DISCARD

Hoover's Handbook of

Private Companies

2019

HOOVERS™
A D&B COMPANY

Austin, Texas

Hoover's Handbook of Private Companies 2019 is intended to provide readers with accurate and authoritative information about the enterprises covered in it. Hoover's researched all companies and organizations profiled, and in many cases contacted them directly so that companies represented could provide information. The information contained herein is as accurate as we could reasonably make it. In many cases we have relied on third-party material that we believe to be trustworthy, but were unable to independently verify. We do not warrant that the book is absolutely accurate or without error. Readers should not rely on any information contained herein in instances where such reliance might cause financial loss. The publisher, the editors, and their data suppliers specifically disclaim all warranties, including the implied warranties of merchantability and fitness for a specific purpose. This book is sold with the understanding that neither the publisher, the editors, nor any content contributors are engaged in providing investment, financial, accounting, legal, or other professional advice.

The financial data (Historical Financials sections) in this book are from a variety of sources. Mergent Inc., provided selected data for the Historical Financials sections of publicly traded companies. For private companies and for historical information on public companies prior to their becoming public, we obtained information directly from the companies or from trade sources deemed to be reliable. Hoover's, Inc., is solely responsible for the presentation of all data.

Many of the names of products and services mentioned in this book are the trademarks or service marks of the companies manufacturing or selling them and are subject to protection under US law. Space has not permitted us to indicate which names are subject to such protection, and readers are advised to consult with the owners of such marks regarding their use. Hoover's is a trademark of Hoover's, Inc.

10 9 8 7 6 5 4 3 2 1

Publishers Cataloging-in-Publication Data
Hoover's Handbook of Private Companies 2019
    Includes indexes.
    ISBN: 978-1-64141-143-1
    ISSN 1073-6433
    1. Business enterprises — Directories. 2. Corporations — Directories.
HF3010 338.7

U.S. AND WORLD BOOK SALES

Mergent Inc.

580 Kingsley Park Drive
Fort Mill, SC
29715
Phone: 800-342-5647
e-mail: orders@mergent.com
Web: www.mergentbusinesspress.com

Mergent Inc.

Executive Managing Director: John Pedernales

Publisher/Managing Director of Print Products: Thomas Wecera

Director of Print Products: Charlot Volny

Quality Assurance Editor: Wayne Arnold

Production Research Assistant: Davie Christna

Data Manager: Jason Horvat

MERGENT CUSTOMER SERVICE
Support & Fulfillment: Melanie Horvat

ABOUT MERGENT INC.

For over 100 years, Mergent, Inc. has been a leading provider of business and financial information on public and private companies globally. Mergent is known to be a trusted partner to corporate and financial institutions, as well as to academic and public libraries. Today we continue to build on a century of experience by transforming data into knowledge and combining our expertise with the latest technology to create new global data and analytical solutions for our clients. With advanced data collection services, cloud-based applications, desktop analytics and print products, Mergent and its subsidiaries provide solutions from top down economic and demographic information, to detailed equity and debt fundamental analysis. We incorporate value added tools such as quantitative Smart Beta equity research and tools for portfolio building and measurement. Based in the U.S., Mergent maintains a strong global presence, with offices in New York, Charlotte, San Diego, London, Tokyo, Kuching and Melbourne. Mergent, Inc. is a member of the London Stock Exchange plc group of companies. The Mergent business forms part of LSEG's Information Services Division, which includes FTSE Russell, a global leader in indexes.

MERGENT
BUSINESS PRESS
by FTSE Russell

Abbreviations

AFL-CIO – American Federation of Labor and Congress of Industrial Organizations

AMA – American Medical Association

AMEX – American Stock Exchange

ARM – adjustable-rate mortgage

ASP – application services provider

ATM – asynchronous transfer mode

ATM – automated teller machine

CAD/CAM – computer-aided design/ computer-aided manufacturing

CD-ROM – compact disc – read-only memory

CD-R – CD-recordable

CEO – chief executive officer

CFO – chief financial officer

CMOS – complementary metal oxide silicon

COO – chief operating officer

DAT – digital audiotape

DOD – Department of Defense

DOE – Department of Energy

DOS – disk operating system

DOT – Department of Transportation

DRAM – dynamic random-access memory

DSL – digital subscriber line

DVD – digital versatile disc/digital video disc

DVD-R – DVD-recordable

EPA – Environmental Protection Agency

EPS – earnings per share

ESOP – employee stock ownership plan

EU – European Union

EVP – executive vice president

FCC – Federal Communications Commission

FDA – Food and Drug Administration

FDIC – Federal Deposit Insurance Corporation

FTC – Federal Trade Commission

GATT – General Agreement on Tariffs and Trade

GDP – gross domestic product

HMO – health maintenance organization

HR – human resources

HTML – hypertext markup language

ICC – Interstate Commerce Commission

IPO – initial public offering

IRS – Internal Revenue Service

ISP – Internet service provider

kWh – kilowatt-hour

LAN – local-area network

LBO – leveraged buyout

LCD – liquid crystal display

LNG – liquefied natural gas

LP – limited partnership

Ltd. – limited

mips – millions of instructions per second

MW – megawatt

NAFTA – North American Free Trade Agreement

NASA – National Aeronautics and Space Administration

NASDAQ – National Association of Securities Dealers Automated Quotations

NATO – North Atlantic Treaty Organization

NYSE – New York Stock Exchange

OCR – optical character recognition

OECD – Organization for Economic Cooperation and Development

OEM – original equipment manufacturer

OPEC – Organization of Petroleum Exporting Countries

OS – operating system

OSHA – Occupational Safety and Health Administration

OTC – over-the-counter

PBX – private branch exchange

PCMCIA – Personal Computer Memory Card International Association

P/E – price to earnings ratio

RAID – redundant array of independent disks

RAM – random-access memory

R&D – research and development

RBOC – regional Bell operating company

RISC – reduced instruction set computer

REIT – real estate investment trust

ROA – return on assets

ROE – return on equity

ROI – return on investment

ROM – read-only memory

S&L – savings and loan

SEC – Securities and Exchange Commission

SEVP – senior executive vice president

SIC – Standard Industrial Classification

SOC – system on a chip

SVP – senior vice president

USB – universal serial bus

VAR – value-added reseller

VAT – value-added tax

VC – venture capitalist

VoIP – Voice over Internet Protocol

VP – vice president

WAN – wide-area network

Contents

Companies Profiled

Companies Profiled (continued)

Companies Profiled (continued)

Companies Profiled (continued)

Companies Profiled (continued)

Companies Profiled (continued)

Companies Profiled (continued)

Companies Profiled (continued)

Companies Profiled (continued)

Companies Profiled (continued)

Companies Profiled (continued)

Companies Profiled (continued)

About Hoover's Handbook of Private Companies 2019

Finding current relevant information about nonpublic companies can be a challenge, as many of these organizations see secrecy as a competitive strategy. In this edition of *Hoover's Handbook of Private Companies*, we have done for you the tough work of compiling these hard-to-find facts.

We consider this volume to be one of the premier sources of business information on privately held enterprises in the US. It features the facts on 900 of the largest and most influencial of those enterprises. Entries feature overviews of company operations, up to five years of financial information, product information, and lists of company executives as found in Hoover's huge database of company information. Some larger and more visable companies will feature an additional History section.

HOOVER'S ONLINE FOR BUSINESS NEEDS

In addition to Hoover's widely used MasterList and Handbooks series, comprehensive coverage of more than 40,000 business enterprises is available in electronic format on our website at www.hoovers.com. Our goal is to provide our customers with the fastest path to business with insight and actionable information about companies, industries, and key decision makers, along with the powerful tools to find and connect to the right people to get business done. Hoover's has partnered with other presigious business information and service providers to bring you all the right business information, services, and links in one place.

We welcome the recognition we have received as a provider of high-quality company information — online, electronically, and in print — and continue to look for ways to make our products more available and more useful to you.

Hoover's Handbook of Private Companies is one of our four-title series of handbooks that covers, literally, the world of business. The series is available as an indexed set, and also includes *Hoover's Handbook of American Business*, *Hoover's Handbook of World Business*, and *Hoover's Handbook of Emerging Companies*. This series brings you information on the biggest, fast-growing, and most influential enterprises in the world.

We believe that anyone who buys from, sells to, invests in, lends to, competes with, interviews with, or works for a company should know all there is to know about that enterprise. Taken together, this book and the other Hoover's products and resources represent the most complete source of basic corporate information readily available to the general public.

HOW TO USE THIS BOOK

This book has four sections:

1. "Using Hoover's Handbooks" describes the contents of our profiles and explains the ways in which we gather and compile our data.

2. "A List-Lover's Compendium" contains lists of the largest and fastest-growing private companies. The lists are based on the information in our profiles, or compiled from well-known sources.

3. The company profiles section makes up the largest and most important part of the book — 900 profiles of major private enterprises, arranged alphabetically.

4. Three indexes complete the book. The first sorts companies by industry groups, the second by headquarters location. The third index is a list of all the executives found in the Executives section of each company profile.

Using Hoover's Handbooks

SELECTION OF THE COMPANIES PROFILED

The 900 enterprises profiled in this book include the largest and most influential companies in America. Among them are:

- private companies, from the giants (Cargill and Koch) to the colorful and prominent (Bad Boy Entertainment and L.L. Bean)
- mutuals and cooperative organizations owned by their customers (State Farm Insurance, Ace Hardware, Ocean Spray Cranberries)
- not-for-profits (Red Cross, Kaiser Permanente, Smithsonian Institution)
- joint ventures (Motiva Enterprises, Dow Corning)
- partnerships (PricewaterhouseCoopers, Baker & McKenzie)
- universities (Columbia, Harvard, University of California)
- government-owned corporations (US Postal Service and New York City's Metropolitan Transportation Authority)
- and a selection of other enterprises (National Basketball Association, AFL-CIO, Texas Lottery Commission).

ORGANIZATION

The profiles are presented in alphabetical order. You will find the commonly used name of the enterprise at the beginning of the profile; the full, legal name is found in the Locations section. If a company name is also a person's name, such as Henry Ford Health System or Mary Kay, it will be alphabetized under the first name; if the company name starts with initials, for example, L.L. Bean or S.C. Johnson, look for it under the combined initials (in the above examples, LL and SC, respectively).

Basic financial data are listed under the heading Historical Financials. The annual financial information contained in the profiles is current through fiscal year-ends occuring as late as October 2014. We have included certain nonfinancial developments , such as officer changes, through December 2014.

OVERVIEW

In the first section of the profile, we have tried to give a thumbnail description of the company and what it does. The description will usually include information on the company's strategy, reputation, and ownership. We recommend that you read this section first.

HISTORY

This extended section, which is available for some of the larger and more well-known companies, reflects our belief that every enterprise is the sum of its history and that you have to know where you came from in order to know where you are going. While some companies have limited historical awareness, we think the vast majority of the enterprises in this book have colorful backgrounds. We have tried to focus on the people who made the enterprises what they are today. We have found these histories to be full of twists and ironies; they make fascinating reading.

EXECUTIVES

Here we list the names of the people who run the company, insofar as space allows. In the few cases where available, we have shown the ages and pay of key officers. In some instances the published data is for the previous year, although the company has announced promotions or retirements since year-end. The pay represents cash compensation, including bonuses, but excludes stock option programs.

Although companies are free to structure their management titles any way they please, most modern corporations follow standard practices. The ultimate power in any corporation lies with the shareholders, who elect a board of directors, usually including officers or "insiders" as well as individuals from outside the company. The chief officer, the person on whose desk the buck stops, is usually called the chief executive officer (CEO). Often, he or she is also the chairman of the board.

As corporate management has become more complex, it is common for the CEO to have a "right-hand person" who oversees the day-to-day operations of the company, allowing the CEO plenty of time to focus on strategy and long-term issues. This right-hand person is usually designated the chief operating officer (COO) and is often the president of the company. In other cases one person is both chairman and president.

A multitude of other titles exists, including chief financial officer (CFO), chief administrative officer, and vice chairman. We have always tried to include the CFO, the chief legal officer, and the chief human resources or personnel officer.

The people named in the Executives section are indexed at the back of the book.

The Executives section also includes the name of the company's auditing (accounting) firm, where available.

LOCATIONS

Here we include the company's full legal name and its headquarters, street address, telephone and fax numbers, and Web site, as available. The back of the book includes an index of companies by headquarters locations.

In some cases we have also included information on the geographic distribution of the company's business, including sales and profit data. Note that these profit numbers, like those in the Products/Operations section below, are usually operating or pretax profits rather than net profits. Operating profits are generally those before financing costs (interest income and payments) and before taxes, which are considered costs attributable to the whole company rather than to one division or part of the world. For this reason the net income figures (in the Historical Financials section) are usually much lower, since they are after interest and taxes. Pretax profits are after interest but before taxes.

Headquarters for companies that are incorporated in Bermuda, but whose operational headquarters are in the US, are listed under their US address.

PRODUCTS/OPERATIONS

This section contains selected lists of products, services, brand names, divisions, subsidiaries, and joint ventures. We have tried to include a company's major lines and most familiar brand names.

The nature of this section varies by company and the amount of information contained in Hoover's storehouse of business information. If the company publishes sales and profit information by type of business, we have included it.

COMPETITORS

In this section we have listed companies that compete with the profiled company. This feature is included as a quick way to locate similar companies and compare them. The universe of competitors includes all public companies and all private companies with sales in excess of $500 million. In a few instances we have identified smaller private companies as key competitors.

HISTORICAL FINANCIALS

Here we have tried to present as much data about each enterprise's financial performance as we could compile in the allocated space. The information varies somewhat from industry to industry and is less complete in the case of private companies that do not release data. (We have always tried to provide annual sales and employment, although in some instances those numbers are simply not available). There are a few industries, venture capital and investment banking, for example, for which revenue numbers are not reported as a rule. In the case of private companies that do not publicly dis-close financial information, we have statistics when reliable sources are available.

The following information is generally present.

A five-year table, with relevant annualized compound growth rates, covers:
- Sales — fiscal year sales (year-end assets for most financial companies)
- Net income — fiscal year net income (before accounting changes)
- Net profit margin — fiscal year net income as a percent of sales (as a percent of assets for most financial firms)
- Employees — fiscal year-end or average number of employees

The information on the number of employees is intended to aid the reader interested in knowing whether a company has a long-term trend of increasing or decreasing employment. As far as we know, we are the only company that publishes this information in print format.

The numbers on the left in each row of the Historical Financials section give the month and the year in which the company's fiscal year actually ends. Thus, a company with a March 31, 2019, year-end is shown as 3/19. The last item in the Financials section is a graph, which for private companies shows net income, or, if that is unavailable, sales.

Key year-end statistics are included in this section for insurance companies and companies required to file reports with the SEC. They generally show the financial strength of the enterprise, including:
- Debt ratio (long-term debt as a percent of shareholders' equity)
- Return on equity (net income divided by the average of beginning and ending common shareholders' equity)
- Cash and cash equivalents
- Current ratio (ratio of current assets to current liabilities)
- Total long-term debt (including capital lease obligations)
- Fiscal year sales for financial institutions

Hoover's Handbook of

Private Companies

A List-Lover's Compendium

The 300 Largest Private Companies by Sales 2019

Rank	Company	Sales ($ mil.)
1	STATE OF CALIFORNIA	$255,725
2	STATE OF TEXAS	$115,336
3	SAINT PAUL REGIONAL WATER SERVICES	$57,543
4	NOVARTIS PHARMACEUTICALS CORPORATION	$49,436
5	MCLANE COMPANY, INC.	$48,016
6	JOHNSON CONTROLS, INC.	$37,179
7	FINCANTIERI MARINE SYSTEMS NORTH AMER	$35,834
8	PUBLIX SUPER MARKETS, INC.	$34,274
9	CITGO PETROLEUM CORPORATION	$24,100
10	ASCENSION HEALTH ALLIANCE	$22,633
11	BNSF RAILWAY COMPANY	$20,747
12	STATE OF OKLAHOMA	$17,175
13	WHOLE FOODS MARKET, INC.	$16,030
14	TELCO INTERCONTINENTAL CORP	$15,168
15	CATHOLIC HEALTH INITIATIVES	$14,982
16	PROVIDENCE HEALTH & SERVICES	$14,434
17	PLUMAS LAKE ELEMENTARY SCHOOL DISTRICT	$14,359
18	GENERAL ELECTRIC INTERNATIONAL, INC.	$14,100
19	DAIRY FARMERS OF AMERICA, INC.	$13,803
20	UNIVERSITY OF TEXAS SYSTEM	$13,282
21	UNIVERSITY OF PITTSBURGH MEDICAL CENTER	$12,848
22	SUTTER HEALTH	$12,444
23	ALLEGIS GROUP, INC.	$12,297
24	MAYO CLINIC HOSPITAL-ROCHESTER	$11,993
25	PARTNERS HEALTHCARE SYSTEM, INC.	$11,666
26	THE TURNER CORPORATION	$10,524
27	LAWRENCE TOWNSHIP SCHOOL DISTRICT INC	$10,232
28	ADVENTIST HEALTH SYSTEM SUNBELT HEALTH	$10,083
29	EQUINOR MARKETING & TRADING (US) INC.	$9,874
30	ASSOCIATED WHOLESALE GROCERS, INC.	$9,704
31	CHEVRON PHILLIPS CHEMICAL COMPANY LLC	$9,622
32	NEW YORK CITY HEALTH AND HOSPITALS	$9,551
33	BAYLOR SCOTT & WHITE HOLDINGS	$9,477
34	THE TRUSTEES OF THE UNIVERSITY OF PENNSY	$9,194
35	WHEATLAND UNION HIGH SCHOOL DISTRICT	$9,187
36	ONEOK PARTNERS, L.P.	$8,918
37	THE HERTZ CORPORATION	$8,803
38	ALTICOR INC.	$8,783
39	JARDEN CORPORATION	$8,604
40	GROWMARK, INC.	$8,522
41	NEW YORK UNIVERSITY	$8,500
42	THE CLEVELAND CLINIC FOUNDATION	$8,407
43	SHI INTERNATIONAL CORP.	$8,244
44	TATA AMERICA INTERNATIONAL CORPORATION	$8,197
45	CHEVRON PHILLIPS CHEMICAL COMPANY LP	$7,919
46	BANNER HEALTH	$7,835
47	COMPUTER SCIENCES CORPORATION	$7,607
48	REGENTS OF THE UNIVERSITY OF MICHIGAN	$7,467
49	FEDERAL-MOGUL HOLDINGS LLC	$7,434
50	STATE OF RHODE ISLAND AND PROVIDENCETIO	$7,013
51	PRECISION CASTPARTS CORP.	$7,002
52	ZEN-NOH GRAIN CORPORATION	$6,971
53	INTERMOUNTAIN HEALTH CARE INC	$6,940
54	EATON CORPORATION	$6,925
55	JOHNS HOPKINS HEALTH SYS CORP	$6,558
56	GEISINGER HEALTH	$6,537

Rank	Company	Sales ($ mil.)
57	SSM HEALTH CARE CORPORATION	$6,497
58	CONSOLIDATED GRAIN & BARGE COMPANY	$6,431
59	ALLY BANK	$6,427
60	MERCY HEALTH	$6,254
61	THE WHITING-TURNER CONTRACTING COMPANY	$6,173
62	NIELSEN HOLDINGS PLC	$6,172
63	AEROTEK, INC.	$6,070
64	THE PENNSYLVANIA STATE UNIVERSITY	$6,059
65	JOHNS HOPKINS UNIVERSITY	$6,021
66	SPECTRUM HEALTH SYSTEM	$6,000
67	THE CHARLOTTE-MECKLENBURG HOSPITAL AU	$5,991
68	HENRY FORD HEALTH SYSTEM	$5,977
69	WORLD WIDE TECHNOLOGY, LLC	$5,928
70	ALASKA PERMANENT FUND CORPORATION	$5,671
71	THE NEW YORK AND PRESBYTERIAN HOSPITAL	$5,616
72	LELAND STANFORD JUNIOR UNIVERSITY	$5,605
73	MEDSTAR HEALTH, INC.	$5,604
74	IHC HEALTH SERVICES, INC.	$5,483
75	ADVOCATE HEALTH CARE NETWORK	$5,393
76	ACE HARDWARE CORPORATION	$5,388
77	TEXAS PERMANENT SCHOOL FUND MANAGEMEN	$5,375
78	AURORA HEALTH CARE, INC.	$5,334
79	AIRGAS, INC.	$5,305
80	SENTARA HEALTHCARE	$5,298
81	FAIRVIEW HEALTH SERVICES	$5,275
82	BOARD OF EDUCATION OF CITY OF CHICAGO	$5,273
83	MEMORIAL HERMANN HEALTH SYSTEM	$5,258
84	BOARD OF REGENTS OF THE UNIVERSITY SYST	$5,101
85	UNIVERSITY OF SOUTHERN CALIFORNIA	$4,937
86	SPECTRA ENERGY CORP	$4,916
87	NEW YORK CITY TRANSIT AUTHORITY	$4,912
88	GILBANE BUILDING COMPANY	$4,899
89	UNIVERSITY OF WASHINGTON INC	$4,893
90	FAIRFAX COUNTY VIRGINIA	$4,806
91	MERCY HEALTH	$4,738
92	BALFOUR BEATTY, LLC	$4,690
93	TEXAS HEALTH RESOURCES	$4,689
94	HOBBY LOBBY STORES, INC.	$4,544
95	NEW YORK PRESBYTERIAN HOSPITAL WEILL COR	$4,506
96	MARYLAND DEPARTMENT OF TRANSPORTATION	$4,491
97	STANFORD HEALTH CARE	$4,454
98	BEAUMONT HEALTH	$4,439
99	SANFORD HEALTH	$4,411
100	SANFORD	$4,411
101	THE SCOULAR COMPANY	$4,367
102	THE UNIVERSITY OF CHICAGO	$4,355
103	TEKSYSTEMS, INC.	$4,351
104	UNIVERSITY OF COLORADO HEALTH	$4,341
105	CHRISTUS HEALTH INTERNATIONAL	$4,212
106	COUNTY OF MONTGOMERY	$4,191
107	IOWA HEALTH SYSTEM	$4,157
108	BRIGHTSTAR US, INC.	$4,138
109	ADVENTIST HEALTH SYSTEM/WEST	$4,115
110	AVAYA HOLDINGS CORP.	$4,081
111	OHIOHEALTH CORPORATION	$4,046
112	CORNELL UNIVERSITY	$4,014
113	THOMAS JEFFERSON UNIVERSITY	$3,952

Rank	Company	Sales ($ mil.)
114	ALLINA HEALTH SYSTEM	$3,948
115	TALEN ENERGY SUPPLY, LLC	$3,913
116	HOUSTON METHODIST HOSPITAL	$3,887
117	WHITEWAVE FOODS COMPANY	$3,866
118	BALFOUR BEATTY CONSTRUCTION GROUP, INC.	$3,853
119	YALE UNIVERSITY	$3,848
120	BALFOUR BEATTY CONSTRUCTION, LLC	$3,809
121	MONTEFIORE MEDICAL CENTER	$3,763
122	THE REGENTS OF THE UNIVERSITY OF COLOR	$3,728
123	THE SCHOOL BOARD OF MIAMI-DADE COUNTY	$3,728
124	MCCARTHY HOLDINGS, INC.	$3,666
125	MASSACHUSETTS INSTITUTE OF TECHNOLOGY	$3,627
126	DUKE UNIVERSITY HEALTH SYSTEM, INC.	$3,598
127	MCCARTHY BUILDING COMPANIES, INC.	$3,575
128	SCRIPPS NETWORKS INTERACTIVE, INC.	$3,562
129	HCL AMERICA INC.	$3,559
130	THE WASHINGTON UNIVERSITY	$3,543
131	CITY OF BOSTON	$3,542
132	COUNTY OF RIVERSIDE	$3,504
133	CEDARS-SINAI MEDICAL CENTER	$3,470
134	AG PROCESSING INC A COOPERATIVE	$3,411
135	VCU HEALTH SYSTEM AUTHORITY	$3,400
136	LONG ISLAND POWER AUTHORITY	$3,399
137	SHARP HEALTHCARE	$3,397
138	MONSTER BEVERAGE 1990 CORPORATION	$3,369
139	BLACK & VEATCH HOLDING COMPANY	$3,364
140	BVH, INC.	$3,364
141	HENSEL PHELPS CONSTRUCTION CO.	$3,360
142	NOBLE HOLDING (U.S.) CORPORATION	$3,352
143	CLARK COUNTY SCHOOL DISTRICT	$3,313
144	SWINERTON BUILDERS	$3,306
145	NATIONAL RAILROAD PASSENGER CORPORATION	$3,306
146	WESTERN & SOUTHERN FINANCIAL GROUP, INC.	$3,302
147	PRODUCTION TECHNOLOGIES, INC.	$3,289
148	DRIVETIME AUTOMOTIVE GROUP, INC.	$3,267
149	RAYMOND JAMES & ASSOCIATES INC	$3,256
150	THE SCHOOL DISTRICT OF PHILADELPHIA	$3,251
151	PHILADELPHIA CONSOLIDATED HOLDING CORP.	$3,234
152	COUNTY OF SUFFOLK	$3,175
153	REGAL ENTERTAINMENT GROUP	$3,163
154	SCHWAB CHARITABLE FUND	$3,147
155	SALT RIVER PROJECT AGRICULTURAL MPROVE	$3,085
156	OREGON HEALTH & SCIENCE UNIVERSITY	$3,050
157	API GROUP INC.	$3,046
158	TEXAS COUNTY AND DISTRICT RETIREMENT SY	$3,030
159	TRAMMO, INC.	$3,006
160	J.E. DUNN CONSTRUCTION GROUP, INC.	$2,947
161	AMC ENTERTAINMENT INC.	$2,947
162	J.E. DUNN CONSTRUCTION COMPANY	$2,946
163	SCRIPPS HEALTH	$2,944
164	DO IT BEST CORP.	$2,926
165	CALIFORNIA INSTITUTE OF TECHNOLOGY	$2,895
166	COUNTY OF CLARK	$2,874
167	THE UNIVERSITY OF IOWA	$2,860
168	OCHSNER HEALTH SYSTEM	$2,812
169	UNIVERSITY OF MISSOURI SYSTEM	$2,800
170	METALDYNE PERFORMANCE GROUP INC.	$2,791

SOURCE: HOOVER'S, INC., DATABASE, FEBRUARY 2019

The 300 Largest Private Companies by Sales 2019 (continued)

Rank	Company	Sales ($ mil.)
171	LEHIGH VALLEY HEALTH NETWORK, INC.	$2,740
172	SCHOOL BOARD OF BROWARD COUNTY, THE (INC)	$2,739
173	ESTES EXPRESS LINES, INC.	$2,732
174	FRANCISCAN ALLIANCE, INC.	$2,731
175	EXPRESS SERVICES INC	$2,722
176	HOUSTON INDEPENDENT SCHOOL DISTRICT	$2,696
177	BAPTIST HEALTHCARE SYSTEM, INC.	$2,688
178	HEARTLAND PAYMENT SYSTEMS, LLC	$2,682
179	HARTFORD HEALTHCARE CORPORATION	$2,678
180	BROWARD COUNTY PUBLIC SCHOOLS	$2,630
181	NEW YORK POWER AUTHORITY	$2,573
182	J M SMITH CORPORATION	$2,566
183	OSF HEALTHCARE SYSTEM	$2,561
184	CLARK EQUIPMENT COMPANY	$2,544
185	PRATT CORRUGATED HOLDINGS, INC.	$2,518
186	THE ORANGE COUNTY PUBLIC SCHOOL DIST.	$2,506
187	BARTON MALOW ENTERPRISES, INC.	$2,503
188	BARTON MALOW COMPANY	$2,502
189	SUFFOLK CONSTRUCTION COMPANY, INC.	$2,500
190	PRATT INDUSTRIES, INC.	$2,499
191	MARTIN RESOURCE MANAGEMENT CORP.	$2,494
192	THE CARLE FOUNDATION	$2,493
193	THE MASSACHUSETTS GENERAL HOSPITAL	$2,452
194	UNIVERSITY OF MASSACHUSETTS	$2,443
195	PAREXEL INTERNATIONAL CORPORATION	$2,442
196	JOHNS HOPKINS HOSPITAL	$2,423
197	NORTHERN INDIANA PUBLIC SERVICE CO	$2,418
198	MULTICARE HEALTH SYSTEM	$2,416
199	YALE-NEW HAVEN HOSPITAL, INC.	$2,389
200	COBANK, ACB	$2,380
201	HDR, INC.	$2,362
202	WGL HOLDINGS, INC.	$2,342
203	ST. LUKE'S HEALTH SYSTEM, LTD.	$2,327
204	NATIONWIDE CHILDREN'S HOSPITAL	$2,317
205	UNIVERSITY OF ARKANSAS SYSTEM	$2,298
206	UNIVERSITY OF PITTSBURGH	$2,276
207	RUSH UNIVERSITY MEDICAL CENTER	$2,268
208	ALEX LEE, INC.	$2,262
209	TRUSTEES OF INDIANA UNIVERSITY	$2,256
210	HOSPITAL OF THE UNIVERSITY OF PENNSYLVANIA	$2,237
211	MEMORIAL HEALTH SERVICES	$2,232
212	SNYDER'S-LANCE, INC.	$2,227
213	LONG ISLAND JEWISH MEDICAL CENTER	$2,223
214	MEMORIAL SLOAN-KETTERING CANCER CENTER	$2,220

Rank	Company	Sales ($ mil.)
215	DST SYSTEMS, INC.	$2,218
216	THE UNIVERSITY OF CHICAGO MEDICAL CENTER	$2,212
217	NORTHWESTERN UNIVERSITY	$2,201
218	NEIGHBORHOOD HEALTH PLAN, INCORPORATED	$2,178
219	WEST VIRGINIA UNITED HEALTH SYSTEM, INC.	$2,173
220	THE SCHOOL DISTRICT OF WEST PALM BEACH	$2,146
221	HILLSBOROUGH COUNTY SCHOOL DISTRICT	$2,133
222	THE BRIGHAM AND WOMEN'S HOSPITAL INC	$2,129
223	TRUMAN ARNOLD COMPANIES	$2,119
224	LEGACY HEALTH	$2,118
225	BASIN ELECTRIC POWER COOPERATIVE	$2,112
226	SAINT MARYS HOSPITAL	$2,092
227	DARTMOUTH-HITCHCOCK HEALTH	$2,069
228	AMERICAN HONDA FINANCE CORPORATION	$2,066
229	SMMH PRACTICE PLAN, INC.	$2,061
230	PLY GEM HOLDINGS, INC.	$2,056
231	GRUMA CORPORATION	$2,051
232	FRANCISCAN MISSIONARIES OF OUR LADY HEAL	$2,030
233	MOUNT SINAI HOSPITALS GROUP, INC.	$2,025
234	BOSTON UNIVERSITY	$2,018
235	CHEMIUM INTERNATIONAL CORP.	$2,016
236	SOUTH BROWARD HOSPITAL DISTRICT	$2,015
237	THE TRUSTEES OF PRINCETON UNIVERSITY	$2,013
238	PORTLAND GENERAL ELECTRIC COMP	$2,009
239	WESTCHESTER COUNTY HEALTH CARE CORP	$2,009
240	NORTHSIDE HOSPITAL, INC.	$2,003
241	THE MOSES H CONE MEMORIAL HOSPITAL	$2,002
242	ESSENTIA HEALTH	$1,990
243	EQUINOR NATURAL GAS LLC	$1,967
244	MIDCOAST ENERGY PARTNERS, L.P.	$1,966
245	THE UNIVERSITY OF VERMONT HEALTH NET	$1,934
246	TRIBOROUGH BRIDGE & TUNNEL AUTHORITY	$1,932
247	MICHIGAN STATE UNIVERSITY	$1,932
248	PERMANENT UNIVERSITY FUND	$1,907
249	SPECTRUM HEALTH HOSPITALS	$1,905
250	UNIVERSITY OF FLORIDA	$1,898
251	UNIVERSITY OF NORTH CAROLINA HOSPITALS	$1,892
252	JEA	$1,875
253	JOHNSON CONTROLS FIRE PROTECTION LP	$1,871
254	GWINNETT COUNTY BOARD OF EDUCATION	$1,869
255	THE FRESH MARKET INC	$1,857
256	ST. LUKE'S HEALTH NETWORK, INC.	$1,845
257	CROWLEY HOLDINGS, INC.	$1,841
258	HMO MINNESOTA	$1,840

Rank	Company	Sales ($ mil.)
259	THE FINISH LINE INC	$1,839
260	THE MOSES H CONE MEMORIAL HOSPITAL	$1,837
261	JOHN MUIR HEALTH	$1,832
262	NORTH SHORE UNIVERSITY HOSPITAL	$1,827
263	PETROLEUM TRADERS CORPORATION	$1,816
264	WHEATON FRANCISCAN SERVICES, INC.	$1,809
265	UNIVERSITY OF NEW MEXICO	$1,808
266	DESAROLLADORA DEL NORTE S E	$1,802
267	JERSEY CENTRAL POWER & LIGHT COMPANY	$1,801
268	ARIZONA STATE UNIVERSITY	$1,782
269	LOMA LINDA UNIVERSITY MEDICAL CENTER	$1,777
270	UNIVERSITY OF NORTH CAROLINA AT CHA HILL	$1,774
271	SCOTTSDALE HEALTHCARE CORP.	$1,763
272	SOUTH CAROLINA PUBLIC SERVICE AUTHORITY	$1,757
273	KETTERING ADVENTIST HEALTHCARE	$1,754
274	MISSION HEALTH SYSTEM, INC.	$1,753
275	BROTHER INTERNATIONAL CORPORATION	$1,751
276	MAIN LINE HEALTH SYSTEM	$1,742
277	AMERICAN LEBANESE SYRIAN ASSOCIATED CHA.	$1,741
278	CATHOLIC HEALTH INITIATIVES COLORADO	$1,735
279	DALLAS COUNTY HOSPITAL DISTRICT	$1,734
280	HARRIS COUNTY HOSPITAL DISTRICT	$1,732
281	BARNES-JEWISH HOSPITAL	$1,726
282	SAINT LUKE'S HEALTH SYSTEM, INC.	$1,721
283	OCEAN SPRAY CRANBERRIES, INC.	$1,719
284	NORTON HOSPITALS, INC	$1,712
285	HDR ENGINEERING, INC.	$1,707
286	NEW JERSEY TURNPIKE AUTHORITY INC	$1,699
287	ALRO STEEL CORPORATION	$1,691
288	INTEGRIS HEALTH, INC.	$1,673
289	UNIVERSITY OF TEXAS AT AUSTIN	$1,670
290	UMASS MEMORIAL MEDICAL CENTER, INC.	$1,669
291	UC HEALTH, LLC.	$1,662
292	EASTERN MAINE HEALTHCARE SYSTEMS	$1,654
293	NEW PRIME, INC.	$1,654
294	AARP	$1,644
295	LUCILE SALTER PACKARD CHILDREN'S HOS STA	$1,638
296	BRIGHAM YOUNG UNIVERSITY	$1,634
297	NORTH CAROLINA BAPTIST HOSPITAL	$1,634
298	BAPTIST HEALTH SYSTEM, INC.	$1,630
299	SERVCO PACIFIC INC.	$1,629
300	UMASS MEMORIAL MEDICAL CENTER, INC.	$1,622

The 300 Largest Private Companies by Employees 2019

Rank	Company	Employees	Rank	Company	Employees	Rank	Company	Employees
1	EXPRESS SERVICES INC	373,869	61	HENRY FORD HEALTH SYSTEM	23,000	121	SHARP HEALTHCARE	14,000
2	STATE OF CALIFORNIA	208,580	62	UNIVERSITY OF SOUTHERN CALIFOR	22,700	122	ESTES EXPRESS LINES, INC.	14,000
3	PUBLIX SUPER MARKETS, INC.	193,000	63	YALE NEW HAVEN HEALTH SER CORR	22,490	123	JEFFERSON COUNTY BOARD OF ED	14,000
4	STATE OF TEXAS	144,175	64	HOUSTON INDEPENDENT SCHOOL DIS	22,440	124	MORTON HOSPITAL AND MEDICAL CEN	14,000
5	JOHNSON CONTROLS, INC.	139,000	65	YALE-NEW HAVEN HOSPITAL, INC.	22,000	125	NORTHSIDE INDEPENDENT SCH	13,698
6	ASCENSION HEALTH ALLIANCE	111,719	66	GOODWILL INDUSTRIES, INC.	22,000	126	STATE OF RHODE ISLAND AND PRO	13,535
7	ASCENSION HEALTH	109,000	67	UNIVERSITY OF TEXAS AT AUSTIN	21,513	127	SCRIPPS HEALTH	13,445
8	WHOLE FOODS MARKET, INC.	89,000	68	TEXAS HEALTH RESOURCES	21,277	128	UNIVERSITY OF MASSACHUSETTS	13,196
9	ALLEGIS GROUP, INC.	85,000	69	THE SCHOOL DISTRICT OF PHIL	21,065	129	GEISINGER HEALTH	13,030
10	MAYO CLINIC HOSPITAL-ROCHESTER	82,000	70	NEW YORK UNIVERSITY	21,000	130	JOHNS HOPKINS HEALTH SYS CORP	13,000
11	UNIVERSITY OF TEXAS SYSTEM	81,260	71	THE VANDERBILT UNIVERSITY	21,000	131	CYPRESS-FAIRBANKS INDEP SCH	13,000
12	UNIVERSITY OF PITTSBURGH MEDICAL	80,000	72	THE TRUSTEES OF THE UNIV PENN	20,433	132	DUVAL COUNTY PUBLIC SCHOOLS	13,000
13	ADVENTIST HEALTH SYS HEALTH CORP	78,000	73	MCLANE COMPANY, INC.	20,128	133	WILLOW VALLEY COMMUNITIES	13,000
14	CATHOLIC HEALTH INITIATIVES	72,500	74	COUNTY OF RIVERSIDE	20,000	134	THE REGENTS OF THE UNIV OF COL	12,980
15	PARTNERS HEALTHCARE SYSTEM, INC.	67,000	75	LARSEN & TOUBRO INFOTECH LIMITED	20,000	135	COUNTY OF SUFFOLK	12,814
16	UHS OF PEACHFORD LP	66,575	76	STAFF FORCE, INC.	20,000	136	THE FINISH LINE INC	12,700
17	COMPUTER SCIENCES CORPORATION	66,000	77	THE ORANGE COUNTY PUBLIC SCHOOL	19,858	137	UNIVERSITY OF HOUSTON SYSTEM	12,608
18	THE CHARLOTTE-MECKLENBURG HOS	62,000	78	AMC ENTERTAINMENT INC.	19,700	138	BAPTIST HEALTHCARE SYSTEM, INC.	12,601
19	ST MARY'S MEDICAL CENTER	56,605	79	ADVENTIST HEALTH SYSTEM/WEST	19,512	139	THE FRESH MARKET INC	12,600
20	FEDERAL-MOGUL HOLDINGS LLC	53,700	80	OREGON HEALTH & SCIENCE UNIV	19,500	140	NORTH CAROLINA BAPTIST HOSPITAL	12,563
21	SUTTER HEALTH	48,000	81	OCHSNER HEALTH SYSTEM	19,000	141	MOUNT SINAI HOSPITALS GROUP, INC.	12,559
22	NEW YORK CITY TRANSIT AUTHORITY	47,956	82	FRANCISCAN ALLIANCE, INC.	19,000	142	CORNELL UNIVERSITY	12,207
23	THE CLEVELAND CLINIC FOUNDATION	44,000	83	IOWA HEALTH SYSTEM	18,923	143	UNI OF NORTH CAR AT CHAPEL HILL	12,204
24	THE PENNSYLVANIA STATE UNIVERSITY	44,000	84	PAREXEL INTERNATIONAL CORP	18,900	144	THE UNIVERSITY OF CHICAGO	12,120
25	NIELSEN HOLDINGS PLC	43,061	85	CITY OF BOSTON	18,760	145	FAIRFAX COUNTY VIRGINIA	12,000
26	BOARD OF EDUCATION OF CITY OF CH	43,000	86	PURDUE UNIVERSITY	18,715	146	MASSACHUSETTS INSTITUTE OF TECH	12,000
27	BNSF RAILWAY COMPANY	41,000	87	NATIONAL RAILROAD PASSENGER COR	18,650	147	METALDYNE PERFORMANCE GROUP	12,000
28	BD OF REGENTS OF THE UN SYS GEO	40,000	88	UNIVERSITY OF NEW MEXICO	18,362	148	LEHIGH VALLEY HEALTH NET	12,000
29	STATE OF OKLAHOMA	37,613	89	WILLIAM BEAUMONT HOSPITAL	18,050	149	JOHNS HOPKINS HOSPITAL	12,000
30	JOHNS HOPKINS UNIVERSITY	37,600	90	FAIRVIEW HEALTH SERVICES	18,000	150	NATIONWIDE CHILDREN'S HOSPITAL	12,000
31	CLARK COUNTY SCHOOL DISTRICT	37,361	91	WHEATON FRANCISCAN SERVICES, INC.	18,000	151	THE MOSES H CONE MEMORIAL HOS	12,000
32	THE HERTZ CORPORATION	37,000	92	CHILDREN'S HOSPITAL MEDICAL CEN	18,000	152	MISSION HEALTH SYSTEM, INC.	12,000
33	NEW YORK CITY HEALTH AND HOSP	35,700	93	UNIVERSITY OF GEORGIA	17,800	153	UNIVERSITY OF MARYLAND MEDICAL	12,000
34	BANNER HEALTH	35,000	94	MAIN LINE HEALTH SYSTEM	17,485	154	THE GEISINGER CLINIC	12,000
35	INTERMOUNTAIN HEALTH CARE INC	35,000	95	SANFORD	17,400	155	JEFFERSON COUNTY SCH DIS NO. R-1	12,000
36	MERCY HEALTH	35,000	96	AIRGAS, INC.	17,070	156	UNIVERSITY OF HAWAII	12,000
37	BEAUMONT HEALTH	35,000	97	JARDEN CORPORATION	17,000	157	TESLA ENERGY OPERATIONS, INC.	12,000
38	MAXIM HEALTHCARE SERVICES, INC.	35,000	98	THE UNIVERSITY OF IOWA	17,000	158	CHICAGO TRANSIT AUTHORITY	12,000
39	REGENTS OF THE UNIV OF MICHIGAN	34,624	99	SCOTTSDALE HEALTHCARE CORP.	17,000	159	PORTLAND ADVENTIST MEDICAL	12,000
40	MEDSTAR HEALTH, INC.	33,000	100	SPECTRUM HEALTH SYSTEM	16,996	160	HCL AMERICA INC.	11,993
41	HEARTLAND HEALTH	32,000	101	WAKEMED	16,933	161	WELLSTAR HEALTH SYSTEM, INC.	11,985
42	BROWARD COUNTY PUBLIC SCHOOLS	31,174	102	DUKE UNIVERSITY HEALTH SYSTEM,	16,627	162	VIA CHRISTI HEALTH, INC.	11,970
43	UNIVERSITY OF MISSOURI SYSTEM	30,282	103	TRUSTEES OF INDIANA UNIVERSITY	16,000	163	AVAYA HOLDINGS CORP.	11,701
44	HOBBY LOBBY STORES, INC.	30,218	104	ALSCO INC.	16,000	164	METHODIST LE BONHEUR HEALTHCARE	11,459
45	PRECISION CASTPARTS CORP.	30,100	105	UNIVERSITY SYSTEM OF NEW HAMP	16,000	165	MICHIGAN STATE UNIVERSITY	11,100
46	AURORA HEALTH CARE, INC.	30,000	106	BAPTIST HEALTH SOUTH FLORIDA, INC.	16,000	166	YALE UNIVERSITY	11,000
47	THE SCHOOL DISTRICT OF WEST PAL	29,653	107	MINNETONKA INDEPEND SCHOOL 276	16,000	167	MONTEFIORE MEDICAL CENTER	11,000
48	NPC RESTAURANT HOLDINGS, LLC	29,000	108	DST SYSTEMS, INC.	15,700	168	SPECTRUM HEALTH HOSPITALS	11,000
49	SENTARA HEALTHCARE	28,000	109	BOARD OF REGENTS OF UNIV OF NEB	15,200	169	DALLAS COUNTY HOSPITAL DISTRICT	11,000
50	NYSARC, INC.	28,000	110	LELAND STANFORD JUNIOR UNIVERSITY	15,000	170	PUBLIC HEALTH OF MIAMI DADE CO	11,000
51	UNIVERSITY OF WASHINGTON INC	27,228	111	OHIOHEALTH CORPORATION	15,000	171	VIRGINIA COMMONWEALTH UNIV	11,000
52	ALLINA HEALTH SYSTEM	26,400	112	UNIV HEALTH SYSTEMS OF EASTECA	15,000	172	BEAUMONT UNIFIED SCHOOL DISTRICT	11,000
53	REGAL ENTERTAINMENT GROUP	25,359	113	PITT COUNTY MEMORIAL HOSPITAL,	15,000	173	LEGACY HEALTH	10,675
54	ADVOCATE HEALTH CARE NETWORK	25,000	114	ESSENTIA HEALTH	14,700	174	THOMAS JEFFERSON UNIVERSITY	10,625
55	CHRISTUS HEALTH INTERNATIONAL	25,000	115	ALMOST FAMILY, INC.	14,200	175	GORDON FOOD SERVICE, INC.	10,600
56	HILLSBOROUGH COUNTY SCHOOL	25,000	116	ADVANCE SERVICES, INC.	14,200	176	LOYOLA UNIVERSITY OF CHICAGO INC	10,500
57	BARNABAS HEALTH, INC.	24,600	117	MILWAUKEE PUBLIC SCHOOLS (INC)	14,154	177	THE SALVATION ARMY	10,447
58	SSM HEALTH CARE CORPORATION	24,230	118	UNIVERSITY OF ARKANSAS SYSTEM	14,025	178	FORT WORTH INDEPENDENT SCH	10,360
59	THE EVANGELICAL LUTHERAN GOOD	24,000	119	ALTICOR INC.	14,000	179	THE MASSACHUSETTS GEN HOSPITAL	10,156
60	THE NEW YORK AND PRESBYTERIAN	23,709	120	MEMORIAL HERMANN HEALTH SYSTEM	14,000	180	BOSCOV'S, INC.	10,003

SOURCE: HOOVER'S, INC., DATABASE, FEBRUARY 2019

Rank	Company	Employees		Rank	Company	Employees		Rank	Company	Employees
181	MCLAREN HEALTH CARE CORPORATION	10,003		221	TUCSON UNIFIED SCHOOL DISTRICT	9,000		261	BENEDICTINE HEALTH SYSTEM	8,000
182	RAYMOND JAMES & ASSOCIATES INC	10,000		222	KENTUCKY COMM AND TECH SYSTEM	9,000		262	LIFESPAN CORPORATION	8,000
183	HDR, INC.	10,000		223	MERCY HEALTH	8,800		263	NORTHEAST GEORGIA HEALTH SYS	8,000
184	UC HEALTH, LLC.	10,000		224	MEMORIAL HEALTH CARE SYSTEM, INC.	8,800		264	UNIVERSITY OF OREGON	7,971
185	COUNTY OF HILLSBOROUGH	10,000		225	SPECTRA ENERGY CORP	8,700		265	ST. LUKE'S HEALTH SYSTEM, LTD.	7,891
186	THE UNIVERSITY OF KANSAS HOSPITAL	10,000		226	UNIVERSITY OF MISSISSIPPI	8,700		266	CAMPUS CRUSADE FOR CHRIST INC	7,688
187	COBB COUNTY PUBLIC SCHOOLS	10,000		227	MOHEGAN TRIBAL GAMING AUTHORITY	8,640		267	UNIVERSITY OF IOWA HOSPITALS AND	7,638
188	FULTON COUNTY BOARD OF EDUCATI	10,000		228	CREIGHTON ALEGENT HEALTH	8,600		268	SAN ANTONIO INDEPENDENT SCHOOL	7,600
189	FARM CREDIT SERVICES OF AMERICA	10,000		229	IVY TECH COMMUNITY COLLEGE OF I	8,553		269	UNIVERSITY OF COLORADO HEALTH	7,593
190	COLUMBUS PUBLIC SCHOOL DISTRICT	10,000		230	COUNTY OF CLARK	8,528		270	HARTFORD HOSPITAL	7,500
191	MERCY HOSPITALS EAST COMMUNITIES	10,000		231	NCH CORPORATION	8,500		271	PIMA COUNTY	7,500
192	MISSION HOSPITAL, INC.	10,000		232	WAYNE STATE UNIVERSITY	8,500		272	COUNTY OF MONTGOMERY	7,400
193	NORTH EAST INDEPENDENT SCH	10,000		233	BLACK & VEATCH HOLDING COMPANY	8,495		273	VCU HEALTH SYSTEM AUTHORITY	7,399
194	COOPERATIVE FOR ASSISTA AND RE	10,000		234	BVH, INC.	8,495		274	GARLAND INDEPENDENT SCHOOL DI	7,307
195	UMASS MEMORIAL COMMUNITY HOSP	10,000		235	THE BRIGHAM AND WOMEN'S HOSPITAL	8,376		275	COUNTY OF DEKALB	7,300
196	BAPTIST MEMORIAL HEALTH CARE SYS	9,877		236	AVERITT EXPRESS INCORPORATED	8,210		276	COBORN'S, INCORPORATED	7,200
197	ONEAMERICA FINANCIAL PARTNERS,	9,875		237	AVERITT EXPRESS, INC.	8,208		277	LIBERTY UNIVERSITY, INC.	7,200
198	LOUDOUN COUNTY PUBLIC SCHOOL	9,822		238	EASTERN MAINE HEALTHCARE SYSTEMS	8,175		278	YSLETA INDEPENDENT SCHOOL DIST	7,155
199	KENTUCKYONE HEALTH, INC.	9,807		239	CEDARS-SINAI MEDICAL CENTER	8,000		279	CATHOLIC RELIEF SERVICES -	7,100
200	PROVIDENCE HEALTH & SERVICES	9,700		240	RUSH UNIVERSITY MEDICAL CENTER	8,000		280	CINCINNATI PUBLIC SCHOOLS	7,070
201	BEALL'S, INC.	9,700		241	DARTMOUTH-HITCHCOCK HEALTH	8,000		281	ORLEANS PARISH SCHOOL DISTRICT	7,062
202	SWEDISH HEALTH SERVICES	9,700		242	NORTHSIDE HOSPITAL, INC.	8,000		282	NOVARTIS PHARMACEUTICALS CORPO	7,000
203	THE GEORGETOWN UNIVERSITY	9,700		243	ARIZONA STATE UNIVERSITY	8,000		283	DAIRY FARMERS OF AMERICA, INC.	7,000
204	MESA UNIFIED SCHOOL DISTRICT 4	9,621		244	CATHOLIC HEALTH INITIATIVES COL	8,000		284	GROWMARK, INC.	7,000
205	UNIVERSITY OF PITTSBURGH	9,607		245	THE HEALTH CARE CITY OF HUNTSVI	8,000		285	WEST VIRGINIA UNITED HEALTH SYS	7,000
206	THE WASHINGTON UNIVERSITY	9,600		246	MOUNT CARMEL HEALTH SYSTEM	8,000		286	GRUMA CORPORATION	7,000
207	SAINT LUKE'S HOSPITAL OF BETH	9,599		247	FLORIDA HEALTH SCIENCES CENTER	8,000		287	BAPTIST HEALTH SYSTEM, INC.	7,000
208	SOUTHERN ILLINOIS UNIVERSITY INC	9,576		248	SCOTT & WHITE MEMORIAL HOSPITAL	8,000		288	THE UNIVERSITY OF VERMONT MEDICA	7,000
209	JOHNSON CONTROLS FIRE PROT	9,500		249	RIVERSIDE HEALTHCARE ASSOCIAT	8,000		289	NORTH BROWARD HOSPITAL DISTRICT	7,000
210	INTEGRIS HEALTH, INC.	9,500		250	SOUTHEASTERN FREIGHT LINES, INC.	8,000		290	MERCY CHILDREN'S HOSPITAL	7,000
211	LOS ANGELES DEPARTMENT OF WAT	9,500		251	NEVADA SYSTEM OF HIGHER EDUCA	8,000		291	THE LANCASTER GENERAL HO	7,000
212	CLEVELAND MUNICIPAL SCHOOL DIS	9,500		252	GEISINGER MEDICAL CENTER	8,000		292	THEDACARE, INC.	7,000
213	MANAGEMENT & TRAINING CORP	9,500		253	THE CHILDREN'S HOSPITAL CORPO	8,000		293	ALDINE INDEPENDENT SCHOOL	7,000
214	MEMORIAL SLOAN-KETTERING CANCER	9,325		254	INTERNATIONAL RESCUE COMMI	8,000		294	THE UNIVERSITY OF TOLEDO	7,000
215	ALEX LEE, INC.	9,200		255	OMAHA PUBLIC SCHOOLS	8,000		295	ALBANY MEDICAL CENTER	7,000
216	SOUTH BROWARD HOSPITAL DISTRICT	9,200		256	ALPINE SCHOOL DISTRICT	8,000		296	WASHOE COUNTY SCHOOL	7,000
217	PLY GEM HOLDINGS, INC.	9,000		257	ARLINGTON INDEPENDENT SCHOOL	8,000		297	THE JUDGE GROUP INC	7,000
218	FRANCISCAN MISSIONARIES OF .	9,000		258	RIVERSIDE HOSPITAL, INC.	8,000		298	UNITED STATES BEEF CORP	7,000
219	MINNEAPOLIS PUBLIC SCHOOL DIST	9,000		259	GRANITE SCHOOL DISTRICT	8,000		299	YOUNG MEN'S CHRISTIAN OF THE G	7,000
220	EL PASO INDEPENDENT SCHOOL DIS	9,000		260	UNIVERSITY COMMUNITY HOSPITAL,	8,000		300	MAINEHEALTH	7,000

The 100 Largest Private Companies by Net Income 2019

Rank	Company Headquarters	Net Income ($bil)
1	SAINT PAUL REGIONAL WATER SERVICES	$13,928
2	BNSF RAILWAY COMPANY	$12,119
3	NOVARTIS PHARMACEUTICALS CORPORATION	$6,698
4	FINCANTIERI MARINE SYSTEMS NORTH AMERICA, INC.	$6,671
5	ALASKA PERMANENT FUND CORPORATION	$5,109
6	AMERICAN BALANCED FUND, INC.	$4,903
7	STATE OF CALIFORNIA	$4,799
8	TEXAS PERMANENT SCHOOL FUND MANAGEMENT INC.	$4,155
9	YALE UNIVERSITY	$3,271
10	LELAND STANFORD JUNIOR UNIVERSITY	$2,972
11	THE TRUSTEES OF PRINCETON UNIVERSITY	$2,583
12	MASSACHUSETTS INSTITUTE OF TECHNOLOGY	$2,392
13	PUBLIX SUPER MARKETS, INC.	$2,026
14	PERMANENT UNIVERSITY FUND	$1,964
15	STATE OF TEXAS	$1,883
16	TEXAS COUNTY AND DISTRICT RETIREMENT SYSTEM	$1,761
17	THE TRUSTEES OF THE UNIVERSITY OF PENNSYLVANIA	$1,735
18	JOHNSON CONTROLS, INC.	$1,679
19	ASCENSION HEALTH ALLIANCE	$1,639
20	UNIVERSITY OF TEXAS SYSTEM	$1,589
21	SCHWAB CHARITABLE FUND	$1,552
22	CHEVRON PHILLIPS CHEMICAL COMPANY LLC	$1,446
23	SUNOCO PIPELINE L.P.	$1,420
24	CENTRAL PUGET SOUND REGIONAL TRANSIT AUTHORITY	$1,292
25	ALLY BANK	$1,273
26	ADVENTIST HEALTH SYSTEM SUNBELT HEALTHCARE	$1,168
27	THE CLEVELAND CLINIC FOUNDATION	$1,150
28	ONEOK PARTNERS, L.P.	$1,072
29	INTERMOUNTAIN HEALTH CARE INC	$1,062
30	SUTTER HEALTH	$1,060
31	SPECTRA ENERGY CORP	$1,020
32	THE WASHINGTON UNIVERSITY	$1,012
33	CORNELL UNIVERSITY	$986
34	THE UNIVERSITY OF CHICAGO	$980
35	COBANK, ACB	$937
36	REGENTS OF THE UNIVERSITY OF MICHIGAN	$920
37	IHC HEALTH SERVICES, INC.	$885
38	TEXAS HEALTH RESOURCES	$870
39	MAYO CLINIC HOSPITAL-ROCHESTER	$856
40	CHEVRON PHILLIPS CHEMICAL COMPANY LP	$841
41	THE CHARLOTTE-MECKLENBURG HOSPITAL AUTHORITY	$830
42	EATON CORPORATION	$821
43	MONSTER BEVERAGE 1990 CORPORATION	$821
44	PRECISION CASTPARTS CORP.	$817
45	SCRIPPS NETWORKS INTERACTIVE, INC.	$814
46	PLAINS PIPELINE, L.P.	$783
47	THE NEW YORK AND PRESBYTERIAN HOSPITAL	$763
48	BAYLOR SCOTT & WHITE HOLDINGS	$755
49	AMERICAN HONDA FINANCE CORPORATION	$753
50	UNIVERSITY OF TEXAS AT AUSTIN	$752
51	UNIVERSITY OF COLORADO HEALTH	$747
52	DARTMOUTH COLLEGE	$740
53	THE BLOOMBERG FAMILY FOUNDATION INC	$737
54	BANNER HEALTH	$728
55	EQUINOR NATURAL GAS LLC	$722
56	CITGO PETROLEUM CORPORATION	$715
57	JOHNS HOPKINS UNIVERSITY	$705
58	THOMAS JEFFERSON UNIVERSITY	$700
59	TRUSTEES OF DARTMOUTH COLLEGE	$691
60	DUKE UNIVERSITY HEALTH SYSTEM, INC.	$688
61	GENERAL ELECTRIC INTERNATIONAL, INC.	$686
62	HOUSTON METHODIST HOSPITAL	$682
63	AMERICAN LEBANESE SYRIAN ASSOCIATED CHARITIES, INC.	$658
64	THE ANDREW W MELLON FOUNDATION	$656
65	NATIONWIDE CHILDREN'S HOSPITAL	$647
66	THE PENNSYLVANIA STATE UNIVERSITY	$636
67	NOBLE HOLDING (U.S.) CORPORATION	$607
68	PRESIDIAN DESTINATIONS, LTD.	$583
69	PRODUCTION TECHNOLOGIES, INC.	$580
70	SENTARA HEALTHCARE	$580
71	NIELSEN HOLDINGS PLC	$575
72	SAINT MARYS HOSPITAL	$557
73	OHIOHEALTH CORPORATION	$519
74	BOSTON UNIVERSITY	$517
75	FARM CREDIT SERVICES OF AMERICA, PCA	$514
76	FAIRVIEW HEALTH SERVICES	$511
77	THE VANDERBILT UNIVERSITY	$511
78	COLONIAL PIPELINE COMPANY	$509
79	BRIGHAM YOUNG UNIVERSITY	$492
80	UNIVERSITY OF SOUTHERN CALIFORNIA	$489
81	MICHIGAN STATE UNIVERSITY	$482
82	MERCY HEALTH	$457
83	DST SYSTEMS, INC.	$452
84	STANFORD HEALTH CARE	$450
85	THE SCHOOL BOARD OF MIAMI-DADE COUNTY	$449
86	HARTFORD HEALTHCARE CORPORATION	$440
87	AURORA HEALTH CARE, INC.	$438
88	CEDARS-SINAI MEDICAL CENTER	$418
89	CALIFORNIA INSTITUTE OF TECHNOLOGY	$413
90	THE PEW CHARITABLE TRUSTS	$408
91	UNIVERSITY OF MISSOURI SYSTEM	$402
92	MAGELLAN PIPELINE COMPANY, L.P.	$397
93	BEAUMONT HEALTH	$393
94	WESTERN & SOUTHERN FINANCIAL GROUP, INC.	$388
95	SIGNATURE FINANCIAL LLC	$387
96	UNIVERSITY OF PITTSBURGH	$382
97	BAYLOR UNIVERSITY MEDICAL CENTER	$379
98	ENTERPRISE CRUDE PIPELINE LLC	$378
99	SUNLIGHT GIVING FOUNDATION	$378
100	GORDON RESEARCH CONFERENCES INC	$372

SOURCE: MERGENT DATA , FEBRUARY 2019

The 100 Largest Private Companies by Total Assets 2019

Rank	Company Headquarters	Net Income ($bil)
1	SAINT PAUL REGIONAL WATER SERVICES	$335,832
2	STATE OF CALIFORNIA	$333,689
3	STATE OF TEXAS	$323,008
4	NOVARTIS PHARMACEUTICALS CORPORATION	$130,124
5	ALLY BANK	$123,548
6	COBANK, ACB	$117,471
7	AMERICAN BALANCED FUND, INC.	$87,395
8	BNSF RAILWAY COMPANY	$83,098
9	AMERICAN HONDA FINANCE CORPORATION	$69,854
10	ALASKA PERMANENT FUND CORPORATION	$67,671
11	UNIVERSITY OF TEXAS SYSTEM	$66,887
12	NEW YORK CITY TRANSIT AUTHORITY	$44,805
13	WESTERN & SOUTHERN FINANCIAL GROUP, INC.	$44,750
14	TEXAS PERMANENT SCHOOL FUND MANAGEMENT COMPANY	$44,517
15	FINCANTIERI MARINE SYSTEMS NORTH AMERICA, INC.	$44,240
16	STATE OF OKLAHOMA	$43,483
17	SIGNATURE FINANCIAL LLC	$43,120
18	LELAND STANFORD JUNIOR UNIVERSITY	$41,954
19	YALE UNIVERSITY	$41,873
20	SPECTRA ENERGY CORP	$36,842
21	ASCENSION HEALTH ALLIANCE	$34,320
22	AGFIRST FARM CREDIT BANK	$32,487
23	THE TRUSTEES OF PRINCETON UNIVERSITY	$31,582
24	JOHNSON CONTROLS, INC.	$29,673
25	EATON CORPORATION	$27,466
26	TEXAS COUNTY AND DISTRICT RETIREMENT SYSTEM	$26,387
27	COUNTY OF CLARK	$26,120
28	MASSACHUSETTS INSTITUTE OF TECHNOLOGY	$26,073
29	FARM CREDIT SERVICES OF AMERICA, PCA	$24,773
30	THE TRUSTEES OF THE UNIVERSITY OF PENNSYLVANIA	$23,083
31	PERMANENT UNIVERSITY FUND	$22,404
32	NEW JERSEY TRANSPORTATION TRUST FUND AUTHORITY	$22,218
33	REGENTS OF THE UNIVERSITY OF MICHIGAN	$22,063
34	FARM CREDIT BANK OF TEXAS	$21,222
35	MARYLAND DEPARTMENT OF TRANSPORTATION	$21,134
36	CATHOLIC HEALTH INITIATIVES	$20,595
37	PRECISION CASTPARTS CORP.	$20,497
38	THE HERTZ CORPORATION	$20,058
39	ONEAMERICA FINANCIAL PARTNERS, INC.	$19,921
40	GENERAL ELECTRIC INTERNATIONAL, INC.	$19,615
41	NEW YORK STATE HOUSING FINANCE AGENCY	$18,240
42	PUBLIX SUPER MARKETS, INC.	$17,464
43	SUTTER HEALTH	$17,081
44	NEW YORK UNIVERSITY	$16,876
45	CHEVRON PHILLIPS CHEMICAL COMPANY LLC	$16,767
46	MAYO CLINIC HOSPITAL-ROCHESTER	$16,307
47	FAIRFAX COUNTY VIRGINIA	$15,883
48	THE CLEVELAND CLINIC FOUNDATION	$15,866
49	PROVIDENCE HEALTH & SERVICES	$15,740
50	ONEOK PARTNERS, L.P.	$15,469
51	ADVENTIST HEALTH SYSTEM SUNBELT HEALTHCARE COR	$15,468
52	NIELSEN HOLDINGS PLC	$15,303
53	NATIONAL RAILROAD PASSENGER CORPORATION	$15,253
54	THE UNIVERSITY OF CHICAGO	$15,237
55	PARTNERS HEALTHCARE SYSTEM, INC.	$15,070
56	STATE OF RHODE ISLAND AND PROVIDENCE PLANTATIONS	$14,901
57	NEW JERSEY TURNPIKE AUTHORITY INC	$14,831
58	JARDEN CORPORATION	$14,293
59	MILTON HERSHEY SCHOOL & SCHOOL TRUST	$14,224
60	THE PENNSYLVANIA STATE UNIVERSITY	$14,030
61	NORTHWESTERN UNIVERSITY	$13,660
62	BOARD OF REGENTS OF THE UNIVERSITY SYSTEM OF GEO	$13,505
63	THE WASHINGTON UNIVERSITY	$13,321
64	SOUTH CAROLINA PUBLIC SERVICE AUTHORITY (INC)	$13,200
65	CORNELL UNIVERSITY	$13,184
66	LONG ISLAND POWER AUTHORITY	$13,101
67	CHEVRON PHILLIPS CHEMICAL COMPANY LP	$12,987
68	NOBLE HOLDING (U.S.) CORPORATION	$12,876
69	COUNTY OF MONTGOMERY	$12,816
70	SALT RIVER PROJECT AGRICULTURAL IMPROVE	$12,657
71	UNIVERSITY OF SOUTHERN CALIFORNIA	$12,603
72	BAYLOR SCOTT & WHITE HOLDINGS	$12,138
73	THE FORD FOUNDATION	$12,114
74	INTERMOUNTAIN HEALTH CARE INC	$12,008
75	BANNER HEALTH	$11,670
76	UNIVERSITY OF WASHINGTON INC	$11,609
77	COUNTY OF HILLSBOROUGH	$11,550
78	THE NEW YORK AND PRESBYTERIAN HOSPITAL	$11,488
79	UNIVERSITY OF PITTSBURGH MEDICAL CENTER	$11,485
80	LAWRENCE TOWNSHIP SCHOOL DISTRICT INC	$11,407
81	CENTRAL PUGET SOUND REGIONAL TRANSIT AUTHORITY	$11,387
82	IHC HEALTH SERVICES, INC.	$10,973
83	JOHNS HOPKINS UNIVERSITY	$10,648
84	CITY OF LONG BEACH	$10,637
85	SCHWAB CHARITABLE FUND	$10,634
86	UNIVERSITY OF TEXAS AT AUSTIN	$10,584
87	LOS ANGELES DEPARTMENT OF WATER AND POWER	$10,299
88	TALEN ENERGY SUPPLY, LLC	$10,240
89	GENERAL ELECTRIC INTERNATIONAL OPERATIONS COM	$9,968
90	RAYMOND JAMES & ASSOCIATES INC	$9,918
91	PHILADELPHIA CONSOLIDATED HOLDING CORP.	$9,719
92	BOARD OF EDUCATION OF CITY OF CHICAGO	$9,663
93	ADVOCATE HEALTH CARE NETWORK	$9,634
94	THE CHARLOTTE-MECKLENBURG HOSPITAL AUTHORITY	$9,320
95	THE REGENTS OF THE UNIVERSITY OF COLORADO	$9,273
96	METROPOLITAN WATER RECLAMATION DISTR	$9,187
97	TESLA ENERGY OPERATIONS, INC.	$9,131
98	TRUSTEES OF THE ESTATE OF BERNICE PAUAHI BISHOP	$9,072
99	HEWLETT, WILLIAM AND FLORA FOUNDATION (INC)	$9,023
100	MUNICIPAL ELECTRIC AUTHORITY OF GEORGIA	$8,995

Hoover's Handbook of

Private Companies

The Companies

AAA COOPER TRANSPORTATION

They might not give you a map like that other AAA but AAA Cooper Transportation can freight your cargo from point A to point B. A non-union regional less-than-truckload (LTL) freight hauler AAA Cooper (ACT) operates in a dozen southeastern US states as well as Puerto Rico; it also maintains facilities in Chicago and a few other industrial crossroads. (LTL carriers combine freight from multiple shippers into a single truckload.) ACT operates a fleet of approximately 2400 tractors and 6000 trailers. ACT also offers freight brokerage services and dedicated contract carriage.

Operations
The company's five primary service offerings are LTL Services dedicated services international Services (including port services) managed services and fleet maintenance services.

Its port services provide services to the port the shipper and the customer. It transloads the goods from the container to its trailer or dock and returns the container to the port. Its fleet maintenance services provide maintenance services for all types of diesel engines including the CAT VOLVO International Detroit and Cummins brands.

The company's distribution operations offer assembly operations manufacturing plant transfers warehouse transfers wholesale distribution and retail distribution.

Geographic Reach
ACT operates more than 70 facilities in the Southeast Southwest Midwest and Puerto Rico. It has nearly 40 maintenance facilities nationwide and partners with carriers to extend its coverage into Canada and Mexico. The company's international partnerships allow it for operate across the Caribbean Latin America Europe Asia Africa and Australia.

Sales and Marketing
ATC serves a range of sectors including Automotive Manufacturing Automotive Parts Heavy Equipment Parts Building Materials Retail and HVAC. ACT customers include Schneider Logistics Volvo Logistics Mastio & Company GlobalTranz Technicolor John Deere and Nissan.

Strategy
As part of its growth strategy ACT seeks to offer new services and expand into new geographies. In 2014 the company launched a new Managed Services offering adding Truckload Brokerage and Parcel Audit to its services.

In 2013 the company opened a service center at Corpus Christi Texas.

Company Background
The ATC was founded in 1955.

EXECUTIVES

President And Coo, Reid Dove
Cfo, Steve Roy
Director Dedicated Services, Charles (Charlie) Prickett
Vp Operations, Lee McMillan
Vp Information Services, Dan Christian
Vice President Of Safety And Maintenance, Steven Aronhalt
Vice President Enterprise Development, John Hammons
National Account Manager, Joe Hanks
National Account Manager, Bob Mazzeffi
Vice President, CORY Bingham
National Account Manager, Chris Holden
National Account Manager, Tom Glaser

LOCATIONS
HQ: AAA COOPER TRANSPORTATION
1751 KINSEY RD, DOTHAN, AL 363035877
Phone: 334 793-2284
Web: WWW.AAACOOPER.COM

PRODUCTS/OPERATIONS

Selected Services
Dedicated
  Company branding
  Specialized equipment
International LTL
LTL
Port
  Consolidation
  Drayage
  Transloading

COMPETITORS

ArcBest	Saia
Averitt Express	Southeastern Freight
Estes Express	Lines
FedEx Freight	UPS Freight
Old Dominion Freight	YRC Worldwide
R+L Carriers	

HISTORICAL FINANCIALS
Company Type: Private

Income Statement   FYE: December 31

	REVENUE ($ mil.)	NET INCOME ($ mil.)	NET PROFIT MARGIN	EMPLOYEES
12/17*	664	31	4.8%	4,933
01/17	592	17	3.0%	—
01/16	595	14	2.4%	—
12/14	576	20	3.5%	—
Annual Growth	4.8%	16.5%		—

*Fiscal year change

2017 Year-End Financials
Return on assets: 1.5%   Cash ($ mil.): —
Return on equity: 4.8%
Current ratio: 1.20

AARP

Turn 50 and the doors of the AARP will open for you as they have for nearly 38 million current members. On behalf of its members the not-for-profit AARP acts as an advocate on public policy issues such as health care and financial security publishes information (the monthly AARP Bulletin and the bimonthly AARP The Magazine and through Spanish language media) promotes community service and works with business partners to offer products and services (including discounts on insurance and travel). The group is organized into some 1300 local chapters throughout the US. Royalties from businesses eager to reach AARP members account for about half of the group's revenue.

Operations
It may not be the most exclusive club around but AARP is one of the most powerful. As the largest advocacy group in the US the organization has a loud voice on Capitol Hill in part because older Americans tend to vote in greater relative numbers than many other segments of the population. AARP through its Foundation organization is focused on the national budget Medicare elder abuse and Social Security. To this end the organization operates Government Watch an interactive website designed to allow older Americans to hold Congress and the President's administration accountable on key issues that affect them.

AARP oversees volunteer services as well. The AARP Experience Corps is for volunteers aged 50+ who want to tutor and mentor youth in their communities primarily literacy for children in kindergarten through third grade. It operates in nearly 20 cities across the country.

Geographic Reach
The organization boasts staffed offices in all 50 US states the District of Columbia Puerto Rico and the US Virgin Islands.

Financial Performance
AARP generates revenue from several sources including royalties from businesses that partner with it membership dues advertising and investment income. For the year 2016 AARP generated $1.6 billion in operating revenue up 4% from the previous year. Royalties (mainly from United Healthcare Corp.) totaled $880 million membership dues amounted to $300 million and advertising sales were $150 million.

As a non-profit AARP does not report net income or earnings but instead records a change in its net assets. For the year 2016 the change in net assets due to operating activities was $3.9 million well below the $47 million of the prior year. Despite higher operating revenues the agency spent enough additional monies on program services (community outreach publications & communications membership engagement) that it eroded the upward movement in sales.

Strategy
AARP in 2016 achieved notable marks for its constituents. Its policy arm helped pass caregiver legislation in 14 US states; it entered the national conversation about updating the US Social Security program with its Take a Stand campaign and helped 2.7 million taxpayers file tax returns free of charge through the AARP Foundation Tax-Aide.

The group has worked to attract baby boomers with its 50+ campaign in anticipation of the aging generation. AARP continues to advance its legislative agendas at the state and federal government levels championing policies that aid its older membership base. Such policies include safe & affordable housing senior hunger issues reconnecting families & communities and helping seniors attain a stable source of income.

It?s programs and services through which it directly interacts with its members and communities includes: Back to Work 50+ Drive to End Hunger Experience Corps and Work for Yourself@50+.

Employers who engage in age discrimination are likely to hear from the AARP which joins several age discrimination cases each year. It is watching with interest cases against Google and Spirit AeroSystems. It recently helped resolve a lawsuit pertaining to Northrup Grumman?s 401k plan.

AARP offers insurance through partnerships with Aetna and UnitedHealth Group. The AARP-branded products includes policies designed to supplement Medicare coverage and policies intended to cover people ages 50 to 64. Other insurance partners include New York Life Insurance and The Hartford Financial Services Group.

EXECUTIVES

Evp And Cfo, Robert R. Hagans
Ceo, Jo Ann C. Jenkins
Evp And President Life Reimagined, Emilio Pardo
Evp And Chief Of Staff, Kevin Donnellan
Evp State And National Group, Nancy A. LeaMond
President And Ceo Aarp Services Inc., John J. Wider
Evp Membership And Integrated Value, Steve Cone
Evp Multicultural Markets And Engagement, Lorraine Cortés-V¨zquez
Evp States And Communities, Harroll (Hop) Backus

Evp And Cio, Hollis (Terry) Bradwell
Evp Policy Strategy And International Affairs,
 Debra Whitman
President Aarp Foundation, Lisa M. Ryerson
Executive Vice President Of Media, Beth Ellard
Chief Operating Officer, Scott Frisch
Senior Vice President Editorial Director, Myrna
 Blyth
Senior Vice President Data Analytics And
 Performance Management, Jason Mugg
Vice President Quality And Compliance, Michael
 Lewis
Vice President, Sanjay Khurana
Senior Vice President And Senior Associate
 General Counsel, David Morales
Vice President My Home And Family Portfolio,
 Robert Stephen
Vice President, Margaret Mannix
Senior Vice President Aarp Experience, Jim
 Pendergast
Senior Vice President And Treasurer, Karen Mercer
Chairman, Carol Raphael
Vice Chairman, Ronald E. Daly
Auditors: GRANT THORNTON LLP WASHINGTON

LOCATIONS

HQ: AARP
 601 E ST NW, WASHINGTON, DC 200490003
Phone: 202 434-2277
Web: WWW.AARP.ORG

PRODUCTS/OPERATIONS

2016 sales

	$ mil.	% of total
Royalties	880	55
Membership dues	299	19
Publications advertising	150	9
Contributions	96	6
Grant	97	6
Program income	73	5
Other	5	-
Total	**1,603**	**100**

Selected Operations & Programs

AARP Bulletin (monthly news update)
AARP Driver Safety (classroom refresher)
AARP Foundation Experience Corps
AARP Legal Services Network
AARP Services (taxable product management marketing
 and e-commerce subsidiary)
AARP The Magazine (bimonthly magazine)
Back to Work 50+
Financial Planning
Public Policy Institute
Research Information Center
Senior Community Service Employment Program
 (SCSEP)
Tax-Aide

HISTORICAL FINANCIALS

Company Type: Private

Income Statement

	REVENUE ($ mil.)	NET INCOME ($ mil.)	NET PROFIT MARGIN	EMPLOYEES
12/17	1,643	279	17.0%	1,800
12/16	1,604	141	8.8%	—
12/14	1,399	84	6.0%	—
12/13	1,438	408	28.4%	—
Annual Growth	**3.4%**	**(9.1%)**	**—**	**—**

FYE: December 31

2017 Year-End Financials

Return on assets: 11.9%   Cash ($ mil.): 460
Return on equity: 17.0%
Current ratio: —

AARP FOUNDATION

EXECUTIVES

Pres, Lisa Marsh Ryerson
Communications Manager, Luci De Haan
Procurement Staff, Vince Coutee
Staff, Carlton Crudup
Executive Officer, Barbara Hvasta
Designer, Courtney Murphy
Management Vice-President, Tom Malloy
Management Vice-President, Tracey Merchant
Staff, Lynn Wiles
Executive Officer, Phil Hawkins
Staff, George McGrath
Auditors: GRANT THORNTON LLP WASHINGTON

LOCATIONS

HQ: AARP FOUNDATION
 601 E ST NW, WASHINGTON, DC 200490003
Phone: 202 434-6755
Web: WWW.AARP.ORG

HISTORICAL FINANCIALS

Company Type: Private

Income Statement

	REVENUE ($ mil.)	NET INCOME ($ mil.)	NET PROFIT MARGIN	EMPLOYEES
12/16	341	133	39.0%	232
12/15	1,541	108	7.0%	—
12/14	146	2	1.4%	—
12/13	0	0	—	—
Annual Growth	**—**	**—**	**—**	**—**

FYE: December 31

2016 Year-End Financials

Return on assets: —   Cash ($ mil.): 11
Return on equity: 39.0%
Current ratio: —

ABINGTON MEMORIAL HOSPITAL INC

Abington Memorial Hospital brings health care to residents of southeastern Pennsylvania. The not-for-profit community hospital has some 670 beds. In addition to general medical and surgical care the hospital offers specialized care centers for cancer and cardiovascular conditions operates high-tech orthopedic and neurological surgery units and serves as a regional trauma care facility. It also runs an inpatient pediatric unit in affiliation with The Children's Hospital of Philadelphia. Abington Memorial also known as Abington Health operates the neighboring 125-bed Lansdale Hospital and several area outpatient facilities.

Operations

The not-for-profit community hospital has some 670 beds and employs about 1400 physicians. Its specialty units include the Pilla Heart Center the Rosenfeld Cancer Center the Diamond Stroke Center as well as a level II trauma center and institutes for senior health and bariatric surgeries. Abington Memorial is affiliated with several medical schools including the Temple University School of Medicine and offers residency programs and postgraduate medical education.

In addition to its hospitals Abington Memorial operates an extensive outpatient care facility named Abington Health Center-Warminster. The Warminster facility is located in Bucks County and features an inpatient hospice center. Other outpatient facilities include Abington Health Center-Schilling (in Willow Grove) Abington Health Center-Blue Bell and Abington Physicians at Montgomeryville.

Altogether the organization's facilities handle 677000 outpatient visits and 33000 inpatient admissions each year.

Additionally Abington Memorial operates a nursing school and a clinical research center.

Geographic Reach

Abington Memorial provides care to residents of southeastern Pennsylvania. The hospital serves Montgomery Bucks and Philadelphia counties.

Strategy

Abington Memorial began using the Abington Health moniker to reflect its larger network of facilities after it acquired Lansdale Hospital which was previously known as Central Montgomery Medical Center from Universal Health Services in 2008. Abington Memorial has since invested in a number of improvements at the acquired hospital. The main Abington Memorial facility has also been enhanced including a new hybrid operating room for cardiac procedures in 2013.

Mergers and Acquisitions

In 2013 Abington Memorial acquired a home health agency the North Penn Visiting Nurse Association (NPVNA). The purchase expanded the geographic reach of Abington Memorial's home health operations.

Company Background

Abington Memorial first opened its doors in 1914.

EXECUTIVES

Senior Vice President For Finance, Michael Walsh
President Abington Hospitals, Margaret M. (Meg)
 McGoldrick
Chief Medical Officer, John J. Kelly
Medical Director, Gerard Cleary
Executive Vice President Of Information
 Technology, Jan Seip
Respiratory Therapy Director, Kathy Sebastian
Director Of Radiology, Kristin Crisci
Medical Records Director, Theresa Jones
Vice President Oncologist, Michael S Yoon
Infection Control Director, ROGER NIEMAN
Executive Vice President And Administrator,
 Michelle Henrie
Vice President Of Administration, Regina Harte
Secretary To Director Of Material Management,
 Joanne Jones

LOCATIONS

HQ: ABINGTON MEMORIAL HOSPITAL INC
 1200 OLD YORK RD, ABINGTON, PA 190013788
Phone: 215 481-2000
Web: WWW.ABINGTONHEALTH.ORG

PRODUCTS/OPERATIONS

Selected Facilities

Abington Health Center — Blue Bell Campus
 (Blue Bell PA)
Abington Health Center — Schilling Campus
 (Willow Grove PA)
Abington Health Center — Warminster Campus
 (Warminster PA)
Abington Memorial Hospital (Abington PA)
Abington Physicians at Montgomeryville (North Wales
 PA)
Lansdale Hospital (Lansdale PA)

COMPETITORS

Albert Einstein Healthcare Network
Aria Health
Crozer-Keystone Health System
Doylestown Hospital
Grand View
Main Line Health System

Memorial Hospital (PA)
Mercy Health System
Moses Taylor Hospital
North Philadelphia Health System
TUHS
Tenet Healthcare
University of Pennsylvania Health System
Virtua Memorial

HISTORICAL FINANCIALS
Company Type: Private

Income Statement				FYE: June 30
	REVENUE ($ mil.)	NET INCOME ($ mil.)	NET PROFIT MARGIN	EMPLOYEES
06/16	740	35	4.8%	4,018
06/15	697	28	4.1%	—
06/14	697	0	0.1%	—
06/13	708	20	2.9%	—
Annual Growth	1.5%	19.2%	—	—

2016 Year-End Financials
Return on assets: 5.5% Cash ($ mil.): 176
Return on equity: 4.8%
Current ratio: 1.80

ACCESS BUSINESS GROUP LLC

Somehow all those Amway products have to get from factories to the sales floor and that's where Access Business Group (ABG) comes in. The company manufactures and distributes cosmetics nutritional supplements home care and personal care products for its sister company Amway. (Both companies are units of Alticor.) It also offers contract manufacturing services for third-party consumer goods companies but to a lesser extent. Other offerings include product packaging services as well as catalog and direct mail printing services. In addition the company operates R&D labs that develop and test products for Amway.

Operations
A major function of ABG is the manufacturing and distribution of some 200 products in Amway's NUTRILITE line which includes nutritional food supplements in liquid powder food bar tablet and capsule form. Other key operations include manufacturing and distributing products in the ARTISTRY cosmetics and skin care line.

Geographic Reach
ABG owns and operates 10 manufacturing plants that comprise more than 1 million sq. ft. of space.

Sales and Marketing
The company offers its products through distributors and retailers both in North America and Internationally.

Strategy
Amway announced in 2012 it was investing nearly $180 million to expand manufacturing and processing capacity to meet growing global demand for its NUTRILITE brand of vitamin mineral and dietary supplements. The investment includes a new $81 million nutrition plant at the company's Spaulding Avenue site in Ada Michigan near Amway's headquarters. In support of this initiative the Michigan government has approved a $1.6 million incentive from a fund to support construction of this nutrition products manufacturing facility for ABG.

EXECUTIVES
Vice President Brand Management, Jackie Nickel
Vice President, Jim Siewertsen
Vice President Contract Sales, Ed VanEssendelft

LOCATIONS
HQ: ACCESS BUSINESS GROUP LLC
7575 FULTON ST E, ADA, MI 493550001
Phone: 616 787-6000
Web: WWW.ACCESSBUSINESSGROUP.COM

PRODUCTS/OPERATIONS

Selected Services and Products
Beauty
  Blushes
  Eye shadows
  Lipsticks
  Mascara
  Skin care
Fulfillment
  A-Frame
  B2B & B2C
  Customized order picking at the store level
  High volume pick pack & ship
  Pick-to-light
  Tilt tray sorter
Home Care
  Household cleaners
  Plastic bottles
  Powder and liquid dish washing detergents
  Powder and liquid laundry detergents
Nutrition
  Antioxidants/supplements/herbals
  Food bars
  Granulation
  Multiminerals/multivitamins
  OTC tableting
  Powdered drinks
Personal Care
  Bar soaps
  Bath oils
  Body mist
  Conditioners
  Lotions
  Plastic bottles
  Shampoos
  Shower gels
  Styling products
Print
  Catalogs
  Corrugated cases
  Fine printing
  Labels
  L-Boards
  Paperboard packaging

COMPETITORS

AppTech	Pfizer
Berry Global	Procter & Gamble
Botanical Laboratories	Strathmore
Essential Nutrition	UPS Supply Chain
Johnson & Johnson	Solutions

HISTORICAL FINANCIALS
Company Type: Private

Income Statement				FYE: December 31
	REVENUE ($ mil.)	NET INCOME ($ mil.)	NET PROFIT MARGIN	EMPLOYEES
12/16	974	0	—	3,000
12/15	1,009	0	—	—
12/14	1,068	0	—	—
12/13	1,135	0	—	—
Annual Growth	(5.0%)	—	—	—

ACCESS MANAGEMENT SERVICES, LLC

EXECUTIVES
President, Marshall Thomas
Vice President, Cody Belzley
Regional Commissioner, Richard Gonz Lez
Coordinator, Jenny Han
Coordinator, Lauren Barocas
Information Specialist, Lois Ellison
Manager, Ashley Davis
Manager, Lori Chavez
Vice President of Legal Servic, Ann Edelman
External Resource Coordinator, Charlene Frazier-Flores
Credentialing Coordinator Cred, Chelene Harris
Auditors: ERNST & YOUNG US LLP PHOENIX

LOCATIONS
HQ: ACCESS MANAGEMENT SERVICES, LLC
11100 E BETHANY DR, AURORA, CO 800142630
Phone: 720 744-5100
Web: WWW.COACCESS.COM

HISTORICAL FINANCIALS
Company Type: Private

Income Statement				FYE: December 31
	REVENUE ($ mil.)	NET INCOME ($ mil.)	NET PROFIT MARGIN	EMPLOYEES
12/15	319	(13)	—	325
12/09	158	(1)	—	—
12/08*	0	0	—	—
06/05	0	0	—	—
Annual Growth	—	—	—	—

*Fiscal year change

2015 Year-End Financials
Return on assets: 13.7% Cash ($ mil.): 17
Return on equity: (-4.2%)
Current ratio: 1.10

ACCESSLEX INSTITUTE

EXECUTIVES
Ceo, Christopher P Chapman
Chb, Hannah R Arterian
Coo, Charles Albano
Human Resources Manager, Tanya Papahristos
Marketing Staff, Krysten Levin
Vice President of Legal Affair, Debbie Swartz
Auditors: GRANT THORNTON LLP PHILADELPH

LOCATIONS
HQ: ACCESSLEX INSTITUTE
10 N HIGH ST STE 400, WEST CHESTER, PA
193803014
Phone: 484 653-3300
Web: WWW.ACCESSGROUP.ORG

COMPETITORS

Bank of America	First Marblehead
College Loan	JPMorgan Chase
Corporation	Nelnet
Discover	Sallie Mae

HISTORICAL FINANCIALS
Company Type: Private

Income Statement
FYE: March 31

	ASSETS ($ mil.)	NET INCOME ($ mil.)	INCOME AS % OF ASSETS	EMPLOYEES
03/17	4,584	91	2.0%	60
03/16	5,056	16	0.3%	—
03/11	8,767	58	0.7%	—
03/10	10,316	(0)	—	—
Annual Growth	(10.9%)	—	—	—

2017 Year-End Financials

Return on assets: —
Return on equity: 150.0%
Sales ($ mil): 60

ACCORD HEALTHCARE, INC.

EXECUTIVES

Pres, Gerald Price
Vice President, Burt Sullivan
Executive Officer, David Demello
Executive Officer, Grzegorz Orlik
Senior Director of Marketing, Shannon Price
Auditors: JANSEN VALK THOMPSON REAHM PC

LOCATIONS

HQ: ACCORD HEALTHCARE, INC.
 1009 SLATER RD STE 210B, DURHAM, NC 277038446
Phone: 919 941-7878
Web: WWW.ACCORD-HEALTHCARE.COM

HISTORICAL FINANCIALS
Company Type: Private

Income Statement
FYE: March 31

	REVENUE ($ mil.)	NET INCOME ($ mil.)	NET PROFIT MARGIN	EMPLOYEES
03/17	281	5	2.1%	35
03/16*	223	8	3.7%	—
12/12	105	0	0.4%	—
12/11	64	2	4.6%	—
Annual Growth	34.4%	15.0%	—	—

*Fiscal year change

2017 Year-End Financials

Return on assets: 0.8%
Return on equity: 2.1%
Current ratio: 0.80
Cash ($ mil.): 1

ACE HARDWARE CORPORATION

In an age of big-box home improvement centers (Home Depot Lowes) wholesaler Ace makes the case for the local hardware store. By sales it is the #1 hardware cooperative in the US ahead of Do It Best. Ace dealer-owners operate more than 95% of the 4800 Ace Hardware-branded stores home centers and lumber and building materials locations selling more than 75000 products across all 50 US states and about 70 other countries. Stores range in size from small urban shops to large rural locations. From about 15 warehouses Ace distributes such products as electrical and plumbing supplies garden equipment hand tools housewares and power tools. Ace was founded in 1924 by a group of Chicago hardware store owners.

HISTORY

A group of Chicago-area hardware dealers — William Stauber Richard Hesse Gern Lindquist and Oscar Fisher — decided in 1924 to pool their hardware buying and promotional costs. In 1928 the group incorporated as Ace Stores named in honor of the superior WWI fliers dubbed aces. Hesse became president the following year retaining that position for the next 44 years. The company also opened its first warehouse in 1929 and by 1933 it had 38 dealers.

The organization had 133 dealers in seven states by 1949. In 1953 Ace began to allow dealers to buy stock in the company through the Ace Perpetuation Plan. During the 1960s Ace expanded into the South and West and by 1969 it had opened distribution centers in Georgia and California — its first such facilities outside Chicago. In 1968 it opened its first international store in Guam.

By the early 1970s the do-it-yourself market began to surge as inflation pushed up plumber and electrician fees. As the market grew large home center chains gobbled up market share from independent dealers such as those franchised through Ace. In response Ace and its dealers became a part of a growing trend in the hardware industry — cooperatives.

Hesse sold the company to its dealers in 1973 for $6 million (less than half its book value) and the following year Ace began operating as a cooperative. Hesse stepped down in 1973. In 1976 the dealers took full control when the company's first Board of Dealer-Directors was elected.

After signing up a number of dealers in the eastern US Ace had dealers in all 50 states by 1979. The co-op opened a plant to make paint in Matteson Illinois in 1984. By 1985 Ace had reached $1 billion in sales and had initiated its Store of the Future Program allowing dealers to borrow up to $200000 to upgrade their stores and conduct market analyses. Former head coach John Madden of the National Football League's Oakland Raiders signed on as Ace's mouthpiece in 1988.

A year later the co-op began to test ACENET a computer network that allowed Ace dealers to check inventory send and receive e-mail make special purchase requests and keep up with prices on commodity items such as lumber. In 1990 Ace established an International Division to handle its overseas stores. (It had been exporting products since 1975.) EVP and COO David Hodnik became president in 1995. That year the co-op added a net of 67 stores including a three-store chain in Russia. Expanding further internationally Ace signed a five-year joint-supply agreement in 1996 with Canadian lumber and hardware retailer Beaver Lumber. Hodnik added CEO to his title in 1996.

Ace fell further behind its old rival True Value in 1997 when ServiStar Coast to Coast and True Value merged to form TruServ (renamed True Value in 2005) a hardware giant that operated more than 10000 outlets at the completion of the merger.

Late in 1997 Ace launched an expansion program in Canada. (The co-op already operated distribution centers in Ontario and Calgary.) In 1999 Ace merged its lumber and building materials division with Builder Marts of America to form a dealer-owned buying group to supply about 2700 retailers. Ace gained 208 member outlet stores in 2000 but saw 279 member outlets terminated. The next year it gained 220 but lost 255.

Sodisco-Howden bought all the shares of Ace Hardware Canada in February 2003. To better serve international members Ace opened its first international buying office in Hong Kong in April 2004.

In all the company added 131 new stores in 2005. That year after 33 years with the company David F. Hodnik retired as president and CEO of Ace Hardware. He was succeeded by COO Ray A. Griffith.

In 2007 Griffith sent a letter to Ace's retailers saying the company was considering changing from a cooperative to a traditional corporation to become more competitive and to better fuel growth. Shortly after the company announced an accounting shortfall of about $150 million or nearly half of its equity which was uncovered while Ace prepared to convert formats. The error turned out to be an accident by a mid-level employee.

In 2009 Ace launched Aisle411 a free product-location service that can be accessed via phone similar to dialing for information. The company launched the service after learning that shoppers who were unable to find a product either left (about 20% of the time) or asked store associates for assistance (about 60%) which created a high demand for staff attention. Dedicated to pleasing its shoppers Ace was ranked "Highest in Customer Satisfaction among Home Improvement Stores" by J.D. Power and Associates in 2007 2008 and 2009.

In mid-2010 the hardware store chain became the first retailer — outside of Sears and Kmart stores — to sell Craftsman brand tools.

In January 2011 the company reorganized its international division into a stand-alone entity: Ace Hardware International Holdings. Ace Hardware owns about 78% of the newly-created entity.

In December 2012 Ace exited the paint manufacturing business with the sale of its paint manufacturing division including two paint manufacturing plants near Chicago to Valspar Corp. for about $45 million. Under the terms of the sale Valspar will continue to make and supply Ace-branded paint under a long-term supply agreement. Also it will supply a comprehensive line of Valspar-branded paints to Ace retail stores.

EXECUTIVES

President And Ceo, John S. Venhuizen, age 48
Vp Information Technology And Cio, Karen Fedyszyn
Evp Cfo And Chief Risk Officer, Bill Guzik
Chairman, Jim Ackroyd
Auditors: ERNST & YOUNG LLP CHICAGO IL

LOCATIONS

HQ: ACE HARDWARE CORPORATION
 2200 KENSINGTON CT, OAK BROOK, IL 605232100
Phone: 866 681-1836
Web: WWW.ACEHARDWAREINTL.COM

PRODUCTS/OPERATIONS

2014 Sales

	$ mil.	% of total
Wholesale Revenues	4,466	95
Retail Revenues	233	5
Total	**4,700**	**100**

Selected Services
Assembly
Automotive chip key cutting
Blade sharpening
Glass & Acrylic sheet cutting
Glass Repair
Hunting/Fishing license
In-store lock servicing
Selected Brands

ACCO BRANDS
ACE
ACME
ADANACBIG BENBILCOEUREKAEVEREADY

COMPETITORS

84 Lumber	McCoy Corp.
Akzo Nobel	Menard
BMC Stock	Northern Tool
Costco Wholesale	Orgill
Do it Best	Sears
Fastenal	Sutherland Lumber
Grossman's	True Value
Home Depot	United Hardware
Kmart	Distributing
Lowe's	Wal-Mart

HISTORICAL FINANCIALS

Company Type: Private

Income Statement				FYE: December 30
	REVENUE ($ mil.)	NET INCOME ($ mil.)	NET PROFIT MARGIN	EMPLOYEES
12/17	5,388	147	2.7%	4,500
12/16*	5,125	161	3.1%	—
01/16	5,045	156	3.1%	—
01/15	4,700	141	3.0%	—
Annual Growth	4.7%	1.4%	—	—

*Fiscal year change

2017 Year-End Financials

Return on assets: 12.7%
Return on equity: 2.7%
Current ratio: 0.50
Cash ($ mil.): 23

ACT, INC.

A C and T... three little letters that can strike fear in the hearts of high school students across the US. ACT most notably develops and administers the ACT national college admission exam with about 2 million high school seniors taking the test each year. ACT also designs other educational assessment tests and programs as well as career planning and workforce development programs for people of all ages around the world. Other operations provide assessment training and consulting to employers. The not-for-profit organization was founded in 1959 by E. F. Lindquist and Ted McCarrel who sought to create an exam to measure potential college students' capacity for critical thinking.

Operations

The organization's College and Career Readiness System culminates in the ACT test but it also includes the PLAN assessment test for 10th graders and the EXPLORE assessment test for eighth or ninth grade students. The ACT test has been taken by millions of people seeking to enter college and all four-year colleges and universities in the US accept ACT scores.

ACT maintains the ACT Center Network which delivers computer-based testing and training services to individuals employers and professional organizations. Located primarily at two- and four-year colleges ACT Center locations serve as a comprehensive resource for developing and serving a community's workforce and economy.

ACT has a strategic plan to invest in its product and service portfolios to ensure their effectiveness in meeting the challenges and opportunities of the rapidly changing world. ACT also plans to take a more pronounced position as a participant in national and international discussions regarding education and success in the workplace.

The company also engages in research and publishes reports aimed at policymakers researchers and educators. ACT's policy-related publications cover national topics that describe the implementation of education and workforce solutions or that focus on a single topic. Its research efforts are focused on test and test-item fairness test reliability and validity the meaning of test-score differences improving achievements of at-risk populations and the determinants of academic and career success. For educators ACT conducts free and fee-based research services to help postsecondary institutions recruit and better understand how to serve their students.

Geographic Reach

ACT operates globally from about a dozen US offices and international offices in Seoul Shanghai Singapore and Sydney. The company offers its services in all 50 states and in more than 130 countries worldwide.

On the global front ACT operates ACT International a for-profit subsidiary divided into two divisions: ACT Education Solutions which provides English-language instruction for international students hoping to attend English-speaking universities and ACT Business Solutions which focuses on employers. The latter includes a program English WorkKeys that analyzes key skill abilities and language proficiency of potential employees.

Mergers and Acquisitions

As part of its plan to use technology to improve its products ACT in 2016 acquired OpenEd a K-12 standards-aligned open educational resource provider. OpenEd offers half a million assessments homework assignments videos games and lesson plans to teachers schools and districts across the country.

EXECUTIVES

Svp And Cfo, Thomas J. Goedken
Coo, Janet E. Godwin
Ceo, Marten Roorda
Chief Commercial Officer, Suzana Delanghe
Cto, Lucas Kuhlmann
Chief Officer Center For Equity In Learning, Jim Larimore
Chief Talent Officer, Jennifer Yi Boyer
Director, Robert M. (Bob) Berdahl, age 81
Vice Chairman, Chad P. Wick
Auditors: MCGLADREY LLP CEDAR RAPIDS I

LOCATIONS

HQ: ACT, INC.
500 ACT DR, IOWA CITY, IA 522439003
Phone: 319 337-1000
Web: WWW.ACT.ORG

Selected US Locations

Atlanta
Aurora Colorado
Austin Texas
Chattanooga Tennessee (KeyTrain)
Gahanna Ohio
Hunt Valley Maryland
Iowa City Iowa (headquarters)
Lansing Michigan
Lincolnshire Illinois
Rancho Cordova California
Southborough Massachusetts
Tallahassee Florida
Washington DC

PRODUCTS/OPERATIONS

Selected Programs

ACT Online Prep (practice tests with real ACT®; test questions)
The ACT®; Test (curriculum-based achievement exam that measures skills and knowledge deemed important for college success)
ACT Pro (customized testing services)
ASSET®; (course placement assessment for college and university students)

CAAP (Collegiate Assessment of Academic Proficiency is a standardized nationally normed assessment program)
COMPASS®; (postsecondary placement test)
COMPASS®;/ESL (postsecondary placement test with assessment of English language ability levels)
CoreWork®; Diagnostics (online research-based benchmarking program)
CPAt (career programs assessment test)
Engage™ (academic behavior assessment)
Educational Opportunity Service (a tool to help colleges and universities build a pool of qualified prospective students)
EXPLORE®; (career investigation for 8th and 9th grade students)
Global Assessment Certificate™ and English Language Programs (GAC - university preparation program for students who do not have English as their first language; ELP - a suite of general and academically oriented English language programs)
KeyTrain®; and Career Ready 101®; (interactive training system for career readiness skills; comprehensive career training course)
NCRC™ - NCRC Plus - ICRC (career-readiness certificates)
PLAN®; (pre-ACT for 10th grade students)
QualityCore®; (high school instructional improvement component of ACT's College and Career Readiness System)
Research Services (survey services free and fee-based research services policy reports research and information services for educational institutions)
Scholarship and Recognition Services (consultation in scholarship and recognition program management for organizations)
State Services (Statewide adoption of one or more key ACT assessment products)
WorkKeys®; (workplace skills assessment)

Selected Operations

ACT Centers (training and testing sites)
ACT Education Solutions (English-language education)
National Center for Educational Accountability (public school data collection)

COMPETITORS

Bridges Transitions	Huntington Learning
College Board	Centers
College Coach	Kaplan
ETS	Questar Assessment
Edmentum	S&P Global
Educate	The Princeton Review

HISTORICAL FINANCIALS

Company Type: Private

Income Statement				FYE: August 31
	REVENUE ($ mil.)	NET INCOME ($ mil.)	NET PROFIT MARGIN	EMPLOYEES
08/16	350	17	5.1%	1,200
08/14	328	9	3.0%	—
08/05	179	208	116.2%	—
08/03	151	15	10.2%	—
Annual Growth	6.7%	1.2%	—	—

2016 Year-End Financials

Return on assets: 7.2%
Return on equity: 5.1%
Current ratio: 0.80
Cash ($ mil.): 21

ACTION CAPITAL CORPORATION

EXECUTIVES

Ceo, Becky J Cronister
Executive Vice President, Patrick Thom
Cfo, John J Canning
Stckhldr, Cicero Garner

Stckhldr, Hugh Inman Jr
Portfolio Manager Vice Preside, Bo Boyet
Auditors: MCGREGOR & COMPANY LLP COLUMB

LOCATIONS

HQ: ACTION CAPITAL CORPORATION
230 PEACHTREE ST NW # 810, ATLANTA, GA
303031568
Phone: 404 524-3181
Web: WWW.ACTIONCAPITAL.COM

HISTORICAL FINANCIALS

Company Type: Private

Income Statement   FYE: December 31

	ASSETS ($ mil.)	NET INCOME ($ mil.)	INCOME AS % OF ASSETS	EMPLOYEES
12/17	170	6	3.8%	17
12/16	146	4	3.0%	—
12/15	140	6	4.3%	—
12/14	128	5	4.6%	—
Annual Growth	9.8%	3.5%	—	—

2017 Year-End Financials

Return on assets: —   Sales ($ mil.): 1,539
Return on equity: 0.4%

ACTIONET, INC.

EXECUTIVES

President And Ceo, Ashley W. Chen
Evp And Cto, Jeffrey D. (Jeff) Abish
Vp And Cfo, Steven A. Crespy
Vice President Of Health Services, David Collignon
Vice President Global Operations, Alliant Small
Vice President Science And Research, Ramon De Guzman
Auditors: ARONSON LLC ROCKVILLE MD

LOCATIONS

HQ: ACTIONET, INC.
2600 PARK TWR DR STE 1000, VIENNA, VA 22180
Phone: 703 204-0090
Web: WWW.ACTIONET.COM

COMPETITORS

Amadeus Consulting	Leidos
CACI International	Lockheed Martin
Computer Sciences Corp.	ManTech
	Northrop Grumman
HP Enterprise Services	Unisys
IBM Global Services	

HISTORICAL FINANCIALS

Company Type: Private

Income Statement   FYE: December 31

	REVENUE ($ mil.)	NET INCOME ($ mil.)	NET PROFIT MARGIN	EMPLOYEES
12/16	425	32	7.7%	1,400
12/15	411	32	7.8%	—
12/14	352	25	7.2%	—
12/13	298	23	8.0%	—
Annual Growth	12.5%	11.3%	—	—

2016 Year-End Financials

Return on assets: 4.6%   Cash ($ mil.): 55
Return on equity: 7.7%
Current ratio: 4.10

ADAMS 12 FIVE STAR SCHOOLS

EXECUTIVES

Supt, Christopher E Gdowski
Help Desk Technician, Sandy Noon
Coordinator, Julie Campbell
Manager, Linda Lee
Coordinator, Stacey Bernstein
Psychologist, Catherine Sura
Assistant, D Eipper
Secretary, Heather Davis
Teacher, Vince Berger
Teacher, Rose Gifford
Teacher, Suzy Lucier
Auditors: CLIFTONLARSONALLEN LLP BROOMF

LOCATIONS

HQ: ADAMS 12 FIVE STAR SCHOOLS
1500 E 128TH AVE, THORNTON, CO 802412601
Phone: 720 972-4000
Web: WWW.ADAMS12.ORG

HISTORICAL FINANCIALS

Company Type: Private

Income Statement   FYE: June 30

	REVENUE ($ mil.)	NET INCOME ($ mil.)	NET PROFIT MARGIN	EMPLOYEES
06/18	448	(55)		5,040
06/17	427	270	63.3%	—
06/15	394	24	6.2%	—
06/14	379	9	2.4%	—
Annual Growth	4.3%	—	—	—

2018 Year-End Financials

Return on assets: 4.4%   Cash ($ mil.): 79
Return on equity: (-12.5%)
Current ratio: —

ADAMS COUNTY MEMORIAL HOSPITAL

EXECUTIVES

Ceo, Jo Ellen Eidam
Mng Dir, Robert Judge
V Chm, Russ Flueckiger
SEC, Dennis Bieberich
Cfo, Dane Wheeler
Director of Laboratory, Rhonda Brune
Security Staff, John Ginter
Supervisor, Janice Muhlenkamp
Director, Allison Kukelhan
Pharmacist, John Pasalich
Manager, Karen Cox
Auditors: SOMERSET CPAS PC INDIANAPOLI

LOCATIONS

HQ: ADAMS COUNTY MEMORIAL HOSPITAL
1100 MERCER AVE, DECATUR, IN 467332303
Phone: 260 724-2145
Web: WWW.ADAMSHOSPITAL.ORG

HISTORICAL FINANCIALS

Company Type: Private

Income Statement   FYE: December 31

	REVENUE ($ mil.)	NET INCOME ($ mil.)	NET PROFIT MARGIN	EMPLOYEES
12/16	315	10	3.3%	50
12/15	45	(1)	—	—
12/14	0	0	47.5%	—
12/13	0	0	55.4%	—
Annual Growth	1391.7%	485.0%	—	—

2016 Year-End Financials

Return on assets: 19.7%   Cash ($ mil.): 68
Return on equity: 3.3%
Current ratio: 1.60

ADVANCED TECHNOLOGY INTERNATIONAL

EXECUTIVES

Pres, Chris Van Metre
Treasurer, Julia Martin
Program Manager, Dennis Simon
Senior Vice-President, Curtis Holcomb
Sales and Marketing Staff, Ron Glover
Manager, Allison Moody
Administrative Assistant, Amanda Ballou
Scientist, Gerry Graves
Coordinator, Marcia Lytton
Program Manager, Mike Atkinson
Purchasing Administrator, Dee Green
Auditors: BDO USA LLP RALEIGH NC

LOCATIONS

HQ: ADVANCED TECHNOLOGY INTERNATIONAL
315 SIGMA DR, SUMMERVILLE, SC 294867790
Phone: 843 760-4500
Web: WWW.ATI.ORG

HISTORICAL FINANCIALS

Company Type: Private

Income Statement   FYE: September 30

	REVENUE ($ mil.)	NET INCOME ($ mil.)	NET PROFIT MARGIN	EMPLOYEES
09/17*	718	(11)	—	117
06/16	423	(2)	—	—
06/15	385	1	0.4%	—
06/14	273	2	1.0%	—
Annual Growth	38.0%	—	—	—

*Fiscal year change

2017 Year-End Financials

Return on assets: 16.9%   Cash ($ mil.): 206
Return on equity: (-1.6%)
Current ratio: 1.00

ADVANTECH CORPORATION

EXECUTIVES

Ceo, Ke-Cheng Liu
President, Chaney Ho
Vice President, Deryu Yin
Vice President, Eric Chen
Director of Engineering, Alan Koch
Marketing Staff, Russell Barber
Human Resources Executive, Ween Niu
Engineer of Sales, Dan Pierangeli
Quality Control Manager, Eric Huang
Engineer of Sales, George Renth
Vice-President, Kenny Deng
Auditors: CHEN & FAN SAN JOSE CALIFORN

LOCATIONS

HQ: ADVANTECH CORPORATION
380 FAIRVIEW WAY, MILPITAS, CA 950353062
Phone: 408 519-3800
Web: WWW.ADVANTECH.COM

HISTORICAL FINANCIALS
Company Type: Private

Income Statement · FYE: December 31

	REVENUE ($ mil.)	NET INCOME ($ mil.)	NET PROFIT MARGIN	EMPLOYEES
12/16	343	7	2.1%	5,390
12/15	340	4	1.4%	—
12/11	247	5	2.4%	—
12/09	116	0	0.7%	—
Annual Growth	16.6%	38.2%	—	—

2016 Year-End Financials

Return on assets: 9.9%
Return on equity: 2.1%
Current ratio: 0.20
Cash ($ mil.): 8

ADVENTIST HEALTH SYSTEM SUNBELT HEALTHCARE CORPORATION

EXECUTIVES

Pres, Donald Jernigan
V Pres, Robert Henderschedt
Coordinator, Pennie Moore

LOCATIONS

HQ: ADVENTIST HEALTH SYSTEM SUNBELT
HEALTHCARE CORPORATION
900 HOPE WAY, ALTAMONTE SPRINGS, FL
327141502
Phone: 407 357-1000
Web: WWW.ADVENTISTHEALTHSYSTEM.COM

HISTORICAL FINANCIALS
Company Type: Private

Income Statement · FYE: December 31

	REVENUE ($ mil.)	NET INCOME ($ mil.)	NET PROFIT MARGIN	EMPLOYEES
12/17	10,083	1,167	11.6%	78,000
12/16	9,651	806	8.4%	—
12/14	519	26	5.1%	—
12/13	530	73	13.9%	—
Annual Growth	108.8%	99.6%	—	—

2017 Year-End Financials

Return on assets: 10.9%
Return on equity: 11.6%
Current ratio: 0.30
Cash ($ mil.): 338

ADVENTIST HEALTH SYSTEM/WEST

Not content to wait around for the advent of good health Adventist Health System/West operates about 20 hospitals in the western US. Its health care facilities sprinkled throughout California Hawaii Oregon and Washington also include more than 260 physicians' clinics. Additionally the not-for-profit organization runs more than a dozen home health care agencies and a handful of retirement centers. The system has more than 5000 physicians on staff. Adventist Health maintains strong ties to the Seventh-day Adventist Church but is independently owned. A sister organization Adventist Health System operates in the central and southern parts of the country.

Operations

Adventist Health System/West works with its own churches and those of other denominations to offer such preventive health services as medical screenings immunizations and health education. The majority of Adventist Health's acute care hospitals are concentrated in California with the rest scattered throughout Hawaii Oregon and Washington. The system's nearly 300 clinics vary from small one or two provider offices to large facilities with primary care specialty medical services dental behavioral health perinatal and other services. Other facilities include home care agencies and four retirement centers.

Annually Adventist Health System/West has more than 150000 admissions 685000 emergency department visits and 2.9 million outpatient visits.

Geographic Reach

Adventist Health System/West serve patients throughout California Hawaii and Oregon. It also has a retirement center in Washington.

Financial Performance

In fiscal 2016 Adventist Health System/west received $3.95 billion in net revenue including patient care income and other sources of income. Its operating expenses totaled $3.77 billion that year.

Strategy

Adventist Health System/West often partners with others including organizations related to the Seventh-day Adventist church to enhance and grow its health care offerings. In early 2018 for example it joined forces with another not-for-profit health system Rideout Health (which operates acute care hospital Rideout Regional Medical Center). The partners aim to improve the wellness of California's Yuba City/Marysville community by providing expanded health care services.

EXECUTIVES

Svp And Cfo, Jack W. Wagner
President And Ceo Southern California Region, Beth D. Zachary
President And Ceo, Scott Reiner
President And Ceo Central California Region, Wayne Ferch
President And Ceo Northern California Region, Jeff Eller
President And Ceo Northwest Region, Joyce Newmyer
Evp And Coo, Bill Wing
Vice President Cno, Gloria Bancarz
Vice President Hospital Finance, Stan Adams
Senior Vice President, James Brewster
Second Vice President, Rebecca Williams
Vice President Of Advocacy And Public Policy, Michael Griffin
Vice President Human Resources, Shane Voshell
Secretary, Kirk Iverson

LOCATIONS

HQ: ADVENTIST HEALTH SYSTEM/WEST
2100 DOUGLAS BLVD, ROSEVILLE, CA 956613898
Phone: 916 781-2000
Web: WWW.ADVENTISTHEALTH.ORG

COMPETITORS

Community Health Systems	Providence St. Joseph Health
Dignity Health	Queen's Medical Center
HCA	Shasta Regional Medical Center
Hawai'i Pacific Health	Sisters of Charity of Leavenworth
John Muir Health	
Kuakini Health System	Stanford Health Care
Legacy Health System	
LifePoint Health	Sutter Health
Memorial Health Services	Tenet Healthcare
	UCSF Medical

HISTORICAL FINANCIALS
Company Type: Private

Income Statement · FYE: December 31

	REVENUE ($ mil.)	NET INCOME ($ mil.)	NET PROFIT MARGIN	EMPLOYEES
12/17	4,114	199	4.9%	19,512
12/16	3,945	185	4.7%	—
12/15	251	10	4.3%	—
12/14	3,262	133	4.1%	—
Annual Growth	8.0%	14.3%	—	—

2017 Year-End Financials

Return on assets: 6.2%
Return on equity: 4.9%
Current ratio: 1.80
Cash ($ mil.): 728

ADVENTIST HEALTHCARE, INC.

From the newest newborn to the most senior Adventist HealthCare takes care of residents in the Washington DC region. The not-for-profit system with more than 1700 physicians and medical providers is home to two acute care hospitals two specialty hospitals and dozens of specialty clinics urgent care clinics and medical offices. Its acute care hospitals are Adventist HealthCare Shady Grove Medical Center and Adventist HealthCare Washington Adventist Hospital. Adventist HealthCare which is affiliated with the Seventh-day Adventist Church has been in operation since 1907.

Operations

Adventist HealthCare's Lourie Center for Children's Social & Emotional Wellness promotes the emotional health of parent-child relations through education training research early prevention and intervention. Its offerings include an early head start program to benefit low-income families parent-child programs a therapeutic nursery and the state-approved Lourie Center School a non-public elementary school for children with emotional and multiple disabilities. Another system school The Ridge School of the Eastern Shore provides general and special education to adolescents with emotional learning or behavioral health problems.

Additionally Adventist provides employee assistance programs and behavioral health and wellness services through its LifeWork Strategies subsidiaries.

The system has about 110000 emergency visits 424000 outpatient visits and delivers some 7000 babies a year.

Geographic Reach

Adventist HealthCare operates facilities in Maryland northwestern New Jersey and Washington DC. Its home health agencies operate throughout much of Maryland and parts of Washington DC.

Strategy

Adventist HealthCare is focused on physician integration and providing greater access to health care based on needs at the community level. Collaboration is part of a larger consolidation trend among the industry in order to strengthen all health care organizations financially and geographically.

The system is moving its Washington Adventist Hospital to an integrated campus currently under construction in White Oak Maryland. The new campus expected to open in 2019 will feature 170 beds in a seven-story building. It will be renamed Adventist HealthCare White Oak Medical Center.

The network is also taking measures to operate more efficiently and effectively by eliminating processes that are unnecessary and adopting green practices to lower energy costs.

EXECUTIVES

President Adventist Healthcare Behavioral Health And Wellness Services, Kevin Young
President And Ceo, Terry Forde
Evp And Coo; President Adventist Healthcare Shady Grove Medical Center, John Sackett
Evp And Cfo, James G. Lee
Vp Public Relations And Marketing, Thomas Grant
Vp And Cio, Christopher Ghion
President Adventist Healthcare Washington Adventist Hospital, Erik Wangsness
Svp Physician Integration Strategy; President Adventist Medical Group, Patrick Garrett
Senior Vice President And Chief Human Resources Officer, Marta Perez
Vice President Of Human Resources, Carlos Vargas
Chairman, David E. Weigley
Vice Chairman, Robert T. Vandeman
Auditors: BAKER TILLY VIRCHOW KRAUSE LL

LOCATIONS

HQ: ADVENTIST HEALTHCARE, INC.
820 W DIAMOND AVE STE 600, GAITHERSBURG, MD 208781469
Phone: 301 315-3030
Web: WWW.ADVENTISTHEALTHCARE.COM

PRODUCTS/OPERATIONS

Selected Home Health Services
Nursing and Home Health
  Adult nursing
  Diabetes management
  Maternal/child care
  Nutrition management
  Pediatric nursing
  Personal care
  Pre- and post-op care
  Rehabilitation
  Wound care
Home Assistance
  Laundry and linens
  Light housekeeping
  Meal preparation
  Medication reminders
  Personal care

COMPETITORS

Bon Secours Health
Calvert Memorial Hospital
Dimensions Healthcare
Frederick Memorial
GBMC
Johns Hopkins Health System
MedStar Health
Trinity Health (Novi)
University of Maryland Medical System

HISTORICAL FINANCIALS

Company Type: Private

Income Statement   FYE: December 31

	REVENUE ($ mil.)	NET INCOME ($ mil.)	NET PROFIT MARGIN	EMPLOYEES
12/16	779	0	0.1%	5,236
12/14	695	11	1.6%	—
12/13	659	11	1.7%	—
12/12	0	(0)	—	—
Annual Growth	462.0%	—	—	—

ADVENTIST MIDWEST HEALTH

EXECUTIVES

V Pres-SEC, James R Garvell
V Pres-Nursing, Patricia A Sutton
V Pres-Marketing, Steve Davis
V Pres-Patients, Todd S Werner Jr
Executive Vice-President Marke, Susan King
Regional Pacs Admin, Dave Golitko
Pathologist, Adam Dubin
Pathologist, Agnieszka Piotrowski
Pathologist, Anthony Dombrowski
Program Director, Clara Carls
Pathologist, Dino Vallera

LOCATIONS

HQ: ADVENTIST MIDWEST HEALTH
120 N OAK ST, HINSDALE, IL 605213829
Phone: 630 856-9000
Web: WWW.ADVENTISTHEALTHPARTNERS.COM

HISTORICAL FINANCIALS

Company Type: Private

Income Statement   FYE: December 31

	REVENUE ($ mil.)	NET INCOME ($ mil.)	NET PROFIT MARGIN	EMPLOYEES
12/16	305	10	3.4%	2,470
12/15	289	17	5.9%	—
12/14	287	0	0.3%	—
Annual Growth	3.1%	230.7%	—	—

2016 Year-End Financials

Return on assets: 3.6%   Cash ($ mil.): 62
Return on equity: 3.4%
Current ratio: 1.50

ADVOCATE HEALTH AND HOSPITALS CORPORATION

Advocate Lutheran General Hospital also known simply as Lutheran General provides acute and long-term medical and surgical care to the residents of Park Ridge Illinois and the surrounding northern suburban Chicago area. As one of the largest hospitals in the region Lutheran General boasts nearly 640 beds and a Level I trauma center. Its operations also include a complete children's hospital and pediatric critical care center. Lutheran General serves as a teaching hospital and its specialized programs include oncology cardiology women's health emergency medicine and hospice care. Lutheran General is part of the Advocate Health Care network.

Operations

Lutheran General the sixth largest hospital in the Chicago area is a not-for-profit faith-based organization related to the Evangelical Lutheran Church in America and the United Church of Christ. With some 1150 physicians representing more than 50 specialties and subspecialties Advocate Lutheran General saw 62500 patients in its emergency department in 2012.

That year the company reported more than 29000 admissions 19000 surgeries and more than 4000 births.

Geographic Reach

The hospital system is the primary academic referral hospital for northwest Chicago and north Greater Chicago.

Strategy

Increase its services to meet specific demographics in 2012 Lutheran General opened a new South Asian Cardiovascular Center in the Midwest; it also launched Expressions a program aimed at helping seniors in the early stages of Alzheimer's disease.

That year thee hospital introduced a new Pet Therapy program to the Adult Oncology unit. It also launched of its neuroendovascular program to expand Lutheran General's acute stroke care to provide advanced acute stroke care to patients throughout the northern Chicago area.

Company Background

Lutheran General serves those who live in the northern suburban Chicago area specifically Park Ridge Illinois.

The hospital was founded in 1897.

EXECUTIVES

Dir, Michael Wegel
Plastic Surgeon, Christopher V Pelletiere
Administrative Assistant, Sara Pezzuto
Staff, Tenisha Matthews
Chief Information Officer, Antonella R Salerno
Vice-President, Michael Ploszek
Coordinator, Richard Schoemer
Doctor, Suresh Havalad
Administrative Assistant, Valerie Green
Senior Project Manager Project, Daniel Hull
Family Practitioner, Haydee Cantu

LOCATIONS

HQ: ADVOCATE HEALTH AND HOSPITALS CORPORATION
1775 DEMPSTER ST, PARK RIDGE, IL 600681143
Phone: 847 723-6610
Web: WWW.ADVOCATEHEALTH.COM

Selected Hospitals
Advocate BroMenn Medical Center
Advocate Children's Hospital - Oak Lawn

Advocate Children's Hospital - Park Ridge
Advocate Christ Center for Breast Care
Advocate Christ Medical Center
Advocate Christ Medical Center - Physical Rehabilitation
 Center Center for Hearing and Sleep Center
Advocate Christ Outpatient Center
 Advocate C
Advocate Condell Medical Center
Advocate Eureka Hospital
Advocate Good Samaritan Hospital
Advocate Good Shepherd Hospital
Advocate Illinois Masonic Medical Center
Advocate Lutheran General Hospital
Advocate South Suburban Hospital
Advocate Trinity Hospital

PRODUCTS/OPERATIONS

Selected Services
Adult Day Hospital
Adult Down Syndrome Center
Anticoagulation Center
Behavioral Health
Caldwell Breast Center
Cancer Care
Center for Fetal Care
Children's Services
The Comprehensive Continence Center
Emergency Services
Heart and Vascular
Hyperbaric Treatment
Interventional Radiology
Joint Reconstruction & Replacement
Nutrition Services Opthamology
Outpatient Testing Prep Instructions
Pain Management Center
Rehabilitation
Senior Services
Sleep Disorders
Surgical Services
The Center for Robotic Surgery
Women's Services
Wound Care

COMPETITORS

Children's Hopsital of
 Chicago
Gottleib Memorial
 Hospital
NorthShore University
 HealthSystem
Northwest Community
 Healthcare

Northwestern Lake
 Forest Hospital
Northwestern Memorial
 HealthCare
Rush System for Health
University of Chicago
 Medical Center

HISTORICAL FINANCIALS
Company Type: Private

| Income Statement | | | | FYE: December 31 |
	REVENUE ($ mil.)	NET INCOME ($ mil.)	NET PROFIT MARGIN	EMPLOYEES
12/17	790	79	10.0%	4,818
12/16	785	118	15.1%	—
12/15	752	104	13.9%	—
12/14	741	107	14.5%	—
Annual Growth	2.1%	(9.6%)	—	—

2017 Year-End Financials

Return on assets: 43.8%   Cash ($ mil.): 229
Return on equity: 10.0%
Current ratio: 0.70

ADVOCATE HEALTH CARE NETWORK

Advocating wellness in the Midwest Advocate Aurora Health is a not-for-profit integrated health care network with some 500 care sites serving Illi-

nois and Wisconsin. Formerly named Advocate Health Care Advocate operates about nearly 30 acute and specialty care hospitals (including Advocate BroMenn Medical Center Aurora BayCare Medical Center Aurora Lakeland Medical Center and Lutheran General Hospital) with more than 7150 beds as well as community health clinics and home health care and hospice services. Illinois-based Advocate Health merged with Wisconsin-based Aurora Health Care in 2018; the merger created one of the nation's largest not-for-profit health systems in the US.

Operations
With more than 70000 associates Advocate Aurora Health is one of the largest employers in the region. Its staff also includes more than 8100 affiliated physicians.

The system has teaching affiliations with area medical schools such as the University of Illinois at Chicago and the University of Chicago Pritzker School of Medicine. Its three major teaching hospitals — Christ Medical Center Illinois Masonic Medical Center and Lutheran General Hospital — train 600 residents and fellows per year and provide more than 1600 medical student rotations annually

Geographic Reach
Advocate Aurora Health operates more than 500 care sites serving eastern Wisconsin and northeast Illinois.

Strategy
Even prior to merging with Aurora Health Care Advocate Health had grown through a series of acquisitions. Recent purchases include central Illinois health network BroMenn Healthcare System the 280-bed Condell Medical Center the Midwest Physician Group (now part of the Advocate Medical Group division) and Sherman Health Systems.

In 2017 Advocate Health dropped its plans to merge with NorthShore University Health System another Illinois hospital operator. The combination would have created a 16-hospital market leader in Chicago's North Shore area. The merger was blocked by the FTC which claimed that it would harm consumers by raising prices and lowering health care quality.

Later that year Advocate Health and Wisconsin-based Aurora Health Care agreed to combined forces. The merged company now named Advocate Aurora Health Care operates 27 hospitals and more than 500 care sites; it has the capacity to serve nearly 3 million patients annually. The two companies already had a working relationship through their ACL Laboratories joint venture.

Company Background
Advocate Health was formed in 1995 by the United Church of Christ and the Evangelical Lutheran Church in America.

EXECUTIVES

Evp And Chief Medical Officer; President Advocate Physician Partners, Lee B. Sacks
Svp Cfo Treasurer, Dominic J. Nakis
President Advocate Condell Medical Center, Ann Errichetti
President, Karen A. Lambert
President Advocate Home Health Services, Denise M. Keefe
President Advocate Physician Partners, Martin F. (Marty) Manning, age 63
President Advocate Medical Group, James R. Dan
President Recognized Associates, John Bruss
Svp And Chief Marketing Officer, Kelly Jo Golson
President Dreyer Clinic, Donna Copper
President Acl Laboratories, Barbara Bigler
Coo, Dana Gilbert
Vice President Talent Management And Staffing, Anne Callen

Vice President Physician And Ambulatory Services, Lois Elia
Vice President Corporate Is Physician Services, John Norenberg
Vice President Of Clinical Effectiveness, Debra Oconnor
Vice President App Advisors, Charlyn Slade
Medical Director, Martin Doot
Vice President Public Affairs, Lisa Lesniak
Vice President Development, Doug Hutchings
Pharmacy Manager, Paul Miller
Vice President Operations, Karen Moore
Vice President Professional Arrangements Professional Arrangements, Peg Stone
Assistant To Vice President Network Sales Vice President Govt And Community Relations Vice President Marketing, Judy Zumpano
Secretary, Olga Wegehaupt
Auditors: ERNST & YOUNG LLP CHICAGO IL

LOCATIONS

HQ: ADVOCATE HEALTH CARE NETWORK
 3075 HIGHLAND PKWY FL 6, DOWNERS GROVE, IL
 605155563
Phone: 630 572-9393
Web: WWW.ADVOCATEHEALTH.COM

PRODUCTS/OPERATIONS

Selected Locations
Advocate BroMenn Medical Center (Normal Illinois) - 221 beds
Advocate Christ Medical Center (Oak Lawn Illinois) - 695 beds
Advocate Condell Medical Center (Libertyville Illinois) - 281 beds
Advocate Good Samaritan Hospital (Downers Grove Illinois) -340 beds
Advocate Eureka Hospital (Eureka Illinois)- 25 beds
Advocate Good Shepherd Hospital (Barrington Illinois) -183 beds
AdvoAdvocate Hope Children's Hospital (Oak Lawn Illinois)
Advocate Illinois Masonic Medical Center (Chicago Illinois) -408 beds
Advocate Lutheran General Hospital (Park Ridge Illinois) - 639 beds
Advocate Sherman Hospital (ElginIllinois)- 225 beds
Advocate South Suburban Hospital (Hazel Crest Illinois) - 284 beds
Advocate Trinity Hospital (Chicago Illinois) - 250 beds

COMPETITORS

Alexian Brothers
 Health System
Central DuPage
 Hospital
Children's Hopsital of
 Chicago
Covenant Ministries
Elmhurst Memorial
 Healthcare
Gottleib Memorial
 Hospital
HCA
Hospital Sisters
 Health System
KishHealth
Loyola University
 Health System

Mercy Hospital and
 Medical Center
NorthShore University
 HealthSystem
Northwest Community
 Healthcare
Northwestern Lake
 Forest Hospital
Northwestern Memorial
 HealthCare
Pronger Smith
Rush System for Health
SSM Health Care
Silver Cross Hospital
Sinai Health System
University of Chicago
 Medical Center

HISTORICAL FINANCIALS
Company Type: Private

| Income Statement | | | | FYE: December 31 |
	REVENUE ($ mil.)	NET INCOME ($ mil.)	NET PROFIT MARGIN	EMPLOYEES
12/15	5,392	60	1.1%	25,000
12/06	3,268	286	8.8%	—
12/05	2,973	140	4.7%	—
12/04	2,779	143	5.2%	—
Annual Growth	6.2%	(7.6%)	—	—

2015 Year-End Financials

Return on assets: 7.7%   Cash ($ mil.): 203
Return on equity: 1.1%
Current ratio: 0.60

AEP OHIO TRANSMISSION COMPANY, INC

EXECUTIVES

Ceo, Nick Akins
Pres-Coo, Liza Barton
Svp, Wade Smith
Svp, Scott Smith

LOCATIONS

HQ: AEP OHIO TRANSMISSION COMPANY, INC
1 RIVERSIDE PLZ, COLUMBUS, OH 432152355
Phone: 614 716-1000
Web: WWW.AEP.COM

HISTORICAL FINANCIALS
Company Type: Private

Income Statement				FYE: December 31
	REVENUE ($ mil.)	NET INCOME ($ mil.)	NET PROFIT MARGIN	EMPLOYEES
12/17	383	140	36.7%	18
12/16	275	89	32.4%	—
Annual Growth	39.4%	57.7%	—	—

AEROTEK, INC.

Aerotek a unit of staffing powerhouse Allegis Group offers commercial and technical staffing services throughout North America. Through several divisions Aerotek staffs workers such as engineers mechanics scientists and technical professionals as well as administrative staff members general laborers and tradespeople. The company also provides training and support services. Along with aerospace auto and engineering companies Aerotek's clients include companies from the construction energy manufacturing health care and finance industries.

Geographic Reach
Aerotek is headquartered in Hanover Maryland. The company has office locations in Asia Australia Europe and North America. Aerotek also operates a network of more than 250 non-franchised offices.

Sales and Marketing
Aerotek serves a wide variety of industries including the accounting construction engineering financial services government and public administration health care manufacturing and pharmaceutical industries among others. The company serves more than 18000 clients and 300000 contract employees every year.

Strategy
Aerotek has expanded its operations over the years through organic growth and acquisitions especially in niche markets such as the biotechnology health care clinical research chemical and plastics sectors. Despite the economic downturn demand within these industries has been consistent along with engineering giving Aerotek some continuity during the recession. Aerotek has also widened its client focus to include the niche market of minority and woman-owned companies.

EXECUTIVES

Vp Technical And Professional Services, Mark Cooper
President, Todd M. Mohr
Cfo, Thomas B. (Tom) Kelly
Svp Operations, John Flanigan
Regional Vp Northeast, John Rudy
Regional Vp Midwest, Marty Schager
Regional Vp Central, Mike Hansen
Regional Vp West, Tony Bartolucci
Regional Vp Northwest, Brooks Wells
Vp Canada, Bryan Toffey
Regional Vp Southwest, Brad Kennedy
Regional Vp Mid-atlantic, Jeff Colvin
Regional Vp Southeast, Greg Jones
Vice President Client Delivery, Vinayak Nayak
Vice President Of Finance, James Mann
Auditors: PRICEWATERHOUSECOOPERS LLP B

LOCATIONS

HQ: AEROTEK, INC.
7301 PARKWAY DR, HANOVER, MD 210761159
Phone: 410 694-5100
Web: WWW.AEROTEK.COM

PRODUCTS/OPERATIONS

INDUSTRIES SERVED
Accounting
Administrative & Support Services
Aerospace Aviation & Defense
Architecture & Design
Automotive
Construction
Customer Service
Energy & Utilities
Engineering
Environmental
Financial Services
Government & Public Administration
Healthcare
Manufacturing
Pharmaceutical
Sciences
Warehouse & Distribution

COMPETITORS

AMN Healthcare	MSX International
Adecco	ManpowerGroup
Bryant Bureau	On Assignment
CDI	Pinnacle Staffing
COMFORCE	Randstad Holding
Kelly Services	Robert Half
Kforce	

HISTORICAL FINANCIALS
Company Type: Private

Income Statement				FYE: December 31
	REVENUE ($ mil.)	NET INCOME ($ mil.)	NET PROFIT MARGIN	EMPLOYEES
12/17	6,070	0	—	4,200
12/16	5,565	0	—	—
12/15	5,492	0	—	—
12/14	5,353	0	—	—
Annual Growth	4.3%	—	—	—

2017 Year-End Financials
Return on assets: 1.7% Cash ($ mil.): 8
Return on equity: —
Current ratio: 3.50

AFFILIATED FOODS MIDWEST COOPERATIVE, INC.

Affiliated Foods Midwest Cooperative is a wholesale food distribution cooperative that supplies more than 800 independent grocers in some 15 states in the Midwest. From its handful of distribution centers in Kansas Nebraska and Wisconsin the co-op distributes fresh produce meats deli items baked goods dairy products and frozen foods as well as general merchandise and equipment. It distributes goods under the Shurfine brand (from Topco Associates) and IGA labels. Additionally Affiliated Foods Midwest provides marketing merchandising and warehousing support services for its members. The cooperative was formed in 1931 to make wholesale purchases for a group of retailers in Nebraska.

Geographic Reach
Norfolk Nebraska-based Affiliated Foods Midwest Cooperative has distribution centers in Norfolk Elwood Kansas and Kenosha Wisconsin. It serves customers in 15 states across the Midwest.

Financial Performance
Affiliated Foods Midwest rang up an estimated $1.6 billion in sales in fiscal 2013 (ended June).

Auditors: BKD LLP LINCOLN NEBRASKA

LOCATIONS

HQ: AFFILIATED FOODS MIDWEST COOPERATIVE, INC.
1301 W OMAHA AVE, NORFOLK, NE 687015872
Phone: 402 371-0555
Web: WWW.AFMIDWEST.COM

PRODUCTS/OPERATIONS

Selected Private-Label Brands
CharKing
ChuckWagon (pet food)
Clear Value
Cow Belle Creamery (ice cream)
Domestix (household products)
Full Circle (organic natural products)
IGA
PAWS Premium (pet products)
Shurfine
TopCare (OTC drugs health and beauty)
Valu Time
Wide Awake Coffee Co. (coffee)
World Classics Trading Company

COMPETITORS

Associated Wholesale Grocers	Kroger
C&S Wholesale	McLane
Central Grocers	SUPERVALU
Certco	Wal-Mart
Dearborn Wholesale Grocers	

HISTORICAL FINANCIALS
Company Type: Private

Income Statement				FYE: June 26
	REVENUE ($ mil.)	NET INCOME ($ mil.)	NET PROFIT MARGIN	EMPLOYEES
06/15	1,527	1	0.1%	850
06/14	1,477	2	0.2%	—
06/13	1,391	2	0.2%	—
06/12	1,486	2	0.2%	—
Annual Growth	0.9%	(19.5%)	—	—

AFFILIATED FOODS, INC.

This company helps keep pantries stocked in the Texas Panhandle and elsewhere. Affiliated Foods is a leading wholesale distribution cooperative that supplies grocery stores and restaurants in about a half a dozen states including Texas New Mexico and Oklahoma. It distributes fresh produce meat and non-food products as well as dairy products and beverages through its Plains Dairy unit. Its Tri State Baking Company supplies bread and other baked goods. In addition Affiliated Foods owns a stake in private-label products supplier Western Family Foods. The company was founded in 1946 as Panhandle Associated Grocers which merged with South Plains Associated Grocers to form Affiliated Foods in 1968.

Geographic Reach
Based in Amarillo Texas Affiliated Foods supplies grocery stores and restaurants in Texas Oklahoma Kansas New Mexico Colorado Arizona and Arkansas.

Financial Performance
While privately-owned Affiliated Foods doesn't report its financial results the cooperative reported an estimated $1.5 billion in sales in fiscal 2012 (ends October).

EXECUTIVES

National Account Manager, Yolanda Davis

LOCATIONS

HQ: AFFILIATED FOODS, INC.
1401 W FARMERS AVE, AMARILLO, TX 791186134
Phone: 806 372-3851
Web: WWW.AFIAMA.COM

PRODUCTS/OPERATIONS

Selected Subsidiaries
Affiliated Food Service (restaurant supply)
Plains Dairy (Amarillo Texas)
Tri-State Baking Co. (Amarillo Texas)

COMPETITORS

Affiliated Foods Midwest	GSC Enterprises
Associated Wholesale	IGA
Grocers	McLane
C&S Wholesale	SUPERVALU

HISTORICAL FINANCIALS
Company Type: Private

Income Statement   FYE: September 30

	REVENUE ($ mil.)	NET INCOME ($ mil.)	NET PROFIT MARGIN	EMPLOYEES
09/17*	1,421	1	0.1%	1,200
10/16	1,440	0	0.1%	—
09/06	1,137	0	0.0%	—
10/05	1,133	1	0.1%	—
Annual Growth	1.9%	0.7%	—	—

*Fiscal year change

2017 Year-End Financials

Return on assets: 3.1%   Cash ($ mil.): 10
Return on equity: 0.1%
Current ratio: 0.30

AG FOUNDATION

EXECUTIVES

Pres, Robert W Beatty
Auditors: GARDNER & GARDNER CPAS LLC EA

LOCATIONS

HQ: AG FOUNDATION
517 BROADWAY ST STE 300, EAST LIVERPOOL, OH 439203167
Phone: 330 385-3400

HISTORICAL FINANCIALS
Company Type: Private

Income Statement   FYE: December 31

	REVENUE ($ mil.)	NET INCOME ($ mil.)	NET PROFIT MARGIN	EMPLOYEES
12/16	303	296	97.5%	2
12/15	8	1	20.7%	—
12/14	13	6	48.1%	—
12/13	7	0	9.5%	—
Annual Growth	237.3%	633.0%	—	—

2016 Year-End Financials

Return on assets: 5.1%   Cash ($ mil.): 59
Return on equity: 97.5%
Current ratio: —

AG PROCESSING INC A COOPERATIVE

Soy far soy good for Ag Processing (AGP) the largest farmer-owned soybean processor in the world and roughly the fourth-largest soybean processor in the US based on capacity. It purchases and processes more than 5.5 million acres of members' soybeans per year. The farmer-owned cooperative is also a leading supplier of refined vegetable oil in the US. It procures processes markets and transports grains and grain products ranging from human food ingredients to livestock feed to renewable fuels. AGP is owned by about 180 local and regional cooperatives and represents more than 250000 farmers in 15 states throughout the US.

Operations
In addition to its soybean processing and vegetable oil refining facilities AGP operates a merchandising and trading group called Ag Products subdivided into three areas of focus: Grain Protein and Export. Ag Products Grain focuses on marketing grain for members seeking to better compete in the global grain industry. Ag Products Protein markets soybean meal and soy hulls; it also manufactures AMINOPLUS a protein that improves milk production. Ag Products Export offers international marketing of soybean meal oilseeds grains and other bulk agricultural commodities. Its main gateway to the fast growing Pacific Rim market is through a West Coast export shipping terminal in Washington state.

AGP also holds investment stakes in Masterfeeds a Canadian feed manufacturing business and in Protinal/Proagro Venezuela's largest poultry processor and one of country's largest animal feed producers.

Geographic Reach
AGP operates nine soybean processing plants including six located in Iowa. Other soybean pro-

cessing plants are located in Minnesota Missouri and Nebraska. The company operates a growing ethanol plant in Nebraska to serve the renewable fuels market and soybean methyl ester plants in Iowa and Missouri. (Soy methyl ester an alternative to petroleum-based products is a byproduct that is used in everything from biodiesel to solvents.)

Financial Performance
AGP recorded its fourth best earnings year in the company's history in fiscal 2011. Its earnings from continuing operations (before income taxes) nearly doubled from 2010. Soybean processing rebounded from the previous year partly due to more aggressive export efforts. The company's vegetable oil business had its most profitable year yet as a result of improved demand from the soy biodiesel market improved oil quality and improved plant efficiency. Its renewable fuels business (ethanol and biodiesel) started slowly but finished 2011 strong posting improved earnings over 2010.

Strategy
With evolving EPA mandates the potential is still strong for integrated biodiesel producers like AGP which led it to acquire a 60-million gallon biodiesel plant in Algona Iowa in 2011. The acquisition doubled AGP's biodiesel production capacity now totaling about 120 million gallons.

Another major component of AGP's strategy is investing in expanding upgrading and modernizing various facilities for improved capacity and efficiency. In 2011 the company initiated major upgrade and modernization projects at soy processing plants in Sergeant Bluff Iowa and Dawson Minnesota. It also undertook a multi-million dollar expansion project at its Aberdeen Washington-based export terminal as overseas shipments to Pacific Rim countries increases.

In 2012 Ag Processing merged its Masterfeeds subsidiary with the Canadian commercial feed business (Feed-Rite) of Ridley to form the second-largest feed provider in Canada Masterfeeds LP. The new entity operates 22 manufacturing plants across the Quebec Ontario and Prairie provinces. Ridley and Ag Processing each own relative shares in Masterfeeds LP.

EXECUTIVES

Vice President Management Information Systems, Ramanathan Narayanan
Senior Vice President Engineering, Chuck Janiszewski
Vice President And Corporate Controller, Dennis Rademacher
Vice President, JC Gum
Vice President Of Human Resources, Rachel Warden
Vice President Human Resources, Matt Bendler

LOCATIONS

HQ: AG PROCESSING INC A COOPERATIVE
12700 W DODGE RD, OMAHA, NE 681546102
Phone: 402 496-7809
Web: WWW.AGP.COM

PRODUCTS/OPERATIONS

Selected Brands
Masterfeeds
  AMINOPLUS (dairy cattle feed additive)
  DIRECTOR (dairy cattle feed additive)
  FUSION (horse feed additive)
Proagro/Protinal
  Corral (Prepared chicken products Venezuela only)
SOYGOLD (bio-diesel fuel additives herbicides solvents surfacants fuel additives)

Selected Exported Products
Barley
Corn
Distillers dried grains (DDGS)
Feeding peas
High-protein soybean meal

Lecithin
Low-protein soybean meal
Oats
Soybean hulls
Soybean oil
Soybeans
Sunflowers
Wheat

Selected Operations and Products
Animal feed
Corn processing
Corn-based ethanol
Grain processing merchandising and sales
Industrial products (ethanol and methyl esters)
Soybean processing
Soybean oil
Soybean biodiesel
Prepared chicken products (Venezuela only)

COMPETITORS

ACH Food Companies	Liberty Vegetable Oil
ADM	Luckey Farmers
Bunge Limited	Marfrig
CGB	POET
CGC	Smucker
CHS	South Dakota Soybean
Cargill	Processors
ConAgra	Spectrum Foods
J-OIL MILLS	West Central Co-op
Land O'Lakes Purina	Zeeland Farm
Feed	

HISTORICAL FINANCIALS
Company Type: Private

Income Statement				FYE: August 31
	REVENUE ($ mil.)	NET INCOME ($ mil.)	NET PROFIT MARGIN	EMPLOYEES
08/16*	3,410	134	3.9%	1,456
12/10	3	0	1.3%	—
08/06	2,360	62	2.7%	—
Annual Growth	3.7%	7.9%	—	—

*Fiscal year change

2016 Year-End Financials
Return on assets: 2.5%   Cash ($ mil.): 210
Return on equity: 3.9%
Current ratio: 1.30

AGFIRST FARM CREDIT BANK

The expenses involved in equipping and operating a farm add up quickly which is where AgFirst Farm Credit Bank comes in. AgFirst is one of a half-dozen members of the Farm Credit System a federally chartered network of agricultural and rural lending cooperatives. Boasting $30 billion in assets the bank provides financing to 19 farmer-owned agricultural credit associations. The associations in turn offer mortgages and loans to some 80000 farmers agribusinesses and rural home-owners through 280 branches in 15 eastern states and Puerto Rico. They also offer crop insurance credit-related life insurance and financial planning services. Instead of accepting deposits AgFirst raises money by selling bonds and notes on the capital markets.

Operations
AgFirst's capital markets arm arranges participates in and sells loan syndications for agribusinesses. Its correspondent lending unit buys sells and services agricultural and rural home loans throughout the US. About 68% of the bank's loan portfolio consisted of direct notes in 2014 while

purchased participations/syndications made up another 19% of loan assets. The rest of the portfolio consisted of correspondent lending (12%) and loans to OFIs (less than 1%).

The bank makes almost all of its money from interest income. About 79% of its total revenue came from loan interest in 2014 with another 18% of revenue coming from interest on investment securities and other assets. The remainder of its revenue mostly came from loan fees.

Geographic Reach
Columbia South Carolina-based AgFirst serves 15 eastern US states and Puerto Rico. Its largest markets are in Florida North Carolina Georgia Virginia and Pennsylvania. The bank is also active in Alabama Delaware the District of Columbia Kentucky Louisiana Maryland Mississippi Ohio South Carolina Tennessee West Virginia and Puerto Rico.

Financial Performance
AgFirst Farm Credit Bank has struggled to grow its annual revenues and profits over the past several years as its loan assets have not increased and as interest margins continue to be squeezed in the low-interest environment.

The bank's revenue fell 7% to $703.8 million during 2014 as its loan assets barely grew to $20.9 billion or about the same levels as they've been since 2010.

Revenue declines in 2014 coupled with a rise in insurance fund premiums and salaries caused AgFirst's net income to shrink 17% to $380.3 million for the year. The bank's operating cash levels fell sharply to $370.9 million on lower cash earnings and unfavorable working capital changes mostly related to changes in accounts receivables balances.

Strategy
AgFirst has focused on maintaining strong personal relationships with its local customer base. It's also been investing more in security-based IT investments to protect its customers from security breaches. In 2015 it built a modern Data Center to accommodate the bank's growth with 1 Petabyte of data.

Company Background
The Farm Credit System was established by Congress in 1916 to provide a reliable source of credit for US farmers and ranchers.

EXECUTIVES
Ceo, Leon T. (Timmy) Amerson
Svp And Cfo, Charl L. Butler
Svp And Cio, Benjamin F. Blakewood
Vice President, Felicia Morant
Vice President Capital Mkts, John Burnside
Vice President Correspondent Lending, Eric Wilkowski
Vice Chairman, Dale R. Hershey
Chairman, Robert H. Spiers
Auditors: PRICEWATERHOUSECOOPERS LLP MI

LOCATIONS
HQ: AGFIRST FARM CREDIT BANK
1901 MAIN ST, COLUMBIA, SC 292012443
Phone: 803 799-5000
Web: WWW.AGFIRST.COM

PRODUCTS/OPERATIONS
2014 Sales

	$ mil.	% of total
Interest		
Loans	566	79
Investment securities & other	127	18
Non-interest		
Loan fees	8	2
Building lease income	3	-
Net other-than-temporary impairment losses	(1.4)	-
Gains (losses) on called debt	(7.7)	-
Gains (losses) on investments net	0	-
Gains (losses) on other transactions	0	-
Other	7	1
Total	703	100

COMPETITORS

AgriBank	Farm Family Holdings
Bank of America	First National of
COUNTRY Financial	Nebraska
Cat Financial	Rabo AgriFinance

HISTORICAL FINANCIALS
Company Type: Private

Income Statement				FYE: December 31
	ASSETS ($ mil.)	NET INCOME ($ mil.)	INCOME AS % OF ASSETS	EMPLOYEES
12/17	32,487	344	1.1%	530
12/15	30,620	336	1.1%	—
Annual Growth	3.0%	1.2%		

2017 Year-End Financials
Return on assets: 40.3%   Sales ($ mil): 883
Return on equity: 39.0%

AGNESIAN HEALTHCARE, INC.

EXECUTIVES
Pres, John St Peter
Pres, Mr Robert Fale
Registered Nurse, Beth Wilke
Administrator, Bonnie R Schmitz
Chief of Cardiology, Colleen Priest
Registered Nurse, Denise Madel
Manager, Jamie Ausloos
Coordinator, Matthew White
Director, Nicole Gill
Public Relations Director, Shelley Haberman
Vice-President, Susan Edminster
Auditors: WIPFLI LLP GREEN BAY WI

LOCATIONS
HQ: AGNESIAN HEALTHCARE, INC.
430 E DIVISION ST, FOND DU LAC, WI 549354560
Phone: 920 929-2300
Web: WWW.AGNESIAN.COM

HISTORICAL FINANCIALS
Company Type: Private

Income Statement				FYE: June 30
	REVENUE ($ mil.)	NET INCOME ($ mil.)	NET PROFIT MARGIN	EMPLOYEES
06/17	479	11	2.3%	2,012
06/10	281	11	4.0%	—
06/09	276	0	—	—
06/08	220	0	—	—
Annual Growth	9.0%	—	—	—

2017 Year-End Financials
Return on assets: 3.0%   Cash ($ mil.): 15
Return on equity: 2.3%
Current ratio: 1.70

AGRI-AFC, LLC

EXECUTIVES

Pres-Ceo, Mike Malone
MBR-Cfo, Jamie Bowling
Information Technology Support, Amanda Cole
Administrative Specialist, Barbara Russell
Commodity Seed Buyer, Brandon Walls
Office Administrator, Carla Givens
Inside Sales, Chris Brooks
Warehouse Manager, Clint Paulk
Director of Credit, Dee Mears
Retail Accountant, Jenny Bowen
Assistant Controller, Lindsay Darnell

LOCATIONS

HQ: AGRI-AFC, LLC
   121 SOMERVILLE RD NE, DECATUR, AL 356012659
Phone: 256 560-2848
Web: WWW.AGRI-AFC.COM

HISTORICAL FINANCIALS
Company Type: Private

Income Statement				FYE: July 31
	REVENUE ($ mil.)	NET INCOME ($ mil.)	NET PROFIT MARGIN	EMPLOYEES
07/18	384	13	3.5%	165
07/17	347	15	4.5%	—
07/16	339	11	3.4%	—
07/15	344	8	2.5%	—
Annual Growth	3.8%	17.1%	—	—

2018 Year-End Financials
Return on assets: —
Return on equity: 3.5%
Current ratio: 0.70
Cash ($ mil.): —

AGSOUTH FARM CREDIT ACA

EXECUTIVES

Ceo-Pres, J Pat Calhoun
Director, Arthur Q Black
Director, James C Carter Jr
Director, Thomas H Coward
Director, Jimmy B Metts
Director, Jerome G Parker
Director, Charles C Rucks
Director, Hugh E Weathers
Director, Phillip E Love
Director, David H Womack
Director, Loy D Cowart
Auditors: PRICEWATERHOUSECOOPERS LLP FO

LOCATIONS

HQ: AGSOUTH FARM CREDIT ACA
   26 S MAIN ST, STATESBORO, GA 304585256
Phone: 912 764-9091
Web: WWW.AGSOUTHFC.COM

HISTORICAL FINANCIALS
Company Type: Private

Income Statement				FYE: December 31
	ASSETS ($ mil.)	NET INCOME ($ mil.)	INCOME AS % OF ASSETS	EMPLOYEES
12/17	1,800	55	3.1%	226
12/16	1,722	40	2.3%	—
12/15	1,651	39	2.4%	—
12/14	1,594	49	3.1%	—
Annual Growth	4.1%	3.8%	—	—

2017 Year-End Financials
Return on assets: 1.8%
Return on equity: 42.4%
Sales ($ mil.): 130

AGTEGRA COOPERATIVE

EXECUTIVES

Pres, Hal Clemensen
Vice President, Dave Thorson
Gen Mgr-Treas, Dale Locken
SEC-Tres, Todd Bushong
Cfo, Robert Porter
Fleet Manager, James Brandner
Auditors: GARDINER THOMSEN PC DES MOIN

LOCATIONS

HQ: AGTEGRA COOPERATIVE
   908 LAMONT ST S, ABERDEEN, SD 574015515
Phone: 605 225-5500
Web: WWW.WHEATGROWERS.COM

Selected Counties of Operation
North Dakota
   Dickey
   LaMoure
   Stutsman
South Dakota
   Aurora
   Beadle
   Brown
   Brule
   Clark
   Corson
   Day
   Edmunds
   Faulk
   Hand
   Hyde
   Jerauld
   Lyman
   Marshall
   Sanborn
   Spink

COMPETITORS

ADM	North Central Farmers
CHS	Elevator
Cargill	Northern Growers
Country Pride	

HISTORICAL FINANCIALS
Company Type: Private

Income Statement				FYE: July 31
	REVENUE ($ mil.)	NET INCOME ($ mil.)	NET PROFIT MARGIN	EMPLOYEES
07/18	1,544	32	2.1%	638
07/17	1,275	22	1.8%	—
07/16	1,209	6	0.6%	—
07/15	1,283	40	3.1%	—
Annual Growth	6.3%	(6.8%)	—	—

2018 Year-End Financials
Return on assets: 1.0%
Return on equity: 2.1%
Current ratio: 0.10
Cash ($ mil.): —

AHS HILLCREST MEDICAL CENTER, LLC

Hillcrest Medical Center as part of the Hillcrest HealthCare System provides a helping hand to health care patients in northeastern Oklahoma. The medical center operates health care facilities in Tulsa and surrounding areas. The main hospital facility has about 730 beds and offers emergency cancer cardiology neurology rehabilitation and other acute and specialty care services. Hillcrest Medical Center also operates outpatient and extended care facilities including general health and specialty clinics and provides home health foster care and hospice services. The health care organization is part of Ardent Health Services.

Operations

Hillcrest HealthCare System operates six hospitals and Utica Park Clinic. Operating under the Hillcrest Hospital name to better reflect their affiliation they include Hillcrest Hospital Claremore Hillcrest Hospital Cushing Hillcrest Hospital Henryetta and Hillcrest Hospital South.

As part of its services the medical center also provides patients with The Alexander Burn Center The Peggy V. Helmerich Women's Health Center The Spine & Orthopedic Center Kaiser Rehabilitation Center The Hillcrest Center for Diabetes Management Oklahoma CyberKnife and the Oklahoma Heart Institute.

Operation of the Oklahoma State University Medical Center was transferred from Ardent Health Services to a public trust in 2009. St. John Health System now manages the facility.

Geographic Reach

Located in Tulsa Oklahoma's midtown area Hillcrest Medical Center consists of half a dozen hospitals and several other facilities for specialty care.

EXECUTIVES

Respiratory Therapy Director, Tim Markus
Operating Room Director, Davena Talley

LOCATIONS

HQ: AHS HILLCREST MEDICAL CENTER, LLC
   1120 S UTICA AVE, TULSA, OK 741044012
Phone: 918 579-1000
Web: WWW.HILLCRESTMEDICALCENTER.COM

PRODUCTS/OPERATIONS

Selected Services
Alexander Burn Center
Behavioral Health Services
Cancer Care
Diabetes
Emergency Care
Exercise & Lifestyle Program
Home Care
Hospice
Medical & Neurological Rehab
Medicare Incentive Payment
Oklahoma Heart Institute
Palliative Care
Pastoral Care Department
Pregnancy
Silver Elite
Spine & Orthopedics
Women's Health Center

COMPETITORS

Deaconess Health Care	North Memorial Health
Fairview Health	Care
HealthEast Care System	Saint Francis Health
INTEGRIS Health	System
Marian Health System	St. John Health System

HISTORICAL FINANCIALS

Company Type: Private

Income Statement

FYE: June 30

	REVENUE ($ mil.)	NET INCOME ($ mil.)	NET PROFIT MARGIN	EMPLOYEES
06/16	507	14	2.9%	2,126
06/15	472	7	1.6%	—
Annual Growth	7.5%	89.4%	—	

2016 Year-End Financials

Return on assets: 3.7%   Cash ($ mil.): 17
Return on equity: 2.9%
Current ratio: 2.50

AIDS HEALTHCARE FOUNDATION

EXECUTIVES

Ceo, Michael Arthur Weinstein
M.D., Chairman*, Rodney L Wright
Cfo, Lyle Honig
Sr Vice President, Peter Reis
Prin, Scott Carruthers
Coordinator, Santiago Leal
Director of Business, Arlette De
Department Coordinator, Bower Luna
Media Buyer, Chris Grace
Assistant Phlebotomist, Gerardo Diaz
Manager Community Outreach, Kendall Moore
Auditors: VASQUEZ & COMPANY LLP LOS ANG

LOCATIONS

HQ: AIDS HEALTHCARE FOUNDATION
6255 W SUNSET BLVD FL 21, LOS ANGELES, CA
900287422
Phone: 323 860-5200
Web: WWW.AIDSHEALTH.ORG

HISTORICAL FINANCIALS

Company Type: Private

Income Statement

FYE: December 31

	REVENUE ($ mil.)	NET INCOME ($ mil.)	NET PROFIT MARGIN	EMPLOYEES
12/16	1,163	40	3.5%	2,331
12/15	1,039	56	5.4%	—
12/14	879	30	3.5%	—
12/13	772	16	2.1%	—
Annual Growth	14.6%	35.2%	—	—

2016 Year-End Financials

Return on assets: 6.0%   Cash ($ mil.): 63
Return on equity: 3.5%
Current ratio: 1.10

AIR METHODS CORPORATION

It's a bird it's a plane ... it's an ambulance! With a fleet of more than 400 medically equipped aircraft mainly helicopters Air Methods is the largest provider of emergency medical air-transportation services in the US. The company operates through three divisions. A community-based operating segment which represents roughly 85% of revenues offers transportation and in-flight medical care from hubs in some two dozen states. It also provides tourism operations around the Grand Canyon and Hawaiian Islands. The smallest division United Rotorcraft designs manufactures and installs aircraft medical-transport products.In 2017 Air Methods was acquired by a private equity firm.

Operations

The company mainly provides air medical transportation services throughout the US and designs manufactures and installs medical aircraft interiors and other aerospace and medical transport products. It also provides tourism operations in and around the Grand Canyon and Hawaiian Islands.

Geographic Reach

The company has more than 300 bases of operations that serve 48 states in the US. It operates eight maintenance centers throughout the country and a national communications center.

Financial Performance

Air Methods has achieved extraordinary growth over the years with 2014 revenues peaking at the $1 billion mark for the first time in its history. Profits also climbed 52% from $62 million in 2013 to a record-setting $95 million in 2014.

The historic growth was fueled by an explosion in tourism segment revenue — this segment more than doubled its revenue from 2013 to 2014. Air Methods also generated additional sales from new revenue generated from the addition of 41 new bases throughout the year.

Strategy

Business acquisitions are part of the company's strategy to gain market share. It in 2013 acquired Helicopter Consultants of Maui LLC (doing business as Blue Hawaiian Helicopters) for a cash purchase price of $67 million. The deal enhanced Air Methods' tourism segment and helped it to post milestone revenues during 2014.

EXECUTIVES

Ceo And Director, Aaron D. Todd, $765,000 total compensation
President Sundance Helicopters, James (Jim) Greiner
President Domestic Air Medical Services, Michael D. Allen, $459,000 total compensation
Vp Information Technology, Doni Perry
Director Operations, Dennis McCall
Evp Business Development, David M. Doerr, $408,000 total compensation
Cfo And Treasurer, Peter P. Csapo
Senior Vice President Patient Business Services, Mark Keene
Vice President Of Corporate Development, Craig Yale
Medical Director, Justin Fairless
Chairman, C. David Kikumoto
Auditors: KPMG LLP DENVER COLORADO

LOCATIONS

HQ: AIR METHODS CORPORATION
5500 S QUEBEC ST STE 310, GREENWOOD VILLAGE, CO 801111926
Phone: 303 792-7400
Web: WWW.AIRMETHODS.COM

PRODUCTS/OPERATIONS

2014 Sales

	$ mil.	% of total
AMS	863	85
Tourism	116	11
United Rotorcraft	36	4
Corporate Activities	86	0
Adjustments	(11.4)	-
Total	**1,004**	**100**

Fleets

Fleets
AS 350
EC 135
EC 130
Bell 407
EC 145
Bell 429
BK 117
A-109
SA 365
Bell 222
Bell 430
Bell 206
MD 902
King Air
PC 12
Agusta 119Kx

Services

AirCom
Complete Billing Solutions
DirectCall
TAMMA
United Rotorcraft
LifeShield Alliance

COMPETITORS

Acadian Ambulance Service Inc.	CHC Group
Bristow Group Inc	Evergreen Holdings
	PHI Inc.

HISTORICAL FINANCIALS

Company Type: Private

Income Statement

FYE: December 31

	REVENUE ($ mil.)	NET INCOME ($ mil.)	NET PROFIT MARGIN	EMPLOYEES
12/15	1,085	109	10.1%	5,133
12/14	1,004	95	9.5%	—
12/13	881	62	7.0%	—
Annual Growth	11.0%	32.7%	—	—

2015 Year-End Financials

Return on assets: 2.8%   Cash ($ mil.): 5
Return on equity: 10.1%
Current ratio: 2.60

AIRGAS, INC.

Airgas hopes its industrial customers walk on its air. The US industrial gas distributor's North American network of more than 1100 locations includes retail stores gas fill plants specialty gas labs production facilities (17 air separation plants) and distribution centers. Airgas distributes argon carbon dioxide hydrogen nitrogen oxygen and a variety of medical and specialty gases as well as dry ice and protective equipment (hard hats goggles). Its gases production unit operates air-separation plants that produce oxygen nitrogen and argon. The company also sells welding machines. The company is owned by Air Liquide SA.

Operations

The industrial manufacturing and repair and maintenance industries account for about a quarter each of the Airgas' sales; customers primarily make fabricated metal products industrial transportation and equipment chemical products and primary metal products. Other industries served include medical and health services agriculture mining repair and maintenance and wholesale trade.

Airgas' distribution business accounts for 88% of the company's 2016 sales. Almost all of its sales come from distributing bulk gases (nitrogen oxygen argon helium) gas cylinders and welding equipment. Airgas also produces gases to supply its regional distribution companies. Its other operations consist of six business units that manufacture and/or distribute carbon dioxide dry ice nitrous oxide ammonia and refrigerant gases. Gas and rent represented 61% of the distribution business segment's sales in fiscal 2016; hard goods 39%.

The distribution business operates a network of multiple use facilities consisting of 900 branches 300 cylinder fill plants 70 regional specialty gas laboratories 11 national specialty gas laboratories one research and development center two specialty gas equipment centers 11 acetylene plants and 16 air separation units as well as six national hard-goods distribution centers and various customer call centers buying centers and administrative offices.

Airgas' All Other Operations business segment consists of six operating segments all of which primarily manufacture and/or distribute single gas product lines (carbon dioxide dry ice nitrous oxide ammonia and refrigerant gases along with a nitrogen services business). It has 90 branch/distribution locations eight liquid carbon dioxide and 14 dry ice production facilities and three nitrous oxide production facilities.

Geographic Reach

Operating in all 50 states Airgas is the largest distributor of packaged gases in the US with a 25% market share. Outside the US it conducts operations mostly in Canada but also operates in the UAE Mexico Russia and in parts of Europe. It got less than 2% of its fiscal 2016 (ending in March) revenues from outside the US.

Sales and Marketing

The company serves customers in a range of industries including Manufacturing and Metal Fabrication Non-Residential (Energy and Infrastructure) Construction Life Sciences and Healthcare Food Beverage and Retail Energy and Chemical Production and Distribution Basic Materials and Services. It also has government clients.

Airgas markets its products and services through multiple sales channels including branch-based representatives retail stores telesales strategic customer account programs catalogs e-Business and other distributors.

Manufacturing & Metal Fabrication customers account for 30% of sales while Non-Residential (Energy & Infrastructure) Construction accounts for 15% and Food Beverage & Retail for 13%. Each bringing in more than 10% of sales are its Energy & Chemical Production & Distribution and Basic Materials & Services customers. Government & Other Life and Sciences & Healthcare customers account for the rest.

Strategy

Prior to its 2016 acquisition by global rival Air Liquide Airgas had grown its operations through acquisitions in its core businesses. It has bought more than 500 companies since its founding in 1986 and focuses on high-growth products with strong cross-selling opportunities. In fiscal 2016 it purchased 18 businesses (22 in fiscal 2015) with historical annual sales of $85 million. Airgas also grew through organic expansion.

HISTORY

In the early 1980s Peter McCausland was a corporate attorney involved in mergers and acquisitions for Messer Griesheim a large German industrial gas producer. When the German firm declined McCausland's recommendation in 1982 to buy Connecticut Oxygen he raised money from private sources and bought it himself. He acquired other distributors and then left Messer Griesheim in 1987 to run Airgas full-time.

Airgas began buying mostly small local and regional gas distributors in the US. By 1994 strategy shifted to purchasing larger "superregional" distributors such as Jimmie Jones Co. and Post Welding Supply of Alabama which added about $70 million combined to the company's revenues.

Airgas then began "rolling up" additional similar businesses. In 1995 it bought more than 25 companies and two years later it added more than 20 gas distributors. Also in 1997 Airgas expanded its manufacturing capabilities by building three plants that could fast-fill whole pallets of gas cylinders (the old manual system rolls cylinders two at a time). By 2000 the company had about 100 cylinder fill plants.

Struggling to integrate acquisitions while dealing with softening markets Airgas began a companywide realignment in 1998. To that end it sold its calcium carbide and carbon products operations to former partner Elkem ASA later that year; the company also consolidated 34 hubs into 16 regional companies and sold its operations in Poland and Thailand to Germany-based Linde in 1999.

In 2000 Airgas acquired distributor Mallinckrodt's Puritan-Bennett division (gas products for medical uses) with 36 locations in the US and Canada. The company also acquired the majority of Air Products' US packaged gas business excluding its electronic gases and magnetic resonance imaging-related helium operations in 2002.

In 2004 and 2005 it bought units from giants like Air Products and Chemicals BOC and LaRoche Industries. In 2006 Airgas continued to build with the purchase of 10 businesses including Union Industrial Gas which supplies Texas and much of the Southwest and then Linde's US bulk gas business for $495 million the next year. Linde in the process of integrating its 2006 acquisition of BOC then sold to Airgas a portion of its US packaged gas business for $310 million.

Rival Air Products had made a major bid to buy Airgas in 2010 but was rebuffed. Air Products extended its tender offer to Airgas stockholders several times and made a "best and final offer" of $70 a share (almost $6 billion) in December 2010. Airgas said it was holding out for $78 a share and rejected that offer too. In early 2011 a Delaware judge ruled for Airgas in a suit brought by Air Products to set aside a "poison pill" defense used by the Airgas board to fend off the takeover try. Following the verdict Air Products dropped its bid.

Airgas acquired six businesses in 2010 including Tri-Tech an independent distributor with 16 locations throughout Florida Georgia and South Carolina and annual sales of $31 million.

In 2011 Airgas reorganized its 12 regional segments into four new business support divisions — North South Central and West — to leverage a new SAP information systems platform in 2011. Each of the units is headed by a division president. The new company structure is designed to accelerate sales growth and pricing management and create operating efficiencies.

In fiscal 2012 the company added eight businesses with total annual sales of about $106 million. The largest of the busines

EXECUTIVES

Coo, Andrew R. (Andy) Cichocki, $296,936 total compensation
Svp Human Resources, Pamela J. (Pam) Claypool
Svp Sales And Marketing, Ronald J. (Ron) Stark
Svp And Cio, Robert A. Dougherty, $263,779 total compensation
President Airgas South, John F. Sheehan
Svp And Cfo, Robert M. (Bob) McLaughlin, $470,453 total compensation
Division President Gases Production, Thomas S. Thoman
Division President West, Douglas L. (Doug) Jones
Svp And General Counsel, Robert H. Young, $397,272 total compensation
Division President Central, Terry L. Lodge
President East Region, Jack Appolonia
Ceo, Pascal Vinet
Area Vice President, Denton Thompson
Vice President Human Resources, Tom Sheridan
Vice President Area Sales, Ross Jones
Vice President Of Information Technology Airgas Mid South, George Turner
Vice President, James Cook
National Sales Manager, Jerry Anderskow
Vice President Sales And Marketing, David Webb
Vice President Of Plant Operations, Roger Weber
Vice President Of Bulk Operations, Steve Scheuring
Vice President, Ted Schulte
Area Vice President, Jake Lucier
Vice President Of Finance, Michael Maley
Area Vice President, Jeff Mann
Assistant Vice President Corporate Development, Brian Shammo
Senior Vice President, Ken Beringer
National Account Manager, Ken Ashworth
Division Vice President Of Sales, Mark Johnston
Vice President, Wayne Wilson
National Account Manager, Don Wallenfelsz
Vice President Operations, Robbie Cosner
National Account Manager, Victoria Ektarian
Vice President Bulk Gases, David Stockmal
Vice President Strategic Accounts, Jim Meyer
National Account Manager, Earl Dyck
Vice President, Kathryn Shuler
National Account Manager Metal Fabrication Markets, James Doyle
Vice President Gulf Coast Region, Scott Koonce
National Account Manager, Joe Sebastian
Vice President Credit And Collections, Ed Burke
Vice President Bulk Gases, Stephanie Benham
Vice President Bulk Sales And Operations, Richard Cassano
National Account Manager, Danielle Pogue
Vp Safety And Compliance, Curtis Henson
Vice President Safety And Compliance North Division, Benson Scott
Chairman, Pierre Dufour
Vice Chairman, Michael J. (Mike) Graff
Auditors: KPMG LLP PHILADELPHIA PENNSY

LOCATIONS

HQ: AIRGAS, INC.
259 N RADNOR CHESTER RD # 100, RADNOR, PA 190875240
Phone: 610 687-5253
Web: WWW.AIRGAS.COM

PRODUCTS/OPERATIONS

2016 sales

	% of total
Manufacturing & Metal Fabrication	29
Non Residential (Energy & Infrastructure) construction	15
Life Science & Healthcare	14
Food Beverage & Retail	13
Energy & Chemical Production & Distribution	12
Basic Material & Services	11
Government & Others	6
Total	**100**

2016 sales

	$ mil.	% of total
Distribution	4,716	88
Other Operations	635	12
Adjustments	(38.2)	
Total	**5,313**	**100**

Selected Products and Services

Products
Carbon dioxide
Dry ice
Industrial gases
Argon
Helium
Hydrogen
Liquid oxygen
Nitrogen
Nitrous oxide
Oxygen
Safety equipment
Specialty gases

Services
Container rental
Welding equipment rental

Selected Subsidiaries

Airgas Canada
Airgas Carbonic
Airgas East
Airgas Great Lakes
Airgas Intermountain
Airgas Medical Services
Airgas Mid America
Airgas Mid South
Airgas Nitrous Oxide
Airgas Nor Pac
Airgas North Central
Airgas Northern California & Nevada
Airgas Refrigerant
Airgas Safety
Airgas South
Airgas Southwest
Airgas Specialty Gases
Airgas Specialty Products
Airgas West
National Welders Supply Company dba Airgas National
  Welders
Nitrous Oxide Corp.
Red-D-Arc
WorldWide Welding LLC

COMPETITORS

Air Products	Praxair Distribution
Lincoln Electric	Valley National Gases
Matheson Tri-Gas	W.W. Grainger

HISTORICAL FINANCIALS

Company Type: Private

Income Statement — FYE: March 31

	REVENUE ($ mil.)	NET INCOME ($ mil.)	NET PROFIT MARGIN	EMPLOYEES
03/15	5,304	368	6.9%	17,070
03/13	4,957	340	6.9%	—
Annual Growth	**3.4%**	**3.9%**	**—**	**—**

2015 Year-End Financials

Return on assets: 3.9%   Cash ($ mil.): 50
Return on equity: 6.9%
Current ratio: 0.70

ALAMEDA COUNTY TRANSPORTATION COMMISSION

EXECUTIVES

Ex Dir, Arthur Dao
Director of Finance, Patricia Reavey
Manager, Rebecca Kaplan
Assistant, Chris Van Alstyne
Associate, Erika Cheng
Assistant Transportation Engin, Ashley Tam
Consultant, Christina Ramos

LOCATIONS

HQ: ALAMEDA COUNTY TRANSPORTATION
  COMMISSION
  1111 BROADWAY STE 800, OAKLAND, CA 946074006
Phone: 510 208-7400
Web: WWW.ALAMEDACTC.ORG

HISTORICAL FINANCIALS

Company Type: Private

Income Statement — FYE: June 30

	REVENUE ($ mil.)	NET INCOME ($ mil.)	NET PROFIT MARGIN	EMPLOYEES
06/17	351	46	13.3%	21
06/16	344	92	27.0%	—
Annual Growth	**2.0%**	**(49.5%)**	**—**	**—**

ALASKA NATIVE TRIBAL HEALTH CONSORTIUM

The Alaska Native Tribal Health Consortium (ANTHC) brings good health to Alaska Natives. The company is a not-for-profit statewide health care organization managed by regional tribal governments and their respective regional health organizations. The organization connects disparate medical providers by providing a range of health programs and services including community health care public health advocacy and education initiatives health research (including water and sanitation) and medical supply distribution. The 150-bed Alaska Native Medical Center (ANMC) a native-owned hospital is jointly managed by ANTHC and Southcentral Foundation a regional health corporation based in the Cook Inlet region.

Operations

ANMC's services are reserved primarily for Alaska Native Tribal groups with the exception of its Urgent Care centers and Emergency Room. (Emergency rooms are compelled to take patients of all types under US fair care guidelines.) The hospital handles about 8000 patient admissions each year as well as 300000 outpatient and 57000 emergency room visits. It also conducts some 11000 surgeries and 1600 births. ANMC has about 100 physicians.

The organization's primary mission is to improve the health of Alaska natives through health sanitation technology and advocacy services. It conducts a number of community outreach programs and it works to create a continuum of care for its members so they can move smoothly through the health care process (including initial specialist and follow-up care visits). The hospital is the regional hub of that health care continuum offering general and specialist care in a range of fields. ANTHC also operates outpatient care centers and it operates an extensive telemedicine network (allow providers to care for and consult with patients in outlying areas).

ANTHC provides administrative support to Alaska's Tribal health groups and it supports state legislative efforts such as the reauthorization of the Indian Health Care Improvement Act. The consortium formed in 1997 also works to improve the Alaskan health system by participating in strategic summit meetings and sponsoring electronic health record initiatives.

Geographic Reach

ANTHC and ANMC are located in Anchorage Alaska. The organization provides services throughout the state.

Financial Performance

The company's 2014 revenues stood at $643 million about 33% of which came from patient revenues. Other major operating segments include compact revenue (25% of sales) and grant and project income (17%).

Strategy

Infrastructure and service expansions are a key means of growth for ANTHC.

In 2015 ANTHC awarded Neeser Construction Inc. a contract to build the new ANMC patient housing facility on the Alaska Native Health Campus in Anchorage. The building will house patients and their families travelling to ANMC for medical care. The a new patient housing facility is expected to open in fall 2016. It will have 202 private rooms and six floors with a dedicated floor for new families.

In 2015 Alaska Governor Walker introduced legislation declaring his plan for Medicaid reform and expansion. ANTHC supports the Governor's efforts to expand Medicaid coverage to more than 41000 Alaskans.

Company Background

In 2012 ANMC expanded its maternal child health and neurosurgery departments due to increasing patient populations in the Anchorage area. In 2010 the medical center opened the only Level II trauma center in Alaska making it a referral hospital for major trauma cases.

The organization has also improved its health care technology resources; it expanded the use of electronic health records at ANMC in 2012 and it is expanding its telemedicine operations (as telemedicine is becoming an increasingly popular way for specialists to see patients without the expense of a personal visit). It has increased other community outreach efforts as well such as smoking cessation and behavioral health programs.

EXECUTIVES

**Vp Professional And Support Services Alaska
  Native Medical Center Hospital,** Vivian Echavarria
Cfo, Garvin Federenko
Ceo And Administrator, Roald Helgesen
Cio, Stewart Ferguson
Chief Medical Officer, Paul Franke
**Chief Nursing Executive Alaska Native Medical
  Center Hospital,** Richard Hall
Chairman And President, Andy Teuber
Vice Chairman, Lincoln A. Bean
Auditors: BDO USA LP ANCHORAGE AK

LOCATIONS

HQ: ALASKA NATIVE TRIBAL HEALTH CONSORTIUM
  4000 AMBASSADOR DR, ANCHORAGE, AK 995085909
Phone: 907 729-1900
Web: WWW.ANTHC.ORG

PRODUCTS/OPERATIONS

2014 Sales

	$ mil.	% of total
Patient revenue	213	33
Compact revenue	161	25
Grant & project revenue	109	17
Warehouse revenue	22	3
Investment income	4	1
Other	133	21
Total	**643**	**100**

Selected Services

Ear Nose Throat
Emergency and Trauma
Family Medicine
Imaging and Laboratory Services
Internal Medicine Clinic
Maternal Fetal Medicine
OB/GYN Services
Oncology
Orthopedics Clinic
Pediatric ICU
Pediatrics
Pharmacy Services
Pregnancy and Childbirth
Primary Care Services
Respiratory Care

COMPETITORS

HCA	South Peninsula
Immediate Care	Hospital
PeaceHealth	Tenet Healthcare
Providence St. Joseph	
Health	

HISTORICAL FINANCIALS

Company Type: Private

Income Statement   FYE: September 30

	REVENUE ($ mil.)	NET INCOME ($ mil.)	NET PROFIT MARGIN	EMPLOYEES
09/16	587	72	12.4%	1,850
09/15	511	3	0.7%	—
09/14	618	154	24.9%	—
09/13	459	21	4.6%	—
Annual Growth	**8.5%**	**50.5%**	—	—

2016 Year-End Financials

Return on assets: 13.0%   Cash ($ mil.): 121
Return on equity: 12.4%
Current ratio: 1.20

ALASKA PERMANENT FUND CORPORATION

EXECUTIVES

Ceo, Angela Rodell
Coo, Marcus Frampton
Chief Financial Officer, Valerie Mertz
Portfolio Manager, Chris Cummins
Information Specialist, Andrew Loney
Principal, Chris Poag
Communications Manager, Paulyn Swanson
Executive Officer, Stephen Moseley
Portfolio Manager, Yup Kim
Information Technology Special, Anthony Shaw
Credit Analyst, Matthew Olmsted
Auditors: KPMG LLP ANCHORAGE AK

LOCATIONS

HQ: ALASKA PERMANENT FUND CORPORATION
801 W 10TH ST STE 302, JUNEAU, AK 998011878
Phone: 907 796-1500
Web: WWW.APFC.ORG

HISTORICAL FINANCIALS

Company Type: Private

Income Statement   FYE: June 30

	ASSETS ($ mil.)	NET INCOME ($ mil.)	INCOME AS % OF ASSETS	EMPLOYEES
06/18	67,671	5,109	7.6%	50
06/17	61,824	6,675	10.8%	—
06/16	55,346	(30)	—	—
06/15	55,900	1,586	2.8%	—
Annual Growth	**6.6%**	**47.7%**	—	—

ALBANY MEDICAL CENTER

Albany Medical Center (AMC) provides medical care in upstate New York. Serving residents of northeastern New York and western New England the health system has at its heart the 730-bed Albany Medical Center Hospital. The general medical-surgical facility also provides specialty care in such areas as oncology rehabilitation and organ transplantation. AMC also features a children's hospital an outpatient surgery center and a group medical practice. It employs some 400 full-time physicians. Its Albany Medical College is one of the nation's first private medical schools. It offers undergraduate and graduate medical degrees and residency programs as well as fellowships and continuing medical education.

Operations

AMC's assets includes a biomedical research enterprise and one of the region's largest physicians practices with more than 400 doctors. Its physicians have extensive training and experience in 34 subspecialties of pediatric medicine. The system's subsidiaries include the Albany Medical Center Kidskeller Corporation a not-for-profit day care facility and Madison Avenue Services Corporation a taxable corporation.

AMC is affiliated with several community physician groups including Albany Vascular Group Capital Cardiology Associates and Capital Region Orthopaedic Group.

In 2013 the system reported some 33000 admissions 581000 outpatient visits 28000 surgical cases and 68000 emergency department visits.

Geographic Reach

AMC offers services in 25 counties in northeastern New York and western New England. In addition to treating patients at the main site in Albany providers also treat patients at community-based locations throughout the region including Clifton Park Latham Malta North Greenbush Delmar and others.

Sales and Marketing

HMOs account for around a third of net patient revenue while Medicare and Medicaid represent about 20% and 15% respectively.

Financial Performance

The company's revenues grew by 3% to $752 million in 2013 (versus $728 million in 2012) due to an increase in net patient revenue; this was partially offset by declines in interest income dividends and other revenue. Net income grew 21% to $63

million in 2013 as net realized gains on sales of securities and impairment charges rose. Other gains were made in pension-related changes and net unrealized gains and losses in investments.

Cash flow from operations fell 55% that year to $37 million as more was used in receivables and other liabilities.

Strategy

AMC grows through organic expansion partnerships and product initiatives. The company is in the midst of a $360 million expansion including a new patient tower with more than 100 beds and increased intensive care resources. The project — expected to last several years — will also increase Albany Medical Center Hospital's bed count to more than 700.

In 2014 The Neurology Group and The Endocrine Group joined AMC's Albany Med Faculty Physician Group.

AMC and Union Graduate College joined forces in 2013 to offer a new joint degree combining medical school with an MBA.

That year AMC and Saratoga Hospital formed a joint venture and opened the $17.5 million Malta Med Emergent Care to provide area residents an alternative to hospital emergency rooms for all but the most serious medical circumstances.

On the product innovation side in 2013 AMC introduced advanced imaging technologies in a pair of its new Patient Pavilion operating rooms that provide for greater precision and patient safety during brain and spinal surgeries.

Also that year the company opened a Chronic Kidney Disease Clinic as the sole source for comprehensive care for 6000 people in its service area suffering from the slow loss of kidney function.

AMC also engages in research and development of new pharmaceuticals through partnerships with companies like Aegis Therapeutics with which it is developing an anti-obesity peptide to benefit patients with type 2 diabetes. The college's research department is also studying brain mapping techniques as well as Alzheimer's disease vascular disease and cancer and multiple sclerosis treatments.

Company Background

AMC which produced Nobel prize winners in both 2009 and 2011 annually awards its own $500000 prize the largest monetary award in medicine and biomedical research in the US. In 2010 combined federal-state entities awarded the center $10 million the center's largest grant since its founding which will be used to expand research labs at Albany Medical College.

AMC's status as the Capital Region's reigning health care giant was toppled by the 2011 merger of four locals hospitals to form St. Peter's Health Partners with nearly 12000 employees vs. 6000 at AMC. Post merger the newly-merged group has nearly 50% of the Capital Region market while AMC has 25%. While AMC is no longer the area's largest hospital as the region's trauma center and only medical school it continues to draw many patients from outside the four-county area.

Albany Medical College was formed in 1839; the hospital's predecessor was formed in 1849. The two combined under the AMC umbrella in 1982.

EXECUTIVES

President And Ceo, James J. Barba
Coo, Gary J. Kochem
Evp And Cfo, William C. Hasselbarth
Evp And Cio, George T. Hickman
Evp Ids And Hospital Systems General Director, Steven M. Frisch
Evp Policy Planning And Communications, Kim Fine
Svp Hospital Business Services And Coo Hospital, Bernadette Pedlow

Dean And Evp Healthâ Affairs, Vincent Verdile
Svp And Chief Nursing Officer, Mary Ellen Plass
Senior Vice President And Chief Compliance
 Officer, Noel Hogan
Vice President, Michael Gruenthal
Chairman, Robert Cushing
Auditors: KPMG LLP ALBANY NEW YORK

LOCATIONS

HQ: ALBANY MEDICAL CENTER
 43 NEW SCOTLAND AVE, ALBANY, NY 122083478
Phone: 518 262-3125
Web: WWW.AMC.EDU

PRODUCTS/OPERATIONS

2013 Sales

	% of total
Net patient service	96
Inter-institutional	1
Interest & dividends	-
Other	2
Net assets released from restrictions	1
Total	**100**

2013 Net Patient Service Revenue

	% of total
Health maintenance organizations	32
Medicare	19
Medicaid	15
Blue Cross and Blue Shield	14
Commercial carriers	9
No fault & worker's compensation	5
Private pay	2
Other third-party payors	4
Total	**100**

Selected Services

Cancer center
Children's Hospital
Center for Donation and Transplant
Diabetes service
Emergency medical services
Hearing center
HIV medicine
Pain management
Perinatal
Physical therapy
Radiology
Rheumatology
Surgical
Trauma center
Women's wellness center

COMPETITORS

Berkshire Health	St. Joseph's Hospital
Systems	Health Center
Ellis Hospital	St. Peter's Health
SUNY Upstate Medical	Partners
University	United Health Services
Southwestern Vermont	Hospitals
Health Care	

HISTORICAL FINANCIALS
Company Type: Private

Income Statement   FYE: December 31

	REVENUE ($ mil.)	NET INCOME ($ mil.)	NET PROFIT MARGIN	EMPLOYEES
12/17	664	267	40.2%	7,000
12/16	317	77	24.5%	—
12/15	1,167	5	0.5%	—
12/13	980	115	11.7%	—
Annual Growth	(9.3%)	23.4%	—	—

2017 Year-End Financials

Return on assets: 4.9%   Cash ($ mil.): 113
Return on equity: 40.2%
Current ratio: 1.30

ALBANY MEDICAL CENTER HOSPITAL

EXECUTIVES

Pres, James J Barba
Coo, Gary J Kochem
SEC, Sabine Needham
Contrl, Patrick Kelly
Auditors: KPMG LLP ALBANY NY

LOCATIONS

HQ: ALBANY MEDICAL CENTER HOSPITAL
 43 NEW SCOTLAND AVE, ALBANY, NY 122083478
Phone: 518 262-3125
Web: WWW.AMC.EDU

HISTORICAL FINANCIALS
Company Type: Private

Income Statement   FYE: December 31

	REVENUE ($ mil.)	NET INCOME ($ mil.)	NET PROFIT MARGIN	EMPLOYEES
12/17	1,017	38	3.8%	1,568
12/16	960	46	4.8%	—
12/15	893	16	1.9%	—
12/14	812	51	6.3%	—
Annual Growth	7.8%	(9.5%)	—	—

2017 Year-End Financials

Return on assets: 5.5%   Cash ($ mil.): 95
Return on equity: 3.8%
Current ratio: 1.40

ALBANY MEDICAL COLLEGE

EXECUTIVES

Exec V Pres, Vincent P Verdile
Exec V Pres-Cfo, William Hasselbarth
Manager, Kevin Pumiglia
Cardiac Physician, Steven Fein
Assistant Professor, Toinette Hartshorne
Auditors: KPMG LLP ALBANY NY

LOCATIONS

HQ: ALBANY MEDICAL COLLEGE
 47 NEW SCOTLAND AVE, ALBANY, NY 122083479
Phone: 518 262-6008

HISTORICAL FINANCIALS
Company Type: Private

Income Statement   FYE: December 31

	REVENUE ($ mil.)	NET INCOME ($ mil.)	NET PROFIT MARGIN	EMPLOYEES
12/17	389	37	9.7%	1,568
12/16	362	(3)	—	—
12/13	290	3	1.2%	—
Annual Growth	7.6%	81.8%	—	—

2017 Year-End Financials

Return on assets: 1.4%   Cash ($ mil.): 8
Return on equity: 9.7%
Current ratio: 0.80

ALBERICI CONSTRUCTORS, INC.

EXECUTIVES

Pres, Gregory J Kozicz
V Pres, John S Alberici
V Pres, Leroy Stromberg
Cfo, Gregory T Hesser
Sr Acct, Sherry Morrow
Chief Information Officer, Frank C Kropiunik
Manager of Information, Deborah Sparrow
Superintendent, Curt Davidson
Project Manager, Glenn Murphy
Coordinator, Katie Schaper
Director of Risk Management, Joe Gallagher

LOCATIONS

HQ: ALBERICI CONSTRUCTORS, INC.
 8800 PAGE AVE, SAINT LOUIS, MO 631146106
Phone: 314 733-2000
Web: WWW.ALBERICI.COM

HISTORICAL FINANCIALS
Company Type: Private

Income Statement   FYE: December 31

	REVENUE ($ mil.)	NET INCOME ($ mil.)	NET PROFIT MARGIN	EMPLOYEES
12/17	782	0	—	2,000
12/16	960	0	—	—
12/15	1,028	0	—	—
12/14	729	0	—	—
Annual Growth	2.4%	—	—	—

2017 Year-End Financials

Return on assets: 8.5%   Cash ($ mil.): 76
Return on equity: —
Current ratio: 1.00

ALBERICI CORPORATION

Alberici helped shape the St. Louis skyline; it now sets its sights — or its construction sites — across North America. As the parent company of Alberici Constructors the company encompasses a group of enterprises with a presence in North America Central America South America and Europe. Operations include construction services building materials and steel fabrication and erection units. Alberici offers general contracting design/build construction management demolition and specialty contracting services while also offering facilities management. Founded in 1918 the Alberici family still holds the largest share of the employee-owned firm.

Operations

The company boasts more than a dozen operating companies in the US Canada and Mexico that serve the automotive energy health care industrial manufacturing and wastewater treatment markets. Its Gunther-Nash subsidiary provides construction services to the mining industry. Another division Vertegy specializes in construction consulting for green and sustainable projects.

Geographic Reach

Alberici is active throughout North America and has offices in St. Louis Missouri; Detroit Michigan; Atlanta Georgia; Topeka Kansas; Burlington and Cambridge Ontario; Saskatoon Saskatchewan; and LA©on Mexico.

Sales and Marketing

Alberici serves a range of different companies including those that are automotive building energy healthcare heavy industrial industrial process mining infrastructure or water-related.

Some of Alberici's completed projects include casinos for Ameristar modernization and new facilities for Anheuser-Busch and factories for Boeing. Nearly 80% of its revenue comes from repeat clients.

Financial Performance

While full financial information was not available for the privately held company Alberici reports that its annual revenue typically exceeds $1 billion. In 2013 the company took home $1.9 billion and was ranked the 46th largest contractor in the US by the Engineering News-Record .

In 2012 the company reported more than $530 million in industrial-related revenue thanks to a recovering economy supporting demand for major industrial projects in the US and Canada.

Strategy

In recent years the heavy construction firm has pursued acquisitions to better diversify its business both geographically and by entering new specialty markets. In 2013 for example Alberici purchased contractor Flintco LLC to broaden its reach into new markets in the southern and southwestern regions of the US. In early 2012 Alberici acquired a water treatment facility specialist to expand its service offerings in the water plant construction market.

Alberici has also become a recognized contractor in recent years which could help give the company a higher profile and thus more exposure to new potential clients. In 2013 the Associated General Contractors of St. Louis awarded Alberici with top prizes at its 16th Annual Keystone Awards for the company's work on the Seabrook Gates Complex and the Knights of Columbus Child Development Center. To date Alberici has won 14 Keystone Awards more than any other general contractor.

So far its high standing hasn't hurt business. In July 2014 Alberici was chosen to lead in the engineering procurement and construction of a major air quality improvement project — with the goal of installing environmental controls and reducing sulfur dioxide emissions by 90% — at one of the generating stations owned and operated by Alliant Energy's Wisconsin utility Wisconsin Power and Light Company.

Mergers and Acquisitions

Expanding it range of capabilities in January 2012 Alberici acquired water treatment facility specialist CAS Construction. The addition of CAS which has built facilities throughout the central and western US strengthens Alberici's capabilities in the water market. The company was renamed CAS Constructors.

In early 2013 Alberici closed on its acquisition of Flintco LLC a century-old Native American-owned contractor based in Tulsa Oklahoma. With offices in Oklahoma New Mexico Texas Arkansas and California Flintco presented an attractive geographic diversification opportunity for Alberici.

EXECUTIVES

Pres, Gregory J Kozicz
Chb, John S Alberici
Coordinator, Keeley Vickers
Director of Information Techno, Ron Borror
Accounting Staff, Amanda Dolan
Coordinator, Matt Rogge
Accounting Staff, Sharon Govreau
Coordinator, Tyler Rickett
Assistant To President and CHI, Anna Colalillo
Position In Coordinator and Pu, Brandon Mills
Constructors Director of Busin, Bruno Presutto

LOCATIONS

HQ: ALBERICI CORPORATION
8800 PAGE AVE, SAINT LOUIS, MO 631146106
Phone: 314 733-2000
Web: WWW.ALBERICI.COM

PRODUCTS/OPERATIONS

Selected Markets

Automotive
Building
Energy
Green building
Health care
Industrial
Manufacturing/Food and Beverage
Mining infrastructure
Steel fabrication
Water and Wastewater Treatment

Selected Subsidiaries and Brands

Alberici Global Group GmbH
  Alberici Constructors Ltd. (Canada)
  Alberici Construcciones S.A. de C.V. (Mexico)
Alberici Group Inc.
  Alberici Constructors Inc.
  Alberici Global Automotive Constructors (automotive construction)
  Alberici Healthcare Constructors
  Alberici Industrial LLC
  CAS Construction LLC (water wastewater)
  Flintco LLC (Native American-owned contractor)
  Gunther-Nash Inc. (shaft slope and tunnel construction for mining industry)
  Hillsdale Fabricators (steel fabrication)
  Kienlen Constructors (structural concrete structural steel)
  Vertegy (green building consulting)

COMPETITORS

Barton Malow	Jacobs Engineering
Bechtel	McCarthy Building
Black & Veatch	Parsons Corporation
DPR Construction	Peter Kiewit Sons'
Fluor	TIC Holdings
Hensel Phelps Construction	Tutor Perini
	Walbridge Aldinger
Hoffman Corporation	Walsh Group
Hunt Construction	Zachry Inc.

HISTORICAL FINANCIALS

Company Type: Private

Income Statement				FYE: December 31
	REVENUE ($ mil.)	NET INCOME ($ mil.)	NET PROFIT MARGIN	EMPLOYEES
12/17	1,531	0	—	2,080
12/16	1,742	0	—	—
12/15	1,885	0	—	—
12/14	1,532	0	—	—
Annual Growth	(0.0%)	—	—	—

2017 Year-End Financials

Return on assets: 14.1%   Cash ($ mil.): 182
Return on equity: —
Current ratio: 1.10

ALBERICI GROUP, INC.

EXECUTIVES

Ceo, Gregory J Kozicz
Chb, John S Alberici
Coo, Leroy J Stromberg Jr
Exe Vice President, Michael W Burke
Coordinator, Keeley Vickers
Safety Project Coordinator, Matt Walters
Director of Preconstruction, Frederick Biermann

LOCATIONS

HQ: ALBERICI GROUP, INC.
8800 PAGE AVE, SAINT LOUIS, MO 631146106
Phone: 314 733-2000
Web: WWW.ALBERICI.COM

HISTORICAL FINANCIALS

Company Type: Private

Income Statement				FYE: December 31
	REVENUE ($ mil.)	NET INCOME ($ mil.)	NET PROFIT MARGIN	EMPLOYEES
12/17	838	0	—	2,000
12/16	1,036	0	—	—
12/15	1,124	0	—	—
12/14	729	0	—	—
Annual Growth	4.8%	—	—	—

2017 Year-End Financials

Return on assets: 9.2%   Cash ($ mil.): 105
Return on equity: —
Current ratio: 1.00

ALBERT C. KOBAYASHI, INC

EXECUTIVES

Ceo, Russell Young
V Pres, George Ballao
V Pres, Warren Leong
V Pres, Kendall Korenaga
SEC, Colette Ruiz
Cfo, Clyde Sugawa
Controller, Shaun Shimizu
Project Engineer, Clifford Garcia
Project Engineer, Jason Ohara
Project Manager, Brian Niitani
Manager, Deron Matsuoka
Auditors: N&K CPAS INC HONOLULU HAWA

LOCATIONS

HQ: ALBERT C. KOBAYASHI, INC
94-535 UKEE ST STE 101, WAIPAHU, HI 967974275
Phone: 808 671-6460
Web: WWW.ACK-INC.COM

HISTORICAL FINANCIALS

Company Type: Private

Income Statement				FYE: July 31
	REVENUE ($ mil.)	NET INCOME ($ mil.)	NET PROFIT MARGIN	EMPLOYEES
07/16	383	5	1.4%	200
07/15	280	4	1.7%	—
07/14	180	9	5.5%	—
07/13	127	8	6.6%	—
Annual Growth	44.2%	(13.4%)	—	—

2016 Year-End Financials

Return on assets: 24.2%   Cash ($ mil.): 46
Return on equity: 1.4%
Current ratio: 1.20

ALBERT EINSTEIN MEDICAL CENTER

EXECUTIVES

Pres, Richard Greenberg
Doctor Internal Medici, Ken Hoellein
Pharmacist, Debbie Hauser
Director, Raymond Schwartz
Osteopathy, Sandra S Jones
Doctor Geriatrics, Andrew Rosenzweig
Placement Coordinator, Ardenia Dublin
Director, Cheryl Mittl
Anesthesiologist, Glenn Shopper
Msw, Paula Glazier

LOCATIONS

HQ: ALBERT EINSTEIN MEDICAL CENTER
5501 OLD YORK RD STE 1, PHILADELPHIA, PA
191413098
Phone: 215 456-7890
Web: WWW.EINSTEIN.EDU

HISTORICAL FINANCIALS

Company Type: Private

Income Statement · FYE: June 30

	REVENUE ($ mil.)	NET INCOME ($ mil.)	NET PROFIT MARGIN	EMPLOYEES
06/18	820	7	1.0%	52
06/16	746	9	1.3%	—
06/15	679	38	5.7%	—
06/11	744	52	7.1%	—
Annual Growth	1.4%	(23.7%)	—	—

2018 Year-End Financials

Return on assets: 11.4%
Return on equity: 1.0%
Current ratio: 0.90
Cash ($ mil.): 15

ALBUQUERQUE MUNICIPAL SCHOOL DISTRICT NUMBER 12

EXECUTIVES

Supt, Jason Martinez
Superintendent, Raquel Martinez Reedy
Assistant Superintendent, Karen Rudys
Auditors: MOSS ADAMS LLP ALBUQUERQUE N

LOCATIONS

HQ: ALBUQUERQUE MUNICIPAL SCHOOL DISTRICT
NUMBER 12
6400 UPTOWN BLVD NE, ALBUQUERQUE, NM
871104202
Phone: 505 880-3700
Web: WWW.APS.EDU

HISTORICAL FINANCIALS

Company Type: Private

Income Statement · FYE: June 30

	REVENUE ($ mil.)	NET INCOME ($ mil.)	NET PROFIT MARGIN	EMPLOYEES
06/17	946	57	6.0%	8
06/16	998	11	1.2%	—
06/11	924	114	12.4%	—
Annual Growth	0.4%	(10.9%)	—	—

2017 Year-End Financials

Return on assets: 0.2%
Return on equity: 6.0%
Current ratio: 0.60
Cash ($ mil.): 97

ALDINE INDEPENDENT SCHOOL DISTRICT

EXECUTIVES

Supt, Dr Latonya Goffney
Principal, Ruth Dimmick
Principal, Jeannette Ross
Social Worker, Desiree Baham
Information Technology/Interne, Jamila Ashmeade-Brown
Coordinator, Randle Lanell
Assistant, Sonia Pace
Assistant, Akua Twumasi
Teacher, David Barfield
Assistant Director, Mario Williams
Administrator, Pat Leon-Wade
Auditors: WHITLEY PENN LLP HOUSTON TEX

LOCATIONS

HQ: ALDINE INDEPENDENT SCHOOL DISTRICT
2520 WW THORNE BLVD, HOUSTON, TX 770733406
Phone: 281 449-1011
Web: WWW.ALDINE.K12.TX.US

HISTORICAL FINANCIALS

Company Type: Private

Income Statement · FYE: June 30

	REVENUE ($ mil.)	NET INCOME ($ mil.)	NET PROFIT MARGIN	EMPLOYEES
06/17	743	(276)		7,000
06/16	766	104	13.7%	—
06/13	625	26	4.2%	—
06/12	607	12	2.0%	—
Annual Growth	4.1%	—	—	—

2017 Year-End Financials

Return on assets: 6.1%
Return on equity: (-37.2%)
Current ratio: —
Cash ($ mil.): 47

ALDRIDGE ELECTRIC, INC.

Aldridge Electric powers up the Windy City and other parts of the Midwest. The electrical contractor divides its business into six main areas: airport industrial power drilling highway and transit. It works on projects ranging from Chicago's subway system to its airport runways. Additional activities include services for street lighting traffic signals high-voltage cabling and splicing and foundation drilling. Aldridge Electric has worked for clients such as Commonwealth Edison Company and Exelon Corporation. It sister companies in the family-owned AldridgeGroup include Aldridge Construction GFS Construction and Woodward Brothering.

Operations

Aldridge Electric has more than 1200 pieces of equipment.

It is the general contractor and subcontractor of choice for the multi-million dollar O'Hare Modernization Program (OMP) intended to reduce delays and improve efficiency at the Chicago international airport. Aldridge completed several OMP contracts involving the construction extension and relocation of several runways in addition to the installation of taxiway lights and navigational equipment.

The company is also participating in a $130 million project the Oak Glen Substation a two-circuit 34.5-kV to 69-kV collection substation on the site of Oak Glen Wind Farm near Blooming Prairie Minnesota. It was selected to provide electrical service and maintenance lighting DelDOT Intelligent Traffic Management Systems (ITMS) bridge monitoring instrumentation and the design and installation of a sand-bypass system over the main span of on a new cable stay bridge.

Aldridge Electric's drilling division has enjoyed a robust backlog due to the growing demand in the wind energy market. The division has worked to drill foundations for wind turbines and transmission lines that criss-cross the US.

Company Background

Leonard "Len" Aldridge started the business in 1932 and incorporated it in 1952.

EXECUTIVES

Vice President, Wayne Gearig
Executive Vice President, Tim Bradley
Vice President, Keith George
Vice President, Paul Legg
Executive Vice President, Frank Manna
Vice President, Martin Bradley

LOCATIONS

HQ: ALDRIDGE ELECTRIC, INC.
844 E ROCKLAND RD, LIBERTYVILLE, IL 600483358
Phone: 847 680-5200
Web: WWW.ALDRIDGE-ELECTRIC.COM

PRODUCTS/OPERATIONS

Selected Divisions and Services

Airport
Approach lighting systems
Control system
Electrical vaults
Hangar facility electrical
High-voltage cable pulling splicing and terminating
Hold pad perimeter lighting and limit lighting
Parking lot lighting
Parking structure rehabilitation
Runway and taxiway lighting
Site utility work
Terminal rehabilitation work
Traffic management and control

Drilling
Bridge foundations
Building structure foundations
Communication tower foundations
Drilled shafts for sewer lift stations
Drilling for earth-retention systems
High-mast lighting tower foundations
Sign foundations
Transmission line foundations

Highway

Closed-loop detection
High-mast lighting
Highway lighting
Intelligent transportation systems
Lighting systems design/build
Municipal street lighting
RTMS detection systems
Subdivision street lighting
Surveillance camera systems
Surveillance systems
Traffic interconnect systems
Traffic signal systems
Variable message signs
Industrial
Design/build capabilities
Electrical maintenance and renovations
Electrical power distribution and lighting for new
construction and existing facilities
Energy conservation upgrades and retrofits
Fire alarm and security
Movable bridge power lighting and control systems
Process control systems
Supervisory control and data acquisition systems
Tenant build-out
Voice data communication systems and CCTV
Power
Design/build
Fiber optic cabling
Interconnect yard construction
Project management
Overhead elecrical construction
Substation construction
Solar panal installation
Turbine wiring
Underground electrical construction
Transit
Catenary systems
Communications systems
Traction power 3rd rail systems
Train control
Affiliates in the AldridgeGroup
Aldridge Canada
GFS Construction LLC
Woodward Brothering

COMPETITORS

Bayview Electric Company	IES Holdings
EEI	Kelso-Burnett
EMCOR	Mass Electric
Faith Technologies	Motor City Electric

HISTORICAL FINANCIALS

Company Type: Private

Income Statement   FYE: March 31

	REVENUE ($ mil.)	NET INCOME ($ mil.)	NET PROFIT MARGIN	EMPLOYEES
03/17	417	0	—	850
03/11	208	2	1.0%	—
03/10	272	10	3.8%	—
Annual Growth	6.3%	—	—	—

2017 Year-End Financials

Return on assets: 7.4%   Cash ($ mil.): 26
Return on equity: —
Current ratio: 1.40

ALEGENT HEALTH-BERGAN MERCY HEALTH SYSTEM

EXECUTIVES

Ceo, Cliff Robertson
Pres, Lawrence Beckman
Sr V Pres, Bonnie Burnett

Cfo, Jeanette Wojtalewicz
V Pres, Leigh Bertholf
Coo, Joan Neuhaus
Manager, Angie Peters
Executive Director, Ann E Oasan
Staff Pharmacist, Brian Rickley
Operations Director, Don Mandel
Registered Nurse, Jean Danielson

LOCATIONS

HQ: ALEGENT HEALTH- BERGAN MERCY HEALTH SYSTEM
7500 MERCY RD, OMAHA, NE 681242319
Phone: 402 398-6060
Web: WWW.ALEGENT.COM

HISTORICAL FINANCIALS

Company Type: Private

Income Statement   FYE: June 30

	REVENUE ($ mil.)	NET INCOME ($ mil.)	NET PROFIT MARGIN	EMPLOYEES
06/17	727	23	3.2%	1
06/14	543	88	16.3%	—
Annual Growth	10.2%	(35.7%)	—	—

2017 Year-End Financials

Return on assets: 7.1%   Cash ($ mil.): 20
Return on equity: 3.2%
Current ratio: 1.60

ALEX LEE, INC.

The business of wholesaling groceries is only part of the bigger picture for Alex Lee. The company is a leading distributor of food and other products to retailers and food service operators. Its Merchants Distributors Inc. (MDI) subsidiary supplies food and general merchandise to more than 600 retailers in nearly a dozen mostly southeastern states. MDI's own Consolidation Services business provides warehousing and logistics services. As part of its business Alex Lee also operates Lowe's Food Stores a chain of about 100 grocery stores located in the Carolinas and Virginia. Alex and Lee George started the company in 1931. The George family continues to control Alex Lee.

Operations

Alex Lee named after Lebanese immigrant founder Moses George's two sons Alex and Lee boasts two operating companies: Merchants Distributors Inc. and Lowe's Food Stores Inc. Run as a division of MDI Consolidation Services operates under the Alex Lee and MDI umbrellas.

Geographic Reach

The company's reach extends to about a dozen US states. Alex Lee operates its Merchants Distributors Inc. (MDI) retail distribution unit across the Carolinas Georgia Tennessee Virginia Alabama West Virginia Ohio Florida Pennsylvania and Kentucky. Regional supermarket chain Lowe's Food Stores serves customers in Virginia South Carolina and North Carolina.

Strategy

The company's retail arm has grown to account for half of its total sales increasing Alex Lee's exposure to the competitive low-margin retail grocery business. Alex Lee is keeping its Lowe's stores network lean to maintain its focus on key markets. In 2012 it sold 10 stores to rival Harris Teeter in exchange for half a dozen Harris Tweeter stores. The deal which gave Lowe's $26.5 million allows Lowe's to focus on core areas such as the Triad the Triangle and Hickory. However the chain

---

closed two stores in the Triangle region in September 2013 ahead of Publix Supermarkets entry and as grocery giant Kroger prepares to take of Harris Teeter Supermarkets. With these two grocery giants encroaching on Lowe's Food's turf the chain can look forward to more intense competition.

EXECUTIVES

Ceo, Boyd L. George, age 76
President Lowe's Food Stores, Steve Hall
President, Brian George
Svp And Cfo, Joyce Reto
Vice President, Roger Henderson
Auditors: MCGLADREY LLP CHARLOTTE NC

LOCATIONS

HQ: ALEX LEE, INC.
120 4TH ST SW, HICKORY, NC 286022947
Phone: 828 725-4424
Web: WWW.ALEXLEE.COM

PRODUCTS/OPERATIONS

Selected Operations
Lowe's Food Stores Inc.
Merchants Distributors Inc.
Consolidation Services Inc.

COMPETITORS

ALDI	Kroger
Associated Wholesale Grocers	MAINES
Ben E. Keith	McLane
C&S Wholesale	Meadowbrook Meat Company
Food Lion	SUPERVALU
H. T. Hackney	Southeastern Grocers
Harris Teeter Supermarkets	Sysco
Ingles Markets	US Foods
K-VA-T Food Stores	Wal-Mart
	Winn-Dixie

HISTORICAL FINANCIALS

Company Type: Private

Income Statement   FYE: September 30

	REVENUE ($ mil.)	NET INCOME ($ mil.)	NET PROFIT MARGIN	EMPLOYEES
09/17*	2,261	4	0.2%	9,200
10/16	2,229	8	0.4%	—
10/15	2,287	25	1.1%	—
09/14	30	(1)	—	—
Annual Growth	319.3%	—	—	—

*Fiscal year change

2017 Year-End Financials

Return on assets: 8.5%   Cash ($ mil.): 4
Return on equity: 0.2%
Current ratio: 0.30

ALEXANDRIA INOVA HOSPITAL

EXECUTIVES

Ceo, Jennifer McCarthy
President, J Knox Singleton
Vice President, H Patrick Walters
SEC-Treas, Richard C Magenheimer
Cfo, Thomas Knight
SEC, John Gaul
Assoc Admn of Foundation, Steve Meyerson

Assoc Admn of Human Resources, Bernardine Dunn
Assoc Admn For Performance Imp, Judy Perry
Coordinator, Ashley Fitzgerald
Coordinator, Dawn Benedicto

LOCATIONS

HQ: ALEXANDRIA INOVA HOSPITAL
4320 SEMINARY RD, ALEXANDRIA, VA 223041535
Phone: 703 504-3000

COMPETITORS

Ascension Health	Johns Hopkins Health
Bon Secours Health	System
HCA	MedStar Health

HISTORICAL FINANCIALS
Company Type: Private

Income Statement				FYE: December 31
	REVENUE ($ mil.)	NET INCOME ($ mil.)	NET PROFIT MARGIN	EMPLOYEES
12/17	387	52	13.5%	1,750
12/15	369	63	17.2%	—
12/14	361	56	15.6%	—
12/08	276	24	9.0%	—
Annual Growth	3.8%	8.6%	—	—

2017 Year-End Financials
Return on assets: 2.5%   Cash ($ mil.): 6
Return on equity: 13.5%
Current ratio: 1.90

ALEXIAN BROTHERS MEDICAL CENTER INC

EXECUTIVES

Ceo-Pres, John Werrbach
Treas, James Sances
Cfo, Sherri Vincent
Director of Operating Room, Ann Harie Herlehy
Nursing Staff Secy, Deb Pelka
Director, Lynwood A Jones
Health Care Director, Patty Christenson
Manager, Edwin Arquines
Administrative Assistant, Joan Matthys
Cardiac Physician, Mark Wernick
Chief Operating Officer, Christopher Novak

LOCATIONS

HQ: ALEXIAN BROTHERS MEDICAL CENTER INC
800 BIESTERFIELD RD FL 1, ELK GROVE VILLAGE, IL 600073310
Phone: 847 437-5500
Web: WWW.ALEXIANBROTHERSHEALTH.ORG

HISTORICAL FINANCIALS
Company Type: Private

Income Statement				FYE: June 30
	REVENUE ($ mil.)	NET INCOME ($ mil.)	NET PROFIT MARGIN	EMPLOYEES
06/16	457	58	12.8%	3,500
06/15	449	47	10.6%	—
06/14	450	29	6.6%	—
06/13	439	28	6.6%	—
Annual Growth	1.3%	26.7%	—	—

2016 Year-End Financials
Return on assets: 0.6%   Cash ($ mil.): —
Return on equity: 12.8%
Current ratio: 0.60

ALFRED I.DUPONT HOSPITAL FOR CHILDREN

EXECUTIVES

Ceo, Thomas Ferry
Vice President, Stephen T Lawless
Cfo, William Britton
Pharmacist, Stacey Collings
Editor, Dustin Samples
Coordinator, Carol Eade-Viele
Coordinator, Julia Morrison
Director of Laboratory, Sonia Fair
Administrative Coordinator, Julia Mayne
Revenue Manager, Kimberley Frantsi
Micro Supervisor, Liz Marek

LOCATIONS

HQ: ALFRED I.DUPONT HOSPITAL FOR CHILDREN
1600 ROCKLAND RD, WILMINGTON, DE 198033607
Phone: 302 651-4000
Web: WWW.NEMOURS.ORG

HISTORICAL FINANCIALS
Company Type: Private

Income Statement				FYE: December 31
	REVENUE ($ mil.)	NET INCOME ($ mil.)	NET PROFIT MARGIN	EMPLOYEES
12/17	525	34	6.6%	3,068
12/16	516	(31)	—	—
12/15	450	28	6.4%	—
12/09	706	150	21.4%	—
Annual Growth	(3.6%)	(16.9%)	—	—

2017 Year-End Financials
Return on assets: 4.4%   Cash ($ mil.): —
Return on equity: 6.6%
Current ratio: 2.50

ALGONQUIN GAS TRANSMISSION, LLC

EXECUTIVES

Pres, William T Yardley
V Pres, Frederick S Steve Bush
V Pres, Patricia M Rice
V Pres, John V Adams
V Pres, Allen C Capps
Vice-President Marketing, Bill Yardley
Senior Vice-President, Richard Kruse Jr
Auditors: DELOITTE & TOUCHE LLP HOUSTO

LOCATIONS

HQ: ALGONQUIN GAS TRANSMISSION, LLC
5400 WESTHEIMER CT, HOUSTON, TX 770565353
Phone: 713 627-5400
Web: WWW.SPECTRAENERGY.COM

HISTORICAL FINANCIALS
Company Type: Private

Income Statement				FYE: December 31
	REVENUE ($ mil.)	NET INCOME ($ mil.)	NET PROFIT MARGIN	EMPLOYEES
12/17	504	166	32.9%	151
12/16	324	131	40.4%	—
Annual Growth	55.8%	26.9%	—	—

ALHAMBRA UNIFIED SCHOOL DISTRICT

EXECUTIVES

V Pres, Jane Canderson
Supt, Laura Tellez-Gagliano
Coo, Cynthia Martin
Prin, Pat Rodriguez-Mackintosh
Acct/Budgeting Mgr, Juanita Orta
Education Specialist, Byron Yip
Psychologist, Stephanie Cohen
Bus/Finance/Purchasing Directo, Elizabeth Roman
Teacher, Ann Wilson
Chief Technology Officer, Ashton Potter
Teacher, Brittany Doan

LOCATIONS

HQ: ALHAMBRA UNIFIED SCHOOL DISTRICT
1515 W MISSION RD, ALHAMBRA, CA 918031618
Phone: 626 943-3000
Web: WWW.AUSD.US

HISTORICAL FINANCIALS
Company Type: Private

Income Statement				FYE: June 30
	REVENUE ($ mil.)	NET INCOME ($ mil.)	NET PROFIT MARGIN	EMPLOYEES
06/17	283	(3)	—	1,800
06/16	287	(1)	—	—
06/05	184	36	19.9%	—
06/04	201	41	20.8%	—
Annual Growth	2.7%	—	—	—

ALIEF INDEPENDENT SCHOOL DISTRICT

EXECUTIVES

Superintendent, H D Chambers
Cfo, Deanna Wentz
Administrative Assistant, Brian Pilgreen
Board of Directors, John Hansen
Management Info Dir, Doug Brown
Director of Teacher Personnel, Theresa Adame

LOCATIONS

HQ: ALIEF INDEPENDENT SCHOOL DISTRICT
    4250 COOK RD, HOUSTON, TX 770721115
Phone: 281 498-8110
Web: WWW.ALIEFISD.NET

HISTORICAL FINANCIALS

Company Type: Private

Income Statement   FYE: August 31

	REVENUE ($ mil.)	NET INCOME ($ mil.)	NET PROFIT MARGIN	EMPLOYEES
08/17	519	(5)	—	6,000
08/16	514	38	7.5%	—
08/07	400	2	0.6%	—
08/06	402	23	6.0%	—
Annual Growth	2.3%	—	—	—

2017 Year-End Financials

Return on assets: 3.7%   Cash ($ mil.): 187
Return on equity: (-1.1%)
Current ratio: —

ALLAN MYERS, INC

American Infrastructure provides heavy civil construction services for projects in the Mid-Atlantic. Operating as Allan A. Myers in Pennsylvania and Delaware and as American Infrastructure in Maryland and Virginia the family-run business builds and reconstructs highways water treatment plants medical facilities and shopping centers and offers site development for homebuilders. Its quarries and asphalt plants operate under the Independence Construction Materials (ICM) subsidiary which supplies aggregates asphalt and ready-mixed concrete to its construction companies. The company is ranked by Engineering News-Record as 25th on the country's Top 50 list of heavy civil contractors.

Operations

American Infrastructure builds projects ranging from $100000 to more than $100 million per project.

As a land developer interested in conservation American Infrastructure offers a unique all-terrain tree spade vehicle that is designed to carry large mature trees harvested from heavily wooded sites intended to be replanted on developed sites. The process allows mature trees to be saved and relocated on a developed site.

Geographic Reach

American Infrastructure and its subsidiaries operate in the Mid-Atlantic region through about 20 locations (including quarries and plants) in Pennsylvania Maryland Virginia Delaware and Washington DC as well as four satellite offices in the region. The company also has 15 materials mining and/or asphalt production facilities in four states.

Sales and Marketing

American Infrastructure serves private developers general contractors departments of transportation utilities local and state governments and federal military customers throughout the Mid-Atlantic region.

Customers include CRB Military Housing Frederick Winchester Service Authority O'Brien & Gere Delaware Department of Transportation The Goldenberg Group Morgan-Keller Construction Forest Park Water Uniwest Construction Divinity Trucking Nardi Construction Hunt Building Company the City of Wilmington and Maryland State Highway Administration.

Strategy

American Infrastructure's financial capacity is strengthened by a bonding capacity of $800 million which allows it to tackle major projects. Selected projects includes Richmond Airport Connector Route 715/40 Interchange Virginia SR 29 Bridge Jersey Shore Pump Station Aberdeen Test Track Argonne Drive Bridge MARC Wedge Railyard Nicodemus Bridge Route 52 Ballenger McKinney wastewater treatment plant and Mount Holly wastewater treatment plant.

Company Background

Some past projects include Eagle Heights at Dover Air Force Base ($13.3 million) Cool Springs Reservoir ($18.6 million) and MD 43 ($46.7 million) in Baltimore County Maryland.

The company was established in 1939 as Allan A. Myers and Son a local hauling company in the suburbs of Philadelphia.

EXECUTIVES

Vice President General Manager, Mark Carroll
Auditors: PRICEWATERHOUSECOPPERS LLP PH

LOCATIONS

HQ: ALLAN MYERS, INC
    1805 BERKS RD, WORCESTER, PA 19490
Phone: 610 222-8800
Web: WWW.ALLANMYERS.COM

PRODUCTS/OPERATIONS

Selected Services

Site Development
    Concrete flatwork
    Excavation and grading
    Hauling
    Large-diameter tree relocation
    Milling and paving
    Rock drilling and blasting
    Soft dig capabilities
    Stone and curb
    Stormwater management
    Survey and stakeout
    Underground utilities
Transportation
    Asphalt paving
    Box culverts
    Bridges and structures
    Concrete paving
    Maintenance of traffic
Water Resources
    New water/wastewater treatment plants
    Reservoirs and dams
    Underground reservoirs
    Water and sewer transmission lines
    Wetland mitigation and reconstruction

Selected Subsidiaries

Allan A. Myers Inc.
American Infrastructure-Maryland
American Infrastructure-Virginia
Independence Construction Materials

COMPETITORS

Angelo Iafrate	English Construction
Balfour Beatty	Company
Infrastructure	Lane Construction
Barnhill Contracting	Peter Kiewit Sons'
Branch Group	Skanska USA Civil
Cherry Hill	Traylor Bros.
Construction	Vecellio & Grogan

HISTORICAL FINANCIALS

Company Type: Private

Income Statement   FYE: December 31

	REVENUE ($ mil.)	NET INCOME ($ mil.)	NET PROFIT MARGIN	EMPLOYEES
12/17	751	21	2.8%	2,000
12/16	756	15	2.0%	—
12/15	745	14	1.9%	—
Annual Growth	0.4%	22.0%	—	—

2017 Year-End Financials

Return on assets: 11.6%   Cash ($ mil.): 140
Return on equity: 2.8%
Current ratio: 0.90

ALLEGHENY GENERAL HOSPITAL INC

If there is a critical trauma anywhere near Pittsburgh Allegheny General Hospital (AGH) is ready to take it on. The roughly 630-bed hospital is the Level I Shock Trauma Center for the five-state region surrounding Steel City. AGH offers traditional medical and surgical services as well as cardiology care and organ transplants. The hospital also is engaged in research in areas such as neuroscience oncology trauma and genetics. AGH which treats nearly 22000 patients each year has about 800 physicians on its staff. The hospital which is affiliated with Philadelphia's Drexel University College of Medicine is a subsidiary of Allegheny Health System which itself is owned by Highmark Inc.

Operations

AGH receives more than 50000 emergency visits each year as well as had 300000 outpatient visits and more than 21000 surgical procedures. In order to receive those emergencies in an expedient manner the hospital also operates a LifeFlight aero medical service.

The hospital's cancer center provides programs for a wide range of diseases such as lung breast colon prostate brain and liver cancer.

AGH also operates a smaller satellite facility in the northern Pittsburgh suburb of McCandless as well as an outpatient facility in suburban Pittsburgh.

Strategy

In 2014 AGH proposed investing part of $175 million from Highmark Inc. in renovations and technology upgrades at its AGH and West Penn hospitals anticipating that they will accommodate more patients when Highmark insurance subscribers lose in-network access to the University of Pittsburgh Medical Center in 2015.

Company Background

AGH first opened in 1885.

EXECUTIVES

Interim President Chief Executive Officer, Michael Harlovic
Vice President Of Finance, Rick Fries
Chief Operating Officer, Ronald Andro

LOCATIONS

HQ: ALLEGHENY GENERAL HOSPITAL INC
    320 E NORTH AVE, PITTSBURGH, PA 152124772
Phone: 412 359-3131
Web: WWW.WPAHS.ORG

COMPETITORS

Butler Health System
Excela Health
Heritage Valley Health
Jefferson Regional Medical Center of Pennsylvania
Ohio Valley General
St. Clair Health
The Western Pennsylvania Hospital
UPMC
UPMC Mercy
Weirton Medical Center

HISTORICAL FINANCIALS

Company Type: Private

Income Statement   FYE: June 30

	REVENUE ($ mil.)	NET INCOME ($ mil.)	NET PROFIT MARGIN	EMPLOYEES
06/16	720	73	10.2%	5,064
06/15	700	107	15.4%	—
06/08	0	(0)	—	—
06/05	559	16	2.9%	—
Annual Growth	2.3%	14.8%	—	—

2016 Year-End Financials

Return on assets: 4.9%   Cash ($ mil.): 1
Return on equity: 10.2%
Current ratio: 1.00

ALLEGIS GROUP, INC.

Allegis Group is one of the world's largest staffing and recruitment firms. Among its group of staffing companies are Aerotek (engineering automotive and scientific professionals) Stephen James Associates (recruitment for accounting financial and cash management positions) and TEKsystems (information technology staffing and consulting). Other Allegis Group units include sales support outsourcer MarketSource. Allegis Group operates through more than 500 offices worldwide. Chairman Jim Davis helped found the company (originally known as Aerotek) in 1983 to provide contract engineering personnel to two clients in the aerospace industry.

Operations

Allegis Group has more than 12000 internal employees including 3000 dedicated recruiters and 130000 contract employees working with customers around the world.

Geographic Reach

Allegis Group's corporate headquarters are located in Hanover Maryland. Outside of the US the company has operations in Canada Europe the Middle East the Pacific Rim Puerto Rico and the UK.

Financial Performance

Allegis Group averages about $11 billion in annual revenue.

Strategy

Allegis Group has expanded its geographical footprint and improved its position in specialist staffing markets through the use of acquisitions. The company's specialized staffing firms cater to various industries.

Mergers and Acquisitions

In 2016 Allegis Group acquired Switzerland-based staffing recruiting and services organization The Stamford Group. The deal increased Allegis Group's global footprint and strengthened its European presence.

EXECUTIVES

Cfo, Paul J. Bowie
President, Andy Hilger
V President-tax, Michael Bison
Chairman, James C. (Jim) Davis
Auditors: PRICEWATERHOUSECOOPERS LLP BA

LOCATIONS

HQ: ALLEGIS GROUP, INC.
7301 PARKWAY DR, HANOVER, MD 210761159
Phone: 410 579-3000
Web: WWW.ALLEGISGROUP.COM

PRODUCTS/OPERATIONS

Selected Subsidiaries
Aerotek
  Aerotek Automotive
  Aerotek Aviation LLC
  Aerotek Canada
  Aerotek CE
  Aerotek Commercial Staffing
  Aerotek E&E
  Aerotek Energy Services
  Aerotek Germany
  Aerotek Netherlands
  Aerotek Professional Services
  Aerotek Scientific LLC
  Aerotek United Kingdom
Allegis Group Canada
Allegis Group Europe
Allegis Group India
Allegis Group Services
InSearch Worldwide
Major Lindsey & Africa
MarketSource Inc
Stephen James Associates
TEKsystems
  TEKsystems Canada
  TEKsystems Germany
  TEKsystems Netherlands
  TEKsystems United Kingdom

COMPETITORS

ASG Renaissance	Kelly Services
Adecco	Korn/Ferry
CDI	ManpowerGroup
Curran Partners	RDL Corporation
ExecuNet	Randstad Holding
Heidrick & Struggles	Robert Half
Horton International	Snelling Staffing
Innovative Management Solutions Group	Volt Information

HISTORICAL FINANCIALS

Company Type: Private

Income Statement   FYE: December 31

	REVENUE ($ mil.)	NET INCOME ($ mil.)	NET PROFIT MARGIN	EMPLOYEES
12/17	12,296	0	—	85,000
12/16	11,502	0	—	—
12/15	11,222	0	—	—
12/14	10,827	0	—	—
Annual Growth	4.3%	—	—	—

2017 Year-End Financials

Return on assets: 1.0%   Cash ($ mil.): 414
Return on equity: —
Current ratio: 2.80

ALLEGRO MICROSYSTEMS, LLC

Allegro MicroSystems' chips don't need touch to make contact. The company is one of the world's top makers of Hall-effect sensors which reduce mechanical wear by using magnets to produce contactless sensors. Automakers use these specialized components — named after an electromagnetic phenomenon called "the Hall effect" — in braking steering suspension and other systems. Allegro also makes power integrated circuits (ICs) used in printers and portable electronics along with driver controller and power interface ICs used in a variety of applications. The company is a subsidiary of Sanken Electric.

Operations

Allegro collaborates with parent Sanken which specializes in power semiconductors and Polar Semiconductor (another Sanken subsidiary) to speed development of chips used in power management energy efficiency and motion control applications.

Allegro Sanken and Polar collaborate on production as well. Production is handled by the Polar facility located in Minnesota. Testing and some assembly is done at a wholly owned subsidiary in the Philippines. Allegro also uses Taiwan-based United Microelectronics as a contract manufacturer.

Geographic Reach

Outside of Massachusetts Allegro has offices in Michigan and New Hampshire. It has global sales and design offices in Argentina France Scotland and the UK. As part of an initiative to increase business in China Allegro is building a second back-end assembly plant in Asia.

Sales and Marketing

Sales are about evenly split across North and South America Europe and Asia. Its products are sold primarily to OEMs through a sales channel that includes a direct sales force manufacturers representatives and distributors such as Digi-Key.

Strategy

Allegro has targeted the growing automotive sensors market and in 2016 it released what it called the industry's first automotive LED buck driver. The A6214 and A6216 devices are aimed at automotive lighting applications in which reliability is desired.

EXECUTIVES

Ceo, Ravi Vig
Cfo, Mark A Feragne
Vice President, Andre G Labrecque
Exec Vice President, Yoshihiro Suzuki
Vice President, Steven Miles
Treas, Diane Macaluso
Marketing Manager, Walter Sullivan Jr
Assistant Engineer, Nathan B Baribeau
Layout, Peter Van Hoesen
Assistant Engineer, Patricia Borglund
Tech, Edward Beaudoin

LOCATIONS

HQ: ALLEGRO MICROSYSTEMS, LLC
955 PERIMETER RD, MANCHESTER, NH 031033353
Phone: 603 626-2300
Web: WWW.ALLEGROMICRO.COM

PRODUCTS/OPERATIONS

Selected Products
Current sensor integrated circuits (ICs)
  Conductor sensor chips
  High-side hot-swap Hall-effect current monitor chips

Magnetic digital position sensor chips
  Bipolar switches
  Dual-element switches
  Hall-effect latches and bipolar switches
  Hall-effect unipolar switches
  Micropower switches and latches
Magnetic linear and angular position sensor chips
  Angular position sensor chips
  Linear position sensor chips
Magnetic speed sensor ICs (camshaft crankshaft transmission and wheel-speed sensor ICs)
Motor driver and interface ICs
  Bipolar stepper motor drivers
  Brushless DC motor drivers
  Photo and ion smoke detector ICs
Regulators and lighting
  LED drivers for backlighting and lighting
  Regulators (single-output multiple output low-noise block)
  Xenon photoflash drivers

COMPETITORS

Fairchild	NXP Semiconductors
Semiconductor	ON Semiconductor
Honeywell	Optek Technology
International	Power Integrations
Infineon Technologies	STMicroelectronics
Linear Technology	Sypris Solutions
Maxim Integrated	Texas Instruments
Products	Toshiba Semiconductor
Micronas Semiconductor	& Storage Products
Micropac Industries	Vishay Intertechnology
NVE	

HISTORICAL FINANCIALS
Company Type: Private

Income Statement				FYE: March 30
	REVENUE ($ mil.)	NET INCOME ($ mil.)	NET PROFIT MARGIN	EMPLOYEES
03/18	654	72	11.1%	3,500
03/17	600	65	10.9%	—
03/16	526	43	8.3%	—
03/13	489	45	9.3%	—
Annual Growth	6.0%	9.7%	—	—

2018 Year-End Financials
Return on assets: 4.6%   Cash ($ mil.): 114
Return on equity: 11.1%
Current ratio: 2.30

ALLEN LUND COMPANY, LLC

The Allen Lund Company (ALC) knows loads; it matches shippers' loads with a network of truckload and less-than-truckload (LTL) carriers. (LTL carriers collect consolidate and haul freight from multiple shippers.) The brokerage firm arranges the transport of dry refrigerated (predominantly produce) and flatbed cargo. It operates from 30 offices throughout more than 20 US states. ALC Logistics ALC Perishable Logistics and ALC International (an international division) assist shippers in managing transportation costs tracking and tracing shipments managing appointments and executing freight forward management services overseas. The company was founded in 1976 by Allen Lund and his wife Kathie Lund.

Operations

ALC has a Logistics & Software division ALC Logistics.

Geographic Reach

The company's international division provides transportation services worldwide along with transportation to and from the US including Puerto Rico Hawaii Alaska and ground transportation for Canada and Mexico.

Strategy

In an effort to expand its operation in 2012 the company opened a new office in Joplin Missouri and another in McAllen Texas which mainly focuses on handling heavy haul flatbed particularly in and out of Mexico. In addition the company opened four additional offices in 2012.

Mergers and Acquisitions

In an effort to grow its business in early 2014 ALC acquired Wisconsin based Northern Freight Service Inc. a company provides truckload LTL and intermodal services to the customers ranging from small shippers to FORTUNE 500 shippers.

EXECUTIVES

Vice President Sales And Branch Operations, Ed Lund
National Accounts Manager, James Lofton

LOCATIONS

HQ: ALLEN LUND COMPANY, LLC
  4529 ANGELES CREST HWY # 300, LA CANADA FLINTRIDGE, CA 910113247
Phone: 818 790-1110
Web: WWW.ALLENLUND.COM

PRODUCTS/OPERATIONS

Selected Services
Software and Logistics
  LTL Freight
  Scheduling
  Spot Pricing and Bid Management
  Truck Load
Transportation Services
  Dry Van
  Flatbed Trucking
  International Freight Shipping
  LTL Freight
  Refrigerated Transportation

COMPETITORS

C.H. Robinson	Ryder System
Worldwide	Universal Logistics
CEVA Logistics	

HISTORICAL FINANCIALS
Company Type: Private

Income Statement				FYE: December 31
	REVENUE ($ mil.)	NET INCOME ($ mil.)	NET PROFIT MARGIN	EMPLOYEES
12/17	515	10	2.0%	310
12/16	426	12	2.9%	—
12/15	457	13	2.9%	—
12/14	476	8	1.9%	—
Annual Growth	2.7%	5.1%	—	—

2017 Year-End Financials
Return on assets: 5.5%   Cash ($ mil.): 6
Return on equity: 2.0%
Current ratio: 1.90

ALLIANCE FOR SUSTAINABLE ENERGY, LLC

EXECUTIVES

MBR-Pres, Martin Keller
Member-Gen Counsel, Steven Sibergleid
MBR-Cfo, Owen Barwell
Asst. SEC, Karen Stiveson
MBR-V Pres, Peter Green
Coo, Bobi Garrett
Auditors: ANTON COLLINS MITCHELL LLP GR

LOCATIONS

HQ: ALLIANCE FOR SUSTAINABLE ENERGY, LLC
  15013 DENVER WEST PKWY, LAKEWOOD, CO 804013111
Phone: 720 279-6746
Web: WWW.NREL.GOV

HISTORICAL FINANCIALS
Company Type: Private

Income Statement				FYE: September 30
	REVENUE ($ mil.)	NET INCOME ($ mil.)	NET PROFIT MARGIN	EMPLOYEES
09/15	388	4	1.2%	1,678
09/14	378	5	1.5%	—
09/13	382	4	1.1%	—
09/11	532	6	1.2%	—
Annual Growth	(7.6%)	(8.2%)	—	—

2015 Year-End Financials
Return on assets: 15.6%   Cash ($ mil.): 4
Return on equity: 1.2%
Current ratio: 1.30

ALLIANCE PIPELINE L.P.

EXECUTIVES

Ptnr-Prin, Murray Birch
Ptnr-Prin, Andy Beissel
Ceo, Terrance Kutryk
Vice President, William Christensen
Sr Vice President, Michael McGonagill
Cfo, Keith Palmer
Vice President, Robyn Waters
Director of Risk Management, Eric McMurray
Manager, Brian Troicuk
Compliance Staff, Michael McGrath
Vice-President Information Ser, Derek Riphagen

LOCATIONS

HQ: ALLIANCE PIPELINE L.P.
  6385 OLD SHADY OAK RD # 150, EDEN PRAIRIE, MN 553447705
Phone: 952 944-3183
Web: WWW.ALLIANCEPIPELINE.COM

HISTORICAL FINANCIALS

Company Type: Private

Income Statement

	REVENUE ($ mil.)	NET INCOME ($ mil.)	NET PROFIT MARGIN	EMPLOYEES
				FYE: December 31
12/17	285	143	50.4%	50
12/16	286	139	48.7%	—
Annual Growth	(0.7%)	2.9%	—	—

2017 Year-End Financials

Return on assets: 2.2% Cash ($ mil.): 1
Return on equity: 50.4%
Current ratio: —

ALLIED BUILDING STORES, INC.

EXECUTIVES

Pres, Dale Mercer
Cfo, Gary McManus
Vice President, Kevin Cockrell
Vice President, Tommy Ormond
Vice President, Mike Cunningham
Vice President, Larry Whitmire
Human Resources Director, Sherry Lewis
Senior Analyst, Mike Lindsay
Administrative Assistant, Robert Johnson
Accounting Staff, Shirley Hinton
Merchandise Manager, Bill Harris
Auditors: HEARD MCELROY & VESTAL LLC

LOCATIONS

HQ: ALLIED BUILDING STORES, INC.
850 KANSAS LN, MONROE, LA 712034776
Phone: 318 699-9100

HISTORICAL FINANCIALS

Company Type: Private

Income Statement

	REVENUE ($ mil.)	NET INCOME ($ mil.)	NET PROFIT MARGIN	EMPLOYEES
				FYE: August 31
08/17	529	0	0.0%	125
08/16	497	0	0.0%	—
08/15	485	0	0.0%	—
08/14	487	0	0.0%	—
Annual Growth	2.8%	(2.7%)		

2017 Year-End Financials

Return on assets: 6.2% Cash ($ mil.): 3
Return on equity: —
Current ratio: 0.90

ALLINA HEALTH SYSTEM

Allina Health System is a not-for-profit health care system that works to protect people's #1 asset — their good health. The system owns and operates a dozen hospitals a network of nearly 100 clinics and specialty centers and a whole bunch of pharmacies. It has licensed bed capacity of 2451 acute care beds. Its vast system of provider locations serve residents throughout Minnesota and western Wisconsin providing disease prevention programs along with specialized inpatient and outpatient services. Allina's Aspen Medical Group division also operates a range of outpatient clinics providing primary and specialty care.

Operations

Allina has 12 hospitals (about 1800 beds) more than 90 clinics and 15 pharmacies. The largest hospital in the group is Abbott Northwestern Hospital (600 beds) followed by United Hospital which has about 570 beds. Five of Allina's hospitals are in the Minneapolis/St. Paul metropolitan area (where the system has more than a 30% share of the health care market) five are scattered throughout the rest of Minnesota and one is in western Wisconsin. The health system reported more than 103000 inpatient admissions in 2016; it also had some 1.4 million outpatient admissions. Each year it has around 360000 emergency care visits about 16000 births and more than 7 million clinic visits.

Regina Hospital has a 57-bed acute care hospital a 61-bed skilled care nursing home and a 134-bed assisted living facility. It also operates three outpatient multi-specialty clinics. Located in Minneapolis/St. Paul District One Hospital provides a broad range of health care services to Faribault and the surrounding communities.

Geographic Reach

The health care system's hospitals are located in Burnsville Champlin Coon Rapids Edina Inver Grove Heights Maplewood Plymouth St. Paul Shakopee and Woodbury in Minnesota and in River Falls in Wisconsin.

Financial Performance

In 2016 Allina Health had $3.9 billion in revenue a 4% increase over the prior year thanks to a 3% gain on hospital net patient revenue. A nurse's strike cut into operating income and the system reported a $27.4 million operating loss in 2016 (versus operating income of $155.3 million in 2015). Among the striking nurses' complaints was the Minnesota Nurses Association's allegations that estimate Allina Health has lost $80 million investing in interest-rate swaps — $80 million that could have been used to improve pay benefits and patient care.

Strategy

Despite Allina's already hefty size the system has a partnership with retail clinic provider MinuteClinic which offers basic health care at CVS Health stores. The hospital also has a multi-year collaboration with HealthPartners designed to reduce total medical costs at both hospitals.

In early 2017 Allina Health and insurance giant Aetna created a health plan joint venture — Allina Health and Aetna Insurance Company — to serve employers and individuals in the Minneapolis/St. Paul area. The venture is designed to streamline the patient experience by coordinating health care services with insurance benefits and administrative services.

The system's wide-ranging locations combined with its huge number of facilities have prompted Allina to embark on a multi-year initiative to install electronic medical records (EMR) at all of its hospitals and clinics. The installation gives medical providers the ability to track a patient's progress through any of the myriad health care settings operated by Allina. The EMR also gives patients access to coordinated care between the different providers as well as the ability to see portions of their medical records and lab results online. Patients can also schedule appointments and make use of a number of health and wellness tools all via the internet.

Allina was the first Minnesota health care organization to earn the Davies Award the industry's preeminent award for health information technology.

EXECUTIVES

System Vp; President Mercy Hospital, Sara Criger
Evp Clinics And Home Care Services, Robert A. Wieland
Ceo, Penny Ann Wheeler
System Vp; President Abbott Northwestern Hospital, Ben Bache-Wiig
System Vp; President United Hospital, Thomas (Tom) O'Connor
Evp Administration And Cfo, Duncan P. Gallagher
Evp Hospital And Specialty Services, Daniel McGinty
Medical Director For Quality, Steven Bergeson
Supervisor Of Medical Records, Jessica Dalton
Director Of Pharmacy Ambulatory, Lee Mork
Vice President Of Marketing, Cathy Runck
Director Of Nursing, Karen Tennis
Director Of Operating Room, Lisa Heutmaker
Medical Director, John Mageli
Senior Vice President Chief Compliance Officer, Katherine Tarvestad
Supervisor Of Medical Records, Louise Brandt
Vice President Payor Contract Reimb, Margaret Hasbrouck
Senior Vice President, Lisa Smith
Chairman, Mark S. Jordahl
Treasurer, Anne Uttermark

LOCATIONS

HQ: ALLINA HEALTH SYSTEM
2925 CHICAGO AVE, MINNEAPOLIS, MN 554071321
Phone: 612 262-5000
Web: WWW.ALLINA.COM

PRODUCTS/OPERATIONS

Selected Services

Care at home
Chronic and advanced illness
Clinics
Home oxygen and medical equipment
Hospitals
Lab services
Medical Services
Medical transportation
Pharmacies
Providers
Specialty services
Urgent care

Selected Hospitals

Abbott Northwestern Hospital (Minneapolis MN)
Buffalo Hospital (Buffalo MN)
Cambridge Medical Center (Cambridge MN)
District One Hospital (Faribault MN)
Mercy Hospital (Coon Rapids MN)
New Ulm Medical Center (New Ulm MN)
Owatonna Hospital (Owatonna MN)
Phillips Eye Institute (Minneapolis MN)
Regina Hospital (Hastings MN)
River Falls Area Hospital (River Falls WI)
St. Francis Regional Medical Center (Shakopee MN)
United Hospital (St. Paul MN)
Unity Hospital (Fridley MN)

COMPETITORS

Bethesda Hospital
Catholic Health Initiatives
CentraCare Health
Children's Hospitals and Clinics of Minnesota
Fairview Health
Hazelden Betty Ford
HealthEast Care System
Mayo Clinic
Methodist Hospital (MN)
North Memorial Health Care
Park Nicollet Health Services
Regions Hospital
St. John's Hospital (Minnesota)
University of Minnesota Medical Center

	REVENUE ($ mil.)	NET INCOME ($ mil.)	NET PROFIT MARGIN	EMPLOYEES
12/16	3,947	74	1.9%	26,400
12/13	3,420	374	10.9%	—
12/12	3,246	154	4.8%	—
12/11	2,743	225	8.2%	—
Annual Growth	7.6%	(19.8%)	—	—

2016 Year-End Financials

Return on assets: 11.7% Cash ($ mil.): 172
Return on equity: 1.9%
Current ratio: 1.10

ALLY BANK

EXECUTIVES

Chb-Pres-Ceo, Diane E Morais
Exec V Pres, Jeffrey J Brown
Cfo, James N Young
Secretary, Cathy L Quenneville
Senior Director of Business De, Craig Nalitt
Portfolio Manager, Janice Waye
Director of Remarketing Sales, Mark Juday
Operations Manager, Michael Snel

LOCATIONS

HQ: ALLY BANK
 6985 S UNION PARK CTR # 435, MIDVALE, UT
 840474177
Phone: 801 790-5005
Web: WWW.ALLY.COM

COMPETITORS

Bank of America	Citibank
BofI	E*TRADE Bank
Charles Schwab	State Farm

HISTORICAL FINANCIALS
Company Type: Private

Income Statement   FYE: December 31

	ASSETS ($ mil.)	NET INCOME ($ mil.)	INCOME AS % OF ASSETS	EMPLOYEES
12/16	123,547	1,273	1.0%	42
12/07*	28,472	291	1.0%	—
06/06	3,586	0	0.0%	—
Annual Growth	38.0%	114.3%	—	—

*Fiscal year change

2016 Year-End Financials

Return on assets: — Sales ($ mil): 6,427
Return on equity: 19.8%

ALMOST FAMILY, INC.

EXECUTIVES

Pres, Steven Guenthner
Senior Living Coordinator, Jackie Alexander
Branch Director, Shawna Holzer
Board Member, Donald G McClinton
Board Member, Jonathan Goldberg
Board Member, Steven B Bing
Board Member, Tyree G Wilburn
Branch Director, Debra Love
Auditors: ERNST & YOUNG LLP LOUISVILLE

LOCATIONS

HQ: ALMOST FAMILY, INC.
 9510 ORMSBY STATION RD # 300, LOUISVILLE, KY
 402235016
Phone: 502 891-1000
Web: WWW.ALMOSTFAMILY.COM

COMPETITORS

Amedisys	HCR ManorCare
Apria Healthcare	Home Instead
Capital Senior Living	Hooper Holmes
Chemed	LHC Group
Continucare	NHC
Diversicare Healthcare Services	National Home Health
	Odyssey HealthCare
Gentiva	Providence Service
Girling Health Care	U.S. Physical Therapy

HISTORICAL FINANCIALS
Company Type: Private

Income Statement   FYE: December 29

	REVENUE ($ mil.)	NET INCOME ($ mil.)	NET PROFIT MARGIN	EMPLOYEES
12/17	796	20	2.6%	14,200
12/16*	623	18	2.9%	—
01/16	532	19	3.7%	—
12/14	495	13	2.7%	—
Annual Growth	17.1%	14.7%	—	—

*Fiscal year change

2017 Year-End Financials

Return on assets: 2.8% Cash ($ mil.): 11
Return on equity: 2.6%
Current ratio: 1.80

ALPINE SCHOOL DISTRICT

EXECUTIVES

Supt, Vern Henshaw
Supt, Samuel Y Jarman
Coordinator, Alex Goold
Buyer, Susan Jones
Management Info Dir, Matt Johnson
Executive of Information Techn, Paul Lewis
Business Manager, James Hansen
Accounting Staff, Steven Reese
Public Information Director, David Stephenson
Teacher, Robert Smith
Coordinator, Barbara Langford
Auditors: SQUIRE & COMPANY PC OREM UT

LOCATIONS

HQ: ALPINE SCHOOL DISTRICT
 575 N 100 E, AMERICAN FORK, UT 840031758
Phone: 801 610-8400
Web: WWW.ALPINESCHOOLS.ORG

Income Statement   FYE: June 30

	REVENUE ($ mil.)	NET INCOME ($ mil.)	NET PROFIT MARGIN	EMPLOYEES
06/18	680	77	11.4%	8,000
06/17	638	129	20.3%	—
Annual Growth	6.7%	(40.3%)	—	—

ALRO STEEL CORPORATION

Alro Steel runs its service centers like a grocery store for metals keeping what customers need in easy reach. The service center operator which has a dozen facilities in the US Northeast Midwest and Southeast provides processing services such as aluminum circle cutting CNC flame cutting forming and machining. The company carries an extensive inventory of steel products along with industrial tools and supplies. It also offers plastic sheet rod tube and film through its Alro Plastics division and distributes industrial tools and materials through subsidiary Alro Industrial Supplies.

Operations

Led by its steel activities Alro Steel operates several other businesses: Alro Metals Service Center Alro Metals Plus (steel bars plates and sheet and brass copper aluminum and other products); Alro Plastics (fiberglass acrylics nylon urethanes and other); and Alro Industrial Supplies (threading milling boring holemaking reaming and other machinery and equipment).

Geographic Reach

Alro Steel has more than 50 facilities in 12 US states (Florida Illinois Indiana Kentucky Michigan Missouri New York North Carolina Ohio Oklahoma Pennsylvania and Wisconsin).

Sales and Marketing

The company distributes metals industrial supplies and plastics through its online store.

Strategy

Alro Steel is expanding its operations to meet demand.

In 2014 the company expanded its presence in Greensboro North Carolina by opening a 42000-sq.-ft. facility. It plans to potentially double the work force there within five years.

In 2013 it opened a new 70000 sq. ft. facility in St. Louis to provide regional manufacturers with Alro's broad range of metal products and extensive processing capabilities. That year the company also opened a new 98000 sq. ft. facility in Imperial Pennsylvania to serve manufacturers in western and central Pennsylvania and northern West Virginia.

Company Background

The company was established in 1948.

EXECUTIVES

Ceo, Alvin Glick
President, David Schmidt
E Vice President, Randy Glick
Cfo, Steve Laten
Treas, Jim Norman
V Chm, Barry Glick
Dir of Cust Acct Serv, John Rumler
Board of Directors, Jason Cook
Technician, Patrick Gardner
Manager, Rebecca Armstrong

LOCATIONS

HQ: ALRO STEEL CORPORATION
   3100 E HIGH ST, JACKSON, MI 492036413
Phone: 517 787-5500
Web: WWW.ALRO.COM

COMPETITORS

Carlisle Companies	Mill Steel
Central Steel & Wire	Peerless Steel
Contractors Steel	
Flame Metals	
Processing	

HISTORICAL FINANCIALS

Company Type: Private

Income Statement   FYE: May 31

	REVENUE ($ mil.)	NET INCOME ($ mil.)	NET PROFIT MARGIN	EMPLOYEES
05/17	1,691	122	7.2%	2,400
05/13	1,553	0	—	—
05/12	1,605	0	—	—
Annual Growth	1.0%	—	—	—

2017 Year-End Financials

Return on assets: 3.6%   Cash ($ mil.): 185
Return on equity: 7.2%
Current ratio: 3.80

ALSCO INC.

Alsco has built a big business outfitting its customers in uniforms linens and related products. Operating from more than150 branches in about 10 countries worldwide the company (whose name stands for American linen supply company) rents and sells uniforms linens towels and clean room garments to more than 300000 customers in North America. It also manages janitorial services provides washroom supplies and launders and sterilizes garments. Alsco serves the automotive food processing restaurant medical and IT industries as well as the federal government. Founded in 1889 by George Steiner the company is owned and operated by the Steiner family.

Geographic Reach

Utah-based Alsco has locations in Australia Brazil Canada China Germany Italy New Zealand Singapore Switzerland Thailand and the US.

Strategy

Alsco heavily promotes its green cleaning solutions and the company has focused on international expansion in recent years. In 2014 the company expanded its uniform and linen services in Texas with a branch in San Antonio and service centers in Austin Houston and Waco.

In addition to uniforms and linens Alsco supplies promotional products for trade shows conventions golf outings sales meetings and other special events and occasions.

EXECUTIVES

Vice President, Kennedy Donald

LOCATIONS

HQ: ALSCO INC.
   505 E 200 S STE 101, SALT LAKE CITY, UT
   841022053
Phone: 801 328-8831
Web: WWW.ALSCO.COM

PRODUCTS/OPERATIONS

Selected Products and Services
Clean room garments
Gown room management
Hospitality/restaurant apparel
Laundry services
Linens
Mats
Mops
Napkins
Restroom service
Towels
Uniform rental and sales
Vacuum filters
Washroom supplies

COMPETITORS

ARAMARK	ISS A/S
Angelica Corporation	Rentokil Initial
Berendsen	ServiceMaster
Cintas	Sodexo USA
Crothall Healthcare	Superior Uniform Group
Diversey	Swisher Hygiene
Ecolab	Tranzonic
G&K Services	UniFirst
Healthcare Services	

HISTORICAL FINANCIALS

Company Type: Private

Income Statement   FYE: December 31

	REVENUE ($ mil.)	NET INCOME ($ mil.)	NET PROFIT MARGIN	EMPLOYEES
12/17	892	64	7.2%	16,000
12/16	704	38	5.5%	—
12/15	683	30	4.5%	—
12/14	658	25	3.8%	—
Annual Growth	10.6%	36.8%	—	—

2017 Year-End Financials

Return on assets: 8.0%   Cash ($ mil.): 22
Return on equity: 7.2%
Current ratio: 1.20

ALSTON CONSTRUCTION COMPANY, INC.

EXECUTIVES

Vice President General Manager, William Hancock
Auditors: CAMPBELL TAYLOR & COMPANY AC

LOCATIONS

HQ: ALSTON CONSTRUCTION COMPANY, INC.
   8775 FOLSOM BLVD STE 201, SACRAMENTO, CA
   958263725
Phone: 916 340-2400
Web: WWW.ALSTONCO.COM

COMPETITORS

Alter Group	H and M Construction
Balfour Beatty	KPRS Construction
Construction	Skanska USA Building
Bechtel	Turner Corporation
Fluor	

HISTORICAL FINANCIALS

Company Type: Private

Income Statement   FYE: December 31

	REVENUE ($ mil.)	NET INCOME ($ mil.)	NET PROFIT MARGIN	EMPLOYEES
12/17	865	13	1.6%	200
12/15	642	6	1.1%	—
12/14	470	3	0.8%	—
12/13	332	4	1.3%	—
Annual Growth	27.0%	33.6%	—	—

2017 Year-End Financials

Return on assets: 20.5%   Cash ($ mil.): 43
Return on equity: 1.6%
Current ratio: 1.10

ALTA CALIFORNIA REGIONAL CENTER, INC.

EXECUTIVES

Pres, James Huyck
Coordinator, Diane Morris
Chief Operating Officer, Peter Tiedemann
Receptionist, Veronica Fisher
Coordinator, Michelle Adams
Human Resources Director, Brianne Harris
Director, Lori Banales
Information Technology Special, Jeff Nguyen
Coordinator, Karen Partch
Coordinator, Lori Hickey
Human Resources Administrator, Bonita Adame
Auditors: STROUB THOMPSON NOBLE CPAS SA

LOCATIONS

HQ: ALTA CALIFORNIA REGIONAL CENTER, INC.
   2241 HARVARD ST STE 100, SACRAMENTO, CA
   958153332
Phone: 916 978-6400
Web: WWW.ALTAREGIONAL.ORG

HISTORICAL FINANCIALS

Company Type: Private

Income Statement   FYE: June 30

	REVENUE ($ mil.)	NET INCOME ($ mil.)	NET PROFIT MARGIN	EMPLOYEES
06/17	383	0	0.0%	487
06/15	322	0	0.0%	—
06/14	300	(0)	—	—
06/13	291	(0)	—	—
Annual Growth	7.1%	—	—	—

2017 Year-End Financials

Return on assets: 6.7%   Cash ($ mil.): 22
Return on equity: —
Current ratio: 1.00

ALTICOR INC.

Where there's a will (and an army of independent sales representatives) there's Amway. Operated through holding company Alticor Amway is the world's top direct-selling company with millions of individual ABOs (Amway Business Owners) pitching everything from air filters to vitamins. The company makes some 450 unique products across the categories of nutrition (which generates about half of sales) beauty and personal care and home. It is active in more than 100 countries across the globe with Asia (led by China) its largest market. Alticor is controlled by the families of Rich DeVos and Jay Van Andel who founded Amway in 1959.

Operations

Nutrition products (supplements skin care products weight management programs) account for about 50% of total Amway sales. Beauty and personal care items (makeup shampoo toothpaste) generate about a quarter of sales and home products (water and air filters cookware cleaners) contribute about 20%. The company's top products include Nutrilite supplements Artistry color cosmetics eSpring water treatment systems and XS energy drinks.

Geographic Reach

Based in Ada Michigan Amway operates in more than 100 countries. Its top markets by sales are China the US and South Korea; other leading markets include India Japan Malaysia Russia Taiwan and Thailand.

The company has manufacturing facilities farms and warehouses in Brazil China Hungary India Japan Mexico the Netherlands Poland Russia South Korea Taiwan Thailand Vietnam and the US.

Sales and Marketing

Amway's 450-plus products are marketing worldwide by more than 3 million independent distributors who purchase the products and resell them. The company provides a host of support services including personal mentors brand centers online learning tools and call centers.

Financial Performance

While privately-owned Alticor doesn't report full results Amway reported global sales of $8.6 billion in 2017 down from $8.8 billion in 2016.The company points to a challenging Chinese market for its revenue decline over the past few years

Strategy

Amway's strategy is pretty straight-forward: continue to enhance and expand its line of products to serve more markets and appeal to more customers and create tools that make selling those products easier for the 3+ million ABOs (Amway Business Owners).

In 2017 Amway introduced a new formula for its Nutrilife Double X product one of the best-selling supplements in the world that includes a phytonutrient blend designed to help the body fight free radicals. Other additions to the company's product portfolio that year include a reformulated Essentials by Artistry skincare line and its first in-car air filtration system Atmosphere Drive. Amway also pushed its XS brand of energy drinks into new countries in 2017 including China and India with more launches planned for 2018. The company has more than 800 patents worldwide and another 250 pending applications.

Direct selling of course looks a lot different in the age of Amazon than it did some 60 years ago when Amway was founded. The company has been making significant investment in tools and technologies in recent years to enable its ABOs to better compete. It has spent some $70 million in mobile apps for ABOs including the flagship Amway MyBiz app which provides back office data and analytics. In addition Amway has boosted its own customer service capabilities with instant messaging bots and other technologies to help it handle the more than 12 million annual customer requests. Other recent initiatives include a content sharing app for ABOs in the Philippines a beauty app for customers in South Korea and a one-stop product education and purchase portal in for ABOs in China.

EXECUTIVES

President, Doug DeVos
Vice President, Richard Holwill
Senior Vice President Information Technology, Craig Datema
Vice President Of Purchasing, Judy West
Vice President Supply Chain Planning, Jennifer Williamson
Chairman, Steve Van Andel

LOCATIONS

HQ: ALTICOR INC.
7575 FULTON ST E, ADA, MI 493550001
Phone: 616 787-1000
Web: WWW.ALTICOR.COM

PRODUCTS/OPERATIONS

2017 Sales

	% of total
Nutrition	50
Beauty & personal care	26
Home	21
Other	3
Total	**100**

Selected Brands

Nutrition
  Nutrilite
Beauty & personal care
  Artistry
  G&H
  Glister
  Satinique
Home
  Amway Home
  Atmosphere Sky
  eSpring
  iCook
Other
  XS

COMPETITORS

Avon	Melaleuca
Bath & Body Works	New Avon
Bluestem Brands	Newell Brands
Colgate-Palmolive	Nikken
Estée Lauder	Nu Skin
Forever Living	Procter & Gamble
GNC	Revlon
Herbalife Ltd.	Shaklee
Johnson & Johnson	Tupperware Brands
L'Oréal	Unilever PLC
Mary Kay	

HISTORICAL FINANCIALS

Company Type: Private

Income Statement   FYE: December 31

	REVENUE ($ mil.)	NET INCOME ($ mil.)	NET PROFIT MARGIN	EMPLOYEES
12/16	8,783	0	—	14,000
12/15	9,459	0	—	—
12/14	10,804	0	—	—
12/13	11,754	0	—	—
Annual Growth	(9.3%)	—	—	—

2016 Year-End Financials

Return on assets: 4.7%   Cash ($ mil.): 1,457
Return on equity: —
Current ratio: 0.80

ALTRU HEALTH SYSTEM

Altru Health System provides medical care throughout northeastern North Dakota and northwestern Minnesota. The integrated health care network administers everything from primary care to inpatient medical and surgical care through its Altru Hospital (with roughly 265 beds) and about a dozen primary care clinics. It also operates a cancer center a rehabilitation center dialysis facilities and home health providers. For area seniors Altru Health operates Parkwood Place a senior living facility that provides several levels of care to residents depending on need. The not-for-profit center was formed in 1997 by the integration of Grand Forks Clinic and United Health Services.

Operations

The system employs more than 200 physicians and serves over 200000 residents. Altru Hospital with a Level II Trauma designation has a 16-bed critical care unit a 10-bed surgical critical care unit pulmonary and sleep labs and cardio and pulmonary rehabilitation facilities.

In 2013 Altru Health System had 12603 inpatient discharges 275000 outpatient discharges 1600 births and some 29000 emergency visits.

Sales and Marketing

Medicare and Medicaid payments accounted for more than 50% of net patient revenue in 2013; Blue Cross accounted for more than 30%. Self-pay and other third-party accounts represented the rest of patient revenue.

In 2013 the system paid $901799 for advertising up from $892641 in 2012.

Financial Performance

Altru Health System's net revenue increased 1% to $457 million in 2013 due to increased patient services charges. Net income also rose 5% to $26 million due to gains on investments. Cash flow also held steady rising 3% to $40 million due to a decline in cash used in receivables plus an increase in cash generated from accounts payable and accrued expenses.

Strategy

The system looks for opportunities to expand both its locations and its services. To that end it is building a new hospital in Grand Forks to replace Altru. The replacement will be built in three stages and is expected to be complete by 2020. The replacement for its main clinic is expected to be operational by 2022.

Altru opened its newest hospital the 45-bed Altru Specialty Center in Grand Forks North Dakota in 2014. The center has four operating rooms and offers such services as elective orthopedic and podiatry surgeries joint replacement and inpatient rehabilitation.

In 2013 Altru opened clinics in Thief River Falls Minnesota and East Grand Fork; it also expanded a clinic in Devils Lake North Dakota.

Company Background

The system was created in 1997 when United Hospital merged with the Grand Forks Clinic.

EXECUTIVES

Ceo, David Molmen
Cfo, Dwight Thompson
Chief Medical Executive, Eric Lunn
Administrative Director Primary Care, Renee Axtman
Chief Nurse Executive, Margaret Reed
Administrative Director Information Services, Mark Waind
Administrative Director Medical Specialty Care, Kerry Carlson
Coo, Brad Wehe
Executive Director Altru Health Foundation, Jon Green
Medical Director Primary Care, Colleen Swank
Medical Director Surgical Services, Scott Charette
Administrative Director Cardiology And Musculoskeletal Services, Kelly Hagen
Administrative Director Surgical Services, Joseph Myers

Vice President For Finance Operations University Of North Dakota, Liz Brekke
Chairman, John Snustad
Vice Chairman, Kris Compton
Treasurer Home Care Advisory Meadowbrook Township, Marie Rose

LOCATIONS

HQ: ALTRU HEALTH SYSTEM
1200 S COLUMBIA RD, GRAND FORKS, ND
582014044
Phone: 701 780-5000
Web: WWW.ALTRU.ORG

PRODUCTS/OPERATIONS

2013 Sales

	% of total
Net patient service	93
Other operating revenue	7
Total	**100**

2013 Net Patient Revenue

	% of total
Medicare	41
Blue Cross	31
Medicaid	11
Other third party	14
Patients	3
Total	**100**

Selected Centers

Bariatric Center
Breast Center
Cancer Center
Diabetes Center
Family Birthing Center
Grief Center
Hand Therapy Center
Hearing Center
Heart and Vascular Center
Joint Replacement Center
Medical Fitness Center
Outpatient Procedure Center
Pre-Admission Center
Psychiatry Center
Truyu Aesthetic Center

COMPETITORS

Avera Health	St. Alexius Medical
Catholic Health	Center
Initiatives	St. Mary's Innovis
First Care	Health
Sanford	
Health-MeritCare	

HISTORICAL FINANCIALS

Company Type: Private

Income Statement				FYE: December 31
	REVENUE ($ mil.)	NET INCOME ($ mil.)	NET PROFIT MARGIN	EMPLOYEES
12/17	549	20	3.7%	3,800
12/16	549	10	1.9%	—
12/15	488	16	3.3%	—
12/14	456	19	4.3%	—
Annual Growth	**6.4%**	**0.5%**	**—**	**—**

2017 Year-End Financials

Return on assets: 3.3%   Cash ($ mil.): 32
Return on equity: 3.7%
Current ratio: 2.00

ALVAREZ LLC

EXECUTIVES

Ceo, Everett Alvarez Jr
Clo, Marc Alvarez
Coo, Alex Waugh
Training Manager, Jennifer Kaiser
Auditors: KELLY & COMPANY LLC TYSONS CO

LOCATIONS

HQ: ALVAREZ LLC
8251 GREENSBORO DR # 230, TYSONS CORNER, VA
221023817
Phone: 703 635-7040
Web: WWW.ALVAREZIT.COM

HISTORICAL FINANCIALS

Company Type: Private

Income Statement				FYE: December 31
	REVENUE ($ mil.)	NET INCOME ($ mil.)	NET PROFIT MARGIN	EMPLOYEES
12/17	323	0	0.1%	13
12/16	285	0	0.2%	—
12/15	241	0	0.0%	—
12/14	287	0	0.1%	—
Annual Growth	**4.0%**	**11.5%**	**—**	**—**

2017 Year-End Financials

Return on assets: 18.0%   Cash ($ mil.): —
Return on equity: 0.1%
Current ratio: 1.00

ALVIN INDEPENDENT SCHOOL DISTRICT

EXECUTIVES

Ed.d., Supt, Buck Gilcrease
Deputy Supt, Tommy King
SEC, Charles McCauley
SEC, Regan Metoyer
Prin, Tiffany Wennerstrom
H R Mgr, Glenna Niceswanger
Bookkeeper, Sandra Webb
Administrator, Thomas Bennett
Teacher Personnel Director, Kathy Windsor
Superintendent, Beck Gilcrease
Assistant Superintendent, Lisa Butler

LOCATIONS

HQ: ALVIN INDEPENDENT SCHOOL DISTRICT
301 E HOUSE ST, ALVIN, TX 775113579
Phone: 281 388-1130
Web: WWW.ALVINISD.NET

HISTORICAL FINANCIALS

Company Type: Private

Income Statement				FYE: June 30
	REVENUE ($ mil.)	NET INCOME ($ mil.)	NET PROFIT MARGIN	EMPLOYEES
06/18	333	(105)	—	2,100
06/17*	305	1	0.6%	—
08/06	118	(24)	—	—
08/02	80	19	24.8%	—
Annual Growth	**9.3%**	**—**	**—**	**—**

*Fiscal year change

2018 Year-End Financials

Return on assets: 9.0%   Cash ($ mil.): 7
Return on equity: (-31.7%)
Current ratio: —

AMARILLO INDEPENDENT SCHOOL DISTRICT

EXECUTIVES

Prin, David Bishop
Supt, Rod Schroder
SEC, Kae Austin
Dir, Judy Brewster
Project Coordinator, Sylvia Hughes
Accounting Staff, Ashley Schweitzer
Coordinator, Annette Ortega
Program Director, Cheryl Reed
Coordinator, Sandra Gonzalez
Employee Benefits Manager, David Joza
Assistant, Brad Hoeksema
Auditors: CONNOR MCMILLOM MITCHELL SH

LOCATIONS

HQ: AMARILLO INDEPENDENT SCHOOL DISTRICT
7200 W INTERSTATE 40, AMARILLO, TX 791062528
Phone: 806 326-1000
Web: WWW.AMAISD.ORG

HISTORICAL FINANCIALS

Company Type: Private

Income Statement				FYE: June 30
	REVENUE ($ mil.)	NET INCOME ($ mil.)	NET PROFIT MARGIN	EMPLOYEES
06/17	322	27	8.6%	5,288
06/16	317	(9)	—	—
06/15	312	(17)	—	—
06/14	300	53	18.0%	—
Annual Growth	**2.5%**	**(19.9%)**	**—**	**—**

2017 Year-End Financials

Return on assets: 1.3%   Cash ($ mil.): 154
Return on equity: 8.6%
Current ratio: —

AMC ENTERTAINMENT INC.

EXECUTIVES

Manager, Beth Olson
Auditors: KPMG LLP KANSAS CITY MISSOUR

LOCATIONS

HQ: AMC ENTERTAINMENT INC.
11500 ASH ST, LEAWOOD, KS 662117804
Phone: 913 213-2000
Web: WWW.AMCENTERTAINMENT.COM

HISTORICAL FINANCIALS
Company Type: Private

Income Statement   FYE: December 31

	REVENUE ($ mil.)	NET INCOME ($ mil.)	NET PROFIT MARGIN	EMPLOYEES
12/15	2,946	103	3.5%	19,700
12/14	2,695	64	2.4%	—
12/13	2,749	364	13.3%	—
12/12	811	(37)	—	—
Annual Growth	**53.7%**	—	—	—

2015 Year-End Financials
Return on assets: 10.6%   Cash ($ mil.): 209
Return on equity: 3.5%
Current ratio: 0.40

AMERICAN ASSETS TRUST, INC.

American Assets Trust is a self-administered real estate investment trust (REIT) that owns develops and operates upscale retail office and residential property mostly in Northern and Southern California but also in Oregon Washington Texas and Hawaii. Its 6 million square foot portfolio includes around 10 shopping centers more than handful of office buildings a 369-room hotel and retail complex and five multi-family residential properties. Its tenants include SalesForce Autodesk the Veterans Benefits Administration and well-known retailers such as Kmart Lowe's Sports Authority Old Navy and Vons. Formed in 1967 as American Assets the firm went public in 2011.

Operations
The REIT leases retail office and multifamily properties as well as hotels. Its retail portfolio which made up 35% of its revenue during 2015 spans 3 million rentable square feet while its office holdings (34% of revenue) measure 2.7 million square feet.

In addition American Assets Trust mixed-use property (19% of revenue) the Embassy Suites at Waikiki Beach Walk in Honolulu is a 369-room all-suite hotel with approximately 97000 square feet of accompanying retail space. The REIT generates the rest of its revenue from its more than 1500 multifamily units in San Diego and Imperial Beach California.

Geographic Reach
San Diego-based American Assets Trust's primary markets include San Diego; the San Francisco Bay area; Portland Oregon; Bellevue Washington; and Oahu Hawaii. More than 50% of its property by square footage was located in Southern and Northern California at the end of 2015 while over 15% of its property space was in Oregon. The rest of its properties were in Hawaii (11% of square footage) Texas (10%) and Washington state (9%).

Sales and Marketing
The REIT's largest five tenants by revenue in 2015 included: Salesforce (8% of annualized base rent) Autodesk (3%) Kmart (3%) Lowe's (3%) the Veterans Benefits Administration (2%) and the Insurance Company of the West (2%). Its properties that year were 98.6% leased.

The company has been increasing its marketing spend in recent years. It spent $2.1 million on marketing during 2015 up from $1.62 million and $1.55 million in 2014 and 2013 respectively.

Financial Performance
America Assets Trusts' annual revenues have risen more than 35% since 2011 as its property valuations have appreciated and have commanded higher rental rates. While more volatile its annual profits have more than doubled over the period on declining interest expenses as the REIT has paid down its long-term debt.

The REIT's revenue climbed 6% to $275.6 million during 2015 thanks to rental income growth mostly from its office properties which benefited from higher occupancy and rental rates. Rental income also grew from its mixed-use property as its hotel occupancy rate jumped by almost 10 percentage points to 89.6% and as its revenue per available room (revPAR) grew 13%. Retail rental revenue grew with higher rental rates while its multifamily rental revenue also rose with the completion of its Hassalo on Eighth property late in the year.

Revenue growth in 2015 combined with a $7.1 million gain from the sale of its Rancho Carmel Plaza property drove the American Asset Trust's net income up 73% to almost $54 million. The REIT's operating cash levels rose 5% to $110.7 million as cash-based rental income increased.

Strategy
American Assets Trust's properties are in located in developed areas where new construction is difficult which helps to keep competition out and rental and occupancy rates stable. The REIT prefers to develop or acquire properties in such high-barrier-to-entry areas in its core markets which include San Diego; the San Francisco Bay area; Portland Oregon; Bellevue Washington; and Oahu Hawaii.

American Asset Trust's other key strategy is redeveloping and improving existing properties to command higher rental rates. It also makes its properties more attractive to potential tenants by signing well-known brands such as Apple Store Banana Republic Pottery Barn and Starbucks as retail tenants.

Company Background
American Assets Trust went public in January 2011 with an offering valued at about $564 million. (About $4 million of that figure went to chairman Ernest Rady who controlled the company prior to its IPO.) The IPO proceeds were used to repay debt and to purchase and renovate property.

EXECUTIVES

Chairman President And Ceo, Ernest S. Rady, $259,616 total compensation
Ceo And President, John W. Chamberlain
Evp And Cfo, Robert F. Barton, $373,846 total compensation
Vp Construction And Development, Jerry Gammieri, $186,923 total compensation
Vp Retail Properties, Chris Sullivan
Vp Office Properties, Jim Durfey
Vp And Regional Manager Portland, Wade Lange
Auditors: ERNST & YOUNG LLP SAN DIEGO

LOCATIONS

HQ: AMERICAN ASSETS TRUST, INC.
  11455 EL CAMINO REAL # 200, SAN DIEGO, CA 921302047
Phone: 858 350-2600
Web: WWW.AMERICANASSETSTRUST.COM

2015 Properties

	No.
Southern California	7
Northern California	4
Hawaii	3
Oregon	2
Texas	1
Washington	1
Total	**18**

PRODUCTS/OPERATIONS

2015 Sales

	% of total
Rental Income	
Retail	35
Office	34
Mixed-Use	19
Multifamily	7
Other Property Income	5
Total	**100**

Selected Tenants
Alliant International University
Autodesk Inc.
California Bank & Trust
Caradigm USA LLC
Drug Enforcement Administration
Foodland Super Market
HDR Engineering
Inome Inc.
Insurance Company of the West
Integra Telecom Holdings
Kmart
Lowe's
Marshalls
McDermott Will & Emery
Nordstrom Rack
Officemax
Old Navy
Portland Energy Conservation
Quiksilver
salesforce.com inc.
Sports Authority
Sprouts Farmers Market
Treasury Call Center
Veterans Benefits Administration
Vons

Selected Properties
Retail
  Alamo Quarry
  Carmel County Plaza
  Carmel Mountain Plaza
  Del Monte Shopping Center
  Lomas Sante Fe Plaza
  Rancho Carmel Plaza
  Solana Beach Towne Centre
  South Bay Market Place
  The Shops at Kalakaua
  Waikele Center
Mixed-use
  Waikiki Beach Walk - Hotel
  Waikiki Beach Walk - Retail
Multi-family
  Imperial Beach Gardens
  Loma Palisades
  Mariner's Point
  Santa Fe Park RV Resort
Office
  Fireman's Fund Headquarters
  Solana Beach Corporate Centre
  The Landmark at One Market
  Torrey Reserve Campus
  Valencia Corporate Center

COMPETITORS

CBL & Associates Properties	Macerich
GGP	Simon Property Group
Hersha Hospitality	Taubman Centers

HISTORICAL FINANCIALS
Company Type: Private

Income Statement   FYE: December 31

	ASSETS ($ mil.)	NET INCOME ($ mil.)	INCOME AS % OF ASSETS	EMPLOYEES
12/17	2,259	40	1.8%	113
12/16	1,986	45	2.3%	—
12/15	1,978	53	2.7%	—
12/14	1,941	31	1.6%	—
Annual Growth	**5.2%**	**8.8%**	—	—

2017 Year-End Financials
Return on assets: 12.1%   Sales ($ mil): 314
Return on equity: 12.7%

AMERICAN ASSOCIATED PHARMACIES

EXECUTIVES

Pres-Ceo, Jon Copeland
SEC-Treas, Kevin Foshee
Vice-President, Tracie Heyrman
Manager, Wendy Radicy
Vice President of Information, Bob Vaden
Territory Manager, Jim Kilborn
Director of Merchandising, Mark Metzger
Territory Manager, Richard Nastasi
Territory Manager, James Lovelady
Coordinator, Kimberly Johnson
Auditors: GANT CROFT ASSOCIATES PC SC

LOCATIONS

HQ: AMERICAN ASSOCIATED PHARMACIES
201 LNNIE E CRAWFORD BLVD, SCOTTSBORO, AL
357697408
Phone: 256 574-7521
Web: WWW.UNITEDDRUGS.COM

HISTORICAL FINANCIALS
Company Type: Private

Income Statement   FYE: December 31

	REVENUE ($ mil.)	NET INCOME ($ mil.)	NET PROFIT MARGIN	EMPLOYEES
12/15	642	(0)	—	220
12/14	513	0	0.0%	—
12/13	498	0	0.0%	—
12/12	476	0	0.1%	—
Annual Growth	10.5%	—	—	—

2015 Year-End Financials
Return on assets: 10.5%   Cash ($ mil.): 34
Return on equity: —
Current ratio: 0.50

AMERICAN BALANCED FUND, INC.

EXECUTIVES

Chb-Ceo, Robert G O'Donnell
Pres, Paul G Haaga Jr
V Pres, Hilda L Applbaum
Sr V Pres, Abner Goldstine
Sr V Pres, John H Smet
V Pres, J Dale Harvey
V Pres, Jeffrey T Lager
Asst Treas, R Marcia Gould
SEC, Patrick F Quan
Auditors: DELOITTE & TOUCHE LLP

LOCATIONS

HQ: AMERICAN BALANCED FUND, INC.
1 MARKET, SAN FRANCISCO, CA 941051596
Phone: 707 864-3945

HISTORICAL FINANCIALS
Company Type: Private

Income Statement   FYE: December 31

	ASSETS ($ mil.)	NET INCOME ($ mil.)	INCOME AS % OF ASSETS	EMPLOYEES
12/15	87,394	4,903	5.6%	9
12/00	6,203	832	13.4%	—
12/99	5,996	218	3.6%	—
Annual Growth	18.2%	21.4%	—	—

AMERICAN ELECTRIC POWER SERVICE CORPORATION

EXECUTIVES

Chb, Nicholas K Akins
Ex Vp Policy-Fin-Strat Plannin, Susan Tomasky
Deputy Gen Counsel, Jeffrey D Cross
Sr Vp Reg Svcs, J Craig Baker
Vp Corp Comm, Dale E Heydlauff
Exec V Pres- Cfo, Holly Koeppel
Svp Gen Counsel & SEC, John B Keane
Executive Vice President, Donald M Clements Jr
Dir Federal Agency Relations, Sabrina V Campbell
Vice-President, Van Der Walde
Information Specialist, Carole Root

LOCATIONS

HQ: AMERICAN ELECTRIC POWER SERVICE
CORPORATION
1 RIVERSIDE PLZ FL 1 # 1, COLUMBUS, OH
432152373
Phone: 614 716-1000
Web: WWW.AEP.COM

HISTORICAL FINANCIALS
Company Type: Private

Income Statement   FYE: December 31

	REVENUE ($ mil.)	NET INCOME ($ mil.)	NET PROFIT MARGIN	EMPLOYEES
12/16	1,348	0	—	2,152
12/05	12,111	1,037	8.6%	—
12/02	1,391	0	—	—
Annual Growth	(0.2%)	—	—	—

2016 Year-End Financials
Return on assets: 6.6%   Cash ($ mil.): 16
Return on equity: —
Current ratio: —

AMERICAN FOREIGN SERVICE PROTECTIVE ASSOCIATION

EXECUTIVES

Ceo, Paula Jakub
Coo, Kyle Longton
Health Benefits Officer, Brandon Rowles
Senior Nealth Benefits Officer, Shalonda Hunter

LOCATIONS

HQ: AMERICAN FOREIGN SERVICE PROTECTIVE
ASSOCIATION
1620 L ST NW STE 800, WASHINGTON, DC
200362902
Phone: 202 833-4910
Web: WWW.AFSPA.ORG

HISTORICAL FINANCIALS
Company Type: Private

Income Statement   FYE: December 31

	REVENUE ($ mil.)	NET INCOME ($ mil.)	NET PROFIT MARGIN	EMPLOYEES
12/17	353	14	4.0%	64
12/16	324	31	9.7%	—
12/15	280	13	4.7%	—
12/14	250	(15)	—	—
Annual Growth	12.1%	—	—	—

AMERICAN FRIENDS OF BAR-ILAN UNIVERSITY

EXECUTIVES

Pres, Moshel Straus
Ceo, Matthew J Maryles
Cfo, Stacy Goodman
Instructor, Dror Goldberg
Auditors: GRANT THORNTON LLP NEW YORK

LOCATIONS

HQ: AMERICAN FRIENDS OF BAR-ILAN UNIVERSITY
160 E 56TH ST FL 5, NEW YORK, NY 100223609
Phone: 212 906-3900
Web: WWW.AFBIU.ORG

HISTORICAL FINANCIALS
Company Type: Private

Income Statement   FYE: September 30

	REVENUE ($ mil.)	NET INCOME ($ mil.)	NET PROFIT MARGIN	EMPLOYEES
09/16	329	(7)	—	30
09/15	320	(67)	—	—
09/14	363	(17)	—	—
09/13	343	(30)	—	—
Annual Growth	(1.4%)	—	—	—

2016 Year-End Financials
Return on assets: 8.9%   Cash ($ mil.): 7
Return on equity: (-2.2%)
Current ratio: 0.50

AMERICAN FURNITURE WAREHOUSE CO INC

Tony the Tiger hawking home furnishings might give some marketers pause but the combination seems to work for American Furniture Warehouse. American Furniture's television commercials often spotlight white-haired president and CEO Jake Jabs (who has become a well-known personality in the state as well as in the home furnishings industry) accompanied by baby exotic animals mostly tigers. The company sells furniture electronics and decor at discounted prices. It boasts about a dozen retail locations in Colorado and Arizona and sells through its website which also features bridal and gift registries. The company has built a reputation as a home-spun local furniture retailer. Jabs bought the company in 1975.

Geographic Reach

American Furniture has locations in the Colorado cities of Aurora Englewood Centennial Lakewood Thornton Westminster Colorado Springs Firestone/Longmont Fort Collins Glenwood Springs Pueblo and Grand Junction. In Arizona it has locations in Phoenix Gilbert and Glendale. It serves customers in the neighboring states of Wyoming Utah Kansas Nevada and New Mexico.

Financial Performance

American Furniture's 2013 sales reached more than $390 million.

Strategy

In 2013 the company made its first move outside Colorado when it opened a 630000-sq.-ft. store in Gilbert Arizona (near Phoenix). It opens another store — in Glendale Arizona — in late 2014. American Furniture hopes to net $3.4 million in direct revenue from the Glendale store during its first year in operation. The furniture retailer also has an eye on expanding into north Scottsdale.

EXECUTIVES

Vice President, Jackie Brookshire
Auditors: BAUERLE AND COMPANY PC DEN

LOCATIONS

HQ: AMERICAN FURNITURE WAREHOUSE CO INC
 8820 AMERICAN WAY, ENGLEWOOD, CO 801127056
Phone: 303 799-9044
Web: WWW.AFWONLINE.COM

PRODUCTS/OPERATIONS

Selected Products

Decorative accessories
Electronics
Furniture
 Bedroom
 Chairs
 Dining room
 Home office
 Indoor/outdoor
 Living room
 Occasional tables
 Sectionals
 Sofas
 Youth bedroom
Lighting
Mattresses
Rugs

COMPETITORS

Ashley Furniture	Pier 1 Imports
Big Lots	Rooms To Go
Costco Wholesale	Sears
J. C. Penney	Target Corporation
Kmart	Wal-Mart

HISTORICAL FINANCIALS

Company Type: Private

Income Statement | | | | FYE: March 31

	REVENUE ($ mil.)	NET INCOME ($ mil.)	NET PROFIT MARGIN	EMPLOYEES
03/18	673	28	4.2%	1,900
03/17	652	25	3.9%	—
03/16	615	23	3.7%	—
03/15	530	20	3.8%	—
Annual Growth	8.3%	11.5%	—	—

2018 Year-End Financials

Return on assets: 3.7%   Cash ($ mil.): 79
Return on equity: 4.2%
Current ratio: 1.40

AMERICAN HONDA FINANCE CORPORATION

If you're fonda the idea of driving a Honda you might want to call on American Honda Finance. Operating as Honda Financial Services the company provides retail financing in the US for Honda and Acura automobiles motorcycles all-terrain vehicles power equipment and outboard motors. Its American Honda Service division administers service contracts while Honda Lease Trust offers leases on new and used vehicles. Honda Financial Services also offers dealer financing and related dealer services. Ancillary services include servicing loans and securitizing and selling loans into the secondary market. A subsidiary of American Honda Motor the company began as a wholesale motorcycle finance provider in 1980.

Operations

American Honda Finance (AHF) acquires retail installment contracts and closed-end vehicle lease contracts from purchasers and lessees and authorized Honda and Acura dealers. It also provides these authorized dealers with wholesale flooring and commercial loans.

AHF also acquires used auto loans of non-Honda and non-Acura vehicles and provides these third-party dealers iwth wholesale loans. Additionally the company offers vehicle service contracts services underwriting and pricing of consumer financing services and incentive financing programs for Honda and Acura products.

Geographic Reach

The company is headquartered in Torrance California and operates nine regional offices that support all authorized Honda and Acura dealers across North America.

Financial Performance

While full financials of the subsidiary were not available American Honda Finance's (AHF) revenue has been on the uptrend as auto sales continue to strengthen along with the US economy. Revenue in fiscal 2014 (ended March 31 2014) grew by 22% to A?5.97 trillion ($58.1 billion) thanks to larger revenues from its parent company's auto business and positive foreign currency exchange rates.

Despite higher selling general and administrative expenses and R&D expenses AHF's operating income also increased 39% to A?290.9 billion ($2.83 billion) in 2014 after the company continued its cost reduction measures.

Strategy

American Honda Finance Corp. (AHFC) exists to provide stability to support sales of new and used Honda and Acura vehicles throughout North America Honda Motor's largest market. To that end AHFC seeks to preserve funding diversity balanced liquidity and maintain a prudent maturity profile. To spur growth of its US business in 2012 the company opened its ninth regional office a 25000-square-foot facility in Charlotte North Carolina to serve Honda buyers in the Carolinas Maryland Tennessee Virginia and West Virginia.

EXECUTIVES

Ceo, Hideo Tamaka
Sr Vice President, Stephan Smith
V Pres-Cfo, John Weisickle
Information Specialist, Hung Le
Recruiter, Breanna Robinson
Assistant Sales Manager, Kevin Dorman
Lead Customer Represen, Rodrigo Mascarenhas
Assistant Manager Administrati, Jennifer Shafer
Manager Mc, Jose Basterrechea
Information Manager, Vern Paylor
Information Technology Directo, Grace Jean
Auditors: KPMG LLP LOS ANGELES CALIFOR

LOCATIONS

HQ: AMERICAN HONDA FINANCE CORPORATION
 20800 MADRONA AVE, TORRANCE, CA 905034915
Phone: 310 972-2239
Web: WWW.HONDAFINANCIALSERVICES.COM

Selected Offices

Alpharetta GA
Charlotte NC
Cypress CA
Elgin IL
Holyoke MA
Irving TX
San Ramon CA
Torrance CA
Wilmington DE

COMPETITORS

Ally Financial
 Automotive Finance Corporation
Bank of America
Credit Acceptance
Ford Motor Credit
Mercedes-Benz Financial Services USA
Mitsubishi Motors Credit of America
Toyota Motor Credit

HISTORICAL FINANCIALS

Company Type: Private

Income Statement | | | | FYE: March 31

	ASSETS ($ mil.)	NET INCOME ($ mil.)	INCOME AS % OF ASSETS	EMPLOYEES
03/17	69,854	753	1.1%	1,000
03/16	66,653	910	1.4%	—
03/08	50,526	(45)	—	—
03/07	41,431	394	1.0%	—
Annual Growth	5.4%	6.7%	—	—

2017 Year-End Financials

Return on assets: —   Sales ($ mil.): 2,066
Return on equity: 36.4%

AMERICAN INSTITUTES FOR RESEARCH IN THE BEHAVIORAL SCIENCES

The American Institutes for Research (AIR) lives and breathes to enhance human performance. The not-for-profit organization conducts behavioral and social science research on topics related to education and educational assessment health international development and work and training. Clients including several federal agencies use AIR's research in developing policies. As a major ongoing initiative the organization provides tools to improve education both in the US and internationally particularly in disadvantaged areas. John C. Flanagan who developed the Critical Incident Technique personnel-selection tool to identify human success indicators in the workplace founded the organization in 1946.

Operations

AIR has organized its group into six program areas: Analysis of Longitudinal Data in Education Research Assessment Education Healthand Social Development Workforce and International Development Evaluation and Research.

AIR's assessment program focuses on score reports and online reporting tools to translate large-scale testing data on student achievement into a benchmark for school performance. International human and social development programs aim to improve the quality of life and education in developing areas. It works to achieve this through teacher and school administrator training curriculum development and teaching materials coupled with mobilizing health communications HIV/AIDS education and raising awareness about such issues as child labor exploitation. Working with governments private health care providers and the general public AIR's health programs design implement and evaluate the impact of health care policies.

Geographic Reach

Begun as a small research group affiliated with the University of Pittsburgh AIR's corporate headquarters and business offices are located in Washington DC. The group maintains about a dozen offices in the US. Domestic offices are located in San Mateo and Sacramento California; Atlanta Georgia; Honolulu Hawaii; Chicago and Naperville Illinois; Indianapolis Indiana; Baltimore Frederick and Silver Spring Maryland; Portland Oregon; Columbus Ohio; Chapel Hill North Carolina; New York New York; and Waltham Massachusetts. AIR also operates nearly 10 international offices located in Egypt Honduras Kyrgyzstan Liberia Tajikistan Cote d'Ivoire and Zambia.

Strategy

The National Center for Education Statistics a key source for statistical data about education and AIR team up to develop large-scale databases for policymaking. Among various efforts AIR designs surveys and assessments develops questionnaires and tests items as well as informational materials. It also helps in producing The Condition of Education the agency's chief report. The organization's successes include campaigns that address public health emergencies such as the flu and H1N1 and the prevention of HIV/AIDS heart disease and birth defects.

Adding to its educational research capabilities AIR has pursued a number of strategic alliances and acquisitions. In 2015 SEDL joined forced with AIR. The combined organizations will have new and enhanced capabilities around for example disability research as well as an increased capacity to conduct large-scale randomized control trials and provide technical assistance to diverse populations across a broader geographic area.

In 2015 AIR awarded a $500000 grant to Impact Network a nonprofit seeking to make high-quality education in Zambia sustainable.

Company Background

In 2011 the National Center for Analysis of Longitudinal Data in Educational Research (CALDER) began operating as a joint project of AIR. CALDER examines how public policies and community conditions impact teacher-student results. A year earlier AIR acquired Learning Point Associates a Chicago-based firm that delivers research in the educational sector. Its clients include state education agencies single-school districts private foundations and for-profit organizations.

EXECUTIVES

Chm, Patricia B Gurin
Pres-Ceo, David Myers
Cfo-Sr Vice President, Marijo Ahlgrimm
Business Spe, Yvonne Dupree
Scientist, San Keller
Auditors: RUBINO & COMPANY CHARTERED BE

LOCATIONS

HQ: AMERICAN INSTITUTES FOR RESEARCH IN THE BEHAVIORAL SCIENCES
1000 THMAS JFFERSON ST NW, WASHINGTON, DC 200073835
Phone: 202 403-5000
Web: WWW.AIR.ORG

PRODUCTS/OPERATIONS

Selected Program Areas
Education
Education assessment
Human development
International development
Work & training

HISTORICAL FINANCIALS

Company Type: Private

Income Statement

FYE: December 31

	REVENUE ($ mil.)	NET INCOME ($ mil.)	NET PROFIT MARGIN	EMPLOYEES
12/17	497	55	11.1%	1,700
12/16	474	43	9.2%	—
12/15	488	45	9.2%	—
12/14	396	24	6.2%	—
Annual Growth	7.9%	30.6%	—	—

2017 Year-End Financials

Return on assets: 5.9%   Cash ($ mil.): 33
Return on equity: 11.1%
Current ratio: 1.30

AMERICAN KIDNEY FUND, INC.

EXECUTIVES

Exec Dir, Lavarne Burton
Cfo, Donald Roy
Mgr, Rae Kelley
Program Manager, Dennis Cooper
Vice President, Carol Cohen
Finance Director, Beverly Matlock
Information Technology/Interne, Jose Ramos
Director, Brock Field
Coordinator, Chad Stewart
Director, Fiona Lawless
Auditors: CLIFTONLARSONALLEN LLP TIMONI

LOCATIONS

HQ: AMERICAN KIDNEY FUND, INC.
11921 ROCKVILLE PIKE # 300, ROCKVILLE, MD 208522737
Phone: 301 881-3690
Web: WWW.KIDNEYFUND.ORG

HISTORICAL FINANCIALS

Company Type: Private

Income Statement

FYE: December 31

	REVENUE ($ mil.)	NET INCOME ($ mil.)	NET PROFIT MARGIN	EMPLOYEES
12/16	310	5	1.9%	40
12/15	265	(0)	—	—
12/14	239	2	1.1%	—
12/13	219	1	0.9%	—
Annual Growth	12.2%	43.9%	—	—

2016 Year-End Financials

Return on assets: 0.6%   Cash ($ mil.): 17
Return on equity: 1.9%
Current ratio: 8.60

AMERICAN LEBANESE SYRIAN ASSOCIATED CHARITIES, INC.

EXECUTIVES

Pres-Ceo, Rick Shadyac Jr
Cmo, Emily Callahan
Chief Admin Ofcr, Emily S Greer
CIO, Robert Machen
Cfo, Jeffrey T Pearson
Svp-Ceo Ops, Betty Macdougall
Executive Director of Fin, Sherri Tagg
Auditors: DELOITTE & TOUCHE LLP MEMPHIS

LOCATIONS

HQ: AMERICAN LEBANESE SYRIAN ASSOCIATED CHARITIES, INC.
501 SAINT JUDE PL, MEMPHIS, TN 381051905
Phone: 901 578-2000
Web: WWW.STJUDE.ORG

HISTORICAL FINANCIALS

Company Type: Private

Income Statement

FYE: June 30

	REVENUE ($ mil.)	NET INCOME ($ mil.)	NET PROFIT MARGIN	EMPLOYEES
06/17	1,741	658	37.8%	1,300
06/16	1,161	(27)	—	—
06/15	1,182	251	21.2%	—
06/13	976	210	21.5%	—
Annual Growth	15.6%	33.0%	—	—

2017 Year-End Financials

Return on assets: 0.9%   Cash ($ mil.): 178
Return on equity: 37.8%
Current ratio: —

AMERICAN MEDICAL ASSOCIATION INC

The AMA knows whether there's a doctor in the house. The American Medical Association (AMA) prescribes the standards for the medical profession. The membership group's activities include advocacy for physicians promoting ethics standards in the medical community and improving health care education. Policies are set by the AMA's House of Delegates comprised of elected representatives. The AMA is also a publisher of books for physicians and provides an online physician network through a partnership with Medfusion sells medical malpractice insurance and helps doctors fight legal claims. Founded in 1847 by a physician to establish a code of medical ethics AMA has nearly 225000 members.

Financial Performance

The AMA's revenue declined 4% in 2012 versus 2011 to about $274 million largely due to a material drop in print advertising sales and a downturn in coding book sales. Publishing-related revenue declined by more than $9 million mainly due to the $10 million drop in ad revenues. Continued growth in site licensing helped to offset revenue losses from print subscriptions and reprints. Print book sales fell $9.8 million in 2012 as migration to online products continued. Current Procedural Terminology royalties and online product revenues partially offset the decline in print book sales up $4.5 million in total. Proceeds from membership dues increased 3% in 2012 over 2011 to account for 14% of total revenue. Indeed membership increased more than 3% in 2012 compared with 2011 to approach 225000. Despite the uptick in its ranks AMA membership is still below 2009 when it boasted 228000 members.

Net income increased 8% over the same period due to the decline in cost of goods sold and selling expenses. Cash provided by operating activities increased 11% from $26.2 million in 2011 to $37.6 million in 2012.

Strategy

During this time of historical change for the nation's health care system the AMA's five-year strategic plans emphasizes three core areas of focus: improving health outcomes; accelerating change in medical education; and enhancing physician satisfaction and practice sustainability by shaping delivery and payment models. The group has been an active and vocal participant concerning health care and insurance reform both huge issues in recent years. National campaigns such as the "Voice for the Uninsured" waged by the AMA call attention to deficiencies in our health care system. It is also stridently against Medicare cuts.

As part of the AMA affiliated groups have sprouted to support the association and fund some of its efforts. The American Medical Association Alliance is a large grassroots group established to support and represent physician spouses. The AMA Foundation founded in 1950 funds medical education research and service through its focus on health care. AMA extends its reach internationally through its AMA Office of International Medicine established in 1978.

EXECUTIVES

Vice President Of Market Research And, Jayne Gretz
Vice President, Deborah Harvey
Vice President Corporate Services, Robert Hobart
Vice President Of Government, Cynthia Brown
Legal Secretary, Jacqueline Krupka
Vice President, John Harrison
Vice President, Denise Friday
Vice President Sales And Marketing, Lisa Manoogian
Vice President Hsg Business Operations, Denise Foy
Auditors: DELOITTE TAX LLP INDIANAPOLIS

LOCATIONS

HQ: AMERICAN MEDICAL ASSOCIATION INC
330 N WABASH AVE # 39300, CHICAGO, IL 606115885
Phone: 312 464-5000
Web: WWW.AMA-ASSN.ORG

PRODUCTS/OPERATIONS

2012 Sales

	$ mil.	% of total
Royalties &credentialing products	83	30
Books newsletters &online products	39	14
Membership dues	38	14
Insurance commissions	36	13
Advertising	19	7
Periodical online	17	6
Grants & other	10	4
Investment income	9	4
Periodical printsubscriptions	9	4
Other publishing	9	3
Other	0	1
Total	**273**	**100**

HISTORICAL FINANCIALS

Company Type: Private

Income Statement   FYE: December 31

	REVENUE ($ mil.)	NET INCOME ($ mil.)	NET PROFIT MARGIN	EMPLOYEES
12/15	284	30	10.6%	1,150
12/14	261	29	11.1%	—
12/13	258	(6)	—	—
12/08	3	(0)	—	—
Annual Growth	**90.1%**	—	—	—

2015 Year-End Financials

Return on assets: 16.4%   Cash ($ mil.): 5
Return on equity: 10.6%
Current ratio: 0.40

AMERICAN MITSUBA CORPORATION

EXECUTIVES

Pres, Yoshimasa Kimura
SEC, David M Stevens
Vice President, Shigeki Miyazaki
Vice President, Mishel Ashtary
Vice President, Yutaka Iijima
Vice President, Tetsuya Onai
Asst Acctg Mgr, Marlene Dehner
Treasurer, Higeki Miyazaki
Acct Mgr, Ken Garber
Auditors: PLANTE & MORAN PLLC AUBURN H

LOCATIONS

HQ: AMERICAN MITSUBA CORPORATION
2945 THREE LEAVES DR, MOUNT PLEASANT, MI 488584596
Phone: 989 779-4962
Web: WWW.AMERICANMITSUBA.COM

HISTORICAL FINANCIALS

Company Type: Private

Income Statement   FYE: December 31

	REVENUE ($ mil.)	NET INCOME ($ mil.)	NET PROFIT MARGIN	EMPLOYEES
12/16	697	(2)	—	800
12/15	687	9	1.4%	—
12/14	558	5	0.9%	—
12/13	557	17	3.1%	—
Annual Growth	**7.7%**	—	—	—

2016 Year-End Financials

Return on assets: 13.0%   Cash ($ mil.): 24
Return on equity: (-0.3%)
Current ratio: 0.70

AMERICAN MUNICIPAL POWER, INC.

Power to the Public is the motto of American Municipal Power (AMP). The non-profit membership organization supplies wholesale power to more than 80 community-owned distribution utilities in Ohio 30 in Pennsylvania 6 in Michigan 5 in Virginia 3 in Kentucky 2 in West Virginia 1 in Indiana and 1 in Delaware (a joint action agency). AMP and its members own and operate plants that generate more than 1500 MW of power. The company also handles projects on behalf of the Ohio Municipal Electric Generating Agency (OMEGA) Joint Ventures program (jointly owned generation and transmission projects). The power generation company is owned by its member municipalities. AMP member utilities serve some 635000 customers.

Operations

The company provides electric capacity and energy and furnishes other services to its members on a cooperative basis. As part of its joint venture responsibilities American Municipal Power also operates the Belleville Hydroelectric Plant a 42 MW plant located in Belleville West Virginia. AMP's wholly-owned subsidiary AMPO provides assistance in establishing electric and gas aggregation programs to benefit local consumers.

Geographic Reach

Ohio-based American Municipal Power serves 130 members - 129 member municipal electric communities in the states of Ohio Pennsylvania Michigan Indiana Virginia Kentucky and West Virginia as well as the Delaware Municipal Electric Corporation a joint action agency headquartered in Smyrna Delaware.

Financial Performance

American Municipal Power (AMP) reported $982.5 million in revenue in 2013 representing a 19% increase over 2012. Rising electric revenues and service fees up 19% and 44% respectively drove growth in 2013. AMP's net margin expanded to $5.3 million from $1.9 million over the same period.

Strategy

Expanding into Indiana in 2014 AMP gained its newest member the city of Cannelton.

Implementing a strategy to reduce carbon emissions the company is building six hydroelectric projects on the Ohio River. The Meldahl plant (with 105 MW of capacity) will be the largest hydroelectric plant on the Ohio River. American Municipal Power also has a deal to develop up to 300 MW of solar power with solar panel company Standard Energy. It also has wind power and landfill gas operations. Indeed AMP members' projected energy resource mix will be approximately 21% renewable by 2015.

In 2013 American Municipal Power and the Vermont Energy Investment Corporation agreed to extend the operation of Efficiency Smart beyond the end of the year. The program provides a broad range of energy efficiency services for the power coop's member utilities. Some 49 member communities in Ohio Pennsylvania and Michigan participated in Efficiency Smart in 2013.

Company Background

To replace lost capacity in 2011 it acquired the Fremont Energy Center in Fremont Ohio from FirstEnergy for $500 million. The 707-MW natural gas combined-cycle facility commenced commercial operation in early 2012. In 2010 American Municipal Power also secured a 368-MW ownership stake in the Prairie State Energy Campus in Illinois.

Expanding geographically American Municipal Power moved into a seventh state in 2011 when it made Delaware Municipal Electric its 129th member.

American Municipal Power was founded in 1971.

EXECUTIVES

Pres, Marc Gerken

Chb, Jon Bisher
Sr V Pres-Cfo, Robert W Trippe
Sr Vice President, Jolene Thompson
Sr Vice President, Pam Sullivan
Sr Vice President, John Bentine
Sr Vice President, Bobby Little
Asst V Pres of Acctng-Treasury, Ray Merrill
Dir of Energy Marketing, Jerry Willman
Security Manager, David Fields
General Manager, Dan Moats
Auditors: PRICEWATERHOUSECOOPERS LLP CO

LOCATIONS

HQ: AMERICAN MUNICIPAL POWER, INC.
1111 SCHROCK RD STE 100, COLUMBUS, OH
432291155
Phone: 614 540-1111
Web: WWW.AMPPARTNERS.ORG

PRODUCTS/OPERATIONS

2013 Sales

	% of total
Electric revenues	97
Service fees	1
Programs & other	2
Total	**100**

Selected Services

Aggregation
Business Development
Clean Energy & Conservation
Community Outreach
Financial
Legislative Regulatory & Legal
Power Supply / AMP Energy Control Center
Safety Programs
Scholarship Programs
Technical Services

COMPETITORS

Dominion Energy   Ohio Valley Electric
Duke Energy Ohio

HISTORICAL FINANCIALS

Company Type: Private

Income Statement   FYE: December 31

	REVENUE ($ mil.)	NET INCOME ($ mil.)	NET PROFIT MARGIN	EMPLOYEES
12/15	1,127	5	0.5%	229
12/14	1,039	2	0.2%	—
12/13	982	5	0.5%	—
12/12	823	1	0.2%	—
Annual Growth	11.0%	45.0%	—	—

2015 Year-End Financials

Return on assets: 10.7%   Cash ($ mil.): 107
Return on equity: 0.5%
Current ratio: 0.50

AMERICAN TRANSMISSION COMPANY, LLC

American Transmission Company is an entrepreneur in the US power grid business — a for-profit multi-state transmission-only utility. Connecting electricity producers to distributors American Transmission owns operates monitors and maintains 9480 miles of high-voltage electric transmission lines and 529 substations in portions of Illinois Michigan Minnesota and Wisconsin. The company a member of the Midwest Independent Transmission System Operator (MISO) regional transmission organization operates the former transmission assets of some of its shareholders. About 30 utilities municipalities electric companies and cooperatives in its service area have an ownership stake in American Transmission.

Operations
Unlike most other power utilities American Transmission is not engaged in the generation distribution or marketing of electricity. Its duties include reliable operation of the transmission system growing the system to meet current and future needs and upgrading and maintain the transmission equipment as needed.

American Transmission is a member of the MISO regional transmission organization and provides nondiscriminatory service to all customers supporting effective competition in energy markets without favoring any market participant.

Geographic Reach
American Transmission meets the power needs of about 5 million people in 72 counties in Illinois Michigan Minnesota and Wisconsin. It operates North central Wisconsin Michigan's Upper Peninsula and Northern Wisconsin South Central/Southwest Wisconsin and North Central Illinois Northeast Wisconsin and Southeast Wisconsin.

Sales and Marketing
The company's customers include local electric distribution companies municipal utilities and co-operative utilities (that procure primary network transmission service and are interconnected or plan on interconnecting to its transmission system) local and national marketers generators and utilities (that procure primarily point-to-point transmission service generators and other transmission systems that want to interconnect with American Transmission's system).

Financial Performance
American Transmission reported revenues of about $603 million in 2012 a 6% increase over 2011 revenues.

Strategy
The company is trying to use its single focus on power transmission to win more customers. American Transmission has invested more than $2.8 billion on infrastructure upgrades (since 2001) including 2305 miles of power line. It has also built more 560 miles of new lines during this time period. By 2021 the company plans to spend a further $3.9-$4.8 billion on infrastructure improvement with a focus on adding new renewable sources to its expanded grid.

In 2014 American Transmission filed applications with the Public Service Commission of Wisconsin to rebuild a 12.5 mile 138000-volt transmission line in western Kenosha County at a cost $12.2 million and a 69000-volt transmission line between Dyckesville Wisconsin and Sturgeon Bay Wisconsin (for $23 million).

In 2013 American Transmission received authorizing to build two new 138-kilovolt transmission lines needed to improve electric system reliability in western Milwaukee County and began construction activities on a new 5.8-mile 345-kilovolt electric transmission line to strengthen the electric system in southeastern Wisconsin and northeastern Illinois. That year it energized the 32-mile 345-kilovolt Rockdale-West Middleton Transmission Line; and placed in service. In 2013 American Transmission

In 2012 it teamed up with ALLETE to study transmission options for transporting Midwestern wind energy as well as Canadian hydroelectric power into Minnesota Wisconsin and Michigan to help local utilities enhance reliability and meet renewable energy goals. To further enable movement of renewable energy that year the company and Minnesota Power agreed to develop a 50-mile double-circuit 345-kilovolt transmission line from the Mesabi Iron Range to the companies' jointly owned Arrowhead Substation in Duluth. The project is due to come into service in 2020.

Company Background
In 2010 it signed two agreements with the Department of Energy to access $12.7 million in investment grants for incorporating smart grid technologies into its transmission system.

In 2011 it announced a plan to build seven new transmission line projects (1800 miles of new line) aimed at filling gaps in the existing transmission grid improving grid reliability and enabling increased delivery of renewable power in Iowa Wisconsin Illinois Indiana and Ohio. The projects in total will cost about $4 billion. It also agreed to purchase of the Zephyr Power Transmission Project (950 miles of transmission line between Wyoming and southern Nevada) in another $4 billion deal.

Boosting its transmission assets in 2011 American Transmission formed a transmission utility joint venture with Duke Energy. Duke-American Transmission Co. builds owns and operates new power transmission infrastructure across North America.

American Transmission is one of the first for-profit transmission companies formed (in 2001) when the US market deregulated in the early 2000s. It is 88% owned by investor-owned utilities and 12% owned by municipalities municipal electric companies and electric cooperatives.

EXECUTIVES

Chb-Pres-Ceo, Patricia Kampling
Pres-Ceo, Michael Peters
President, Allen Leverett
Chm-Pres-Ceo, Gary Wolter
Mng Dir, Stephen Yanisch
Prof, Alan Schriber
Ceo, John Jamar
President, Gale Norton
Exec, Lawrence Borgard
MBR-Exec Vice President, Mike Rowe
Dir of Federal Affairs, Tonja L Wicks
Auditors: DELOITTE & TOUCHE LLP MILWAU

LOCATIONS

HQ: AMERICAN TRANSMISSION COMPANY, LLC
W234N2000 RDGVIEW PKY CT, WAUKESHA, WI
531881022
Phone: 262 506-6700
Web: WWW.ATCLLC.COM

PRODUCTS/OPERATIONS

Contributing Owners
Adams-Columbia Electric Cooperative
Alger Delta Cooperative Electric Association
Badger Power Marketing Authority
Central Wisconsin Electric Cooperative
City of Algoma
City of Columbus
City of Kaukauna
City of Menasha
City of Oconto Falls
City of Plymouth
City of Reedsburg
City of Sheboygan Falls
City of Sturgeon Bay
City of Sun Prairie
City of Wisconsin Rapids
Cloverland Electric Cooperative
Edison Sault Electric Company
Madison Gas & Electric Company
Manitowoc Public Utilities
Marshfield Electric and Water Department
Ontonagon County Rural Electrification Association
Rainy River Energy
Rock Energy Cooperative
Stoughton Utilities

Upper Peninsula Public Power Agency
Wisconsin Electric Power Company
Wisconsin Power & Light Company
Wisconsin Public Service Corporation
WPPI Energy

COMPETITORS

AES
Ameren
Duke Energy
Exelon
FirstEnergy

HISTORICAL FINANCIALS

Company Type: Private

Income Statement   FYE: December 31

	REVENUE ($ mil.)	NET INCOME ($ mil.)	NET PROFIT MARGIN	EMPLOYEES
12/17	714	172	24.2%	547
12/16	650	147	22.7%	—
12/15	615	200	32.5%	—
12/14	635	238	37.6%	—
Annual Growth	4.0%	(10.3%)	—	—

AMERICAN TRANSMISSION SYSTEMS, INCORPORATED

EXECUTIVES

Pres, Richard R Grigg
Director, Richard A Ziegler

LOCATIONS

HQ: AMERICAN TRANSMISSION SYSTEMS, INCORPORATED
76 S MAIN ST, AKRON, OH 443081812
Phone: 330 761-4370
Web: WWW.FIRSTENERGYCORP.COM

HISTORICAL FINANCIALS

Company Type: Private

Income Statement   FYE: December 31

	REVENUE ($ mil.)	NET INCOME ($ mil.)	NET PROFIT MARGIN	EMPLOYEES
12/17	656	165	25.2%	1
12/16	540	133	24.7%	—
Annual Growth	21.6%	23.8%	—	—

AMERICAN UNIVERSITY

Fulfilling the vision of George Washington for a national university in the country's capital American University was chartered by an Act of Congress in 1893 as a private independent co-educational institution under the auspices of the United Methodist Church. Today the school offers a broad range of undergraduate and graduate degree programs to more than 12000 students from more than 120 countries. Its student-teacher ratio is 12:1. American University has schools devoted to arts and sciences business communications international service public affairs and law. It is one of the top producers of Peace Corps volunteers serving overseas. Nine US presidents have served on American University's Board of Trustees.

Operations

American University is known for what else political activism (it has been named most politically active university in the nation by Princeton Review). But you don't have to be pursuing a degree in political science to attend American University; the school offers about 60 undergraduate degrees 50 master's and 10 doctoral degrees.

The school's research centers and institutes include projects focused on chemistry social sciences art design and business behavior. Its academic centers explore research areas that range from social media to war crimes and global peace.

Financial Performance

American University revenue grew from $541.3 million in fiscal 2015 to $555.8 million in fiscal 2016 primarily due to increases in revenue from net tuition and fees.

Strategy

The school has added 15 million square feet of infrastructure since 2011. It 2017 it was scheduled to open four new buildings for student housing parking and academic retail and administrative functions.

Academically with a eye on future trends the university is focusing on hiring faculty with expertise in behavioral and cognitive neurosciences global economic governance and public health policy.

Company Background

In 2010 American University ended a seven year fund-raising campaign that raised $211 million to support a number of campus initiatives. The money is being used to strengthen the school's academic programs develop new facilities and help secure American University's financial future.

The school was founded in 1893.

EXECUTIVES

Cfo; Vp And Treasurer, Douglas Kudravetz
Cio, David G. Swartz
Provost, Scott A. Bass
President, Cornelius M. Kerwin
Vice President, Paula Warrick
Assistant Vice President For Creative Services, Kevin Grasty
Assistant Vice President Of Campus Life And Dean Of Students, Robert Hradsky
Assistant Vice President Financial, Donald Myers
Vice President For Publications, Esther Lee
Vice President Marketing, Yara Altamimi
Vice President Development And Alumni Relations, Courtney Surls
Vice President Moot Court Honor Society, Lucas Novaes
Assistant Vice President Of Planning And Project Management, David Dower
Chairman, Jeffrey A. Sine
Vice Chairman, Jack C. Cassell
Chairman Emeritus And Senior Advisor Of Vanguard, John Brennan
Auditors: PRICEWATERHOUSECOOPERS LLP BA

LOCATIONS

HQ: AMERICAN UNIVERSITY
4400 MASSACHUSETTS AVE NW, WASHINGTON, DC 200168200
Phone: 202 885-1000
Web: WWW.AMERICAN.EDU

PRODUCTS/OPERATIONS

Selected Schools and Colleges
College of Arts and Sciences (CAS)

Kogod School of Business (Kogod)
School of Communication (SOC)
School of International Service (SIS)
School of Professional and Extended Studies (SPExS)
School of Public Affairs (SPA)
Washington College of Law (WCL)

HISTORICAL FINANCIALS

Company Type: Private

Income Statement   FYE: April 30

	REVENUE ($ mil.)	NET INCOME ($ mil.)	NET PROFIT MARGIN	EMPLOYEES
04/18	608	88	14.6%	2,000
04/12	605	55	9.1%	—
04/09	54	(108)	—	—
04/08	398	23	6.0%	—
Annual Growth	4.3%	14.1%	—	—

2018 Year-End Financials

Return on assets: 10.6%   Cash ($ mil.): 127
Return on equity: 14.6%
Current ratio: —

AMERICARES FOUNDATION, INC.

AmeriCares Foundation provides emergency medical aid around the world. The not-for-profit charitable organization helps victims of natural disasters and supports long-term humanitarian programs by collecting medical supplies in the US and overseas and delivering them to places where they are needed. AmeriCares has provided aid in more than 90 countries worldwide. In the US the organization offers medical assistance runs a camp for kids with HIV/AIDS and conducts HomeFront a program that renovates housing for the needy in parts of Connecticut and New York. Robert C. Macauley founded AmeriCares in 1982.

Geographic Reach

The company has presence in US Latin America Caribbean Asia and Eurasia Africa and Middle East.

Financial Performance

AmeriCares' revenue decreased 9% to $572 million in 2014 due to a decline in public support and loss on investments.

EXECUTIVES

Pres-Ceo, Michael Nyenhuis
Svp-Operations, Richard K Trowbridge Jr
Vp-US Programs & Partnership, Lindsay O'Brien
Manager, Jennifer Martins
Auditors: GRANT THORNTON LLP NEW YORK

LOCATIONS

HQ: AMERICARES FOUNDATION, INC.
88 HAMILTON AVE, STAMFORD, CT 069023100
Phone: 203 658-9500
Web: WWW.AMERICARES.ORG

HISTORICAL FINANCIALS
Company Type: Private

Income Statement				FYE: June 30
	REVENUE ($ mil.)	NET INCOME ($ mil.)	NET PROFIT MARGIN	EMPLOYEES
06/15	742	101	13.7%	231
06/14	560	(4)	—	—
06/12	526	5	1.1%	—
06/11	671	(0)	—	—
Annual Growth	2.5%	—	—	—

2015 Year-End Financials
Return on assets: 0.6%   Cash ($ mil.): 10
Return on equity: 13.7%
Current ratio: —

AMES CONSTRUCTION, INC.

Ames Construction aims right for the heart of heavy construction. The company is a general contractor providing heavy civil and industrial construction services to the transportation mining and power industries mainly in the West and Midwest. The family-owned company works on highways airports bridges rail lines mining facilities power plants and other infrastructure projects. Ames also performs flood control environmental remediation reclamation and landfill work. Additionally the firm builds golf courses and undertakes commercial and residential site development projects. Ames typically partners with other companies to perform the engineering and design portion of construction jobs.

Operations
Some of Ames Construction's project include the Arlington Power Plant Dry Fork Station Unit 1 Site Work and Substructure Construction Rentech ClearFuels Cortez Hills Mine and Mills Site and Airport Extension Projects such as its MSP International Airport work.

Geographic Reach
Ames Construction has offices in the US in Minnesota Arizona California Colorado Nevada and Utah as well as in Canada.

Strategy
Through its subcontracting activities Ames Construction contributed to the construction of the Minnesota Twins ballpark and served as subcontractor and partner in a joint venture with Fluor and Balfour Beatty Rail that that undertook a $1 billion design/build portion of a rail line project for the Denver Regional Transit District.

EXECUTIVES

Vice President Of Engineering, John Tripi
Vice President Of Management Services, Roger L Mcbride
Regional Vice President Of Engineering, Robert Gillis
Vice President Of Engineering, Butch Trebesch
Vice President Director Manager It Is, Tony W Meyers
Auditors: CLIFTONLARSONALLEN LLP MINNEA

LOCATIONS

HQ: AMES CONSTRUCTION, INC.
14420 COUNTY ROAD 5, BURNSVILLE, MN 553066997
Phone: 952 435-7106
Web: WWW.AMESCONSTRUCTION.COM

Selected Locations
Arizona
California
Canada
Colorado
Minnesota
Nevada
Utah

PRODUCTS/OPERATIONS

Selected Markets
Commercial
  Commercial site development
  Environmental remediation/ landfills
  Residential site development
Mining
  Contract mining
  Leach pad construction
  Mine development
  Mine infrastructure
  Mine reclamation/remediation
  Mine tailings dam
Power
  Coal fired
  Combined-cycle/natural gas
  Nuclear
  Transmission
  Wind
Transportation
  Airports
  Bridges
  Highways
  Railroads
Water resources
  Dams reservoirs and flood control
  Wastewater/water treatment
  Water delivery
  Water retention structures

COMPETITORS

American Civil Constructors Holdings
Balfour Beatty Construction
Clyde Companies
Granite Construction
Meadow Valley
Peter Kiewit Sons'
SEMA Construction
Skanska USA Civil
Sterling Construction
Tutor-Saliba

HISTORICAL FINANCIALS
Company Type: Private

Income Statement				FYE: November 30
	REVENUE ($ mil.)	NET INCOME ($ mil.)	NET PROFIT MARGIN	EMPLOYEES
11/16	845	2	0.3%	2,200
11/15	1,068	5	0.5%	—
11/14*	1,074	26	2.4%	—
12/12	582	5	1.0%	—
Annual Growth	9.8%	(19.4%)	—	—

*Fiscal year change

2016 Year-End Financials
Return on assets: 8.2%   Cash ($ mil.): 40
Return on equity: 0.3%
Current ratio: 0.90

ANAHEIM UNION HIGH SCHOOL DIST

EXECUTIVES

Supt, Michael Matsuda
Supt, Elizabeth I Novack
Purchasing Director, Brad Minami
Academic Advisor, Jennifer Mele
Teacher, Kelly Gallagher
Food Director, Teresa Alvarez
Secretary, Jenni Smith
Manager, Scott McDonough
Teacher, Steven Graves
Teacher, William Hoffman
Teacher, Adelia Cheng
Auditors: VAVRINEK TRINE DAY & CO LL

LOCATIONS

HQ: ANAHEIM UNION HIGH SCHOOL DIST
501 N CRESCENT WAY, ANAHEIM, CA 928015401
Phone: 714 999-3511
Web: WWW.AUHSD.US

HISTORICAL FINANCIALS
Company Type: Private

Income Statement				FYE: June 30
	REVENUE ($ mil.)	NET INCOME ($ mil.)	NET PROFIT MARGIN	EMPLOYEES
06/17	435	56	13.0%	2,300
06/16	417	11	2.7%	—
06/15	365	41	11.2%	—
06/14	343	7	2.1%	—
Annual Growth	8.3%	99.8%	—	—

2017 Year-End Financials
Return on assets: 3.7%   Cash ($ mil.): 208
Return on equity: 13.0%
Current ratio: —

ANDERSON AND DUBOSE, INC.

EXECUTIVES

Pres, Warren Anderson
Customer Staff, Nancy Wilson

LOCATIONS

HQ: ANDERSON AND DUBOSE, INC.
5300 TOD AVE SW, WARREN, OH 444819767
Phone: 440 248-8800
Web: WWW.ANDERSON-DUBOSE.COM

COMPETITORS

Golden State Foods	Meadowbrook Meat
Gordon Food Service	Company
Keystone Foods	Reinhart FoodService
MAINES	Sysco
Martin-Brower	US Foods

HISTORICAL FINANCIALS
Company Type: Private

Income Statement   FYE: December 30

	REVENUE ($ mil.)	NET INCOME ($ mil.)	NET PROFIT MARGIN	EMPLOYEES
12/16	518	2	0.4%	100
12/15	546	2	0.4%	—
12/14	550	2	0.5%	—
12/11	372	1	0.3%	—
Annual Growth	6.8%	11.0%	—	—

2016 Year-End Financials
Return on assets: 1.9%   Cash ($ mil.): —
Return on equity: 0.4%
Current ratio: 0.30

ANMED HEALTH

EXECUTIVES
Pres-Ceo, John A Miller Jr
Dir, Jimmy Kimbell
Compliance Staff, Chandra Snyder
Surgeon, Felice Moody

LOCATIONS
HQ: ANMED HEALTH
800 N FANT ST, ANDERSON, SC 296215708
Phone: 864 261-1000
Web: WWW.ANMEDHEALTH.ORG

HISTORICAL FINANCIALS
Company Type: Private

Income Statement   FYE: December 31

	REVENUE ($ mil.)	NET INCOME ($ mil.)	NET PROFIT MARGIN	EMPLOYEES
12/17	513	41	8.0%	2,600
12/16	504	40	8.0%	—
12/15	590	(1)	—	—
12/14	570	37	6.6%	—
Annual Growth	(3.5%)	2.7%	—	—

2017 Year-End Financials
Return on assets: 3.3%   Cash ($ mil.): 20
Return on equity: 8.0%
Current ratio: 1.20

ANNE ARUNDEL MEDICAL CENTER, INC.

The ill and infirm get the royal treatment at Anne Arundel Medical Center. The full-service acute-care hospital serves the residents of Anne Arundel Calvert Prince George's and Queen Anne counties in Maryland. With about 425 beds the hospital administers care for women's health oncology pediatrics (it has a level III neonatal intensive care unit) neurology orthopedics and cardiovascular care. The medical center also has weight loss sleep disorder and rehabilitation centers. Anne Arundel which opened its doors in 1902 and is part of the Anne Arundel Health System has expanded its service offerings through various affiliations with regional specialty and primary care clinics. It also has a partnership with Johns Hopkins Medicine.

Operations
With more than 1000 staff members Anne Arundel handles some 26000 inpatient visits and 102000 outpatient visits per year. It also manages more than 5000 births and 93000 emergency room visits.

Johns Hopkins and the not-for-profit Anne Arundel share some services faculty and patients through their collaboration. They also operate a joint outpatient urgent-care facility. Additionally the two organizations work together to perform clinical research projects and conduct physician graduate medical education programs.

Geographic Reach
In addition to its 57-acre Annapolis campus Anne Arundel has outpatient centers in Bowie Kent Island Odenton Pasadena and Waugh Chapel.

Sales and Marketing
In 2014 Medicare payments accounted for about one-third of net patient revenues.

Financial Performance
In 2014 revenue grew 3% to $591 million as net patient services revenues increased. However net income fell 23% to $42 million due to a decline in non-operating income (investment earnings). Cash flow from operations spike 188% to $56 million as cash generated from patient receivables prepaid expenses and other sources rose.

Strategy
Anne Arundel has in recent years added new facilities to better keep up with a continued growth in demand for health care services throughout its service area. In 2015 it opened the second phase of its Pasadena Pavilion adding physical therapy orthopedics and sports medicine capabilities. It also opened a new FastCare walk-in clinic in a grocery store/pharmacy in Annapolis. In 2014 the system opened an outpatient mental health clinic in Annapolis which provides services for patients 13 years of age and older.

In 2013 Anne Arundel opened a training center — the James and Sylvia Earl Simulation to Advance Innovation and Learning (SAIL) Center — to enhance its medical education programs and improve the quality and safety of care in the region. It also opened the Hackerman-Patz House that year to provide an affordable and convenient housing option for families of patients.

Also in 2013 the organization was designated as a Medicare accountable care organization (ACO) by the US government. ACOs work to coordinate care for Medicare patients to improve quality and reduce expenses.

EXECUTIVES
Chb, Florence B Kurdle
V Chb, James F McEncaney Jr
President, Martin L Doordan
V Pres-Fin, Bill Hughes
R V Pres, Joseph D Moser
President, Stephen L Clarke
Vice President, Shirley J Knelly
SEC, Patricia Troy
Treas, John M Suit II
Cso, Paula Widerlite
Fo, Bob Reilly
Auditors: SC&H TAX & ADVISORY SERVICES L

LOCATIONS
HQ: ANNE ARUNDEL MEDICAL CENTER, INC.
2001 MEDICAL PKWY, ANNAPOLIS, MD 214013773
Phone: 443 481-1000
Web: WWW.AAHS.ORG

PRODUCTS/OPERATIONS

Selected Centers and Services
Blood Donor Center
Breast Center
Cardiac Cath Lab
Chest Pain Center
DeCesaris Cancer Institute
Diabetes Wound and Hyperbaric Center
Diagnostic Imaging
Heart and Vascular Institute
Joint Center
Laboratory
Pediatrics
Rehabilitation
Research Institute
Sleep Disorder Center
Spine Center
Stroke Center
Surgery
Women's and Children's Center

COMPETITORS
Ascension Health
Bon Secours Health
Dimensions Healthcare
Franklin Square Hospital Center
GBMC
Harbor Hospital
Johns Hopkins Health System
Johns Hopkins Medicine
LifeBridge Health
MedStar Health
Sinai Hospital of Baltimore
St. Agnes HealthCare
University of Maryland Medical System

HISTORICAL FINANCIALS
Company Type: Private

Income Statement   FYE: June 30

	REVENUE ($ mil.)	NET INCOME ($ mil.)	NET PROFIT MARGIN	EMPLOYEES
06/15	526	39	7.6%	1,890
06/14	492	20	4.1%	—
06/13	493	16	3.4%	—
06/11	445	24	5.4%	—
Annual Growth	4.2%	13.4%	—	—

2015 Year-End Financials
Return on assets: 16.6%   Cash ($ mil.): 59
Return on equity: 7.6%
Current ratio: 0.30

ANNE ARUNDEL MEDICAL CENTER, INC.

EXECUTIVES
Ceo, Victoria W Bayless
Vice President, Stephen L Clarke
Cfo, Bob Reilly
Director of Information Techno, Chuck Daniel
Director of Information Techno, Joan Harris
General Practitioner, Mark D Phillips
Internal Medicine Practitioner, Anthony M Caputo
Health Professional, Adeeb Jaber
Coordinator, Barbara Peterson
Coordinator, Doreen Curry-Briggs
Health Professional, Eileen B Macdonald

LOCATIONS
HQ: ANNE ARUNDEL MEDICAL CENTER, INC.
2001 MEDICAL PKWY, ANNAPOLIS, MD 214013773
Phone: 443 481-1000
Web: WWW.AAHS.ORG

HISTORICAL FINANCIALS
Company Type: Private

Income Statement   FYE: June 30

	REVENUE ($ mil.)	NET INCOME ($ mil.)	NET PROFIT MARGIN	EMPLOYEES
06/16	515	(12)	—	4,000
06/15	498	(16)	—	—
06/14	1	0	23.5%	—
06/13	1	0	16.2%	—
Annual Growth	592.7%	—	—	—

2016 Year-End Financials
Return on assets: 3.1%   Cash ($ mil.): 34
Return on equity: (-2.4%)
Current ratio: 0.80

ANOKA-HENNEPIN SCHOOL DIST NO 11

EXECUTIVES

Supt, David Law
Accounting Mgr, Renee Rodewald
Cfo, Michelle Vargas
Coordinator, Jeff Mueller
Coordinator, Dorothy Olsen
Coordinator, James Greer
Coordinator, Mark Hansen
Coordinator, Noella Fath
Coordinator, Tim Dahlheimer
Site Leader, Chrisanne Way
Site Leader, Donna Riley

LOCATIONS

HQ: ANOKA-HENNEPIN SCHOOL DIST NO 11
2727 N FERRY ST, ANOKA, MN 553031650
Phone: 763 506-1000
Web: WWW.ANOKA.K12.MN.US

HISTORICAL FINANCIALS
Company Type: Private

Income Statement   FYE: June 30

	REVENUE ($ mil.)	NET INCOME ($ mil.)	NET PROFIT MARGIN	EMPLOYEES
06/17*	538	0	0.1%	6,100
08/09	0	0	3.6%	—
06/09	469	51	11.0%	—
06/08	448	(9)	—	—
Annual Growth	2.1%	—	—	—

*Fiscal year change

ANR PIPELINE COMPANY

ANR Pipeline keeps natural gas in line a pipeline that is. The company operates one of the largest interstate natural gas pipeline systems in the US. A subsidiary of TransCanada Corp. ANR controls about 10350 miles of pipeline and delivers more than 1 trillion cu. ft. of natural gas per year. The company primarily serves customers in the Midwest but through its network is capable of connecting to all major gas basins in North America. In tandem with its ANR Storage and Blue Lake Gas Storage subsidiaries ANR Pipeline also pro-

vides natural gas storage services and has ownership interests in more than 250 billion cu. ft. of underground natural gas storage capacity.

Operations
The ANR System is part of TransCanada's network 37000 miles of wholly owned and 4900 miles of partially owned pipelines connecting major supply basins with major markets all across North America.

Geographic Reach
ANR transports natural gas from producing fields in Texas and Oklahoma from offshore and onshore regions of the Gulf of Mexico and from the US midcontinent for delivery mainly to Illinois Indiana Michigan Ohio and Wisconsin.

Strategy
To create greater operating efficiency in 2012 ANR Pipeline Company sold assets and certain related onshore facilities to its wholly owned subsidiary TC Offshore LLC.

To support the growing natural gas production in the Haynesville Shale play in Texas and Louisiana the company is developing the ANR Haynesville Lateral Project to transport up to 1.8 billion cu. ft. of natural gas a day. The Haynesville Lateral pipeline enables producers to transport shale gas to markets in the Southeast Midwest and Northeast.

Company Background
ANR Pipeline was founded as Michigan-Wisconsin Pipe Line Company in 1945 and adopted its current name in 1984.

El Paso Corp. sold ANR Pipeline to TransCanada in 2007. The deal gave TransCanada a regulated natural gas pipeline and storage assets that complemented its other North American gas transmission operations.

EXECUTIVES

Pres-Ceo, Lee Hobbs
Pres-Ceo, Lee G Hobbs
V Pres-Commercial Oprs, Gary C Charette
V Pres-Commercial Sls, Dean Patry
Contrl, Thomas Janish
Information Technology Manager, Kay Dennison

LOCATIONS

HQ: ANR PIPELINE COMPANY
700 LOUISIANA ST STE 700 # 700, HOUSTON, TX 770022873
Phone: 832 320-2000

COMPETITORS

Alliance Pipeline	Transcontinental Gas
Buckeye Pipe Line	Pipe Line
Columbia Gulf	Vector Pipeline
Transmission	Williams Companies
Duke Energy	Williston Basin
OGE Energy	Interstate Pipeline
ONEOK Partners	
Panhandle Eastern Pipe	
Line	

HISTORICAL FINANCIALS
Company Type: Private

Income Statement   FYE: December 31

	REVENUE ($ mil.)	NET INCOME ($ mil.)	NET PROFIT MARGIN	EMPLOYEES
12/17	758	139	18.5%	1,000
12/16	686	54	8.0%	—
12/06	540	152	28.1%	—
12/05	548	147	26.8%	—
Annual Growth	2.7%	(0.4%)	—	—

2017 Year-End Financials
Return on assets: 11.5%   Cash ($ mil.): —
Return on equity: 18.5%
Current ratio: 0.40

ANTELOPE VALLEY HOSPITAL, INC.

EXECUTIVES

Pres-Ceo, Michael Wall
Chm, Abdallah Farrukh
Cfo, Dennis Empey
Cardiology, Timothy W Casarez
Physician Recruiter, Richard Cook
Radiology, Mark Beller
General, Barbara Pierce
Coordinator, Ellen Gaines
Information Specialist, Ellis Hicks
Recruiter, Jennifer Phy
Director of Laboratory, Larry Walker
Auditors: BURKEY COX EVANS & BRADFORD P

LOCATIONS

HQ: ANTELOPE VALLEY HOSPITAL, INC.
1600 W AVENUE J, LANCASTER, CA 935342894
Phone: 661 949-5000
Web: WWW.AVHOSPITAL.ORG

HISTORICAL FINANCIALS
Company Type: Private

Income Statement   FYE: June 30

	REVENUE ($ mil.)	NET INCOME ($ mil.)	NET PROFIT MARGIN	EMPLOYEES
06/17	456	31	6.9%	2,200
06/16	0	0	20.3%	—
06/15	380	6	1.8%	—
06/08	265	(1)	—	—
Annual Growth	6.2%	—	—	—

2017 Year-End Financials
Return on assets: 4.4%   Cash ($ mil.): 56
Return on equity: 6.9%
Current ratio: 2.30

API GROUP INC.

EXECUTIVES

Pres-Ceo, Russell Becker
Chb, Lee R Anderson Sr
Treas-Cfo, Gregory Keup
SEC, William M Beadie
Senior Manager, Michael Shibrowski
Creative Director, Shelly Pagano
Controller, Jason Hult
Information Technology Manager, John Horner
Manager, Kelli Mireles
Senior Web Developer, Kevin Roth
Director Business Information, Chinh Huynh
Auditors: KPMG

LOCATIONS

HQ: API GROUP INC.
1100 OLD HIGHWAY 8 NW, SAINT PAUL, MN 551126447
Phone: 651 636-4320
Web: WWW.APIDISTRIBUTION.COM

PRODUCTS/OPERATIONS

Selected Subsidiaries
Fire Protection Systems
Alliance Fire Protection Inc.
APi National Service Group

Davis-Ulmer Sprinkler Company
Delta Fire Systems Inc.
Grunau Company
Halon Banking Systems
International Fire Protection Inc.
Island Fire Sprinkler Inc.
Reliance Fire Protection
Rich Fire Protection Co Inc.
Security Fire Protection Company
United States Fire Protection Company
VFP Fire Systems Inc.
Viking Automatic Sprinkler Company
Vipond Fire Protection Inc. (Canada)
Vipond Fire Protection Ltd. (UK)
Western States Fire Protection Inc.
Industrial and Specialty Construction Services
3S Incorporated
Anco Products Inc.
APi CAD Services
APi Construction Company
APi Distribution Inc.
APi Electric
APi Supply Inc.
Classic Industrial Services Inc.
Doody Mechanical Inc.
Garage Door Store
Grunau Company Inc.
Industrial Contractors Inc.
Industrial Fabricators Inc.
Jamar Company
Jomax Construction Co.
LeJeune Steel Company
NYCO Inc.
Tessier's Inc.
Twin City Garage Door Company
Low Voltage
APi Systems Group Inc.
APi Systems Integrators
Vipond Systems Group

COMPETITORS

Comfort Systems USA	TDIndustries
EMCOR	Team
IES Holdings	Turner Industries
Irex	Tyco Fire & Security
John E. Green	

HISTORICAL FINANCIALS

Company Type: Private

Income Statement   FYE: December 31

	REVENUE ($ mil.)	NET INCOME ($ mil.)	NET PROFIT MARGIN	EMPLOYEES
12/17	3,046	112	3.7%	4,237
12/16	2,608	104	4.0%	—
12/15	2,448	106	4.3%	—
12/14	2,419	103	4.3%	—
Annual Growth	8.0%	3.0%		

2017 Year-End Financials

Return on assets: 5.0%   Cash ($ mil.): 41
Return on equity: 3.7%
Current ratio: 0.80

APIO, INC.

EXECUTIVES

Ceo, Ron Midyett
Controller, Jeff Kraetsch
Management Vice-President, Debra Vanhorsen
Management Vice-President, Tim Nykoluk
Safety Manager, Janice Van Ryn
Reedley Business S, Kent Huckabay
Director of Communications, Dennis Flynn
Coordinator, Jill Merritt
General Manager, Doug Larose
Director, Martin McGrail
Director, Micah Fuson

LOCATIONS

HQ: APIO, INC.
  4575 W MAIN ST, GUADALUPE, CA 93434
Phone: 800 454-1355
Web: WWW.APIOINC.COM

HISTORICAL FINANCIALS

Company Type: Private

Income Statement   FYE: May 28

	REVENUE ($ mil.)	NET INCOME ($ mil.)	NET PROFIT MARGIN	EMPLOYEES
05/17	470	3	0.8%	90
05/16	488	(31)	—	—
05/14	430	19	4.4%	—
Annual Growth	3.0%	(42.3%)	—	—

2017 Year-End Financials

Return on assets: 4.6%   Cash ($ mil.): —
Return on equity: 0.8%
Current ratio: 1.10

APPALACHIAN REGIONAL HEALTHCARE, INC.

Under-the-weather coal miners (and their daughters) can turn to Appalachian Regional Healthcare (ARH) for medical services. The not-for-profit health system serves residents of eastern Kentucky and southern West Virginia through a dozen hospitals with more than 1000 beds as well as dozens of clinics home health care agencies HomeCare Stores and retail pharmacies. Its largest hospital in Hazard Kentucky has 310 beds and features an inpatient psychiatric unit that serves as the state mental health facility. Several of the system's hospitals are Critical Access Hospitals a federal government designation for rural community hospitals that operate in medically underserved areas.

Operations

ARH's HomeCare Stores provide home medical equipment and oxygen delivery as well as 24-hour support through eight respiratory therapists. Its HomeCare Stores are supported by the ARH Home Health Agencies which provide access to nursing care occupational and physical therapy and social services.

Among the system's hospitals are Beckley ARH Hospital a not-for-profit 173-bed acute-care facility; Harlan ARH Hospital a state-licensed 150-bed acute-care facility; and Mary Breckinridge ARH Hospital a critical access facility.

ARH is the largest provider of care and single largest employer in southeastern Kentucky and the third-largest private employer in southern West Virginia. It employs almost 5000 people and has a network of more than 600 medical staff members. In 2013 the system had 153000 emergency department visits 482000 outpatient visits some 1500 births and about 12000 outpatient surgeries.

Geographic Reach

ARH serves residents of eastern Kentucky and southern West Virginia. It has hospitals in Harlan Hazard Hyden Martin McDowell Middlesboro Morgan County South Williamson and Whitesburg Kentucky; and in Beckley and Summers County West Virginia.

Strategy

As the primary provider of health care to medically underserved populations ARH doles out millions of dollars in uncompensated care each year to un- or underinsured residents of the Appalachian region.

Along with a larger population of uninsured patients and the resulting unpaid medical bills that come along with them rural health care providers face a number of hardships not encountered by their urban brethren. For example physician recruitment is more difficult at rural hospitals especially for some higher-risk specialties such as obstetrics. In order to attract and retain doctors ARH and other rural health care providers have to offer more competitive compensation packages pay for relocation and invest in technology and facility upgrades.

Also patients in rural areas are more likely to suffer from chronic health problems such as diabetes and obesity which can become a significant drain on a health system's resources. ARH is one of many health care providers looking to benefit from changes to the health care system outlined in Affordable Care Act especially the requirement that all US citizens carry health insurance.

To keep up with patient demand ARH also focuses on building and acquiring new facilities as well as investing in new technology and medical capacities.

Beckley ARH Hospital is undergoing a nearly $7 million renovation project that will add 19 more private rooms decrease utility costs and improve patient flow processes. In 2014 ARH completed a $47 million expansion project at the Hazard ARH Regional Medical Center that added an additional 100000 sq. ft. to the medical center including a new patient tower a new 24-bed emergency department on the first floor a dedicated 16-bed cardiac critical care unit and 34 private rooms. Hazard ARH is now the largest hospital in southeastern Kentucky.

Mergers and Acquisitions

In 2018 Appalachian Regional Healthcare acquired its twelfth hospital — the 25-bed Saint Joseph Martin Hospital — and its clinics. That facility now operates as ARH Our Lady of the Way.

Company Background

Appalachian Regional Healthcare was formed in 1956 by the United Mine Workers of America but became an independent not-for-profit entity in the early 1960s.

EXECUTIVES

Vice President Sales And Marketing, Holly Harris
Auditors: MOUNTJOY CHILTON MEDLEY LLP L

LOCATIONS

HQ: APPALACHIAN REGIONAL HEALTHCARE, INC.
  2260 EXECUTIVE DR, LEXINGTON, KY 405054808
Phone: 859 226-2440
Web: WWW.ARH.ORG

PRODUCTS/OPERATIONS

Selected Facilities

Beckley ARH Hospital (Beckley West Virginia)
Hazard ARH Regional Medical Center (Hazard Kentucky)
Harlan ARH Hospital (Harlan Kentucky)
McDowell ARH Hospital (McDowell Kentucky)
Middlesboro ARH Hospital (Middlesboro Kentucky)
Morgan County ARH Hospital (West Liberty Kentucky)
Summers County ARH Hospital (Hinton West Virginia)
Tug Valley ARH Regional Medical Center (South Williamson Kentucky)
Whitesburg ARH Hospital (Whitesburg Kentucky)

Selected Services

Bariatrics
Behavioral Health
Cancer Care
Clinics
Emergency
Heart Care
Home Health
HomeCare Stores
Imaging
Laboratory
Medical Spa
Nephrology
Obstetrics and Gynecology
Pediatrics
Pharmacy
Rehabilitation Therapy
Respiratory Therapy
Rheumatology
Senior Care
Skilled Nursing
Sleep Lab
Surgery
Swing Beds

COMPETITORS

Baptist Health
Bon Secours Health
Carilion Clinic
Catholic Health
  Initiatives
Community Health
  Systems
Highlands Health
Jewish Hospital & St.
  Mary's HealthCare
Kindred Healthcare

Mercy Medical Center
  (NY)
Montgomery Regional
  Hospital
Norton Healthcare
Pikeville Medical
  Center
University of Kentucky
  Chandler Hospital
University of Virginia
  Health System

HISTORICAL FINANCIALS

Company Type: Private

Income Statement | | | | FYE: June 30

	REVENUE ($ mil.)	NET INCOME ($ mil.)	NET PROFIT MARGIN	EMPLOYEES
06/17	657	43	6.6%	4,520
06/16	653	17	2.6%	—
06/15	620	48	7.8%	—
06/13	610	19	3.2%	—
Annual Growth	1.9%	22.0%	—	—

2017 Year-End Financials

Return on assets: 4.1% Cash ($ mil.): 63
Return on equity: 6.6%
Current ratio: 0.60

AQUA PENNSYLVANIA, INC.

EXECUTIVES

Chm-Ceo, Nicholas Debenedictis
President, Marc Lucca
President, Steven Tagert
V Pres-Engg, William Ross
V Pres Corp Dev-Corp Counsel, Mark J Kropilak
Vice President, Bill Miller
Vice President, Anthony Donatoni
Cfo, David P Smeltzer
Contrl, Leon Chain
Field Supervisor, Randall Simmons
Manager Electrical Engineering, Steve Marrano
Auditors: PRICEWATERHOUSECOOPERS LLP PH

LOCATIONS

HQ: AQUA PENNSYLVANIA, INC.
  762 W LANCASTER AVE, BRYN MAWR, PA 190103489
Phone: 610 525-1400
Web: WWW.AQUARESOURCESPA.COM

HISTORICAL FINANCIALS

Company Type: Private

Income Statement | | | | FYE: December 31

	REVENUE ($ mil.)	NET INCOME ($ mil.)	NET PROFIT MARGIN	EMPLOYEES
12/17	414	177	42.9%	1,309
12/16	418	172	41.3%	—
Annual Growth	(1.0%)	2.6%	—	—

2017 Year-End Financials

Return on assets: 8.6% Cash ($ mil.): 1
Return on equity: 42.9%
Current ratio: 0.30

ARCHBOLD MEDICAL CENTER, INC.

EXECUTIVES

Ceo, J Perry Mustian
Pres, Ken Beverly
Chief Financial Officer, Charles Hightower
Chief Operating Officer, Kevin Taylor
Human Resources Director, Zach Wheeler
Accountant, Donna Johnson
Director, Robin Godwin
Vice-President, Amy Griffin
Physician Assistant, Valerie Bush
Human Resources Coordinator, Beverly Hurst
Director of Radiology, Allison Donaldson
Auditors: DRAFFIN & TUCKER LLP ALBANY

LOCATIONS

HQ: ARCHBOLD MEDICAL CENTER, INC.
  GORDON AVE AT MIMOSA DR, THOMASVILLE, GA
  31792
Phone: 229 228-2739
Web: WWW.ARCHBOLD.ORG

HISTORICAL FINANCIALS

Company Type: Private

Income Statement | | | | FYE: September 30

	REVENUE ($ mil.)	NET INCOME ($ mil.)	NET PROFIT MARGIN	EMPLOYEES
09/16	363	20	5.6%	2,700
09/14	24	0	—	—
09/13	23	0	—	—
Annual Growth	148.7%	—	—	—

2016 Year-End Financials

Return on assets: 3.0% Cash ($ mil.): 47
Return on equity: 5.6%
Current ratio: 2.10

ARENA ENERGY, LP

EXECUTIVES

Mng MBR, Michael J Minarovic
MBR, Todd L Stone
MBR, Bryan L Nelson
Scientist, Don Metz
Accounting Staff, Shannon Coffell
Engineer, Ben Frederick
Engineer, Brett Ozene
Marketing Manager, Mike McGinnis
Managing Director, Bryan Nelson
Manager, Allen White
Scientist, John Austin
Auditors: ERNST & YOUNG LLP

LOCATIONS

HQ: ARENA ENERGY, LP
  4200 RES FREST DR STE 500, THE WOODLANDS,
  TX 77381
Phone: 281 681-9500
Web: WWW.ARENAENERGY.COM

HISTORICAL FINANCIALS

Company Type: Private

Income Statement | | | | FYE: December 31

	REVENUE ($ mil.)	NET INCOME ($ mil.)	NET PROFIT MARGIN	EMPLOYEES
12/16	317	(418)	—	8
12/15	275	(347)	—	—
12/08	244	116	47.6%	—
12/07	188	64	34.0%	—
Annual Growth	5.9%	—	—	—

2016 Year-End Financials

Return on assets: 24.6% Cash ($ mil.): 3
Return on equity: (-132.0%)
Current ratio: 0.20

ARIA HEALTH

Aria Health wants to get you back to singing arias in no time flat. Aria Health provides medical care from two acute care hospitals in Philadelphia (Frankford Campus and Torresdale Campus) as well as the Bucks County Campus in Langhorne Pennsylvania. Combined the three facilities boast about 480 beds and offer a full range of specialty care from anesthesiology and pain management to women's care and invasive oncology as well as cardiac and surgical procedures. Aria Health also operates primary care and specialty outpatient facilities throughout its service area. In 2016 Aria announced plans to rejoin forces with Thomas Jefferson University Hospitals eight years after the systems separated.

Operations

Aria Health has more than 4000 employees. It has a staff of more than 1000 medical professionals.

Geographic Reach

Aria Health has three hospital campuses (Bucks County Frankford and Torresdale) two outpatient centers and a network of physicians that serve the Northeast Philadelphia and Bucks County communities.

Strategy

In early 2016 the system announced a definitive agreement to merge with Thomas Jefferson University Hospitals which has been on a merger spree as of late. The transaction will allow for Aria Health to have equal representation on the combined organization's governing board.

The company is also looking to expand its facilities to meet growing demand.

Aria Health is planning a new hospital in the area to be named the Lower Makefield Campus but has met with some resistance from local citizens who say it will cause higher taxes and traffic congestion. Aria Health plans to relocate the services currently offered at its Bucks County Campus to the new $300 million 455000 sq.-ft. replacement hospital. Services would include maternity and birthing as well as advanced technology such as robotic-assisted surgery. In late 2013 the system was still waiting on approval from the town's board of supervisors before beginning construction on the 225-bed facility.

In 2013 the company broke ground on $37 million emergency department expansion at its Torresdale campus in Northeast Philadelphia. The project is expected to increase the facility's emergency adAmisAsions annual capacity by more than 25000 paAtient visits.

In 2013 Aria Health officials met with Lower Makefield officials and area residents to propose a healthcare village on the 41-acre tract of land at the corner of Stony Hill Road and the Newtown Bypass. The 180000 square foot village would include a medical office building an area to conduct clinical research an ambulatory care center as well as restaurants and a spa.

Company Background

To improve its information technology systems and comply with health reform incentive measures Aria Health joined an accountable care organization (ACO) in 2010. The ACO is a collaborative effort among regional care providers to improve quality and efficiency in the health care system.

The organization changed its name from Frankford Health Care System to Aria Health in early 2009 to reflect its independence and growing presence in the Philadelphia area. The health system was part of the larger Jefferson Health System until the end of 2008 when the two entities realigned their relationship after determining that they could better serve customers as independent entities.

Aria Health was formed in 1902 after a resident of the Frankford section of Philadelphia contracted typhoid fever.

EXECUTIVES

Vice President And Medical Director Physician Services, Katherine Behan

LOCATIONS

HQ: ARIA HEALTH
10800 KNIGHTS RD, PHILADELPHIA, PA 191144299
Phone: 215 612-4000
Web: WWW.ARIAHEALTH.ORG

PRODUCTS/OPERATIONS

Selected Medical Services
Allergy and Immunology
Anesthesiology
Bariatrics
Behavioral Health
Breast Health
Breast Surgery
Cancer
Colorectal Surgery
Cardiothoracic Surgery
Cardiovascular Disease/Cardiology
Clinical Trials & Research
Diabetes
Dermatology
Endocrine Surgery
Endocrinology
Emergency Medicine
Eye Care
Family Practice

Gastrointestinal Disease/Gastroenterology
General Surgery
General Practice
Gynecology & Women's Health
Heart Care
Hematology Medical Oncology
Home Health
Infectious Diseases
Internal Medicine
Joint Replacement Program
Medicine (Department of Medicine)
Medical Oncology
Mental Health
Minimally Invasive Surgery
Nephrology
Neurology
Neurosurgery
Occupational Health
Oncology
Ophthalmology
Oral Medicine
Orthopedic Surgery
Otolaryngology (Ear Nose & Throat)
Pain Management
Pathology
Physical Medicine & Rehabilitation
Plastic/Reconstructive Surgery
Podiatry
Primary Care
Psychiatry
Pulmonary Medicine
Radiation Oncology
Radiology
Radiosurgery
Respiratory Disease
Rheumatology
Robotic Surgery
Sleep Medicine
Smoking Cessation and Lung Screening Program
Sports Medicine
Stroke
Surgery
Surgical Oncology
Thoracic Surgery
Trauma
Urology
Vascular Surgery
Weight Loss
Wellness
Women's Health

COMPETITORS

Abington Memorial Hospital
Albert Einstein Healthcare Network
Children's Hospital of Philadelphia
Crozer-Keystone Health System
Doylestown Hospital
Fox Chase Cancer Center
Liberty Healthcare
Lourdes Health
Main Line Health System
Mercy Health System
North Philadelphia Health System
Our Lady of Lourdes Medical Center
TUHS
The Cooper Health System
Thomas Jefferson University
Universal Health Services
University of Pennsylvania Health System
Virtua Health

HISTORICAL FINANCIALS
Company Type: Private

Income Statement   FYE: June 30

	REVENUE ($ mil.)	NET INCOME ($ mil.)	NET PROFIT MARGIN	EMPLOYEES
06/15	432	31	7.3%	4,000
06/13	460	51	11.3%	—
Annual Growth	(3.1%)	(21.9%)	—	—

2015 Year-End Financials

Return on assets: 5.1%   Cash ($ mil.): 12
Return on equity: 7.3%
Current ratio: 0.50

ARISTEO CONSTRUCTION COMPANY

EXECUTIVES

Pres, Michelle Barton
Vice President, Anne Martinelli
Cfo, William Litz
SEC, Ryan McCarthy
Controller, Bill Dupuie
Project Manager, Kevin Wolf
Project Engineer, Patrick McCarthy
Project Manager, Ricky Hayes
Information Technology Special, Robert Copeland
Director of Information Techno, Travis Roy
General Manager, David Nadeau
Auditors: YEO & YEO PC ANN ARBOR MI

LOCATIONS

HQ: ARISTEO CONSTRUCTION COMPANY
12811 FARMINGTON RD, LIVONIA, MI 481501607
Phone: 734 427-9111
Web: WWW.ARISTEO.COM

HISTORICAL FINANCIALS
Company Type: Private

Income Statement   FYE: December 31

	REVENUE ($ mil.)	NET INCOME ($ mil.)	NET PROFIT MARGIN	EMPLOYEES
12/17	283	29	10.4%	1,025
12/16	274	28	10.3%	—
12/15	289	19	6.6%	—
12/14	259	10	4.1%	—
Annual Growth	2.9%	40.1%	—	—

2017 Year-End Financials

Return on assets: 10.9%   Cash ($ mil.): 23
Return on equity: 10.4%
Current ratio: 1.40

ARIZONA STATE UNIVERSITY

Sun lovers and knowledge seekers can turn to Arizona State University (ASU) for a well-rounded college education. The research university offers a wide variety of bachelor's master's and doctoral degree programs with more than 300 majors through some 18 schools teaching a range of disciplines including nursing journalism and engineering. It has an enrollment of more than 98100 undergraduate graduate and professional students on its six campuses in metropolitan Phoenix; most students attend the Tempe campus. The university has a student-teacher ratio of 23:1. ASU was founded in 1885 as a teachers college and has become widely known for its extensive research programs.

Operations

ASU offers more than 90 undergraduate and graduate degrees and certificates online through some of its colleges including the W. P. Carey School of Business Mary Lou Fulton Teachers College College of Nursing and Health Innovation and the Ira A. Fulton School of Engineering. ASU also partners with Pearson Digital Learning to administer online courses; Pearson also monitors and analyzes student performance trends.

The university's extensive research programs cover a variety of fields in life science medicine and physical science categories. In addition subsidiary Arizona Technology Enterprises (AzTE) manages technology ventures for ASU. AzTE manages the university's intellectual property (much of which is the result of its research programs) and facilitates startup businesses which have led to the formation of 80 companies and attracted $500 million in funding between 2002 and 2016.

Geographic Reach
ASU has an enrollment of students from more than 130 countries.

Financial Performance
The university's revenues increased by 11% (or $162 million) to $1.6 billion in fiscal 2016 primarily due a 10% increase in enrollment including a 23% growth in nonresident enrollment. Research grants and contracts revenue primarily funded by federal agencies rose by 7%.

Operating expenses grew by $143 million (or 7%) that year largely related to the increase in enrollment. Instruction and academic support expenses experienced the largest rise of $81 million.

Strategy
The university is working to become a top research university in interdisciplinary fields of science and technology. As part of that goal ASU is seeking to expand its AzTE entrepreneur business through additional technology discoveries and startup formations. It also seeks to help stimulate the Arizona economy by reaching out to local businesses and encouraging startups that will maintain a presence in the state.

ASU is also working to improve graduation rates increase graduate enrollment and enhance individual learning programs. The university intends to increase the quality of its academic programs and its student facilities.

In 2015 and 2016 the US News & World Report named ASU as the most innovative school in the US.

In 2016 the school opened the $130 million Arizona Center for Law and Society at its downtown campus. The center provides law students with greater access to Arizona's judicial political and economic centers. Other planned facilities include new educational and research centers near Phoenix's Mayo Clinic Hospital; they will deepen ASU's partnership with the Mayo Clinic and provide learning opportunities for ASU students.

In 2014 the university launched a partnership with Starbucks to provide tuition reimbursement to employees nationwide attending ASU online.

EXECUTIVES

Evp Treasurer And Cfo, Morgan R. Olsen
President, Michael M. Crow, age 63
Cio And Professor Of Parctice, Lev S. Gonick, age 58
Svp And President Asu Alumni Association, Christine K. Wilkinson
Evp And University Provost, Mark Searle
Cio, Gordon Wishon
Evp Knowledge Enterprise Development And Chief Research & Innovation Officer, Sethuraman (Panch) Panchanathan
Svp And Chief Marketing Officer, Daniel Dillon
Dean Educational Initiatives And Ceo Edplus, Philip Regier
Ceo And Director General Thunderbird School Of Global Management And Professor Of Global Strategy And Leadership, Allen Morrison
Auditors: DEBBIE K DAVENPORT CPA PHOE

LOCATIONS
HQ: ARIZONA STATE UNIVERSITY
  300 E UNIVERSITY DR # 410, TEMPE, AZ 852812061
Phone: 480 965-2100
Web: WWW.ASU.EDU

PRODUCTS/OPERATIONS

2014 Sales

	% of total
Tuition & fees	67
Research grants and contracts	18
Auxiliary enterprises	10
Other operating revenues	5
Total	**100**

Selected Colleges and Schools
Barrett Honors College
College of Health Solutions
College of Liberal Arts and Sciences
College of Nursing and Health Innovation
College of Public Programs
College of Technology and Innovation
Graduate College
Herberger Institute for Design and the Arts
Ira A. Fulton Schools of Engineering
Mary Lou Fulton Teachers College
New College of Interdisciplinary Arts and Sciences
Sandra Day O'Connor College of Law
School of Letters and Sciences
School of Sustainability
Thunderbird School of Global Management
University College
Walter Cronkite School of Journalism and Mass Communication
W.P. Carey School of Business

HISTORICAL FINANCIALS
Company Type: Private

Income Statement   FYE: June 30

	REVENUE ($ mil.)	NET INCOME ($ mil.)	NET PROFIT MARGIN	EMPLOYEES
06/17	1,782	99	5.6%	8,000
06/16	1,644	108	6.6%	—
06/13	1,227	85	6.9%	—
06/12	1,155	121	10.5%	—
Annual Growth	9.1%	(3.9%)	—	—

2017 Year-End Financials
Return on assets: 7.1%   Cash ($ mil.): 167
Return on equity: 5.6%
Current ratio: 0.80

ARIZONA STATE UNIVERSITY

LOCATIONS
HQ: ARIZONA STATE UNIVERSITY
  951 S PALM WALK, TEMPE, AZ 852870001
Phone: 480 965-4385
Web: WWW.ASU.EDU

HISTORICAL FINANCIALS
Company Type: Private

Income Statement   FYE: June 30

	REVENUE ($ mil.)	NET INCOME ($ mil.)	NET PROFIT MARGIN	EMPLOYEES
06/15	1,482	92	6.2%	26
06/14	1,348	103	7.7%	—
Annual Growth	9.9%	(10.7%)	—	—

2015 Year-End Financials
Return on assets: 6.4%   Cash ($ mil.): 47
Return on equity: 6.2%
Current ratio: 0.60

ARKANSAS CHILDREN'S HOSPITAL

As the only pediatric medical center in the state Arkansas Children's Hospital (ACH) serves the youngest Razorbacks from birth to age 21. The not-for-profit hospital with its 370 beds specializes in childhood cancer pediatric orthopedics and neonatology. Besides acute care services it operates more than 80 specialty clinics and outpatient centers. One of the US's largest pediatric hospitals ACH is also engaged in teaching and medical research through its affiliation with the University of Arkansas for Medical Sciences. Its Arkansas Children's Hospital Research Institute focuses on biological mechanisms underlying birth defects diabetes-related complications and childhood diseases.

Operations
ACH each year performs more than 14500 operations and boasts 55000-plus emergency department visits nearly 330000 outpatient visits and about 14800 inpatient admissions.

ACH's Circle of Friends clinic treats more than 20000 patients annually. The clinic which opened in 2008 provides primary care as well as a broad range of specialty care services related to endocrinology dermatological conditions hemophilia and tuberculosis.

The hospital also offers community outreach services that include help for children of domestic abuse and wellness programs as well as a number of clinics to support those with eating disorders and diabetes.

As a prime destination for treatment ACH also runs Angel One Transport an intensive care medical transportation system that brings critically ill and injured infants children and adolescents as well as adult burn patients from throughout Arkansas and the surrounding states to ACH. It also boasts a high risk obstetric transport program in partnership with the University of Arkansas for Medical Sciences.

ACH has a staff of 500 physicians including 95 residents in pediatrics and pediatric specialties. Its mobile clinics annually serve more than 6000 patients and provide more than $3 million in dental treatment.

Geographic Reach
Based in Little Rock Arkansas on a campus that extends nearly 30 city blocks ACH serves children nationwide as one of the largest pediatric hospitals in the US. It has several locations across Arkansas in Little Rock Jonesboro and Lowell.

Financial Performance
The hospital gets about 82% of its net sales from net patient service revenues.

Strategy
In 2015 ACH announced plans to build a $184 million hospital in Springdale. The 24-bed hospital will be located on 37 acres of land near Arvest Ballpark. The hospital is targeted to be completed in 2018.

In 2013 ACH inked a contract with Aetna health insurance under which patients with Aetna health insurance will be able to seek in-network care at ACH. The contract allows the company to reach more families throughout the region.

Company Background

The hospital opened a new $121 million south wing in mid-2012 that added more than 50 inpatient beds to the hospital's capacity. The nearly 260000-sq.-ft. four-story building features telemedicine technology (for remote patient care) new trauma rooms a dedicated orthopedics suite and a decontamination unit.

To its benefit ACH became the state's only pediatric Level I trauma center in 2010 after receiving a four-year designation from the Arkansas Department of Health. The designation means that the hospital is equipped for and capable of taking care of children with the most severe of traumas. Level I trauma centers serve as referral locations for hospitals that are unable to provide the same level of care.

EXECUTIVES

President Ceo And Director, Jonathan R. (Jon) Bates
Coo, Scott R. Gordon
Director; President Arkansas Children's Hospital Research Institute, Richard F. Jacobs
Svp And Cio, Darrell T. Leonhardt
Svp And Cfo, Gena G. Wingfield
Svp And Coo, David T. Berry
President Ach Foundation, Fred Scarborough
Senior Vice President Chief Quality Officer, Jayant K. Deshpande
Senior Vice President Medical Director, W. Robert Morrow
Vice President Operations, Jennifer Carlisle
Nursing Director, Terri Songer
Director Of Pharmacy, Marita Q Nazarian
Vice President Of Ancillary Services, Cindy Holland
Vice President Of Information Technology Applications, Michael Hart
Senior Vice President, Katherine Friend
Vice President Of Financial Operations, Cheryl Edwards
Vice President Of Facilities, Larry Beckius
Senior Vice President Of Human Resource, Kimberly Frisbee
Medical Director, Stephen Schexnayder
Vice President And General Counsel, Rhonda Thornton
Vice President Finance, Cheryl Edward
Government Relations Vice President, Rosi Smith
Secretary To Vice President Human Resources, Charlotte Johnson
Auditors: KPMG LLP MEMPHIS TN

LOCATIONS

HQ: ARKANSAS CHILDREN'S HOSPITAL
1 CHILDRENS WAY, LITTLE ROCK, AR 722023500
Phone: 501 364-1100
Web: WWW.ARCHILDRENS.ORG

PRODUCTS/OPERATIONS

Selected Services
Ambulatory Surgery
Audiology
Center for Good Mourning
Cleft Clinic
Dennis Developmental Center
Dental Clinic
ECMO
Gastroenterology Clinic
Genetic and Metabolic Clinic
Infectious Diseases
Neuroscience Unit
Physical Medicine & Rehab Outreach Clinics
Sleep Disorders Center
Volunteer Services
WHAM (Wellness Health Action & Motivation) Clinic

COMPETITORS

Arkansas Heart Hospital
Baptist Health (Arkansas)
Children's Healthcare of Atlanta
Children's Medical Center of Dallas
Children's Mercy Hospital
Children's National Medical Center
Cook Children's Health Care System
Dell Children's Medical Center
East Tennessee Children's Hospital
Jefferson Regional Medical Center of Arkansas
Methodist Healthcare
Shriners Hospitals For Children
St. Joseph's Mercy Health Center
St. Jude Children's Research Hospital
St. Vincent Health System
Texas Children's Hospital
Universal Health Services
White County Medical Center

HISTORICAL FINANCIALS

Company Type: Private

Income Statement
FYE: June 30

	REVENUE ($ mil.)	NET INCOME ($ mil.)	NET PROFIT MARGIN	EMPLOYEES
06/18	660	57	8.7%	3,700
06/17	615	59	9.7%	—
06/16	585	70	12.1%	—
06/15	562	44	8.0%	—
Annual Growth	5.5%	8.5%	—	—

2018 Year-End Financials
Return on assets: 5.8%   Cash ($ mil.): 91
Return on equity: 8.7%
Current ratio: 2.20

ARKANSAS ELECTRIC COOPERATIVE CORPORATION

Having access to power is the natural state in the Natural State thanks to Arkansas Electric Cooperative Corporation (AECC) the sole wholesale power provider for 17 Arkansas electric distribution cooperatives. The company operates power plants with 3418 MW of generating capacity owns transmission assets and buys wholesale power to meet its members' demands. Affiliate Arkansas Electric Cooperatives Inc. (AECI) provides administrative and maintenance services to the distribution companies. The distribution utilities serve about 500000 customers in more than 60% of Arkansas. AECC and AECI along with the state's 17 electric distribution cooperatives are known as the Electric Cooperatives of Arkansas.

Operations

AECC's diverse generation assets include three hydropower plants three natural gas/oil-based plants and three natural gas-based-only plants. It also co-owns portions of four low-cost coal-based plants and has a long-term power purchase agreement for 51 MW wind energy. The coop also has four transmission lines.

Sales and Marketing

In fiscal 2013 co-op members Mississippi County Electric Cooperative First Electric Cooperative Carroll Electric Cooperative and Arkansas Valley Electric Corporation together accounted for 59% of AECC's total revenues.

Financial Performance

Thanks to a rebounding economy and growing demand for power the company saw its revenues grow by 13% in fiscal 2013.

Net income declined by 37% in fiscal 2013 due to higher operations maintenance generation and transmission expenses as well as an increase in administration and general expenses.

Strategy

AECC is ramping up its renewable energy resources in order to meet state and federal clean energy power requirements.

In 2013 the company signed a long-term deal to buy 150 MW of wind energy from RES America Developments Inc. a subsidiary of Renewable Energy Systems Americas Inc.

In 2012 it reached a long-term purchase power agreement for 51 MW of wind energy from the Flat Ridge 2 South Wind Farm in Kansas. AECC's 51 MW of capacity is part of 470 MW of potential generation provided by the farm's 294 GE wind turbines. BP and Sempra U.S. Gas & Power are equal joint venture partners for the facility which has a combined investment of more than $800 million. A wholly-owned affiliate of BP Wind Energy will monitor and maintain the farm

Mergers and Acquisitions

In another move to cut back on the use of coal-fired power plants in 2012 AECC bought a 746-MW combined cycle natural gas-fired power plant near Magnet Cove for $240 million.

Company Background

The first electric cooperative in Arkansas was formed in Jacksonville in 1938 as part of the Roosevelt Administration's national rural electrification drive.

EXECUTIVES

Ceo, Gary Voigt
Exec Vice President, Michael W Henderson
Senior Vice President, Robert M Lyford
Controller, Lisa Sigler
Vice President, Jonathan Oliver
Ceo, Duane D Highley
Payroll Staff, Denise Garrison
Auditors: BKD LLP LITTLE ROCK ARKANSA

LOCATIONS

HQ: ARKANSAS ELECTRIC COOPERATIVE CORPORATION
1 COOPERATIVE WAY, LITTLE ROCK, AR 722095493
Phone: 501 570-2200
Web: WWW.AECC.COM

HISTORICAL FINANCIALS

Company Type: Private

Income Statement
FYE: December 31

	REVENUE ($ mil.)	NET INCOME ($ mil.)	NET PROFIT MARGIN	EMPLOYEES
12/16	498	38	7.8%	220
12/15	462	35	7.7%	—
12/14*	455	30	6.6%	—
10/11	657	35	5.4%	—
Annual Growth	(5.4%)	1.6%	—	—

*Fiscal year change

2016 Year-End Financials
Return on assets: 3.9%   Cash ($ mil.): 96
Return on equity: 7.8%
Current ratio: 2.60

ARKANSAS ELECTRIC COOPERATIVES, INC.

EXECUTIVES

Pres, Duane Highley
Vice-President, Doug White
Engineer, Pat Patterson
Auditors: BKD LLP LITTLE ROCK ARKANSA

LOCATIONS

HQ: ARKANSAS ELECTRIC COOPERATIVES, INC.
1 COOPERATIVE WAY, LITTLE ROCK, AR 722095493
Phone: 501 570-2200
Web: WWW.AECC.COM

HISTORICAL FINANCIALS

Company Type: Private

Income Statement				FYE: December 31
	REVENUE ($ mil.)	NET INCOME ($ mil.)	NET PROFIT MARGIN	EMPLOYEES
12/17	564	44	7.8%	840
12/15	462	35	7.7%	—
12/13	416	32	7.7%	—
12/12	438	35	8.0%	—
Annual Growth	5.2%	4.7%	—	—

2017 Year-End Financials

Return on assets: 2.9%   Cash ($ mil.): 95
Return on equity: 7.8%
Current ratio: 2.40

ARLINGTON INDEPENDENT SCHOOL DISTRICT (INC)

EXECUTIVES

Supt, Marcelo Bavazls
Principal, Webb Elementary, Michael Martin
Coordinator, Kathy Hitt
Tech Prep Coordinator, Craig Wright
Tech Prep Coordinator, Ed Cannady
Auditors: WHITLEY PENN LLP HOUSTON TEX

LOCATIONS

HQ: ARLINGTON INDEPENDENT SCHOOL DISTRICT (INC)
1203 W PIONEER PKWY, ARLINGTON, TX 760136246
Phone: 682 867-4611
Web: WWW.AISD.NET

HISTORICAL FINANCIALS

Company Type: Private

Income Statement				FYE: June 30
	REVENUE ($ mil.)	NET INCOME ($ mil.)	NET PROFIT MARGIN	EMPLOYEES
06/17	641	(35)	—	8,000
06/16	636	115	18.1%	—
06/15	613	143	23.4%	—
06/14	592	12	2.1%	—
Annual Growth	2.7%	—	—	—

ARNOLD MACHINERY COMPANY

Arnold Machinery helps keep construction on the move. Through its many divisions the company distributes construction mining industrial and material handling equipment as well as farm machinery throughout the US. Arnold Machinery also offers used equipment and provides repair and maintenance rebuild exchange and rental services. The company's divisions include General Implement Distributors Mining Equipment Construction Equipment and Material Handling. Arnold Machinery operates about 20 branch facilities covering some 15 states in the Western US.

Strategy

Since its founding the company has expanded geographically and built its product offerings by acquiring complementary businesses. Arnold Machinery continues to acquire other distributors in its territory and to expand its facilities in many markets.

Company Background

L. E. "Doc" Arnold and Floyd Stannard founded predecessor company StannardA-Arnold Machinery Company in 1929. The company's name was changed to Arnold Machinery Company upon the resignation of Stannard later that year.

EXECUTIVES

President And Ceo, Russ Fleming
President Material Handling Division, Rex Mecham
Co-president Mh Division, Kirk Reese
Corporate Vp; President Gid Division, Wendell Nelson
Corporate Vp; President Mining Division, John Ragsdale
Vice President Sales, Mark Tibbitts
Chairman, Alvin Richer
Auditors: GRANT THORNTON LLP SALT LAKE

LOCATIONS

HQ: ARNOLD MACHINERY COMPANY
2975 W 2100 S, SALT LAKE CITY, UT 841191273
Phone: 801 972-4000
Web: WWW.ARNOLDMACHINERY.COM

COMPETITORS

Cashman Equipment	NES Rentals
Cummins	Sunbelt Rentals
Empire Southwest	United Rentals

HISTORICAL FINANCIALS

Company Type: Private

Income Statement				FYE: September 30
	REVENUE ($ mil.)	NET INCOME ($ mil.)	NET PROFIT MARGIN	EMPLOYEES
09/17	306	11	3.9%	450
09/16	298	5	1.9%	—
09/15	309	12	3.9%	—
09/14	319	13	4.1%	—
Annual Growth	(1.4%)	(3.4%)	—	—

2017 Year-End Financials

Return on assets: 7.4%   Cash ($ mil.): 545
Return on equity: (-5.5%)
Current ratio: —

ARROWHEAD REGIONAL MEDICAL CENTER

Find yourself dehydrated after searching the Inland Empire deserts for arrowheads? Arrowhead Regional Medical Center (ARMC) can fix you up. The San Bernardino County owned and operated hospital provides a range of health services from general medical and surgical care to emergency services rehabilitation inpatient psychiatric care pediatric and women's health services. It also serves as a Level II trauma center a regional burn center and medical training facility. ARMC with some 460 beds (370 inpatient and 90 behavioral) opened in 1999 to replace the aging San Bernardino County Hospital. The hospital also offers outpatient services on its main campus and at area clinics.

Operations

Along with a full range of health care services ARMC offers about 10 residency programs including emergency and family medicine general surgery geriatrics orthopedics neurosurgery and gynecology. The hospital trains about 170 residents each year and also provides training programs for nurses pharmacists clinical laboratory scientists and radiologic technologists.

The ARMC emergency room handles about 140000 visits each year. The hospital's inpatient capacity handles about 25000 patients annually while its outpatient centers see some 250000 patients.

The Medical Center's Internal Medicine Primary Care Clinic offers services for individuals ranging in age from 18 to 100. Its Outpatient Care facility offers more than 60 different specialty services including pediatrics geriatrics orthopedics surgery internal medicine women's health and rehabilitation services.

ARMC's two Breath Mobiles provide pediatric asthma care management at sites throughout San Bernardino County.

Geographic Reach

The company serves patients in San Bernardino Riverside Inyo and Mono counties in California. ARMC's main facility campus in Colton includes an outpatient services complex. It also runs three primary care Family Health Centers in the nearby towns of Fontana Rialto and San Bernadino as well as wound care and elder care clinics.

Financial Performance

ARMC's revenues dropped by 1% to $385 million in 2012 due to a decline in net patient service revenues.

However net income decreased by 63% to $12 million in 2012 due to higher operating expenses (salaries benefits and purchased services) partially offset by a rise in non-operating revenues due to an increase in state funding.

Strategy

To better serve the needs of patients in its service territory ARMC looks to expand services in high-demand areas.

To enable doctors and technologists to provide a vastly expanded number of procedures for cardiac patients neurology patients and those requiring interventional radiology in 2013 ARMC opened its new Dual Purpose Interventional Lab (medical suite).

2017 Year-End Financials

Return on assets: 3.4%   Cash ($ mil.): 3
Return on equity: 3.9%
Current ratio: 1.00

That year it also opened a new and larger West-side Family Health Center which was expanded from 12 to 21 exam rooms in a new co-location facility in Rialto. It also expanded its Breath Mobile service to the High Desert with service to sites including Adelanto Apple Valley Barstow Hesperia Phelan Victorville and Trona.

Company Background

An increase in cases of asthma (particularly among children) in the Central Valley led ARMC to expand its Breathmobile program an asthma clinic on wheels that travels to schools throughout San Bernadino County in 2010.

The hospital is also enhancing stationary outpatient care clinics. It added the ARMC Medical Office Building to its main campus in 2011; the center includes physician practices and an internal medicine clinic.

EXECUTIVES

Director Of Pharmacy, Cliff Hiroshige

LOCATIONS

HQ: ARROWHEAD REGIONAL MEDICAL CENTER
400 N PEPPER AVE, COLTON, CA 923241819
Phone: 909 580-1000
Web: WWW.ARROWHEADMEDCENTER.ORG

PRODUCTS/OPERATIONS

Selected Services
Audiology
Breast Cancer Clinic
Cardiology
Child Health Disability Program
Dialysis Center
Emergency Medicine
Family and Elder Care
Internal Medicine
Level II Trauma Center
Oncology/Infusion Therapy
Ophthalmology
Orthopedics
Pediatric Clinic
Psychiatric Emergency Services
Radiation Oncology
Rehabilitation Clinic
Surgery
Women's Health

COMPETITORS

Anaheim Regional Medical Center	HCA Loma Linda University Medical Center
Cedars-Sinai Medical Center	Memorial Health Services
Children's Hospital of Orange County	St. Jude Medical Center
City of Hope	Tenet Healthcare
Community Hospital of San Bernardino	Trinity Health (Novi)
Dignity Health	

HISTORICAL FINANCIALS
Company Type: Private

Income Statement				FYE: June 30
	REVENUE ($ mil.)	NET INCOME ($ mil.)	NET PROFIT MARGIN	EMPLOYEES
06/15	468	74	15.8%	2,500
06/09	225	25	11.3%	—
06/04	439	3	0.8%	—
06/03	313	(1)	—	—
Annual Growth	3.4%	—	—	—

2015 Year-End Financials
Return on assets: 4.4%   Cash ($ mil.): 72
Return on equity: 15.8%
Current ratio: 1.00

ASCENSION HEALTH ALLIANCE

EXECUTIVES

Pres, Anthony R Tersigni
Sr Exec Advsr, Sister Bernice Coreil DC
Evp, John D Doyle
Evp, Robert J Henkel
Evp-Gen Coun, Joseph R Impicciche
Evp, Susan Nestor Levy
Evp, Sister Maureen McGuire DC
Evp, David B Pryor
Evp-Cfo, Anthony J Speranzo
Executive Assistant, Barbara Flick
Chief Information Oficer, Mark Barner
Auditors: ERNST & YOUNG LLP ST LOUIS M

LOCATIONS

HQ: ASCENSION HEALTH ALLIANCE
101 S HANLEY RD STE 450, SAINT LOUIS, MO 631053463
Phone: 314 733-8000
Web: WWW.HEALTHMART.COM

HISTORICAL FINANCIALS
Company Type: Private

Income Statement				FYE: June 30
	ASSETS ($ mil.)	NET INCOME ($ mil.)	INCOME AS % OF ASSETS	EMPLOYEES
06/17	34,320	1,638	4.8%	111,719
06/16	32,469	(339)	—	—
06/15	30,963	(42)	—	—
Annual Growth	5.3%	—	—	—

2017 Year-End Financials
Return on assets: 12.1%   Sales ($ mil): 22,633
Return on equity: 7.2%

ASCENSION HEALTH WELFARE BENEFITS TRUST

EXECUTIVES

V Pres, Eric Feinftein

LOCATIONS

HQ: ASCENSION HEALTH WELFARE BENEFITS TRUST
11775 BORMAN DR STE 200, SAINT LOUIS, MO 631464134
Phone: 314 733-8648

HISTORICAL FINANCIALS
Company Type: Private

Income Statement				FYE: December 31
	ASSETS ($ mil.)	NET INCOME ($ mil.)	INCOME AS % OF ASSETS	EMPLOYEES
12/16	186	2	1.1%	2
12/15	169	(3)	—	—
12/14	177	0	—	—
Annual Growth	2.6%	—	—	—

2016 Year-End Financials
Return on assets: 0.1%   Sales ($ mil): 318
Return on equity: 0.6%

ASCENSION PARISH SCHOOLS

EXECUTIVES

Supt, Patrice B Pujol
President, A J Nickens
Coordinator, Shelly M Simmons
Coordinator, Melissa Langlois
Human Resources Generalist, Lisa Carter
Coach, Mark Hernandez
Facilities Director, Glenn Bourgeois
Auditors: POSTLETHWAITE & NETTERVILLE G

LOCATIONS

HQ: ASCENSION PARISH SCHOOLS
1100 WEBSTER ST, DONALDSONVILLE, LA 703462754
Phone: 225 257-2000
Web: WWW.APSB.ORG

HISTORICAL FINANCIALS
Company Type: Private

Income Statement				FYE: June 30
	REVENUE ($ mil.)	NET INCOME ($ mil.)	NET PROFIT MARGIN	EMPLOYEES
06/17	305	(8)	—	3,300
06/16	273	(17)	—	—
06/15	270	(4)	—	—
06/14	259	31	12.1%	—
Annual Growth	5.6%	—	—	—

2017 Year-End Financials
Return on assets: 4.2%   Cash ($ mil.): 44
Return on equity: (-2.6%)
Current ratio: —

ASHLAND HOSPITAL CORPORATION

EXECUTIVES

Pres-Ceo, Fred L Jackson
V Pres Fin-Cfo, Paul McDowell
Manager, Merida Johnson
Physician Recruiter, Michael Reeves
Senior Network Engineer, Nate Smithson
Emergency Medicine Specialist, Pavan Kolluri
Information Technology/Interne, Roger Hensley
Chief of Surgery, William Boykin
Chief of Pediatric, Barry J Belcher
General, Mary Adam
Chief of Ob/Gyn, Tony Dotson
Auditors: PARENTEBEARD LLC PHILADELPHIA

LOCATIONS

HQ: ASHLAND HOSPITAL CORPORATION
2201 LEXINGTON AVE, ASHLAND, KY 411012843
Phone: 606 408-4000
Web: WWW.KDMC.COM

HISTORICAL FINANCIALS

Company Type: Private

Income Statement				FYE: September 30
	REVENUE ($ mil.)	NET INCOME ($ mil.)	NET PROFIT MARGIN	EMPLOYEES
09/15	408	12	3.0%	4,200
09/12	530	50	9.4%	—
09/10	600	4	0.8%	—
Annual Growth	(7.4%)	19.9%	—	—

2015 Year-End Financials

Return on assets: 10.9%   Cash ($ mil.): 14
Return on equity: 3.0%
Current ratio: 0.20

ASPIRUS WAUSAU HOSPITAL, INC.

EXECUTIVES

Ceo, Duane Erwin
President, Darrell Lentz
Chief Operating Officer, Dean Danner
Project Manager, Dave Bosio
Information Technology Special, Joan Klehr
Technician, Jonah Glodowski
Program Director, Timothy Nikstad
Administrative Assistant, Carol Iczaowski
Scientist, Cindy Geiss
Supervisor, George Marks
Doctor, James Cygan
Auditors: WIPFLI LLP WAUSAU WI

LOCATIONS

HQ: ASPIRUS WAUSAU HOSPITAL, INC.
425 PINE RIDGE BLVD # 1, WAUSAU, WI 544014122
Phone: 715 847-2121
Web: WWW.ASPIRUS.ORG

HISTORICAL FINANCIALS

Company Type: Private

Income Statement				FYE: June 30
	REVENUE ($ mil.)	NET INCOME ($ mil.)	NET PROFIT MARGIN	EMPLOYEES
06/18	497	8	1.7%	3,500
06/16	456	51	11.4%	—
06/14	369	42	11.4%	—
06/10	319	33	10.4%	—
Annual Growth	5.7%	(15.8%)	—	—

2018 Year-End Financials

Return on assets: 2.2%   Cash ($ mil.): 4
Return on equity: 1.7%
Current ratio: 1.50

ASPIRUS, INC.

Aspirus aspires to provide care for Midwesterners in need. The health system provides a comprehensive range of health and medical services to residents in a 14-county region of central and northern Wisconsin as well as Michigan's Upper Peninsula. Aspirus operates the Aspirus Wausau Hospital a 325-bed multi-specialty regional health center and seven smaller community hospitals. Its hospitals and network of community clinics provide specialized primary and emergency care. Aspirus also operates imaging centers hospice services home health care long-term care facilities and an outpatient dialysis center.

Operations
Other facilities in Aspirus' network include the 25-bed Aspirus Medford Hospital the Catholic Aspirus Langlade Hospital specialist hospital Riverview Family Clinic and 25-bed critical care access hospitals Aspirus Ontonagon and NORTHSTAR. In all it operates four hospitals in Michigan and four in Wisconsin as well as 50 clinics home health and hospice care helicopter transport nursing homes and pharmacies.

Sales and Marketing
Aspirus takes payments from most health plans and payers in the region in which it operates. It also contracts directly with employers and community business coalitions.

Mergers and Acquisitions
Michigan-based NORTHSTAR Health System became an Aspira subsidiary in 2014. It added a 25-bed critical access hospital as well as clinics to Aspira's network.

EXECUTIVES

President And Ceo, Duane L. Erwin, age 67
Senior Vice President Of Finance And Cfo Aspirus Wausau Hospital Aspirus Inc., Sidney Sczygelski
Executive Director Aspirus Network Inc., Joel Rueber
Interim President/coo Aspirus Wausau Hospital, Marita Hattem
President Of Aspirus Clinics And Chief Clinical Integration Officer For Aspirus, Bud Chumbley
Vice President Of Patient Care/chief Nursing Officer, Kathy Drengler
Ceo Of Aspirus Grand View, Carol Goffnett
Vice President Marketing And Planning, Rick L. Nevers
Executive Director Of Aspirus Health Foundation, Kalynn Pempek
Vice President Of Intormation Technology/chief Information Officer, Todd Richardson
Senior Vice President Of Business Development, Eric Anderson
Physical Therapy, Nathan Weiler
Senior Vice President Of Legal Services And General Counsel For Aspirus, Cari Logemann
Clinic Manager, Jody Baeseman
Clinic Manager, Denise Draves
Vice President Of Finance, Sara Lusignan
Clinical Director, Rae Kaare
Director Of Pharmacy, Jessica Bessner
Vice Chair, William Nietert
Auditors: WIPFLI LLP WAUSAU WISCONSIN

LOCATIONS

HQ: ASPIRUS, INC.
425 PINE RIDGE BLVD, WAUSAU, WI 544014123
Phone: 715 847-2121
Web: WWW.GOODNEIGHBORPHARMACY.COM

Selected Facilities

U.P. of Michigan
Aspirus Grand View Aspirus Keweenaw Hospital

Aspirus Ontonagon Hospital
NORTHSTAR Health System Wisconsin
Aspirus Wausau Hospital
Aspirus Langlade Hospital
Aspirus Medford Hospital
Riverview Hospital

PRODUCTS/OPERATIONS

Selected Services
Alzheimer's & Memory Disorders
Anesthesia Services
Angioplasty
Anticoagulation Clinic
Cardiac Electrophysiology
Cardiac Rehab
Cardioversion
Dentistry
Oral & Maxillofacial Surgery
Prosthodontics
Psychiatry
Psychology
Pulmonary Medicine
Sleep Disorders

COMPETITORS

Dean Health Systems Inc.
Howard Young Health Care
Luther Midelfort
ThedaCare Inc.
University of Wisconsin Hospital and Clinics

HISTORICAL FINANCIALS

Company Type: Private

Income Statement				FYE: June 30
	REVENUE ($ mil.)	NET INCOME ($ mil.)	NET PROFIT MARGIN	EMPLOYEES
06/18	911	78	8.6%	3,900
06/13	536	47	8.9%	—
06/12	529	26	4.9%	—
Annual Growth	9.5%	20.0%	—	—

2018 Year-End Financials

Return on assets: 2.6%   Cash ($ mil.): 104
Return on equity: 8.6%
Current ratio: 1.80

ASSOCIATED WHOLESALE GROCERS, INC.

Associated Wholesale Grocers (AWG) knows its customers can't live on bread and milk alone. The second-largest retailer-owned distribution cooperative in the US (behind Wakefern Food Corporation) AWG supplies more than 3800 grocery retail outlets in more than half of the US states from 10 distribution centers which collectively have some 7 million square feet of space. In addition to its wholesale grocery operation AWG offers a variety of business services to its members including marketing and merchandising programs retail accounting supermarket development and access to low-cost merchandise through its Value Merchandisers subsidiary. AWG was founded by a group of independent grocers in 1924.

Geographic Reach
Kansas City-headquartered Associated Wholesale Grocers began in Missouri and its operations are generally centered on that state. It operates ten wholesale divisions in Missouri Nebraska

Kansas Oklahoma Louisiana Alabama Tennessee and Wisconsin. Its distribution activities extend into another 25 states.

AWG?s Valu Merchandisers subsidary is gaining a foothold in non-US regions such as the Caribbean Central & South America and the Middle East.

Sales and Marketing

As a cooperative AWG serves the needs of its members who collectively determine how best to utilize the co-ops operations. Its board of directors is made up of nearly 20 people each a key executive at a grocer retail chain which receives products from AWG.

AWG serves up several private label brands to stores. They include Superior Selections Clearly Organic Best Choice Always Save and IGA.

Financial Performance

Associated Wholesale Grocers (AWG) has grown net sales in recent years from $7.8 billion in 2016 to more recent results exceeding $9.0 billion. Net income has trended positively over the same period from $175 million in 2012 to a spiked of more than $225 million in 2014 to a current result near $190 million.

For the year 2016 net sales grew 3% to $9.2 billion. Product price deflation pushed sales lower as did the loss of Albertsons? membership in the distribution co-op. AWG gained 800 new member stores in conjunction with its unification with Affiliated Foods Midwest which increased sales sufficiently to overcome the negative influencers.

Net income for the year was $190 million 4% lower than the prior year due to a corresponding increase in the co-op?s general and administrative expenses.

Strategy

As a supplier to primarily independent and non-national grocers the co-op must retain size in order to compete with larger corporate firms. Years 2016 and 2017 saw its size shrink in Texas particularly in the hotly contested Dallas-Fort Worth market. Associated Wholesale Grocers lost two key members Albertsons (owner of Tom Thumb?s and Safeway) and WinCo. It countered this by uniting with Affiliated Foods Midwest a distribution co-op with some 800 retail stores but the loss of such notable members is expected influence AWG?s posturing within the North Texas area.

AWG continues to build sales of its billion-dollar private-label products line which includes the Best Choice IGA and Always Save brands. In addition to marketing the products as lower-cost alternatives to brand-name products the co-op has been investing in efforts to make sure the quality of its private-label items matches competing national brands. The company also owns and operates the Value Merchandisers Company (VMC) which offers some 22000 nonfood items to its members including health and beauty care general merchandise and seasonal and promotional products.

Operating in a fragmented business AWG competes with a large number of local and regional suppliers as well as distributors of specialty items. The food wholesale business also has its share of national giants including C & S Wholesale Nash-Finch and wholesale grocery and retail company SUPERVALU.

EXECUTIVES

Svp And Division Manager Nashville, Mike Danes
Evp And Chief Marketing Officer, Steve Arnold
Svp And Division Manager Memphis, Gary Jennings
Svp Finance, David Carl
Svp Distribution, Richard Kearns
Svp And Cio, Jon Payne
Svp And Division Manager Fort Worth, Linda Lawson
Svp Springfield, Tim Bellanti

President And Ceo, David Smith
Svp And Division Manager Oklahoma City, Danny Lane
Svp Grocery Products, Dan Funk
Svp Perishables, Jerry Edney
Svp And Division Manager Gulf Coast, Bob Durand
President Valu Merchandisers Company (vmc), Dave Sutton
President Always Fresh, Michael Schumacher
Vp Sales And Merchandising Memphis Division, David Gates
Senior Vice President, Maurice Henry
Vice President Of Sales Great Lakes, Sonny Leon
Director, Bob Hufford
Vice Chairman, Don Woods

LOCATIONS

HQ: ASSOCIATED WHOLESALE GROCERS, INC.
5000 KANSAS AVE, KANSAS CITY, KS 661061135
Phone: 913 288-1000
Web: WWW.AWGINC.COM

COMPETITORS

Affiliated Foods	GSC Enterprises
Affiliated Foods Midwest	H. T. Hackney
	McLane
Albertsons	SUPERVALU
Alex Lee	SpartanNash
C&S Wholesale	Wakefern Food
Central Grocers	Wal-Mart
Dearborn Wholesale Grocers	WinCo Foods

HISTORICAL FINANCIALS

Company Type: Private

Income Statement				FYE: December 31
	REVENUE ($ mil.)	NET INCOME ($ mil.)	NET PROFIT MARGIN	EMPLOYEES
12/17	9,703	199	2.1%	5,500
12/15	8,935	198	2.2%	—
12/14	8,934	226	2.5%	—
12/13	8,380	192	2.3%	—
Annual Growth	3.7%	0.8%	—	—

2017 Year-End Financials

Return on assets: 6.4%
Return on equity: 2.1%
Current ratio: 0.50
Cash ($ mil.): 166

ATLAS WORLD GROUP, INC.

Willing to carry the weight of a moving world agent-owned Atlas World Group is the holding company for Atlas Van Lines one of the largest moving companies in the US. Atlas Van Lines' more than 500 agents transport household goods domestically and between the US and Canada; it also offers specialized transportation of items such as trade show exhibits fine art and electronics. Atlas Van Lines International provides international corporate relocation and freight forwarding services. Its Atlas Canada unit moves household goods in that country while American Red Ball International specializes in military relocations and serves van lines outside Atlas' network.

Operations

Atlas World Group oversees a family of companies that deliver transportation and related services globally through a network agents and select service partners. Several of its key locations are concentrated in Evansville Indiana.

Strategy

The company continues to grow by adding offices and regional moving agents. In 2013 Atlantic Relocation Systems the second largest agency group within the Atlas Van Lines' US network expanded both its national footprint as well as its local service area in Colorado by opening a new office in Colorado Springs.

EXECUTIVES

Vice President, Steve Hermann
Vice President Human Resources, Nancy Priebe
Auditors: ERNST & YOUNG LLP INDIANAPOLI

LOCATIONS

HQ: ATLAS WORLD GROUP, INC.
1212 SAINT GEORGE RD, EVANSVILLE, IN 477112364
Phone: 812 424-2222
Web: WWW.ATLASVANLINES.COM

PRODUCTS/OPERATIONS

Selected Companies

American Red Ball International (international freight forwarding)
American Vanpac Carriers (international freight forwarding)
Atlas Terminal Company (relocation-related supplies and equipment)
Atlas Van Lines (transportation services)
Atlas Van Lines (Canada) (transportation services)
Atlas Van Lines International (transportation services)
Atlas World Class Travel (travel agency)
Avail Move Management (management programs)
AWG Logistics (transportation warehousing and distribution)
Cornerstone Relocation Group (relocation services)
Smart Move Transportation (containerized shipping)
Titan Global Distribution (logistics)

COMPETITORS

A-Mrazek Moving	Graebel
ALTAIR Global Relocation	Penske Truck Leasing
	SIRVA
AMERCO	Starving Students
Bekins	UniGroup
Budd Van Lines	
Business Products Group	

HISTORICAL FINANCIALS

Company Type: Private

Income Statement				FYE: December 31
	REVENUE ($ mil.)	NET INCOME ($ mil.)	NET PROFIT MARGIN	EMPLOYEES
12/17	842	4	0.6%	726
12/16	795	6	0.8%	—
12/15	845	8	1.0%	—
12/14	878	9	1.1%	—
Annual Growth	(1.4%)	(20.6%)	—	—

2017 Year-End Financials

Return on assets: 2.1%
Return on equity: 0.6%
Current ratio: 1.80
Cash ($ mil.): 9

ATRIUS HEALTH, INC.

Not-for-profit multi-specialty group Atrius Health provides health care services in Boston and surrounding regions. The 900-physician (and some 6000 other health care professionals) medical group operates more than 30 offices throughout eastern Massachusetts providing primary and specialty care to some 720000 adult and pediatric patients. For acute health care services Harvard Vanguard patients have access to more than a dozen hospitals including Beth Israel-Deaconess Hospital Boston Children's Hospital and Emerson Hospital.

Operations

Atrius Health's network of doctors represent more than 50 medical specialties including primary care oncology cardiology and neurology. In addition to providing health care services the group conducts research in health systems clinical trials and epidemiological studies.

Members of Atrius Health include Dedham Medical Associates Granite Medical Group Harvard Vanguard Medical Associates and PMG Physician Associates. Subsidiary VNA Care provides home health and hospice services.

Geographic Reach

Atrius Health has four locations in the City of Boston about 30 locations in Greater Boston and two administrative offices in Newton and Needham.

Sales and Marketing

Atrius Health accepts insurance from most major health plans including Aetna Blue Cross and Blue Shield of Massachusetts Harvard Pilgrim Health Care Neighborhood Health Plan and Tufts Health Plan.

Strategy

Atrius Health collaborates with universities hospitals and other organizations locally and nationally to improve clinical practices and outcomes evaluate the effectiveness of drug treatments and protocols and increase patient involvement in their care. It receives funding from government agencies foundations and other external sponsors.

The system has been working steadily from being a fee-for-service provider to one that relies on value-based payments. Part of this evolution has involved improving efficiency and minimizing waste but it has also launched new initiatives to make more wide-ranging changes. For example its Care in Place program allows nurses to provide care to elderly patients in their homes; this reduces the need for costly emergency department visits.

The group relies heavily on health data analytics to find high-risk populations and intervene to prevent serious illnesses and costly emergency room visits.

Mergers and Acquisitions

PMG Physician Associates joined Atrius Health in 2017; the move added seven new office locations to the group's network.

Company Background

The group practices of Atrius Health include Dedham Medical Associates Granite Medical Group Harvard Vanguard Medical Associates and PMG Physician Associates. The companies work together to coordinate care in a number of ways including sharing an electronic medical records system. In 2015 the groups merged to create one not-for-profit group named Atrius Health. Reliant Medical Group Southboro Medical Group and South Shore Medical Center were no longer affiliated with the group after the transformation.

EXECUTIVES

Cfo Atrius Health And Harvard Vanguard Medical Associates, Thomas M. Congoran
Coo, Mary Dawley
Vp Nursing, Deborah S. Morsi
Interim President And Interim Ceo, H. Eugene (Gene) Lindsey
Chief Information Officer, Daniel Moriarty
Evp And Interim Chief Medical Officer, Michael Pinnolis

Interim Chief Medical Officer, Steven Lampert
Auditors: PKF PC QUINCY MA

LOCATIONS

HQ: ATRIUS HEALTH, INC.
275 GROVE ST STE 3-300, AUBURNDALE, MA 024662274
Phone: 617 559-8444
Web: WWW.ATRIUSHEALTH.ORG

PRODUCTS/OPERATIONS

Selected Specialty Affiliations
Massachusetts Eye and Ear Infirmary
New England Baptist Hospital

Selected OB/GYN Affiliations
Beth Israel Deaconess Medical Center
Beth Israel Deaconess Hospital - Milton
Emerson Hospital
Lowell General Hospital
Mount Auburn Hospital
Newton-Wellesley Hospital
South Shore Hospital

Selected Services
Allergy
Andrology
Audiology
Behavioral Health
Cardiology
Central Patient Registration
Complex Chronic Care Program
Cosmetic Dermatology
Dermatology
Developmental and Behavioral Pediatrics
Ear Nose & Throat
Endocrinology
Endoscopy
Eye Care
Family Medicine
Fertility & Reproductive Health
Gastroenterology
Genetics
Geriatrics
Hematology/Oncology
Imaging/Radiology
Infectious Disease
Internal Medicine
Interpreter Services
Laboratory
Medical Billing
Medical Records
Minimally-Invasive GYN Surgery
Nephrology
Neurology
Nutrition
Obstetrics/Gynecology
Occupational
Hand Therapy
Orthopedics & Sports Medicine
Pain Management
Palliative Care
Pediatrics
Pharmacy
Physical Therapy
Podiatry
Pulmonology
Rheumatology
Speech and Language Therapy
Surgery
Travel Medicine
Urgent Care
Urology
Weight Management/HMR®; Program

COMPETITORS

Boston Medical Center
 Hallmark Health
 Massachusetts General
 Hospital
St. Elizabeth's
 Medical Center
Winchester Healthcare

HISTORICAL FINANCIALS

Company Type: Private

Income Statement — FYE: December 31

	REVENUE ($ mil.)	NET INCOME ($ mil.)	NET PROFIT MARGIN	EMPLOYEES
12/15	1,577	(28)	—	3,906
12/14	28	(0)	—	—
12/01	0	0	—	—
Annual Growth	—	—	—	—

2015 Year-End Financials
Return on assets: 18.5%   Cash ($ mil.): 118
Return on equity: (-1.8%)
Current ratio: —

ATTORNEY GENERAL, TEXAS

EXECUTIVES

Exec Dir, Ken Paxton
Cfo, Greg Herbert
Sergeant, Ingrid Retzer
Sergeant, Lamont Smith
Coordinator, Meghan Rainwater
Analyst, Dale Oliverio
Administrator, Jarrod Walton
Assistant District, Chari Kelly
Deputy Chief of Staff, Reed Clay

LOCATIONS

HQ: ATTORNEY GENERAL, TEXAS
300 W 15TH ST, AUSTIN, TX 787011649
Phone: 512 475-4375
Web: WWW.TEXASATTORNEYGENERAL.GOV

HISTORICAL FINANCIALS

Company Type: Private

Income Statement — FYE: August 31

	REVENUE ($ mil.)	NET INCOME ($ mil.)	NET PROFIT MARGIN	EMPLOYEES
08/16	659	45	6.8%	4,202
08/15	561	8	1.5%	—
08/14	571	(6)	—	—
08/06	0	0	—	—
Annual Growth	—	—	—	—

2016 Year-End Financials
Return on assets: 2.0%   Cash ($ mil.): 87
Return on equity: 6.8%
Current ratio: 1.40

AUBURN UNIVERSITY

Most of us bleed red but studentsA and alumni ofA this university bleed auburn. One of the largest schools in the South Auburn University has an enrollment of more than 30000 students on two campuses andA offersA bachelors master's and doctoral degrees in more than 140 different fields of study through about a dozen colleges and schools. Fields of study include agriculture business education construction forestry and mathematics and science as well as medical fields includingA nursingA pharmacy and veterinary medicine.A Auburn has 1200 faculty members and a student-to-teacher ratioA of 18:1.

Operations

Unique research institutes at Auburn include the Space Research Institute the National Center for Asphalt Technology the Alabama Agricultural Experiment Station and the Canine and Detection Research Institute.

Geographic Reach

Auburn's main campus is in Auburn Alabama.A The universityA alsoA has a branch campus in Montgomery Alabama. More than 800 students participate in the university's study abroad programs each year.

Financial Performance

Auburn reported a 5%A rise in revenues to some $602 millionA in 2012 due to increased income from tuition and fees state and local grants and contracts and sales and services from educational departments. Net income fell 12% to $87 millionA in 2012 however due to higher operating expenses from benefits and compensation as well as due to the absence of federal stimulus funds (streamed through the state during 2011).

Company Background

Auburn was founded by the Alabama Conference of the Methodist Episcopal Church in 1856 as the East Alabama Male College. It became a state land-grantA institution in 1872 (known as the Agricultural and Mechanical College of Alabama)A and adopted its current name in 1960. The university is governed by a board of trustees appointed by the Alabama governor.

EXECUTIVES

Pres, Jay Gogue
Exec V Pres, Donald L Large Jr
Vp Academic Affairs and Provos, Mary Ellen Mazey
Coordinator, Amy Douglas
Alumni Professor, Chwan Hwa Wu
Trustee, Paul J Spina Jr
Assistant Professor, Glendia Edwards
Assistant Professor, James Smith
Assistant Professor, Leonard Laroux
Assistant Professor, Joan Powell
Assistant Professor, Lisa W Kensler
Auditors: PRICEWATERHOUSECOOPERS LLP BI

LOCATIONS

HQ: AUBURN UNIVERSITY
107 SAMFORD HALL, AUBURN, AL 368490001
Phone: 334 844-4539
Web: WWW.AUBURN.EDU

PRODUCTS/OPERATIONS

Selected Colleges and Schools
College of Agriculture
College of Architecture Design and Construction
College of Business
College of Education
College of Human Sciences
College of Liberal Arts
College of Sciences and Mathematics
College of Veterinary Medicine
Graduate School
Harrison School of Pharmacy
Honors College
Samuel Ginn College of Engineering
School of Forestry and Wildlife Sciences
School of Nursing

HISTORICAL FINANCIALS

Company Type: Private

Income Statement   FYE: September 30

	REVENUE ($ mil.)	NET INCOME ($ mil.)	NET PROFIT MARGIN	EMPLOYEES
09/17	805	79	9.9%	6,000
09/16	775	129	16.8%	—
09/11	574	99	17.3%	—
09/10	525	110	21.1%	—
Annual Growth	6.3%	(4.6%)	—	—

2017 Year-End Financials

Return on assets: 7.9%
Return on equity: 9.9%
Current ratio: 0.50
Cash ($ mil.): 143

AUGUSTA HEALTH CARE, INC.

EXECUTIVES

Ceo-Pres, Mary N Mannix
Chb, Stewart Crow
President, Richard H Graham
Cfo, John Heider
Chief of Medicine, Kevin Kollar
Sales and Marketing Assistant, Brian McGill
Chief of Anesthesiology, Jacob Chacko
Manager, Randy Gregory
Director, George Lindbeck
Manager, Kent Colvin
Human Resources Director, Mignon Holly

LOCATIONS

HQ: AUGUSTA HEALTH CARE, INC.
78 MEDICAL CENTER DR, FISHERSVILLE, VA 229392332
Phone: 540 332-4000
Web: WWW.AUGUSTAHEALTH.COM

HISTORICAL FINANCIALS

Company Type: Private

Income Statement   FYE: December 31

	REVENUE ($ mil.)	NET INCOME ($ mil.)	NET PROFIT MARGIN	EMPLOYEES
12/17	315	59	18.9%	2,100
12/16	296	31	10.5%	—
12/14	254	50	20.0%	—
12/13	246	76	31.1%	—
Annual Growth	6.3%	(6.1%)	—	—

2017 Year-End Financials

Return on assets: 4.2%
Return on equity: 18.9%
Current ratio: 1.30
Cash ($ mil.): 24

AURORA BAYCARE MEDICAL CENTER

EXECUTIVES

Pres, Daniel Meyer
Vice President, J Richard Ludgin MD JD
Vice President, Gwendolyn Christensen
Vice President, Heather Schroeder
Director, Chuck Geurts
Coordinator, Heather Vardon
Director of Operating Room, Maria Klim
Vice-President Finance, Sandra Ewald
Director, Tom Ginter
Registered Nurse, Rose Sommerfeldt
Radiologist, Wolfgang F Dahnert

LOCATIONS

HQ: AURORA BAYCARE MEDICAL CENTER
2845 GREENBRIER RD, GREEN BAY, WI 543116519
Phone: 920 288-8000
Web: WWW.AURORABAYCARE.COM

HISTORICAL FINANCIALS

Company Type: Private

Income Statement   FYE: December 31

	REVENUE ($ mil.)	NET INCOME ($ mil.)	NET PROFIT MARGIN	EMPLOYEES
12/17	440	121	27.6%	95
12/16	419	113	27.0%	—
12/15	375	105	28.1%	—
12/14	341	116	34.0%	—
Annual Growth	8.8%	1.5%	—	—

2017 Year-End Financials

Return on assets: 3.8%
Return on equity: 27.6%
Current ratio: 1.00
Cash ($ mil.): —

AURORA HEALTH CARE METRO, INC

EXECUTIVES

President, Marie Golanowski
Project Sys Dev, Shafei Fahim
Specialist, John Halverson
Human Resources Director, Heidi Grow
Chief of Medicine, Scott Hardin
Coordinator, Amy Confare
Director, Mark Prodoehl
Manager of Information, Tim Harden
Surgery Director, John Niedziejko
Internal Auditor, Kerry Engels
Supervisor, Steve Lamonte

LOCATIONS

HQ: AURORA HEALTH CARE METRO, INC
2900 W OKLAHOMA AVE, MILWAUKEE, WI 532154330
Phone: 414 649-6000
Web: WWW.AURORASTLUKES.ORG

HISTORICAL FINANCIALS

Company Type: Private

Income Statement   FYE: December 31

	REVENUE ($ mil.)	NET INCOME ($ mil.)	NET PROFIT MARGIN	EMPLOYEES
12/17	1,428	141	9.9%	4,000
12/16	1,416	164	11.6%	—
Annual Growth	0.8%	(14.0%)	—	—

2017 Year-End Financials

Return on assets: 4.0%
Return on equity: 9.9%
Current ratio: 19.30
Cash ($ mil.): 1,804

AURORA HEALTH CARE, INC.

EXECUTIVES

Ceo-Pres, Nick Turkal
Clinic Manager, Anna Biancuzzo
Supervisor Loss Prevention, Arthur Smith
Environmental Manager, Brad Winnie
Manager of Distribution, David Orlovsky
Recruiter, Debbie Gast
Certified Clinical Research Co, Debra Smith
Operations Manager, Ellen Whitehall
Director Hospice, Glenn Ragalie
Human Resources Assistant, Jean Yunker
Lead Project Coordinator, Michele Johnson
Auditors: DELOITTE & TOUCHE LLP MILWAUK

LOCATIONS

HQ: AURORA HEALTH CARE, INC.
 750 W VIRGINIA ST, MILWAUKEE, WI 532041539
Phone: 414 647-3000

HISTORICAL FINANCIALS

Company Type: Private

Income Statement				FYE: December 31
	REVENUE ($ mil.)	NET INCOME ($ mil.)	NET PROFIT MARGIN	EMPLOYEES
12/17	5,334	437	8.2%	30,000
12/16	5,124	385	7.5%	—
12/15	4,930	428	8.7%	—
Annual Growth	4.0%	1.1%	—	—

2017 Year-End Financials

Return on assets: 4.6% Cash ($ mil.): 192
Return on equity: 8.2%
Current ratio: 1.10

AURORA PUBLIC SCHOOLS

EXECUTIVES

Supt, Rico Munn
Contrl, Gina Lanier
Chief Operating Officer, Anthony Sturges
Board of Directors, Dawn Mills
Project Manager, Guillermo Barriga
Assistant, Tonia Norman
Education Specialist, Jim McDermott
Executive Officer, Matthew Eckert
Coordinator, Stephanie Gianneschi
Assistant, Christopher Capron
Assistant To Director of M, Debra Stoller
Auditors: BKD LLP DENVER COLORADO

LOCATIONS

HQ: AURORA PUBLIC SCHOOLS
 15701 E 1ST AVE STE 106, AURORA, CO 800119037
Phone: 303 344-8060
Web: WWW.AURORAK12.ORG

HISTORICAL FINANCIALS

Company Type: Private

Income Statement				FYE: June 30
	REVENUE ($ mil.)	NET INCOME ($ mil.)	NET PROFIT MARGIN	EMPLOYEES
06/18	492	(8)	—	6,000
06/17	466	193	41.5%	—
06/16	451	(8)	—	—
06/15	420	(25)	—	—
Annual Growth	5.4%	—	—	—

2018 Year-End Financials

Return on assets: 4.2% Cash ($ mil.): 102
Return on equity: (-1.7%)
Current ratio: 1.60

AVAYA HOLDINGS CORP.

EXECUTIVES

Chb, Charles H Giancarlo
Pres-Ceo, Kevin J Kennedy
Sr V Pres-Cfo, David Vellequette
Sr V Pres-CIO, Fariborz Ebrahimi
Sr V Pres-Cmo, Morag Lucey
Sr V Pres-General Counsel, Amy Fliegelman Olli
Chief Revenue Officer, Tara Dunning
Pres-Avaya Services, Ed Nalbandian
Vp-System Integrator Relations, Ron Griggs
Pres-Strategic Partners, Dino Di Palma
Board Member, Ronald Rittenmeyer

LOCATIONS

HQ: AVAYA HOLDINGS CORP.
 4655 GREAT AMERICA PKWY, SANTA CLARA, CA 950541236
Phone: 908 953-6000
Web: WWW.AVAYA.COM

COMPETITORS

Alcatel-Lucent	Logitech
Aspect Software	Mitel Networks
Brocade Communications	NEC
Cisco Systems	NSN
Fujitsu	ShoreTel
Hitachi	Tellabs
Huawei Technologies	ZTE

HISTORICAL FINANCIALS

Company Type: Private

Income Statement				FYE: September 30
	REVENUE ($ mil.)	NET INCOME ($ mil.)	NET PROFIT MARGIN	EMPLOYEES
09/15	4,081	(168)	—	11,701
09/14	4,371	(253)	—	—
09/13	4,708	(376)	—	—
09/11	5,547	(863)	—	—
Annual Growth	(7.4%)	—	—	—

2015 Year-End Financials

Return on assets: 9.3% Cash ($ mil.): 323
Return on equity: (-4.1%)
Current ratio: 0.60

AVERITT EXPRESS INCORPORATED

EXECUTIVES

Pres, Gary D Sasser
Exec V Pres, Phil Pierce
Exec V Pres, George Johnson
Corporate Os and D Reliance Ne, Ashley Ferrell
Senior Site Manager, Benji Brown
Flatbed Area Manager, Bryan Aldridge
Associate Open Line, Connie Glover
Center Director, Dewayne Williams
Admin and Osd, Dora Allman
Operations Manager, Dwayne Gribble
Inside Sales Representative, Hannah Fox
Auditors: DUNCAN WHEELER & WILKERSON P

LOCATIONS

HQ: AVERITT EXPRESS INCORPORATED
 1415 NEAL ST, COOKEVILLE, TN 385014328
Phone: 931 526-3306
Web: WWW.AVERITTEXPRESS.COM

HISTORICAL FINANCIALS

Company Type: Private

Income Statement				FYE: December 31
	REVENUE ($ mil.)	NET INCOME ($ mil.)	NET PROFIT MARGIN	EMPLOYEES
12/17	1,157	93	8.1%	8,210
12/16	1,097	52	4.8%	—
12/15	1,104	52	4.8%	—
12/14	1,088	55	5.1%	—
Annual Growth	2.1%	18.8%	—	—

2017 Year-End Financials

Return on assets: 2.5% Cash ($ mil.): 132
Return on equity: 8.1%
Current ratio: 3.00

AVERITT EXPRESS, INC.

Small loads add up at Averitt Express. The company provides less-than-truckload (LTL) freight transportation service. (LTL carriers combine freight from multiple shippers into a single trailer.) It operates a fleet of about 4100 tractors and 12250 trailers from a network of 80 terminals. Averitt Express directly serves the southern US and Mexico and it provides service elsewhere in North America through partnerships with other carriers such as Lakeville Motor Express and DATS. The company also offers truckload and expedited freight transportation along with logistics warehousing and international freight forwarding. Customers have included Home Depot Shoe Carnival and V.F. Corporation.

Geographic Reach

Averitt Express has a total of roughly 140 facilities that serve thousands of points throughout the Southern US (in about 20 states) Canada Mexico and the Caribbean.

Strategy

The company aims to grow from solely a LTL carrier based in the Southeast to an international transportation and logistics company. To this end it continues to strategically broaden its geographic reach and range of services. Averitt Express over the years has launched a new business unit zeroing in on retailers in need of distribution services. The new unit Averitt Retail Distribution Services offers customized delivery services catering to the unique requirements of retailers and is targeting retailers needing delivery in large Southern markets.

EXECUTIVES

President And Ceo, Gary D. Sasser
Evp And Coo, Wayne Spain
Evp Sales And Marketing, Phil Pierce
Evp And Cfo, George Johnson
Auditors: DUNCAN WHEELER & WILKERSON P

LOCATIONS

HQ: AVERITT EXPRESS, INC.
  1415 NEAL ST, COOKEVILLE, TN 385014328
Phone: 931 526-3306
Web: WWW.AVERITTEXPRESS.COM

PRODUCTS/OPERATIONS

Selected Services
Cross-border/domestic offshore (Canada Mexico Puerto Rico/Virgin Islands)
Dedicated
Expedited
Intermodal
International ocean/air (ocean/air Asia-Memphis Express)
LTL (regional nationwide distribution/consolidation)
Portside
Retail specialized services
Transportation management
Truckload (dry van flatbed brokerage)
Warehousing

COMPETITORS

AAA Cooper Transportation	Old Dominion Freight R+L Carriers
ArcBest	Schneider National
C.H. Robinson Worldwide	Southeastern Freight Lines
Estes Express	Swift Transportation
FedEx Freight	UPS Freight
J.B. Hunt	YRC Worldwide

HISTORICAL FINANCIALS

Company Type: Private

Income Statement				FYE: December 31
	REVENUE ($ mil.)	NET INCOME ($ mil.)	NET PROFIT MARGIN	EMPLOYEES
12/17	1,142	98	8.7%	8,208
12/16	1,088	45	4.1%	—
12/15	1,091	44	4.1%	—
12/14	1,075	46	4.3%	—
Annual Growth	2.1%	28.9%	—	—

2017 Year-End Financials
Return on assets: 2.5%   Cash ($ mil.): 232
Return on equity: 8.7%
Current ratio: 4.60

AXOS BANK

EXECUTIVES

Ceo, Greg Garrabants
Sr V Pres-Cfo, Andrew Micheletti
Evp-Chief Credit Offr-Chief RE, Tom Constantine
Gen Counsel, Eshel Bar-Adon
Exec V Pres, Brian Swanson
Svp-Business Banking Division, Robert Armstrong
Vice-President, Randall Becker
Account Executive, Cari Anderson
Manager, Judy Davidtz

Manager, Rudy Villa
Executive Vice-President, Adriaan Van Zyl

LOCATIONS

HQ: AXOS BANK
  4350 LA JOLLA VILLAGE DR, SAN DIEGO, CA 921221243
Phone: 858 350-6200
Web: WWW.BOFIFEDERALBANK.COM

HISTORICAL FINANCIALS

Company Type: Private

Income Statement				FYE: December 31
	ASSETS ($ mil.)	NET INCOME ($ mil.)	INCOME AS % OF ASSETS	EMPLOYEES
12/17	8,908	150	1.7%	102
12/16	8,162	137	1.7%	—
12/15	6,656	104	1.6%	—
12/14	5,190	71	1.4%	—
Annual Growth	19.7%	28.1%	—	—

2017 Year-End Financials
Return on assets: —   Sales ($ mil.): 483
Return on equity: 31.2%

BABCOCK POWER INC.

EXECUTIVES

Pres-Ceo, Michael D Leclair
Evp-Cfo-Treas, Anthony Brandano
Dir, Nathan Hevrony
Dir, Dale Miller
Dir, Timothy Statton
Dir, William Sigmon
Dir, John H Heffernan
Evp-Admin-Gen Counsel-Sec, William J Ferguson Jr
Vp-Strategic Ops, Douglas J Harding
1st V Pres, James Dougherty
1st V Pres, Edward Dean

LOCATIONS

HQ: BABCOCK POWER INC.
  6 KIMBALL LN STE 210, LYNNFIELD, MA 019402684
Phone: 978 646-3300
Web: WWW.BABCOCKPOWER.COM

HISTORICAL FINANCIALS

Company Type: Private

Income Statement				FYE: September 30
	REVENUE ($ mil.)	NET INCOME ($ mil.)	NET PROFIT MARGIN	EMPLOYEES
09/17	509	10	2.0%	1,120
09/16	678	14	2.1%	—
09/15	627	15	2.5%	—
09/14	746	16	2.2%	—
Annual Growth	(12.0%)	(14.3%)	—	—

2017 Year-End Financials
Return on assets: 8.6%   Cash ($ mil.): 43
Return on equity: 2.0%
Current ratio: 0.80

BAKERSFIELD CITY SCHOOL DISTRICT

EXECUTIVES

Ceo, Don Vereen
Clerk, Bertha Baca
Communications Supervisor, Martin Ramirez
Nutrition Manager, Richard Andrews
Auditors: VAVRINEK TRINE DAY & CO LL

LOCATIONS

HQ: BAKERSFIELD CITY SCHOOL DISTRICT
  1300 BAKER ST, BAKERSFIELD, CA 933054326
Phone: 661 631-4600
Web: WWW.BCSD.COM

HISTORICAL FINANCIALS

Company Type: Private

Income Statement				FYE: June 30
	REVENUE ($ mil.)	NET INCOME ($ mil.)	NET PROFIT MARGIN	EMPLOYEES
06/16	378	31	8.4%	42
06/15	324	(9)	—	—
Annual Growth	16.7%	—	—	—

BAKERSFIELD MEMORIAL HOSPITAL

EXECUTIVES

Ceo, Jon Van Boening
Chb, Gordon K Foster
Chief Staff, Robert L Waguespack
Vp Affairs, R Mark R Root
Dietician, Rachel Larsen
Operations Manager, Gary De Risio
Director, Gary Stevens
Respiratory Therapy Director, Kathy Genter
Infection Control Coordinator, Martha Chapman
Marketing, Michelle Willow
Benefits Specialist, Shana Gonsman

LOCATIONS

HQ: BAKERSFIELD MEMORIAL HOSPITAL
  420 34TH ST, BAKERSFIELD, CA 933012237
Phone: 661 327-1792

HISTORICAL FINANCIALS

Company Type: Private

Income Statement				FYE: June 30
	REVENUE ($ mil.)	NET INCOME ($ mil.)	NET PROFIT MARGIN	EMPLOYEES
06/16	401	19	4.8%	1,100
06/15	423	71	16.9%	—
06/14	373	45	12.1%	—
06/13	338	30	9.0%	—
Annual Growth	5.8%	(13.8%)	—	—

2016 Year-End Financials
Return on assets: 4.1%   Cash ($ mil.): 21
Return on equity: 4.8%
Current ratio: 1.00

BALDWIN COUNTY BOARD OF EDUCATION

EXECUTIVES

Pres, Shannon Cauley
SEC, April Salter
Manager, Rusty Downey
Auditors: RONALD L JONES MONTGOMERY A

LOCATIONS

HQ: BALDWIN COUNTY BOARD OF EDUCATION
2600A HAND AVE, BAY MINETTE, AL 365074180
Phone: 251 937-0306
Web: WWW.BCBE.ORG

HISTORICAL FINANCIALS

Company Type: Private

Income Statement				FYE: September 30
	REVENUE ($ mil.)	NET INCOME ($ mil.)	NET PROFIT MARGIN	EMPLOYEES
09/17	363	35	9.8%	50
09/13	294	32	11.1%	—
09/12	278	20	7.4%	—
09/11	281	26	9.3%	—
Annual Growth	4.4%	5.3%	—	—

2017 Year-End Financials
Return on assets: 1.3%   Cash ($ mil.): 189
Return on equity: 9.8%
Current ratio: —

BALFOUR BEATTY CONSTRUCTION GROUP, INC.

Balfour Beatty Construction is deep in the heart of Texas — and beyond. The company provides start-to-finish project management pre-construction and related services for commercial construction projects. Offerings include site evaluation and analysis general contracting cost consulting process equipment installation turnkey medical facility development capital equipment planning and closeout services. The company works on a range of facilities including hotels office buildings civic centers airports hospitals schools public buildings and retail locations. UK firm Balfour Beatty plc acquired the company then named Centex Construction from Centex Corp. in 2007.

Operations

Balfour Beatty Construction ranks as the fifth largest general builder in the US. The firm is also active in the construction services infrastructure investment and professionals and support services markets.

Geographic Reach

Dallas-based Balfour Beatty Construction has locations in the West Mid-Atlantic and Southeast.

Strategy

The US arm of the international infrastructure group Balfour Beatty Construction is poised to profit from the recovery of the US economy. Indeed the US market has seen a quicker return to growth that its UK counterpart with more private and complex construction projects coming to the market.

To that end the construction service firm is expanding its Houston Division to capitalize on growing demand from the energy and multifamily housing markets in the Houston area. To build its Campus Solutions business which specializes in the construction of education facilities Balfour Beatty Construction absorbed Charter Builders a specialist in educational facilities in 2012. Recent student housing projects include a 1274-bed student housing project at Texas A&M University. Construction of the $104 million project began in mid-2014 with completion and occupancy set for August 2015.

Some of the company's more notable projects include NASA Mission Control (Houston) Texas Stadium (home of the Dallas Cowboys) the Mayo Clinic The James Madison Library of Congress One America Plaza Miami International Airport and Cinderella's Castle at Walt Disney World.

EXECUTIVES

Chb-Ceo, Mark Layman
Exec Vice President, Doug Jones
Exec Vice President, John Tarpey
Sr Vice President, John Parolisi
Exec Vice President, Glenn Burns
Exec Vice President, Eric Stenman
Exec Vice President, John Woodcock
Cfo, Richard Jaggers
Vice President, Mark Crouser
Asst Contrl, Richard Howarth

LOCATIONS

HQ: BALFOUR BEATTY CONSTRUCTION GROUP, INC.
3100 MCKINNON ST FL 10, DALLAS, TX 752017007
Phone: 214 451-1000
Web: WWW.BALFOURBEATTYUS.COM

PRODUCTS/OPERATIONS

Selected Key Markets
Airports
Defense housing
Education
Health care
Judicial & institutional
Rail
Roads

Selected Projects
Air Force Memorial (Arlington VA)
Army/Air Force Exchange Shopping Center (Fort Jackson SC)
Bank of America (Charlotte NC)
Broward County Convention Center (Fort Lauderdale FL)
Burger King corporate headquarters (Miami)
Cape Coral Parkway Expansion (Cape Coral FL)
Carnival Cruise Lines corporate headquarters (Miami)
Children's Hospital & Health Center (San Diego CA)
Cisco Systems corporate headquarters (Research Triangle Park NC)
Disney's Wilderness Lodge Resort (Lake Buena Vista FL)
Duke University Levine Science Research Center (Durham NC)
Harrah's Casino (New Orleans)
Harris Methodist Hospital (Fort Worth TX)
James Madison Memorial Building Library of Congress (Washington DC)
J.P. Morgan International Plaza (Dallas)
Lucayan Beach Resort (Grand Bahama Island Bahamas)
Mescalero Apache K-12 (Mescalero NM)
Music City Central MTA Bus Facility (Nashville TN)
NASA Space Station Control Center (Houston)
Osceoloa County Courthouse (Kissimmee FL)
Port of Miami (Miami)
Southwest Airlines corporate headquarters (Dallas)
United Spirit Arena (Lubbock TX)
Vanderbilt University Medical Center (Nashville TN)
Walter Reed Army Medical Center military housing (Silver Spring MD)
White Sands Missile Range military housing (White Sands NM)

COMPETITORS

American Constructors	Hardaway Construction
Ames Construction	LeChase Construction
Axis Construction	M & H Enterprises
Bechtel	MW Builders
Cutler Associates	McGough Construction
Engelberth Construction	Panattoni Construction
Falkenberg Construction	Rayco Construction
Fluor	Satterfield & Pontikes
G. A. Johnson & Son	Skanska USA Building
	Turner Construction

HISTORICAL FINANCIALS

Company Type: Private

Income Statement				FYE: December 31
	REVENUE ($ mil.)	NET INCOME ($ mil.)	NET PROFIT MARGIN	EMPLOYEES
12/15	3,852	(14)	—	2,200
12/14	3,932	17	0.4%	—
12/13	3,816	24	0.6%	—
12/12	3,459	19	0.6%	—
Annual Growth	3.7%	—	—	—

2015 Year-End Financials
Return on assets: 5.7%   Cash ($ mil.): 69
Return on equity: (-0.4%)
Current ratio: 0.10

BALFOUR BEATTY CONSTRUCTION, LLC

EXECUTIVES

MBR, Mark Layman
MBR, John Woodcock
MBR, Eric Stenman
MBR, Richard Jaggers
MBR, Glenn Burns
MBR, John Parolisi
MBR, John Tarpey
Performance Awareness Cnsltnt, Patricia Laprade
Executive Officer, Stephanie Mills
Project Coordinator, Leonicio Alonzo
Information Technology Interne, Anthony Mathis
Auditors: KPMG LLP DALLAS TX

LOCATIONS

HQ: BALFOUR BEATTY CONSTRUCTION, LLC
3100 MCKINNON ST FL 10, DALLAS, TX 752017007
Phone: 214 451-1000
Web: WWW.BALFOURBEATTYUS.COM

HISTORICAL FINANCIALS

Company Type: Private

Income Statement				FYE: December 31
	REVENUE ($ mil.)	NET INCOME ($ mil.)	NET PROFIT MARGIN	EMPLOYEES
12/16	3,809	13	0.3%	2,190
12/13	3,816	23	0.6%	—
12/12	3,365	8	0.3%	—
12/10	0	0	—	—
Annual Growth	—	—	—	—

2016 Year-End Financials
Return on assets: 7.3%   Cash ($ mil.): 53
Return on equity: 0.3%
Current ratio: 0.40

BALFOUR BEATTY INFRASTRUCTURE, INC.

Balfour Beatty Infrastructure is the North American heavy construction and civil engineering arm of UK-based Balfour Beatty plc. The contractor has expertise in transportation and water infrastructure projects ranging in size from about $3 million to $400 million and specializes in constructing bridges highways tunnels rail lines and water treatment plants. The firm's primary clients are public agencies including municipalities and state departments of transportation. Beyond stand-alone projects it is involved in multiple joint ventures and works on some of the nation's largest public works projects including the design and construction of the $1.5 billion Texas State Highway 130 toll road.

Operations

The company acquired rail infrastructure contractor Balfour Beatty Rail and Fru-Con Construction in 2014 to operate as divisions under its company brand. Fru-Con is an expert in the construction of water and wastewater treatment plants and serves Virginia Maryland and Washington DC.

Balfour Beatty Infrastructure and its sister companies ranked 11th in the Engineering New Record's Top 400 Contractors in the United States in 2014. That year it also ranked 12th in the Top 50 Domestic Heavy Contractors list 14th among the Top 20 Transportation Contractors 10th among the Top 100 Contractors by New Contracts and third among the Top 50 in Domestic Building/Manufacturing Revenue.

Geographic Reach

Atlanta-based Balfour Beatty Infrastructure has a regional office in Wilmington North Carolina. Parent-company Balfour Beatty plc operates in more than 80 countries. Its rail services office is in Fleming Island Florida its rail transit office is in Denver and its Fru-Con Construction office is in Woodbridge Virginia.

Strategy

The infrastructure arm of Balfour Beatty has performed more than 100 major heavy civil construction projects since its founding. The company is focused on expanding its regional presence in existing markets. Roadway contracts with the North Carolina Department of Transportation for instance are helping it grow in the Southeast. In the Pacific Northwest region the company completed retrofitting work on the Seattle Transit Tunnel light rail system. Some of its recent infrastructure projects (around 2015) include the Harry S. Truman Parkway in Savannah Georgia; work on the Golden Gate Bridge; the Sikorsky Bridge in New Bern North Carolina; and Bridgeport I-95 in Bridgeport Connecticut.

Its recently acquired Balfour Beatty Rail group in 2015 continued working on rail projects (including the South Sacramento Corridor Phase II and the Burlington Station projects in San Francisco) in California Denver Philadelphia and Boston. Its Fru-Con Construction projects that year included work in Virginia on the Arlington Water Pollution Control Facility the Broad Run Water Reclamation Facility and the Flat Branc Pump Station & Force Main project; as well as work on water treatment plants in Galveston in Texas and Frederick and Baltimore in Maryland.

Since the global financial crisis Balfour Beatty Infrastructure has relied more heavily on government projects. More than half of the company's work comes from the government which had implemented stimulus programs to kickstart the economy and update outdated infrastructure. The company also has benefited from the realignment of the Department of Defense and several military housing projects.

EXECUTIVES

Vp Fru-con, Michael R. (Mike) Fischer
President And Ceo, Ray Bond
Cfo, Mark Birch
Vp And General Manager Southeast Region, Mark Johnnie
Vp And General Manager Southwest Region, John Rempe
Vp And General Manager Western Region, Crandall Bates
Auditors: KPMG LLP DALLAS TX

LOCATIONS

HQ: BALFOUR BEATTY INFRASTRUCTURE, INC.
999 PEACHTREE ST NE # 900, ATLANTA, GA 303093915
Phone: 404 875-0356
Web: WWW.BBIIUS.COM

Selected Services

Architectural detailing
Concrete
Earthworks
Foundations
Mechanical systems installation
Paving
Structural steel erection
Surface finishing

Selected Project Types

Bridges
Highways
Pumping stations
Roadways
Rail systems
Water and wastewater infrastructure

PRODUCTS/OPERATIONS

Selected Mergers and Acquisitions
FY2011
Fru-Con Construction
FY2009
RT Dooley Construction ($40 million)

COMPETITORS

American Civil Constructors Holdings
American Infrastructure
Flatiron Construction
Granite Construction
Lane Construction
Peter Kiewit Sons'
Skanska USA Civil
Traylor Bros.
Walsh Group

HISTORICAL FINANCIALS
Company Type: Private

Income Statement | | | | FYE: December 31

	REVENUE ($ mil.)	NET INCOME ($ mil.)	NET PROFIT MARGIN	EMPLOYEES
12/15	517	(3)	—	1,100
12/14	555	9	1.8%	—
12/13	509	9	1.9%	—
Annual Growth	0.8%	—	—	—

2015 Year-End Financials
Return on assets: 14.3% Cash ($ mil.): 50
Return on equity: (-0.6%)
Current ratio: 0.60

BALFOUR BEATTY, LLC

EXECUTIVES

Mng MBR-Pres, Mark Crouser
V Pres, Peter Zinkin
V Pres, Leslie Cohn
V Pres-Asst SEC, Joanne Bonfiglio
Treas, Barry Crozier
SEC, Christine Schiltz
Asst Treas, Vicki Sizemore
Vp and Business Unit Leader Fo, Ed Prendergast
Auditors: DELOITTE & TOUCHE LLP DALLAS

LOCATIONS

HQ: BALFOUR BEATTY, LLC
1011 CENTRE RD STE 322, WILMINGTON, DE 198051266
Phone: 302 573-3873
Web: WWW.BALFOURBEATTYUS.COM

HISTORICAL FINANCIALS
Company Type: Private

Income Statement | | | | FYE: December 31

	REVENUE ($ mil.)	NET INCOME ($ mil.)	NET PROFIT MARGIN	EMPLOYEES
12/15	4,690	(18)	—	2,200
12/12	4,378	43	1.0%	—
12/11	4,078	58	1.4%	—
Annual Growth	3.6%	—	—	—

2015 Year-End Financials
Return on assets: 7.3% Cash ($ mil.): 391
Return on equity: (-0.4%)
Current ratio: 0.60

BANNER HEALTH

Banner Health is one of the largest secular not-for-profit health systems in the US. The organization operates about 30 acute-care hospitals (with roughly 4000 beds). It also operates clinics nursing homes clinical laboratories ambulatory surgery centers home health agencies and other health care-related organizations including physician practices and a captive insurance company. Banner Health participates in medical research in areas such as Alzheimer's disease and spinal cord injuries through its Banner Sun Health Research division. The company which has more than 400000 members provides services in seven states in the western US; its largest concentration of facilities is in Arizona.

Operations

Banner Health is one of the first not-for-profit hospital operators to reinsure its employees through its captive insurance company Samaritan Insurance Funding. By offering this service Banner Health is able to diversify its risk improve cash flow and lower life insurance costs by about half a million dollars a year.

The multi-specialty system also operates a health plan in Arizona for Medicare-eligible patients. Its MediSunONE plan includes Medicare and Medicare Part D. The company has joined forces with Aetna in what is called an accountable care collaboration (ACO). An ACO uses technology and a team-based approach to care for the hospital's patients. Doctors and hospitals assume accountability for patient outcomes and are rewarded financially for achieving higher quality greater efficiency and overall better patient outcomes. The partnership also includes a new product called Aetna Whole Health that allows Banner's patients access to a line of Aetna services including their own electronic patient record.

The system's specialty centers include Banner Alzheimer's Institute Banner Concussion Center Banner Heart Hospital and the Western States Burn Center. In addition Banner Health trains 270 doctors per year at Banner Good Samaritan and Northern Colorado Medical Center.

Banner Health also partners with M.D. Anderson Cancer Center to operate a comprehensive cancer center in Phoenix. Services include medical oncology radiation oncology surgical oncology pathology laboratory diagnostic imaging as well as other supportive clinical services. M.D. Anderson has clinical oversight for all aspects of care delivery.

Education looms large on Banner Health's list of priorities — the hospital operates one of the country's largest simulation education centers at its Banner Corporate Center-Mesa. Simulation education is an expanding field in which medical students use computerized mannequins to improve their surgical and medical skills. The school's research has paid off and with Scottsdale Healthcare Osborn Medical Center Banner Health invented the Sapien Transcatheter Heart Valve an artificial heart valve that can replace a diseased aortic heart valve without the open heart surgery that previously was required.

Geographic Reach

Banner Health operates in Alaska Arizona California Colorado Nebraska Nevada and Wyoming.

The system's Banner Health Network is a group of health care providers located in Arizona's Maricopa and Pinal counties.

Financial Performance

Banner Health's income is generally derived through three channels: third-party payers such as commercial insurance managed care agreements Medicare and Medicaid and a small portion of self-pay patients as well as by borrowing funds and receiving philanthropic donations.

Its revenues grew by 29% in 2015 from $5.4 billion to $7 billion; higher net patient service medical insurance premium and other revenues drove that increase. However rising expenses and a $49.3 million loss for ACO Banner Health Network led to a drop in net income which fell 65% to $83.7 million.

Strategy

The health system has grown through construction. Banner Health is nearly always engaged in some sort of construction renovation or upgrading at its numerous facilities. The organization has more than $1 billion in construction projects in progress or completed in recent years. The system has expanded its facilities at Banner Baywood Medical Center Banner Del E. Webb Medical Center Banner Desert Medical Center Banner Thunderbird Medical Center Cardon Children's Medical Center and McKee Medical Center.

In 2015 Banner Health opened a Fort Collins facility on a 28-acre campus with a two-story hospital featuring an emergency department a 24-bed inpatient unit labor and delivery rooms medical imaging women's services surgical services and lab services.

Also that year the system merged with the University of Arizona Health Network (now named Banner - University Medicine) as well as establishing a 30-year affiliation with the University of Arizona. The moves align with its strategy of combining health care provision with medical schools and academic training as well as expanding operations into new markets (in this case the Tuscon region). Banner Health hopes to both improve access to health care through a consumer-focused system and to provide opportunities for medical professionals to remain in Arizona. As part of the merger

the company plans to build a new hospital and renovate an existing ambulatory campus.

In 2017 Banner Health restructured operations including cutting some 500 employees' positions. The move was part of its efforts to become more consumer-focused and included changes to its leadership lineup. Later that year after the restructuring was completed the company began recruiting to fill 1000 positions including spots for specialty nurses and physical and occupational therapists.

Mergers and Acquisitions

Banner Health does occasionally pick up a new hospital through acquisition. For instance in 2015 the company acquired The University of Arizona Health Network (now Banner - University Medicine). As a result University Medicine is the new academic medicine division of Banner Health which includes three academic medical centers: Banner - University Medical Center Tucson Banner - University Medical Center Phoenix and Banner - University Medical Center South.

In mid-2016 the company acquired more than 30 Arizona urgent-care centers from Urgent Care Extra. The centers to be rebranded under the Banner banner are among the expected 50 the company plans to have in Arizona by 2018.

In 2017 Banner Health acquired Medicare-certified home health agency SunLife Home Health which is based in Tucson Arizona. That deal allowed the system to expand its home care operations into southern Arizona.

Company Background

Banner Good Samaritan Medical Center first opened its doors as a 20-bed hospital in 1911. The medical center which is four months older than the state of Arizona marked its 100th anniversary in October 2011.

EXECUTIVES

Evp And Chief Administrative Officer, Ronald R. (Ron) Bunnell
President Ceo And Director, Peter S. Fine, age 66
Evp And Chief Clinical Officer, John Hensing
Evp University Medicine, Kathy Bollinger
Coo, Rebecca (Becky) Kuhn
Ceo Banner University Medical Center South And Banner University Medical Center Tucson, Tom Dickson
Cfo, Dennis L. Laraway
President Western Region, Jim Ferando
Ceo East Morgan County Hospital And Sterling Regional Medcenter, Linda Thorpe
President Arizona East Division, Todd S. Werner, age 50
Ceo Banner Desert Medical Center And Interim Ceo Cardon Children's Medical Center, Laura Robertson
Ceo Platte County Memorial Hospital And Community Hospital, Shelby Nelson
Ceo Banner Thunderbird Medical Center, Deb Krmpotic
Ceo Banner Research, Eric (Bill) Reiman
President Banner Health Network, Chuck Lehn
Ceo Banner Del E. Webb Medical Center And Banner Boswell Medical Center, Debbie Flores
Ceo University Medical Center Phoenix, Steve Narang
Ceo Banner Ironwood Medical Center And Banner Goldfield Medical Center, Sharon Lind
President And Ceo Banner Health Foundation And Banner Alzheimer's Foundation, Andy Kramer Petersen
Cio, Ryan Smith
Ceo Banner Casa Grande Medical Center, Rona Curphy
Ceo Banner Estrella Medical Center, Courtney Ophaug

Ceo Banner Gateway Medical Center Banner Md Anderson Cancer Center Banner Baywood Medical Center And Banner Heart Hospital, Lamont Yoder
Vp Post Acute Services And Ceo Banner Home Care/hospice, Lynn Rosenbach
Ceo Banner Lassen Medical Center, Catherine Harshbarger
Ceo Banner Churchill Community Hospital, Hoyt Skabelund
Ceo Washakie Medical Center, Jay Stallings
Ceo Ogallala Community Hospital, Drew Dostal
Ceo Banner Behavioral Health Hospital, Brian Beutin
Ceo Page Hospital, Brian Kellar
Interim Ceo Northern Colorado Service Area Including: Banner Fort Collins Medical Center Mckee Medical Center North Colorado Medical Center, Scott Baker
Vice President, Tony Blake
System Vice President Information Technology Business Services, Bryce Carder
Vice President Consumer Experience Center, Dave Kriesand
Director Of Pharmacy, E-J Chane
Director Of Pharmacy, Kurt Weibel
Vice Chair, Christopher H. (Chris) Volk
Chairman, Larry S. Lazarus
Auditors: ERNST & YOUNG LLP PHOENIX AZ

LOCATIONS

HQ: BANNER HEALTH
2901 N CENTRAL AVE # 160, PHOENIX, AZ 850122702
Phone: 602 747-4000
Web: WWW.BANNERHEALTH.COM

FEATURED SERVICES

Academic Medicine
Alzheimer's
Cancer
Heart
Insurance (Networks)
Maternity
Orthopedics
Pediatrics
Pharmacy
Physicians & Specialists
Research
Women's Health

COMPETITORS

Community Health Systems	Poudre Valley Health System
Dignity Health	Providence St. Joseph Health
HCA	
Inova	Scottsdale Healthcare
John C. Lincoln Health Network	Tenet Healthcare
	Texas Health Resources
Memorial Health System of East Texas	Wyoming Medical Center
Northern Arizona Healthcare	Yuma Regional Medical Center
Phoenix Children's Hospital	

HISTORICAL FINANCIALS

Company Type: Private

Income Statement   FYE: December 31

	REVENUE ($ mil.)	NET INCOME ($ mil.)	NET PROFIT MARGIN	EMPLOYEES
12/17	7,835	728	9.3%	35,000
12/16	7,633	309	4.1%	—
12/15	6,971	119	1.7%	—
12/14	5,397	261	4.8%	—
Annual Growth	13.2%	40.8%	—	—

2017 Year-End Financials

Return on assets: 2.8%   Cash ($ mil.): 292
Return on equity: 9.3%
Current ratio: 0.60

BANNER HEALTH

EXECUTIVES

Ceo, John Harrington
Director, Jagveer Sandhu
Scientist, Stacey Parman
Pharmacist, William Mostow
Internal Medicine Practitioner, Arvind Satyanarayan
Health Professional, Chukwuemeka Oji
Health Professional, Christopher Dubay
Chief of Medicine, Jeffrey Ronn
Director, Jo Wroblewski
Director, Marci Feddersen
Health Professional, Nonihal Singh

LOCATIONS

HQ: BANNER HEALTH
  14502 W MEEKER BLVD, SUN CITY, AZ 853755282
Phone: 623 524-4000
Web: WWW.BANNERHEALTH.COM

HISTORICAL FINANCIALS

Company Type: Private

Income Statement — FYE: December 31

	REVENUE ($ mil.)	NET INCOME ($ mil.)	NET PROFIT MARGIN	EMPLOYEES
12/16	289	29	10.2%	1,700
12/15	277	26	9.5%	—
Annual Growth	4.2%	11.4%	—	—

2016 Year-End Financials

Return on assets: 2.5% Cash ($ mil.): —
Return on equity: 10.2%
Current ratio: 2.10

BAPTIST HEALTH SOUTH FLORIDA, INC.

Baptist Health South Florida (BHSF) has a good grip on Miami's health. The faith-based not-for-profit enterprise operates 10 acute-care hospitals including a children's hospital in the Miami area. Its flagship facility Baptist Hospital with more than 680 beds provides a comprehensive range of medical and surgical services. The system also includes South Miami Hospital with 460 beds as well as several smaller inpatient facilities in surrounding communities. In all BHSF hospitals contain about 1500 beds. In addition to inpatient services the organization provides ambulatory surgery primary and urgent care diagnostic imaging rehabilitation and home health services. The system is merging with Boca Raton Regional Hospital.

Operations

In addition to Boca Raton Regional Hospital BHSF includes some 50 outpatient facilities and more than 40 physician practices.

Strategy

BHSF's strategic goals focus on organic expansion through new construction and additions but also by acquisitions and through select partnerships when they meet its purposes. Additionally the health system works to improve patient care through medical equipment and information technology upgrades.

Mergers and Acquisitions

As part of an ongoing wave of consolidation among hospital operators BHSF has agreed to merge with another South Florida-based health care organization the not-for-profit Boca Raton Regional Hospital. That deal will close in 2019.

In 2017 the system merged with the not-for-profit Bethesda Health adding two hospitals in Boynton Beach.

EXECUTIVES

Evp And Cfo, Ralph E. Lawson
President And Ceo, Brian E. Keeley
Ceo And Executive Medical Director Miami Cancer Institute, Michael J. Zinner
Evp And Coo, D. Wayne Brackin
Evp And Chief Physician Executive, Jack A. Ziffer
Evp And Chief Administrative Officer, Joe Natoli
Chairman, Rev. William W. White
Auditors: DELOITTE & TOUCHE LLP

LOCATIONS

HQ: BAPTIST HEALTH SOUTH FLORIDA, INC.
  6855 S RED RD, SOUTH MIAMI, FL 331433647
Phone: 305 596-1960
Web: WWW.SALUDEJECUTIVABAPTIST.COM

PRODUCTS/OPERATIONS

2013 Sales

	$ mil.	% of total
Managed Care	1,655	69
Medicare	278	12
Medicaid	122	5
Other	331	14
Total	**0**	**100**

Selected Florida Facilities

Baptist Hospital of Miami (Kendall)
  Baptist Cardiac & Vascular Institute
  Baptist Children's Hospital
Doctors Hospital (Coral Gables)
Homestead Hospital (Homestead)
Mariners Hospital (Tavernier)
South Miami Hospital (South Miami)
West Kendall Baptist Hospital (Kendall)

Selected Services

Addiction treatment
Behavorial medicine
Blood conservation program
Cancer services
Cardiovascular services
Care and counseling services
Children's health
Community wellness
Critical care center
Diabetes
eICU LifeGuard
Emergency
Endoscopy
Executive health
Gamma knife center
Heart surgery
Home care
Hyperbaric services
Imaging
Intensive care unit
International services
Interventional/surgical Services
Laboratory
Maritime medical services
Neonatal
Neuroscience
Nutrition counseling services
Occupational health
Online appointments
Orthopedics
Outpatient/diagnostic services
Pain center
Pastoral care
Pediatric
Pelvic health
Physical and speech therapy
Pregnancy and childbirth
Progressive care unit
Prostate cancer
Pulmonary services
Radiation oncology
Rehabilitation services
Robotic surgery
Senior services
Sleep diagnostic center
Sports medicine and orthopedic programs
Stroke services
Surgery
Weight-loss surgery
Wellness Center
Women's health
Wound care

COMPETITORS

Adventist Health System Sunbelt Healthcare
Boca Raton Regional Hospital
Broward Health
HCA
Holy Cross Hospital Fort Lauderdale
Jackson Health System
Lakeland Regional Medical Center
Miami Children's Hospital
Mount Sinai Medical Center of Florida
South Broward Hospital District
Tenet Healthcare
The Cleveland Clinic
University of Miami Hospital

HISTORICAL FINANCIALS

Company Type: Private

Income Statement — FYE: September 30

	REVENUE ($ mil.)	NET INCOME ($ mil.)	NET PROFIT MARGIN	EMPLOYEES
09/17	608	244	40.2%	16,000
09/15	846	137	16.2%	—
09/09*	616	121	19.7%	—
12/08	2	(1)	—	—
Annual Growth	83.2%	—	—	—

*Fiscal year change

2017 Year-End Financials

Return on assets: 2.9% Cash ($ mil.): 106
Return on equity: 40.2%
Current ratio: 0.50

BAPTIST HEALTH SYSTEM, INC.

Even if you don't root for the Jacksonville Jaguars you can still seek care from Baptist Health System. Baptist Health serves the Jacksonville Florida area through four acute care hospitals and a children's hospital with a combined total of more than 1000 beds. Baptist Medical Center its flagship facility is a full-service hospital that also houses Baptist Heart Hospital. Across the street Wolfson Children's Hospital also cares for the city's youngest residents. The system's satellite acute-care facilities include Baptist Medical Center Beaches Baptist Medical Center Nassau and Baptist Medical Center South.

Operations

Baptist Health's flagship tertiary care hospital Baptist Medical Center is centrally located in Jacksonville and is a full-service medical center representing nearly all major health care specialties. Its Baptist Heart Hospital offers comprehensive cardiovascular care.

In addition to its hospitals Baptist Health System operates a network of about 200 outpatient centers including primary and specialty care physician practices and clinics (including cardiology and cancer care centers) as well as urgent care rehabilitation pharmacy and occupational health locations. In total Baptist Health System has 1200 physicians and handles some 51000 inpatient stays nearly 250000 emergency visits 44000 surgeries and 7000 births each year.

Financial Performance

In 2014 Baptist Health's net revenues increased by 3% due to higher net patient service revenues less provision for bad debts. Net patient service revenue by major payor source was: Medicare 40%; Blue Cross 23%; Medicaid 7%; other third-party payors 25%; and self pay 5%.

The hospital incurred a net loss of $8.9 million in 2014 (a 190% drop compared to 2013) despite the increase in net revenues.

Cash outflow decreased by 102% compared to 2013.

Strategy

Baptist Health is expanding certain programs to cater to targeted population segments in the Jacksonville area. For instance it is expanding its Baptist AgeWell Institute program at the Jacksonville hospital as well as the pastoral care program in Nassau. It is also enhancing its emergency room at the Beaches hospital and is conducting community outreach programs for low-income families.

In 2015 Baptist Health and The University of Texas MD Anderson Cancer Center moved forward with multidisciplinary cancer care for adult patients throughout their region by opening the Baptist MD Anderson Cancer Center.

Company Background

A major construction project was completed in late 2012 with the opening of a new 11-story patient tower at Baptist Jacksonville. The new $200 million tower features all private patient rooms and high-tech surgical suites.

Baptist Health was founded in 1955.

EXECUTIVES

Evp And Coo, John F. Wilbanks
Hospital President Baptist Medical Center South, Ron Robinson
Hospital President Wolfson Childrens Hospital, Michael D. Aubin
President And Ceo, A. Hugh Greene
Administrator Baptist Medical Center Beaches, Joseph M. (Joe) Mitrick
Svp Medical Affairs And Clinical Effectiveness; Chief Medical Officer, Keith L. Stein
Svp And Cfo, Scott Wooten
Hospital President Baptist Medical Center Jacksonville, Michael A. Mayo
Svp And Chief Nursing Officer, Diane S. Raines
President Physician Integration, Edward Sim
Svp And Cio, Roland Garcia
Chief Medical Officer Wolfson Children's Hospital, Jerry A. Bridgham
Hospital President Baptist Medical Center Nassau, Stephen Lee
Executive Vice President Corporate Development, Melanie Husk
Senior Vice President Social Responsibility And Community Advocacy, Audrey Moran
Medical Director, Mark Stich
Vice President Human Resources, Elizabeth Mehaffey
Vice President Of Operations, Keon Falkner
Vice President Of Community Investment And Impact, Melanie Patz
Auditors: ERNST & YOUNG LLP JACKSONVIL

LOCATIONS

HQ: BAPTIST HEALTH SYSTEM, INC.
800 PRUDENTIAL DR, JACKSONVILLE, FL 322078202
Phone: 904 202-2000
Web: WWW.HEALTHMART.COM

PRODUCTS/OPERATIONS

Selected facilities
Baptist Medical Center Beaches (Jacksonville Beach Florida)
Baptist Medical Center Jacksonville (Jacksonville Florida)
Baptist Heart Hospital
Baptist Medical Center Nassau (Fernandina Beach Florida)
Baptist Medical Center South (Jacksonville Florida)
Wolfson Children's Hospital (Jacksonville Florida)

COMPETITORS

Bay Medical Center	Munroe Regional Health
Brooks Rehabilitation	System
Florida Hospital Tampa Bay Division	Nemours Foundation
Florida Hospital Waterman	Orlando Health
	St. Vincent's Health
HCA	System
Mayo Clinic Jacksonville	UF Health Jacksonville

HISTORICAL FINANCIALS

Company Type: Private

Income Statement				FYE: September 30
	REVENUE ($ mil.)	NET INCOME ($ mil.)	NET PROFIT MARGIN	EMPLOYEES
09/17	1,630	304	18.7%	7,000
09/16	1,587	189	11.9%	—
09/09	0	(1)	—	—
09/06	871	49	5.7%	—
Annual Growth	5.9%	18.0%	—	—

2017 Year-End Financials

Return on assets: 12.8% Cash ($ mil.): 93
Return on equity: 18.7%
Current ratio: 1.40

BAPTIST HEALTHCARE SYSTEM, INC.

Baptist Healthcare System which goes by Baptist Health wants to keep all its followers healthy. The system owns eight acute-care hospitals one a long-term facility in Kentucky with a total capacity of more than 2100 beds. The not-for-profit health system's largest facility is Baptist Hospital East a 520-bed hospital in Louisville that provides a wide range of health services with special expertise in cardiology rehabilitation and women's health. In addition to its owned facilities Baptist Health manages Hardin Memorial a 300-bed hospital located in Elizabethtown and Russell County Hospital with 25 beds. The growing Baptist Health was founded as a single hospital in Louisville in 1924.

Operations

Along with inpatient acute care services Baptist Health offers home health care services runs two outpatient surgery centers provides urgent care through a handful of clinics and operates a regional physicians' practice group. It also runs a community-based not-for-profit health care plan Baptist Health Plan which operates across the state and into parts of Indiana and Tennessee. Baptist Health plans to shut the struggling health plan down in 2018.

Strategy

Baptist Health faced major losses during 2017 and laid off more than 500 employees that year. It announced plans to realign its structure and shut down its not-for-profit Baptist Health Plan.

Mergers and Acquisitions

In mid-2017 Baptist Health agreed to buy Hardin Memorial for an undisclosed amount. Hardin Memorial (which Baptist Health already manages) operates some 50 outpatient facilities as well as its 300-bed hospital.

EXECUTIVES

President And Ceo Bluegrass Family Health, James S. Fritz
President Baptist Hospital East, David L. Gray
President Central Baptist Hospital, William G. Sisson
President Baptist Hospital Northeast, Christopher M. (Chris) Roty
President Baptist Regional Medical Center, Larry W. Gray
President Hardin Memorial Hopsital, Dennis Johnson
Ceo, Stephen C. Hanson
Chief Clinical Officer, Timothy Jahn
Cio, David J. Bensema
Cfo, Carl G. Herde
Chief Health Integration Officer; President Baptist Health Medical Group, Isaac J. Myers
President Baptist Health Richmond, C. Todd Jones
Regional Executive And President Baptist Health Paducah, William A. Brown
President Baptist Health Madisonville, Michael A. Baumgartner
Clinic Manager, Sean Sullivan
Auditors: DELOITTE & TOUCHE LLP LOUISVI

LOCATIONS

HQ: BAPTIST HEALTHCARE SYSTEM, INC.
2701 EASTPOINT PKWY, LOUISVILLE, KY 402234166
Phone: 502 896-5000
Web: WWW.BHSI.COM

PRODUCTS/OPERATIONS

Selected Facilities and Operations (Kentucky)
Hospitals
Managed
Baptist Health Corbin
Baptist Health La Grange
Baptist Health Lexington
Baptist Health Louisville
Baptist Health Richmond
Baptist Health Madisonville
Baptist Health Paducah
ContinueCARE Hospital (Corbin)
Owned
Hardin Memorial Hospital (Elizabethtown)
Russell County Hospital (Russell Springs)
Other operations
Baptist East Milestone Wellness Center (Louisville)
Baptist Express Care (various Walmarts in state)
Baptist Medical Associates (medical practice group Louisville area)
Baptist Urgent Care (Louisville)
Bluegrass Family Health (provider-sponsored insurance)

COMPETITORS

Appalachian Regional Healthcare	Norton Healthcare
Catholic Health Initiatives	Pikeville Medical Center
Jewish Hospital & St. Mary's HealthCare	University Health Care
Kindred Healthcare	University of Kentucky Chandler Hospital

HISTORICAL FINANCIALS

Company Type: Private

Income Statement				FYE: August 31
	REVENUE ($ mil.)	NET INCOME ($ mil.)	NET PROFIT MARGIN	EMPLOYEES
08/17	2,688	5	0.2%	12,601
08/16	2,331	1	0.0%	—
08/15	2,136	17	0.8%	—
08/14	1,440	204	14.2%	—
Annual Growth	23.1%	(69.4%)	—	—

2017 Year-End Financials

Return on assets: 3.8% Cash ($ mil.): 207
Return on equity: 0.2%
Current ratio: 1.60

BAPTIST HOSPITAL OF MIAMI, INC.

Baptist Hospital of Miami can treat many vices for Miami residents. The flagship facility of the Baptist Health South Florida health system provides residents of the city with a full range of health care services including pediatric cancer home health rehabilitation neurology and cardiovascular care. The hospital has more than 680 beds and includes the Baptist Children's Hospital which offers a pediatric emergency room and a neonatal intensive care unit. Baptist Hospital of Miami also includes the Baptist Cardiac & Vascular Institute a regional cancer program and a diabetes care center. Baptist Hospital of Miami was founded in 1960.

Operations

Baptist Children's Hospital offers 24-hour emergency care as well as two intensive care units and specialist services including pediatric cancer care. Baptist Hospital of Miami also contains the Baptist Cardiac and Vascular Institute which conducts treatment and research programs. The hospital's international care unit provides services to patients from the Caribbean Latin America and other regions. Other specialist divisions include a sleep diagnostic center and a spine care facility as well as a maternity ward. Baptist Hospital of Miami also operates several wellness centers.

As part of Baptist Health South Florida the Baptist Hospital of Miami is part of a network of six hospitals including South Miami Hospital Doctors Hospital and the West Kendall Baptist Hospital. In addition the health system includes outpatient care clinics including emergency surgery imaging and primary care centers.

Strategy

Controlling expenses through data management quality and wellness initiatives and other measures becomes increasingly important for the hospital and its affiliates as the cost of medical care in the US market continues to skyrocket. Maintaining an efficient organization is also imperative as the level of charity care provided by the system's facilities continues to rise in the face of economic difficulties.

As the largest hospital in the Baptist Health system Baptist Hospital of Miami takes a leading role in technology programs such as medical equipment and data management system upgrades. The Baptist Health network is in the process of installing an electronic health record (EHR) system to connect patient records across its facilities.

In 2012 Baptist Hospital of Miami launched a $90 million construction effort to expand the Cardiac and Vascular Institute. The new expanded institute facility will open in 2016 and will include centers for aneurysm treatment structural heart therapy and endovascular therapy. The project also includes expansion efforts on the hospital's surgery center which will have enhanced capabilities for neurological cardiac and robotic surgery procedures.

EXECUTIVES

Prin, William W White
Chm, Calvin Babcock
Cfo, Ralph Lawson
Treas, Manuel Lasaga
Chief of Pediatrics, Ernesto Valdez
Director, George Weiss
Coordinator, Suzanne Balbosa
Director, Olga Manrique
Pulmonary Disease Specialist, Mark J Hauser
Internal Medicine Practitioner, Ivette Acosta-Trant
Internal Medicine Practitioner, Nick Zilieris

LOCATIONS

HQ: BAPTIST HOSPITAL OF MIAMI, INC.
8900 N KENDALL DR, MIAMI, FL 331762197
Phone: 786 596-1960
Web: WWW.BAPTISTHEALTH.NET

PRODUCTS/OPERATIONS

Selected Centers and Services

Baptist Cardiac & Vascular Institute (Heart Care)
Baptist Children's Hospital (Pediatrics)
Breast Care
Cancer Services
Center for Spine Care
Children's Cancer Services
Children's Emergency Center
Clinical Research Trials
Community Wellness
Critical Care/eICU LifeGuard
Diabetes Care
Diagnostic Imaging
Emergency Services
Endoscopy
Gynecology
Home Care
Intensive Care
International Services
Interventional
Maternity
Neonatal Intensive Care Unit
Neuroscience Center
Neurosurgery
Orthopedic Services
Pain Management
Physical & Speech Therapy
Pulmonary Services
Rehabilitation Services
Robotic Surgery
Senior Services
Sleep Diagnostic Center
Spine Care
Stroke Services
Surgery
Women's Services

COMPETITORS

Broward Health
H. Lee Moffitt Cancer Center & Research Institute
HCA
Jackson Health System
Larkin Community Hospital
Miami Children's Hospital
Mount Sinai Medical Center of Florida
South Broward Hospital District
University of Miami Hospital

HISTORICAL FINANCIALS

Company Type: Private

Income Statement				FYE: December 31
	REVENUE ($ mil.)	NET INCOME ($ mil.)	NET PROFIT MARGIN	EMPLOYEES
12/17*	1,004	73	7.3%	4,200
09/16	867	39	4.6%	—
09/15	889	108	12.2%	—
09/14	913	140	15.4%	—
Annual Growth	3.2%	(19.6%)	—	—

*Fiscal year change

2017 Year-End Financials

Return on assets: — Cash ($ mil.): —
Return on equity: 7.3%
Current ratio: 0.60

BAPTIST HOSPITAL, INC.

EXECUTIVES

Pres-Ceo, Alfred G Stubblefield
Sr V Pres-Cfo, Joseph Felkner
President, Mark Faulkner
Vice President, Sandy Rogers
Sr Vice President, Gary Bembry
Vice President, Bob Harriman
Sr Vice President, Kent Skolrood
Vice President, David Wildebrandt
Cfo, Kerry Vermillion
Chief Technical Officer, Brian Matson
Sr Vice President, Scott Raynes

LOCATIONS

HQ: BAPTIST HOSPITAL, INC.
1000 W MORENO ST, PENSACOLA, FL 325012316
Phone: 850 434-4011
Web: WWW.EBAPTISTHEALTHCARE.ORG

HISTORICAL FINANCIALS

Company Type: Private

Income Statement				FYE: September 30
	REVENUE ($ mil.)	NET INCOME ($ mil.)	NET PROFIT MARGIN	EMPLOYEES
09/17	318	36	11.4%	1,652
09/16	309	36	11.8%	—
09/15	278	20	7.4%	—
09/14	271	23	8.6%	—
Annual Growth	5.4%	16.0%	—	—

2017 Year-End Financials

Return on assets: 8.8% Cash ($ mil.): 143
Return on equity: 11.4%
Current ratio: 2.10

BAPTIST MEMORIAL HOSPITAL

When most of us think of Memphis we think of Elvis Presley. When doctors think of Memphis they think of Elvis and Baptist Memorial Hospital-Memphis. As the flagship facility of Baptist Memorial Health Care the 710-bed hospital often simply called Baptist Memphis offers patients the full spectrum of health care services including cancer treatment orthopedics surgical services and neurology. The campus also features the Baptist Heart Institute for cardiovascular care and research a pediatric emergency room a skilled nursing facility and the Plaza Diagnostic Pavilion for outpatient health care. Baptist Memphis established in 1979 is one of the state's highest volume hospitals.

Operations

Doctors at the hospital see more than 27000 admissions 54000 emergency department visits and nearly 116000 outpatient visits each year. The emergency department houses more than 30 treatment bays. In addition Baptist Memphis' skilled nursing center includes 30 beds. The hospital also operates a 30-bed rehabilitation hospital and a 165000 sq. ft. heart institute for diagnostic and surgical cardiac care. The facility boasts advanced surgical systems including the CyberKnife radiation system for cancerous and non-cancerous tumor removal.

EXECUTIVES

Operating Room Director, Tracy Godsey
Senior Vice President General Counsel, Gregg Duckett
Medical Records Director, Janet Chapman

LOCATIONS

HQ: BAPTIST MEMORIAL HOSPITAL
6019 WALNUT GROVE RD, MEMPHIS, TN 381202113
Phone: 901 226-5000
Web: WWW.BAPTISTONLINE.ORG

COMPETITORS

Methodist Healthcare
Parkwest Medical Center
Shelby County Health Care

St. Jude Children's Research Hospital
Tenet Healthcare

HISTORICAL FINANCIALS

Company Type: Private

Income Statement				FYE: September 30
	REVENUE ($ mil.)	NET INCOME ($ mil.)	NET PROFIT MARGIN	EMPLOYEES
09/15	691	(1)	—	6,000
09/14	663	(47)	—	—
09/13	504	17	3.4%	—
09/12	697	15	2.2%	—
Annual Growth	(0.3%)	—	—	—

2015 Year-End Financials

Return on assets: 1.5%
Return on equity: (-0.2%)
Current ratio: 0.90

Cash ($ mil.): 28

BAPTIST MEMORIAL HOSPITAL-DESOTO, INC.

EXECUTIVES

Ceo, Randy King
Chief of Nursing, Mary Banks
Staff Coordinator, Rosemary Phillips
Internal Medicine Practitioner, Albert Weeks
Director, Cedric Benson
Anesthesiologist, Darron Johnson
Health Professional, Fazila Khaliq
Internal Medicine Practitioner, Jo Wood
Internal Medicine Practitioner, Leonidas Vieron

LOCATIONS

HQ: BAPTIST MEMORIAL HOSPITAL-DESOTO, INC.
7601 SOUTHCREST PKWY, SOUTHAVEN, MS 386714739
Phone: 662 772-4000
Web: WWW.BAPTISTONLINE.ORG

HISTORICAL FINANCIALS

Company Type: Private

Income Statement				FYE: September 30
	REVENUE ($ mil.)	NET INCOME ($ mil.)	NET PROFIT MARGIN	EMPLOYEES
09/16	287	25	9.0%	600
09/15	322	10	3.3%	—
09/14	337	13	4.0%	—
09/13	280	35	12.8%	—
Annual Growth	0.8%	(10.5%)	—	—

2016 Year-End Financials

Return on assets: 4.4%
Return on equity: 9.0%
Current ratio: 0.30

Cash ($ mil.): 7

BAPTIST ST. ANTHONY'S HOSPITAL CORPORATION

EXECUTIVES

Pres-Ceo, John D Hicks
V Pres-Fin-Cfo, Elizabeth Pulliam
V Pres, Kenneth Johnston
Vice President, Robert D Williams
VPresident, Michael Cruz
Vice President, Belinda Gibson
SEC, Emily Kohn
Director of Nursing, Sharon Hutchinson
Administrator, Laura Reyher
Director, Diane Dyess
Director, Eileen Harpole
Auditors: ERNST & YOUNG LLP DALLAS TEX

LOCATIONS

HQ: BAPTIST ST. ANTHONY'S HOSPITAL CORPORATION
1600 WALLACE BLVD, AMARILLO, TX 791061799
Phone: 806 212-2000
Web: WWW.BSAHS.ORG

HISTORICAL FINANCIALS

Company Type: Private

Income Statement				FYE: December 31
	REVENUE ($ mil.)	NET INCOME ($ mil.)	NET PROFIT MARGIN	EMPLOYEES
12/16	477	60	12.8%	2,500
12/15	424	77	18.3%	—
12/08*	285	3	1.3%	—
06/05	0	0	—	—
Annual Growth	—	—	—	—

*Fiscal year change

2016 Year-End Financials

Return on assets: 3.2%
Return on equity: 12.8%
Current ratio: 2.00

Cash ($ mil.): 1

BARNABAS HEALTH, INC.

EXECUTIVES

Ceo-Pres, Barry Ostrowsky
Cao, Stephen Jones
Program Director, Anthony Carlino
Administrative Assistant, Elana Miklaszewski
Executive Assistant, Joan Zwan
Director of Operations, Julie Owen
Associate, Karly Mintz
Bookkeeper, Kisha Chiles
Manager, Maria Nelson
Director of Laboratory, Maria Sterenski
Vice-President, Patricia Balsamini

LOCATIONS

HQ: BARNABAS HEALTH, INC.
95 OLD SHORT HILLS RD, WEST ORANGE, NJ 070521008
Phone: 973 322-5000
Web: WWW.BARNABASHEALTH.ORG

HISTORICAL FINANCIALS

Company Type: Private

Income Statement				FYE: December 31
	REVENUE ($ mil.)	NET INCOME ($ mil.)	NET PROFIT MARGIN	EMPLOYEES
12/17	624	293	47.0%	24,600
12/02	2,159	(92)	—	—
12/01	2,224	58	2.7%	—
12/00	2,006	62	3.1%	—
Annual Growth	(6.6%)	9.5%	—	—

2017 Year-End Financials

Return on assets: 9.8%
Return on equity: 47.0%
Current ratio: 0.10

Cash ($ mil.): 292

BARNES-JEWISH HOSPITAL

LOCATIONS

HQ: BARNES-JEWISH HOSPITAL
1 B J HOSPITAL PLAZA DR, SAINT LOUIS, MO 63110
Phone: 314 747-3000
Web: WWW.BARNESJEWISH.COM

HISTORICAL FINANCIALS

Company Type: Private

Income Statement				FYE: December 31
	REVENUE ($ mil.)	NET INCOME ($ mil.)	NET PROFIT MARGIN	EMPLOYEES
12/15	1,726	68	4.0%	30
12/14	1,664	83	5.0%	—
Annual Growth	3.7%	(18.2%)	—	—

2015 Year-End Financials

Return on assets: 3.1%
Return on equity: 4.0%
Current ratio: 2.40

Cash ($ mil.): —

BARRICK ENTERPRISES, INC.

EXECUTIVES

President, Robert L Barrick
Capital Reporting Manager, Charl Smit
Manager of Projects, John Gillman
Corporate Director, Bernie Gosevitz
Auditors: CROSKEY LANNI PC ROCHESTER

LOCATIONS

HQ: BARRICK ENTERPRISES, INC.
  4338 DELEMERE BLVD, ROYAL OAK, MI 480731876
Phone: 248 549-3737
Web: WWW.BARRICKENT.COM

HISTORICAL FINANCIALS

Company Type: Private

Income Statement   FYE: December 31

	REVENUE ($ mil.)	NET INCOME ($ mil.)	NET PROFIT MARGIN	EMPLOYEES
12/17	534	0	0.1%	35
12/16	491	3	0.6%	—
12/15	552	3	0.7%	—
12/14	781	6	0.8%	—
Annual Growth	(11.9%)	(58.8%)	—	—

2017 Year-End Financials

Return on assets: 1.7%   Cash ($ mil.): 10
Return on equity: 0.1%
Current ratio: 1.80

BARTON MALOW COMPANY

Barton Malow scores by building end zones and home plates. The construction management and general contracting firm which has built its share of sporting facilities also focuses on projects such as schools hospitals offices and plants. Across the eastern US and Mexico the company offers design/build and program management services ranging from the pre-planning stage to completion. Projects have included the Detroit Institute of Arts and Cultural Center and the Baltimore Orioles stadium. Affiliate Barton Malow Design provides architecture and engineering services while Barton Malow Rigging installs process equipment and machinery. Carl Osborn Barton founded the employee-owned firm as C.O. Barton Company in 1924.

Operations

Barton Malow is a general contractor and construction manager. It provides a variety of building services including building information modeling (BIM) planning & scheduling service conceptual and hard dollar estimating services. It specializes in several areas such as routine boiler installation & service foundation & architectural concrete forming machinery moving & equipment installation and procurement & erection of steel building framework.

The company addresses niche markets in its geography focusing on energy health industrial and sports industries along with K-12 education and government institutions.

Geographic Reach

Michigan-based Barton Malow operates about a dozen offices in the eastern third of the US. It also has an office in San Luis Potosi Mexico.

Financial Performance

A private company Barton Malow provides little financial information. However Forbes Magazine estimates its revenue to be $2.4 billion in 2016.

Strategy

Headquartered in a Detroit suburb Barton Malow has historically maintained a healthy relationship with the steel and auto industries. It is somewhat atypical in that it maintains a staff of workers to perform its trade-based services as with boiler servicing and steel erection; other firms commonly hire out such work.

In 2017 the company received a Best Projects award from trade magazine Engineering News-Record (ENR) for its work on a MATS (Mercury and Air Toxics Standards) compliance project with energy client DTE Energy. In that same year the company completed a complete redesign of Bloomfield Hills (Michigan) High School which involved a partial demolition and partial renovation of existing structures and the design and buildout of a new open-plan educational campus.

EXECUTIVES

Evp And Corporate Secretary, Doug Maibach
Chairman And Ceo, Ben C. Maibach
Vp K12 Education, Michael (Mike) Stobak
Vp Central Region, Todd Ketola
Vp Charlottesville Operations, Phil Kirby
Vp Eastern Region And Virginia, Carrie Shaeffer
Vp Southeast Region, David Price
Vp National Sports, Len Moser
President, Ryan Maibach
General Manager Quality Concrete, Chuck Binkowski
Vp Project Financial Control, Michael Dishaw
Svp Southeast Region, Rod Creach
Vp Central Region, Dan Kovoch
Vice President, Jennifer Brown
Senior Vice President Sports Facilities, Harvey Oliva
Vice President, Joe Benvenuto
Vice President, Matt Lentini
Senior Vice President, Bob Grottenthaler
Auditors: PRICEWATERHOUSECOOPERS LLP DE

LOCATIONS

HQ: BARTON MALOW COMPANY
  26500 AMERICAN DR, SOUTHFIELD, MI 480342252
Phone: 248 436-5000
Web: WWW.BARTONMALOW.COM

Selected Locations
Atlanta
Baltimore
Charlottesville
Chicago
Columbus
Fairfax
Jacksonville
Oak Park
Orlando
Richmond
Southfield

PRODUCTS/OPERATIONS

Selcted Services
Architecture and planning
Building Information Management (BIM)
Concrete trade services
Construction management
Design/build
Facility audits
Facility services
  Administration
  Engineering
  Maintenance repair and operations
General contracting
Interior design

Interior trade services
Preconstruction
Program management
Rigging
Special projects
Technology consulting

COMPETITORS

Alberici	M. A. Mortenson
Clark Enterprises	McCarthy Building
Gilbane	Miron Construction
H.J. Russell	Skanska USA Building
Hensel Phelps	Turner Corporation
Construction	Walbridge Aldinger
Hunt Construction	Walsh Group
KBR Building Group	Whiting-Turner

HISTORICAL FINANCIALS

Company Type: Private

Income Statement   FYE: March 31

	REVENUE ($ mil.)	NET INCOME ($ mil.)	NET PROFIT MARGIN	EMPLOYEES
03/18	2,502	11	0.4%	1,600
03/17	2,361	0	0.0%	—
03/16	1,777	(2)	—	—
03/15	1,454	4	0.3%	—
Annual Growth	19.8%	36.5%	—	—

2018 Year-End Financials

Return on assets: 18.9%   Cash ($ mil.): 55
Return on equity: 0.4%
Current ratio: 0.80

BARTON MALOW ENTERPRISES, INC.

EXECUTIVES

Pres, Benjamin C Maibach III
SEC-Exec V Pres, Douglas L Maibach
Treas-Cfo, Michael F Dishaw
V Pres, Ronald J Torbert
Dir, Sheryl B Maibach
Project Manager, Tyler Smith
Auditors: PRICEWATERHOUSECOOPERS LLP DE

LOCATIONS

HQ: BARTON MALOW ENTERPRISES, INC.
  26500 AMERICAN DR, SOUTHFIELD, MI 480342252
Phone: 248 436-5000
Web: WWW.BARTONMALOW.COM

HISTORICAL FINANCIALS

Company Type: Private

Income Statement   FYE: March 31

	REVENUE ($ mil.)	NET INCOME ($ mil.)	NET PROFIT MARGIN	EMPLOYEES
03/18	2,502	18	0.7%	1,815
03/17	2,361	14	0.6%	—
03/16	1,777	9	0.6%	—
03/15	1,454	8	0.6%	—
Annual Growth	19.8%	27.8%	—	—

2018 Year-End Financials

Return on assets: 18.8%   Cash ($ mil.): 80
Return on equity: 0.7%
Current ratio: 0.90

BASIN ELECTRIC POWER COOPERATIVE

Ranges at home on the range depend on Basin Electric Power Cooperative as do other electric-powered items in nine states from Montana to Iowa to New Mexico. The consumer-owned power generation and transmission co-op provides power to 138 rural electric member systems which serve about 2.8 million people. It had generating capacity of 5478 MW (mostly coal-fired) in 2014. Basin Electric's subsidiaries include Dakota Gasification (which produces natural gas from coal) Dakota Coal (markets lignite and limestone) Basin Telecommunications (Internet access) Basin Co-operative Services (property management) PrairieWinds (wind power) and Souris Valley Pipeline (CO2 pipeline).

Operations

The company maintains about 2250 miles of high-voltage transmission 70 switchyards and about 150 telecommunication locations. It generates about 990 MW for participants in the Missouri Basin Power Project (a group of six regional consumer-owned energy entities that built the Laramie River Station in Wyoming). Its generation portfolio includes 4913 MW of wholesale electric generating capacity.

Geographic Reach

Basin Electric serves customers in Colorado Iowa Minnesota Montana Nebraska New Mexico North Dakota South Dakota and Wyoming. The enterprise's generation facilities are located in Iowa Minnesota Montana North Dakota South Dakota and Wyoming.

Financial Performance

In 2013 Basin Electric's revenues grew by 12% due to higher members sales as a result of an increase in higher electricity resales.

The coop's net income decreased by 62% that year as the result of to higher operating expenses caused by an increase in depreciation and amortizations.

The company's operating cash inflow decreased to $306.56 million in 2013 (from $354.18 million in 2012) due to lower net income and a change in working capital as a result of higher customer account receivables and inventories.

Strategy

Basin Electric like all power utilities is under regulatory pressure to lower the carbon emissions from its power production. As part of its commitment to cleaner energy production the company has established two wind power subsidiaries to build wind farms in the Dakotas.

In 2013 Basin Electric signed two power purchase agreements with California-based Infinity Wind Power associated with the development of two new wind projects in North Dakota with a combined capacity is 278 MW.

Company Background

The company generated 437 MW of its total capacity of 482 MW of renewable energy in 2012 from wind power sources. That year about 16% of Basin Electric's generating capacity came from renewable sources.

In 2011 Basin Electric opened the Crow Lake Wind Project (Nebraska) its largest renewable project to date with 162 MW of power generating capacity. Basin Electric's operations are overseen by a 10-member board of directors elected by and representing individual membership districts. Dakota Gasification and Dakota Coal have separate boards.

The not-for-profit generation and transmission cooperative was formed in 1961.

EXECUTIVES

Coo And Svp Dakota Coal Company And Montana Limestone Company, Robert J. Bartosh
Svp Financial Services And Cfo, Paul Sukut
Svp Transmission, Michael Risan
Coo And Svp Dakota Gasification Company, Dave Sauer
Svp Generation, Matt Greek
Vp Marketing And Trading, Kenneth S. Rutter
Vice President Basin Electric Board, Kermit Pearson
Vice President Basin Electric Board, Wayne Peltier
Auditors: DELOITTE & TOUCHE LLP MINNEAP

LOCATIONS

HQ: BASIN ELECTRIC POWER COOPERATIVE
1717 E INTERSTATE AVE, BISMARCK, ND 585030564
Phone: 701 223-0441
Web: WWW.BASINELECTRIC.COM

PRODUCTS/OPERATIONS

2013 Power Generation Fuel Mix

	% of total
Coal	60
Renewables	15
Natural gas	14
Hydro	6
Oil	4
Nuclear	1
Total	**100**

2012 Sales

	% of total
Utility	62
Synthetic gas	13
Lignite coal	7
Byproducts co-products & other	18
Total	**100**

Regional Member Cooperatives

Regional Member Cooperatives
Central Montana Electric Power Cooperative (District 6)
  Beartooth Electric Cooperative (Red Lodge MT)
  Big Flat Electric Cooperative (Malta MT)
  Fergus Electric Cooperative (Lewistown MT)
  Hill County Electric Cooperative (Havre MT)
  Marias River Electric Cooperative (Shelby MT)
  Mid-Yellowstone Valley Electric Cooperative (Hysham MT)
  Northern Electric Cooperative (Opheim MT)
  Park Electric Cooperative (Livingston MT)
  Sun River Electric Cooperative (Fairfield MT)
  Tongue River Electric Cooperative (Ashland MT)
  Valley Electric Cooperative (Glasgow MT)
  Vigilante Electric Cooperative (Dillon MT)
  Yellowstone Valley Electric Cooperative (Huntley MT)
Central Power Electric Cooperative (District 3)
  Capital Electric Cooperative (Bismarck ND)
  Dakota Valley Electric Cooperative (Milnor ND)
  McLean Electric Cooperative (Garrison ND)
  North Central Electric Cooperative (Bottineau ND)
  Northern Plains Electric Cooperative (Carrington ND)
  Verendrye Electric Cooperative (Velva ND)
Corn Belt Power Cooperative (Humboldt IA)
District 9
  Grand Electric Cooperative (Bison SD)
  KEM Electric Cooperative (Linton ND)
  Minnesota Valley Cooperative Light & Power Association (Montevideo MN)
  Mor-Gran-Sou Electric Cooperative (Flasher ND)
  Oliver-Mercer Electric Cooperative (Hazen ND)
  Rosebud Electric Cooperative (Gregory SD)
  Wright-Hennepin Cooperative Electric Association (Rockford MN)
  Wyoming Municipal Power Agency (Lusk WY)
East River Electric Power Cooperative (District 1)
  Bon Homme-Yankton Electric Association (Tabor SD)
  Central Electric Cooperative
  Charles Mix Electric Association (Lake Andes SD)
  Clay-Union Electric Corp. (Vermillion SD)
  Codington-Clark Electric Cooperative (Watertown SD)
  Dakota Energy Cooperative (Huron SD)
  Douglas Electric Cooperative (Armour SD)
  FEM Electric Association (Ipswich SD)
  H-D Electric Cooperative (Clear Lake SD)
  Kingsbury Electric Cooperative (De Smet SD)
  Lake Region Electric Association (Webster SD)
  Lyon-Lincoln Electric Cooperative (Tyler MN)
  McCook Electric Cooperative (Salem SD)
  Northern Electric Cooperative (Bath SD)
  Oahe Electric Cooperative (Blunt SD)
  Renville-Sibley Cooperative Power Association (Danube MN)
  Sioux Valley-Southwestern Cooperative (Colman SD)
  Southeastern Electric Cooperative (Marion SD)
  Traverse Electric Cooperative (Wheaton MN)
  Union County Electric Cooperative (Elk Point SD)
  Whetstone Valley Electric Cooperative (Milbank SD)
Flathead Electric Cooperative (Kalispell MT)
L & O Power Cooperative (District 2)
  Lyon Rural Electric Cooperative (Rock Rapids IA)
  Osceola Electric Cooperative (Sibley IA)
Northwest Iowa Power Cooperative (NIPCO) (District 4)
  Harrison County Electric Cooperative (Woodbine)
  Iowa Lakes Electric Cooperative (Estherville)
  Nishnabotna Valley Rural Electric Cooperative (Harlan)
  North West Rural Electric Cooperative (Orange City)
  Western Iowa Municipal Electric Association (Manning)
  Western Iowa Power Cooperative
  Woodbury County Rural Electric Cooperative (Moville)
Powder River Energy Corp. (District 10 Sundance WY)
Rushmore Electric Power Cooperative (District 7)
  Black Hills Electric Cooperative (Custer SD)
  Butte Electric Cooperative (Newell SD)
  Cam Wal Electric Cooperative (Selby SD)
  Cherry-Todd Electric Cooperative (Mission SD)
  Lacreek Electric Association (Martin SD)
  Moreau-Grand Electric Cooperative (Timber Lake SD)
  West Central Electric Cooperative (Murdo SD)
  West River Electric Association (Wall SD)
Tri-State Generation and Transmission Association (District 5)
  Big Horn Rural Electric Co. (Basin WY)
  Carbon Power & Light (Saratoga WY)
  Central New Mexico Electric Cooperative (Mountainair NM)
  Chimney Rock Public Power District (Bayard NE)
  Columbus Electric Cooperative (Deming NM)
  Delta-Montrose Electric Association (Delta CO)
  Empire Electric Association (Cortez CO)
  Garland Light & Power Co. (Powell WY)
  Gunnison County Electric Association (Gunnison CO)
  Highline Electric Association (Holyoke CO)
  High Plains Power Inc. (Thermopolis and Riverton WY)
  High West Energy (Pine Bluffs WY)
  Jemez Mountains Electric Cooperative (Hernandez NM)
  K. C. Electric Association (Hugo CO)
  Kit Carson Electric Cooperative (Taos NM)
  La Plata Electric Association (Durango CO)
  Midwest Electric Cooperative Corp. (Grant NE)
  Morgan County Rural Electric Association (Fort Morgan CO)
  Mountain Parks Electric (Granby CO)
  Mountain View Electric Association (Limon CO)
  Niobrara Electric Association (Lusk WY)
  Northern Rio Arriba Electric Cooperative (Chama NM)
  Northwest Rural Public Power District (Hay Springs NE)
  Panhandle Rural Electric Membership Association (Alliance NE)
  Poudre Valley Rural Electric Association (Fort Collins CO)
  Roosevelt Public Power District (Mitchell NE)
  San Isabel Electric Association (Pueblo CO)
  San Luis Valley Rural Electric Cooperative (Monte Vista CO)
  San Miguel Power Association (Nucla CO)
  Sangre De Cristo Electric Association (Buena Vista CO)
  Sierra Electric Cooperative Inc. (Elephant Butte NM)
  Southeast Colorado Power Association (La Junta)
  Springer Electric Cooperative (Springer MN)
  United Power (Brighton CO)
  Wheat Belt Public Power District (Sidney NE)
  Wheatland Rural Electric Association (Wheatland WY)
  White River Electric Association (Meeker CO)
  Wyrulec Co. (Lingle WY)
  Y-W Electric Association (Akron CO)
Upper Missouri Generation and Transmission Electric Cooperative (District 8)
  Burke-Divide Electric Cooperative (Columbus ND)
  Goldenwest Electric Cooperative (Wibaux MT)

Lower Yellowstone Rural Electric Association (Sidney MT)
McCone Electric Cooperative (Circle MT)
McKenzie Electric Cooperative (Watford City ND)
Mountrail-Williams Electric Cooperative (Williston ND)
Sheridan Electric Cooperative (Medicine Lake MT)
Slope Electric Cooperative (New England ND)
Southeast Electric Cooperative (Ekalaka MT)
West Plains Electric Cooperative (Dickinson ND)
????

COMPETITORS

Alliant Energy	Nebraska Public Power
Berkshire Hathaway Energy	NorthWestern
	Omaha Public Power
Black Hills	Otter Tail
MDU Resources	Xcel Energy

HISTORICAL FINANCIALS
Company Type: Private

Income Statement   FYE: December 31

	REVENUE ($ mil.)	NET INCOME ($ mil.)	NET PROFIT MARGIN	EMPLOYEES
12/17	2,112	72	3.4%	1,527
12/16	1,561	54	3.5%	—
12/15	1,445	8	0.6%	—
12/14	1,481	49	3.4%	—
Annual Growth	12.6%	13.3%	—	—

2017 Year-End Financials
Return on assets: 9.6%   Cash ($ mil.): 142
Return on equity: 3.4%
Current ratio: 0.30

BATON ROUGE GENERAL MEDICAL CENTER

The first hospital founded in Louisiana's capital Baton Rouge General Medical Center is a not-for-profit full-service community hospital offering patients general medical and surgical care. Through the hospital's two locations Bluebonnet and Mid City Baton Rouge General also provides specialty services for cancer heart and neonatal care. In addition the nearly 530-bed health care facility provides services in areas such as burn treatment diabetes sleep disorders and behavioral health. Baton Rouge General Medical Center is the flagship facility of General Health System.

Operations
Baton Rouge General Medical Center is affiliated with and also serves as a satellite campus of Tulane University School of Medicine. In addition to serving as a satellite campus for Tulane medical students in the Leadership Education Advocacy and Discovery Academy program Baton Rouge General Medical Center also offers a Family Medicine Residency Program an Internal Medicine Residency Program a Sports Medicine Fellowship Program a School of Nursing and a School of Radiologic Technology.

In 2012 the Center had more than 1000 physicians and about 950 nurses on its medical staff and served 153000 patients and had about 91000 emergency department visits.

Geographic Reach
Through the hospital's two locations Bluebonnet and Mid City Baton Rouge General Medical Center also provides specialty services for cancer heart and neonatal care. Baton Rouge General is affiliated with and also serves as a satellite campus of Tulane University School of Medicine.

Financial Performance
In 2012 Baton Rouge General Medical Center reported gross revenues of $820 million and a net income of $10 million.

Strategy
The Center is expanding its infrastructure to keep up with demand. In 2014 Baton Rouge General Medical Center and Lane Regional Medical Center opened a $4.5 million state-of-the-art Radiation Oncology Center in Zachary Louisiana. In 2013 Baton Rouge General Medical Center announced plans to add two floors and 64 beds to an existing patient tower at the Bluebonnet campus a project that will cost an estimated $24 million and which will be completed by early 2015.

In 2013 Baton Rouge General Medical Center completed the steel beam structure for the hospital's patient tower expansion project.

In 2012 the Center initiated OneVision a program aimed at investing in minimally invasive technology and strengthening its physician network. That year it also opened the Behavioral Wellness Center at Jackson.

Company Background
In 2011 Baton Rouge General Medical Center broke ground on a $40 million expansion at the Bluebonnet campus. The project included a new five-story medical office building with 105000 sq. ft. of space and four large operating rooms. Part of the hospital's larger Bluebonnet expansion project the new construction projects follow the surgical services expansion and new heart and vascular tower. The surgical expansion included the addition of four new operating rooms equipped with an innovative hybrid build out and minimally invasive robotics.

The Center which has been an accredited teaching hospital since 1991 first opened its doors in 1900.

EXECUTIVES

Ceo, Milton Sietman
Cao, Ted Lewis
Dir, Chris W Barnette
Dir, Cheryl Matusicky
Dir, Milton Siepman
Auditors: POSTLETHWAITE & NETTERVILLE B

LOCATIONS

HQ: BATON ROUGE GENERAL MEDICAL CENTER
3600 FLORIDA BLVD, BATON ROUGE, LA 708063842
Phone: 225 387-7000
Web: WWW.BRGENERAL.ORG

PRODUCTS/OPERATIONS

Selected Products and Services
Birth Center
Cancer
Heart & Vascular
Pediatrics
Emergency Room (ER)
Behavioral Health
Burn
Gastroenterology
Hyperbarics & Wound Care
Imaging/Radiology
Neurosciences
Orthopedics
Rehabilitation/Therapy
Seniors
Weight Loss
Wellness
Clinical Trials
Limbs For Life
Sleep Center

COMPETITORS

Lane Regional Medical Center	River Parishes Hospital
Our Lady of the Lake RMC	Woman's Hospital

HISTORICAL FINANCIALS
Company Type: Private

Income Statement   FYE: September 30

	REVENUE ($ mil.)	NET INCOME ($ mil.)	NET PROFIT MARGIN	EMPLOYEES
09/15	403	20	5.2%	394
09/09	304	0	0.2%	—
09/08*	281	2	0.9%	—
12/05	2,026	0	—	—
Annual Growth	(14.9%)	280.1%	—	—

*Fiscal year change

2015 Year-End Financials
Return on assets: 7.0%   Cash ($ mil.): 71
Return on equity: 5.2%
Current ratio: 4.10

BATON ROUGE GENERAL MEDICAL CENTER

EXECUTIVES

Ceo, Mark F Slyter
Treas, Cfo, Kendal Johnson
Engineer, Todd Lemmiksoo
Auditors: POSTLETHWAITE & NETTERVILLE B

LOCATIONS

HQ: BATON ROUGE GENERAL MEDICAL CENTER
8490 PICARDY AVE STE 200, BATON ROUGE, LA 708093733
Phone: 225 237-1547
Web: WWW.BRGENERAL.ORG

HISTORICAL FINANCIALS
Company Type: Private

Income Statement   FYE: September 30

	REVENUE ($ mil.)	NET INCOME ($ mil.)	NET PROFIT MARGIN	EMPLOYEES
09/16	400	25	6.3%	17
09/15	403	20	5.2%	—
09/14	406	17	4.3%	—
Annual Growth	(0.8%)	20.0%	—	—

2016 Year-End Financials
Return on assets: 6.2%   Cash ($ mil.): 80
Return on equity: 6.3%
Current ratio: 5.10

BATTERY PARK CITY AUTHORITY INC

EXECUTIVES

Chb, James F Gill
President, Timothy S Carey
Exec Vice President, Alexandria Altman
Sr V Pres-Treas-Cfo, Robert M Serpico
Chief Financial Officer, Robert Serpico
Human Resources, Angela Whitehead

LOCATIONS

HQ: BATTERY PARK CITY AUTHORITY INC
1 WRLD FNCL CTR FL 24, NEW YORK, NY 102811802
Phone: 212 417-2000

HISTORICAL FINANCIALS

Company Type: Private

Income Statement   FYE: October 31

	ASSETS ($ mil.)	NET INCOME ($ mil.)	INCOME AS % OF ASSETS	EMPLOYEES
10/17	1,085	22	2.1%	65
10/03	1,111	(285)	—	—
10/02	801	24	3.1%	—
10/00	878	(12)	—	—
Annual Growth	1.3%	—	—	—

BAYHEALTH MEDICAL CENTER, INC.

EXECUTIVES

Pres, Terry Murphy
Controller, Susan Doughty
Information Department, Bob Mucha
Director, Craig Hochstein
Doctor, Cathy Diven
Network Engineer, Kevin Seiwell
Manager of Management Informat, Kimberly Billings
Doctor, Lawrence Piccioni
Warehouse Manager, David Webb
Board of Directors, Harjinder Grewal
Network Technician, Jason Tanis
Auditors: GRANT THORNTON LLP PHILADELPH

LOCATIONS

HQ: BAYHEALTH MEDICAL CENTER, INC.
640 S STATE ST, DOVER, DE 199013530
Phone: 302 422-3311
Web: WWW.BAYHEALTH.ORG

HISTORICAL FINANCIALS

Company Type: Private

Income Statement   FYE: June 30

	REVENUE ($ mil.)	NET INCOME ($ mil.)	NET PROFIT MARGIN	EMPLOYEES
06/17	583	86	14.9%	2,790
06/16	570	19	3.4%	—
06/15	551	39	7.1%	—
06/14	511	86	17.0%	—
Annual Growth	4.5%	0.0%	—	—

2017 Year-End Financials

Return on assets: 7.1%   Cash ($ mil.): 26
Return on equity: 14.9%
Current ratio: 0.80

BAYLOR ALL SAINTS MEDICAL CENTER

EXECUTIVES

Pres, Steve Newton
President, David G Klein
SEC, Preshie M Wilson
SEC, Charles Langham
Chief of Staff, Larry Reaves
Asst To V Pres-Fin, Leigh Anne Gates
Executive of Information Techn, Sandy Vaughn
Vice President Engineering, Bobby Wallace
Payroll Specialist, Bryan Bartlett
Lab Director, Flora McCright
Lab Technician, Karen Abbott

LOCATIONS

HQ: BAYLOR ALL SAINTS MEDICAL CENTER
1400 8TH AVE, FORT WORTH, TX 761044110
Phone: 817 926-2544

HISTORICAL FINANCIALS

Company Type: Private

Income Statement   FYE: September 30

	REVENUE ($ mil.)	NET INCOME ($ mil.)	NET PROFIT MARGIN	EMPLOYEES
09/15	347	19	5.7%	1,800
09/14	364	38	10.6%	—
09/13	341	16	4.8%	—
09/12	367	3	0.9%	—
Annual Growth	(1.8%)	83.6%	—	—

2015 Year-End Financials

Return on assets: 1.6%   Cash ($ mil.): 110
Return on equity: 5.7%
Current ratio: 2.90

BAYLOR SCOTT & WHITE HOLDINGS

EXECUTIVES

Exec Dir, Paul E Madeley
Director of External Digital C, Jacob Sloan
Vice President of Corporate Co, Jamie Rambo
Auditors: PRICEWATERHOUSECOOPERS LLP DA

LOCATIONS

HQ: BAYLOR SCOTT & WHITE HOLDINGS
350 N SAINT PAUL ST # 2900, DALLAS, TX
752014234
Phone: 214 820-3151
Web: WWW.BAYLORSCOTTANDWHITE.COM

HISTORICAL FINANCIALS

Company Type: Private

Income Statement   FYE: June 30

	REVENUE ($ mil.)	NET INCOME ($ mil.)	NET PROFIT MARGIN	EMPLOYEES
06/18	9,476	754	8.0%	1
06/17	9,084	630	6.9%	—
06/15	7,535	356	4.7%	—
Annual Growth	7.9%	28.4%	—	—

2018 Year-End Financials

Return on assets: 3.6%   Cash ($ mil.): 1,263
Return on equity: 8.0%
Current ratio: 1.20

BAYLOR UNIVERSITY

EXECUTIVES

Pres-Ceo, Robert Sloan PHD
President, Ken Starr
Vice President, John M Barry
Vice President, Elizabeth Davis
Vice President, Tommye Lou Davis
Coordinator, Stephen Rylander
Scientist, Diane Hartman
Assistant Professor, Brent Phillips
Assistant Professor, Lorin Matthews
Assistant Professor, Terry Hudson
Coordinator, Rebecca Derosa
Auditors: GRANT THORNTON LLP DALLAS TX

LOCATIONS

HQ: BAYLOR UNIVERSITY
700 S UNIVERSITY PARKS DR, WACO, TX 767061003
Phone: 254 710-1561
Web: WWW.BAYLOR.EDU

PRODUCTS/OPERATIONS

Selected Colleges and Schools
College of Arts and Sciences
George W. Truett Theological Seminary
Graduate School
Hankamer School of Business
Honors College
Law School
Louise Herrington School of Nursing
School of Education
School of Engineering and Computer Science
School of Music
School of Social Work

Selected Institutes
Allbritton Art Institute
Institute for Air Science
Institute for Faith and Learning
Institute for Oral History
Institute of Biblical and Related Languages
Institute of Biomedical Studies
J. M. Dawson Institute of Church-State Studies

HISTORICAL FINANCIALS

Company Type: Private

Income Statement   FYE: May 31

	REVENUE ($ mil.)	NET INCOME ($ mil.)	NET PROFIT MARGIN	EMPLOYEES
05/18	674	96	14.3%	2,500
05/16	656	(20)	—	—
Annual Growth	1.4%	—	—	—

2018 Year-End Financials

Return on assets: 4.3%   Cash ($ mil.): 75
Return on equity: 14.3%
Current ratio: —

BAYLOR UNIVERSITY MEDICAL CENTER

Baylor University Medical Center at Dallas is the flagship institution of the Baylor Health Care System. The medical center (known as Baylor Dallas) serves more than 300000 patients annually with more than 1000 inpatient beds and some 1200 physicians. It offers general medical and surgical services to specialty care in a wide range of fields including oncology cardiovascular disease and neuroscience. The hospital also features a Level I trauma center neonatal ICU and organ transplantation center. Founded in 1903 the Baylor Dallas campus includes the Charles A. Sammons Cancer Center and the Baylor Research Institute which conducts basic and clinical research across numerous medical specialties.

Operations

The Baylor University Medical Center campus consists of 20 specialty centers for treating a range of medical conditions. Primary facilities include the Charles A. Sammons Cancer Center Neuroscience Center Annette C. and Harold C. Simmons Transplant Institute James M. and Dorothy D. Collins Womens and Children's Center and the George Truett James Orthopaedic Institute as well as a top trauma center digestive care program and heart and vascular unit. The Heart and Vascular Institute conducts more than 50 research studies a year.

Strategy

The hospital received a boost in 2011 when Texas A&M's Health Science Center struck an affiliation with Baylor Health Care System. The two parties agreed to make Baylor Dallas a primary teaching hospital for A&M's third and fourth-year medical students. No hospital in the Baylor Health Care System held such a designation after it became independent from Baylor University in 1997.

As one of only two adult Level 1 trauma centers in the region Baylor Dallas has worked to bolster its emergency services to keep up with increasing demand. To this end it has broadened its Level 1 trauma capabilities increased the size of its minor emergency care area and added more patient care areas. The Riggs Emergency Department treats some 67000 patients each year.

Baylor Dallas' transplant program is considered a national leader in solid organ transplantation and in partnership with the program at Baylor All Saints Medical Center is one of only three programs worldwide to have performed more than 3000 adult liver transplants. The program is also known for its kidney pancreas heart and lung small bowel and blood and marrow transplants.

EXECUTIVES

Vice President Medical Staff Affairs And Chief Medical Officer, Irving D Prengler
Vice President Finance, Bryan Nichols
Vice President Finance Decision Support Services, Lavone Neal

LOCATIONS

HQ: BAYLOR UNIVERSITY MEDICAL CENTER
2001 BRYAN ST STE 2200, DALLAS, TX 752013024
Phone: 214 820-3151
Web: WWW.BAYLORHEALTH.COM

Selected Locations
A. Webb Roberts Hospital
Baylor Charles A. Sammons Cancer Center
Baylor Jack and Jane Hamilton Heart and Vascular Hospital
Carr P. Collins Hospital

Erik and Margaret Jonsson Medical and Surgical Hospital
George W. Truett Memorial Hospital
Karl and Esther Hoblitzelle Memorial Hospital
Baylor Specialty Hospital
Our Children's House at Baylor

PRODUCTS/OPERATIONS

Selected Speciality Centers
Baylor Cancer Hospital
Baylor Center for Pain Management
Baylor Diagnostic Imaging Centers
Baylor George Truett James Orthopaedic Institute
Baylor Geriatric and Senior Center
Baylor Heart and Vascular Institute
Baylor Heart Failure Program
Baylor Motion and Sports Performance Center
Baylor Neuroscience Center
Baylor Radiosurgery Center
Baylor Ruth Collins Diabetes Center
Baylor Sammons Bone Tumor Center
Baylor Sammons Lung Cancer Center
Baylor Spine Center
Baylor SportsCare
Comprehensive Wound Center
Darlene G. Cass Women's Imaging Center
Digestive Care Services
Ernie's Appearance Center
Gastrointestinal and Endoscopy Laboratory
Hereditary Cancer Risk Program
Infectious Disease Center
James M. and Dorothy D. Collins Women and Children's Center
Kimberly H. Courtwright and Joseph W. Summers Institute of Metabolic Disease
Louise Gartner Center for Hyperbaric Medicine
Martha Foster Lung Care Center
Non-invasive Heart and Vascular Laboratory
Reuben H. Adams Family Health Center
Simply Mom's Mother and Baby Boutique
Sleep Center
TINY TOTS Clinic
Virginia R. Cvetko Cancer Patient Education Center
Visual Function Testing Center
W.H. and Peggy Smith Baylor Sammons Breast Center
Weight Loss Surgery Program

COMPETITORS

CHRISTUS Health	Presbyterian Hospital
Children's Medical	of Dallas
Center of Dallas	Southwestern Medical
Dynacq Healthcare	Center
Harris Methodist Fort	Texas Health Denton
Worth Hospital	Texas Health Resources
Parkland Health &	The Methodist Health
Hospital System	System

HISTORICAL FINANCIALS
Company Type: Private

Income Statement   FYE: June 30

	REVENUE ($ mil.)	NET INCOME ($ mil.)	NET PROFIT MARGIN	EMPLOYEES
06/15	1,394	378	27.2%	5,003
06/09	1,072	0	—	—
06/08	155	16	10.3%	—
06/06	937	114	12.2%	—
Annual Growth	4.5%	14.3%	—	—

2015 Year-End Financials
Return on assets: 3.7%   Cash ($ mil.): —
Return on equity: 27.2%
Current ratio: 2.80

BAYSTATE HEALTH INC.

Baystate Medical Center is the flagship facility of the not-for-profit Baystate Health System. It is a tertiary care facility and Level I trauma center that provides comprehensive acute care services

to residents of Springfield Massachusetts and the surrounding region. The more than 700-bed medical center is also a teaching hospital serving as a secondary campus for Tufts University School of Medicine. The Baystate Medical Center campus includes Baystate Children's Hospital a 110-bed/57-bassinette unit that boasts neonatal and pediatric ICUs. Other Baystate Medical Center operations include specialty programs in radiology cardiac care cancer and neurology.

Operations

As the only Level I trauma center in western Massachusetts Baystate Medical Center is responsible for treating the most critical and urgent cases in the region. The hospital is also home to the second-busiest emergency department in the state. Along with performing its own research activities Baystate Medical Center collaborates with the University of Massachusetts Amherst on biomedical technology research projects through the Pioneer Valley Life Sciences Institute. The center is home to one of only about 40 American College of Surgeons-accredited Level I Comprehensive Education Institutes in the world.

Other Baystate Health System facilities include Baystate Franklin Medical Center and Baystate Mary Lane Hospital.

Strategy

In partnership with nine other area not-for-profit hospitals Baystate Medical Center is working to improve its region's access to health care services and overall well-being. Social and economic factors impeding access to care include the community's poverty levels poor housing conditions and lack of transportation. Health conditions include high rates of obesity diabetes asthma and cardiovascular disease as well as the growing incidence of opioid overdoses. The coalition of hospitals aims to improve matters by working together combining resources to increase care capabilities.

EXECUTIVES

President And Ceo, Mark A. Keroack
Svp Coo And Chief Nursing Officer, Nancy Shendell-Falik
Vice President Sales And Marketing, Lisa Hill
Vice President Sales, Holly Dinnie
Vice President Human Resources, Paul Judd
Director Of Pharmacy, Aaron J Michelucci
Vice President Marketing, Walter Hollihan

LOCATIONS

HQ: BAYSTATE HEALTH INC.
759 CHESTNUT ST, SPRINGFIELD, MA 011991001
Phone: 413 784-0000
Web: WWW.BAYSTATEHEALTH.ORG

PRODUCTS/OPERATIONS

Selected Programs and Services
Baystate Children's Hospital
Baystate Heart & Vascular Program
Baystate Regional Cancer Program
Department of Surgery
Regional Sleep Program
Women's Health

COMPETITORS

Berkshire Health Systems
Boston Medical Center
CareGroup
Children's Hospital Boston
Connecticut Children's Medical Center
Harrington Memorial Hospital
Hartford Health Care
Hospital of Central Connecticut
Partners HealthCare
Saint Francis Hospital and Medical Center
St. Elizabeth's Medical Center
University of Connecticut Health Center
Yale New Haven Health System

HISTORICAL FINANCIALS

Company Type: Private

Income Statement — FYE: September 30

	REVENUE ($ mil.)	NET INCOME ($ mil.)	NET PROFIT MARGIN	EMPLOYEES
09/17	1,217	107	8.8%	4,691
09/16	1,095	108	9.9%	—
09/15	1,048	76	7.3%	—
09/13	13	(1)	—	—
Annual Growth	207.7%	—	—	—

2017 Year-End Financials

Return on assets: 5.0%
Return on equity: 8.8%
Current ratio: 0.40
Cash ($ mil.): 65

BEA JAVON HOSPITAL

EXECUTIVES

Ceo, Gary E Kaatz
Emergency Medicine Specialist, George D Tsonis
Analyst, Douglas Lundin
Supervisor, Barry Britton
Doctor, Bharati Roy
Chief of Cardiology, Bill Anderson
Programmer Analyst, Cory Gehrke
Emergency Medicine Specialist, John Rudzinski
Member, Marcia Donaldson
Chief of Medicine, Ray Davis
Training Specialist, Sheryl Andreasen

LOCATIONS

HQ: BEA JAVON HOSPITAL
2400 N ROCKTON AVE, ROCKFORD, IL 611033655
Phone: 815 971-5000
Web: WWW.RHSNET.ORG

HISTORICAL FINANCIALS

Company Type: Private

Income Statement — FYE: June 30

	REVENUE ($ mil.)	NET INCOME ($ mil.)	NET PROFIT MARGIN	EMPLOYEES
06/18	387	14	3.8%	2,200
06/15*	186	22	12.1%	—
12/14	307	42	13.7%	—
12/13	346	49	14.2%	—
Annual Growth	2.8%	(25.9%)	—	—

*Fiscal year change

2018 Year-End Financials

Return on assets: 6.5%
Return on equity: 3.8%
Current ratio: 1.50
Cash ($ mil.): 70

BEALL'S, INC.

Residents of the Sun Belt have been known to leave their homes with Beall's on. The retail holding company operates through subsidiaries Beall's Department Stores Beall's Outlet and Burke's Outlet Stores in a dozen states. The multi-brand retailer has more than 530 department and outlet stores (about 200 are in Florida) located throughout states in the southern and western US including Arizona California Georgia Louisiana and Texas. Products range from off-price clothing and footwear for men and women to cosmetics gifts and housewares. Each chain has its own online shopping destination. The family-owned company was founded in 1915 by the grandfather of chairman Robert Beall (pronounced "bell").

Operations

Beall's Inc. oversees operations of its three operating companies. Beall's Florida operates some 190 stores in the Sunshine State. Beall's Outlet operates about 300 stores in Arizona Florida Texas and Georgia while Burke's Outlet operates more than 190 stores in 16 states.

Geographic Reach

Beall's trio of chain's operate stores in Alabama Arkansas Arizona California Florida Georgia Kentucky Louisiana Mississippi Nevada New Mexico North Carolina South Carolina Tennessee Texas Virginia and West Virginia.

Financial Performance

Privately-owned Beall's rings ups more than $1 billion in sales annually.

Strategy

The company has aspirations to transform itself into a major discount retailer much like its larger rivals TJX and Ross Stores. To that end the company plans to add new stores outside its traditional markets with an eye on establishing a national retail presence. Targets include adding 30 to 50 stores a year for the next several years and raising brand awareness beyond Florida.

With many of its stores in Arizona Florida and California (three of the states hit hardest by the housing crisis and deep recession) Beall's Inc. should have been in a heap of retail trouble. However its largest chain — Beall's Outlet —proved to be quite popular during this recession. Indeed the budget-priced outlet chain outperformed its two sister chains as well as more moderately priced department stores. The retailer has also benefited from the demise of other retailers including Goody's Linens 'n Things and Mervyn's.

The three operating companies share resources provided by Beall's Inc. such as distribution finance loss prevention and information systems. Conversely each chain is responsible for its purchasing product development real estate and advertising activities.

Company Background

Stores operating under the Bealls name in Alabama New Mexico and Texas are owned by Stage Stores and are not affiliated with Beall's Inc.

EXECUTIVES

Vice President Gmm Home, Kelley Wotton-Gantner
Auditors: CHRISTOPHER SMITH LEONARD B

LOCATIONS

HQ: BEALL'S, INC.
1806 38TH AVE E, BRADENTON, FL 342084700
Phone: 941 747-2355
Web: WWW.BEALLSINC.COM

PRODUCTS/OPERATIONS

Selected Retail Operations

Bealls Department Stores (Florida)
Bealls Outlet (deep-discount outlet stores in Arizona Florida Georgia)
Burke's Outlet (11 southern states)

COMPETITORS

Bed Bath & Beyond	Ross Stores
Costco Wholesale	Sears
Dillard's	Stage Stores
J. C. Penney Company	TJX Companies
Kohl's	Target Corporation
Macy's	The Gap
Nordstrom	Wal-Mart

HISTORICAL FINANCIALS

Company Type: Private

Income Statement — FYE: August 1

	REVENUE ($ mil.)	NET INCOME ($ mil.)	NET PROFIT MARGIN	EMPLOYEES
08/15*	1,321	25	1.9%	9,700
07/12	1,232	14	1.1%	—
07/11	1,166	15	1.3%	—
Annual Growth	3.2%	12.8%	—	—

*Fiscal year change

2015 Year-End Financials

Return on assets: 10.5%
Return on equity: 1.9%
Current ratio: 0.50
Cash ($ mil.): 107

BEAUMONT HEALTH

EXECUTIVES

Medical Director Microbiology, Bobby Boyanton
Vice President System Compliance, Edward Grima
Director Of Patient Care Nursing, Randy Whitney
Associate Vice President Corporate And Foundation Giving, Laura Charbonneau
Vice President Finance, Mark Leonard
System Vice President Quality And Patient Safety, Paula Levesque
Vice President Finance, Steve Collard
Senior Vice President Of Human Resources, Andrew Melnyczenko
Vice President Information Technology Service Delivery And Crm, Neha Yale
Senior Vice President Chief Marketing And Communications Officer, Mark Bohen
Executive Vice President And Chief Nursing Officer, Susan Grant
Vice President Financial Operations And Corporate Accounting, Donna Zuk

LOCATIONS

HQ: BEAUMONT HEALTH
3601 W 13 MILE RD, ROYAL OAK, MI 480736712
Phone: 248 898-5000
Web: WWW.BEAUMONT.ORG

Selected Michigan Locations

Lake Orion
Macomb
Rochester Hills
Royal Oak
St. Clair Shores
Sterling Heights
Warren
West Bloomfield

PRODUCTS/OPERATIONS

Selected Michigan Facilities

Health Wellness and Outpatient Care
  Beaumont Bon Brae Center (fitness; St. Clair Shores)
  Beaumont Health and Wellness Center (Rochester Hills)
  Beaumont Health Center (outpatient services; Royal Oak)
  Beaumont Medical Centers
Hospitals
  Beaumont Hospital Grosse Pointe
  Beaumont Hospital Royal Oak
  Beaumont Hospital Troy
Nursing and Rehabilitation
  Evergreen Health and Living Center (Southfield)
  Shelby Nursing Center (Shelby Township)
  ShorePointe Nursing Care (St. Clair Shores)
  ShorePointe Village Assisted Living (St. Clair Shores)
  West Bloomfield Nursing Center
  Woodward Hills Nursing Center (Bloomfield Hills)
Research and Education

Oakland University William Beaumont School of Medicine (Royal Oak)

Selected Centers of Excellence
Cancer
Children's Hospital
Digestive health
Heart and vascular
Neuroscience
Orthopedics
Women's health

COMPETITORS

Children's Hospital of Michigan
Crittenton Hospital
Detroit Medical Center
Garden City Hospital
Henry Ford Health System
Kindred Healthcare
Mayo Clinic
McLaren Health Care
Mount Clemens Regional Medical Center
Providence Hospital and Medical Centers
Sinai-Grace Hospital
St. John Health
St. John Hospital & Medical Center
Trinity Health (Novi)
University of Michigan Health System

HISTORICAL FINANCIALS
Company Type: Private

Income Statement | | | | FYE: December 31

	REVENUE ($ mil.)	NET INCOME ($ mil.)	NET PROFIT MARGIN	EMPLOYEES
12/17	4,438	392	8.8%	35,000
12/16	4,373	286	6.6%	—
Annual Growth	1.5%	37.0%	—	—

2017 Year-End Financials
Return on assets: 4.2%   Cash ($ mil.): 390
Return on equity: 8.8%
Current ratio: 1.30

BEAVERTON SCHOOL DISTRICT

EXECUTIVES

Supt, Jerome Colonna
Asst Supt, Sarah Boly
Asst Supt, Bud Moore
Cfo, Janice Essenberg
CIO, Stephen Langford
Information Technology Manager, Lori Morgan
Chief Financial Officer, Claire Hertz
Coordinator, Jill Bogle
Transportation Director, Chuck Beck
Project Coordinator, Jay Dwyer
Coordinator, Kara Yunck
Auditors: GROVE MUELLER & SWANK PC

LOCATIONS

HQ: BEAVERTON SCHOOL DISTRICT
    16550 SW MERLO RD, BEAVERTON, OR 970035179
Phone: 503 591-8000
Web: WWW.BEAVERTON.K12.OR.US

HISTORICAL FINANCIALS
Company Type: Private

Income Statement | | | | FYE: June 30

	REVENUE ($ mil.)	NET INCOME ($ mil.)	NET PROFIT MARGIN	EMPLOYEES
06/17	529	119	22.5%	4,000
06/16	513	(137)	—	—
06/15	495	431	87.0%	—
06/13	396	(6)	—	—
Annual Growth	7.5%	—	—	—

BEEBE MEDICAL CENTER, INC.

Sea shells on the sea shore can be found near Beebe Medical Center. The health care provider offers emergency inpatient long-term care women's health and other medical services to residents of Sussex County Delaware. The hospital is located in the town of Lewes near Rehoboth Beach. It hasA approximatelyA 210 beds and offers specialized services including cardiology orthopedic rehabilitation and oncology treatments. Beebe Medical Center offers outpatientA services includingA woundA care diabetes managementA surgery radiology and sleep disorder diagnosis. It alsoA operatesA senior care centers home health agenciesA medical laboratories and a nursing school.

Operations
Beebe Medical Center has a staff of some 1400 health professionals including about 300 doctors. It handles some 50000 emergency room visits per year. In addition to the primary hospital facilities the health care provider operates the Beebe Health Campus (outpatient services) and theA nearby Millville Emergency Center (a summertime clinic near Bethany Beach).

Strategy
Beebe Medical Center has expanded its facilities over the years to better serve area residents. It began an expansion aiming to double enrollment of the nursing school in 2012.A Construction efforts at the main hospital facility include a new emergency and critical care wing added in 2008.

Company Background
Beebe Medical Center was founded in 1916 by two brothers Dr. James Beebe and Dr. Richard Beebe. The Beebe School of NursingA opened in 1921 and the outpatient Beebe Health Campus was completed in 2003.

EXECUTIVES

Director Of Pharmacy, Samuel Roberts
Vice President Management, Gerald Smith
Vice President Of Operations, Donna Streletzky
Medical Records Director, Steven D Berlin
Auditors: GRANT THORNTON LLP PHILADELPH

LOCATIONS

HQ: BEEBE MEDICAL CENTER, INC.
    424 SAVANNAH RD, LEWES, DE 199581462
Phone: 302 645-3300
Web: WWW.BEEBEMED.ORG

Selected Delaware Locations
Beebe Health Campus (Rehoboth Beach)
Beebe Lab Express (Milton)
Beebe School of Nursing (Lewes)

Diabetes Management and Wound Care Center (Long Neck)
Georgetown Professional Park (Georgetown)
Gull House Adult Activities Center (Lewes)
Home Health Agency (Lewes)
Millville Walk-in Health Center (Millville)
Sleep Disorders Center (Rehoboth Beach)
Tunnell Cancer Center (Rehoboth Beach)

PRODUCTS/OPERATIONS

Selected Services
Bariatric
Cancer care
Cardiac & vascular
Community health
Diabetes management
Emergency
Home health
Hospitalist program
Imaging
Integrative health
Orthopedics
Rehabilitation
Senior care
Sleep Disorder
Surgical
Walk-in Healthcare
Wellness
Women's Health
Wound Care

COMPETITORS

Anne Arundel Medical Center
AtlantiCare
Christiana Care
Crozer-Keystone Health System
Inspira Health Network
Shore Memorial Hospital

HISTORICAL FINANCIALS
Company Type: Private

Income Statement | | | | FYE: June 30

	REVENUE ($ mil.)	NET INCOME ($ mil.)	NET PROFIT MARGIN	EMPLOYEES
06/18	419	54	13.1%	1,606
06/17	410	37	9.3%	—
06/16	365	41	11.5%	—
06/15	325	29	9.2%	—
Annual Growth	8.8%	22.4%	—	—

2018 Year-End Financials
Return on assets: 10.9%   Cash ($ mil.): 65
Return on equity: 13.1%
Current ratio: 1.90

BELLIN HEALTH SYSTEMS, INC.

EXECUTIVES

Pres, George Kerwin
Cfo, Jim Dietsche
Controller, Kevin Mc Gurk
Manager, Paul Vlies
Director, Jason Perry
Financial Executive, Stacey Burt
Secretary, Tracy Ledocq
Coordinator, Diane Koepke
Vice-President Business Develo, Randy Vanstraten
Registered Nurse, Courtney Batal
Health Professional, Francis Lee
Auditors: WIPFLI LLP GREEN BAY WISCONS

LOCATIONS

HQ: BELLIN HEALTH SYSTEMS, INC.
744 S WEBSTER AVE, GREEN BAY, WI 543013505
Phone: 920 433-3500
Web: WWW.BELLIN.ORG

HISTORICAL FINANCIALS
Company Type: Private

Income Statement				FYE: September 30
	REVENUE ($ mil.)	NET INCOME ($ mil.)	NET PROFIT MARGIN	EMPLOYEES
09/17	571	43	7.6%	2,300
09/16	533	31	6.0%	—
09/15	502	27	5.5%	—
09/14	460	34	7.4%	—
Annual Growth	7.5%	8.4%	—	—

2017 Year-End Financials
Return on assets: 2.6% Cash ($ mil.): 89
Return on equity: 7.6%
Current ratio: 2.30

BELLIN MEMORIAL HOSPITAL, INC.

EXECUTIVES

Pres, George Kerwin
Cfo, Jim Dietsche
Director of Information Techno, Troy Schiesl
Director of Risk Management, Mary Mueller
Information Specialist, Kerry Calba
Administrative Assistant, Laura Winnekens
Licensed Practical Nurse, Ann Conley
Nurse Practitioner, Patti Marquardt
Internal Medicine Practitioner, Andrea Akpoguma
Administrator, Kevin J McGurk
Security Staff, Tom Brault
Auditors: WIPFLI LLP GREEN BAY WISCONS

LOCATIONS

HQ: BELLIN MEMORIAL HOSPITAL, INC.
744 S WEBSTER AVE, GREEN BAY, WI 543013581
Phone: 920 433-3500
Web: WWW.BELLINHEALTHPHARMACY.COM

HISTORICAL FINANCIALS
Company Type: Private

Income Statement				FYE: September 30
	REVENUE ($ mil.)	NET INCOME ($ mil.)	NET PROFIT MARGIN	EMPLOYEES
09/17	571	42	7.5%	1,725
09/16	488	32	6.7%	—
09/15	462	27	6.0%	—
09/14	399	32	8.3%	—
Annual Growth	12.7%	9.0%	—	—

2017 Year-End Financials
Return on assets: 2.6% Cash ($ mil.): 89
Return on equity: 7.5%
Current ratio: 2.30

BENEFIS HEALTH SYSTEM, INC

EXECUTIVES

Chm, Susan Humble
SEC, David Richards
Executive Director, Lloyd V Smith
Vice-President Information Ser, Sonia Puckett
Coordinator, Peggy Randono
Auditors: MOSS ADAMS LLP PORTLAND OR

LOCATIONS

HQ: BENEFIS HEALTH SYSTEM, INC
1101 26TH ST S, GREAT FALLS, MT 594055161
Phone: 406 455-5000
Web: WWW.BENEFIS.ORG

HISTORICAL FINANCIALS
Company Type: Private

Income Statement				FYE: December 31
	REVENUE ($ mil.)	NET INCOME ($ mil.)	NET PROFIT MARGIN	EMPLOYEES
12/16	413	15	3.8%	94
12/15	69	7	10.5%	—
12/12	46	6	14.4%	—
Annual Growth	72.6%	24.1%	—	—

BENEFIS HOSPITALS, INC

EXECUTIVES

Ceo-Cfo, John Goodnow
President, Laura Goldhahn
Vice President, Steven Ballock
Dentist, Will Daniels DDS
Vice-President Information Ser, Alexander N Chung
Vice-President Information Ser, Mary Davis
General Practitioner, Justin Madill
Coordinator, Stacy McKittrick
Doctor, Paul G Dolan

LOCATIONS

HQ: BENEFIS HOSPITALS, INC
1101 26TH ST S, GREAT FALLS, MT 594055161
Phone: 406 455-5000
Web: WWW.BENEFIS.ORG

HISTORICAL FINANCIALS
Company Type: Private

Income Statement				FYE: December 31
	REVENUE ($ mil.)	NET INCOME ($ mil.)	NET PROFIT MARGIN	EMPLOYEES
12/16	865	26	3.0%	2,419
12/15	860	20	2.4%	—
12/14*	363	14	4.0%	—
05/06	86	9	10.5%	—
Annual Growth	23.3%	10.1%	—	—

*Fiscal year change

BENTLEY UNIVERSITY

Bentley University is not the Rolls-Royce of universities but is fairly prestigious nevertheless. It offers undergraduate graduate and doctoral degree programs to its nearly 5670 enrolled students from 82 countries. The university also offers professional development and certificate programs for executives and corporations. The focus at Bentley is on business; the school was a pioneer in integrating information technology into the business curriculum. In the belief that businesspeople need a broad education Bentley requires a liberal arts core of classes in behavioral and social sciences English and other subjects in the humanities as well as math and natural sciences.

Operations

The university has a student-faculty ratio of 14:1 with 78% of its faculty holding doctoral degrees. It offers 23 majors and 36 minors in business the arts and sciences. Tuition and fees are about $44020 per year.

Bentley offers numerous on-campus activities outside its academic and research functions. These include cultural events athletics the arts volunteering and more than 100 student organizations.

Geographic Reach

Bentley University is situated on about 165 acres in Waltham west of Boston. In partnership with Bahrain Institute of Banking and Finance Bentley launched its "Bentley in Bahrain" degree program in 2002 expanding its campus to students in Bahrain and surrounding Gulf States in the Middle East. It also has a campus in San Francisco

Strategy

Bentley is working to implement what it calls a fused curriculum where courses are taught by faculty from both the business and the arts and sciences sides academia. As part of the movement it offers an 11-month MBA that pulls from multiple disciplines.

Seeing a market for students on the West Coast in 2013 Bentley opened a campus in San Francisco.

Company Background

Harry Bentley founded the institution as the Bentley School of Accounting and Finance in 1917.

Bentley's university designation and name change occurred in 2008.

EXECUTIVES

Vice President Business Finance Treas, Paul Clemente
Vice President For Administration And Finance, Kenneth Cody
Vice President For University Advancement, William Torrey
Senior Business Systems Analyst Office Of Vice President For Enrollment Mgmnt, Jay DeFrank
Executive Vice President For Administration, Betts Robyn
Vice President For Schools And Scholarships, Savageau Thomas
Vice President For Student Affairs Dean Of Students, Andrew Shepardson
Vice President For Student Affair, Pine Deborah
Assistant Treasurer, James Fuerst
Auditors: KPMG LLP BOSTON MA

LOCATIONS

HQ: BENTLEY UNIVERSITY
175 FOREST ST, WALTHAM, MA 024524713
Phone: 781 891-2000
Web: WWW.BENTLEY.EDU

HISTORICAL FINANCIALS

Company Type: Private

Income Statement				FYE: June 30
	REVENUE ($ mil.)	NET INCOME ($ mil.)	NET PROFIT MARGIN	EMPLOYEES
06/15	288	18	6.5%	911
06/13	192	40	21.0%	—
06/12	185	(21)	—	—
06/11	183	34	18.9%	—
Annual Growth	12.0%	(14.2%)	—	—

2015 Year-End Financials

Return on assets: 9.0%
Return on equity: 6.5%
Current ratio: 0.30

Cash ($ mil.): 47

BERGELECTRIC CORP.

One of the nation's top electrical contractors Bergelectric provides design/build and design/assist services on projects that include office buildings public-sector facilities bioscience labs entertainment complexes hotels data centers and hospitals. Its projects also consist of parking garages water treatment plants residential towers and correctional facilities. The company boasts expertise in building information modeling fire alarms and security and telecommunications and data infrastructure. Bergelectric operates mainly in the western and southeastern US from about a dozen offices.

Operations

The electrical company keeps a lengthy list of projects past and current. More recent projects have included the San Ysidro Land Port of Entry Lackland Ambulatory Care Center Northwest Water Reclamation Facility Naval Hospital Camp Pendleton Fort Riley Community Replacement Hospital Wilshire Boulevard Temple California Health Care Facility Visitors Center at King Gillette Ranch Variety Special Education School Greenlaw Partners and Sandy High School.

The company has more than $550 million in backlog.

Geographic Reach

From its headquarters in Los Angeles Bergelectric maintains a presence in California through a handful of offices in San Diego Los Angeles Orange County Sacramento and Ventura. It also serves as an electrical contractor in half a dozen cities including Austin Texas; Denver Colorado; Las Vegas Nevada; Orlando Florida; Phoenix Arizona; Portland Oregon; and Raleigh North Carolina.

Strategy

The company is also focused on green initiatives completing Leadership in Energy and Environmental Design (LEED) construction projects for the likes of Sony the FBI the EPA and the University of Oregon. To this end the company formed the Fire-Alarm/Security Division which provides projects and clients with comprehensive electrical services for such fire alarm projects as the Morongo Casino & Hotel Pechanga Hotel & Casino and San Manuel Indian Bingo & Casino.

Bergelectric has extended the reach of its traditional electrical contracting operations by expanding into new markets including sustainable building structures and renewable energy systems such as wind farms. Through a partnership with telecommunications firm Teo Bergelectric provides communications services to wind energy produc-

ers. As part of the agreement Bergelectric designs and installs fiber connections and equipment while Teo supplies phones switches and other hardware.

To simplify the integration of complex systems Bergelectric established a national Technology Systems group which serves to consolidate all of the company's existing low-voltage divisions under one management umbrella. The move aims to differentiate Bergelectric from the traditionally fragmented industry of electrical and systems components.

Company Background

Bergelectric was founded in 1946.

EXECUTIVES

Vice President, Rik Becker
Vice President, Douglas Crumby
Vice President Preconstruction, Chris Billig
Vice President Field Operations, Darren Murray
Vice President Northern California Region, Peter Casazza
Auditors: MOSS LEVY & HARTZHEIM LLP B

LOCATIONS

HQ: BERGELECTRIC CORP.
5650 W CENTINELA AVE, LOS ANGELES, CA 900451501
Phone: 310 337-1377
Web: WWW.BERGELECTRIC.COM

Selected Locations
Agoura Hills CA
Austin TX
Costa Mesa CA
Denver
Durham NC
Escondido CA
Los Angeles
North Las Vegas NV
Orlando FL
Portland OR
Rancho Cordova CA
Tempe AZ

COMPETITORS

Cupertino Electric	MYR Group
EMCOR	Morrow-Meadows
Fisk Electric	Rosendin Electric
Henkels & McCoy	Sachs Electric
IES Holdings	

HISTORICAL FINANCIALS

Company Type: Private

Income Statement				FYE: January 31
	REVENUE ($ mil.)	NET INCOME ($ mil.)	NET PROFIT MARGIN	EMPLOYEES
01/17	483	4	0.9%	2,100
01/16	507	2	0.4%	—
01/15	494	1	0.2%	—
01/14	525	4	0.9%	—
Annual Growth	(2.7%)	(5.0%)	—	—

2017 Year-End Financials

Return on assets: 5.0%
Return on equity: 0.9%
Current ratio: 1.20

Cash ($ mil.): 16

BERING STRAITS NATIVE CORPORATION

EXECUTIVES

Ceo, Gail Schubert
Chm, Henry Ivanoff
Board Member, Tim Towarak
Vice President, Jerald Brown
President, Carolyn Crowder
Exec Vice President, Moriah Sallaffie
SEC-Treas, Clara Langton
Information Technology Manager, Kevin Ivanoff
Corporate Communications Manag, Miriam Aarons
Director, Louis Green
Director, Robert Evans
Auditors: RSM US LLP FREDERICK MARYLAN

LOCATIONS

HQ: BERING STRAITS NATIVE CORPORATION
110 FRONT ST STE 300, NOME, AK 99762
Phone: 907 443-5252
Web: WWW.BERINGSTRAITS.COM

HISTORICAL FINANCIALS

Company Type: Private

Income Statement				FYE: March 31
	REVENUE ($ mil.)	NET INCOME ($ mil.)	NET PROFIT MARGIN	EMPLOYEES
03/17	357	12	3.5%	280
03/16	326	13	4.3%	—
03/15	304	13	4.6%	—
03/14	229	9	4.2%	—
Annual Growth	16.0%	8.7%	—	—

2017 Year-End Financials

Return on assets: 8.4%
Return on equity: 3.5%
Current ratio: 1.50

Cash ($ mil.): 36

BERKSHIRE MEDICAL CENTER, INC.

EXECUTIVES

Pres- Ceo, David E Phelps
Treas, Michael R Cullen
Dir, Ann Trabulsi
Health Professional, Jessica Bridgmon
Health Professional, Azade Izadi
Internal Medicine Practitioner, Jansen Jones
Internal Medicine Practitioner, Katsiaryna Tsyrkunova
Internal Medicine Practitioner, Kipp Spencer
Internal Medicine Practitioner, Nidhi Aggarwal
Internal Medicine Practitioner, Shams Jubouri
Coordinator, Michelle Richard

LOCATIONS

HQ: BERKSHIRE MEDICAL CENTER, INC.
725 NORTH ST, PITTSFIELD, MA 012014124
Phone: 413 447-2000
Web: WWW.BERKSHIREHEALTHSYSTEMS.ORG

HISTORICAL FINANCIALS
Company Type: Private

Income Statement				FYE: September 30
	REVENUE ($ mil.)	NET INCOME ($ mil.)	NET PROFIT MARGIN	EMPLOYEES
09/17	448	36	8.1%	1,375
09/16	437	34	7.9%	—
09/15	424	46	10.9%	—
09/14	377	38	10.3%	—
Annual Growth	5.9%	(2.4%)	—	—

2017 Year-End Financials

Return on assets: 3.8% Cash ($ mil.): 27
Return on equity: 8.1%
Current ratio: 0.90

BERRY GLOBAL FILMS, LLC

Making plastic cling is this company's thing. AEP Industries manufactures plastic packaging films — more than 15000 types — including stretch wrap for industrial pallets packaging for foods and beverages and films for agricultural uses such as wrap for hay bales. AEP also makes dispenser-boxed plastic wraps which are sold to consumers as well as institutions ranging from schools to hospitals. Other industries courted by AEP are packaging transportation food autos chemicals textiles and electronics. The company operates in the US and in Canada. In the summer of 2016 AEP agreed to be acquired by rival Berry Plastics Group.

Change in Company Type

AEP agreed to be acquired by Berry Plastics Group in mid-2016 in a deal valued at $765 million a price that includes AEP's debt load. AEP will be combined with Berry's Engineered Materials Division.

Geographic Reach

AEP conducts about 95% of its business in the US market. Remaining sales take place in Canada. It has about 15 manufacturing facilities in the US (about 11 states) and Canada. The company also exports its products to Latin America through its office in Waxahachie Texas.

Sales and Marketing

About two-thirds of AEP's sales are made to distributors and the remainder directly to end-users of its products. It serves about 3000 customers. The company works to maintain customer relationships and it provides technical training to its sales personal so that they are able to provide customer support and communicate customer needs to the company's product development team. Distribution functions are mostly contracted to third parties.

Financial Performance

AEP's revenues have fluctuated over the years. After peaking at $1.19 billion in 2014 revenues fell by 4% to $1.14 billion in 2015. The revenue decrease for 2015 was fueled by a 3% dip in average selling prices primarily due to the pass-through of lower resin costs negatively affecting net sales by $31 million.

The company in 2015 also experienced a 1% decrease in sales volumes attributed to volatility in the resin markets. This resulted in soft customer demand in certain stock product lines customer bankruptcies and the impact of exiting certain low-margin businesses during fiscal 2014.

After experiencing a net loss of $6 million in 2014 AEP posted positive net income of $29 million in 2015. This was the result of a decline in costs coupled with a larger amount of income tax benefits.

Strategy

With little product differentiation among plastic film producers AEP positions itself as the low-cost source with technological expertise to customize value-added flexible films to satisfy myriad manufacturing and processing applications. The company aims to provide long-term value to shareholders by becoming the preferred provider of flexible packaging products in the North American market.

To strengthen its finances and increase manufacturing output and productivity AEP is investing heavily in capital improvements. During the last decade it has purchased or leased new equipment and made equipment upgrades intended to optimize its manufacturing footprint in high-growth product categories.

The company looks for success in its sales and distribution model by establishing long-term relationships with its customers. To mitigate the volatility of raw material prices the company pursues volume raw material rebates by making most of its purchases from three primary suppliers.

Company Background

Brendan Barba a former salesman for polyethylene film maker PPD formed Flexible Plastics in 1967 in Lodi New Jersey. In 1970 his partner bought him out. That year Barba founded AEP Industries briefly called Automatically Extruded Products. In 1982 the company moved into the specialty and premium films market. It established a plant in Waxahachie Texas in 1985 and went public a year later.

EXECUTIVES

Vp Manufacturing Polyvinyl Chloride Products, Richard Boyette
Evp Operations, Paul C. Vegliante, $317,300 total compensation
President And Coo, John J. Powers, $349,300 total compensation
Evp Finance Cfo And Director, Paul M. Feeney, $463,800 total compensation
Chairman President And Ceo, J. Brendan Barba, $958,700 total compensation
Evp National Accounts, Robert Cron
Vp Custom Films Division, Robert Covella
Vp Stretch Film Division, Brian Ochsner
Vp Proformance Films Products, Gary Bobko
Vice President Engineering, Carl Opperman
Vice President Of Information Technology, Ken Ribe

LOCATIONS

HQ: BERRY GLOBAL FILMS, LLC
95 CHESTNUT RIDGE RD, MONTVALE, NJ 076451801
Phone: 201 641-6600
Web: WWW.AEPINC.COM

2015 Sales

	$ mil.	% of total
US	1,073	94
Canada	68	6
Total	**1,141**	**100**

PRODUCTS/OPERATIONS

2015 Sales

	$ mil.	% of total
Custom films	357	31
Stretch (pallet) wrap	332	29
Food contact	165	14
Canliners	144	13
PROformance films	63	6
Printed & converted films specialty films & other	77	7
Total	**1,141**	**100**

Selected Products

Canliners
 Kitchen and standard garbage bags
Custom films (polyethylene co-extruded and monolayer custom designed film)
 Drum box carton pail liners
 Films to cover high value products
 Furniture and mattress bags
 Magazine overwrap
PROformance films (co-extruded and monolayer polyolefin films)
 Cereal box liners
 Fresh cut produce packaging
 Frozen foods
 Medical
Polyvinyl chloride wrap
 Food and freezer wrap
Printed and converted films (polyethylene)
 Printed laminated converted films for flexible packaging to consumer markets
 Printed shrink films
Stretch (pallet) wrap (polyethylene)
 Pallet wrap
Other products and specialty films (unplasticized polyvinyl chloride polyethylene)
 Agricultural films
 Battery labels
 Canliners
 Credit card laminate
 Retail and institutional films and products
 Table covers aprons bibs and gloves
 Twist wrap

COMPETITORS

Acme Packaging	Intertape Polymer
Ampac	Pactiv
Bemis	Plastic Suppliers
Berry Global	Primex Plastics
Dow Chemical	Printpack
DuPont	S.C. Johnson
FlexSol Packaging	Sealed Air Corp.
Griffon	Sigma Plastics
Inteplast	Tredegar

HISTORICAL FINANCIALS
Company Type: Private

Income Statement				FYE: October 31
	REVENUE ($ mil.)	NET INCOME ($ mil.)	NET PROFIT MARGIN	EMPLOYEES
10/15	1,141	28	2.5%	2,600
10/14	1,192	(5)	—	—
10/13	1,143	10	0.9%	—
Annual Growth	(0.1%)	63.8%	—	—

2015 Year-End Financials

Return on assets: 5.8% Cash ($ mil.): 20
Return on equity: 2.5%
Current ratio: 1.10

BEST PETROLEUM CORPORATION

EXECUTIVES

Pres, Antonio De Jesus Nieves
Head of Business Development, Manuel F Rojas
Auditors: JESUS OYOLA CUADRADO BAYAMON

LOCATIONS

HQ: BEST PETROLEUM CORPORATION
KM 20 HM 5 RR 2, TOA BAJA, PR 00951
Phone: 787 251-6218

HISTORICAL FINANCIALS

Company Type: Private

Income Statement   FYE: December 31

	REVENUE ($ mil.)	NET INCOME ($ mil.)	NET PROFIT MARGIN	EMPLOYEES
12/17	547	26	4.8%	130
12/16	439	16	3.7%	—
12/15	479	11	2.4%	—
12/98	0	0	—	—
Annual Growth	—	—	—	—

2017 Year-End Financials

Return on assets: 1.4%   Cash ($ mil.): 75
Return on equity: 4.8%
Current ratio: 10.20

BETH ISRAEL DEACONESS MEDICAL CENTER, INC.

Not just a mouthful Beth Israel Deaconess Medical Center (BIDMC) is a hospital in Boston. Though it's the official hospital for Major League Baseball's Red Sox and the flagship hospital of CareGroup it's perhaps best known for being a teaching hospital of Harvard Medical School. BIDMC has about 675 beds and provides general medical and surgical care as well as outpatient services at its facilities. In addition to a Level I trauma center BIDMC offers specialized care in such areas as organ transplantation breast cancer care and cardiac surgery. BIDMC traces its roots to Deaconess Hospital founded in 1896 and Beth Israel Hospital established in 1916. It plans to merge with Lahey Health to create a stronger rival to Massachusetts' largest system Partners Health-Care.

Operations

In addition to its main campus in Boston BIDMC operates eight other Massachusetts hospitals four satellite locations two urgent care centers a half-dozen community health centers and about 40 primary care locations.

Most of BIDMC's physicians hold faculty appointments at Harvard Medical School. Along with helping students become doctors BIDMC provides clinical education to students in social work radiology and pharmacy.

The Carl J. Shapiro Institute for Education and Research provides medical students and physicians in training with an on-site centralized educational facility.

Financial Performance

BIDMC is very active in medical research and consistently ranks among the top recipients of biomedical research funding from the National Institutes of Health totaling nearly $200 million annually. The health system is also home to the Harvard-Thorndike Laboratory the nation's oldest clinical research laboratory.

Strategy

Being on the forefront of medical education goes hand-in-hand with using cutting-edge technology and BIDMC does just that with its Carl J. Shapiro Institute for Education and Research administers training for learners at all levels and from all disciplines using progressive teaching methods to replicate real-life patient care situations from routine procedures to acute management crises. The institute features a range of technologically advanced educational resources including realistic models simulators virtual reality experiences computer-based materials ultrasound technology and filmed operations.

In late 2017 the hospital announced plans to build a 10-story patient tower its largest such project in more than 20 years. The facility will have private patient rooms operating rooms imaging suites and a landing pad for helicopters.

Mergers and Acquisitions

In early 2017 BIDMC agreed to merge with Lahey Health to become Massachusetts' second-largest health system (after Partners HealthCare). Other hospitals have agreed to join the combined system including Anna Jaques Hospital of Newburyport New England Baptist Hospital and Mount Auburn Hospital. The combined system will have 11 hospitals.

EXECUTIVES

Svp Information Systems And Cio, John D. Halamka, age 55
Svp Finance And Cfo, Steven Fischer
President And Ceo Beth Israel Deaconess Hospital Plymouth, Peter J. Holden
Coo, Nancy Formella
President And Ceo Affiliated Physicians Group, John Christoforo
Chief Department Of Medicine, Mark L. Zeidel
President Ceo And Director, Kevin Tabb
Chief Nursing Officer And Svp Patient Care Services, Marsha Maurer
President And Ceo Beth Israel Deaconess Hospital - Needham, John Fogarty
President, Peter Healy
Svp Communications And Marketing, Paul Donovan
Interim President And Ceo Beth Israel Deaconess Care Organization, Jeff Hulburt
President And Ceo Harvard Medical Faculty Physicians, Stuart Rosenberg
Deputy Cio/cto, Manu Tandon
Medical Director Of Cytogenetics, Christine Bryke
Medical Director, Karen Lee
Vice President Clinical Applications And Development, Larry Markson
Clinic Manager, Marie Hardy
Associate Medical Director, Jeff Odiet
Director, Ronald P. (Ron) O'Hanley, age 61
Vice Chair, Margaret A. McKenna, age 73
Vice Chair, Edward H. (Ted) Ladd
Chairman, Daniel Jick

LOCATIONS

HQ: BETH ISRAEL DEACONESS MEDICAL CENTER, INC.
330 BROOKLINE AVE, BOSTON, MA 022155400
Phone: 617 667-7000
Web: WWW.BIDMC.ORG

PRODUCTS/OPERATIONS

Centers and Departments
Cancer Center
CardioVascular Institute
Digestive Disease Center
Spine Center
Transplant Institute
Clinical Departments
Anesthesia Critical Care and Pain Medicine
Dermatology
Emergency Medicine
Medicine
Neonatology
Neurology
Obstetrics and Gynecology
Orthopedic Surgery
Pathology
Psychiatry
Radiation Oncology
Radiology
Rehabilitation Services
Surgery

Selected Facilities
Beth Israel Deaconess HealthCare-Chelsea
Beth Israel Deaconess HealthCare-Chestnut Hill
Beth Israel Deaconess HealthCare-Lexington
Beth Israel Deaconess Hospital-Milton
Beth Israel Deaconess Hospital-Needham
Beth Israel Deaconess Hospital-Plymouth

COMPETITORS

Boston Medical Center
Brigham and Women's Hospital
Cambridge Health Alliance
Care New England
Children's Hospital Boston
Dana-Farber
Massachusetts General Hospital
Newton-Wellesley Hospital
Northeast Health System
Southcoast Hospitals Group
Spaulding Rehabilitation Hospital
Steward Health Care

HISTORICAL FINANCIALS

Company Type: Private

Income Statement   FYE: September 30

	REVENUE ($ mil.)	NET INCOME ($ mil.)	NET PROFIT MARGIN	EMPLOYEES
09/17	1,335	37	2.8%	6,500
09/16	1,279	28	2.3%	—
09/15	1,198	44	3.7%	—
09/14	1,113	37	3.4%	—
Annual Growth	6.3%	(0.1%)	—	—

2017 Year-End Financials

Return on assets: 15.0%   Cash ($ mil.): 17
Return on equity: 2.8%
Current ratio: 0.70

BETHESDA HOSPITAL, INC.

From modest beginnings as a informal cottage hospital Bethesda North Hospital has grown into the fourth largest medical center in Cincinnati Ohio. Bethesda North is a full-service acute care hospital with some 360 beds for adults and 60 for children. It provides comprehensive medical and surgical care including maternity and fertility services emergency care and diagnostic imaging. The hospital joined with fellow Cincinnati health care provider Good Samaritan Hospital in 1995 to form TriHealth. Together the two hospitals offer care at some 80 locations including primary care offices fitness centers and occupational health facilities.

Operations

The full-service 420-bed acute care hospital handles some 24000 inpatient admissions each year as well as 260000 outpatient visits 77000 emergency room visits and 4000 births. It employs 165 full-time doctors and dentists and provides more than $30 million in community outreach efforts (including charity care programs) each year.

Specialty units at Bethesda North Hospital include institutes for cancer heart surgical and digestive care as well as centers for outpatient imaging breast stroke obstetrics-gynecology orthopedics and emergency trauma care. As a regional teaching center the hospital offers residency programs in a number of specialties including family medicine internal medicine OB-GYN and surgery.

Geographic Reach

Bethesda North is located in northern Cincinnati Ohio and serves as a regional trauma center as well as a major teaching hospital in the area.

Strategy

Parent organization TriHealth has aligned skilled physicians specialists surgeons and its staff to create specialty institutes offering best-of-class medical assistance in fields including heart and cancer care. To further enhance its facilities in 2013 the organization renovated the labor and delivery wing at Bethesda North Hospital. Other recent projects include the addition of a seven-story patient tower and a new outpatient imaging center.

Additionally the company has invested in TriHealth Connect the electronic medical records system that will help access accurate patient information.

Company Background

In early 2012 TriHealth unveiled a new logo. Bethesda North traces it roots to 1896 and a cottage occupied by seven German Methodist deaconesses ministering to the poor and sick.

EXECUTIVES

Pres, John Prout
Cfo, Craig Rucker
Controller, Brian Krause
Corporate Counsel/Legal, Donna Nenaber
Chief of Orthopedic Surgery, Nicholas S Mirkopoulos
Manager of Information, Thomas Barnes
Auditors: LB BKD LLP CINCINNATI OH

LOCATIONS

HQ: BETHESDA HOSPITAL, INC.
4750 WESLEY AVE, CINCINNATI, OH 452122244
Phone: 513 569-6100
Web: WWW.TRIHEALTH.COM

PRODUCTS/OPERATIONS

List of Selected Services
Breast health
Cancer care
Digestive diseases
Heart and vascular care
Maternity (OB-GYN childbirth)
Orthopedics
Outpatient imaging
Pallative Care
Pharmacy
Robotic-assisted surgery
Stroke care
Trauma/Emergency services

COMPETITORS

Cincinnati Children's Hospital	St. Elizabeth Healthcare
Deaconess Associations	The Christ Hospital Corporation
Kettering Health Network	UC Health
Miami Valley Hospital	
Premier Health Partners	

HISTORICAL FINANCIALS
Company Type: Private

Income Statement				FYE: June 30
	REVENUE ($ mil.)	NET INCOME ($ mil.)	NET PROFIT MARGIN	EMPLOYEES
06/18	639	52	8.2%	3,000
06/15	551	71	13.0%	—
06/14	552	76	13.8%	—
06/13	534	57	10.8%	—
Annual Growth	3.7%	(1.9%)	—	—

2018 Year-End Financials
Return on assets: 5.4%
Return on equity: 8.2%
Current ratio: 0.80

Cash ($ mil.): —

BETHESDA HOSPITAL, INC.

EXECUTIVES

Pres, Roger L Kirk
V Pres-Fin-Cfo, Joanne Aquilina
V Pres Strategy*, Robert Broadway
SEC, Marie Bedner
Vice-President, Kenneth Peltzie
Managing Officer, Ralph Breslaw
Vice-President, Robert Taylor
Telecommunications Manager, Ron Bean
Internal Auditor, Michael Shafer
Offc Mgr, Kerry Young
Clinical Educator, Martha Morales

LOCATIONS

HQ: BETHESDA HOSPITAL, INC.
2815 S SEACREST BLVD, BOYNTON BEACH, FL 334357995
Phone: 561 737-7733
Web: WWW.BETHESDAWEB.COM

HISTORICAL FINANCIALS
Company Type: Private

Income Statement				FYE: September 30
	REVENUE ($ mil.)	NET INCOME ($ mil.)	NET PROFIT MARGIN	EMPLOYEES
09/17	317	(24)	—	304
09/16	297	(10)	—	—
09/15	287	(24)	—	—
09/14	271	(0)	—	—
Annual Growth	5.3%	—	—	—

2017 Year-End Financials
Return on assets: 2.7%
Return on equity: (-7.6%)
Current ratio: 1.60

Cash ($ mil.): 4

BETHESDA, INC.

EXECUTIVES

Pres, J James Pearce Jr
V Pres, Chip Crowther
SEC, Ellen Katz
Treas, William A Tsacalis
V Chm, Michael F Haverkamp
Executive Assistant, Cindy Auger
Director, Jennifer Zimmerman
Auditors: BKD LLP CINCINNATI OH

LOCATIONS

HQ: BETHESDA, INC.
619 OAK ST 7N, CINCINNATI, OH 452061613
Phone: 513 569-6400
Web: WWW.TRIHEALTH.COM

HISTORICAL FINANCIALS
Company Type: Private

Income Statement				FYE: June 30
	REVENUE ($ mil.)	NET INCOME ($ mil.)	NET PROFIT MARGIN	EMPLOYEES
06/18	679	78	11.6%	5,543
06/17	615	91	14.8%	—
06/15	53	7	14.7%	—
06/13	9	5	61.1%	—
Annual Growth	134.4%	68.1%	—	—

2018 Year-End Financials
Return on assets: 5.3%
Return on equity: 11.6%
Current ratio: 0.80

Cash ($ mil.): —

BEXAR COUNTY HOSPITAL DISTRICT

As the hospital system of the Bexar County Hospital District University Health System serves residents of San Antonio and the surrounding region. Its flagship facility University Hospital boasts about 720 beds and is the primary teaching facility for The University of Texas Health Science Center at San Antonio. In addition to general medical and surgical care the hospital is a designated Level I trauma center and a Level II pediatric trauma and burn center. The system provides health care for families near its clinic locations including the Robert B. Green Campus Texas Diabetes Institute more than a dozen neighborhood clinics five ExpressMed urgent-care clinics and four outpatient renal dialysis centers.

Operations

The system which has about 800 physicians also operates preventive care centers including the Texas Diabetes Institute which provides treatment research and education for diabetes patients and health care professionals. The University Transplant Center performs a range of procedures such as kidney liver and lung transplants. The Harlandale Independent School District school-based Health Center is a collaboration with Harlandale ISD that helps keep students healthy and learning.

University Health System's emergency department is the busiest in the area taking in nearly 70000 visits annually. In 2013 it had about 22000 inpatient discharges 3000 births and 139000 outpatient visits.

As part of its operations University Health System is joint owner of San Antonio AirLIFE which provides emergency air medical transport services aboard its fleet of Bell 430 helicopters.

University Health System provides health insurance through its Community First Health Plans a not-for-profit HMO with thousands of members in Bexar and surrounding counties.

Geographic Reach

The system's University Hospital is the lead trauma hospital for a 22-county area of Texas serving patients from Bexar County to South Texas and beyond.

Financial Performance

University Health System's revenue rose 11% to $564 million in 2013 thanks to net patient revenue growth. Net income decreased 24% to $75 million that year as operating expenses including salaries and benefits purchased services and supplies rose.

Strategy

To its benefit University Hospital is the only pediatric trauma center that serves San Antonio and the greater South Texas area. Its emergency center remains the busiest in the region averaging nearly 70000 visits annually.

The organization is in the midst of a system-wide capital improvement program aimed at "right-sizing" its facilities to meet growing demand. To this end the system in 2014 completed construction on a $778 million 10-story Sky Tower at University Hospital that features an expanded emergency department 35 new surgical suites and 420 new private patient rooms. It also opened a six-story Clinical Pavilion at its Robert B. Green Campus in 2013. In 2015 the system was granted approval to renovate and expand its emergency department which will convert most semi-private rooms to fully private rooms and provide additional observance and recovery space. The new facilities are part of University Health System's $900 million Capital Improvement Program to expand and renovate facilities at University Hospital and its downtown Robert B. Green Campus.

Additionally University Health System's downtown health center has added services that include acute and crisis care diagnostic imaging and pharmacy.

In 2014 the system launched its healthyUexpress2 mobile health vehicle which extends its new school-based health care initiative throughout Bexar County.

Company Background

University Health System was founded in 1968.

EXECUTIVES

Evp And Cfo, Peggy Deming
Vice President Chief Information Officer, Bill Phillips
Executive Vice President Chief Operating Officer, Christann Vasquez
Vp Managed Care; President Community First Health Plans, Greg Gieseman
Senior Vice President Chief Nursing Officer, Nancy Ray
Evp Chief Medical Officer, Bryan Alsip
President And Ceo Community Medicine Associates, Priti Mody-Baily
President And Ceo, George B. Hernandez
Senior Vice President, Emily Volk
Chairman, James R. Adams

LOCATIONS

HQ: BEXAR COUNTY HOSPITAL DISTRICT
4502 MEDICAL DR MS651, SAN ANTONIO, TX 782294402
Phone: 210 358-4000
Web: WWW.UNIVERSITYHEALTHSYSTEM.COM

PRODUCTS/OPERATIONS

2013 Sales

	% of total
Net patient services revenue	60
Premium revenue	34
Other revenue	6
Total	**100**

2013 Net Patient Revenue

	% of total
Medicare	22
Medicaid	21
Self-Pay including CareLink	37
Commercial insurance	19
Other	1
Total	**100**

Selected Locations

University Hospital
University Health Care
Texas Diabetes Institute
University Family Health Centers

Selected Medical Services

Audiology
Blood Bank
Breast Health
Cancer
Cardiology
Craniosynostosis
Diabetes
ExpressMed
Emergency Center
Endoscopy
Epilepsy
Gynecology
Health Education
Hepatology
HIV/AIDS
Mammography
Maternal-fetal Medicine
Men's Health
Neurosciences
Newborn Services
NICU
Obstetrics
Outpatient Surgery
Pharmacy Services
Pediatrics
Primary Care
Rehabilitation
Respiratory Care
Robot Assisted Surgery
Stroke
Texas Diabetes Institute
Transcatheter Aortic Valve Replacement
Transplant Center
Trauma Center
Vascular
Women's Health

COMPETITORS

CHRISTUS Health	Tenet Healthcare
Methodist Healthcare System	Valley Baptist Health System (Texas)

HISTORICAL FINANCIALS

Company Type: Private

Income Statement   FYE: December 31

	REVENUE ($ mil.)	NET INCOME ($ mil.)	NET PROFIT MARGIN	EMPLOYEES
12/17	1,349	54	4.1%	3,998
12/16	1,253	82	6.6%	—
Annual Growth	7.6%	(33.1%)	—	—

2017 Year-End Financials

Return on assets: 16.1%   Cash ($ mil.): 91
Return on equity: 4.1%
Current ratio: 0.70

BI-RITE RESTAURANT SUPPLY CO., INC.

Bi-Rite Restaurant Supply which does business as BiRite Foodservice Distributors is a leading food service supplier serving the San Francisco Bay area and Northern California. The company distributes a full line of food equipment and supplies including meat and dairy items seafood frozen foods dry groceries cleaning supplies china kitchen equipment and disposables. Its customers include restaurant operators hotels universities and hospitals. The company's international arm supplied food to the Middle East and Asia. A member of the UniPro Foodservice cooperative the family-owned company was founded in 1966 by cousins Victor and John Barulich.

Geographic Reach

Brisbane-based Bi-Rite's coverage area ranges from Cloverdale in Northern California east to Reno (Nevada) and South to Fresno and Monterey. Beyond California the company supplies food and equipment to Afghanistan Jordan Kuwait Turkey China Japan South Korea Singapore Thailand Vietnam and several other territories.

Mergers and Acquisitions

In December 2012 the company acquired family-owned A&B Produce which supplies food to restaurants throughout the San Francisco Bay area.

EXECUTIVES

Vice President Sales And Marketing, Michael Pendergast
Executive Vice President Of Purchasing, Tom Whiteside
Vice President Marketing, Dan Lorenz

LOCATIONS

HQ: BI-RITE RESTAURANT SUPPLY CO., INC.
123 S HILL DR, BRISBANE, CA 940051203
Phone: 415 656-0187
Web: WWW.BIRITE.COM

PRODUCTS/OPERATIONS

Selected Product Categories

Disposables
Equipment & supply
Food
Fresh cut produce
Fresh next-day protein
Fresh seafood
Janitorial

COMPETITORS

Dot Foods	McLane Foodservice
Golden State Foods	Sysco
Jacmar	US Foods
MAINES	

HISTORICAL FINANCIALS

Company Type: Private

Income Statement   FYE: December 31

	REVENUE ($ mil.)	NET INCOME ($ mil.)	NET PROFIT MARGIN	EMPLOYEES
12/17	314	13	4.2%	300
12/16	305	12	4.0%	—
12/15	321	8	2.7%	—
12/14	310	6	2.2%	—
Annual Growth	0.4%	25.8%	—	—

2017 Year-End Financials

Return on assets: 3.3%   Cash ($ mil.): 8
Return on equity: 4.2%
Current ratio: 2.40

BIG RIVER RESOURCES, LLC.

EXECUTIVES

Ceo-Pres, Raymond E Defenbaugh
Coo, Jim Leiting
Cfo, Jim Hall
MBR-Treas, Les Allen
MBR-V Pres, Andy Brader
MBR, Gene Youngquist
Production Manager, John Wolf

Accountant, Tina McCulloch
Plant Manager, Duane Salmon
Scientist, Jeannette Peterson
Marketing Director, Brian Schasel
Auditors: CHRISTIANSON PLLP WILLMAR MI

LOCATIONS

HQ: BIG RIVER RESOURCES, LLC.
211 N GEAR AVE STE 200, WEST BURLINGTON, IA
526551027
Phone: 319 753-1100
Web: WWW.BIGRIVERRESOURCES.COM

HISTORICAL FINANCIALS

Company Type: Private

Income Statement | | | | FYE: December 31

	REVENUE ($ mil.)	NET INCOME ($ mil.)	NET PROFIT MARGIN	EMPLOYEES
12/17	817	33	4.2%	250
12/16	851	74	8.8%	—
12/15	863	74	8.7%	—
12/14	1,184	224	18.9%	—
Annual Growth	(11.6%)	(46.7%)	—	—

2017 Year-End Financials

Return on assets: 3.6%   Cash ($ mil.): 54
Return on equity: 4.2%
Current ratio: 1.50

BILLINGS CLINIC

Billings Clinic is an integrated health care system that serves the residents of Big Sky Country. Through a group of more than 320 doctors and other providers the clinic caters to some 570000 people in Billings Montana and in surrounding communities. It offers 50-plus specialties such as emergency and trauma cancer orthopedics birthing cardiovascular neurosciences dialysis and pediatrics. Its operations include a more than 285-bed hospital and the organization's main clinic. Additionally Billings Clinic operates the 90-bed Aspen Meadows Retirement Community and provides support services to several regional community hospitals. The not-for-profit health care system is owned by the community.

Operations

With its vast service area the health care system provides a MedFlight advanced life support fixed-wing aircraft service that transports critically ill or injured patients from rural communities. The service averages 700 flights per year.

As part of its operations Billings Clinic runs a Level II emergency and trauma center 14-suite family birthing center Level III neonatal intensive care unit inpatient cancer care unit and a 15-bed transitional care unit. The health care system's cancer center provides both inpatient and outpatient care in Billings and the surrounding four-state region.

Billings Clinic is governed by a 12-member board consisting of mostly community members but also a pair of doctors and a physician CEO.

In 2014 Billings Clinic's Community Benefit totaled $37.6 million including $14.8 million in financial assistance (charity care) provided to 5744 patients.

Geographic Reach

As the largest health care organization in the area Billings Clinic's service area comprises 40 counties and extends more than 120000 miles in Montana Wyoming and the western Dakotas.

Strategy

Billings Clinic works with pharmaceutical sponsors on a variety of clinical research trials in various phases and indications. To this end it operates a research center with more than 20 years of experience in the areas of basic and clinical research. The center has participated in more than 200 clinical research studies with the help of some 5000 volunteer subjects since 1988.

The health care system has been growing. In 2014 it completed construction of a 24-bed Intensive Care Unit located on the second floor of the hospital directly above the Emergency and Trauma Center. That year Billings Clinic also opened a second ExpressCare retail clinic in the Albertsons store and opened two new major cardiac facilities.

In 2014 Billings Clinic began offering a new non-invasive surgery for the brain using Gamma Knife Perfexion an advanced technology for stereotactic radiosurgery.

Company Background

It expanded its capacity for infusions in 2012 when its Billings Clinic Cody location opened an infusion center. In late 2012 the organization also opened a new Stillwater Billings Clinic medical facility which combines Stillwater Community Hospital and Billings Clinic Columbus and integrates the billing process for the two health care facilities.

The Billings Clinic evolved from the general practice of Dr. Arthur J. Movius who founded his Billings practice in 1911.

EXECUTIVES

Vp And Cio, Chris Stevens
Physician In Chief, Mark C. Rumans
President Billings Clinic Foundation, Jim Duncan
Vp Hospital Operations, Lu Byrd
Cfo, Connie F. Prewitt
Ceo, Randall Gibb
Director Of Radiology, Douglas Bell
Director Of Patient Relations, Karrie Cleveland
Director Of Medical Records, Lorraine Jelle
Chairman, J. Scott Millikan
Director, David Brown

LOCATIONS

HQ: BILLINGS CLINIC
2800 10TH AVE N, BILLINGS, MT 591010703
Phone: 406 657-4000
Web: WWW.BILLINGSCLINIC.COM

PRODUCTS/OPERATIONS

Selected Services
Advance Medical Directives
Allergy Asthma Immunology
Aspen Meadows - Skilled Nursing and Assisted Living
Anticoagulation Clinic
Breast Center
Cancer Center
Cardiovascular Services
Cardiovascular Surgery
Children's Services
Continence Center
Community Training Center
Cosmetic Surgery
da Vinci Surgical System
Dermatology Center
Diabetes Management Center
Diagnostic Imaging
Diabetes
Dialysis Center
Eldercare Solutions
Emergency & Trauma Center
Emmi Educational Videos
Employer Services - Occupational Health
Endocrinology
Eye Center
Facial Plastic Surgery
Family Medicine
Family Birth Center
Gastroenterology
General Surgery

Genetic Counseling
Geriatric Assessment Program
Gynecologic Cancer
Heart Services
Heart Surgery
Home Oxygen & Medical Equipment
Hospitalist Program
Infectious Diseases
Insurance Finder
Internal Medicine
Laboratory Services
LifeFit
Maternal-Fetal Medicine
MedFlight Air Ambulance
Mental Health Services
Metabolism Center
Mohs Surgery
Nutrition Services
Neurosciences
Obstetrics & Gynecology
Occupational Health - Employer Services
Ophthalmology
Orthopedics & Sports Medicine
Palliative Care
Pediatrics
 Pediatric Center
 Pediatric Cancer
 Pediatric Diabetes
 Pediatric Gastroenterology
 Pediatric Pulmonology
 Rehabilitation (Therapy)
Pharmacy
Physical Medicine & Rehabilitation
Plastic Surgery
Primary Care for Adults
Pulmonary Rehabilitation Program
Radiology Services
Reproductive Medicine and Fertility Care
Robotic Surgery
SameDay Care
Senior Services
Sleep Disorders Center
Sports Medicine
Sports Specific Camps
Stroke Care
Surgery Center
Transitional Care Unit
Urology Services
Vascular Surgery
Vein Clinic
Women's Free Screenings
Women's and Children's Services

Selected Affiliate Hospitals and Clinics
Beartooth Billings Clinic - Red Lodge
Colstrip Medical Center - Colstrip
Daniels Memorial Healthcare - Scobey
Livingston HealthCare - Livingston
North Big Horn Hospital - Lovell
Pioneer Medical Center - Big Timber
Roundup Memorial Healthcare - Roundup
Sheridan Memorial Hospital Association
Stillwater Billings Clinic

COMPETITORS

Glendive Medical Center
St. Alexius Medical Center
St. James Healthcare
St. Patrick Hospital
Wyoming Medical Center

HISTORICAL FINANCIALS

Company Type: Private

Income Statement | | | | FYE: June 30

	REVENUE ($ mil.)	NET INCOME ($ mil.)	NET PROFIT MARGIN	EMPLOYEES
06/16	586	(2)	—	3,300
06/15	565	30	5.4%	—
06/14	593	38	6.6%	—
06/13	560	14	2.6%	—
Annual Growth	1.6%	—	—	—

2016 Year-End Financials

Return on assets: 4.2%   Cash ($ mil.): 13
Return on equity: (-0.4%)
Current ratio: 1.30

BIOMEDICAL RESEARCH FOUNDATION OF NORTHWEST LOUISIANA

EXECUTIVES

Chb, Stephen F Skrivanos
Vice President, James D Dean
Vice President, Dennis Lower
Prin, John F George Jr
SEC, Johnette Magner
Treas, Arthur Thompson
Director, Joseph Sarpy Jr
Director, John F Sharp
Director, Virginia K Shehee
Director, Elaine Joyce Simpkins PHD
Director, W Juan Watkins
Auditors: POSTLETHWAITE & NETTERVILLE B

LOCATIONS

HQ: BIOMEDICAL RESEARCH FOUNDATION OF NORTHWEST LOUISIANA
2031 KINGS HWY, SHREVEPORT, LA 711033600
Phone: 318 716-4100
Web: WWW.BIOMED.ORG

HISTORICAL FINANCIALS

Company Type: Private

Income Statement				FYE: September 30
	REVENUE ($ mil.)	NET INCOME ($ mil.)	NET PROFIT MARGIN	EMPLOYEES
09/15	564	14	2.6%	50
09/14	502	(1)	—	—
09/13*	10	(5)	—	—
12/09	15	0	2.1%	—
Annual Growth	81.9%	88.0%	—	—

*Fiscal year change

2015 Year-End Financials

Return on assets: 18.6%
Return on equity: 2.6%
Current ratio: 1.00
Cash ($ mil.): 8

BLACK & VEATCH HOLDING COMPANY

EXECUTIVES

Chb-Pres-Ceo, Steven L Edwards
Exec V Pres-Cfo, Karen L Daniel
Sr V Pres-Treas, Angela L Hoffman
Exec V Pres & SEC, Timothy W Triplett
V Pres-RE & Facilities, Ralph J Dyro
V Pres-Tax Councel, Jeffrey J Stamm
Cfo, Ken Williams
Chief Officer, Tel, Harold R Hoagland
Pres Management Consulting Div, John Chevrette
Procurement Staff, Hal E Smith
Project Manager, Benjamin Whitehead

LOCATIONS

HQ: BLACK & VEATCH HOLDING COMPANY
11401 LAMAR AVE, OVERLAND PARK, KS 662111598
Phone: 913 458-2000
Web: WWW.BV.COM

HISTORICAL FINANCIALS

Company Type: Private

Income Statement				FYE: December 31
	REVENUE ($ mil.)	NET INCOME ($ mil.)	NET PROFIT MARGIN	EMPLOYEES
12/17	3,364	87	2.6%	8,495
12/16*	3,207	75	2.3%	—
01/16	2,955	109	3.7%	—
01/15	0	0	—	—
Annual Growth	—	—	—	—

*Fiscal year change

2017 Year-End Financials

Return on assets: 22.5%
Return on equity: 2.6%
Current ratio: 0.70
Cash ($ mil.): 344

BLESSING HOSPITAL

Blessing Hospital is a not-for-profit acute care medical center that provides a wide range of health services to residents in areas of western Illinois northeast Missouri and southeast Iowa. Through its main campus location it provides primary and emergency care as well as specialty services including diagnostics and surgery. The hospital is home to centers of excellence in the treatment of cancer heart and cardiovascular ailments wound care and women's health issues. Blessing Hospital provides outpatient and behavioral health services at a nearby campus. It also operates family practice centers and provides home and hospice care services. It is part of the Blessing Health System.

Operations

Blessing Health System includes two hospitals a physician group medical specialty operations a foundation and a four-year nursing education program.

Blessing Hospital boasts a medical staff of more than 240 physicians with an additional 2000 health care personnel. Its operations consist of a behavioral center body motion center breast center cancer center heart and vascular center sleep center and wound center as well as family practice centers.

The hospital typically sees more than 13400 inpatients and 245000 outpatients each year.

Geographic Reach

Blessing Hospital serves those who reside in western Illinois southeast Iowa and northeast Missouri.

Strategy

Blessing Hospital is working to boost its range of tertiary (acute specialty care) services to keep residents in the area from heading to larger towns more than 150 miles away. To this end it has built up its cardiac services and brought in a robotic surgical system.

EXECUTIVES

Vice President Human Resources, Joellen Randall
Vice President Planning And Compliance, Betty Kasparie
Radiology Director, Sharon Dieker
Vice President Operations, Gregg Hamilton
Director Of Pharmacy Illini Community Hospital, Mary Tatum
Auditors: GRAY HUNTER STENN LLP QUINCY

LOCATIONS

HQ: BLESSING HOSPITAL
BROADWAY AT 11TH ST, QUINCY, IL 62301
Phone: 217 223-1200
Web: WWW.BLESSINGHOSPITAL.ORG

PRODUCTS/OPERATIONS

Selected Services
Bariatric Services
Behavioral Center
Blessing FastCare Clinic
Body Motion Center
Breast Center
Cancer Center
Emergency Center
Heart & Vascular Center
Home Care
Hospice & Palliative Care
Hospital Medicine Program
Maternity Care
Nutrition Services
Orthopedic Surgical Services
Pain Management Service
Radiology
Rehabilitation Services
Renal Dialysis Services
Sleep Center
Surgical Services
Wound Center

COMPETITORS

Advocate BroMenn
Hospital Sisters
Health System
Memorial Health System
St. John's Hospital
(Illinois)

HISTORICAL FINANCIALS

Company Type: Private

Income Statement				FYE: September 30
	REVENUE ($ mil.)	NET INCOME ($ mil.)	NET PROFIT MARGIN	EMPLOYEES
09/16	355	52	14.8%	2,500
09/15	316	15	4.8%	—
09/12	289	14	5.1%	—
09/08	238	(2)	—	—
Annual Growth	5.1%	—	—	—

2016 Year-End Financials

Return on assets: 11.2%
Return on equity: 14.8%
Current ratio: 0.80
Cash ($ mil.): 46

BLOUNT INTERNATIONAL, INC.

Folks at Blount International have their work cut out for them. The manufacturer produces cutting chain guide bars sprockets and accessories for chainsaws concrete-cutting equipment and lawnmower blades. Blount's lineup is sold under brands Oregon Carlton Tiger and Windsor to outdoor equipment OEMs including Husqvarna and the replacement and retail markets. Other subsidiaries supply log splitters post-hole diggers and other agriculture add-ons. End users are professionals and consumers engaged in forestry lawn and garden farming and construction activities. The company's manufacturing facilities dot Brazil Canada China and the US. About two-thirds of Blount's sales are made outside the US. In early 2016 it was acquired by private-equity firms American Securities and P2 Capital Partners.

Operations

Blount sells its products across two segments: forestry lawn and garden (FLAG) and farm ranch and agriculture (FRAG). The former segment represents about 70% of its total sales each year while the latter accounts for the remainder.

The company also operates a concrete cutting and finishing (CCF) equipment business that is reported within the "corporate and other" category. This business manufactures and markets diamond-cutting chains assembles and markets concrete cutting chain saws and purchases other concrete cutting products that are marketed to the construction and utility industries.

Sales and Marketing
The company sells its products through a global sales and distribution network of over 300 distributors 30000 dealers direct sales companies and mass merchants which sell to the global forestry lawn and garden; farm ranch and agriculture; and construction products end markets. The company also sells through nearly 100 original equipment manufacturers.

Financial Performance
After posting a decline in 2013 Blount saw its revenues rebound for 2014 increasing 5% to peak at a record-setting $945 million. Profits also skyrocketed over 650% from $5 million in 2013 to $37 million in 2014. Its operating cash flow has fluctuated over the years rising sharply in 2013 but declining by 15% during 2014.

The historic growth for 2014 was driven by a 5% increase from its FLAG segment due to a rise in demand across most geographic regions especially South America (increased by 8%) and North America (7%). Its FRAG operations experienced a 3% increase in 2014 due to higher unit sales volumes (led by increased sales of log splitters and tractor attachments) and higher average selling prices across North America.

Blount's surge in profits for 2014 was attributed to the improved revenue coupled with lower expenses related to the impairment of acquired intangible assets along with charges related to restructuring activities.

Strategy
Blount has also fueled its momentum by strategically expanding its product portfolio and customer base through acquisitions. In 2014 the company acquired Arizona-based Pentruder. As part of the transaction the company became the exclusive distributor of Pentruder high-performance concrete cutting systems in North and South America. Pentruder now operates under Blount's concrete cutting and finishing (CCF) equipment business.

EXECUTIVES

Svp And Cfo, Calvin E. Jenness, age 62, $385,000 total compensation

Ceo And Chairman, Joshua L. (Josh) Collins, age 53, $565,000 total compensation

President Frag Division, Gerald D. (Jerry) Johnson, $350,000 total compensation

Vp Flag Manufacturing Operations, William C. Alford

President And Coo, David A. Willmott, age 48, $500,000 total compensation

Svp Global Supply Chain, David K. Parrish

Vp And Cio, Kevin M. Trepa

Svp Global Sales And Marketing Flag Division, Dave P. Gillrie

Auditors: KPMG LLP PORTLAND OREGON

LOCATIONS

HQ: BLOUNT INTERNATIONAL, INC.
4909 SE INTERNATIONAL WAY, PORTLAND, OR 972224679
Phone: 503 653-8881
Web: WWW.BLOUNT.COM

PRODUCTS/OPERATIONS

Selected Products
Chain drive sprockets
Chainsaw guide bars
Concrete-cutting chainsaws and circular saws (gasoline and hydraulic powered)
Cutting chain (for chainsaws)
Diamond-segmented chain (for cutting concrete)
Farm accessories
Lawn and garden cutting attachments
Lawnmower and edger cutting blades
Log splitters
Maintenance tools (for chainsaws and mechanical timber harvesting equipment)
Tractor driven post-hole diggers
Tractor three-point linkage parts

COMPETITORS

Alamo Group	Great Plains
Ariens	Manufacturing
Briggs & Stratton	Husqvarna
Caterpillar	Kubota
Champion Cutting Tool	MTD Products
Deere	Metso
Dover Corp.	STIHL Incorporated
Emak Group	Terex

HISTORICAL FINANCIALS
Company Type: Private

Income Statement   FYE: December 31

	REVENUE ($ mil.)	NET INCOME ($ mil.)	NET PROFIT MARGIN	EMPLOYEES
12/15	828	(49)	—	4,000
12/14	944	36	3.9%	—
12/13	900	4	0.5%	—
12/12	927	39	4.3%	—
Annual Growth	(3.7%)	—	—	—

2015 Year-End Financials
Return on assets: 5.2%   Cash ($ mil.): 25
Return on equity: (-6.0%)
Current ratio: 1.00

BLUE BUFFALO PET PRODUCTS, INC.

Blue Buffalo Pet Products is converting pet parents into what it refers to as "True Blue Believers" with its wholesome pet food offerings. The company makes natural dog and cat food using whole meats fruits and vegetables with no by-products or artificial ingredients; some products are also grain-free. By riding the wave of people forking over big bucks for natural and wholesome food for themselves and their families Blue Bufallo has positioned dogs and cats as members of the family and has risen to be the #1 brand in the Wholesome Natural pet food market segment. The company sells its products internationally but the majority of net sales remains in the US. Bill Bishop started the company when his dog Blue developed cancer but recovered after eating food he formulated. Cereal giant General Mills bought Blue Buffalo in 2018.

Change in Company Type
In mid-2018 consumer packaged goods company General Mills paid some $8 billion for Blue Buffalo in its quest to reshape its portfolio with more natural and organic brands. Blue Buffalo will operate as an independent subsidiary while taking advantage of the supply chain distribution and sales capabilities of its new parent.

Operations
Blue Buffalo operates its business in one reportable segment. It makes five main lines of pet food covering different product types diet types breed sizes for dogs and life stages.

The company has traditionally sold its products through specialty channels such as pet stores in the past but has recently expanded its distribution into the food drug and mass (FDM) markets (such as grocery stores) in the US where it now generates more than half its revenues.

The company produces 55% of its dry food in its own food production facility in Joplin MO and plans to open a new facility in Richmond IN by the end of 2018. Blue Buffalo hopes to handle 85% of its dry food production at these two sites over the next several years. The remainder of food production is through third-party contract manufacturers.

Geographic Reach
Blue Bufallo's BLUE brand products are sold in the US Canada Japan and Mexico. The US accounts for more than 95% of net sales.

Sales and Marketing
Blue Buffalo BLUE products are sold through multiple distributors who also provide logistics services and some in-field sales support. Products appear in specialty channels such as national and regional pet stores farm and feed stores e-commerce retailers and select grocery stores. The company has minimal sales through veterinary clinics and hospitals. Its sales teams are organized by type of retail accounts they sell to — National Accounts Regional Accounts eCommerce and Food-Drug-Mass (FDM).

The company promotes and markets its products through television internet and print advertisements produced by an in-house agency. Blue Buffalo has increased its advertising spend about 60% in the past three years ($132.3 million in 2016 $101.2 million in 2016 and $83.6 million in 2015).

In 2017 almost 60% of Blue Buffalo's sales were generated from its two largest customers PetSmart and Petco. Other customers include Tractor Supply Company Pet Supermarket Target Kroger Meijer and Publix.

Financial Performance
Blue Buffalo has enjoyed double digit growth over the past several years with sales in 2017 amounting to $1.3 billion (an 11% increase over 2016). Net sales were driven by a favorable product mix growth in sales in national pet superstores and expansion in farm and feed stores and e-commerce retailers.

Net income increased 49% to $193.5 million in 2017 compared with $130.2 million in 2016 mainly due to increased volume supply chain efficiencies and lower tax rates.

Cash at the end of fiscal 2017 was $282.2 million a decrease of $10.3 million from the prior year. Cash from operations contributed $193.9 billion to the coffers while investing activities used $171.0 million mainly for capital expenditures for a three-year program to expand its internal manufacturing capabilities. Financing activities used another $33.5 million for repurchases of common stock.

Strategy
Blue Buffalo touts its extensive product line and continuous innovation as differentiators for the company. It also includes educating "pet parents" as part of the company's strategy for attracting new customers; it uses part-time employees it calls Pet Detectives to interact with and market directly to customers shopping for pet food in stores in the US and Canada. The company has also significantly increased spending on advertising over the past three years. Some of Blue Buffalo's key initiatives going forward include expanding distribution

in the US growing its FDM business expanding the wet food and pet treat lines and increasing its focus on e-commerce sales.

The company is leveraging General Mills' resources and expertise to expand its FDM distribution in the US and refine its supply chain and category management operations. It will also capitalize on General Mills' customer relationship management (CRM) capabilities to to increase communication with customers.

In the pet specialty channel Blue Buffalo is investing in media advertising to support sales as well as new packaging and products in the wet food and treats categories an area it feels is currently underdeveloped.

The company aims to continue manufacturing operations at both company-owned as well as co-manufacturing facilities. It will open a new facility in Richmond IN in 2018 and a new treat facility at its existing location in Joplin MO.

EXECUTIVES

Evp Cfo And Treasurer, Michael (Mike) Nathenson, $318,270 total compensation
Ceo, William (Billy) Bishop, $269,088 total compensation
Auditors: KPMG LLP STAMFORD CONNECTICU

LOCATIONS

HQ: BLUE BUFFALO PET PRODUCTS, INC.
11 RIVER RD STE 103, WILTON, CT 068976011
Phone: 203 762-9751
Web: WWW.BLUEBUFFALO.COM

PRODUCTS/OPERATIONS

2017 Sales

	$ mil.	% of total
Dry foods	1,013	80
Wet foods treats and other	261	20
Total	**1,274**	**100**

Selected Product Lines
BLUE Life Protection Formula
BLUE Wilderness
BLUE Basics
BLUE Freedom
BLUE Natural Veterinary Diet

COMPETITORS

Big Heart Pet Brands	OurPet's Co.
Breeder's Choice	Pet Supermarket
Hill's Pet Nutrition	Pet Valu
Iams	Procter & Gamble
Mars Incorporated	Royal Canin
Nestlé Purina PetCare	Simmons Foods
Nutro Products	WellPet

HISTORICAL FINANCIALS

Company Type: Private

Income Statement   FYE: December 31

	REVENUE ($ mil.)	NET INCOME ($ mil.)	NET PROFIT MARGIN	EMPLOYEES
12/17	1,274	193	15.2%	1,800
12/16	1,149	130	11.3%	—
12/15	1,027	89	8.7%	—
Annual Growth	11.4%	47.1%	—	—

2017 Year-End Financials
Return on assets: 5.0%   Cash ($ mil.): 282
Return on equity: 15.2%
Current ratio: 3.10

BNSF RAILWAY COMPANY

BNSF Railway operates one of the largest railroad networks in North America. A wholly-owned subsidiary of Burlington Northern Santa Fe itself a unit of Berkshire Hathaway the company provides freight transportation over a network of about 32500 route miles of track across two-thirds of the western US and two provinces in Canada. BNSF Railway owns or leases a fleet of about 8000 locomotives. It also has some 30 intermodal facilities that help to transport agricultural consumer and industrial products as well as coal. In addition to major cities and ports BNSF Railway serves smaller markets in alliance with short-line partners.

Operations
BNSF Railway serves more than 40 ports and 30 intermodal facilities and operates 1600 trains per day.

In 2014 it hauled nearly 1 million carloads of agricultural commodities; more than 5 million intermodal shipments (truck trailers or containers); nearly 2 million carloads of industrial products; and almost 2.3 million coal shipments. All told the company hauled more than 10 million carloads in 2014.

Geographic Reach
The company's network is spread across 28 US states and three Canadian provinces.

Sales and Marketing
BNSF Railway serves smaller markets by working closely with 200 shortline partners. It has also forms marketing agreements with other rail carriers expanding the marketing reach for each railroad and their customers.

Financial Performance
In 2014 the company's revenues rose by 5.6% due to increased capacity offset by the negative effects of severe winter weather conditions early in the year which dampened transportation activities.

BNSF Railway generated 31% of its revenues in 2014 from consumer products; 28% from industrial products; 22% from coal; and 19% from agricultural products.

It also reported a 1.8% increase in cars/units handled and a 3.5% increase in average revenue per car/unit for the year.

The company accounted for more than 56% of Burlington Northern Santa Fe's net revenues for 2014.

Strategy
As part of its capital plan of $6 billion for 2015 the company has planned some major capital projects to maintain and grow its rail network.

In its northern region the company has plans to invest $1.5 billion across eight states for engineering maintenance and line expansion projects of which $700 million is planned for projects to expand the rail lines and Positive Train Control (PTC advanced technologies designed to automatically stop or slow a train before accidents occur) in that region. In the southern region it plans to spend $800 million in nine states for engineering maintenance and line expansion projects of which $175 million is planned for line expansion initiatives and continued implementation of PTC.

The overall $6 billion investment for 2015 includes $2.9 billion to replace and maintain core network and related assets nearly $1.5 billion on expansion and efficiency projects $200 million for continued implementation of PTC and $1.4 billion for locomotives freight cars and other equipment acquisitions.

In 2014 the company made capital investments for line expansion system improvement projects

additional equipment and new employee hires. BNSF Railway had a 2013 capital program (to strengthen its infrastructure) valued at $4.1 billion.

EXECUTIVES

President And Ceo, Carl R. Ice, age 61
Evp Law And Corporate Affairs, Roger Nober, age 53
Evp And Cfo, Julie A. Piggott
Evp And Chief Marketing Officer, Stevan B. Bobb
Evp Operations, Gregory C. Fox
Executive Chairman, Matthew K. (Matt) Rose, age 59
Auditors: DELOITTE & TOUCHE LLP FORT WO

LOCATIONS

HQ: BNSF RAILWAY COMPANY
2650 LOU MENK DR, FORT WORTH, TX 761312830
Phone: 800 795-2673
Web: WWW.BNSF.COM

COMPETITORS

American Commercial Lines	Kansas City Southern Railway
American Commercial Lines	Kansas City Southern Railway
Canadian National Railway	Kirby Corporation
Canadian National Railway	Kirby Corporation
Canadian Pacific Railway	Landstar System
Canadian Pacific Railway	Landstar System
Ingram Industries	Norfolk Southern
Ingram Industries	Norfolk Southern
J.B. Hunt	Schneider National
J.B. Hunt	Schneider National
	Union Pacific Railroad
	Union Pacific Railroad
	Werner Enterprises
	Werner Enterprises

HISTORICAL FINANCIALS

Company Type: Private

Income Statement   FYE: December 31

	REVENUE ($ mil.)	NET INCOME ($ mil.)	NET PROFIT MARGIN	EMPLOYEES
12/17	20,747	12,119	58.4%	41,000
12/16	19,278	4,260	22.1%	—
12/14	22,714	4,397	19.4%	—
12/13	21,552	4,271	19.8%	—
Annual Growth	(0.9%)	29.8%	—	—

2017 Year-End Financials
Return on assets: 14.8%   Cash ($ mil.): 516
Return on equity: 58.4%
Current ratio: 0.70

BOARD OF EDUCATION FOR THE CITY OF SAVANNAH AND THE COUNTY OF CHATHAM (INC)

EXECUTIVES

Pres, Jolene Byrne
Contrl, Beth Stanford
Auditors: KRT CPAS PC SAVANNAH GEORG

LOCATIONS

HQ: BOARD OF EDUCATION FOR THE CITY OF
SAVANNAH AND THE COUNTY OF CHATHAM (INC)
208 BULL ST, SAVANNAH, GA 314013997
Phone: 912 395-1000
Web: WWW.SAVANNAH.COM

HISTORICAL FINANCIALS
Company Type: Private

Income Statement — FYE: June 30

	REVENUE ($ mil.)	NET INCOME ($ mil.)	NET PROFIT MARGIN	EMPLOYEES
06/17	500	(30)	—	4,781
06/16	493	21	4.3%	—
06/15	478	(11)	—	—
06/14	447	36	8.1%	—
Annual Growth	3.8%	—	—	—

BOARD OF EDUCATION OF CARROLL COUNTY

EXECUTIVES

President, James L Doolan
Administrator, Michille Caples
Purchasing Agent, Nancy Codner
Education Specialist, Diana Haines
Network Analyst, James Paul
Education Assistant, Jeannette Dowling
Network Engineer, Jimmy Garrett
Transportation Associate, Pat Wall
Academic Advisor, Sean Hembree
Auditors: CLIFTONLARSONALLEN LLP BALTIM

LOCATIONS

HQ: BOARD OF EDUCATION OF CARROLL COUNTY
125 N COURT ST, WESTMINSTER, MD 211575192
Phone: 410 751-3000
Web: WWW.CARROLLK12.ORG

HISTORICAL FINANCIALS
Company Type: Private

Income Statement — FYE: June 30

	REVENUE ($ mil.)	NET INCOME ($ mil.)	NET PROFIT MARGIN	EMPLOYEES
06/15	358	(6)	—	121
06/14	361	(5)	—	—
06/13	372	0	0.3%	—
06/12	375	10	2.7%	—
Annual Growth	(1.6%)	—	—	—

2015 Year-End Financials
Return on assets: 1.4%   Cash ($ mil.): 10
Return on equity: (-1.8%)
Current ratio: 0.30

BOARD OF EDUCATION OF CITY OF CHICAGO

EXECUTIVES

Pres, Frank Clark
Technology, James V Dispensa
Coordinator, Samantha Treworgy
Information Technology Influen, Hallie Askuvich
Technology Manager, Denise Sangster
Chief Public Policy Officer, Frank Bilecki
Director, Ryan Crosby
Auditors: MCGLADREY LLP CHICAGO ILLINO

LOCATIONS

HQ: BOARD OF EDUCATION OF CITY OF CHICAGO
42 W MADISON ST FL 2, CHICAGO, IL 606024309
Phone: 773 553-1600
Web: WWW.CPS.K12.IL.US

HISTORICAL FINANCIALS
Company Type: Private

Income Statement — FYE: June 30

	REVENUE ($ mil.)	NET INCOME ($ mil.)	NET PROFIT MARGIN	EMPLOYEES
06/16	5,272	(381)	—	43,000
06/12	5,760	324	5.6%	—
06/11	5,660	238	4.2%	—
06/08	17	(0)	—	—
Annual Growth	103.8%	—	—	—

BOARD OF REGENTS OF THE UNIVERSITY OF NEBRASKA

EXECUTIVES

Svp Business And Finance, David E. Lechner
Chancellor University Of Nebraska Lincoln, Harvey S. Perlman
Chancellor University Of Nebraska Kearney, Douglas A. (Doug) Kristensen
Interim Chancellor Omaha Campus, John Christenson
Evp And Provost, Susan M. Fritz
Interim President, James Linder
Chancellor University Of Nebraska Medical Center, Jeffrey P. Gold
Cio, Walter Weir
President, Hank M. Bounds
Assistant Vice President And Director Of Budget And Planning, Chris Kabourek
Vice President Administrative Services, Janet Means
Chairman, Howard L. Hawks
Vice Chairman, Bob Phares
Auditors: NEBRASKA AUDITOR OF PUBLIC ACC

LOCATIONS

HQ: BOARD OF REGENTS OF THE UNIVERSITY OF NEBRASKA
3835 HOLDREGE ST, LINCOLN, NE 685031435
Phone: 402 472-3906
Web: WWW.UNMC.EDU

PRODUCTS/OPERATIONS

University Campuses
The University of Nebraska at Kearney
The University of Nebraska-Lincoln
The University of Nebraska Medical Center
The University of Nebraska at Omaha

HISTORICAL FINANCIALS
Company Type: Private

Income Statement — FYE: June 30

	REVENUE ($ mil.)	NET INCOME ($ mil.)	NET PROFIT MARGIN	EMPLOYEES
06/16	1,490	215	14.5%	15,200
06/15	1,405	221	15.8%	—
06/14	1,333	222	16.7%	—
06/13	1,313	254	19.4%	—
Annual Growth	4.3%	(5.4%)	—	—

2016 Year-End Financials
Return on assets: 10.1%   Cash ($ mil.): 613
Return on equity: 14.5%
Current ratio: 1.70

BOARD OF REGENTS OF THE UNIVERSITY SYSTEM OF GEORGIA

EXECUTIVES

Chancellor, Hank Huckaby
Director For Grants Accounting, Jennifer Shaw
Procurement Staff, Michael Haun
Coordinator, Taylor Smith
Coordinator, Charlotte Stauffer
Customer Representativ, Justina Washington
Senior Human Resources General, Andrea Mitchell
Administrative Coordinator, Blair Witte
Administrator, Britt Freeman
Director, Cherry Zhang
Ecampus Director, Christy Talley-Smith
Auditors: GREG S GRIFFIN ATLANTA GEOR

LOCATIONS

HQ: BOARD OF REGENTS OF THE UNIVERSITY SYSTEM OF GEORGIA
270 WASHINGTON ST SW FL 7, ATLANTA, GA 303349009
Phone: 404 962-3050
Web: WWW.USG.EDU

HISTORICAL FINANCIALS
Company Type: Private

Income Statement — FYE: June 30

	REVENUE ($ mil.)	NET INCOME ($ mil.)	NET PROFIT MARGIN	EMPLOYEES
06/17	5,100	57	1.1%	40,000
06/15	4,704	124	2.6%	—
06/11	0	0	—	—
06/08	266	5	1.9%	—
Annual Growth	38.8%	31.2%	—	—

2017 Year-End Financials
Return on assets: 3.1%   Cash ($ mil.): 1,515
Return on equity: 1.1%
Current ratio: 2.30

BOCA RATON REGIONAL HOSPITAL, INC.

EXECUTIVES

Prin, Jerry Fedele
Vice President, Dawn Javersack
Vice President, Mindy Raymond
Coo, Mindy Shikiar
Materials Director, Laurie Leon
Director, Kathy Schilling
Director, Caroline Ferraiuolo
Senior Manager, Richard Aronsohn
Vice-President, Alex Eremia
Executive Director, Denise Caccioppo
Assistant Controller, Jeanne Wiener

LOCATIONS

HQ: BOCA RATON REGIONAL HOSPITAL, INC.
800 MEADOWS RD, BOCA RATON, FL 334862304
Phone: 561 395-7100
Web: WWW.BRRH.COM

HISTORICAL FINANCIALS

Company Type: Private

Income Statement				FYE: June 30
	REVENUE ($ mil.)	NET INCOME ($ mil.)	NET PROFIT MARGIN	EMPLOYEES
06/16	424	20	4.9%	1,917
06/15	386	22	5.8%	—
06/14	390	38	9.8%	—
06/13	362	21	6.0%	—
Annual Growth	5.4%	(1.8%)	—	—

BON SECOURS-MARYVIEW HEALTH CORPORATION

Auditors: DELOITTE TAX LLP MCLEAN VA

LOCATIONS

HQ: BON SECOURS-MARYVIEW HEALTH CORPORATION
7007 HARBOUR VIEW BLVD # 114, SUFFOLK, VA 234353657
Phone: 757 889-5000

HISTORICAL FINANCIALS

Company Type: Private

Income Statement				FYE: August 31
	REVENUE ($ mil.)	NET INCOME ($ mil.)	NET PROFIT MARGIN	EMPLOYEES
08/17	417	(10)	—	3
08/16	417	(1)	—	—
08/15	402	2	0.7%	—
08/14	393	9	2.4%	—
Annual Growth	2.0%	—	—	—

2017 Year-End Financials

Return on assets: 9.4%   Cash ($ mil.): 1
Return on equity: (-2.5%)
Current ratio: 0.50

BOONE HOSPITAL CENTER

EXECUTIVES

Pres, Paul Machuk
Pres, Jim Sinek
Internal Medicine Practitioner, Martha J Herring
Director of Risk Management, Mary Kingsley
Chief Operating Officer, Randy M Morrow
Recruiter, Teri Kaune
Internal Medicine Practitioner, Jeffrey Robinson
Blood Bank Manager, Grant Darkow
General Manager, Michael Szewczyk
Director, Myrl Frevert
Director of Plant Operations, Gary Wilburn

LOCATIONS

HQ: BOONE HOSPITAL CENTER
1600 E BROADWAY, COLUMBIA, MO 652015897
Phone: 573 815-8000
Web: WWW.BOONE.ORG

COMPETITORS

Alexian Brothers Health System	HCA
	Mercy Health
Ascension Health	SSM Health Care
CHRISTUS Health	Saint Luke's Health
Carle Physician Group	System
Catholic Health Initiatives	Tenet Healthcare

HISTORICAL FINANCIALS

Company Type: Private

Income Statement				FYE: December 31
	REVENUE ($ mil.)	NET INCOME ($ mil.)	NET PROFIT MARGIN	EMPLOYEES
12/17	288	(10)	—	3,150
12/16	299	6	2.1%	—
12/15	284	(1)	—	—
12/14	288	16	5.6%	—
Annual Growth	0.1%	—	—	—

2017 Year-End Financials

Return on assets: 1.9%   Cash ($ mil.): 8
Return on equity: (-3.8%)
Current ratio: 2.10

BORGESS MEDICAL CENTER

Borgess Medical Center is part of the Borgess Health Alliance which is a member of the Ascension Health network. The general acute care facility which serves residents of southwestern Michigan houses more than 420 beds. It has a comprehensive offering of medical and surgical services including specialty care in areas such as cancer heart disease neuroscience and orthopedics. Borgess Medical Center also serves as a Level II trauma center and features a research institute a sleep disorders clinic a weight loss surgery center no-wait emergency room and outpatient facilities. The hospital was founded in 1889 by a local priest.

Operations

Borgess Medical Center sees more than 60000 visitors at its emergency and trauma facilities each year. Its specialist surgical facilities include operat-

ing rooms with comprehensive monitoring services for brain surgery spinal surgery and other complex procedures. The facility also serves as a regional behavioral health center. Its Stryker Center features extensive cardiovascular and neurological diagnosis and treatment resources as well as radiology pharmacy and same-day surgery units.

EXECUTIVES

Vice President Human Resources, Laura Lentenbrink
Vice President Operations, Jason Nicolai

LOCATIONS

HQ: BORGESS MEDICAL CENTER
1521 GULL RD, KALAMAZOO, MI 490481666
Phone: 269 226-7000
Web: HEALTHCARE.ASCENSION.ORG/SITES-OF-CARE/MICHIGAN/

PRODUCTS/OPERATIONS

Selected Centers and Services
Behavioral Health
Birthing Center
Brain & Spine
Breast Care Centers
Cancer & Oncology
Cardiology Group
Critical Care
Dietary Services
Emergency & Trauma
Fibroid Center
Henry Ford
Inpatient Services
Laboratory Services
Osteoporosis Centers
Palliative Care
Radiology
Rehabilitation Services
Sleep Disorders
Vascular
Women's Services

COMPETITORS

Bronson Health Care	Sheridan Community
Covenant HealthCare	Hospital
Gerber Memorial	Sparrow Health System
McLaren Health Care	Spectrum Health
Memorial Hospital & Health System	Trinity Health (Novi)

HISTORICAL FINANCIALS

Company Type: Private

Income Statement				FYE: June 30
	REVENUE ($ mil.)	NET INCOME ($ mil.)	NET PROFIT MARGIN	EMPLOYEES
06/16	394	60	15.4%	2,200
06/15	382	28	7.4%	—
06/14	449	64	14.3%	—
06/10	455	(6)	—	—
Annual Growth	(2.4%)	—	—	—

2016 Year-End Financials

Return on assets: 1.8%   Cash ($ mil.): 10
Return on equity: 15.4%
Current ratio: 0.40

BOSCOV'S, INC.

EXECUTIVES

Ceo, Albert Boscov
President, Kenneth S Lakin
Treas, Russell C Diehm
Exec Vice President, Toni Miller

Vice President, Peter D Lakin
Prin, Edwin A Lakin
Executive Officer, Kathleen Houck
Purchasing Coordinator, Mary Dunn
Consultant, Patricia Creque
Staff, Ronnie Eddinger
Sales Staff, Chantal Van Bauwel
Auditors: KPMG LLP PHILADELPHIA PA

LOCATIONS

HQ: BOSCOV'S, INC.
  4500 PERKIOMEN AVE, READING, PA 196063946
Phone: 610 779-2000
Web: WWW.BOSCOVS.COM

HISTORICAL FINANCIALS

Company Type: Private

Income Statement   FYE: February 3

	REVENUE ($ mil.)	NET INCOME ($ mil.)	NET PROFIT MARGIN	EMPLOYEES
02/18*	1,192	37	3.2%	10,003
01/17	1,139	32	2.8%	—
01/16	1,101	27	2.5%	—
Annual Growth	4.1%	17.9%	—	—

*Fiscal year change

2018 Year-End Financials

Return on assets: 4.1%   Cash ($ mil.): 73
Return on equity: 3.2%
Current ratio: 0.70

BOSTON MEDICAL CENTER CORPORATION

Located in Boston's South End neighborhood Boston Medical Center (BMC) offers a full spectrum of health care services from prenatal care and obstetrics to surgery and rehabilitation. BMC is also the city's largest provider of indigent care spending millions of dollars annually on care for uninsured patients and offering free screenings and other community outreach programs. The not-for-profit hospital boasts nearly 500 licensed beds more than 700 physicians and includes a Level 1 trauma center acute rehabilitation facilities and neonatal and pediatric intensive care units. The center is the primary teaching hospital of Boston University's School of Medicine.

Operations

BMC also operates Boston HealthNet a network affiliation of the medical center Boston University School of Medicine and more than a dozen community health centers. Boston HealthNet provides outreach prevention primary care and specialty care and dental services at sites located throughout the community.

Hand-in-hand with being a major teaching hospital is engaging in extensive medical research. BMC oversees more than 590 research and service projects and conducts both biomedical and clinical research programs exploring infectious disease cardiology vascular biology Parkinson's disease geriatrics and endocrinology among other areas. With Boston University BMC also operates a 16-acre research and business park called BioSquare that serves as a collaborative center for the development and commercialization of new biomedical technologies.

In 2015 BMC had more than 712 000 outpatient clinic visits 204000 outpatient ancillary visits 125000 emergency department visits and 24000 admissions.

Sales and Marketing

In addition to its medical and research services BMC provides health insurance through its BMC HealthNet Plan a managed care plan that has more than 240000 Medicaid and low-cost health plan members. The center markets its services through social media.

Financial Performance

BMC received more than $119 million in sponsored research funding in fiscal 2015; it oversees 594 research and service projects separate from research activities at Boston University School of Medicine.

Strategy

In late 2014 BMC's Center for Regenerative Medicine and Boston University were awarded a $2.7 million grant from the National Heart Lung and Blood Institute to establish a stem cell repository that researchers across the US can access for free. The first-of-its-kind repository will help promote stem cell research particularly in the area of lung disease.

EXECUTIVES

Svp Finance And Cfo, Richard Silveria
President And Ceo, Kate E. Walsh
Svp And Chief Nursing Officer, Nancy Gaden
Svp And Chief Medical Officer, Ravin Davidoff
Coo, Alastair Bell
President And Ceo Faculty Practice Foundation, William Creevy
Svp Quality Safety And Technology; Chief Quality Officer, Stanley Hochberg
Vice President Operations, Gary Nicksa
Pharmacy Manager, Jose Barria
Chairman, James S. Phalen, age 67

LOCATIONS

HQ: BOSTON MEDICAL CENTER CORPORATION
  1 BOSTON MEDICAL CTR PL # 1, BOSTON, MA
  021182999
Phone: 617 414-5000
Web: WWW.BMC.ORG

PRODUCTS/OPERATIONS

Selected Services and Programs

Alzheimer's Disease Center
Anesthesiology
Boston HealthNet
Boston University Affiliated Physicians
Boston University Cosmetic and Laser Center
Cardiovascular Center
Care Management
Dermatology
Diabetes
Elders Living at Home Program
Emergency Medicine
Facial Plastic and Reconstructive Surgery
General Internal Medicne / Primary Care
Geriatrics
Head and Neck Cancer Center of Excellence
Hematology & Medical Oncology
Immigrant & Refugee Health Program
Integrative Medicine
LocoMotor Training
Mattapan Community Health Center
Melanoma Program
Neurosurgery
Nursing
Ophthalmology
Oral and Maxillofacial Surgery
Pediatrics - bWell Center
 Pediatrics
Rehabilitation Therapies
Renal Medicine
South End Community Health Center
Special Kids Special Help
Thoracic Surgery
Transplant Surgery
Uphams Corner Health Center
Urology
Vascular Center
Vascular and Endovascular Surgery
Weight Loss Surgery (Bariatric Surgery)
Whittier Street Health Center

COMPETITORS

Beth Israel Deaconess Medical Center
 Brigham and Women's Hospital
 Cambridge Health Alliance
 Care New England
 CareGroup
 Children's Hospital Boston
 Dana-Farber
 Massachusetts General Hospital
 Newton-Wellesley Hospital
 Northeast Health System
 Partners HealthCare
 Shriners Hospitals For Children
 Spaulding Rehabilitation Hospital
 St. Elizabeth's Medical Center
 Steward Health Care

HISTORICAL FINANCIALS

Company Type: Private

Income Statement   FYE: September 30

	REVENUE ($ mil.)	NET INCOME ($ mil.)	NET PROFIT MARGIN	EMPLOYEES
09/17	1,089	12	1.2%	4,200
09/15	1,004	7	0.8%	—
09/12	886	2	0.3%	—
09/09	1,004	(12)	—	—
Annual Growth	1.0%	—	—	—

2017 Year-End Financials

Return on assets: 14.0%   Cash ($ mil.): 125
Return on equity: 1.2%
Current ratio: 0.90

BOSTON UNIVERSITY

EXECUTIVES

Pres, Robert Brown
Cfo, Martin Howard
Vice President, Todd Klipp
Director of Finance, Alison English
Co-Director, Ellen Shell
Associate, Hamid Nawab
Scientist, Jeffrey Baumgardner
Scientist, Karen Hirsch
Director, Mariko Henstock
Manager, Todd Blute
Professor, Abraham Matta

LOCATIONS

HQ: BOSTON UNIVERSITY
  590 COMMONWEALTH AVE # 255, BOSTON, MA
  022152521
Phone: 617 353-2600
Web: WWW.BU.EDU

HISTORICAL FINANCIALS

Company Type: Private

Income Statement   FYE: June 30

	REVENUE ($ mil.)	NET INCOME ($ mil.)	NET PROFIT MARGIN	EMPLOYEES
06/18	2,018	517	25.6%	70
06/17	1,895	507	26.8%	—
Annual Growth	6.5%	2.0%	—	—

2018 Year-End Financials

Return on assets: 6.0%   Cash ($ mil.): 148
Return on equity: 25.6%
Current ratio: —

BOTSFORD GENERAL HOSPITAL

EXECUTIVES

Ceo-Prin, Paul E Lacasse
Cfo, David L Marcellino
Cntrl, Barb Hrit
Programmer, Doug Warren
Purchasing Director, Kathy Leach
Supervisor, Maryjo McKenzie
Chief of Medicine, David Walters
Marketing Manager, Lynn Anderson
Coordinator, Peter Newberry
Coordinator, Debbie Sherman
Administrative Assistant, Debbie Wozniak

LOCATIONS

HQ: BOTSFORD GENERAL HOSPITAL
  28050 GRAND RIVER AVE, FARMINGTON HILLS, MI
  483365933
Phone: 248 471-8000
Web: WWW.BOTSFORD.ORG

HISTORICAL FINANCIALS
Company Type: Private

Income Statement			FYE: December 31	
	REVENUE ($ mil.)	NET INCOME ($ mil.)	NET PROFIT MARGIN	EMPLOYEES
12/15	283	(1)	—	1,859
12/14	286	7	2.5%	—
12/06	527	10	2.1%	—
12/05	279	7	2.6%	—
Annual Growth	0.1%	—	—	—

2015 Year-End Financials

Return on assets: 6.6%   Cash ($ mil.): 15
Return on equity: (-0.5%)
Current ratio: 1.30

BOULDER VALLEY SCHOOL DISTRICT RE-2

EXECUTIVES

Supt, George Garcia
Sup, Chris King
Asst Sup, Ellen Brown
Treas, Linda Clausen
Sup, Bruce Messinger PHD
Education Specialist, Carolina Henderson
Academic Advisor, Cindy Maxfield
Health Professional, Jeanne Franklin
Teacher, Kate Villarreal
Academic Advisor, Victor Sanchez
Manager, John Shortridge
Auditors: S&G SWANHORST & COMPANY LLC G

LOCATIONS

HQ: BOULDER VALLEY SCHOOL DISTRICT RE-2
  6500 ARAPAHOE RD, BOULDER, CO 803031407
Phone: 303 447-1010
Web: WWW.BVSD.ORG

HISTORICAL FINANCIALS
Company Type: Private

Income Statement				FYE: June 30
	REVENUE ($ mil.)	NET INCOME ($ mil.)	NET PROFIT MARGIN	EMPLOYEES
06/17	415	84	20.4%	3,815
06/16	393	(55)	—	—
06/12	319	(36)	—	—
06/11	324	(42)	—	—
Annual Growth	4.2%	—	—	—

BOWLING GREEN-WARREN COUNTY COMMUNITY HOSPITAL CORPORATION

EXECUTIVES

Ceo, Connie D Smith
Exec Vice President, Ronald Sowell
Sr V Pres-Contrl, Chris Roszman
Dir, Bob Hovious
Coordinator, Sandra Webb
Staff, Emily Jernigan
Vice-President, Mark Robison
Marketing Director, Sandy Feria
Health Professional, Arshad H Banday
Nurse, Christopher M Tarter
Plant Manager, Ken Offutt

LOCATIONS

HQ: BOWLING GREEN-WARREN COUNTY
  COMMUNITY HOSPITAL CORPORATION
  250 PARK ST, BOWLING GREEN, KY 421011760
Phone: 270 745-1000
Web: WWW.MCBG.ORG

HISTORICAL FINANCIALS
Company Type: Private

Income Statement				FYE: March 31
	REVENUE ($ mil.)	NET INCOME ($ mil.)	NET PROFIT MARGIN	EMPLOYEES
03/18	377	32	8.7%	1,900
03/17	365	23	6.4%	—
03/12	312	23	7.6%	—
03/05	208	16	7.9%	—
Annual Growth	4.7%	5.4%	—	—

2018 Year-End Financials

Return on assets: 4.1%   Cash ($ mil.): 29
Return on equity: 8.7%
Current ratio: 1.30

BOY SCOUTS OF AMERICA

Scouts enter dens as Tigers and eventually take flight as Eagles. Boy Scouts of America (BSA) one of the nation's largest youth organizations has about 2.6 million youth members and more than 1 million adult leaders in its ranks. BSA offers educational and character-building programs emphasizing leadership citizenship personal development and physical fitness. In addition to traditional scouting programs (Tiger Cub Webelos and Boy Scouts ranging up to Eagle rank) it offers the Venturing program for boys and girls ages 14-21. BSA generates revenue through membership and council fees food and magazine sales and contributions. The organization was founded by Chicago publisher William Boyce in 1910.

Operations

BSA's group membership is supported through about 300 local Boy Scout councils. Additionally it hosts a National Scout Jamboree each year to bring all scouts together. The organization also operates a high-adventure base in West Virginia. The bases offer scouts a range of outdoor activities including backpacking camping canoeing and diving. The West Virginia location serves as the organization's permanent location for its annual Jamboree. BSA operates also bases in Florida Minnesota and New Mexico.

BSA also publishes Boys' Life monthly magazine which boasts more than 1 million subscribers and Scouting magazine for adults registered in Cub Scouting Boy Scouting Varsity Scouting and Venturing.

Financial Performance

BSA's revenue increased 24% in 2013 to $283 over 2012's $229 million. The uptick was due to a bump in fees (44% of total revenue) primarily from the 2013 National Scout Jamboree as well as from contributions and bequests.

Strategy

BSA boasts programs that remain popular but in recent years membership growth has slowed with the recession and other societal forces including video games social media and other entertainment.

In 2013 Cub Scout membership (which accounts for more than 50% of total youth membership) dipped by about 7% while the ranks of the Boy Scouts decreased by 3%. Overall total youth membership declined by about 6% for the year continuing its downward trend. To boost membership and grow its organization BSA developed a strategic plan that involves reaching out to new groups of parents and students. To this end it has developed and maintained relationships with civic religious and fraternal organizations across the US including those that serve African-American Asian and Latino families. It has also analyzed Generation X and Millennial parents to determine how to best bring scouting to their families.

EXECUTIVES

Deputy Chief Scout Executive And Coo, Gary P. Butler
National President, Robert M. Gates
Cfo, Michael Ashline
Chief Scout Executive, Michael Surbaugh
Auditors: PRICEWATERHOUSECOOPERS LLP DA

LOCATIONS

HQ: BOY SCOUTS OF AMERICA
  1325 W WALNUT HILL LN, IRVING, TX 750383096
Phone: 972 580-2000

PRODUCTS/OPERATIONS

2015 Youth Membership

	No.
Cub Scout-Age	1,261,340
Boy Scout	840,654
Venturing and Sea Scouts	142,892
Explorers	110,445
Life Character	385,535
Total	**2,612,955**

2015 Revenue

	$ mil.	% of total
Fees	126	4
Net investment gain	4	2
Contributions & bequests	28	14
Supply operations	23	12
Magazines	14	8
Other (includes trading post sales)	(0.8)	0
Total	**197**	**100**

HISTORICAL FINANCIALS
Company Type: Private

Income Statement				FYE: December 31
	REVENUE ($ mil.)	NET INCOME ($ mil.)	NET PROFIT MARGIN	EMPLOYEES
12/15	335	(25)	—	2,800
12/14	244	46	19.0%	—
12/13	0	(33)	—	—
12/10	310	90	29.0%	—
Annual Growth	1.6%	—	—	—

2015 Year-End Financials
Return on assets: 9.4% Cash ($ mil.): 44
Return on equity: (-7.6%)
Current ratio: 0.10

BRANDEIS UNIVERSITY

Brandeis University offers more than 40 undergraduate majors and 45 minors programs in the creative arts humanities sciences and social sciences. Located just west of Boston it comprises the College of Arts and Sciences the Graduate School of Arts and Sciences the International Business School the Heller School for Social Policy and Management the Lown School for Near Eastern and Judaic Studies and the Rabb School of Continuing Studies. The university has an enrollment of more than 5000 students; the student/faculty ratio is 10-to-1. A non-sectarian Jewish community-sponsored institution named after the late Justice Louis Brandeis of the US Supreme Court Brandeis University was founded in 1948.

Operations
Brandeis University's tuition fee for 2016-17 was $49586 per year. The students are instructed by about 650 faculty members. The university provided more than $51 million in funded grants and scholarships to undergraduates.

Geographic Reach
The university is located in 235 acres campus in Waltham Massachusetts comprising more than 100 academic and residential buildings.

Financial Performance
Revenues increased by 5% in 2015 due to growth in net tuition fees residence hall and dining revenues contributions and endowment return utilized revenues.

Net income decreased by 36% due to a decline in investment returns and higher operating expenses (including instruction and academic support expenses).

Operating cash outflow decreased in 2015 by 53% due to a change in operating assets.

EXECUTIVES

President, Ronald D. Liebowitz, age 62
Svp And Coo, Steven S. Manos
Interim Dean Heller School For Social Policy And Management, Marty W. Krauss
Cio, John Unsworth
Dean International Business School, Bruce R. Magid
Svp Finance And Treasurer, Marianne Cwalina
Dean College Of Arts And Sciences, Susan J. Birren
Dean Graduate School Of Arts And Sciences, Eric Chasalow
Interim Provost, Irving R. Epstein
Assistant Vice President Corporate And Foundation Relations, Michael Dettelbach
Assistant Vice President For Budget And Planning, John Richard
Vice President, April French
Vice Chairman, Stephen B. Kay
Chairman, Perry M. Traquina
Vice Chairman, Jonathan G. Davis
Auditors: KPMG LLP BOSTON MA

LOCATIONS

HQ: BRANDEIS UNIVERSITY
298 CRESCENT ST, WALTHAM, MA 024533803
Phone: 781 736-8318
Web: WWW.BRANDEIS.EDU

PRODUCTS/OPERATIONS

2015 Sales

	% of total
Net tuition fees residence hall and dining revenues	55
Sponsored programs-direct	15
Endowment return utilized	13
Contributions	6
Others	11
Total	**100**

Selected Programs
African and Afro-American Studies
American Studies
Anthropology
Biochemistry
Biological Physics
Biology
Business
Classical Studies
Comparative Literature
East Asian Studies
Economics
English
Film Television and Interactive Media
French and Francophone Studies
German Studies
Hispanic Studies
History of Ideas
International and Global Studies
Journalism
Language and Linguistics
Legal Studies
Music
Neuroscience
Philosophy
Politics
Russian Studies
Sexuality and Queer Studies
South Asian Studies

HISTORICAL FINANCIALS
Company Type: Private

Income Statement				FYE: June 30
	REVENUE ($ mil.)	NET INCOME ($ mil.)	NET PROFIT MARGIN	EMPLOYEES
06/16	333	(64)	—	1,200
06/15	508	80	15.7%	—
06/10	323	(24)	—	—
06/09	248	(173)	—	—
Annual Growth	4.3%	—	—	—

2016 Year-End Financials
Return on assets: 7.3% Cash ($ mil.): 30
Return on equity: (-19.4%)
Current ratio: —

BRAZOS EDUCATION LOAN AUTHORITY, INC

EXECUTIVES

Pres, Murray Watson Jr
Exec Vp - Ceo, Ricky Turman
Exec Vp, David Horner

LOCATIONS

HQ: BRAZOS EDUCATION LOAN AUTHORITY, INC
2600 WASHINGTON AVE, WACO, TX 767107449
Phone: 254 753-0915
Web: WWW.BRAZOSFOUNDATION.ORG

HISTORICAL FINANCIALS
Company Type: Private

Income Statement				FYE: June 30
	ASSETS ($ mil.)	NET INCOME ($ mil.)	INCOME AS % OF ASSETS	EMPLOYEES
06/18	2,224	8	0.4%	3
06/17	2,477	11	0.5%	—
06/16	2,770	19	0.7%	—
Annual Growth	(10.4%)	(34.7%)	—	—

BRE GLACIER L.P.

EXECUTIVES

Pres-ceo, Jack Cuneo

LOCATIONS

HQ: BRE GLACIER L.P.
90 PARK AVE FL 32, NEW YORK, NY 100161316
Phone: 212 297-1000
Web: WWW.GPTREIT.COM

HISTORICAL FINANCIALS
Company Type: Private

Income Statement				FYE: December 31
	ASSETS ($ mil.)	NET INCOME ($ mil.)	INCOME AS % OF ASSETS	EMPLOYEES
12/17	6,456	86	1.3%	109
12/16	5,603	33	0.6%	—
12/15	5,840	(48)	—	—
Annual Growth	5.1%			

Return on assets: 10.9%   Sales ($ mil.): 545
Return on equity: 15.8%

BRENTWOOD UNION FREE SCHOOL DISTRICT

EXECUTIVES

Ceo, Dr Levy McIntyre
Superintendent, Joseph Bond
Coordinator, Jolynn Sapia
Coordinator, Ann Palmer
Coordinator, Joel Ratner
Auditors: COUGHLIN FOUNDOTOS CULLEN & DA

LOCATIONS

HQ: BRENTWOOD UNION FREE SCHOOL DISTRICT
52 3RD AVE, BRENTWOOD, NY 117174651
Phone: 631 434-2335
Web: WWW.BRENTWOOD.K12.NY.US

HISTORICAL FINANCIALS
Company Type: Private

Income Statement   FYE: June 30

	REVENUE ($ mil.)	NET INCOME ($ mil.)	NET PROFIT MARGIN	EMPLOYEES
06/18	414	3	0.8%	2,500
06/17	398	5	1.3%	—
06/09	325	24	7.5%	—
06/08	304	6	2.1%	—
Annual Growth	3.1%	(6.4%)	—	—

2018 Year-End Financials
Return on assets: 3.1%   Cash ($ mil.): 60
Return on equity: 0.8%
Current ratio: —

BRIDGEPORT HOSPITAL

EXECUTIVES

Pres-Ceo, William M Jennings
Sr V Pres-Med Staff, Bruce Mc Donald
V Pres-Hr, Joseph E Janell
Executive Vice President Chief, Norman Roth
Dir, David Bindelglass
Recruiter, Lorraine Iversen
Benefits Specialist, Marge Stehman
Human Resources Coordinator, Maria Alicea
Pediatrician, Mary Gaeta
Administrative Secretary, Mary Piskura
Senior Vice-President, Maryellen Kosturko

LOCATIONS

HQ: BRIDGEPORT HOSPITAL
267 GRANT ST, BRIDGEPORT, CT 066102870
Phone: 203 384-3000
Web: WWW.BRIDGEPORTHOSPITAL.ORG

HISTORICAL FINANCIALS
Company Type: Private

Income Statement   FYE: September 30

	REVENUE ($ mil.)	NET INCOME ($ mil.)	NET PROFIT MARGIN	EMPLOYEES
09/17	482	25	5.4%	200
09/16	470	46	9.9%	—
09/15	466	55	11.9%	—
09/14	439	42	9.8%	—
Annual Growth	3.1%	(15.5%)	—	—

2017 Year-End Financials
Return on assets: 3.6%   Cash ($ mil.): 26
Return on equity: 5.4%
Current ratio: 0.90

BRIGHAM YOUNG UNIVERSITY

Mormons looking for faith-based higher education don't have to look far — they can go to Brigham Young University (BYU) where they can get schooling based on the values of The Church of Jesus Christ of Latter-Day Saints (also known as the Mormon Church). Through 10 colleges the Mormon-owned university offers bachelor's degrees in some 180 academic programs master's in almost 70 and doctorates in another 26. BYU's enrollment includes more than 33360 students with about 99% identifying themselves as Mormon. The university's student-to-teacher ratio is about 21:1.

Operations

BYU's most-popular majors include exercise science management psychology English accounting communications computer science economics political science and public health. The university employs about 1500 faculty members. Tuition for Latter-Day Saints (LDS) members (those whose families pay tithes to the church) is about $5460 per two-semesters for undergraduates.

The school operates one of the largest university-based CE programs in the country. The division administers independent study evening school conferences and workshops and with the help of the Church Educational System religious education classes and lectures.

Geographic Reach

BYU is located in Provo Utah. It also has extension campuses in Laie Hawaii and Rexburg Idaho as well as a learning center in Jerusalem. Its Provo campus includes a missionary training center and the university also operates a business school in Salt Lake City Utah.

About 6% of BYU's students hail from outside of the US. Its continuing education (CE) division enrolls students from 50 states and locations outside the US that include Brazil China England Germany the Philippines Mexico and Switzerland. In addition BYU conducts about 150 study abroad programs in 56 countries.

Company Background

BYU was founded in 1875 by Brigham Young who led some 3500 church members fleeing religious persecution to found their own settlement in Salt Lake City. Utah became a US state in 1876.

EXECUTIVES

Vp Information Technology And Cio, J. Kelly Flanagan

Cfo, Brian K. Evans
Dean Of Students, Vernon L. Heperi
President, Kevin J. Worthen
Dean College Of Life Sciences, Rodney J. Brown
Dean Ira A. Fulton College Of Engineering And Technology, Alan R. Parkinson
Dean College Of Fine Arts And Communications, Stephen M. Jones
Dean College Of Humanities, John R. Rosenberg
Dean David O. Mckay School Of Education, K. Richard Young
Dean College Of Nursing, Beth V. Cole
Dean School Of Continuing Education, Wayne J. Lott
Dean College Of Family Home And Social Sciences, Benjamin M. Ogles
Dean Undergraduate Education, John D. Ball
Dean Religious Education, Terry B. Ball
Dean Marriott School Of Management, Gary C. Cornia
Dean College Of Physical And Mathematical Sciences, Scott D. Sommerfeldt
Dean Clark Law School, James R. Rasband
Dean Of Graduate Studies, Wynn C. Stirling
Chairman, Thomas S. Monson

LOCATIONS

HQ: BRIGHAM YOUNG UNIVERSITY
A 41 ASB BRGHAM YUNG UNIV, PROVO, UT 84602
Phone: 801 422-1211
Web: WWW.BYU.EDU

PRODUCTS/OPERATIONS

Selected Schools Colleges and Departments
Continuing Education
David M. Kennedy Center for International Studies
David O. McKay School of Education
Family Home and Social Sciences
Fine Arts and Communications
Graduate Studies
Humanities
Ira A. Fulton College of Engineering and Technology
J. Reuben Clark Law School
Life Sciences
Marriott School of Management
Nursing
Physical and Mathematical Sciences
Religious Education
Undergraduate Education

HISTORICAL FINANCIALS
Company Type: Private

Income Statement   FYE: December 31

	REVENUE ($ mil.)	NET INCOME ($ mil.)	NET PROFIT MARGIN	EMPLOYEES
12/17	1,633	492	30.1%	3,767
12/05	0	(4,294)	—	—
Annual Growth	146.8%	—	—	—

2017 Year-End Financials
Return on assets: 5.1%   Cash ($ mil.): 76
Return on equity: 30.1%
Current ratio: —

BRIGHTSTAR US, INC.

EXECUTIVES

Pres, Ray Roman
Dir-SEC, Oscar J Fumagali
Dir, Noel Marsden
Dir, Catherine Smith
Director Forward Operations, Ruta Ladd

HISTORICAL FINANCIALS

Company Type: Private

Income Statement				FYE: December 31
	REVENUE ($ mil.)	NET INCOME ($ mil.)	NET PROFIT MARGIN	EMPLOYEES
12/16	4,137	52	1.3%	225
12/15	4,418	50	1.1%	—
Annual Growth	(6.4%)	2.8%	—	—

BRONSON HEALTH CARE GROUP, INC.

Bronson Health Care Group has a strong presence as a provider of a wide range of medical services in southern Michigan and northern Indiana. The company operates several regional hospitals and health clinics including Bronson Methodist Hospital (some 400 beds) Bronson Battle Creek (220 beds) and Bronson Lakeview Hospital (35 beds). The not-for-profit health care system's facilities provide general and specialty services including trauma stroke burn cancer and cardiac care as well as emergency medicine pediatrics obstetrics rehabilitation and home health care.

Operations

Bronson Health Care Group serves about 24000 patients each year at more than 60 locations. The medical system offers a full range of services from primary care to critical care; it has more than 1000 medical staff members and 812 licensed beds.

The hospital group provides $94 million in community benefits a year including charity care for under-insured or uninsured patients.

Geographic Reach

Bronson Health Care Group operates hospitals clinics and physician practice facilities in Kalamazoo Calhoun and Van Buren counties in southwestern and south central Michigan; its locations also serve patients from areas of northern Indiana.

Strategy

Expanded its infrastructure to meet demand in 2013 the company opened Bronson Commons a rehabilitation and skilled nursing community in Mattawan. The all-private room healthcare facility has the capacity to serve 100 patients.

That year 2013 Bronson Battle Creek opened a new outpatient center on Beckley Road.

Mergers and Acquisitions

In 2013 HealthCare Midwest a multidisciplinary physician group (with 80 doctors) serving southwest Michigan joined the Bronson family of companies and became Bronson HealthCare Midwest. That year Associated Internal Medicine Specialists a medical practice focused on internal medicine and rheumatology joined Bronson Battle Creek and was renamed Bronson Internal Medicine & Rheumatology.

In 2012 Colon and Rectal Surgery Center PC joined the Bronson network and became Bronson Center for Colon & Rectal Diseases.

Company Background

To expand its services and geographic reach in 2011 Bronson Health Care System acquired the Battle Creek Health System (now named Bronson Battle Creek located in south central Michigan. The purchase added acute care inpatient mental health cancer care occupational health and other specialized services in the region.

The not-for-profit health care system was founded in 1900.

EXECUTIVES

Vice President Of Clinical Operations, Katie Harrelson
Senior Vice President Strategy And Communication, Sue Birch
Vice President, Vivian Burch
Board Member, Brenda Hunt

LOCATIONS

HQ: BRONSON HEALTH CARE GROUP, INC.
301 JOHN ST, KALAMAZOO, MI 490075295
Phone: 269 341-6000
Web: WWW.BRONSONHEALTH.COM

PRODUCTS/OPERATIONS

Selected Facilities
Bronson Athletic Club
Bronson Battle Creek
Bronson Commons
Bronson Health Foundation
Bronson HealthCare Midwest
Bronson Home Health Care
Bronson LakeView Hospital
Bronson LakeView Outpatient Center
Bronson Lifestyle Improvement & Research Center
Bronson Medical Group
Bronson Methodist Hospital
Bronson Vicksburg Outpatient Center
Van Buren Emergency Medical Services

COMPETITORS

Ascension Health	Mercy Health Hackley
Gerber Memorial	Sheridan Community
Hayes Green Beach	Hospital
Memorial Hospital	Spectrum Health

HISTORICAL FINANCIALS

Company Type: Private

Income Statement				FYE: December 31
	REVENUE ($ mil.)	NET INCOME ($ mil.)	NET PROFIT MARGIN	EMPLOYEES
12/17	1,233	63	5.1%	4,180
12/16	1,136	28	2.5%	—
12/09	119	16	13.8%	—
12/08	588	(62)	—	—
Annual Growth	8.6%	—	—	—

2017 Year-End Financials

Return on assets: 1.4%   Cash ($ mil.): 103
Return on equity: 5.1%
Current ratio: 2.00

BRONSON METHODIST HOSPITAL INC

EXECUTIVES

Director Of Nursing, Melissa Brown
Director Of Nursing, Tresa Kruis
Director Of Nursing, Season Marinich
Auditors: PLANTE & MORAN PLLC CHICAGO

LOCATIONS

HQ: BRONSON METHODIST HOSPITAL INC
601 JOHN ST STE E-012, KALAMAZOO, MI
490075346
Phone: 269 341-7654
Web: WWW.BRONSONHEALTH.COM

PRODUCTS/OPERATIONS

Selected Services
Anticoagulation
Bereavement
Breast Health
Burn
Cancer Care
Critical Care
Diabetes
Flu
Heart and Vascular
Home Health
Hyperbaric Oxygen Therapy
Infusion
Laboratory
Medical and Surgical Weight Management
Neurosciences
Nutrition
Occupational Health
Orthopedics
Palliative Care
Pediatrics
Pharmacy
Pregnancy and Childbirth
Rehabilitation
Respiratory Care
Sleep
Surgery
Stomal Therapy
Testing and Imaging
Trauma and Emergency
Women's Health
Wound

COMPETITORS

Ascension Health	Holland Hospital
Borgess Health	Spectrum Health
Bronson Battle Creek	Trinity Health (Novi)
Community Hospital	Zeeland Community
Elkhart General	Hospital
Healthcare System	
Hayes Green Beach	
Memorial Hospital	

HISTORICAL FINANCIALS

Company Type: Private

Income Statement				FYE: December 31
	REVENUE ($ mil.)	NET INCOME ($ mil.)	NET PROFIT MARGIN	EMPLOYEES
12/17	864	85	9.8%	2,861
12/15	726	69	9.5%	—
12/13	647	(8)	—	—
12/09	524	41	7.9%	—
Annual Growth	6.5%	9.5%	—	—

2017 Year-End Financials

Return on assets: 0.9%   Cash ($ mil.): 95
Return on equity: 9.8%
Current ratio: 3.30

BRONXCARE HEALTH SYSTEM

Bronx-Lebanon Hospital Center cares for patients in the central and south Bronx no doubt while rooting for the Yankees a few blocks away. The health care provider maintains more than 970 beds across its two campuses as well as psychiatric and nursing home facilities. Hospital specialty units include chest pain orthopedic cancer and women's health centers. Bronx-Lebanon also manages a network of about 70 owned and affiliated medical practices (under the BronxCare brand). This network includes primary care doctors and specialty clinics as well as rehabilitation facilities. The hospital is also a primary teaching hospital for the Albert Einstein College of Medicine.

Operations

Aside from its two major hospitals Bronx-Lebanon operates a psychiatric facility a pair of specialized long-term care facilities and the BronxCare network of medical practices that include Dr. Martin Luther King Jr. Health Center and a 51-unit facility to house seniors and low-income residents. Bronx-Lebanon cares for those with mental or substance abuse problems through the Family Wellness Center. It also operates a 240-bed Special Care Center and the 90-bed Highbridge Woodycrest Center to provide long term health care to geriatric AIDS and disabled residents. Its ER Department responds to about 141000 patient visits a year.

Geographic Reach

The hospital system's 37 locations serve residents of central and south Bronx in New York.

Sales and Marketing

In 2013 the company spent about $144000 on advertising.

Financial Performance

The Hospital Center is supported primarily by patient service fees paid by Medicaid Medicare and commercial insurance carriers. In 2013 the Medicaid contributed 63% of the revenue whereas Medicare contributed 28% and the rest 9% was contributed other third-party insurance carriers.

In 2013 Bronx-Lebanon's net revenues increased by about 5% due to a rise in patient service revenues and grants partially offset by a decrease in auxiliary services.

The company's net income increased by more than 790% in 2013 as the result of an increase in revenues.

Bronx-Lebanon's operating cash flows increased by 53% thanks to higher income.

Strategy

Bronx-Lebanon emphasizes its role as a community health care provider not only through its BronxCare network but through a number of community outreach and service efforts including school-based programs mobile health units free health screening and even a weekly live television show that discusses health issues.

To accommodate the growing population in and around the Bronx the hospital system has expanded in recent years with a new children's wing for inpatient and outpatient services; a nine-story ambulatory care facility; and an extensive emergency room modernization. Bronx-Lebanon also maintains a short stay observation unit in the emergency room area to monitor and evaluate patients in cardiac distress prior to admission or discharge.

Bronx-Lebanon is one of many hospital organizations to have joined a regional health information organization (RHIO) to allow medical professionals to access a patient's medical records at any number of health care locations. Other members of the Bronx RHIO include Montefiore Medical Center Jacobi Medical Center St. Barnabas Hospital and Hebrew Home at Riverdale.

Bronx-Lebanon is also one of the few hospitals in New York that is fully computerized with a complete inpatient and outpatient electronic medical record.

The hospital center's expansion plans include a $42 million 60000 sq. ft ambulatory care facility

and a $34 million 56000 sq. ft. life recovery center for chemical dependency services.

In 2014 the company completed the construction of its Health and Wellness Center a new state-of-the-art outpatient facility with general and specialty services and new treatment rooms and diagnostic equipment. It also completed the construction of its Life Recovery Center to combine inpatient outpatient and residential services for individuals suffering from chemical dependency.

The company also expanded its Emergency room adding a new 11-bay treatment area.

In the same year it also relocated and expanded its main Dentistry Practice adding 39 dental chairs (a 50% increase).

EXECUTIVES

Vice President Rcm, George Irizarry

LOCATIONS

HQ: BRONXCARE HEALTH SYSTEM
1276 FULTON AVE, BRONX, NY 104563402
Phone: 718 590-1800
Web: WWW.BRONX-LEB.ORG

PRODUCTS/OPERATIONS

Selected Services
Anesthesiology
Asthma
  Adult
  Pediatric
Cardiology
Dentistry
Diabetes
  Adult
  Pediatric
Ear Nose & Throat
Gastroenterology
Hematology & Oncology
Neonatology
Neurology
Ophthalmology
Orthopaedics
Pediatrics
Physical Medicine
Psychiatry
Radiology
Special Care Center
Urology & Men's Health

Selected Academic Affiliations

Albert Einstein College of Medicine
Bronx Community College
Hostos Community College
Lehman College City University of New York
State University of New York at Stony Brook

COMPETITORS

Beth Israel Medical Center	Montefiore Medical
Catholic Healthcare System	New York City Health and Hospitals
Continuum Health Partners	NewYork-Presbyterian Healthcare
Lenox Hill Hospital	Northwell Health
Maimonides Medical Center	Winthrop-University Hospital
Memorial Sloan-Kettering	

HISTORICAL FINANCIALS

Company Type: Private

Income Statement   FYE: December 31

	REVENUE ($ mil.)	NET INCOME ($ mil.)	NET PROFIT MARGIN	EMPLOYEES
12/16	641	6	1.0%	4,000
12/15	631	18	3.0%	—
12/14	598	(34)		—
12/13	631	0	0.1%	—
Annual Growth	0.5%	165.3%	—	—

BROOKLYN HOSPITAL CENTER

The Brooklyn Hospital Center has been taking care ofA ailing Kings County residentsA since before Brooklyn was a borough. Established in 1845 (before Brooklyn became part of New York City) the hospital houses some 460 beds and is a member of the NewYork-Presbyterian Healthcare System. It provides general medical and surgical care as well as aA wide variety of specialty medical services including dialysis pediatrics obstetricsA andA cardiovascular care.A The Brooklyn Hospital Center is affiliated with Weill Medical College of Cornell University. The hospital also operates a network of outpatient clinics providingA primary and specialty care throughout the borough.

Operations

Each year the Brooklyn Hospital Center handles about 65000 ERA visits 19000 inpatient staysA and 150000 outpatient care visits. It has a medical staff of about 600 doctors. The hospital also conducts nursing and medical education programs.

Financial Performance

The Brooklyn Hospital Center has an annual operating budget of about $380 million.

Strategy

The Brooklyn Hospital Center is striving to increase the quality of its clinical programs and upgrade its infrastructure. It also aims to retain a quality medical staff and increase the hospitals educational and research activities.

Company Background

The Brooklyn Hospital Center filed for bankruptcyA protectionA in 2005 when expensive expansion projects that didn't pay off as well as malpractice litigation left the company in more debt than it could manage. The hospital emerged from bankruptcy in 2007.

EXECUTIVES

Vice President Internal Audit And Corporate Compliance, Lora Myers
Physical Therapy Director, Rita Hamburgh
Vice Chair, Armand Asarian

LOCATIONS

HQ: BROOKLYN HOSPITAL CENTER
121 DEKALB AVE, BROOKLYN, NY 112015493
Phone: 718 250-8000
Web: WWW.TBH.ORG

PRODUCTS/OPERATIONS

Selected Services
Bariatric Surgery
Cancer Care
Dental Care and Oral Surgery
Dialysis Services
Emergency Medicine
Family Medicine
The Family Medicine Residency
Geriatric Care
Home Health Services
Imaging and Radiology
Inpatient Hospitalist Care
Obstetrics and Gynecology
Orthopaedic Surgery
Pediatrics
Pediatric Cancer Care

Pediatric Emergency Services
Pediatric and Neonatal Critical Care
Sleep Center
Spine and Neurosurgery
Stroke Center
TeleHealth
Vascular Surgery
Wound Care

COMPETITORS

Brookdale University Hospital	Montefiore Medical
Catholic Healthcare System	New York City Health and Hospitals
Continuum Health Partners	Northwell Health
Kingsbrook Jewish Medical Center	SUNY Downstate
Maimonides Medical Center	Winthrop-University Hospital

HISTORICAL FINANCIALS

Company Type: Private

Income Statement   FYE: December 31

	REVENUE ($ mil.)	NET INCOME ($ mil.)	NET PROFIT MARGIN	EMPLOYEES
12/17	347	(9)	—	3,300
12/16	349	4	1.2%	—
12/15	345	3	1.0%	—
12/14	328	13	4.2%	—
Annual Growth	1.9%	—	—	—

2017 Year-End Financials

Return on assets: 15.4%   Cash ($ mil.): 23
Return on equity: (-2.9%)
Current ratio: 0.70

BROOKWOOD BAPTIST MEDICAL CENTER

EXECUTIVES

Ceo, Garry Gause
Coo, Kerry R Tirman
Cdo, Sheila O McKenna
Cfo, Joe Benton
Chief Officer, Sheila Mc Kenna
Pharmacist, Shondra Sholar
Administrative Director Women', Amy Beard
Manager of Womens or, Debbie Phillips
Buyer, Lori Butler
GI Manager, Patricia Burrage
Pacs Administrator, Stanley Jones

LOCATIONS

HQ: BROOKWOOD BAPTIST MEDICAL CENTER
2010 BROOKWOOD MED CTR DR, BIRMINGHAM, AL 352096804
Phone: 205 877-1000

HISTORICAL FINANCIALS

Company Type: Private

Income Statement   FYE: December 31

	REVENUE ($ mil.)	NET INCOME ($ mil.)	NET PROFIT MARGIN	EMPLOYEES
12/17	365	19	5.3%	2,218
12/16	377	38	10.2%	—
12/15	375	35	9.4%	—
12/14	350	23	6.7%	—
Annual Growth	1.4%	(6.0%)	—	—

2017 Year-End Financials

Return on assets: 4.0%   Cash ($ mil.): —
Return on equity: 5.3%
Current ratio: 1.90

BROTHER INTERNATIONAL CORPORATION

Brother International is part of one big global family. A subsidiary of Japan-based Brother Industries Brother International sells inkjet and laser printers fax machines scanners typewriters stamp-making systems laminators electronic label printers sewing machines garment printers gear motors and machine tools manufactured by its parent company. Its products are marketed to consumers and businesses in North America and across Latin America. Through its subsidiaries Brother International operates production and sales facilities in the US Canada Mexico Argentina Brazil Chile and Peru. The business which accounts for more than 25% of its parent's sales was formed in 1954.

Operations

Brother International maintains offices in California and Tennessee to support its headquarters. It also has a production and sales presence across North America Argentina Brazil Chile and Peru.

Geographic Reach

New Jersey-based Brother International serves customers across the Americas while also having an eye on expanding globally.

Sales and Marketing

The company caters to several sectors such as education government mid to large enterprises and healthcare organizations.

Financial Performance

Thanks to exchange rate benefits and rising demand for both equipment and consumables Brother International's printing and solutions segment revenue rose some 23% in fiscal 2014 as compared to 2013.

Strategy

True to its name Brother International is taking a global view by seeking to expand its business in emerging countries. Brother aims to accelerate the expansion of its existing businesses and to develop new ones by seeking out opportunities for mergers acquisitions and alliances with other firms in each of its business segments and regions of operation.

Keeping up with the latest platforms Brother International in 2014 launched BR-Docs a cloud-based document management service that aims to help improve business processes primarily for small to medium businesses.

Looking to expand its selection of specialty products the company acquired San Diego-based Nefsis which provides video conferencing software and cloud computing online services in 2011. Nefsis operates under brands such as ePop Nefsis and WiredRed and provides services to customers in the business government non-profit and educational industries.

EXECUTIVES

Chairman Brother International Corporation, Tadashi Ishiguro

LOCATIONS

HQ: BROTHER INTERNATIONAL CORPORATION
200 CROSSING BLVD, BRIDGEWATER, NJ 088072861
Phone: 908 704-1700
Web: WWW.BROTHER-USA.COM

PRODUCTS/OPERATIONS

Selected Services

Brother Business Solutions
Brother Cloud

Selected Products

Fax machines
Garment printers
Gear motors
Home sewing & embroidery
Industrial printing & sewing
Labeling systems
Machine tools
Mobile products (portable scanners printers industrial labelers)
Printers
Scanners
Sewing and embroidery machines
Stamp-making systems
Typewriters
Web conferencing

COMPETITORS

Canon USA	OKI Data Americas
Epson	Oracle
HP	RISO Inc.
IBM	Retail Holdings
Kyocera Document Solutions America	Ricoh Americas
Microsoft	Xerox

HISTORICAL FINANCIALS

Company Type: Private

Income Statement   FYE: March 31

	REVENUE ($ mil.)	NET INCOME ($ mil.)	NET PROFIT MARGIN	EMPLOYEES
03/18	1,751	33	1.9%	2,000
03/15	1,852	3	0.2%	—
03/14	1,826	26	1.5%	—
Annual Growth	(1.0%)	6.1%	—	—

2018 Year-End Financials

Return on assets: 6.3%   Cash ($ mil.): 29
Return on equity: 1.9%
Current ratio: 1.60

BROWARD COUNTY PUBLIC SCHOOLS

EXECUTIVES

Supt, Robert W Runcie
Acct, Paul Purrier
Executive of Information Techn, Sharon Simmons
Customer Staff, Kendra Demme
Director, Angela St Hubert
Athletic Director, Lisa Bailey
Purchasing Agent, Debra Swain
Education Specialist, Dwayne Murray
Teacher, Melissa Atkinson
Teacher, Paula Johnson
Professor, Randolph Black

LOCATIONS

HQ: BROWARD COUNTY PUBLIC SCHOOLS
600 SE 3RD AVE, FORT LAUDERDALE, FL 333013125
Phone: 754 321-0000
Web: WWW.BROWARDSCHOOLS.COM

HISTORICAL FINANCIALS

Company Type: Private

Income Statement FYE: June 30

	REVENUE ($ mil.)	NET INCOME ($ mil.)	NET PROFIT MARGIN	EMPLOYEES
06/16	2,630	(37)	—	31,174
06/15	2,536	186	7.3%	—
06/11	2,515	(37)	—	—
Annual Growth	0.9%	—	—	—

2016 Year-End Financials

Return on assets: 6.8% Cash ($ mil.): 671
Return on equity: (-1.4%)
Current ratio: 1.40

BROWARD GENERAL MEDICAL CENTER

EXECUTIVES

Ceo, James Thaw
SEC, Beverly Virago
Admin, Maxine James Francis
Pathologist, Julian Garcia
Pathologist, Larry Hirschfield
Compliance Director, Natassia Orr
Chief of Pathology, Peter S Johnson
Doctor, Erol Yoldas
Health Care Director, Linda Stanic
Manager, Marco Ruiz
Scientist, Maryluz Osorio

LOCATIONS

HQ: BROWARD GENERAL MEDICAL CENTER
  1600 S ANDREWS AVE, FORT LAUDERDALE, FL
  333162510
Phone: 954 355-4400
Web: WWW.BROWARDHEALTH.ORG

HISTORICAL FINANCIALS

Company Type: Private

Income Statement FYE: June 30

	REVENUE ($ mil.)	NET INCOME ($ mil.)	NET PROFIT MARGIN	EMPLOYEES
06/16	455	26	5.9%	95
06/15	458	58	12.8%	—
Annual Growth	(0.7%)	(54.2%)	—	—

2016 Year-End Financials

Return on assets: 9.0% Cash ($ mil.): —
Return on equity: 5.9%
Current ratio: 1.10

BRYAN HEALTH

EXECUTIVES

President, Kimberly Russel
Chairperson, Gene Brake
Vice Chairman*, Steven Erwin
Trustee, Andrew Hove Jr
Trustee, William Lester
Trustee, Donde Plowman PHD

Trustee, David Dyke
Trustee, Jon Hinrichs
Trustee, Prem Paul Dvm
Trustee, Jack Huck
Trustee, Renee Sjulin

LOCATIONS

HQ: BRYAN HEALTH
  1600 S 48TH ST, LINCOLN, NE 685061299
Phone: 402 481-1111
Web: WWW.BRYANLGH.ORG

HISTORICAL FINANCIALS

Company Type: Private

Income Statement FYE: December 31

	REVENUE ($ mil.)	NET INCOME ($ mil.)	NET PROFIT MARGIN	EMPLOYEES
12/17	682	87	12.8%	4,344
12/16	650	70	10.9%	—
12/15	6	50	769.7%	—
12/14	3	30	796.7%	—
Annual Growth	465.5%	42.8%	—	—

2017 Year-End Financials

Return on assets: 3.1% Cash ($ mil.): 218
Return on equity: 12.8%
Current ratio: 2.90

BRYAN MEDICAL CENTER

Bryan Medical Center is the centerpiece of a not-for-profit health care system serving residents of Lincoln Nebraska and surrounding communities. The medical center which operates as part of Bryan Health features two acute-care hospitals (Bryan East and Bryan West) housing a combined 670 beds. In addition to providing general medical and surgical care it serves as a regional trauma center and provides specialty care in areas such as cancer orthopedics and cardiology. The Bryan Health organization also includes a rural hospital and several outpatient clinics and it provides medical training home health care services and wellness programs.

Operations

In addition to Bryan Medical Center the Bryan Health organization operates the Crete Area Medical Center a 25-bed community hospital. Outpatient facilities include the Bryan Heart Institute (cardiology and cardiothoracic surgery) the Bryan Physician Network (family practice urgent care and specialist locations) and Bryan LifePointe (wellness and fitness programs). In addition the network includes the Bryan College of Health Sciences which provides bachelor's and master's degrees in nursing and health professional fields and the Bryan Foundation. It also conducts community education activities.

In the latest year for which data is available the hospital had 5912 inpatient visits; 6650 outpatient surgeries; and 68352 emergency department visits.

Geographic ReachBryan Medical Center serves patients throughout Nebraska as well as portions of neighboring states including Kansas Iowa and Missouri with clinics in more than 30 communities including Lincoln Columbus and Hastings.

Sales and Marketing

Bryan Medical Center advertises through magazines and through the Internet.

Strategy

In 2015 the hospital became the first in Nebraska to utilize the CardioMEMS HF System a miniaturized and wireless monitoring device to manage heart failure and reduce hospital admissions. That year it also began using the Kiva VCF Treatment System for the treatment of patients with vertebral compression fractures.

Company Background

The BryanLGH system was formed through the 1997 combination of Bryan Memorial Hospital (named after populist firebrand William Jennings Bryan) and Lincoln General Hospital. Bryan Health is part of the Heartland Health Alliance a group of about 40 Nebraska hospitals that work together to improve rural health care services through shared services and best practices.

In 2012 the health organization rebranded itself to reflect its expanded position in the region's health care market. BryanLGH Medical Center was renamed Bryan Medical Center and the broader health organization changed its name from the BryanLGH Health System to simply Bryan Health.

EXECUTIVES

Ceo, Kim Russel
Ceo, R Lynn Wilson
President, Craig Ames
Exec Dir, Keith Miller
Cfo, Russell Gronewold
Chief of Pediatric, Robert Koch
Coordinator, Aaron Delahoyde
Scientist, Sandy Houser
Registered Nurse, Tricia Splichal
Program Manager, Brenda Lieske
Major Gift Officer, Deetta Mayrose

LOCATIONS

HQ: BRYAN MEDICAL CENTER
  1600 S 48TH ST, LINCOLN, NE 685061283
Phone: 402 481-1111
Web: WWW.BRYANHEALTH.COM

PRODUCTS/OPERATIONS

Selected Services

Bariatrics
Cardiac Services
Cancer
Cardiothoracic Surgery
Childbirth/Family Birthplace
Corporate & Community Wellness
Diabetes Center
Early Detection
Emergency Department
Heart Valve Center of Excellence
Hospitalists
Independence Center
Inpatient Rehabilitation
Neuroscience
Mental Health
Orthopedics
Outpatient Specialty Clinic
Radiation Oncology
Radiology
Rehabilitation/Therapy
Robotic Surgery
Sleep Medicine
StarCare Air Ambulance
Substance Abuse
Trauma Center
Urgent Care
Vascular Services
Women's & Children's

COMPETITORS

Catholic Health Initiatives
Children's Hospital & Medical Center
Madonna Rehabilitation Hospital
Methodist Health System
Nebraska Medical Center

HISTORICAL FINANCIALS
Company Type: Private

Income Statement
FYE: December 31

	REVENUE ($ mil.)	NET INCOME ($ mil.)	NET PROFIT MARGIN	EMPLOYEES
12/17	606	74	12.3%	3,970
12/16	586	60	10.3%	—
12/15	558	43	7.8%	—
12/14	507	34	6.8%	—
Annual Growth	6.1%	29.4%	—	—

2017 Year-End Financials
Return on assets: 3.1% Cash ($ mil.): 190
Return on equity: 12.3%
Current ratio: 2.90

BUCKEYE PIPE LINE COMPANY, L P

EXECUTIVES

Pres, William Shea
Project Coordinator, Brian Parker
Board Member, Joseph A Lasala

LOCATIONS

HQ: BUCKEYE PIPE LINE COMPANY, L P
5002 BUCKEYE RD, EMMAUS, PA 180495347
Phone: 484 232-4000
Web: WWW.BUCKEYE.COM

COMPETITORS

ExxonMobil Pipeline   Shell Pipeline
NuStar Energy

HISTORICAL FINANCIALS
Company Type: Private

Income Statement
FYE: December 31

	REVENUE ($ mil.)	NET INCOME ($ mil.)	NET PROFIT MARGIN	EMPLOYEES
12/16	335	173	51.7%	504
12/04	323	82	25.6%	—
12/03	196	14	7.2%	—
12/02	179	55	30.9%	—
Annual Growth	4.6%	8.5%	—	—

BUCKEYE POWER, INC.

EXECUTIVES

Chb, Steven Nelson
Pres-Ceo, Anthony J Ahern
V Pres-Fin, Bobby Daniel
Dir, James Walker Jr
Manager, Paul Jackson
Auditors: BDO USA LLP CHICAGO ILLINO

LOCATIONS

HQ: BUCKEYE POWER, INC.
6677 BUSCH BLVD, COLUMBUS, OH 432291101
Phone: 614 781-0573
Web: WWW.BUCKEYEPOWER.COM

COMPETITORS

AEP   Ohio Valley Electric
FirstEnergy

HISTORICAL FINANCIALS
Company Type: Private

Income Statement
FYE: June 30

	REVENUE ($ mil.)	NET INCOME ($ mil.)	NET PROFIT MARGIN	EMPLOYEES
06/18	708	45	6.5%	300
06/12	626	31	5.0%	—
06/11	580	32	5.7%	—
Annual Growth	2.9%	4.9%	—	—

2018 Year-End Financials
Return on assets: 8.1% Cash ($ mil.): 24
Return on equity: 6.5%
Current ratio: 0.60

BVH, INC.

EXECUTIVES

Chb-Pres-Ceo, Steve L Edwards
Vp Real Estate & Facilities, Ralph J Dyro
Sr Vp & Treas, Angela L Hoffman
Cfo/Exec Vp, Karen L Daniel
Cao, James R Lewis
Vp Tax Counsel, Jeffrey J Stamm
Exec Vp & SEC, Timothy W Triplett
Project Engineer, Sierra McCreary
Traffic Coordinator, Courtney Collins
Auditors: KPMG LLP KANSAS CITY MO

LOCATIONS

HQ: BVH, INC.
11401 LAMAR AVE, OVERLAND PARK, KS 662111508
Phone: 913 458-2000
Web: WWW.BV.COM

HISTORICAL FINANCIALS
Company Type: Private

Income Statement
FYE: December 29

	REVENUE ($ mil.)	NET INCOME ($ mil.)	NET PROFIT MARGIN	EMPLOYEES
12/17	3,363	87	2.6%	8,495
12/16*	3,207	75	2.4%	—
01/16	2,955	108	3.7%	—
01/15	3,029	113	3.7%	—
Annual Growth	3.6%	(8.3%)	—	—

*Fiscal year change

2017 Year-End Financials
Return on assets: 18.6% Cash ($ mil.): 344
Return on equity: 2.6%
Current ratio: 0.70

C C 1 LIMITED PARTNERSHIP

EXECUTIVES

Ceo-Pres-Ptn, Alberto De La Cruz
Ptnr, Carlos De La Cruz Sr
Ptnr, Rosa De La Cruz

Controller, Brenda Cevillano
Manager of Management Informat, Oscar Rosado
Auditors: RSM PUERTO RICO SAN JUAN PUE

LOCATIONS

HQ: C C 1 LIMITED PARTNERSHIP
107 CARR 174, BAYAMON, PR 009591910
Phone: 787 288-6400
Web: WWW.COCA-COLA.COM

HISTORICAL FINANCIALS
Company Type: Private

Income Statement
FYE: December 31

	REVENUE ($ mil.)	NET INCOME ($ mil.)	NET PROFIT MARGIN	EMPLOYEES
12/17	344	14	4.1%	816
12/16	338	7	2.3%	—
12/15	345	15	4.4%	—
12/14	337	0	0.1%	—
Annual Growth	0.6%	277.4%	—	—

2017 Year-End Financials
Return on assets: 6.2% Cash ($ mil.): 5
Return on equity: 4.1%
Current ratio: 0.30

CABELL HUNTINGTON HOSPITAL INC

EXECUTIVES

Pres-Ceo, Brent A Marsteller
Vice President, David Graley
SEC, Steven L Burton
Treas, Floyd Eharlow Jr
Dir, Carolyn L Bagby
Executive Officer, Judith Riley
Chief of Medicine, Ross Patton
General Practitioner, Hadassah Frye
Analyst, Jason Hill
Customer Staff, Jonathon Pritt
Coordinator, Amy Bullington
Auditors: BAKER TILLY VIRCHOW KRAUSE LL

LOCATIONS

HQ: CABELL HUNTINGTON HOSPITAL INC
1340 HAL GREER BLVD, HUNTINGTON, WV
257010195
Phone: 304 526-2000
Web: WWW.CABELLHUNTINGTON.ORG

HISTORICAL FINANCIALS
Company Type: Private

Income Statement
FYE: September 30

	REVENUE ($ mil.)	NET INCOME ($ mil.)	NET PROFIT MARGIN	EMPLOYEES
09/17	587	76	13.0%	2,300
09/16	559	18	3.2%	—
09/15	473	17	3.8%	—
09/14	417	8	2.0%	—
Annual Growth	12.0%	109.3%	—	—

2017 Year-End Financials
Return on assets: 1.4% Cash ($ mil.): 70
Return on equity: 13.0%
Current ratio: 1.80

CADDO PARISH SCHOOL BOARD

EXECUTIVES

II Coo, James W Woolfolk
Supt, Ollie Tyler
Supt, Dr T Lamar Goree
Principal, Mary D Rounds
Auditors: ALLEN GREEN & WILLIAMSON LLP

LOCATIONS

HQ: CADDO PARISH SCHOOL BOARD
  1961 MIDWAY ST, SHREVEPORT, LA 711082200
Phone: 318 603-6300
Web: WWW.CADDOSCHOOLS.ORG

HISTORICAL FINANCIALS
Company Type: Private

Income Statement				FYE: June 30
	REVENUE ($ mil.)	NET INCOME ($ mil.)	NET PROFIT MARGIN	EMPLOYEES
06/17	457	(7)	—	5,680
06/16	468	0	0.0%	—
06/08	448	15	3.4%	—
06/07	420	9	2.2%	—
Annual Growth	0.8%	—	—	—

2017 Year-End Financials
Return on assets: 2.2%   Cash ($ mil.): 141
Return on equity: (-1.7%)
Current ratio: —

CAJUN CONSTRUCTORS, LLC

EXECUTIVES

Ceo, Ken Jacob
Pres, Todd W Grigsby
Chm of The Board, L Lane Grigsby
Exec V Pres, Milton Graugnard
Cfo, Shane Recile
Mis, Jason Davis
Senior Vice-President, Michael Calabrese
Vice-President Operations, Todd Grigsby
Senior Vice-President, Euclid Michel
Marketing Staff, Kelly Wolf
Vice-President, Mike Barber
Auditors: HANNIS T BOURGEOIS LLP BATO

LOCATIONS

HQ: CAJUN CONSTRUCTORS, LLC
  15635 AIRLINE HWY, BATON ROUGE, LA 708177318
Phone: 225 753-5857
Web: WWW.CAJUNUSA.COM

HISTORICAL FINANCIALS
Company Type: Private

Income Statement				FYE: September 30
	REVENUE ($ mil.)	NET INCOME ($ mil.)	NET PROFIT MARGIN	EMPLOYEES
09/17	573	47	8.2%	1,000
09/16	658	41	6.3%	—
09/15	521	25	4.9%	—
09/14	431	10	2.5%	—
Annual Growth	9.9%	64.1%	—	—

2017 Year-End Financials
Return on assets: 4.9%   Cash ($ mil.): 6
Return on equity: 8.2%
Current ratio: 1.60

CAJUN INDUSTRIES, LLC

EXECUTIVES

Vice President Texas Operations, Carlton Janise
Vice President Operations, Lee Mayeux
Auditors: HANNIS T BOURGEOIS LLP BATO

LOCATIONS

HQ: CAJUN INDUSTRIES, LLC
  15635 AIRLINE HWY, BATON ROUGE, LA 708177318
Phone: 225 753-5857
Web: WWW.CAJUNUSA.COM

PRODUCTS/OPERATIONS

Selected Divisions
Cajun Constructors Inc.
Cajun Deep Foundations LLC
Cajun Equipment Services LLC
Cajun Maritime LLC

Selected Services
ASME code work
Bridge construction and repair
Building construction
Coastal restoration
Dock facility construction and repair
Deep foundation work
  Drill shafts
  Driven piles
  Earth retention
  Marine piles
Design/build
Emergency response
Hauling
Maintenance
Marsh and marine power transmission and distribution
Oilfield construction
Paving
Pipeline installation and repair
Plant dismantling and relocation
Procurement
Project management
Retrofits
Stevedoring
Structural steel erection
Turnarounds
Water quality

COMPETITORS

Bechtel	Jacobs Engineering
Boh Bros Construction	KBR
Eby	Performance
Fluor	Contractors

HISTORICAL FINANCIALS
Company Type: Private

Income Statement				FYE: September 30
	REVENUE ($ mil.)	NET INCOME ($ mil.)	NET PROFIT MARGIN	EMPLOYEES
09/17	616	56	9.2%	1,500
09/16	721	56	7.9%	—
09/15	559	28	5.2%	—
09/14	476	11	2.5%	—
Annual Growth	9.0%	69.0%	—	—

2017 Year-End Financials
Return on assets: 4.7%   Cash ($ mil.): 17
Return on equity: 9.2%
Current ratio: 1.20

CALCASIEU PARISH SCHOOL BOARD

EXECUTIVES

Pres, Mack Dellafosse
Superintendent, Wayne Savoy
Asst Supt, Leo Miller
Asst Supt, Gary Anderson
Director*, Dennis Bent
Admin, Barbara I Bankens
Dir, Dr George Reado
Admin, Dolores Hicks
Admin, David Buller
Cfo, Karl Bruchhaus
Food Director, Mary Thomas
Auditors: ALLEN GREEN & WILLIAMSON LLP

LOCATIONS

HQ: CALCASIEU PARISH SCHOOL BOARD
  3310 BROAD ST, LAKE CHARLES, LA 706153808
Phone: 337 217-4000
Web: WWW.CPSB.ORG

HISTORICAL FINANCIALS
Company Type: Private

Income Statement				FYE: June 30
	REVENUE ($ mil.)	NET INCOME ($ mil.)	NET PROFIT MARGIN	EMPLOYEES
06/17	438	39	9.1%	4,500
06/16	427	5	1.2%	—
06/04	249	(16)	—	—
06/03	234	(3)	—	—
Annual Growth	4.6%	—	—	—

2017 Year-End Financials
Return on assets: 10.4%   Cash ($ mil.): 118
Return on equity: 9.1%
Current ratio: —

CALGON CARBON CORPORATION

Calgon wants impurities in water and air gone. A global leader in activated carbons and purification systems it offers purification separation and concentration services to industrial process and environmental markets. Services include ballast water treatment ultraviolet light disinfection and advanced ion-exchange technologies used in the treatment of drinking water wastewater ballast water air emissions and manufacturing processes. Its products find usage more than 700 discrete market applications including air drinking water foods and pharmaceuticals purification and the removal of mercury emissions from coal-powered electrical plants. More than half of the Calgon?s sales comes from the US. In 2017 Calgon was acquired by Kuraray and became its subsidiary.

Change in Company Type

In 2017 the company entered into a definitive merger agreement with Kuraray Co under which Calgon became a wholly owned subsidiary of the latter for a transaction value of $1.3 billion.

Operations

Calgon has three segments?Activated Carbon Alternative materials and Advanced Water Purification.

Activated Carbon makes granular and powdered activated carbon to remove organic compounds from liquids and gases bringing in roughly 90% of total sales.

The Alternative Materials unit (some 10%) offers diatomaceous earth and perlite filtration media which are primarily used as filter aids in beverage food and industrial applications. Products also includes carbon cloth which is activated carbon in cloth form.

Its Advance Water Purification (less than 5%) unit makes and sells a broad line of UV light disinfection.

Geographic Reach
Calgon Carbon operates in a geographically diverse array of markets. It operates about 20 production plants in Belgium China France Italy Japan the UK and the US. It has about 40 warehouses service centers and sales office facilities in various locations in US Europe and Asia-Pacific region.

Financial Performance
Calgon Carbon's revenues increased by 4% in 2012 due to 43% jump in Equipment revenues driven by ultraviolet light systems principally ballast water treatment which rose by 71%. Consumer revenues went up by 20% thanks to higher demand for activated carbon cloths. The increases were partially offset by 0.15% decrease in the Activated Carbon and Service sales due to the negative impact of foreign currency translation.

The company posted a net income of $23.2 million in 2012 (41% down on 2011) due to higher interest expenses and restructuring charges.

Mergers and Acquisitions
In 2016 Calgon Carbon completed the acquisition of CECA's wood-based activated carbon reactivation and mineral-based filtration media business for $153 million. The business joined Calgon Carbon?s European operations under the name Chemviron.

EXECUTIVES

Evp And Coo, Robert P. (Bob) O'Brien, age 68, $378,325 total compensation
Evp Advanced Materials Manufacturing And Equipment Division, Stevan R. Schott, age 55, $322,500 total compensation
Chairman President And Ceo, Randall S. (Randy) Dearth, age 55, $560,000 total compensation
Evp Core Carbon And Services Division, James A. Coccagno, age 47
Svp And Cfo, Robert Fortwangler
Senior Vice President Global Procurement And Strategic Initiatives, Jim Coccagno
Senior Vice President General Counsel Secretary, Chad Whalen
Auditors: DELOITTE & TOUCHE LLP PITTSBU

LOCATIONS

HQ: CALGON CARBON CORPORATION
3000 GSK DR, MOON TOWNSHIP, PA 151081381
Phone: 412 787-6700
Web: WWW.CALGONCARBON.COM

2015 sales

	$ mil.	% of total
United States	288	53
United Kingdom	43	8
Japan	35	7
France	20	4
China	17	3
Germany	17	3
Canada	17	3
South Korea	12	2
Belgium	10	2
Singapore	9	2
Netherlands	5	1
Denmark	4	1
Switzerland	3	1
Spain	3	1
Thailand	3	1
Other	41	8
Total	**535**	**100**

PRODUCTS/OPERATIONS

2015 Sales

	$ mil.	% of total
Activated Carbon & Service	486	91
Equipment	39	7
Consumer	9	2
Total	**535**	**100**

Selected Products
Ballast Water Treatment
Energy Storage
Environmental Air Treatment
Environmental Water Treatment
Food and Beverage
Industrial Processes
Medical
Mercury Removal
Metals Recovery
Municipal Water Treatment
Personal Protection Equipment
Residential Point of Use/Entry

COMPETITORS

3M Purification	Norit
ITT Water & Wastewater	Siemens Water
Herford	Technologies
Met-Pro	Trojan Technologies

HISTORICAL FINANCIALS
Company Type: Private

Income Statement   FYE: December 31

	REVENUE ($ mil.)	NET INCOME ($ mil.)	NET PROFIT MARGIN	EMPLOYEES
12/17	619	21	3.4%	1,334
12/16	514	13	2.7%	—
12/15	535	43	8.1%	—
12/14	555	49	8.9%	—
Annual Growth	3.7%	(24.7%)	—	—

2017 Year-End Financials
Return on assets: 15.0%
Return on equity: 3.4%
Current ratio: 1.40
Cash ($ mil.): 42

CALIFORNIA HOSPITAL MEDICAL CENTER FOUNDATION

EXECUTIVES

Chb, Phillip C Hill
Ceo-President, Nathan R Nusbaum
V Pres-Fin-Cfo, Clark Underwood
V Pres-Hr, David Milovich
V Pres-Chief Nursing Officer, Linda Bolor
Acting Coo, John Kramar
President, Margaret R Peterson
Vice President, Bob Quarfoot
Coo, Harold Newton
Coordinator, Deborah Liu
Coordinator, Dolores Molina

LOCATIONS

HQ: CALIFORNIA HOSPITAL MEDICAL CENTER FOUNDATION
1401 S GRAND AVE, LOS ANGELES, CA 900153010
Phone: 213 748-2411

HISTORICAL FINANCIALS
Company Type: Private

Income Statement   FYE: June 30

	REVENUE ($ mil.)	NET INCOME ($ mil.)	NET PROFIT MARGIN	EMPLOYEES
06/15	396	63	16.0%	1,500
06/09	241	31	13.2%	—
06/06	5	3	66.2%	—
06/05	4	2	47.0%	—
Annual Growth	55.2%	39.3%	—	—

2015 Year-End Financials
Return on assets: 3.9%
Return on equity: 16.0%
Current ratio: 2.00
Cash ($ mil.): 84

CALIFORNIA INSTITUTE OF TECHNOLOGY

The California Institute of Technology (Caltech) has an enlightened perspective on science. The institute enrolls about 2250 students and offers about two dozen majors across six academic divisions focused on biology chemistry engineering geology humanities and physics. Caltech has a very low student-teacher ratio of 3:1. The school receives about half of its operating revenue through research grants primarily from government agencies. Caltech operates the Jet Propulsion Laboratory (JPL) which supervises robotic Mars exploration programs and other interplanetary missions under contract to NASA. The school was founded in 1891.

Operations
CalTech's most popular majors are chemical engineering computer science electrical engineering mechanical engineering and physics. The school's primary research focus areas include energy medical science information science the universe the environment and nanoscience.

The JPL lab is responsible for about two dozen spacecraft missions in a given year.

Geographic Reach
Caltech has a student population that comes from more than 30 US states and 11 countries; international students account for more than 20% of enrollment. In addition to its facilities in California the institute has a network of about a dozen astronomy observatories across the US and in Antarctica and Chile.

Financial Performance
Caltech has a budget of about $2.3 billion and an endowment of about $2.1 billion. It gets some 54% of its revenue from contracts and grants and 19% from its endowment. Tuition and fees only account for about 6% of revenue.

Strategy
The institute has established new divisions of biology and biological engineering in recent years.

Company Background
Caltech's professors and graduates have snared more than 30 Nobel Prizes. Other alumni include filmmaker Frank Capra and Apollo 17 astronaut Harrison Schmitt.

EXECUTIVES

Provost, Edward M. Stolper
Vp Business And Finance, Dean W. Currie
Cio, Richard E. (Rich) Fagen
Vp; Director Jet Propulsion Laboratory, Charles Elachi, age 71

Chair Biology And Biological Engineering Division, Stephen L. Mayo
President, Thomas F. Rosenbaum
Chief Investment Officer, Scott Richland
Chair Chemistry And Chemical Engineering Division, Jacqueline K. Barton
Chair Physics Mathematics And Astronomy Division, B. Thomas Soifer
Chair Engineering And Applied Science Division, Guruswami Ravichandran
Chair Geological And Planetary Sciences Division, John P. Grotzinger
Chair Humanities And Social Sciences Division, Jean-Laurent Rosenthal
Chairman, David L. Lee, age 62
Vice Chairman, Ronald K. Linde
Auditors: PRICEWATERHOUSECOOPERS LLP LO

LOCATIONS

HQ: CALIFORNIA INSTITUTE OF TECHNOLOGY
1200 E CALIFORNIA BLVD, PASADENA, CA
911250001
Phone: 626 395-6811
Web: WWW.CALTECH.EDU

PRODUCTS/OPERATIONS

Selected Academic Divisions
Academics
  Biology
  Chemistry and Chemical Engineering
  Engineering and Applied Science
  Geological and Planetary Sciences
  Humanities and Social Sciences
  Physics Mathematics and Astronomy
Jet Propulsion Laboratory (NASA partnership)
  Galaxy Evolution Explorer Science Center
  Infrared Processing and Analysis Center
  NASA Exoplanet Science Institute
  NASA Herschel Science Center
  Spitzer Space Telescope Science Center

HISTORICAL FINANCIALS

Company Type: Private

Income Statement   FYE: September 30

	REVENUE ($ mil.)	NET INCOME ($ mil.)	NET PROFIT MARGIN	EMPLOYEES
09/17	2,894	412	14.3%	3,980
09/16	2,561	203	7.9%	—
09/14	2,153	154	7.2%	—
09/13	2,005	182	9.1%	—
Annual Growth	9.6%	22.7%	—	—

2017 Year-End Financials
Return on assets: 13.1%   Cash ($ mil.): 6
Return on equity: 14.3%
Current ratio: 0.20

CALIFORNIA'S VALUED TRUST

EXECUTIVES

Exec Dir, Valerie Cornuelle
Exec Dir, David Vaughn
Receptionist, Lois Casey
Member, Ashley Aguilar
Accountant, MAI Thao

LOCATIONS

HQ: CALIFORNIA'S VALUED TRUST
520 E HERNDON AVE, FRESNO, CA 937202907
Phone: 559 437-2960
Web: WWW.CVTRUST.ORG

HISTORICAL FINANCIALS

Company Type: Private

Income Statement   FYE: September 30

	ASSETS ($ mil.)	NET INCOME ($ mil.)	INCOME AS % OF ASSETS	EMPLOYEES
09/17	157	21	13.3%	1
09/15	136	(5)	—	—
Annual Growth	7.5%	—	—	—

2017 Year-End Financials
Return on assets: 0.2%   Sales ($ mil): 802
Return on equity: 2.6%

CALLAHAN, INC.

EXECUTIVES

Pres, Patrick Callahan
Vice President, Tim Callahan
V Pres-Cfo, Dennis Sheehan
Project Executive, Joe Roche
Assistant, Justin Valentim
Research and Engin, Robert Sanda
Project Manager, Brian Parmenter
Office Manager, Gail Dibona
Manager, Jim Fikiet
Marketing Director, Raj Bhangoo
Superintendent, Derek Mahar
Auditors: CITRIN COOPERMAN & COMPANY LLP

LOCATIONS

HQ: CALLAHAN, INC.
80 1ST ST, BRIDGEWATER, MA 023241071
Phone: 508 279-0012
Web: WWW.CALLAHAN-INC.COM

HISTORICAL FINANCIALS

Company Type: Private

Income Statement   FYE: December 31

	REVENUE ($ mil.)	NET INCOME ($ mil.)	NET PROFIT MARGIN	EMPLOYEES
12/16	391	13	3.5%	130
12/13	140	2	2.1%	—
12/12	159	3	2.5%	—
Annual Growth	25.2%	36.6%	—	—

2016 Year-End Financials
Return on assets: 20.8%   Cash ($ mil.): 36
Return on equity: 3.5%
Current ratio: 1.10

CALLISONRTKL INC.

RTKL Associates has a global appetiteA forA architecture and engineering projects. Ranked among the top providers of architecture and engineering services to the public sector RTKL also caters to the hospitality retail and entertainment health care and academic markets. The firm offers a variety of servicesA such as planning and urban design interior architecture historic preservation structural engineering and mechanical and electrical engineering. to clients in the Americas Europe and the Middle East.A Other services include graphic design landscape design and information technology planning. RTKL was founded in 1946 and is owned by Dutch consulting and engineering firm ARCADIS.

Geographic Reach

Baltimore-baed RTKL Associates has offices in Chicago Dallas Los Angeles Miami and Washington DC. Beyond the US it has operations in Abu Dhabi Beijing Dubai London Jeddah SA?o Paulo and Shanghai.

Financial Performance

In 2011 RTKL grew as a result of successful expansion in Asia and the Middle East offsetting stagnation in the US market.

Strategy

With the backing of ARCADIS which acquired the RTKL in 2007 the firm has extended its portfolio of servicesA intoA critical geographic markets around the world. Lured the strong economic growht and a ripe market for its planning and architectural design services RTKL inA late 2012 opened an office in SA?o Paulo Brazil. The company now serves clients in more than 50 countries on six continents although its primary areas of concentration are North America Europe and Asia. In those regions RTKLA hasA worked on projects ranging fromA the US FDA headquarters in Washington DC to the Shanghai Science and Technology Museum in China.

RTKL makes strategic acquisitions to extend its global reach.A In 2010 the firm purchased Beijing-based architecture firm AHS International and opened an office in Beijing — its second in China. The company also began working in Abu Dhabi that year. Previously itA opened an office in Dubai.

EXECUTIVES

Vice President, Dan Freed

LOCATIONS

HQ: CALLISONRTKL INC.
901 S BOND ST, BALTIMORE, MD 212313339
Phone: 410 537-6000
Web: WWW.CALLISONRTKL.COM

PRODUCTS/OPERATIONS

Selected Services
Architecture
Brand building
Building information modeling
Environmental graphic design
Health care facility transitioning
Health care strategic facility planning
Health care technologies
Historical preservation
Interior architecture and design
Mechanical electrical and plumbing engineering
Planning and urban design
Protective planning
Special systems design
Structural engineering

COMPETITORS

AECOM	Leo A Daly
Callison Architecture	Mancini Duffy
FRCH Design	NBBJ
Gensler	Parsons Corporation
HDR	Perkins+Will
HOK	RMJM
Jacobs Engineering	Skidmore Owings
KBR Building Group	SmithGroupJJR
Kimley-Horn and	Thorton Tomasetti
Associates	Zimmer Gunsul Frasca
Kohn Pedersen Fox	

HISTORICAL FINANCIALS
Company Type: Private

Income Statement
FYE: December 31

	REVENUE ($ mil.)	NET INCOME ($ mil.)	NET PROFIT MARGIN	EMPLOYEES
12/16	294	9	3.3%	1,236
12/13	205	10	5.1%	—
12/12	202	11	5.4%	—
12/11	201	9	4.6%	—
Annual Growth	7.8%	0.8%	—	—

2016 Year-End Financials
Return on assets: 21.2%
Return on equity: 3.3%
Current ratio: 1.10
Cash ($ mil.): 65

CAMPUS CRUSADE FOR CHRIST INC

EXECUTIVES

Ceo-Pres, Stephen B Douglass
Dir, Vonette Z Bright
Analyst, Michael Schmitt
Recruiter, Ada Morgan
Human Resources Administrator, Barbara Beecher
Director, Dave Dickens
Engineer, David Wilkins
Vice-President, Dela Adadevoh
Senior Manager, Joanna Bailey
Leader, John Emmans
Staff, Kim Swanson

LOCATIONS

HQ: CAMPUS CRUSADE FOR CHRIST INC
100 LAKE HART DR, ORLANDO, FL 328320100
Phone: 407 826-2000
Web: WWW.PERSPECTIVECARDS.COM

HISTORICAL FINANCIALS
Company Type: Private

Income Statement
FYE: August 31

	REVENUE ($ mil.)	NET INCOME ($ mil.)	NET PROFIT MARGIN	EMPLOYEES
08/17	598	26	4.4%	7,688
08/08	7	1	25.1%	—
08/05	0	0	—	—
08/04	423	414	97.7%	—
Annual Growth	2.7%	(19.0%)	—	—

2017 Year-End Financials
Return on assets: 0.6%
Return on equity: 4.4%
Current ratio: 0.40
Cash ($ mil.): 45

CANDLER HOSPITAL, INC.

EXECUTIVES

Pres-Ceo, Paul P Hinchey
Cfo, Greg Schaack
SEC, Julie Foster
Manager, Beverly Albury

Vice-President Human Resources, Don Stubbs
Administrative Assistant, Lynda Beebe
Vice-President Human Resources, Steve Pound
Doctor, Sheila Lowe
Nurse, Cary Freeland
Director, Howard Zaren
Coordinator, Jean Peeples
Auditors: DRAFFIN & TUCKER LLP ALBANY

LOCATIONS

HQ: CANDLER HOSPITAL, INC.
5353 REYNOLDS ST, SAVANNAH, GA 314056015
Phone: 912 819-6000
Web: WWW.SJCHS.ORG

HISTORICAL FINANCIALS
Company Type: Private

Income Statement
FYE: June 30

	REVENUE ($ mil.)	NET INCOME ($ mil.)	NET PROFIT MARGIN	EMPLOYEES
06/17	301	18	6.1%	1,600
06/16	291	17	5.9%	—
06/14	250	15	6.0%	—
06/13	242	15	6.3%	—
Annual Growth	5.6%	5.0%	—	—

2017 Year-End Financials
Return on assets: 5.2%
Return on equity: 6.1%
Current ratio: 2.90
Cash ($ mil.): —

CANYONS SCHOOL DISTRICT

EXECUTIVES

Suptd, Ginger Rhode
Suptd, James Briscoe
Senior Buyer, Jay Caldwell
Building and Grounds Director, Rick Conger
Assistant, Brenda McCann
Teacher, Caitlin Moser
Assistant, Jan Hansen
Human Resources Administrator, Jo Jolley
Board of Directors, Robert Green
Administrative Assistant, Shela Barker
Coordinator, Jake Thomas
Auditors: SQUIRE & COMPANY PC OREM UT

LOCATIONS

HQ: CANYONS SCHOOL DISTRICT
9361 S 300 E, SANDY, UT 840702902
Phone: 801 826-5340
Web: WWW.CANYONSDISTRICT.ORG

HISTORICAL FINANCIALS
Company Type: Private

Income Statement
FYE: June 30

	REVENUE ($ mil.)	NET INCOME ($ mil.)	NET PROFIT MARGIN	EMPLOYEES
06/17	335	(38)	—	4,500
06/13	0	0	16.2%	—
06/12	0	0	16.9%	—
06/11	290	90	31.1%	—
Annual Growth	2.4%	—	—	—

CAPE COD HEALTHCARE, INC.

Cape Cod Healthcare (CCHC) is a not-for-profit healthcare organization that operates two acute care hospitals (Cape Cod Hospital and Falmouth Hospital) with a total of more than 350 beds. Specializations include heart and vascular women's health bones and muscles cancer care and brain spine and nerves. CCHC also operates a home health services agency (Visiting Nurse Association of Cape Cod) primary and specialized care clinics a 130-bed skilled nursing and rehabilitation facility (JML Care Center) and a 60-unit assisted living facility (Heritage at Falmouth). The health care system has an affiliation with UMass Medical School whereby students can receive hands-on training at Cape Cod Hospital.

Operations

CCHC is the Cape's largest private employer with nearly 5000 staff members including more than 450 physicians. The system has about 120000 emergency department visits each year and facilitates about 1200 births and performs more than 14000 surgical procedures annually.

Financial Performance

CCHC's net patient revenue numbers have been increasing over the past five years. In fiscal 2016 it increased 8% to $817 million. Like most hospitals net patient revenue represents the bulk of CCHC's total revenue.

Strategy

While CCHC enjoys a strong market share in the Cape Cod region it also struggles with seasonal fluctuations and high Medicare and Medicaid numbers within its patient load. As such the company could be impacted by reform measures that could decrease Medicare reimbursement levels. CCHC plans to continue its efforts to control costs and increase efficiencies to keep its operations nimble and keep pace with the changing health care environment.

Faced with rising operating costs and lower reimbursement rates the system in 2017 agreed to sell its outreach lab services operations to Quest Diagnostics. As a focused lab services provider Quest is able to provide testing at a lower cost than the typical hospital-based laboratory. The two companies will partner to provide an expanded array of diagnostics to the Cape Cod community.

EXECUTIVES

Senior Vice President, Jeff Dykens
President And Ceo, Michael K. (Mike) Lauf, age 47
Coo, Michael Bundy
Svp Communications And Business Development, Patrick Kane
Svp Finance And Cfo, Michael L. Connors
Chief Medical Officer, Donald A. Guadagnoli
Svp And Cio, Jeanne M. Fallon
President And Ceo Vna Of Cape Cod, Dianne C. Kolb
Vice President Patient Financial Services, Victor Oliveira
Vice Chairman, William Zammer
Vice Chairman, DeWitt Davenport
Auditors: PRICEWATERHOUSECOOPERS LLP B

LOCATIONS

HQ: CAPE COD HEALTHCARE, INC.
27 PARK ST, HYANNIS, MA 026015230
Phone: 508 862-5030
Web: WWW.GIVETOCAPECODHEALTH.ORG

PRODUCTS/OPERATIONS

Selected Massachusetts Facilities
Bourne Health Center
Cape Cod Hospital (Hyannis)
Davenport Mugar Cancer Center (Hyannis)
Falmouth Hospital
   Clark Cancer Center
Fontaine Medical Center (Harwich)
Heritage at Falmouth
JLM Care Center (Falmouth)
Mashpee Health Center
Sandwich Health Center
Wilkins Outpatient Medical Complex (Hyannis)

COMPETITORS

Baystate Health	Partners HealthCare
Boston Medical Center	Southcoast Hospitals
Cambridge Health	Group
Alliance	Steward Health Care
Care New England	Universal Health
CareGroup	Services
Milford Regional	Winchester Healthcare
Medical Center	
Northeast Health	
System	

HISTORICAL FINANCIALS

Company Type: Private

Income Statement   FYE: September 30

	REVENUE ($ mil.)	NET INCOME ($ mil.)	NET PROFIT MARGIN	EMPLOYEES
09/17	872	74	8.5%	1,850
09/16	837	74	8.9%	—
09/12	680	80	11.9%	—
09/11	648	37	5.7%	—
Annual Growth	5.1%	12.2%	—	—

2017 Year-End Financials
Return on assets: 12.8%   Cash ($ mil.): 32
Return on equity: 8.5%
Current ratio: 0.80

CAPE COD HOSPITAL

Get too much sun or eat too much lobster while visiting Cape Cod? Never fear Cape Cod Hospital can treat whatever ails you. Cape Cod Hospital a subsidiary of Cape Cod Healthcare is a 260-bed acute care hospital that serves the Cape Cod Massachusetts area. Its specialty services include pediatrics maternity care cancer treatment and infectious disease therapeutics. The not-for-profit Cape Cod Hospital also includes a specialty cardiovascular center a psychiatry unit a surgical pavilion and a diagnostic imaging facility as well as outpatient medical offices.

Operations

Cape Cod Hospital's emergency department treats about 85000 patients each year. The medical center also performs more than 12500 surgeries and 1000 birth procedures each year as well as about 2 million laboratory tests. Its 20-bed Cape Psych Center provides inpatient and outpatient mental and behavioral services. The campus also includes more than a dozen medical offices buildings and a community health center. Cape Cod Hospital's staff includes about 300 physicians.

Geographic Reach

Cape Cod Hospital is located on a 40-acre campus on the shoreline of Hyannis Massachusetts.

Strategy

To keep its facilities modern and efficient in 2015 the company opened a new emergency cen-

ter located adjacent to the existing emergency center. The 18-month $22 million project added 25000 sq. ft. of space and 72 patient treatment rooms.

In 2013 Cape Cod Hospital reopened the renovated and expanded Intensive Care Unit. That project cost $4.9 million and doubled the size of the original area.

To control the cost of providing hospital care parent Cape Cod Healthcare has also been expanding its outpatient and ambulatory care services. It is adding new urgent care centers and surgery centers both near the hospital and in surrounding communities.

Company Background

Cape Cod Hospital was established in Hyannis in 1920.

EXECUTIVES

Medical Director, Kelsey Rezendes
Vice President, Stephanie Nadolny
Medical Records Director, Tim Greene

LOCATIONS

HQ: CAPE COD HOSPITAL
27 PARK ST, HYANNIS, MA 026015203
Phone: 508 862-7575
Web: WWW.CAPECODHEALTH.ORG

PRODUCTS/OPERATIONS

Selected Services
Allergy and Immunology
Behavioral Health
Blood Center
Dermatology
Foot Care & Surgery
Hand Surgery
Orthopedics
Pregnancy & Birth
Sports Medicine
Women's Health

COMPETITORS

Baystate Health	Northeast Health
Boston Medical Center	System
Cambridge Health	Partners HealthCare
Alliance	Southcoast Hospitals
Care New England	Group
CareGroup	Steward Health Care
Children's Hospital	Sturdy Memorial
Boston	Universal Health
Milford Regional	Services
Medical Center	Winchester Healthcare

HISTORICAL FINANCIALS

Company Type: Private

Income Statement   FYE: September 30

	REVENUE ($ mil.)	NET INCOME ($ mil.)	NET PROFIT MARGIN	EMPLOYEES
09/17	526	47	9.0%	1,700
09/16	515	43	8.4%	—
09/15	462	33	7.2%	—
09/14	439	24	5.7%	—
Annual Growth	6.3%	24.0%	—	—

2017 Year-End Financials
Return on assets: 6.1%   Cash ($ mil.): 11
Return on equity: 9.0%
Current ratio: 1.10

CAPE FEAR VALLEY MEDICAL CENTER

LOCATIONS

HQ: CAPE FEAR VALLEY MEDICAL CENTER
1638 OWEN DR, FAYETTEVILLE, NC 283043424
Phone: 910 615-4000
Web: WWW.CAPEFEARVALLEY.COM

HISTORICAL FINANCIALS

Company Type: Private

Income Statement   FYE: September 30

	REVENUE ($ mil.)	NET INCOME ($ mil.)	NET PROFIT MARGIN	EMPLOYEES
09/15	630	23	3.8%	2,711
09/14	590	40	6.8%	—
09/13	823	398	48.4%	—
Annual Growth	(12.5%)	(75.5%)	—	—

2015 Year-End Financials
Return on assets: 4.6%   Cash ($ mil.): 38
Return on equity: 3.8%
Current ratio: 0.70

CAPISTRANO UNIFIED SCHOOL DISTRICT

EXECUTIVES

Ceo, John M Alpay
SEC Brd, Jane Boss
Supt, Joseph M Farley
Dir of Fin, Philippa Geiger
Mng MBR, Joel Drew
Interm Dep Superintendent, Robyn Phillips
Superintendent, Lois Anderson
Information Technology Manager, Barbara Scholl
Director, Kristin Nelson
Administrative Manager, T K Frantz
Transportation Director, Carlos Chicas
Auditors: VAVRINEK TRINE DAY & CO LL

LOCATIONS

HQ: CAPISTRANO UNIFIED SCHOOL DISTRICT
33122 VALLE RD, SAN JUAN CAPISTRANO, CA 926754859
Phone: 949 234-9200
Web: WWW.CAPOUSD.ORG

HISTORICAL FINANCIALS

Company Type: Private

Income Statement   FYE: June 30

	REVENUE ($ mil.)	NET INCOME ($ mil.)	NET PROFIT MARGIN	EMPLOYEES
06/17	521	(3)	—	4,500
06/16	528	29	5.6%	—
06/05	3	0	—	—
06/03	380	(66)	—	—
Annual Growth	2.3%	—	—	—

2017 Year-End Financials
Return on assets: 4.6%   Cash ($ mil.): 155
Return on equity: (-0.7%)
Current ratio: —

CARE NEW ENGLAND HEALTH SYSTEM INC

EXECUTIVES

Senior Vice President Marketing Communications, May Kernan
Auditors: PRICEWATERHOUSECOOPERS LLP BO

LOCATIONS

HQ: CARE NEW ENGLAND HEALTH SYSTEM INC
45 WILLARD AVE, PROVIDENCE, RI 029053218
Phone: 401 453-7900
Web: WWW.CARENEWENGLAND.ORG

COMPETITORS

Baystate Health
Community Health
  Systems
Lifespan Corporation
Partners HealthCare
Roger Williams Medical
  Center
Southcoast Hospitals
  Group
Tenet Healthcare
Universal Health
  Services
Yale New Haven Health
  System

HISTORICAL FINANCIALS
Company Type: Private

Income Statement — FYE: September 30

	REVENUE ($ mil.)	NET INCOME ($ mil.)	NET PROFIT MARGIN	EMPLOYEES
09/17	1,132	21	1.9%	6,500
09/16	1,154	(63)	—	—
09/15	126	(8)	—	—
09/13	94	1	2.1%	—
Annual Growth	86.0%	82.7%	—	—

2017 Year-End Financials
Return on assets: 11.0%   Cash ($ mil.): 54
Return on equity: 1.9%
Current ratio: 0.90

CAREALLIANCE HEALTH SERVICES

CareAlliance Health Services (doing business as Roper St. Francis Healthcare) operates four hospitals — the 370-bed Roper Hospital the 200-bed Bon Secours St. Francis Hospital the 85-bed Mount Pleasant Hospital and the Roper Rehabilitation Hospital. Besides providing home health services it also operates outpatient emergency primary care and diagnostic facilities. Roper St. Francis Healthcare serves Charleston South Carolina and surrounding communities. Its Roper St. Francis Physician Partners is one of the region's largest physician practices.

Operations

The health system comprises Roper Hospital Bon Secours St. Francis Hospital Roper St. Francis Mount Pleasant Hospital Roper St. Francis Foundation and Roper St. Francis Physicians Network. Altogether it boasts three acute care hospitals with 655-plus beds one specialty hospital 15 centers for outpatient services three industrial medicine sites five emergency rooms and two urgent care centers.

Roper St. Francis Healthcare has a medical staff of some 800 physicians. The Roper St. Francis Physician Partners organization has more than 230 physicians who offer primary and specialty care including family practice internal medicine and pediatrics.

Geographic Reach

Altogether Roper St. Francis Healthcare operates about 90 facilities in seven counties in the lowcountry region of South Carolina.

Strategy

The health system in 2014 signed an agreement with Trendlines Lab to collaborate on the development of new medical device inventions as well as low-cost solutions for clinical problems. The partnership will work to create devices that will address unmet needs identified by physicians and other health care providers.

Company Background

Roper St. Francis Healthcare was formed through the merger of Roper Hospital and Bon Secours St. Francis Hospital in 1998.

Roper St. Francis Physician Partners was formed through the 2009 combination of Roper St. Francis Physicians' Network and Lowcountry Medical Associates.

EXECUTIVES

President And Ceo, David L. Dunlap
Vp And Cio, Mike Taylor
Vice President Of Medical Affairs & Chief Medical Officer, Steven Shapiro
Svp And Cfo, Bret Johnson
Ceo Roper Hospital And Svp Operations, Matthew Severance
Ceo Roper St. Francis Mount Pleasant Hospital And Vp Operations, John Sullivan
Ceo Bon Secours St. Francis Hospital And Svp Operations, Allen Carroll
Chairman Roper St. Francis Foundation, John B. Holloway
Vice Chairman Roper St. Francis Foundation, Charles T. Cole
Vice President Nursing & Senior Nurse Executive Bon Secours St. Francis, Pennie Peralta
Ceo Rsf Physician Partners & Rsfh Vice President & Chief Strategy Officer, Douglas Bowling
Interim Chief Nursing Officer Vice President Nursing Roper Hospital, Susan Bennett
Vice President Quality And Training, Tanya Lott
Vice President Human Resources, Melanie Stith
Director Of Pharmacy, Holly Balcer
Vice President Of Nursing And Senior Nurse Executive, Lisa Irvin
Chairman Of The Board, Pierre Manigault
Auditors: DELOITTE & TOUCHE LLP CHARLO

LOCATIONS

HQ: CAREALLIANCE HEALTH SERVICES
316 CALHOUN ST, CHARLESTON, SC 294011113
Phone: 843 724-2000
Web: WWW.RSFH.COM

Selected South Carolina Facilities
Hospitals
  Mt. Pleasant Hospital Campus - Mount Pleasant Roper Hosp
  Roper Rehabilitation Hospital
  St. Franci
Outpatient Centers
  After Hours Care - James Island
  Kiawah-Seabrook Medical & Urgent Care Roper Hosp
  Roper Hospital Ambulatory Surgery & Pain Management - James Island
  Roper Hosp
  Roper Hosp
  Roper Hosp
  Roper Hosptial Diagnostics - Goose Creek
  Roper Hosptial Diagnostics - James Island
  Roper Hosp
  Roper Hosptial Diagnostics - Moncks Corner
  Roper Hospital Imaging - Wesley Drive
  Roper Hospital Imaging - Wingo Way

COMPETITORS

Beaufort Memorial
  Hospital
Conway Medical Center
Georgetown Hospital
  System
Grand Strand Regional
  Medical Center
HCA
Medical University of
  South Carolina
Tenet Healthcare

HISTORICAL FINANCIALS
Company Type: Private

Income Statement — FYE: December 31

	REVENUE ($ mil.)	NET INCOME ($ mil.)	NET PROFIT MARGIN	EMPLOYEES
12/15	827	16	1.9%	5,000
12/14	793	(2)	—	—
12/09	682	56	8.3%	—
12/08	618	(51)	—	—
Annual Growth	4.3%	—	—	—

2015 Year-End Financials
Return on assets: 7.0%   Cash ($ mil.): 31
Return on equity: 1.9%
Current ratio: 0.90

CAREOREGON, INC.

EXECUTIVES

Pres, Chris Krenk
Exec Dir, Mylia Christensen
Coordinator, Crystal Page
Accounting Manager, Timothy Benak
Customer Representativ, Brian M McManus
Personnel Assistant, Vicki Greenwald
Administrative Assistant, Kim Wiseman
Case Manager, Sherry Hansen
Accounting Manager, Kate Koustareva
Isnetwork Engineer II, Dean Brummet
Quality Improvement Coordinato, Jerrie Nelson
Auditors: LB KPMG LLP SEATTLE WA

LOCATIONS

HQ: CAREOREGON, INC.
315 SW 5TH AVE STE 900, PORTLAND, OR 972041739
Phone: 503 416-4100
Web: WWW.CAREOREGON.ORG

HISTORICAL FINANCIALS
Company Type: Private

Income Statement — FYE: December 31

	REVENUE ($ mil.)	NET INCOME ($ mil.)	NET PROFIT MARGIN	EMPLOYEES
12/16	886	(9)	—	140
12/14	851	87	10.3%	—
12/13	564	(0)	—	—
12/08	343	22	6.5%	—
Annual Growth	12.6%	—	—	—

2016 Year-End Financials
Return on assets: 1.8%   Cash ($ mil.): 49
Return on equity: (-1.1%)
Current ratio: 5.00

CARILION MEDICAL CENTER

EXECUTIVES

Ceo, Nancy Howell Agee
President, Steve Arner
SEC, Briggs Andrews
V Pres-Treas, Rob Vaughan
Treas, George Robert Vaughan Jr
Cfo, Donald E Lorton
Prin, Edward Murphy
Department SEC, Donna Webb
Director of Pastoral Care, Richard A Brown
Manager, Sam Garber
Chief of Surgery, Joseph T Moskal
Auditors: DELOITTE & TOUCHE LLP CHARLOT

LOCATIONS

HQ: CARILION MEDICAL CENTER
1906 BELLEVIEW AVE SE, ROANOKE, VA 240141838
Phone: 540 981-7000

HISTORICAL FINANCIALS
Company Type: Private

Income Statement   FYE: September 30

	REVENUE ($ mil.)	NET INCOME ($ mil.)	NET PROFIT MARGIN	EMPLOYEES
09/17	1,232	134	10.9%	6,390
09/16	1,177	4	0.4%	—
09/15	1,064	(36)	—	—
09/13	896	116	12.9%	—
Annual Growth	8.3%	3.6%	—	—

2017 Year-End Financials

Return on assets: 2.3%   Cash ($ mil.): —
Return on equity: 10.9%
Current ratio: 1.20

CARLE FOUNDATION HOSPITAL

Carle Foundation Hospital is a 393-bed acute-care facility that serves the residents of east central Illinois. The hospital includes the region's only Level I trauma center as well as a Level III perinatal center a neonatal ICU and centers devoted to cardiac and cancer care. It also runs a handful of specialty centers in the region. Carle Foundation Hospital is the primary teaching hospital for the University of Illinois College of Medicine at Urbana-Champaign. It is controlled by the not-for-profit Carle Foundation; sister company Carle Physician Group which boasts more than 400 physicians representing 80 specialties is one of the nation's largest private physician groups.

Operations
The hospital averages more than 22000 annual patient admissions and treats 63000-plus emergency room patients. It offers services related to bariatrics stroke sports medicine women's health and heart and cancer care.

Geographic Reach
Carle Foundation Hospital's service area spans 14 communities across east-central Illinois.

Sales and Marketing
Revenue increased 12% to $2 billion in 2014 as patient service earnings and rental income grew.

However due to an increase in medical benefits of insured and pension-related changes net income fell 65% to $112 million that year.

Despite the lower net income cash flow from operations rose 20% to $193 million on changes in medical claims payable as well as an increase in cash generated fro third-party payor settlements.

Strategy
Construction has been key to Carle Foundation Hospital's growth in recent years. The hospital built a $6 million center for children with hearing loss; the center houses the Expanding Children's Hearing Opportunities Center and the Carle Auditory Oral School. Carle Foundation Hospital Research Institute opened an $11-million Biomedical Research Center that houses hospital and University of Illinois staff conducting research in breast cancer gastrointestinal and cardiovascular disease and neuroscience.

The hospital in 2013 added a $200 million seven-story patient tower that houses the heart and vascular institute. The new patient capacity replaced patient beds in older parts of the hospital and provides for future growth opportunities. Carle Foundation Hospital now plans to build a new facility to address the region's needs for increased orthopedic and sports medicine services.

In 2015 Crawford Memorial Hospital and Carle Foundation Hospital entered into an affiliation agreement. Crawford's 25-bed facility joined Carle's network of rural care centers to better provide care for patients in the area.

EXECUTIVES

President And Ceo, James C. Leonard
Vice President Of Facility, Scott Harding
Medical Director, Andy Arwari
Medical Director, Douglas Filipov
Medical Records Director, Tricia Truscott
Vice President, Bonnie Standley
Operating Room Director, Julie Cox
Medical Director, Thomas Scaggs
Vice President, Carol Hovis
Radiology Director, Tim Sapyta
Occupational Medicine, Martina Stika
Senior Vice President Chief Medical Director, Kirk Moberg
Vice President, Matthew Kolb
Vice President Primary Care And Medical Specialties, Eli Smith

LOCATIONS

HQ: CARLE FOUNDATION HOSPITAL
611 W PARK ST, URBANA, IL 618012529
Phone: 217 326-2900
Web: WWW.CARLE.ORG

PRODUCTS/OPERATIONS

2014 Sales

	% of total
Net premium revenue-health insurance	63
Net patient service revenue	34
Rental income	1
Net assets released from restrictions	-
Other	2
Loss on the disposal of property & equipment	-
Total	**100**

Selected Medical Services

Bariatrics
Cancer
Cancer
Cardiology & Heart Surgery
Diabetes & Endocrinology
Ear Nose & Throat
Gastroenterology & GI Surgery
Geriatrics
Gynecology
Heart
Nephrology
Neurology & Neurosurgery
Sports Medicine
Stroke
Women's Health

COMPETITORS

Advocate BroMenn
Decatur Memorial Hospital
Hospital Sisters Health System
Iroquois Memorial Hospital
Memorial Health System
Morris Hospital
OSF Healthcare System
Sarah Bush Lincoln Health Center
Silver Cross Hospital
St. Elizabeth Regional Health
St. John's Hospital (Illinois)
Union Hospital (Indiana)

HISTORICAL FINANCIALS
Company Type: Private

Income Statement   FYE: December 31

	REVENUE ($ mil.)	NET INCOME ($ mil.)	NET PROFIT MARGIN	EMPLOYEES
12/17	900	247	27.5%	2,500
12/16	812	185	22.8%	—
12/15	754	163	21.7%	—
12/13	616	180	29.2%	—
Annual Growth	9.9%	8.3%	—	—

CARNEGIE MELLON UNIVERSITY

If you can't act maybe Carnegie Mellon University can help. The university is known around the world for churning out award-winning actors from its highly regarded drama school. Drama isn't all Carnegie teaches though — the school has seven colleges and schools that offer academic programs in areas such as psychology computer science engineering biology and public policy. It has more than 13000 students and 5300 faculty and staff and it has a relatively small student-teacher ratio of 10:1. Carnegie Mellon was founded by philanthropist and industrialist Andrew Carnegie who established the Carnegie Technical Schools in 1900 for the sons and daughters of Pittsburgh's blue-collar workers.

Operations
Along with its undergraduate and graduate degree programs Carnegie offers working adults a chance to continue their learning through the Professional & Distance Learning arm of the school. Students there can hone their international business management skills and bone up on information technology health systems and human resources among other topics.

Carnegie prides itself on its innovation efforts and to support them operates more than 100 research institutes and centers across its campus. Carnegie's CyLab is one of the largest university-based cybersecurity education and research centers in the country. Cylab focuses on seven primary areas of research and development spanning a wide range of technologies and systems and users.

Tuition for residential undergraduates in the fiscal year ending 2017 totals more than $51000.

The school's alumni network includes about 20 Nobel Prize laureates some 100 Emmy Award winners and a half-dozen Academy Award winners.

Geographic Reach
The school's main campus nearly 150 acres with more than 100 buildings is located in Pittsburgh; Carnegie Mellon also has branch campuses in

Qatar and Silicon Valley California. Additionally the university offers degrees in nearly 20 locations around the world including Australia Greece Japan Mexico Portugal and Singapore.

Financial Performance
The university's revenue increased 5% to $1.1 billion in 2015. This was driven by increases in tuition and fees and higher enrollments. Contributions revenue rose 15% that year and investment income rose nearly that much.

However net income dropped 36% to $161 million as investment returns declined. An increase in accounts payable and other factors led the school's operating cash to rise 14% to $75 million that year.

Strategy
In 2015 Carnegie Mellon focused on four major capital projects. Among those were the addition of a classroom and central hub in its Heinz College Hamburg Hall and the addition of fitness amenities to the Cohon University Center. The David A. Tepper Quadrangle which will include the Tepper School of Business and the Swartz Center for Entrepreneurship is scheduled to be completed in 2018.

Company Background
Carnegie Tech merged with the Mellon Institute of Research to become Carnegie Mellon University in 1967.

EXECUTIVES

Provost, Farnam Jahanian
Ceo Software Engineering Institute, Paul D. Nielsen, age 67
Dean Student Affairs, Gina Casalegno
Dean Qatar Campus, Ilker Baybars
President, Subra Suresh
Dean Heinz College, Ramayya Krishnan
Chief Investment Officer, Charles A. Kennedy
Vp Finance And Cfo, Amir Rahnamay-Azar
Dean College Of Engineering, James H. Garrett
Dean College Of Fine Arts, Dan Martin
Dean Mellon College Of Science, Fred Gilman
Dean Tepper School Of Business, Robert M. Dammon
Vp Marketing And Communications, Steve Kloehn
Interim Cio, David Baisley
Dean School Of Computer Science, Andrew Moore
Dean Dietrich College Of Humanities And Social Sciences, Richard Scheines
Dean Of Admission, Michael Steidel
Dean University Libraries, Keith Webster
Department Head, Terry Hurlbert
Vice President Marketing, Peter Boatwright
Senior Management (senior Vice President General Manager Director), Gretchen Beck
Associate Vice President, Tim McNulty
Assistant Vice President For Marketing Communications, Marilyn Kail
Vice President Of Technology, Neel Kishan
Contracts Manager Associate Vice President For Re, Lynn Young
Vice President Of Membership Development, Jean Sloat
Assistant Vice President For Research Compliance, Ann Mathias
Vice President, Brandon Davis
Department Head, Stephen Garoff
Vice President, Robert Sekerka
Associate Vice President Campus Design Facility Development, Ralph Horgan
Vice President Of Finance, Lapah Mofor
Vice President Of Technology, Daniel Dallala
Vice President Of Finance, Peter Tran
Vice President Of Finance, Jorge Carvallo
Assistant Vice President Internationa, Carrie Nelson
Vice President Of Finance, Sam Phong

Vice President Of Technology Education, Silvio Tannert
Vice President Finance, Maneesh Lekkala
Co Vice President Of Finance, Sahil Jain
Vice President Of Education Technology, Georgia Tech
Vice President Of Finance, Kevin Gallagher
Vice President Of Finance And Technology, Daniel Robinson
Vice President Of Corporate Finance, Mark Flemming
Vice President, Egon Balas
Associate Vice President Government Relations, Timothy McNulty
Assistant Vice President Advancement Marketing And Communications, Brian Thornton
Chairman, James E. (Jim) Rohr, age 70
Vice Chairman, Edward H. (Ed) Frank, age 61
Treasurer, Michelle Martin
Secretary, Alice Yochum

LOCATIONS

HQ: CARNEGIE MELLON UNIVERSITY
5000 FORBES AVE, PITTSBURGH, PA 152133890
Phone: 412 268-2000
Web: WWW.CMU.EDU

Selected Locations
Adelaide Australia
Athens Greece
Aveiro and Coimbra Portugal
Doha Qatar
Kobe Japan
Lisbon Portugal
Los Angeles
Madeira Portugal
Minho and Porto Portugal
Mexico
Silicon Valley
Singapore

PRODUCTS/OPERATIONS

2015 Sales

	% of total
Tuition and other educational fees revenue net of financial aid	39
Sponsored projects revenue	32
Contributions revenue	12
Auxiliary services revenue	5
Investment income	3
Other sources	9
Total	**100**

Selected Departments
Chemical Engineering
Civil and Environmental Engineering
Energy Science Technology & Policy
Electrical and Computer Engineering
Engineering and Public Policy
Engineering & Technology Innovation Management
Information Networking Institute
Materials Science Engineering
Mechanical Engineering
Software Engineering and
Software Management
Architecture
Art
Design
Drama
Master of Arts Management
Master of Entertainment Industry Management
Music
English
History
Modern Languages
Philosophy
Psychology
Social and Decision Sciences
Statistics

Selected Schools
Carnegie Institute of Technology
School of Computer Science
College of Fine Arts
College of Humanities & Social Sciences
H. John Heinz III College
Mellon College of Science
Tepper School of Business

HISTORICAL FINANCIALS
Company Type: Private

Income Statement   FYE: June 30

	REVENUE ($ mil.)	NET INCOME ($ mil.)	NET PROFIT MARGIN	EMPLOYEES
06/18	1,313	296	22.6%	4,913
06/17	1,229	556	45.2%	—
06/13	1,106	182	16.5%	—
06/12	1,061	44	4.2%	—
Annual Growth	3.6%	37.1%	—	—

2018 Year-End Financials
Return on assets: 15.4%   Cash ($ mil.): 481
Return on equity: 22.6%
Current ratio: —

CAROLINA NORTH HOUSING FINANCE AGENCY

EXECUTIVES

Director, Robert Qucab
Board of Directors, James W O Glesby
Paralegal, Liz Hair
Training, Jane Buchholz

LOCATIONS

HQ: CAROLINA NORTH HOUSING FINANCE AGENCY
3508 BUSH ST, RALEIGH, NC 276097509
Phone: 919 877-5700
Web: WWW.NCHFA.COM

HISTORICAL FINANCIALS
Company Type: Private

Income Statement   FYE: June 30

	REVENUE ($ mil.)	NET INCOME ($ mil.)	NET PROFIT MARGIN	EMPLOYEES
06/18	363	43	12.1%	108
06/17*	381	39	10.2%	—
12/06	0	0	—	—
Annual Growth	—	—	—	—

*Fiscal year change

2018 Year-End Financials
Return on assets: 0.9%   Cash ($ mil.): 15
Return on equity: 12.1%
Current ratio: 0.20

CAROLINAEAST MEDICAL CENTER

EXECUTIVES

Pres, G Raymond Leggett III
Vice President, Rosanne Leahy
Vice President, Cindy Turco
Vp of Hr, Leslie Hunter
Cfo, Tammy Sherron

Director of Pharmacy, Genelle Butz
Vice-President, Lesley Hunter
Director, Lynda Honaker
Manager, Megan McGarvey
Administrative Assistant, Deb Rogers
Internal Medicine Practitioner, Chete Eze-Nliam

LOCATIONS

HQ: CAROLINAEAST MEDICAL CENTER
  2000 NEUSE BLVD, NEW BERN, NC 285603449
Phone: 252 633-8111
Web: WWW.CAROLINAEASTHEALTH.COM

HISTORICAL FINANCIALS

Company Type: Private

Income Statement				FYE: September 30
	REVENUE ($ mil.)	NET INCOME ($ mil.)	NET PROFIT MARGIN	EMPLOYEES
09/17	363	40	11.1%	1,630
09/16	345	31	9.2%	—
09/15	320	2	0.7%	—
09/14	301	25	8.4%	—
Annual Growth	6.4%	17.0%	—	—

2017 Year-End Financials

Return on assets: —
Return on equity: 11.1%
Current ratio: 2.50
Cash ($ mil.): 115

CAROLINAS MEDICAL CENTER NORTHEAST

EXECUTIVES

Ceo, Michael C Tarwater
President, Phyllis Wingate-Jones
Chief Information Officer, Keith Mc Neice
Director, Linda K Bresnahan
Director of Emergency Room, Mary Anne Nolan
Chief Operating Officer, Bill Hubbard
Director of Information Techno, Linda Bresnahan
Director of Information Techno, Mark Williams
Assistant Administrator, Donna Harless
Executive Director, Gale Deal
Director, Richard Ozment

LOCATIONS

HQ: CAROLINAS MEDICAL CENTER NORTHEAST
  920 CHURCH ST N, CONCORD, NC 280252927
Phone: 704 783-3000
Web: WWW.CAROLINASHEALTHCARE.ORG

HISTORICAL FINANCIALS

Company Type: Private

Income Statement				FYE: December 31
	REVENUE ($ mil.)	NET INCOME ($ mil.)	NET PROFIT MARGIN	EMPLOYEES
12/17	576	158	27.4%	4,500
12/16	552	130	23.6%	—
12/15	557	117	21.0%	—
Annual Growth	1.7%	16.3%	—	—

2017 Year-End Financials

Return on assets: 0.4%
Return on equity: 27.4%
Current ratio: 5.00
Cash ($ mil.): —

CAROMONT HEALTH, INC.

CaroMont Health is an independent not-for-profit health care system serving residents of North Carolina's Piedmont region. Anchoring CaroMont Health is Gaston Memorial Hospital a 435-bed medical and surgical facility that features a birthing center an inpatient psychiatric ward and specialized facilities for heart disease cancer sleep disorders diabetes and wound care. Other operations include a nearly 100-bed nursing home outpatient surgery and urgent care centers and a network of primary and specialty medical practices. CaroMont Health also provides home health and hospice care services. CaroMont Health is governed by the North Carolina Medical Care Commission.

Operations
CaroMont Health employs a total of some 3900 health professionals including about 450 physicians. Its CaroMont Medical Group physician practice organization includes 140 doctors that serve patients from 45 outpatient locations including primary and specialty practices surgery centers and urgent and immediate care clinics.

Geographic Reach
CaroMont's primary facilities are located in Gastonia a community just west of Charlotte North Carolina. The health network also operates clinics and offices in Cleveland Mecklenburg Mountain Island Lake and Lincoln North Carolina as well as in York South Carolina.

Strategy
Like many medical networks CaroMont Health is establishing urgent care and walk-in immediate care centers to offset unnecessary use of hospital emergency rooms. Such facilities help to lower costs and increase efficient patient care management.

In other efforts to meet area population needs CaroMont has begun an expansion program to significantly increase the size of its Gaston Hospice facility. It is also expanding and renovating the emergency department of its main campus; the facility will gain 10000 sq. ft. of new space and a pediatric emergency area. In 2015 the system opened the CaroMont Regional Medical Center in Mount Holly which is designed to meet the emergency care needs of eastern Gaston southern Lincoln and western Mecklenburg counties.

Partnering with community groups is another way CaroMont works to improve general health and medical services. In 2014 it partnered with Gaston County Schools to begin providing athletic training services; the following year it initiated a two-year pilot program with North Carolina State Health Plan encouraging plan members' physicians to improve engagement and improve member experiences in general.

EXECUTIVES

Medical Director Cardiac Surgery, James Greelish
Director Of Radiology Cardiology, Deanna Roe
Medical Director, Andrew Matthews
Auditors: DIXON HUGHES GOODMAN LLP ASHE

LOCATIONS

HQ: CAROMONT HEALTH, INC.
  2525 COURT DR, GASTONIA, NC 280542140
Phone: 704 834-2000
Web: WWW.CAROMONTHEALTH.ORG

PRODUCTS/OPERATIONS

Selected Service Areas
Cancer (oncology)
Diabetes
Emergency care
Heart and vascular
Hospice and palliative care
Immediate care
Long-term care
Mental health
Mobile screening
Neuroscience
Orthopedics
Pain management
Rehabilitation
Sleep medicine
Surgery
Trauma
Wellness programs
Women's health
Wound care

COMPETITORS

Blue Ridge HealthCare
Carolinas HealthCare System
Community Health Systems
High Point Regional Health System
Mission Hospitals
New Hanover Regional Medical Center
Novant Health
Tenet Healthcare

HISTORICAL FINANCIALS

Company Type: Private

Income Statement				FYE: June 30
	REVENUE ($ mil.)	NET INCOME ($ mil.)	NET PROFIT MARGIN	EMPLOYEES
06/18	602	63	10.5%	2,400
06/17	552	80	14.6%	—
06/15	38	36	95.3%	—
06/14	37	35	95.9%	—
Annual Growth	100.7%	15.4%	—	—

2018 Year-End Financials

Return on assets: 3.0%
Return on equity: 10.5%
Current ratio: 0.70
Cash ($ mil.): 25

CARROLLTON-FARMERS BRANCH INDEPENDENT SCHOOL DISTRICT

EXECUTIVES

Supt, Dr John E Chapman III
Auditors: HANKINS EASTUP DEATON TONN

LOCATIONS

HQ: CARROLLTON-FARMERS BRANCH INDEPENDENT SCHOOL DISTRICT
  1445 N PERRY RD, CARROLLTON, TX 750066134
Phone: 972 968-6100
Web: WWW.CFBISD.EDU

HISTORICAL FINANCIALS

Company Type: Private

Income Statement | | | | FYE: August 31

	REVENUE ($ mil.)	NET INCOME ($ mil.)	NET PROFIT MARGIN	EMPLOYEES
08/17	339	16	4.9%	4,020
08/16	316	(10)	—	—
08/15	306	(13)	—	—
08/14	290	(11)	—	—
Annual Growth	5.3%	—	—	—

2017 Year-End Financials

Return on assets: 1.6%   Cash ($ mil.): 213
Return on equity: 4.9%
Current ratio: —

CARSON TAHOE REGIONAL HEALTHCARE

EXECUTIVES

Operating Room Director, Cindy Kuperus
Admissions Director, Melissa Williams
Vice President Clinical Integration, Pam Puckett

LOCATIONS

HQ: CARSON TAHOE REGIONAL HEALTHCARE
  1600 MEDICAL PKWY, CARSON CITY, NV 897034625
Phone: 775 445-8000
Web: WWW.CARSONTAHOE.COM

PRODUCTS/OPERATIONS

Selected Services
Behavioral Health Services Inpatient
Cancer Center
Carson Tahoe Cardiology Locations
Carson Tahoe Surgery Center
Dayton Medical Building
Eagle Medical Center
Holbrook Therapy
Minden Medical Center
Regional Medical Center
Sierra Surgery Hospital
Specialty Medical Center
Therapy at N. Roop Prof. Center
Urgent & Emergent Care
Walmart Clinics
Womens Health/Cardiology

COMPETITORS

Dignity Health   Universal Health
HCA   Services
Sutter Health

HISTORICAL FINANCIALS

Company Type: Private

Income Statement | | | | FYE: December 31

	REVENUE ($ mil.)	NET INCOME ($ mil.)	NET PROFIT MARGIN	EMPLOYEES
12/17	284	20	7.1%	2,000
12/16	270	26	9.9%	—
12/15	245	21	8.6%	—
12/14	202	10	5.0%	—
Annual Growth	12.0%	25.6%	—	—

2017 Year-End Financials

Return on assets: 2.9%   Cash ($ mil.): 22
Return on equity: 7.1%
Current ratio: 1.80

CARTER-JONES COMPANIES, INC.

EXECUTIVES

Pres-Ceo, Neil Sackett
Sr V Pres-Cfo, Jeffrey Donley
SEC, Judy Lee
Controller, Brian Horning
Auditors: BDO USA LLP AKRON OHIO

LOCATIONS

HQ: CARTER-JONES COMPANIES, INC.
  601 TALLMADGE RD, KENT, OH 442407331
Phone: 330 673-6100
Web: WWW.DOITBEST.COM

HISTORICAL FINANCIALS

Company Type: Private

Income Statement | | | | FYE: December 31

	REVENUE ($ mil.)	NET INCOME ($ mil.)	NET PROFIT MARGIN	EMPLOYEES
12/17	1,365	29	2.1%	3,225
12/16	1,241	15	1.2%	—
12/15	1,109	17	1.6%	—
Annual Growth	10.9%	27.8%	—	—

2017 Year-End Financials

Return on assets: 5.0%   Cash ($ mil.): 7
Return on equity: 2.1%
Current ratio: 0.90

CASE WESTERN RESERVE UNIVERSITY

Looking for a research-oriented university? Case Western Reserve University (CWRU) is a private research school with an enrollment of more than 11300 students from all US states and more than 90 countries more than half of whom are graduate and professional students. CWRU offers about 200 undergraduate and graduate degree programs from its eight colleges and schools — business engineering law arts and sciences dentistry social work nursing and medicine — as well as a graduate school at its campus in Cleveland. The university has 3360 faculty members and a student-to-teacher ratio of 8:1.

Operations

The school receives close to $400 million in external funding each year to pay for its various research enterprises. CWRU provides research opportunities to more than 5100 undergraduates and partners with corporations foundations and other universities to operate more than 100 research centers and institutes. Some of its priority research initiatives include energy and the environment culture creativity and design social justice and ethics. Medical studies are conducted in coordination with health care entities; its most predominant partner is the Cleveland Clinic.

Geographic Reach

CWRU is located on the a 178-acre campus in Cleveland Ohio; the campus is located within the 500-acre University Circle district; and houses more than 40 educational medical cultural social and religious institutions. CWRU's students come from all 50 US states and more than 90 countries.

Financial Performance

Research grants and contracts account for about 33% of CWRU's revenues while tuition accounts for another 25%. Other sources of revenue include investment returns overhead cost recovery and gifts and pledges from private sources. The university reported a 10% increase in revenues to $1 billion in fiscal 2016 due to an increase in tuition and higher undergraduate enrollment. CWRU also saw a 50% increase in gifts and pledges that year.

Operating margin grew from to $7.4 million in 2015 to $9 million in 2016 as a result of higher tuition and fees and an increase in grant gifts and auxiliary services income.

CWRU has an endowment of about $1.7 billion.

Strategy

CWRU's core priorities include enhancing its education and research programs advancing institutional resources strengthening partnerships and building a diverse community.

In 2016 CWRU launched the Master of Arts in Military Ethics program the nation?s first in a field of study that contends with questions of how advancing military technologies relate to the common humanity of both enemy and ally.

In 2014 the university reached its initial goal of raising $1 billion to increase financial support for students grow the number of endowed professorships and support capital projects. That year it launched a $64 million renovation and expansion of the Temple-Tifereth Israel complex as part of its 21-acre campus expansion; the project will turn the facility into a performing arts center that will house the school's dance theatre and music departments.

Company Background

The university's origins date back to 1826 in the Ohio region then known as the Western Reserve of Connecticut; its current structure was formed in 1967 with the combination of neighboring Case Institute of Technology and Western Reserve College.

EXECUTIVES

Vice President For Campus Services, Dick Jamieson
Director Media Relations, Lisa Chiu
President, Barbara R. Snyder, age 62
Dean School Of Graduate Studies, Charles Rozek
Dean Undergraduate Studies, Jeffrey Wolcowitz
Chief Investment Officer, Sally J. Staley
Dean School Of Dental Medicine, Kenneth B. Chance
Dean Mandel School Of Applied Social Sciences, Grover C. (Cleve) Gilmore
Provost And Evp, William A. (Bud) Baeslack
Svp Finance And Cfo, John F. Sideras
Dean School Of Medicine, Pamela Bowles Davis
Dean College Of Arts And Sciences, Cyrus Taylor
Vp University Marketing And Communications, Chris Sheridan
Dean Case School Of Engineering, Jeffrey Duerk
Dean Weatherhead School Of Management, Robert E. Widing
Dean Bolton School Of Nursing, Mary E. Kerr
Vp Information Technology Services And Cio, Sue B. Workman
Dean School Of Law, Jessica Berg
Dean School Of Law, Michael P. Scharf
Medical Director Professor, Kingman Strohl
Senior Vice President Of University Relations And Development, Bruce Loessin
Vice President Information Services, Lev Gonick
Vice President Financial Advisor, William Bruner
Vice President, Stephen Campbell
Associate Vice President For Operations And Planning, Dennis Rupert

Krieger Mueller Associate Professor Of Applied History Krieger Mueller Historian Vice President For Collections Wrhs, John Grabowski
Vice President Of Planning, Kenneth Basch
Chair Department Of Nutrition, Henri Brunengraber
Vice President For Enrollment Management, Richard Bischoff
Vice President Of Planning, Christine Ash
Vice President For Biomedical Science In Technology Transfer Office, Joseph Jankowski
Director Of Admissions, Christian Essman
Vice President For Development, Terese Perchinske
Student Affairs Associate Vice President, Sue Nickel-Schindewolf
Vice President For Student Affairs, Lou Stark
Associate Vice President Of Institutional Development, Kaye Ridolfi
Medical Director Of Respiratory Therapy, Tony Dimarco
Vice President, Marissa Wong
Vice President Of Membership Development, Akash K Menon
Vice President Finance Executive, Anthony D Kinslow
Vice President Finance, Shreenath Nedungadi
Director Of Admissions, Albert Difranco
Associate Vice President Information Technology, Michael Edwards
Vice President, Jacqueline Musacchia
Medical Director Clinical Microbiology, Michael Jacobs
Medical Director, Ted Parran
Vice President Of Marketing, Jim Hammerstone
Vice President Its, Dean Bianchi
Vice President Technology, Karmar Clifton
Vice President, Ken Basch
Vice President, Tom Mullen
Senior Vice President Secretary And General Counsel, Elizabeth Keefer
Associate Vice President And Treasurer, NORMAN CANNON
Vice President Of Marketing, Juanita Cutler
Associate Vice President For Student Affairs, Dean Patterson
Vice President For Financial Planning, Jonathan Carlson
Director Of Nursing, Wayne MacKenzie
Vice President, Casandra Tice
Vice President, Ray Braun
Associate Vice President Of University Relations And Development, Taylor Gladys
Chairman, Charles D. (Chuck) Fowler
Board Member, Fred Collopy
Treasurer, Eric Bower
Secretary, Ellen Rothchild
Secretary Iv, Kellie Shaffer
Vice Chair Of Research And Professor, Irina Pikuleva
Secretary, Susan Grimm
Secretary, Kimberly Racut
Secretary, Tiana Wilson
Auditors: PRICEWATERHOUSECOOPERS LLP CL

LOCATIONS

HQ: CASE WESTERN RESERVE UNIVERSITY
10900 EUCLID AVE, CLEVELAND, OH 441064901
Phone: 216 368-2000
Web: WWW.CASE.EDU

PRODUCTS/OPERATIONS

2014 Sales

	% of total
Grants and contracts	27
Student tuition and fees	24
Gifts and pledges	9
CCLCM grants and contracts	9
Facilities and administrative cost recovery	8
Others	23
Total	100

Selected Schools and Programs

Case School of Engineering
College of Arts and Sciences
Cleveland Clinic (part of the School of Medicine)
Frances Payne Bolton School of Nursing
Mandel Center for Nonprofit Organizations
Mandel School of Applied Social Sciences
School of Dental Medicine
School of Graduate Studies
School of Law
School of Medicine
Weatherhead School of Management

HISTORICAL FINANCIALS

Company Type: Private

Income Statement

FYE: June 30

	REVENUE ($ mil.)	NET INCOME ($ mil.)	NET PROFIT MARGIN	EMPLOYEES
06/18	1,016	111	10.9%	6,599
06/17	1,022	208	20.4%	—
06/15	1,093	48	4.4%	—
06/14	926	214	23.2%	—
Annual Growth	2.3%	(15.2%)	—	—

2018 Year-End Financials

Return on assets: 6.2%   Cash ($ mil.): 105
Return on equity: 10.9%
Current ratio: —

CATHOLIC HEALTH INITIATIVES

For Catholic Health Initiatives (CHI) returning sick people to good health is more than a business — it's a mission. Formed in 1996 through the merger of three Catholic hospital systems the giant not-for-profit organization is one of the largest Catholic hospital operators in the US. It covers more than 90 sites including hospitals and clinics as well as long-term care assisted-living and senior residential facilities in about 20 states from Washington to Maryland. Its hospitals range from large urban medical centers (many with educational and research programs) to small hospitals in rural areas. All told CHI has more than 14000 acute-care beds. It is sponsored by a dozen different congregations of nuns. In 2019 CHI merged with San Francisco-based hospital system Dignity Health to create the $29 billion not-for-profit organization CommonSpirit Health.

Change in Company Type

After the merger with Dignity Health CHI operates as a part of CommonSpirit Health which has more than 140 hospitals and serves 21 states. CommonSpirit Health is headquartered in Chicago.

Operations

CHI's network includes 105 hospitals four of which are academic and teaching facilities and 30 rural facilities with critical-care access as well as nursing colleges home-health agencies community health services organizations long-term care facilities assisted-care and residential senior homes research and development programs and labs.

Geographic Reach

CHI operates in Arkansas Colorado Indiana Iowa Kansas Kentucky Minnesota Nebraska New Jersey New Mexico North Dakota Ohio Oregon Pennsylvania South Dakota Tennessee Texas Washington and Wisconsin — 19 states in all.

Strategy

CHI whose mission covers "expressing Christ's love by caring for those in need" is issuing nearly

$2 billion in taxable and tax-exempt bonds to fund several initiatives including a system-wide IT infrastructure upgrade (in part to facilitate its federally mandated conversion to universal electronic health records) virtual health programs (telemedicine) insurance products and clinic networks.

In 2016 the company announced plans to exit the health insurance business by selling its Qual-Choice Health insurance subsidiary acquired in 2014. The unit lost nearly $97 million in the first three quarters of fiscal 2016 (ended March) and CHI posted an operating loss of some $19 million.

Mergers and Acquisitions

After years of discussions CHI and Dignity Health merged in early 2019. The combined health system with 142 hospitals in 21 states is the largest not-for-profit hospital system in the US. The size of the system allows for it to provide expanded care to patients through such methods as virtual appointments a broader range of clinical programs and advanced technologies. The new organization named CommonSpirit Health is headquartered in Chicago. Individual hospitals continue to operate under their existing names.

HISTORY

In 1860 the Sisters of St. Francis established a hospital in Philadelphia laying the foundation for a larger health care organization. In 1981 Franciscan Health System was formally established to be a national holding company for Catholic hospitals and related organizations. By the mid-1990s the system consisted of 12 member and two affiliate hospitals and 11 long-term-care facilities located in the mid-Atlantic states and the Pacific Northwest.

Sisters of Charity of Cincinnati and the Sisters of St. Francis Perpetual Adoration of Colorado Springs co-sponsored The Sisters of Charity Health Care Systems incorporated in 1979 as a multi-institutional health care network. By the mid-1990s the system included 20 hospitals in Colorado Kentucky Nebraska New Mexico and Ohio.

Three congregations collaborated to form Catholic Health Corporation in 1980 one of the first such health care partnerships between religious communities within the Roman Catholic Church in the US. By 1996 this coalition operated 100 health care facilities in 12 states.

The development of modern managed care health care systems put pressure on the smaller Catholic hospital operations so the three systems established Catholic Health Initiatives (CHI) in 1996 as a national entity serving five geographic regions. Patricia Cahill a lay health care veteran who previously served the Archdiocese of New York was appointed president and CEO of CHI. The following year CHI absorbed the 10-hospital Sisters of Charity of Nazareth Health Care System based in Bardstown Kentucky (founded in a log cabin in 1812).

That year CHI continued to seek new partnerships to improve efficiency. With Alegent Health it formed provider network Midwest Select with nearly 200 hospitals marketing discounted rates to businesses. CHI allied with the Daughters of Charity to form for-profit joint venture Catholic Healthcare Audit Network to provide operational financial compliance and information systems audits as well as due diligence reviews. CHI also joined insurance joint venture NewCap Insurance with the Daughters of Charity and Catholic Health East; the firm allowed CHI to operate independently of commercial insurers.

CHI made a secular tie-in with the University of Pennsylvania Health System in 1998 whereby the university's system would offer care through five Catholic hospitals (CHI made plans to transfer these hospitals to Catholic Health East in 2001).

The next year CHI announced its first loss due to lackluster performance in the Midwest. During 2000 the company responded by streamlining operations and changing management resulting in a positive bottom line. In 2001 it sold three hospitals in Pennsylvania one in Delaware and one in New Jersey to Catholic Health East.

EXECUTIVES

President Ceo And Trustee, Kevin E. Lofton, age 63
President Enterprise Business Lines And Cfo, J. Dean Swindle
Svp Divisional Operations (texas), Michael H. Covert
Svp Marketing And Communications, Joyce M. Ross
Executive Vice President Mission, Thomas R. Kopfensteiner
Svp Divisional Operations And Ceo Chi Memorial (tennessee), Larry Schumacher, age 60
Evp Corporate Affairs And Chief Legal Officer, Mitch H. Melfi
Evp Growth And Business Acquisitions, Paul W. Edgett
Svp Human Resources And Chief Human Resources Officer, Patricia G. (Pat) Webb
Svp Divisional Operations And Ceo Chi Health (nebraska And Southwest Iowa), Cliff A. Robertson
Senior Vice President And Division Executive Officer, Jeffrey S. Drop
Svp And Chief Nursing Officer, Kathleen D. Sanford
Svp Divisional Operations And Ceo Mercy Health Network (iowa), David H. Vellinga
Svp Divisional Operations And Ceo Chi Franciscan Health (tacoma), Ketul J. Patel
Svp And President And Ceo Kentuckyone Health, Ruth W. Brinkley
Ceo Chi St. Alexius Health, Matt Grimshaw, age 43
Interim Evp Operations, Anthony Jones
Svp And Chief Medical Officer, Robert J. Weil
Senior Vice President And Chief Medical Officer, Stephen L Moore
Senior Vice President Divisional Operationsceo, Robert Ratzi
Vice President Treasury, Linda Macdonald
Vice President Human Resource Business Practices, Thomas Sams
Vice President Supply Chain Data Analytics, Kevin Kakuda
Vice President Public Policy, Marcia Desmond
Vice President And Chief Nursing Informatics And Telehealth Officer, Ann Shepard
Vice President National Hospitalist, Amanda Trask
Vice President Legal Transactions And Tax, Cynthia Leon
Vice President Of Patient Care, Deb Haagenson
Vice President Outreach, Ellen Lee
Director Of Pharmacy, Nicki Bohl
Senior Vice President Performance Excellence, Robert Strickland
Vice President Of Nursing, Heike Duban
Vice President Real Estate, Dave Glasscock
Senior Vice President Strategy Development, Meta Dooley
Vice President Ministry Formation, Alan BowmanCHI
Svp Ciso, Sheryl Rose
Vice President, Deeanna Opstedahl
Senior Vice President Capital Finance, Nick Barto
Auditors: ERNST & YOUNG LLP DENVER CO

LOCATIONS

HQ: CATHOLIC HEALTH INITIATIVES
198 INVERNESS DR W, ENGLEWOOD, CO 801123637
Phone: 303 298-9100
Web: WWW.CATHOLICHEALTHINITIATIVES.ORG

Selected Facilities and Operations
Arkansas
St. Vincent Health System
St. Vincent Doctors Hospital (Little Rock)
St. Vincent Infirmary Medical Center (Little Rock)
St. Vincent Medical Center North (Sherwood)
St. Vincent Morrilton (formerly St. Anthony's Medical Center Morrilton)
St. Vincent Rehabilitation Hospital (Sherwood)
Colorado
Centura Health
Centura Senior Services
The Gardens at St. Elizabeth (Denver)
Medalion Retirement Center (Colorado Springs)
Namaste Alzheimer Center (Colorado Springs)
Progressive Care Center (Canon City)
Villa Pueblo (Pueblo)
The Villas at Sunny Acres (Thornton)
Mercy Regional Medical Center (Durango)
Penrose-St. Francis Health Services
Penrose Hospital (Colorado Springs)
St. Francis Health Center (Colorado Springs)
St. Francis Medical Center (Colorado Springs)
St. Anthony Hospitals
St. Anthony Central Hospital (Denver)
St. Anthony North Hospital (Westminster)
St. Anthony Summit Medical Center (Frisco)
St. Mary-Corwin Medical Center (Pueblo)
St. Thomas More Hospital (Canon City)
Iowa
Alegent Health
Alegent Health-Mercy Hospital (Corning)
Alegent Health-Mercy Hospital (Council Bluffs)
Mercy Health Network
Bishop Drumm Retirement Center (Johnston)
Mercy Clinics (Des Moines)
Mercy College of Health Sciences (Des Moines)
Mercy Court (Des Moines)
Mercy Franklin Center (Des Moines)
Mercy Medical Center - Centerville (Centerville)
Mercy Medical Center - West Lakes (Des Moines)
Mercy Park Apartments (Des Moines)
Kansas
St. Rose Ambulatory and Surgery Center (formerly Central Kansas Medical Center Great Bend)
St. Catherine Hospital (Garden City)
Kentucky
KentuckyOne Health
Jewish Hospital and St. Mary's HealthCare (with Jewish Hospital HealthCare Services)
Our Lady of Peace (Louisville)
Sts. Mary & Elizabeth Hospital (Louisville)
Saint Joseph Health System
Continuing Care Hospital Inc. (Lexington)
Flaget Memorial Hospital (Bardstown)
Saint Joseph Berea Hospital (Berea)
Saint Joseph Hospital (Lexington)
Saint Joseph Hospital East (Lexington)
Saint Joseph Hospital Mount Sterling (Mt. Sterling)
Marymount Medical Center (London)
Maryland
St. Joseph Medical Center (Towson)
Minnesota
LakeWood Health Center (Baudette)
St. Francis Healthcare Campus (Breckenridge)
St. Francis Home (Breckenridge)
St. Joseph's Area Health Services (Park Rapids)
Unity Family Healthcare (dba St. Gabriel's Healthcare)
Albany Area Hospital and Medical Center
Alverna Apartments (Little Falls)
St. Camillus Place (Little Falls)
St. Gabriel's Hospital (Little Falls)
Nebraska
Alegent Health (joint venture with Immanuel Healthcare System)
Alegent Health-Bergan Mercy Medical Center (Omaha)
Alegent Health-Mercy Hospital (Council Bluffs)
Good Samaritan Hospital (Kearney)
Richard H. Young Hospital (Kearney)
Saint Elizabeth Regional Medical Center (Lincoln)
Saint Francis Medical Center (Grand Island)
St. Mary's Community Hospital (Nebraska City)
New Jersey
Saint Clare's Health System (Denville)
Saint Clare's Hospital (Boonton)
Saint Clare's Hospital (Denville)
Saint Clare's Hospital (Dover)
Saint Clare's Hospital (Sussex)
New Mexico
St. Joseph Community Health (Albuquerque)
North Dakota
CHI North Dakota
Carrington Health Center (Carrington)
Lisbon Area Health Services
Mercy Hospital (Valley City)
Oakes Community Hospital
Mercy Hospital (Devils Lake)
Mercy Medical Center (Williston)
St. Joseph's Hospital and Health Center (Dickinson)
Villa Nazareth Corporation
Friendship (Fargo)
Riverview Place (Fargo)
Ohio
Premier Health Partners
Good Samaritan Hospital (Dayton)
The Maria-Joseph Center (Dayton)
TriHealth
Good Samaritan Hospital (Cincinnati)
Oregon
Mercy Medical Center
Linus Oakes Inc. (Roseburg)
St. Anthony Hospital (Pendleton)
Pennsylvania
St. Joseph Health Ministries (Lancaster)
St. Joseph Regional Health Network
St. Joseph Medical Center (Reading)
South Dakota
St. Mary's Healthcare Center
Gettysburg Medical Center
Maryhouse Long-term Care Facility (Pierre)
ParkWood Retirement Apartments (Pierre)
Oahe Manor (Gettysburg)
Oahe Villa (Gettysburg)
St. Mary's Hospital (Pierre)
Tennessee
Memorial Health Care System
Memorial Hospital (Chattanooga)
Memorial North Park Hospital (Hixson)
Washington
Franciscan Health System
Enumclaw Regional Hospital (Enumclaw)
St. Anthony Hospital (Gig Harbor)
St. Clare Hospital (Lakewood)
St. Francis Hospital (Federal Way)
St. Joseph Medical Center (Tacoma)
Wisconsin
Franciscan Villa (South Milwaukee)

COMPETITORS

Adventist Health System Sunbelt Healthcare
Allina Hospitals
Ascension Health
Baptist Health
Baptist Health (Arkansas)
BryanLGH Medical Center
Denver Health and Hospital Authority
Exempla Healthcare
Golden Horizons
HCA
Kettering Health Network
Life Care Centers
Memorial Health System (Colorado)
Methodist Health System
MultiCare Health System
OhioHealth
Tenet Healthcare
UC Health
Universal Health Services
University of Colorado Hospital

HISTORICAL FINANCIALS

Company Type: Private

Income Statement				FYE: June 30
	REVENUE ($ mil.)	NET INCOME ($ mil.)	NET PROFIT MARGIN	EMPLOYEES
06/18	14,982	222	1.5%	72,500
06/17	15,547	128	0.8%	—
06/16	15,942	(703)	—	—
06/07	7,731	902	11.7%	—
Annual Growth	6.2%	(12.0%)	—	—

2018 Year-End Financials
Return on assets: 9.9%   Cash ($ mil.): 510
Return on equity: 1.5%
Current ratio: 0.60

CATHOLIC HEALTH INITIATIVES - IOWA, CORP.

EXECUTIVES

Ceo, David Vellinga
Purchasing Coordinator, Matt Rouse
Coordinator, Kelli Cain
Coordinator, Valerie Diehl
Information Technology Manager, Becky Booth
Clerical Supervisor, Kristi Steinbronn
Surgery Education Coordinator, Lori Sheely
Registered Nurse Sales Mscn Ne, Valerie Stickel-Diehl
Midwest Regional Sales Manager, Jeff Johnston
Physician, Mark Tannenbaum
Network Administrator, Terry Anderson
Auditors: CATHOLIC HEALTH INITIATIVES E

LOCATIONS

HQ: CATHOLIC HEALTH INITIATIVES - IOWA, CORP.
1111 6TH AVE, DES MOINES, IA 503142613
Phone: 515 247-3121
Web: WWW.MERCYDESMOINES.ORG

HISTORICAL FINANCIALS
Company Type: Private

Income Statement				FYE: June 30
	REVENUE ($ mil.)	NET INCOME ($ mil.)	NET PROFIT MARGIN	EMPLOYEES
06/16	804	58	7.3%	6,100
06/14	733	(14)	—	—
06/10	691	39	5.8%	—
06/08	577	36	6.3%	—
Annual Growth	4.2%	6.2%	—	—

2016 Year-End Financials
Return on assets: 8.3%   Cash ($ mil.): 82
Return on equity: 7.3%
Current ratio: 3.30

CATHOLIC HEALTH INITIATIVES COLORADO

EXECUTIVES

Ceo, Kevin E Lofton
President, Gregory H Burfitt
Corporate Revenue Integrity, Shelly Vendemo
Chief Officer, Terry Orourke
Orsos Reimbursement Coordinato, Terry Walb
Senior Vice-President, Nancy Hoffman
Vice President of Operations, Geoffrey Lawton Pharmd
Chief Operating Officer, Jameson Smith Fache
Senior Network Engineer, Shawn Crockett
Open Manager, Eric Merredith
Webmaster, Julie Lindsay
Auditors: LB CATHOLIC HEALTH INITIATIVES

LOCATIONS

HQ: CATHOLIC HEALTH INITIATIVES COLORADO
198 INVERNESS DR W, ENGLEWOOD, CO 801123637
Phone: 303 290-6500
Web: WWW.CATHOLICHEALTH.NET

HISTORICAL FINANCIALS
Company Type: Private

Income Statement				FYE: June 30
	REVENUE ($ mil.)	NET INCOME ($ mil.)	NET PROFIT MARGIN	EMPLOYEES
06/15	1,735	101	5.8%	8,000
06/14	1,689	96	5.7%	—
06/10	1,307	50	3.9%	—
06/09	1,226	24	2.0%	—
Annual Growth	6.0%	26.4%	—	—

2015 Year-End Financials
Return on assets: 12.7%   Cash ($ mil.): 45
Return on equity: 5.8%
Current ratio: 1.30

CATHOLIC MEDICAL MISSION BOARD INC

EXECUTIVES

Pres, John F Galbraith
President, Bruce Wilkinson
Marketing Staff, Kate M Seo
Senior Vice-President, Marivette Cannon
Director, Chris Foster
Vice-Chairman, F W Smullen
Government Affairs Manager, Jennifer Paulk
Director of Information Techno, Joshua Freeman
Financial Controller, Patrick Opembe
Program Manager, Syndie Saint Hilaire
Auditors: MARKS PANETH & SHRON LLP NEW

LOCATIONS

HQ: CATHOLIC MEDICAL MISSION BOARD INC
100 WALL ST FL 9, NEW YORK, NY 100055765
Phone: 212 242-7757
Web: WWW.CMMB.ORG

HISTORICAL FINANCIALS
Company Type: Private

Income Statement				FYE: September 30
	REVENUE ($ mil.)	NET INCOME ($ mil.)	NET PROFIT MARGIN	EMPLOYEES
09/17	603	19	3.2%	38
09/16	371	(12)	—	—
09/15	290	(3)	—	—
09/14	387	(6)	—	—
Annual Growth	16.0%	—	—	—

2017 Year-End Financials
Return on assets: 0.4%   Cash ($ mil.): 6
Return on equity: 3.2%
Current ratio: 1.30

CATHOLIC RELIEF SERVICES - UNITED STATES CONFERENCE OF CATHOLIC BISHOPS

EXECUTIVES

Ceo, Sean Callahan
Exec V Pres, Schuyler Thorup
Exec V Pres, Joan Rosenhauer
Exec V Pres, Annemarie Reilly
Exec V Pres-Dir, Mark Melia
Exec V Pres-Dir, Shawn Mood
Cfo-Dir, James Bond
Communications Officer, Kim Pozniak
Chief Financial Officer, Mark Palmer
Auditors: RSM US LLP GAITHERSBURG MARY

LOCATIONS

HQ: CATHOLIC RELIEF SERVICES - UNITED STATES CONFERENCE OF CATHOLIC BISHOPS
228 W LEXINGTON ST, BALTIMORE, MD 212013443
Phone: 410 625-2220
Web: WWW.CRS.ORG

HISTORICAL FINANCIALS
Company Type: Private

Income Statement				FYE: September 30
	REVENUE ($ mil.)	NET INCOME ($ mil.)	NET PROFIT MARGIN	EMPLOYEES
09/17	978	20	2.1%	7,100
09/16	917	(47)	—	—
09/15	738	(11)	—	—
09/13	639	8	1.3%	—
Annual Growth	11.2%	25.6%	—	—

2017 Year-End Financials
Return on assets: 9.0%   Cash ($ mil.): 114
Return on equity: 2.1%
Current ratio: 0.80

CCF BRANDS LLC

EXECUTIVES

Pres- Ceo, Justin Whaley
Chb, Ron Whaley
Cfo, Doug Parker
Coo, Bob Hodges
Sr V Pres- Gen Counsel- SEC, Sean Hatch
Sr V Pres Fin, Dennis McDowell
Vice-President Marketing, Jodie Daniels
Director, Jose Chipollini
Manager, Morgan Stellpflug
Accountant, Jessica Porch
Vice President, Monte Terry
Auditors: FROST PLLC LITTLE ROCK ARKAN

LOCATIONS

HQ: CCF BRANDS LLC
5211 W VILLAGE PKWY # 101, ROGERS, AR 727588104
Phone: 479 464-0544
Web: WWW.CCFBRANDS.COM

HISTORICAL FINANCIALS
Company Type: Private

Income Statement   FYE: April 30

	REVENUE ($ mil.)	NET INCOME ($ mil.)	NET PROFIT MARGIN	EMPLOYEES
04/18	433	8	2.0%	58
04/17	323	3	1.1%	—
04/16	732	11	1.6%	—
04/15	0	0	—	—
Annual Growth	—	—	—	—

2018 Year-End Financials
Return on assets: 7.9%   Cash ($ mil.): 2
Return on equity: 2.0%
Current ratio: 0.80

CDM CONSTRUCTORS INC.

EXECUTIVES

Pres, Peter W Tunnicliffe
Treas, Eric J Hartmann
Asst Treas, Christopher Campbell
SEC, Mario J Marcaccio
Asst SEC, Paul T Milligan
Dir, Timothy B Wall
Dir, Thierry Desmaris
Dir, Anthony B Bouchard
Dir, Francesco M Terrasi
Business Operations, Sheron Maxwell
Manager, Consuelo Del Castillo
Auditors: PRICEWATERHOUSECOPPERS LLP BO

LOCATIONS

HQ: CDM CONSTRUCTORS INC.
   75 STATE ST STE 701, BOSTON, MA 021091940
Phone: 617 452-6000
Web: WWW.CDM.COM

HISTORICAL FINANCIALS
Company Type: Private

Income Statement   FYE: December 30

	REVENUE ($ mil.)	NET INCOME ($ mil.)	NET PROFIT MARGIN	EMPLOYEES
12/17	307	(15)	—	500
12/16*	347	(7)	—	—
01/16	414	8	2.0%	—
12/12	392	10	2.8%	—
Annual Growth	(4.7%)	—	—	—

*Fiscal year change

2017 Year-End Financials
Return on assets: 18.9%   Cash ($ mil.): 5
Return on equity: (-5.1%)
Current ratio: 0.70

CEB INC.

EXECUTIVES

Ceo, Thomas L Monahan III
Cfo, Richard S Lindahl
Cao, J Barron Anschutz
Information Specialist, Gary Banks

Executive Officer, Christoffer Ellehuus
Executive Officer, Teresa Green
Head, Corporate Strategy and D, Jesse Levin
Chief Administrative Officer, Melody L Jones
Staff, Kevin Hoyle
Senior Director, Brian Slatas
Associate Director, Jaclyn Jensen
Auditors: ERNST & YOUNG LLP MCLEAN VIR

LOCATIONS

HQ: CEB INC.
   1919 N LYNN ST, ARLINGTON, VA 222091742
Phone: 571 303-3000
Web: WWW.CEBGLOBAL.COM

COMPETITORS

Accenture	Conference Board
Booz Allen	Kantar Group
Boston Consulting	McKinsey & Company

HISTORICAL FINANCIALS
Company Type: Private

Income Statement   FYE: December 31

	REVENUE ($ mil.)	NET INCOME ($ mil.)	NET PROFIT MARGIN	EMPLOYEES
12/16	949	(34)	—	4,600
12/15	928	92	10.0%	—
12/14	908	51	5.6%	—
12/13	820	31	3.9%	—
Annual Growth	5.0%	—	—	—

2016 Year-End Financials
Return on assets: 9.5%   Cash ($ mil.): 134
Return on equity: (-3.6%)
Current ratio: 0.70

CEDARS-SINAI MEDICAL CARE FOUNDATION

EXECUTIVES

Exec Dir, Tom Gordeon
Exec Dir, Tom Gordon
Director, Delia Vogel
Facilities Director, Mark Kruse

LOCATIONS

HQ: CEDARS-SINAI MEDICAL CARE FOUNDATION
   200 N ROBERTSON BLVD # 101, BEVERLY HILLS, CA
   902111769
Phone: 800 700-6424
Web: WWW.CEDARS-SINAI.EDU

HISTORICAL FINANCIALS
Company Type: Private

Income Statement   FYE: June 30

	REVENUE ($ mil.)	NET INCOME ($ mil.)	NET PROFIT MARGIN	EMPLOYEES
06/18	394	8	2.2%	4
06/14	216	19	9.1%	—
06/11	145	6	4.2%	—
Annual Growth	15.4%	5.1%	—	—

2018 Year-End Financials
Return on assets: 7.3%   Cash ($ mil.): 28
Return on equity: 2.2%
Current ratio: 1.60

CEDARS-SINAI MEDICAL CENTER

Many a star has been born literally at Cedars-Sinai Medical Center. The 886-bed teaching and research hospital is located right where Los Angeles meets Beverly Hills and West Hollywood and has tended to the medical needs of a number of celebrities since its founding in 1902. However the center is also a major teaching hospital for UCLA's David Geffen School of Medicine and is engaged in hundreds of research programs in areas such as cancer neuroscience and genetics. It also includes two multi-specialty physician associations Cedars-Sinai Medical Group and Ceders-Sinai Health Associates and operates a number of community health centers and outreach programs (such as mobile health clinics).

Operations
The not-for-profit hospital's more than 2100 physicians represent just about every clinical specialty out there. Cedars-Sinai is consistently listed as a top-ranked hospital by U.S. News & World Report in such specialties as cancer cardiology endocrinology gastrointestinal disorders gynecology heart surgery kidney disease neurology orthopaedics and respiratory disorders.

Cedars-Sinai is the only private hospital with a Level 1 trauma center in Los Angeles County; as such the hospital sees about 1600 trauma patients a year. The hospital also provides a number of outpatient services.

Federal funding from the National Institutes of Health and other sources have provided the hospital with some $40 million towards research. Cedars-Sinai currently has some 1300 research projects.

The hospital sees some 660000 outpatient visits and 85000 emergency department visits each year.

Geographic Reach
Cedars-Sinai's hospital is located in Los Angeles; it has an administrative office in Beverly Hills California.

Financial Performance
Revenues from patient care and other sources totaled nearly $2.77 billion in fiscal 2015 while net income amounted to $472.9 million.

Strategy
To meet increasing patient demand and expand its capacity for research projects Cedars-Sinai added nearly 7000 sq. ft. of space to house the Cedars-Sinai Biobank and Translational Research Core Facility in 2015. The previous year it opened a new clinic dedicated to the evaluation of heart and vascular disease patients for participation in stem cell medical studies.

EXECUTIVES

Senior Vice President Legal Affairs, Peter Braveman
President And Ceo, Thomas M. (Tom) Priselac
Evp Finance And Cfo, Edward M. Prunchunas
Evp Hospital Operations And Coo Medical Center, Mark R. Gavens
Evp Academic Affairs And Dean Of The Faculty, Shlomo Melmed
Svp Medical Affairs And Chief Medical Officer, Michael L. Langberg
Evp System Development And Chief Strategy Officer, Richard B. Jacobs
Svp Enterprise Information Systems And Cio, Darren Dworkin
Evp Medical Network, John Jenrette
Medical Director, Matthew Wilson
Pharmacy Manager, Melsen Kwong

Vice President Strategic Planning And Business Development, Lori Weise
Vice President Of Marketing And Public Relations, Richard Elbaum
Medical Director, Spencer Koerner
Senior Vice President Community Relations, Arthur Ochoa
Medical Director, Jaime Moriguchi
Medical Director, Syed Naqvi
Vice President Service Line Operations, Bryan Croft
Mph Chc Vice President Corporate Integrity Program, Ginny Kim
Medical Director, Edward Wolin
Chairman, Marc H. Rapaport
Vice Chair, Steven Romick

LOCATIONS

HQ: CEDARS-SINAI MEDICAL CENTER
8700 BEVERLY BLVD, WEST HOLLYWOOD, CA 900481804
Phone: 310 423-3277
Web: WWW.CEDARS-SINAI.ORG

PRODUCTS/OPERATIONS

Selected Centers and Services
Ambulatory Care Center
Cedars-Sinai Center for Chest Disease
Cedars-Sinai Center for Digestive Diseases
Cedars-Sinai Heart Institute
Cedars-Sinai Institute Spine Center
Cedars-Sinai Health Associates (affiliated independent physician association)
Cedars-Sinai Medical Group (multi-specialty physicians group)
Cedars-Sinai Orthopedic Center
Diagnostic imaging center
Emergency department and trauma center
Hospice services
Kidney and pancreas transplant center
Neuroscience services
Pediatric services
Psychiatry and mental health services
Samuel Oschin Comprehensive Cancer Institute
Surgical services
Organ and bone marrow transplantation
Radiation therapy
Radiology
Stroke program
Pain management services
Women's health services

COMPETITORS

Adventist Health System West
Brotman Medical Center
Childrens Hospital Los Angeles
City of Hope
Community Health Systems
Dignity Health
Eisenhower Medical Center
Glendale Adventist Medical Center
Glendale Memorial Hospital
Golden State Health Centers
Good Samaritan Hospital (IN)
HCA
Hollywood Presbyterian Medical Center
Newhall Memorial Hospital
Pasadena Hospital Association
Providence Health System Southern California
Scripps Health
Tenet Healthcare
UCSF Medical
White Memorial Medical Center

HISTORICAL FINANCIALS

Company Type: Private

Income Statement   FYE: June 30

	REVENUE ($ mil.)	NET INCOME ($ mil.)	NET PROFIT MARGIN	EMPLOYEES
06/18	3,470	418	12.0%	8,000
06/17	3,788	380	10.0%	—
06/16	2,910	301	10.4%	—
06/15	2,760	366	13.3%	—
Annual Growth	7.9%	4.5%		

2018 Year-End Financials
Return on assets: 9.7%   Cash ($ mil.): 320
Return on equity: 12.0%
Current ratio: 1.20

CEDARWOOD-YOUNG COMPANY

EXECUTIVES

Pres-Ceo, Jason Young
Chm-SEC, Stephen Young
Cfo, Michael Ochniak
Vp Operations, Richard Hubbard
Vp Mrktng, Don Rogers
Vp Export, Yun Koo
Vp Sales, Adam Holt
P, Francisco Del Rincon
Auditors: DOUGHERTY & COMPANY GLENDALE

LOCATIONS

HQ: CEDARWOOD-YOUNG COMPANY
14620 JOANBRIDGE ST, BALDWIN PARK, CA 917061750
Phone: 626 962-4047
Web: WWW.ALLANCOMPANY.COM

HISTORICAL FINANCIALS

Company Type: Private

Income Statement   FYE: December 31

	REVENUE ($ mil.)	NET INCOME ($ mil.)	NET PROFIT MARGIN	EMPLOYEES
12/17	299	5	1.7%	275
12/16	275	0	0.2%	—
12/14	338	1	0.6%	—
12/13	365	2	0.8%	—
Annual Growth	(4.8%)	16.8%		

2017 Year-End Financials
Return on assets: 3.3%   Cash ($ mil.): 9
Return on equity: 1.7%
Current ratio: 3.20

CENTEGRA HEALTH SYSTEM FOUNDATION

Centegra Health System seeks integrity in the health care services realm. The health network serves residents of the greater McHenry County region in northern Illinois and southern Wisconsin.

The company operates two main medical centers Centegra Hospital-McHenry and Centegra Hospital-Woodstock with a total of some 325 beds. They offer emergency and trauma care as well as general medicine surgery and obstetrics services. Centegra has dedicated cancer diabetes and heart centers and also offers rehabilitation behavioral health and fitness services. In addition the community-based health system operates a network of primary care and specialty outpatient clinics.

Operations

In 2014 the hospital delivered 1634 babies conducted 12227 Surgeries 134656 Outpatient imaging procedures and 181234 Outpatient laboratory procedures. It has 59608 Emergency department visits and 16183 participiants in its Centegra Health Bridge Fitness program.

Strategy

Centegra's strategic plan calls for expanding the hospital's advanced treatments and wellness services.

In 2014 the company announced a partnership with Loyola University Health System to provide advanced heart failure care at Centegra Hospital-McHenry location.

Company Background

Centegra became a "system" when two northern Illinois area hospitals Memorial Medical Center and Northern Illinois Medical Center joined forces in 1995. Memorial Medical Center was founded in 1914 and is now named Centegra Hospital-Woodstock while Northern Illinois Medical Center was established in 1956 and is called Centegra Hospital-McHenry.

EXECUTIVES

Senior Vice President Chief Nursing Offi, Bob Murphy
Auditors: KPMG LLP CHICAGO ILLINOIS

LOCATIONS

HQ: CENTEGRA HEALTH SYSTEM FOUNDATION
385 MILLENNIUM DR STE A, CRYSTAL LAKE, IL 600123761
Phone: 815 788-5800
Web: WWW.CENTEGRA.ORG

PRODUCTS/OPERATIONS

Selected Medical Services
Anticoagulation Management
Bone and Joint Services
Cancer Services
Centegra Clinical Laboratories
Centegra Immediate Care
Centegra Physician Care
Corporate Health Services
Diabetes Services
Emergency and Trauma Services
Family Birth Centers
Heart Services
Home Health Services
Medical Imaging/X-Ray
Mental Health Services
Nursing
Nutrition
Orthopedic Services
Outpatient Services
Rehabilitation Services
Respiratory Care Services
Screenings
Sleep Services
Surgical Services
Weight-Loss Surgery
Wellness Services
Women's Services
Wound Care and Hyperbaric Services

COMPETITORS

Advocate Health Care	OSF Healthcare System
Alexian Brothers Health System	Rockford Health System
	Rush System for Health
KishHealth	Sherman Health Systems

NorthShore University HealthSystem
Northwest Community Healthcare
Northwestern Memorial HealthCare
Silver Cross Hospital
SwedishAmerican Health System
University of Chicago Medical Center

HISTORICAL FINANCIALS

Company Type: Private

Income Statement				FYE: June 30
	REVENUE ($ mil.)	NET INCOME ($ mil.)	NET PROFIT MARGIN	EMPLOYEES
06/17	564	(45)	—	3,700
06/12	427	(13)	—	
06/11	0	0	—	
06/10	80	(11)	—	
Annual Growth	32.0%	—	—	—

2017 Year-End Financials

Return on assets: 2.2%
Return on equity: (-8.0%)
Current ratio: 0.90

Cash ($ mil.): 13

CENTIMARK CORPORATION

Shout it from the rooftops Centimark is one of the largest commercial and industrial roofing contractors in North America. The company provides roof installation inspection repair and emergency leak service. Centimark typically works on flat roofs using EPDM rubber thermoplastic bitumen metal and coatings. Top customers have included NASA and the US Army Corps of Engineers. Its Quest-Mark division offers commercial industrial and retail flooring do-it-yourself (DIY) products and floor maintenance and cleaning products. The company which has about 80 offices throughout North America.

Operations

The company offers roof and floor services roof replacement roof repairs floor repairs emergency services preventative maintenance programs energy efficient solutions safety options and accessories online project management and DIY floor products. Centimark also provides systems such as thermoplastic solutions sprayed polyurethane foams roof coatings modified bitumen and built-up roofing metal products and steep slope products. In addition it engages in the online retail of flooring products such as patch and repair and maintenance/floor care products and coatings.

QuestMark a division of Centimark offers materials for commercial retail and industrial floors. It specializes in DiamondQuest polished concrete flooring epoxy flooring floor repair materials floor maintenance and floor cleaning products.

Centimark's Asset Management service provides extensive roof surveys roof life expectancy models return-on-investment analysis for roof repairs and evaluations for roof repair or roof replacement.

Geographic Reach

Pittsburgh Pennsylvania-based Centimark also does business in Canada through subsidiary Centimark Ltd. which has offices in Calgary Edmonton Toronto and Vancouver.

Sales and Marketing

The company serves customers in different segments including retail industrial general contractors and education.

Financial Performance

Centimark's 2014 sales totaled $485 million.

Strategy

In response to customer demand for more energy-efficient options Centimark has been increasing its use of spray polyurethane foam (which adds insulation and a waterproof barrier to roofs). The company also installs electricity-producing photovoltaic solar panels onto roofs. Other green options available from Centimark include skylights and garden roofs.

The company also tries to stay ahead of the pack with technological innovations such as its MyCentimark service. The online resource allows property owners to view invoices work authorizations before-and-after photos and recommendations for future roof maintenance. In 2014 the company launched a tablet and smartphone app that allows customers to request service and find the nearest Centimark office based on their current location.

Company Background

Chairman and CEO Edward Dunlap founded Centimark as an industrial cleaning business in 1967. Centimark is owned by its employees.

EXECUTIVES

Vice President Applications, Joe Filtz
Chairman And Ceo, Edward B. Dunlap
President And Coo, Timothy M. Dunlap
Evp And Northern Group Director, Robert J. Rudzik
Evp And Western Group Director, Steven M. Ferencz
Evp National And Regional Sales, John T. Godwin
Evp And Cfo, John L. Heisey
Evp And Southern Group Director, Sherman L. Gaskins
Evp And Questmark Flooring Group Director, John P. Scanlon
Evp And Eastern Group Director, Mark A. Cooper
Vp And Canada Group Director Centimark Ltd, Robert T. Penney
Svp And Southern Group Director, Keith Battenfield
Evp Service, Kenneth W. Zmich
National Accounts Manager, Cindy Molnar
Vice President Of Human Resources, Landon Connolly
Vice President Benefits And Compensation, Laura Kickbusch
National Account Manager, Eric Gorman
National Account Manager, Clint Snowden
National Account Manager, Mark Misencik
National Accounts Manager, Keith O'Brien
Executive Vice President, John Rudzik
Senior Vice President, Michael Rew
Vice President National Accounts Questmark Flooring, Jim Gasper
National Account Manager, Brian Cerilli
National Account Manager, Art Collias
National Account Manager, Shaun Bynum
National Accounts Manager, Chuck Blair
Auditors: SCHNEIDER DOWNS & CO INC P

LOCATIONS

HQ: CENTIMARK CORPORATION
12 GRANDVIEW CIR, CANONSBURG, PA 153178533
Phone: 724 514-8700
Web: WWW.CENTIMARK.COM

PRODUCTS/OPERATIONS

Selected Operations

CentiMark (roofing)
CentiMark ltd. (Canada roofing)
QuestMark (flooring)

Selected Systems

Roof Systems
EPDM
Green Roofing
Metal Roofs
Modified Bitumen and Built-Up Roofs
Roof Coatings
SPF
Steep Slope
TPO & PVC
Floor Systems
Chemical Resistant Systems
Decorative Broadcast
Decorative Concrete
Electric Static Dissipative
Heavy Duty Resurfacer
High Build Coating
Polished Concrete
Thin Mil

COMPETITORS

Armstrong World Industries
Cabral Roofing & Waterproofing
D. C. Taylor
Duro-Last Roofing
Garcia Roofing
Holland Roofing
Pickens Roofing
Tecta America

HISTORICAL FINANCIALS

Company Type: Private

Income Statement				FYE: April 30
	REVENUE ($ mil.)	NET INCOME ($ mil.)	NET PROFIT MARGIN	EMPLOYEES
04/18	670	54	8.1%	3,500
04/17	625	51	8.2%	—
04/15	540	46	8.7%	—
04/14	508	42	8.3%	—
Annual Growth	7.2%	6.4%	—	—

2018 Year-End Financials

Return on assets: 2.5%
Return on equity: 8.1%
Current ratio: 2.80

Cash ($ mil.): 161

CENTRA HEALTH, INC.

Centra Health is a constellation of hospitals and medical practices targeting the health care needs of residents in central and southern Virginia. At the not-for-profit entity's core are two acute care facilities in Lynchburg: the 358-bed Lynchburg General which is the region's main emergency center and specializes in orthopedic pediatric and cardiac care; and Virginia Baptist a 161-bed facility focused on surgery women's health infant care mental health and rehabilitation. Centra also operates a nearby community hospital and an array of primary care physician practices home health agencies retirement centers and other physical and behavioral health businesses.

Operations

In addition to Lynchburg General and Virginia Baptist Centra's acute care facilities include Southside Community Hospital (Farmville). Southside Community Hospital serves as a central acute care and birthing facility for an eight-county region. Centra also operates the Bedford Memorial Hospital through a partnership with Carilion Health System; it plans to buy out Carilion's shares in the partnership.

Outside of its acute care operations Centra Health administers senior care services through The Summit assisted living and independent living facilities. The Summit offers senior residents private apartments medical care and personal assistance. Centra also operates a network of treatment centers for patients of all ages with behavioral and psychiatric disorders. The network includes facilities that specialize in treating children and adolescents with emotional and behavioral disorders.

Altogether the network handles more than 300000 patient visits each year including more than 90000 emergency room visits and more than 5000 cardiac procedures. Its hospitals have a medical staff of about 500 doctors who perform more than 6300 inpatient and 9300 outpatient surgeries annually. Centra also operates the Centra Medical Group which includes about 140 primary care and specialist physicians.

Geographic Reach

Centra Health serves Lynchburg and surrounding communities in central Virginia including Farmville (located in Prince Edward County) Bedford Danville/Gretna and Moneta/Smith Mountain Lake Virginia.

Strategy

Centra Health is expanding its breadth of services as well as its network of facilities. Recent additions include new behavioral health facilities and an expansion of Bedford Memorial's orthopedic center. In 2015 it announced plans to buy out Carilion Clinic's shares of Bedford Memorial Hospital and the Oakwood Health and Rehabilitation Center for $11 million.

Company Background

Centra Health was founded in 1987 through the merger of Lynchburg General and Virginia Baptist. Southside Community Hospital joined the network in 2006.

EXECUTIVES

Chairman Centra Foundation, George A. Hurt
President And Ceo, E. W. Tibbs
Vp And Ceo Centra Southside Community Hospital, William L. Bass
Chairman, Walker P. Sydnor
Vice Chairman, Amy G. Ray

LOCATIONS

HQ: CENTRA HEALTH, INC.
1920 ATHERHOLT RD, LYNCHBURG, VA 245011120
Phone: 434 200-3204
Web: WWW.CENTRAHEALTH.COM

PRODUCTS/OPERATIONS

Selected Facilities
Bedford Memorial Hospital (Bedford Virginia; partnership with Carilion Health System)
Lynchburg General Hospital (Lynchburg Virginia)
Virginia Baptist Hospital (Lynchburg Virginia)
Southside Community Hospital (Farmville Virginia)
Physician Practices
 Altavista Medical Center (Altavista Virginia)
 Big Island Medical Center (North Big Island Virginia)
 Brookneal Family Medical Center (Brookneal Virginia)
 Gretna Medical Center (Gretna Virginia)
 Lynchburg Family Medicine Center (Lynchburg Virginia)
Other Facilities
 Bridges Treatment Center (Lynchburg Virginia)
 Fairmont Crossing Health and Rehabilitation Center (Amherst Virginia)
 Guggenheimer Health and Rehabilitation Center (Lynchburg Virginia)
 Piedmont Psychiatric Center (Lynchburg Virginia)
 Rivermont Schools (regional)
 The Summit (regional)

COMPETITORS

Alleghany Regional Hospital	Martha Jefferson Hospital
Bon Secours Health	Mary Washington Healthcare
Carilion Clinic	Montgomery Regional Hospital
Clinch Valley Medical Center	Sentara Healthcare
Danville Regional Medical Center	University of Virginia Health System
Encompass Health	
Henrico Doctors' Hospital	

HISTORICAL FINANCIALS
Company Type: Private

Income Statement   FYE: December 31

	REVENUE ($ mil.)	NET INCOME ($ mil.)	NET PROFIT MARGIN	EMPLOYEES
12/15	742	25	3.4%	6,000
12/14	553	63	11.5%	—
12/09	534	16	3.1%	—
12/08	419	33	7.9%	—
Annual Growth	8.5%	(3.9%)	—	—

2015 Year-End Financials

Return on assets: 8.0%   Cash ($ mil.): 25
Return on equity: 3.4%
Current ratio: 0.40

CENTRAL BUCKS SCHOOL DISTRICT

EXECUTIVES

Spdt, John Kopicki
Treas-Dir of Fin, Thomas McCambridge
President, Steven Corr
Principal, Jeanann M Kahley
Principal, Greg Nolan
Principal, Alan J Bernabei
Supt, David Weitzel
Supt, Robert Laws
Auditors: MAILLIE LLP OAKS PA

LOCATIONS

HQ: CENTRAL BUCKS SCHOOL DISTRICT
20 WELDON DR, DOYLESTOWN, PA 189012359
Phone: 267 893-2000
Web: WWW.CBSD.ORG

HISTORICAL FINANCIALS
Company Type: Private

Income Statement   FYE: June 30

	REVENUE ($ mil.)	NET INCOME ($ mil.)	NET PROFIT MARGIN	EMPLOYEES
06/17	331	20	6.1%	2,800
06/16	315	16	5.1%	—
06/06	0	0	—	—
06/02	159	(4)	—	—
Annual Growth	5.0%	—	—	—

2017 Year-End Financials

Return on assets: 1.8%   Cash ($ mil.): 68
Return on equity: 6.1%
Current ratio: —

CENTRAL ELECTRIC POWER COOPERATIVE, INC.

EXECUTIVES

Ceo, Ronald J Calcaterra
Sr Vice President, Art Fusco
Sr Vice President, Jim Lamb
Dir, David Logeman
Cfo, John Brantley
Prin, John Tiencken
Human Resources Coordinator, Tina Smedes
Program Manager, Scott Hammond
Manager, Cynthia Hickman
Analyst, Katherine Bridges
Administrator, Kevin Wood

LOCATIONS

HQ: CENTRAL ELECTRIC POWER COOPERATIVE, INC.
20 COOPERATIVE WAY, COLUMBIA, SC 292103112
Phone: 803 779-4975
Web: WWW.CEPCI.ORG

HISTORICAL FINANCIALS
Company Type: Private

Income Statement   FYE: December 31

	REVENUE ($ mil.)	NET INCOME ($ mil.)	NET PROFIT MARGIN	EMPLOYEES
12/15	1,220	0	0.0%	44
12/14	1,254	0	0.0%	—
12/13	1,198	0	0.0%	—
12/09	1,037	1	0.2%	—
Annual Growth	2.8%	(33.9%)	—	—

2015 Year-End Financials

Return on assets: 7.3%   Cash ($ mil.): 8
Return on equity: —
Current ratio: —

CENTRAL FLORIDA EXPRESSWAY AUTHORITY

EXECUTIVES

Exec V Pres, Joseph Berenis
Exec Vice President, Laura Kelley
Cfo, Lisa Lumbard
Asst Acct Mgr, Marc Ventura
Operations Executive, Armando Corominas
Buyer, Saul Rivas
Manager, Ben Dreiling
Finance Administrator, Angie Carloss
Education Specialist, Charles Muniz
Senior Analyst, Charles Tate
Rector, Corey Quinn
Auditors: MOORE STEPHENS LOVELACE PA O

LOCATIONS

HISTORICAL FINANCIALS

Company Type: Private

Income Statement				FYE: June 30
	REVENUE ($ mil.)	NET INCOME ($ mil.)	NET PROFIT MARGIN	EMPLOYEES
06/17	433	235	54.3%	50
06/16	400	203	50.8%	—
06/09	208	74	35.6%	—
06/07	205	72	35.4%	—
Annual Growth	7.8%	12.5%	—	—

2017 Year-End Financials

Return on assets: 8.7% Cash ($ mil.): 94
Return on equity: 54.3%
Current ratio: 0.50

CENTRAL HUDSON GAS & ELECTRIC CORPORATION

EXECUTIVES

Chb-ceo, Stephen Lant

LOCATIONS

HQ: CENTRAL HUDSON GAS & ELECTRIC CORPORATION
284 SOUTH AVE DEPT 100, POUGHKEEPSIE, NY 126014839
Phone: 845 452-2700
Web: WWW.CHENERGYGROUP.COM

HISTORICAL FINANCIALS

Company Type: Private

Income Statement				FYE: December 31
	REVENUE ($ mil.)	NET INCOME ($ mil.)	NET PROFIT MARGIN	EMPLOYEES
12/17	671	55	8.2%	869
12/16	640	52	8.2%	
/	0	0	—	
Annual Growth	—	—	—	—

2017 Year-End Financials

Return on assets: 7.4% Cash ($ mil.): 14
Return on equity: 8.2%
Current ratio: 0.80

CENTRAL IOWA HOSPITAL CORP

EXECUTIVES

Ceo, Eric Crowell
Executive Director-Finance, Kara Dunham
Chief of Urology, Markham J J Anderson
Regional Vice-President, Jean Shelton

Coordinator, Anne Alesch
Pediatrician, Andrew Fondell
Emergency Medicine Specialist, Brooke Johnson
Director of Reimbursement, Crystal Estabrook
Pediatrician, Greg Kolb
Pediatrician, Jennifer Hess
Pediatrician, Katie Lilly

LOCATIONS

HQ: CENTRAL IOWA HOSPITAL CORP
1200 PLEASANT ST, DES MOINES, IA 503091406
Phone: 515 241-6212
Web: WWW.BLANKCHILDRENS.ORG

HISTORICAL FINANCIALS

Company Type: Private

Income Statement				FYE: December 31
	REVENUE ($ mil.)	NET INCOME ($ mil.)	NET PROFIT MARGIN	EMPLOYEES
12/16	573	153	26.8%	3,495
12/15	548	152	27.9%	—
12/14	534	145	27.2%	—
12/13	703	52	7.5%	—
Annual Growth	(6.6%)	42.6%	—	—

2016 Year-End Financials

Return on assets: 6.2% Cash ($ mil.): —
Return on equity: 26.8%
Current ratio: 1.00

CENTRAL MICHIGAN UNIVERSITY

Academic advancement is central at Central Michigan University (CMU). The university offers more than 200 academic programs for undergraduate graduate and professional coursework through eight colleges including business communication and fine arts medicine and education and human services. The university enrolls more than 20000 students at the main campus in Mt. Pleasant. The institution also enrolls another 7000 students online and at 50 locations throughout North America. In addition CMU offers study abroad programs in 40 countries.

Operations

CMU has 1000 faculty members and a student-to-faculty ratio of about 21:1. It has 22 residence halls. The university also has division I athletic programs for men and women. Its CMU Public Broadcasting unit operates 10 television and seven radio stations.

Financial Performance

CMU has pioneer in distance learning since 1971 when it was one of the first universities to provide education off campus and directly to students and adults. In 2014 it had nearly 40 locations in the US and Canada including on more than 20 military bases.

Company Background

Notable alumni include former US Senator Robert P. Griffin and actor Jeff Daniels.

CMU was founded in 1892 as a teachers' college.

EXECUTIVES

Assistant Vice President, Stan Shingles
Associate Vice President Institutional D, Carolyn Dunn
Associate Vice President Residences And Auxiliary Services, John Fisher

Vice Chairman, John Hurd
Secretary, Jody Dittenber
Auditors: PLANTE & MORAN PLLC EAST LAN

LOCATIONS

HQ: CENTRAL MICHIGAN UNIVERSITY
1200 S FRANKLIN ST, MOUNT PLEASANT, MI 488592001
Phone: 989 774-4000
Web: WWW.CMICH.EDU

PRODUCTS/OPERATIONS

Selected Colleges and Schools
College of Business Administration
College of Communication and Fine Arts
College of Education and Human Services
College of Graduate Studies
College of Health Professions
College of Humanities and Social and Behavioral Sciences
College of Medicine
College of Science and Technology
Global Campus & Online

HISTORICAL FINANCIALS

Company Type: Private

Income Statement				FYE: June 30
	REVENUE ($ mil.)	NET INCOME ($ mil.)	NET PROFIT MARGIN	EMPLOYEES
06/18	328	21	6.6%	2,388
06/17	333	55	16.7%	—
06/16	334	8	2.5%	—
06/15	336	1	0.4%	—
Annual Growth	(0.8%)	152.7%	—	—

2018 Year-End Financials

Return on assets: 20.2% Cash ($ mil.): 35
Return on equity: 6.6%
Current ratio: 0.60

CENTRAL PENINSULA GENERAL HOSPITAL, INC.

EXECUTIVES

Ceo, Ryan Smith
Cfo, Jason Paret
Cno, Andrea Posey
Cfo, Richard Davis
Pres, Loren Karp Weimer
V Pres, Trena Richardson
SEC-Treas, Son Stogsdill
General Surgeon, M Todd Boling
Chief Information Security Off, Richard Davidson
Chief of Medicine, Greg Motonaga
Chief of Medicine, Henry Krull

LOCATIONS

HQ: CENTRAL PENINSULA GENERAL HOSPITAL, INC.
250 HOSPITAL PL, SOLDOTNA, AK 996696999
Phone: 907 262-4404
Web: WWW.CPGH.ORG

HISTORICAL FINANCIALS
Company Type: Private

Income Statement
FYE: June 30

	REVENUE ($ mil.)	NET INCOME ($ mil.)	NET PROFIT MARGIN	EMPLOYEES
06/16	311	24	7.7%	611
06/15	274	17	6.2%	—
06/14	234	13	5.6%	—
06/13	0	14	—	—
Annual Growth	—	19.2%	—	—

2016 Year-End Financials
Return on assets: 4.5%
Return on equity: 7.7%
Current ratio: 0.90
Cash ($ mil.): 37

CENTRAL WASHINGTON HEALTH SERVICES ASSOCIATION

EXECUTIVES

Ceo, Peter Rutherford
Vice Chb, Mark Heminger
Chief of Staff, Malcolm Butler
Coordinator, John Swenson
Information Specialist, Deborah Carroll
Chief of Medicine, Stuart Freed
Coordinator, Renee Rahne
Internal Medicine Practitioner, Toby Long

LOCATIONS

HQ: CENTRAL WASHINGTON HEALTH SERVICES ASSOCIATION
1201 S MILLER ST, WENATCHEE, WA 988013201
Phone: 509 662-1511
Web: WWW.CWHS.COM

HISTORICAL FINANCIALS
Company Type: Private

Income Statement
FYE: December 31

	REVENUE ($ mil.)	NET INCOME ($ mil.)	NET PROFIT MARGIN	EMPLOYEES
12/16	312	31	10.1%	1,100
12/15	288	(8)	—	—
12/14	259	18	7.0%	—
12/13	0	16	—	—
Annual Growth	—	25.4%	—	—

2016 Year-End Financials
Return on assets: 0.8%
Return on equity: 10.1%
Current ratio: 4.20
Cash ($ mil.): 62

CENTRASTATE HEALTHCARE SYSTEM INC

CentraState Healthcare System makes healing its central mission while serving residents of central New Jersey. The health system operates CentraState Medical Center an acute-care teaching hospital with more than 280 beds that offers emergency surgical and diagnostic imaging services as well as specialty services including cardiovascular care and women's health. Other CentraState Healthcare facilities include three nursing homes wellness centers and outpatient clinics. CentraState Healthcare is an affiliate of the Robert Wood Johnson Health System and Network.

Operations

In addition to medical care CentraState Healthcare's main hospital provides medical training including a family medicine residency program through affiliations with the Rutgers Robert Wood Johnson Medical School and other colleges.

In addition to CentraState Medical Center the organization operates three nursing homes (Applewood Estates Manor Health and Monmouth Crossing) and the Star and Barry Tobias Ambulatory Campus which includes fitness and wellness centers. It also runs family medicine practices and its CentraState Healthcare Foundation supports the company's community health and expansion initiatives.

Strategy

CentraState has added on to its main medical campus over the years including the addition of the Star and Barry Tobias Ambulatory Campus a full-service outpatient care center located adjacent to the CentraState Medical Center. The company has also expanded its senior care facilities. And in 2014 it added certified counselors to help uninsured patients sign up for coverage under the Affordable Care Act.

In 2012 it opened a new $160 million proton therapy clinic (one of ten such facilities in the US) through a partnership with Princeton Radiation Oncology and ProCure Cancer Centers. CentraState also expanded radiation oncology capabilities at CentraState Medical Center that year.

In partnership with other area hospitals CentraState Medical Center is working to improve efficiencies and reduce expenses during the care of Medicare and Medicaid patients. The program is called the Bundled Payments for Care Improvement initiative and is facilitated by the Centers for Medicare and Medicaid.

EXECUTIVES

President Ceo And Trustee, John T. Gribbin
Svp And Cfo, John A. Dellocono
Vp Patient Services, Linda Geisler
Vp Senior Services, Jay S. Solomon
Vp Clinical Services, Kim A. Kelly
Vp And Chief Medical Officer, Jack H. Dworkin
Vp Physician Practice Management, James Richvalsky
Vp And Chief Information Officer, John W. Ulett
Svp And Coo, Thomas W. Scott
Assistant Vice President Cancer Services, Barry Asch
Assistant Vice President Finance, Robert Nyman
Vice President Of Sales, Miah Kim
Assistant Vice President Nursing, Cathleen Janzekovich
Director Of Radiology Services Nuclear Medicine Director, Mandy Wortman
Director Of Radiology, Stephen C Keklak
Director Of Radiology, Ann M Hughes
Senior Vice President, Martin Schneider
Vice President Of Business Development, Alexander Goldberg
Vice President Of Patient Satisfaction, Ellen Gutter
Vice President Information Technology, Michael Sordo
Vice President Director Of Marketing Webmaster, Keshav Prasad
Assistant Vice President Integrative Health, Kim Simers
Director Of Radiology, Mandi Wortman
Chairperson, Joseph R. Iantosca
Vice Chairperson, Stephen J. Walsh
Auditors: ERNST & YOUNG LLP ISELIN NJ

LOCATIONS

HQ: CENTRASTATE HEALTHCARE SYSTEM INC
901 W MAIN ST, FREEHOLD, NJ 077282537
Phone: 732 431-2000
Web:
WWW.CENTRASTATEHEALTHCAREPARTNERS.COM

PRODUCTS/OPERATIONS

Selected Services
Cardiac catheterization lab
Cardiology services
Computed tomography (CT)
Coronary CTangiography (CTA)
Diabetes services (Novo Nordisk Diabetes Center)
Dialysis unit
Emergency services
Endovascular surgery
Inpatient psychiatric services
Magnetic resonance imaging (MRI)
Maternity care (single room) and special care nursery
Oncology
Radiation oncology
Rehabilitation
Short stay unit
Sleep disorders center
Women's Health Center

COMPETITORS

Bergen Regional Medical
Capital Health System
Princeton HealthCare
Raritan Bay Medical Center
Robert Wood Johnson University Hospital
Saint Peter's University Hospital
St. Joseph's Healthcare System
Trinitas Regional Medical Center

HISTORICAL FINANCIALS
Company Type: Private

Income Statement
FYE: December 31

	REVENUE ($ mil.)	NET INCOME ($ mil.)	NET PROFIT MARGIN	EMPLOYEES
12/17	326	9	2.9%	2,527
12/16	322	13	4.1%	—
12/15	313	(33)	—	—
12/14	0	0	—	—
Annual Growth	—	—	—	—

2017 Year-End Financials
Return on assets: 11.4%
Return on equity: 2.9%
Current ratio: 1.00
Cash ($ mil.): 22

CENTURY HEALTH ALLIANCE JOINT VENTURE

EXECUTIVES

Director, Emily Avery
Credentials Coordinator, Mitzi Carter
Director, Gary Harrelson
Manager, Brent Sutton
Compensation Manager, Lori Royer
Orthopedist, Beverly Vanoy
Manager, Jerry Tucker
Executive Vice President and, Bill Cassels
Director, James Askew
Manager Information, Kelly Wells
Registered Nurse, Kimberly Parker

LOCATIONS

HQ: CENTURY HEALTH ALLIANCE JOINT VENTURE
809 UNIVERSITY BLVD E, TUSCALOOSA, AL
354012029
Phone: 205 759-7111
Web: WWW.DCHSYSTEM.COM

HISTORICAL FINANCIALS
Company Type: Private

Income Statement				FYE: September 30
	REVENUE ($ mil.)	NET INCOME ($ mil.)	NET PROFIT MARGIN	EMPLOYEES
09/17	469	13	2.8%	1
09/16	475	25	5.3%	—
09/15	450	34	7.6%	—
09/14	420	15	3.7%	—
Annual Growth	3.7%	(5.3%)	—	—

2017 Year-End Financials
Return on assets: 2.6%　　Cash ($ mil.): 245
Return on equity: 2.8%
Current ratio: 2.00

CERES SOLUTIONS, LLP

EXECUTIVES

Vice President Of Agronomy, Daryl Warren
Auditors: BLUE & CO LLC SEYMOUR IN

LOCATIONS

HQ: CERES SOLUTIONS, LLP
2112 INDIANAPOLIS RD, CRAWFORDSVILLE, IN
479333137
Phone: 765 362-6108
Web: WWW.CERESLLP.COM

COMPETITORS

ADM
　Ag Processing Inc.
　CHS
Cargill
GROWMARK
Premier AG Co-Op Inc.

HISTORICAL FINANCIALS
Company Type: Private

Income Statement				FYE: July 31
	REVENUE ($ mil.)	NET INCOME ($ mil.)	NET PROFIT MARGIN	EMPLOYEES
07/17	309	13	4.5%	125
07/16	299	10	3.6%	—
07/15	368	16	4.5%	—
07/14	412	22	5.4%	—
Annual Growth	(9.1%)	(14.4%)	—	—

2017 Year-End Financials
Return on assets: 8.7%　　Cash ($ mil.): 10
Return on equity: 4.5%
Current ratio: 0.60

CHA HOLLYWOOD MEDICAL CENTER LP

As one might expect from a Hollywood hospital the staff at Hollywood Presbyterian Medical Center (HPMC) includes bellmen concierges and parking valets in addition to nurses and doctors. HPMC aims to blur the lines between acute-care hospital and hotel caring for the oft-pampered community of Hollywood California. Its health care services include a cancer treatment center; physical speech and occupational therapy; and the Institute of Maternal Fetal Health which performs fetal surgeries. Other services include community health outreach programs and The Chalet a skilled nursing facility. The 430-plus-bed hospital with 500 physicians is part of CHA Health Systems.

Operations
CHA Health Systems headed by fertility specialist Dr. Kwang Yul Cha is based in Korea where it operates hospitals clinics and a medical school in Seoul. The group is heavily involved in stem cell research and also operates two infertility medical centers one in Korea and one in Los Angeles (as part of HPMC).

In 2012 HPMC had more than 92000 inpatient days and 50785 outpatient visits.

HPMC offers a number of residency programs some in affiliation with the Keck School of Medicine at the University of Southern California. Selected programs include OB/GYN (fellowship and residency) OB/GYN for emergency medicine rotation pediatrics residency (affiliated with Children's Hospital Los Angeles) a pharmacy residency and a neonatal-perinatal medicine fellowship program.

Strategy
CHA Health Systems plans to acquire other US hospitals.

Company Background
HPMC was founded in 1924. CHA Health Systems acquired it from Tenet in 2004.

EXECUTIVES

Ceo, Jeff A Nelson
Cfo, Galen Gorman
ADM Asst, Christy Jacobs
Director of Pharmacy, Sofia Gezalyan
Director, Carrie Roberts
Chief Technology Officer, Destina Hopkins
Director of Information Techno, Carrie Robert
Chief of Anesthesiology, Romeo Velasco
Vice President of Security, Ryan Reichert
Director, Donalda Dunnett

LOCATIONS

HQ: CHA HOLLYWOOD MEDICAL CENTER LP
1300 N VERMONT AVE, LOS ANGELES, CA
900276098
Phone: 213 413-3000
Web: WWW.HOLLYWOODPRESBYTERIAN.COM

PRODUCTS/OPERATIONS

Selected Services
Cardiac Care
Cancer Care
Emergency Care
Fetal Therapy
Imaging Services
Maternity Services
Neurosciences
Orthopedic Services
Pediatric Services
Rehabilitation
Support Services
Transitional Care-Chalet

COMPETITORS

Anaheim Regional Medical Center
Brotman Medical Center
Cedars-Sinai Medical Center
Childrens Hospital Los Angeles
Dignity Health
Glendale Adventist Medical Center
Glendale Memorial Hospital
Good Samaritan Hospital (IN)
Hoag Memorial Hospital
Methodist Hospital of Southern California
Pasadena Hospital Association
Providence St. Joseph Health
Scripps Health
White Memorial Medical Center

HISTORICAL FINANCIALS
Company Type: Private

Income Statement				FYE: December 31
	REVENUE ($ mil.)	NET INCOME ($ mil.)	NET PROFIT MARGIN	EMPLOYEES
12/16	288	33	11.7%	1,500
12/15	260	18	7.1%	—
Annual Growth	10.9%	83.0%	—	—

2016 Year-End Financials
Return on assets: 5.1%　　Cash ($ mil.): 10
Return on equity: 11.7%
Current ratio: 0.80

CHAFFEY JOINT UNION HIGH SCHOOL DISTRICT

EXECUTIVES

Supt, Mathew Holton
Supt, Barry Cadwallader
Suprtnt, Matthew Holton
Coordinator, Jonna Pyles
Payroll Staff, Shelli Boshart
Project Manager, Michael Weaver
Administrative Assistant, Bertica Johnson
Athletic Director, Bill Blades
Ontario High School Athletic D, Bryan Grant
Counselor, David Berry
Operations, Georgann Harmon

LOCATIONS

HQ: CHAFFEY JOINT UNION HIGH SCHOOL DISTRICT
211 W 5TH ST, ONTARIO, CA 917621653
Phone: 909 988-8511
Web: WWW.CJUHSD.K12.CA.US

HISTORICAL FINANCIALS
Company Type: Private

Income Statement   FYE: June 30

	REVENUE ($ mil.)	NET INCOME ($ mil.)	NET PROFIT MARGIN	EMPLOYEES
06/17	322	55	17.4%	2,000
06/16	315	(65)	—	—
06/11	226	14	6.5%	—
06/09	243	10	4.3%	—
Annual Growth	3.5%	23.2%	—	—

2017 Year-End Financials
Return on assets: 15.2%   Cash ($ mil.): 323
Return on equity: 17.4%
Current ratio: —

CHAMBERSBURG HOSPITAL

EXECUTIVES

V Chm, Philip Fague
Ceo, Patrick O Donnell
Chb-President, Nancy Meyers
Treas, Dennis Wilson
SEC, Michael Colli
Coordinator, Rebecca Sucke
Specialist, Mary Rine
Health Professional, Anthony Kehr
Internal Medicine Practitioner, Glenn Vanderver
Internal Medicine Practitioner, Kemsha Huslin
Auditors: SMITH ELLIOTT KEARNS & COMPANY

LOCATIONS

HQ: CHAMBERSBURG HOSPITAL
    112 N 7TH ST, CHAMBERSBURG, PA 172011700
Phone: 717 267-3000
Web: WWW.SUMMITHEALTH.ORG

HISTORICAL FINANCIALS
Company Type: Private

Income Statement   FYE: June 30

	REVENUE ($ mil.)	NET INCOME ($ mil.)	NET PROFIT MARGIN	EMPLOYEES
06/18	352	22	6.5%	1,729
06/17	345	73	21.3%	—
06/16	317	(43)	—	—
06/15	290	(0)	—	—
Annual Growth	6.7%	—	—	—

2018 Year-End Financials
Return on assets: 3.0%   Cash ($ mil.): 16
Return on equity: 6.5%
Current ratio: 1.00

CHANDLER REGIONAL MEDICAL CENTER

EXECUTIVES

Pres, Tim Bricker
Coordinator, Janet Shepard
Supervisor, Martha Tilley
Nurse Practitioner, Chris T Tran

Microbology Supervisor, Denise Schauer
Director of Food, Gregory Codkind
Manager Data Communications, James Gosser
Assistant To Bob Campbell, Peggy Hall
Director of Patient Care Nursi, Veronica Harder

LOCATIONS

HQ: CHANDLER REGIONAL MEDICAL CENTER
    1955 W FRYE RD, CHANDLER, AZ 852246282
Phone: 480 728-3000
Web: WWW.CHW.EDU

HISTORICAL FINANCIALS
Company Type: Private

Income Statement   FYE: June 30

	REVENUE ($ mil.)	NET INCOME ($ mil.)	NET PROFIT MARGIN	EMPLOYEES
06/15	438	40	9.2%	1,900
06/08	3	0	20.3%	—
06/05	0	0	—	—
Annual Growth	—	—	—	—

2015 Year-End Financials
Return on assets: 3.7%   Cash ($ mil.): 169
Return on equity: 9.2%
Current ratio: 5.30

CHANDLER UNIFIED SCHOOL DISTRICT

EXECUTIVES

Superintendent, Camille Casteel
Building and Grounds Director, Roosevelt De Leon
Academic Advisor, Lisa Edwards
Assistant Superintendent, Joel Wirth
Coordinator, Lourdes Nieto
Accounting Staff, Tammy Schroeder
Senior Manager, Liz Judd
Teacher, Michael Garcia
Athletic Director, Shawn Rustad
Teacher, Tara Spears
Coordinator, Tim Owens
Auditors: HEINFELD MEECH & CO PC P

LOCATIONS

HQ: CHANDLER UNIFIED SCHOOL DISTRICT
    1525 W FRYE RD, CHANDLER, AZ 852246112
Phone: 480 812-7000
Web: WWW.CHANDLER.K12.AZ.US

HISTORICAL FINANCIALS
Company Type: Private

Income Statement   FYE: June 30

	REVENUE ($ mil.)	NET INCOME ($ mil.)	NET PROFIT MARGIN	EMPLOYEES
06/17	377	6	1.8%	4,500
06/16	353	49	14.0%	—
06/05	207	0	—	—
06/04	207	(11)	—	—
Annual Growth	4.7%	—	—	—

CHAPMAN UNIVERSITY

Chapman UniversityA enrollsA 7000 students at campuses throughout CaliforniaA as well as in Washington State. From its main campus in Orange California the university offers traditionalA undergraduate graduate and professional programs at seven colleges and schools. It also confers bachelor and master's degrees and teaching credentials to non-traditional students at its two-dozen satellite campuses. The universityA offersA someA 50 undergraduate majorsA and 40 graduate programs. It has 650 faculty members and a student-to-teacher ratio of 15:1.A Chapman University includes Brandman University a distance learning program for some 10000 working adultsA that operatesA two dozenA locations andA offers online courses.

Financial Performance

Chapman University reported a 9% increase in revenues to $304 millionA in 2011 due to higher income from tuition fees gifts grants and bequests. Net income also increased 27% to $70 million due to increased endowment returns offset slightly by increased general educational and auxiliary expenses.

Strategy

Chapman University is expanding programs to widen opportunities for students. In 2011 theA School of LawA launched a new business law program and in 2013 the Argyros School of Business and Economics opened a new financial center for real-time student investor trading and portfolio management training. Facilities expansions include the construction of a new center for the arts and a new health sciences campus; both projects were launched in 2012.

Company Background

Chapman University was founded in 1861 as Hesperian College; it was re-named Chapman College in 1934 in honor of philanthropist Charles C. Chapman.

EXECUTIVES

Vice President, Rebecca Haber
Vice President Of Finance, Ernest Wang
Vice President Finance, Hannah Brown
Vice President, Katie Walsh
Vice President Campus Planning And Operations, Kris Olsen
Vice President And Chief Information Officer, Helen Norris
Vice President President Elect Faculty Senate Jimmy Blalock, Gordon Babst
Vice President Scholarship And Standards, Jacqueline Hudspeth
Vice President Strategic Marketing And Communications, Jamie Ceman
Auditors: KPMG LLP IRVINE CA

LOCATIONS

HQ: CHAPMAN UNIVERSITY
    1 UNIVERSITY DR, ORANGE, CA 928661005
Phone: 714 997-6815
Web: WWW.CHAPMAN.EDU

PRODUCTS/OPERATIONS

Selected Colleges and Schools
College of Educational Studies
College of Performing Arts
George L. Argyros School of Business and Economics
Lawrence and Kristina Dodge College of Film and Media Arts
Schmid College of Science and Technology
School of Law
Wilkinson College of Humanities and Social Sciences

HISTORICAL FINANCIALS

Company Type: Private

Income Statement
FYE: May 31

	REVENUE ($ mil.)	NET INCOME ($ mil.)	NET PROFIT MARGIN	EMPLOYEES
05/18	483	90	18.8%	3,300
05/17	437	76	17.6%	—
05/16	424	31	7.4%	—
05/15	400	50	12.7%	—
Annual Growth	6.5%	21.4%	—	—

2018 Year-End Financials

Return on assets: 11.6%
Return on equity: 18.8%
Current ratio: 0.90
Cash ($ mil.): 88

CHARLES COUNTY BOARD OF EDUCATION

EXECUTIVES

Chb, Roberta Wise
Chb, Virginia McGraw
Director of Finance, Cynthia McRoy
Manager, Carol Crouse
Teacher, Allison Lee
Nurse, Deborah Heim
Occupational Specia, Teresa Whigham
Teacher, Jacy Wolfe
Advisor, Carol Compton
Coordinator, Linda Johnson
Vice-President, Maura Cook

LOCATIONS

HQ: CHARLES COUNTY BOARD OF EDUCATION
5980 RADIO STATION RD, LA PLATA, MD 206463337
Phone: 301 934-7224
Web: WWW.CCBOE.COM

HISTORICAL FINANCIALS

Company Type: Private

Income Statement
FYE: June 30

	REVENUE ($ mil.)	NET INCOME ($ mil.)	NET PROFIT MARGIN	EMPLOYEES
06/15	391	(3)	—	3,300
06/14	403	5	1.3%	—
06/13	393	9	2.5%	—
06/12	365	8	2.3%	—
Annual Growth	2.3%	—	—	—

2015 Year-End Financials

Return on assets: 3.1%
Return on equity: (-0.8%)
Current ratio: —
Cash ($ mil.): 68

CHARLESTON AREA MEDICAL CENTER, INC.

CAMC Health System is a catalyst for care in Charleston. The health network includes flagship facility Charleston Area Medical Center (CAMC) which is the largest hospital in West Virginia and consists of three campuses with some 840 beds total. The system also includes the CAMC Health Education and Research Institute which coordinates education programs for medical students from West Virginia University. In addition the health system operates smaller rural hospital CAMC Teays Valley and several urgent care and family practice clinics. CAMC Health System operates an online medical information system and physician services company Integrated Health Care Providers.

Operations

The three campuses of CAMC include CAMC General Hospital CAMC Memorial Hospital and CAMC Women and Children's Hospital all of which are located in Charleston. Specialty services at the hospitals include cardiology kidney transplants trauma and pediatrics. The CAMC Institute conducts graduate and continuing education courses; it also connects education and health care through clinical research projects in areas such as cancer and cardiovascular clinical science studies. The Teays Valley Hospital is a 70-bed facility located in nearby Hurricane West Virginia.

CAMC General Hospital is home to the highest level Trauma Center nationally-accredited Medical Rehabilitation and Stroke Centers The Center for Joint Replacement Neurosciences Center one of two Facial Surgery Centers Charleston's only accredited Sleep Center and West Virginia's only kidney transplant program affiliated with the Cleveland Clinic.

CAMC Memorial Hospital hosts one of highest volume heart programs in the US which performs 8000 procedures in the cardiac catheterization labs and more than 1600 open-heart bypass surgeries a year.

CAMC Women and Children's Hospital facilitates the birth of more than 3000 babies (including many high-risk births) per year.

Teays Valley Hospital is a not-for-profit 70-bed hospital. More than 100 doctors are authorized to practice at the hospital.

CAMC serves as a clinical training site for 700 additional learners per year through educational affiliations with regional colleges and universities.

Sales and Marketing

Commercial insurance providers and other third parties accounted for more than half of CAMC's net patient revenue in 2013; Medicare and Medicaid account for 30% and 13% respectively.

Financial Performance

The company's revenue grew by 4% to $969 million in 2013 due to higher net patient revenues and investment income. Net income fell 8% to $86 million though as expenses including salaries and employee benefits rose. Cash flow from operations dropped 48% to $33 million both as a result of the lower net income and an increase in cash used in short-term trading investments.

Strategy

In 2013 CAMC teamed up with The Ohio State University University of Michigan and West Virginia University to raise awareness and educate the community about cervical cancer. Community Awareness Resources and Education (CARE) is one of OSU Cancer Center's programs sponsored by the National Cancer Institute that focuses on an important health disparity among an underserved Appalachian population.

The following year CAMC teamed with Alliance Oncology a division of Alliance HealthCare Services to work on establishing a department of radiation therapy at CAMC Cancer Center.

Upgrading its infrastructure in 2013 Teays Valley Hospital completed a $3.7 million ICU expansion project.

EXECUTIVES

Director Of Utilization Review, Janice Kiser
Director Of Operating Room, Marcy Myers
Operating Room Director, Glen Martin
Director Of Radiology, John J Anton
Respiratory Therapy Director, Chuck Menders
Director Of Radiology, Michael E Anton
Interim Vice President For Medical Affairs, Joan Phillips
Director Of Radiology, Jeffrey C Dameron
Medical Director, Bruce Horswell
Managing Director, Janet Jenkins
Vice President Chief Medical Officer, Pinckney Mcilwain
Board Member, Gail Pitchford
Board Member, Asif Rahman
Secretary And Receptionist, Diana Gallik

LOCATIONS

HQ: CHARLESTON AREA MEDICAL CENTER, INC.
501 MORRIS ST, CHARLESTON, WV 253011326
Phone: 304 348-5432
Web: WWW.CAMC.ORG

PRODUCTS/OPERATIONS

2013 Net Patient Revenue

	% of total
Commercial insurance & other third-party payment programs	51
Medicare	30
Medicaid	13
Self-pay	1
PEIA	5
Total	**100**

2013 Sales

	of total
Net patient revenue less provision for bad debts	91
Investment income	5
Other revenue	4
Net assets released from restrictions	-
Total	**100**

Selected Service Areas

Behavioral health
Cancer
Cardiac
Children's medicine
Craniofacial surgery
Endoscopy
Fertility
Gynecology
Hemophilia
Kidney transplant
Orthopedics
Palliative care
Perinatal
Plastic surgery
Stroke
Trauma
Urology
Vascular

COMPETITORS

Charleston Hospital
Ohio Valley Medical Center
Princeton Community Hospital
St. Mary's Medical Center
WVUHS
Weirton Medical Center
West Virginia University Hospitals

HISTORICAL FINANCIALS
Company Type: Private

Income Statement
FYE: December 31

	REVENUE ($ mil.)	NET INCOME ($ mil.)	NET PROFIT MARGIN	EMPLOYEES
12/16	1,044	(17)	—	4,000
12/15	932	36	4.0%	—
12/14	877	42	4.9%	—
12/13	861	54	6.3%	—
Annual Growth	6.6%	—	—	—

2016 Year-End Financials
Return on assets: 14.6%
Return on equity: (-1.7%)
Current ratio: 0.70
Cash ($ mil.): 106

CHEMIUM INTERNATIONAL CORP.

EXECUTIVES

Pres, Ofer Levy
V Pres, Thomas Holzmann
Software Developer, Nicolas Folgado
Vice-President, Sanjeev Vora
Manager, Steve Williams
Accounting Team Member, Jimena Ferrufino
Human Resources, Zoyla Hernandez

LOCATIONS

HQ: CHEMIUM INTERNATIONAL CORP.
3773 RICHMOND AVE STE 600, HOUSTON, TX 770463725
Phone: 713 622-7766
Web: WWW.CHEMIUMCORP.COM

HISTORICAL FINANCIALS
Company Type: Private

Income Statement
FYE: December 31

	REVENUE ($ mil.)	NET INCOME ($ mil.)	NET PROFIT MARGIN	EMPLOYEES
12/15	2,015	3	0.2%	24
12/06	450	3	0.9%	—
12/03	103	0		—
Annual Growth	28.1%	—	—	—

2015 Year-End Financials
Return on assets: 2.9%
Return on equity: 0.2%
Current ratio: 0.80
Cash ($ mil.): 5

CHENEGA CORPORATION

An Alaska Native Corporation Chenega Corporation has gone from landowner to business titan. Representing the Chenega people residing in the central Alaskan Prince William Sound region it operates mostly through its subsidiaries. Chenega Integrated Systems and Chenega Technology Services offer information technology security training manufacturing research and development network engineering and military operation support services. Chenega Corporation's clients have included the Department of Defense Department of Homeland Security and EPA.

Geographic Reach
The company's headquarters are located in Anchorage Alaska. Chenega Corporation and its subsidiaries operate in 45 states and 11 countries.

Strategy
Government contracts are a source of revenue growth. Chenega Corporation began to participate in the Government Services marketplace in 1997. By 2012 it was performing on more than 158 prime contracts and 100 principal sub-contracts through a combination of competitive and negotiated best-value awards.

EXECUTIVES

Director Of Government Relations, Kristina Woolston
Vice President Human Resources, Peggy O'keefe
Vice President, Ronald Lee
Vice President Of Financial, Kathy Kowals
Senior Vice President, Ken Bishop

LOCATIONS

HQ: CHENEGA CORPORATION
3000 C ST STE 301, ANCHORAGE, AK 995033975
Phone: 907 277-5706

PRODUCTS/OPERATIONS

Selected Services
Base operations and maintenance
Environmental management
Information technology
Intel and military operations
Light manufacturing
Logistics support
Telecommunications
Tourism and hospitality
Training services
Security services

COMPETITORS

Akal Security	Halliburton
Arctic Slope Regional Corporation	IBM Global Services
	Parsons Corporation
Computer Sciences Corp.	TKC Communications
	chugach alaska
HP Enterprise Services	

HISTORICAL FINANCIALS
Company Type: Private

Income Statement
FYE: September 30

	REVENUE ($ mil.)	NET INCOME ($ mil.)	NET PROFIT MARGIN	EMPLOYEES
09/17	875	12	1.4%	4,500
09/16	926	14	1.5%	—
09/15	881	12	1.4%	—
09/14	134	5	3.9%	—
Annual Growth	86.6%	32.5%	—	—

2017 Year-End Financials
Return on assets: 4.9%
Return on equity: 1.4%
Current ratio: 1.70
Cash ($ mil.): 45

CHEROKEE NATION BUSINESSES LLC

EXECUTIVES

MBR-Ceo, Shawn Slaton
MBR-Chm, Gary Cooper
MBR-Cfo, Doug Evans
MBR-Board MBR, Bob Berry
MBR-Chb, Harold Sam Ray Hart
Snr Dir Fin, Kimberly Barnette
Regional Vice-President, David Mullen
Information Specialist, Aaron Lowther
Information Specialist, Cody Hardy
Information Specialist, Curtis Starling
Information Specialist, Daniel Basden
Auditors: BKD LLP TULSA OKLAHOMA

LOCATIONS

HQ: CHEROKEE NATION BUSINESSES LLC
777 W CHEROKEE ST, CATOOSA, OK 740153235
Phone: 918 384-7474
Web: WWW.CHEROKEENATIONBUSINESSES.COM

HISTORICAL FINANCIALS
Company Type: Private

Income Statement
FYE: September 30

	REVENUE ($ mil.)	NET INCOME ($ mil.)	NET PROFIT MARGIN	EMPLOYEES
09/17	1,018	40	4.0%	3,117
09/16	1,021	50	4.9%	—
09/15	925	32	3.5%	—
09/14	829	52	6.4%	—
Annual Growth	7.1%	(8.4%)	—	—

2017 Year-End Financials
Return on assets: 5.4%
Return on equity: 4.0%
Current ratio: 2.20
Cash ($ mil.): 202

CHEVRON PHILLIPS CHEMICAL COMPANY LLC

Among the world's largest petrochemical firms Chevron Phillips Chemical (CPChem) produces ethylene propylene polyethylene and polypropylene — sometimes used as building blocks for the company's other products such as pipe. Chevron Phillips Chemical also produces aromatics such as benzene and styrene specialty chemicals such as acetylene black (a form of carbon black) and mining chemicals. Chevron Phillips Chemical Company LP is CPChem's wholly-owned primary US operating subsidiary. CPChem is 50% owned by Chevron U.S.A. Inc. an indirect wholly-owned subsidiary of Chevron Corporation and 50% by wholly-owned subsidiaries of Phillips 66.

Operations
CPChem is a leading global producer of olefins and polyolefins (more than 80% of total sales) and a major supplier of aromatics alpha olefins styrenics specialty chemicals as well as piping material and other proprietary plastics. It is the Western Hemisphere's largest producer of high-density polyethylene — used in blow/injection molding plastic bags and pipes and films. CPChem also is near the top in styrene ethylene and aromatics production.

CPChem has several petrochemical joint ventures in the Middle East including Saudi Chevron Phillips Company (50%) and Qatar Chemical Company (not quite 50%). Subsidiary Chevron Oronite produces fuel additives.

The company's chemical products are used in more than 70000 consumer and industrial products. Its brands include Marlex Aromax Scentinel Soltex and K-Resin.

Geographic Reach

CPChem operates 35 manufacturing facilities and two research and development centers in Belgium China Colombia Qatar Saudi Arabia Singapore South Korea and the US.

Sales and Marketing

The company serves a range of markets including Adhesives and Sealants Agricultural Appliances Automotive Building and Construction Chemical Manufacturing Drycleaning Textiles Pharmaceuticals Paint and Coatings Imaging and Photography Packaging and Electronics.

Strategy

CPChem is growing its complex of chemical plants taking advantage of the deep pockets of its multinational parents increased demand for chemical products (especially in Asia) and the abundance of chemical raw materials generated by natural gas production in North American shale basins.

In 2015 the company completed an expansion of its normal alpha olefins capacity at its Cedar Bayou plant in Baytown. Alpha olefins are used in synthetic motor oils lubricants surfactants and other specialty applications.

Growing its infrastructure during 2014 CPChem completed the construction of a 1-hexene plant (the world's largest) at the company's Cedar Bayou complex in Baytown Texas with a design capacity of 250000 metric tons per year. The product 1-hexene is a component used in the manufacture of polyethylene a plastic resin commonly converted into film plastic pipe milk jugs detergent bottles and food and beverage containers.

In 2014 CPChem completed an ethylene expansion at its Sweeny complex in Old Ocean Texas.

That year to take advantage of chemical supply from nearby oil and gas basins the company committed $6 billion to build a 1.5-million-metric-tons/year (3.3 billion pounds/year) ethane cracker and two ethylene derivatives facilities on the US Gulf Coast. The two new polyethylene facilities will each have an annual capacity of 500000 metric tons (1.1 billion pounds). The projects are due to be completed in 2017.

To raise cash in 2015 the company sold its its Ryton polyphenylene sulfide business to Solvay for $220 million.

Company Background

In 2011 to expand its portfolio in Europe the company acquired a polyalphaolefin plant in Beringen Belgium from Neste Oil. The acquisition also added to the company's existing production of polyalphaolefins (PAOs) which are used in high-performance lubricants.

A coin toss determined whose name would go first when Chevron and Phillips Petroleum (now Phillips 66) formed 50-50 joint venture Chevron Phillips Chemical Company in 2000.

EXECUTIVES

Svp Petrochemicals, D. S. (Dave) Smith
President And Ceo, Mark E. Lashier
Vp And Cio, Peggy Colsman
Svp Cfo And Controller, Tim D. Leveille
Svp Projects And Supply Chain, R. E. (Ron) Corn
Svp Manufacturing, M. S. (Scott) Sharp
Svp Polymers, David Morgan
Vice President Of Human Resources, Greg Wagner
Vice President, Ken Hope
Vice President Human Resources, Donald Kremer
Vice President Manufacturing, Todd Monette
Auditors: ERNST & YOUNG LLP HOUSTON TX

LOCATIONS

HQ: CHEVRON PHILLIPS CHEMICAL COMPANY LLC
10001 SIX PINES DR, THE WOODLANDS, TX
773801498
Phone: 832 813-4100
Web: WWW.CPCHEM.COM

PRODUCTS/OPERATIONS

Selected Products

Olefins and polyolefins
  Ethylene
  Polyethylene
  Polyethylene pipe
  Polypropylene
  Propylene
Aromatics and styrenics
  Benzene
  Cumene
  Cyclohexane
  Paraxylene
  Styrene
Specialty products
  Acetylene black
  Alpha olefins
  Dimethyl sulfide
  Drilling specialty chemicals
  High-purity hydrocarbons and solvents
  Mining chemicals
  Neohexene
  Performance and reference fuels
  Polyalpha olefins
  Polystyrene

Selected Joint Ventures

Americas Styrenics (50%)
Chevron Phillips Singapore Chemicals (Private) Limited (50%)
KR Copolymer Co. Ltd. (60% South Korea)
Qatar Chemical Company Ltd. (Q-Chem 49%)
Saudi Chevron Phillips Company (50%)
Shanghai Golden Phillips Petrochemical Co. Ltd. (40%)

COMPETITORS

Dow Chemical	NOVA Chemicals
DuPont	SABIC
ExxonMobil Chemical	Sasol
Kraton	Total Petrochemicals
LyondellBasell	Westlake Chemical

HISTORICAL FINANCIALS

Company Type: Private

Income Statement   FYE: December 31

	REVENUE ($ mil.)	NET INCOME ($ mil.)	NET PROFIT MARGIN	EMPLOYEES
12/17	9,622	1,446	15.0%	5,000
12/16	8,769	1,687	19.2%	—
12/15	9,859	2,651	26.9%	—
12/14	14,148	3,288	23.2%	—
Annual Growth	(12.1%)	(24.0%)	—	—

2017 Year-End Financials

Return on assets: 9.7%
Return on equity: 15.0%   Cash ($ mil.): 676
Current ratio: 1.10

CHEVRON PHILLIPS CHEMICAL COMPANY LP

EXECUTIVES

Ceo, Peter L Cella
Exec V Pres, Mark E Lashier
Sr V Pres, Ron Corn
Sr V Pres, Tim Hill
V Pres, Mitch Eichelberger
Director of Operations, Tommy Gilligan
Coordinator, Aprile Turner
Finance Administrator, Jacqueline Ray
Marketing Manager, Lee Fixmer
Marketing Director, Marty Utterback
Technical Manager, Michael Rhodes
Auditors: ERNST & YOUNG LLP HOUSTON T

LOCATIONS

HQ: CHEVRON PHILLIPS CHEMICAL COMPANY LP
10001 SIX PINES DR, THE WOODLANDS, TX
773801498
Phone: 832 813-4100
Web: WWW.CPCHEM.COM

HISTORICAL FINANCIALS

Company Type: Private

Income Statement   FYE: December 31

	REVENUE ($ mil.)	NET INCOME ($ mil.)	NET PROFIT MARGIN	EMPLOYEES
12/17	7,919	841	10.6%	5,000
12/16	7,106	1,301	18.3%	—
12/15	7,990	2,020	25.3%	—
12/14	11,758	2,444	20.8%	—
Annual Growth	(12.3%)	(29.9%)		

2017 Year-End Financials

Return on assets: 14.4%
Return on equity: 10.6%   Cash ($ mil.): 519
Current ratio: 1.00

CHG FOUNDATION

EXECUTIVES

Director, Sheila Martz
Chief Information Officer, Jonathan Tamayo
Chief Financial Officer, William Rice
Auditors: MOSS ADAMS LLP SAN FRANCISCO

LOCATIONS

HQ: CHG FOUNDATION
740 BAY BLVD, CHULA VISTA, CA 919105254
Phone: 619 422-0422
Web: WWW.CHGSD.COM

HISTORICAL FINANCIALS

Company Type: Private

Income Statement   FYE: December 31

	REVENUE ($ mil.)	NET INCOME ($ mil.)	NET PROFIT MARGIN	EMPLOYEES
12/16	1,098	206	18.8%	1
12/14	622	34	5.5%	—
12/13	323	(11)	—	—
12/09	133	1	1.0%	—
Annual Growth	35.1%	106.8%	—	—

2016 Year-End Financials

Return on assets: 32.0%
Return on equity: 18.8%   Cash ($ mil.): 659
Current ratio: —

CHICAGO COMMUNITY TRUST

EXECUTIVES

Vice Chair, Adele Simmons
Auditors: O BDO USA LLP CHICAGO IL

LOCATIONS

HQ: CHICAGO COMMUNITY TRUST
225 N MICHIGAN AVE # 2200, CHICAGO, IL
606017672
Phone: 312 616-8000
Web: WWW.CCT.ORG

HISTORICAL FINANCIALS
Company Type: Private

Income Statement				FYE: September 30
	REVENUE ($ mil.)	NET INCOME ($ mil.)	NET PROFIT MARGIN	EMPLOYEES
09/16	389	135	34.8%	66
09/15	363	136	37.5%	—
09/14	291	105	36.3%	—
09/10	33	(36)	—	—
Annual Growth	50.8%	—	—	—

2016 Year-End Financials
Return on assets: 1.2% Cash ($ mil.): 86
Return on equity: 34.8%
Current ratio: 3.10

CHICAGO PARK DISTRICT

EXECUTIVES

Ceo, Michael P Kelly
President, Mona Castillo
Treasurer, Melinda Molloy
Commissioner, Margaret T Burroughs
Commissioner, William C Batholomay
Commissioner, Robert Pickens
Commissioner, Anita M Cummings
Commissioner, Gerald M Sullivan
General Superintendent, David Doig
General Counsel, Kevin Ridley
Chief Financial Officer, Stephen Hughes

LOCATIONS

HQ: CHICAGO PARK DISTRICT
541 N FAIRBANKS CT # 300, CHICAGO, IL 606113653
Phone: 312 742-7529
Web: WWW.CHICAGOPARKDISTRICT.COM

HISTORICAL FINANCIALS
Company Type: Private

Income Statement				FYE: December 31
	REVENUE ($ mil.)	NET INCOME ($ mil.)	NET PROFIT MARGIN	EMPLOYEES
12/17	445	(44)	—	3,100
12/16	490	54	11.0%	—
12/06	0	0	—	—
12/05	0	0	—	—
Annual Growth	—	—	—	—

2017 Year-End Financials
Return on assets: 16.3% Cash ($ mil.): 252
Return on equity: (-9.9%)
Current ratio: 1.70

CHICAGO TRANSIT AUTHORITY

The CTA is focused on making its ETA. The Chicago Transit Authority operates the second-largest public transportation system in the US behind the New York City Transit Authority. On a typical weekday CTA passengers take about 1.7 million rides on the agency's buses and trains which travel in and around Chicago and about 35 suburbs. The CTA operates a fleet of 1865 buses on almost 130 routes. Its rail system includes eight rail lines with some 1356 rail cars operating on 224 miles of track at more than 145 stations. The agency created by the Illinois legislature in 1947 is part of the state's Regional Transportation Authority which also oversees Metra (commuter rail system) and Pace (suburban bus system).

Financial Performance
The agency generates the majority of its revenue from fare and passes; the remainder comes from a reduced fare subsidy from the state of Illinois advertising and concessions investment income parking fees the sale of real estate and the sale of CTA merchandise.

The company's net revenue increased the last three years (2012-2014). In fiscal 2014 revenues jumped by 1% primarily due to increases in farebox revenue. CTA's net income has fluctuated the last three years; however it decreased by 81% in 2014 mainly due to a surge in provision for depreciation and labor and fringe benefits.

Strategy
CTA has raised prices several times to keep up with the cost of doing business.

EXECUTIVES

Cfo And Treasurer, Karen Walker, $180,000 total compensation
Inspector General, Paul Sidrys, $160,000 total compensation
Coo, Peter Ousley
President, Forrest Claypool
Chairman, Terry Peterson
Auditors: CROWE HORWATH LLP CHICAGO IL

LOCATIONS

HQ: CHICAGO TRANSIT AUTHORITY
567 W LAKE ST STE CTA, CHICAGO, IL 606611465
Phone: 312 664-7200
Web: WWW.TRANSITCHICAGO.COM

PRODUCTS/OPERATIONS

2014 Sales

	$ mil.	% of total
Farebox	364	57
Pass	219	35
Advertising & Concessions	27	4
Other Revenue	22	4
Total	**633**	**100**

HISTORICAL FINANCIALS
Company Type: Private

Income Statement				FYE: December 31
	REVENUE ($ mil.)	NET INCOME ($ mil.)	NET PROFIT MARGIN	EMPLOYEES
12/16	625	(79)	—	12,000
12/10	548	(323)	—	—
12/05	448	(153)	—	—
12/04	397	(9)	—	—
Annual Growth	3.8%	—	—	—

2016 Year-End Financials
Return on assets: 23.9% Cash ($ mil.): 79
Return on equity: (-12.7%)
Current ratio: 0.20

CHILDREN'S HOSPITAL

EXECUTIVES

Pres, Kurt Newman
Director, Carole Helmandollar
Facilities Director, Robert Beckwith
Pediatric Nurse Practitioner, Debbie Lafond
Admissions Manager, Jennifer Cameron
Director, Jyoti Jaiswal
Auditors: GRANT THORNTON LLP MC LEAN V

LOCATIONS

HQ: CHILDREN'S HOSPITAL
111 MICHIGAN AVE NW, WASHINGTON, DC 200102916
Phone: 202 232-0521
Web: WWW.CHILDRENSNATIONAL.ORG

HISTORICAL FINANCIALS
Company Type: Private

Income Statement				FYE: June 30
	REVENUE ($ mil.)	NET INCOME ($ mil.)	NET PROFIT MARGIN	EMPLOYEES
06/15	1,076	118	11.0%	6,000
06/14	983	43	4.4%	—
Annual Growth	9.4%	174.2%	—	—

2015 Year-End Financials
Return on assets: 13.2% Cash ($ mil.): 114
Return on equity: 11.0%
Current ratio: 0.50

CHILDREN'S HOSPITAL COLORADO

Rocky Mountain rugrats can count on Children's Hospital Colorado. The not-for-profit organization runs a network of health facilities in Colorado anchored by its nearly 50-acre main campus in Aurora. The campus includes a 260-bed inpatient hospital and numerous outpatient clinics. Children's Hospital Colorado also operates more than a dozen satellite locations in and around Denver that specialize in providing children with emergency and specialty care. Affiliated with the University of Colorado Denver School of Medicine the hospital provides medical training and performs a wide range of research into pediatric illnesses including cancer and HIV/AIDS.

Operations
The main hospital is located on the Anschutz Medical Campus with the medical school and the University of Colorado Hospital Authority's 620-bed acute care center. With help from its medical staff of 2330 Children's Hospital Colorado had 18500 inpatient admissions; 21000 surgeries 527000 outpatient visits and about 158000 emergency department visits in 2014.

The hospital boasts two additional emergency locations at Exempla Saint Joseph Hospital in Denver and Centura's Parker Adventist Hospital in Parker. Children's Hospital Colorado provides urgent care through three nearby community locations: Centura Littleton Adventist Hospital Children's Hospital North Campus at Broomfield and Exempla Lutheran Medical Center in Wheat Ridge. In addition it has about 10 specialty care clinics in the Denver area that provide cancer pulmonary and surgery services.

The health care facility's research initiatives are conducted at the Children's Hospital Colorado Research Institute. Along with its affiliation with the university the Children's Hospital works with the Pediatric Clinical Translational Research Center to conduct research and clinical trials in a number of fields including cardiology gastroenterology oncology orthopedics pulmonology and psychiatry.

Geographic Reach
Children's Hospital Colorado established in 1908 serves a seven-state region through its Level 1 trauma center. Its other facilities cater to residents of the Denver metropolitan area.

Sales and Marketing
Medicaid accounted for 47% of the hospital's net patient revenue in 2014; managed care accounted for 45%.

Financial Performance
Gross patient services revenue totaled $2.2 billion in 2014; other operating revenue totaled $60.7 million.

Strategy
Children's Hospital Colorado boasts the capacity to handle the most challenging emergencies as the only dedicated Level 1 trauma center in a seven-state region. Through its affiliation with the University of Colorado the hospital conducts physician assistant residency fellowship and internship programs in a variety of fields including anesthesiology orthopedics dentistry and neurology. It also provides continuing education programs for doctors and nurses.

The health care facility is expanding its footprint in the Colorado Springs area as the region experiences noteworthy growth. To this end it is building a new $110 million hospital on the University of Colorado Health Memorial North campus that will house 100 inpatient beds an emergency room neonatal and pediatric intensive care units and operating rooms. The complex is expected to open in 2018.

EXECUTIVES

President And Ceo Children's Hospital Colorado Foundation, Steve Winesett
President Ceo And Director, James E. Shmerling, age 64
Svp Patient Care Services And Chief Nursing Officer, Kelly M. Johnson
Surgeon-in-chief, Timothy M. Crombleholme
Pediatrician-in-chief, Stephen Daniels
Chief Medical Officer, Joan Bothner
President And Ceo, Jena Hausmann
Svp And Cio, Mary Anne Leach
Svp And Cfo, Jeff Harrington
Chief Research Officer, Frederick J. Suchy
Medical Director Pediatric Sports Medicine, Aaron Provance
Clinical Director, Sheila Kaseman
Vice President Operations, Jerrod Milton
Nursing Director, Norine Hemphill
Medical Director, Teri Schreiner
Finance Vice President, Jeffrey Harrington
Medical Director, George Wang
Vice President Of Support Services, Dan Coxall
Senior Vice President And Chief Information Officer, Dana Moore
Chairman, Kevin Reidy

LOCATIONS

HQ: CHILDREN'S HOSPITAL COLORADO
13123 E 16TH AVE, AURORA, CO 800457106
Phone: 720 777-1234
Web: WWW.CHILDRENSCOLORADO.ORG

Selected Locations
Children's Hospital Colorado Main Campus
Children's Hospital Colorado at Saint Joseph Hospital
Children's Hospital Colorado KidStreet
Children's Hospital Colorado Orthopedic Care Centennial

Children's Hospital Colorado Outpatient Specialty Care Centennial
Children's Hospital Colorado Outpatient Specialty Care Colorado Springs
Children's Hospital Colorado Outpatient Specialty Care Parker
Children's Hospital Colorado Therapy Care Parker
Children's Hospital Colorado Therapy Care Pueblo
Children's Hospital Colorado Urgent and Outpatient Specialty Care Wheat Ridge

PRODUCTS/OPERATIONS

Selected Departments
Adolescent Medicine Program
Adult Congenital Heart Disease Program
Aerodigestive Program
Allergy Program
Arrhythmia Center
Asthma Program
Audiology Speech and Learning Program
Bill Daniels Center for Children's Hearing
Bone Marrow Transplant Program
Breathing Institute
Burn program
Cardiac Anesthesia
Cardiac Catheterization
Cardiology Clinic
Cardiology Outreach Programs
Cardiomyopathy Program
Center for Cancer and Blood Disorders
Center for Celiac Disease
Child Abuse Services
Child Development Unit
Child Health Clinic
Colorado Fetal Care Center
Colorado Institute for Maternal and Fetal Health
Colorectal and Complex Pelvic Floor Disorders Program
Complex Congenital Heart Disease and Development Clinic
Craniofacial Center
Critical Care
Cystic Fibrosis Research and Care Center
Dental
Dermatology
Digestive Health Institute
Ear Nose and Throat
Eating Disorder Program
Emergency Department
Endocrinology
Endoscopy Clinic (ATECh)
Experimental Therapeutics Program
Extracorporeal Membrane Oxygenation (ECMO) Program
Eye
Fetal Cardiology Program
Fiberoptic Endoscopic Evaluation of Swallowing (FEES) Clinic
Flight for Life
Gastroenterology
Gastrointestinal Eosinophilic Diseases
Genetics Program
Gynecology
Healthy Expectations Perinatal Mental Health Program
Heart Institute
Heart Surgery
Heart Transplant Program
HOPE Clinic for Cancer Survivors
Hospitalist Services

COMPETITORS

Banner Health
Catholic Health Initiatives
Centura Health
Denver Health and Hospital Authority
Exempla Healthcare
HealthONE
North Colorado Medical Center
Presbyterian/St. Luke's Medical Center
Rose Medical Center
Shriners Hospitals For Children
The Memorial Hospital

HISTORICAL FINANCIALS
Company Type: Private

Income Statement   FYE: December 31

	REVENUE ($ mil.)	NET INCOME ($ mil.)	NET PROFIT MARGIN	EMPLOYEES
12/17	960	76	8.0%	2,200
12/16	911	50	5.5%	—
12/15	908	25	2.8%	—
12/14	879	58	6.6%	—
Annual Growth	3.0%	9.8%	—	—

2017 Year-End Financials
Return on assets: 8.0%   Cash ($ mil.): 70
Return on equity: 8.0%
Current ratio: 1.40

CHILDREN'S HOSPITAL MEDICAL CENTER

Cincinnati Children's Hospital Medical Center has a special place in its heart for kids. The pediatric health care facility offers specialty treatments for children and adolescents suffering from just about any malady including ailments of the heart and liver as well as blood diseases and cancer. Cincinnati Children's Hospital has some 600 beds and operates about a dozen outpatient care centers. Founded in 1883 the not-for-profit hospital runs the only level I pediatric trauma center in the region and serves as a teaching and research facility for the University of Cincinnati College of Medicine. It is also ranked in the top 10 for all 10 pediatric specialties by U.S. News & World Report

Operations
With a staff of some 1500 physicians Cincinnati Children's Hospital serves more than 1 million patients each year including about 100000 emergency room visits and 32000 surgical procedures. Its outpatient centers include community urgent and emergency care facilities and general and specialty physician practices as well as laboratory radiology dentistry and physical therapy clinics.

The Cincinnati Children's Research Foundation conducts research and clinical trials of pediatric medical innovations including new vaccines and surgical techniques. It has research partnerships with hospitals in Africa Asia Latin America and the Middle East. The hospital and research foundation's contributions to pediatric medicine include the rotavirus vaccine and Albert Sabin's discovery of the oral polio vaccine (first tested in 1960).

The hospital's educational programs are also renowned.

Geographic Reach
Reaching beyond Cincinnati Cincinnati Children's Hospital also provides services to communities in southeastern Indiana and northern Kentucky through its network of outpatient clinics. The hospital serves patients from all 50 US states as well as from about 60 international countries. It has international research collaborations with institutions in Bangladesh Brazil China Honduras Israel Malawi Mexico Nepal and the United Arab Emirates.

Financial Performance
In 2014 revenue grew 10% to $2.1 billion as the center saw rises in revenue from net patient services capitation professional services and other

operations. Net income rose 13% to $172 million due to the higher revenue.

Strategy

Cincinnati Children's Hospital regularly expands its facilities to improve medical services and enhance research and education programs. In 2015 it opened a new 15-story clinical research building at its main campus in Avondale. In 2014 it opened a new urgent care center at its Liberty Campus.

In addition the institution forms collaborations to expand its operations. In 2015 it signed a three-year partnership with Shire to research rare diseases. The partners will work to discover and develop novel therapies to treat these diseases.

The hospital has remained on the forefront of the digital revolution that has swept the health care industry. In recent years the organization has linked its emergency inpatient radiology pharmacy and specialty department patient data together to create an electronic medical record (EHR). The EHR system helps to reduce patient errors (such as medication errors) and improves communication between departments.

To prepare for health reform measures Cincinnati Children's Hospital is also reducing costs through workflow purchasing and care delivery improvement programs.

EXECUTIVES

Vice President Family Relations, David Anderson
Vice President Marketing, Phyllis Goodman Goodman
Vice President Operations Cincinnati Children's Research Foundation, John Maybury
President And Ceo, Michael Fisher, age 59
Evp And Coo, Scott J. Hamlin
Svp Information Services And Cio, Marianne F. James
Cfo, Mark D. Mumford, age 56
Chief Medical Officer, Margaret Hostetter
Medical Director, Paul Edward Steele
Vice President Facilities Management, Thomas Kinman
Assistant Vice President, Carolyn Karageorges
Clinical Director, Victoria Decastro
Clinical Director, Natalie Elsbrock
Assistant Vice President, Melissa Saladonis
Assistant Vice President, Stephanie Ebken
Assistant Vice President Patient Service, Deborah Browning
Assistant Vice President Of Development, Karen Kratz
Clinical Director, Wendy Ungard
Clinical Director, Thomas Cahill
Vice President Business Development, Jim Barter
Assistant Vice President, Maria Britto
Medical Director Pediatric Environmental Health And Lead Clinic, Nicholas Newman
Assistant Vice President Biodiagnostics, Sally May
Clinical Director, Tonya Honeycutt
Clinical Director, Linda Richey
Assistant Vice President Executive Director, Abram Gordon
Clinical Toxicologist Business Specialist Mt Pharmd Dabat, Jan Scaglione
Vice President Patient Services, Mary Sitterding
Clinical Director, Kandice Ferdon
Clinical Director, Barbara Valerius
Assistant Vice President Business Intelligence, Mike Naber
Clinical Director, Travee Sanderson
Clinical Director, Andrea Shaffer Ellis
Clinical Director, Megan Isley
Pharmd Bcps, Breann Taylor
Vp Budget And Finance, Sidney Norton
Chair, Thomas G. Cody, age 76
Assistant Treasurer, Alex Miller

LOCATIONS

HQ: CHILDREN'S HOSPITAL MEDICAL CENTER
3333 BURNET AVE, CINCINNATI, OH 452293039
Phone: 513 636-4200
Web: WWW.CINCINNATICHILDRENS.ORG

PRODUCTS/OPERATIONS

Selected Locations
Anderson
Batesville
Burnet Campus
  Children's
College Hill Campus
Drake
Eastgate
Fairfield
Harrison
Hopple Street Center
Kenwood
Liberty Campus
Lindner Center of Hope (Mason)
Mason Campus
Northern Kentucky
Oak Campus

Selected Treatment Areas
Abdomen and Digestive Tract
Allergy Asthma Immunology
Anesthesia
Arthritis and Rheumatology
Babies / Infants
Bones Joints and Muscles
Brain Spinal Cord and Nerves
Cancer
Cerebral Palsy
Chest and Lungs
Craniofacial Anomalies
Dental and Oral Health
Developmental Disabilities
Ear Nose Throat
Endocrine Metabolism and Diabetes
Eyes
Genetics
Growth and Development
Heart
Hemangiomas and Vascular Malformations
Hematology and Blood
Infectious Diseases
Injuries and Poisonings
Kidney Bladder and Genitals
Liver
Medications
Mental Health
Nutrition and Diet
Pain Management
Rehabilitation
Safety and Injury Prevention
Skin
Speech
Sports Medicine
Surgery
Teen Health
X-Ray / Radiology

COMPETITORS

Bethesda North
Children's Hospital of Philadelphia
Deaconess Associations
Kettering Health Network
Nationwide Children's Hospital
Nemours Foundation
Premier Health Partners
Shriners Hospitals For Children
St. Elizabeth Healthcare
St. Jude Children's Research Hospital
The Christ Hospital Corporation
TriHealth
UC Health

HISTORICAL FINANCIALS

Company Type: Private

Income Statement
FYE: June 30

	REVENUE ($ mil.)	NET INCOME ($ mil.)	NET PROFIT MARGIN	EMPLOYEES
06/16	1,597	213	13.4%	18,000
06/15	1,527	209	13.7%	—
06/14	2,116	140	6.6%	—
06/11	1,693	53	3.2%	—
Annual Growth	(1.2%)	32.0%	—	—

2016 Year-End Financials
Return on assets: 14.1%   Cash ($ mil.): 148
Return on equity: 13.4%
Current ratio: 1.60

CHILDREN'S HOSPITAL OF ORANGE COUNTY

EXECUTIVES

Ceo-Pres, Kimberly Cripe
Chb, L Kenneth Heuler DDS
Pediatric Hematology Oncology, David K Buchbinder
Vice-President Engineering, Sally Gallagher
Patient Safety Officer, Cathy Mc Donnell
Nurse Practitioner, Jill D Stites
Security Staff, Cathy McDonnell
Technical Manager, Michael Kunz
Manager, Dorit Ben Ezer
Director of Case Management, Karen Pugh
Nursing Director, Linda Glenn
Auditors: KPMG LLP LOS ANGELES CA

LOCATIONS

HQ: CHILDREN'S HOSPITAL OF ORANGE COUNTY
1201 W LA VETA AVE, ORANGE, CA 928684203
Phone: 714 997-3000
Web: WWW.CHOCCHILDRENS.ORG

HISTORICAL FINANCIALS

Company Type: Private

Income Statement
FYE: June 30

	REVENUE ($ mil.)	NET INCOME ($ mil.)	NET PROFIT MARGIN	EMPLOYEES
06/16	523	10	2.0%	3,200
06/15	518	20	3.9%	—
06/14	517	(15)	—	—
06/13	548	29	5.3%	—
Annual Growth	(1.6%)	(28.7%)	—	—

2016 Year-End Financials
Return on assets: 6.3%   Cash ($ mil.): 93
Return on equity: 2.0%
Current ratio: 2.10

CHILDREN'S HOSPITAL OF THE KINGS DAUGHTERS INC

EXECUTIVES

Pres, James D Dahling
Vice President, Beth M Duke
Vice President, Kathy Abshire
Vice President, Deborah Barnes
Vice President, David G Bowers
Vice President, Jo-Ann Burke
Vice-President Finance, Kathryn Abshire
Doctor, Scott Nottingham
Information Specialist, Steve Williamson
Otolaryngologist, Joseph Han
Database Administrator, Andrew Xie

LOCATIONS

HQ: CHILDREN'S HOSPITAL OF THE KINGS
DAUGHTERS INC
601 CHILDRENS LN, NORFOLK, VA 235071910
Phone: 757 668-7000
Web: WWW.CHKD.COM

HISTORICAL FINANCIALS
Company Type: Private

Income Statement				FYE: June 30
	REVENUE ($ mil.)	NET INCOME ($ mil.)	NET PROFIT MARGIN	EMPLOYEES
06/16	361	47	13.1%	1,211
06/15	332	49	14.8%	—
06/14	342	44	13.1%	—
06/13	337	50	15.0%	—
Annual Growth	2.3%	(2.2%)	—	—

2016 Year-End Financials

Return on assets: 4.9%   Cash ($ mil.): 60
Return on equity: 13.1%
Current ratio: 3.00

CHILDREN'S MEDICAL CENTER OF DALLAS

Children's Medical Center of Dallas (operating as Children's Health) treats children with various medical needs from birth to age 18. Specialties include craniofacial deformities cystic fibrosis gastroenterology cancer and heart disease. Children's is also a major pediatric center for heart kidney bone marrow and other transplant procedures. The not-for-profit hospital has about 600 beds and is the pediatric teaching facility for UT Southwestern Medical. Children's also operates a network of about 20 primary care and specialty clinics in and around Dallas in addition to its two full-service campuses.

Operations

The Children's system serves patients through two full-service hospitals a specialty care center in Southlake and a network of primary care offices called MyChildren's located throughout the Metroplex. As the primary pediatric teaching facility for UT Southwestern Children's supports a three-year residency program for physicians and academic fellowships in numerous subspecialties.

Children's Health's Dallas campus operates the city's only pediatric emergency room and the region's only pediatric-centered teaching hospital. It was also the first Level I trauma center for pediatrics in the state. Together the Dallas and Plano hospital campuses serve some 800000 patients annually and provide more than 50 sub-specialty programs. Additionally the organization provides primary health care services to the county's children living in under-served areas; some of these care services are provided through academic programs for doctors in training.

The system's research and development areas includes cancer cardiothoracic neonatology kidney disease infectious disease pharmacology sickle cell disease and psychiatry. It also provides Level IV Neonatal Intensive Care Unit.

In 2014 Children's logged some 173000 patient visits in its emergency departments in Dallas and Plano.

Geographic Reach

Children's main hospital campuses are in Dallas and Plano Texas. It has a handful of specialty centers and 16 primary care locations in the Dallas suburbs and area communities including Southlake.

Financial Performance

Children's receives revenues from a mix of third-party payers including HMOs and PPOs as well as Medicaid and Medicare and the state Children's Health Insurance Program (CHIP). It also relies heavily on private donations and fundraising efforts but provides a hefty amount of charity care each year for the region's uninsured children.

Strategy

Children's introduced its Children's Health brand in 2014. The new identity serves to reflect its operations as an integrated health system beyond the two primary campus locations.

At any given time it seems that Children's is building or opening one facility or another. In 2015 it opened the nation's second Pitt Hopkins Syndrome clinic treating a rare genetic condition that can cause development delays intellectual disabilities breathing issues and seizures.

Mergers and Acquisitions

In 2015 the system bought Our Children's House which provides rehabilitative and transitional care to children with special needs from Baylor Scott & White. Children's took over operations of Our Children's House's inpatient and outpatient facilities as well as eight outpatient clinics.

Company Background

In the four-year period between 2001 and 2005 the center spent more than $250 million on new construction and expansion projects. It opened a 72-bed Children's Legacy Hospital in nearby Plano in 2008 and in 2009 Children's completed construction of a new $150 million tower on its main Dallas campus to house its heart center cancer center and neonatal intensive care unit.

The company was founded in 1913.

EXECUTIVES

Evp And Chief Administrative Officer Corporate Services, Michele Chulick
Chief Clinical Officer And Evp, W. Robert (Bob) Morrow
Evp Population Health And Business Development, Peter W. Roberts
President Childrenâ's Medical Center Dallas Foundation And Evp Childrenâ's Health System Texas, Kern Wildenthal
President And Ceo, Christopher J. Share
President And Coo, Douglas G. Share

LOCATIONS

HQ: CHILDREN'S MEDICAL CENTER OF DALLAS
1935 MEDICAL DISTRICT DR, DALLAS, TX 752357701
Phone: 214 456-7000
Web: WWW.CHILDRENS.COM

Children's Medical Center Selected Locations
Chase Bank Building Specialty Center (Dallas)
Children's Medical Center and Ambulatory Care Pavilion at Legacy (Plano)
Children's Medical Center of Dallas Main Campus
Dallas Ambulatory Care Pavilion
Irving Specialty Center
Mesquite Specialty Center
MyChildren's Primary Care (about 16 locations)
Pediatric Urology Clinic at Rockwall
Southlake Specialty Care Center
Walnut Hill Urology Clinic

PRODUCTS/OPERATIONS

Children's Medical Center Selected Services
Allergy/Immunology/Asthma
Audiology
Cystic fibrosis
Day surgery
Dentistry
Dermatology
Diabetes
Ear/Nose/Throat
Endocrinology
Gastroenterology
General surgery
Genetics/Metabolism
International adoption medicine
Laboratory services
Neurology
Nutrition
Obesity program
Occupational therapy
Ophthalmology
Orthodontics
Orthopaedics
Physical therapy
Plastic Surgery
Pulmonary function lab
Pulmonology
Radiology
Rheumatology
Sickle cell treatment
Sleep disorders
Speech therapy
Trauma
Urology

COMPETITORS

Baylor University Medical Center
Cook Children's Health Care System
Dell Children's Medical Center

HCA
Parkland Health & Hospital System
Tenet Healthcare
Texas Children's Hospital

HISTORICAL FINANCIALS
Company Type: Private

Income Statement				FYE: December 31
	REVENUE ($ mil.)	NET INCOME ($ mil.)	NET PROFIT MARGIN	EMPLOYEES
12/15	712	(185)	—	5,318
12/14	1,120	135	12.1%	—
12/13	1,111	166	15.0%	—
12/08	744	(4)	—	—
Annual Growth	(0.6%)	—	—	—

2015 Year-End Financials

Return on assets: 4.9%   Cash ($ mil.): 9
Return on equity: (-26.0%)
Current ratio: 1.80

CHILDRENS HOSPITAL & MEDICAL CENTER

Junior Cornhuskers can have their medical needs met at Children's Hospital & Medical Center. The not-for-profit center Nebraska's only pediatric hospital (and a top US children's hospital) is a 150-bed facility offering pediatric inpatient services. The Omaha hospital has neonatal and pediatric intensive care units along with units dedicated surgery child development eating disorders and conditions including asthma allergies cardiac care diabetes nephrology and respiratory care. Children's serves as the teaching hospital for the University of Nebraska and Creighton University. It also operates urgent care and outreach clinics in the area.

Operations
Children's handles about 370000 patient visits each year including 8000 inpatient stays 8000 surgeries and 40000 emergency room and urgent care center visits. Children's main hospital building includes a level II pediatric trauma center a 20-bed pediatric intensive care unit (ICU) and a 45-bed newborn ICU. Its specialty centers also include a 30-bed day hospital (the Children's Ambulatory Recovery and Express Stay or CARES unit) and a fetal medicine center operated in partnership with Alegent Creighton Health.

The hospital's research programs include studies of translational medicine basic medicine and health outcomes conducted in partnership with the University of Nebraska's Medical Center and College of Medicine.

Geographic Reach
Children's is located in a nine-story 290000 sq. ft. facility. In addition to the main hospital in Omaha Children's operates urgent care centers in Omaha and a specialty clinic in Lincoln Nebraska. It also operates outreach clinics in communities including Columbus Grand Island Hastings Holdrege Kearney Norfolk and North Platte Nebraska; Sioux Falls and Rapid City South Dakota; and Sioux City Iowa.

About half of Children's patients come from outside the Omaha area including areas of South Dakota Iowa Kansas and Missouri. Its metabolic bone disease program offers treatment for brittle bones to children from around the country.

Financial Performance
The Children's Hospital enjoys a healthy market share in Omaha despite increasing competition from neighboring hospitals offering pediatric services. The organization reported some $249 million in net operating revenues in 2011 an increase of 5% from 2010 results. Net assets also increased by 3% to $279 million that year. However net income fell 65% to some $8 million.

Strategy
Children's Hospital has been expanding its facilities to provide a broader breadth of services to existing patients as well as to attract new patients. For instance in 2012 it launched a new fetal care center through a venture with Alegent Creighton Health. In 2010 it opened its Specialty Pediatric Center an outpatient facility providing diagnostic and treatment services for chronic conditions and diseases including childhood cancers diabetes rare diseases birth defects and congenital heart defects. The five-story building houses some 30 specialty clinics.

Mergers and Acquisitions
Children's Hospital acquired an outpatient pediatric therapy clinic in Lincoln in 2018. This will allow it to offer services to patients in the area more easily.

Company Background
The hospital was founded in 1948 as Children's Memorial Hospital by two local philanthropists Dr. C.W.M. Poynter and publisher Henry Doorly to establish a children's facility accessible to patients of all financial means. It relocated in 1981 (to a larger building) and 2000 (to a newly built nine-floor medical center). In 2009 Children's Hospital added "& Medical Center" to its name in hopes of more accurately reflecting its specialty offerings.

EXECUTIVES

President Ceo, Gary A. Perkins
Evp And Coo, Kathy English
Svp And Cfo, Mike Brown
Vp Marketing And Community Relations, Martin W. Beerman
Executive Director Children's Hospital & Medical Center Foundation, Roger Lewis
Vp Cio And Cmio, George Reynolds
Director Of Surgery, Barbara Schwarz
Vice President Cno, Debra Arnow
Vice President Of Strategy, Darla Qassem
Medical Director, Hana Niebur
Treasurer, Cynthia Hinkel

LOCATIONS

HQ: CHILDRENS HOSPITAL & MEDICAL CENTER
8200 DODGE ST, OMAHA, NE 681144113
Phone: 402 955-5400
Web: WWW.CHILDRENSOMAHA.ORG

PRODUCTS/OPERATIONS

List of Items
Access Center
Aerodigestive Clinic (GI Clinic)
Aerodigestive Clinic (Pulmonary Medicine)
Asthma Allergy Clinic
Audiology (Hearing)
Behavioral Health (Family Support)
CDC (Children's Developmental Clinic)
Child Life Services
Craniofacial Clinic
Cystic Fibrosis
Developmental Pediatric Clinic
Diabetes Clinic
Ear Nose Throat Clinic (ENT)
Eating Disorders Program
Emergency Department
Endocrine Clinic
Fetal Care Center
GI Clinic (Gastroenterology)
Hand-In-Hand/Palliative Care
Heart Center (Cardiology)
Helmet Clinic
Hematology and Oncology Clinic
Home Health Services
Hospitalist Service
Infectious Disease Clinic
Medical Surgical Floors
Metabolic Management Clinic
Newborn Intensive Care Unit (NICU)
Neurodiagnostic Services
Neurology Clinic
NICU Follow-Up Clinic
Orthopaedics Clinic
Pathology
Pediatric Intensive Care Unit (PICU)
Plastic Surgery
Pulmonary Medicine
Radiology
Rehab Services (Speech Occupational & Physical Therapies)
Renal Clinic
Rheumatology Clinic
Sleep Center
Social Work
Speech Therapy Clinic
Surgical Services
Transport (Critical Care Transport Team)
Urgent Care
Urology Clinic
Weight Management (HEROES)

COMPETITORS

BryanLGH Medical Center
CHI Health
Fremont Area Medical Center
Heartland Health
Mercy Health Network
Methodist Health System
Nebraska Medical Center
Saint Elizabeth Regional Medical Center
Shriners Hospitals For Children
Tenet Healthcare
UNMC Physicians
UnityPoint Health
University of Nebraska

HISTORICAL FINANCIALS
Company Type: Private

Income Statement				FYE: December 31
	REVENUE ($ mil.)	NET INCOME ($ mil.)	NET PROFIT MARGIN	EMPLOYEES
12/17	373	81	21.9%	1,400
12/16	339	57	17.0%	—
12/15	327	42	13.1%	—
12/14	297	64	21.6%	—
Annual Growth	7.8%	8.3%	—	—

2017 Year-End Financials
Return on assets: 5.4% Cash ($ mil.): 50
Return on equity: 21.9%
Current ratio: 2.00

CHILDRENS HOSPITAL MEDICAL CENTER OF AKRON

Akron Children's Hospital is the largest pediatric health care system in northeast Ohio. The health system operates through more than 80 locations scattered around the state including its flagship 253-bed hospital in Akron. Among Children's specialized services are cardiology orthopedics rehabilitation and home care. It also has a second 50-bed inpatient hospital called the Akron Children's Beeghly Campus. The main hospital's emergency department treats nearly 70000 patients each year. Its regional burn center sees about 3700 visits per year. Akron Children's Hospital started as a nursery more than 100 years ago.

Operations
Each year Akron Children's Hospital sees some 800000 outpatients performs more than 15000 surgeries and admits more than 10000 inpatients.

Geographic Reach
Akron Children's Hospital is a major teaching facility affiliated with Northeastern Ohio Medical University and offering nearly a dozen subspecialty fellowship training programs. Children's also runs one of the state's largest pediatric primary care networks with 15 offices in seven counties including Cuyahoga Medina Wayne Tuscawaras and Portage.

Sales and Marketing
In 2014 Medicaid payments accounted for 52% of gross patient service revenue while commercial payments accounted for 44%.

Financial Performance
The hospital's net revenue was about $701000 in fiscal 2014 with about 90% of that coming from patient services revenues.

Strategy

The system has expanded its campuses and opened new facilities to broaden its care offerings. In 2014 it opened its first location in Columbiana County opened a pediatric specialty care office in Mansfield and expanded its sports rehabilitation hours and services at LifeCenter Plus in Hudson.

EXECUTIVES

President And Ceo, William H. (Bill) Considine
Vp Medical Services; Clinical Leader Ohio Children's Hospitals Solutions For Patient Safety, Michael Bird
Vp Managed Care, Karen Richter
Vp Operations And Coo, Grace Wakulchik
Evp, Shawn Lyden
Vp Akron Children's Hospital Foundation, John Zoilo
Noah Miller Chair Department Of Pediatrics, Norman C. Christopher
Vp Akron Children's Mahoning Valley, Sharon Hrina
Cfo, Michael Trainer
Vp Patient Services And Chief Nursing Officer, Lisa Aurilio
Cio, Tom Ogg
Vp Department Of Pediatrics, Cindy Dormo
Chief Medical Information Officer, Amy Maneker
Vp Surgical Subspecialty Practices, Craig McGhee
Chief Medical Officer, Robert McGregor
Vice President Marketing, Carolyn Davis
Medical Librarian, Judy Griggs
Medical Director Of The Locust Pediatric Care Group, Cooper White
Director Of Government Relations, Charlie Solley
Vice President Of Public Policy And Government Affairs, Rhonda Perkins
Auditors: ERNST & YOUNG LLP CLEVELAND

LOCATIONS

HQ: CHILDRENS HOSPITAL MEDICAL CENTER OF AKRON
1 PERKINS SQ, AKRON, OH 443081063
Phone: 330 543-1000
Web: WWW.AKRONCHILDRENS.ORG

COMPETITORS

Akron General Medical Center	OhioHealth
Aultman Health Foundation	Parma Community General Hospital
Lake Health	Robinson Memorial Hospital
Mercy Medical Center (NY)	Summa Health System
MetroHealth System	The Cleveland Clinic
Nationwide Children's Hospital	University Hospitals Health System

HISTORICAL FINANCIALS

Company Type: Private

Income Statement   FYE: December 31

	REVENUE ($ mil.)	NET INCOME ($ mil.)	NET PROFIT MARGIN	EMPLOYEES
12/15	747	47	6.3%	4,763
12/14	701	93	13.3%	—
12/13	623	80	13.0%	—
12/12	579	46	8.1%	—
Annual Growth	8.8%	0.3%	—	—

2015 Year-End Financials

Return on assets: 2.9%   Cash ($ mil.): 52
Return on equity: 6.3%
Current ratio: 1.40

CHILDRENS HOSPITAL PEDIATRIC ASSOCIATES, INC.

EXECUTIVES

Pres, William Tarvainen
Trustee, Mark Schuster
Trustee, Raif Geha
Auditors: BAKER NEWMAN & NOYES LC PORTL

LOCATIONS

HQ: CHILDRENS HOSPITAL PEDIATRIC ASSOCIATES, INC.
20 OVERLAND ST, BOSTON, MA 022153336
Phone: 617 919-2822
Web: WWW.CHILDRENSHOSPITAL.ORG

HISTORICAL FINANCIALS

Company Type: Private

Income Statement   FYE: September 30

	REVENUE ($ mil.)	NET INCOME ($ mil.)	NET PROFIT MARGIN	EMPLOYEES
09/17	289	15	5.2%	4
09/15	246	11	4.7%	—
09/14	241	10	4.3%	—
09/13	228	25	11.4%	—
Annual Growth	6.1%	(12.6%)	—	—

2017 Year-End Financials

Return on assets: 4.6%   Cash ($ mil.): 47
Return on equity: 5.2%
Current ratio: 5.20

CHRISTUS HEALTH ARK-LA-TEX

EXECUTIVES

Ceo-Pres, Chris Karam
Treas, Shawn Barnett
Vice President, Jason Rounds
Vice President, Glen Boles
Vice President, John Graham
Vice President, Pam Kennedy
Specialist, Janet Curry
Physician Assistant, Nazaneen Cauthron
Director, Jannice Phillips
Director, Javier Enriquez
Marketing Manager, Francine Francis

LOCATIONS

HQ: CHRISTUS HEALTH ARK-LA-TEX
2600 SAINT MICHAEL DR, TEXARKANA, TX 755035220
Phone: 903 614-1000
Web: WWW.CHRISTUSHEALTH.ORG

HISTORICAL FINANCIALS

Company Type: Private

Income Statement   FYE: June 30

	REVENUE ($ mil.)	NET INCOME ($ mil.)	NET PROFIT MARGIN	EMPLOYEES
06/16	305	20	6.8%	1,800
06/15	258	21	8.5%	—
06/14*	278	21	7.8%	—
05/14	243	20	8.3%	—
Annual Growth	12.1%	1.4%	—	—

*Fiscal year change

2016 Year-End Financials

Return on assets: 6.7%   Cash ($ mil.): 181
Return on equity: 6.8%
Current ratio: 9.60

CHRISTUS HEALTH INTERNATIONAL

In CHRISTUS there is no east or west but plenty of care nonetheless. The not-for-profit Catholic health care system operates about 350 medical facilities from its more than 60 hospitals including general hospitals and long-term acute care facilities to clinics and outpatient centers. It operates mostly in Louisiana and Texas where its hospitals are but also has facilities in Arkansas Georgia Iowa Missouri and New Mexico and in six states in Mexico and one in Chile. In addition to its acute care facilities CHRISTUS runs medical groups home health and hospice agencies and senior living facilities. Specialized services include oncology pediatrics rehabilitation and women's and children's health care.

Operations

In addition to its more than 30 hospitals CHRISTUS also operates about 20 long-term care facilities 175 clinics and outpatient centers and dozens of other "health ministries" including mobile clinics fitness centers and daycare centers for adults and children.

Geographic Reach

CHRISTUS has a dozen hospitals in Texas and Louisiana one in Puebla Mexico and one in Santiago Chile. Its clinics outpatient centers long-term care facilities (under the Dubois and Advanced Care names) are found in Texas Louisiana Iowa Georgia Missouri and New Mexico in the US and in the Mexican states of Chihuahua Coahuila Nuevo LeA?n Puebla San Luis PotosA and Tamaulipas.

Financial Performance

In 2013 CHRISTUS reported a 3% increase in revenue from $3.6 billion to $3.7 billion based on increased net patient and premium revenues. Net income was $261 million against net loss in 2012 due to an increase in investment returns.

Strategy

CHRISTUS has been expanding its Continuing Care division which includes non-acute care operations like home care hospice palliative care residential facilities and fitness centers.

Another goal of CHRISTUS Health is to reduce overcrowding and such misuses as patients being seen for routine illnesses in its emergency rooms. To that end and to make primary care a bit more accessible the company has opened immediate care clinics in a number of Texas Wal-Mart stores.

CHRISTUS Health has plans to expand the clinics into Wal-Marts in Louisiana.

CHRISTUS Health has taken other steps to try to offset some costs of indigent care including pushing for the establishment of hospital districts to pay for charity care costs in some of its markets. It has also sold some of it facilities.

The organization has been focused on growing its operations in Mexico where it operates about a dozen clinics in six states. CHRISTUS Health's Mexico operations are a majority-owned partnership with Monterrey-based Muguerza. The organization's main Monterrey facility became the first Mexican hospital to win accreditation from the Joint Commission International a unit of the organization that certifies US hospitals.

Because Mexican citizens overwhelmingly rely on public hospitals run by the national health care system CHRISTUS Muguerza markets itself as a "medical tourism" destination where Americans can go for cheaper and lower-hassle medical care. Services include acute and primary care dental care urgent care and post-surgical rehabilitation.

Company Background

CHRISTUS Health was formed through the 1999 merger of Incarnate Word Health System and Sisters of Charity Health System. Both systems have their roots in the religious order Sisters of Charity of the Incarnate Word founded when three French nuns arrived in Texas in 1866 to care for the poor and sick.

EXECUTIVES

Evp And Chief Clinical Officer, John A. Gillean
President And Ceo, Ernie W. Sadau
Evp And Chief Administrative Officer, Linda McClung
Svp And Cio, George S. Conklin
Evp And Coo, Jeffrey M. (Jeff) Puckett
Evp And Cfo, Randolph W. Safady
Evp And Chief Strategy And Health Network Officer, Paul Generale
Evp Corporate Services And Chief Human Resources Officer, Marty Margetts
President And Ceo Good Shepherd Hospital Longview, Todd Hancock
Chairman, Arthur M. Southam
Vice Chair, Maricela S. Moore
Auditors: ERNST & YOUNG LLP DALLAS TX

LOCATIONS

HQ: CHRISTUS HEALTH INTERNATIONAL
919 HIDDEN RDG, IRVING, TX 750383813
Phone: 469 282-2000
Web: WWW.CHRISTUSHEALTH.ORG

PRODUCTS/OPERATIONS

2015 Payor Mix

	% of total
Managed care organizations	47
Medicare	22
Self-pay	14
Medicaid	9
Commercial insurance	8
Total	**100**

2015 Revenues

	$ mil.	% of total
Patient services	3,233	90
Premium revenue	161	4
Other revenue	188	5
Equity in income of unconsolidated organizations	25	1
Total	**3,609**	**100**

Selected Facilities in Texas

CHRISTUS HomeCare - Corpus Christi
CHRISTUS HomeCare - Texarkana
CHRISTUS Hospital - St. Elizabeth
CHRISTUS Hospital - St. Mary
CHRISTUS Jasper Memorial Hospital
CHRISTUS Santa Rosa Alamo Heights Imaging Center

CHRISTUS Santa Rosa Ambulatory Surgery Center
CHRISTUS Santa Rosa Cancer Center
CHRISTUS Santa Rosa Children's Hospital
CHRISTUS Santa Rosa Hospital - City Centre
CHRISTUS Santa Rosa Hospital - Medical Center
CHRISTUS Santa Rosa Hospital - New Braunfels
CHRISTUS Santa Rosa Hospital - Westover Hills
CHRISTUS Santa Rosa Imaging Center
CHRISTUS Santa Rosa Outpatient Rehabilitation Center
CHRISTUS Santa Rosa Rehabilitation Hospital
CHRISTUS Santa Rosa Rehabilitation Services - Downtown
CHRISTUS Santa Rosa Rehabilitation Services - Medical Center
CHRISTUS Santa Rosa Wound Care and Hyperbaric Center - Downtown
CHRISTUS Santa Rosa Wound Care and Hyperbaric Center - Medical Center
CHRISTUS Spohn Family Center Northside
CHRISTUS Spohn Family Health Center
CHRISTUS Spohn Family Health Center Falfurrias
CHRISTUS Spohn Family Health Center Padre Island
CHRISTUS Spohn Family Health Center Robstown
CHRISTUS Spohn Family Health Center San Diego
CHRISTUS Spohn Family Health Center Westside
CHRISTUS Spohn Health System
CHRISTUS Spohn Hospital Alice
CHRISTUS Spohn Hospital Beeville
CHRISTUS Spohn Hospital Corpus Christi - Memorial
CHRISTUS Spohn Hospital Corpus Christi - Shoreline
CHRISTUS Spohn Hospital Corpus Christi - South
CHRISTUS Spohn Hospital Kleberg
CHRISTUS Spohn Medical Group - Obstetrics and Gynecology Associates
CHRISTUS St. Catherine Hospital
CHRISTUS St. John Hospital
CHRISTUS St. Michael Health System
CHRISTUS St. Michael Rehabilitation Hospital
CHRISTUS Transplant Institute
CHRISTUS Visiting Nurse Association - Houston
CHRISTUS Visiting Nurse Association - Nassau Bay
CHRISTUS Visiting Nurse Association - San Antonio
David Christopher Goldsbury Center for Children and Families
Dubuis Hospital of Beaumont
Dubuis Hospital of Bryan Texas
Dubuis Hospital of Corpus Christi
Dubuis Hospital of Houston Texas (long-term acute care)
Dubuis Hospital of Paris
Dubuis Hospital of Port Arthur Texas (long-term acute care)
Dubuis Hospital of Texarkana

Selected Other US Facilities

Advance Care Hospital of Fort Smith (Arkansas)
Advance Care Hospital of Hot Springs (Arkansas)
CHRISTUS Coushatta Health Care Center (Coushatta Louisiana)
CHRISTUS HomeCare - Jennings (Louisiana)
CHRISTUS HomeCare - Lake Charles (Louisiana)
CHRISTUS HomeCare - Shreveport (Louisiana)
CHRISTUS Hospice and Palliative Care - Alexandria (Louisiana)
CHRISTUS Schumpert Health System (Shreveport Louisiana)
CHRISTUS Schumpert Highland (Shreveport Louisiana)
CHRISTUS Schumpert St. Mary Place (Shreveport Louisiana)
CHRISTUS St. Frances Cabrini Hospital (Alexandria Louisiana)
CHRISTUS St. Patrick Hospital (Lake Charles Louisiana)
CHRISTUS St. Vincent (Santa Fe New Mexico)
Dubuis Hospital of Alexandria (Louisiana)
Dubuis Hospital of Lake Charles (Louisiana)
Dubuis Hospital of Shreveport (Louisiana)
Dubuis Hospital of St. Louis (Chesterfield Missouri)
Natchitoches Parish Hospital (Louisiana)
Southern Crescent Hospital for Specialty Care (Riverdale Georgia)

Selected Facilities in Mexico

CHRISTUS MUGUERZA Hospital Alta Especialidad (Monterrey Nuevo Leon)
CHRISTUS MUGUERZA Hospital Conchita (Monterrey Nuevo Leon)
CHRISTUS MUGUERZA Hospital Del Parque (Chihuahua)
CHRISTUS MUGUERZA Hospital Reynosa (Tamaulipas¸ C.P.)
CHRISTUS MUGUERZA Hospital Saltillo (Coahuila)

CHRISTUS MUGUERZA Hospital Sur (Monterrey Nuevo Leon)
CHRISTUS MUGUERZA Hospital UPAEP (Puebla)

COMPETITORS

Ascension Health
Catholic Health Initiatives
Community Health Systems
HCA
Intermountain Health Care
LifePoint Health
MD Anderson Cancer Center
Memorial Health Services
Memorial Hermann Healthcare
Mercy Health
Methodist Hospital System
St. Luke's Episcopal Hospital
Tenet Healthcare
Texas Children's Hospital
Universal Health Services
University of Utah Hospitals & Clinics

HISTORICAL FINANCIALS

Company Type: Private

Income Statement

FYE: June 30

	REVENUE ($ mil.)	NET INCOME ($ mil.)	NET PROFIT MARGIN	EMPLOYEES
06/16	4,212	149	3.6%	25,000
06/15	658	(44)	—	—
06/14	673	25	3.8%	—
06/13	646	124	19.3%	—
Annual Growth	86.7%	6.3%	—	—

2016 Year-End Financials

Return on assets: 11.0%
Return on equity: 3.6%
Current ratio: 1.20
Cash ($ mil.): 483

CHRISTUS SANTA ROSA HEALTH CARE CORPORATION

EXECUTIVES

Pres, Don Beeler
Pres, Patrick B Carrier
Dir, Melissa Krause
Coo, Renato Baciarelli
Cfo, Kenneth Kolb
Coordinator, Carl Zepeda
Coordinator, Amy Lopez
Chief of Emergency Room, Greg Roth
Chief of Medicine, Hugo Castaneda
Executive of Information Techn, Ron Love
Food Director, Hedar Almaznaai
Auditors: ERNST & YOUNG US LLP INDIANAP

LOCATIONS

HQ: CHRISTUS SANTA ROSA HEALTH CARE CORPORATION
333 N SANTA ROSA ST, SAN ANTONIO, TX 782073108
Phone: 210 704-2011
Web: WWW.CHRISTUSHEALTH.ORG

HISTORICAL FINANCIALS

Company Type: Private

Income Statement   FYE: June 30

	REVENUE ($ mil.)	NET INCOME ($ mil.)	NET PROFIT MARGIN	EMPLOYEES
06/15	656	(14)	—	3,700
06/14	635	6	1.1%	—
06/13	612	2	0.4%	—
06/10	577	(19)		—
Annual Growth	2.6%	—	—	—

2015 Year-End Financials

Return on assets: 8.5%   Cash ($ mil.): 2
Return on equity: (-2.2%)
Current ratio: 1.90

CHRISTUS TRINITY MOTHER FRANCES HEALTH SYSTEM

EXECUTIVES

Pres, Chris Glenney
Cmo, Steve Keuer
Coo, Jason Proctor
Cfo, Elizabeth Tulliam
Dir of Human Resources, Laura Lockhart
Office Manager, Karla Boles
It Manager, Gena King
Director, Daryl Pritchard
Clinic Manager III, Boyce Johnson
Direct of Sports Medicine, James Rapp
Director of Pastoral Care, Stephen Murray
Auditors: ERNST & YOUNG LLP DALLAS TX

LOCATIONS

HQ: CHRISTUS TRINITY MOTHER FRANCES HEALTH SYSTEM
800 E DAWSON ST, TYLER, TX 757012036
Phone: 903 593-8441
Web: WWW.CHRISTUSTMF.ORG

HISTORICAL FINANCIALS

Company Type: Private

Income Statement   FYE: June 30

	REVENUE ($ mil.)	NET INCOME ($ mil.)	NET PROFIT MARGIN	EMPLOYEES
06/17	789	42	5.4%	4,000
06/15	752	48	6.4%	—
Annual Growth	2.5%	(5.6%)	—	—

CHUGACH ALASKA CORPORATION

At the heart of Chugach Alaska Corporation is a vision of indigenous people running their own businesses on their own land. Chugach Alaska was formed following the activation of the Alaska Na-tive Claims Settlement Act (which was passed by the US Congress in 1971) to provide land management services for the 928000-acre Chugach region of Alaska. The company derives the bulk of its sales from oil and gas production mining commercial timber and tourist activities that occur in the region and from its engagement in military base construction projects at more than 30 locations in Alaska the US Pacific Northwest and the Western Pacific. Chugach Alaska's shareholders consist of Aleut Eskimo and Indian natives.

Operations

In 2011 the company's Chugach World Services unit secured a $32 million contract (with the option for an additional $33 million) for housing and maintenance operations at Naval Base Guam and Andersen Air Force Base Guam.

In late 2010 the Chugach Alaska Services unit won a renewal of its existing oil spill prevention and response contract with Alyeska Pipeline Service Company. The new contract to service the Alaska Pipeline runs from 2011 to 2016.

Geographic Reach

With operations in Alaska the Pacific Northwest and the Western Pacific the company has major offices in Alabama Alaska Hawaii and Nevada.

Financial Performance

To raise cash in 2013 Chugach Alaska sold its three-story former headquarters building in downtown Anchorage.

Strategy

Developing and sustaining multiple revenues streams has been a key to the company's growth. Chugach Alaska is looking to continue to grow its Alaskan gas natural gas projects while diversifying into markets that are not traditional for the company such as the niche market of environmentally responsible guided tourism.

Expanding its global engineering footprint in 2012 the company acquired bankrupt Hawaii-based engineering firm Heide & Cook LLC.

Company Background

Chugach Alaska was founded in 1972 as an Alaska Native Claims Settlement Act Corporation. A nine-person board of directors elected from the corporation's more than 2300 shareholders oversees Chugach Alaska's management and operations. The company has gone from filing bankruptcy protection in 1990 (in the wake of the Exxon Valdez oil spill and a major cannery fire) to generating about $1 billion in annual revenues.

EXECUTIVES

Executive Vice President And General Counsel, Melanie Osborne
Senior Vice President Of Operations, Scott Davis

LOCATIONS

HQ: CHUGACH ALASKA CORPORATION
3800 CNTRPINT DR STE 1200, ANCHORAGE, AK 99503
Phone: 907 563-8866
Web: WWW.CHUGACH-AK.COM

PRODUCTS/OPERATIONS

Selected Services

Base Operating Services
Construction Services
Educational Services
Engineering Services
IT/Telecommunications
Manufacturing Services
Oil and Gas Services

Selected Subsidiaries

Chugach Alaska Services Inc. (CASI)
Chugach Education Services Inc. (CESI)
Chugach Federal Solutions Inc. (CFSI)
Chugach Government Services Inc. (CGSI)
Chugach Industries Inc. (CII)
Chugach Information Technology Inc. (CITI)
Chugach Management Services Inc. (CMSI)
Chugach McKinley Inc. (CMI)
Chugach Support Services Inc. (CSSI)
Chugach Systems Integration Llc (CSI)
Chugach World Services Inc. (CWSI)
Heide & Cook LLC. (H&C)
Wolf Creek Federal Services Inc. (WCFS)

COMPETITORS

ConocoPhillips Alaska	Freegold Ventures
Doyon	Jacobs Engineering
Fluor	Sealaska

HISTORICAL FINANCIALS

Company Type: Private

Income Statement   FYE: December 31

	REVENUE ($ mil.)	NET INCOME ($ mil.)	NET PROFIT MARGIN	EMPLOYEES
12/17	919	20	2.3%	4,822
12/16	842	35	4.2%	—
12/15	758	22	3.0%	—
12/14	7	(12)		—
Annual Growth	387.6%	—	—	—

2017 Year-End Financials

Return on assets: 5.4%   Cash ($ mil.): 66
Return on equity: 2.3%
Current ratio: 2.00

CHULA VISTA ELEMENTARY SCHOOL DISTRICT

EXECUTIVES

Supt, Dr Francisco Escobedo
Cfo, Susan Fahle
President, Larry Cunningham
Vice President, Glendora Tremper
Fin Dir, Orcar Esquivel
Director, Olivia Guerrero
Public Information Director, Anthony Millican
Instructional Media Svcs Dir, Gloria Ciriza
Transportation Director, Theron Neal
Director, Joseph Dombrowski
Teacher, Sandy Pembleton

LOCATIONS

HQ: CHULA VISTA ELEMENTARY SCHOOL DISTRICT
84 E J ST, CHULA VISTA, CA 919106115
Phone: 619 425-9600
Web: WWW.CVESD.ORG

HISTORICAL FINANCIALS

Company Type: Private

Income Statement   FYE: June 30

	REVENUE ($ mil.)	NET INCOME ($ mil.)	NET PROFIT MARGIN	EMPLOYEES
06/17	365	11	3.2%	2,500
06/05	228	(28)	—	—
06/03	217	0	0.3%	—
06/02	0	0		—
Annual Growth	—	—	—	—

2017 Year-End Financials

Return on assets: 6.2%   Cash ($ mil.): 197
Return on equity: 3.2%
Current ratio: —

CIANBRO CORPORATION

One of the East Coast's largest civil and heavy industrial construction companies Cianbro welcomes requests from clients to help a brother out. Operating in a dozen sector markets in 40-plus states the employee-owned contractor specializes in modular construction marine and piling work transportation projects and pulp and paper construction projects. Other areas of expertise include chemical plants hydroelectric dams biotech and warehouses. Working with a fleet of 3500 owned equipment units Cianbro provides construction services from concept through implementation and works start-up commissioned and turn-key operations. Its clients have included L.L. Bean International Paper and the US government.

Operations

Cianbro specializes in civil structural mechanical electrical instrumentation fabrication and coating. While the company serves as a prime/general contractor and joint venture/partner Cianbro also acts as a construction manager subcontractor fabrication supplier and consultant for construction services. Its equipment fleet valued at nearly $150 million consists of about 3500 numbered pieces.

Cianbro works on projects in a dozen US markets (as of early 2016) including the Building (commercial and institutional industry); Industrial & Manufacturing; Infrastructure (bridges water and waste-water and marine projects); Oil Gas & Chemical (oil chemicals natural-gas and related facilities) and Power & Energy (power generation facilities).

Geographic Reach

Pittsfield Maine-based Cianbro works on projects in 42 US states. Its offices are in Baltimore; Bloomfield Connecticut; Pittsfield Maine; Brewer Maine; Portland Maine; and Georgetown Massachusetts.

Strategy

Cianbro continues to work on big projects around the US. In early 2016 after winning ABC National Excellence in Construction Awards on its Bates Bridge Replacement project in Massachusetts and its White Compressor Station Project in Pennsylvania it continued its work on the Hadley Falls Fish Passage project and the North Grand Island Bridges Rehabilitation project.

In 2015 it worked on the Holtwood Dam Sarah Mildred Long Bridge Replacement project the restoration of the historic A. Piatt Andrew Bridge in Gloucester and the EMMC modernization project among others. In 2014 Cianbro was chosen to build ESP for Maine's offshore Cape Wind project valued at more than $100 million.

Company Background

Four Cianchette brothers — Carl Ken Bud and Chuck — pooled their savings and used Chuck's 1934 pickup truck to found Cianbro in 1949.

The company's Starcon International business which it acquired in 2010 specialized in serving the refinery and petrochemical industries. Based in La Porte Texas Starcon has regional offices in Illinois California Louisiana and West Virginia.

EXECUTIVES

Chairman And Ceo, Peter G. (Pete) Vigue
President And Coo, Andi Vigue
Cfo, Aldo Servello
Vice President And General Manager For Northern New England Region, Charlie Cianchette
Auditors: BERRY DUNN MCNEIL & PARKER LL

LOCATIONS

HQ: CIANBRO CORPORATION
101 CIANBRO SQ, PITTSFIELD, ME 049676301
Phone: 207 487-3311
Web: WWW.CIANBRO.COM

COMPETITORS

American Bridge Company	KBR Building Group
Clark Construction Company	Louis Berger
Edward Kraemer & Sons	SW&B Construction
Fru-Con Construction	Sargent Corp
Jacobs Engineering	Skanska USA Civil
	Weeks Marine
	Yates Companies

HISTORICAL FINANCIALS

Company Type: Private

Income Statement | FYE: December 31

	REVENUE ($ mil.)	NET INCOME ($ mil.)	NET PROFIT MARGIN	EMPLOYEES
12/16	384	(6)	—	1,639
12/08	428	0	—	—
12/07	0	0	—	—
12/06	0	0	—	—
Annual Growth	—	—	—	—

2016 Year-End Financials

Return on assets: 11.0%
Return on equity: (-1.7%)
Current ratio: 1.10

Cash ($ mil.): 26

CINCINNATI PUBLIC SCHOOLS

EXECUTIVES

Spdt, Laura Mitchell
SEC, Denae Coco
Cfo-Treas, Jonathan Boid
Facilities, Michael L Burson
Reading Specialist, Angela Campos
Teacher, Chyla Barner
Coordinator, Melvina Stokes
Manager, Michelle Taylor
Manager, Kevin Hudson
Information Technology/Interne, Christine Shields
Teacher, Gary Favors
Auditors: CAUDILL & ASSOCIATES CPA POR

LOCATIONS

HQ: CINCINNATI PUBLIC SCHOOLS
2651 BURNET AVE, CINCINNATI, OH 452192551
Phone: 513 363-0000
Web: WWW.CPS-K12.ORG

HISTORICAL FINANCIALS

Company Type: Private

Income Statement | FYE: June 30

	REVENUE ($ mil.)	NET INCOME ($ mil.)	NET PROFIT MARGIN	EMPLOYEES
06/17	703	17	2.5%	7,070
06/16	650	13	2.1%	—
06/15	654	(0)	—	—
06/05	402	0	—	—
Annual Growth	4.8%	—	—	—

CIRCLE HEALTH, INC.

EXECUTIVES

Ceo, Joseph White
Manager, Pam Gordon
Team Lead, Greg Green
Project Manager, Marie Voltaire
Emergency Medicine, Rugg Christopher

LOCATIONS

HQ: CIRCLE HEALTH, INC.
295 VARNUM AVE, LOWELL, MA 018542134
Phone: 978 937-6000
Web: WWW.LOWELLGENERAL.ORG

HISTORICAL FINANCIALS

Company Type: Private

Income Statement | FYE: September 30

	REVENUE ($ mil.)	NET INCOME ($ mil.)	NET PROFIT MARGIN	EMPLOYEES
09/17	509	7	1.6%	3,000
09/16	0	(0)	—	—
Annual Growth	295	19	251.1%	—

2017 Year-End Financials

Return on assets: 19.4%
Return on equity: 1.6%
Current ratio: 0.90

Cash ($ mil.): 46

CITGO PETROLEUM CORPORATION

From the get-go CITGO Petroleum has been refining and marketing petroleum products including jet fuel diesel fuel heating oils and lubricants. It markets CITGO branded gasoline through about 6500 independent retail outlets in 28 US states mainly east of the Rockies. CITGO Petroleum owns oil refineries in Illinois Louisiana and Texas. The company has the refining capacity to process more than 749000 barrels per day. It markets more than 600 types of lubricants and sold 15.5 billion gallons of refined products in 2015. CITGO Petroleum is the operating subsidiary of PDV America itself a subsidiary of Venezuela's national oil company PDVSA.

Operations

In addition to its refineries CITGO Petroleum has almost 50 storage terminals (which together process more than 10 billion gallons of fuel per year) and access to an additional 140 facilities. It also has three fully-owned pipelines and six jointly owned pipelines.

Geographic Reach

The company is based in Houston and operates three refineries in Lemont Illinois; Corpus Christi Texas; and Lake Charles Louisiana; and three lubricant blending plants in Cicero Illinois; Oklahoma City and Atlanta.

Sales and Marketing

The company markets automotive fuels to independent marketers which sell to nearly 6000 branded retail outlets. It markets jet fuel directly to airlines. CITGO Petroleum produces a variety of agricultural automotive industrial and private label lubricants which are sold to independent distributors mass marketers and industrial customers. It also sells petrochemicals and industrial products directly to various manufacturers and industrial companies across the US.

Company Background

The company had an agreement to access the St. Croix Virgin Islands refinery jointly owned by PDVSA and US-based Hess but the parties shut down the HOVENSA refinery in 2012 due to poor market conditions and high operating expenses.

Growing its retail network in 2011 the company converted 42 locally owned gas station in Maine and New Hampshire to the CITGO brand.

That year CITGO Petroleum completed and started up a 42500 barrel-per day unit at its Corpus Christi Texas refinery to produce Ultra Low Sulfur Diesel.

One of CITGO Petroleum's public relations initiatives is that it annually provides low-cost heating oil to selected low income communities as a way to offset high fuel prices. In early 2011 the company supplied 132000 low-income households in 25 states as well as 250 tribal communities and 234 homeless shelters. That year it invested more than $75 million in contributions for community activities.

CITGO Petroleum traces its history to Cities Service Company founded in Oklahoma in 1910. PDVSA took control of the company in 1990. In 2010 Venezuelan President Hugo Chavez announced a long term interest in selling CITGO Petroleum in order to generate cash for parent company PDVSA but PDVSA scrapped the idea in 2014.

EXECUTIVES

Chairman President And Ceo, Alejandro Granado
Vp Finance And Treasurer, Maritza Villanueva
Vp Refining And General Manager Lake Charles Manufacturing Complex, Eduardo Assef
Vp Supply And Marketing, Gustavo Vel˜squez
Vp And General Manager Lemont Refinery, Jim Cristman
Vice President General Manager, Tomeu Vadell
Vice President And General Manager Corpus Christi Refinery, Randy Flowers
Vice President Manager Director, Bob Pennington
Vice President Supply Marketing, Fernando Valera
Vice President Finance, Jose Pereira
Auditors: KPMG LLP HOUSTON TEXAS

LOCATIONS

HQ: CITGO PETROLEUM CORPORATION
1293 ELDRIDGE PKWY, HOUSTON, TX 770771670
Phone: 832 486-4000
Web: WWW.CITGOLUBES.COM

PRODUCTS/OPERATIONS

Selected Products
Lubricants and Oils
Petrochemicals
Retail Gasoline

COMPETITORS

BP	Motiva Enterprises
CRI/Criterion Catalyst	Shell Oil Products
Chevron	Sunoco
ConocoPhillips	TransMontaigne
Exxon Mobil	Partners
Kimber Petroleum	Valero Energy
Marathon Petroleum	

HISTORICAL FINANCIALS

Company Type: Private

Income Statement

FYE: December 31

	REVENUE ($ mil.)	NET INCOME ($ mil.)	NET PROFIT MARGIN	EMPLOYEES
12/17	24,100	715	3.0%	4,000
12/16	19,914	234	1.2%	—
/	0	0	—	—
Annual Growth	—	—	—	—

2017 Year-End Financials

Return on assets: 6.4%   Cash ($ mil.): 276
Return on equity: 3.0%
Current ratio: 0.50

CITRUS VALLEY MEDICAL CENTER, INC.

EXECUTIVES

Pres-Ceo, Robert Curry
Coo, Elvia Foulke
Chief Operating Officer, Roger Sharma
Risk Management Director, Jill Jacobs
Corporate Director Finance, Debbie Cooper
Clinical Coordinator, Paul Morris
Director, Donna Brotman
Auditors: ERNST & YOUNG LLP LOS ANGELE

LOCATIONS

HQ: CITRUS VALLEY MEDICAL CENTER, INC.
1115 S SUNSET AVE, WEST COVINA, CA 917903940
Phone: 626 962-4011
Web: WWW.CVHP.ORG

HISTORICAL FINANCIALS

Company Type: Private

Income Statement

FYE: December 31

	REVENUE ($ mil.)	NET INCOME ($ mil.)	NET PROFIT MARGIN	EMPLOYEES
12/17	502	90	18.0%	3,500
12/16	452	43	9.5%	—
12/14	397	31	7.9%	—
12/12	384	22	5.8%	—
Annual Growth	5.5%	32.3%	—	—

2017 Year-End Financials

Return on assets: 5.5%   Cash ($ mil.): 14
Return on equity: 18.0%
Current ratio: 0.50

CITY OF ALEXANDRIA

EXECUTIVES

Mayor, Allison Silberberg
City Mgr, Mark Jinks
Deputy Cty Mgr, Emily A Baker
Senior Project Manager, Adrian King
Auditors: CLIFTONLARSONALLEN LLP ARLING

LOCATIONS

HQ: CITY OF ALEXANDRIA
301 KING ST, ALEXANDRIA, VA 223143211
Phone: 703 746-4000
Web: WWW.ALEXANDRIACITYWEBSITE.COM

HISTORICAL FINANCIALS

Company Type: Private

Income Statement

FYE: June 30

	REVENUE ($ mil.)	NET INCOME ($ mil.)	NET PROFIT MARGIN	EMPLOYEES
06/18	842	108	12.9%	2,375
06/16	751	15	2.0%	—
06/15	730	3	0.5%	—
06/14	0	0	—	—
Annual Growth	—	—	—	—

2018 Year-End Financials

Return on assets: —   Cash ($ mil.): 336
Return on equity: 12.9%
Current ratio: —

CITY OF BOSTON

EXECUTIVES

Mayor, Martin J Walsh
Assistant Director Office of H, Alysha Glazier
Marketing, Kate Sullivan
Controller, Lisa Obrien
H R Director, Vivian Leonard
Auditors: KPMG LLP

LOCATIONS

HQ: CITY OF BOSTON
1 CITY HALL STE 242, BOSTON, MA 022011020
Phone: 617 635-4545
Web: WWW.AFTMA.NET

HISTORICAL FINANCIALS

Company Type: Private

Income Statement

FYE: June 30

	REVENUE ($ mil.)	NET INCOME ($ mil.)	NET PROFIT MARGIN	EMPLOYEES
06/17	3,542	93	2.7%	18,760
06/16	3,393	138	4.1%	—
06/15*	3,278	79	2.4%	—
12/13	11	1	9.4%	—
Annual Growth	578.2%	344.2%	—	—

*Fiscal year change

CITY OF COLORADO SPRINGS

EXECUTIVES

Mgr, Lorne Kramer
Account Exec, Rebecca L Smith
Technology, Tiffany M Vaughn
Auditors: RUBINBROWN LLP DENVER CO

LOCATIONS

HQ: CITY OF COLORADO SPRINGS
107 N NEVADA AVE STE 300, COLORADO SPRINGS, CO 809031305
Phone: 719 385-2489
Web: WWW.SPRINGSGOV.COM

HISTORICAL FINANCIALS
Company Type: Private

Income Statement   FYE: December 31

	REVENUE ($ mil.)	NET INCOME ($ mil.)	NET PROFIT MARGIN	EMPLOYEES
12/16	387	34	8.9%	111
12/13	279	(2)	—	—
Annual Growth	11.6%	—	—	—

HISTORICAL FINANCIALS
Company Type: Private

Income Statement   FYE: September 30

	REVENUE ($ mil.)	NET INCOME ($ mil.)	NET PROFIT MARGIN	EMPLOYEES
09/17	281	(8)	—	2,100
09/16*	280	14	5.0%	—
12/15	275	23	8.7%	—
09/14	0	0	—	—
Annual Growth	—	—	—	—

*Fiscal year change

2017 Year-End Financials

Return on assets: 4.8%   Cash ($ mil.): 2
Return on equity: (-3.1%)
Current ratio: 0.40

Executive Officer, Eddie Carr
Purchasing Coordinator, John Paine
Council Member, William Carroll
Auditors: SMITH DUKES & BUCKALEW LLP M

LOCATIONS

HQ: CITY OF MOBILE
205 GOVERNMENT ST, MOBILE, AL 366020001
Phone: 251 208-7416
Web: WWW.CITYOFMOBILE.ORG

HISTORICAL FINANCIALS
Company Type: Private

Income Statement   FYE: September 30

	REVENUE ($ mil.)	NET INCOME ($ mil.)	NET PROFIT MARGIN	EMPLOYEES
09/16	302	7	2.6%	2,300
09/15	294	22	7.6%	—
09/09	239	(44)	—	—
09/07	0	0	—	—
Annual Growth	—	—	—	—

CITY OF HOPE MEDICAL FOUNDATION

EXECUTIVES

Prin, Robert W Stone
Auditors: ERNST & YOUNG US LLP IRVINE

LOCATIONS

HQ: CITY OF HOPE MEDICAL FOUNDATION
1500 DUARTE RD, DUARTE, CA 910103012
Phone: 626 256-4673
Web: WWW.CITYOFHOPE.ORG

HISTORICAL FINANCIALS
Company Type: Private

Income Statement   FYE: September 30

	REVENUE ($ mil.)	NET INCOME ($ mil.)	NET PROFIT MARGIN	EMPLOYEES
09/17	287	3	1.1%	1
09/16	248	12	4.8%	—
09/15	228	(11)	—	—
09/14	142	(1)	—	—
Annual Growth	26.4%	—	—	—

2017 Year-End Financials

Return on assets: 9.6%   Cash ($ mil.): 21
Return on equity: 1.1%
Current ratio: 1.80

CITY OF LONG BEACH

EXECUTIVES

Mayor, Robert Garcia
Mayor, Bob Foster
City Treas, David Nakamoto
Mayor, Robert G Foster
City, Robert E Shannon
Director Financial Management, Lori Ann Farrell
Document Specialist, Frederick Wagner
Information Department, Sergeant Bell
Project Manager, Teresa Gomez
City Manager, Patrick H West
Administrative Director, Roberto Uranga

LOCATIONS

HQ: CITY OF LONG BEACH
333 W OCEAN BLVD, LONG BEACH, CA 908024664
Phone: 562 570-6450
Web: WWW.CITYAUDITORLAURADOUD.COM

HISTORICAL FINANCIALS
Company Type: Private

Income Statement   FYE: September 30

	REVENUE ($ mil.)	NET INCOME ($ mil.)	NET PROFIT MARGIN	EMPLOYEES
09/17	716	9	1.3%	5,028
09/16	675	(1)	—	—
09/15	648	(119)	—	—
09/14	676	1	0.2%	—
Annual Growth	2.0%	97.4%	—	—

2017 Year-End Financials

Return on assets: 22.2%   Cash ($ mil.): 439
Return on equity: 1.3%
Current ratio: 1.10

CITY OF SANTA MONICA

EXECUTIVES

Mayor, Ed Winterer
Prin, Rod Gould
Coordinator, Melissa Lindley
Marketing Manager, Norma Angel
Information Specialist, Ivy Weston
Staff, Brian Mondragon
Coordinator, Diane Cancino
Information Specialist, Michelle Dimas
Staff, Constance Babos
Assistant, Terry White
Auditors: MACIAS GINI & O'CONNELL LLP L

LOCATIONS

HQ: CITY OF SANTA MONICA
1685 MAIN ST, SANTA MONICA, CA 904013248
Phone: 310 458-8281
Web: WWW.SANTA-MONICA.ORG

HISTORICAL FINANCIALS
Company Type: Private

Income Statement   FYE: June 30

	REVENUE ($ mil.)	NET INCOME ($ mil.)	NET PROFIT MARGIN	EMPLOYEES
06/17	450	(4)	—	2,100
06/16	453	27	6.0%	—
06/15	419	11	2.6%	—
06/08	394	(47)	—	—
Annual Growth	1.5%	—	—	—

CITY OF LAREDO

EXECUTIVES

Mayor, Pete Saenz
City Manager, Horacio De Leon Jr
City of Laredo Human Resources, Monica Flores
Chief of Police, Claudio Trevino Jr
Deputy City Manager, Cynthia Collazo
City Managers Office, Alejandra Quintanilla
Auditors: CANALES GARZA & BAUM PLLC C

LOCATIONS

HQ: CITY OF LAREDO
1110 HOUSTON ST, LAREDO, TX 780408019
Phone: 956 791-7308

CITY OF MOBILE

EXECUTIVES

Mayor, Sandy Stimpson
Council Member, Fred Richardson
Council Member, Thomas Sullivan
Council Member, Clinton L Johnson
Council Member, Reggie Copeland Sr
Principal, Ben Brooks

CITY OF STAMFORD

EXECUTIVES

Mayor, David Martin
Sergeant, Diedrich Hohn
Project Coordinator, Laura Labosky
Manager, Domenick Tramontozzi
Customer Staff, Frank Fedeli

Executive Assistant, Judith Isidro
Officer, Karen Cammarota
Human Resources, Melissa Wills
Manager, Robert Robitaille
Administrative Assistant, Alec Iogman
Superintendent, Earl Kim
Auditors: BLUM SHAPIRO & COMPANY PC

LOCATIONS

HQ: CITY OF STAMFORD
888 WASHINGTON BLVD, STAMFORD, CT 069012902
Phone: 203 977-4150
Web: WWW.CI.STAMFORD.CT.US

HISTORICAL FINANCIALS

Company Type: Private

Income Statement | | | | FYE: June 30

	REVENUE ($ mil.)	NET INCOME ($ mil.)	NET PROFIT MARGIN	EMPLOYEES
06/17	678	5	0.8%	2,878
06/16	648	29	4.5%	—
06/15	627	19	3.0%	—
06/14	628	(14)	—	—
Annual Growth	2.6%	—	—	—

2017 Year-End Financials

Return on assets: 4.0%
Return on equity: 0.8%
Current ratio: 1.40
Cash ($ mil.): 69

CITY UTILITIES OF SPRINGFIELD MO

City Utilities of Springfield Missouri springs to action with multiple services and products. The multi-utility supplies electricity natural gas and water for residents and businesses in the southwestern Missouri town. It has about 1870 miles of power lines and 1260 miles of natural gas mains serves about 110000 electric customers 82000 natural gas customers and 81000 water customers. It also operates the municipal bus system which has 25 regular street buses and five demand/response buses and serves about 790 broadband contracts through SpringNet Telecommunications. City Utilities of Springfield has a service region of 320 sq. ml. and serves a base population of 229000.

Geographic Reach

The multi-utility's service territory covers Springfield Missouri portions of Greene county and a part of northern Christian county.

Financial Performance

In 2012 City Utilities of Springfield's revenues declined by 4% primarily due to milder-than-usual weather crimping demand (heating degree days were 21% below normal). This drop was partially offset by an increase in revenues from its Transportation Telco/Broadband and Water segments. In 2012 revenues from electric retail sales increased 5% thanks to rate increases. However off-system sales volumes decreased 38%.

Natural gas sales decreased 15% as a direct result of lower volumes due to a mild winter and lower natural gas prices.

Water retail sales increased in 2012 to $36.4 million as compared to $32.8 million in 2011 thanks in part to lower-than-usual rainfall.

Telco/Broadband had 25 new SpringNet customers billed in 2012 and saw its revenues rise by 6%.

Strategy

With coal-fired plants accounting for 62% of its power generation capacity City Utilities of Springfield is looking to boost its green power options. The utility offers its customers the option of using renewable wind-generated electricity imported to Springfield from a Kansas wind farm (the 50 MW Smoky Hills Wind Farm in Salina).

In 2013 City Utilities of Springfield was working on a deal to buy solar power from Missouri's largest solar energy farm - a 5 MW plant on a 40 acre site in eastern Greene County near to the multi-utility's McCartney natural gas turbine between Springfield and Strafford.

Company Background

The utility traces its origins to the gas works of Springfield Gas Lighting Company which opened in 1874. In 1945 Springfield Gas and Electric was bought by the City of Springfield resulting in the creation of City Utilities of Springfield.

EXECUTIVES

Vice President Customer Sales And Service,
Marsha McClanahan
Vice President, Andrew Foster
Secretary, Sharon Gott
Auditors: BKD LLP SPRINGFIELD MISSOUR

LOCATIONS

HQ: CITY UTILITIES OF SPRINGFIELD MO
301 E CENTRAL ST, SPRINGFIELD, MO 658023858
Phone: 417 863-9000
Web: WWW.CITYUTILITIES.NET

HISTORICAL FINANCIALS

Company Type: Private

Income Statement | | | | FYE: September 30

	REVENUE ($ mil.)	NET INCOME ($ mil.)	NET PROFIT MARGIN	EMPLOYEES
09/17	432	34	8.1%	980
09/16	417	41	9.9%	—
Annual Growth	3.7%	(15.8%)	—	—

2017 Year-End Financials

Return on assets: 3.8%
Return on equity: 8.1%
Current ratio: 0.70
Cash ($ mil.): 36

CLARCOR INC.

CLARCOR cleans up with filters. The company's industrial and environmental filtration unit makes air and antimicrobial filters for commercial industrial and residential buildings along with filters used in industrial processes. Brands include Airguard Facet ATI Transweb UAS Keddeg MKI TF-Sand Purolator. Companies in CLARCOR's engine and mobile filtration business make products under brands such as Baldwin Hastings Filters and Clark that filter the air oil fuel coolant and hydraulic fluids. In 2017 in order to expand its filtration portfolio Parker-Hannifin acquired CLARCOR for about $4.3 billion.

Operations

CLARCOR operates in two industry segments: Engine/Mobile Filtration and Industrial/Environmental Filtration.

The Engine/Mobile Filtration segment (about 60% of total revenue) makes and sells filtration products for engines used in stationary power generation and for engines in mobile equipment applications including trucks automobiles buses and locomotives and marine construction industrial mining and agricultural equipment. The company manufactures and sells both 'First-fit' filtration systems and replacement products such as oil air fuel coolant transmission and hydraulic filters.

The company's Industrial/Environmental Filtration segment (about 40%) centers around the manufacturing and marketing of filtration products used in industrial and commercial processes and in buildings and infrastructures of various types. Its liquid process filtration products include specialty industrial process liquid filters; filters for pharmaceutical processes and beverages; and filtration systems and filters for the oil and natural gas industry sewage treatment and water recycling and other industrial uses.

Its air filtration products represent air filters and systems including advanced medias and treatments and high efficiency first-fit systems used in gas turbine power generation systems heavy industrial manufacturing processes thermal power plants commercial buildings hospitals general factories residential buildings paint spray booths medical devices and facilities motor vehicle systems aircraft cabins clean rooms compressors and compressor stations.

Geographic Reach

CLARCOR makes and sells its products worldwide and more than 30% of the company's sales come from outside the US. The company has manufacturing distribution and service facilities in US Brazil China France Germany India Italy Malaysia Netherlands the UAE the UK Japan and Mexico.

Sales and Marketing

The company's filtration products are sold through independent distributors and dealers for OEMs as well as directly to end users.

The 10 largest customers of the Engine/Mobile Filtration segment accounted for 35% of 2016 fiscal year (November year end) segment sales.

The 10 largest customers of the Industrial/Environmental Filtration segment accounted for more than 15% of that segment's revenue.

Financial Performance

In fiscal 2016 CLARCOR's revenue declined by 6% ($91 million) due to a number of factors including the 2015 divestiture of J.L. Clark (the former Packaging Segment) which accounted for $40.9 million; decreased net sales volume (due to lower industrial demand) of $26.3 million in the Industrial/Environmental Filtration segment; and $25.1 from a negative currency exchange rate impact due to the strong dollar.

CLARCOR's net income grew by 3.4% to $139.3 million primarily due to Other net income of $20.7 million (flat in 2015) which primarily reflected $27.3 million from 3M to settle a patent litigation case.

Net cash provided by operating activities increased by $131.7 million in 2016 to $285.4 million. Some $18.1 million of this increase came from the 3M patent litigation award and the remainder primarily from cost cutting activities including lowering inventory levels by $36.4 million (resulting in a $58.5 million improvement in cash from operations). The company also reported a $26 million impact from lower cash taxes paid driven by the timing of tax payments in 2016 and 2015.

Strategy

Following the closing of its acquisition by Parker Hannifin in 2017 CLARCOR will be combined with Parker's Filtration Group to form a diverse global filtration business.

Restructuring to focus on two core business lines in 2015 CLARCOR sold its J.L. Clark business (the former Packaging Segment) to CC Industries.

Mergers and Acquisitions

In addition to organic growth CLARCOR has pursued a strategy of expanding its portfolio through acquisitions.

To support its global growth and innovation activities in 2016 the company acquired certain assets of US-based FibeRio Technology (a technology company focused on the research development and commercialization of performance fabric and filtration media) for $11.9 million. That year its CLARCOR Industrial Air division acquired TDC Filter Manufacturing a top US manufacturer and supplier of pleated filter bags dust collection cartridges and gas turbine air filters for $11 million.

In 2014 the company acquired Stanadyne's diesel fuel filtration business for $327.7 million and changed its name to CLARCOR Engine Mobile Solutions. That year it also bought Filter Resources Inc. Filtration Inc. and Fabrication Specialties Inc. for $21.9 million.

Company Background

In 2013 CLARCOR purchased the air filtration business of General Electric's power and water division for $260.3 million.

In 2013 CLARCOR announced plans to invest $40 million for subsidiary Baldwin Filters Inc. to build a new 400000 sq. ft. warehouse and distribution center adjacent to Baldwin's manufacturing facility in Kearney Nebraska.

In 2012 the company acquired Modular Engineering Pty Ltd. an Australian manufacturer of natural gas filtration products as well as a distributor of aftermarket elements. Modular a longtime supplier to CLARCOR's PECOFacet division became part of the division. PECOFacet is included in the company's Industrial/Environmental Filtration segment. Modular produces skid-mounted equipment for the natural gas industry in the Asia/Pacific region and expands CLARCOR's presence in that region in both manufacturing and aftermarket sales.

In 2011 the company purchased one of its suppliers of filtration media Transweb LLC. New Jersey-based Transweb manufactures and supplies media used in end-market applications including respirators and HVAC filters.

CLARCOR was founded in 1904 and reincorporated in 1969.

EXECUTIVES

Senior Business Development Officer, Sam Ferrise, $400,795 total compensation
Vp Finance And Cfo, David J. Fallon, $394,808 total compensation
Chairman President And Ceo, Christopher L. Conway, $689,615 total compensation
Group President Clarcor Industrial Air, Keith A. White
President Engine And Mobile Group, Jacob Thomas
Vice President Business Systems, John Campbell
Vice President Strategic Business Systems, Chris Schechter
Vice President And Managing Director, Rahul Dharmadhikary
Vice President Of Business Development, Naimesh Dave
Vice President Operations, Nick Salimbene
Vice President Human Resources, Pam K Kile
Vice President Operations, Richard Jensen
Vice President Advanced Product And Process Engineering, Thomas B Green
National Account Manager, Heather Swanson
Vice President Finance, Dennis M Haun
Vice President Innovation Product And Process Engineering, Monte A Crabtree
Vice President Sales National Accounts And Exports, Andrew Sisler
Vice President General Manager, Jeff Orlando
Vice President Strategic Accounts, David Amato

Vice President Engineering Industrial Filtration, Mark Gerken
Vice President Innovation Product And Process Engineering, Monte Crabtree
Vice President Human Resources, Pam Kile
Auditors: PRICEWATERHOUSECOOPERS LLP NA

LOCATIONS

HQ: CLARCOR INC.
840 CRESCENT CENTRE DR # 600, FRANKLIN, TN 370674687
Phone: 615 771-3100
Web: WWW.CLARCORWATER.COM

Sales 2016

	$ mil.	% of total
United States	944	68
Europe	152	11
Asia	144	10
Other International	148	11
Total	**1,389**	**100**

PRODUCTS/OPERATIONS

sales 2016

	% of total
Industrial/Environmental Filtration	58
Engine/Mobile Filtration	42
Total	**100**

COMPETITORS

Crown Holdings	EMD Millipore
Cummins	ESCO Technologies
Dana	Pall Corporation
Delphi Automotive Systems	Parker-Hannifin
Donaldson Company	W rth Group

HISTORICAL FINANCIALS

Company Type: Private

Income Statement FYE: November 30

	REVENUE ($ mil.)	NET INCOME ($ mil.)	NET PROFIT MARGIN	EMPLOYEES
11/16	1,389	139	10.0%	5,773
11/15	1,481	134	9.1%	—
11/14	1,512	144	9.5%	—
11/13	1,130	118	10.5%	—
Annual Growth	7.1%	5.6%	—	—

2016 Year-End Financials

Return on assets: 6.4%
Return on equity: 10.0%
Current ratio: 1.80

Cash ($ mil.): 134

CLARK COUNTY SCHOOL DISTRICT

EXECUTIVES

Supt, Patrick Skorkowsky
Coordinator, Monica Robles
Executive of Information Techn, Alisha Bragg
Coordinator, Ransom Terrell
Project Coordinator, Steven Holyoak
Executive of Information Techn, Chris Ahrens
Executive Officer, Teresa Holden
Executive of Information Techn, Robin Thomas
Security Staff, Tashaan Swayne
Information Specialist, Jonathan Swaby
Program Coordinator, Sherie Moore
Auditors: EIDE BAILLY LLP LAS VEGAS NE

LOCATIONS

HQ: CLARK COUNTY SCHOOL DISTRICT
5100 W SAHARA AVE, LAS VEGAS, NV 891463406
Phone: 702 799-5000
Web: WWW.CCSD.NET

HISTORICAL FINANCIALS

Company Type: Private

Income Statement FYE: June 30

	REVENUE ($ mil.)	NET INCOME ($ mil.)	NET PROFIT MARGIN	EMPLOYEES
06/18	3,313	134	4.1%	37,361
06/17	3,178	(112)	—	—
06/16	3,048	328	10.8%	—
06/15	2,971	(52)	—	—
Annual Growth	3.7%	—	—	—

CLARK EQUIPMENT COMPANY

EXECUTIVES

Ceo-Pres, Richard Goldsbury
Customer Staff, Phil Bogner
Design Engineer, Chris Gillund
Manager, Christopher Young
Executive of Sales, Dirk Pettit
Vice-President, Joel Honeyman
Administrator, Glenn Comegys
Manager, Justin Odegaard
Information Technology Project, Chad Huffman
Sales Staff, Heather Messmer
Manager, Paul White
Auditors: DELOITTE & TOUCHE LLP

LOCATIONS

HQ: CLARK EQUIPMENT COMPANY
250 E BEATON DR, WEST FARGO, ND 580782656
Phone: 701 241-8700

HISTORICAL FINANCIALS

Company Type: Private

Income Statement FYE: December 31

	REVENUE ($ mil.)	NET INCOME ($ mil.)	NET PROFIT MARGIN	EMPLOYEES
12/17	2,543	174	6.9%	5,000
12/16	2,415	166	6.9%	—
12/15	0	0	—	—
12/14	2,539	492	19.4%	—
Annual Growth	0.1%	(29.3%)	—	—

2017 Year-End Financials

Return on assets: 14.8%
Return on equity: 6.9%
Current ratio: 0.60

Cash ($ mil.): 127

CLASSIC STAR GROUP, LP

EXECUTIVES

Gen Ptnr, Michael Ali
Ptnr, Gulamali Barwani
Ptnr, Muradali Barwani
Contrl, Chethan Shah
Credit Manager, Barbara Rhodes
Auditors: MWH GROUP PC WICHITA FALLS

LOCATIONS

HQ: CLASSIC STAR GROUP, LP
6324 EDEN DR, HALTOM CITY, TX 761176129
Phone: 817 834-2868
Web: WWW.CLASSICSTARGROUP.COM

HISTORICAL FINANCIALS

Company Type: Private

Income Statement				FYE: December 31
	REVENUE ($ mil.)	NET INCOME ($ mil.)	NET PROFIT MARGIN	EMPLOYEES
12/15	404	3	0.8%	17
12/14	591	2	0.5%	—
12/13	639	3	0.5%	—
12/12	555	2	0.4%	—
Annual Growth	(10.0%)	18.2%	—	—

2015 Year-End Financials

Return on assets: 1.9%   Cash ($ mil.): 1
Return on equity: 0.8%
Current ratio: 1.00

CLAY ELECTRIC COOPERATIVE, INC.

Clay Electric Cooperative covers a lot of ground in Florida. The utility distributes electricity to 14 counties in the northeastern part of the state including the suburbs of Jacksonville and Gainesville. It delivers power to about 170000 residential commercial and industrial members over more than 13000 miles of distribution and transmission lines. The consumer-owned utility offers electronic funds transfer average billing and a seniors' payment plan to residential customers and backup diesel power generation and special rate plans to businesses. The consumer-owned utility has a stake in Seminole Electric Cooperative which provides generation services to Clay Electric and nine other cooperatives.

Geographic Reach

The cooperative serves customers in the Florida counties of Alachua Baker Bradford Clay Columbia Flagler Gilchrist Lake Levy Marion Putnam Suwannee Union and Volusia. It has six district offices (Gainesville Keystone Heights Lake City Orange Park Palatka and Salt Springs).

Strategy

To encourage conservation and green energy use the coop also supports customers' installation of small photovoltaic solar displays on their own homes through an arrangement whereby Seminole Electric purchases electricity generated and delivered to Clay Electric from any of its members' qualifying solar power systems.

Like other non-profit cooperatives Clay Electric refunds any annual profits to its members as credit refunds. In 2012 the company made $5.25 million in refunds available to its members or about $19 a customer.

That year Clay Electric announced that it would further cut its members' bills due to weak natural gas prices lowering the costs of power production from its gas-fired plants.

Company Background

The company was founded in 1937 as part of a national rural electrification drive.

EXECUTIVES

Ceo, Richard K Davis
Director of Finance, Mark Maxwell
District Manager, Dale Furlong
Senior Engineer, Michael Grantham
Project Manager, Tammy Edinger
Coordinator, Neal Wilkerson
Information Technology/Interne, Corry Blankenship
Human Resources Director, Chip Gray
Network Technician, Tom Rozier
Coordinator, Lisa Richardson
Coordinator, Steve Howard
Auditors: NICHOLS CAULEY & ASSOCIATES

LOCATIONS

HQ: CLAY ELECTRIC COOPERATIVE, INC.
225 W WALKER DR, KEYSTONE HEIGHTS, FL
326567617
Phone: 352 473-8000
Web: WWW.CLAYELECTRIC.COM

COMPETITORS

Florida Power & Light	Gainesville Regional
Florida Public	Utilities
Utilities	JEA

HISTORICAL FINANCIALS

Company Type: Private

Income Statement				FYE: December 31
	REVENUE ($ mil.)	NET INCOME ($ mil.)	NET PROFIT MARGIN	EMPLOYEES
12/17	355	16	4.6%	444
12/16	359	17	4.9%	—
12/15	362	22	6.3%	—
12/14	368	25	6.8%	—
Annual Growth	(1.2%)	(13.5%)	—	—

2017 Year-End Financials

Return on assets: 1.3%   Cash ($ mil.): 2
Return on equity: 4.6%
Current ratio: 0.20

CLEAR LAKE REGIONAL MEDICAL CENTER, INC.

EXECUTIVES

Ceo, Michael Roussos
Director, Irene Taylor
Diagnostic Radiologist, John Hyun
Director of Mis/Is, Ley Sampson
Administrator, Sharon Holdorff
Quality Assurance Director, Carol Heckenkemper
Diagnostic Radiologist, Larry Schock
Diagnostic Radiologist, Steven Gerguis
Board Member, Eduardo Ramirez
Director, Glenda Parish

LOCATIONS

HQ: CLEAR LAKE REGIONAL MEDICAL CENTER, INC.
500 W MEDICAL CENTER BLVD, WEBSTER, TX
775984220
Phone: 713 371-5000
Web: WWW.CLEARLAKERMC.COM

HISTORICAL FINANCIALS

Company Type: Private

Income Statement				FYE: December 31
	REVENUE ($ mil.)	NET INCOME ($ mil.)	NET PROFIT MARGIN	EMPLOYEES
12/16	476	54	11.5%	720
12/15	469	56	12.0%	—
Annual Growth	1.5%	(2.6%)	—	—

2016 Year-End Financials

Return on assets: 2.2%   Cash ($ mil.): —
Return on equity: 11.5%
Current ratio: —

CLEVELAND MUNICIPAL SCHOOL DISTRICT

EXECUTIVES

Ceo, Eric Gordon
Coo, Patrick Zohn
Chb, Denise W Link
Cfo, John Scanlan
Exec Dir, Megan Obryan
Executive Assistant, Stephanie Hobbs
Coordinator, Tyanna Blanchard
Executive Director, Jessica Baldwin
Registered Nurse, Vanessa Jones
Coordinator, Carolyn Hoover
Coordinator, Chris Callender
Auditors: DAVE YOST-AUDITOR OF STATE CL

LOCATIONS

HQ: CLEVELAND MUNICIPAL SCHOOL DISTRICT
1111 SUPERIOR AVE E # 1800, CLEVELAND, OH
441142500
Phone: 216 838-0000
Web: WWW.CLEVELANDMETROSCHOOLS.ORG

HISTORICAL FINANCIALS

Company Type: Private

Income Statement				FYE: June 30
	REVENUE ($ mil.)	NET INCOME ($ mil.)	NET PROFIT MARGIN	EMPLOYEES
06/17	854	(71)	—	9,500
06/16	902	18	2.1%	—
06/11	888	38	4.3%	—
06/09	914	(49)	—	—
Annual Growth	(0.9%)	—	—	—

2017 Year-End Financials

Return on assets: 2.8%   Cash ($ mil.): 1
Return on equity: (-8.3%)
Current ratio: —

CLIFTONLARSONALLEN LLP

CliftonLarsonAllen (CLA) is all about the CPAs. Boasting more than $3 billion in client assets under management and 500 partners CLA is the US' 10th-largest accounting firm that serves privately-owned firms and their principals along with not-for-profits and government agencies. Also serving as a financial advisory and business consultancy CLA is organized as a holding company with three main business segments: Public Accounting Wealth Management and Outsourcing Services. It mostly serves clients in the agribusiness financial employee benefit plan healthcare manufacturing and government sectors. With 1800 CPAs and nearly 3000 other professionals the firm's annual revenues exceed $750 million.

Operations
The company's service areas include audit accounting tax consulting outsourcing and wealth advisory. Its investment advisory services are conducted through CliftonLarsonAllen Wealth Advisors LLC. CLA serves clients outside the US through its affiliations with Nexia International.

Geographic Reach
Minnesota-based CLA boasts nearly 100 offices in about 20 states and the District of Columbia.

Sales and Marketing
CLA which counts more than 150000 clients serves privately-held businesses individuals not-for-profits and governmental entities. Its major client groups include agribusiness and cooperatives dealerships employee benefit plans federal government financial institutions healthcare manufacturing and distribution companies as well as state and local governments.

Financial Performance
CLA's revenue has risen more than 36% since the end of 2012. The company's revenue reached $750 million at the end of 2015.

Strategy
CLA has been acquiring local accounting and consulting firms around the US to expand into new geographic markets while bolstering its service offerings and client list.

Mergers and Acquisitions
In February 2016 CLA bought Bruner Cox LLP the 10th-largest accounting firm in Northeast Ohio (according to the Crain's 2016 Book of Lists). The deal was expected to take effect in June.

In November 2015 the firm purchased Pittsburgh-based KFMR Katz McMurtry PC the region's 19th-largest accounting firm.

In April 2014 the company acquired accounting and consulting firm Illinois Agricultural Auditing Association expanding its presence in Illinois to more than a dozen locations with the addition of IAAA's Bloomington/Normal and Springfield locations.

In January 2014 CLA purchased several companies to expand its consultancy including: Massachusetts consulting firm Bankers Advisory Inc.; Maryland-based OneSource Professional Services Group a consulting technology accounting and tax services firm; and Sullivan Rogers & Company a Massachusetts CPA and consulting firm dedicated to the state and local government market.

In 2013 in looking to take advantage of the implementation of healthcare reform in the US CLA acquired Idaho-based national healthcare consulting firm Beck Advisory Group. That year it also bought accounting firm Monaghan Group boosting its outsourcing practice and services in the Charlotte North Carolina area as well as Indiana-based Nonprofit Financial Solutions a firm focused on providing nonprofits with CFO consulting and outsourcing services.

Company Background
CLA was formed in 2011 by the merger of Clifton Gunderson and LarsonAllen. Prior to the pairing both companies had been active in expanding across the country by purchasing smaller firms and parts of other firms.

EXECUTIVES

Coo, David E. Bailey
Cfo, Sharon Ten Clay
Cio, Steve Noble
Ceo Cliftonlarsonallen Wealth Advisors Llc, Tony Hallada
Ceo And Chief Business Officer, Denny Schleper

LOCATIONS

HQ: CLIFTONLARSONALLEN LLP
220 S 6TH ST STE 300, MINNEAPOLIS, MN 554021418
Phone: 612 376-4500
Web: WWW.CLIFTONLARSONALLEN.COM

Selected Locations
Arizona
California
Colorado
Florida
Idaho
Illinois
Indiana
Iowa
Maryland
Massachusetts
Michigan
Minnesota
Mississippi
Missouri
New Jersey
New Mexico
New York
North Carolina
Ohio
Pennsylvania
Texas
Virginia
Washington
Wisconsin

PRODUCTS/OPERATIONS

Selected Services:
Audit and assurance
Consulting
CLA Intuition financial modeling
Employee benefit plans
Executive search
Forensic
Information security
Intacct software
Litigation support
Risk management
Technology
Transaction support
Valuation
International
Outsourci

COMPETITORS

BDO	Grant Thornton
BKD LLP	KPMG L.L.P.
Baker Tilly Virchow Krause	Moore Stephens International
Crowe Horwath	PricewaterhouseCoopers UK
Deloitte & Touche	
Eide Bailly	RSM US
Ernst & Young LLP	SVA

HISTORICAL FINANCIALS
Company Type: Private

Income Statement — FYE: December 31

	REVENUE ($ mil.)	NET INCOME ($ mil.)	NET PROFIT MARGIN	EMPLOYEES
12/16	755	226	30.1%	4,786
12/15	650	170	26.3%	—
12/14	598	163	27.3%	—
12/13	563	154	27.5%	—
Annual Growth	10.3%	13.6%	—	—

2016 Year-End Financials
Return on assets: 0.5%
Return on equity: 30.1%
Current ratio: 2.40
Cash ($ mil.): 11

COACHELLA VALLEY UNIFIED SCHOOL DISTRICT

EXECUTIVES

Spdt, Edwin Gomez
Fin Mgr, Ray Rivas
Facilities Specialist, Manuel Leal
Director of Activities, Megan C Ramirez
Auditors: VAVRINEKTRINEDAY & CO LLP RAN

LOCATIONS

HQ: COACHELLA VALLEY UNIFIED SCHOOL DISTRICT
87225 CHURCH ST, THERMAL, CA 922748901
Phone: 760 399-5137
Web: WWW.CVUSD.US

HISTORICAL FINANCIALS
Company Type: Private

Income Statement — FYE: June 30

	REVENUE ($ mil.)	NET INCOME ($ mil.)	NET PROFIT MARGIN	EMPLOYEES
06/17	283	20	7.3%	1,189
06/16	272	38	14.2%	—
06/13	1	(0)	—	—
06/12	181	(1)	—	—
Annual Growth	9.4%	—	—	—

COAST CITRUS DISTRIBUTORS

EXECUTIVES

Chb-Pres-Ceo, James M Alvarez
SEC, Margarita Alvarez
Transportation Associate, Norma Pequeno
Administrator, Erica Alvarez
Manager Operations, Miguel Lara
Operations Manager, Miguel Liar
Chief Operations Officer, Nick Alvarez
Credit Manager, Pattie Arias

LOCATIONS

HQ: COAST CITRUS DISTRIBUTORS
7597 BRISTOW CT, SAN DIEGO, CA 921547419
Phone: 619 661-7950
Web: WWW.COASTCITRUS.COM

COMPETITORS

A. Duda & Sons	Fresh Del Monte
Albert's Organics	Produce
American Fruit &	FreshPoint
Produce	General Produce
Borg Produce	Interfresh
Chiquita Brands	The Oppenheimer Group

HISTORICAL FINANCIALS

Company Type: Private

Income Statement

FYE: December 30

	REVENUE ($ mil.)	NET INCOME ($ mil.)	NET PROFIT MARGIN	EMPLOYEES
12/17	293	1	0.7%	320
12/16*	290	1	0.6%	—
01/15	331	2	0.7%	—
12/11	297	3	1.0%	—
Annual Growth	(0.3%)	(6.8%)	—	—

*Fiscal year change

2017 Year-End Financials

Return on assets: 5.6%
Return on equity: 0.7%
Current ratio: 1.40

Cash ($ mil.): 4

COBANK, ACB

You could say CoBank is dependent on its rural customers and vice versa. A member of the Farm Credit System (which is regulated by the FCA) the $110 billion cooperative bank provides seasonal and wholesale loans to agribusinesses as well as to rural power water and communications cooperatives across the US. The bank also leases vehicles farming equipment and agricultural facilities through various Farm Credit System affiliates. Its core agribusiness customers range from local and regional farmers' cooperatives to multinational food companies. It has counted Land O' Lakes Blue Diamond Almonds and National Beef as among its larger customers. Formed in 1989 CoBank merged with US AgBank in early 2012.

Operations

CoBank operates three main business segments: Strategic Relationships Agribusiness and Rural Infrastructure. Its Strategic Relationships loans made up 50% of its $80 billion loan portfolio at the end of 2014 while Agribusiness and Rural Infrastructure made up another 30% and 20% respectively.

About 76% of CoBank's total revenue came from loan interest in 2014 while another 16% came from interest income on investment securities. The rest of its revenue came from fee income (5% of revenue) prepayment income (1%) and other miscellaneous sources.

Geographic Reach

Based in Colorado the bank operates 15 regional offices throughout the US including locations in Iowa Georgia Texas Connecticut Kansas Missouri and Kentucky. It also has an international office in Singapore.

Sales and Marketing

CoBank mainly serves clients in rural America in the agribusiness water communications and power sectors.

Financial Performance

CoBank's annual revenues and profits have been rising over the past several years thanks to steady loan asset growth across all three of its target loan types (Strategic Relationships Agribusiness and Rural Infrastructure).

The bank's revenue jumped 5% to $2.2 million during 2014 mostly thanks to higher average loan volume and increased earnings from a strengthened balance sheet. CoBank's lending business grew with food and agribusiness customers Farm Credit Association customers and rural energy and communications customers which all in turn contributed to its top-line growth.

Revenue growth in 2014 drove CoBank's net income up 6% to $904.3 million for the year. The bank's operating cash levels dipped 2% to $883.1 million during the year due to unfavorable working capital changes related to accrued interest balance changes.

EXECUTIVES

Cfo, David P. Burlage
Chief Risk Officer, Lori L. O'Flaherty
Coo, Ann Trakimas
Evp Banking Services Group, Antony M. Bahr
Svp And Cio, James R. Bernsten
Evp Regional Agribusiness Banking Group, Amy H. Gales
Central Region President Regional Agribusiness Banking Group, Mike Hechtner
Chief Credit Officer, Daniel Key
Evp Corporate Agribusiness Banking Group, Jonathan B. Logan
Southern Region President Regional Agribusiness Banking Group, Lynn Scherler
Svp And Manager Communications Division, Robert F. (Rob) West
Eastern Region President Regional Agribusiness Banking Group, David Sparks
Western Region President Regional Agribusiness Banking Group, Leili Ghazi
Ceo, Robert B. Engel, $880,000 total compensation
President, Mary E. McBride
Chief Banking Officer; Member Management Executive Committee, Thomas Halverson
Vp And Managing Counsel Legal And Loan Processing Division, Chris Clayton
President Farm Credit Leasing, Mike Romanowski
Svp Power Energy And Utilities Banking Division, Todd E. Telesz
Svp Electric Distribution Water And Community Facilities, Nivin Elgohary
Regional Vice President, Todd Sogge
Senior Vice President, Karen Lowe
Vice President, Marshall Essig
Vice President Lead Relationship Manager, David James
Vice President, Andrew Haberern
Vice President Infrastructure, Shawn Dombowsky
Vice President, Bryan Ervin
Vice President Senior Relationship Manager, Natalya Rivkin
Regional Vice President Electric Distribution Division Acb, Tamra Reynolds
Regional Vice President, Brett Challenger
Senior Vice President Corporate Communications, Arthur Hodges
Sector Vice President Managing Director, Michael Tousignant
Vice President, Andy Glover
Vice President Energy Banking, Allison Dunn
Vice President, Tom Houser
Vice President Agribusiness Banking Group, Kurt Harris
Sector Vice President, Dave Dornbirer
Vice President, James Matzat
Vice President Government Affairs, Sarah Tyree
Senior Vice President Of Operations, Horst Kisch
Vice President Appraisal Services, Ray Wagester
Vice President Project Finance, Jennifer Daurio
Senior Vice President, Brian Cavey
Vice President Digital Business Solutions Sales, Noelle Daghe
Sector Vice President Of Project Finance Group, Brian Goldstein
Second Vice Chair, Kevin A. Still
First Vice Chair, Daniel T. (Dan) Kelley
Chairman, Everett M. Dobrinski
Auditors: PRICEWATERHOUSECOOPERS LLP DE

LOCATIONS

HQ: COBANK, ACB
6340 S FIDDLERS GREEN CIR, GREENWOOD VILLAGE, CO 801114951
Phone: 303 740-6527
Web: WWW.COBANK.COM

Selected Regional Offices
Ames IA
Atlanta GA
Austin TX
Enfield CT
Fargo ND
Louisville KY
Lubbock TX
Minneapolis MN
Omaha NE
Roseville CA
Spokane WA
St. Louis MO
Washington D.C.
Wichita KS

COMPETITORS

AgFirst	Northwest Farm Credit
AgStar	Rabo AgriFinance
AgriBank	Wells Fargo
Bank of America	
Farm Credit Services of Mid-America	

HISTORICAL FINANCIALS

Company Type: Private

Income Statement

FYE: December 31

	ASSETS ($ mil.)	NET INCOME ($ mil.)	INCOME AS % OF ASSETS	EMPLOYEES
12/15	117,470	936	0.8%	500
12/14	107,428	904	0.8%	—
12/10	67,700	818	1.2%	—
12/09	58,160	565	1.0%	—
Annual Growth	12.4%	8.8%	—	—

2015 Year-End Financials

Return on assets: —
Return on equity: 39.4%

Sales ($ mil): 2,379

COBB COUNTY BOARD OF EDUCATION

EXECUTIVES

Chair, Randy Scamihorn
Cfo, Cathy Adams
Staff, Cherry Herron
Staff, Danielle Jesko
Auditors: MAULDIN & JENKINS LLC ATLANT

LOCATIONS

HQ: COBB COUNTY BOARD OF EDUCATION
514 GLOVER ST SE, MARIETTA, GA 300602750
Phone: 770 426-3300
Web: WWW.COBBK12.ORG

Income Statement				FYE: June 30
	REVENUE ($ mil.)	NET INCOME ($ mil.)	NET PROFIT MARGIN	EMPLOYEES
06/17	1,299	(13)	—	115
06/16	1,238	(1)	—	—
06/15	1,166	(29)	—	—
06/14	532	67	12.6%	—
Annual Growth	34.7%	—	—	—

2017 Year-End Financials

Return on assets: 2.2% Cash ($ mil.): 247
Return on equity: (-1.0%)
Current ratio: —

COBB COUNTY PUBLIC SCHOOLS

EXECUTIVES

Principal, Dr Ashley Hosey
Director of Communications, Donna Lowry
Consultant, Katherine Williams
Assistant Bbe, Sandra Evans
Auditors: MAULDIN & JENKINS ATLANTA GE

LOCATIONS

HQ: COBB COUNTY PUBLIC SCHOOLS
  4575 WADE GREEN RD NW, ACWORTH, GA
  301023407
Phone: 678 594-8320
Web: WWW.COBBK12.ORG

HISTORICAL FINANCIALS
Company Type: Private

Income Statement				FYE: June 30
	REVENUE ($ mil.)	NET INCOME ($ mil.)	NET PROFIT MARGIN	EMPLOYEES
06/17	1,299	(13)	—	10,000
06/16	1,238	(1)	—	—
06/15	1,166	(29)	—	—
06/14	0	0	13.9%	—
Annual Growth	1017.7%	—	—	—

2017 Year-End Financials

Return on assets: 2.2% Cash ($ mil.): 247
Return on equity: (-1.0%)
Current ratio: —

COBB ELECTRIC MEMBERSHIP CORPORATION

Cobb Electric Membership Corporation (Cobb EMC) makes sure that Cobb County Georgia residents can cook corn on the cob (and anything else) using either electric power or natural gas. The utility distributes electricity to more than 200000 meters (more than 177000 residential commercial and industrial members) in Cobb County and four other north metro Atlanta counties. Cobb EMC operates about 10000 miles of power lines. The company's Gas South unit markets natural gas to customers who receive their service on Atlanta Gas & Light's natural gas distribution pipelines in Georgia.

Operations

Its Cobb Energy Management provides administrative and labor support to Cobb EMC and offers phone and Internet services to Cobb EMC's customers primarily through subsidiaries. Cobb Energy Management provides call center training tree trimming and billing software services and other ancillary support to EMC's core activities.

Geographic Reach

One of the largest of Georgia's 41 EMCs Cobb EMC's distribution system covers approximately 1434 square miles (Cobb Bartow Cherokee Fulton and Paulding counties in the north metro Atlanta area and Randolph Calhoun Quitman and Clay counties in Southwest Georgia).

Financial Performance

In 2012 the company reported a 46% increase in revenues thanks to a 10% rise in natural gas sales which outpaced a 2% decline in electric revenues. Net income grew by 194% in 2012 as a result of higher net sales and lower operating costs.

Strategy

Cobb EMC is a partner in Power4Georgians a consortium of six Georgia EMCs that collectively is developing a comprehensive strategy to provide reliable and affordable energy to the EMC members.

In 2013 as part of its ongoing transition out of non-energy businesses Cobb EMC announced today plans to cut its workforce by up to 20% percent through a company-wide offer of voluntary separation packages.

In 2012 Smart Energy Capital LLC and Jacoby Development Inc. signed a power purchase deal with Cobb EMC to provide power from the Azalea Solar Facility the largest solar power plant (10MW) in Georgia and one of the largest in the Southeast.

Company Background

The cooperative has been embroiled in litigation in recent years and in 2011 a Cobb County grand jury indicted Cobb EMC Dwight Brown on 31 counts of theft and racketeering. Brown was replaced as CEO by W.T. "Chip" Nelson.

The gas and support companies were merged into EMC as wholly owned units in 2009 as a way to streamline EMC's overall operations. The company has also sold a number of former assets to raise cash including Cooperative Business Ventures in 2009 for $2 million and the health and welfare brokerage business of Cooperative Benefits and Financial Services for a gain of $470000 in 2010.

Formed in 1938 Cobb EMC began life as an electric utility with 489 residential members and 14 commercial customers.

EXECUTIVES

Associate Vice President, Jim Gantt
Vice President, Steve Paolucci
Vice President Member Care, Tim Sosebee
Treasurer, Cheryl Meadows
Secretary Treasurer, Malcolm Swanson
Auditors: MCNAIR MCLEMORE MIDDLEBROOKS &

LOCATIONS

HQ: COBB ELECTRIC MEMBERSHIP CORPORATION
  1000 EMC PKWY NE, MARIETTA, GA 300607908
Phone: 770 429-2100
Web: WWW.COBBEMC.COM

Income Statement				FYE: April 30
	REVENUE ($ mil.)	NET INCOME ($ mil.)	NET PROFIT MARGIN	EMPLOYEES
04/18*	849	25	3.0%	548
12/13	416	(8)	—	—
04/09	641	3	0.6%	—
Annual Growth	3.2%	24.4%	—	—
*Fiscal year change				

2018 Year-End Financials

Return on assets: 5.3% Cash ($ mil.): 20
Return on equity: 3.0%
Current ratio: 0.60

COBB HOSPITAL, INC.

EXECUTIVES

Ceo, Reynold J Jennings
President, Kem Mullen
Cfo, A James Budzinski
SEC, Leo E Reichert
Director of Radiology, Lynn Hanks
Registered Nurse, Lee Balos
Radiologist, Mark Wetherly
Diagnostic Radiologist, Martin Silbiger
Anesthesiologist, Nabeel Khan
Emergency Medicine Specialist, Orrin Ahola
Hospitalist, Benadette Makori-Nelson

LOCATIONS

HQ: COBB HOSPITAL, INC.
  3950 AUSTELL RD, AUSTELL, GA 301061121
Phone: 770 792-7600
Web: WWW.COBBWOMENSHEALTH.COM

HISTORICAL FINANCIALS
Company Type: Private

Income Statement				FYE: June 30
	REVENUE ($ mil.)	NET INCOME ($ mil.)	NET PROFIT MARGIN	EMPLOYEES
06/16	329	29	9.0%	2,500
06/15*	287	(7)	—	—
05/05	651	0	—	—
06/99	148	54	36.4%	—
Annual Growth	4.8%	(3.5%)	—	—
*Fiscal year change				

2016 Year-End Financials

Return on assets: 0.5% Cash ($ mil.): —
Return on equity: 9.0%
Current ratio: 7.20

COBORN'S, INCORPORATED

Coborn's hopes you'll shop at your convenience. The company operates 52 stores across Minnesota North Dakota South Dakota Iowa Illinois and Wisconsin under the Coborn's Cash Wise Foods and Save-A-Lot banners. To support its more than 100 retail locations Coborn's operates its own central bakery dry cleaning facility and grocery distribution center. It supplies its stores with baked goods deli items and meat from its own central bakery and manufacturing plant. Along with its grocery stores the firm owns and operates pharmacies and convenience liquor and video stores.

Operations
As part of its business Coborn's operates under several banner names including Cash Wise Foods Save-A-Lot Economart Food Pride Mike's Super Value and namesake Coborn's. These supermarkets are supported by their own central bakery dry cleaning facility and grocery distribution center. The company also runs more than 65 stand-alone convenience liquor video and pharmacy locations.

Geographic Reach
Based in Minnesota Coborn's operates across the Upper Midwest in Minnesota the Dakotas Iowa Illinois and Wisconsin.

Strategy
Independently-owned Corborn's is building a sizable empire in the Upper Midwest through acquisitions and organic growth. In 2015 it purchased Marketplace Foods which owns four grocery/liquor stores in Western Wisconsin. The four Marketplace Foods stores are located in Hayward Menomonie Rice Lake and St. Croix Falls and will continue to operate as Marketplace Foods.

In fall 2013 it acquired four Captain Jack's liquor stores in Bismarck North Dakota as well as a single Bill's Liquor store in Mandan. (North Dakota's economy is growing rapidly thanks to the oil boom.)

Company Background
Founded in 1921 when Chester Coborn started a single produce market the company opened its first Cash Wise Foods store in 1979 and its first convenience store in 1986.

EXECUTIVES

Vp Information Technology, Dale D. Monson
Cfo, Tom Velin
President And Ceo, Chris Coborn
Evp, Greg Sandeno
Vp Operations, Dave Meyer
Auditors: RSM US LLP MINNEAPOLIS MINNE

LOCATIONS

HQ: COBORN'S, INCORPORATED
  1921 COBORN BLVD, SAINT CLOUD, MN 563012100
Phone: 320 252-4222
Web: WWW.COBORNSINC.COM

PRODUCTS/OPERATIONS

Selected Store Formats
Convenience stores (Little Dukes Holiday)
Hardware stores (Ace)
Liquor stores
Pharmacies
Restaurants (Subway)
Supermarkets (Coborn's Cash Wise Foods JK Markets Save-A-Lot)
Video stores

COMPETITORS

7-Eleven	Kroger
ALDI	Lunds
Couche-Tard	Target Corporation
Cub Foods	Wal-Mart
Kowalski's Markets	

HISTORICAL FINANCIALS
Company Type: Private

Income Statement   FYE: December 31

	REVENUE ($ mil.)	NET INCOME ($ mil.)	NET PROFIT MARGIN	EMPLOYEES
12/16	1,403	15	1.1%	7,200
12/13	1,246	30	2.5%	—
12/12	1,220	32	2.7%	—
Annual Growth	3.6%	(17.0%)		

2016 Year-End Financials
Return on assets: 4.1%   Cash ($ mil.): 19
Return on equity: 1.1%
Current ratio: 0.30

COC PROPERTIES, INC.

EXECUTIVES

Chb, Harry D Stephenson
Pres, Don Stephenson
V Pres, Betty Phillips
V Pres, Mark Maddox
V Pres, Jim Bosworth
Auditors: BATCHELOR TILLERY & ROBERTS

LOCATIONS

HQ: COC PROPERTIES, INC.
  110 MACKENAN DR STE 300, CARY, NC 275117901
Phone: 919 462-1100
Web: WWW.CARYOIL.COM

HISTORICAL FINANCIALS
Company Type: Private

Income Statement   FYE: December 31

	ASSETS ($ mil.)	NET INCOME ($ mil.)	INCOME AS % OF ASSETS	EMPLOYEES
12/16	90	9	10.3%	100
12/15	77	4	6.1%	—
12/14	79	7	8.8%	—
12/13	77	3	4.4%	—
Annual Growth	5.4%	40.3%	—	—

2016 Year-End Financials
Return on assets: 3.7%   Sales ($ mil): 1,133
Return on equity: 0.8%

COLONIAL PIPELINE COMPANY

With a reach that extends far beyond the original English colonies Colonial Pipeline delivers about 105 million gallons of gasoline diesel jet fuel home heating oil aviation and military fuels per day to cities and businesses across the eastern and southern US. The more than 5500-mile Colonial Pipeline system transports these fuels from Alabama Louisiana Mississippi and Texas to more than 265 marketing terminals near major urban centers in the Southeast and along the Eastern Seaboard. The company owns more than 3000 miles of right of way. Colonial Pipeline is owned by a consortium of companies including Koch a KKR affiliate Caisse de depot et placement du Quebec and Shell Pipeline.

Operations
The company operates an underground pipeline system that originates in the Houston Texas area and terminates at Linden New Jersey on the New York harbor. The Colonial Pipeline system connects refineries in the Gulf Coast and other locations to more than 260 marketing terminals. Colonial Pipeline delivers 100 million gallons of gasoline kerosene home heating oil diesel fuel and national defense fuels a day to shipper terminals in 13 states and Washington DC. The batches of oil shipments carried by the pipeline vary from 75000 barrels to 3.2 million barrels.

The Colonial Pipeline system services seven airports directly and provides fuel to multiple Department of Defense installations each day. It has 15 storage tanks strategically positioned along the pipeline to serve its customers' requirements.

Geographic Reach
Colonial Pipeline's network of customer-operated pipelines and terminals serves communities across the Southeast and Eastern US. It has shipper terminals in 13 states and the District of Columbia.

Strategy
The company is used to battling rough weather due to its pipeline being close to the hurricane-prone Gulf Coast. It has portable generators and emergency procedures it brings into action when confronted by power outages and other storm damage and is developing new infrastructure projects and additions to better serve its customers. In 2013 Colonial Pipeline outlined a strategy for expanding services. One project adds 100000 barrels of capacity to Colonial Pipeline's main gasoline pipeline which originates in Houston and terminates at Greensboro North Carolina; a second project adds 60000 barrels of daily capacity to the Greensboro-to-Linden New Jersey mainline which will be transported by Colonial Pipeline. Once completed Colonial Pipeline's capacity to carry gasoline diesel fuel jet fuel heating oil and other refined petroleum products through the pipeline would increase to 2.4 million barrels per day.

Other new projects include Clear Skies (a facilities modification program to support the delivery of ultra low sulfur diesel); Bengal Pipeline (a joint venture between Colonial Pipeline and Shell Pipeline serving refineries in Louisiana and Texas); and the Dulles Expansion Project (which links Colonial Pipeline's Line 3 mainline directly to Washington Dulles International Airport enabling the delivery of jet fuel to an onsite 579000-barrel tank farm).

Colonial Pipeline and Buckeye Pipe Line teamed up in 2013 to enable Gulf Coast refineries to supply eastern Pennsylvania and upstate New York markets. The deal allows Colonial Pipeline barrels to transfer to Buckeye's Paulsboro Pipeline and on to the Malvern and Macungie Pennsylvania terminals

The company also plans to further harden the Northeast infrastructure against another severe storm like Sandy. Modeled on its Gulf Coast contingency operations the improved system will add portable generators capable of replacing the loss of commercial power during a storm or other emergency.

Company Background
Responding to increased customer demand in 2011 Colonial Pipeline expanded the northern part of its Houston-to-New York system adding 100000 barrels per day of capacity (increasing its capacity in the New York Harbor market by 14%). In 2011 and 2012 it also conducted a series of system upgrades including adding 55000 barrels of daily capacity for diesel fuel home heating oil jet fuel and

fuels and other petroleum products for the US military.

Taking advantage of the Yorktown Virginia refinery shut down and the conversion of its storage tanks to a delivery facility serving the Tidewater area in 2011 the company announced a capacity expansion to increase deliveries to the Tidewater region by 24000 barrels a day.

In 2010 Chevron sold its 23% stake in Colonial Pipeline to a KKR affiliate as part of its plan to sell non-core assets. In 2014 KKR-Keats Pipeline Investors L.P. owned 28% of Colonial Pipeline.

EXECUTIVES

Interim Ceo, John W. Somerhalder
Vp Operations, Doug Belden
Vp Technical Services, Rob Barbeauld
Vp And Cfo, Dave Doudna
Vice President Of Human Resources, Eve Brooks
Vice President Human Resources, James America

LOCATIONS

HQ: COLONIAL PIPELINE COMPANY
1185 SANCTUARY PKWY # 100, ALPHARETTA, GA
300094765
Phone: 678 762-2200
Web: WWW.COLPIPE.COM

Colonial Pipeline operates a pipeline system that spans from Texas to New Jersey.

PRODUCTS/OPERATIONS

Selected Customers
American Airlines Inc
Apex Oil Company
Astra Oil Co. Inc.
Atlantic Trading & Marketing
BP Oil Company
Cargill Incorporated
Center Oil Company
Chalmette Refinery
Charter-Triad Terminals LLC
Chevron Corporation
CHS Inc
CITGO Petroleum Corp.
ConocoPhillips
Continental Airlines Fuel Mgmt.Inc
Cummins Terminal Inc.
Department Of Defense
Energy Merchant LLC
Epsilon Trading Inc.
Equiva Trading
ExxonMobil Oil Corporation
Flint Hills Resources
George E. Warren Corporation
Glencore Ltd
Global Companies LLC
Gulf Oil Limited Partnership
Hess Corporation
Hunt Refining Co.
J. Aron & Company
Kinder Morgan Energy
Koch Petroleum Group LP
Lion Oil Company
Louis Dreyfus Energy Services LP
Mabanaft
Maples Gas Company Inc.
Marathon Petroleum Co. LLC
Metroplex Energy Inc
Morgan Stanley Capital Group Inc.
Motiva
Murphy Oil USA Inc.
Musket Corporation
NIC Holding Corp
NWA Fuel Services Corp.
Petro Services
Petrocom Energy Group Ltd
Petroleum Traders Corporation
Phibro Inc.
Pilot Corporation
Placid Refining Company
Premcor Refining Group Inc
Quiktrip Corp.
Rwe Trading Americas Inc
Sheetz Inc
Shell Oil Products US

Shell Trading
Societe Generale Energie (USA) Corp
South Padre Energy LTD
Southwest Airlines
Sprague Energy Corporation
Sun Refining & Marketing
Tauber Oil Co.
Trafigura AG
Transmontaigne
Truman Arnold
United Parcel Service
US Airways Inc
Valero Marketing And Supply
Valley Oil Company LLC
Vitol S.A. Inc.
WAWA Incorporated
Williams Energy Marketing And Trading
World Fuel Services

COMPETITORS

Buckeye Partners	Magellan Midstream
Enterprise Products	Sunoco Logistics
Gateway Energy	TransMontaigne
Kinder Morgan Energy Partners	

HISTORICAL FINANCIALS

Company Type: Private

Income Statement | FYE: December 31

	REVENUE ($ mil.)	NET INCOME ($ mil.)	NET PROFIT MARGIN	EMPLOYEES
12/17	1,231	509	41.4%	700
12/16	1,214	233	19.2%	—
12/06	798	192	24.1%	—
12/05	718	186	26.0%	—
Annual Growth	4.6%	8.7%	—	—

2017 Year-End Financials

Return on assets: 12.4%
Return on equity: 41.4%
Current ratio: 0.60
Cash ($ mil.): 99

COLORADO HOUSING AND FINANCE AUTHORITY

EXECUTIVES

Ceo, Cris A White
Chief Operating Officer, Jaime Gomez
Cfo, Patricia Hippe
Compliance Manager, Emily Jensik
Executive Officer, Julie Chelin
Compliance Staff, Shelia Anderson
Executive Officer, Margaret Miller
Quality Assurance Director, Sugin Sim
Manager, Beth Truby
General Counsel, Charles Knight
Public Relations Staff, Heather Johnson
Auditors: CLIFTON & GUNDERSON LLP GREEN

LOCATIONS

HQ: COLORADO HOUSING AND FINANCE AUTHORITY
1981 BLAKE ST, DENVER, CO 802021229
Phone: 303 297-2432
Web: WWW.CHFAINFO.COM

HISTORICAL FINANCIALS

Company Type: Private

Income Statement | FYE: December 31

	ASSETS ($ mil.)	NET INCOME ($ mil.)	INCOME AS % OF ASSETS	EMPLOYEES
12/17	2,192	52	2.4%	150
12/16	2,037	24	1.2%	—
12/09	3,671	(15)	—	—
12/08	4,059	13	0.3%	—
Annual Growth	(6.6%)	16.5%	—	—

2017 Year-End Financials

Return on assets: —
Return on equity: 30.2%
Sales ($ mil): 173

COLORADO INTERSTATE GAS COMPANY LLC

EXECUTIVES

Pres, Mark A Kissel
Exec V Pres, Steven J Kean
V Pres-Cfo, David P Michels
V Pres, David R Deveau

LOCATIONS

HQ: COLORADO INTERSTATE GAS COMPANY LLC
1001 LA ST STE 1000, HOUSTON, TX 77002
Phone: 713 369-9000

COMPETITORS

Black Hills	Enterprise Products
DTE	Kinder Morgan
Energen	Questar Pipeline

HISTORICAL FINANCIALS

Company Type: Private

Income Statement | FYE: December 31

	REVENUE ($ mil.)	NET INCOME ($ mil.)	NET PROFIT MARGIN	EMPLOYEES
12/17	319	91	28.6%	4
12/16	365	97	26.6%	—
Annual Growth	(12.5%)	(6.1%)	—	—

COLORADO SEMINARY

Want a mile-high education? Colorado Seminary which does business as University of Denver (DU) offers graduate and undergraduate degrees in more than 100 fields of study including law government humanities education engineering and psychology. About 11600 undergraduate and graduate students from across the US and more than 80 countries are enrolled at the school. Founded in 1864 the university has a staff of 700 full-time faculty members; its student-to-faculty ratio is 11:1. DU is located on a 125-acre campus. Former Secretary of State Condoleezza Rice former Interior Secretary Gale Norton and former Coors Brewing CEO Peter Coors attended DU.

Strategy

DU has added about 20 buildings since 1997 to enhance its academic administrative athletic and residential capacities. Projects have included a soccer stadium and a center for international security and diplomacy within the School of International Studies. In 2016 it opened the Daniel Felix Ritchie School of Engineering and Computer Science.

Despite campus growth between 2006 and 2015 the University shrank its carbon footprint by 27% due the use of carbon offsets and vehicles fueled by compressed natural gas (CNG). It operates the only CNG fueling station on a Colorado university campus.

EXECUTIVES

Provost, Robert D. (Bob) Coombe
Dean Josef Korbel School Of International Studies, Christopher R. Hill
Vice Chancellor Business And Financial Affairs, Craig W. Woody
Dean Women's College, Lynn Gangone
Provost, Gregg Kvistad
Dean Divisions Of Arts Humanities And Social Sciences, Anne E. McCall
Dean Sturm College Of Law, Martin J. (Marty) Katz
Dean Graduate School Of Professional Psychology, Shelly Smith-Acuna
Dean Natural Sciences And Mathematics, Andrei Kutateladze
Interim Dean Daniel Felix Ritchie School Of Engineering And Computer Science, Michael Keables
Vice Chancellor Division Of Marketing & Communications And Chief Marketing Officer, Kevin Carroll
Auditors: CLIFTONLARSONALLEN LLP GREEN

LOCATIONS

HQ: COLORADO SEMINARY
2199 S UNIVERSITY BLVD, DENVER, CO 802104711
Phone: 303 871-2000
Web: WWW.DU.EDU

PRODUCTS/OPERATIONS

Selected Schools and Programs
Undergraduate Schools and Colleges
Daniels College of Business
Division of Natural Sciences & Mathematics
Division of Arts Humanities and Social Sciences
Josef Korbel School of International Studies
Morgridge College of Education
School of Engineering and Computer Science
University College
Women's College
Graduate and Professional Programs
Daniels College of Business
Divisions of Arts Humanities and Social Sciences
Divisions of Natural Sciences and Mathematics
Graduate School of Professional Psychology (GSPP)
Graduate School of Social Work (GSSW)
Graduate Tax Program
Interdisciplinary Degree Programs
Josef Korbel School of International Studies
Morgridge College of Education (MCE)
School of Engineering and Computer Science
The Sturm College of Law
University College

HISTORICAL FINANCIALS

Company Type: Private

Income Statement				FYE: June 30
	REVENUE ($ mil.)	NET INCOME ($ mil.)	NET PROFIT MARGIN	EMPLOYEES
06/17	467	86	18.6%	2,770
06/16	458	9	2.2%	—
06/15	431	69	16.0%	—
06/14	396	122	31.0%	—
Annual Growth	5.7%	(10.9%)	—	—

2017 Year-End Financials
Return on assets: 14.5% Cash ($ mil.): 52
Return on equity: 18.6%
Current ratio: —

COLORADO STATE UNIVERSITY SYSTEM

EXECUTIVES

Chancellor, Joe Blake
Chancellor, Michael Martin
Cfo, Henry Sobanet
Pres-Colorado State Univ.-Glob, Becky Takeda
Executive Assistant To Boa, Sharon Teufel
Deputy General Counsel, Johnna Doyle
Auditors: BKD LLP DENVER CO

LOCATIONS

HQ: COLORADO STATE UNIVERSITY SYSTEM
475 17TH ST STE 1550, DENVER, CO 802024012
Phone: 303 534-6290
Web: WWW.CSUSYSTEM.EDU

HISTORICAL FINANCIALS

Company Type: Private

Income Statement				FYE: June 30
	REVENUE ($ mil.)	NET INCOME ($ mil.)	NET PROFIT MARGIN	EMPLOYEES
06/15	1,011	33	3.3%	6,701
06/14	938	(5)	—	—
06/13	884	22	2.6%	—
Annual Growth	6.9%	21.7%	—	—

2015 Year-End Financials
Return on assets: 4.2% Cash ($ mil.): 352
Return on equity: 3.3%
Current ratio: 2.00

COLTON JOINT UNIFIED SCHOOL DISTRICT

EXECUTIVES

Supt, Jerry Almendarez
Administrative Assistant, Yolanda Guerrero
Member, Frank Ibarra
Director, Amanda Cordidan
Assistant, Frances Frost
Facilities, Craig Sandifer
Project Manager, Owen Chang
Accountant, Anna Leon
Communications Specialist, Jacqueline Paul

LOCATIONS

HQ: COLTON JOINT UNIFIED SCHOOL DISTRICT
1212 VALENCIA DR, COLTON, CA 923241798
Phone: 909 580-5000
Web: WWW.COLTON.K12.CA.US

HISTORICAL FINANCIALS

Company Type: Private

Income Statement				FYE: June 30
	REVENUE ($ mil.)	NET INCOME ($ mil.)	NET PROFIT MARGIN	EMPLOYEES
06/17	297	25	8.7%	1,800
06/05	187	0	—	—
06/02	160	5	3.7%	—
06/01	156	16	10.6%	—
Annual Growth	4.1%	2.8%	—	—

2017 Year-End Financials
Return on assets: 14.8% Cash ($ mil.): 153
Return on equity: 8.7%
Current ratio: —

COLUMBIA GAS OF OHIO, INC.

Columbia Gas of Ohio takes pride in the fact that it can deliver gas first class en masse without impasse to the working class the middle class and the upper class. The utility is the largest natural gas utility in the state serving 1.4 million customers (including about 1.3 million residential 112000 commercial and 2600 industrial customers in more than 1030 communities in more than 60 of Ohio's 88 counties). The NiSource subsidiary offers a customer choice program which allows customers to choose their energy suppliers while Columbia Gas of Ohio continues to deliver the gas.

Operations
In addition to operating more than 19160 miles of distribution mains the company also provides other gas products services and programs across its 25400-sq.-mi. service area. Columbia Gas of Ohio is part of the NiSource's Gas Distribution segment which contributed about 54% of the total sales in fiscal 2013.

Geographic Reach
Columbia Gas of Ohio distributes natural gas to residential commercial and industrial customers in Columbus Mansfield Parma Springfield and Toledo. It is one of a handful of NiSource's distribution companies which collectively serve about 3.4 million gas and electric customers in seven states and operates about 58000 miles of pipeline.

Financial Performance
Columbia Gas of Ohio is part of the NiSource's Gas Distribution segment which reported an increase of 9% in 2013 due primarily to an increase for regulatory and service programs (including the impact from the rate cases at Columbia of Pennsylvania and Columbia of Massachusetts and the implementation of rates under Columbia of Ohio's approved infrastructure replacement program); the effects of colder weather which increased residential commercial and industrial usage; and an increase in the numbers of residential and commercial customers.

Strategy
The company's strategy includes spending about $2 billion over 25 years to improve its underground pipeline system.

In 2014 it asked state regulators for permission to replace a mile-long 12-inch diameter pipeline that crosses the Maumee River between Maumee and Perrysburg with a new 20-inch pipeline.

Upgrading its main offices in order to be more efficient in 2013 Columbia Gas of Ohio announced plans to relocated to the Arena District of Columbus taking about 208000 sq. ft. of a planned 288000-sq.-ft. office complex.

In 2012 Columbia Gas of Ohio has finished work on its $14 million Ackerman Road natural gas pipeline replacement project in Columbus.

That year it moved more than 722000 customers to independent suppliers as part of a decade-long deregulation plan by the state.

Company Background

In 2011 Columbia Gas of Ohio announced plans to secure permission from the Public Utilities Commission of Ohio for a five year extension of its energy efficiency programs (home energy audits weatherization and other initiatives) aimed at bringing down energy costs for individual customers.

In 2010 Columbia Gas of Ohio commenced a $1.3 million gas mains upgrade in two neighborhoods in Toledo.

EXECUTIVES

Pres, Jack Partridge
V Pres Trea Cro, Devit Vajda
Acct Dept, Ms Jaime Hartenback
Executive Officer, Trudy Zielinski
Vice-President Information Ser, Dick James

LOCATIONS

HQ: COLUMBIA GAS OF OHIO, INC.
290 W NATIONWIDE BLVD # 114, COLUMBUS, OH 432151082
Phone: 614 460-6000
Web: WWW.COLUMBIAGASOHIO.COM

COMPETITORS

Dominion East Ohio	The Illuminating
Duke Energy Ohio	Company
Ohio Edison	Toledo Edison
Ohio Power	Vectren Energy
Stand Energy	Delivery of Ohio

HISTORICAL FINANCIALS
Company Type: Private

Income Statement				FYE: December 31
	REVENUE ($ mil.)	NET INCOME ($ mil.)	NET PROFIT MARGIN	EMPLOYEES
12/17	908	96	10.7%	2,500
12/16	854	114	13.4%	—
12/15	872	113	13.0%	—
12/14	993	102	10.3%	—
Annual Growth	(3.0%)	(1.9%)	—	—

2017 Year-End Financials

Return on assets: 16.9%   Cash ($ mil.): 7
Return on equity: 10.7%
Current ratio: —

COLUMBIA ST. MARY'S HOSPITAL MILWAUKEE, INC.

EXECUTIVES

Pres, Travis Andersen
President, Leo Burdeau
Coo, Treasie Pandl
Exec Asst, Angie Madigan

Coordinator, Evan Solochek
Doctor, Anil Dogra
Director, Chris Frank
Doctor, Anita Thakur
Manager, Diana Lenhardt
Internal Medicine Practitioner, Erik Stilp
Chief Financial Officer, Dennis Langer

LOCATIONS

HQ: COLUMBIA ST. MARY'S HOSPITAL MILWAUKEE, INC.
2301 N LAKE DR, MILWAUKEE, WI 532114508
Phone: 414 291-1000
Web: WWW.COLUMBIA-STMARYS.ORG

HISTORICAL FINANCIALS
Company Type: Private

Income Statement				FYE: June 30
	REVENUE ($ mil.)	NET INCOME ($ mil.)	NET PROFIT MARGIN	EMPLOYEES
06/15	447	(35)	—	2,100
06/04	222	6	2.8%	—
06/03	507	29	5.9%	—
06/02	1,032	0	0.0%	—
Annual Growth	(6.2%)	—	—	—

2015 Year-End Financials

Return on assets: 1.7%   Cash ($ mil.): 2
Return on equity: (-8.0%)
Current ratio: 1.90

COLUMBUS PUBLIC SCHOOL DISTRICT

EXECUTIVES

Supt, Gene T Harris
Dpty Supt, Marvenia Bosley
Treas, Mike Kinneer
Vice President, Terry Boyd
Nurse, Regina Hinterschied
Executive Officer, Blain Waldron
Executive Officer, Carol Rood
Auditing Manager, Carolyn Smith
Executive Officer, Craig Bickley
Executive Officer, David Nelson
Executive Officer, Lean Katterheinrich
Auditors: DAVE YOST COLUMBUS OHIO

LOCATIONS

HQ: COLUMBUS PUBLIC SCHOOL DISTRICT
270 E STATE ST FL 3, COLUMBUS, OH 432154312
Phone: 614 365-5000
Web: WWW.CCSOH.US

HISTORICAL FINANCIALS
Company Type: Private

Income Statement				FYE: June 30
	REVENUE ($ mil.)	NET INCOME ($ mil.)	NET PROFIT MARGIN	EMPLOYEES
06/17	1,038	106	10.3%	10,000
06/16	972	(13)	—	—
06/06	667	(51)	—	—
06/05	0	0	—	—
Annual Growth	—	—	—	—

2017 Year-End Financials

Return on assets: 0.6%   Cash ($ mil.): 440
Return on equity: 10.3%
Current ratio: —

COMFORT SYSTEMS USA (ARKANSAS), INC.

EXECUTIVES

Pres, Clyde A Jester
Vice President, Trent McKenna
SEC, Dawn McElyea
General Manager, Tad Hankins
Auditors: ERNST & YOUNG LLP HOUSTON TE

LOCATIONS

HQ: COMFORT SYSTEMS USA (ARKANSAS), INC.
4806 RIXIE RD, NORTH LITTLE ROCK, AR 721171537
Phone: 501 834-3320
Web: WWW.COMFORTAR.COM

HISTORICAL FINANCIALS
Company Type: Private

Income Statement				FYE: December 31
	REVENUE ($ mil.)	NET INCOME ($ mil.)	NET PROFIT MARGIN	EMPLOYEES
12/15	1,580	49	3.1%	102
12/14	1,410	28	2.0%	—
12/13	1,357	28	2.1%	—
Annual Growth	7.9%	31.5%	—	—

2015 Year-End Financials

Return on assets: 6.7%   Cash ($ mil.): 56
Return on equity: 3.1%
Current ratio: 1.20

COMMERCIAL CONTRACTING GROUP, INC.

EXECUTIVES

Ceo-Pres, Stephen Fragnoli
Cfo, Steven Teper
Exec Vice President, Bradford Kimmel
Exec Vice President, Joel Lewandowski

LOCATIONS

HQ: COMMERCIAL CONTRACTING GROUP, INC.
4260 N ATLANTIC BLVD, AUBURN HILLS, MI 483261578
Phone: 248 209-0500
Web: WWW.CCCNETWORK.COM

HISTORICAL FINANCIALS
Company Type: Private

Income Statement				FYE: December 31
	REVENUE ($ mil.)	NET INCOME ($ mil.)	NET PROFIT MARGIN	EMPLOYEES
12/17	480	0	—	300
12/16	284	0	—	—
12/15	281	0	—	—
12/14	289	0	—	—
Annual Growth	18.4%	—	—	—

2017 Year-End Financials

Return on assets: 15.5%   Cash ($ mil.): 12
Return on equity: —
Current ratio: 1.20

COMMUNITY BEHAVIORAL HEALTH

EXECUTIVES

Director, Arthur C Evans Jr
Director*, Estelle Richmond
Director*, Nancy Luckas
Human Resources Director, Peter Bezrucik
Auditors: MITCHELL & TITUS LLP PHILADEL

LOCATIONS

HQ: COMMUNITY BEHAVIORAL HEALTH
801 MARKET ST STE 7000, PHILADELPHIA, PA
191073158
Phone: 215 413-3100
Web: WWW.DBHIDS.ORG

HISTORICAL FINANCIALS
Company Type: Private

Income Statement				FYE: December 31
	REVENUE ($ mil.)	NET INCOME ($ mil.)	NET PROFIT MARGIN	EMPLOYEES
12/16	919	0	—	270
12/15	811	0	—	—
12/02	453	(0)	—	—
12/01	443	(0)	—	—
Annual Growth	5.0%	—	—	—

2016 Year-End Financials
Return on assets: 16.3%   Cash ($ mil.): 82
Return on equity: —
Current ratio: —

COMMUNITY CARE, INC.

EXECUTIVES

Ceo, Kenneth Munson
Pres, Kirby Shoaf
Coo, Alicia Modjeska
Exec Asst, Jean Schoessow
Director, Donna Henning
Information Specialist, Peter Kather
Manager, Lorie Hadel
Manager, Tanya Knox
Case Manager, Aaron Quam
Family Care Case Manager, Adrienne Calcagnino
Executive Assistant, Alyce Nawrocki
Auditors: RSM US LLP MADISON WI

LOCATIONS

HQ: COMMUNITY CARE, INC.
205 BISHOPS WAY OFC, BROOKFIELD, WI
530056272
Phone: 414 385-6600
Web: WWW.COMMUNITYCAREINC.ORG

HISTORICAL FINANCIALS
Company Type: Private

Income Statement				FYE: December 31
	REVENUE ($ mil.)	NET INCOME ($ mil.)	NET PROFIT MARGIN	EMPLOYEES
12/15	407	(5)	—	1,100
12/14	381	(0)	—	—
12/13	351	4	1.4%	—
12/12	333	11	3.3%	—
Annual Growth	6.9%	—	—	—

2015 Year-End Financials
Return on assets: 1.5%   Cash ($ mil.): 46
Return on equity: (-1.4%)
Current ratio: 8.00

COMMUNITY FOUNDATION OF NORTHWEST INDIANA, INC.

EXECUTIVES

Pres, Frankie Fesko
SEC, James J Richards
Treas, David E Wickland
Registered Nurse, Jennifer Phelps
Nurse, Jennifer White
Administrative Assistant, Kathryn Johnson
Registered Nurse, Pamela Wilson
Registered Nurse, Annette Haney
Nurse, Cheryl Filler
Registered Nurse, David Gasper
Security Staff, Derek Gilliam

LOCATIONS

HQ: COMMUNITY FOUNDATION OF NORTHWEST
INDIANA, INC.
905 RIDGE RD, MUNSTER, IN 463211773
Phone: 219 836-0130
Web: WWW.COMHS.ORG

HISTORICAL FINANCIALS
Company Type: Private

Income Statement				FYE: June 30
	REVENUE ($ mil.)	NET INCOME ($ mil.)	NET PROFIT MARGIN	EMPLOYEES
06/18	1,150	137	12.0%	2,000
06/17	1,084	122	11.2%	—
06/15	108	(4)	—	—
Annual Growth	119.5%	—	—	—

2018 Year-End Financials
Return on assets: 2.0%   Cash ($ mil.): 18
Return on equity: 12.0%
Current ratio: 1.00

COMMUNITY HEALTH CHOICE, INC.

EXECUTIVES

Ceo, Kenneth Janda
Coo, Karen Love
Cfo, Brian Maude
Associate Web Developer, Becky Cantu
Human Resources Manager, Claudia Garcia
Coordinator, Richard Hobbs
Director, John Coakley
Vice-President, John Petrosino

Sales Staff, Leticia Neri
Administrative Assistant, Delwin Beene
Coordinator of Marketing, Jenna McCormick
Auditors: I KPMG LLP OKLAHOMA CITY OK

LOCATIONS

HQ: COMMUNITY HEALTH CHOICE, INC.
2636 S LOOP W STE 700, HOUSTON, TX 770545630
Phone: 713 295-2200
Web: WWW.COMMUNITYCARES.COM

HISTORICAL FINANCIALS
Company Type: Private

Income Statement				FYE: December 31
	ASSETS ($ mil.)	NET INCOME ($ mil.)	INCOME AS % OF ASSETS	EMPLOYEES
12/15	239	1	0.5%	700
12/14	192	16	8.6%	—
12/13	166	(3)	—	—
12/12	172	(17)	—	—
Annual Growth	11.6%	—	—	—

2015 Year-End Financials
Return on assets: 1.1%   Sales ($ mil.): 851
Return on equity: 0.1%

COMMUNITY HOSPITAL OF THE MONTEREY PENINSULA

Community Hospital of the Monterey Peninsula has a sunny disposition when it comes to medical care. The not-for-profit health care facility provides general medical and surgical services to residents of Monterey California. It has about 235 acute care and skilled nursing beds and offers specialty services including cardiac and cancer care obstetrics orthopedics and rehabilitation. In addition to its main facility the hospital operates several ancillary centers including a mental health clinic an inpatient hospice medical laboratory branches and several outpatient centers offering diagnostic imaging diabetes care and other services.

Operations

Community Hospital offers a broad range of healthcare services at 15 locations including the main hospital outpatient facilities satellite laboratories a mental health clinic a short-term skilled nursing facility Hospice of the Central Coast and business offices.

In 2012 the hospital systems served 12130 inpatients in 2012. It also had 49565 emergency visits 283181 outpatient visits and assisted in 1193 births.

Geographic Reach

The company has facilities in Carmel Marina Monterey and Seaside counties in California.

Financial Performance

Medicare accounted for 53% of Community Hospital of the Monterey Peninsula's revenues in 2012; commercial insurance 23% and Medi-Cal 10%.

Strategy

To improve care in its service territory the hospital is working to increase best-practice sharing among physicians. It is also supporting information sharing by coordinating electronic health records (EHRs).

In 2014 the hospital received a $200000 contribution from the Auxiliary of Community Hospital of the Monterey Peninsula completing a five-year $1 million pledge by the service organization to support the hospital.

Company Background

As health care costs skyrocket in the US Community Hospital of the Monterey Peninsula has worked to lower its expenses. Between 2008 and 2011 the organization lowered annual costs by about $44 million.

Community Hospital of the Monterey Peninsula was founded in 1934.

EXECUTIVES

Vice President Nursing, Terril Lowe

LOCATIONS

HQ: COMMUNITY HOSPITAL OF THE MONTEREY PENINSULA
23625 HOLMAN HWY, MONTEREY, CA 939405902
Phone: 831 624-5311
Web: WWW.CHOMP.ORG

PRODUCTS/OPERATIONS

Selected Community Hospital Service Locations
Community Hospital of the Monterey Peninsula: Monterey
Carol Hatton Breast Care Center: Monterey
Development/Patient Business Services: Monterey
Hartnell Professional Center: Monterey Peninsula
Primary Care/Satellite Laboratory: Carmel
Peninsula Wellness Center: Marina
Ryan Ranch Outpatient Campus: Monterey
Seaside Satellite Laboratory: Seaside
Westland House: Monterey

Selected Services
Bariatric Surgery
Behavioral Health Services
Carol Hatton Breast Care Center
Comprehensive Cancer Center
Diabetes
Diagnostic and Interventional Radiology
Emergency
Family Birth Center
Hospice of the Central Coast
Intermediate Intensive Care Nursery
Laboratory Services
Nutrition Therapy Program
Orthopedics
Outpatient Immunology Services
Outpatient Surgery Center
Pulmonary Wellness Services
Radiation Oncology
Rehabilitation Services
Sleep disorders
Social Services
Stroke Program
Tyler Heart Institute (Cardiac Care)
Westland House Skilled Nursing Facility
Wound Care and Hyperbaric Healing

COMPETITORS

Dignity Health	Stanford Health Care
John Muir Health	Sutter Health
Queen of the Valley Medical Center	The Palo Alto Medical Foundation
Salinas Valley Memorial	UCSF Medical
Sequoia Healthcare District	

HISTORICAL FINANCIALS
Company Type: Private

Income Statement   FYE: December 31

	REVENUE ($ mil.)	NET INCOME ($ mil.)	NET PROFIT MARGIN	EMPLOYEES
12/16	526	71	13.7%	1,947
12/15	560	66	11.9%	—
12/12	442	81	18.4%	—
12/09	475	26	5.6%	—
Annual Growth	1.5%	15.2%	—	—

2016 Year-End Financials
Return on assets: 8.3%   Cash ($ mil.): 73
Return on equity: 13.7%
Current ratio: 1.70

COMMUNITY HOSPITALS OF CENTRAL CALIFORNIA

EXECUTIVES

Pres, Tim Joslin
Coordinator, Jennifer Trytten
Senior Vice-President, Margaret Breen
Doctor, Dalpinder Sandhu
Manager, Denise Curry
Human Resources Director, Linda Jeffers
Registered Nurse, Mark Osburn
Doctor, Mohinder Poonia
Pharmacist, Staci Anderson
Rn, Bonnie Harkins
Manager, Jonathan Miller
Auditors: MOSS ADAMS LLP STOCKTON CA

LOCATIONS

HQ: COMMUNITY HOSPITALS OF CENTRAL CALIFORNIA
2823 FRESNO ST, FRESNO, CA 937211324
Phone: 559 459-6000
Web: WWW.COMMUNITYMEDICAL.ORG

HISTORICAL FINANCIALS
Company Type: Private

Income Statement   FYE: August 31

	REVENUE ($ mil.)	NET INCOME ($ mil.)	NET PROFIT MARGIN	EMPLOYEES
08/17	1,529	48	3.1%	1,000
08/14	127	0	0.5%	—
Annual Growth	128.9%	320.6%	—	—

2017 Year-End Financials
Return on assets: 5.2%   Cash ($ mil.): 64
Return on equity: 3.1%
Current ratio: 1.20

COMMUNITY MEDICAL CENTER, INC.

EXECUTIVES

Cfo, Mark Ostrander
Coordinator, Meg Ford
General, Chris Filippone
Pathologist, Bich Pham
It Director, David McHenry
Lab Technician, Denise Drew
Informatics Manager, Jaala Wickman
Buyer, Keith Stokey
Lab Director, Naomi Matten

LOCATIONS

HQ: COMMUNITY MEDICAL CENTER, INC.
99 ROUTE 37 W, TOMS RIVER, NJ 087556423
Phone: 732 557-8000
Web: WWW.COMMUNITYMED.ORG

HISTORICAL FINANCIALS
Company Type: Private

Income Statement   FYE: December 31

	REVENUE ($ mil.)	NET INCOME ($ mil.)	NET PROFIT MARGIN	EMPLOYEES
12/17	380	25	6.8%	2,500
12/15	372	33	9.0%	—
12/14	360	21	6.1%	—
12/13	320	3	1.2%	—
Annual Growth	4.4%	61.9%	—	—

2017 Year-End Financials
Return on assets: 3.3%   Cash ($ mil.): —
Return on equity: 6.8%
Current ratio: 0.70

COMMUNITY MEMORIAL HEALTH SYSTEM

EXECUTIVES

Pres, Gary Wilde
V Pres-Oprs, Adam Thunell
V Pres-Fin, David Glyar
Director Records, Mary Jane Greene
Staff Pharmacist, Mary Ann Edwards
Chief Staff, Mark A Beaghler
Benefits Coordinator, Evelyn Beckett
Vice-President Corporate Commu, Steve Caryer
Health Professional, Luke Rwanczyk
Director, Fermin Cortes
Nurse, Jody C McDonald
Auditors: ERNST & YOUNG US LLP IRVINE

LOCATIONS

HQ: COMMUNITY MEMORIAL HEALTH SYSTEM
147 N BRENT ST, VENTURA, CA 930032809
Phone: 805 652-5011
Web: WWW.CMHSHEALTH.ORG

HISTORICAL FINANCIALS

Company Type: Private

Income Statement				FYE: December 31
	REVENUE ($ mil.)	NET INCOME ($ mil.)	NET PROFIT MARGIN	EMPLOYEES
12/17	406	30	7.4%	2,200
12/14	353	41	11.7%	—
12/13	320	24	7.7%	—
12/09	279	9	3.4%	—
Annual Growth	4.8%	15.4%	—	—

2017 Year-End Financials

Return on assets: 8.9% Cash ($ mil.): 26
Return on equity: 7.4%
Current ratio: 0.90

COMMUNITYBANK OF TEXAS NATIONAL ASSOCIATION

EXECUTIVES

Prin, George Casseb
Fo, Donna Dillon
Manager, Trudy Jones
Senior Vice-President, Michael Mallette
Senior Vice-President, Paul Broussard
Senior Vice-President, N Felan

LOCATIONS

HQ: COMMUNITYBANK OF TEXAS NATIONAL ASSOCIATION
5999 DELAWARE ST, BEAUMONT, TX 777067607
Phone: 409 861-7200
Web: WWW.COMMUNITYBANKOFTX.COM

HISTORICAL FINANCIALS

Company Type: Private

Income Statement				FYE: December 31
	ASSETS ($ mil.)	NET INCOME ($ mil.)	INCOME AS % OF ASSETS	EMPLOYEES
12/17	3,079	28	0.9%	60
12/16	2,950	28	1.0%	—
12/15	2,881	25	0.9%	—
12/14	2,629	23	0.9%	—
Annual Growth	5.4%	6.2%	—	—

2017 Year-End Financials

Return on assets: — Sales ($ mil): 131
Return on equity: 21.7%

COMPASSION INTERNATIONAL INC

EXECUTIVES

Pres-Ceo, Santiago Mellado
Gen Dir, Ronald Mathieu

V Chm, Laurent Mbanda
Chm, Karen Wesolowski
Gen Dir, Jean-Franois Bussy
Gen Dir, Robert Hawkins
Gen Dir, Mike Jeffs
Gen Dir, Francisco Batres
SEC, Judy Briscoe Golz
Gen Mgr, Kenneth Morgan
Gen Dir, Chris Knepper
Auditors: CAPIN CROUSE LLP COLORADO SPR

LOCATIONS

HQ: COMPASSION INTERNATIONAL INC
12290 VOYAGER PKWY, COLORADO SPRINGS, CO 809213694
Phone: 719 487-7000
Web: WWW.COMPASSION.COM

HISTORICAL FINANCIALS

Company Type: Private

Income Statement				FYE: June 30
	REVENUE ($ mil.)	NET INCOME ($ mil.)	NET PROFIT MARGIN	EMPLOYEES
06/16	800	13	1.6%	2,002
06/15	768	(8)	—	—
06/14	719	8	1.2%	—
06/13	659	15	2.3%	—
Annual Growth	6.6%	(4.4%)	—	—

2016 Year-End Financials

Return on assets: 3.1% Cash ($ mil.): 95
Return on equity: 1.6%
Current ratio: 1.30

COMPTON UNIFIED SCHOOL DISTRICT

EXECUTIVES

Supt, Darin Brawley
Maintenance Manager, Arthur Thompson
Research Director, Irene Lee
Payroll Staff, Francine Lee
Payroll Staff, Brittney Young
Director, Aaron Walker
Administrator, Doc Gonzales
Financial Analyst, Stephanie Dewitt
Senior Director of Ed Tech, Michelle Dawson
Purchasing, Randy Farley
Administrative Secretary, Regina S Moss

LOCATIONS

HQ: COMPTON UNIFIED SCHOOL DISTRICT
501 S SANTA FE AVE, COMPTON, CA 902213814
Phone: 310 604-6508
Web: WWW.COMPTON.K12.CA.US

HISTORICAL FINANCIALS

Company Type: Private

Income Statement				FYE: June 30
	REVENUE ($ mil.)	NET INCOME ($ mil.)	NET PROFIT MARGIN	EMPLOYEES
06/17	335	19	5.8%	3,800
06/16	337	30	9.2%	—
06/05	302	0	—	—
06/02	175	14	8.3%	—
Annual Growth	4.4%	1.9%	—	—

COMPUTER SCIENCES CORPORATION

Computer Sciences Corporation (CSC) has been one of the world's leading providers of systems integration and other information technology services. It offers application development data center management communications and networking development IT systems management and business consulting. It also provides business process outsourcing (BPO) services in such areas as billing and payment processing customer relationship management (CRM) and human resources. CSC boasts 2500 clients in more than 70 countries. In 2017 CSC merged with the Enterprise Services segment of Hewlett-Packard Enterprise to form DXC Technology Co. This report is based on CSC's last year as an independent company.

Change in Company Type

DXC is the result of mixing and matching of downsizing and upsizing corporate units. Computer Sciences Corp. spun out its government service unit several years ago which reduced CSC's revenue. Hewlett Packard Enterprise Services was part of Hewlett Packard Enterprise one of two companies created with Hewlett-Packard split up. The combination of HP Enterprise Services and CSC began in 2016 and concluded in April 2017 when DXC formally began operations. The new company is expected to have annual revenue of about $26 billion. This report reflects the final year of CSC as an independent company.

Operations

Prior to the creation of DXC CSC conducted business in through Global Business Services (GBS) and Global Infrastructure Services (GIS). GBS (55% of revenue) addresses key business challenges such as consulting applications services and software. GIS (45% of revenue) provides IT infrastructure services such as managed and virtual desktop solutions unified communications and collaboration services data center management cyber security and cloud-based offerings.

Geographic Reach

CSC has major operations throughout North America Europe Asia and Australia. The company has clients in more than 70 countries. About 40% of sales are made in the US and about 20% are in the UK the second biggest market.

Sales and Marketing

CSC's clients have included AboveNet Communications Deutsche Telekom DirecTV Vodafone and Ryman Hospitality Properties (formerly Gaylord Entertainment).

Financial Performance

After seven straight years of revenue declines CSC's sales rebounded in 2017 (ended March) to $7.6 billion a 7% increase from 2016. The increase was driven by the Global Business Services unit?s business processing services offerings and contributions from recent acquisitions in the Digital Applications business. The Global Infrastructure Services unit posted a small revenue increase from new business and sales from acquisitions.

CSC lost about $123 million in 2017 down from a $251 million profit in 2016 mainly due to large restructuring charges.

Cash flow from operating activities rose to $978 million in 2017 from $802 million in 2016. The increase flowed from an increase in trade payables and a decrease in net account receivables.

Strategy

After going through corporate breakups DXC Technology bets that bigger will be better and stronger in competing in the worldwide market for IT services. The companies have a wide footprint and with some $26 billion in annual revenue and will have some weight to throw around. A question will be if the company can effectively compete with companies that provide similar services such as Cognizant WiPro Accenture IBM Global Service and Dell Technologies.

DXC has bulked up to ride the wave of digital transformation that its customers and potential customers are going through. The company's range of services could lead customers from legacy systems to private or public or hybrid cloud systems.

Mergers and Acquisitions

In 2016 CSC acquired Xchanging plc provider of technology-enabled business services for $633 million. Xchanging brings its Xuber software which is used by commercial insurance companies around the world.

Also in 2016 CSC acquired Aspediens a European provider in the service-management sector and a preferred partner of ServiceNow. The deal extended CSC?s reach in software-as-a-service in Europe.

EXECUTIVES

Vice President Of Global Human Resources And Trans, Mike Darcy
Division Director Deputy Vice President General Manager, Richard Morrow
Vice President Global Sales Excellence, Cherie Gartner
Vice President, Brad Canel
Auditors: DELOITTE & TOUCHE LLP MCLEAN

LOCATIONS

HQ: COMPUTER SCIENCES CORPORATION
1775 TYSONS BLVD STE 1000, TYSONS, VA 221024284
Phone: 703 245-9675
Web: WWW.DXC.TECHNOLOGY

2017 Sales

	$ mil.	% of total
United States	2,986	40
United Kingdom	1,482	19
Australia	921	12
Other Europe	1,594	21
Other International	624	8
Total	**7,607**	**100**

PRODUCTS/OPERATIONS

2017 Sales

	$ mil.	% of total
Global Business Services	4,173	55
Global Infrastructure Services	3,434	45
Total	**7,607**	**100**

Selected Service Areas

Application outsourcing
Business process outsourcing
Customer relationship management
Data hosting
Enterprise application integration
Knowledge management
Management consulting
Risk management
Security
Supply chain management

Selected Solutions

Application Services
Big Data & Analytics
Business & Technology Consulting
Cloud Solutions & Services
Cybersecurity
Industry Software & Solutions
Infrastructure Services
Managed Services & Outsourcing
Mobility Solutions

COMPETITORS

ADP
Accenture
Atos
Booz Allen
CACI International
CIBER
Capgemini
Cognizant Tech Solutions
Computacenter
Convergys
Dell
Deloitte Consulting
Dimension Data
General Dynamics Information Technology
Getronics
HCL Technologies
Honeywell International
IBM Global Services
Infosys
Leidos
ManTech
NTT Data
Northrop Grumman
Siemens AG
Tata Consultancy
Tech Mahindra
Unisys
Wipro
Wipro Technologies

HISTORICAL FINANCIALS

Company Type: Private

Income Statement

FYE: March 31

	REVENUE ($ mil.)	NET INCOME ($ mil.)	NET PROFIT MARGIN	EMPLOYEES
03/17*	7,607	(100)	—	66,000
04/16	7,106	263	3.7%	—
04/15	12,173	7	0.1%	—
03/14	12,998	690	5.3%	—
Annual Growth	(16.4%)	—	—	—

*Fiscal year change

2017 Year-End Financials

Return on assets: 5.4%
Return on equity: (-1.3%)
Current ratio: 1.00

Cash ($ mil.): 1,263

CONCORD HOSPITAL, INC.

Concord Hospital is agreeably an acute care regional hospital serving central New Hampshire. The hospital has some 300 licensed beds and provides general inpatient and outpatient medical care as well as specialist centers for cardiology orthopedics cancer care urology and women's health. Concord Hospital operates other medical facilities either on its main campus or nearby including surgery imaging diagnostic hospice and rehabilitation facilities as well as physician practice locations. With roots reaching back to 1884 Concord Hospital is part of the Capital Region Health Care system which also offers mental health and home health care services.

Operations

With a staff of some 350 doctors Concord Hospital sees about 18000 patients (including some 9000 rehabilitation patients) performs more than 9600 surgeries and handles about 65000 emergency room visits and 1200 births each year. The hospital provides services in about 40 specialty medical fields.

As part of Capital Region Health Care Concord Hospital shares education purchasing and outpatient service functions (and expenses) with its network sister entities which include the Concord Regional Visiting Nurse Association and the Riverbend Community Mental Health center. Through Capital Regional Health Care Concord Hospital also has affiliations with area organizations including Dartmouth-Hitchcock Medical Center Concord Ambulatory Center and Concord Imaging Center.

Concord Hospital is also part of a collaborative network the Granite Healthcare Network with four regional New Hampshire health care providers: Elliot Health System (which operates the Elliot Hospital) LRGHealthcare (consisting of Lakes Region General Hospital and Franklin Regional Hospital) Southern New Hampshire Health System (operating the Southern New Hampshire Medical Center) and Wentworth-Douglass Hospital. Hospitals in the network remain independently managed and owned and have the option to participate or not participate in each of the group efforts.

Geographic Reach

Concord Hospital is located on a 110-acre campus in Concord New Hampshire. It provides services in area communities including Allenstown Andover Barnstead Boscawen Bow Bradford Canterbury Chichester Deering Dunbarton Epsom Henniker Hillsboro Hopkinton Loudon Northwood Pembroke Pittsfield Salsibury Warner Washington Weare Webster and Windsor.

Sales and Marketing

Medicare and Medicaid accounted for some 27% and 3% of net patient revenues respectively in 2014.

Financial Performance

Annual operating revenues increased 3% to some $440 million due to higher net patient revenues in 2014. However net income fell 72% to $18 million due to factors including loss from pension adjustments and declines in net unrealized gains. Cash flow from operations rose 14% to $32 million as less cash was used in accounts receivable and towards supplies and other assets.

Strategy

To help control the spiraling costs of medical care in the US as well as to meet health reform mandates Concord and its affiliated facilities are launching programs to share technology and administrative resources such as claims management software data storage linen service liability insurance pooling and Medicare patient management.

Concord Hospital has also launched independent initiatives to improve quality and patient safety programs including putting infection reduction protocols in place consolidating electronic health record (EHR) consolidation efforts and enacting medication management practices.

EXECUTIVES

Director Of Health Information Medical Records Director, Jodi Panzino
Vice President Acute Care Nursing, Jean Haken
Vp Operations, James Thorne
Vice President Of Medical Records, Mark Carwell
Vice President Provider Services, Bill Dooley
Vice President, Allyson Hicks

LOCATIONS

HQ: CONCORD HOSPITAL, INC.
250 PLEASANT ST, CONCORD, NH 033012598
Phone: 603 227-7000
Web: WWW.CONCORDHOSPITAL.ORG

2014 Sales

	% of total
Net patient service revenue	93
Other revenue	6
Disproportionate share revenue	1
Net assets released from restrictions for operations	-
Total	**100**

Selected Services

Ambulatory Care Center
Behavioral Health
Breast Care Center
Cancer
Cardiac
Center for Health Promotion
Child Life
Clinical Decision Unit
Day Surgery Center
Diabetes Self-Management Education
Concord Hospital Medical Group
Emergency Services
End Of Life
Family Health Centers
Infectious Disease
Intensive Care
Laboratory Services
Maternity
Neurology
Occupational Health
Orthopedics
Pediatrics
Primary Care
Radiology
Rehabilitation
Sleep Center
Surgery
Urology
Walk-in Urgent Care
Women's Health
Wound Care

COMPETITORS

Cambridge Health Alliance
Catholic Medical Center
Elliot Health System
Exeter Health Resources
Frisbie Memorial Hospital
HCA
Partners HealthCare
Southern New Hampshire Medical Center
Steward Health Care

HISTORICAL FINANCIALS

Company Type: Private

Income Statement

FYE: September 30

	REVENUE ($ mil.)	NET INCOME ($ mil.)	NET PROFIT MARGIN	EMPLOYEES
09/17	481	35	7.3%	2,000
09/16	447	15	3.4%	—
09/15	396	24	6.3%	—
09/14	386	28	7.3%	—
Annual Growth	**7.6%**	**7.9%**	**—**	**—**

2017 Year-End Financials

Return on assets: 8.2%
Return on equity: 7.3%
Current ratio: 0.50
Cash ($ mil.): 3

CONNECTICUT CHILDREN'S MEDICAL CENTER

When their tiny tykes need some TLC Nutmeg Staters turn to Connecticut Children's Medical Center. The roughly 190-bed children's hospital is located on two campuses and provides a variety of pediatric services including surgery behavioral care and emergency medicine. Its facilities house pediatric trauma and intensive care units that receive referral patients from hospitals throughout the region. The not-for-profit medical center also conducts clinical research and is the primary pediatric teaching facility for the UConn School of Medicine. In addition Connecticut Children's operates outpatient facilities throughout Connecticut and a school for children with physical and behavioral challenges.

Operations

Connecticut Children's employs some 1100 medical professionals practicing in more than 30 specialty care fields. The hospital handles about 6500 inpatient admissions more than 55000 emergency department visits and 10000 surgeries each year. The medical center also operates the Faculty Practice Plan an integrated multi-specialty pediatric practice providing care to children and their families. The practice employs about 170 physicians and mid-level practitioners.

The system is the only academic medical center dedicated exclusively to pediatric care in western New England making it a popular destination for medical training and research program participants. The hospital is home to a number of clinical research and physician training programs including several two-year fellowships in pediatric subspecialties and a three-year fellowship in pediatric emergency medicine. Other hospital divisions conduct clinical trials in fields including oncology hematology endocrinology gastroenterology and infectious disease.

Geographic Reach

Connecticut Children's operates about a dozen locations across Connecticut. Its main hospital campus is in Hartford while its secondary acute care center is in Waterbury (on the campus of Saint Mary's Hospital). Other locations include ambulatory surgery specialty care and general pediatric care offices.

Strategy

Connecticut Children's grows by expanding its facilities and its range of patient services. It also strives to expand its services into new territories in southern New England including through partnerships with other area health care providers. In addition the medical center is working to increase its participation in basic and clinical research programs.

EXECUTIVES

Surgeon-in-chief And Evp Clinical Affairs, Fernando A. Ferrer
Ceo, James E. Shmerling, age 64
Vp Operations And Cio, Kelly R. Styles
President Medical Staff, Craig C. Bonanni
Evp Community Child Health, Paul H. Dworkin
Evp And Coo, Theresa Hendricksen
Evp And Chief Administrative Officer, Ann Taylor
President Connecticut Children's Medical Center Foundation, Martha E. Schall
Chief Strategy Officer And Vp Marketing And Communications, Thomas C. Richardson
President Connecticut Children's Specialty Group, Dean Rapoza
Vp Clinical Services And Chief Nursing Officer, Cheryl Hoey
President And Coo, Gil Peri
Svp And Cfo, Patrick Garvey
Physician-in-chief, Juan C. Salazar
Director Of Nursing, Gail Karas
Assistant Vice President Development, Greg Latz
Director Of Him And Revenue Cycle Initiatives, Kim Garvey

LOCATIONS

HQ: CONNECTICUT CHILDREN'S MEDICAL CENTER 282 WASHINGTON ST, HARTFORD, CT 061063322
Phone: 860 545-9000
Web: WWW.CONNECTICUTCHILDRENS.ORG

PRODUCTS/OPERATIONS

Selected Programs and Services

Acute Inpatient Rehabilitation
Adolescent Health
Asthma Center
Anesthesiology
Audiology
Bereavement
Cardiology
Cardiovascular Surgery
CCMC School
Center for Motion Analysis
Child and Family Support
Child Health Data Center
Child Protection
Childhood Injury Prevention
Childhood Obesity Awareness and Prevention
Clinical Nutrition
Craniofacial
Critical Care/Pediatric Intensive Care
Cyto-Genetics and Genetic Testing
Day Surgery
Dentistry
Developmental and Behavioral Pediatrics
Diagnostic Cardiology
Digestive Diseases Hepatology and Nutrition
Ear Nose and Throat
Echocardiography
EKG
Emergency Medicine
Emergency Psychiatry
Endocrinology and Diabetes
Feeding
Food Allergy
Genetics
General Surgery
Gynecology
Hand Surgery
Hematology and Oncology
High Risk Infant Follow Up
HIV
Infectious Diseases
Inpatient Medicine
Lead Prevention
Neonatology
Nephrology
Neurogenetics
Neurology
Neurophysiology Lab (EEG)
Neurophysiology - Video Telemetry
Neurosurgery
Occupational Therapy
Ophthalmology
Oral and Maxillofacial Surgery
Organ Transplantation Care
Orthopaedics
Orthotics and Prosthetics
Otolaryngology
Pain Medicine
Pediatric Medicine
Pediatric Pathology
Physical Therapy
Plastic Surgery
Primary Care
Pro-Kids: Primary Care for substance abuse exposed infants
Psychiatry/Psychology
Pulmonary Medicine
Pulmonary Function and Exercise Lab

Radiology
Rehabilitation Medicine
Research
Respiratory Care
Rheumatology
Sleep Diagnostic Laboratory
Special Kids Support Center
Speech-Language Pathology
Sports Medicine
Sports Physical Therapy
TEAM Club: weight management
Trauma Program - Video Telemetry
Urology

COMPETITORS

Backus	MidState Medical
Bridgeport Hospital	Center
Bristol Hospital	New Milford Hospital
Day Kimball Hospital	Saint Francis Hospital
Griffin Health	and Medical Center
Harrington Memorial	St. Vincent's Health
Hospital	Services
Hartford Health Care	Yale-New Haven
Lawrence & Memorial	Hospital
Hospital	

HISTORICAL FINANCIALS

Company Type: Private

Income Statement   FYE: September 30

	REVENUE ($ mil.)	NET INCOME ($ mil.)	NET PROFIT MARGIN	EMPLOYEES
09/15	293	28	9.6%	1,117
09/14	256	(1)	—	—
09/13	264	(2)	—	—
09/10	210	10	4.8%	—
Annual Growth	6.9%	22.7%	—	—

2015 Year-End Financials

Return on assets: 12.1%   Cash ($ mil.): 8
Return on equity: 9.6%
Current ratio: 0.50

CONNECTICUT STATE UNIVERSITY SYSTEM

The Connecticut State University System (CSUS) is the largest public university system in Connecticut and consists of four universities — Central Connecticut State University Eastern Connecticut State University Southern Connecticut State University and Western Connecticut State University. CSUS has an enrollment of more than 36000 students and its schools offer undergraduate and graduate degrees in some 180 subjects. Programs include courses in liberal arts sciences (including meteorology) business nursing education and technology. CSUS traces its roots to 1849 when Central Connecticut State University was founded. It is part of the broader Connecticut State Colleges & Universities (ConnSCU) system.

Operations

Tuition and fees account for 60% of the CSUS' revenues; the rest come from auxiliary activities grants and other sources.

Altogether the ConnSCU organization includes the four universities of CSUS and some 12 community colleges as well as the Charter Oak State College. ConnSCU entities offer more than 1200 degrees and certificates and enroll some 92000 students.

Geographic Reach

CSUS has university locations in Danbury New Britain New Haven and Willimantic Connecticut.

Financial Performance

Revenue was relatively flat in fiscal 2012 falling less than 1% to some $425.5 million as CSUS saw a decrease in revenue from tuition fees grants contracts and auxiliary activity. Net assets decreased 31% to $38.5 million on lower state appropriations.

Strategy

Originally overseen by a board of trustees in 2011 oversight of CSUS was placed under the Connecticut Board of Regents for Higher Education. The Board of Regents also governs the state's community and technical college system and the state's Charter Oak online college. As part of the coordinated system CSUS has raised its minimum standards for admissions and is collaborating with local school districts to improve high school students' readiness for college. The effort has reduced the number of students requiring remedial classes in core academic areas.

To meet the needs of a changing student population the ConnSCU entities are increasing their online course offerings.

EXECUTIVES

Pres, Gregory W Gray
Chb, Lawrence D McHugh
V Chb, Karl J Krapek
Cfo, Pamela J Kedderis
Telecommunications Department, Lawrence McHugh
Asst Cfo, Rosr Butler
Associate Exec Offcr, Germ N Berm Dez
Accounting Staff, Melentina Pusztay
Security Staff, Jeffrey Clark
Coordinator, Cheryl Putnam
Director, Aj Bilotta
Auditors: PRICEWATERHOUSECOOPERS LLP HA

LOCATIONS

HQ: CONNECTICUT STATE UNIVERSITY SYSTEM
61 WOODLAND ST, HARTFORD, CT 061052345
Phone: 860 493-0000
Web: WWW.CT.EDU

HISTORICAL FINANCIALS

Company Type: Private

Income Statement   FYE: June 30

	REVENUE ($ mil.)	NET INCOME ($ mil.)	NET PROFIT MARGIN	EMPLOYEES
06/17	429	(55)	—	2,800
06/11	428	55	13.0%	—
06/10	413	22	5.5%	—
06/09	373	39	10.7%	—
Annual Growth	1.7%	—	—	—

2017 Year-End Financials

Return on assets: 3.8%   Cash ($ mil.): 212
Return on equity: (-12.9%)
Current ratio: 1.60

CONROE INDEPENDENT SCHOOL DISTRICT

EXECUTIVES

Supt, Don Stockton
Asst Supt For Elementary Schl, Cathy Gibson
Assistant, Dawn Poole
Special Education Assistant, Colleen Hruska

Assistant Students H, Paul Fleming
Staff Accountant, Rachael Batalla
Director of Communications, Sarah Blakelock
Police Officer, Steve Esch

LOCATIONS

HQ: CONROE INDEPENDENT SCHOOL DISTRICT
3205 W DAVIS ST, CONROE, TX 773042039
Phone: 936 709-7751
Web: WWW.CONROEISD.NET

HISTORICAL FINANCIALS

Company Type: Private

Income Statement   FYE: August 31

	REVENUE ($ mil.)	NET INCOME ($ mil.)	NET PROFIT MARGIN	EMPLOYEES
08/17	609	7	1.2%	6,223
08/16	590	81	13.9%	—
08/15	552	24	4.4%	—
08/14	510	(4)	—	—
Annual Growth	6.1%	—	—	—

2017 Year-End Financials

Return on assets: 4.8%   Cash ($ mil.): 7
Return on equity: 1.2%
Current ratio: 0.10

CONSOLIDATED GRAIN & BARGE COMPANY

EXECUTIVES

Ceo, Kevin D Adams
Vice President, Gregory Beck
Credit Manager, Randolph Hart
Information Technology, Sean Goodrion
Controller, Robin Gerarve
Accounting Assistant, Melody Bradfoot
Manager, Bill McBee
Human Resources Director, Judy Keitel
Manager, Paul Kelly
Auditors: KPMG LLP NEW ORLEANS LA

LOCATIONS

HQ: CONSOLIDATED GRAIN & BARGE COMPANY
1127 HWY 190 E SERVICE RD, COVINGTON, LA 704334929
Phone: 985 867-3500

HISTORICAL FINANCIALS

Company Type: Private

Income Statement   FYE: May 31

	REVENUE ($ mil.)	NET INCOME ($ mil.)	NET PROFIT MARGIN	EMPLOYEES
05/17	6,430	16	0.3%	2,000
05/16	5,759	21	0.4%	—
05/14	7,093	44	0.6%	—
05/12	5,996	50	0.8%	—
Annual Growth	1.4%	(20.4%)	—	—

2017 Year-End Financials

Return on assets: 0.7%   Cash ($ mil.): —
Return on equity: 0.3%
Current ratio: 0.10

CONSOLIDATED PIPE & SUPPLY COMPANY, INC.

Consolidated Pipe and Supply lives up to its name: Its nine divisions supply pipe and pipeline materials to a swath of industries from energy to water and waste treatment chemical mining nuclear oil and gas and pulp and paper. Its industrial unit specializes in carbon and stainless alloy pipe valves and fittings. Vulcan makes all types of PVC. Corrosion resistant coatings are offered by a Line Pipe and Tubular unit and liquid applied coatings by Specialty Coatings. Its Consolidated Power Supply is the largest in the business of safety related metallic materials for commercial nuclear generation. Another unit caters to utilities. Consolidated also provides engineering services and inventory systems.

Operations

Consolidated Pipe and Supply is one of nearly 20 US Steel distributors authorized to sell seamless and electric resistance welded products in North America. Not limited to its branch and sales centers Consolidated Pipe and Supply's fitted semi-trailers complete with area row and bin and bar coded shelving serve as mobile warehouses for construction customers requiring on-site materials management.

The company operates through nine divisions: Industrial Line Pipe Structural Pipeline Coatings Utility Products Specialty Coatings Consolidated Power Vulcan Plastics and Consolidated Controls.

Geographic Reach

The company's reach extends to 19 US states including Alabama Arkansas Florida Georgia Illinois Indiana Kentucky Missouri Mississippi North Carolina Pennsylvania South Carolina Tennessee Texas and Virginia. It has nearly 50 sales offices in 15 states.

EXECUTIVES

Pres, Howard J Kerr
Exec Vice President, Robert W Kerr
SEC-Treas, Barry Howton
Accounting Staff, Dana Grimes
Staff, Jeff Hallmark
Executive Vice President, Bob Kerr
Sales Staff, Michael Murray

LOCATIONS

HQ: CONSOLIDATED PIPE & SUPPLY COMPANY, INC.
1205 HILLTOP PKWY, BIRMINGHAM, AL 352045002
Phone: 205 323-7261
Web: WWW.CONSOLIDATEDPIPE.COM

PRODUCTS/OPERATIONS

Selected Industries Served
Chemical
Energy
Mining
Nuclear Generation
Oil and Gas
Petro-Chemical
Pulp and Paper
Water and Waste Treatment

Selected Divisions
Consolidated Controls (valves)
Consolidated Power (provides materials to energy industries)
Industrial (provides materials construction commercial energy pulp and paper chemical petro-chemical mining and fabrication industries)
Line Pipe (line pipe and tubular products)
Pipeline Coatings
Specialty Coatings (specialty linings for use in jet fuel and military applications)

Structural (1/8" through 48" structural and prime grades of carbon steel pipe)
Utility Products (provides utilities with products such as steel ductile iron PVC polyethylene and brass fittings and valves and steel PVC and polyethylene pipe)
Vulcan Plastics (water and sewer pipe)

COMPETITORS

American Cast Iron Pipe	Phoenix Tube
Bristol Metals	Seymour Tubing
Bull Moose Tube	Southland Tube
Chicago Tube & Iron	Steel Ventures
Kelly Pipe Co. LLC	U.S. Pipe

HISTORICAL FINANCIALS
Company Type: Private

Income Statement				FYE: December 31
	REVENUE ($ mil.)	NET INCOME ($ mil.)	NET PROFIT MARGIN	EMPLOYEES
12/16	550	17	3.3%	700
12/15	575	7	1.3%	—
12/14	667	23	3.5%	—
12/13	602	19	3.2%	—
Annual Growth	(3.0%)	(2.3%)	—	—

2016 Year-End Financials
Return on assets: 5.4%
Return on equity: 3.3%
Current ratio: 1.40
Cash ($ mil.): 1

CONSUMER PRODUCT DISTRIBUTORS, INC.

EXECUTIVES

Vice President Of Sales, Steve Peterson
Vice President, Lori Polep
Vice President Trade Development And Sales Analytics, Joe Normand
Auditors: MEYERS BROTHERS KALICKA PC

LOCATIONS

HQ: CONSUMER PRODUCT DISTRIBUTORS, INC.
705 MEADOW ST, CHICOPEE, MA 010134820
Phone: 413 592-4141
Web: WWW.JPOLEP.COM

PRODUCTS/OPERATIONS

Selected Products
Alcohol
  Spirits
  Wine
Automotive
  Branded Motor Oils
  Mag 1
  Additives
  Cleaning Supplies
Bakery/Pastry
  Rachael's Gourmet
  Mrs. Freshley's
  Dolly Madison
  Bon Appetite
  Bellow's House
  Diana's
  Table Talk
Beverages
  Poland Springs (Nestle Waters)
  Adirondack Soda
  Arizona
  Florida's Natural
  Simply Juices
  Sweet Leaf Tea
  Trade Winds
  Daily Juice

Selected Services
Credit & Return Policy
Management Information Systems
Merchandising Support
Sales and Marketing Support

COMPETITORS

Atlantic Dominion	Harold Levinson
C&S Wholesale	McLane
Core-Mark	SUPERVALU
Eby-Brown	Tripifoods
H. T. Hackney	

HISTORICAL FINANCIALS
Company Type: Private

Income Statement				FYE: September 30
	REVENUE ($ mil.)	NET INCOME ($ mil.)	NET PROFIT MARGIN	EMPLOYEES
09/17*	1,101	5	0.5%	400
10/16	1,005	5	0.6%	—
10/15	968	2	0.3%	—
09/14	898	2	0.3%	—
Annual Growth	7.0%	27.1%	—	—

*Fiscal year change

2017 Year-End Financials
Return on assets: 3.0%
Return on equity: 0.5%
Current ratio: 2.20
Cash ($ mil.): 4

COOK CHILDREN'S HEALTH PLAN

EXECUTIVES

Pres, Doris Hunt
Director, Claire Murtha
Project Manager, Barbara Flores
Coordinator, Chase Robinson
Senior Network Engineer, Lud Pendery
Coordinator, Allyson Tate
Manager, Beatriz Ruiz
Orthotist, Caitlin Denmark
Coordinator, Michael Miller
Senior Project, Anne Mullins
Vice President, Cory Rhoades
Auditors: BKD LLP HOUSTON TX

LOCATIONS

HQ: COOK CHILDREN'S HEALTH PLAN
801 7TH AVE, FORT WORTH, TX 761042733
Phone: 817 334-2247
Web: WWW.COOKCHILDRENS.ORG

HISTORICAL FINANCIALS
Company Type: Private

Income Statement				FYE: September 30
	REVENUE ($ mil.)	NET INCOME ($ mil.)	NET PROFIT MARGIN	EMPLOYEES
09/15	307	17	5.8%	27
09/14	284	11	3.9%	—
09/13	259	5	2.0%	—
09/09	126	(3)	—	—
Annual Growth	16.0%	—	—	—

2015 Year-End Financials
Return on assets: 9.0%
Return on equity: 5.8%
Current ratio: 2.30
Cash ($ mil.): 62

COOK CHILDREN'S MEDICAL CENTER

EXECUTIVES

Pres-Ceo, Rick W Merrill
Director, Winney King
Director of Infection Control, Lisa La Rue
Director Staff Svs, Karen Baker
Credentaling Coordinator, Sandy Martin
Director of Human Resources, Beth Schmidt
Coordinator Audio Visual/Media, Terry Wilder
Trustee, Joann Sanders
Scientist, Anita Gonzales
Human Resources Information MA, Jill Wegman
Osteopathy, Orlando Chapa Do

LOCATIONS

HQ: COOK CHILDREN'S MEDICAL CENTER
801 7TH AVE, FORT WORTH, TX 761042796
Phone: 682 885-4000
Web: WWW.COOKCHILDRENS.ORG

HISTORICAL FINANCIALS
Company Type: Private

Income Statement				FYE: September 30
	REVENUE ($ mil.)	NET INCOME ($ mil.)	NET PROFIT MARGIN	EMPLOYEES
09/15	753	159	21.1%	2,000
09/14	753	107	14.2%	—
09/13	828	160	19.4%	—
09/09	563	99	17.7%	—
Annual Growth	5.0%	8.1%	—	—

2015 Year-End Financials

Return on assets: 4.2%   Cash ($ mil.): 255
Return on equity: 21.1%
Current ratio: 0.70

COOK CHILDREN'S PHYSICIAN NETWORK

EXECUTIVES

Pres, W Britt Nelson
Chm, Howard Kelfer
Vice President, Ryan Champlin
V Pres-Cfo, Ted Matthews
Treas, Clive Daniels
SEC, Kimberly Aaron
V Chm, Michael Beachman
V Chm, Kevin Wylie
Doctor, Christopher Mann
Financial Executive, Pam Foster
Nurse, Jimmy Uselton

LOCATIONS

HQ: COOK CHILDREN'S PHYSICIAN NETWORK
801 7TH AVE, FORT WORTH, TX 761042733
Phone: 682 885-6800
Web: WWW.COOKCHILDRENS.ORG

HISTORICAL FINANCIALS
Company Type: Private

Income Statement				FYE: September 30
	REVENUE ($ mil.)	NET INCOME ($ mil.)	NET PROFIT MARGIN	EMPLOYEES
09/16	282	(0)	—	801
09/15	250	0	0.1%	—
09/14	230	(0)	—	—
09/13	216	3	1.5%	—
Annual Growth	9.2%	—	—	—

2016 Year-End Financials

Return on assets: 2.9%   Cash ($ mil.): 11
Return on equity: (-0.1%)
Current ratio: 2.80

COOP WHEATON-DUMONT ELEVATOR INC

EXECUTIVES

Chb-Pres, Vaughn Maudal
Ceo, Philip Deal
V Pres, Chuck Grimes
SEC-Treas, Chadd Berger
Cfo-Controller, Mark Suek
Director, Greg Frisch
Director, Ron Lenzen
Director, Dan Nigg
Plant Manager, Jeremy Ostby
Plant Manager, Brian Montonye
Plant Manager, Casey Loosmore

LOCATIONS

HQ: COOP WHEATON-DUMONT ELEVATOR INC
6587 US HIGHWAY 75, WHEATON, MN 562965441
Phone: 320 563-8152
Web: WWW.WDCOOP.COM

HISTORICAL FINANCIALS
Company Type: Private

Income Statement				FYE: August 31
	REVENUE ($ mil.)	NET INCOME ($ mil.)	NET PROFIT MARGIN	EMPLOYEES
08/17	284	1	0.5%	120
08/16	234	3	1.4%	—
08/09	159	5	3.6%	—
08/08	163	2	1.5%	—
Annual Growth	6.3%	(5.9%)	—	—

2017 Year-End Financials

Return on assets: 1.6%   Cash ($ mil.): 2
Return on equity: 0.5%
Current ratio: 0.10

COOPERATIVE ENERGY, A MISSISSIPPI ELECTRIC COOPERATIVE

EXECUTIVES

Pres, Henry C Waterer Jr
Vice President, Harlan Rogers
Vice President, Billy Harden
SEC, W T Shows
Gen Mgr, James M Compton
Plant Manager, Jerry Hudson

LOCATIONS

HQ: COOPERATIVE ENERGY, A MISSISSIPPI
ELECTRIC COOPERATIVE
7037 U S HIGHWAY 49, HATTIESBURG, MS
394029128
Phone: 601 579-0215
Web: WWW.SMEPA.COOP

HISTORICAL FINANCIALS
Company Type: Private

Income Statement				FYE: December 31
	REVENUE ($ mil.)	NET INCOME ($ mil.)	NET PROFIT MARGIN	EMPLOYEES
12/16	822	0	—	238
12/13	811	0	—	—
12/12	771	0	—	—
12/11	766	0	—	—
Annual Growth	1.4%	—	—	—

2016 Year-End Financials

Return on assets: 17.4%   Cash ($ mil.): 41
Return on equity: —
Current ratio: 0.60

COOPERATIVE FOR ASSISTANCE AND RELIEF EVERYWHERE, INC. (CARE)

The Cooperative for Assistance and Relief Everywhere (CARE) strives to be the beginning of the end of poverty. The organization works to reduce poverty in about 85 countries by helping communities in areas such as health education economic development emergency relief and agriculture. CARE supports more than 1100 projects to combat poverty.A It also operates a small economic activity development (SEAD) unit that supports moneymaking activities. Through SEAD CAREA provides technical training and savings and loans programs to help people — particularlyA women —A open or expand small businesses. CARE was founded in 1945 to give aid to WWII survivors.

Operations

In addition to its home office in Georgia CARE maintains field offices in about 10 US cities including Boston Chicago Miami New York and Wash-

ington DC. The group'sA internationalA field offices are located inA more than 55 countries.

CARE's 1100 projects reach 122 million people
more than half of which are women. About 90%
of the funds that CARE receives go toward its aid
efforts. The organization helps people in the poor-
est communities of developing nations. (It does
not provide assistance in the US.)

Geographic Reach

From its headquarters in Atlanta CARE serves
poor communities in nearly 85 countries. It does
not provide assistance in the US.

Financial Performance

CARE's revenue increasedA a modest 1% to
$590 million in fiscal 2011 as compared to 2010.
While it logged a drop in revenues from the US
government the organization saw a boost in private contributions — totaling $310 million — from
CARE international members.

Strategy

CARE is supported by donations from thousands of individuals and dozens of corporations
foundations and other charitable organizations in
the US. Some of the participating organizations
include World Wildlife Fund Covance Merck
Meredith Corporation and the Wal-Mart Foundation. The group also receives funding and supplies
from government agencies including the United
Nations and European Union.A As a result of the
economicA downturn CARE hasA beenA working
to raise contribution levels as governments businesses and individuals cut back their spending including charitable donations.

EXECUTIVES

**Vice President Finance And Information
Technology And Chief Financial Officer,** Peter
Buijs
Vice President, Phil Mazzara
**Vice President Individual Fundraising And
Marketing,** Tolli Love
Auditors: ERNST & YOUNG LLP ATLANTA GA

LOCATIONS

HQ: COOPERATIVE FOR ASSISTANCE AND RELIEF
EVERYWHERE, INC. (CARE)
151 ELLIS ST NE, ATLANTA, GA 303032420
Phone: 404 681-2552
Web: WWW.CARE.ORG

PRODUCTS/OPERATIONS

Selected International Partner Organizations
Covance Inc.
Merck Foundation
Meredith Corporation
The Wal-mart Foundation
WWF

HISTORICAL FINANCIALS
Company Type: Private

Income Statement				FYE: June 30
	REVENUE ($ mil.)	NET INCOME ($ mil.)	NET PROFIT MARGIN	EMPLOYEES
06/16	530	(21)	—	10,000
06/13	492	(18)	—	—
06/11	589	10	1.7%	—
06/08	713	40	5.6%	—
Annual Growth	(3.6%)	—	—	—

2016 Year-End Financials
Return on assets: 8.4%   Cash ($ mil.): 74
Return on equity: (-4.1%)
Current ratio: 0.90

COPPEL CORPORATION

EXECUTIVES

Cfo, Olegario Gomez
Administrative Assistant, Gloria Perez
Auditors: BEACH FLEISCHMAN PC TUCSON A

LOCATIONS

HQ: COPPEL CORPORATION
503 SCARONI AVE, CALEXICO, CA 922319791
Phone: 760 357-3707
Web: WWW.COPPEL.COM

HISTORICAL FINANCIALS
Company Type: Private

Income Statement				FYE: December 31
	REVENUE ($ mil.)	NET INCOME ($ mil.)	NET PROFIT MARGIN	EMPLOYEES
12/17	329	2	0.8%	80
12/16	335	3	1.0%	—
12/15	335	4	1.5%	—
12/14	332	4	1.4%	—
Annual Growth	(0.3%)	(18.1%)	—	—

2017 Year-End Financials
Return on assets: 4.7%   Cash ($ mil.): 1
Return on equity: 0.8%
Current ratio: 0.20

CORE CONSTRUCTION GROUP, LTD.

EXECUTIVES

Pres, Mark A Steffen
Exec Vice President, Dennis Barber
Treas, Michael J Thomas
Manager, Tim Hickey

LOCATIONS

HQ: CORE CONSTRUCTION GROUP, LTD.
866 N MAIN ST, MORTON, IL 615501602
Phone: 309 263-0808

HISTORICAL FINANCIALS
Company Type: Private

Income Statement				FYE: December 31
	REVENUE ($ mil.)	NET INCOME ($ mil.)	NET PROFIT MARGIN	EMPLOYEES
12/17	1,007	0	—	450
12/15	782	0	—	—
12/12	624	0	—	—
12/06	620	0	—	—
Annual Growth	4.5%	—	—	—

2017 Year-End Financials
Return on assets: 16.7%   Cash ($ mil.): 37
Return on equity: —
Current ratio: 1.00

CORNELL UNIVERSITY

To excel at Cornell you'll need every one of your
brain cells. The Ivy League school's 22000 students can select undergraduate graduate and professional courses from 14 colleges and schools. In
addition to its Ithaca New York campus the university has medical and professional programs in
New York City and Doha Qatar. Cornell's faculty
includes a handful of Nobel laureates and the university has a robust research component studying
everything from animal health to space to waste
management. It has a student-faculty ratio of about
9:1. Notable alumni include author E. B. White
and US Supreme Court Justice Ruth Bader Gins-
burg.

Operations

Cornell awarded the nation's first university degree in veterinary medicine and first doctorates in
electrical engineering and industrial engineering.
It awarded the world's first degree in journalism
(and taught the first university course in that subject) and established the first four-year schools of
hotel administration and industrial and labor relations.

Cornell is deeply involved in research with more
than 100 interdisciplinary research organizations
pursuing research teaching and outreach on broad
topics like nanofabrication life sciences computing
and information science environmental sustainability human development agriculture space research and international issues. Cornell has dozens
of research centers such as the Cornell High Energy Synchrotron Source (CHESS) the Cornell
Electroacoustic Music Center (CEMC) the Cornell
Center for Wildlife Conservation (CCWC) the National Biomedical Center for Advanced ESR Technology (ACERT) and the Laboratory of Elemen-
tary-Particle Physics (LEPP).

Geographic Reach

Cornell's main campus in Ithaca NY is comprised of endowed colleges and contract colleges
(operated on behalf of the state) spanning a 2300
acre campus in New York State?s Finger Lakes
region. Its location in New York City primarily consists of the Sanford I. Weill Medical College which
has an extension campus in Doha Qatar and the
Graduate School of Medical Sciences.

Financial Performance

University operating revenues grew by 25% between 2012 and 2017 from $3.2 billion to $4.0
billion. The largest area of growth was the Medical
Physician Organization at the Weill Cornell Medicine which makes up more than 25% of Cornell?s
operating revenue.

In FY2017 (ended June 30 2017) operating revenue was $4.0 billion with tuition & fees and the
Medical Physician Organization each contributing
about $1.0 billion. Grants contracts and similar
agreements accounted for another $600 million. It
also garnered money through gifts & contributions
of $535 million in FY2017. Because it operates
contract colleges on behalf of the State University
of New York (SUNY) it received appropriations of
about $132 million for the year.

Non-operating revenue which includes contributions for its endowment change in value of its
endowment investments and other items accounted for a $424 million rise in overall asset
value leading to a FY2017 year-end amount exceeding $3.1 billion.

The university?s endowment is more than $6.5
billion.

Company Background

The Ivy League university has been educating
young minds since its founding in 1865.

EXECUTIVES

Evp And Cfo, Joanne M. DeStefano
Dean School Of Continuing Education And Summer Sessions, Glenn C. Altschuler
Provost, Michael I. Kotlikoff
Dean College Of Human Ecology, Alan D. Mathios
Dean And Provost Cornell Nyc Tech, Daniel P. Huttenlocher
President, Martha E. Pollack
Dean College Of Agriculture And Life Sciences, Kathryn J. Boor
Dean College Of Engineering, Lance R. Collins
Dean Of The Cornell Sc Johnson College Of Business, Soumitra Dutta
Dean College Of Architecture Art And Planning, Kent Kleinman
Dean Graduate School, Barbara A. Knuth
Dean Graduate School Of Medical Sciences And Senior Associate Dean For Research At Weill Cornell Medicine, Gary Koretzky
Dean College Of Arts And Sciences, Gretchen Ritter
Dean School Of Law, Eduardo M. Pe ±alver
Provost For Medical Affairs And Dean Of Weill Cornell Medicine, Augustine M.K. Choi
Vp Information Technology And Chief Information Office, David Lifka
Dean Of The School Of Industrial And Labor Relations (ilr), Kevin F. Hallock
Interim Dean School Of Applied Economics And Management, Edward W. McLaughlin
Dean Of The Faculty Of Computing And Information Science, J. Gregory Morrisett
Dean Of The Samuel Curtis Johnson Graduate School Of Management, Mark W. Nelson
Interim Dean Of The School Of Hotel Administration And E. M. Statler Professor Of Hotel Administration, Kate Walsh
Dean Of The College Of Veterinary Medicine, Lorin D. Warnick
Vice Chairman, David D. Croll
Chairman, Robert S. Harrison
Vice Chairman, Barton J. Winokur
Auditors: PRICEWATERHOUSECOOPERS LLP RO

LOCATIONS

HQ: CORNELL UNIVERSITY
308 DUFFIELD HALL, ITHACA, NY 148532700
Phone: 607 254-4636
Web: WWW.CORNELL.EDU

HISTORICAL FINANCIALS
Company Type: Private

Income Statement				FYE: June 30
	REVENUE ($ mil.)	NET INCOME ($ mil.)	NET PROFIT MARGIN	EMPLOYEES
06/17	4,013	985	24.6%	12,207
06/16	3,809	(442)	—	—
06/12	2,956	(341)	—	—
06/11	2,955	814	27.5%	—
Annual Growth	5.2%	3.2%	—	—

2017 Year-End Financials
Return on assets: 15.9% Cash ($ mil.): 181
Return on equity: 24.6%
Current ratio: —

CORONA-NORCO UNIFIED SCHOOL DISTRICT

EXECUTIVES

Ceo, Cathy L Sciortino
Supt, Kent Bechler
Prin, Ted Rozzi
President, John Z Zickefoose
Vice President, Jose W Lalas
SEC, Linda Hawkins
Vice-President, Alia Morales
Teacher, Scott Foster
Vice-President, Andrea Rangel
Administrator, Benjamin Odipo
Director, Nancy Baker
Auditors: VAVRINEK TRINE DAY & CO LL

LOCATIONS

HQ: CORONA-NORCO UNIFIED SCHOOL DISTRICT
2820 CLARK AVE, NORCO, CA 928601903
Phone: 951 736-5000
Web: WWW.CNUSD.K12.CA.US

HISTORICAL FINANCIALS
Company Type: Private

Income Statement				FYE: June 30
	REVENUE ($ mil.)	NET INCOME ($ mil.)	NET PROFIT MARGIN	EMPLOYEES
06/17	637	(8)	—	614
06/16	635	113	17.8%	—
06/11	1	(20)	—	—
06/10	0	0	92.3%	—
Annual Growth	214.6%	—	—	—

CORPORATION FOR PUBLIC BROADCASTING

EXECUTIVES

Senior Vice President Radio, Greg Schnirring
Senior Vice President, Debra Sanchez
Vice President Business Affairs, Jeffrey R Breslow
Senior Vice President General Counsel, Westwood Smithers
Vice President Radio, Erika Pulley-Hayes
Auditors: GRANT THORNTON LLP BALTIMORE

LOCATIONS

HQ: CORPORATION FOR PUBLIC BROADCASTING
401 9TH ST NW STE 200, WASHINGTON, DC 200042129
Phone: 202 879-9600
Web: WWW.CPB.ORG

HISTORICAL FINANCIALS
Company Type: Private

Income Statement				FYE: September 30
	REVENUE ($ mil.)	NET INCOME ($ mil.)	NET PROFIT MARGIN	EMPLOYEES
09/16	510	31	6.1%	99
09/15	461	(11)	—	—
09/14	463	1	0.4%	—
09/13	446	(18)	—	—
Annual Growth	4.6%	—	—	—

2016 Year-End Financials
Return on assets: 1.2% Cash ($ mil.): 78
Return on equity: 6.1%
Current ratio: 1.00

COUNTY OF CLARK

EXECUTIVES

County Mgr, Don Burnette
County Manager, Don Burnett
Cfo, Yolanda King
Staff, Hanks Jeffrey
Information Specialist, Bill Bonner
Coordinator, Fernando Martinez
Deputy Chief Information Offic, Michael Lane
Auditors: KAFOURY ARMSTRONG & CO CPAS

LOCATIONS

HQ: COUNTY OF CLARK
500 S GRAND CENTRAL PKWY # 6, LAS VEGAS, NV 891554502
Phone: 702 455-3530

HISTORICAL FINANCIALS
Company Type: Private

Income Statement				FYE: June 30
	REVENUE ($ mil.)	NET INCOME ($ mil.)	NET PROFIT MARGIN	EMPLOYEES
06/17	2,873	96	3.4%	8,528
06/16	2,768	74	2.7%	—
06/15	2,595	(26)	—	—
06/13	2,372	(133)	—	—
Annual Growth	4.9%	—	—	—

2017 Year-End Financials
Return on assets: 18.2% Cash ($ mil.): 3,389
Return on equity: 3.4%
Current ratio: —

COUNTY OF CLAYTON

EXECUTIVES

Chm, Eldrin Bell
Cfo, Ramona Thurman
Coo, Anthony Brister
Commissioner, Jeffrey Turner
Manager, Angie Roberts
Vice-President Marketing, Deborah Nichols
Coordinator, Kenn Cook
Coordinator, Ricardo Newman
Manager, Twana Hudson
Legal Assistant, Ashley Patterson
Manager, Cyd Cox
Auditors: MAULDIN & JENKINS LLC MACON

LOCATIONS

HQ: COUNTY OF CLAYTON
112 SMITH ST, JONESBORO, GA 302363539
Phone: 770 477-3208
Web: WWW.CLAYTONCOUNTYGA.GOV

HISTORICAL FINANCIALS
Company Type: Private

Income Statement
FYE: June 30

	REVENUE ($ mil.)	NET INCOME ($ mil.)	NET PROFIT MARGIN	EMPLOYEES
06/17	287	3	1.3%	2,400
06/16	276	(11)	—	—
06/15	260	(2)	—	—
06/14	0	0	—	—
Annual Growth	—	—	—	—

2017 Year-End Financials
Return on assets: 4.7% Cash ($ mil.): 299
Return on equity: 1.3%
Current ratio: —

COUNTY OF DAUPHIN

EXECUTIVES

Chm, Jeffrey T Haste
Vice President, Mike Pries
SEC, George P Hartwick III
County Solicitor, William T Tully
Chief Clerk Administrator, Chad Saylor
Auditors: ZELENKOFSKE AXELROD LLC HARRI

LOCATIONS

HQ: COUNTY OF DAUPHIN
MARKET & FRONT STS, HARRISBURG, PA 17101
Phone: 717 780-6300
Web: WWW.DAUPHINC.ORG

HISTORICAL FINANCIALS
Company Type: Private

Income Statement
FYE: December 31

	REVENUE ($ mil.)	NET INCOME ($ mil.)	NET PROFIT MARGIN	EMPLOYEES
12/17	288	5	2.0%	1,500
12/16	288	0	0.0%	—
12/15	272	9	3.5%	—
12/14	0	0	—	—
Annual Growth	—	—	—	—

2017 Year-End Financials
Return on assets: 4.3% Cash ($ mil.): 59
Return on equity: 2.0%
Current ratio: —

COUNTY OF DEKALB

EXECUTIVES

Ceo, Vernon Jones
Interim Ceo, Lee May
Cpo, Talisa R Clark
Attorney, Jonathan Weintraub
Gis Specialist, Tony Hall
Administrator, Felecia Alston

Coordinator, Larry Thomas
Acting Sheriff, Ruth M Stringer
Assistant Director of Informat, Austin Brown
Deputy Chief Operating Officer, Luz Borrero
Senior Risk Control Manager, Steadman Scavella
Auditors: KPMG LLP ATLANTA GA

LOCATIONS

HQ: COUNTY OF DEKALB
1300 COMMERCE DR, DECATUR, GA 300303222
Phone: 404 371-2881
Web: WWW.CO.DEKALB.GA.US

HISTORICAL FINANCIALS
Company Type: Private

Income Statement
FYE: December 31

	REVENUE ($ mil.)	NET INCOME ($ mil.)	NET PROFIT MARGIN	EMPLOYEES
12/17	628	20	3.2%	7,300
12/16	577	15	2.7%	—
12/15	599	(3)	—	—
12/10	583	(39)	—	—
Annual Growth	1.1%	—	—	—

2017 Year-End Financials
Return on assets: 16.3% Cash ($ mil.): 690
Return on equity: 3.2%
Current ratio: —

COUNTY OF HARFORD

EXECUTIVES

County Exec, David Craig
Council President, William Boniface
Treas, Kathryn Hewitt
Procurement Staff, James P Barker
Procurement Staff, Stacy R Appold
Procurement Staff, Peter D Wakefiel
Procurement Staff, Stephanie L Si
Procurement Staff, Walter Ballesteros
Administration Director, Mary Chance
Information Specialist, Constance Hirsch
Council Member, Joseph Woods
Auditors: SB & COMPANY LLC HUNT VALLEY

LOCATIONS

HQ: COUNTY OF HARFORD
220 S MAIN ST, BEL AIR, MD 210143820
Phone: 410 638-3000
Web: WWW.HARFORDCOUNTYMD.GOV

HISTORICAL FINANCIALS
Company Type: Private

Income Statement
FYE: June 30

	REVENUE ($ mil.)	NET INCOME ($ mil.)	NET PROFIT MARGIN	EMPLOYEES
06/18	630	22	3.5%	1,400
06/17	603	47	7.9%	—
06/13	553	(7)	—	—
06/09	1	0	—	—
Annual Growth	96.5%	—	—	—

COUNTY OF HILLSBOROUGH

EXECUTIVES

County Admin, Mike Merrill
Dep County Admin, Gregory Horwedel
Chief Fin Admin, Bonnie Wise
Chief Development Svs, Lucia Garsys
Chief of Human Svs, Carl Harness
Grants Admin, Wayne Finley
Executive of Information Techn, Hammond R Powes
Program Inspector, Bobby Jackson
Program Inspector, Wayne New
Admin Splst, Catherine Achat
Manager, Renee Lee
Auditors: CHERRY BEKAERT LLP TAMPA FL

LOCATIONS

HQ: COUNTY OF HILLSBOROUGH
601 E KENNEDY BLVD, TAMPA, FL 336024156
Phone: 813 276-2720
Web: WWW.HILLSBOROUGHCOUNTY.ORG

HISTORICAL FINANCIALS
Company Type: Private

Income Statement
FYE: September 30

	REVENUE ($ mil.)	NET INCOME ($ mil.)	NET PROFIT MARGIN	EMPLOYEES
09/17	1,613	83	5.2%	10,000
09/16	1,521	(9)	—	—
09/15	1,434	64	4.5%	—
09/14	1,370	(32)	—	—
Annual Growth	5.6%	—	—	—

2017 Year-End Financials
Return on assets: 2.8% Cash ($ mil.): 258
Return on equity: 5.2%
Current ratio: 0.60

COUNTY OF MONTGOMERY

EXECUTIVES

County Executive, Marc Elrich
Pres, Hans Riemer
Exec Dir, Linda Herman
Prin, Amy Moskowitz
Captain, Dan Ogren
Captain, Gary Rebsch
Captain, Mike Green
Program Inspector, Brian Keeler
Program Inspector, Kevin Embry
Coordinator, Lili Rojas
Coordinator, Michael Brown
Auditors: CLIFTONLARSONALLEN LLP BALTIM

LOCATIONS

HQ: COUNTY OF MONTGOMERY
101 MONROE ST FL 15, ROCKVILLE, MD 208502503
Phone: 240 777-8220

HISTORICAL FINANCIALS
Company Type: Private

Income Statement
FYE: June 30

	REVENUE ($ mil.)	NET INCOME ($ mil.)	NET PROFIT MARGIN	EMPLOYEES
06/17	4,191	52	1.3%	7,400
06/16	3,874	(89)	—	—
06/15	0	0	—	—
06/14	0	70	—	—
Annual Growth	—	(9.0%)	—	—

2017 Year-End Financials
Return on assets: 4.8%
Return on equity: 1.3%
Current ratio: —

Cash ($ mil.): 309

COUNTY OF RIVERSIDE

EXECUTIVES

1st Dist Sup, Bob Buster
2nd Dist Sup, John Tavaglinoe
3rd Dist Sup, Jeff Stone
Sup, Cynthia R
Sup, Marion Ashley
SEC, Judy Green
Dir, Jean Strey
Dir, John Mooney
Dir, Lucas Robert
Analyst II, Carmela Dunderman
Sales, Ron Kirk
Auditors: BROWN ARMSTRONG ACCOUNTANCY CO

LOCATIONS

HQ: COUNTY OF RIVERSIDE
4080 LEMON ST FL 11, RIVERSIDE, CA 925013609
Phone: 951 955-1110
Web: WWW.COUNTYOFRIVERSIDE.US

HISTORICAL FINANCIALS
Company Type: Private

Income Statement
FYE: June 30

	REVENUE ($ mil.)	NET INCOME ($ mil.)	NET PROFIT MARGIN	EMPLOYEES
06/17	3,504	(132)	—	20,000
06/16	3,390	(124)	—	—
06/15	3,245	293	9.0%	—
Annual Growth	3.9%	—	—	—

COUNTY OF SUFFOLK

EXECUTIVES

County Exec, Steven Bellone
Comptroller, John Kennedy Jr
Treasurer, Angie M Carpenter
Controller, Joseph Sawicki
Coordinator, David Rubin
Comptroller, Joseph Junior
Coordinator, Louise Taylor
Assistant Operations Superviso, Dale Grudier
Chief Deputy County Executive, Dennis Cohen
Bureau Chief, Phyllis Seidman
Operations, Robert Braun
Auditors: CHERRY BEKAERT LLP RICHMOND

LOCATIONS

HQ: COUNTY OF SUFFOLK
100 VETERANS HWY, HAUPPAUGE, NY 117885402
Phone: 631 853-4000

HISTORICAL FINANCIALS
Company Type: Private

Income Statement
FYE: December 31

	REVENUE ($ mil.)	NET INCOME ($ mil.)	NET PROFIT MARGIN	EMPLOYEES
12/17	3,174	(9)	—	12,814
12/16	3,069	(83)	—	—
12/15	2,938	(71)	—	—
12/12	2,712	(138)	—	—
Annual Growth	3.2%	—	—	—

2017 Year-End Financials
Return on assets: 16.0%
Return on equity: (-0.3%)
Current ratio: 0.60

Cash ($ mil.): 834

COUNTY OF TARRANT

EXECUTIVES

Judge, B Glen Whitely
County Judge, B Glen Whiitely
Commissioner, Roy Brooks
Comissioner, Andy H Nguyen
Commissioner, J D Johnson
Information Specialist, Hannelore Baker
Coordinator, Velina Willis
Coordinator, Donna Zavala
Coordinator, Joyce Kirk
Coordinator, Linda Blair
Coordinator, Mary Chaisson
Auditors: KPMG LLP DALLAS TX

LOCATIONS

HQ: COUNTY OF TARRANT
100 E WEATHERFORD ST, FORT WORTH, TX 761960206
Phone: 817 884-1205
Web: WWW.TARRANTCOUNTY.COM

HISTORICAL FINANCIALS
Company Type: Private

Income Statement
FYE: September 30

	REVENUE ($ mil.)	NET INCOME ($ mil.)	NET PROFIT MARGIN	EMPLOYEES
09/16	597	5	1.0%	139
09/15	580	52	9.1%	—
09/14	0	0	—	—
09/13	537	20	3.8%	—
Annual Growth	3.6%	(33.8%)	—	—

COUNTY SANITATION DISTRICT NO. 2 OF LOS ANGELES COUNTY

EXECUTIVES

Gen Mgr, Stephen Maguin
Acctg, Sherry Rachman
Acct Mgr, Kim Black
Sales and Marketing Staff, Cheryl Shea
Human Resources Manager, Jennifer Allen
Scientist, Ryan Reinke
Director, Debra Bogdanoff
Administrative Assistant, Denise Mays
Director, Dan Sanchez
Education Manager, Earle Hartling
Chief Technology Officer, Thomas Tran
Auditors: MOSS LEVY & HARTZHEIM LLP CU

LOCATIONS

HQ: COUNTY SANITATION DISTRICT NO. 2 OF LOS ANGELES COUNTY
1955 WORKMAN MILL RD, WHITTIER, CA 906011415
Phone: 562 699-7411
Web: WWW.LACSD.ORG

HISTORICAL FINANCIALS
Company Type: Private

Income Statement
FYE: June 30

	REVENUE ($ mil.)	NET INCOME ($ mil.)	NET PROFIT MARGIN	EMPLOYEES
06/16	545	144	26.4%	1,700
06/15	555	92	16.7%	—
06/12	550	74	13.6%	—
06/11	575	115	20.0%	—
Annual Growth	(1.1%)	4.6%	—	—

2016 Year-End Financials
Return on assets: 6.2%
Return on equity: 26.4%
Current ratio: 0.90

Cash ($ mil.): 115

COVENANT HEALTH

EXECUTIVES

Vice President Human Resources, Debi Welch

LOCATIONS

HQ: COVENANT HEALTH
100 FORT SANDERS W BLVD, KNOXVILLE, TN 379223353
Phone: 865 531-5555
Web: WWW.COVENANTHEALTH.COM

PRODUCTS/OPERATIONS

Selected Tennessee Facilities
Fort Loudon Medical Center (Lenoir City TN)
Fort Sanders Regional Medical Center (Knoxville TN)
LeConte Medical Center (formerly Fort Sanders Sevier Medical Center; Sevierville TN)
Methodist Medical Center of Oak Ridge (Oak Ridge TN)
Parkwest Medical Center (Knoxville TN)
Peninsula Hospital (behavioral health care Louisville TN)
Roane Medical Center (Harriman TN)

COMPETITORS

Blount Memorial Hospital	Saint Thomas Rutherford Hospital
East Tennessee Children's Hospital	Tennova Healthcare
Kindred Healthcare	University Health System Inc.
LifePoint Health	Vanderbilt University Medical Center
Parkridge Medical Center	
Saint Thomas Midtown Hospital	

HISTORICAL FINANCIALS
Company Type: Private

Income Statement   FYE: December 31

	REVENUE ($ mil.)	NET INCOME ($ mil.)	NET PROFIT MARGIN	EMPLOYEES
12/17	1,268	144	11.4%	2,469
12/16	1,246	57	4.6%	—
12/05	1,056	32	3.1%	—
12/04	971	30	3.1%	—
Annual Growth	2.1%	12.8%	—	—

2017 Year-End Financials
Return on assets: 9.5%
Return on equity: 11.4%
Current ratio: 0.80
Cash ($ mil.): 51

COVENANT HEALTH SYSTEM

EXECUTIVES

Vice President, Sharon Prather
Auditors: ERNST & YOUNG US LLP IRVINE

LOCATIONS

HQ: COVENANT HEALTH SYSTEM
3615 19TH ST, LUBBOCK, TX 794101209
Phone: 806 725-1011

COMPETITORS

Baptist St. Anthony's Health System	Tenet Healthcare
Del Sol Medical Center	Texas Health Resources
Encompass Health	The Methodist Health System
Hunt Memorial	University Medical Center of El Paso
NW Texas Healthcare	
Parkland Health & Hospital System	

HISTORICAL FINANCIALS
Company Type: Private

Income Statement   FYE: June 30

	REVENUE ($ mil.)	NET INCOME ($ mil.)	NET PROFIT MARGIN	EMPLOYEES
06/15	703	76	10.9%	5,000
06/13	552	35	6.5%	—
06/09	1,185	(38)	—	—
Annual Growth	(8.3%)	—	—	—

2015 Year-End Financials
Return on assets: 5.6%
Return on equity: 10.9%
Current ratio: 3.00
Cash ($ mil.): 39

COVENANT HEALTH, INC.

EXECUTIVES

Pres-Ceo, David R Lincoln
SEC, Patricia Karl
Treas, Harold R Acres
Chm, Dorothy Cooper
V Chb, Richard J Hanley
Dir, Margaret Mary Modde
Asst Cfo, Laural Haug
Assistant Controller, Becky Lehoux
Executive Assistant, Nicole Goodreau
Vice President Quality Improve, Anne Berger
Radiology Supervisor, Donna Hale
Auditors: WILLIAM STEELE & ASSOCIATES PC

LOCATIONS

HQ: COVENANT HEALTH, INC.
100 AMES POND DR STE 102, TEWKSBURY, MA 018761240
Phone: 978 654-6363
Web: WWW.COVENANTHEALTH.NET

HISTORICAL FINANCIALS
Company Type: Private

Income Statement   FYE: December 31

	REVENUE ($ mil.)	NET INCOME ($ mil.)	NET PROFIT MARGIN	EMPLOYEES
12/17	670	38	5.8%	6,500
12/16	645	18	2.9%	—
12/12	12	1	12.0%	—
12/09	9	(0)	—	—
Annual Growth	71.3%	—	—	—

2017 Year-End Financials
Return on assets: 2.6%
Return on equity: 5.8%
Current ratio: 1.10
Cash ($ mil.): 32

COVENANT MEDICAL CENTER, INC.

Covenant Medical Center (operating as Covenant HealthCare) has made a pact with Wolverine Staters to try to keep them in good health. The not-for-profit health care provider operates more than 20 inpatient and outpatient care facilities including its two main Covenant Medical Center campuses. It serves residents in a 20-county area of east-central Michigan with additional facilities in Bay City Frankenmuth and Midland. Specialized care services include cardiovascular health cancer treatment and obstetrics. The regional health care system has more about 650 beds.

Operations
Covenant HealthCare programs and services range from high-risk obstetrics and neonatal/pediatric intensive care to acute care. Its assets include cardiology oncology orthopedics robotic surgery and Level II Adult and Pediatric Trauma Center.

The health system has more than 20 inpatient and outpatient facilities and a trauma/emergency department that provides 85000 visits per year. The system employs more than 500 physicians from 52 medical specialties.

Sales and Marketing
Covenant HealthCare markets its services via social media.

Financial Performance
In 2014 the company's revenue increased 4% to $528 million as patient service revenue rose; this gain was partially offset by a decline in realized gain and other revenues. An increase in salaries and wages as well as higher supplies expenses led to a 12% decline in net income (to $57 million).

Cash flow from operations also fell slipping 20% to $48 million as accounts receivable increased.

Strategy
Expanding its infrastructure to keep up with demand in 2014 Covenant HealthCare added 11456 sq. ft. to its Emergency Department. The addition allows for more efficient triage enhanced patient waiting areas and additional space for current technology. It added 18 treatment bays to the existing 47 and also brought a dedicated CT scanner and mini-laboratory within the department.

Also that year it opened the assisted living community of Covenant Glen in Frankenmuth. The 35000 sq. ft. structure has 45 rooms (15 dedicated to memory care and 30 with assisted living beds).

Company Background
Covenant HealthCare was formed in 1998 through the merger of Saginaw General and St. Luke's Hospitals.

EXECUTIVES

Ceo, Edward Bruff
President, Spencer T Maidlow
Cfo, Mark Gronda
Dir of Info Tech, Keith Grantham
Administrator, Melissa K Grew

LOCATIONS

HQ: COVENANT MEDICAL CENTER, INC.
1447 N HARRISON ST, SAGINAW, MI 486024727
Phone: 989 583-0000
Web: WWW.COVENANTHEALTHCARE.COM

PRODUCTS/OPERATIONS

2014 Revenues

	% of total
Net patient service revenues	95
Other revenues	5
Total	**100**

Selected services
Bariatrics
Birth Center
Cancer Care
Cardiology - Center for the Heart
Childbirth Classes
da Vinci Robotic Surgery
Diabetes Self-Management Program
Emergency Care Center
Imaging and Diagnostics
Neonatal Intensive Care
Neurology
Osteoporosis
Orthopaedics
Pediatrics
Physical Medicine and Rehab.
Pulmonary/Respiratory Care
Sleep Center
Surgical Services
Trauma
Urologic Surgery
Women's Health
Wound Healing Center

COMPETITORS

Genesys Health System	McLaren Health Care
Genesys Regional Medical Center	Munson Healthcare
Hurley Medical Center	Sparrow Health System
McLaren Bay	University of Michigan Health System

HISTORICAL FINANCIALS
Company Type: Private

Income Statement				FYE: June 30
	REVENUE ($ mil.)	NET INCOME ($ mil.)	NET PROFIT MARGIN	EMPLOYEES
06/16	579	40	7.0%	4,000
06/15	535	31	5.8%	—
06/14	566	34	6.1%	—
06/10	508	28	5.5%	—
Annual Growth	2.2%	6.2%	—	—

2016 Year-End Financials
Return on assets: 2.4%
Return on equity: 7.0%
Current ratio: 1.20

Cash ($ mil.): 21

COVENANT MEDICAL CENTER, INC.

EXECUTIVES

Pres, Jack Dusenbery
Contrl, Timothy Huber
Podiatrist, Paul Lantz

LOCATIONS

HQ: COVENANT MEDICAL CENTER, INC.
3421 W 9TH ST, WATERLOO, IA 507025401
Phone: 319 272-8000
Web: WWW.WHEATONIOWA.ORG

HISTORICAL FINANCIALS
Company Type: Private

Income Statement				FYE: June 30
	REVENUE ($ mil.)	NET INCOME ($ mil.)	NET PROFIT MARGIN	EMPLOYEES
06/18	290	4	1.4%	2,300
06/14	275	26	9.5%	—
Annual Growth	1.4%	(37.2%)	—	—

2018 Year-End Financials
Return on assets: 11.7%
Return on equity: 1.4%
Current ratio: 1.50

Cash ($ mil.): 10

COWAN SYSTEMS, LLC

Not cowed by competition from bigger transportation companies Cowan Systems provides truckload freight transportation primarily in the eastern half of the US. The company's coverage area includes the mid-Atlantic states the Midwest New England and the southeastern US. Cowan has about 2000 tractors and 5000 trailers and its largest customer is Coca-Cola Enterprises. The company arranges the transportation of freight through its logistics unit. Other offerings include ground transportation of airfreight between airports and dedicated contract carriage in which drivers and equipment are assigned to a customer long-term.

Operations

Cowan Systems' fleet consists of 2000 company owned trucks 20 intermodal terminals and more than 15000 contract carriers to handle any type of shipments.

Geographic Reach

Cowan Systems has its presence in Maryland Utah California Texas Arizona Illinois Kansas Mississippi Tennessee Kentucky Indiana Ohio Georgia Virginia and Pennsylvania.

Company Background

The company has its roots in a trucking company that was founded in 1924.

EXECUTIVES

President, Dennis Morgan
Svp Operations, Richard Warner
Vp Operations, Kristin Morgan
Vice President, Dan Colhoun

LOCATIONS

HQ: COWAN SYSTEMS, LLC
4555 HOLLINS FERRY RD, BALTIMORE, MD 212274610
Phone: 410 247-0800
Web: WWW.COWANSYSTEMS.COM

PRODUCTS/OPERATIONS

Selected Services
Dedicated freight transportation
Driver leasing
Intermodal freight transportation
Logistics
Truckload freight transportation
Warehousing

COMPETITORS

C.H. Robinson Worldwide	Swift Transportation
Forward Air	U.S. Xpress
J.B. Hunt	UPS Supply Chain Solutions
Landstar System	Werner Enterprises
Schneider National	

HISTORICAL FINANCIALS
Company Type: Private

Income Statement				FYE: December 31
	REVENUE ($ mil.)	NET INCOME ($ mil.)	NET PROFIT MARGIN	EMPLOYEES
12/16	434	21	4.8%	1,800
12/15	435	0	—	—
12/14	421	0	—	—
12/13	0	0	—	—
Annual Growth	—	—	—	—

2016 Year-End Financials
Return on assets: 1.6%
Return on equity: 4.8%
Current ratio: 1.00

Cash ($ mil.): 15

CREIGHTON ALEGENT CLINIC

EXECUTIVES

Principal, Richard Hachten II
Principal, Cindy Johnson
Director of Information Techno, Kurt Powers
Operations Director Quality MA, Christine Daly
Manager, Haizhen Zhu
Director Public Relations, Kelly Grinnell

Vice President Information TEC, Ken Lawonn
Operations Director, Marilyn Rhoten
Operations Director, Ann Schriner
Auditors: CATHOLIC HEALTH INITIATIVES O

LOCATIONS

HQ: CREIGHTON ALEGENT CLINIC
12809 W DODGE RD, OMAHA, NE 681542155
Phone: 402 343-4343
Web: WWW.ALEGENT.COM

HISTORICAL FINANCIALS
Company Type: Private

Income Statement				FYE: June 30
	REVENUE ($ mil.)	NET INCOME ($ mil.)	NET PROFIT MARGIN	EMPLOYEES
06/17	318	(72)	—	5
06/15	244	(77)	—	—
06/14	235	(106)	—	—
06/13	222	(69)	—	—
Annual Growth	9.4%	—	—	—

2017 Year-End Financials
Return on assets: 6.3%
Return on equity: (-22.9%)
Current ratio: 1.30

Cash ($ mil.): —

CREIGHTON ALEGENT HEALTH

CHI Health (formerly Alegent Creighton Health) pledges allegiance to medical well-being in its corner of the Midwest. The not-for-profit health care system operates 15 hospitals with about 3000 beds in Omaha and surrounding communities in eastern Nebraska and southwestern Iowa including Bergan Mercy Medical Center and Immanuel Medical Center. Alegent Creighton Health's hospitals provide specialty services including cardiovascular orthopedic and cancer care; it also operates psychiatric long-term care home health and outpatient centers. The health system is sponsored by Catholic Health Initiatives and is affiliated with Creighton University.

Operations

CHI Health is the primary provider of teaching locations for the Creighton University School of Medicine with academic programs in a number of fields including psychiatry women's health nursing and pharmacy. Its hospitals have some 1500 physicians on staff and include 10 acute care facilities and one psychiatric hospital. Specialty units include an orthopedic hospital and skilled nursing centers.

In addition to its acute care facilities the organization provides primary and specialty outpatient care services through its CHI Health Alegent Creighton Clinic unit. The division has more than 20 specialties and operates about 100 physician practices and clinics in Omaha and surrounding areas. There are also two Express Care clinics that offer urgent care for non-life-threatening ailments and six Quick Care clinics in Omaha (located in Hy-Vee retail stores) that provide minor medical ailment treatment as well as sports physicals and vaccinations. The idea behind the clinics is to divert patients who might otherwise end up at ERs with non-emergency symptoms (thus lowering hospital expenses).

Geographic Reach

The network's hospitals are located in Omaha (five medical centers) Papillion Plainview and Schuyler Nebraska; as well as in Corning Council Bluffs and Missouri Valley Iowa.

Strategy

The company has been pursuing growth to signify its presence as a unified regional health network. The efforts are intended to allow it to better compete and thrive in the changing US health care landscape by expanding its facilities training programs and resources in the Omaha area. Growth efforts include the formation of an intensive care partnership with Good Samaritan Hospital in 2013. The network has also opened several new community care clinics in recent years.

In 2015 CHI Health partnered with Aetna to create Nebraska's first commercial product-based accountable care organization (ACO). The ACO offers employers a health care option that is designed to improve quality of care outcomes and patient experiences.

EXECUTIVES

Pres-Ceo, Cliff Robertson
Sr V Pres, Bonnie Burnett
Sr V Pres, Nancy Wallace
Svp-Coo, Joan Neuhaus
Cfo, Jeanette Wojtalewicz
Pres-Ceo, Alegent Cr Clinic, Richard Rolston
Manager, Lori McCormack
Phlebotomist, Tammy Sill
Head of Compliance, Lee Bertholf
Purchasing, Kris McDonald
Auditors: LB CATHOLIC HEALTH INITIATIVES

LOCATIONS

HQ: CREIGHTON ALEGENT HEALTH
12809 W DODGE RD, OMAHA, NE 681542155
Phone: 402 343-4300
Web: WWW.ALEGENT.ORG

PRODUCTS/OPERATIONS

Selected Facilities and Operations
Alegent Creighton Health Clinics (primary care multiple locations in Iowa and Nebraska)
Alegent Creighton Health Urgent Care clinics (urgent care three locations in Nebraska)
Alegent Creighton Health Quick Care (minor care clinics; seven locations in Omaha Nebraska in Hy-Vee stores)
Alegent Health at Home (home health care)
Bergan Mercy Medical Center (Omaha Nebraska; 300 beds)
Community Memorial Hospital (Missouri Valley Iowa; 20 beds)
Creighton University Medical Center (Omaha Nebraska; 400 beds)
Immanuel Communities (independent and assisted living in Omaha and Lincoln)
Immanuel Fontenelle (nursing home in Omaha)
Immanuel Medical Center (Omaha Nebraska; 280 beds)
Immanuel Rehabilitation Center (Omaha Nebraska)
Lakeside Hospital (Omaha Nebraska; 160 beds)
Lasting Hope Recovery Center (Omaha Nebraska; psychiatric hospital with 120 beds)
Memorial Hospital (Schuyler Nebraska; 25 beds)
Mercy Corning Hospital (Corning Iowa; 20 beds)
Mercy Hospital (Council Bluffs Iowa; 160 beds)
Midlands Hospital (Papillion Nebraska; 50 beds)
Plainview Hospital (Plainview Nebraska)

COMPETITORS

BryanLGH Medical Center
Children's Hospital & Medical Center
Fremont Area Medical Center
Heartland Health
Madonna Rehabilitation Hospital
Mercy Health Network
Methodist Health System
Nebraska Medical Center
Saint Elizabeth Regional Medical Center
UNMC Physicians
UnityPoint Health

HISTORICAL FINANCIALS
Company Type: Private

Income Statement				FYE: June 30
	REVENUE ($ mil.)	NET INCOME ($ mil.)	NET PROFIT MARGIN	EMPLOYEES
06/15	516	(147)	—	8,600
06/13	525	63	12.2%	—
Annual Growth	(0.9%)	—	—	

2015 Year-End Financials
Return on assets: 8.9%   Cash ($ mil.): 20
Return on equity: (-28.7%)
Current ratio: 2.00

CREST INDUSTRIES, LLC

EXECUTIVES

Pres-Ceo, Kenneth L Robison
Contrl, Joseph R Bareswill
Cfo, Robert L Brinkerhoff
Vice-President Human Resources, Joy Williford
Information Technology Manager, Donald Stewart
Vice-President, John Doggett
Human Resources, Sarah Sasser
Human Resources, Kristina U Hickman
Manager, Stuart Tichenor
Information Specialist, Charles Neal
Auditors: LESTER MILLER & WELLS ALEXAN

LOCATIONS

HQ: CREST INDUSTRIES, LLC
4725 HIGHWAY 28 E, PINEVILLE, LA 713604730
Phone: 318 767-5530
Web: WWW.CRESTOPERATIONS.COM

HISTORICAL FINANCIALS
Company Type: Private

Income Statement				FYE: December 31
	REVENUE ($ mil.)	NET INCOME ($ mil.)	NET PROFIT MARGIN	EMPLOYEES
12/17	286	(5)	—	415
12/16	259	3	1.2%	—
12/15	259	9	3.6%	—
12/14	251	12	4.9%	—
Annual Growth	4.4%	—	—	

2017 Year-End Financials
Return on assets: 7.9%   Cash ($ mil.): 24
Return on equity: (-2.0%)
Current ratio: 1.20

CROUSE HEALTH HOSPITAL, INC.

EXECUTIVES

Ceo, Kimberly Boynton
A/C Payable Supervisor, Deborah Montrond
Coordinator, Barbara Carpenter
Executive Assistant, Betty Oconnor
Nurse Practitioner, Elizabeth Casazza
Network Engineer, Greg Ellison
Nurse Practitioner, Karen Bennett

Manager, Malcolm Cowling
Purchasing Agent, Michael Fegley
Human Resources Administrator, Myra Seikaly
Supervisor, Amy Graham

LOCATIONS

HQ: CROUSE HEALTH HOSPITAL, INC.
736 IRVING AVE, SYRACUSE, NY 132101687
Phone: 315 470-7521
Web: WWW.CROUSE.ORG

HISTORICAL FINANCIALS
Company Type: Private

Income Statement				FYE: December 31
	REVENUE ($ mil.)	NET INCOME ($ mil.)	NET PROFIT MARGIN	EMPLOYEES
12/15	391	0	0.2%	2,700
12/14	367	13	3.7%	—
12/13	3	1	44.4%	—
12/09	3	0	27.2%	—
Annual Growth	122.8%	(2.7%)	—	—

2015 Year-End Financials
Return on assets: 5.1%   Cash ($ mil.): 19
Return on equity: 0.2%
Current ratio: 1.20

CROWDER CONSTRUCTORS, INC.

EXECUTIVES

President, Lynn L Hansen
Executive Vice President, Carlos W Norris
Chief Executive Officer, Otis A Crowder
Chief Operating Officer, William T Crowder
Manager, Billy Waller
Engineer, Grady McClamrock
Vice President, Greg Cochran
Manager, Paul Stephenson
Auditors: GREEN WALKER LLP CHARLOTTE N

LOCATIONS

HQ: CROWDER CONSTRUCTORS, INC.
6425 BROOKSHIRE BLVD, CHARLOTTE, NC 282160301
Phone: 704 372-3541
Web: WWW.CROWDERUSA.COM

HISTORICAL FINANCIALS
Company Type: Private

Income Statement				FYE: March 31
	REVENUE ($ mil.)	NET INCOME ($ mil.)	NET PROFIT MARGIN	EMPLOYEES
03/18	306	0	—	1,062
03/17	298	15	5.2%	—
Annual Growth	2.5%	—	—	

2018 Year-End Financials
Return on assets: 10.9%   Cash ($ mil.): 33
Return on equity: —
Current ratio: 1.00

CROWE LLP

EXECUTIVES

Ceo, James Powers
Cfo-Ptnr, Todd Welu
Cro-Ptnr, Fred J Bauters
Cmo, Ann Lathrop
CIO, Yvonne Scott
Coo, Joseph P Santucci Jr
Chief Strategy & Innovation of, Derek Bang
Cdso, Justin Bass
Manager, John Kurkowski
Business Manager, Kevin Starchvill
Assistant Director, Maureen McCoige
Auditors: CROWE HORWATH

LOCATIONS

HQ: CROWE LLP
225 W WACKER DR STE 2600, CHICAGO, IL
606061228
Phone: 312 899-7000
Web: WWW.CROWEHORWATH.COM

HISTORICAL FINANCIALS

Company Type: Private

Income Statement				FYE: March 31
	REVENUE ($ mil.)	NET INCOME ($ mil.)	NET PROFIT MARGIN	EMPLOYEES
03/15	700	204	29.2%	3,130
03/14	670	163	24.4%	—
03/13	0	0	—	—
Annual Growth	—	—	—	—

2015 Year-End Financials

Return on assets: 0.1%   Cash ($ mil.): 6
Return on equity: 29.2%
Current ratio: 1.80

CROWLEY HOLDINGS, INC.

EXECUTIVES

Chb-Pres, Thomas B Crowley Jr
V Chb-Exec Vice President, William A Pennella
Sr V Pres-Gc, Arthur F Mead III
Sr V Pres-Controller, John C Calvin
Sr Vice President, Carl Fox
Sr Vice President, Dan Warner
Sr V Pres-Treas, Daniel L Warner
Sr V Pres Admin, Susan L Rodgers
Manager, Jeffery White
Director, Larry Miles
Superintendent Engineer, Andre Zibrov
Auditors: DELOITTE & TOUCHE LLP JACKSON

LOCATIONS

HQ: CROWLEY HOLDINGS, INC.
9487 REGENCY SQUARE BLVD # 101,
JACKSONVILLE, FL 322257800
Phone: 904 727-2200
Web: WWW.CROWLEY.COM

HISTORICAL FINANCIALS

Company Type: Private

Income Statement				FYE: December 31
	REVENUE ($ mil.)	NET INCOME ($ mil.)	NET PROFIT MARGIN	EMPLOYEES
12/16	1,841	117	6.4%	4,500
12/15	2,158	153	7.1%	—
12/14	2,059	48	2.4%	—
12/13	2,030	71	3.5%	—
Annual Growth	(3.2%)	18.2%	—	—

2016 Year-End Financials

Return on assets: 9.4%   Cash ($ mil.): 152
Return on equity: 6.4%
Current ratio: 1.10

CUMBERLAND COUNTY SCHOOLS

EXECUTIVES

Supt, William Harrison
Supt, Frank Till
Upt Admin Asst, Betsy Horne
Administrative Assistant, Jeannette Mason
Finance Manager, Kenneth Villareal
Director of Risk Management, Henry Smith
Data Processing Executive, Erika White
Compliance Staff, Linda Annas
Teacher, Lydia Stewart
Secretary, Rachel Velazquez
Teacher, Tara Weymouth
Auditors: CHERRY BEKAERT LLP FAYETTEVI

LOCATIONS

HQ: CUMBERLAND COUNTY SCHOOLS
2465 GILLESPIE ST, FAYETTEVILLE, NC 283063053
Phone: 910 678-2300
Web: WWW.CCS.K12.NC.US

HISTORICAL FINANCIALS

Company Type: Private

Income Statement				FYE: June 30
	REVENUE ($ mil.)	NET INCOME ($ mil.)	NET PROFIT MARGIN	EMPLOYEES
06/16	411	3	0.8%	6,210
06/15	413	(0)	—	—
06/14	399	(6)	—	—
06/11	444	3	0.8%	—
Annual Growth	(1.5%)	(2.2%)	—	—

2016 Year-End Financials

Return on assets: 1.0%   Cash ($ mil.): 62
Return on equity: 0.8%
Current ratio: —

CVR NITROGEN, LP

EXECUTIVES

Ceo, Keith B Forman
Pres, John H Diesch
Cfo, Jeffrey R Spain
Sr Vp -Finance & Admin, Wilfred Bahl Jr
Vp-Investor & Comm, Julie Dawoodjee Cafarella
Regional Sales Manager, Steve Sheline
Auditors: PRICEWATERHOUSECOOPERS LLP LO

LOCATIONS

HQ: CVR NITROGEN, LP
10877 WILSHIRE BLVD FL 10, LOS ANGELES, CA
900244251
Phone: 310 571-9800
Web: WWW.RENTECHNITROGEN.COM

HISTORICAL FINANCIALS

Company Type: Private

Income Statement				FYE: December 31
	REVENUE ($ mil.)	NET INCOME ($ mil.)	NET PROFIT MARGIN	EMPLOYEES
12/15	340	(101)	—	145
12/14	334	(1)	—	—
12/13	311	4	1.3%	—
12/11	63	10	16.6%	—
Annual Growth	52.5%	—	—	—

2015 Year-End Financials

Return on assets: 3.5%   Cash ($ mil.): 15
Return on equity: (-29.8%)
Current ratio: 0.50

CYPRESS-FAIRBANKS INDEPENDENT SCHOOL DISTRICT

EXECUTIVES

Supt, Mark Henry
Supt, Richard E Berry
General, Mary Jadlowski
Assistant Director, Eric May
Rector, David Villareal
Bus/Finance/Purchasing Directo, Stuart Snow
Auditors: HEREFORD LYNCH SELLARS & KIR

LOCATIONS

HQ: CYPRESS-FAIRBANKS INDEPENDENT SCHOOL
DISTRICT
10300 JONES RD, HOUSTON, TX 770654208
Phone: 281 897-4000
Web: WWW.CFISD.NET

HISTORICAL FINANCIALS

Company Type: Private

Income Statement				FYE: June 30
	REVENUE ($ mil.)	NET INCOME ($ mil.)	NET PROFIT MARGIN	EMPLOYEES
06/17	1,208	(58)	—	13,000
06/12	926	(4)	—	—
06/09	858	43	5.1%	—
06/06	654	42	6.5%	—
Annual Growth	5.7%	—	—	—

2017 Year-End Financials

Return on assets: 6.6%   Cash ($ mil.): 23
Return on equity: (-4.9%)
Current ratio: —

DAIRY FARMERS OF AMERICA, INC.

Dairy Farmers of America (DFA) is one of the world's largest dairy cooperatives with nearly 15000 member farmers across the US. Millions of cows belonging to member farmers produce 64 billion pounds of milk a year (roughly 30% of milk production in the US) which DFA markets. Along with fresh and shelf-stable fluid milk the co-op produces cheese butter dried milk powder and other dairy products for industrial wholesale and retail customers. It also offers contract manufacturing services. The co-op owns more than 40 manufacturing plants nationwide. DFA whose profits are shared based on member contribution is a major supplier to dairy giant Dean Foods as well as joint venture partners such as Hiland Dairy.

Operations

DFA owns more than 40 manufacturing plants nationwide. The facilities are focused on several functions and product categories including consumer cheese and butter consumer fluid ingredient cheese and protein and contract manufacturing.

The company's brands include Borden and Cache Valley for consumer cheese; Keller?s Creamery Plugra Breakstone?s Falfurrias and Hotel Bar for butter; and other dairy products under Sport Shake (sports beverage) La Vaquita (queso) Kemps Guida?s Dairy and Dairy Maid Dairy.

Geographic Reach

DFA is based in Kansas City Missouri and divides the US into seven areas: Central (which shares the main headquarters) Mideast (Medina OH) Mountain (Salt Lake City UT) Northeast (East Syracuse NY) Southeast (Knoxville TN) Southwest (Grapevine TX) and Western (Corona CA).

Sales and Marketing

DFA's customers include big names in the dairy food and retail businesses including Hiland Dairy Borden supermarket giant Kroger Dean Foods Kraft Foods Nestle and many others.

Financial Performance

In 2017 DFA reported revenue of $14.7 billion up nearly 10% from the prior year due to unit sales growth as well as higher milk prices.

Net income that year was $127.4 million.

Strategy

In a statement that could be written about most companies across most industries DFA's strategic focus is on technology and innovation. In late 2018 it invested in SomaDetect a startup that promotes artificial intelligence as way for dairy farmers to more closely monitor herd health and improve milk quality. Also that year it partnered with startup ripe.io to evaluate the usefulness of blockchain technology in the food supply chain.

As far as product innovation DFA introduced a new cheese brand (Craigs Creamery) in early 2019 and invested in a whey protein-infused yogurt (MOPRO) in 2018.

The cooperative also continues to invest in its facilities expanding existing plants and acquiring new ones.

Mergers and Acquisitions

In late 2018 DFA agreed to purchase a St. Paul Minnesota facility from Canada-based dairy cooperative Agropur which will expand DFA's extended shelf-life capabilities and introduce aseptic processing into its business portfolio.

Company Background

DFA was established in 1998 by leaders of four of the nation?s leading milk cooperatives: Associated Milk Producers Mid-America Dairymen Milk Marketing and Western Dairymen Cooperative.

HISTORY

Mid-America Dairymen (Mid-Am) the largest of the cooperatives that merged to form Dairy Farmers of America (DFA) was born in 1968. At that time several Midwestern dairy co-ops banded together to attack common economic problems such as reduced government subsidies price drops resulting from a rising milk surplus dealer consolidation and improvements in production processing and packaging. The merging organizations — representing 15000 dairy farmers — were Producers Creamery Company (Springfield Missouri) Sanitary Milk Producers (St. Louis) Square Deal Milk Producers (Highland Illinois) Mid-Am (Kansas City Missouri) and Producers Creamery Company of Chillicothe (north central Missouri).

During the early 1970s Mid-Am struggled with internal restructuring. Most dairy farmers and co-ops were hit hard by the energy crisis and the government's decision to allow increased dairy imports in 1973 the same year the US Justice Department filed an antitrust suit against Mid-Am. (A judge cleared the co-op 12 years later.)

In 1974 Mid-Am lost almost $8 million on revenues of $625 million chalked up to record-high feed prices a weakened economy a milk surplus and a massive inventory loss. Co-op veteran Gary Hanman was named CEO that year. Over the next two years Mid-Am cut costs sold corporate frills downsized management and began marketing more of its own products under the Mid-America Farms label thus reducing dependency on commodity sales.

Mid-Am expanded its research and development efforts throughout the 1980s. The co-op opened its services to farmers in California and New Mexico in 1993 and a series of mergers in 1994 and 1995 nearly doubled its size. In 1997 it purchased some of Borden's dairy operations including rights to the valuable Elsie the Cow and Borden's trademarks.

Wary of falling milk prices Mid-Am merged with Western Dairymen Cooperative Milk Marketing and the Southern Region of Associated Milk Producers at the end of 1997 to form DFA. Hanman moved into the seat of CEO at the new co-op. DFA began a series of joint ventures with the #1 US dairy processor Suiza Foods (now Dean Foods).

DFA added California Gold (more than 330 farmers 1998) and Independent Cooperative Milk Producers Association (730 dairy farmer members in Michigan and parts of Ohio and Indiana 1999). In another joint venture with Suiza in early 2000 DFA sold its 50% stake in the US's #3 fluid milk processor Southern Foods in exchange for 34% of a new company named Suiza Dairy Group.

After mollifying the government's antitrust fears DFA acquired the butter operations of Sodiaal North America in 2000. It then molded all its butter businesses into a new entity Keller's Creamery. However another acquisition did not fare as well. The same year DFA acquired controlling interest in Southern Belle Dairy only to have the merger challenged three years later by the Department of Justice. Arguing that the merger formed a monopoly in school milk sales in several states the Department of Justice filed suit which a federal judge later dismissed.

During 2001 the cooperative went in with Land O'Lakes 50/50 to purchase a cheese plant from Kraft. Later in the year as Suiza Foods acquired Dean Foods (and took on its name) DFA sold back its stake in Suiza Dairy Group to the new Dean Foods. DFA then teamed up with a group of dairy investors to form a new 50/50 joint venture National Dairy Holdings which received 11 processing plants from Dean Foods as part of the exchange for Suiza Dairy.

HISTORICAL FINANCIALS

Company Type: Private

Income Statement				FYE: December 31
	REVENUE ($ mil.)	NET INCOME ($ mil.)	NET PROFIT MARGIN	EMPLOYEES
12/15	13,803	98	0.7%	7,000
12/14	17,856	48	0.3%	—
12/13	12,826	58	0.5%	—
12/12	12,082	(126)	—	—
Annual Growth	4.5%	—	—	—

2015 Year-End Financials

Return on assets: 4.7%   Cash ($ mil.): 228
Return on equity: 0.7%
Current ratio: 0.70

DAIRYLAND POWER COOPERATIVE

Dairyland Power Cooperative provides its customers with lots of juice in the land of lactose. The firm provides electricity generation (1366 MW of generating capacity) and transmission services for 25 member distribution cooperatives and 16 municipal utilities in five states (including Wisconsin). The member cooperatives and municipal utilities in turn distribute electricity to almost 254460 consumers. Dairyland Power generates 1030 MW of capacity from its coal-fired power plants; it also operates more than 3180 miles of transmission lines and 228 substations. The power cooperative also markets electricity and offers energy management services.

Operations

In addition to its traditional fossil fuel-powered plants the company to meet green energy regulations also contracts renewable and alternative energy power plants including "cow power" animal waste to energy facilities (8 farms with manure digesters which collectively produce 3 MW of power). It also has 40 MW of contracted biomass energy 47 MW of wind and 14 MW of landfill gas. In 2012 it expanded its wind portfolio agreeing to buy 5 MW of electricity from a wind farm near Lewiston Minnesota. It also agreed that year to buy the excess energy output from a new 368 kW solar photovoltaic installation at the City of Galena wastewater treatment plant in Illinois.

Geographic Reach

Dairyland Power Cooperative has member coops in Illinois Iowa Minnesota North Dakota and Wisconsin.

Financial Performance

In 2012 Dairyland Power Cooperative's revenues grew by 2% thanks to an increase in margins. Net income grew by 11% as the result of an increase in net sales.

Strategy

While admitting no violations of law in 2012 the company settled litigation with the EPA and Sierra Club agreeing to install hundreds of millions of dollars of air emission controls at its fossil-fueled power plants.

Company Background

In 2010 the cooperative integrated fully into regional transmission operator Midwest ISO. The move gave Dairyland Power Cooperative access to the Midwest ISO's wholesale ancillary services and other markets helping to improve the coop's regional grid reliability by giving it access to more energy sources to help avoid power shortages.

Dairyland Power Cooperative was founded in 1941.

EXECUTIVES

Pres-Ceo, Barbara Nick
V Pres-Gen Div, Rob Palmberg
Vice President, Mary Lund
Vice President, Phillip Moilien
Vice President, John Carr
V Pres Power Delivery*, Ben Porath
Coordinator, Jodi Roesler
Auditors: DELOITTE & TOUCHE LLP MINNEAP

LOCATIONS

HQ: DAIRYLAND POWER COOPERATIVE
3200 EAST AVE S, LA CROSSE, WI 546017291
Phone: 608 788-4000
Web: WWW.DAIRYNET.COM

COMPETITORS

ALLETE	DTE
Alliant Energy	MGE Energy
Berkshire Hathaway	WEC Energy
Energy	Xcel Energy

HISTORICAL FINANCIALS

Company Type: Private

Income Statement   FYE: December 31

	REVENUE ($ mil.)	NET INCOME ($ mil.)	NET PROFIT MARGIN	EMPLOYEES
12/17	441	27	6.1%	500
12/16	414	23	5.6%	—
12/15	418	26	6.4%	—
12/14	447	22	5.1%	—
Annual Growth	(0.5%)	5.7%	—	—

2017 Year-End Financials

Return on assets: 5.3%   Cash ($ mil.): 30
Return on equity: 6.1%
Current ratio: 0.30

DAKOTA GASIFICATION COMPANY INC

EXECUTIVES

Chb, Don Applegate
Ceo, Paul M Sukut
Coo, David Sauer
Cfo, Steve Johnson
SEC, Mark Foss
Auditors: DELOITTE & TOUCHE LLP MINNEAP

LOCATIONS

HQ: DAKOTA GASIFICATION COMPANY INC
420 COUNTY RD 26, BEULAH, ND 58523
Phone: 701 873-2100
Web: WWW.DAKOTAGAS.COM

PRODUCTS/OPERATIONS

Selected Products
Ammonium sulfate
Anhydrous ammonia
Carbon dioxide
Dephenolized cresylic acid
Krypton and xenon gases
Liquid nitrogen
Naphtha
Phenol

COMPETITORS

Chevron	SM Energy
Global Energy	Sasol Chemicals USA
Pioneer Natural Resources	Synthesis Energy Systems
Range Resources	Syntroleum

HISTORICAL FINANCIALS

Company Type: Private

Income Statement   FYE: December 31

	REVENUE ($ mil.)	NET INCOME ($ mil.)	NET PROFIT MARGIN	EMPLOYEES
12/17	337	(87)	—	725
12/16	312	(94)	—	—
12/14	582	7	1.3%	—
12/08	566	127	22.6%	—
Annual Growth	(5.6%)	—	—	—

2017 Year-End Financials

Return on assets: 8.7%   Cash ($ mil.): 15
Return on equity: (-25.9%)
Current ratio: 0.10

DAKOTA SUPPLY GROUP, INC.

EXECUTIVES

Ceo, Paul Kennedy
Cfo, Ross Westby
President, Tom Rosendahl
Vice President, Mike Tupa
Cfo, Mark Feeney
CIO, Tracy Koenig
Coo, Mike Meiresonne
Sales Associate, Eric Sharpe
Auditors: EIDE BAILLY LLP FARGO NORTH

LOCATIONS

HQ: DAKOTA SUPPLY GROUP, INC.
2601 3RD AVE N, FARGO, ND 581024016
Phone: 701 237-9440
Web: WWW.DAKOTASUPPLYGROUP.COM

COMPETITORS

Border States Electric	Viking Electric
J. H. Larson	

HISTORICAL FINANCIALS

Company Type: Private

Income Statement   FYE: December 31

	REVENUE ($ mil.)	NET INCOME ($ mil.)	NET PROFIT MARGIN	EMPLOYEES
12/17	364	6	1.8%	720
12/16	359	5	1.6%	—
12/15	401	11	2.8%	—
12/14	380	15	4.0%	—
Annual Growth	(1.4%)	(24.8%)	—	—

2017 Year-End Financials

Return on assets: 4.7%   Cash ($ mil.): 1
Return on equity: 1.8%
Current ratio: 0.80

DALLAS COUNTY HOSPITAL DISTRICT

Many people know Dallas County Hospital District doing business as Parkland Health and Hospital System or PHHS as Parkland Memorial Hospital the hospital where JFK died. Parkland Memorial sits at the heart of the health system and is Dallas' only public hospital. PHHS also manages a network of about 20 community clinics as well as Parkland Community Health Plan a regional HMO for Medicaid and CHIP (Children's Health Insurance Program) members. Additionally the system offers Parkland Financial Assistance a program to help residents of Dallas County pay for health care services. Parkland Memorial Hospital has more than 700 beds and is the primary teaching institution of The University of Texas Southwestern Medical Center.

Operations

PHHS is one of the largest public hospital systems in the US. In addition to its community-based clinics it offers a number of outreach and education programs to improve wellness in its service area.

Parkland Memorial Hospital has 870 single-patient rooms and is a Level I trauma center. Each year the hospital has some 39000 inpatient discharges and some 260000 emergency department visits. Specialty community and women's clinic outpatient visits total more than 1 million.

The system also manages the health system for Lew Sterrett — Dallas County Jail one of the nation's largest jails.

Sales and Marketing

Medicare and Medicaid payments account for about 15% and 30% of PHHS's net patient service revenues respectively.

Strategy

PHHS's original hospital location was established in 1954; more recently the system replaced the aging facility with a new hospital. The expansion included an 870-bed hospital an outpatient center an office center and parking. PHHS also invested in new and replacement information systems and medical equipment.

Additionally the system is working to open more primary care health clinics and launch new programs to reach further into its community.For example in 2016 it introduced the Acute Integrated Mental Health Services (AIMS) program to assist underserved patients with complex behavioral health issues and diabetes. It combines health care and social work services to connect patients with valuable resources and help them manage their health in an integrated manner.

Similarly the Parkland Information Exchange Portal (IEP) launched by PHHS health IT think tank Parkland Center for Clinical Innovation services to connect underserved individuals with social services including homeless shelters and food banks.

In early 2017 the system completed construction of a new five-story clinic with 171 exam rooms MRI's CT scanners radiology and ultrasound rooms laboratories and a pharmacy.

EXECUTIVES

Coo, David S. Lopez
President And Ceo, Frederick P. (Fred) Cerise, age 55
Evp And Chief Administrative Officer Population Health, Sharon Phillips
Evp And General Counsel, Paul Leslie
Evp And Chief Nursing Officer, Karen Watts
Evp And Chief Medical Officer, Roberto de la Cruz
Evp And Chief Talent Officer, Jim Dunn
Evp And Chief Strategy And Integration Officer, Esmaeil Porsa
Evp And Cfo, Richard Humphrey
Medical Director Of Homeless Outreach Medical Services, Susan Spalding
Vice President And Chief Compliance Offi, Mary Findley
Medical Director Of Adult Medicine, Noel Santini
Director Of Pharmacy, Vivian Johnson
Senior Vice President (internal Audit Service), Vic Summers
Vice President Finance And Controller, Elizabeth Mcmullen
Senior Vice President Quality Safety And Performance Improvement, Jacqueline Sullivan
Operating Room Dir, SUZANNE SIMS
Radiology Director, Terry Napper
Vice Chair, Michael D. (Mike) Williams
Chair Board Of Managers, Winfred Parnell
Auditors: GRANT THORNTHON LLP DALLAS T

LOCATIONS

HQ: DALLAS COUNTY HOSPITAL DISTRICT
5200 HARRY HINES BLVD, DALLAS, TX 752357709
Phone: 214 590-8000
Web: WWW.PARKLANDHOSPITAL.COM

PRODUCTS/OPERATIONS

Selected Facilities
Bluitt Flowers Health Center
de Haro-Saldivar Health Center
East Dallas Health Center
Garland Health Center
Oak West Health Center
Pediatric Primary Care Center
Simmons Ambulatory Surgery Center
Southeast Dallas Health Center
Vickery Health Center

COMPETITORS

Baylor University Medical Center
CHRISTUS Health
Children's Medical Center of Dallas
Community Health Systems
HCA
Harris Methodist Fort Worth Hospital
JPS Health Network
Presbyterian Hospital of Dallas
Tenet Healthcare
Texas Health Resources
The Methodist Health System

HISTORICAL FINANCIALS
Company Type: Private

Income Statement   FYE: September 30

	REVENUE ($ mil.)	NET INCOME ($ mil.)	NET PROFIT MARGIN	EMPLOYEES
09/17	1,734	(17)	—	11,000
09/16	1,641	(71)	—	—
09/15	665	33	5.1%	—
09/14	755	3	0.4%	—
Annual Growth	31.9%	—	—	—

2017 Year-End Financials
Return on assets: 13.4%   Cash ($ mil.): 316
Return on equity: (-1.0%)
Current ratio: 1.20

DALLAS/FORT WORTH INTERNATIONAL AIRPORT

Many things are bigger in Texas and Dallas/Fort Worth International Airport (DFW) is no exception. Covering some 30 square miles DFW is one of the world's largest airports by land mass. The facility includes seven runways two active control towers five terminals and 165 gates. Some 65 million passengers pass through DFW annually to destinations domestic and international. Aside from airport fare DFW provides private warehouse and distribution centers to tenants and features Grand Hyatt and Hyatt Regency hotels. Opened in 1974 DFW is owned by the cities of Dallas and Fort Worth; it is situated halfway between them and within about a four-hour flight time of most US destinations.

Operations

DFW?s primary operating goal is the facilitation of movement of people cargo and airplanes. Beyond that it leases land to travel-related businesses (car rental agencies) provide parking coordinates concessions and permits hotels to operate within its confines. About 45% of revenue comes from airlines (landing fees terminal usage fees) and 55% comes from non-airline activities.

With about 1800 flights per day serving 65 million customers a year DFW is the world's fourth busiest airport. Airlines flying out of DFW provide nonstop service to 163 domestic and 55 international non-stop destinations through about 25 passenger carriers and nearly 20 cargo carriers.

DFW is the home airport for the world?s largest carrier American Airlines (AA) which operates 745 flights per day to nearly 200 domestic destinations and some 50 international destinations. AA is constructing a new headquarters on a 300-acre campus on DFW property.

Financial Performance

In FY2016 (ended September 30 2016) Dallas Fort Worth International Airport generated revenue of $745 million a 10% increase from the prior year.

The airport?s earnings in FY2016 had a hard landing losing almost $94 million. Although its operations incurred a relatively small $4.6 million loss the big contributor was massive interest expense on its revenue bonds. The interest is a recurring annual charge and the airport has recently been running at an annual loss.

Strategy

DFW is in the midst of a $2.34 billion terminal improvement project that's expected to be completed in late 2018. Improvements include new gates and a new concourse light rail connections to downtown Dallas and renovations to existing terminals. Improvements to Terminals A B and E completed in 2017 and work on Terminal C is on hold due to financing decisions. The physical airfield is also on tap to receive capital funding: runway 17C to get $250 million and end-around taxiways to get $430 million.

The airport has excellent connectivity to Latin & South America and to Asia and believes it is well positions to serve as a gateway between the two world regions. It is geographically situated in an advantageous place and already has an extensive network of destinations into Mexico and Latin & South America.

EXECUTIVES

Ceo, Sean P. Donohue
Evp Operations, James M. (Jim) Crites
Evp And Cfo, Christopher A. Poinsatte
Evp Administration, Linda Valdez Thompson
Vp Marketing, Sharon McCloskey
Evp Revenue Management, Kenneth (Ken) Buchanan
Evp Global Strategy And Development, John Ackerman
Evp Airport Development And Planning, Khaled Naja
Svp Information Technology Services, Stephen Shaffer
Assistant Vice President Of Operations, Rosa Rivera
Vice President Information Technology, Michael Youngs
Chairman, Sam Coats, age 77
Vice Chairman, William W. (Bill) Meadows

LOCATIONS

HQ: DALLAS/FORT WORTH INTERNATIONAL AIRPORT
3200 E AIRFIELD DR, DFW AIRPORT, TX 752614904
Phone: 972 973-8888
Web: WWW.DFWAIRPORT.COM

HISTORICAL FINANCIALS

Company Type: Private

Income Statement   FYE: September 30

	REVENUE ($ mil.)	NET INCOME ($ mil.)	NET PROFIT MARGIN	EMPLOYEES
09/16	745	(88)	—	1,700
09/07	567	28	5.0%	
09/06	388	140	36.2%	—
09/05	388	140	36.2%	—
Annual Growth	6.1%	—	—	—

2016 Year-End Financials

Return on assets: —
Return on equity: (-11.9%)
Current ratio: 0.50
Cash ($ mil.): 164

DANA-FARBER CANCER INSTITUTE, INC.

The Dana-Farber Cancer Institute fights cancer on two fronts: It provides treatment to cancer patients young and old and researches new cancer diagnostics treatments and preventions. The organization's scientists also research AIDS treatments and cures for a host of other deadly diseases. Patients receive treatment from Dana-Farber through its cancer centers operated in conjunction with Brigham and Women's Hospital Children's Hospital Boston and Massachusetts General Hospital. The institute is also a principal teaching affiliate of Harvard Medical School. Dana-Farber is funded by the National Cancer Institute the National Institute of Allergy and Infectious Diseases and private contributions.

Operations

Dana-Farber reports more than 38300 patient visits a year and is involved in some 700 clinical trials.

Dana-Farber provides care to children and adults with cancer while advancing the understanding diagnosis treatment cure and prevention of cancer and related diseases. As an affiliate of Harvard Medical School and a Comprehensive Cancer Center designated by the National Cancer Institute the Institute also provides training for new generations of physicians and scientists designs programs that promote public health particularly among high-risk and underserved populations and disseminates innovative patient therapies and scientific discoveries to target community across the US and around the world. In 2014 the hospital has a community benefit of $6.75 million.

Geographic Reach

The institute primarily serves patients in New England. Dana-Farber's main campus is in Boston's Longwood Medical Area and it also has facilities in Brighton Milford South Weymouth and Pittsfield (all in Massachussets); Londonderry New Hampshire; and Waterford Connecticut.

Dana-Farber Community Cancer Care physician practices are in seven communities throughout eastern Massachusetts.

Financial Performance

The institute reported a 7% rise in revenues in 2014 thanks to an increase in patient service revenues unrestricted contributions and bequests and other operating revenues. Revenues from the Medicare and Medicaid programs accounted for approximately 25% and 5% respectively of Dana-Farber's net patient service revenue in 2014

Net income decreased by 11% due to an increase in temporarily restricted net assets and contributions.

Strategy

When it comes to patient care Dana-Farber emphasizes the importance of forming research and treatment partnerships with other health care organizations. To that end the institute has opened a handful of treatment clinics on other medical campuses including one at Faulkner Hospital in southwest Boston and another at Milford Regional Medical Center in Massachusetts.

Along with expanding on other campuses Dana-Farber built a new cancer care center on its main campus in Boston.

Although Dana-Farber directs its research efforts toward saving lives from deadly diseases some of its discoveries also bring in a tidy income as the company and its research partners occasionally license out their drug discoveries to pharmaceutical companies.

In 2015 new research by Dana-Farber scientists raised the prospect of cancer therapy that works by converting a tumor's best friends in the immune system into its gravest enemies. In a study published in the journal Science an international collaboration of investigators from Dana-Farber Harvard Medical School Boston Children's Hospital and the University of Strasbourg uncovered a mechanism that allows key immune system cells to keep a steady rein on their more belligerent brother cells thereby protecting normal healthy tissue from assault. The discovery has powerful implications for cancer. By blocking the mechanism with a drug it may be possible to turn the attack-suppressing cells into tumor-attacking cells.

Company Background

In 2013 the institute and Lawrence + Memorial Cancer Center opened a $34.5 million 47000 sq.-ft. cancer facility in Waterford Connecticut.

The Yawkey Center for Cancer Care named in honor of long-time contributor The Yawkey Foundation opened in 2011 to serve a growing number of patients. The 275000-sq.-ft center's 14-stories house most of Dana-Farber's adult outpatient care. The building has more than 100 exam rooms about 140 infusion chairs and a number of consultation rooms for family and patients. It also connected Dana-Farber to other campus buildings and to its clinical partners Brigham and Women's Hospital and Children's Hospital Boston.

Dana-Farber Cancer Institute was founded as a children's cancer research foundation in 1947 by Dr. Sidney Farber. The institute later expanded its services to provide programs for adults as well as children.

EXECUTIVES

President And Ceo, Laurie H. Glimcher, age 66
Evp Cfo And Assistant Treasurer, Dorothy E. Puhy, age 66
Vp And Chief Marketing Officer, David A. Feinberg
Svp Patient Care Services And Chief Nursing Officer, Anne Gross
Chair Department Of Medical Oncology, James D. Griffin
Chief Scientific Officer, Barrett J. Rollins
Svp And Cfo, Michael L. Reney
Chief Department Of Imaging, Annick D. Van den Abbeele
Chief Surgical Officer, Scott J. Swanson
Chief Medical Officer, Craig A. Bunnell
Chief Clinical Research Officer, Bruce E. Johnson
Chair Department Of Pediatric Oncology, Scott A. Armstrong
Chief Medical Officer Dana-farber/boston Childrenâ's Cancer And Blood Disorders Center, Lisa R. Diller

Professor And Chair Department Of Radiation Oncology Dana-farber Cancer Institute/brigham And Womenâ's Hospital/boston Childrenâ's Hospital, Daphne Haas-Kogan
Chair Executive Committee For Research (ecr), William C. Hahn
Chair Executive Committee For Clinical Programs (eccp), Robert J. Soiffer
Chair Executive Committee For Clinical Research (eccr), Mary-Ellen Taplin
Chair Department Of Psychosocial Oncology And Palliative Care, James Tulsky
President Dana-farber/boston Childrenâ's Cancer And Blood Disorders Center, David A. Williams
Clinical Director Adult Leukemia, Martha Wadleigh
Vice President, Melissa Shore
Senior Vice President Communications, Steven R Singer
Vice President Clinical Bussiness Development, Elizabeth Liebow
Senior Vice President For Patient Care Services And Chief Of Nur, Patricia Reid-ponte

LOCATIONS

HQ: DANA-FARBER CANCER INSTITUTE, INC.
450 BROOKLINE AVE, BOSTON, MA 022155450
Phone: 617 632-3000
Web: WWW.DANA-FARBER.ORG

PRODUCTS/OPERATIONS

2014 Sales

	% of total
Patients Services	62
Research	30
Unrestricted Contributions and Bequests	6
Other revenue	2
Total	**100**

Selected Clinical Affiliations

Dana-Farber/Brigham and Women's Cancer Center (outpatient services for adult cancer patients provided by Dana-Farber; and inpatient care provided by Brigham and Women's Hospital)
Dana-Farber/Children's Hospital Cancer Center (Dana-Farber Cancer Institute and Children's Hospital Boston outpatient care for children provided at Dana-Farber's Jimmy Fund Clinic)
Dana-Farber/Harvard Cancer Center (Beth Israel Deaconess Medical Center Brigham and Women's Hospital Children's Hospital Boston and Massachusetts General Hospital collaborate on research cancer prevention and treatments and therapies for cancer patients)
Dana-Farber/Lawrence + Memorial Cancer Center (cancer facility Waterford Connecticut).
Dana-Farber/Partners Cancer Care (consolidated adult oncology programs and clinical research of Dana-Farber Cancer Institute Brigham and Women's Hospital and Massachusetts General Hospital)

Selected Satellite Centers

Dana-Farber/Brigham and Women's Cancer Center at Faulkner Hospital in Jamaica Plain (southwest Boston area)
Dana-Farber/Brigham and Women's Cancer Center at Milford Regional Medical Center (Massachusetts)
Dana-Farber/Brigham and Women's Cancer Center in clinical affiliation with South Shore Hospital (South Weymouth Massachusetts)
Dana-Farber/New Hampshire Oncology-Hematology (Londonderry)
Adult Treatment Centers and Clinical Services
Blood Cancers
Breast Cancer
Cancer Genetics and Prevention
Cutaneous (Skin) Cancer
Gastrointestinal Cancer
Genitourinary Cancer
Gynecologic Cancer
Head and Neck Cancer
Hematology
Melanoma
Neuro-Oncology
Sarcoma
Thoracic (Lung) Cancer
Pediatric Treatment Centers and Clinical Services

Blood Disorders Center
Brain Tumor Center
Hematologic Malignancies Center
Solid Tumors Center
Stem Cell Transplant Center

COMPETITORS

Baystate Health	Johns Hopkins Medicine
Beth Israel Deaconess Medical Center	MD Anderson Cancer Center
Boston Medical Center	Mayo Clinic
Brigham and Women's Hospital	Memorial Sloan-Kettering
Care New England	Partners HealthCare
CareGroup	Roswell Park Cancer Institute
Children's National Medical Center	St. Elizabeth's Medical Center
Emory Healthcare	St. Jude Children's Research Hospital
Fox Chase Cancer Center	

HISTORICAL FINANCIALS

Company Type: Private

Income Statement   FYE: September 30

	REVENUE ($ mil.)	NET INCOME ($ mil.)	NET PROFIT MARGIN	EMPLOYEES
09/15	739	4	0.6%	3,000
09/14	672	34	5.1%	—
09/13	635	56	8.8%	—
09/10	894	16	1.9%	—
Annual Growth	(3.7%)	(22.7%)		

2015 Year-End Financials

Return on assets: 16.8%   Cash ($ mil.): 28
Return on equity: 0.6%
Current ratio: 0.50

DARTMOUTH-HITCHCOCK HEALTH

EXECUTIVES

Ceo, James Weinstein
Cfo, Daniel Jantzen
General Counsel, John Kacavas
Cao, Stephen Leblanc
Director of Treasury and Inves, Michael J Waters
Auditors: PRICEWATERHOUSECOOPERS LLP

LOCATIONS

HQ: DARTMOUTH-HITCHCOCK HEALTH
  1 MEDICAL CENTER DR, LEBANON, NH 037560001
Phone: 603 653-1118
Web: WWW.DARTMOUTH-HITCHCOCK.ORG

HISTORICAL FINANCIALS

Company Type: Private

Income Statement   FYE: June 30

	REVENUE ($ mil.)	NET INCOME ($ mil.)	NET PROFIT MARGIN	EMPLOYEES
06/18	2,069	87	4.2%	8,000
06/16	1,791	(44)	—	—
Annual Growth	7.5%	—	—	—

2018 Year-End Financials

Return on assets: 4.6%   Cash ($ mil.): 200
Return on equity: 4.2%
Current ratio: 1.60

DAVIDSON'S, INC.

EXECUTIVES

Chm, Bryan Tucker
President, Tim Mulder
Vice President, Larry M Massimo
Vice President, Daniel Leonard
Director of Information Techno, Richard Gutierrez
Information Technology Manager, Josh Tucker
Web Developer, Diane Anderson
Human Resources Director, Aaron Rogos
Account Manager, Kevin Wilson
Sales Manager, Matt Nicholson
Account Executive, Dennis Sullivan
Auditors: EIDE BAILLY LLP PHOENIX ARIZ

LOCATIONS

HQ: DAVIDSON'S, INC.
  6100 WILKINSON DR, PRESCOTT, AZ 863016162
Phone: 928 776-8055
Web: WWW.DAVIDSONSINC.COM

HISTORICAL FINANCIALS

Company Type: Private

Income Statement   FYE: November 30

	REVENUE ($ mil.)	NET INCOME ($ mil.)	NET PROFIT MARGIN	EMPLOYEES
11/17	374	9	2.7%	89
11/16	513	26	5.2%	—
11/15	342	16	4.7%	—
11/14	322	15	4.7%	—
Annual Growth	5.1%	(13.1%)	—	—

2017 Year-End Financials

Return on assets: 5.4%   Cash ($ mil.): 2
Return on equity: 2.7%
Current ratio: 1.70

DARTMOUTH COLLEGE

EXECUTIVES

Mgr, James Fries
Assistant Professor, Ethan M Berke
Assistant Professor, WEI Wang
Public Relations Manager, Michael Barwell
Coordinator, Ben Myers
Auditors: PRICEWATERHOUSECOOPERS LLP BO

LOCATIONS

HQ: DARTMOUTH COLLEGE
  6193 HINMAN, HANOVER, NH 037554007
Phone: 603 646-2191
Web: WWW.DARTMOUTHCOOP.COM

HISTORICAL FINANCIALS

Company Type: Private

Income Statement   FYE: June 30

	REVENUE ($ mil.)	NET INCOME ($ mil.)	NET PROFIT MARGIN	EMPLOYEES
06/18	893	739	82.8%	10
06/17	887	691	77.9%	—
06/16	859	(301)	—	—
06/15	876	236	27.0%	—
Annual Growth	0.7%	46.2%	—	—

2018 Year-End Financials

Return on assets: 10.3%   Cash ($ mil.): 203
Return on equity: 82.8%
Current ratio: 0.80

DAUGHTERS OF CHARITY SERVICES OF ST. LOUIS

EXECUTIVES

President-Ceo, Robert G Porter
General Accounting Manager, Flo Cramper
Chief Financial Officer, Mark Oconnor

LOCATIONS

HQ: DAUGHTERS OF CHARITY SERVICES OF ST. LOUIS
  12303 DE PAUL DR, BRIDGETON, MO 630442512
Phone: 314 344-6000
Web: WWW.SSMHEALTH.COM/LOCATIONS/DEPAUL-HOSPITAL-ST-LOUIS

HISTORICAL FINANCIALS

Company Type: Private

Income Statement   FYE: December 31

	REVENUE ($ mil.)	NET INCOME ($ mil.)	NET PROFIT MARGIN	EMPLOYEES
12/15	396	41	10.4%	1,550
12/14	368	40	11.0%	—
Annual Growth	7.7%	2.3%	—	—

2015 Year-End Financials

Return on assets: 4.2%   Cash ($ mil.): 14
Return on equity: 10.4%
Current ratio: 0.30

DAYTON PUBLIC SCHOOL DISTRICT

EXECUTIVES

Superintendent, Lori Ward
Director, Roy Hollis
Food Director, Travis Grant
Secretary, Jennifer Dennis
General Manager, Jerry Hays
Treasurer, John McManus
Supervisor, Richard Knight
Administrator, Debora Wotring
Teacher, Judy Scroggins
Administrative Assistant, Kimberly Lewis
Teacher, Lorry Creech
Auditors: DAVE YOST AUDITOR OF STATE C

LOCATIONS

HQ: DAYTON PUBLIC SCHOOL DISTRICT
  115 S LUDLOW ST, DAYTON, OH 454021812
Phone: 937 542-3000
Web: WWW.DPS.K12.OH.US

HISTORICAL FINANCIALS

Company Type: Private

Income Statement				FYE: June 30
	REVENUE ($ mil.)	NET INCOME ($ mil.)	NET PROFIT MARGIN	EMPLOYEES
06/17	319	23	7.2%	197
06/16	294	16	5.5%	—
Annual Growth	8.5%	43.1%		

2017 Year-End Financials

Return on assets: 0.5% Cash ($ mil.): 10
Return on equity: 7.2%
Current ratio: —

DB US HOLDING CORPORATION

EXECUTIVES

Pres-Ceo, Dr Josef Blank
Ex V Pres-Cfo, Joseph L Groneman
V Pres-SEC, Brian P Lynch
Assistant General Counsel, Dennis St George
Manager, Laura Beckmeyer
Senior Internal Auditor, Dominic Huang
Auditors: PRICEWATERHOUSECOOPERS LLP N

LOCATIONS

HQ: DB US HOLDING CORPORATION
120 WHITE PLAINS RD, TARRYTOWN, NY 105915526
Phone: 914 366-7200
Web: WWW.DBUSHOLDING.COM

HISTORICAL FINANCIALS

Company Type: Private

Income Statement				FYE: December 31
	REVENUE ($ mil.)	NET INCOME ($ mil.)	NET PROFIT MARGIN	EMPLOYEES
12/16	914	(2)	—	6,300
12/15	1,766	(10)	—	—
/	0	0	—	—
Annual Growth	—	—	—	—

2016 Year-End Financials

Return on assets: — Cash ($ mil.): 122
Return on equity: (-0.3%)
Current ratio: 100.60

DE PAUL UNIVERSITY

In the land of da Bulls and da Bears there's De-Paul. One of the largest private not-for-profit universities in the US DePaul has some 23000 students attending classes at its Chicago-area campuses and its increasing offerings of online learning courses. The university offers more than 300 undergraduate and graduate programs through 10 colleges and schools including the Kellstadt Graduate School of Business and the College of Communication. It has a student teacher ratio of 15 to 1. One of the country's largest Catholic institutions of higher learning DePaul was founded in 1898 by the Vincentian religious community

and is named after 17th century French priest St. Vincent de Paul.

Geographic Reach

DePaul's five Chicago-area campuses are located in Lincoln Park the Loop and the O'Hare area. Although 67% of its students come from Illinois DePaul's student body hosts learners from the 50 US states and more than 100 countries.

Financial Performance

DePaul has an annual budget of about $550 million and its endowment is about $420 million. Undergraduate tuition for the 2017-2018 academic year was $39000.

EXECUTIVES

Vice President, Bonnie Frankel
Evp Financial Affairs, Robert L. (Bob) Kozoman
Vp Facilities, Robert (Bob) Janis
Dean Driehaus College Of Business And Kellstadt Graduate School Of Business, Ray Whittington
Dean School For New Learning, Marisa Alicea
Dean Theatre School, John Culbert
Dean College Of Computing And Digital Media, David Miller
President, A. Gabriel Esteban
Vp Information Services, Bob McCormick
Dean College Of Communication, Salma Ghanem
Provost, Marten denBoer
Vp Planning And Presidential Administration, Jay Braatz
Svp Enrollment Management, David Kalsbeek
Dean College Of Science And Health, Gerald P. Koocher
Athletic Director, Jean Lenti-Ponsetto
Interim Dean College Of Liberal Arts And Social Sciences, Lucy Rinehart
Dean College Of Law, Jennifer Rosato Perea
Dean School Of Education, Paul Zionts
Vice President And General Counsel, Jose Padilla
Executive Vice President For Operations Loop, Susan Carolan
Acting Vice President Finance, Bonnie Hirsch
Vice President Of Finance Operating Loop Campus, Rebecca Awells
Assistant Vice President Academic Affairs, Charles Strain
Director Of Admissions, Dennis Shea
Assistant Vice President Planned Giving, Joel Schaeffer
Assistant Vice President For Marketing Communications, Gwyn Friend
Assistant Vice President For Cross College Initiatives; Accreditation, Caryn Chaden
Vice President Teaching Learning Resources, Edward Udovic
Vice President Student Affairs, James Doyle
Assistant Vice President Gems Loop Campus, Suzanne Adepeder
Vice President Student Affairs Lincoln Park Campus, Kathryn Ao'brien
Associate Vice President, Barbara M Schaffer
Associate Vice President, Doris Brown
Executive Vice President For Academic Affairs, Michael Greene
Vice President Facility Operations, Bob Janis
Board Member, R Ostrander
Auditors: KPMG LLP CHICAGO ILLINOIS

LOCATIONS

HQ: DE PAUL UNIVERSITY
1 E JACKSON BLVD, CHICAGO, IL 606042287
Phone: 312 362-6714
Web: WWW.DEPAUL.EDU

HISTORICAL FINANCIALS

Company Type: Private

Income Statement				FYE: June 30
	REVENUE ($ mil.)	NET INCOME ($ mil.)	NET PROFIT MARGIN	EMPLOYEES
06/18	575	67	11.7%	3,895
06/17	575	67	11.7%	—
06/15	562	38	6.9%	—
06/14	564	59	10.5%	—
Annual Growth	0.5%	3.1%	—	—

2018 Year-End Financials

Return on assets: 9.9% Cash ($ mil.): 59
Return on equity: 11.7%
Current ratio: —

DEACON HOLDINGS, INC.

EXECUTIVES

Ceo, Steven D Deacon
President, Richard Smith
Partner, Meridian Park Oncolog, Bob Miller
Principal, Portland, Pete Snook
Director, Kendra Howell
Administrator, Curt Mills
Superintendent, Eric Fleming
Manager, Julie Earnest
Superintendent, Bob Doyle
Information Specialist, Chuck Moua
Superintendent, Kevin Frank
Auditors: BFBA LLP SACRAMENTO CALIFOR

LOCATIONS

HQ: DEACON HOLDINGS, INC.
7745 GREENBACK LN STE 250, CITRUS HEIGHTS, CA 956105865
Phone: 916 969-0900

HISTORICAL FINANCIALS

Company Type: Private

Income Statement				FYE: October 31
	REVENUE ($ mil.)	NET INCOME ($ mil.)	NET PROFIT MARGIN	EMPLOYEES
10/15	391	5	1.5%	340
10/14	389	1	0.4%	—
10/13	388	1	0.4%	—
10/12	384	7	1.9%	—
Annual Growth	0.6%	(7.8%)	—	—

2015 Year-End Financials

Return on assets: 24.0% Cash ($ mil.): 23
Return on equity: 1.5%
Current ratio: 1.00

DEACONESS HEALTH SYSTEM, INC.

While it primarily presides over numerous health care facilities in the southwestern corner of Indiana Deaconess Health System also serves residents in parts of southeastern Illinois and western Kentucky. The system consists of two general acute-care hospitals as well as specialty hospitals for women's health mental health and medical rehabilitation. Its flagship Deaconess Hospital boasts 365 beds and serves as a regional referral center. Deaconess Health also operates a standalone cancer treatment center medical group practice Deaconess Clinic and about 20 outpatient and urgent care clinics. Its Deaconess Health Plans unit is a PPO network that contracts with various health insurers.

Operations

As part of its operations the health system comprises half a dozen facilities including Deaconess Hospital (365 beds) Deaconness Gateway Hospital (120 beds) The Women's Hospital (50 beds) Deaconess Cross Pointe (60 beds) HealthSouth Deaconess Rehabilitation Hospital (80 beds) and The Heart Hospital of Deaconess Gateway (24 beds). It also operates primary care locations such as Deaconess Clinic Deaconess Primary Care for Seniors and Deaconess Urgent Care.

The hospital treats 18000 inpatients 350000 outpatients 65000 emergency patients and 7500 surgical patients each year.

Geographic Reach

Deaconess Health System primarily serves those who reside in 26 counties in Southern Indiana Southeast Illinois and West Kentucky.

Financial Performance

In 2014 net sales increased by 13% due to higher revenues from net patient service.

Deaconess Health System's net patient service revenue increased due to increased contractual adjustments. Medicare and Medicaid together accounted 57% of total net sales in 2014. Commercial and managed care and Self pay and other accounted for 36% and 7% respectively

In 2014 net income increased by 40% compared to 2013. The primary reason was due to increased sales partially offset by decreased benefit related changes other than net periodic benefit cost.

Deaconess Health System's net cash provided by the operating activities increased by 28%.

Strategy

Deaconess Health System has been focused on improving information technology systems including the implementation of an electronic health record (EHR) system. It has increased efficiencies through IT initiatives by installing new automated medication dispensing and prescription management programs.

MyChart is available at Deaconess Hospital Main Deaconess Gateway Deaconess Riley Hospital for Children The Heart Hospital Cross Point all Deaconess Clinic locations Deaconess Critical Care Deaconess Family Practice and Residency and Deaconess Primary Care for Seniors physician offices. MyChart is a secure online health management tool that connects MyChart patients to their personalized health information. MyChart contains inpatient and outpatient test results and information.

In 2015 the company finalized a letter of intent to partner directly with Methodist Hospital on a not-for-profit joint venture to bring additional and enhanced healthcare services to Henderson. The joint venture will improve access to care providers and quality of care in Henderson. Deaconess Health System purchased 10-plus acres of land off Barret Boulevard near Walmart in Henderson in 2014.

Company Background

Founded in 1892 Deaconess Hospital is a teaching facility that offers residency and clinical education programs in addition to providing general and specialty inpatient care. It also conducts medical research programs.

EXECUTIVES

Vice President Business Development, Jared Florence
Nursing Director, Jill Buttry
Auditors: BLUE & CO LLC INDIANAPOLIS I

LOCATIONS

HQ: DEACONESS HEALTH SYSTEM, INC.
  600 MARY ST, EVANSVILLE, IN 477101658
Phone: 812 450-5000
Web: WWW.DEACONESS.COM

PRODUCTS/OPERATIONS

Selected Services
Back & Spine
Behavioral Health
Cancer
Children's Health
Clinical Research
Diabetes
Emergency Care
Joint Replacement
Orthopedic
Pain Management
Physical Medicine
Radiology
Respiratory
Senior Health
Weight Loss
Women's Health
Wound Care

COMPETITORS

Ball Memorial Hospital
Baptist Health
  Madisonville
Commonwealth Health
  Corporation
Community Health
  Network
Daviess Community
  Hospital
Good Samaritan
  Hospital (IN)
Henry County Memorial
  Hospital
Kosciusko Community
  Hospital
Memorial Hospital
  (Logansport)
St. Mary's Medical
  Center of Evansville

HISTORICAL FINANCIALS

Company Type: Private

Income Statement				FYE: September 30
	REVENUE ($ mil.)	NET INCOME ($ mil.)	NET PROFIT MARGIN	EMPLOYEES
09/17	930	127	13.7%	6,086
09/16	2	(27)	—	—
09/15	2	(24)	—	—
09/14	3	(20)	—	—
Annual Growth	548.9%	—	—	—

2017 Year-End Financials

Return on assets: 7.2%   Cash ($ mil.): 78
Return on equity: 13.7%
Current ratio: 1.60

DEACONESS HOSPITAL INC

Deaconess Hospital provides benevolent medical assistance to residents of southern Indiana western Kentucky and southeastern Illinois. The not-for-profit hospital is a 365-bed acute care medical facility that is the flagship hospital of the Deaconess Health System. Specialized services include cardiovascular surgery cancer treatment orthopedics neurological and trauma care. The hospital also offers home health care hospice services and medical equipment rental and it operates outpatient family practice surgery wellness and community outreach centers. Founded in 1892 Deaconess Hospital is a teaching and research facility affiliated with the Indiana University School of Medicine.

Operations

Deaconess handles about 18000 inpatient visits per year. It also sees about 350000 outpatients and 65000 emergency room visitors and it handles about 7500 annual surgery procedures.

Geographic Reach

Deaconess Hospital is located in Evansville Indiana and provides services to about 26 surrounding counties.

Strategy

To improve services to area residents Deaconess Hospital is expanding its outpatient care facilities and enhancing its IT resources. For instance in 2013 it moved its urgent care center to a larger more efficient facility. The hospital is also pursuing recognition for specialist programs such as its stroke center which was certified as a level one facility in 2013.

EXECUTIVES

Vice President Facilities Support Services, Bruce E Epmeier

LOCATIONS

HQ: DEACONESS HOSPITAL INC
  600 MARY ST, EVANSVILLE, IN 477101674
Phone: 812 450-5000
Web: WWW.DEACONESS.COM

Selected Services
24-hour Emergency Center
Cancer Services
Corporate Wellness
Family Medicine Clinic
Heart Services
Home Medical Equipment
Home-based Medical Care
Hospice Care
Inpatient and Outpatient Surgery
Mental Health Services
Neuro Services
Orthopedics
Pediatrics
Physician Referral Service
Radiology Services
Residency Program
Support Groups and Programs
Women's Hospital

COMPETITORS

Ball Memorial Hospital
Baptist Health
Baptist Health
  Madisonville
Commonwealth Health
  Corporation
Community Health
  Network
Daviess Community
  Hospital
Good Samaritan
  Hospital (IN)
Henry County Memorial
  Hospital
Jewish Hospital & St.
  Mary's HealthCare
Kosciusko Community
  Hospital
Memorial Hospital
  (Logansport)
Norton Healthcare
St. Mary's Medical
  Center of Evansville

HISTORICAL FINANCIALS

Company Type: Private

Income Statement				FYE: September 30
	REVENUE ($ mil.)	NET INCOME ($ mil.)	NET PROFIT MARGIN	EMPLOYEES
09/17	725	94	13.0%	5,300
09/16	698	108	15.5%	—
09/15	680	138	20.3%	—
09/14	623	113	18.1%	—
Annual Growth	5.2%	(5.9%)	—	—

2017 Year-End Financials
Return on assets: 7.7%   Cash ($ mil.): 66
Return on equity: 13.0%
Current ratio: 1.60

DECATUR HOSPITAL AUTHORITY

EXECUTIVES

Pres, Brian Stephens
Ceo, Steve Summers
V Pres, Jay Bearden
SEC, Kevin Haney
MBR, Chris Forbis
Chief of Orthopedic Surgery Sv, Wade Mc Kenna
Health Professional, Brandi Stowe
Fit N Wise Sports and Fitness, Dana Hale
Chief Financial Officer, Leon Fuqua
Emergency Medicine Specialist, Phillip Chapa
Audit Manager, Robert Olson
Auditors: BKD LLP WACO TX

LOCATIONS

HQ: DECATUR HOSPITAL AUTHORITY
   609 MEDICAL CENTER DR, DECATUR, TX 762343836
Phone: 940 627-5921
Web: WWW.WISEREGIONAL.COM

HISTORICAL FINANCIALS

Company Type: Private

Income Statement				FYE: December 31
	REVENUE ($ mil.)	NET INCOME ($ mil.)	NET PROFIT MARGIN	EMPLOYEES
12/17	427	21	5.0%	1,084
12/16	415	28	6.7%	—
12/10	105	(0)	—	—
12/09	103	(1)	—	—
Annual Growth	19.3%	—	—	—

2017 Year-End Financials
Return on assets: 7.6%   Cash ($ mil.): 65
Return on equity: 5.0%
Current ratio: 2.60

DEER PARK REFINING LIMITED PARTNERSHIP

EXECUTIVES

Prin, Bruce A Henderson
Auditors: ERNST & YOUNG LLP HOUSTON TX

LOCATIONS

HQ: DEER PARK REFINING LIMITED PARTNERSHIP
   5900 HIGHWAY 225, DEER PARK, TX 775362434
Phone: 713 246-7280
Web: WWW.DEERPARKTX.GOV

HISTORICAL FINANCIALS

Company Type: Private

Income Statement				FYE: December 31
	REVENUE ($ mil.)	NET INCOME ($ mil.)	NET PROFIT MARGIN	EMPLOYEES
12/17	867	97	11.2%	3
12/16	897	154	17.2%	—
Annual Growth	(3.3%)	(36.9%)		

2017 Year-End Financials
Return on assets: —   Cash ($ mil.): 77
Return on equity: 11.2%
Current ratio: 0.50

DEER VALLEY SCHOOL DISTRICT 97

EXECUTIVES

Supt, James R Veitenheimer
Assoc Supt Suppt Serv, Dr Kent Davis
Coordinator, Bob Rambole
Coordinator, Debbie Habgood
Accounting Staff, Joanne Douglas
Accounting Staff, Karen Kelner
Accounting Staff, Sheila Stodghill
Facilities Manager, Garry Glay
Teacher, Janet Gilbert
Teacher, Angela Larson
Academic Advisor, Beth Harvill
Auditors: HEINFELD MEECH & CO PC P

LOCATIONS

HQ: DEER VALLEY SCHOOL DISTRICT 97
   20402 N 15TH AVE, PHOENIX, AZ 850273636
Phone: 623 445-5000
Web: WWW.DVUSD.ORG

HISTORICAL FINANCIALS

Company Type: Private

Income Statement				FYE: June 30
	REVENUE ($ mil.)	NET INCOME ($ mil.)	NET PROFIT MARGIN	EMPLOYEES
06/17	292	(6)	—	3,500
06/16	276	17	6.5%	—
06/13	274	2	1.0%	—
06/11	294	8	2.9%	—
Annual Growth	(0.1%)	—	—	—

DEKALB MEDICAL CENTER, INC.

As far as DeKalb is concerned da healthier da better! Beginning as a rural hospital DeKalb Regional Health System now serves all of the Atlanta metropolitan area. The health system operating as DeKalb Medical is home to two acute care hospitals - DeKalb Medical at North Decatur and DeKalb Medical at Hillandale (with a combined total of about 550 beds). It also operates a 75-bed long-term rehabilitation hospital — DeKalb Medical at Downtown Decatur. Specialty hospital services include oncology cardiology orthopedics and diabetes care. The health system which was founded in 1961 also operates primary specialty and mobile health care clinics partly through the DeKalb Medical Physicians Group. DeKalb is merging with Emory Healthcare.

Operations
DeKalb's network of three hospitals staffs more than 800 physicians who represent about 50 medical specialties including neurosurgery interventional radiology sports medicine endovascular surgery gynecology emergency medicine and infectious disease. Altogether DeKalb Medical's facilities had some 27000 inpatient visits 123000 outpatient encounters 120000 emergency department visits and delivered some 5000 babies during 2014.

In addition to medical services DeKalb Medical offers educational residency programs in subjects including pharmacy nursing and podiatry. It also operates a school for radiology technicians.

Geographic Reach
In addition to its main facilities in Decatur and Hillandale DeKalb has operations in Lilburn Lithonia Snellville Stone Mountain and Tucker Georgia.

Strategy
DeKalb Medical is a self-supporting not-for-profit community hospital that does not receive tax dollars as part of its funding. The hospital system's operating budget comes solely from patient fees; DeKalb Medical reinvests any excess income into expanding or updating its services and facilities to meet Atlanta's growing population. The DeKalb Medical Foundation was established in 1991 and since then has funded improvements in facilities technology and community outreach programs.

Mergers and Acquisitions
In late 2017 DeKalb Medical and fellow Georgia health system Emory Healthcare agreed to join forces. The arrangement should help DeKalb which had operating losses of more than $20 million in 2016 and 2017 by giving it access to the larger Emory's resources and support.

EXECUTIVES

Vp Patient Care Services And Chief Nursing Officer, Susan Breslin
Evp And Coo, Dane Henry
Svp And Cfo, John Katsianis
Svp And Chief Strategy Officer, Jim Forstner
Vp Information Systems And Cio, Elizabeth Patino
Vp Medical Affairs, Raoul Mayer
Ceo And Director, Robert Wilson
Medical Director, Leslie Pope
Chairman, David L. Jollay

LOCATIONS

HQ: DEKALB MEDICAL CENTER, INC.
   2701 N DECATUR RD, DECATUR, GA 300335918
Phone: 404 501-1000
Web: WWW.DEKALBMEDICAL.ORG

PRODUCTS/OPERATIONS

Selected Specialties
Cancer Center
Community Programs
Corporate Health Services
Emergency Department
Heart and Vascular Services
Orthopedic Services
Podiatry
Radiology and Medical Imaging
Rehabilitation Services
Senior Services
Sleep Center
Surgical Weight Loss
Volunteers

Wellness Center
Women's Services
Workswell Services
Wound Care

COMPETITORS

Children's Healthcare of Atlanta	HCA
Emory Healthcare	Northside Hospital
Grady Health System	Piedmont Healthcare
Gwinnett Health System	St. Mary's Health Care
	WellStar Health System

HISTORICAL FINANCIALS
Company Type: Private

Income Statement   FYE: June 30

	REVENUE ($ mil.)	NET INCOME ($ mil.)	NET PROFIT MARGIN	EMPLOYEES
06/15	303	4	1.6%	2,700
06/14	524	1	0.3%	—
06/11	422	0	0.2%	—
06/10	397	(15)	—	—
Annual Growth	(5.3%)	—	—	—

2015 Year-End Financials
Return on assets: 5.4%   Cash ($ mil.): 4
Return on equity: 1.6%
Current ratio: 1.10

DEKALB REGIONAL HEALTH SYSTEM, INC.

EXECUTIVES

Ceo, Eric Norwood
Cfo, Diane Harden
Ceo, John A Shelton
SEC, Robert Wilson
Information Technology Adminis, Darian Brooks
Information Technology Support, Keith Carter
Information Technology Analyst, Laura Bridges
Auditors: DIXON HUGHES GOODMAN LLP ATLA

LOCATIONS

HQ: DEKALB REGIONAL HEALTH SYSTEM, INC.
2701 N DECATUR RD, DECATUR, GA 300335918
Phone: 404 501-1000
Web: WWW.DEKALBMEDICAL.ORG

HISTORICAL FINANCIALS
Company Type: Private

Income Statement   FYE: June 30

	REVENUE ($ mil.)	NET INCOME ($ mil.)	NET PROFIT MARGIN	EMPLOYEES
06/17	487	(6)	—	2,827
06/15	4	(7)	—	—
06/14	5	(5)	—	—
06/13	4	(9)	—	—
Annual Growth	215.4%	—	—	—

2017 Year-End Financials
Return on assets: 10.1%   Cash ($ mil.): 3
Return on equity: (-1.3%)
Current ratio: 1.40

DELAWARE RIVER PORT AUTHORITY

The famous painting of George Washington crossing the Delaware would have lacked a good deal of its drama if the Delaware River Port Authority of Pennsylvania and New Jersey (DRPA) had been around in 1776. DRPA keeps commuters (and leaders of revolutionary armies) out of small boats by operating the Benjamin Franklin Betsy Ross Commodore Barry and Walt Whitman toll bridges over the Delaware River which divides Pennsylvania from New Jersey. Bridge operations account for 90% of the agency's revenue. Through its Port Authority Transit Corp. (PATCO) subsidiary DRPA operates PATCO a rail service that links Philadelphia with communities on the New Jersey side of the Delaware.

Operations

The Benjamin Franklin Bridge opened in 1926 hosts average weekday traffic of more than 105000. DRPA's second-oldest bridge Walt Whitman opened in 1957 provides crossings for average weekday traffic of more than 108000. DRPA opened two more bridges during the mid-1970s that carry significantly less traffic than their older counterparts. Commodore Barry opened in 1974 has average weekday traffic of more than 39000.

Betsy Ross opened in 1976 provides passage for more than 32000 on an average weekday. PATCO launched in 1969 boasts an average weekday ridership of more than 36000. Since 2000 DRPA has operated the RiverLink Ferry System which annually transports about 110000 passengers between Philadelphia and Camden New Jersey.

Financial Performance

Mainly because of toll and fare increases DRPA's revenue grew by almost 10% in 2012 compared with 2011. It was helped by a 10% surge in bridge toll revenue and an 8% spike in PATCO sales. In addition the amount it earned on interest income jumped 17% from 2011 to 2012.

Strategy

PATCO is spending about $200 million to overhaul its some 120 rail cars. Another major DRPA project is redecking the suspended span and anchorage spans of the Walt Whitman Bridge for about $140 million. These improvements are part of a larger DRPA $1 billion five-year capital improvement plan. To gather money for capital improvements DRPA raised fares by 25% on its tollbridges and 10% on PATCO in 2011.

Also in 2011 DRPA ended some major operations. The DRPA board voted to discontinue economic development spending and DRPA closed the Philadelphia Cruise Terminal at Pier 1 which had been operating in the Philadelphia Navy Yard for more than 10 years.

Company Background

DRPA was established by the New Jersey and Pennsylvania legislatures in 1919 as the Delaware River Bridge Joint Commission; it became the Delaware River Port Authority by an act of the US Congress in 1951.

EXECUTIVES

V Chm, Jeffrey L Nash
Jr Cfo/Treasurer, James M White
Chairman of Board, Ryan Boyer
General Legal Practice, Brooke D Schmoll
Coordinator, Sheila Milner
Law Specialist, Jan Odjemski
Captain, Gary Smith
Captain, John Stief

LOCATIONS

HQ: DELAWARE RIVER PORT AUTHORITY
2 RIVERSIDE DR STE 603, CAMDEN, NJ 081031019
Phone: 856 968-2000
Web: WWW.DRPA.ORG

HISTORICAL FINANCIALS
Company Type: Private

Income Statement   FYE: December 31

	REVENUE ($ mil.)	NET INCOME ($ mil.)	NET PROFIT MARGIN	EMPLOYEES
12/16	354	66	18.9%	900
12/15	341	102	30.0%	—
12/14	75	0	0.8%	—
12/13	328	92	28.2%	—
Annual Growth	2.6%	(10.3%)	—	—

2016 Year-End Financials
Return on assets: 3.1%   Cash ($ mil.): 37
Return on equity: 18.9%
Current ratio: 0.30

DELNOR-COMMUNITY HOSPITAL

EXECUTIVES

Pres-Ceo, Craig Livermore
Treas, Bob White
Cfo, Michael Kittoe
Coo, Tom Wright
Doctor, Brian S Chang
Computer Specialist, Wayne V Polek
Pharmacist, Karen Matuszewski
Coordinator, Lisa Klonowski
Pediatrician, Ruthann Birr
Chief of Anesthesiology, Scott Helm
Education Specialist, Shannon McCall

LOCATIONS

HQ: DELNOR-COMMUNITY HOSPITAL
300 RANDALL RD, GENEVA, IL 601344202
Phone: 630 208-3000
Web: WWW.DELNOR.COM

HISTORICAL FINANCIALS
Company Type: Private

Income Statement   FYE: August 31

	REVENUE ($ mil.)	NET INCOME ($ mil.)	NET PROFIT MARGIN	EMPLOYEES
08/15	305	(210)	—	1,600
08/14*	44	5	11.4%	—
06/13	216	20	9.4%	—
06/12	214	21	10.2%	—
Annual Growth	12.5%	—	—	—

*Fiscal year change

2015 Year-End Financials
Return on assets: 34.6%   Cash ($ mil.): 3
Return on equity: (-68.9%)
Current ratio: 0.20

DELRAY MEDICAL CENTER, INC.

EXECUTIVES

Pres, Mark H Bryan
SEC, Kristina A Mack
Treas, Tyler Murphy
C-Level Human Resources, Shannon Lutlow
Director of Information Techno, Robens Rosena
Director, Cheri Silveria
Director of Operations, Michael Cronan
Registered Nurse Msn Crrn Clin, Gail Rubin
Supervisor Plant Operations, Patrick Gray
Anesthesiology, David Ritter
Office Manager, Janice Berry

LOCATIONS

HQ: DELRAY MEDICAL CENTER, INC.
  5352 LINTON BLVD, DELRAY BEACH, FL 334846514
Phone: 561 498-4440
Web: WWW.TENETHEALTH.COM

HISTORICAL FINANCIALS

Company Type: Private

Income Statement				FYE: December 31
	REVENUE ($ mil.)	NET INCOME ($ mil.)	NET PROFIT MARGIN	EMPLOYEES
12/16	336	41	12.4%	10
12/15	313	38	12.1%	—
12/14	294	37	12.8%	—
12/12	0	37	—	—
Annual Growth	—	2.5%	—	—

2016 Year-End Financials

Return on assets: 4.7%   Cash ($ mil.): —
Return on equity: 12.4%
Current ratio: 1.70

DENTON INDEPENDENT SCHOOL DISTRICT

EXECUTIVES

Pres, Mia Price
Manager, Jamie Wilson
Supt, Ray Braswell
Vice President, Glenna G Harris
SEC, Rudy Rodriguez
Coordinator, Donna Kearley
Auditors: HANKINS EASTUP DEATON TONN

LOCATIONS

HQ: DENTON INDEPENDENT SCHOOL DISTRICT
  1307 N LOCUST ST, DENTON, TX 762013037
Phone: 940 369-0000
Web: WWW.DENTONISD.ORG

HISTORICAL FINANCIALS

Company Type: Private

Income Statement				FYE: June 30
	REVENUE ($ mil.)	NET INCOME ($ mil.)	NET PROFIT MARGIN	EMPLOYEES
06/17	335	(74)	—	3,300
06/16	313	105	33.7%	—
06/15	291	(49)	—	—
06/14	269	174	64.8%	—
Annual Growth	7.6%	—	—	—

2017 Year-End Financials

Return on assets: 4.0%   Cash ($ mil.): 341
Return on equity: (-22.0%)
Current ratio: —

DENVER BOARD OF WATER COMMISSIONERS

Denver Water keeps the Broncos' troughs full. The Board of Water Commissioners City and County of Denver Colorado which operates as Denver Water distributes water to more than 1.3 million people in the Denver metropolitan area. The company serves some 1.2 million residential commercial and industrial customer accounts within the city and county and it serves more than 175000 suburban customers through retail and wholesale service contracts. The utility gets its water primarily from the Blue River and the South Platte River. Denver Water is an independently operated division of the City and County of Denver.

Operations

The utility's system includes 30 underground reservoirs 23 pumping stations more than 3000 miles of water mains which in addition to serving customers supplies water to about 19818 fire hydrants.

Strategy

In recent years Denver Water has been tightening its rules on water usage (mainly regarding lawn and plant watering) to protect its supply in the face of a growing population and persistent drought conditions.

In 2012 the company completed the first of several treated water reservoir projects by building a new 10-million-gallon concrete reservoir in Lone Tree. It also rebuilt two dams including the 140-year-old Harriman Lake Dam that year.

By 2022 Denver Water plans to spend $120 million on treated water storage tank projects throughout its system. As part of a $40 million four-year project at the Ashland Treated Water Reservoir in Wheat Ridge the utility will demolish two tanks and replace them with new reservoirs.

Company Background

The utility which was founded in 1918 when Denver citizens purchased the city's water system from a private company is the oldest and largest water utility in Colorado.

EXECUTIVES

Director Information Technology, Christopher R. Dermody
Director Engineering, Robert J. Mahoney
Director Operations And Maintenance, Tom Roode
President, Greg Austin
Ceo And Manager, Jim Lochhead
Director Finance, Angela Bricmont
Vice President Manager Director, Alan Chotiner

Board Member, Jarrod Loran
Auditors: KPMG LLP DENVER CO

LOCATIONS

HQ: DENVER BOARD OF WATER COMMISSIONERS
  1600 W 12TH AVE, DENVER, CO 802043412
Phone: 303 893-2444
Web: WWW.DENVERWATER.ORG

PRODUCTS/OPERATIONS

2013 Sales

	% of total
Water sales	95
Power generation & other	5
Total	**100**

HISTORICAL FINANCIALS

Company Type: Private

Income Statement				FYE: December 31
	REVENUE ($ mil.)	NET INCOME ($ mil.)	NET PROFIT MARGIN	EMPLOYEES
12/17	298	83	27.8%	1,100
12/16	284	87	30.7%	—
12/11	249	55	22.2%	—
12/10	233	31	13.5%	—
Annual Growth	3.6%	14.9%	—	—

2017 Year-End Financials

Return on assets: 10.2%   Cash ($ mil.): 6
Return on equity: 27.8%
Current ratio: 0.40

DENVER HEALTH AND HOSPITALS AUTHORITY INC

When you live a mile high you sometimes need a safety net; that's where Denver Health and Hospital Authority comes in. Though it serves all the people of Colorado's capital annually attending to a fourth of the city's population and a third of its children Denver Health is also the "safety net" care provider for the city's indigent uninsured mentally ill and other high-risk patients. The medical system's primary facility is the Denver Health Medical Center a 525-bed hospital offering care in more than 50 medical specialties that also houses a regional trauma center. It also includes a network of family health and dental clinics; a poison and drug center; and a 911 response system for Denver County.

Operations

Denver Health's principal facility Denver Health Medical Center is a teaching hospital affiliated with the University of Colorado at Denver and is one of the busiest medical centers in the state. The trauma center (known as Rocky Mountain Regional Trauma Center) has Level I status and is known for having one of the highest survival rates in the nation. In addition the hospital operates an ambulance service a pediatric emergency center and a terrorism and catastrophe response center. Denver Health operates Denver's 911 medical emergency response system. Annually Denver Health paramedics respond to about 90000 calls for emergency medical assistance and transport more than 61000 patients to 11 area hospitals.

The health system provides medical care at 16 K-12 school-based health centers as well as eight family health centers located throughout the city. It also runs a number of public health clinics that offer immunizations infectious disease treatment detoxification and behavioral health consultation.

Denver Health cares for some 66000 children each year. In 2013 the system delivered 3175 babies and reported 55511 emergency department visits.

Financial Performance

Denver Health's revenue increased 7% to $793 million in 2013 due to an increase in net patient service revenue as well as safety net reimbursements and government grants. The number of uninsured patients has fallen dramatically under the Affordable Care Act which has helped the system improve its earnings. However the company reported a net loss of $15 million as non-operating revenue declined and fair value of investments fell.

Strategy

Denver Health integrates acute hospital and emergency care with public and community health offerings to deliver preventive primary and acute care services.

The health system's health plan covers 17000 city and hospital employees members of Medicaid's child plan and Medicare and another 53000 Medicaid patients. It expects to serve 40000 new Medicaid customers over the next few years as a result of the 2014 Affordable Care Act including about 15000 the hospital already sees without any payment.

In 2014 the company opened the Lowry Family Health Center adding new exam rooms to its operations. It also opened a new dental clinic and Women Infants and Children (WIC) office location.

Company Background

Denver Health traces its beginnings back to territorial days in 1860. As Denver General Hospital it operated as an agency of Denver's city and county governments until 1997 when it became a freestanding authority.

Denver Health's flagship medical center joined forces with Children's Hospital Colorado in late 2010 to share best practices and resources to expand and improve pediatric care throughout the region. Through the collaboration the two have increased access to pediatric mental health services; they also coordinate recruitment and sharing of highly specialized pediatric providers.

EXECUTIVES

Coo, Stephanie Thomas
Ceo, Arthur A. Gonzalez
Chief Nursing Officer, Kathy Boyle
Cfo, Peg Burnette
Director Rocky Mountain Poison And Drug Center, Richard C. Dart
Chief Medical Officer, Phillip S. Mehler
Executive Director Denver Health Foundation, Paula Herzmark
Director Of Nursing, Keith Moorhead
Clinic Director, Edward Gardner
Nursing Director, Nicole Stafford
Medical Director, Jeanne Rozwadowski
Pharmacy Manager, Paul Lehr
Vice President, Christy Allen
Pharmacy Manager, Renee Toner
Director Of Radiology, Linda Fielding
Second Vice Chairman, Hubert A. Farbes
Chair, Caz Matthews
Vice Chair, Rus Heise

LOCATIONS

HQ: DENVER HEALTH AND HOSPITALS AUTHORITY INC
777 BANNOCK ST, DENVER, CO 802044597
Phone: 720 956-2580
Web: WWW.DENVERHEALTHMEDICAID.ORG

PRODUCTS/OPERATIONS

2013 Sales

	% of total
Net patient service	46
Captation earned net of reinsurance expense	16
Medicaid disproportionate share & other safety net reimbursements	16
Federal state & other grants	9
Others	13
Total	**100**

Selected Medical Centers Clinics and Affiliates

Denver Emergency Center for Children
Denver Health Dental Care Clinics
Denver Health Medical Center
Denver Health Medical Plan (for Denver Health employees)
Denver Health Primary Care Clinics
Denver Paramedics
Denver Public Health
Rocky Mountain Center for Medical Response to Terrorism Mass Casualties and Epidemics
Rocky Mountain Poison & Drug Center
Rocky Mountain Regional Trauma Center

COMPETITORS

Banner Health	HealthONE
Catholic Health Initiatives	Porter Adventist Hospital
Centura Health	Rose Medical Center
Children's Hospital Colorado	University of Colorado Hospital
Exempla Healthcare	

HISTORICAL FINANCIALS
Company Type: Private

Income Statement   FYE: December 31

	REVENUE ($ mil.)	NET INCOME ($ mil.)	NET PROFIT MARGIN	EMPLOYEES
12/17	1,056	14	1.3%	3,541
12/16	505	(6)	—	—
12/14	449	45	10.2%	—
12/06	514	22	4.3%	—
Annual Growth	6.8%	(4.1%)	—	—

2017 Year-End Financials

Return on assets: 4.8%   Cash ($ mil.): 47
Return on equity: 1.3%
Current ratio: 0.60

DESAROLLADORA DEL NORTE S E

EXECUTIVES

Pres, Gabriel Escarrer
V Pres of Devel, Edgar Motta
Buyer, Luis Molina

LOCATIONS

HQ: DESAROLLADORA DEL NORTE S E
200 COCO BCH BL HWY 955, RIO GRANDE, PR 00745
Phone: 787 657-1026

HISTORICAL FINANCIALS
Company Type: Private

Income Statement   FYE: December 31

	REVENUE ($ mil.)	NET INCOME ($ mil.)	NET PROFIT MARGIN	EMPLOYEES
12/16	1,801	102	5.7%	500
12/15	1,738	0	—	—
Annual Growth	3.7%	—	—	—

2016 Year-End Financials

Return on assets: 25.5%   Cash ($ mil.): 366
Return on equity: 5.7%
Current ratio: 0.70

DESERT SANDS UNIFIED SCHOOL DISTRICT SCHOOL BUILDING CORPORATION

EXECUTIVES

Ceo-Myr, Richard Oliphant
Security Staff, John Stull
Executive Assistant, Adriana Romero
Network Technician, Anthony Padilla
Administrator, Cindy McDaniel
Purchasing Director, Nancy Lavrusky
Director, Matthew Howe
Director, Peggy Reyes
Security Staff, Jess Thomas
Manager, Joel Parks
Maintenance Director, John Vallesillo
Auditors: VAVRINEK TRINE DAY & CO LL

LOCATIONS

HQ: DESERT SANDS UNIFIED SCHOOL DISTRICT SCHOOL BUILDING CORPORATION
47950 DUNE PALMS RD, LA QUINTA, CA 922534000
Phone: 760 771-8567
Web: WWW.DSUSD.US

HISTORICAL FINANCIALS
Company Type: Private

Income Statement   FYE: June 30

	REVENUE ($ mil.)	NET INCOME ($ mil.)	NET PROFIT MARGIN	EMPLOYEES
06/17	403	(12)	—	3,200
06/16	395	77	19.7%	—
06/08	2	(2)	—	—
06/07	0	0	—	—
Annual Growth	—	—	—	—

DEUTZ CORPORATION

EXECUTIVES

Ceo, Robert Mann
Pres-Ceo, Steve Corley

Exec V Pres-Cfo, Christian Vorspel-Rueter
Corp SEC, Debra Gable
Treas, Wallace Evans III
Asst Treas, Cecilia Marrero
Accounting, Nancy McMillan
Executive Officer, Nicholas Price

LOCATIONS

HQ: DEUTZ CORPORATION
　3883 STEVE REYNOLDS BLVD, NORCROSS, GA
　300933066
Phone: 770 564-7100
Web: WWW.DEUTZAMERICAS.COM

HISTORICAL FINANCIALS

Company Type: Private

Income Statement			FYE: December 31	
	REVENUE ($ mil.)	NET INCOME ($ mil.)	NET PROFIT MARGIN	EMPLOYEES
12/15	306	1	0.4%	115
12/11	242	11	4.9%	—
12/09	100	(10)	—	—
12/07	1,635	0	—	—
Annual Growth	—	246.2%	—	—

2015 Year-End Financials

Return on assets: 1.1%　　　　Cash ($ mil.): 2
Return on equity: 0.4%
Current ratio: 0.40

DEVCON CONSTRUCTION INCORPORATED

Devcon Construction has built a sturdy business from building in the Bay Area. One of the area's top general building contractors Devcon has constructed more than 30 million sq. ft. of office industrial and commercial space. Its focus is on Northern California mainly in the San Francisco Bay Area and Silicon Valley. The company provides engineering design/build and interior design services. It specializes in high-tech projects including data centers and industrial research and development facilities. In addition to building company facilities and offices Devcon works on such projects as hotels restaurants parking structures retail stores sports facilities and schools.

Geographic Reach

Based in Milpitas California Devcon maintains several satellite offices in California in Petaluma Stockton and Santa Cruz as well as an office in Reno Nevada.

Strategy

Although most of Devcon's work is in California the company also has completed projects in Nevada Oregon Idaho Texas Massachusetts and Florida. Recent projects in the San Francisco Forty Niners Stadium in Santa Clara San Jose Sharks Ice Center in Pleasanton and the Stanford Research Computing Facility.

The company partnered with US-based Central Concrete in 2012 to supply its high-performing low-CO2 concrete for the new San Francisco 49er Stadium. The move showcases Devcon's focus on sustainability as part of its projects.

EXECUTIVES

Pres-Ceo, Gary Filizetti
Chief Financial Officer, Justine Pereira
Cfo, Brett Sisney
Security Staff, Ken Sullivan

Superintendent, Rich Van Kirk
Information Specialist, Kimberly Stein
Accounting Staff, Jennifer Chavez
Foreman, Everardo Ramirez
Senior Project Engineer, Amy Wilson
Project Engineer, Andrew White
Project Engineer, Chris Arce
Auditors: JOHANSON & YAU ACCOUNTANCY COR

LOCATIONS

HQ: DEVCON CONSTRUCTION INCORPORATED
　690 GIBRALTAR DR, MILPITAS, CA 950356317
Phone: 408 942-8200
Web: WWW.DEVCON-CONST.COM

PRODUCTS/OPERATIONS

Selected Projects

Anderson Collection At Stanford University Stanford
Barnes & Nobles Palo Alto
Cisco Parking Structure 1 San Jose
Cisco Parking Structure 2 San Jose
Downtown Sunnyvale Town Center Sunnyvale
El Camino Family Housing South San Francisco
Fresno Hyatt Place Hotel Fresno
Friedenrich Center For Translational Research At 800
　Welch Road
Lawson Lane East - Buildings A & B Santa Clara
Oakland Air Traffic Control Tower (ATCT) Oakland
San Francisco 49ers Stadium Santa Clara
San Jose Earthquakes - MLS Soccer Stadium San Jose
SanDisk Milpitas
Santa Clara University Admissions & Enrollment
　Services Building Santa Clara
Sharks Ice Center Pleasanton
Stanford Research Computing Facility Stanford
The Plaza At Triton Park Foster City
University Plaza Palo Alto
Villa Siena Nursing Care Units Mountain View

COMPETITORS

Charles Pankow Builders	KPRS Construction
DPR Construction	Obayashi
Hathaway Dinwiddie Construction	Rudolph & Sletten
Hensel Phelps Construction	Structure Tone
	Swinerton
	Turner Corporation
	Webcor Builders

HISTORICAL FINANCIALS

Company Type: Private

Income Statement			FYE: December 31	
	REVENUE ($ mil.)	NET INCOME ($ mil.)	NET PROFIT MARGIN	EMPLOYEES
12/15	1,224	14	1.2%	350
12/14	1,181	20	1.7%	—
12/13	1,012	12	1.2%	—
12/12	779	3	0.5%	—
Annual Growth	16.3%	60.4%	—	—

2015 Year-End Financials

Return on assets: 17.1%　　　Cash ($ mil.): 7
Return on equity: 1.2%
Current ratio: 0.90

DIALYSIS CLINIC, INC.

Dialysis Clinic Inc. or DCI is dedicated to caring for patients with end-stage renal disease (ESRD). The not-for-profit company which operates a network of more than 210 dialysis centers serving more than 14000 patients in 27 states also provides kidney transplant assistance services. Affiliate DCI Donor Services is an organ and tissue procurement agency. DCI also funds kidney-related research and educational programs and is affiliated

with various universities and teaching hospitals throughout the US including Tufts University the University of Arizona and Tulane University.

Geographic Reach

The company has its locations in Alabama Arizona Arkansas California Colorado Connecticut Florida Georgia Indiana Iowa Kentucky Louisiana Maine Massachusetts Missouri Montana Nebraska Nevada New Jersey New Mexico New York North Carolina Ohio Pennsylvania South Carolina Tennessee and Texas.

Strategy

DCI grows its network of facilities by forming partnerships with health care providers and other organizations. The company provides funding for construction and operation of the facility and it provides clinic support services including supply procurement and central laboratory services (through its DCI Lab subsidiary).

In 2012 the company opened a dialysis clinic in Albuquerque its first dialysis clinic in the South Valley region of New Mexico.

Company Background

DCI was established in 1971 by nephrologist Keith Johnson.

EXECUTIVES

Chb, H Keith Johnson
Dir, James Perry
President, Ed Attrill
SEC-Treas, William Wood
Attorney, Karin A Barrett
Human Resources Director, Audrey Semke
Director of Operations, Bill Wood
Senior Consultant, Jeff Arnold
Analyst, Jessica Porter
Compliance Officer, Peggy Williams
Administrative Assistant, Stuart Redpath
Auditors: DELOITTE & TOUCHE LLP NASHVIL

LOCATIONS

HQ: DIALYSIS CLINIC, INC.
　1633 CHURCH ST STE 500, NASHVILLE, TN
　372032948
Phone: 615 327-3061
Web: WWW.DCIINC.ORG

COMPETITORS

DaVita	Renal Advantage
FMCNA	U.S. Renal Care
Fresenius	

HISTORICAL FINANCIALS

Company Type: Private

Income Statement			FYE: September 30	
	REVENUE ($ mil.)	NET INCOME ($ mil.)	NET PROFIT MARGIN	EMPLOYEES
09/17	736	23	3.3%	5,000
09/16	719	22	3.2%	—
09/15	712	29	4.1%	—
09/14	663	35	5.4%	—
Annual Growth	3.5%	(12.4%)	—	—

2017 Year-End Financials

Return on assets: 2.3%　　　Cash ($ mil.): 175
Return on equity: 3.3%
Current ratio: 3.70

DIRECT RELIEF

EXECUTIVES

Ceo, Thomas Tighe
Cfo, Bhupi Singh
Philanthropic Investment Syste, Anthony Morain
Project Coordinator, Amy Mata
Coordinator, Dan Hovey

LOCATIONS

HQ: DIRECT RELIEF
  6100 WALLACE BECKNELL RD, SANTA BARBARA, CA
  931173265
Phone: 805 964-4767
Web: WWW.DIRECTRELIEF.ORG

HISTORICAL FINANCIALS

Company Type: Private

Income Statement

FYE: June 30

	REVENUE ($ mil.)	NET INCOME ($ mil.)	NET PROFIT MARGIN	EMPLOYEES
06/17	1,114	105	9.5%	2
06/12	299	(17)	—	—
06/11	405	95	23.6%	—
06/09	1,554	0	—	—
Annual Growth	—	200.1%	—	—

2017 Year-End Financials

Return on assets: 0.2%   Cash ($ mil.): 2
Return on equity: 9.5%
Current ratio: 1.10

DLL FINANCE LLC

EXECUTIVES

Mng MBR, Dave Roszak
MBR, Dan Kronlage
Business Manager, Gustavo Lichtenberger
Director, Eugene Purcell
Relationslrip Manager, Geoffrey Hoffman
Sales Representati, Stewart Ibsen
Senior Sales Repre, Chris Seymour
Business Manager, John Sugden
Financial Advisor, Josh Nielsen
Marketing Executive, Kelly Whitelaw

LOCATIONS

HQ: DLL FINANCE LLC
  8001 BIRCHWOOD CT STE C, JOHNSTON, IA
  501312889
Phone: 800 873-2474
Web: WWW.AGRICREDIT.COM

HISTORICAL FINANCIALS

Company Type: Private

Income Statement

FYE: December 31

	ASSETS ($ mil.)	NET INCOME ($ mil.)	INCOME AS % OF ASSETS	EMPLOYEES
12/16	2,327	14	0.6%	250
12/15	1,578	10	0.7%	—
12/14	1,454	14	1.0%	—
12/13	1,321	17	1.3%	—
Annual Growth	20.8%	(5.8%)	—	—

2016 Year-End Financials

Return on assets: —   Sales ($ mil): 73
Return on equity: 19.4%

DO IT BEST CORP.

For home builders and Mr. (and Ms.) Fix-its hardware cooperative Do it Best wants you to make the best even better. One of the industry's largest hardware cooperatives it boasts more than 3800 member-owned stores in 50-plus countries but primarily the US. Besides the usual tools and building materials merchandise includes automotive items bicycles camping gear housewares office supplies and small appliances. Customers also can have products specially shipped to their local stores through Do it Best's e-commerce site. The co-op's buying power enables members to offer items at competitive prices.

Operations

The company has eight retail service centers.

Some of the suppliers of the company are All American Do It Center Rogers Do It Best Hardware Your Building Centers and Building Depot.

With a wholesale sales volume of nearly $3 billion Do it Best provides affiliated stores with the buying power and services they need to remain competitive in the hardware and building materials industry.

The company has more than 67000 items available for distribution and more than 1400 in its no-adder drop ship vendor program.

Geographic Reach

Based in Fort Wayne Indiana Do it Best operates member-owned hardware stores primarily in the US in Illinois Missouri South Carolina Ohio Nevada New York Texas and Oregon as well as in more than 50 countries globally.

Sales and Marketing

Nearly all of the Do it Best's sales are to dealer-members. Members are required to buy 20 voting common shares at $50 per share on becoming a member.

It incurred $16.4 million in advertising costs in 2015.

Financial Performance

In 2015 the company's net revenues increased by 5% due to a growth in shipment volumes and positive sales from lumber.

Do it Best's net income decreased by 45% due to higher sales costs and a decrease in other income.

In 2015 cash from operating activities grew by 52% as a result of changes in inventories payable; and accounts and notes receivable net.

Strategy

Do it Best works to set itself apart from other hardware cooperatives (such as Ace and True Value) by pursuing licensing opportunities. To this end its member stores offer an exclusive line of tools made by Channellock including lockback knives flashlights and vacuums. The alliance with Channellock is part of Do it Best's long-term strategy as it looks to attract more consumers to the Channellock brand which has a following among serious do-it-yourselfers and professionals.

Through its Voice Picking/Warehouse Management System software the company reduces warehouse returns and allowances as well as outbound freight expenses.

In 2015 the company re-launched doitbest.com their ecommerce platform and launched Do it Best INCOM SupplySM to better help its retail hardware and LBM members.

In the past three years Do it Best's members have completed 220 store enhancement and expansion projects across the US and in more than a dozen other countries with another 150 in progress including Do it Centers in Saudi Arabia. It also invested more than $14 million towards growth via its Retail Performance Loan Program.

During the year the company also co-branded Signature.

Company Background

Formerly named Hardware Wholesalers Do it Best was founded in 1945 by Arnold Gerberding.

EXECUTIVES

Vp Finance And Cfo, Doug Roth
Vp Information Technology, Michael J. (Mike) Altendorf
Evp And Coo, Daniel B. (Dan) Starr
Vp Marketing, Timothy (Tim) Miller
Vp Merchandising, Steve Markley
Vp Lumber And Building Materials, Gary Nackers
Gm Vice President Business Unit Manager, Dori Meighan
Vice President Information Technology, John Mergy
Vp Of It, Mike Altendorf
Vice President Of Marketing, Bruce Baldridge
Vice Chairman, Brad McDaniel
Chairman, John Holmes
Auditors: CROWE HORWATH LLP FORT WAYNE

LOCATIONS

HQ: DO IT BEST CORP.
  6502 NELSON RD, FORT WAYNE, IN 468031947
Phone: 260 748-5300
Web: WWW.DOITBESTCORP.COM

PRODUCTS/OPERATIONS

Selected Programs
ADpak
Do it Best Rental Center
INCOM Distributor Supply
Opportunity program

COMPETITORS

84 Lumber	Orgill
Ace Hardware	Sears
Home Depot	Sutherland Lumber
Lowe's	True Value
Menard	Wal-Mart
Northern Tool	

HISTORICAL FINANCIALS

Company Type: Private

Income Statement

FYE: June 25

	REVENUE ($ mil.)	NET INCOME ($ mil.)	NET PROFIT MARGIN	EMPLOYEES
06/16	2,925	0	0.0%	1,519
06/11	2,328	0	0.0%	—
06/10	2,296	0	0.0%	—
Annual Growth	4.1%	(5.7%)	—	—

2016 Year-End Financials

Return on assets: 12.6%   Cash ($ mil.): 20
Return on equity: —
Current ratio: 0.80

DOCTORS HOSPITAL AT RENAISSANCE, LTD.

EXECUTIVES

Ceo, Lawrence Gelman
President, Susan Turley
Administrative Assistant, Alyssa Trevino
Transportation Associate, Frank Nunez
Accounting Staff, Joyce Lustgarten

Analyst, Michelle Olivarez
Vice-President, Patrick Blackwell
Coordinator, Ricardo Maldonado
Manager, Rick Gomez
Program Director, Steve Butler
Case Manager, Aracely Gillett

LOCATIONS

HQ: DOCTORS HOSPITAL AT RENAISSANCE, LTD.
5501 S MCCOLL RD, EDINBURG, TX 785395503
Phone: 956 362-8677
Web: WWW.DHR-RGV.COM

HISTORICAL FINANCIALS

Company Type: Private

Income Statement   FYE: December 31

	REVENUE ($ mil.)	NET INCOME ($ mil.)	NET PROFIT MARGIN	EMPLOYEES
12/16	580	80	13.9%	176
12/14	436	63	14.4%	—
Annual Growth	15.3%	13.1%	—	—

2016 Year-End Financials

Return on assets: 7.7%   Cash ($ mil.): 49
Return on equity: 13.9%
Current ratio: 1.10

DOCTORS HOSPITAL OF AUGUSTA, LLC

Doctors Hospital of Augusta serves up physician care in eastern Georgia and western South Carolina. The general and acute health care facility has more than 350 beds and is part of hospital giant HCA. Its specialty units include the Joseph M. Still Advanced Wound and Burn Clinic and the Healthy Living Center. In addition the hospital offers centers for cardiopulmonary health digestive diseases occupational medicine orthopedics cancer care sleep disorders stroke care surgery and women's health. Doctors Hospital of Augusta also operates freestanding surgical centers diagnostic imaging centers and Human Motion Institute rehabilitation clinics.

Operations

Doctors Hospital of Augusta employs more than 500 physicians and handles about 190000 patient visits each year including 13000 inpatient admissions and 50000 emergency room visits. The medical center has an economic impact of some $200 million annually.

The Joseph M. Still Advanced Wound and Burn Clinic (which has a special burn designation as part of the Georgia Trauma Care Network) includes 20 patient rooms and a hyperbaric treatment area.

Geographic Reach

Doctors Hospital of Augusta is located in Augusta Georgia which is located on the border of Richmond and Columbia counties.

Strategy

The hospital has improved technology systems in recent years to enhance patient services. Improvements to communication systems included the addition of SurgiTrak which lets patients update friends and family on their progress during 2013.

Company Background

In 2012 it added the CyberKnife robotic radiosurgery system. It also operates a da Vinci robotic surgery system for minimally invasive procedures.

Facility improvements have included the 2012 construction of a Lydia House a respite facility for female cancer patients undergoing treatment and needing a place to stay. In addition in 2011 the hospital renovated its burn treatment unit expanding its capacity from about 60 beds to 70 beds and adding new ICU and operating facilities; it also completed renovations of its emergency department and its women's health center that year.

To better serve regional residents Doctors Hospital of Augusta expanded its facility in a $55 million project completed in 2010. The medical center gain a three-story bed tower with about 50 patient rooms for medical surgical and intensive care purposes as well as new administration and surgery facilities.

EXECUTIVES

Physical Therapy Director, ANGELA TAYLOR
Medical Director, Fred Mullins
Vice President, Lee Gray
Vice President Technology Director, Cynthia Crabtree
Infection Control Director, ERIC STUCKART
Operating Room Dir, MARTHA STRATTON
Respiratory Therapy Director, CYNTHIA GREENE

LOCATIONS

HQ: DOCTORS HOSPITAL OF AUGUSTA, LLC
3651 WHEELER RD, AUGUSTA, GA 309096426
Phone: 706 651-3232
Web: WWW.DOCTORS-HOSPITAL.NET

PRODUCTS/OPERATIONS

Selected Centers and Services
24-Hour emergency Services
Accredited Cancer Care Center
Accredited Chest pain Center with PCI
Accredited EEG Laboratory
Accredited inpatient Rehabilitation Facility
Accredited primary Stroke Center
Advanced Burn and Wound Clinic
Advanced Surgical Services
American Burn Association Verified Burn Center
Aquatic therapy
Cardiopulmonary exercise testing
Center for Women/pelvic Health
da Vinci Robotic Surgical System
Diagnostic Services
Endoscopy
Family-Centered maternity Care with Level ii NICU
Hand Center
H2uprogram
Human motion institute - Joint/Spine Center
Hyperbaric oxygen therapy
Intensive Care unit
Outpatient Rehabilitation Health Centers
Outpatient Surgery Centers - Augusta and Evans Locations
Physical and occupational therapy
Sports medicine
Vestibular Balance Center

COMPETITORS

MCG Health
Memorial Health University Medical Center
South Georgia Medical Center
Tenet Healthcare
Tift Regional Medical Center
University Health Services
Walton Rehabilitation Hospital
WellStar Health System

HISTORICAL FINANCIALS

Company Type: Private

Income Statement   FYE: March 31

	REVENUE ($ mil.)	NET INCOME ($ mil.)	NET PROFIT MARGIN	EMPLOYEES
03/17	392	121	31.0%	1,300
03/09*	271	89	33.0%	—
12/02	162	28	17.3%	—
12/01	1,254	0	—	—
Annual Growth	—	72.5%	—	—

*Fiscal year change

2017 Year-End Financials

Return on assets: 2.4%   Cash ($ mil.): —
Return on equity: 31.0%
Current ratio: 0.20

DOCTORS MEDICAL CENTER OF MODESTO, INC.

EXECUTIVES

Ceo, Warren J Kirk
Cfo, Greg Berry
Manager, Cindy Vingerhoets
Scientist, Dan Martin
Supervisor, Amandip Mahil
Director, Cynthia Baccellieri
Manager, Janice Halloran
Executive Secretary, Wendy Zollinger
Administrative Assistant, Jill Fisher
Manager, Joseph Garcia
Anesthesiologist, Edward Verde

LOCATIONS

HQ: DOCTORS MEDICAL CENTER OF MODESTO, INC.
1441 FLORIDA AVE, MODESTO, CA 953504404
Phone: 209 578-1211
Web: WWW.DMC-MODESTO.COM

HISTORICAL FINANCIALS

Company Type: Private

Income Statement   FYE: May 31

	REVENUE ($ mil.)	NET INCOME ($ mil.)	NET PROFIT MARGIN	EMPLOYEES
05/16	587	86	14.6%	2,000
05/09	306	4	1.4%	—
Annual Growth	9.8%	52.8%	—	—

2016 Year-End Financials

Return on assets: 2.9%   Cash ($ mil.): —
Return on equity: 14.6%
Current ratio: 0.90

DOMINICAN HOSPITAL

EXECUTIVES

Director, Robert Quinn
Coordinator Quality Assurance, Kathy Dean
Chief of Medicine, David Kipps
Plant Manager, Kevin Keith
Facilities Manager, Lauren Smith
Anesthesiologist, Mark L Rigler

Anesthesiologist, Linda L Leum
Pathologist, Paula Quinn
Pathologist, Kenneth Westphal
Family Practitioner, Robert C Potts
Anesthesiologist, Steven Plumb

LOCATIONS

HQ: DOMINICAN HOSPITAL
  1555 SOQUEL DR, SANTA CRUZ, CA 950651794
Phone: 831 462-7700
Web: WWW.DIGNITYHEALTH.ORG

HISTORICAL FINANCIALS

Company Type: Private

Income Statement				FYE: June 30
	REVENUE ($ mil.)	NET INCOME ($ mil.)	NET PROFIT MARGIN	EMPLOYEES
06/16	447	57	12.8%	6
06/15	418	69	16.6%	
Annual Growth	7.0%	(17.5%)	—	—

2016 Year-End Financials

Return on assets: 2.9%   Cash ($ mil.): 19
Return on equity: 12.8%
Current ratio: 1.40

DON FORD SANDERSON INC

EXECUTIVES

Pres, David Kimmerle
Chb, La Verne Sanderson
SEC-Treas, Stephen C Wendt
Prin, Sandra Sue Kimmerle
Information Technology Manager, Mark Crites
Sales Associate, Brad Bailey
Parts Manager, Dave Beard
Sales Associate, Florin Nichitean
Graphic Designer, Jenny Kester
Sales Manager, John Pratt
Advertising Director, Max Sirstins

LOCATIONS

HQ: DON FORD SANDERSON INC
  6400 N 51ST AVE, GLENDALE, AZ 853014600
Phone: 623 842-8600
Web: WWW.SANDERSONFORD.COM

HISTORICAL FINANCIALS

Company Type: Private

Income Statement				FYE: December 31
	REVENUE ($ mil.)	NET INCOME ($ mil.)	NET PROFIT MARGIN	EMPLOYEES
12/15	679	3	0.5%	416
12/14	671	4	0.7%	
12/13	692	5	0.8%	
12/12	590	3	0.6%	
Annual Growth	4.8%	(3.8%)	—	—

2015 Year-End Financials

Return on assets: 0.6%   Cash ($ mil.): 1
Return on equity: 0.5%
Current ratio: 0.20

DOUGLAS COUNTY BOARD OF EDUCATION

EXECUTIVES

Chairperson, D T Jackson
Assistant Director, Holly Tinns
Teacher, James Brooks
Teacher, Miranda Stanley
Education Specialist, Payton Millinor
Auditors: MAULDIN & JENKINS LLC ATLANT

LOCATIONS

HQ: DOUGLAS COUNTY BOARD OF EDUCATION
  9030 HIGHWAY 5, DOUGLASVILLE, GA 301341539
Phone: 770 651-2000
Web: WWW.DOUGLAS.K12.GA.US

HISTORICAL FINANCIALS

Company Type: Private

Income Statement				FYE: June 30
	REVENUE ($ mil.)	NET INCOME ($ mil.)	NET PROFIT MARGIN	EMPLOYEES
06/17	293	0	0.3%	3,947
06/16	291	7	2.6%	
06/13	194	(21)	—	
06/11	272	(8)	—	
Annual Growth	1.2%	—	—	—

2017 Year-End Financials

Return on assets: 2.5%   Cash ($ mil.): 100
Return on equity: 0.3%
Current ratio: —

DOWNEY UNIFIED SCHOOL DISTRICT

EXECUTIVES

Supt, Edward A Sussman Edd
Supt, John A Garcia Jr
Deputy Supt, Donna Boose
Supt, Wendy L Doty
Chm, Dianne Lumsdaine
Asst Supt-Admin Svcs, Gary Orsinger Edd
Asst Supt-Personnel, Ed Potter Edd
MBR, John Kennedy
Assistant Director, Andrea Iacovitti
Director, Ruth Valadez
Information Specialist, Daniel D Ramirez

LOCATIONS

HQ: DOWNEY UNIFIED SCHOOL DISTRICT
  11627 BROOKSHIRE AVE, DOWNEY, CA 902414911
Phone: 562 904-3500
Web: WWW.DUSD.NET

HISTORICAL FINANCIALS

Company Type: Private

Income Statement				FYE: June 30
	REVENUE ($ mil.)	NET INCOME ($ mil.)	NET PROFIT MARGIN	EMPLOYEES
06/17	290	(24)	—	2,900
06/05	189	0	—	
06/04	139	1	1.2%	
06/03	133	(3)	—	
Annual Growth	5.7%	—	—	—

DOYLESTOWN HOSPITAL HEALTH AND WELLNESS CENTER, INC.

It takes a village to own a hospital and Doylestown Hospital is owned by the local women's civic organization Village Improvement Association (VIA Health). Founded in 1923 the hospital serves southeastern Pennsylvania and neighboring areas of New Jersey. With some 240 beds Doylestown Hospital provides a variety of acute and tertiary medical services. Specialties include cardiac surgery cancer care (as part of the University of Pennsylvania Cancer Network) and orthopedics. Affiliated with the hospital are two Pine Run nursing and assisted-living centers. Doylestown Hospital the flagship facility of the Doylestown Health system.

Operations

The hospital employs some 420 doctors across 50 specialties including radiology gastroenterology urology and pulmonology. Doylestown is also a certified chest pain center (via The Woodall Chest Pain Center) and a joint commission-certified primary stroke center. Additional hospital departments cover emergency critical care birthing rehabilitation and robotic surgery services.

In addition to the main medical center Doylestown Hospital operates three outpatient locations: The Health and Wellness Center in Warrington an Open MRI center in Hartsville and The Pavilion outpatient building located adjacent to the hospital. The parent organization VIA Health runs the Pine Run retirement centers as well as community health facilities.

Geographic Reach

Doylestown Hospital serves Bucks and Montgomery counties in Pennsylvania (including northern suburbs of Philadelphia) and Hunterdon and Mercer counties in neighboring New Jersey.

EXECUTIVES

Vp And Chief Medical Officer, Scott S. Levy, age 60
President And Ceo, James Brexler
Medical Director, Joseph Auteri
Vice President Patient Services, Eleanor Wilson
Director Of Radiology, Ronald Costanzo
Medical Director Chop Newborn Care At Dh, Gita Jani
Medical Director, Jane Tuller
Chair, Carolyn Della-Rodolfa
Director, Joan Parlee

LOCATIONS

HQ: DOYLESTOWN HOSPITAL HEALTH AND WELLNESS CENTER, INC.
595 W STATE ST, DOYLESTOWN, PA 189012597
Phone: 215 345-2200
Web: WWW.DH.ORG

PRODUCTS/OPERATIONS

Selected Services
Hospice
Medical Imaging/Radiology
Outpatient Testing
Rehab/Therapy
Surgical Services
Visiting Nurse/Home Care
Women's Services
Cardiac-Neuro Services
Diabetes Management
GI/Endoscopy
Fibromyalgia
Lab Services
Medical Library
Mammography
Nutrition Counseling - Healthy Directions

COMPETITORS

Abington Memorial Hospital
Children's Hospital of Philadelphia
LVHN
Main Line Health System
North Philadelphia Health System
Pennsylvania Hospital
Shore Memorial Hospital
St. Luke's University Health Network
Tenet Healthcare
University of Pennsylvania Health System

HISTORICAL FINANCIALS

Company Type: Private

Income Statement				FYE: June 30
	REVENUE ($ mil.)	NET INCOME ($ mil.)	NET PROFIT MARGIN	EMPLOYEES
06/18	310	10	3.3%	2,853
06/16	291	12	4.1%	—
06/15	211	(37)	—	—
06/10	234	3	1.5%	—
Annual Growth	3.6%	14.5%		

2018 Year-End Financials
Return on assets: 8.0%   Cash ($ mil.): 5
Return on equity: 3.3%
Current ratio: 0.70

DREXEL UNIVERSITY

Drexel doesn't want to train its dragons but to educate them in a wide range of disciplines. Drexel University (home of the Drexel Dragons) is a private coeducational institution of higher learning with an enrollment of more than 24200 undergraduate and graduate students and a student-teacher ratio of about 9:1. It operates more than a dozen schools and colleges in the US; the Drexel University College of Medicine is the one of the country's largest private medical schools. Drexel runs a mandatory co-operative education program that helps students gain real-world experience while supplying local employers with trained workers. Philadelphia financier and philanthropist Anthony Drexel founded the university in 1891.

Operations

One of the 15 largest private universities in the US Drexel offers more than 200 degree programs in 15 colleges and schools. Drexel Online was one of the first Internet-based distance education programs. It offers more than 100 degree programs.

Geographic Reach

Besides its three campuses in Philadelphia Drexel has educational operations in Malvern Pennsylvania and Sacramento California and it has research partnerships in China and Israel.

Financial Performance

Drexel's fiscal 2016 (ends June) revenue decreased to $1.03 billion from $1.05 billion a year earlier due to lower net student revenue. Operating expenses came in at $1 billion compared to $979 million in fiscal 2015 due to high college program costs and an increase in research and public service and institutional support expenses among other costs.

Its assets grew to $2.113 billion in 2016 up from $2.078 billion the previous year.

Strategy

Drexel is working with Amtrak and Brandywine Realty Trust to develop a mixed-use project on 75 acres around Philadelphia's 30 th Street Station. Next door to that site Drexel is developing its Innovation Neighborhood project on 12 acres of its campus. That project is designed to attract and start high-tech businesses. It is also working with developer Hospitality 3 to build a 212-room boutique hotel at 33rd and Chestnut Street.

Drexel in 2014 opened a 23000-square-foot facility in Philadelphia's Center City that includes space for clinical services and research for its College of Nursing and Health Professions.

EXECUTIVES

Vice President Facilities, Robert Francis
President And Ceo Academy Of Natural Sciences Of Drexel University, George W. Gephart
Dean College Of Arts And Sciences, Donna Murasko
Dean College Of Nursing And Health Professions, Gloria F. Donnelly
Interim Vp And Cio Information Resources And Technology, Kenneth S. Blackney
Dean Westphal College Of Media Arts And Design, Allen Sabinson
Dean Thomas R. Kline School Of Law, Roger J. Dennis
Athletic Director, Eric Zillmer
Dean University Libraries, Danuta Nitecki
Evp Treasurer And Coo, Helen Y. Bowman
Dean College Of Engineering, Joseph Hughes
President, John A. Fry
Executive Vice Provost And Dean Of The Graduate College, James Herbert
Svp Online Learning And President Drexel Online, Susan C. Aldridge
Dean And Svp Medical Affairs College Of Medicine, Daniel V. Schidlow
Provost And Evp, M. Brian Blake
Director School Of Biomedical Engineering Science And Health Systems, Kenneth A. Barbee
Dean Pennoni Honors College, Paula Marantz Cohen
Dean Close School Of Entrepreneurship, Donna De Carolis
Director Center For Hospitality And Sport Management, Jonathan Deutsch
Vp Finance Cfo And Associate Treasurer, Jeff Eberly
Vp And Dean Admissions, Chris Ferguson
Dean Lebow College Of Business, Frank Linnehan
Interim Dean College Of Computing And Informatics, Spiros Mancoridis
Director A.j. Drexel Autism Institute, Craig Newschaffer
Dean Dornside School Of Public Health, Ana Diez Roux
Dean School Of Education, Nancy Butler Songer

Dean Graduate School Of Biomedical Sciences And Professional Studies College Of Medicine, Elisabeth Van Bockstaele
Vice President And Comptroller, Susan Wilmer
Vice President, Karen Sams
Provost And Executive Vice President, M Blake
Associate Vice President College Of Engi, John Dolan
Assistant Vice President Core Enterprise Systems, Michael Mccabe
Vice President, Derek Bowks
Chairman Board Of Trustees, Richard A. Greenawalt
Auditors: PRICEWATERHOUSECOOPERS LLP PH

LOCATIONS

HQ: DREXEL UNIVERSITY
3141 CHESTNUT ST, PHILADELPHIA, PA 191042875
Phone: 215 895-2000
Web: WWW.DREXEL.EDU

PRODUCTS/OPERATIONS

Selected Schools and Colleges
Antoinette Westphal College of Media Arts & Design
Bennett S. Lebow College of Business
College of Arts and Sciences
College of Engineering
The College of Information Science and Technology
College of Law
College of Nursing and Health Professions
Drexel University College of Medicine
Earle Mack School of Law
Pennoni Honors College
Richard C. Goodwin College of Professional Studies
School of Biomedical Engineering Science and Health Systems
School of Education
School of Public Health

HISTORICAL FINANCIALS

Company Type: Private

Income Statement				FYE: June 30
	REVENUE ($ mil.)	NET INCOME ($ mil.)	NET PROFIT MARGIN	EMPLOYEES
06/17	985	34	3.5%	2,868
06/12	910	34	3.8%	—
06/11*	896	166	18.6%	—
12/08	0	0	—	—
Annual Growth	—	—		—

*Fiscal year change

2017 Year-End Financials
Return on assets: 6.8%   Cash ($ mil.): 51
Return on equity: 3.5%
Current ratio: 0.50

DRIVETIME AUTOMOTIVE GROUP, INC.

In this story the ugly duckling changes into DriveTime Automotive Group. Formerly known as Ugly Duckling the company is a used-car dealership chain that primarily targets low-income customers and those with less-than-stellar credit. To cater to subprime clients it's a "buy here-pay here" dealer meaning it finances and services car loans rather than using outside lenders. DriveTime operates more than 125 dealerships in 50 US metropolitan areas in 24 mostly southern and western states. The company provides customers with a comprehensive end-to-end solution for their automotive needs including the sale financing and maintenance of their vehicle.

Change in Company Type

The company withdrew its SEC registration in 2014.

Operations

The company's activities includes vehicle acquisition vehicle reconditioning and distribution vehicle sales underwriting and finance loan servicing and after sale support. DriveTime has sold more than 750000 used cars to consumers of all credit types and services a $2 billion loan portfolio.

DriveTime's financing business operates under the name DT Acceptance Corporation. The unit generates about a quarter of the company's total revenues

The company also offers DriveCare a 36-month/36000 miled (5-Year/50000 miled in some states) vehicle protection plan and extended powertrain coverage.

Geographic Reach

Phoenix-based DriveTime operates dealerships in 47 US metro areas throughout 24 states. More than a third of the dealerships are located in Florida and Texas.

Sales and Marketing

DriveTime markets its automotive products and services through TV commercials.

Strategy

DriveTime's long-term strategic goal is to expand its network of dealerships throughout the US targeting metropolitan areas with populations of 500000 to 3 million residents. In 2015 the company opened its first New Jersey location in Williamstown. In 2014 it established its presence in the Chicago area with the opening of the Lombard location; it also opened first location in the Washington DC area.

The used car dealer is also expanding in Texas opening a dealership in Corpus Christi in late 2013 its 20th in the Lone Star State.

As part of its business model DriveTime acquires used vehicles at auction. In 2013 the company purchased more than 96000 vehicles nationwide primarily from used vehicle auctions.

That year DriveTime teamed up with fellow car dealer Manheim to form Go Auto Exchange a new separate and independent wholesale auction company focused on independent dealers and the low-end vehicle segment.

Company venture Carvana (launched in early 2013) allows customers to buy its used cars online. Carvana expands the company's customer base by targeting customers outside its traditional credit-impaired low-income cohort.

Company Background

Chairman Ernest Garcia III owns the company through his Verde Investments firm. In 2012 the company abandoned plans to split its finance and used vehicle retail operations by selling the financing arm to Santander Consumer USA and the used car dealerships to a group of third-party investors. Prior to that DriveTime in early 2010 filed to go public but withdrew the proposed offering seven months later. It with drew a second IPO attempt in 2014.

EXECUTIVES

Prin, Ernest C Garcia II
Exec Vice President, Jon D Ehlinger
Cfo, Kurt Wood
Cfo, Matthew Peel
Dir, Gregg Tryhuss
Director, William N Plamondon
Corp Liaison, Kimberly Moon
Information Specialist, Jodi Cook
General Manager, Seth Taylor

LOCATIONS

HQ: DRIVETIME AUTOMOTIVE GROUP, INC.
1720 W RIO SALADO PKWY, TEMPE, AZ 852816590
Phone: 602 852-6600
Web: WWW.DRRICHSCHUTTLER.COM

2014 Stores

	No.
Alabama	5
Arkansas	1
Arizona	6
California	5
Colorado	2
Delware	1
Florida	21
Georgia	9
Illinois	2
Indiana	2
Kentucky	2
Maryland	2
Missouri	4
Mississippi	1
North Carolina	9
New Jersey	1
New Mexico	3
Nevada	2
Ohio	7
Oklahoma	3
South Carolina	4
Tennessee	6
Texas	22
Virginia	7
Total	**127**

COMPETITORS

AutoNation	Gunn Automotive
CarMax	McCombs Enterprises
Gillman Auto	Sonic Automotive

HISTORICAL FINANCIALS

Company Type: Private

Income Statement — FYE: December 31

	REVENUE ($ mil.)	NET INCOME ($ mil.)	NET PROFIT MARGIN	EMPLOYEES
12/17	3,267	(16)	—	3,165
12/15	2,372	32	1.4%	—
Annual Growth	—	—	—	—

2017 Year-End Financials

Return on assets: 5.1%
Return on equity: (-0.5%)
Current ratio: 1.00
Cash ($ mil.): 32

DRYMALLA CONSTRUCTION COMPANY, INC.

EXECUTIVES

Pres, Earl W Pitchford
Vice President, W R Sronce IV
Vice President, Charles Labay
Vice President, Rusty Klaus
SEC, Pat Simons
Information Technology Manager, Janna Christoph
Accounting Staff, Cindy Sronce
Project Manager, Greg Johnson
Assistant Superintendent, Steven Keto
Project Engineer, Matthew Limones
Superintendent, Shawn Brown
Auditors: DESROCHES PARTNERS LLP HOUST

LOCATIONS

HQ: DRYMALLA CONSTRUCTION COMPANY, INC.
608 HARBERT ST, COLUMBUS, TX 789342812
Phone: 281 342-3853
Web: WWW.DRYMALLA.COM

HISTORICAL FINANCIALS

Company Type: Private

Income Statement — FYE: December 31

	REVENUE ($ mil.)	NET INCOME ($ mil.)	NET PROFIT MARGIN	EMPLOYEES
12/17	409	10	2.7%	105
12/16	302	6	2.3%	—
12/15	220	5	2.6%	—
12/14	131	1	0.8%	—
Annual Growth	45.9%	115.0%	—	—

2017 Year-End Financials

Return on assets: 9.0%
Return on equity: 2.7%
Current ratio: 1.10
Cash ($ mil.): 38

DST SYSTEMS, INC.

Financial firms and health institutions focus on making clients wealthy and healthy respectively. So they might be wise to turn to DST Systems to handle their information processing tasks. The company provides information processing software and services to the mutual fund insurance retirement and healthcare industries. The company?s financial services segment offers software and systems used to handle a wide range of tasks including shareowner recordkeeping investment management and business process management. Among the healthcare offerings are claims adjudication and benefit and care management. DST makes most of its sales to customers in the US. The company was acquired by SS&C Technologies Holdings in 2018.

Change in Company Type

In 2018 SS&C Technologies Holdings a financial services software company paid about $5.4 billion for DST. The transaction significantly increased SS&C's scale boosting its revenue to from $1.6 billion to a combined $3.9 billion. The deal SS&C into the US retirement and wealth management markets while adding more than 110 million investor positions across DST's client base. DST become a wholly owned SS&C subsidiary.

Operations

DST Systems? Domestic Financial Services business produces about 55% of revenue. The segment supports direct and intermediary sales of mutual funds alternative investments securities brokerage accounts and retirement plans. Its software also handles reports to investors for confirmations statements and tax forms web access and electronic delivery of documents. Systems include TA 2000 and TRAC. The company offers its AWD workflow software to clients and licenses it to third parties.

The International Financial Services segment which accounts for almost a quarter of its revenue offers investor and policyholder administration and technology services on a Remote and BPO basis in the UK and in Canada Ireland and Luxembourg through the IFDS joint venture.

The Healthcare Services segment which provides medical and pharmacy claims administration generates about a fifth of sales. The segment provides healthcare organizations with pharmacy and healthcare administration software and health outcomes optimization services. Specific tasks handled by DST software include claims adjudication benefit management care management and business intelligence.

DST sold its North American Customer Communications business in 2016 for about $410 million followed by the sale of its UK counterpart in 2017 for about $45 million.

DST operates its own data centers that provide secure infrastructure for its products and services.

Geographic Reach

The US is DST Systems? largest market accounting for about 75% of sales. The UK is its largest international market with about 25% of sales. The Kansas City Missouri-based company also has customers in Australia Canada and several other geographic markets.

Sales and Marketing

DST Systems markets its products directly and through subsidiaries joint venture affiliates and strategic alliances. The Domestic Financial Services business works in some areas through joint ventures with State Street Corp. In the US the companies work through Boston Financial Data Services and through International Financial Data Services overseas.

DST?s five largest customers overall account for about 25% of its revenue. The healthcare business is the more heavily concentrated with its five largest customers generating almost half of revenue including nearly 20% from one customer. International Financial Services? five largest customers supply almost 55% of the segment?s revenue with the largest customer generating nearly 25%.

Primary customers for Financial Services are mutual fund managers insurers and platform providers. The main healthcare customers are managed care organizations preferred provider organizations third-party administrators dental vision and behavioral health organizations. The company also works with government sponsored programs such as the Health Insurance Exchanges that operate under the Patient Protection and Affordable Care Act Medicare Advantage Medicare Part D and Medicaid.

Financial Performance

Charting DST Systems? five-year revenue record shows a dip to about $1.4 billion in 2015 before rebounding in 2015 and 2016 following a series of divestments and acquisitions.

In 2017 revenue jumped about 42% to $2.2 billion which include reimbursements for out-of-pocket expenses (about 6% of total revenue). A good chunk of the increase came from BFDS and IFDS UK in which DST took controlling interest in 2017.

Net income increased about 6% to $451 million in 2017 from 2016 due to the acquired interests in BFDS and IFDS UK. The company also recorded a gain on the sale of securities in 2017.

DST?s cash fell to about $80 million in 2017 from $199 million in 2016. A difference was that the company had about $248 million from discontinued operations that it didn?t have in 2017.

Strategy

The acquisition by DST Systems by SS&C Technologies unites two major players in financial software. The combined product portfolios cover a wide range of financial services and it provides SS&C with DST?s healthcare component. The deal doesn?t do much however to expand their geographic reach other than to deepen their UK business. The companies are not strangers. SS&C bought DST?s Global Solutions subsidiary in 2014.

Mergers and Acquisitions

DST Systems has been active on the acquisition front to complement its product line and expand into new geographic areas. DST has balanced its acquisition strategy by purchasing technology providers and service providers with an emphasis on business process outsourcing concerns and consulting firms.

In 2017 DST acquired the remaining interests in IFDS UK and BFDS that it didn?t own for about $330 million. The businesses have been strategically important to DST which intends to make enhancements as full owner.

In 2016 DST bought Kaufman Rossin Fund Services a provider of administration services to the investment community for $95 million. This acquisition provides DST with products for the alternative investment market.

EXECUTIVES

President And Ceo Dst Healthcare, Jonathan J. Boehm, age 57, $490,000 total compensation

Evp And President Alps, Edmund J. (Ned) Burke, age 57

Cfo, Gregg W. Givens, age 57, $460,000 total compensation

President And Ceo Boston Financial Data Services, Stephen C. Hooley, age 54, $825,000 total compensation

Ceo International Dst Financial Services, William (Willie) Slattery

Evp Dst Financial Services, Vercie Lark, age 55, $460,000 total compensation

President Dst Retirement Solutions, Jude C. Metcalfe

President Dst Brokerage Solutions, Stuart S. Bowers

President Dst Fund Advisor And Investor Solutions, Scott A. Chelton

President Dst Realty, Vince Dasta

Evp And Cio, Maria A. Mann

President And Ceo Dst Health Solutions, Teri L. Mullaney

President And Coo Argus Health Systems, J. Marc Palmer

Executive Director Dst Bluedoor, Martin Spedding

Vice President, Thomas McGee

Executive Vice President Sales And Marketing Canada At Dst Output (canada), Andrew Idzior

Vice President Of Marketing, Mary Carol Morrissey

Senior Vice President Development, Jim Alexander

Vice President Management Information Systems, Jack Dooley

Vice President, Bill Chisholm

Senior Vice President, Roderick Mckinney

Vice President Client Services, Fred Quatrocky

Vice President Human Resources, Susie Herbel

Senior Vice President Operations Argus Health Systems, Wayne Armstrong

Vice President Total Rewards, Steven Gebben

Vice President Field Customer Operations Dst Output, Bruce Splaine

Vice President, Brian Olson

Vice President, Kyle M Mallot

Vice President Total Rewards, Steven G Gebben

Vice President, John D Gallary

Vice President Chief Risk Officer, Blair S Williams

Vice President, James Lawler

Board Member, Samuel Liss

Auditors: PRICEWATERHOUSECOOPERS LLP K

LOCATIONS

HQ: DST SYSTEMS, INC.
333 W 11TH ST, KANSAS CITY, MO 641051773
Phone: 816 435-1000
Web: WWW.DSTSYSTEMS.COM

2017 Sales

	$ mil.	% of total
U.S.	1,641	74
International		
U.K.	504	23
Canada	19	1
Australia	28	1
Others	24	1
Total	**2,218**	**100**

PRODUCTS/OPERATIONS

2017 Sales

	$ mil.	% of total
Domestic Financial Services	1,299	57
International Financial Services	550	24
Healthcare Services	426	19
Elimination Adjustments	(57.4)	-
Total	**2,218**	**100**

2017 Sales

	$ mil.	% of total
Operating revenues	20,864	94
Out-of-pocket reimbursements	131	6
Total	**2,218**	**100**

Selected Products & Services

Alternative Asset Manager Solutions
Asset Manager Solutions
Applied Analytics
Banking Solutions
Brokerage Solutions
Business Process Solutions
Digital Consumer Solutions
Health Outcomes Optimization Healthcare Administration Insura

COMPETITORS

ADP	HealthPort
Algorithmics	Healthcare Holdings
Alliance Data Systems	Iron Mountain Inc
Assurant	McKesson
Bank of New York Mellon	Misys
	NCR
Broadridge	Paychex
CSG Systems International	Pegasystems
	Progress Software
CVS	R.R. Donnelley
Cerner	SEI Investments
Computershare	StatPro Group
Convergys	State Street
Express Scripts	SunGard
Fidelity National Information Services	TIBCO Software
	TMG Health
First Data	TeleTech
Fiserv	Total System Services
GE Healthcare	TriZetto
Greenway Medical Technologies	

HISTORICAL FINANCIALS

Company Type: Private

Income Statement

FYE: December 31

	REVENUE ($ mil.)	NET INCOME ($ mil.)	NET PROFIT MARGIN	EMPLOYEES
12/17	2,218	452	20.4%	15,700
12/16	1,556	426	27.4%	—
12/15	2,825	358	12.7%	—
12/14	2,749	593	21.6%	—
Annual Growth	(6.9%)	(8.7%)	—	—

2017 Year-End Financials

Return on assets: 4.6%   Cash ($ mil.): 80
Return on equity: 20.4%
Current ratio: 0.50

DUKE HEALTH RALEIGH HOSPITAL GUILD

EXECUTIVES

Pres, David Zaas
Coo, Rick Gannotta
Cfo, Terri Newsom
Ceo, Doug Dinsel

Internal Medicine Practitioner, Asghar Yamadi
Licensed Practical Nurse, Patricia Daniel
Manager, Rodger Sage
Registered Nurse, Amanda Eltz
Pulmonologist, Jerry B Hung
Emergency Medicine Specialist, Timothy M Plonk

LOCATIONS

HQ: DUKE HEALTH RALEIGH HOSPITAL GUILD
   3400 WAKE FOREST RD, RALEIGH, NC 276097317
Phone: 919 954-3000
Web: WWW.DUKEHEALTH.ORG/HOSPITALS/DUKE-
   RALEIGH-HOSPITAL/HOME

HISTORICAL FINANCIALS

Company Type: Private

Income Statement — FYE: June 30

	REVENUE ($ mil.)	NET INCOME ($ mil.)	NET PROFIT MARGIN	EMPLOYEES
06/16	384	58	15.3%	600
06/15	348	60	17.3%	—
06/10	0	(0)	—	—
06/09	0	0	51.8%	—
Annual Growth	251.7%	195.5%	—	—

DUKE REGIONAL HOSPITAL

EXECUTIVES

Lab Technician, Tracy Robbins
Educator, Eva McCullock
Assistant Director, Ruth Tolman
Hospitalist, Danielle G Richardson

LOCATIONS

HQ: DUKE REGIONAL HOSPITAL
   3643 N ROXBORO ST, DURHAM, NC 277042702
Phone: 919 470-4000
Web: WWW.DUKEHEALTH.ORG

HISTORICAL FINANCIALS

Company Type: Private

Income Statement — FYE: June 30

	REVENUE ($ mil.)	NET INCOME ($ mil.)	NET PROFIT MARGIN	EMPLOYEES
06/18	342	(9)	—	17
06/17	0	0	12.0%	—
Annual Growth	419185.9%	—	—	—

DUKE UNIVERSITY HEALTH SYSTEM, INC.

More than a campus infirmary the Duke University Health System operates the Duke University Hospital and other medical educational and research facilities on the Duke University grounds. Duke University Hospital has about 960 acute pediatric and psychiatric patient beds and specializes in trauma care diagnostics and cardiac and endoscopic surgeries. The health system also operates two community hospitals — Duke Regional Hospital (370 beds) and Duke Raleigh Hospital (186 beds) — as well as other area health clinics. Duke University Health System's facilities provide primary and specialty care home and hospice care clinical research physician and nurse training and public education programs.

Operations

The system was formed in 1998 to expand the core Medical Center operations and has since added the Durham and Raleigh community hospitals. The Duke University Health System is closely affiliated with the Duke University Medical School as well as with the Duke University School of Nursing. The three entities are all located within the Duke University Medical Center complex (consisting of research educational and clinical care facilities on the Duke campus) also known as Duke Medical. The medical complex also includes the health system's Duke Clinic which provides outpatient and non-emergency specialist care.

Duke University Health System and the university's medical schools train health care professionals in cutting-edge technologies and infrastructures. The entities also work together to advance biomedical and general medical research with the goal of discovering and improving methods of care. Funding for medical research comes from the National Institutes of Health and other government organizations as well as from partnerships with pharmaceutical and medical device companies.

Geographic Reach

While Duke University Health System focuses on medical educational and research work in the US (in the states of North Carolina and Virginia) as part of its business the health system operates a joint venture in India.

Financial Performance

In 2014 revenues increased 2% to $4.9 billion mainly as a result of increases in patient service revenues tuition and fees and investment earnings. The system's net income rose 14% to $1.8 billion led by higher investment returns.

Cash flow from operations fell 90% to $12 million in 2014 due to an increase of cash used for accounts and contributions receivable and changes in inventories.

Strategy

Duke University Health System is working to expand further in existing and new territories and is looking to widen its service offerings in cancer vascular orthopedic musculoskeletal women and children's care and outpatient ambulatory care. To this end the health system is expanding by adding new medical locations and boosting its expertise in technology. For example in 2015 the Duke Eye Center opened a new four-story clinical pavilion. The system also aims to improve efficiencies across all locations and to help community members access needed services.

The company's DLP Healthcare joint venture with LifePoint Health provides management and cost-control services to community hospitals in North Carolina. Maria Parham Medical Center its first client is a small hospital looking for operational support in the face of health reform changes and rising competition in the marketplace. DLP Healthcare holds an 80% stake in the Maria Parham facility through the management agreement. An investment of $15 million in nearby Person Memorial Hospital will go to capital improvements help eliminate its debt and pave the way for DLP Healthcare to acquire the hospital.

Duke Medicine has a partnership with Medanta — The Medicity — through which the pair has established the Medanta Duke Research Institute (MDRI) in India to research medical treatments (drugs and devices). Medanta a 1500-bed institute will fund the creation and operation of the facility as part of the agreement with Duke providing scientific clinical research and operational expertise. Medanta and Duke share joint oversight over implementation and management of the unit.

EXECUTIVES

Svp Cfo And Treasurer, Kenneth C. Morris
Evp, William J. Fulkerson
**Vp Patient Care And System And Chief Nurse
   Executive,** Mary Ann Fuchs
President Duke Regional Hospital, Katie Galbraith
President Private Diagnostic Clinic Pllc, Mark F.
   Newman
Chief Medical Officer, Thomas A. Owens
President Duke Raleigh Hospital, David Zaas
President And Ceo, A. Eugene Washington
Director Of Pharmacy, Matthew Harris
**Vice President Marketing And Communications
   Duke University Health System,** Doug Stokke
Vice President, Philip Stern
**Assistant Vice President Development And
   Alumni Affairs,** Ellen Luken
Associate Vice President, Paul Vick
Chair, Thomas M. Gorrie
Vice Chair, Peter Van Etten
Auditors: KPMG LLP NORFOLK VIRGINIA

LOCATIONS

HQ: DUKE UNIVERSITY HEALTH SYSTEM, INC.
   2301 ERWIN RD, DURHAM, NC 277054699
Phone: 919 684-8111
Web: WWW.DUKECHILDRENS.ORG

Selected Facilities
Duke Clinic (Durham North Carolina)
Duke Raleigh Hospital (Raleigh North Carolina)
Duke University Hospital (Durham North Carolina)
   Duke Children's Hospital & Health Center
Durham Regional Hospital (Durham North Carolina)

PRODUCTS/OPERATIONS

2014 Sales

	% of total
Patient service	50
Grants & contracts	22
Tuition & fees	8
Investment return	8
Auxiliary enterprises	5
Contributions	4
Net assets released from restrictions	2
Other	1
Total	**100**

Selected Services
AIDS Research and Treatment Center (DART)
Anesthesiology
Aortic Disease
Asthma and Allergies
Attention Deficit Hyperactivity Disorder
Breast Cancer
Cardiac Rehabilitation
Children's Health
Coronary Artery Disease
Dermatology
Developmental and Behavioral Pediatrics
Diabetes
Diet & Fitness Center
Duke Heart Center
Duke Medicine
Ear Nose Throat Head & Neck Surgery
Eating Disorders
Endocrinology
Esophageal Cancer
Executive Health
Eye Center
Foot and Ankle
Gastroenterology
Gastrointestinal Cancer
General Orthopaedics
General and Consultative Heart Care
Geriatrics
Gynecologic Cancer
Gynecology
Health & Fitness Center
Health and Wellness
Healthy Lifestyles for Children

Heart Rhythm Services
Hematology
Hereditary Cancer
Hyperbaric Diving and Altitude Medicine
Infectious Diseases
Integrative Medicine
Knee Treatments
Leukemias Lymphomas and Myelomas
Lung Cancer
Men's Health
Neurological Disorders
Neuroscience
Obstetrics and Gynecology
Pain Disorders
Peripheral Vascular Disease
Prostate Cancer
Psychiatry
Pulmonology and Respiratory Medicine
Radiology
Research
Rheumatology and Immunology
Skin Cancer
Sleep Disorders
Smoking/Smoking Cessation
Speech and Audiology
Sports Medicine
Stroke Center
Transplants
Urologic Cancer
Valvular Heart Disease
Vascular Diseases
Women's Health
Women's Heart Care

COMPETITORS

Carolinas HealthCare System	Novant Health
Cone Health	Rex Healthcare
Cumberland County Hospital System	Rowan Regional Medical Center
Danville Regional Medical Center	UNC Hospitals
	Vidant Health
FirstHealth of the Carolinas	WakeMed
	Wesley Long Community Hospital
Morehead Memorial Hospital	

HISTORICAL FINANCIALS

Company Type: Private

Income Statement				FYE: June 30
	REVENUE ($ mil.)	NET INCOME ($ mil.)	NET PROFIT MARGIN	EMPLOYEES
06/18	3,597	688	19.1%	16,627
06/16	3,160	(787)	—	—
06/13	2,539	516	20.4%	—
06/09	2,070	198	9.6%	—
Annual Growth	6.3%	14.8%	—	—

2018 Year-End Financials

Return on assets: 4.6%   Cash ($ mil.): 277
Return on equity: 19.1%
Current ratio: 1.60

DUQUESNE LIGHT COMPANY

Duquesne Light is the first and last resort for light for many residential customers in the Keystone State. The utility company provides electricity to more than 588000 customers (90% of which are residential) in southwestern Pennsylvania via an extensive transmission and distribution system. The utility a subsidiary of Duquesne Light Holdings (formerly DQE) acts as a generation Provider of Last Resort (POLR) for customers who do not

choose an alternative supplier. A consortium led by Macquarie Infrastructure Partners controls the company's parent.

Operations
The company has 212000 utility poles 103000 transformers and more than 45000 miles of overhead [pwer lines.

Geographic Reach
Duquesne Light provides electric service to customers in southwestern Pennsylvania including the city of Pittsburg in a service area that covers 817 square miles in Allegheny and Beaver counties.

Strategy
Duquesne Light which has been hurt by declining margins provided by its POLR service due to unrecovered payments to PJM Interconnection generators implemented a 2011-2013 POLR plan to yield more reliable returns taking advantage of favorable changes in Pennsylvania law regarding POLR costs and surcharges.

In an effort to improve reliability and public safety Duquesne Light has replaced 205 network transformers across its service region since 2002. In 2012 it replaced 29 of these network transformers and was working on replacing 42 more in 2013.

Company Background
The company was founded in 1880.

EXECUTIVES

Vice President Communications And Corporate Citizenship, Jessica Rock

LOCATIONS

HQ: DUQUESNE LIGHT COMPANY
411 7TH AVE 6-1, PITTSBURGH, PA 152191942
Phone: 412 393-6000
Web: WWW.DUQUESNELIGHT.COM

COMPETITORS

Dominion Energy	FirstEnergy
Exelon	PPL Corporation

HISTORICAL FINANCIALS

Company Type: Private

Income Statement				FYE: December 31
	REVENUE ($ mil.)	NET INCOME ($ mil.)	NET PROFIT MARGIN	EMPLOYEES
12/17	911	130	14.3%	1,000
12/16	903	118	13.1%	—
/ 0	0	—	—	—
Annual Growth	—	—	—	—

2017 Year-End Financials

Return on assets: 10.2%   Cash ($ mil.): 24
Return on equity: 14.3%
Current ratio: 0.90

DUQUESNE UNIVERSITY OF THE HOLY SPIRIT

EXECUTIVES

Director Animal Care, J. Douglas Bricker
Assistant Vp And Cio, Charles R. (Chuck) Bartel
President, Ken Gormley
Vp Academic Affairs And Provost, Timothy R. Austin

Dean A.j. Palumbo School Of Business Administration And John F. Donahue Graduate School Of Business, Dean McFarlin
Dean Bayer School Of Natural And Environmental Sciences, Philip Reeder
Dean Mary Pappert School Of Music, Seth Beckman
Dean Mcanulty College And Graduate School Of Liberal Arts, James Swindal
Interim Dean Rangos School Of Health Sciences, Paula Turocy
Dean School Of Education, Cindy Walker
Interim Dean School Of Law, Maureen Lally-Green
Dean School Of Nursing, Mary Ellen Smith Glasgow
Vp Management And Business, Matthew J. Frist
Auditors: GRANT THORNTON LLP PHILADELPH

LOCATIONS

HQ: DUQUESNE UNIVERSITY OF THE HOLY SPIRIT
600 FORBES AVE, PITTSBURGH, PA 152193016
Phone: 412 396-6000
Web: WWW.DUQ.EDU

PRODUCTS/OPERATIONS

2015 Sales

	% of total
Tuition and fees-net of financial aid	72
Auxiliary enterprises	17
Grants and contracts	4
Endowment earnings distributed for operations	3
Gifts and pledges	2
Other	2
Total	**100**

Selected Programs

Accounting
Athletic Training
Behavioral Science
Binary Engineering (Physics/Engineering)
Biochemistry
Biology
Biomedical Engineering (BME)
Biomedical Engineering (BME) - Nursing (BSN)
Business - General
Chemistry
Classical Civilization
Classical Greek
Classical Languages
Classical Latin
Communication Studies
Child Psychology
Clinical Mental Health Counseling
K-12 Latin Education
K-12 School Administration and Supervision
Early Level (PreK- 4)
Educational Studies- Educational Studies Concentration
Educational Studies- Program Evaluation
ESL MSEd and Certificate Program
Instructional Technology
Marriage and Family Counseling

HISTORICAL FINANCIALS

Company Type: Private

Income Statement				FYE: June 30
	REVENUE ($ mil.)	NET INCOME ($ mil.)	NET PROFIT MARGIN	EMPLOYEES
06/17	287	36	12.9%	3,601
06/15	400	25	6.4%	—
06/12	262	7	2.8%	—
06/11	333	21	6.6%	—
Annual Growth	(2.4%)	9.1%	—	—

2017 Year-End Financials

Return on assets: 3.1%   Cash ($ mil.): 16
Return on equity: 12.9%
Current ratio: 0.50

DURHAM PUBLIC SCHOOLS

EXECUTIVES

Supt, Bert L'Homme
Supt, Eric Becoats
Fo, Aaron Beaulieu
Safety Security Director, Terry Brown
Auditors: RIVES & ASSOCIATES LLP RALEI

LOCATIONS

HQ: DURHAM PUBLIC SCHOOLS
   511 CLEVELAND ST, DURHAM, NC 277013334
Phone: 919 560-2000
Web: WWW.DPSNC.NET

HISTORICAL FINANCIALS

Company Type: Private

Income Statement				FYE: June 30
	REVENUE ($ mil.)	NET INCOME ($ mil.)	NET PROFIT MARGIN	EMPLOYEES
06/17	379	(0)	—	4,500
06/11	398	20	5.2%	—
06/10	331	7	2.3%	—
06/09	359	0	0.2%	—
Annual Growth	0.7%	—	—	—

2017 Year-End Financials

Return on assets: 0.7%   Cash ($ mil.): 40
Return on equity: —
Current ratio: —

DUVAL COUNTY PUBLIC SCHOOLS

EXECUTIVES

Supt, John C Fryer Jr
Payroll Staff, Bobbie Johns
Technical Manager, Patricia McClure
Coordinator, Elly Gumera
Psychologist, Tempie Alexander
General Manager, Adora Davis
Technical Manager, Cathy S Maycott
Teacher, Mike Monlezun
Information Technology Special, Rosa Howell
Instructor, Amy Guth
Information Technology/Interne, Byron Copeland

LOCATIONS

HQ: DUVAL COUNTY PUBLIC SCHOOLS
   1701 PRUDENTIAL DR, JACKSONVILLE, FL
   322078152
Phone: 904 390-2000
Web: WWW.DUVALSCHOOLS.ORG

HISTORICAL FINANCIALS

Company Type: Private

Income Statement				FYE: June 30
	REVENUE ($ mil.)	NET INCOME ($ mil.)	NET PROFIT MARGIN	EMPLOYEES
06/17	1,207	(25)	—	13,000
06/16	1,184	(63)	—	—
06/07	1,189	27	2.3%	—
06/06	1,063	(22)	—	—
Annual Growth	1.2%	—	—	—

2017 Year-End Financials

Return on assets: 2.3%   Cash ($ mil.): 68
Return on equity: (-2.1%)
Current ratio: —

DYNASTY FARMS, INC.

EXECUTIVES

Pres, David L Johnson
V Pres, David Black
SEC, Steven Tripp
Human Resources, Andrea Beltran
Chief Financial Officer, DK Michaelson
Marketing Coordinator, Margaret Gerba

LOCATIONS

HQ: DYNASTY FARMS, INC.
   740 AIRPORT BLVD, SALINAS, CA 939014510
Phone: 831 755-1398
Web: WWW.PIM4U.COM

HISTORICAL FINANCIALS

Company Type: Private

Income Statement				FYE: December 31
	REVENUE ($ mil.)	NET INCOME ($ mil.)	NET PROFIT MARGIN	EMPLOYEES
12/16	325	3	1.0%	100
12/15	363	(2)	—	—
12/14	339	1	0.3%	—
12/13	324	(1)	—	—
Annual Growth	0.1%	—	—	—

2016 Year-End Financials

Return on assets: 0.6%   Cash ($ mil.): —
Return on equity: 1.0%
Current ratio: 1.20

DYNETICS, INC.

EXECUTIVES

Chb, Marcus J Bendickson
Ceo, David King
President, Greg Lester
Vice President, Stephen Cook
Vice President, Michael Moody
Cfo, Randy Reynolds
Asst SEC, Michael Stebbins
Vice President, Ronnie Chronister
Vp, Lucinda Griner
Vp, Mark Miller
Vp, Keith McCollum
Auditors: NOEL D TALLON CPA PC HUNTS

LOCATIONS

HQ: DYNETICS, INC.
   1002 EXPLORER BLVD NW, HUNTSVILLE, AL
   358062806
Phone: 256 964-4000
Web: WWW.DYNETICS.COM

HISTORICAL FINANCIALS

Company Type: Private

Income Statement				FYE: June 26
	REVENUE ($ mil.)	NET INCOME ($ mil.)	NET PROFIT MARGIN	EMPLOYEES
06/16	315	4	1.3%	1,914
06/13*	285	16	5.7%	—
07/12	266	17	6.5%	—
07/11	666	0	0.0%	—
Annual Growth	(13.9%)	484.3%	—	—

*Fiscal year change

2016 Year-End Financials

Return on assets: 1.2%   Cash ($ mil.): 28
Return on equity: 1.3%
Current ratio: 2.60

E-Z MART STORES, INC.

E-Z Mart Stores aims to make filling gas tanks and stomachs EZR for small-town America. The regional convenience store chain operates about 295 stores across four neighboring states including Arkansas Louisiana Oklahoma and Texas. Rather than build its own stores the company usually expands through acquisitions. In addition to the standard hot dogs sodas coffee and cigarettes most E-Z Mart locations also offer Shell Conoco Phillips 66 or CITGO gasoline. E-Z Mart was founded in 1970 by Jim Yates in Nashville Arkansas. Yates died in 1998 when the plane he was piloting crashed leaving his daughter Sonja Hubbard at the company's helm as CEO.

Geographic Reach

Ranked #35 on Convenience Store News ' "Top 100 Convenience Stores Report" E-Z Mart is a regional c-store chain that primarily serves Texas and Arkansas as well as Oklahoma and Louisiana.

Sales and Marketing

Aiming to offer the chain's customers access to updated fuel prices a list of locations and in-store promotions among other items E-Z Mart partnered with OpenStore by GasBuddy to roll out a new E-Z Mart website and mobile app. The fully integrated mobile app enables consumers to send feedback from their mobile phones and receive time-sensitive electronic mobile coupons.

Strategy

While E-Z Mart has trimmed its store count during the past decade or so including exiting markets such as Missouri it continues to make strategic acquisitions. Like other convenience store operators seeking to boost in-store sales E-Z Mart is expanding its food and beverage offering adding fresh-brewed iced tea to all of its stores and installing freezers. Outside the company has a deal with Redbox to place its movie rental kiosks outside of E-Z Mart stores.

EXECUTIVES

Ceo, Sonja Hubbard
President, Bob Hubbard
Cfo, Stacy Yates
Offc Mgr, Debbie Flowers
Chief Financial Officer, Stacy Y Flod
Database Administrator, Jack Williams
Marketing Manager, Faellen Yates
Controller, Les Smith
Director, Steve Launius
Auditors: BKD LLP PORT SMITH ARKANSAS

LOCATIONS

HQ: E-Z MART STORES, INC.
602 FALVEY AVE, TEXARKANA, TX 755016677
Phone: 903 832-6502
Web: WWW.EZMART.COM

2014 Stores

	No.
Texas	96
Arkansas	95
Oklahoma	80
Louisiana	18
Total	**289**

COMPETITORS

7-Eleven	Love's Country Stores
Allsup's	QuikTrip
Brookshire Grocery	Racetrac Petroleum
Chevron	Susser Holdings
Exxon Mobil	Valero Energy
Krause Gentle	

HISTORICAL FINANCIALS

Company Type: Private

Income Statement — FYE: December 31

	REVENUE ($ mil.)	NET INCOME ($ mil.)	NET PROFIT MARGIN	EMPLOYEES
12/16	786	16	2.1%	2,100
12/15	827	16	2.0%	—
12/14	1,026	19	1.9%	—
12/13	1,003	15	1.5%	—
Annual Growth	(7.8%)	3.2%	—	—

2016 Year-End Financials

Return on assets: 2.4%
Return on equity: 2.1%
Current ratio: 0.50
Cash ($ mil.): 7

E. C. BARTON & COMPANY

E. C. Barton & Company sells a variety of home-building tools and goods under a handful of banner names. A member of industry cooperative Do It Best the company sells lumber and building materials through more than 100 locations throughout Texas as well as 15 other states in the US Southeast and the Northeast. It operates several divisions including Barton's Builders Material Company E.C.B. Brokerage and Surplus Purchasing Surplus Warehouse and Grossman's Bargain Outlet. E. C. Barton also manages an e-commerce site. Professional builders and remodelers generate most of the company's revenue. The company is employee-owned.

Operations

The company has organized its business into a handful of divisions: Barton's Grossman's Bargain Outlet Builders Material Company E.C.B. Brokerage and Surplus Purchasing and Surplus Warehouse.

Geographic Reach

E. C. Barton operates its 100-plus stores in 16 states including Alabama Arkansas Connecticut Florida Louisiana Massachusetts Missouri Mississippi New York North Carolina Ohio Pennsylvania Rhode Island South Carolina Tennessee and Texas. More than half of its stores are located in four states: Arkansas New York Texas and Massachusetts.

Sales and Marketing

The retailer serves both professional builders and remodelers and is part of cooperative Do It Best.

Company Background

E. C. Barton was founded in 1885.

EXECUTIVES

President And Ceo, Niel Crowson
Secretary And Treasurer, Tom Rainwater
Manager Builders Material Company, Steve Gage
Vice President Of Operations, Kevin Pierce
Auditors: JONES & COMPANY LTD JONESBO

LOCATIONS

HQ: E. C. BARTON & COMPANY
2929 BROWNS LN, JONESBORO, AR 724017208
Phone: 870 932-6673
Web: WWW.BARTONS-LUMBER.COM

PRODUCTS/OPERATIONS

Selected Products

Bath
Ceiling fans and light kits
Ceilings
Composite decking
Doors
Driveway sealer
Electrical
Flooring
Kitchens
Lighting
Moulding
Outdoor living
Paint
Paint sundries
Pine / oak / vinyl boards
Roofing
Screws & nails
Tools & hardware
Wall planking plywood & shims
Water heaters
Windows

Selected Divisions

Barton's
Builders Material Company
E.C.B. Brokerage and Surplus Purchasing
Grossman's Bargain Outlet
Surplus Warehouse

COMPETITORS

84 Lumber
Ace Hardware
BMC Stock
Builders FirstSource Southeast Group
Diamond Hill Plywood
Guardian Building Products Distribution
Home Depot
Lowe's
Northern Tool
Snavely Forest Products
True Value
WinWholesale

HISTORICAL FINANCIALS

Company Type: Private

Income Statement — FYE: October 26

	REVENUE ($ mil.)	NET INCOME ($ mil.)	NET PROFIT MARGIN	EMPLOYEES
10/17	296	13	4.7%	600
10/16	269	10	3.9%	—
10/15	253	5	2.1%	—
10/14	247	0	0.4%	—
Annual Growth	6.2%	145.1%	—	—

2017 Year-End Financials

Return on assets: 2.4%
Return on equity: 4.7%
Current ratio: 0.90
Cash ($ mil.): 17

EARTHLINK HOLDINGS, LLC

EXECUTIVES

Ceo-Pres, Tony Thomas
Cfo, Bob Gunderman
Ezec V Pres-CHR, John Fletcher
Cmo, Joe Harding
Exec V Pres-Enterprises Sales, Jeff Howe
Pres-Consumer, Sarah Day
Pres-Wholesale, Mike Shippey
Exec V Pres-Access, John Dobbins
Exec V Pres, Engr, Jeff Small
Project Manager, Darrell Smith
General Manager, Livona Stitt
Auditors: ERNST & YOUNG LLP ATLANTA GE

LOCATIONS

HQ: EARTHLINK HOLDINGS, LLC
1170 PEACHTREE ST NE # 900, ATLANTA, GA
303097706
Phone: 404 815-0770

HISTORICAL FINANCIALS

Company Type: Private

Income Statement — FYE: December 31

	REVENUE ($ mil.)	NET INCOME ($ mil.)	NET PROFIT MARGIN	EMPLOYEES
12/16	959	7	0.8%	20
12/15	1,097	(43)	—	—
12/14	1,176	(72)	—	—
Annual Growth	(9.7%)	—	—	—

2016 Year-End Financials

Return on assets: 1.6%
Return on equity: 0.8%
Current ratio: 0.90
Cash ($ mil.): 51

EAST ALABAMA HEALTH CARE AUTHORITY

From babies to seniors The East Alabama Health Care Authority cares for all of Alabama's denizens. The authority's flagship facility is East Alabama Medical Center (EAMC) a general acute-care hospital with 340 beds and a skilled nursing facility with about 35 beds. Facilities at the medical center include an adult day care center cancer center hospice sleep disorders lab and surgery center. Services include diagnostic imaging physical therapy respiratory care and behavioral care. The system also operates EAMC-Lanier which includes an emergency department rehabilitation facilities a nursing home and an urgent care clinic.

Operations

The East Alabama Health Care Authority serves residents of east-central Alabama with a medical staff of more than 160 physicians practicing in about 40 different specialties.EAMC is the second-largest employer in Lee County with a staff of some 3000.

Geographic Reach

The East Alabama Health Care Authority services those who reside in Alabama's Lee County as well as five surrounding counties in east-central Alabama.

Financial Performance

The East Alabama Health Care Authority's revenue fell less than 1% in fiscal 2016 due to a decline in patient revenues. Other revenues increased 8% that year.

With the decline in revenue net income decreased 7% in 2016.

Strategy

The East Alabama Health Care Authority has been expanding its operations by opening new units within its facilities particularly at the EAMC-Lanier campus. In 2017 the system opened a new inpatient detox unit to assist patients in withdrawal; it also opened an acute inpatient rehabilitation unit (the first of its kind in the region).

Company Background

EAMC was founded as an 80-bed hospital in 1952.

EXECUTIVES

Vice President Human Resources, Ken Lott
Evp And Cfo, Sam Price
President And Ceo, Terry W. Andrus, age 66
Vp And Chief Medical Officer, Michael Lisenby
Evp And Administrator, Laura D. Gill
Vp And Chief Planning Officer, Carey Owen
Assistant Vice President Information Services, Sarah Gray
Executive Vice President Administrator, Laura D. Grill
Assistant Vice President Operations, Greg Nichols
Ambulatory Services Director, Carol McCrory
Assistant Vice President, Christopher Clark
Assistant Vice President Patient Care Services, Jane Fullum
Vice President, Susan Johnston
Vice President Clinical Services, Eve Milner
Chairman, Joel Pittard
Vice Chairman, Ken McKemie
Secretary, Elaine Thomas

LOCATIONS

HQ: EAST ALABAMA HEALTH CARE AUTHORITY
2000 PEPPERELL PKWY, OPELIKA, AL 368015452
Phone: 334 749-3411
Web: WWW.EAMC.ORG

PRODUCTS/OPERATIONS

Selected Services
Alzheimer's / Dementia Specialty Care
Ambulance Services
Aperian Laboratory Solutions Inc.
Assisted Living/Senior Communities
Auburn Diagnostic Imaging
Auburn MRI Center
Auburn University Medical Clinic
Auxiliary
Azalea Place Assisted and Independent Living

COMPETITORS

Ascension Health
Columbus Regional Healthcare System
Health Care Authority of the City of Huntsville
Jackson Hospital & Clinic of Alabama
Southeast Alabama Medical Center
University of Alabama
West Georgia Health System

HISTORICAL FINANCIALS
Company Type: Private

Income Statement — FYE: September 30

	REVENUE ($ mil.)	NET INCOME ($ mil.)	NET PROFIT MARGIN	EMPLOYEES
09/17	298	9	3.2%	2,250
09/16	6	0	9.5%	—
09/15	288	8	3.1%	—
09/14	255	17	6.9%	—
Annual Growth	5.4%	(18.2%)	—	—

EAST BAY MUNICIPAL UTILITY DISTRICT, WASTEWATER SYSTEM

EXECUTIVES

Gen Mgr, Alexander Coate
Mgr, Wanda H Talley
Mgr, Patty Seu
Data Center Manager, Pat Cho
Electrical Engineer, Michael Nakamura
Controller/Poc, David Klein
Graphic Designer, Mary R Orr
Electrical Engineer, Paresh Gandhi
Buyer, Rebakah Sharpe
Auditors: MAZE & ASSOCIATES PLEASANT HI

LOCATIONS

HQ: EAST BAY MUNICIPAL UTILITY DISTRICT, WASTEWATER SYSTEM
375 11TH ST, OAKLAND, CA 946074246
Phone: 866 403-2683
Web: WWW.EBMUD.COM

HISTORICAL FINANCIALS
Company Type: Private

Income Statement — FYE: June 30

	REVENUE ($ mil.)	NET INCOME ($ mil.)	NET PROFIT MARGIN	EMPLOYEES
06/16	525	118	22.6%	241
06/05	56	51	91.7%	—
06/04	314	40	12.8%	—
Annual Growth	4.4%	9.4%	—	—

2016 Year-End Financials
Return on assets: 16.7%   Cash ($ mil.): 163
Return on equity: 22.6%
Current ratio: 1.20

EAST BAY MUNICIPAL UTILITY DISTRICT, WATER SYSTEM

It is part of the job description of East Bay Municipal Utility District (EBMUD) to keep the mud out of the drinking water. The utility provides potable water to 1.3 million people in a 331-square-mile area (which includes the cities of Alameda Berkeley and Oakland). Its wastewater system serves about 650000 people in an 88-square-mile area of Alameda and Contra Costa counties along San Francisco Bay's east shore. EBMUD operates a wastewater treatment plant that treats wastewater collected by nine East Bay cities and cleans it before discharge to the San Francisco Bay.

Operations

EBMUD has three business segments: The Water System (the collection transmission and distribution of water within Alameda and Contra Costa countries of California); The Wastewater System (the treatment of wastewater in Alameda Albany Berkeley Emeryville Oakland Piedmont and the Stege Sanitary District); and The Pension and Other Employee Benefit Trust which manages the Employees' Retirement System (retirement benefits of the company employees).

Geographic Reach

EBMUD serves the cities and towns of Alameda Albany Berkeley Danville El Cerrito Emeryville part of Hayward Hercules Lafayette Moraga Oakland Orinda Piedmont Pinole part of Pleasant Hill Richmond San Leandro San Pablo San Ramon part of Walnut Creek and the unincorporated communities of Alamo Ashland Blackhawk Castro Valley Cherryland Crockett Diablo El Sobrante Fairview Kensington North Richmond Oleum Rodeo San Lorenzo and Selby.

Financial Performance

The company's overall fiscal 2014 revenues increased by 8%. Water sales grew by 9% due to a 10% increase in water rates and wastewater revenues increased by 6% resulting from a 9% rate increase. Offsetting these gains EBMUD's power sales decreased by 42% as the result of lower precipitation and run-off of power generation.

In fiscal 2014 the company's net income decreased by 5% due to major increase raw water expenses and higher sewer treatment plant costs. This was offset by higher revenues and lower administration expenses.

EBMUD's operating cash flows increased by 14% in fiscal 2014 due to a rise in cash inflows from cash received from customers offset by an increase in payments to suppliers.

Strategy

EBMUD's mission is to provide reliable high quality water and wastewater services at fair and reasonable rates for the people of the East Bay. The company's 2010-2040 strategic plan calls for the company to obtain an additional 32 million gallons a day of supply. Future activities include infrastructure expansion maintaining fiscal stability and increasing rationing to preserve long term water supply. It is also committed to green energy. Some 90% of the electricity needed to power its main wastewater facility comes from a biomass-fired plant that uses waste from food wineries fats greases and oils.

The company has planned a two year budget (fiscal 2016 and 2017) of $1.8 billion that will fund needed water and wastewater capital projects that replace aging pipelines and rehab aging reservoirs continue to pay for long-term water supply infrastructure and account for the increasing costs of drought. Its active projects include Summit Reservoir Replacement; Round Hill Reservoir/Oakshire Place; Danville Pumping Plant Upgrades; Eden Reservoir Replacement; 39th and Bayo Street Pumping Plant; and Crossroads Reservoir.

Company Background

Formed in 1923 by residents of the San Francisco Bay area EBMUD gets most of its water supply from the Mokelumne River watershed. The Sacramento River provides the balance.

EXECUTIVES

Gen Mgr, Alexander Coate
Corp SEC, Rischa Cole
Contrl, David Klein
Fin Dir, Sophia Skoda
Gen Counsel, Craig Spencer
Asst Treas, Robert Hannay
Dir, John Coleman
H R Mgr, Gwen Mc Donald
Sr Graphic Designer, Todd Salerno

2017 Year-End Financials
Return on assets: 2.5%   Cash ($ mil.): 133
Return on equity: 3.2%
Current ratio: 2.10

Supervisor, Michael Hazinski
Data Processing Operations Man, Pat Cho

LOCATIONS

HQ: EAST BAY MUNICIPAL UTILITY DISTRICT, WATER
SYSTEM
  375 11TH ST, OAKLAND, CA 946074246
Phone: 866 403-2683
Web: WWW.EBMUD.COM

PRODUCTS/OPERATIONS

2013 Sales

	% of total
Water	79
Wastewater	16
Wet weather facilities charges	4
Electricity	1
Total	**100**

HISTORICAL FINANCIALS
Company Type: Private

Income Statement				FYE: June 30
	REVENUE ($ mil.)	NET INCOME ($ mil.)	NET PROFIT MARGIN	EMPLOYEES
06/17	534	136	25.5%	1,511
06/16	525	118	22.6%	—
Annual Growth	1.6%	14.7%	—	—

2017 Year-End Financials
Return on assets: 14.6%   Cash ($ mil.): 221
Return on equity: 25.5%
Current ratio: 1.60

EAST CAROLINA HEALTH INC

EXECUTIVES

Prin, Anita Hunt
Board of Directors, David Harris
Auditors: MCGLADREY LLP CHICAGO IL

LOCATIONS

HQ: EAST CAROLINA HEALTH INC
  2100 STANTONSBURG RD, GREENVILLE, NC
  278342818
Phone: 252 847-6156
Web: WWW.VIDANTHEALTH.COM

HISTORICAL FINANCIALS
Company Type: Private

Income Statement				FYE: September 30
	REVENUE ($ mil.)	NET INCOME ($ mil.)	NET PROFIT MARGIN	EMPLOYEES
09/17	389	18	4.6%	2
09/16	375	25	6.7%	—
09/15	367	25	6.9%	—
09/14	366	5	1.4%	—
Annual Growth	2.1%	52.1%	—	—

2017 Year-End Financials
Return on assets: 10.5%   Cash ($ mil.): 40
Return on equity: 4.6%
Current ratio: 2.40

EAST JEFFERSON GENERAL HOSPITAL

EXECUTIVES

Int. Ceo, Raymond Decorte
Ptnr, Martin H Klein
Ptnr, Dr Reita Lawrence
Exec Vice President, Judy Brown
Chm, Jim M Hudson
SEC, Howard I Brenner
Treas, Ashton J Ryan Jr
Manager, Cheryl St Germain
Director of Surgery, Maty Jo D'Amico
Chief of Pediatric, Jeanne M Rademacher
Coordinator, Steve Neilson
Auditors: RSM US LLP DAVENPORT IOWA

LOCATIONS

HQ: EAST JEFFERSON GENERAL HOSPITAL
  4200 HOUMA BLVD, METAIRIE, LA 700062996
Phone: 504 454-4000
Web: WWW.EJGH.ORG

HISTORICAL FINANCIALS
Company Type: Private

Income Statement				FYE: December 31
	REVENUE ($ mil.)	NET INCOME ($ mil.)	NET PROFIT MARGIN	EMPLOYEES
12/17	352	(25)	—	3,436
12/16	365	(13)	—	—
12/15	322	(15)	—	—
12/14	328	(17)	—	—
Annual Growth	2.4%	—	—	—

2017 Year-End Financials
Return on assets: 5.7%   Cash ($ mil.): 7
Return on equity: (-7.3%)
Current ratio: 0.20

EAST TEXAS ELECTRIC COOPERATIVE, INC.

EXECUTIVES

Pres, Debra Robinson
V Pres, John Dugan
SEC, Kyle Kuntz
Cfo, Ryan Thomas
Acct, Mildred Stone
Auditors: I GOFF & HERRINGTON PC LUFKI

LOCATIONS

HQ: EAST TEXAS ELECTRIC COOPERATIVE, INC.
  2905 WESTWARD DR, NACOGDOCHES, TX
  759641231
Phone: 936 560-9532
Web: WWW.ETEC.COOP

HISTORICAL FINANCIALS
Company Type: Private

Income Statement				FYE: December 31
	REVENUE ($ mil.)	NET INCOME ($ mil.)	NET PROFIT MARGIN	EMPLOYEES
12/15	288	8	2.8%	7
12/14	334	10	3.1%	—
12/13	281	10	3.8%	—
12/10	235	12	5.4%	—
Annual Growth	4.2%	(8.5%)	—	—

2015 Year-End Financials
Return on assets: 9.7%   Cash ($ mil.): 91
Return on equity: 2.8%
Current ratio: 4.10

EASTERN MAINE HEALTHCARE SYSTEMS

Eastern Maine Healthcare Systems (EMHS) keeps the folks in the Pine Tree State feeling fine. With more than a dozen member hospitals and multiple medical practices and clinics the organization offers patients emergency primary mental-health laboratory and other specialty services. It primarily serves eastern central and northern portions of rural Maine. Some hospitals include Eastern Maine Medical Center (410 beds) Acadia Hospital (100 beds) Aroostook Medical Center (75 beds) and Inland Hospital (50 beds). The system also operates long-term care hospice and home health facilities as well as emergency transportation and administrative services businesses.

Operations

Besides its Acadia Hospital Aroostook Medical Center Eastern Maine Medical Center and Inland Hospital EMHS operates three smaller community hospitals with 15 to 30 beds each: Blue Hill Memorial Hospital Charles A. Dean Memorial Hospital and Sebasticook Valley Hospital. The system has affiliations with the Houlton Regional Hospital and Millinocket Regional Hospital.

Subsidiaries of EMHS include Affiliated Healthcare Systems (medical communications and retirement ventures) Affiliated Laboratory (pathology services) Affiliated Material Services (medical supplies distribution and pharmacies) and Affiliated Healthcare Management (transcription and employee services).

As part of its operations EMHS also runs the Eastern Maine Medical Center Clinical Research Center which performs clinical studies in several medical disciplines and diseases including cancer hospital-acquired infections heart disease and physician best practices.

In fiscal 2014 EMHS had 105629 emergency room visits; 32964 inpatient and outpatient surgeries; 3017 births; and 388920 primary care visits.

The company's total Community Benefit that year was about $200 million and its philanthropy giving was nearly $3 million.

Geographic Reach

Despite its name Eastern Maine Healthcare System serves those in eastern central and northern portions of rural Maine.

Strategy

EMHS continues to work collaboratively at the national level looking at not only making a difference in healthcare in Maine but to be a change leader throughout the country. The Northern New England Accountable Care Collaborative is creating resources necessary to propel the reinvention of care model. In addition their work in the High Value Healthcare Collaborative (co-owned with Dartmouth MaineHealth and the University of Vermont Medical Center) this past year has been focused on sepsis care and prevention patient engagement and shared decision-making pilot projects.

In fiscal 2015 Maine's largest health insurer teamed up with Eastern Maine Healthcare Systems under a new venture aimed at keeping patients healthier while reducing costs. The deal involves Anthem Blue Cross and Blue Shield in Maine EMHS and an EMHS-led coalition of hospitals and physician practices across the state. EMHS and its partners have agreed to avoid any cost increase for services they deliver to 40000 Anthem policyholders.

In mid-2014 EMHS completed a community health needs assessment of the northern two-thirds of Maine including the counties of Aroostook Cumberland Hancock Kennebec Penobscot Piscataquis Somerset and Washington. This report was seen as foundational to the company achieving its mission of improving the health and well-being of the communities it serves.

Company Background
The system was established in 1982.

EXECUTIVES

Vice President Talent And Diversity Human Resources, Catherine Maclaren
Vice President Of Organizational Effectiveness, Deborah Sanford
Vice President And System Controller, Jeffery Sanford
Vice President Of Finance Chief Finance, Elmer Doucette
Vice President Finance, Thomas Koil
Vice President Application Services, Teri Hohentanner
Vice President Finance, Randy Clark
Medical Director, Jens Rueter
Department Head, Mikele Neal

LOCATIONS

HQ: EASTERN MAINE HEALTHCARE SYSTEMS
43 WHITING HILL RD # 500, BREWER, ME 044121016
Phone: 207 973-7050
Web: WWW.EMH.ORG

PRODUCTS/OPERATIONS

Selected Strategic Affiliates
Houlton Regional Hospital
Millinocket Regional Hospital
Member Hospitals
Acadia Hospital
Affiliated Healthcare Systems
Aroostook Medical Center
Beacon Health
Blue Hill Memorial Hospital
Charles A. Dean Memorial Hospital and Nursing Home
Dirigo Pines Retirement Community
Eastern Maine HomeCare
Eastern Maine Medical Center
Healthcare Charities
Inland Hospital
Rosscare
Sebasticook Valley Hospital

COMPETITORS

Franklin Community Health Network
Maine Coast Memorial Hospital
MaineGeneral Health
MaineHealth
Mercy Health System of Maine
Miles Health Care
Millinocket Regional Hospital
St. Joseph Healthcare

HISTORICAL FINANCIALS
Company Type: Private

Income Statement				FYE: September 30
	REVENUE ($ mil.)	NET INCOME ($ mil.)	NET PROFIT MARGIN	EMPLOYEES
09/17	1,654	43	2.6%	8,175
09/16	1,523	21	1.4%	—
09/15	1,374	(1)	—	—
09/14	1,301	94	7.2%	—
Annual Growth	8.3%	(22.7%)	—	—

2017 Year-End Financials
Return on assets: 4.1%   Cash ($ mil.): 64
Return on equity: 2.6%
Current ratio: 1.10

EASTERN MAINE MEDICAL CENTER

EXECUTIVES

Ceo, Deborah C Johnson
V Pres-Cfo, Elmer Doucette
Vice President, John Doyle
Coor, Melissa Cadieux
Business Analyst, Karen Egan
Manager, Michelle Mayo
Coordinator, Suzie Phillips
Health Professional, Andrea Sornberger
Information Technology/Interne, Darlene Bean
Director, Susan Dow
Administrative Assistant, Michael Donahue
Auditors: BERRY DUNN MCNEIL & PARKER LL

LOCATIONS

HQ: EASTERN MAINE MEDICAL CENTER
489 STATE ST, BANGOR, ME 044016674
Phone: 207 973-7000
Web: WWW.EMMC.ORG

HISTORICAL FINANCIALS
Company Type: Private

Income Statement				FYE: September 24
	REVENUE ($ mil.)	NET INCOME ($ mil.)	NET PROFIT MARGIN	EMPLOYEES
09/16	776	23	3.0%	1,119
09/15	720	41	5.8%	—
09/13	646	56	8.8%	—
09/12	669	67	10.1%	—
Annual Growth	3.8%	(23.2%)	—	—

2016 Year-End Financials
Return on assets: 4.1%   Cash ($ mil.): 65
Return on equity: 3.0%
Current ratio: 1.70

EATON CORPORATION

EXECUTIVES

Chb-Ceo-Pres, Alexander Cutler
Cfo, Richard Fearon
Exec Vice President, Mark McGuire

Sr V Pres-SEC, Thomas Moran
Sr V Pres-Contrl, Billie Rawot
Sr V Pres Corp Devt & Treas, David Foster
Senior Engineer, Fred James
Manager, Gordon Harmon
Sales Manager, Jim Lago
Executive Officer, Matt Greene
Coordinator, Sandy Benzin
Auditors: ERNST & YOUNG LLP CLEVELAND

LOCATIONS

HQ: EATON CORPORATION
1000 EATON BLVD, CLEVELAND, OH 441226058
Phone: 440 523-5000
Web: WWW.EATON.COM

HISTORICAL FINANCIALS
Company Type: Private

Income Statement				FYE: December 31
	REVENUE ($ mil.)	NET INCOME ($ mil.)	NET PROFIT MARGIN	EMPLOYEES
12/15	6,925	821	11.9%	736
12/14	6,990	170	2.4%	—
Annual Growth	(0.9%)	382.9%	—	—

ECTOR COUNTY INDEPENDENT SCHOOL DISTRICT

EXECUTIVES

Ceo, Brian Moersch
President, Nelson Minyard
Vice President, Teri Ervin
SEC, Doyle Woodall
Federal Program Director, Julia Willett Weekly
Auditors: JOHNSON MILLER & CO CPA'S P

LOCATIONS

HQ: ECTOR COUNTY INDEPENDENT SCHOOL DISTRICT
802 N SAM HOUSTON AVE, ODESSA, TX 797613973
Phone: 432 456-0002
Web: WWW.ECTORCOUNTYISD.ORG

HISTORICAL FINANCIALS
Company Type: Private

Income Statement				FYE: June 30
	REVENUE ($ mil.)	NET INCOME ($ mil.)	NET PROFIT MARGIN	EMPLOYEES
06/18	298	13	4.6%	3,900
06/17	266	(35)	—	—
06/16	264	(83)	—	—
06/15	279	(90)	—	—
Annual Growth	2.2%	—	—	—

2018 Year-End Financials
Return on assets: 1.5%   Cash ($ mil.): 4
Return on equity: 4.6%
Current ratio: —

EDEN TOWNSHIP HOSPITAL DISTRICT, INC

EXECUTIVES

Pres-Ceo, Terry Glubka
Cbo Facility Liason, Jennifer Bostic
Security Staff, Paul White
Marketing Director, Cindy Dove
Foreman Supervisor, George Weaver

LOCATIONS

HQ: EDEN TOWNSHIP HOSPITAL DISTRICT, INC
20400 LAKE CHABOT RD # 303, CASTRO VALLEY, CA
945465316
Phone: 510 538-2031
Web: WWW.ETHD.ORG

HISTORICAL FINANCIALS

Company Type: Private

Income Statement — FYE: December 31

	REVENUE ($ mil.)	NET INCOME ($ mil.)	NET PROFIT MARGIN	EMPLOYEES
12/15	334	26	8.1%	968
12/14	0	(0)	—	—
12/13	51	(51)	—	—
12/09	311	16	5.2%	—
Annual Growth	1.2%	8.9%		—

2015 Year-End Financials

Return on assets: 1.9%   Cash ($ mil.): 4
Return on equity: 8.1%
Current ratio: —

EDUCATIONAL TESTING SERVICE INC

Please completely fill in each circle on the answer sheet as prepared by Educational Testing Service (ETS). ETS develops and administers the Graduate Record Examinations (GRE) and Test of English as a Foreign Language (TOEFL). The not-for-profit group develops and administers more than 50 million achievement admissions academic and professional tests a year at some 9000 locations in more than 180 countries. It also develops assessment programs for corporations professional associations and state entities. ETS' research unit conducts education-focused analysis and policy studies; test-development firm Prometric is a for-profit subsidiary.

Operations

ETS' K-12 products include Advanced Placement (AP) exams and tests to meet individual state standards. Teachers are not forgotten — the company also develops and administers the Praxis Series assessments for teacher licensing and certifications. For college-bound scholars ETS supports The College Board's Scholastic Assessment Test (SAT) and the College Level Examination Program (CLEP).

More than 3300 employees work at ETS's offices worldwide. Of these more than 2300 of its professional staff have training and expertise in education psychology statistics psychometrics computer sciences sociology and the humanities. Almost 1000 have advanced degrees and 390 hold doctorates. Some 1150 employees support ETS's wholly owned subsidiary Prometric.

Its Computerized Assessments and Learning subsidiary is a computerized assessment company based in Lawrence Kansas. Edusoft Ltd. a foreign subsidiary is a global leader in technology-based comprehensive English Language Learning solutions serving a range of educational government and corporate sectors worldwide.

Prometric a global leader in technology-enabled testing and assessment services provides test development test delivery and data management capabilities to 500 clients in the academic professional government corporate and information technology markets via the web or by utilizing a robust test center network in 135 countries.

ETS Global the international arm of ETS brings expertise to educational and business communities around the world such as companies language schools academic institutions and public service organizations.

Geographic Reach

ETS serves US customers from offices in California Florida New Jersey Pennsylvania Puerto Rico Washington State and Washington DC. In addition ETS has direct operating subsidiaries in Canada China Korea and other countries in Latin America Asia Europe the Middle East and Africa; these offices provide services to customers in about 80 countries.

Strategy

In addition to launching new graduate and college-preparation tests and online support programs of its own ETS teams with partners such as Pearson SchoolNet and the Kansas State Department of Education to develop new products such as online tutorials assessment tests for elementary and secondary-education students and teacher leadership assessments. ETS is also increasing security measures to ensure that test takers' identities are properly verified such as a voice recognition system.

ETS also works to increase the market share of its existing products. For instance ETS has been steadily nudging its way into the niche previously dominated by the Graduate Management Admission Council — which administers the GMAT for students heading to graduate business schools — by convincing a growing number of business schools that its GRE General Test is a valuable instrument and to accept the test for admissions.

In 2014 ETS launched the 2015 TOEFL Scholarship Program in India. ETS will award a total of US$70000 in TOEFL scholarships to exceptional students in India who have proven their academic excellence.

Mergers and Acquisitions

In early 2017 ETS agreed to buy K-12 testing services firm Questar Assessment for $127.5 million. Questar specializes in state tests for third to eighth grades; its Nextera assessment platform combines content management student-test interface and image-based hand-scoring abilities.

Company Background

In 2011 the company opened several new customer support centers to support international customers seeking to take the TOEFL test.

The company bulked up its testing technology in early 2011 with the acquisition of Computerized Assessments and Learning (CAL). Operating as a subsidiary of ETS CAL offers assessment products for K-12 education systems.

To move beyond assessment and into actual education ETS acquired Edusoft an English language learning firm in 2011. The 2011 acquisition brought in Edusoft's English Discoveries Online product used around the world. The online product is designed to accompany and support classroom instruction with courses for general and technical English language instruction. Edusoft operates as a for-profit subsidiary.

ETS was founded in 1947.

EXECUTIVES

Svp And President Institute For Student Achievement (isa), Gerry House
Svp And Chief Administrative Officer, Yvette Donado
President And Ceo, Walt MacDonald
Svp And Cfo, Jack Hayon
Svp Strategy Marketing And Growth And Chief Marketing Officer, Scott Nelson
Svp Global Education And Workforce, David Hunt
Senior Vice President And General Manager, Nancy Segal
Associate Vice President Research And Technology Transfer, Marissa Farnum
Vice President Operations, Lynn Rodi
Senior Vice President And General Counsel, Glenn Schroeder
Associate Vice President, Richard Patanella
Vice President And Associate General Counsel, Sheree Johnson-Gregory
Vice President Of Research, Joanna Gorin
Senior Strategic Advisor To The Vice President And Chief Operating Officer Of Global Education, Alberto Acereda
Board Treasurer, Jeff Guelcher
Auditors: DELOITTE & TOUCHE LLP

LOCATIONS

HQ: EDUCATIONAL TESTING SERVICE INC
660 ROSEDALE RD, PRINCETON, NJ 085402218
Phone: 609 921-9000
Web: WWW.ETS.ORG

PRODUCTS/OPERATIONS

Selected Testing Programs

Advanced Placement (AP)
Algebra end of course assessment (EOC)
California High School Exit Examination (CAHSEE)
California State University Placement Test (EPT/ELM)
College-Level Examination Program (CLEP)
ETS Literacy
ETS Proficiency Profile
EXADEP
Graduate Record Examinations (GRE)
High Schools That Work Assessment
iSkills Assessment
Major Field Tests (MFT)
Middle Grades Assessment (MGA)
National Assessment of Educational Progress (NAEP)
ParaPro Assessment
The Praxis Series: Professional Assessments for Beginning Teachers
Preliminary SAT/National Merit Scholarship Qualifying Test (PSAT/NMSQT)
Scholastic Aptitude Test (SAT)
School Leaders Licensure Assessment (SLLA)
School Leadership Series (SLS)
School Superintendent Assessment (SSA)
Secondary Level English Proficiency Test (SLEP)
Test Link Test Collection
TFI Test
Test of English as a Foreign Language (TOEFL)
Test of English for International Communication (TOEIC)

Selected Acquisitions

COMPETITORS

ACT Inc.	S&P Global
Houghton Mifflin	Scantron
Harcourt	The Princeton Review
Kaplan	University of Iowa
Questar Assessment	

HISTORICAL FINANCIALS

Company Type: Private

Income Statement				FYE: September 30
	REVENUE ($ mil.)	NET INCOME ($ mil.)	NET PROFIT MARGIN	EMPLOYEES
09/17	1,398	53	3.8%	2,614
09/16	1,592	73	4.6%	—
Annual Growth	(12.2%)	(28.1%)		

2017 Year-End Financials

Return on assets: 3.4%   Cash ($ mil.): 227
Return on equity: 3.8%
Current ratio: 0.70

EDWARD HOSPITAL

EXECUTIVES

System Ceo, Pamela Davis
System Evp-Cfo, William Devoney
System Vp-Physician Ambulatory, Bill Kottman
Vice Pres-Facilities, Gary Mielak
System Evp-Gen Counsel, Chris Mollet
Exec Vice President, Vince Pryor
Vice President, Barbara Byrne
Vice President, Patti Ludwig-Beymer
System Evp-Hr, Susan Mitchell
System Vp-CIO, Bobbie Byrne
System Vp-Cmo, Brian Davis

LOCATIONS

HQ: EDWARD HOSPITAL
801 S WASHINGTON ST, NAPERVILLE, IL 605407499
Phone: 630 355-0450
Web: WWW.EDWARD.ORG

HISTORICAL FINANCIALS

Company Type: Private

Income Statement				FYE: June 30
	REVENUE ($ mil.)	NET INCOME ($ mil.)	NET PROFIT MARGIN	EMPLOYEES
06/16	592	2	0.5%	4,700
06/15	567	39	7.0%	—
06/14	615	106	17.2%	—
06/13	517	52	10.1%	—
Annual Growth	4.6%	(62.8%)	—	—

EDWARD-ELMHURST HEALTHCARE

EXECUTIVES

Pres, Pamela Meyer-Davis
Exec Vice President, Chris Mollet
Exec Vice President, Susan Mitchell
Vice President, Bobbie Byrne
Cfo, Vince Pryor
Vice President-Facilities, Gary Mielak
Neurology, Henry C Echiverri
Executive, Ajitha Antony
Nurse Manager, Emily Wittenkeller
Information Technology Project, Laura Georges
Manager, Paul Boettcher
Auditors: CROWE HORWATH LLP CHICAGO IL

LOCATIONS

HQ: EDWARD-ELMHURST HEALTHCARE
801 S WASHINGTON ST, NAPERVILLE, IL 605407430
Phone: 630 355-0450
Web: WWW.EDWARD.ORG

HISTORICAL FINANCIALS

Company Type: Private

Income Statement				FYE: June 30
	REVENUE ($ mil.)	NET INCOME ($ mil.)	NET PROFIT MARGIN	EMPLOYEES
06/18	1,474	119	8.1%	6,500
06/17	1,372	105	7.7%	—
06/15	75	5	7.3%	—
06/10	62	11	18.6%	—
Annual Growth	48.4%	33.8%		

2018 Year-End Financials

Return on assets: 2.7%   Cash ($ mil.): 55
Return on equity: 8.1%
Current ratio: 0.50

EFFINGHAM EQUITY

EXECUTIVES

Ceo, Bruce Vernon
Cfo, Karen Whitt
Administrative Assistant, Callie Eveland
Agronomy Sales, Dan Eveland
Administrative Assistant, Erin Pope
Grain Location Manager, Paul Porter
Auditors: BLUE & COMPANY LLC SEYMOUR

LOCATIONS

HQ: EFFINGHAM EQUITY
201 W ROADWAY AVE, EFFINGHAM, IL 624012101
Phone: 217 342-4101
Web: WWW.THEEQUITY.COM

HISTORICAL FINANCIALS

Company Type: Private

Income Statement				FYE: December 31
	REVENUE ($ mil.)	NET INCOME ($ mil.)	NET PROFIT MARGIN	EMPLOYEES
12/15	322	9	2.8%	348
12/14	354	10	2.9%	—
12/13	333	9	2.7%	—
12/10	51	12	23.8%	—
Annual Growth	44.4%	(5.6%)	—	—

2015 Year-End Financials

Return on assets: 8.8%   Cash ($ mil.): —
Return on equity: 2.8%
Current ratio: 0.30

EIDE BAILLY LLP

Eide Bailly is how the West was audited. The company which was founded in 1917 provides clients with audit accounting tax and consulting services from more than 20 offices in nearly a dozen western and central US states. Eide Bailly's target industries include construction agricultural processing oil and gas real estate renewable energy government financial services manufacturing health care and not-for-profit organizations. Additional services are provided by subsidiaries and affiliates including Eide Bailly Technology Consulting. International services are provided through Eide Bailly's affiliation with HLB International. The accounting firm serves some 44000 clients annually.

Geographic Reach

Fargo North Dakota-based Eide Bailly has offices in Arizona Colorado Idaho Iowa Minnesota Montana Oklahoma Utah Washington and the Dakotas.

Financial Performance

Edie Bailly's net fees amounted to $192 million in fiscal 2014 (ended April) up from $171 million in the prior year. The firm's tax services audit and assurance and consulting/other businesses accounted for 40% 37% and 21% of the total respectively.

Strategy

Edie Bailly is growing its business through the acquisition of regional accounting firms to better compete with larger national firms.

Mergers and Acquisitions

In August 2014 the accounting firm acquired Fort Collins-based Sample & Bailey CPAs expanding its Colorado presence to Fort Collins. Previously Eide Bailly expanded into Utah in 2012 with the purchase of Schmitt Griffiths Smith & Co. adding about $6 million to its total revenue. More significantly Edie Bailly announced plans to merge with fellow accountancy Milwaukee-based Wipfli in 2012. However the deal was called off later that year when the two firms could not reach an agreement on key terms.

Other recent purchases include Williston North Dakota-based CPA firm Voller Lee Seuss & Associates. The purchase which closed in December 2012 expanded Edie Bailly's resources and services to clients in the rapidly-growing Bakken Oil Region in western North Dakota. Also in late 2012 the firm acquired Clark & Srsich LLC a boutique tax firm in Littleton Colorado.

EXECUTIVES

Mng Ptnr, Dave Stende
Coo, Michael Astrup
Accounting Staff, Terra Ferguson
Executive Officer, Craig Rennich
Information Specialist, Elizabeth Gallagher
Accounting Staff, Nicole Richards
Taxes Manager, Susan Van Plew
Accounting Staff, Chelsie McInelly
Partner In Charge Phoenix, Andy Spillum
Senior Associate, Anne Stoll
Tax Manager, Chandra Foster

LOCATIONS

HQ: EIDE BAILLY LLP
4310 17TH AVE S, FARGO, ND 581033339
Phone: 701 239-8500
Web: WWW.EIDEBAILLY.COM

PRODUCTS/OPERATIONS

2013 Services by Category

	% of total
Tax Services	40
Audit & Assurance	38
Affiliates	2
Consulting and other	20
Total	**100**

Selected Services

Accounting
Audit & assurance
Employee benefits
Enterprise risk management
Financial services
Forensic & valuation

International services
Tax
Technology consulting
Transaction services
Wealth management

COMPETITORS

BDO Seidman	Ernst & Young LLP
BKD LLP	Grant Thornton
CliftonLarsonAllen	KPMG L.L.P.
Crowe Horwath	PricewaterhouseCoopers
Deloitte & Touche	US

HISTORICAL FINANCIALS

Company Type: Private

Income Statement   FYE: April 30

	REVENUE ($ mil.)	NET INCOME ($ mil.)	NET PROFIT MARGIN	EMPLOYEES
04/18	296	100	34.0%	1,720
04/17	269	98	36.6%	—
04/16	259	93	36.2%	—
04/15	224	76	33.9%	—
Annual Growth	9.7%	9.9%	—	—

2018 Year-End Financials

Return on assets: 1.1%   Cash ($ mil.): 12
Return on equity: 34.0%
Current ratio: 1.00

EL PASO COUNTY HOSPITAL DISTRICT

University Medical Center is a community not-for-profit health care system serving West Texas and southern New Mexico. The networkA includes the 330-bed University Medical Center of El Paso (formerly also known asA Thomason General Hospital) several neighborhood primary care clinics and the El Paso First Health Plans HMO.A The hospitalA is an acute-care teaching hospital affiliated with Texas Tech. It specializes in emergency/trauma care obstetrics pediatric medicine and orthopedics. The hospital district through its affiliates provides a range of outpatient services including physical rehabilitation speech therapy family planning dental care cancer treatment diagnostics and pharmacy services.

Company Background

University Medical Center of El Paso openedA in 1915. The hospital was rebranded under the University Medical Center name in 2009 when Texas Tech opened a full four-year medical school on the Thomason General campus.

EXECUTIVES

Secretary Of Medical Executive Committee, Pedro Serrato
Auditors: BKD LLP DALLAS TEXAS

LOCATIONS

HQ: EL PASO COUNTY HOSPITAL DISTRICT
4815 ALAMEDA AVE, EL PASO, TX 799052705
Phone: 915 544-1200
Web: WWW.UMCELPASO.ORG

PRODUCTS/OPERATIONS

Selected Services
After Hours Pediatrics
Aquatic Therapy
Cardiac Cath
CAT Scan
Case Management
Dental Clinic
Diabetes Management
Diagnostic Radiology
Echocardiograms
Electrocardiograms
Emergency Department
Endoscopy/Special Procedures
Family Planning
Infusion Center
Interventional Radiology
Laboratory Services
Labor and Delivery
Laparoscopic Surgery
Lithotripsy
Mammography
Medical Unit
Mother/Baby Unit
MRI
Neonatal Intensive Care
Neonatal Intermediate Care
Neonatal Continuing Care
Newborn Nursery
Neurosurgery
Nuclear Medicine
Nutritional Care
Occupational Health
Occupational Therapy
Patient Financial Services
Pediatric Unit
Pediatric Rehabilitation
Pharmacy
Physical Therapy
Poison Control Center
Prenatal Services
Primary Care Clinics
Public Affairs
Rehabilitative Services
Respiratory Services
Special Care Nurseries
Speech Therapy
Surgical Services
Surgical Unit
Telemetry Unit
Trauma - Level 1
Ultrasound
West Texas Regional Poison Control Center
Wound Care

COMPETITORS

Covenant Health System	Tenet Healthcare
Del Sol Medical Center	Texas Health Resources
Encompass Health	

HISTORICAL FINANCIALS

Company Type: Private

Income Statement   FYE: September 30

	REVENUE ($ mil.)	NET INCOME ($ mil.)	NET PROFIT MARGIN	EMPLOYEES
09/16	578	0	0.1%	1,898
09/15	177	(2)	—	—
09/14	361	(66)	—	—
09/13	393	1	0.3%	—
Annual Growth	13.7%	(26.4%)	—	—

2016 Year-End Financials

Return on assets: 14.0%   Cash ($ mil.): 61
Return on equity: 0.1%
Current ratio: 1.10

EL PASO INDEPENDENT SCHOOL DISTRICT

EXECUTIVES

Spdt, Juan Cabrera
Psychologist, Michael McCormack
Superintendent, Terri Jordan
Food Director, Laura Duran
Auditors: GIBSON RUDDOCK PATTERSON LLC

LOCATIONS

HQ: EL PASO INDEPENDENT SCHOOL DISTRICT
6531 BOEING DR, EL PASO, TX 799251008
Phone: 915 230-2000
Web: WWW.EPISD.ORG

HISTORICAL FINANCIALS

Company Type: Private

Income Statement   FYE: June 30

	REVENUE ($ mil.)	NET INCOME ($ mil.)	NET PROFIT MARGIN	EMPLOYEES
06/18	625	(34)	—	9,000
06/17	621	188	30.3%	—
06/16	651	2	0.4%	—
06/15	620	(13)	—	—
Annual Growth	0.3%		—	—

2018 Year-End Financials

Return on assets: 0.4%   Cash ($ mil.): 347
Return on equity: (-5.6%)
Current ratio: —

EL PASO NATURAL GAS COMPANY, L.L.C.

EXECUTIVES

Pres-Ceo, James J Cleary
Exec V Pres-Cfo, John R Sult
V Pres-Controller-Cao, Rosa P Jackson
Technician, Jesse Watkins
Engineer, Ramiro Leal

LOCATIONS

HQ: EL PASO NATURAL GAS COMPANY, L.L.C.
1001 LOUISIANA ST, HOUSTON, TX 770025089
Phone: 713 420-2600
Web: WWW.ELPASO.COM

HISTORICAL FINANCIALS

Company Type: Private

Income Statement   FYE: December 31

	REVENUE ($ mil.)	NET INCOME ($ mil.)	NET PROFIT MARGIN	EMPLOYEES
12/17	648	141	21.8%	525
12/16	627	128	20.5%	—
/	0	0		
Annual Growth	—	—	—	—

ELECTRIC POWER BOARD OF CHATTANOOGA

Pardon me .... is that the Electric Power Board (EPB) of Chattanooga? EPB keeps on choo-chooin' along by providing electricity to more than

167410 residents and businesses. The utility (a non-profit agency of the City of Chattanooga) distributes energy in a 600 sq.-ml. area that includes greater Chattanooga as well as parts of surrounding counties in Georgia and Tennessee. It gets its wholesale power supply from the Tennessee Valley Authority. EPB also provides telecommunications (telephone and Internet) services to area homes and businesses through its EPB Fiber Optics unit.

Operations

In addition to its electric distribution business the company's all-fiber Internet product gives 50000 businesses and residences access to up to 500 Mbps of bandwidth a capacity 300 times faster than standard DSL cable or T1 connections. This service gives all EFB customers internet bandwidth capacity and service on a par with or superior to that offered in Atlanta Chicago and Los Angeles.

Geographic Reach

EPB serves greater Chattanooga and parts of surrounding counties (Bledsoe Bradley Marion Rhea and Sequatchie) and North Georgia (parts of Catoosa Dade and Walker counties).

Financial Performance

The company saw its operating revenues rise by 1% in 2013 thanks to an increase of $12.4 million in Fiber Optics residential services sales.

Strategy

EFB is pushing technological innovation and the modernization of its systems as a way to increase value and efficiency.

To help reduce power outages in 2013 the company added 200 smart switches to its 46 Kv system (in addition to its 1200 smart swtiches on the 12kV system already in place.

Company Background

During 2009 the company received a $111 million federal stimulus grant to build and operate a Smart Grid (an automated electric system with communication capabilities to help improve response time reduce outages cut down on theft and help clients take charge of their own power use). In 2012 EFB completed the installation of the 1170 IntelliRupterA® PulseCloser (smart switches) making EPB's Smart Grid the most automated system of its size in the US.

The utility was established in 1935 to provide electric power to the people of the greater Chattanooga area.

EXECUTIVES

Vice President Information Technology, David Johnson
Vice President Economic Developmentandgov.rel., Diana Bullock
Vice President Human Resources, Marie Webb
Vice President, Katherine Espeseth
Vice President Finance And Controller, Michael Kaiser
Board Of Directors, Jon Kinsey
Auditors: MAULDIN & JENKINS LLC CHATTA

LOCATIONS

HQ: ELECTRIC POWER BOARD OF CHATTANOOGA
10 W MARTIN LUTHER KING B, CHATTANOOGA, TN 374021813
Phone: 423 756-2706
Web: WWW.EPB.NET

PRODUCTS/OPERATIONS

2013 Sales

	% of total
Electric	86
Fiber Optics	12
Other	2
Total	**100**

COMPETITORS

AT&T	Southern Company Gas
Constellation Energy Group	

HISTORICAL FINANCIALS
Company Type: Private

Income Statement   FYE: June 30

	REVENUE ($ mil.)	NET INCOME ($ mil.)	NET PROFIT MARGIN	EMPLOYEES
06/17	716	35	4.9%	400
06/16	683	32	4.7%	—
06/15	671	17	2.6%	—
06/14	654	17	2.6%	—
Annual Growth	3.1%	26.8%	—	—

2017 Year-End Financials

Return on assets: 10.1%   Cash ($ mil.): 90
Return on equity: 4.9%
Current ratio: 0.80

ELECTRIC POWER BOARD OF THE METROPOLITAN GOVERNMENT OF NASHVILLE & DAVIDSON COUNTY

The Electric Power Board of the Metropolitan Government of Nashville and Davidson County is a mouthful. Its operating name Nashville Electric Service (NES) sounds much better. And talking of sound the legendary "Nashville Sound" would be hard to hear without the resources of this power distributor which serves more thanA 360000 customers in central Tennessee. NES is one of the largest government-owned utilities in the US. The company is required to purchase all its power from another government-owned operator the Tennessee Valley Authority (TVA).

EXECUTIVES

Pres, Decosta Jenkins
Jr.vice Chair Partner, Robert Campbell
Vp and Cfo, Teresa Broyles Aplin
Senior Manager, Ricky Davis
Accounting Staff, Melissa Stenberg
Manager, Nancy Van Horn
Coordinator, Robert Winters
Operations Manager, Jack Baxter
Senior Engineer, Frederick Friton
Auditors: PRICEWATERHOUSECOOPERS LLP N

LOCATIONS

HQ: ELECTRIC POWER BOARD OF THE METROPOLITAN GOVERNMENT OF NASHVILLE & DAVIDSON COUNTY
1214 CHURCH ST, NASHVILLE, TN 372460001
Phone: 615 747-3831
Web: WWW.NESPOWER.COM

COMPETITORS

AEP	Public Service Enterprise Group
Constellation Energy Group	SCANA
MLGW	Southern Company
Piedmont Natural Gas	Southern Company Gas

HISTORICAL FINANCIALS
Company Type: Private

Income Statement   FYE: June 30

	REVENUE ($ mil.)	NET INCOME ($ mil.)	NET PROFIT MARGIN	EMPLOYEES
06/16	1,203	28	2.4%	950
06/15	1,246	55	4.5%	—
06/09	1,146	16	1.4%	—
06/08	1,030	33	3.2%	—
Annual Growth	2.0%	(2.0%)	—	—

ELECTRIC POWER RESEARCH INSTITUTE, INC.

The Electric Power Research Institute (EPRI) knows there's more to electricity than putting a plug in a socket. From its headquarters in Palo Alto California the institute works to bring together investor-owned and government-owned utility companies as well as other industry representatives. EPRI operates as a not-for-profit research consortium that organizes and funds collaborative research. The organization identifies and works on issues related to electricity generation delivery and use including questions related to environmental protection. More than 10% of the organization's members are located outside the US. EPRI was founded in 1973.

Operations

The institute's research portfolio includes Environment & Renewable Energy Generation Nuclear and Power Delivery and Utilization. EPRI works to make electricity production and its use sustainable for current and future generations. It also focused on advanced generation technologies and emissions controls as well as environmentally-responsible technologies that enable the long-term operation of existing nuclear plants and the deployment of advanced nuclear power plants. It's also interested in developing technologies and approaches to facilitate improved grid reliability energy use efficiency and grid transformation.

Geographic Reach

EPRI serves more than 30 countries. Its members provide some 90% of the electricity generated and delivered in the US. To support its operations EPRI maintains offices in Madrid and Tokyo as well as in half a dozen locations in the US. It has offices and laboratories in Palo Alto California; Charlotte North Carolina; Dallas Texas; Lenox Massachusetts; Knoxville Tennessee; and Washington DC.

Strategy

EPRI's technology strategy encompasses long-term and broad societal visions and goals through its Electricity Technology Roadmap. One such goal is the role of the electric sector and electricity-based technologies in reducing greenhouse gas emissions by 2030.

Through collaboration with other research institutes EPRI is able to tackle more research topics. In 2013 EPRI collaborated with the Japan Nuclear Safety Institute (JANSI) and began participating in a number of EPRI's nuclear research programs. Previously EPRI entered a three-year collaboration with the International Atomic Energy Agency (IAEA) to promote public benefit research into nuclear power plant development operation decommissioning and waste disposal. The collaboration which extends through 2015 offers technical engagement on issues regarding nuclear plant development in countries initiating commercial nuclear power programs.

EXECUTIVES

Svp Cfo And Treasurer, Pamela J. Keefe, age 53
Svp Research And Development And Acting Vice President Generation, Michael W. Howard
Vp Member And Technical Services, Robert Chapman
Vp Transmission And Distribution, Robin E. (Rob) Manning, age 62
Vp People And Performance, Carolyn R. Shockley
Vp Generation, C. Thomas (Tom) Alley
Vp Nuclear And Chief Nuclear Officer, Neil Wilmshurst
Vp Distribution And Energy Utilization, Mark F. McGranaghan
Vice President Legal, Salvador Casente
Vice President Nuclear Power, Christian Larsen
Vice Chair, Jeffrey J. (Jeff) Lyash, age 57
Chairman, Warner L. Baxter, age 57
Auditors: DELOITTE & TOUCHE LLP SAN FR

LOCATIONS

HQ: ELECTRIC POWER RESEARCH INSTITUTE, INC.
3420 HILLVIEW AVE, PALO ALTO, CA 943041382
Phone: 650 855-2000
Web: WWW.EPRIJOURNAL.COM

PRODUCTS/OPERATIONS

Selected Research Topics
Cable aging management
Concrete aging management
Controls and monitoring modernization
Extended fuel storage for spent nuclear fuel
Flexible operation of fossil assets
Irradiation effects on nuclear components
Transmission system life extension through inspection technologies

HISTORICAL FINANCIALS
Company Type: Private

Income Statement				FYE: December 31
	REVENUE ($ mil.)	NET INCOME ($ mil.)	NET PROFIT MARGIN	EMPLOYEES
12/17	408	6	1.7%	891
12/16	399	18	4.7%	—
12/15	406	22	5.6%	—
12/14	388	16	4.4%	—
Annual Growth	1.7%	(26.3%)	—	—

2017 Year-End Financials
Return on assets: 9.6%   Cash ($ mil.): 59
Return on equity: 1.7%
Current ratio: 0.30

ELEMENT14 US HOLDINGS INC

EXECUTIVES

Pres, Ralf Buehler
Vp, Gen Counsel and Secretary, Joseph R Daprile
Treasurer and Assistant Secret, Paul M Barlak

LOCATIONS

HQ: ELEMENT14 US HOLDINGS INC
4180 HIGHLANDER PKWY, RICHFIELD, OH
442869352
Phone: 330 523-4280
Web: WWW.PREMIERFARNELL.COM

HISTORICAL FINANCIALS
Company Type: Private

Income Statement				FYE: February 1
	REVENUE ($ mil.)	NET INCOME ($ mil.)	NET PROFIT MARGIN	EMPLOYEES
02/16	598	9	1.6%	1,043
02/15	717	48	6.7%	—
02/14	698	35	5.1%	—
Annual Growth	(7.5%)	(48.4%)	—	—

2016 Year-End Financials
Return on assets: 7.2%   Cash ($ mil.): 70
Return on equity: 1.6%
Current ratio: 2.70

ELLIOT HEALTH SYSTEM

EXECUTIVES

Ceo, Doug Dean
Nurse, Cynthia Gray
Human Resources, Paul Carter
Office Manager, April Toomey
Analyst, Lisa Berger
Doctor, Kenneth Thomas
Physical Medicine Specialist, Jill Mack
Administrative Assistant, Joann Walsh
Analyst, Bob Blanchette
General Manager, Michael Deblasi
Manager Clinical Engineer Depa, Bob Tanguay

LOCATIONS

HQ: ELLIOT HEALTH SYSTEM
1 ELLIOT WAY, MANCHESTER, NH 031033502
Phone: 603 663-1600
Web: WWW.ELLIOTHOSPITAL.ORG

HISTORICAL FINANCIALS
Company Type: Private

Income Statement				FYE: June 30
	REVENUE ($ mil.)	NET INCOME ($ mil.)	NET PROFIT MARGIN	EMPLOYEES
06/17	544	20	3.7%	3,400
06/08	0	0	4.0%	—
Annual Growth	111.7%	109.6%	—	—

2017 Year-End Financials
Return on assets: 4.6%   Cash ($ mil.): 115
Return on equity: 3.7%
Current ratio: 2.30

ELLIOT HOSPITAL OF THE CITY OF MANCHESTER

Elliot Health System provides medical care to southern New Hampshire. The health care organization operates Elliot Hospital an acute care hospital with nearly 300 beds that is home to a regional cancer center a designated regional trauma center and a level III neonatal intensive care unit (NICU). In addition to general and surgical care the hospital offers rehabilitation behavioral health obstetrics cardiology and lab services. The system also operates the Elliot Physician Network which operates primary care centers specialty clinics and surgery centers in various regional communities. Elliot Hospital was founded in 1890.
Operations
Elliot Hospital is Manchester's designated Regional Trauma Center. Additional facilities include the Elliot Breast Health Center Elliot Urgent Care Elliot Senior Health Center and New Hampshire's Hospital for Children.
Strategy
Elliot Health System has expanded throughout the region by constructing new outpatient care centers in nearby towns. Most recently Elliot Health completed construction of satellite facilities including an ambulatory care center and a senior health center. In 2015 it partnered with Northeast Rehabilitation Hospital to create a new rehabilitation floor within its Elliot Hospital.

EXECUTIVES

Vice President Of Services, Carla Braveman
Vice President For Senior Services And Community Health, John Lofaro
Auditors: BAKER NEWMAN & NOYES LLC MANC

LOCATIONS

HQ: ELLIOT HOSPITAL OF THE CITY OF MANCHESTER
1 ELLIOT WAY, MANCHESTER, NH 031033502
Phone: 603 669-5300
Web: WWW.ELLIOTHOSPITAL.ORG

PRODUCTS/OPERATIONS

Selected Centers and Services
Aeronautics Medicine
Adult Day Programs
Bariatric Surgery
Behavioral Health
Breast Health Center
Cardiology Services
Center for Sleep Evaluation
Center for Wound Care & Hyberbaric Medicine
Childbirth And Family Education
Community Health and Wellness
Critical Care at The Elliot
Diabetes and Outpatient Nutrition Services
Diagnostic Imaging
Elliot 1-Day Surgery Center
The Elliot at Hooksett
Elliot Behavioral Health Services
Elliot Endocrinology Associates
Elliot Gastroenterology
Elliot General Surgical Specialists
Elliot Maternal Fetal Medicine
Elliot Medical Center at Londonderry
Elliot Neurology Associates
Elliot Obstetrics and Gynecology
Elliot Orthopaedic Surgical Specialists
Elliot Physician Network
Elliot Regional Cancer Center
Elliot Sports Medicine
Elliot Trauma Center

Elliot Wellness Center
Endoscopy Center
Health Education Library
Home Medical Equipment
Hospitalist Program
Infection Control Department
Inpatient Care/Nursing Units
Laboratory Services
Max K. Willscher Urology Center
Neurophysiology
New England EMS Institute
New Hampshire Arthritis Center
Nursing Units/Inpatient Care
Nutrition Services
Occupational Health & Wellness
Oral Maxillofacial Surgery Center
Oxygen Therapy
Pain Management Center
Pediatric Surgery
Pharmacy Services
Pulmonary Medicine
Pulmonary Rehabilitation
Physical Therapy
Rehabilitation
Respiratory Care
Senior Health Center
Sports Medicine
Surgery
Speech Therapy
  Urgent Car
  Urgent Car
Visiting Nurse Association of Manchester & So. NH Inc.
Weight Management
Wellness Center
Women's & Children's Services
Wound Center

COMPETITORS

Caritas Holy Family	Frisbie Memorial
Hospital	Hospital
Catholic Medical	HCA
Center	Lahey Health System
Concord Hospital	Southern New Hampshire
Exeter Health	Medical Center
Resources	

HISTORICAL FINANCIALS

Company Type: Private

Income Statement				FYE: June 30
	REVENUE ($ mil.)	NET INCOME ($ mil.)	NET PROFIT MARGIN	EMPLOYEES
06/16	394	49	12.5%	2,000
06/15	421	43	10.4%	—
06/10	324	7	2.4%	—
06/09	288	0	—	—
Annual Growth	4.6%	—	—	—

2016 Year-End Financials

Return on assets: 4.1%   Cash ($ mil.): 75
Return on equity: 12.5%
Current ratio: 2.40

ELLIS HOSPITAL

Schenectady-based Ellis Hospital (dba Ellis Medicine) serves the residents of New York's capital area as part of Ellis Medicine a 438-bed community and teaching health care system. The hospital provides emergency inpatient medical/surgical and psychiatric care including diagnostic primary and rehabilitative care. The hospital is also home to centers of excellence in the treatment of and care for heart and cardiovascular ailments cancer women's health issues stroke-related problems and behavioral health concerns. It also operates the Ellis Center the Bellvue Woman's Center the satel-

lite outpatient clinic Ellis Health Center and recently-constructed Medical Center of Clifton Park.

Operations

Ellis Hospital is part of Ellis Medicine a 438-bed community and teaching health care system serving the Albany New York area. Ellis Medicine has four campuses - Ellis Hospital Ellis Health Center Bellevue Woman's Center and Medical Center of Clifton Park - five additional service locations and more than 700 affiliated physicians.

The hospital's specialty services include a nationally recognized Heart Center a New York State designated Stroke Center and advanced surgery programs such as cardiothoracic orthopedic neurological and vascular among others. The facility features diagnostic imaging and a modern 36-bed intensive care unit.

The McClellan Street Health Center offers outpatient services primary care short-stay rehabilitation and nursing home services. Ellis Medicine Bariatric Care Centers offers a surgical weight loss program.

Ellis Hospital also operates academic programs to prepare students for careers in health care and nursing.

Geographic Reach

The hospital serves patients in the Albany Saratoga Schenectady Fulton and Montgomery counties of upstate New York.

Sales and Marketing

Medicare and Medicaid payments accounted for 53% of net patient service revenues in fiscal 2014.

Financial Performance

Ellis Hospital reported a 2% increase in revenue to $388 million in 2014 due to an increase in net patient service revenues. However it reported a net loss of $5.5 million due to losses on extinguishment of debt and changes in net unrealized gains on investments. Affiliate pension and post-retirement-related changes other than net periodic benefit costs also contributed to the loss.

Cash flow from operations rose 54% to $28 million in 2014 as accounts payable and accrued expenses declined.

Strategy

All of the Schenectady facilities are undergoing expansion or improvement efforts to increase service offerings. In 2013 a $61-million project to expand emergency care and parking at Ellis Hospital was begun; it was completed in early 2015. The project expanded treatment stations to 60 (from 47) and added a new two-story 212-space parking garage. Other capital improvements include a $17-million expansion and modernization of Bellevue Women's Center. Recently completed improvements include the relocation of Ellis' 82-bed nursing home and short-stay rehabilitation center and the creation of the Medical Center of Clifton Park.

EXECUTIVES

Medical Director Infomatics, Igor Kraev
Vice President Of Corporate Compliance And Internal Audit, Colleen Susko
Vice President Physician Services, Patti Hammond
Managing Director, Laurie Wasniski

LOCATIONS

HQ: ELLIS HOSPITAL
1101 NOTT ST, SCHENECTADY, NY 123082489
Phone: 518 243-4000
Web: WWW.ELLISMEDICINE.ORG

PRODUCTS/OPERATIONS

2014 Sales

	% of total
Net patient service revenue	98
Other operating revenue	2
Net assets released from restrictions used for operations	-
Total	**100**

Selected Services

Emergency
Cancer/Oncology
Neuroscience
Orthopedics
Primary care
Weight Loss
Women's Health

Selected Facilities

Bariatric Care Center
Bellevue Woman's Center
Ellis Health Center
Ellis Hospital
Medical Center Clifton Park
Primary Care
Clifton Park
Glenville
Latham
Schenectady (Nott St.)
Schenectady (McClellan St.)
School of Nursing

COMPETITORS

Albany Medical Center
Lifetime Health
Oneida Healthcare Center
SUNY Upstate Medical University
St. Joseph's Hospital Health Center
St. Peter's Health Partners
United Health Services Hospitals
Upstate University Hospital at Community General

HISTORICAL FINANCIALS

Company Type: Private

Income Statement				FYE: December 31
	REVENUE ($ mil.)	NET INCOME ($ mil.)	NET PROFIT MARGIN	EMPLOYEES
12/17	401	1	0.4%	3,000
12/16	400	3	0.9%	—
12/15	377	2	0.5%	—
12/14	361	9	2.7%	—
Annual Growth	3.6%	(46.2%)	—	—

2017 Year-End Financials

Return on assets: 6.5%   Cash ($ mil.): 31
Return on equity: 0.4%
Current ratio: 1.10

ELMHURST MEMORIAL HOSPITAL INC

Elmhurst Memorial Healthcare operates Elmhurst Memorial Hospital an acute care facility located in DuPage County Illinois in the western suburbs of Chicago. Founded in 1926 the hospital provides a comprehensive range of medical services — from emergency care to specialty cancer and orthopedics care to behavioral health services. In addition to the 310-bed main hospital Elmhurst Memorial Healthcare operates several facilities such as doctors' offices outpatient centers occupational health programs and other ancillary health care operations. Elmhurst Memorial Healthcare is part of Edward-Elmhurst Healthcare after it merged with Edward Hospital & Health Services and Linden Oaks.

Change in Company Type

Elmhurst Memorial Healthcare Edward Hospital & Health Services and Linden Oaks merged in 2013 to create a larger integrated health system. Combined the system operates three hospitals and more than 50 outpatient facilities. It has some $1 billion in annual revenues.

Operations
Aside from its Elmhurst Memorial Hospital Main Campus Elmhurst Memorial Healthcare operates several other facilities such as the Berteau Campus Center for Health Lombard Health Center Addison Health Center Elmhurst Memorial Sleep Center Occupational Health Services Wood Dale and an outpatient surgery center clinic primary care associates medical associates and hematology oncology associates offices under the Elmhurst banner.

The newer acute care hospital known as the Elmhurst Memorial Hospital Main Campus features about 260 private inpatient rooms as well as a high-tech emergency department and surgical and diagnostic imaging facilities. It includes the Elmhurst Memorial Center for Health which boasts outpatient clinics and a medical office building for general practice and specialty physicians.

Each year Elmhurst Memorial Hospital has some 48000 emergency department visits and performs some 3400 inpatient and 5500 outpatient surgeries.

Geographic Reach
Elmhurst Memorial Healthcare and its hospital serve the western suburbs of Chicago specifically the county residents of DuPage.

Strategy
To provide its communities with quality cancer care Elmhurst Memorial Healthcare constructed a new cancer care facility that boasts medical oncologist offices an infusion center Cyberknife robotic radiosurgery system and radiation oncology services.

In 2015 Elmhurst Memorial Hospital opened a bariatrics and weight management center that provides surgical and non-surgical services.

The system has been expanding by opening new facilities. In 2014 it opened its second walk-in clinic which provides treatment for minor illnesses. The following year Elmhurst broke ground on a new three-story health center in Hinsdale.

There are also plans for the old Elmhurst Memorial Hospital campus known as the Berteau Campus. While the Berteau Campus' inpatient and emergency care operations were transferred to the new Main Campus the Berteau Campus' emergency room became an outpatient urgent care center. The campus also includes inpatient behavioral health and recovery facilities as well as outpatient cancer care physical therapy and occupational health clinics. For the long term Elmhurst Memorial Healthcare plans to transform the Berteau Campus into a senior health and housing center by closing or moving the existing operations to other or new locations.

EXECUTIVES

Ceo, Pamela Davis
Ceo, Mary Lou Mastro
Vice President, Pamela Dunley
Cfo, James Doyle
Coordinator, Andrea White
Coordinator, Chavonne Hardy
Scientist, Mirza Baig
Coordinator, Joan Stramel
Director, Robert Blazek
Assistant Manager, Greg Liedtka
Coordinator, Karen Forte

LOCATIONS

HQ: ELMHURST MEMORIAL HOSPITAL INC
133 E BRUSH HILL RD, ELMHURST, IL 601265659
Phone: 331 221-9003
Web: WWW.EMHC.ORG

PRODUCTS/OPERATIONS

Selected Services
Breast Health Center
Cardiovascular Services
EMH Laboratory
Family Birthing Center
Home Health and Hospice
Immediate Care Centers
Occupational Health
Orthopedics
Radiology
Surgery
Cancer Center
Emergency Department

COMPETITORS

Adventist Health System Sunbelt Healthcare
Advocate Health Care
Alexian Brothers Health System
Central DuPage Hospital
Covenant Ministries
Gottleib Memorial Hospital
Loyola University Health System
Northwest Community Healthcare
Rush System for Health
University of Chicago Medical Center
Wheaton Franciscan Services

HISTORICAL FINANCIALS
Company Type: Private

Income Statement | | | | FYE: June 30

	REVENUE ($ mil.)	NET INCOME ($ mil.)	NET PROFIT MARGIN	EMPLOYEES
06/15	379	(9)	—	2,444
06/09	305	20	6.6%	—
06/08	345	(22)	—	—
06/07	341	43	12.7%	—
Annual Growth	1.3%	—	—	—

ELON UNIVERSITY

EXECUTIVES

Pres, Leo M Lambert
Chb, William NP Herbert
V Chb, Kerrii Brown Anderson
Sr Vice President, Gerald Whittington
Exec Vice President, Gerald Francis
Vice President, Holly Berry
Accounting Staff, Pieter Swanepoel
Assistant Professor, Sirena Hargrove
Administration Executive, Donna Van Bodegraven
Security Staff, Louis Adams
Security Staff, Mike Talley
Auditors: GRANT THORNTON LLP CHARLOTTE

LOCATIONS

HQ: ELON UNIVERSITY
100 CAMPUS DR, ELON, NC 272449423
Phone: 336 278-2000
Web: WWW.ELON.EDU

HISTORICAL FINANCIALS
Company Type: Private

Income Statement | | | | FYE: May 31

	REVENUE ($ mil.)	NET INCOME ($ mil.)	NET PROFIT MARGIN	EMPLOYEES
05/17	289	65	22.6%	1,200
05/16	240	22	9.5%	—
05/15	262	54	20.7%	—
05/14	238	50	21.0%	—
Annual Growth	6.7%	9.4%	—	—

2017 Year-End Financials
Return on assets: 4.0%   Cash ($ mil.): 25
Return on equity: 22.6%
Current ratio: —

ELWYN

Elwyn isn't a character out of Harry Potter or Lord of the Rings . It's a not-for-profit organization that serves more than 13000 disabled and disadvantaged people of all ages at multiple sites through education rehabilitation and vocational counseling. The organization also operates residential communities including more than 80 group homes and apartments and provides a variety of health care services for persons with developmental physical and emotional disabilities. The group also publishes training materials and hosts conferences and seminars for human services professionals. Founded in 1852 as a school for children with mental retardation Elwyn is one of the oldest organizations of its kind in the US.

Operations
Elwyn operates two for-profit subsidiaries. Its PEMS unit an applied technology service provides a variety of enhanced management services. The organization's Grace Pharmacy Inc. is a full-service pharmacy operation that specializes in long-term care clients.

Elwyn Commercial Laundry specializes in laundry services for hospitals nursing homes surgical centers and other health care related organizations.

Geographic Reach
Elwyn's main campus is in Philadelphia with satellite locations in California New Jersey and Delaware.

Company Background
At a time when most people with mental disabilities were left to live on the streets or thrown in prison Dr. Alfred Elwyn proposed a special school to help "feeble-minded children." The school attracted the best minds of the time and grew quickly adding residential services and custodial care of adults in 1877.

EXECUTIVES

Senior Vice President Business Development, H Scott Campbell
Auditors: KREISCHER MILLER HORSHAM PA

LOCATIONS

HQ: ELWYN
111 ELWYN RD, MEDIA, PA 190634622
Phone: 610 891-2000
Web: WWW.ELWYN.ORG

PRODUCTS/OPERATIONS

Selected Services
Behavioral health services
Deaf services

Early childhood services
Education services
Research and health services
Supports for living
Work and adult day services

COMPETITORS

Res-Care

HISTORICAL FINANCIALS

Company Type: Private

Income Statement

FYE: June 30

	REVENUE ($ mil.)	NET INCOME ($ mil.)	NET PROFIT MARGIN	EMPLOYEES
06/17	314	19	6.2%	2,500
06/15	218	2	1.2%	—
06/14	268	13	4.9%	—
06/11	264	14	5.5%	—
Annual Growth	3.0%	4.9%	—	—

2017 Year-End Financials

Return on assets: 9.0%
Return on equity: 6.2%
Current ratio: 0.70
Cash ($ mil.): 13

EMJ CORPORATION

EMJ does it all for the mall. Founded in 1968 by namesake Edgar M. Jolley the company specializes in building and renovating retail outlets and shopping centers throughout the US. It is also known for other building projects such as offices warehouses churches hotels multifamily residences hospitals and wind farms. Working from five offices nationwide EMJ provides general construction and construction management. The company's pre-construction services include creating detailed budgets and construction schedules and coordinating permitting utility companies and municipal requirements. To track a project's progress and monitor costs EMJ offers quality control and safety and warranty management.

Operations

EMJ owns several operating divisions including Signal Energy which engineers and builds renewable energy projects such as wind farms and solar and biomass energy projects. Another division Accent Construction Management provides site selection budgeting scheduling and other services. Its RedStone Construction Services builds commercial retail hospitality healthcare government facilities and others. It is focused on fostering economic growth in Native American communities.

Geographic Reach

From its base in Chattanooga Tennessee EMJ serves clients through a handful of US offices in Massachusetts Tennessee Texas and California.

Sales and Marketing

EMJ has built more than 500 million sq. ft. of construction projects. Its client roster includes Academy Barnes & Noble Bed Bath & Beyond Blue Cross and Blue Shield Home Depot PetSmart and Winn-Dixie.

The company serves several sectors such as airports education entertainment government and civic grocery healthcare hospitality industrial and warehouse and Native American tribal communities office buildings parking lifestyle and mixed use development retail renewable energy renovations and worship centers.

Strategy

The company is working on projects for Whole Foods Market TownPlace Suites Silverdale Baptist

student center and Dick's Sporting Goods. Inked in 2013 EMJ's $250-million deal with Native American Chris Samples operating under the name RedStone Construction Services is building a 500-room hotel and expanding a casino in Tulsa Oklahoma.

EXECUTIVES

Vice President, Christopher Hall
Vice President, Alfonso Leon
Vice President, Earl Carstens
Senior Vice President, Philip Augustino
Senior Vice President, Drew Smith
Vice President Southwest Office, Drew Halsey
Vice President Marketing, Deron Smith
Vice President Of Construction, Steve Rice

LOCATIONS

HQ: EMJ CORPORATION
2034 HAMILTON PLACE BLVD # 400,
CHATTANOOGA, TN 374216102
Phone: 423 855-1550
Web: WWW.EMJCORP.COM

PRODUCTS/OPERATIONS

Selected Projects
Airports
Education
Entertainment
Government/civic
Grocery
Healthcare
Hospitality
Industrial/warehouse
Lifestyle/mixed use development and retail
Native American tribal communities
Office buildings
Parking
Renewable energy
Renovations
Worship centers

Selected Services
Construction
Construction management
General contracting
Pre-construction services
Quality control
Safety consultation
Site evaluation
Warranty

COMPETITORS

Case Contracting	Hoar Construction
Embree Construction	JESCO
Fisher Development	Rodgers Builders
Graycor	S.D. Deacon
Hardaway Construction	Skanska USA Building
Hardin Construction	Weis Builders
Hayward Baker	Workman Commercial

HISTORICAL FINANCIALS

Company Type: Private

Income Statement

FYE: March 7

	REVENUE ($ mil.)	NET INCOME ($ mil.)	NET PROFIT MARGIN	EMPLOYEES
03/17*	960	4	0.5%	210
12/11	437	0	0.1%	—
12/08	821	7	1.0%	—
12/07	959	10	1.1%	—
Annual Growth	0.0%	(7.9%)	—	—

*Fiscal year change

2017 Year-End Financials

Return on assets: 18.0%
Return on equity: 0.5%
Current ratio: 1.10
Cash ($ mil.): 29

EMORY UNIVERSITY HOSPITAL MIDTOWN

EXECUTIVES

Ceo, Robert J Bachman
Dir, Rosalind K Lett
President, John T Fox
Exec Vice President, S Wright Caughman
Attorney, Lorraine Spencer
Chief of Medicine, Harold Ramos
Director, Jakob V Johansen
Assistant Professor, James Weisberg
Coordinator, Crystal Evans
Internal Medicine Practitioner, Sharmila Thadani
Physician Director of Er, Matthew Keadey

LOCATIONS

HQ: EMORY UNIVERSITY HOSPITAL MIDTOWN
550 PEACHTREE ST NE, ATLANTA, GA 303082212
Phone: 404 686-4411
Web: WWW.EMORY.ORG

HISTORICAL FINANCIALS

Company Type: Private

Income Statement

FYE: August 31

	REVENUE ($ mil.)	NET INCOME ($ mil.)	NET PROFIT MARGIN	EMPLOYEES
08/16	735	64	8.7%	2,500
08/15	641	(21)	—	—
08/10	0	(0)	—	—
08/09	1,807	(38)	—	—
Annual Growth	(12.0%)	—	—	—

2016 Year-End Financials

Return on assets: 9.0%
Return on equity: 8.7%
Current ratio: 2.30
Cash ($ mil.): 269

EMPIRE RESOURCES, INC.

EXECUTIVES

Ceo, Johnny Hsieh
AP Administrator, Irina Pisarenkov
Manager, Isaac Piha
Chief Financial Officer, Sandy Kahn
Executive, David Kronfeld
Vice President, Harvey Wrubel
Network Manager, Ross Toombs
Auditors: EISNERAMPER LLP NEW YORK NEW

LOCATIONS

HQ: EMPIRE RESOURCES, INC.
2115 LINWOOD AVE STE 200, FORT LEE, NJ
070245022
Phone: 201 944-2200
Web: WWW.EMPIRERESOURCES.COM

PRODUCTS/OPERATIONS

Selected Aluminum Products
Circles
Coil/sheet
Foil
Plate
Profiles/extruded products
Treadplate

COMPETITORS

Arconic	Rio Tinto Alcan
Commercial Metals	Ryerson
Metal Connection	SASA

HISTORICAL FINANCIALS

Company Type: Private

Income Statement				FYE: December 31
	REVENUE ($ mil.)	NET INCOME ($ mil.)	NET PROFIT MARGIN	EMPLOYEES
12/16	458	3	0.7%	60
12/15	521	2	0.5%	—
12/14	582	3	0.6%	—
12/13	482	2	0.5%	—
Annual Growth	(1.7%)	11.3%	—	—

2016 Year-End Financials

Return on assets: 4.8% Cash ($ mil.): 4
Return on equity: 0.7%
Current ratio: 0.40

EMPLOYERS RESOURCE MANAGEMENT COMPANY

EXECUTIVES

Chb-Ceo, George H Gersema
President, Ray O'Leary
Vice President, Douglas W Gersema
Exec Vice President, Mary D Gersema
Vice-President, Douglas C Neve
Admn Asst, Debby Toncray
Controller, Jerry Hedrick
Manager, Susan Szabo
Manager, Robert Henbest
Auditors: EIDE BAILLY LLP BOISE IDAHO

LOCATIONS

HQ: EMPLOYERS RESOURCE MANAGEMENT COMPANY
1301 S VISTA AVE STE 200, BOISE, ID 837052576
Phone: 208 376-3000
Web: WWW.EMPLOYERSRESOURCE.COM

HISTORICAL FINANCIALS

Company Type: Private

Income Statement				FYE: June 30
	REVENUE ($ mil.)	NET INCOME ($ mil.)	NET PROFIT MARGIN	EMPLOYEES
06/17	515	0	0.1%	95
06/16	489	0	0.1%	—
06/14	456	0	0.1%	—
06/11	357	0	0.1%	—
Annual Growth	6.3%	19.3%	—	—

2017 Year-End Financials

Return on assets: 0.1% Cash ($ mil.): 10
Return on equity: 0.1%
Current ratio: 0.40

ENABLE GAS TRANSMISSION, LLC

EXECUTIVES

Pres, David McClanahan
President, Gregory Harper
Vice President, Peter Kirsch
Treas, Marc Kilbride
V Pres of Fin, Cy Zebot
Senior Analyst, Brian Vantubergen
Vice-President, Doyle McQuillon
District Manager, Jay Reber
Nephrology, Steve Letbetter
Director of Mis/Is, Frank Hughes
Manager, Doug Robins

LOCATIONS

HQ: ENABLE GAS TRANSMISSION, LLC
1111 LOUISIANA ST, HOUSTON, TX 770025230
Phone: 713 207-1111

HISTORICAL FINANCIALS

Company Type: Private

Income Statement				FYE: December 31
	REVENUE ($ mil.)	NET INCOME ($ mil.)	NET PROFIT MARGIN	EMPLOYEES
12/16	483	100	20.9%	310
12/02	232	53	23.1%	—
/ 0	0	—	—	—
Annual Growth	—	—	—	—

ENERGY SYSTEMS GROUP, LLC

EXECUTIVES

Pres, Gregory F Collins
Sr V Pres-Public Sector, Steve Pride
Sr V Pres-Infrastructure, Lawrence Roth
V Pres-Fin-Treas, Dennis Perrey
V Pres-Gen Counsel-Asst SEC, Jonathan D Shell
V Pres of Oprs, W Luke Brockman
SEC-Asst Treas, Michelle D Quinn
Engineering Manager, Mike Johnson
Project Manager, Ron Bresser
Director of Finance, Ted Edgar
Payroll Manager, Melanie Schapker
Auditors: HARDING SHYMANSKI & COMPANY

LOCATIONS

HQ: ENERGY SYSTEMS GROUP, LLC
9877 EASTGATE CT, NEWBURGH, IN 476302368
Phone: 812 492-3734
Web: WWW.ENERGYSYSTEMSGROUP.COM

HISTORICAL FINANCIALS

Company Type: Private

Income Statement				FYE: December 31
	REVENUE ($ mil.)	NET INCOME ($ mil.)	NET PROFIT MARGIN	EMPLOYEES
12/17	281	15	5.4%	238
12/16	63	10	17.4%	—
12/15	199	1	1.0%	—
12/14	129	5	4.2%	—
Annual Growth	29.5%	41.2%	—	—

2017 Year-End Financials

Return on assets: 13.5% Cash ($ mil.): 49
Return on equity: 5.4%
Current ratio: 0.80

ENERGYUNITED ELECTRIC MEMBERSHIP CORPORATION

EXECUTIVES

Ceo, H Wayne Wilkins
Vice President Corporate Servi, Alec Natt
Market Executive, Paul Pipkin
Vice President of Engineerando, David Schleicher
Purchasing Agent, Pam Current
Manager, Brett Alkins
Market Executive, Johnny Mabe
Communications Specialist, Donnie Shoaf
General Manager, Jeff Ruffner
Sales Manager, Jeff Teague
Web Developer, Alex Midgett

LOCATIONS

HQ: ENERGYUNITED ELECTRIC MEMBERSHIP CORPORATION
567 MOCKSVILLE HWY, STATESVILLE, NC 286258269
Phone: 704 873-5241
Web: WWW.ENERGYUNITED.COM

COMPETITORS

Crestwood Equity	SCANA
Duke Energy	

HISTORICAL FINANCIALS

Company Type: Private

Income Statement				FYE: December 31
	REVENUE ($ mil.)	NET INCOME ($ mil.)	NET PROFIT MARGIN	EMPLOYEES
12/17	282	6	2.3%	185
12/16	291	9	3.2%	—
12/15	281	9	3.5%	—
12/14	274	9	3.5%	—
Annual Growth	0.9%	(12.5%)	—	—

2017 Year-End Financials

Return on assets: 8.2% Cash ($ mil.): 5
Return on equity: 2.3%
Current ratio: 0.70

ENGEL MACHINERY INC.

EXECUTIVES

Ceo-Pres, Mark Sankovitch
Controller, Glenn Ness
Sales Director, Jim Moran
Marketing Manager, Kleta Childs
Executive of Information Techn, Bryan Brenneman
Accounting Staff, Michele Kriskie
Account Manager, Mike Wright
Spare Parts Administrator, Cristi Hoover
Sales, Larry Alvey
Vice President, Mike Petrides
Account Manager, Arturo Cuevas
Auditors: GRANT THORNTON LLP KITCHENER

LOCATIONS

HQ: ENGEL MACHINERY INC.
3740 BOARD RD, YORK, PA 174068425
Phone: 717 764-6818
Web: WWW.ENGELGLOBAL.COM

HISTORICAL FINANCIALS

Company Type: Private

Income Statement   FYE: March 31

	REVENUE ($ mil.)	NET INCOME ($ mil.)	NET PROFIT MARGIN	EMPLOYEES
03/18	333	2	0.7%	140
03/17	203	0	0.4%	—
03/16	190	2	1.2%	—
03/15	126	0	0.4%	—
Annual Growth	38.2%	63.5%	—	—

2018 Year-End Financials

Return on assets: 5.4%   Cash ($ mil.): 9
Return on equity: 0.7%
Current ratio: 0.70

ENGINEERED STRUCTURES, INC.

EXECUTIVES

Ceo, Thomas D Hill
President, Neil W Nelson
Cfo, Kevin Smith
Project Manager, Shane Plummer
Project Manager, Bonnie Heinrich
Superintendent, Joe Crutchfield
Director, Michael Papac
Project Engineer, Nathan Miller
Project Manager, Phil Goldman
Project Coordinator, Cheralee Keyes
Superintendent, Dave Cooney
Auditors: HARRIS & CO PLLC MERIDIAN I

LOCATIONS

HQ: ENGINEERED STRUCTURES, INC.
3330 E LOUISE DR STE 300, MERIDIAN, ID 836425123
Phone: 208 362-3040
Web: WWW.ESICONSTRUCTION.COM

HISTORICAL FINANCIALS

Company Type: Private

Income Statement   FYE: December 31

	REVENUE ($ mil.)	NET INCOME ($ mil.)	NET PROFIT MARGIN	EMPLOYEES
12/17	354	8	2.3%	250
12/14	246	5	2.1%	—
12/13	270	6	2.3%	—
12/12	0	0	—	—
Annual Growth	—	125.5%	—	—

2017 Year-End Financials

Return on assets: 9.8%   Cash ($ mil.): 9
Return on equity: 2.3%
Current ratio: 0.80

ENGLEWOOD HOSPITAL AND MEDICAL CENTER FOUNDATION INC.

Englewood Hospital and Medical Center is a 520-bed acute care hospital serving New Jersey's Bergen County which is part of the New York City metro area. The not-for-profit health care provider offers general medical and surgical care along with specialty services in areas such as oncology cardiovascular disease wound care women's health joint replacement and pediatrics. It also maintains a short-term inpatient behavioral health program for adults. The hospital is affiliated with the Mount Sinai School of Medicine and the Mount Sinai Consortium for Graduate Medical Education and provides residency programs to doctors from the Mount Sinai School of Medicine.

Operations

Englewood Hospital and Medical Center has a nursing staff of 800 and medical staff of 380. It serves more than 23000 admitted patients and nearly 47000 emergency cases a year. It conducted some 8000 operations and helped deliver 2000 babies in 2014.

As a teaching hospital it offers education and research programs including Grand Rounds CME Online an Internal Medicine Residency Program a Vascular Surgery Fellowship a Pharmacy Residency Program and a School of Radiography.

Along with the typical acute and chronic medical care services the hospital maintains an infusion center for patients requiring chemotherapy and also offers hyperbaric oxygen treatments for divers with the bends and other patients who will benefit from having oxygen administered under pressure.

To better serve patients for whom blood transfusions are not an option the hospital had established a program for bloodless medicine and surgery. The Institute for Patient Blood Management & Bloodless Medicine and Surgery serves as a leading resource for training health professionals in working in environments where blood transfusions are not readily available.

Geographic Reach

The company operates the largest voluntary acute care hospital in Bergen County and the third largest in New Jersey.

Company Background

The hospital was founded in 1890.

EXECUTIVES

V Pres, Anthony T Orlando
SEC, Warren Geller
Vp Info Tech-CIO, Dimitri J Cruz
Principal, Phil Maneri
Training and Direc, Barbara Wilkinski
Scientist, Mazyar Javidroozi
Anesthesiology, Lorraine V Volpe
Health Professional, Mercedes Delgado
Anesthesiology, Payyanadan V Chithran
Health Professional, Silvia Daici
Manager, Francis Valenzona

LOCATIONS

HQ: ENGLEWOOD HOSPITAL AND MEDICAL CENTER FOUNDATION INC.
350 ENGLE ST, ENGLEWOOD, NJ 076311808
Phone: 201 894-3725
Web: WWW.ENGLEWOODHOSPITAL.COM

PRODUCTS/OPERATIONS

Selected ServicesMedical ServicesAMI of EnglewoodAnesthesiologyAntepartum Testing CenterBerrie Center Same Day SurgeryBariatric SurgeryBloodless Medicine & SurgeryBreast Care CenterBreast Surgical ServicesCancer Center ResourcesCardiac RehabCardiac Surge

COMPETITORS

Bergen Regional Medical
Bronx-Lebanon Hospital
Hackensack University Medical Center
Lenox Hill Hospital
Memorial Sloan-Kettering
NewYork-Presbyterian Healthcare
St. Joseph's Regional Medical Center
The Valley Hospital
Valley Health System

HISTORICAL FINANCIALS

Company Type: Private

Income Statement   FYE: December 31

	REVENUE ($ mil.)	NET INCOME ($ mil.)	NET PROFIT MARGIN	EMPLOYEES
12/16	552	19	3.5%	2,200
12/15	480	12	2.5%	—
12/14	428	13	3.2%	—
12/13	425	11	2.7%	—
Annual Growth	9.1%	19.0%	—	—

2016 Year-End Financials

Return on assets: 8.6%   Cash ($ mil.): 45
Return on equity: 3.5%
Current ratio: 1.00

ENTERGY OPERATIONS, INC.

EXECUTIVES

Pres, Jeff S Forbes
V Pres, Wanda C Curry
V Pres, Clifford Eubanks
SEC, Daniel T Falstad
Engineer, Barbara Johnson
Supervisor, Deepak RAO
Supervisor, Robert Wright
Engineer, Angel Reyes
Vice-President Operations, Joseph P Deroy
Senior Engineer, Eric Lewis
Engineer, Judy A Tin

LOCATIONS

HQ: ENTERGY OPERATIONS, INC.
  1340 ECHELON PKWY STE 100, JACKSON, MS
  392138210
Phone: 601 366-2727
Web: WWW.ENTERGY.COM

HISTORICAL FINANCIALS
Company Type: Private

Income Statement				FYE: December 31
	REVENUE ($ mil.)	NET INCOME ($ mil.)	NET PROFIT MARGIN	EMPLOYEES
12/16	473	0	—	3,600
12/02	20	0	—	—
12/01	19	0	—	—
12/00	701	159	22.8%	—
Annual Growth	(2.4%)	—	—	—

2016 Year-End Financials
Return on assets: 8.9%   Cash ($ mil.): 27
Return on equity: —
Current ratio: 0.50

ENTERGY SERVICES, INC.

EXECUTIVES

Ceo, Leo P Denault
Cfo, Andrew Marsh
Coo, Mark T Savoff
President, Theo Bunting Jr
Exec President, Marcus V Brown
Vice President, Kimberly H Despeaux
Vice President, Jere M Ahrens
Vice President, Kay K Arnold
Vice President, Michael A Balduzzi
Vice President, Kelle J Barfield
Director, Cory Gruntz

LOCATIONS

HQ: ENTERGY SERVICES, INC.
  639 LOYOLA AVE STE 300, NEW ORLEANS, LA
  701137106
Phone: 504 576-4000
Web: WWW.ENTERGY.COM

HISTORICAL FINANCIALS
Company Type: Private

Income Statement				FYE: December 31
	REVENUE ($ mil.)	NET INCOME ($ mil.)	NET PROFIT MARGIN	EMPLOYEES
12/16	1,112	10	0.9%	1,325
12/04	10,123	933	9.2%	—
Annual Growth	(16.8%)	(31.2%)	—	—

2016 Year-End Financials
Return on assets: 14.4%   Cash ($ mil.): 51
Return on equity: 0.9%
Current ratio: 0.20

ENTERPRISE CRUDE PIPELINE LLC

EXECUTIVES

Pres, W Randall Fowler
Senior Project Manager, Lloyd Ruddick

LOCATIONS

HQ: ENTERPRISE CRUDE PIPELINE LLC
  1100 LOUISIANA ST # 1000, HOUSTON, TX
  770027499
Phone: 713 381-6500
Web: WWW.ENTERPRISEPRODUCTS.COM

HISTORICAL FINANCIALS
Company Type: Private

Income Statement				FYE: December 31
	REVENUE ($ mil.)	NET INCOME ($ mil.)	NET PROFIT MARGIN	EMPLOYEES
12/17	596	378	63.5%	300
12/16	472	284	60.2%	—
Annual Growth	26.2%	33.1%	—	—

ENTERPRISE TE PRODUCTS PIPELINE COMPANY LLC

EXECUTIVES

Ceo-MBR, Jerry E Thompson
Cfo-MBR, William G Manias
Specialist, Christopher Santamaria
Supervisor, Harry Johnson
Operations Supervisor, Lewis Brown
Supervisor, Tim Kistner
Technician Pipeline, Paul Deken

LOCATIONS

HQ: ENTERPRISE TE PRODUCTS PIPELINE COMPANY
  LLC
  1100 LOUISIANA ST # 1600, HOUSTON, TX
  770025227
Phone: 713 381-6500
Web: WWW.EPROD.COM

HISTORICAL FINANCIALS
Company Type: Private

Income Statement				FYE: December 31
	REVENUE ($ mil.)	NET INCOME ($ mil.)	NET PROFIT MARGIN	EMPLOYEES
12/17	659	337	51.1%	3
12/16	628	275	43.9%	—
Annual Growth	5.0%	22.3%	—	—

EQUINOR MARKETING & TRADING (US) INC.

EXECUTIVES

Vice President Human Resources, Shild Larsen
Vice President Legal, Paul Owen
Vice President Business Development, Ase Staupe
Vice President Project Management, Erik Westad
Vice President Project Management, Johnny
  Wollberg
Vice President Internal Communication, Kjell
  Hugvik
Senior Vice President International Exploration,
  Nicholas Maden
Vice President Drilling Americas, Erling Meyer
Vice President Organisational Change, Geir Husoy
Vice President Troll A Tpc34 Project, Karl Ulveseth
Vice President International Gas, Philippe Mathieu
Vice President Operations, Anita Solheim
Vice President Operations, Lars Hier
Vice President Operations, Dag Johnsgaard
Vice President Information Technology, Andreas
  Sollie
Executive Vice President, Arne Nylund
Vp Tax, Tom Geczik
Vice President Drilling And Well Engineering,
  Erik Kirkemo
Auditors: KPMG LLP STAMFORD CONNECTICU

LOCATIONS

HQ: EQUINOR MARKETING & TRADING (US) INC.
  120 LONG RIDGE RD 3E01, STAMFORD, CT
  069021839
Phone: 203 978-6900
Web: WWW.STATOIL.COM

COMPETITORS

Global Partners	Irving Oil Limited
Gulf Oil	Shell Oil
Hess Corporation	Tauber Oil

HISTORICAL FINANCIALS
Company Type: Private

Income Statement				FYE: December 31
	REVENUE ($ mil.)	NET INCOME ($ mil.)	NET PROFIT MARGIN	EMPLOYEES
12/17	9,874	(28)	—	85
12/16	5,984	(259)	—	—
12/15	6,947	(132)	—	—
12/14	12,075	(140)	—	—
Annual Growth	(6.5%)	—	—	—

2017 Year-End Financials
Return on assets: 7.6%   Cash ($ mil.): 46
Return on equity: (-0.3%)
Current ratio: 0.70

EQUINOR NATURAL GAS LLC

EXECUTIVES

Pres, Jan Rune Schoepp
Sec-General Counsel, Charles T O'Brien
Vp-Tax & Asst SEC, Martin J Pastore

Controller, Neil Tarling
Chairman, Tor Martin Anfinnsen
Mgr-Ssu, Gary Aucoin
Mgr-Origination, Teddy Muhlfelder
Cfo, Gary A Turiano
Director, William Maloney
Vice-President, Geir Bjornstad
Auditors: KPMG LLP STAMFORD CONNECTICU

LOCATIONS

HQ: EQUINOR NATURAL GAS LLC
120 LONG RIDGE RD, STAMFORD, CT 069021839
Phone: 203 978-6900
Web: WWW.STATOIL.COM

HISTORICAL FINANCIALS

Company Type: Private

Income Statement — FYE: December 31

	REVENUE ($ mil.)	NET INCOME ($ mil.)	NET PROFIT MARGIN	EMPLOYEES
12/15	1,967	722	36.7%	15
12/13	3,507	(127)	—	—
12/10	1,614	149	9.3%	—
12/08	1,640	168	10.3%	—
Annual Growth	2.6%	23.1%	—	—

2015 Year-End Financials

Return on assets: —
Return on equity: 36.7%
Current ratio: 0.20

Cash ($ mil.): 20

ERIE COUNTY MEDICAL CENTER CORP.

EXECUTIVES

Ceo, Jody L Lomeo
Cfo, Michael J Sammarco
Coo, Richard C Cleland
R V Pres, Ronald Krawiec
R V Pres, Karen Ziemianski
Cfo, Steven Gary
Asst Ceo, Kathleen Gellart
Infectious Diseases, Chiu Bin Hsiao
Emergency Medicine Specialist, Kerry Cassel
Manager, Michael Ott
Network Analyst, Mike Pollack
Auditors: FREEDMAXICK CPAS PC BUFFAL

LOCATIONS

HQ: ERIE COUNTY MEDICAL CENTER CORP.
462 GRIDER ST, BUFFALO, NY 142153098
Phone: 716 898-3000
Web: WWW.ECMC.EDU

HISTORICAL FINANCIALS

Company Type: Private

Income Statement — FYE: December 31

	REVENUE ($ mil.)	NET INCOME ($ mil.)	NET PROFIT MARGIN	EMPLOYEES
12/16	616	1	0.3%	3,300
12/14	514	3	0.6%	—
12/13	467	9	2.0%	—
12/12	425	13	3.1%	—
Annual Growth	9.7%	(37.9%)	—	—

2016 Year-End Financials

Return on assets: 5.2%
Return on equity: 0.3%
Current ratio: 0.70

Cash ($ mil.): 15

ERM-NA HOLDINGS CORP.

EXECUTIVES

Ceo, Charles Leichner
Treas, John Stipa
Auditors: KPMG LLP PHILADELPHIA PA

LOCATIONS

HQ: ERM-NA HOLDINGS CORP.
75 VALLEY STREAM PKWY # 200, MALVERN, PA 193551459
Phone: 484 913-0300

HISTORICAL FINANCIALS

Company Type: Private

Income Statement — FYE: March 31

	REVENUE ($ mil.)	NET INCOME ($ mil.)	NET PROFIT MARGIN	EMPLOYEES
03/18	358	14	4.1%	1,573
03/17	356	10	2.9%	—
03/16	388	10	2.7%	—
03/15	387	18	4.7%	—
Annual Growth	(2.6%)	(7.2%)	—	—

2018 Year-End Financials

Return on assets: 7.2%
Return on equity: 4.1%
Current ratio: 0.70

Cash ($ mil.): 1

ESSENTIA HEALTH

EXECUTIVES

Vice President System Accounting, Traci Morris
Auditors: RSM US LLP MINNEAPOLIS MINNE

LOCATIONS

HQ: ESSENTIA HEALTH
502 E 2ND ST, DULUTH, MN 558051913
Phone: 218 786-8376
Web: WWW.ESSENTIAHEALTH.ORG

PRODUCTS/OPERATIONS

2014 Sales

	$ mil.	% of total
Net patient services	1,685	96
Other operating revenue	69	4
Total	1,754	100

COMPETITORS

Children's Hospital and Health System
Children's Hospitals and Clinics of Minnesota
HCA
HealthEast Care System
Hospital Sisters Health System
Olmsted Medical
Regina Medical

University of Minnesota Medical Center
Wheaton Franciscan Services

HISTORICAL FINANCIALS

Company Type: Private

Income Statement — FYE: June 30

	REVENUE ($ mil.)	NET INCOME ($ mil.)	NET PROFIT MARGIN	EMPLOYEES
06/17	1,990	178	9.0%	14,700
06/13	79	7	9.8%	—
06/11	1,593	153	9.6%	—
Annual Growth	3.8%	2.5%	—	—

2017 Year-End Financials

Return on assets: 1.7%
Return on equity: 9.0%
Current ratio: 0.90

Cash ($ mil.): 23

ESTES EXPRESS LINES, INC.

Founded during the Depression with a Chevy truck Estes Express Lines has grown into a multiregional less-than-truckload (LTL) freight hauler. Its fleet of some 7100 tractors and 25700 trailers operates via a network of some 210 terminals dotting the US. Service in Canada is provided by TST Overland Express an ExpressLINK partner and in Mexico through affiliate Almex. Estes Express works with designated carriers to offer door-to-door delivery in the Caribbean and in Mexico. Subsidiary Estes Forwarding Worldwide services ocean/air freight forwarding. The company is owned and run by the family of founder W.W. Estes.

Operations

The company operates through several divisions and companies. Divisions include Estes Time-Critical (offering four levels of shipping) Level2 Logistics (business-to-business and business-to-consumer shipping) Estes Specialized Truckload and Delivery Services and Estes SureMove (customers load shipments themselves and Estes provides transportation). Companies include Estes Forwarding Worldwide Estes Brokerage Estes Leasing and Big E Transportation.

Geographic Reach

Estes Express offers regional service to all 50 US states. It also offers direct service to Canada Mexico and the Caribbean.

Strategy

Estes Express has continued to build out its LTL business by offering expedited delivery volume truckload transportation supply chain management nationwide brokerage services warehousing services and equipment leasing. The latter has provided such rental services as laundry trucks for the Department of Veterans Affairs. Its slate of services are supported by an upgraded wireless onboard pickup and delivery system featuring real-time data enabling terminals and drivers to process freight more efficiently. It has also formed a Mexico third-party logistics subsidiary Estes Logistica for managing freight consolidation and transportation to points south of the US border.

Estes Express over the years has opened new offices in San Francisco Los Angeles Dallas Chicago Miami and New York. To support the continuing market growth in the Midwest in 2015 it opened a new terminal in Oswego Illinois. The next year it opened an additional terminal in the

Chicago area to replace a smaller facility. The new location is in Markham Illinois and is the seventh terminal the company owns in the state.

Company Background
The company was formed in 1931.

EXECUTIVES

Vice President Human Resources, Tom Donahue
President And Ceo, Rob W. Estes, age 66
President And Ceo Estes Forwarding Worldwide, Scott Fisher
Coo, Billy Hupp
Vp And Chief Information Officer, Bob Fowler
Vice President Sales, Patricia Robinson
Vice President Information Technology, Hugh Canden
Vice President Fleet Services, Mike Palmer
Vice President Pricing, Paul Dugent
Vice President Operations, Jt Johnson
Vice President, Wayne Young

LOCATIONS

HQ: ESTES EXPRESS LINES, INC.
3901 W BROAD ST, RICHMOND, VA 232303962
Phone: 804 353-1900
Web: WWW.ESTES-EXPRESS.COM

PRODUCTS/OPERATIONS

Selected Services
Global (airfreight ocean international consolidation/deconsolidation customs brokerage international freight forwarding)
Less-than-truckload (regional national international/offshore)
Time critical (expedited guaranteed time/date definite)
Volume & truckload (LTL full loads backhaul services truckload brokerage dedicated truckload)

COMPETITORS

AAA Cooper Transportation	R+L Carriers
ArcBest	Ryder System
Averitt Express	Saia
FedEx Freight	UPS Freight
Old Dominion Freight	Vitran
Penske Truck Leasing	YRC Worldwide

HISTORICAL FINANCIALS
Company Type: Private

Income Statement · FYE: December 31

	REVENUE ($ mil.)	NET INCOME ($ mil.)	NET PROFIT MARGIN	EMPLOYEES
12/17	2,731	231	8.5%	14,000
12/16	2,403	128	5.3%	—
12/15	2,367	135	5.7%	—
12/14	2,185	112	5.2%	—
Annual Growth	7.7%	27.0%	—	—

2017 Year-End Financials
Return on assets: 3.8%
Return on equity: 8.5%
Current ratio: 1.40
Cash ($ mil.): 62

ESTRELLA BANNER MEDICAL CENTER

EXECUTIVES

Ceo, Deb Krmpotic
Cfo, Patti Rhoden
Chief Staff, Larry Klein
Director of Patient Relations, Kaaren De Shay
Nursing Director, Nancy Adamson
Director, Salene Slader
Internal Medicine Practitioner, Mir Quadri
Health Professional, Punnaiah Marella
Internal Medicine Practitioner, Sarath Bhimineni
Coordinator, Banner Crocco
Manager, Valerie Martinez

LOCATIONS

HQ: ESTRELLA BANNER MEDICAL CENTER
9201 W THOMAS RD, PHOENIX, AZ 850373332
Phone: 623 327-4000
Web: WWW.BANNERHEALTH.COM

HISTORICAL FINANCIALS
Company Type: Private

Income Statement · FYE: December 31

	REVENUE ($ mil.)	NET INCOME ($ mil.)	NET PROFIT MARGIN	EMPLOYEES
12/17	303	50	16.8%	1,400
12/16	288	42	14.6%	—
12/15	276	38	13.9%	—
12/14	268	36	13.6%	—
Annual Growth	4.2%	11.7%	—	—

2017 Year-End Financials
Return on assets: 1.1%
Return on equity: 16.8%
Current ratio: 2.70
Cash ($ mil.): —

EUGENE WATER & ELECTRIC BOARD

"Power (and water) to the people" is the the belief and practice of Eugene Water & Electric Board (EWEB) the source of power and water for residents and businesses in Eugene Oregon. The utility is one of Oregon's largest municipal utilities. It has more than 89000 electric customers and about 52000 water customers. EWEB generates 110 MW of capacity at its hydroelectric and fossil-fueled power plants; it gets the rest of its power supply from other generators including the Bonneville Power Administration. The utility gets its water supply from the McKenzie River.

Operations
EWEB's electric system serves a 236-square mile area including Eugene and adjacent suburban areas. It gets its power supply from hydroelectric sources from its own generation facilities and via purchases from Bonneville Power Administration.

The utility's water system provides water to Eugene and two water districts. It gets water from the McKenzie River and treats itat the Hayden Bridge Filtration Plant one of the largest treatment plants in Oregon. The water distribution system consists of 26 enclosed reservoirs (total storage capacity — 98.5 million gallons) 31 pump stations and 800 miles of distribution mains.

Financial Performance
The utility reported a 5% increase in revenues in 2013 due to higher sales of electricity and water. The electric system's largest revenue increase was from residential including a higher heating load due to an extreme cold weather event of December 2013. The waste system's revenues increased due to a 20% rate increase and an unusually dry spring and summer which drove up consumption.

EWEB's net income grew by 67% to in 2013 primarily due to higher sales and lower operating costs.

Its operating cash flow increased that year due to a higher net income and a rise in receipts from customers.

Strategy
In 2013 EWEB began a project to install a new water transmission pipe under the Beltline Bridge. The $1.8 million project replaces an exposed 36-inch water transmission pipeline river crossing that runs beneath the Willamette River.

After 50 years of supplying steam heat to customers in downtown Eugene the utility ceased its steam operations in 2012 citing a dwindling customer base and an inefficient and aging steam distribution system.

On the green energy front EWEB offer its customers a number of programs that save energy and water including participation in wind and solar power options and other conservation measures. (EWEB broke ground on its first wind power generation project in 1997).

Company Background
EWEB was founded in 1911 largely in response to a 1906 typhoid fever epidemic in Eugene that was traced to the privately-owned water supply. The Walterville hydroelectric plant on the McKenzie River completed in 1911 enabled the powering of water pumps and street lights.

EXECUTIVES

Board Member, Jeannine Parisi
Auditors: FOR MOSS ADAMS LLP PORTLAND

LOCATIONS

HQ: EUGENE WATER & ELECTRIC BOARD
500 E 4TH AVE, EUGENE, OR 974012465
Phone: 541 685-7000
Web: WWW.EWEB.ORG

COMPETITORS

Avista	Seattle City Light
IDACORP	Xcel Energy
NW Natural	
Portland General Electric	

HISTORICAL FINANCIALS
Company Type: Private

Income Statement · FYE: December 31

	REVENUE ($ mil.)	NET INCOME ($ mil.)	NET PROFIT MARGIN	EMPLOYEES
12/17	294	31	10.7%	460
12/16	284	29	10.4%	—
12/15	276	39	14.4%	—
12/14	292	43	14.7%	—
Annual Growth	0.2%	(9.8%)	—	—

2017 Year-End Financials
Return on assets: —
Return on equity: 10.7%
Current ratio: 2.00
Cash ($ mil.): 39

EVERETT PUBLIC SCHOOLS

EXECUTIVES

Pres, Pam Lesesne
Vice President, Carol Andrews
Deputy Supt, Matt McCauley

Ir, Maryhelen Pierce
Prin, Ted Wenta
Prin, Caroline Mason
Prin, Brittni Burgess
Information Technology Manager, Darla Van Duren
Planning Staff, Darcy Walker
Facilities Specialist, Jill Stoffel
Director, Robert Polk

LOCATIONS

HQ: EVERETT PUBLIC SCHOOLS
   3900 BROADWAY, EVERETT, WA 982015033
Phone: 425 385-4000
Web: WWW.EVERETT.K12.WA.US

HISTORICAL FINANCIALS
Company Type: Private

Income Statement   FYE: August 31

	REVENUE ($ mil.)	NET INCOME ($ mil.)	NET PROFIT MARGIN	EMPLOYEES
08/17	296	53	18.0%	2,500
08/16	271	12	4.4%	—
08/06	168	6	4.0%	—
08/05	168	6	4.0%	—
Annual Growth	4.8%	18.9%	—	—

EVERSOURCE ENERGY SERVICE COMPANY

EXECUTIVES

Vice President Finance Treasurer And Secretary Select Energy Services, Linda A Jensen
Vice President Of Sales, John Serrantino
Vice President Investor Relations Media Contact, Jeffrey Kotkin
Vice President Of Electric Field Operations, Steven Gilkey
Vice President Electric System Operations, Joseph Luchini
Vice President Finance, Michael J Ausere
Vice President Supply Chain Real Estate And Property Management, Ellen Angley
Vice President Gas Operations Engineering Sales M, Zohorsky Paul
Vice President Engineering, Ken Bowes
Vice President Operations, W Edmonson
Executive Board Member, GARY LONG

LOCATIONS

HQ: EVERSOURCE ENERGY SERVICE COMPANY
   56 PROSPECT ST, HARTFORD, CT 061032818
Phone: 860 665-5000
Web: WWW.EVERSOURCE.COM

COMPETITORS

Connecticut Water   PSEG Fossil
Service

HISTORICAL FINANCIALS
Company Type: Private

Income Statement   FYE: December 31

	REVENUE ($ mil.)	NET INCOME ($ mil.)	NET PROFIT MARGIN	EMPLOYEES
12/16	831	11	1.4%	4,550
12/08	5,800	260	4.5%	—
12/07	5,822	246	4.2%	—
12/05	0	0	—	—
Annual Growth	—	—	—	—

2016 Year-End Financials
Return on assets: 13.2%   Cash ($ mil.): 11
Return on equity: 1.4%
Current ratio: —

EXECUTIVE COMMITTEE OF THE SOUTHERN BAPTIST CONVENTION

EXECUTIVES

Pres, D August Boto
Cfo, Wiliam Townes
Auditors: CAPIN CROUSE LLP LAWRENCEVILL

LOCATIONS

HQ: EXECUTIVE COMMITTEE OF THE SOUTHERN BAPTIST CONVENTION
   901 COMMERCE ST STE 750, NASHVILLE, TN 372033600
Phone: 615 244-2355
Web: WWW.SBCLIFE.NET

HISTORICAL FINANCIALS
Company Type: Private

Income Statement   FYE: September 30

	REVENUE ($ mil.)	NET INCOME ($ mil.)	NET PROFIT MARGIN	EMPLOYEES
09/17	390	0	0.1%	29
09/16	8	1	12.6%	—
09/15	7	(0)	—	—
09/14	7	(0)	—	—
Annual Growth	268.7%	—	—	—

2017 Year-End Financials
Return on assets: —   Cash ($ mil.): 8
Return on equity: 0.1%
Current ratio: —

EXPLORER PIPELINE SERVICES COMPANY

EXECUTIVES

Pres, Rodney E Sands
V Pres-Cfo, James Dobson
V Pres-Oprs, Thomas J Jensen
Dir of Eng, Jeffrey A Wenzell
Contrl, J Thomas Angleton
Treas, Carol McNern
Vice President, Tom Jensen
Vice President, Curtis Craig
Cfo, Terry Biehl
Executive Assistant, Katrinia Moss
Project Manager, Brian Dedeke

LOCATIONS

HQ: EXPLORER PIPELINE SERVICES COMPANY
   6120 S YALE AVE STE 1100, TULSA, OK 741364250
Phone: 918 493-5100
Web: WWW.EXPL.COM

HISTORICAL FINANCIALS
Company Type: Private

Income Statement   FYE: December 31

	REVENUE ($ mil.)	NET INCOME ($ mil.)	NET PROFIT MARGIN	EMPLOYEES
12/16	414	144	35.0%	185
12/10	225	57	25.4%	—
12/09	219	53	24.4%	—
12/08	238	41	17.6%	—
Annual Growth	7.2%	16.8%	—	—

2016 Year-End Financials
Return on assets: 12.6%   Cash ($ mil.): 18
Return on equity: 35.0%
Current ratio: 0.20

EXPRESS SERVICES INC

When you need a worker fast Express Services delivers. Operating as Express Employment Professionals the professional staffing company provides work at medium-sized businesses for some 400000 employees each year. It operates on a franchise business model from a network of some 700 employment agency offices across Canada South Africa and the US. In addition to temporary staffing it offers professional search and contract staffing services in the accounting engineering IT sales and marketing and HR sectors. The firm was founded in 1983 by Robert Funk William Stoller and James Gray.

Geographic Reach
Express has offices located in the states of Texas California Oklahoma Tennessee Florida Washington Minnesota Missouri Illinois Georgia Wisconsin and Pennsylvania. It has international offices in Canada and South Africa.

Financial Performance
During 2013 sales jumped 8% to more than $2.5 billion. The growth for 2013 was the result of surging temporary staffing sales as the nation's overall economy recovers. It opened nearly 75 franchise locations during 2013 which contributed to the rise in revenue.

Strategy
Express is focusing on expanding its franchise business. It opened nearly 75 franchise locations in 2013 and 100 new locations in 2014 targeting strategic markets in 30 states and Canada. Key areas for growth include the states of Nevada California and Illinois among others.

EXECUTIVES

Senior Vice President Information Systems, Terry Weldon
Chairman And Ceo, Robert A. Funk
Vice President International Headquarters, Harvey Homsey
Coo, Robert E. (Bob) Fellinger
Svp Sales And Marketing, Cory Benton
Cfo, Tony Bostwick
Vice President Central Zone, Dan Healy
Senior Vice President Of Sales And Marketing I, Purdy Chad
Vice President, Sharon Patric
Vice President Of Business Development, Framme Cyndi
Vice President Of Franchising, David Lewis
Vice President, Jonathan Thom
Vice President Regional Manager, Shawn Spalding
Executive Vice President General Counsel And Secretary, Keith McFall
Vice Chairman, William H. (Bill) Stoller
Auditors: RSM US LLP OKLAHOMA CITY OK

LOCATIONS

HQ: EXPRESS SERVICES INC
9701 BOARDWALK BLVD, OKLAHOMA CITY, OK
731626029
Phone: 405 840-5000
Web: WWW.EXPRESS-SERVICES.COM

PRODUCTS/OPERATIONS

Selected Services
Evaluation and direct hire
Human resource services
Professional contract staffing
Temporary and flexible staffing

Selected Staffing Fields
Express Personnel
    General labor
    Government
    Health care
    Industrial
    Office and clerical
    Scientific
    Technical
Express Professional
    Accounting and financial
    Engineering and manufacturing
    Health care
    Human resources
    Information technology
    Sales and marketing
    Technical

COMPETITORS

ADP TotalSource	Kelly Services
Adecco	ManpowerGroup
Barrett Business	Randstad Holding
Services	Robert Half
Butler America	Volt Information
Insperity	

HISTORICAL FINANCIALS

Company Type: Private

Income Statement · FYE: December 31

	REVENUE ($ mil.)	NET INCOME ($ mil.)	NET PROFIT MARGIN	EMPLOYEES
12/16	2,722	89	3.3%	373,869
12/15	2,648	99	3.7%	—
12/14	0	55	—	—
12/13	0	58	—	—
Annual Growth	—	14.8%	—	—

2016 Year-End Financials

Return on assets: 2.8% Cash ($ mil.): 21
Return on equity: 3.3%
Current ratio: 1.10

FACULTY PRACTICE FOUNDATION INC AND AFFILIATES

EXECUTIVES

Prin, Annmarie Cloonan
Treasurer, Diane Holmes
Auditors: PRICEWATERHOUSECOOPERS LLP BO

LOCATIONS

HQ: FACULTY PRACTICE FOUNDATION INC AND
AFFILIATES
660 HARRISON AVE, BOSTON, MA 021182304
Phone: 617 638-8923
Web: WWW.BMC.ORG

HISTORICAL FINANCIALS

Company Type: Private

Income Statement · FYE: June 30

	REVENUE ($ mil.)	NET INCOME ($ mil.)	NET PROFIT MARGIN	EMPLOYEES
06/15	339	(5)	—	21
06/14	18	4	23.1%	—
06/13	30	17	55.6%	—
06/11	331	(1)	—	—
Annual Growth	0.6%	—	—	—

2015 Year-End Financials

Return on assets: 5.0% Cash ($ mil.): 20
Return on equity: (-1.6%)
Current ratio: —

FAIRFAX COUNTY VIRGINIA

EXECUTIVES

City Exec, Anthony H Griffin
Staff, Mark Young
Manager, Matthew Vaughan
Director of Communications, Stephen Brundage
Business Dir, Angela Shaw
Telecommunications Staff, Alton Drew
Program Manager, Robert Grabowski
Information, Tanya Quinonez
Captain, Roger Arnn
Captain, John Piper
Coordinator, Kelly Bachand
Auditors: KPMG LLP WASHINGTON DC

LOCATIONS

HQ: FAIRFAX COUNTY VIRGINIA
12000 GOVERNMENT STE 214, FAIRFAX, VA 22035
Phone: 703 324-3126
Web: WWW.FAIRFAXCOUNTYEDA.ORG

HISTORICAL FINANCIALS

Company Type: Private

Income Statement · FYE: June 30

	REVENUE ($ mil.)	NET INCOME ($ mil.)	NET PROFIT MARGIN	EMPLOYEES
06/18	4,806	71	1.5%	12,000
06/17	4,695	171	3.6%	—
06/16	4,469	49	1.1%	—
06/15	0	60	—	—
Annual Growth	—	5.8%	—	—

2018 Year-End Financials

Return on assets: 3.1% Cash ($ mil.): 1,364
Return on equity: 1.5%
Current ratio: —

FAIRFIELD COUNTRY RADIOOLOGY A

EXECUTIVES

Prin, Shashi Chaddha
Manager, Amy Kurzatkowski
Bs Pharm Dispensary Coordinato, Christine Toni
Administrative Assistant, Ellen Harry
Admin Assistant, Victoria Montoya
Vice President, Ann Carey
Neuroradiology Specialist, Aparna Singhal
Director of Surgical, Brooke Karlsen
Marketing, Christine Howard
Vice President Finance, Christopher Given
Director of Family Practice, Cosmo Filiberto

LOCATIONS

HQ: FAIRFIELD COUNTRY RADIOLOGY A
2800 MAIN ST, BRIDGEPORT, CT 066064201
Phone: 203 576-5033
Web: WWW.STVINCENTS.ORG

HISTORICAL FINANCIALS

Company Type: Private

Income Statement · FYE: September 30

	REVENUE ($ mil.)	NET INCOME ($ mil.)	NET PROFIT MARGIN	EMPLOYEES
09/16	432	(2)	—	4
09/15	466	(32)	—	—
Annual Growth	(7.2%)	—	—	—

2016 Year-End Financials

Return on assets: 6.4% Cash ($ mil.): 1
Return on equity: (-0.7%)
Current ratio: 1.50

FAIRFIELD MEDICAL CENTER

Fairfield Medical Center is a more than 220-bed acute care hospital serving residents in southeastern and central Ohio. In addition to providing comprehensive medical and surgical care Fairfield Medical Center offers specialty services including cancer cardiovascular women's and children's health and rehabilitation services. The not-for-profit hospital also operates offsite facilities for physician practices as well as specialty diagnostic and laboratory services. The Center employs more than 250 physicians and is served by a number of volunteer organizations which help to support and operate it.

Operations

Fairfield Medical Center handles some 10000 inpatient admissions each year. It also sees about 250000 outpatients and handles 2500 surgeries and 1000 birthing procedures.

Geographic Reach

The hospital serves the Ohio counties of Fairfield Perry Hocking and Athens.

Strategy

Fairfield Medical Center has launched a $38 million facility expansion program called Project BRIGHT (Build Revitalize and Innoate for Greater Health care Tomorrow). Through the project the medical center is adding a new hospital wing with

30 private patient rooms a surgery center and clinical support areas.

To further expand services and reach more patients the hospital is also forming collaborations and making acquisitions.

In 2013 Fairfield Medical Center partnered with New Vision to provide a medical stabilization service for individuals who are undergoing detoxification from drugs and/or alcohol.

That year the Center opened Fairfield Healthcare Professionals Bremen to offer occupational health and primary care services. It also opened the Cancer Resource Center.

In 2012 Fairfield Medical Center expanded its services with the opening of the Emery and Evelyn Williams Graduate Medical Education Resource Center and the Fairfield Medical Heartburn Center.

Mergers and Acquisitions

In 2013 Fairfield Medical Center bought River View Imaging Center and renamed it Fairfield Medical Diagnostic Services at River View.

Company Background

The hospital entered into the convenient clinic market by pairing with Wal-Mart to open a seven-day walk-in clinic called the Clinic at Walmart in Canal Winchester Ohio in 2011. Two more Wal-Mart locations were added in Lancaster and Logan. The clinics offer school physicals immunizations treatment for common illnesses and other minor medical treatments.

On the acquisitions side Fairfield bought River View Surgery Center from a group of physician owners (70%) and Mount Carmel Health System (30%) for $8.5 million also in 2011. The hospital also paid about $1 million that year to buy out what had been a joint venture and gain full ownership of Fairfield Diagnostic Imaging.

Fairfield Medical Center's original hospital dates back to 1916.

EXECUTIVES

Medical Records Director, Cheryl Henney
Medical Director, Michelle Graham

LOCATIONS

HQ: FAIRFIELD MEDICAL CENTER
  401 N EWING ST, LANCASTER, OH 431303371
Phone: 740 687-8000
Web: WWW.FMCHEALTH.ORG

PRODUCTS/OPERATIONS

Selected Centers and Services
Bariatrics
Cancer Care
Emergency Care
Ewing Square Infusion Clinic
Fairfield Healthcare Professionals
Fairfield Medical Diagnostic Services
Heartburn Center
Internal Medicine Clinic
Maternity Care
Orthopedic Care
  Outpatient
Physical Therapy & Rehabilitative Services
River View Surgery Services
Snider Cardiovascular Institute
Southeast Ohio Sleep Disorder Center
Surgery
The Pavilion (Surgery and Medical Office)
Womens Health
Wound Clinic

COMPETITORS

Genesis HealthCare System (Ohio)	Mount Carmel Health Nationwide Children's
Licking Memorial Health Systems	Hospital OhioHealth

HISTORICAL FINANCIALS
Company Type: Private

Income Statement
FYE: December 31

	REVENUE ($ mil.)	NET INCOME ($ mil.)	NET PROFIT MARGIN	EMPLOYEES
12/17	283	14	5.0%	2,200
12/16	278	10	3.6%	—
12/15	255	7	3.1%	—
12/14	239	22	9.3%	—
Annual Growth	5.9%	(14.1%)	—	—

2017 Year-End Financials
Return on assets: 2.4%   Cash ($ mil.): 14
Return on equity: 5.0%
Current ratio: 1.50

FAIRVIEW HEALTH SERVICES

EXECUTIVES

Ceo, Rulon F Stacey
Sr V Pres-Cfo, James M Fox
Sr Vice President, Daniel Fromm
Vice President, Bob Beacher
Exec Vice President, Carolyn Wilson
Manager of Lan, D Ick Neubaur
Director, Roby Thompson Jr
Chief of Emergency Room, Kevin S Meyer
Scientist, Gerald August
Scientist, Scott Crow
Family Practitioner, Kimberly De Roche
Auditors: ERNST & YOUNG LLP MINNEAPOLI

LOCATIONS

HQ: FAIRVIEW HEALTH SERVICES
  2450 RIVERSIDE AVE, MINNEAPOLIS, MN 554541450
Phone: 612 672-6300
Web: WWW.SONUSMETROMKE.COM

COMPETITORS

Abbott Northwestern Hospital	Mayo Clinic North Memorial Health Care
Allina Hospitals	Care
Bethesda Hospital	Park Nicollet Health
Catholic Health Initiatives	Services
CentraCare Health	Regions Hospital
HealthEast Care System	St. John's Hospital (Minnesota)

HISTORICAL FINANCIALS
Company Type: Private

Income Statement
FYE: December 31

	REVENUE ($ mil.)	NET INCOME ($ mil.)	NET PROFIT MARGIN	EMPLOYEES
12/17	5,275	511	9.7%	18,000
12/12	3,218	168	5.2%	—
12/11	2,575	4	0.2%	—
Annual Growth	12.7%	120.0%	—	—

2017 Year-End Financials
Return on assets: 5.7%   Cash ($ mil.): 51
Return on equity: 9.7%
Current ratio: 0.80

FAIRVIEW HOSPITAL

EXECUTIVES

Ceo, Toby Cosgrove
Pres-Ceo, Louis Caravella
President, Delos Cosgrove
Cao, Jeffrey A Leimgruber
Business Manager, Adam Miller

LOCATIONS

HQ: FAIRVIEW HOSPITAL
  18101 LORAIN AVE, CLEVELAND, OH 441115612
Phone: 216 476-7000
Web: WWW.FAIRVIEWHOSPITAL.ORG

HISTORICAL FINANCIALS
Company Type: Private

Income Statement
FYE: December 31

	REVENUE ($ mil.)	NET INCOME ($ mil.)	NET PROFIT MARGIN	EMPLOYEES
12/16	474	150	31.7%	2,364
12/15	426	70	16.6%	—
12/14	411	135	32.8%	—
12/05	0	0	17.1%	—
Annual Growth	91.8%	102.8%	—	—

2016 Year-End Financials
Return on assets: 2.1%   Cash ($ mil.): 5
Return on equity: 31.7%
Current ratio: 1.90

FAITH TECHNOLOGIES, INC.

EXECUTIVES

Executive Vice President, George Van Der Linden
Vice President Supply Chain Management, Dan Siebers
Auditors: GRANT THORNTON LLP MILWAUKEE

LOCATIONS

HQ: FAITH TECHNOLOGIES, INC.
  225 MAIN ST, MENASHA, WI 549523186
Phone: 920 738-1500
Web: WWW.FAITHTECHNOLOGIES.COM

COMPETITORS

Aldridge Electric	Guarantee Electrical
EEI	Sachs Electric
EMCOR	

HISTORICAL FINANCIALS
Company Type: Private

Income Statement
FYE: December 31

	REVENUE ($ mil.)	NET INCOME ($ mil.)	NET PROFIT MARGIN	EMPLOYEES
12/15	425	31	7.5%	2,581
12/12	260	9	3.8%	—
12/11	248	4	1.9%	—
12/10	228	2	1.0%	—
Annual Growth	13.3%	69.0%	—	—

2015 Year-End Financials
Return on assets: 5.0%   Cash ($ mil.): 4
Return on equity: 7.5%
Current ratio: 1.40

FAMILY HEALTH INTERNATIONAL INC

EXECUTIVES

Acting Chief Financial Officer, Rasika Padmaperuma
Auditors: ERNST & YOUNG US LLP TAMPA F

LOCATIONS

HQ: FAMILY HEALTH INTERNATIONAL INC
359 BLACKWELL ST STE 200, DURHAM, NC 277012477
Phone: 919 544-7040
Web: WWW.FHI.ORG

PRODUCTS/OPERATIONS

Selected Services
Behavior-change communication
Capacity-building
Clinical trials services
Creative services
Data analysis
Quality assurance
Research services
Social marketing
Training and technical assistance

HISTORICAL FINANCIALS

Company Type: Private

Income Statement — FYE: September 30

	REVENUE ($ mil.)	NET INCOME ($ mil.)	NET PROFIT MARGIN	EMPLOYEES
09/15	610	(0)	—	4,000
09/14	653	(3)	—	—
09/13	664	10	1.5%	—
09/09	327	2	0.9%	—
Annual Growth	10.9%	—	—	—

2015 Year-End Financials
Return on assets: 11.7%   Cash ($ mil.): 116
Return on equity: (-0.1%)
Current ratio: 1.40

FAMILYCARE, INC.

EXECUTIVES

Pres, Jeff Heatherington
Vice-President Finance, Kevin Clancy
Coordinator, Annmarie Rainford
Project Manager, Joanna Langberg
Manager, Scott Crader
Controller, Anthony Jackson
Chief Compliance Officer, Cheri Pfannes
Coordinator, Jon Chao
Msw, Kevin Dickson
Customer Manager, Stephanie Buxton
Manager, Ashlee Sharp
Auditors: PERKINS & COMPANY PC PORTLAND

LOCATIONS

HQ: FAMILYCARE, INC.
825 NE MULTNOMAH ST # 300, PORTLAND, OR 972322135
Phone: 503 222-2880
Web: WWW.FAMILYCAREINC.ORG

HISTORICAL FINANCIALS

Company Type: Private

Income Statement — FYE: December 31

	REVENUE ($ mil.)	NET INCOME ($ mil.)	NET PROFIT MARGIN	EMPLOYEES
12/16	497	(20)	—	61
12/14	410	73	17.9%	—
12/13	168	14	8.7%	—
Annual Growth	43.4%	—	—	—

2016 Year-End Financials
Return on assets: 27.3%   Cash ($ mil.): 128
Return on equity: (-4.2%)
Current ratio: —

FARM CREDIT BANK OF TEXAS

EXECUTIVES

Vice President, Steve Donnell
Vice President And Controller, Vicki Rodriguez
Vice President, Paul Rudd
Vice President Business Systems Unit Manager, Ed Benson
Vice President, Darren Cannon
Vice President Regional Manager, Chris Amend
Vice President Collateral Risk Management, Brad Swinney
Assistant Vice President Operations, William Foley
Vice President, Ronnie Sellers
Board Member, Larry Fairchild
Auditors: PRICEWATERHOUSECOOPERS LLP AU

LOCATIONS

HQ: FARM CREDIT BANK OF TEXAS
4801 PLAZA ON THE LK # 1200, AUSTIN, TX 787461081
Phone: 512 330-9060
Web: WWW.FARMCREDITBANK.COM

HISTORICAL FINANCIALS

Company Type: Private

Income Statement — FYE: December 31

	ASSETS ($ mil.)	NET INCOME ($ mil.)	INCOME AS % OF ASSETS	EMPLOYEES
12/16	21,222	192	0.9%	200
12/13	16,212	179	1.1%	—
/	0	0	—	—
Annual Growth	—	—	—	—

2016 Year-End Financials
Return on assets: —   Sales ($ mil): 530
Return on equity: 36.2%

FARM CREDIT OF THE VIRGINIAS ACA

EXECUTIVES

Ceo, David Lawrence
Cfo, David Sauer
SEC, Carolyn Hite
Auditors: PRICEWATERHOUSECOOPERS LLP FO

LOCATIONS

HQ: FARM CREDIT OF THE VIRGINIAS ACA
106 SANGERS LN, STAUNTON, VA 244016711
Phone: 540 899-0989

HISTORICAL FINANCIALS

Company Type: Private

Income Statement — FYE: December 31

	ASSETS ($ mil.)	NET INCOME ($ mil.)	INCOME AS % OF ASSETS	EMPLOYEES
12/16	1,858	43	2.3%	142
12/15	1,757	44	2.5%	—
12/14	1,654	50	3.1%	—
12/13	1,560	51	3.3%	—
Annual Growth	6.0%	(5.5%)	—	—

2016 Year-End Financials
Return on assets: 3.0%   Sales ($ mil): 112
Return on equity: 38.3%

FARM CREDIT SERVICES OF AMERICA, PCA

EXECUTIVES

Pres-Ceo, Doug Stark
Exec Vice President, Neil Olsen
Sr V Pres-Cfo, Eugene College
Sr Vice President, Michelle Mapes
Sr Vice President, David Martin
Turner Youth Initiative Direct, Twila Phillips
Auditors: PRICEWATERHOUSECOOPERS LLP M

LOCATIONS

HQ: FARM CREDIT SERVICES OF AMERICA, PCA
5015 S 118TH ST, OMAHA, NE 681372210
Phone: 800 884-3276
Web: WWW.FCSAMERICA.COM

HISTORICAL FINANCIALS

Company Type: Private

Income Statement — FYE: December 31

	ASSETS ($ mil.)	NET INCOME ($ mil.)	INCOME AS % OF ASSETS	EMPLOYEES
12/15	24,772	514	2.1%	10,000
12/04	8,475	294	3.5%	—
12/03	7,633	114	1.5%	—
12/02	0	132	—	—
Annual Growth	—	11.0%	—	—

2015 Year-End Financials
Return on assets: —   Sales ($ mil): 1,099
Return on equity: 46.8%

FARMERS COOPERATIVE SOCIETY

EXECUTIVES

Pres, Marvin Wynia
Vice President, Dave Deboer
SEC, Mark Vermeer
Exec Vice President, Steven T White

Manager, Denis Wolff
Officer, Galen Mars

LOCATIONS

HQ: FARMERS COOPERATIVE SOCIETY
317 3RD ST NW, SIOUX CENTER, IA 512501897
Phone: 712 722-2671
Web: WWW.FARMERSCOOPSOCIETY.COM

COMPETITORS

AGRI Industries	Miles Enterprises
Five Star Co-op	Premier AG Co-Op Inc.
Gold-Eagle Cooperative	Sears
Heartland Co-op	True Value
Home Depot	Wal-Mart
Lowe's	West Central Co-op

HISTORICAL FINANCIALS

Company Type: Private

Income Statement   FYE: July 31

	REVENUE ($ mil.)	NET INCOME ($ mil.)	NET PROFIT MARGIN	EMPLOYEES
07/16	384	8	2.3%	160
07/15	405	7	1.9%	—
07/14	418	3	0.9%	—
07/13	496	4	1.0%	—
Annual Growth	(8.2%)	21.7%	—	—

2016 Year-End Financials

Return on assets: 2.4%   Cash ($ mil.): —
Return on equity: 2.3%
Current ratio: 0.30

FATHER FLANAGAN'S BOYS' HOME

EXECUTIVES

Pres, Steven E Boes
Exec Dir, Rev Steve Boes
SEC, Barbara J Vollmer
Coordinator, Colleen Hurst
Auditing Manager, Julie Mattern
Manager Research L, Barbara Peterson

LOCATIONS

HQ: FATHER FLANAGAN'S BOYS' HOME
14100 CRAWFORD ST, BOYS TOWN, NE 680107520
Phone: 402 498-1111
Web: WWW.BOYSTOWN.ORG

HISTORICAL FINANCIALS

Company Type: Private

Income Statement   FYE: December 31

	REVENUE ($ mil.)	NET INCOME ($ mil.)	NET PROFIT MARGIN	EMPLOYEES
12/16	423	17	4.1%	2,000
12/14	465	(8)	—	—
12/10	393	61	15.7%	—
12/09	398	93	23.4%	—
Annual Growth	0.9%	(21.3%)	—	—

2016 Year-End Financials

Return on assets: 6.7%   Cash ($ mil.): 11
Return on equity: 4.1%
Current ratio: —

FAYETTE COMMUNITY HOSPITAL, INC.

EXECUTIVES

Ceo, James Michael Burnette
Cfo, John Miles
Director, Jeremiah Ellis
Health Professional, Merly Marquez
Internal Medicine Practitioner, Deann Bing
Physical Therapist, Keri Sunvold
Executive Director of Communit, Debbie Britt
Point of Care Coordinator, Michael Quick
Internist, Brandi Jouett
Anesthesiologist, Michael Keats
Chief of Orthopedic Surgery, Peter Harvey
Auditors: KPMG LLP GREENSBORO NC

LOCATIONS

HQ: FAYETTE COMMUNITY HOSPITAL, INC.
1255 HIGHWAY 54 W, FAYETTEVILLE, GA 302144526
Phone: 770 719-7000
Web: WWW.PIEDMONT.ORG/LOCATIONS/PIEDMONT-FAYETTE/PFH-HOME

PRODUCTS/OPERATIONS

Selected Specialties

Anesthesiology
Cardiopulmonary services
Colon and rectal surgery
Dermatology
Emergency medicine
ENT (ear nose and throat)
Family practice
Gastroenterology
General surgery
Hematology
Internal medicine
Nephrology
Neurology
OB/GYN
Oncology
Ophthalmology
Orthopedic surgery
Pathology
Pediatric anesthesiology
Pediatric dentistry
Pediatric neurosurgery
Pediatrics
Plastic surgery
Pulmonology
Radiation oncology
Radiology
Urology
Vascular surgery

Selected Facilities

24-hour Emergency Department
Minor Emergency Care
Outpatient Diagnostic Center
Rehabilitation and Fitness Center
Sleep Order Laboratory
Women's Imaging Center

COMPETITORS

Adventist Health System Sunbelt Healthcare
DeKalb Medical
Emory Healthcare
Grady Health System
Gwinnett Health System
Northside Hospital
Upson Regional Medical Center
WellStar Kennestone Hospital
West Georgia Health System

HISTORICAL FINANCIALS

Company Type: Private

Income Statement   FYE: June 30

	REVENUE ($ mil.)	NET INCOME ($ mil.)	NET PROFIT MARGIN	EMPLOYEES
06/16	349	25	7.4%	1,045
06/14	306	29	9.5%	—
06/13	283	23	8.4%	—
06/09	165	18	11.0%	—
Annual Growth	11.3%	5.1%	—	—

2016 Year-End Financials

Return on assets: 3.3%   Cash ($ mil.): —
Return on equity: 7.4%
Current ratio: 1.30

FAYETTEVILLE PUBLIC WORKS COMMISSION

EXECUTIVES

Secretary Treasurer Ncames, Gail Boggs

LOCATIONS

HQ: FAYETTEVILLE PUBLIC WORKS COMMISSION
955 OLD WILMINGTON RD, FAYETTEVILLE, NC 283016357
Phone: 910 223-4005
Web: WWW.FAYPWC.COM

HISTORICAL FINANCIALS

Company Type: Private

Income Statement   FYE: June 30

	REVENUE ($ mil.)	NET INCOME ($ mil.)	NET PROFIT MARGIN	EMPLOYEES
06/18	334	43	12.9%	467
06/17	313	39	12.6%	—
06/16	311	22	7.2%	—
06/15	308	22	7.2%	—
Annual Growth	2.7%	24.7%	—	—

2018 Year-End Financials

Return on assets: 11.9%   Cash ($ mil.): 11
Return on equity: 12.9%
Current ratio: 0.80

FEDERAL WAY PUBLIC SCHOOLS

EXECUTIVES

Supt, Sally McLean
Supt, Robert Neu
Bus/Finance/Purchasing Directo, Jeri Carlson
Superintendent, Tammy Campbell
Office Manager, Christine Young
Assistant, David Stone
Buyer, Lynn Shore
Education Specialist, Anne Carpio
Payroll Manager, Pam Jacobson
Teacher, Rasa Conklin
Nurse, Teri Gibson
Auditors: TROY KELLEY OLYMPIA WA

LOCATIONS

HQ: FEDERAL WAY PUBLIC SCHOOLS
33330 8TH AVE S, FEDERAL WAY, WA 980036325
Phone: 253 830-6246
Web: WWW.FWPS.ORG

HISTORICAL FINANCIALS

Company Type: Private

Income Statement				FYE: August 31
	REVENUE ($ mil.)	NET INCOME ($ mil.)	NET PROFIT MARGIN	EMPLOYEES
08/17	328	13	4.2%	2,309
08/15	273	10	3.9%	—
08/14	262	11	4.4%	—
08/09	238	11	4.9%	—
Annual Growth	4.1%	2.1%	—	—

2017 Year-End Financials

Return on assets: 2.2% Cash ($ mil.): 71
Return on equity: 4.2%
Current ratio: —

FEDERAL-MOGUL HOLDINGS LLC

Auditors: GRANT THORNTON LLP SOUTHFIELD

LOCATIONS

HQ: FEDERAL-MOGUL HOLDINGS LLC
27300 W 11 MILE RD # 101, SOUTHFIELD, MI
480346193
Phone: 248 354-7700
Web: WWW.FEDERALMOGUL.COM

HISTORICAL FINANCIALS

Company Type: Private

Income Statement				FYE: December 31
	REVENUE ($ mil.)	NET INCOME ($ mil.)	NET PROFIT MARGIN	EMPLOYEES
12/16	7,434	90	1.2%	53,700
12/15	7,419	(104)	—	—
12/14	7,317	(161)	—	—
Annual Growth	0.8%	—	—	—

2016 Year-End Financials

Return on assets: 11.9% Cash ($ mil.): 300
Return on equity: 1.2%
Current ratio: 0.90

FERMI RESEARCH ALLIANCE, LLC

EXECUTIVES

MBR, Pier Oddone
Accounting Staff, Patricia Terra
Auditors: LB CROWE HORWATH LLP CHICAGO

LOCATIONS

HQ: FERMI RESEARCH ALLIANCE, LLC
MS 105 WILSON & KIRK RDS, BATAVIA, IL 60510
Phone: 630 840-3211
Web: WWW.FRA-HQ.ORG

HISTORICAL FINANCIALS

Company Type: Private

Income Statement				FYE: September 30
	REVENUE ($ mil.)	NET INCOME ($ mil.)	NET PROFIT MARGIN	EMPLOYEES
09/15	386	2	0.6%	5
09/14	373	2	0.6%	—
09/10	424	1	0.4%	—
09/08	339	1	0.4%	—
Annual Growth	1.9%	8.9%	—	—

2015 Year-End Financials

Return on assets: — Cash ($ mil.): 1
Return on equity: 0.6%
Current ratio: 8.50

FINCANTIERI MARINE SYSTEMS NORTH AMERICA, INC.

EXECUTIVES

Ceo, Dario Deste
President, Domenico Sorvillo
V Pres-Gen Mgr, Richard Dinsmore
Treas, Paolo Pezzulo
Contrl, Martha Rosbrough
Manager, Pamela Thomas
Human Resources Coordinator, Ashley Morningstar

LOCATIONS

HQ: FINCANTIERI MARINE SYSTEMS NORTH
AMERICA, INC.
800 PRINCIPAL CT STE C, CHESAPEAKE, VA
233203681
Phone: 757 548-6000
Web: WWW.FINCANTIERIMARINESYSTEMS.COM

HISTORICAL FINANCIALS

Company Type: Private

Income Statement				FYE: December 31
	REVENUE ($ mil.)	NET INCOME ($ mil.)	NET PROFIT MARGIN	EMPLOYEES
12/17	35,833	6,670	18.6%	56
12/16	37,567	6,365	16.9%	—
12/14	34,753	2,898	8.3%	—
12/13	0	1,229	—	—
Annual Growth	—	52.6%	—	—

2017 Year-End Financials

Return on assets: 4.2% Cash ($ mil.): 1,877
Return on equity: 18.6%
Current ratio: 1.20

FIRELANDS REGIONAL HEALTH SYSTEM

EXECUTIVES

Ceo, Martin E Tursky
Evp-Cfo, Daniel Moncher
Director of Physical Therapy, Shelly De Lamattere
Co-Chief Staff, Anthony J Minotti
Co-Chief Staff, Christopher E Avendano
Co-Chief Staff, Fredric H Itzkowitz
Nurse, Casey Warner
Director of Physical Therapy, Christopher E Parnell
Office Manager, Donna Robinson
Vascular Surgery, Jeffrey Buehrer
Assistant Vice President Opera, Ryan R Chandler
Auditors: PLANTE & MORAN PLLC COLUMBIA

LOCATIONS

HQ: FIRELANDS REGIONAL HEALTH SYSTEM
1111 HAYES AVE, SANDUSKY, OH 448703323
Phone: 419 557-7400

Selected Counties Served

Firelands Counseling and Recovery Services
Erie
Huron
Lorain
Ottawa
Sandusky
Seneca
Wyandot
Firelands Home Health Services
Erie
Huron
Lorain
Ottawa
Richland
Sandusky
Seneca
Wood
Firelands Regional Medical Center
Erie
Huron
Ottawa
Sandusky

PRODUCTS/OPERATIONS

Selected Services and Facilities

Behavioral health
Cancer Center
Clinics
Corporate health
Endocrine and diabetes
Dialysis Center
Digestive Health Center
Emergency room
Firelands 55+ Club
Healthy Lifestyles
Heart and Vascular Institute
Home health services
Imaging services
Infusion Center
Laboratory services
Maternity/Pediatrics
Pain relief
Pharmacy services
Rehabilitation
Respiratory services
Sleep disorders
Spine Center & Neurosciences
Surgical services
Women's health
Wound care programs

Selected Affiliations

Hospital Networks
Community Care Five (five local independent hospitals
collaborating within the region)

University Hospitals Rainbow Babies & Children's
Hospital (collaboration and pediatric hospitalist
physician staffing agreement)
University Hospitals Seidman Cancer Center
(collaboration and physician staffing agreement)
Teaching and Clinical
BGSU Firelands
Bowling Green State University
Erie Huron Ottawa Vocational Education
Lorain County Community College
Lourdes College (Sylvania Ohio)
Medical University of Ohio - Toledo
Midwestern University College of Osteopathic
Medicine (Glendale Arizona)
Ohio University Heritage College of Osteopathic
Medicine (Athens Ohio)
University of Health Sciences College of Osteopathic
Medicine (Kansas City Missouri)
University of Osteopathic Medicine Health Sciences
(Des Moines Iowa)
Sandusky Career Center
Terra Community College

COMPETITORS

Fairfield Medical	ProMedica
Center	Robinson Memorial
Kindred Healthcare	Hospital
Lake Health	Samaritan Regional
Mercy Health Partners	Health System
Toledo	The Cleveland Clinic
Mount Carmel Health	Toledo Hospital
Nationwide Children's	University Hospitals
Hospital	Health System
OhioHealth	

HISTORICAL FINANCIALS
Company Type: Private

Income Statement   FYE: December 31

	REVENUE ($ mil.)	NET INCOME ($ mil.)	NET PROFIT MARGIN	EMPLOYEES
12/17	285	27	9.6%	1,635
12/16	0	0	4383.8%	—
12/15	0	0	15.6%	—
12/12	200	36	18.1%	—
Annual Growth	7.3%	(5.5%)	—	—

2017 Year-End Financials
Return on assets: 2.4%
Return on equity: 9.6%
Current ratio: 1.60
Cash ($ mil.): 15

FIRST AMERICAN TRUST COMPANY

EXECUTIVES

Chm-Ceo, Thomas M Kelley
SEC, Pat Lucado
Sr V Pres-Cfo, Teri Pierce
Sr V Pres-Coo, Kelly Dudley
Sr V Pres Personal Trust, Darliene Evans
V Pres Corporate Council, Dimetria Jackson
Exec V Pres, Robert Daniel Banis
Evp-Chief Fiduciary Officer, Eric R McMullen
Vp-Wealth Management, Mark Monaco
Vice-President, Michael Hinkle
Customer, Barbara Boomgarden
Auditors: PRICEWATERHOUSECOOPERS LLP O

LOCATIONS

HQ: FIRST AMERICAN TRUST COMPANY
5 FIRST AMERICAN WAY, SANTA ANA, CA 927075913
Phone: 714 560-7856
Web: WWW.FIRSTAMTRUST.COM

HISTORICAL FINANCIALS
Company Type: Private

Income Statement   FYE: December 31

	ASSETS ($ mil.)	NET INCOME ($ mil.)	INCOME AS % OF ASSETS	EMPLOYEES
12/17	3,431	27	0.8%	106
12/16	3,124	29	0.9%	—
12/15	2,982	24	0.8%	—
12/14	2,627	18	0.7%	—
Annual Growth	9.3%	13.7%	—	—

2017 Year-End Financials
Return on assets: —
Return on equity: 33.4%
Sales ($ mil.): 82

FIRSTHEALTH OF THE CAROLINAS, INC.

FirstHealth of the Carolinas maintains a health care network that extends to 15 counties across the mid-Carolinas. The health network includes four hospitals — Moore Regional Richmond Memorial Moore Regional - Hoke and Montgomery Memorial — that provide emergency surgical acute care and diagnostic services and have a combined capacity of more than 580 beds. Moore Regional its largest hospital includes an inpatient rehabilitation center and a heart hospital. FirstHealth of the Carolinas also operates satellite facilities including family practice clinics fitness centers and dental practices. The system's FirstCarolinaCare provides home health and hospice services emergency care medical transportation and health insurance.

Operations
In addition to its four hospitals the network includes the Reid Heart Center a rehabilitation center three sleep disorders centers three dental clinics a dozen family medicine clinics five fitness centers four charitable foundations a Hospice program home health services and EMS.

The health care network offers major medical and surgical specialties and subspecialties such as open-heart surgery bariatric weight-loss surgery neurosurgery and neonatology. To provide these specialties FirstHealth maintains an active medical staff of 320 of which 95% are board certified.

Geographic Reach
FirstHealth serves those who reside in a 15-county region of the mid-Carolinas. Altogether it operates nearly 62 locations across North Carolina.

Financial Performance
The not-for-profit took in about 8% more in revenue for 2013 when it rose to $565 from $524 the previous year.

Strategy
Despite the downturn in the economy in recent years the health system worked to maintain its expansion efforts to meet the demand of area residents. On the Moore Regional campus it opened the 60-bed Reid Heart Hospital a cardiology and neurology facility in 2011.

In Hoke County FirstHealth built a medical campus consisting of an urgent care center diagnostic facilities and physician offices along with a new 65-bed acute care hospital in the area. Moore Regional - Hoke the county's first hospital began serving patients in 2013.

FirstHealth had been participating in a 50/50 joint venture with the University of North Carolina

Healthcare System to run Sanford Hematology and Oncology. In 2013 it purchased full ownership of the facility.

EXECUTIVES

Vice President Telecommunications, Wanda Hardister
Medical Director, Steven J Filby
Nursing Director, Cheryl Batchelor
Vice President Finance, Mark Rush
Occupational Therapy Director, Linda Deyoung
Vice President Human Resources, Biediger Daniel
Vice President Finance, Marty Ryan
Clinical Director, Cynthia S Ward
Vice President Quality, Cindy McDonald

LOCATIONS

HQ: FIRSTHEALTH OF THE CAROLINAS, INC.
155 MEMORIAL DR, PINEHURST, NC 283748710
Phone: 910 715-1000
Web: WWW.FIRSTHEALTH.ORG

PRODUCTS/OPERATIONS

2013 Sales

	% of total
Net patient service revenue	81
Net assets released from restrictions used for operations	18
other	1
Total	**100**

Selected Facilities
Montgomery Memorial Hospital (Troy North Carolina)
Moore Regional Hospital (Pinehurst North Carolina)
Moore Regional Hospital (Hoke North Carolina)
Richmond Memorial Hospital (Rockingham North Carolina)

COMPETITORS

Alamance Regional	Morehead Memorial
Medical Center	Hospital
Carolinas HealthCare	Novant Health
System	Rex Healthcare
Cone Health	Stanly Medical Center
Cumberland County	UNC Hospitals
Hospital System	Vidant Health
Duke University Health	WakeMed
System	

HISTORICAL FINANCIALS
Company Type: Private

Income Statement   FYE: September 30

	REVENUE ($ mil.)	NET INCOME ($ mil.)	NET PROFIT MARGIN	EMPLOYEES
09/18	747	43	5.9%	3,897
09/17	744	81	11.0%	—
09/16	695	59	8.5%	—
09/15	652	45	7.0%	—
Annual Growth	4.6%	(1.1%)	—	—

2018 Year-End Financials
Return on assets: 3.0%
Return on equity: 5.9%
Current ratio: 1.50
Cash ($ mil.): 40

FLAGSTAFF MEDICAL CENTER, INC.

Flagstaff Medical Center serves northern Arizona's residents and those who are just passing through. Founded in 1936 the not-for-profit hospital is part of the Northern Arizona Healthcare family. It has some 270 beds and its medical staff includes about 210 physicians. The hospital offers cancer heart sports medicine joint surgery and women and infants' centers. Other medical services include behavioral health audiology diabetes care home health hospice and ambulance and air flight transportation. In addition Flagstaff Medical Center provides training courses for health care professionals. The hospital's emergency department treats about 40000 patients each year.

Operations

Flagstaff Medical Center boasts a regional trauma center open-heart surgery high-tech imaging a cancer center surgical services orthopedic services and women's infants' and children's services. Altogether the medical facility each year logs more than 13000 inpatient hospital visits some 68500 outpatient visits and about 40000 emergency department visits. Flagstaff Medical Center is responsible for birthing about 1300 babies annually.

Through the Guardian Medical Transport division's 15 fully-equipped ambulances the medical center provides emergency medical services and non-emergent transports around the clock.

Geographic Reach

Based in Flagstaff the medical center provides services to the communities of northern Arizona. Its Guardian Medical Transport division serves more than 6200 square miles across the northern part of the state.

Strategy

To maintain and improve its level of service Flagstaff Medical Center has expanded its operations in recent years.

In 2014 Flagstaff Medical Center received a $129412 grant award from the US Department of Agriculture Rural Development office's Distance Learning and Telemedicine Loan and Grant Program.

Company Background

It opened a new outpatient Supportive Care Clinic in 2012 to provide care support and resources to patients living with a chronic or life-threatening illness. The medical center also spent the year renovating and expanding its Emergency Department to provide better customer service and faster care to its patients.

Flagstaff Medical Center has also partnered with technology companies to roll out wireless services for monitoring its patients' health. Through a new program launched in 2012 the center extends care of patients beyond the walls of the hospital or physician's office. Care Beyond Walls and Wires rolled out in collaboration with Qualcomm Incorporated (through its Wireless Reach initiative) Zephyr Technology Verizon Wireless and the National Institutes of Health. Care Beyond Walls and Wires uses advanced 3G wireless technology and health-monitoring devices to enhance the care of patients with congestive heart failure or other related conditions.

EXECUTIVES

Vice President Communications And Invest, Michelle Musich
Secretary Treasurer, Chris Bavasi
Auditors: ERNST & YOUNG US LLP PHOENIX

LOCATIONS

HQ: FLAGSTAFF MEDICAL CENTER, INC.
 1200 N BEAVER ST, FLAGSTAFF, AZ 860013118
Phone: 928 779-3366
Web: WWW.FLAGSTAFFMEDICALCENTER.COM

PRODUCTS/OPERATIONS

Selected Services
Audiology
Neurodiagnostic Services

Bariatric Surgical Weight Loss Center
Northern Arizona Homecare
Behavioral Health Services
Northern Arizona Hospice
Bereavement Services
Nutrition Therapy
 Cancer Cen
Occupational Therapy
Care Coordination/Disease Management
Patient Registration
Children's Health Center
Pediatrics
Complementary Services
Pharmacy Services
da Vinci Surgical System
Physical Therapy
Diabetes Education & Management
Renal Services
Education
Safe Child Center
Emergency Services
Security Services
Fit Kids of Arizona
Speech Therapy
FMC Foundation
Spine & Joint Surgery Center
Guardian Air
Sports Medicine
Guardian Medical Transport
Surgical Services
Heart & Vascular Care
Taylor House
Heart and Vascular Center of Northern Arizona
Team Health
Imaging/Radiology
Telemedicine
Infectious Disease
Therapy Services
Intensive Care Unit
Trauma Services
Laboratory and Blood Bank
Volunteer Services
Library Services
Women & Infants' Center
Massage Therapy

COMPETITORS

Banner Health
 Community Health
  Systems
Dignity Health
John C. Lincoln Health
 Network
Mayo Clinic

Phoenix Children's
 Hospital
Scottsdale Healthcare
University of Arizona
 Health Network
Yuma Regional Medical
 Center

HISTORICAL FINANCIALS

Company Type: Private

Income Statement   FYE: June 30

	REVENUE ($ mil.)	NET INCOME ($ mil.)	NET PROFIT MARGIN	EMPLOYEES
06/16	415	55	13.3%	2,000
06/15	389	53	13.8%	—
06/09	358	0		—
Annual Growth	2.2%	—	—	—

2016 Year-End Financials

Return on assets: 2.5%   Cash ($ mil.): 33
Return on equity: 13.3%
Current ratio: 2.50

FLEMING GANNETT INC

Engineering firm Gannett Fleming has waded through water waste and sludge for nearly a century. Gannett Fleming operates through more than a dozen subsidiaries that offer a variety of services that range from design/build construction management ground testing and soil strengthening site

remediation structural rehabilitation electrical and mechanical installation geophysical mapping and surveying and 3D visualization. Founded in 1915 Gannett Fleming serves the transportation water and wastewater facilities energy and environmental industries working on projects around the world from more than 60 offices across North America and Middle East.

Operations

While the firm is heavily involved in traffic and transportation projects its water and wastewater infrastructure work is perhaps its hallmark. Gannett Fleming has worked on hundreds of treatment plants and pumping stations in addition to thousands of miles of water and sewer systems. Over the past decade Gannett Fleming has designed more than 200 new and renovated dams and has offered its construction management and inspection services for projects with a total construction cost of more than $4 billion.

The company's long list of services has helped it endure dips in the economy. Its 25 lines of business include information technology transportation environmental resources facilities dams and hydraulics site development and construction management services.

Gannett Fleming's design practice GeoDecisions develops master plans for highways railroads bridges and airports. It also designs new dams and modifications on those needing repair.

Geographic Reach

Gannett Fleming has more than 60 offices has offices in the US Canada Mexico Qatar and the United Arab Emirates. It has been involved in infrastructure and community improvement work in more than 65 countries.

Sales and Marketing

Gannett Fleming serves both the private and public sectors on projects throughout the US and abroad. Some of its clients have included JEA Washington Suburban Sanitary Commission the City of Baltimore New Jersey Department of Transportation Michigan Department of Environmental Quality the U.S. Army Corps of Engineers and Chevron.

Strategy

Gannett Flemming has made a series of office relocations to be closer to its clients and project work in recent years. In 2014 the company relocated its office in Milwaukee Wisconsin as part of its partnership with Chicago-based MPR Engineering Corp which specializes in water wastewater and water reclamation and reuse services with the goal of supporting the growing water-related business and research happening in the Midwestern region. That year it also moved its Michigan operations in Detroit to Ann Arbor and moved its San Francisco Bay operations in California from Mill Valley to San Bruno.

The company has also enriched its service offerings and broadened its geographic reach over the past few years through strategic acquisitions. In late 2014 Gannett Fleming bought Pennsylvania-based contractor Innovative Engineering which expanded its electrical engineering procurement and turnkey-construction service offerings. In early 2013 the firm purchased Griffin Engineering and Technical Services to extend its reach into a key research region of North Carolina broaden its HVAC system solution offerings and move it more into the biotech pharma and healthcare markets.

Mergers and Acquisitions

In August 2014 Gannett Fleming acquired electrical design-build contractor Innovative Engineering (doing business as IETC) to expand its electrical engineering procurement and turnkey-construction service offerings.

In January 2013 Gannett Fleming acquired Griffin Engineering and Technical Services which was added to its mechanical and electrical practices group. The purchase expands Gannett Fleming's presence in the Research Triangle region of North Carolina and its testing adjusting and balancing of HVAC systems which increases its reach into the biotech pharmaceutical and healthcare fields.

EXECUTIVES

Vice President And Senior Associate, Judy Hricak
Vice President, Eric E Rensel
Vice President, Mark Pilwallis
Executive Vice President; Board Of Director; Regional Director, Paul Nowicki
Vice President, Terry Snow
Vp Human Resources, Roderick Savidge
Auditors: STAMBAUGH NESS PC HANOVER P

LOCATIONS

HQ: FLEMING GANNETT INC
207 SENATE AVE, CAMP HILL, PA 170112316
Phone: 717 763-7211
Web: WWW.GANNETTFLEMING.COM

PRODUCTS/OPERATIONS

Selected Services
Construction Management
  Bridges
  Commissioning Services
  Dams
  Facilities
  Roads and Highways
  Transit and Rail
  Water/Wastewater
Dams & Hydraulics
  Dam Investigations/Inspections
  Design
  Emergency Response Planning
  Hydrologic and Hydraulic Modeling
  Permitting
Environmental Resources
  Environmental Management
  Industrial Waste Management
  Oil and Gas Services
  Site Investigation and Remediation
  Solid Waste Management
  Water/Wastewater
Facilities
  Architectural
  Electrical
  Elevators and Escalators
  Facilities Management
  Healthcare Regulatory Compliance
  Industrial Process
  Information and Controls
  Mechanical
  Security Services
  Structural
GeoDecisions
  Application Design and Development
  Geographic Information Systems Mapping Analysis and Engineering Support
  Transportation Operations/ITS/Traffic
  Web Services
Geotechnical/Earth Sciences
  Earth Structures
  Foundations
  Geophysics
  Geotechnical Laboratory Services
  Ground Modification
  Groundwater and Hydrogeology
  Site Evaluation
Information Technology
  3D Building Information Modeling (BIM)
  3D Visualization and CADD
  Certified Training
  Digital Printing
  Graphics and Multimedia Design
  IT Services
  Reprographics
Planning
  Community
  Environmental
  Municipal Waste and Recycling
  Transportation
Site Development
  Bid/Construction Phase Services
  Drainage/Stormwater Management
  Environmental/Subsurface Investigations
  Green Design
  Land Development/Subdivision Plans
  Landscape Architecture
  Permitting/Agency Coordination
  Planning
  Traffic/Parking Studies
  Site/Roadway Designs
  Surveys
  Water and Sewer Systems
Sustainability
  Energy
  Facilities
  Industrial/Private
  Military
  Public/Government Agencies
  Technology
  Transportation
  Water Supply
Transportation
  Airports
  Bridges
  Highways
  Transit/Rail
  Transportation Operations/ITS/Traffic

Selected Subsidiaries & Affiliates

GANCOM (reprographics digital printing and graphic design)
Ganflec Architects & Engineers Inc. (general architectural and engineering design)
Gannett Fleming Pharmaceutical & Biotechnology Services (design and construction services on pharmaceutical and biotechnology facilities)
Gannett Fleming Project Development Corp. (design and construction management on commercial and industrial facilities)
Gannett Fleming Transit & Rail Systems (design and construction management on railway and rail transit systems)
Gannett Fleming Valuation and Rate Division (consulting to public utilities and railroads)
Gannett Fleming Williams Geotechnical Group (geotechnical engineering quality control testing construction inspection)
GeoDecisions (computerized mapping and database management services)
IT Services Division (computer consulting)
L.G. Hetager Drilling (exploratory drilling and testing services)
TerraSure (real estate remediation)
Vertical Transportation Excellence (consulting on elevator escalator moving walks material handling design and other specialty services)

COMPETITORS

AECOM	K&M Engineering and
Bechtel	Consulting
Black & Veatch Ltd.	Louis Berger
CH2M HILL	MWH Global
Jacobs Engineering	Parsons Brinckerhoff

HISTORICAL FINANCIALS

Company Type: Private

Income Statement   FYE: December 31

	REVENUE ($ mil.)	NET INCOME ($ mil.)	NET PROFIT MARGIN	EMPLOYEES
12/16	375	10	2.8%	1,743
12/13	309	7	2.3%	—
12/11	286	4	1.6%	—
12/10	287	2	0.8%	—
Annual Growth	4.5%	28.5%	—	—

2016 Year-End Financials

Return on assets: 5.6%   Cash ($ mil.): 10
Return on equity: 2.8%
Current ratio: 2.20

FLORIDA ATLANTIC UNIVERSITY

Who gives a hoot about tertiary education in Southeast Florida? About 30000 "owls" enrolled at Florida Atlantic University (FAU) do. The Southeast Florida university's colleges offer more than 170 undergraduate and graduate degree programs in a range of academic fields including architecture liberal arts education nursing science and engineering. The university has about a half-dozen locations in Boca Raton Ft. Lauderdale Port St. Lucie Dania Beach Jupiter Fort Pierce and Davie. FAU has a student to faculty ratio of 30:1

Financial Performance
The university's revenues decreased 8% in fiscal year 2013 mainly due to increased enrollments as well as higher tuition and fees. Though revenue improved costs rose as well and FAU's total assets are now at $1 billion which is down just a bit from 2012.

Strategy
The university focuses on the rapid development of marine and coastal issues biotechnology and contemporary societal challenges which provide opportunities for faculty and students to build upon FAU's existing strengths in research and scholarship.

In late 2014 the school received its largest donation ever $16 million from The Schmidt Family Foundation and is using that to build The Schmidt Family Complex for Academic and Athletic Excellence.

Company Background
FAU was established in 1964 as an institution solely serving upper-division and graduate students; it allowed its first freshman class 20 years later.

EXECUTIVES

Senior Vice President For Financial Affairs, Dorothy Russell
Vice President And General Counsel, David Kian
Vice President For Public Affairs, Peter Hull
Assistant Vice President, Joanne Davis
Vice President For Student Affairs, Corey King
Vice President I, Bilal Asaad
Assistant Vice President, Scott Silversten
Vice President Research Private Other Grts, Julie Walls-Honeycutt
Vice President Student Affairs Jupiter, Stacey Edens
Vice President For Strategic Planning, Ye Wu
Pharmacy Manager, Carline Applys
Associate Vice President For Research, Karin Scarpinato
Delta Sigma Pi Vice President, Gabriela Heizer
Vice President Of Operations, Sam Nimah
Vice President Business Strategy, Stuart Halberg
Vice President Of Public Relations, Courtney Crawford
Associate Vice President For Student Affairs, Andrea Oliver
Assistant Vice President, Meghan Deford
Assistant Vice President Media Relations And Public Affairs, Joshua D Glanzer
Executive Board Member, Ben Klein
Secretary, Mike Andrews

LOCATIONS

HQ: FLORIDA ATLANTIC UNIVERSITY
777 GLADES RD, BOCA RATON, FL 334316496
Phone: 561 297-3000
Web: WWW.FAU.EDU

COMPETITORS

Florida State	Miami University
University	University of Miami

HISTORICAL FINANCIALS

Company Type: Private

Income Statement   FYE: June 30

	REVENUE ($ mil.)	NET INCOME ($ mil.)	NET PROFIT MARGIN	EMPLOYEES
06/17	282	(1)		3,053
06/11	233	65	28.1%	—
Annual Growth	3.2%	—	—	—

2017 Year-End Financials

Return on assets: 3.0%
Return on equity: (-0.6%)
Current ratio: 0.60
Cash ($ mil.): 13

FLORIDA CLINICAL PRACTICE ASSOCIATION, INC.

EXECUTIVES

Pres, Anthony Mancuso
Exec V Pres, William W Tharp
Information Technology Manager, Aaron Weldon
Director, Stephanie Smith

LOCATIONS

HQ: FLORIDA CLINICAL PRACTICE ASSOCIATION, INC.
1329 SW 16TH ST STE 4250, GAINESVILLE, FL 326081128
Phone: 352 265-8017
Web: WWW.SHANDS.UFL.EDU

HISTORICAL FINANCIALS

Company Type: Private

Income Statement   FYE: June 30

	REVENUE ($ mil.)	NET INCOME ($ mil.)	NET PROFIT MARGIN	EMPLOYEES
06/17	642	(1)	—	2
06/15	598	19	3.3%	—
06/13	419	2	0.5%	—
06/12	360	(11)	—	—
Annual Growth	12.3%	—	—	—

2017 Year-End Financials

Return on assets: 2.1%
Return on equity: (-0.2%)
Current ratio: 8.80
Cash ($ mil.): 82

FLORIDA GAS TRANSMISSION COMPANY, LLC

Florida Gas Transmission gasses up the Gulf Coast. The company transports natural gas to cogeneration facilities electric utilities independent power producers municipal generators and local distribution companies through a 5400-mile natural gas pipeline extending from south Texas to south Florida. It delivers 3.1 billion cu. ft. of natural gas a day to more than 250 delivery points consisting of more than 50 natural gas-fired electric generation facilities. Florida Gas Transmission is operated by Citrus Corp. which is a joint venture of Energy Transfer Partners and Kinder Morgan.

Operations

Florida Gas Transmission is the primary transporter of natural gas to the Florida energy market delivering more than 64% of the natural gas consumed by Floridians. The pipeline system operates and maintains more than 70 interconnects with major interstate and intrastate natural gas pipelines.

Geographic Reach

Florida Gas Transmission's pipeline system receives natural gas from producing basins in Louisiana and along the Texas Gulf Coast Mobile Bay and offshore in the Gulf of Mexico and transports it to markets in Florida.

Strategy

In 2013 the Florida Public Service Commission approved Florida Power & Light's contracts for a $3.5 billion 600-mile pipeline system. The project due for completion in 2017 will connect Florida's two existing pipelines the larger one owned by Florida Gas Transmission and the other by Gulfstream Natural Gas System LLC.

Upping its pipeline investment in 2012 Kinder Morgan invested about $2 billion in Citrus Corp.

Company Background

In 2008 Florida Power & Light agreed to contract for half the capacity of a $2 billion expansion of a natural-gas pipeline.

EXECUTIVES

Vice President Technical Services, Eric Amundsen
Vice President Accounting, Mary Simon
Vice President Market Services, Brad Holmes

LOCATIONS

HQ: FLORIDA GAS TRANSMISSION COMPANY, LLC
1300 MAIN ST, HOUSTON, TX 770026803
Phone: 713 989-7000

COMPETITORS

Columbia Gulf	Gulf South Pipeline
Transmission	Texas Gas Transmission
Enable Oklahoma	Williams Gas Pipeline

HISTORICAL FINANCIALS

Company Type: Private

Income Statement   FYE: December 31

	REVENUE ($ mil.)	NET INCOME ($ mil.)	NET PROFIT MARGIN	EMPLOYEES
12/17	839	247	29.5%	450
12/16	829	238	28.7%	—
/ 0	0	0	—	—
Annual Growth	—	—	—	—

FLORIDA HEALTH SCIENCES CENTER INC

Florida Health Sciences Center which does business as Tampa General Hospital (TGH) provides health care services in west-central Florida. The medical center offers general medical and surgical care as well as tertiary offerings including a Level 1 trauma center a burn unit a pediatric ward women's and cardiovascular centers and an organ transplant unit. The not-for-profit hospital has more than 1000 acute-care beds as well as 60 beds in its rehabilitation unit which specializes in helping patients recover from stroke head or spine trauma and other neuromuscular conditions. TGH is the primary teaching hospital for The University of South Florida College of Medicine.

Operations

TGH division Tampa General Medical Group (TGMG) is a multispecialty physician group with locations in Florida's Hillsborough and Pasco counties. Specialties include family practice internal medicine transplant cardiology endocrinology hepatology nephrology and surgery.

Geographic Reach

One of the largest employers in the Tampa Bay region TGH employs about 6300 workers. It also conducts research and operates community care centers in the Tampa area.

Each year TGH treats more than 91000 patients in its emergency department. This includes pediatric chest pain minor emergency and trauma center patients. The hospital also operates a regional helicopter medical transport program.

Strategy

TGH has added new wing to the hospital to expand patient capacity. TGH has added a new emergency/trauma center as well as cardiovascular diagnostic neurology and women's health units.

The hospital also works to stay on top of the latest medical advances. For example in 2014 TGH acquired the ThermoCool SmartTouch catheter a recently launched high-tech device that helps physicians control the amount of contact force applied to the heart wall during treatments for atrial fibrillation.

EXECUTIVES

Evp Cfo, Steve Short
Evp And Coo, Deana L. Nelson
Svp And Chief Medical Officer, Sally H. Houston
Chief Technology Officer, Balaji Ramadoss
Ceo, James R. Burkhart
Executive Vice President Chief Academic Officer, Charles J. Lockwood
Director Of Patient Relations, Joanna Singleton
Senior Vice President Finance, Judy Ploszek
Senior Vice President Compliance Legal And Risk Management, Jonathan Dixon
Chairman, David A. Straz
Secretary Unit Management, Linda Starkey
Treas, Dee Richardson

LOCATIONS

HQ: FLORIDA HEALTH SCIENCES CENTER INC
1 TAMPA GENERAL CIR, TAMPA, FL 336063571
Phone: 813 844-7000
Web: WWW.TGH.ORG

COMPETITORS

All Children's	Lakeland Regional
Hospital	Medical Center
BayCare Health System	Lee Memorial
Bayfront Health	Manatee Memorial
DeSoto Memorial	Hospital
Florida Hospital Tampa	Sarasota Memorial
Bay Division	Health Care
HCA	Winter Haven Hospital

HISTORICAL FINANCIALS
Company Type: Private

Income Statement
FYE: September 30

	REVENUE ($ mil.)	NET INCOME ($ mil.)	NET PROFIT MARGIN	EMPLOYEES
09/17	1,257	98	7.8%	8,000
09/16	1,055	80	7.6%	—
09/14	1,127	98	8.7%	—
Annual Growth	3.7%	(0.0%)	—	—

2017 Year-End Financials
Return on assets: 9.5% Cash ($ mil.): 129
Return on equity: 7.8%
Current ratio: 0.90

FLORIDA HOSPITAL MEDICAL GROUP, INC.

EXECUTIVES

Pres, Terry Owen
President, Bryan Stiltz
Dir, Lamvu Georgine
Dir, Lay Kevin
Plastic Surgeon, Jason Junker
Marketing Manager, Brian Ahearn
Diagnostic Radiologist, Darren Transue
Customer Experience Director, Zorayma Barnard
Management, Joann McCullough
Administrative Vice President, Scott Hill

LOCATIONS

HQ: FLORIDA HOSPITAL MEDICAL GROUP, INC.
2600 WESTHALL LN STE 400, MAITLAND, FL
327517107
Phone: 407 200-2700
Web: WWW.FPMG.COM

HISTORICAL FINANCIALS
Company Type: Private

Income Statement
FYE: December 31

	REVENUE ($ mil.)	NET INCOME ($ mil.)	NET PROFIT MARGIN	EMPLOYEES
12/15	421	0	0.2%	350
12/14	363	(17)	—	—
12/08	177	0	—	—
Annual Growth	13.1%	—	—	—

2015 Year-End Financials
Return on assets: 8.6% Cash ($ mil.): 1
Return on equity: 0.2%
Current ratio: 1.00

FLORIDA HOUSING FINANCE CORP

EXECUTIVES

Exec Dir, Stephen Auger
Executive Officer, Vicki Robinson
Auditors: ERNST & YOUNG LLP ORLANDO FL

LOCATIONS

HQ: FLORIDA HOUSING FINANCE CORP
227 N BRONOUGH ST # 5000, TALLAHASSEE, FL
323011367
Phone: 850 488-4197
Web: WWW.FLORIDAHOUSING.ORG

PRODUCTS/OPERATIONS

Selected Programs
First Time Homebuyer Program
Down Payment Assistance
Homeownership Loan Program
Mortgage Credit Certificate
Multifamily Development Programs
Multifamily Mortgage Revenue Bonds
Florida Affordable Housing Guarantee Program
HOME Investment Partnerships
Elderly Housing Community Loan Program
Low Income Housing Tax Credits
State Apartment Incentive Loan
Predevelopment Loan Program
State Housing Initiative Partnerships
Demonstration Loans
Affordable Housing Catalyst Program

HISTORICAL FINANCIALS
Company Type: Private

Income Statement
FYE: December 31

	ASSETS ($ mil.)	NET INCOME ($ mil.)	INCOME AS % OF ASSETS	EMPLOYEES
12/17	4,764	206	4.3%	130
12/16	4,567	141	3.1%	—
12/14	5,079	23	0.5%	—
12/12	5,721	0	—	—
Annual Growth	(3.6%)	—	—	—

2017 Year-End Financials
Return on assets: 46.5% Sales ($ mil): 186
Return on equity: 111.2%

FLORIDA MUNICIPAL POWER AGENCY

Unlike some politicians Florida Municipal Power Agency (FMPA) doesn't believe in holding on to power. The non-profit public agency generates and supplies electric power to 31 county or municipally owned distribution utilities which in turn serve 2 million Florida residents and businesses. Each of the distribution utilities appoints one representative to FMPA's board of directors which governs the Agency's activities. The Agency is authorized to undertake joint power supply projects for its members and to issue tax-exempt bonds to finance the costs of such projects. It is also empowered to implement a pooled financing program for utility-related projects.

Operations
FMPA has five distinct power supply projects and has stakes in 15 operating power plants. Each of its members have the option of whether or not to participate in a power supply project. Some members receive all their power from FMPA some receive part of their power and others receive no power. Agency members may participate in more than one project although each project is independent from the others.

FMPA supplies all of the power needs for 13 of its members and some of the power supply needs of seven others. All together FMPA supplies more than 40% of its members' total power needs.

Strategy
The Agency is looking to diversify its fuel mix in the long term adding nuclear and renewable energy powered plants to reduce the carbon emission output from its generation activities.

Company Background
FMPA has also been modernizing its power plant fleet since 2003 and in 2011 it opened a new low-emission high efficiency generator known as Cane Island Unit 4. Plant modernization has led to lower power costs enabling Florida Municipal Power Agency to reduce its wholesale rates to a number of members' cities in 2011 by 20% over 2009 levels.

The Agency was formed in 1978 to support the activities of Florida's locally owned and operated municipal utilities in projects requiring joint action such as the development of large power plants to serve a number of municipalities.

EXECUTIVES

Ceo, Nicholas P Guarriello
Chm, Howard McKinnon
Assistant General Counsel, Jody Finklea
Manager, Richard Montgomery
Member, Sharon Smeenk
Manager, Victoria Bidwell
Buyer, Alan Bradley
General Counsel, Frederick M Bryant
Office Manager, Karen Culpepper
Officer, Larry Mattern
Human Resources Administrative, Sharon Adam
Auditors: PURVIS GRAY & COMPANY LLP OC

LOCATIONS

HQ: FLORIDA MUNICIPAL POWER AGENCY
8553 COMMODITY CIR, ORLANDO, FL 328199002
Phone: 407 355-7767
Web: WWW.FMPA.COM

HISTORICAL FINANCIALS
Company Type: Private

Income Statement
FYE: September 30

	REVENUE ($ mil.)	NET INCOME ($ mil.)	NET PROFIT MARGIN	EMPLOYEES
09/17	618	13	2.2%	67
09/16	588	0	0.0%	—
09/15	613	0	0.1%	—
09/14	677	0	0.0%	—
Annual Growth	(3.0%)	371.4%	—	—

2017 Year-End Financials
Return on assets: 6.0% Cash ($ mil.): 58
Return on equity: 2.2%
Current ratio: 0.50

FLOYD HEALTHCARE MANAGEMENT, INC.

If you need heart help in the Heart of Dixie Floyd Healthcare Management is there for you. Its main hospital Floyd Medical Center has more than 300 beds and serves northwestern Georgia and northeastern Alabama with more than 40 medical speciaties. In addition to medical surgical and emergency care (including a Level II trauma center and Level III neonatal intensive care unit) the hospital offers rehabilitation programs hospice and home health care. It also operates a 25-bed community hospital (Polk Medical Center) and the 53-bed

Floyd Behavioral Health Center. Floyd Healthcare also operates outpatient centers including primary care surgery and urgent care locations. The organization was founded in 1942.

Operations

Floyd Healthcare Management's main hospital facility Floyd Medical Center employs 300 physicians and handles 102500 emergency visits each year. It also manages some 249000 outpatient visits and 2200 births and it specialized in fields including orthopedic surgery stroke care bariatric surgery and breast care. The system also operates about 40 primary care practices and urgent care facilities in surrounding areas.

In partnership with the Floyd County Commission Floyd County Department of Family and Children Services (DFCS) and physicians in the community Floyd sponsors the Floyd County Clinic where low-income uninsured residents of Floyd County can receive free primary medical care services through the faculty and resident medical students enrolled in the Floyd Family Medicine Residency program.

Floyd Medical Center also provides community outreach programs through its mobile mammography vans and a range of other services aimed at improving access to health care throughout the service area.

Geographic Reach

Floyd Healthcare Management serves Rome Rockmart and other communities in Polk and Floyd counties.

Sales and Marketing

Third-party payers contributed some 40% of Floyd Healthcare's net patient service revenue in 2014 followed by Medicare (which contributed 33%).

Financial Performance

Sales increased 2% to $334.8 million in fiscal 2014 for Floyd Healthcare Management due to higher patient service revenue and other earnings. A majority of the company's sales come from patient revenue with more than 30% of that sourced to Medicare reimbursements. Despite the rise in revenue net income fell 34% to $14.9 million that year however due to lower actuarial gains and higher expenses.

Cash flow from operations rose 82% to $34.5 million on inflows from accounts payable.

Strategy

The organization invests in improving care for its service territory. In 2014 community hospital Polk Medical Center opened a new 65000-sq.-ft. medical complex featuring 12 emergency rooms a new surgical program with modern operating rooms improved diagnostic and imaging services and a medical office building. Also in 2014 Floyd Medical Center renovated its sixth floor adding more private beds for patients.

The network launched a technology initiative in 2013 to implement a physician order entry system; the tool will help to reduce medical errors and improve patient care.

EXECUTIVES

Vice President, Greg Polley
Director Of Pharmacy, Robert Purcell

LOCATIONS

HQ: FLOYD HEALTHCARE MANAGEMENT, INC.
304 TURNER MCCALL BLVD SW, ROME, GA
301655621
Phone: 706 509-5000
Web: WWW.FLOYD.ORG

PRODUCTS/OPERATIONS

Selected Services

Adult Psychiatric Services
Alcohol and Chemical Dependency
Bariatric Medicine Surgery and Aftercare
Breast Health
Behavioral Health
Cancer Care
Cardiac Catheterization
Cardiology
Cardiac Rehabilitation
Childbirth and Aftercare
Corporate Health
Dementia and Alzheimer's
Diabetes Care
Echocardiography
Emergency Care
Family Medicine
Family Medicine Residency Program
Gynecology
Hospice
Hospitalist Care
Hyperbarics and Wound Care
Infusion Therapy
Intensive Care
Interventional Cardiology
IV Therapy
Joint Replacement
Laboratory
Level III Neonatal Intensive Care Unit
Level II Trauma Care
Maternity
Neurology
Neuropsychology
Neurosurgery
Occupational Medicine
Oncology
Orthopedics
Pediatrics
Pediatric Intermediate Care
Pharmacy Inpatient and Outpatient
Primary Care
Pulmonary Rehabilitation
Radiology
Inpatient Rehabilitation
Outpatient Rehabilitation
Sleep Disorders
Spine Center
Sports Medicine Services
Stroke
Surgery Inpatient and Outpatient
Urgent Care
Vascular Surgery
Wound Care and Hyperbarics

COMPETITORS

Gadsden Regional Medical Center	WellStar Kennestone Hospital
Hutcheson Medical	
Redmond Regional Medical Center	

HISTORICAL FINANCIALS

Company Type: Private

Income Statement

FYE: June 30

	REVENUE ($ mil.)	NET INCOME ($ mil.)	NET PROFIT MARGIN	EMPLOYEES
06/16	326	13	4.1%	2,400
06/15	316	32	10.4%	—
06/11	332	11	3.4%	—
06/10	288	8	3.0%	—
Annual Growth	2.1%	7.6%	—	—

2016 Year-End Financials

Return on assets: 4.7%   Cash ($ mil.): 74
Return on equity: 4.1%
Current ratio: 2.40

FOGO DE CHAO, INC.

EXECUTIVES

Vice President Talent Management, Richard Lenderman
Global Vice President Operational And Finance, Eulila Oliveira
Vice President Of Talent Management, Jackie Rodriguez
Auditors: PRICEWATERHOUSECOOPERS LLP DA

LOCATIONS

HQ: FOGO DE CHAO, INC.
5908 HDQTR DR STE K200, PLANO, TX 75024
Phone: 972 960-9533
Web: WWW.FOGODECHAO.COM

COMPETITORS

Buckhead Life Restaurants	Morton's Restaurant Group
Clyde's Restaurant Group	Palm Restaurants
Consilient Restaurants	Patina Restaurant Group
Del Frisco's Restaurant	Ruth's Hospitality
Il Fornaio	Smith & Wollensky
Lettuce Entertain You	Tavistock Restaurants
Levy Restaurants	Wolfgang Puck Fine Dining
McCormick & Schmick's	

HISTORICAL FINANCIALS

Company Type: Private

Income Statement

FYE: December 31

	REVENUE ($ mil.)	NET INCOME ($ mil.)	NET PROFIT MARGIN	EMPLOYEES
12/17*	314	28	9.0%	3,154
01/17	288	24	8.4%	—
01/16	271	28	10.3%	—
Annual Growth	7.6%	0.7%	—	—

*Fiscal year change

2017 Year-End Financials

Return on assets: 11.3%   Cash ($ mil.): 38
Return on equity: 9.0%
Current ratio: 1.10

FONTANA UNIFIED SCHOOL DISTRICT

EXECUTIVES

Supt, Leslie Boozer
Human Resources Analyst, Molly Garza
Accounting Manager, Dawn Brooks
Sergeant, Doug Imhof
Project Coordinator, Tom Haugh
Coordinator, Cecilia Henderson
Coordinator, Nathan Hunt
Coordinator, Matt Davis
Administrative Assistant, Steve McGuffey
Assistant Engineer, Graciela Martinez
Auditors: NIGRO NIGRO & WHITE PC TEMEC

LOCATIONS

HQ: FONTANA UNIFIED SCHOOL DISTRICT
9680 CITRUS AVE, FONTANA, CA 923355571
Phone: 909 357-7600
Web: WWW.FONTANA.ORG

HISTORICAL FINANCIALS
Company Type: Private

Income Statement   FYE: June 30

	REVENUE ($ mil.)	NET INCOME ($ mil.)	NET PROFIT MARGIN	EMPLOYEES
06/17	531	27	5.1%	3,627
06/16*	525	23	4.5%	—
12/06	0	0	—	—
06/05	329	(22)	—	—
Annual Growth	4.1%	—	—	—

*Fiscal year change

2017 Year-End Financials
Return on assets: 10.8%   Cash ($ mil.): 272
Return on equity: 5.1%
Current ratio: —

FOOD FOR THE POOR, INC.

EXECUTIVES

Secretary And General Counsel, David Price
Auditors: MAYER HOFFMAN MCCANN PC BOC

LOCATIONS

HQ: FOOD FOR THE POOR, INC.
   6401 LYONS RD, COCONUT CREEK, FL 330733602
Phone: 954 427-2222
Web: WWW.FOODFORTHEPOOR.ORG

HISTORICAL FINANCIALS
Company Type: Private

Income Statement   FYE: December 31

	REVENUE ($ mil.)	NET INCOME ($ mil.)	NET PROFIT MARGIN	EMPLOYEES
12/17	948	(1)	—	335
12/16	994	14	1.5%	—
12/15	1,158	(0)	—	—
12/14	913	(0)	—	—
Annual Growth	1.3%	—	—	—

2017 Year-End Financials
Return on assets: 0.6%   Cash ($ mil.): 22
Return on equity: (-0.2%)
Current ratio: 4.50

FOOD GIANT SUPERMARKETS, INC.

EXECUTIVES

Pres, Kevin Ladd
V Pres-Oprs, Gary Duncan
Asst SEC-Treas, Steve Malone
SEC, Spencer Coates
Information Technology Manager, Brent Benton
Buyer, Candace Halstead
Loan Officer, Dedra Clark
District Manager, Earl Johnson
Supervisor, Shane Riley
Meat Deli Director, Bryan Gilley
Produce Supervisor, Jeff Turner

LOCATIONS

HQ: FOOD GIANT SUPERMARKETS, INC.
   120 INDUSTRIAL DR, SIKESTON, MO 638015216
Phone: 573 471-3500
Web: WWW.FOODGIANT.COM

HISTORICAL FINANCIALS
Company Type: Private

Income Statement   FYE: October 1

	REVENUE ($ mil.)	NET INCOME ($ mil.)	NET PROFIT MARGIN	EMPLOYEES
10/16	725	22	3.1%	4,500
10/15	757	25	3.4%	—
10/10*	616	22	3.6%	—
09/06	468	108	23.1%	—
Annual Growth	4.5%	(14.6%)	—	—

*Fiscal year change

2016 Year-End Financials
Return on assets: 3.2%   Cash ($ mil.): 18
Return on equity: 3.1%
Current ratio: 0.60

FOODCOMM INTERNATIONAL

EXECUTIVES

Ceo, Greg Bourke
Pres, Frank Tarantino
Cfo, Tom Granndsart
National Director of Hri Sales, Dan Moore
Auditors: MOSS ADAMS LLP CAMPBELL CALI

LOCATIONS

HQ: FOODCOMM INTERNATIONAL
   4260 EL CAMINO REAL, PALO ALTO, CA 943064404
Phone: 650 813-1300
Web: WWW.FOODCOMM.COM

HISTORICAL FINANCIALS
Company Type: Private

Income Statement   FYE: December 31

	REVENUE ($ mil.)	NET INCOME ($ mil.)	NET PROFIT MARGIN	EMPLOYEES
12/16	444	8	1.9%	30
12/13	211	4	2.0%	—
12/10	168	1	1.2%	—
12/09	728	0	0.0%	—
Annual Growth	(6.8%)	418.0%	—	—

2016 Year-End Financials
Return on assets: 0.3%   Cash ($ mil.): 6
Return on equity: 1.9%
Current ratio: 0.40

FORDHAM UNIVERSITY

A private Catholic university Fordham offers its more than 16000 students numerous degree programs through about 10 graduate and undergraduate schools. Called the Jesuit University of New York Fordham has multiple locations including the original Rose Hill campus in the Bronx (often the scene of location shooting for movies TV shows and commercials) the Westchester campus and the Lincoln Center campus in Manhattan. It also operates a biological field station in Armonk New York and international centers in China and the UK. Fordham was founded in 1841.

Operations
Fordham offers more than 50 majors in liberal arts sciences and business. It has an undergraduate student/faculty ratio of 15:1. The university has more than 750 full-time instructors (including more than 30 Jesuits). More than 90% of its faculty holds a Ph.D. or other terminal degree.

Some 70% of Fordham's revenue comes from tuition and fees. Auxiliary enterprises bring in more than 10% of revenue. The rest of its income comes from investments contributions and grants and net assets released from restrictions.

Geographic Reach
Fordham's Rose Hill campus is located on 85 acres in the Bronx and offers studies in business liberal arts science and religion. The Lincoln Center campus provides education business administration social services and legal training while the Westchester campus provides graduate programs in a variety of subjects. The Armonk field station is the headquarters for several university research programs.

Financial Performance
In fiscal 2017 (ended June) Fordham had $596.5 million in operating revenues and $738.9 million in endowments and other investments. Operating expenses totaled $592.3 million that year.

Undergraduate tuition in 2016-17 was $47850 per student.

Company Background
The school opened in 1841 as St. John's College. It officially changed its name to Fordham University in 1907.

EXECUTIVES

Vice President, Jeffrey Gray
President, Joseph M. McShane
Provost, Stephen Freedman
Vp Finance, Frank Simio
Vp Technology And Cio, Frank Sirianni
Dean Fordham College At Lincoln Center, Robert R. Grimes
Interim Dean Fordham College At Rose Hill, John Harrington
Dean Gabelli School Of Business, Donna Rapaccioli
Dean Fordham School Of Professional And Continuing Studies, Isabelle Frank
Dean Graduate School Of Arts And Sciences, Eva Badowska
Dean Graduate School Of Education, James J. Hennessy
Dean Graduate School Of Religion And Religious Education, C. Colt Anderson
Dean Graduate School Of Social Service, Debra M. McPhee
Dean School Of Law, Michael M. Martin
Assistant Vice President, Kevin Munnelly
Assistant Vice President, John Carroll
Director Of Admissions And Marketing, Glenn S Berman
Associate Vice President Information Technology, Fleur Eshghi
Interim Assistant Vice President For Academic Records And Services, Catherine Cadigan
Assistant Vice President For Development And University Events, Elizabeth Manigan
Department Chair, Robert Beer
Mba Candidate 18 Vice President Full Time Students, Joe Colandrea
Chairman Board Of Trustees, Robert D. (Bob) Daleo, age 69
Vice Chairman Board Of Trustees, Edward M. Stroz

Secretary Of The University, Margaret Ball
Treasurer, Viliam Litavec
Treasurer, Angela Bates
Treasurer, Gilda Severiano
Auditors: KPMG LLP NEW YORK NY

LOCATIONS

HQ: FORDHAM UNIVERSITY
441 E FORDHAM RD, BRONX, NY 104589993
Phone: 718 817-1000
Web: WWW.FORDHAM.EDU

PRODUCTS/OPERATIONS

2017 Sales

	$ mil.	% of total
Net tuition & fees	424	71
Net auxiliary enterprises	78	13
Investments	27	5
Contributions & private grants	27	4
Government grants	17	3
Net assets released from restrictions	4	1
Other	16	3
Total	**596**	**100**

Selected Colleges

Graduate and Professional
  Graduate School of Arts and Sciences
  Graduate School of Business
  Graduate School of Education
  Graduate School of Religion and Religious Education
  Graduate School of Social Services
  School of Law
Undergraduate
  Fordham College at Lincoln Center
  Fordham College at Rose Hill
  Gabelli School of Business
  School of Professional and Continuing Studies

HISTORICAL FINANCIALS
Company Type: Private

Income Statement				FYE: June 30
	REVENUE ($ mil.)	NET INCOME ($ mil.)	NET PROFIT MARGIN	EMPLOYEES
06/16	588	(52)	—	4,070
06/14	566	100	17.7%	—
06/12	518	60	11.6%	—
06/11	494	283	57.4%	—
Annual Growth	3.5%	—	—	—

2016 Year-End Financials

Return on assets: 11.6%   Cash ($ mil.): 1
Return on equity: (-8.9%)
Current ratio: —

FORREST GENERAL HEALTH SERVICES, INC.

EXECUTIVES

Ceo, Evan Dillard
President, William C Oliver
Cfo, Ed Tucker
Optometrists, Rochelle Hopkins

LOCATIONS

HQ: FORREST GENERAL HEALTH SERVICES, INC.
6051 U S HIGHWAY 49, HATTIESBURG, MS
394017200
Phone: 601 288-7000
Web: WWW.FGHFAMILYMEDICINE.COM

HISTORICAL FINANCIALS
Company Type: Private

Income Statement				FYE: September 30
	REVENUE ($ mil.)	NET INCOME ($ mil.)	NET PROFIT MARGIN	EMPLOYEES
09/15	398	48	12.0%	168
09/08	0	0	29.3%	—
/	0	0	—	—
Annual Growth	—	—	—	—

2015 Year-End Financials

Return on assets: 4.8%   Cash ($ mil.): 97
Return on equity: 12.0%
Current ratio: 2.10

FORSYTH COUNTY BOARD OF EDUCATION

EXECUTIVES

Chairperson, Darla Light
Cfo, Dan Jones
Administrator, Miranda Willingham
Human Resources Director, Kathy Mills
Personnel Assistant, Kayla Cheek
Executive, Deanna Bowen
Executive, Carolyn Boggs
Teacher, Christopher Webb
Executive Officer, Fonda Harrison
Administrator, Jennifer Miller
Teacher, Kaila Copenhaver
Auditors: MAULDIN & JENKINS LLC ATLANT

LOCATIONS

HQ: FORSYTH COUNTY BOARD OF EDUCATION
1120 DAHLONEGA HWY, CUMMING, GA 300404536
Phone: 770 887-2461
Web: WWW.FORSYTH.K12.GA.US

HISTORICAL FINANCIALS
Company Type: Private

Income Statement				FYE: June 30
	REVENUE ($ mil.)	NET INCOME ($ mil.)	NET PROFIT MARGIN	EMPLOYEES
06/17	526	(16)	—	4,160
06/16	472	21	4.5%	—
06/12	354	(6)	—	—
06/11	346	(10)	—	—
Annual Growth	7.2%	—	—	—

2017 Year-End Financials

Return on assets: 1.9%   Cash ($ mil.): 158
Return on equity: (-3.1%)
Current ratio: —

FORT WORTH INDEPENDENT SCHOOL DISTRICT

EXECUTIVES

Sup, Kent Scribner
Executive Officer, Martin Yarobough
Executive Officer, Camille Rodriguez
Executive Officer, Judy Needham
Executive Officer, Blaine Buchenau
Executive Officer, Diana Vargas
Staff, Micheal Lee
Executive Officer, Steven Senevy
Accounting Staff, Deborah Cooper-Boone
Educational Technology Special, Christopher Villagran
School Manager, Stephanie Boatner
Auditors: WEAVER AND TIDWELL LLP FORTH

LOCATIONS

HQ: FORT WORTH INDEPENDENT SCHOOL DISTRICT
100 N UNIVERSITY DR, FORT WORTH, TX 761071360
Phone: 817 871-2000
Web: WWW.FWISD.ORG

HISTORICAL FINANCIALS
Company Type: Private

Income Statement				FYE: June 30
	REVENUE ($ mil.)	NET INCOME ($ mil.)	NET PROFIT MARGIN	EMPLOYEES
06/17	924	133	14.4%	10,360
06/16	909	(101)	—	—
06/15	843	64	7.7%	—
06/12	777	(98)	—	—
Annual Growth	3.5%	—	—	—

FORTIS CONSTRUCTION, INC.

EXECUTIVES

Vice President Information Technology, Mark Callahan
Auditors: ALDRICH CPAS AND ADVISORS LLP

LOCATIONS

HQ: FORTIS CONSTRUCTION, INC.
1705 SW TAYLOR ST STE 200, PORTLAND, OR
972051922
Phone: 503 459-4477
Web: WWW.FORTISCONSTRUCT.COM

PRODUCTS/OPERATIONS

Selected Services

Construction management
General contracting
Green building
Preconstruction
Web-based collaboration and electronic document management

COMPETITORS

Andersen Construction	R&H Construction
Hoffman Corporation	S.D. Deacon

Jacobsen Construction   Swinerton Builders
Panattoni Construction

HISTORICAL FINANCIALS
Company Type: Private

Income Statement   FYE: December 31

	REVENUE ($ mil.)	NET INCOME ($ mil.)	NET PROFIT MARGIN	EMPLOYEES
12/16	782	30	3.9%	175
12/15	468	18	3.9%	—
12/14	282	14	5.0%	—
Annual Growth	66.6%	48.0%	—	—

2016 Year-End Financials
Return on assets: 12.4%   Cash ($ mil.): 41
Return on equity: 3.9%
Current ratio: 1.30

FOUNDATION FOR THE CAROLINAS

EXECUTIVES

Pres-Ceo, Michael Marsicano
Exec Vice President, Laura Meyer Wellman
Sr V Pres, C Barton Landess

LOCATIONS

HQ: FOUNDATION FOR THE CAROLINAS
    220 N TRYON ST, CHARLOTTE, NC 282022137
Phone: 704 973-4500
Web: WWW.FFTC.ORG

HISTORICAL FINANCIALS
Company Type: Private

Income Statement   FYE: December 31

	REVENUE ($ mil.)	NET INCOME ($ mil.)	NET PROFIT MARGIN	EMPLOYEES
12/15	382	84	22.1%	40
12/14	684	330	48.2%	—
12/13	317	121	38.3%	—
12/09	88	(3)	—	—
Annual Growth	27.6%	—	—	—

2015 Year-End Financials
Return on assets: 0.9%   Cash ($ mil.): 200
Return on equity: 22.1%
Current ratio: 7.40

FRANCIS SAINT MEDICAL CENTER

It may be guided by Catholic principles but you don't have to be a saint to get medical care at Saint Francis Medical Center. The hospital serves a five-state region from Missouri (its home base) to Arkansas with about 285 beds. Services include emergency medicine orthopedics cancer rehabilitation and women's health care. It also offers heart and neurosciences institutes as well as diabetes education and wound healing centers. The health care provider which was established in 1875 partners with Poplar Bluff Medical Partners to provide outpatient care at Poplar Bluff Medical Complex. Services include family practice OB-GYN and pain management.

Operations
Saint Francis Medical Center also partners with Landmark Holdings of Missouri to provide long-term acute care services through the 30-bed Landmark Hospital. The only facility of its kind between St. Louis and Memphis the hospital provides long-term care for patients who need complex medical care from catastrophic accidents or chronic diseases.

The hospital partners with the doctor-owned Physicians Alliance Surgery Center to provide outpatient surgery services in the region. Specialties provided at the center include gynecology ophthalmology orthopedic retinal and ENT (ear nose and throat) surgeries as well as general procedures.

Geographic Reach
Saint Francis Medical Center serves about 650000 people in Arkansas Kentucky Missouri Illinois and Tennessee.

Strategy
Saint Francis Medical Center has been expanding its facilities to offer more specialized services. Recent additions include its heart hospital and cancer institute. In 2015 it opened a new five-story patient tower including new and renovated space. It is also working on an orthopedic and neuroscience center and new surgery women's and children's health facilities.

EXECUTIVES

Ceo, Mary Ann Reese
Chb, Clyde Nenninger
Cfo, David Prather
Coordinator, Gisele L Kaahanui
Internal Medicine Practitioner, Alexis Lansing
Scientist, Anita Phillips
Administrative Secretary, Marilyn Curtis
Director of Laboratory, Kim Matthews
Chief of Medicine, Matthew Schumer
Director, Bill Tegel
Admin Secretary II, Debbie Foight

LOCATIONS

HQ: FRANCIS SAINT MEDICAL CENTER
    211 SAINT FRANCIS DR, CAPE GIRARDEAU, MO
    637035049
Phone: 573 331-3000
Web: WWW.SFMC.NET

PRODUCTS/OPERATIONS

Selected Services
Cancer institute
Emergency trauma & urgent care services
Gastroenterology services
Heart hospital
Neurosciences institute
Orthopedic institute
Primary care
Services to business
Women & children's services

COMPETITORS

Barnes-Jewish Hospital   St. Anthony's Medical
Memorial Hospital   Center
  (Illinois)   St. John's Hospital
Southeast Missouri   (Illinois)
  State University
Southern Illinois
  Healthcare

HISTORICAL FINANCIALS
Company Type: Private

Income Statement   FYE: June 30

	REVENUE ($ mil.)	NET INCOME ($ mil.)	NET PROFIT MARGIN	EMPLOYEES
06/16	449	31	6.9%	1,500
06/15	424	41	9.7%	—
06/14	433	37	8.7%	—
06/11	423	48	11.4%	—
Annual Growth	1.2%	(8.4%)	—	—

2016 Year-End Financials
Return on assets: 5.1%   Cash ($ mil.): 56
Return on equity: 6.9%
Current ratio: 1.30

FRANCISCAN ALLIANCE, INC.

The Franciscan Alliance keeps watch over a family of hospitals. The not-for-profit organization operates more than a dozen hospitals in Indiana and south suburban Chicago. The hospitals house about 3500 beds and include specialist centers for cancer care heart and vascular care weight loss pediatrics and women's health. In addition to inpatient acute care services they operate numerous outpatient facilities and medical practices within their local service areas. Other subsidiaries and affiliates perform clinical laboratory tests offer home health services and provide support services to the system. Franciscan Alliance was founded and is sponsored by the Sisters of St. Francis of Perpetual Adoration.

Operations
Franciscan Alliance's hospitals handle about 100000 inpatient visits annually. The organization also handles about 3 million outpatient visits each year at its hospitals clinics and practice offices. Its physician practice organization includes about 700 doctors.

Along with providing a wide range of health care services Franciscan Alliance educates future health care providers through affiliations with area universities. The schools offer a variety of degree programs in fields including nursing medical technician and pharmacy residency.

Geographic Reach
Franciscan Alliance's hospitals are located in about ten communities in Indiana as well as in southern Chicago suburbs. The facilities serve patients in parts of Michigan as well. The organization also operates hundreds of outpatient clinics and physician offices in the area as well as a data center in Beech Grove Indiana.

Strategy
In 2011 the Sisters of St. Francis of Perpetual Adoration decided to change the name of the health system from Sisters of St. Francis Health Services to Franciscan Alliance to spread brand awareness and illustrate cohesiveness among the system's various facilities. The name change came after several months of consumer research and took about a year to be fully implemented across the entire system.

Franciscan Alliance also expanded through new construction in 2011 with the completion of the first phase of its Indianapolis Campus Expansion project. The health system moved a number of services into the new patient tower there including emergency services surgical suites and a wound care institute. In 2012 the company closed its Beech Grove hospital and consolidated services to the expanded Indianapolis center. It also opened a new short-stay hospital in Carmel that year.

In 2013 however the company announced that it would explore options to sell all or part of its two Franciscan St. James Health hospitals. The organization sought a partner to invest in capital improvements at the facilities. No buyer stepped forward but economic conditions improved enough by 2014 that the alliance said it was no longer searching for a buyer or investor. It also broke ground on a Hospice facility opened a specialized wound-care center and started a $10.2 million renovation at its St. Margaret facility.

Mergers and Acquisitions

In 2011 Franciscan Alliance grew its outpatient facilities by acquiring Surgical Hospital of Munster which serves as an outpatient surgery center of Franciscan Physicians Hospital.

EXECUTIVES

President Ceo, Kevin Leahy
President And Ceo Franciscan St. Margaret Health, Michael J. Stenger
Ceo Franciscan Health Dyer Franciscan Health Hammond Franciscan Health Munster, Patrick Maloney
Ceo Western Indiana Region, Terrance E. Wilson
Svp And Coo Inpatient Services, Gene Diamond
President And Ceo Crown Point, Barbara Anderson
President Franciscan St. Anthony Health Michigan City, James Callaghan
President Franciscan St. Margaret Health-dyer And Hammond, Thomas Gryzbek
Auditors: I PNCEWATERHOUSECOOPERS LLP

LOCATIONS

HQ: FRANCISCAN ALLIANCE, INC.
3510 PARK PL W STE 200, MISHAWAKA, IN 465453515
Phone: 574 273-3867
Web: WWW.HEALTHMART.COM

PRODUCTS/OPERATIONS

Selected Operations

St. Anthony Health (Crown Point and Michigan City Indiana)
St. Elizabeth Health (Crawfordsville Lafayette Central Lafayette East Indiana)
St. Francis Health (Carmel Indianapolis and Mooresville Indiana)
St. James Health (Chicago Heights and Olympia Fields Illinois)
St. Margaret Health (Hammond and Dyer Indiana)
Franciscan Healthcare Munster (formerly Physicians Hospital; Munster Indiana)

Selected Services

Anticoagulation Clinics
Behavioral Health
Cancer Care
Colon and Rectal Surgery
Diabetes Care
Ear Nose and Throat
Emergency Medicine
Heart & Vascular
Home Health Care
Hospice
Imaging
Joint & Spine Care
Laboratory Services
Neurology
Neurosurgery
Occupational Health
Ophthalmology
Pain Management
Palliative Medicine
Pediatrics
Plastic Surgery
Primary Care Physicians
Pulmonary Medicine
Registered Dietitians
Rehabilitation Services
Robotic Surgery
Senior Services
Sleep Disorders
Sports Medicine
Surgical Services
Urgent Care
Weight Loss/Bariatrics
Women's Health/OBGYN
Wound Care

Selected Hospitals

Franciscan St. Anthony - Crown Point
Franciscan St. Anthony - Michigan City
Franciscan St. Elizabeth - Lafayette Central
Franciscan St. Elizabeth - Lafayette East
Franciscan St. Elizabeth - Crawfordsville
Franciscan St. Francis - Carmel
Franciscan St. Francis - Indianapolis
Franciscan St. Francis - Mooresville
Franciscan St. James - Chicago Heights
Franciscan St. James - Olympia Fields
Franciscan St. Margaret - Dyer
Franciscan St. Margaret - Hammond
Franciscan Healthcare - Munster

COMPETITORS

Advocate Health Care
Ascension Health
Community Health Network
Covenant Ministries
IU Health
Memorial Hospital & Health System
NorthShore University HealthSystem
Northwestern Memorial HealthCare
Porter Health Care System
Riverview Hospital
Rush System for Health
Sinai Health System
St. Bernard Hospital and Health Care Center
Union Hospital (Indiana)
University of Chicago Medical Center

HISTORICAL FINANCIALS

Company Type: Private

Income Statement   FYE: December 31

	REVENUE ($ mil.)	NET INCOME ($ mil.)	NET PROFIT MARGIN	EMPLOYEES
12/15	2,731	250	9.2%	19,000
12/14	2,661	274	10.3%	—
12/13	2,588	92	3.6%	—
12/12	2,625	136	5.2%	—
Annual Growth	1.3%	22.4%	—	—

2015 Year-End Financials

Return on assets: 6.8%   Cash ($ mil.): 71
Return on equity: 9.2%
Current ratio: 0.30

FRANCISCAN HEALTH SYSTEM

St. Francis himself may have hailed from Italy but his followers look after the health of the residents of the South Puget Sound area through the Franciscan Health System. The not-for-profit system includes five full-service hospitals. The oldest and largest hospital is St. Joseph Medical Center in Tacoma Washington a 320-bed facility. Its facilities include community hospitals St. Clare Hospital (in Lakewood) and St. Francis Hospital (in Federal Way) as well as a hospice program and numerous primary and specialty care clinics. Its St. Anthony Hospital is an 80-bed full service pharmacy and home medical equipment retail location at Gig Harbor.

Geographic Reach

Franciscan Health System serves patients in Tacoma Washington and surrounding areas.

Financial Performance

The company gets most of its revenues from patient services. Other sources of income includes foundation gifts and investment community benefit charity care and uncompensated care (unreimbursed costs of serving patients enrolled in Medicaid and other state-subsidized programs).

Strategy

Franciscan Health System and Harrison Medical Center are looking to join forces while Franciscan's parent continues in talks to combine its Northwest operations with PeaceHealth of Vancouver Washington. If both plans are approved by regulators Harrison will become part of the largest community hospital system in the Northwest with facilities in Alaska Washington and Oregon. Both the Harrison-Franciscan affiliation and that of Franciscan's parent Catholic Health Initiatives with PeaceHealth is slated to be approved in 2013.

In addition Franciscan Health System is collaborating with the MultiCare Health System and TRA Medical Imaging to build a women's imaging and breast cancer care center.

St. Elizabeth Hospital opened its doors in 2011 in Enumclaw replacing Enumclaw Regional Hospital as that community's acute-care facility.

Company Background

St. Joseph Medical Center in Tacoma (the health system's oldest facility) was founded by the Sisters of St. Francis in 1891.

EXECUTIVES

Pharmacy Manager, Michael Bonck
Director Of Pharmacy, Timothy W Lynch
Vice President Of Quality And Associate Chief Marketing Officer, Kimberly Moore
Physical Therapy Director, DAVID LUNDGREN

LOCATIONS

HQ: FRANCISCAN HEALTH SYSTEM
1717 S J ST, TACOMA, WA 984054933
Phone: 253 426-4101
Web: WWW.FHSHEALTH.ORG

PRODUCTS/OPERATIONS

Key Facilities and Services

Carol Milgard Breast Center Tacoma
Franciscan Center for Weight Management Federal Way
Franciscan Dialysis Center Eastside Tacoma
Franciscan Medical Group primary-care and specialty-care clinics
Franciscan Hospice House University Place
Franciscan Port Clinic Tacoma
Gig Harbor Medical Pavilion Gig Harbor
Gig Harbor Ambulatory Surgery Clinic Gig Harbor
St. Anthony Hospital Gig Harbor
St. Clare Hospital Lakewood
St. Clare Specialty Center Lakewood
St. Clare Medical Pavilion Lakewood
St. Elizabeth Hospital Enumclaw
St. Francis Hospital Federal Way
St. Francis Outpatient Center Federal Way
St. Joseph Medical Center Tacoma
St. Joseph Outpatient Center Tacoma
St. Joseph Heart & Vascular Center Tacoma
St. Joseph Dialysis Center Tacoma
St. Joseph Dialysis Center Gig Harbor
St. Joseph Dialysis Center Puyallup
St. Joseph Medical Clinic Tacoma
St. Joseph Medical Pavilion Tacoma
Milgard Medical Pavilion at St. Anthony Gig Harbor
Women's Health & Breast Center Federal Way

COMPETITORS

Harrison Medical Center   Seattle Children's Hospital

MultiCare Health System
Overlake Hospital
PeaceHealth
Providence St. Joseph Health
Swedish Health Services
Yakima Valley Memorial

HISTORICAL FINANCIALS
Company Type: Private

Income Statement
FYE: June 30

	REVENUE ($ mil.)	NET INCOME ($ mil.)	NET PROFIT MARGIN	EMPLOYEES
06/16	637	51	8.0%	3,183
06/15	610	56	9.2%	—
06/14	1,190	(106)	—	—
06/10	1,093	71	6.5%	—
Annual Growth	(8.6%)	(5.4%)	—	—

2016 Year-End Financials
Return on assets: 6.2%
Return on equity: 8.0%
Current ratio: 2.80
Cash ($ mil.): 113

FRANCISCAN MISSIONARIES OF OUR LADY HEALTH SYSTEM, INC.

EXECUTIVES
Ceo, John J Finan
V Pres, Pete Guarisco
SEC-Treas, Sr Helen Cahill
Cfo, Howard Harvill
Information Technology Manager, Kathy Chauvin
Director of Risk Management, Harriet Percy
Manager of Management Informat, Karen Parker
Manager, Rita Finn
Manager, Brittney Sprague
Information Specialist, Chris Jones
Coordinator, David M Murungi
Auditors: KPMG LLP BATON ROUGE LA

LOCATIONS
HQ: FRANCISCAN MISSIONARIES OF OUR LADY HEALTH SYSTEM, INC.
4200 ESSEN LN, BATON ROUGE, LA 708092158
Phone: 225 923-2701
Web: WWW.FMOLSISTERS.COM

HISTORICAL FINANCIALS
Company Type: Private

Income Statement
FYE: June 30

	REVENUE ($ mil.)	NET INCOME ($ mil.)	NET PROFIT MARGIN	EMPLOYEES
06/18	2,029	106	5.3%	9,000
06/17	1,911	112	5.9%	—
06/15	122	(34)	—	—
06/14	106	(19)	—	—
Annual Growth	109.1%	—	—	—

2018 Year-End Financials
Return on assets: 4.9%
Return on equity: 5.3%
Current ratio: 1.30
Cash ($ mil.): 235

FRANKLIN COUNTY BOARD OF COMMISSIONERS

EXECUTIVES
Commissioner, Paula Brooks
Commissioner, Marilyn Brown
Commissioner, John Ogrady
Commissioner, Kevin L Boyce
Treasurer, Edward Leonard
Staff, Jenell Williams
Coordinator, Cecilia Weirick
Coordinator, Kris McDaniel
Coordinator, Kysten Palmore
Coordinator, Patti Froehlich
Coordinator, Phyllis Roberts
Auditors: DAVE YOST AUDITOR OF STATE C

LOCATIONS
HQ: FRANKLIN COUNTY BOARD OF COMMISSIONERS
373 S HIGH ST FL 26, COLUMBUS, OH 432154591
Phone: 614 525-3322
Web: WWW.FRANKLINCOUNTYOHIO.GOV

HISTORICAL FINANCIALS
Company Type: Private

Income Statement
FYE: December 31

	REVENUE ($ mil.)	NET INCOME ($ mil.)	NET PROFIT MARGIN	EMPLOYEES
12/17	1,281	85	6.7%	6,000
12/16	1,226	48	3.9%	—
12/09	1,163	(25)	—	—
12/08	1,169	(38)	—	—
Annual Growth	1.0%	—	—	—

2017 Year-End Financials
Return on assets: 4.4%
Return on equity: 6.7%
Current ratio: —
Cash ($ mil.): 20

FRANKLIN SQUARE HOSPITAL CENTER, INC.

Franklin Square Hospital Center has made a declaration to care for the residents of eastern Baltimore County Maryland. The facility offers a wide range of specialties through some 700 doctors and about 380 beds. Since 1998 the hospital has been part of MedStar Health the region's largest integrated health system. As a teaching hospital Franklin Square offers a number of residency programs including internal and family medicine OB-GYN and surgery. The not-for-profit hospital offers its medical services through half a dozen primary service lines: Medicine Surgery Women's and Children's Care Oncology Behavioral Health and Community Health and Wellness.

Operations

Franklin Square Hospital boasts more than 3000 skilled professions including 1000-plus nurses and 400 staff physicians and more than 750 independently practicing physicians.

Geographic Reach

The only one of its kind in the region Franklin Square's Cancer Institute serves oncology patients

by offering education and prevention services research and diagnostic treatment.

Strategy

The hospital which logs one of the highest numbers of cancer admissions in Maryland is working to expand its cancer services as it anticipates admissions to grow.

In fact the company is expanding other services as well also in anticipation of future patient demand. The hospital built a 300-bed patient tower on the campus that includes an expanded emergency department dedicated pediatric and inpatient suites and an expanded 50-bed critical care unit.

EXECUTIVES
Pres, Samuel E Moskowitz
Cfo, Robert P Lally Jr
Vice President, Anthony Sclama
Vice President, Larry Strassner
Vice President, Karen Robertson-Keck
Occupational Specia, Stacy A Goldstein
Director, Netra Thakur
Information Specialist, Jan Lear
Pediatrician, Fernando V Mena
Chief of Cardiology, Georgia Prichard
Registered Nurse, Keirstin Bueche

LOCATIONS
HQ: FRANKLIN SQUARE HOSPITAL CENTER, INC.
9000 FRANKLIN SQUARE DR, BALTIMORE, MD 212373901
Phone: 410 933-2777
Web: WWW.MEDSTARFRANKLINSQUARE.ORG

PRODUCTS/OPERATIONS

Selected Services
Ambulatory & Minimally Invasive Surgery
Cancer Services
Cyberknife
da Vinci Robotic Surgery
Diagnostic Imaging and Radiology
Obstetrics & Neonatology
Orthopedics & Joint Replacement Therapies
Sleep Disorders
Women's Services

COMPETITORS

Anne Arundel Medical Center	LifeBridge Health
Bon Secours Health	MedStar Union Memorial Hospital
GBMC	Sinai Hospital of Baltimore
Good Samaritan Hospital of Maryland	St. Agnes HealthCare
Harbor Hospital	St. Joseph Medical Center
Johns Hopkins Bayview Medical Center	University of Maryland Medical System
Johns Hopkins Health System	Upper Chesapeake Health
Johns Hopkins Medicine	

HISTORICAL FINANCIALS
Company Type: Private

Income Statement
FYE: June 30

	REVENUE ($ mil.)	NET INCOME ($ mil.)	NET PROFIT MARGIN	EMPLOYEES
06/16	506	10	2.1%	3,019
06/15	492	17	3.5%	—
06/11	452	18	4.0%	—
06/10	439	31	7.1%	—
Annual Growth	2.4%	(16.2%)	—	—

2016 Year-End Financials
Return on assets: 2.1%
Return on equity: 2.1%
Current ratio: 1.10
Cash ($ mil.): 1

FRAZIER INDUSTRIAL COMPANY

This company's racket is structural steel storage systems. Frazier Industrial Co. is a leading manufacturer of structural as opposed to roll-formed steel storage racks at nearly a dozen production centers located across the US Canada and Mexico. These facilities can adapt production to demand and receive just-in-time delivery of raw materials. Customers use Frazier Industrial's storage racks in warehouses factories farms and other industrial and commercial facilities. Among the company's storage products is the Glide 'N Pick pallet cart that automatically rolls out for greater ease in retrieving items. Frazier Industrial is owned by CEO William Mascharka.

Operations

Frazier Industrial has manufacturing locations in Idaho New Jersey New York Pennsylvania South Carolina and Wisconsin. Outside the US it has plants in Mexicali and Monterrey Mexico and in Ontario Canada.

The company boasts sales offices nationwide in Canada and in 10 US states including New Jersey Georgia Massachusetts Texas Ohio Illinois California Washington and New York.

Geographic Reach

The manufacturing company operates throughout North America.

Sales and Marketing

Relying on a network of about a dozen fabrication facilities located throughout the US Mexico and Canada Frazier Industrial is able to meet tight construction deadlines while also guaranteeing manufacturing flexibility.

Customers include some of the world's top suppliers including Procter & Gamble Unilever and Nestle.

Strategy

Frazier Industrial is taking a stand for environmentally sound business practices as green initiatives become a focal point for customers. To this end Frazier sources all of its steel sections from North American mini-mills which only use recycled scrap material. Fittingly all of Frazier Industrial's scrap raw material is fully recyclable. Because the company receives preformed structural sections energy output is minimal; these structural parts require only cutting punching and welding. The location of Frazier Industrial's production centers helps to keep travel time and fuel expenses to a minimum. They are all within 400 miles of the company's raw material suppliers and within 500 miles of major North American population centers.

In 2013 the company launched a semi-automated high-density pallet mole system across North America. The pallet mole system a specific material handling technology maximizes available floor space enabling customers to store pallets up to 6-high and 50 positions deep while measurably increasing warehouse productivity.

Company Background

Frazier Industrial was founded in 1949.

EXECUTIVES

Ceo, William L Mascharka
Chm, Donald Frazier
Pres, Carlos Oliver
V Pres, Domenick Iellimo
Cfo, Peter Acerra
Chief Financial Officer, Robert M Warren
Credit Manager, Christy Nicotra
Project Manager, Arvin Deguzman
Auditors: EISNER AMPER LLP ISELIN NEW

LOCATIONS

HQ: FRAZIER INDUSTRIAL COMPANY
91 FAIRVIEW AVE, LONG VALLEY, NJ 078533381
Phone: 908 876-3001
Web: WWW.FRAZIER.COM

PRODUCTS/OPERATIONS

Selected Products

Drive-In/Drive-Thru Storage
Frazier Design-Build
Glide-In Push-Back Storage
Glide N' Pick Order Picking Cart
Klamp-Fast Cantilever Rack
Pick-to-Belt Systems
Rack Supported Buildings
Safety Accessories
SelecDeck Carton Flow System
Sentinel Selective Pallet Rack
The Pallet Mole

COMPETITORS

Actionrack
Edsal Manufacturing
Interlake Mecalux
Lyon Workspace Products
Steel of West Virginia

HISTORICAL FINANCIALS

Company Type: Private

Income Statement				FYE: December 31
	REVENUE ($ mil.)	NET INCOME ($ mil.)	NET PROFIT MARGIN	EMPLOYEES
12/17	288	11	4.1%	750
12/16	230	5	2.4%	—
12/15	204	5	2.5%	—
12/14	254	5	2.0%	—
Annual Growth	4.2%	31.4%	—	—

2017 Year-End Financials

Return on assets: 4.0%
Return on equity: 4.1%
Current ratio: 0.80
Cash ($ mil.): 11

FREDERICK MEMORIAL HOSPITAL, INC.

Frederick Memorial Healthcare System cares for the sick and unhealthy across The Old Line State. The system operates Frederick Memorial Hospital an acute care facility with some 240 beds and 20 satellite facilities in and around Frederick Maryland. Specialty services include cardiology oncology pediatrics and psychiatry. Other facilities in the system include FMH Immediate Care at Oak Street FMH Crestwood FMH Medical Fitness FMH Rose Hill FMH Wellness FMH Urbana Mt. Airy Health Services and the FMH Regional Cancer Therapy Center. The hospital traces its historical roots all the way back to 1902.

Sales and Marketing

Medicare and Medicaid payments together represent about 45% of Frederick Memorial Healthcare System's net patient revenues. HMOs and PPOs account for about 20% while Blue Cross makes up another 15%.

Financial Performance

Revenue declined 1% in 2014 as net patient services and other operating earnings decreased. Net income fell 67% to $8.6 million that year. That decline was due to realized and unrealized losses on interest rate swaps as well as pension adjustments.

Cash flow from operations rose 24% to $25 million on changes in accounts payable and accrued expenses.

Strategy

The system expands by opening new outpatient facilities expanding into new service areas and adopting new technologies. In 2014 it selected Tableau and FTI Catalyst for its business analytics. Tableau will provide data analysis on admissions discharges surgical outcomes emergency services and other sources while FTI Catalyst will provide data modeling and management services.

EXECUTIVES

Svp Finance And Cfo, Michelle Mahan
President And Ceo, Thomas A. Kleinhanzl
Chief Of Staff, Neil Waravdekar
Vp And Cio, David Quirke
Director Of Pharmacy, Joseph Morrissey
Vice President Ambulatory Services, Don Schilling
Medical Librarian And Cme Coordinator, Lucy Koscielniak
Assistant Vice President Payer Contracting And Government Relations, Jennifer Teeter
Vice President Finance, Hannah Jacobs
Associate Medical Director, Ayodeji Somefun
Medical Director, Patrick Mansky
Vice President Managed Care, White J-amie
Chairman, Anne-Herbert Rollins
Vice Chairman, E. James Reinsch

LOCATIONS

HQ: FREDERICK MEMORIAL HOSPITAL, INC.
400 W 7TH ST, FREDERICK, MD 217014593
Phone: 240 566-3300
Web: WWW.FMH.ORG

PRODUCTS/OPERATIONS

Selected Centers

FMH Crestwood
FMH Immediate Care at Oak Street
FMH Medical Fitness
FMH Regional Cancer Therapy Center
FMH Rose Hill
FMH Urbana
FMH Wellness
Frederick Memorial Hospital
Mt. Airy Health Services

Selected Medical Services

Behavioral Health
Cancer Care
Cardiac Rehabilitation
Cardiology Services
Diabetes Center
Emergency Services
Home Health Services
Hospice/Home Care Information
Hospitalist Care
Imaging Vascular Services
Laboratory Wellness Center
Medical Fitness Women and Children
Occupational Health
Orthopedic Services
Pain and Palliative Care
Pharmacy
Pulmonary Function Lab
Pulmonary Rehab Program
Rehabilitation
Robotics
Sleep Disorders
Smoking Cessation Program
Stroke Center
Surgical Services
Wound Care and Hyperbaric Medicine

COMPETITORS

Adventist HealthCare
Children's National Medical Center
Johns Hopkins Medicine
Loudoun Healthcare
Meritus Health

HISTORICAL FINANCIALS

Company Type: Private

Income Statement
FYE: June 30

	REVENUE ($ mil.)	NET INCOME ($ mil.)	NET PROFIT MARGIN	EMPLOYEES
06/16	341	18	5.5%	2,600
06/15	327	11	3.4%	—
06/14	327	7	2.3%	—
06/13	344	4	1.3%	—
Annual Growth	(0.3%)	61.3%	—	—

2016 Year-End Financials

Return on assets: 9.1%
Return on equity: 5.5%
Current ratio: 0.30
Cash ($ mil.): 31

FREEMAN HEALTH SYSTEM

Freeman Health System (FHS) offers comprehensive health and behavioral health services to the residents of Arkansas Kansas Missouri and Oklahoma through three hospitals with a total of more than 500 beds. Specialty facilities include a full-service cardiothoracic and vascular program at the Freeman Heart Institute and behavioral health services through its Ozark Health Center. Community-owned not-for-profit FHS also operates two urgent care centers a separate sleep center several doctors' office buildings and serves as a teaching hospital with three residency programs (ear nose and throat; emergency medicine; and internal medicine). FHS employs more than 300 physicians in 60 specialties.

Operations

FHS operates three Missouri hospitals - Freeman Hospital West and Freeman Hospital East in Joplin and Freeman Neosho in Neosho. Its Ozark Center provides behavioral health services to patients from Missouri Arkansas Oklahoma and Kansas.

Strategy

Like most health care providers FHS has been working to update it facilities and expand it offerings. To that end in 2013 it opened a transitional living and life skills assistance center for homeless teens and teamed with an autism support group to design an autism treatment program for its Ozark Center. The prior year it christened Will's Place behavioral health center for children and opened a $2 million sports and rehabilitation center.

Company Background

Located in Joplin Missouri — the site of the deadly E5 tornado that killed 161 people in May 2011 — Freeman Health System was the only fully functional hospital in the aftermath of the disaster. Rival St. John's Regional Medical Center just two miles away was destroyed. However Ozark Health Center FHS's behavioral health division lost nine buildings in the disaster.

EXECUTIVES

Pres- Ceo, Paula Baker
Cfo, Steven Graddy
Exec V Pres, Joseph Kirk
Cmo, Richard D Schooler
Specialist, Thomas Coy
Auditors: BKD LLP SPRINGFIELD MISSOUR

LOCATIONS

HQ: FREEMAN HEALTH SYSTEM
  1102 W 32ND ST, JOPLIN, MO 648043503
Phone: 417 347-1111
Web: WWW.GOODNEIGHBORPHARMACY.COM

PRODUCTS/OPERATIONS

Selected Services

Autism Services
Behavioral/mental health
Bladder care
Cancer care
Children's Miracle Network Hospitals
Clinical trials
Cosmetic/reconstructive surgery
Critical Care (ICU)
Diabetes education
Digestive care
Emergency medicine
Family care
Family counseling
Geriatric medicine
Health screenings
Hearing services
Home care
Internal medicine
Internet Addiction Services
Kidney Care
Lung care
Maternity
Neonatal intensive care
Nephrology & dialysis
Neurology & neurosurgery
Occupational medicine
Orthopedics
Pain management
Palliative care
QuickMeds Pharmacy™
Radiology
Rehabilitation
Senior Services
Skilled nursing
Sleep disorders
Sports medicine
Substance abuse services
Surgery
Tobacco cessation
Transitional Care Unit (TCU)
Urgent care
Women's Services
Wound care

Selected Facilities

Freeman Hospital West - Joplin MO
Freeman Hospital East - Joplin MO
Freeman Neosho Hospital - Neosho MO
Freeman Business Center - Joplin MO
Ozark Center - Joplin Missouri

COMPETITORS

Catholic Health Initiatives	Heartland Regional Medical
Children's Mercy Hospital	Mercy Health

HISTORICAL FINANCIALS

Company Type: Private

Income Statement
FYE: March 31

	REVENUE ($ mil.)	NET INCOME ($ mil.)	NET PROFIT MARGIN	EMPLOYEES
03/18	588	51	8.7%	3,887
03/17	564	45	8.1%	—
03/11	452	7	1.7%	—
03/10	474	30	6.5%	—
Annual Growth	2.7%	6.6%	—	—

2018 Year-End Financials

Return on assets: 2.2%
Return on equity: 8.7%
Current ratio: 1.60
Cash ($ mil.): 43

FRESNO COMMUNITY HOSPITAL AND MEDICAL CENTER

EXECUTIVES

Pres-Ceo, Phillip Hinton
Ceo, Tim A Joslin
Cfo, William Grigg
Treas, Roger Fretwell
Sr Vice President, Mike Kingbury
Sr Vice President, Stephen Walter
Vice President, Les Abercrombie
Information Technology/Interne, John Ounesavath
Information Technology/Interne, Karen Christiansen
Information Technology/Interne, Hadi Habib
Manager, John Strubert
Auditors: MOSS ADAMS LLP STOCKTON CA

LOCATIONS

HQ: FRESNO COMMUNITY HOSPITAL AND MEDICAL CENTER
  2823 FRESNO ST, FRESNO, CA 937211324
Phone: 559 459-3948
Web: WWW.COMMUNITYMEDICAL.ORG

HISTORICAL FINANCIALS

Company Type: Private

Income Statement
FYE: August 31

	REVENUE ($ mil.)	NET INCOME ($ mil.)	NET PROFIT MARGIN	EMPLOYEES
08/15	1,571	139	8.9%	5,045
08/10	1,027	9	0.9%	—
08/09	1,010	65	6.5%	—
Annual Growth	7.6%	13.3%	—	—

2015 Year-End Financials

Return on assets: 8.2%
Return on equity: 8.9%
Current ratio: 0.50
Cash ($ mil.): 62

FROEDTERT AND COMMUNITY HEALTH INC

Auditors: KPMG LLP COLUMBUS OH

LOCATIONS

HQ: FROEDTERT AND COMMUNITY HEALTH INC
  9200 W WISCONSIN AVE, MILWAUKEE, WI 532263522
Phone: 414 777-0960

HISTORICAL FINANCIALS

Company Type: Private

Income Statement
FYE: June 30

	REVENUE ($ mil.)	NET INCOME ($ mil.)	NET PROFIT MARGIN	EMPLOYEES
06/15	397	55	14.0%	457
06/10	173	6	3.7%	—
Annual Growth	18.1%	54.4%	—	—

Return on assets: 29.8%   Cash ($ mil.): 4
Return on equity: 14.0%
Current ratio: —

FULTON COUNTY BOARD OF EDUCATION

EXECUTIVES

Pres, Linda McCain
Cfo, Michael Russell
Contrl, W Harold Grindle
Executive Officer, Linda Bryant
Coordinator, Ashley Garrison

LOCATIONS

HQ: FULTON COUNTY BOARD OF EDUCATION
  6201 POWERS FERRY RD, ATLANTA, GA 303392926
Phone: 404 768-3600
Web: WWW.FULTONSCHOOLS.ORG

HISTORICAL FINANCIALS
Company Type: Private

Income Statement				FYE: June 30
	REVENUE ($ mil.)	NET INCOME ($ mil.)	NET PROFIT MARGIN	EMPLOYEES
06/17	1,252	14	1.2%	10,000
06/16	1,201	(32)	—	—
06/11	1,091	142	13.1%	—
Annual Growth	2.3%	(31.6%)	—	—

2017 Year-End Financials

Return on assets: 3.4%   Cash ($ mil.): 400
Return on equity: 1.2%
Current ratio: 2.30

FURST-MCNESS COMPANY

EXECUTIVES

Chb, Frank E Furst
Ceo, Matt Heinrich
Pres, Martha Furst
Exec V Pres, Kevin Gyland
Cfo, Matt Hartman
Fleet Manager, Trinity Zimmerman
Cntrl, Kelly Priewe
Director, Jackie Gyles
Director, Lyle Youngdahl
Consultant, Amanda Wall
Merchandizer, Clark Miller
Auditors: BAKER TILLY VIRCHOW KRAUSE

LOCATIONS

HQ: FURST-MCNESS COMPANY
  120 E CLARK ST, FREEPORT, IL 610323300
Phone: 800 435-5100
Web: WWW.MCNESS.COM

HISTORICAL FINANCIALS
Company Type: Private

Income Statement				FYE: December 31
	REVENUE ($ mil.)	NET INCOME ($ mil.)	NET PROFIT MARGIN	EMPLOYEES
12/16	345	1	0.3%	219
12/15	310	1	0.5%	—
12/14	314	1	0.4%	—
12/13	291	3	1.1%	—
Annual Growth	5.8%	(28.9%)	—	—

2016 Year-End Financials

Return on assets: 7.4%   Cash ($ mil.): 1
Return on equity: 0.3%
Current ratio: 0.80

FUTURE FOAM, INC.

EXECUTIVES

Pres, Bruce Schneider
Vice President, Robert A Heller
SEC-Treas, Michael Blatt
Dir, Cole Schneider
General Manager, Jen Smith
Operations Manager, Michael Phatipat
Regional Sales Manager, Denise Muller
Plant Manager, Marty Lovato
Customer Staff, Laura Dilucchio
Information Technology Manager, Russell Mosemann
General Manager, Brian French
Auditors: FRANKELZACHARIA LLC OMAHA NE

LOCATIONS

HQ: FUTURE FOAM, INC.
  1610 AVENUE N, COUNCIL BLUFFS, IA 515011071
Phone: 712 323-9122
Web: WWW.FUTUREFOAM.COM

HISTORICAL FINANCIALS
Company Type: Private

Income Statement				FYE: January 31
	REVENUE ($ mil.)	NET INCOME ($ mil.)	NET PROFIT MARGIN	EMPLOYEES
01/17	459	42	9.2%	1,000
01/16	424	10	2.5%	—
01/15	408	(8)	—	—
01/14	0	9	—	—
Annual Growth	—	66.5%	—	—

2017 Year-End Financials

Return on assets: 7.5%   Cash ($ mil.): 20
Return on equity: 9.2%
Current ratio: 1.40

GALENCARE, INC.

EXECUTIVES

Pres, Samuel N Hazen
Sr Vice President, Robert T Waterman
Admn, Michael Sencel
SEC, John M Franck
Cfo, Michael Terrell
Vice President, Donald W Stinnett
SEC-Treas, David G Anderson
SEC, Natalie H Cline
Ceo, Bland Eng
Coo, Janice Balzano
Vice President, David Park

LOCATIONS

HQ: GALENCARE, INC.
  119 OAKFIELD DR, BRANDON, FL 335115779
Phone: 813 681-5551
Web: WWW.BRANDONHOSPITAL.COM

HISTORICAL FINANCIALS
Company Type: Private

Income Statement				FYE: December 31
	REVENUE ($ mil.)	NET INCOME ($ mil.)	NET PROFIT MARGIN	EMPLOYEES
12/17	381	124	32.6%	1,300
12/16	370	115	31.1%	—
12/15	350	104	29.8%	—
12/14	358	106	29.6%	—
Annual Growth	2.1%	5.5%	—	—

2017 Year-End Financials

Return on assets: 2.7%   Cash ($ mil.): —
Return on equity: 32.6%
Current ratio: 0.10

GANNETT FLEMING AFFILIATES, INC.

EXECUTIVES

Chb, William Stout
Sr V Pres-V Chm, Robert J Dietz
Treas, Lynn E Knepp
President, Robert Scaer
Director, Robert Skaggs
Auditors: STAMBAUGH NESS PC HANOVER P

LOCATIONS

HQ: GANNETT FLEMING AFFILIATES, INC.
  1105 N MARKET ST, WILMINGTON, DE 198011216
Phone: 717 763-7211

HISTORICAL FINANCIALS
Company Type: Private

Income Statement				FYE: December 31
	REVENUE ($ mil.)	NET INCOME ($ mil.)	NET PROFIT MARGIN	EMPLOYEES
12/17	423	11	2.6%	2,000
12/16	386	11	3.0%	—
12/14	331	9	2.7%	—
12/13	312	7	2.2%	—
Annual Growth	7.9%	12.3%	—	—

2017 Year-End Financials

Return on assets: 7.8%   Cash ($ mil.): 2
Return on equity: 2.6%
Current ratio: 1.70

GARDEN GROVE UNIFIED SCHOOL DISTRICT

EXECUTIVES

Supt, Gabriela Mafi
Supt, Laura Schwalm
Prin, Coleen Cross
SEC, Joyan Spraus
President, George West
Vice President, Lan Quoc Nguyen
Director, Rick Rodriguez
Assistant Director, Steven Nguyen
Accounting Staff, Cathy Joseph
Food Director, Leo Bas
Operations Staff, Marc Aranda

LOCATIONS

HQ: GARDEN GROVE UNIFIED SCHOOL DISTRICT
10331 STANFORD AVE, GARDEN GROVE, CA
928406351
Phone: 714 663-6000
Web: WWW.GGUSD.US

HISTORICAL FINANCIALS
Company Type: Private

Income Statement				FYE: June 30
	REVENUE ($ mil.)	NET INCOME ($ mil.)	NET PROFIT MARGIN	EMPLOYEES
06/17	602	7	1.2%	5,000
06/16	632	(46)	—	—
06/06	0	0	—	—
06/05	62	(9)	—	—
Annual Growth	20.8%	—	—	—

GARLAND INDEPENDENT SCHOOL DISTRICT

EXECUTIVES

Supt, Dr Bob Morrison
Chief of Staff, Linda Chance
Director, Gradyne Brown
Coordinator, Judy Kriehn
Information Technology/Interne, Phat Tran
Buyer, Kay Moore
Coordinator, Deb Tietjen
Director, Susan Dewese
Teacher, Christie Armstrong
Administrator, Curtis Culwell
Public Relations Staff, Kevin Welch
Auditors: WHITLEY PENN LLP HOUSTON TEX

LOCATIONS

HQ: GARLAND INDEPENDENT SCHOOL DISTRICT
501 S JUPITER RD, GARLAND, TX 750427108
Phone: 972 494-8201
Web: WWW.GARLANDISD.NET

GBMC HEALTHCARE, INC.

EXECUTIVES

Pres-Ceo, John B Chessare
V Pres, Richard Borschuk
Cfo, Eric L Melchior
Sr V Pres, John W Ellis
Sr V Pres, Jody Porter
Coo, Keith Poisson
V Pres, Michael A Forthman
V Pres, Deloris Simpson Tuggle
V Pres, Cathy Hamel
V Pres, Jenny Coldiron
V Pres, George Bayless
Auditors: DELOITTE TAX LLP MC LEAN VA

LOCATIONS

HQ: GBMC HEALTHCARE, INC.
6701 N CHARLES ST, BALTIMORE, MD 212046808
Phone: 443 849-2000

HISTORICAL FINANCIALS
Company Type: Private

Income Statement				FYE: June 30
	REVENUE ($ mil.)	NET INCOME ($ mil.)	NET PROFIT MARGIN	EMPLOYEES
06/18	573	30	5.3%	103
06/17	551	49	9.0%	—
06/15	16	14	88.2%	—
06/14	42	40	95.8%	—
Annual Growth	91.8%	(6.8%)	—	—

2018 Year-End Financials
Return on assets: 12.5%
Return on equity: 5.3%
Current ratio: 0.80

Cash ($ mil.): 34

GEISINGER HEALTH

Geisinger Health System provides health care to a large portion of the Keystone State. The health care system serves more than 3 million residents of nearly 50 counties spanning central and northeastern Pennsylvania. Founded in 1915 the organization's flagship facility is Geisinger Medical Center a 400-bed medical-surgical hospital located in Danville. It includes the Janet Weis Children's Hospital. With joint venture partner HealthSouth Geisinger also runs a rehabilitation hospital in Danville. As part of its operations the health system runs the 240-bed Geisinger Wyoming Valley Medical Center as well as numerous outpatient facilities and doctors' offices located throughout the region.

Geographic Reach

Geisinger Health System extends the reach of its health care system to millions of central and northeastern Pennsylvania residents across about 50 counties.

Financial Performance

In fiscal 2014 the hospital reported net revenue of $9.8 billion a $1 billion increase over the prior year.

Strategy

Geisinger Health System has been working to standardize its procedural operations to improve the quality of care at its facilities and cut costs. Initiatives include assigning care coordinators and providing home visits for high-risk patients to avoid repeat hospitalizations. The health network also implemented an electronic medical records system and began using networking technology to reach into rural markets. Known as "telemedicine" the system's networking technologies are used among other things to facilitate remote two-way consultations between system physicians and rural patients. Additionally Geisinger runs the Geisinger Health Plan a not-for-profit HMO with some 230000 members.

In addition to its clinical operations Geisinger Health System also pursues industry partnerships and licensing opportunities through Geisinger Ventures its business development unit. The unit works to commercialize (and sometimes spin off) medical and technology-related innovations.

Mergers and Acquisitions

Geisinger has grown through several strategic acquisitions as of late. The health care system purchased central Pennsylvania's Cancer Care Centers in late 2014 adding four facilities to its network.

EXECUTIVES

Evp And Coo, Frank Trembulak
Evp Finance And Cfo, Kevin F. Brennan
Evp And Chief Medical Officer, Albert Bothe
Evp And Managing Partner Geisinger Consulting Services, Bruce H. Hamory
Evp And System Chief Nursing Officer, Susan M. Robel
Evp Clinical Operations, Lynn Miller
Evp And Chief Scientific Officer, David H. Ledbetter
President And Ceo, David T. Feinberg
President And Ceo Geisinger Health Plans, Steven R. Youso
Chief Medical Executive Geisinger Northeast Region, Robert J. Weil
Vice President Supply Chain Services, Deborah Templeton
Associate Vice President Nursing, Denise Venditti
Vice President Of Media, Wendy Wilson
Assistant To Greg Snow Vice President Of Revenue Cycle, Denise Baylor
Vice President Clinical Informatics, Joan Topper
Associate Vice President Resource, Nancy G Lawton
Vice President Of Sales, Chris Fanning
Vice President Faculty And Curriculum Development, Nicole Woll
Medical Director Government Programs, Perry Meadows
Auditors: KPMG LLP PHILADELPHIA PA

LOCATIONS

HQ: GEISINGER HEALTH
100 N ACADEMY AVE, DANVILLE, PA 178229800
Phone: 800 275-6401
Web: WWW.GEISINGER.ORG

HISTORICAL FINANCIALS
Company Type: Private

Income Statement				FYE: August 31
	REVENUE ($ mil.)	NET INCOME ($ mil.)	NET PROFIT MARGIN	EMPLOYEES
08/17	632	84	13.3%	7,307
08/16	601	(67)	—	—
Annual Growth	5.2%	—	—	—

2017 Year-End Financials
Return on assets: 4.7%
Return on equity: 13.3%
Current ratio: —

Cash ($ mil.): 445

PRODUCTS/OPERATIONS

Selected Services
Adolescent & Young Adult Medicine
Allergy
Anesthesia
Audiology
Bariatric Surgery
Cancer Institute
Cardiology
Colorectal Surgery
Cosmetics Program
Critical Care
Dental Medicine
Dermatology
Ear Nose & Throat
Emergency Medicine
Endocrinology & Metabolism
Fertility Center
Gastroenterology
Gynecology
Gynecologic Oncology
Heart Services
Hip & Knee Center
Imaging Services
Infectious Disease
Internal Medicine
Joint Replacement
Laboratory Medicine
LASIK Surgery
Mammography
Maternal Fetal Medicine
Mental Health
Minimally Invasive Surgery
Mohs Surgery
Neonatology
Nephrology
Neurodevelopmental Pediatrics
Neuroscience Institute
Neurology
Neurosurgery
Obstetrics
Ophthalmology
Orthopaedics
Osteoporosis
Pain Management
Palliative Medicine
Pediatrics (General)
Pediatric Allergy & Immunology
Pediatric Anesthesia & Sedation
Pediatric Cardiology
Pediatric Dental Surgery
Pediatric Dentistry
Pediatric Dermatology
Pediatric Endocrinology
Pediatric Gastroenterology
Pediatric General Surgery
Pediatric Genetics
Pediatric Hematology/Oncology
Pediatric Hospitalists
Pediatric Infectious Disease
Pediatric Intensive Care
Pediatric Interventional Radiology
Pediatric Nephrology
Pediatric Neurology
Pediatric Neuropsychology
Pediatric Neurosurgery
Pediatric Ophthalmology
Pediatric Orthopaedics
Pediatric Otolaryngology
Pediatric Plastic Surgery
Pediatric Psychology & Psychiatry
Pediatric Pulmonology
Pediatric Rehabilitation
Pediatric Rheumatology
Pediatric Transplant Surgery
Pediatric Trauma
Pediatric Urology
Pediatric Weight Management & Nutrition
Plastic & Reconstructive Surgery
Podiatry
Psychiatry
Pulmonary Medicine
Radiology
Rehabilitation
Rheumatology
Sleep Services
Spine Medicine
Sports Medicine
Surgery
Thoracic Surgery
Transplant Surgery
Trauma Center
Urogynecology
Urology
Vascular Surgery
Weight Management Clinic
Women's Health

Selected Facilities
Geisinger HealthSouth Rehabilitation Hospital
 (Danville)
Geisinger Medical Center (Danville)
 The Janet Weis Children's Hospital
Geisinger Wyoming Valley Medical Center (Wilkes-Barre)
 Pearsall Heart Hospital
Geisinger South Wilkes-Barre Outpatient Center
Shamokin Area Community Hospital

COMPETITORS

Ascension Health
 Blue Cross of Northeastern Pennsylvania
 Capital BlueCross
 Community Health Systems
 HealthAmerica
 Highmark
 PinnacleHealth System
 UPMC
 Universal Health Services
 Wyoming Valley Health Care System

HISTORICAL FINANCIALS

Company Type: Private

Income Statement   FYE: June 30

	REVENUE ($ mil.)	NET INCOME ($ mil.)	NET PROFIT MARGIN	EMPLOYEES
06/18	6,536	359	5.5%	13,030
06/17	6,337	552	8.7%	—
06/10	47	31	65.7%	—
Annual Growth	85.1%	35.8%	—	—

2018 Year-End Financials

Return on assets: 2.8%   Cash ($ mil.): 363
Return on equity: 5.5%
Current ratio: 0.80

GEISINGER MEDICAL CENTER

EXECUTIVES

Ceo, Glenn D Steele Jr
Exec Vice President, Frank J Trembulak
Exec Vice President, Joanne E Wade
Exec Vice President, Albert Bothe Jr
Exec Vice President, Lynn Miller
SEC, Jessica Robertson
Chief Medical Officer, Rosemary Leeming
Evp-CIO, Karen Murphy
Evp-Cfo, Kevin V Roberts
Chief of Emergency, John Skiendzielewski
Customer Representativ, Darren Soles

LOCATIONS

HQ: GEISINGER MEDICAL CENTER
 100 N ACADEMY AVE, DANVILLE, PA 178220001
Phone: 570 271-6211
Web: WWW.GEISINGER.EDU

HISTORICAL FINANCIALS

Company Type: Private

Income Statement   FYE: June 30

	REVENUE ($ mil.)	NET INCOME ($ mil.)	NET PROFIT MARGIN	EMPLOYEES
06/16	1,095	108	9.9%	8,000
06/15	1,058	120	11.4%	—
06/10	815	79	9.7%	—
06/09	735	46	6.3%	—
Annual Growth	5.8%	12.8%	—	—

2016 Year-End Financials

Return on assets: 8.9%   Cash ($ mil.): 8
Return on equity: 9.9%
Current ratio: 1.00

GEISINGER SYSTEM SERVICES

EXECUTIVES

Pres, Glenn D Steele Jr
V Pres System Treas Mgmt, Timothy Fitzgerald
Sr V Pres Treas, Frank J Trembulak
Customer Staff, Randall Hutchison
Vice-President Information Ser, David Macko
Recruiter, Deborah Miller
Coordinator, Paul Venarchick
Director, Bob Murcek

LOCATIONS

HQ: GEISINGER SYSTEM SERVICES
 100 N ACADEMY AVE, DANVILLE, PA 178229800
Phone: 570 271-6211
Web: WWW.GEISINGER.EDU

HISTORICAL FINANCIALS

Company Type: Private

Income Statement   FYE: June 30

	REVENUE ($ mil.)	NET INCOME ($ mil.)	NET PROFIT MARGIN	EMPLOYEES
06/15	535	14	2.7%	344
06/14	582	20	3.4%	—
06/13	519	6	1.3%	—
06/10	375	6	1.7%	—
Annual Growth	7.4%	17.1%	—	—

2015 Year-End Financials

Return on assets: 60.3%   Cash ($ mil.): 3
Return on equity: 2.7%
Current ratio: —

GEISINGER WYOMING VALLEY MEDICAL CENTER

EXECUTIVES

Vp, Timothy Fitzgerald
Ceo Pres Chair of Bd, Glenn D Steele Jr
Sr Vp Treasurer, Frank J Trembulak

Chief of Medicine, Steven B Pierdon
Chief of Medicine, Seth Fisher
Internal Medicine Practitioner, Arvind Kumar
Pharm D, Chris Patton

LOCATIONS

HQ: GEISINGER WYOMING VALLEY MEDICAL
  CENTER
  1000 E MOUNTAIN DR, WILKES BARRE, PA
  187110001
Phone: 570 808-7300
Web: WWW.GEISINGER.ORG

HISTORICAL FINANCIALS

Company Type: Private

Income Statement   FYE: June 30

	REVENUE ($ mil.)	NET INCOME ($ mil.)	NET PROFIT MARGIN	EMPLOYEES
06/16	471	25	5.4%	15
06/10	322	11	3.6%	—
Annual Growth	6.6%	14.1%	—	—

2016 Year-End Financials

Return on assets: 6.1%   Cash ($ mil.): 14
Return on equity: 5.4%
Current ratio: 1.60

GENERAL ELECTRIC INTERNATIONAL OPERATIONS COMPANY, INC.

EXECUTIVES

Pres, Robert Smits
Secretary, Kristen Urso
Lead Acct, Kyle Furnish
Auditors: KPMG LLP STAMFORD CT

LOCATIONS

HQ: GENERAL ELECTRIC INTERNATIONAL
  OPERATIONS COMPANY, INC.
  191 ROSA PARKS ST, CINCINNATI, OH 452022573
Phone: 513 813-9133

HISTORICAL FINANCIALS

Company Type: Private

Income Statement   FYE: December 31

	REVENUE ($ mil.)	NET INCOME ($ mil.)	NET PROFIT MARGIN	EMPLOYEES
12/17	966	192	19.9%	43
12/16	925	(55)	—	—
12/15	925	(22)	—	—
12/14	760	(8)	—	—
Annual Growth	8.3%	—	—	—

2017 Year-End Financials

Return on assets: 7.2%   Cash ($ mil.): 101
Return on equity: 19.9%
Current ratio: 0.30

GENERAL ELECTRIC INTERNATIONAL, INC.

EXECUTIVES

Pres, Giuseppe Recchi
V Pres, Candace F Carson
V Pres, Daniel Janki
SEC, Pierrot Christophe
SEC, Kristen Urso-Rio
Treas, Michael J Geary
Senior Specialist, A Carbone
Power Performance Mana, Jerry King
Fbw Integrator, Joseph Desormeaux
Auditors: KPMG LLP CINCINNATI OHIO

LOCATIONS

HQ: GENERAL ELECTRIC INTERNATIONAL, INC.
  191 ROSA PARKS ST, CINCINNATI, OH 452022573
Phone: 617 443-3000
Web: WWW.GE.COM

HISTORICAL FINANCIALS

Company Type: Private

Income Statement   FYE: December 31

	REVENUE ($ mil.)	NET INCOME ($ mil.)	NET PROFIT MARGIN	EMPLOYEES
12/17	14,100	685	4.9%	125
12/16	13,364	1,339	10.0%	—
12/15	13,288	82	0.6%	—
12/14	12,884	(304)	—	—
Annual Growth	3.1%	—	—	—

2017 Year-End Financials

Return on assets: 7.3%   Cash ($ mil.): 961
Return on equity: 4.9%
Current ratio: 0.20

GENESIS HEALTH SYSTEM

Genesis Health System operates three acute care hospitals in Iowa and Illinois that have more than 660 beds total and employ some 700 doctors. Genesis Medical Center in Davenport Iowa with more than 500 beds is the system's flagship facility; the hospital offers a range of general surgical and specialist health services. The system's Illini Campus in Silvis Illinois features an assisted-living center. The Genesis Medical Center Dewitt Campus serves that Iowa town and the surrounding area with its 13-bed hospital nursing home and related care facilities. Genesis Health System also operates physician practices outpatient centers and a home health agency.

Operations

Altogether Genesis Health System has more than 100 locations including hospitals convenient care locations Genesis Health Group sites physical rehabilitation clinics and outpatient service centers.

Strategy

In 2014 the system invested $15 million in the new Genesis HealthPlex in Bettendorf.

The following year Genesis Health System entered into a partnership with technology vendor Cerner Corporation to improve its patient care enterprise management systems.

Company Background

Genesis Health System had its genesis in 1869 with the establishment of Mercy Hospital (one of the first hospitals west of the Mississippi) and in the 1895 founding of St. Luke's Hospital. The two hospitals merged in 1994 to form the health system.

EXECUTIVES

Vice President Human Resources, Edwin Maxwell
Medical Records Director, Betsy Tibbitts
Clinic Supervisor, Kathryn Ellsworth
Vice President Support Services, Mike Sharp
Vp Human Resources, Heidi Kahly Mcmahon
Medical Librarian, Karlene Campbell
Medical Director, Linda Delessio
Board Member, Deborah Stafford
Secretary, Mary Jo McVey
Auditors: MCGLADREY LLP DAVENPORT IA

LOCATIONS

HQ: GENESIS HEALTH SYSTEM
  1227 E RUSHOLME ST, DAVENPORT, IA 528032459
Phone: 563 421-1000
Web: WWW.GENESISHEALTH.COM

PRODUCTS/OPERATIONS

Selected Services
Bariatric Surgery
Behavioral Health
Birthing Services
Cancer
Cardiology
Home Health/Hospice
Neuroscience
Nursing Homes
Physical Medicine & Rehab
Senior Services

COMPETITORS

Blessing Hospital	Mercy Health Network
Catholic Health Initiatives	OSF Healthcare System
McDonough District Hospital	UnityPoint Health

HISTORICAL FINANCIALS

Company Type: Private

Income Statement   FYE: June 30

	REVENUE ($ mil.)	NET INCOME ($ mil.)	NET PROFIT MARGIN	EMPLOYEES
06/18	511	20	4.1%	5,000
06/16	509	32	6.3%	—
06/15	503	59	11.7%	—
06/14	467	26	5.7%	—
Annual Growth	2.3%	(6.0%)	—	—

2018 Year-End Financials

Return on assets: 5.1%   Cash ($ mil.): 33
Return on equity: 4.1%
Current ratio: 1.50

GENESYS REGIONAL MEDICAL CENTER

Genesys Regional Medical Center generates health care services for residents of a six-county region in eastern Michigan. The integrated medical center features a 410-bed hospital providing general medical and surgical care as well as specialty care in areas such as heart disease (through the

Genesys Heart Institute). Additionally Genesys Regional includes family medicine outpatient diagnostic and rehabilitative care centers. It also operates a women and children's center and in cooperation with Flint's Hurley Medical Center it runs the Genesys Hurley Cancer Institute. Genesys Regional is a member the Genesys Health System which is part of Catholic hospital operator Ascension Health.

Operations

Genesys Regional's emergency room serves as a regional level II trauma center and features a rapid diagnostic center for cardiac conditions. In addition to heart cancer pediatric and women's care the hospital offers specialist centers focusing on orthopedics geriatrics neurology and minimally invasive surgery as well as diagnostic laboratories and fitness facilities. Genesys Regional handles some 21000 inpatient admissions each year including 2200 births. It also conducts about 16000 inpatient and outpatient surgical procedures and sees some 65000 visitors at its emergency department.

In addition to acute care Genesys Regional offers a variety of internships fellowships and residency programs for physicians-in-training through its partnership with Michigan State University. Fellowship programs cover cardiology gastroenterology psychology pulmonary care critical care and hematology and oncology. The hospital also provides continuing education programs for health professionals and it conducts medical and clinical research programs.

Geographic Reach

Genesys Regional is located at the Health Park in Grand Blanc Michigan just south of Flint. Its campus consists of about 480 acres and includes nature trails.

The company offers services for residents of a six-county region including Genesee Shiawassee Lapeer Oakland Livingston and Tuscola counties.

Company Background

The medical center opened its doors in 1997.

EXECUTIVES

Director Of Pharmacy, Marc Guzzardo
Vice President Clinical Services, JoAnne Herman
Medical Director Regional Cardiology Associate, Vuong Duthinh
Director Of Pharmacy Physical Therapy Director
Vice President Of Diagnostic Services, Joy Finkenbiner
Infection Control Director, Diane Scully

LOCATIONS

HQ: GENESYS REGIONAL MEDICAL CENTER
1 GENESYS PKWY, GRAND BLANC, MI 484398065
Phone: 810 606-5000
Web: WWW.PUMMILLPLASTICSURGERY.COM

PRODUCTS/OPERATIONS

Selected Services
Allied Health
Behavioral Health
Breast Center
Diabetes and Nutrition
Emergency
Genesys MRI Center
Health Centers
Health Equipment
Heart Institute
Home Health & Hospice
Inpatient Rehab
Laboratory
Neurosciences
Occupational Health
Oncological Surgery
Oncology
Orthopedics
Senior Services
Short-Term Rehab

Sleep Disorders
Surgery
Urgent Care
Women & Children
Wound Treatment

COMPETITORS

Covenant HealthCare	Hurley Medical Center
Crittenton Hospital	McLaren Health Care
Detroit Medical Center	Sparrow Health System
Henry Ford Health System	Trinity Health (Novi)

HISTORICAL FINANCIALS
Company Type: Private

Income Statement — FYE: June 30

	REVENUE ($ mil.)	NET INCOME ($ mil.)	NET PROFIT MARGIN	EMPLOYEES
06/15	403	12	3.0%	3,739
06/14	417	0	0.1%	—
06/13	415	1	0.4%	—
06/10	452	11	2.5%	—
Annual Growth	(2.3%)	0.9%	—	—

2015 Year-End Financials

Return on assets: 7.7% Cash ($ mil.): 4
Return on equity: 3.0%
Current ratio: 0.10

GEORGIA TECH APPLIED RESEARCH CORPORATION

EXECUTIVES

Ceo-Cfo, Stephen Cross
Chm, Leslie R Sibert
President, G Wayne Clough
SEC, Robert McGrath
Director of Sponsored Programs, G Duane Hutchison
Manager of Sponsored Programs, Patricia Head
Controller, Barbara J Alexander
Assistant SEC Treasurer, Barbara Alexander
Auditors: CHERRY BEKAERT LLP ATLANTA G

LOCATIONS

HQ: GEORGIA TECH APPLIED RESEARCH CORPORATION
505 10TH ST NW, ATLANTA, GA 303185775
Phone: 404 894-4819
Web: WWW.GTRC.GATECH.EDU

HISTORICAL FINANCIALS
Company Type: Private

Income Statement — FYE: June 30

	REVENUE ($ mil.)	NET INCOME ($ mil.)	NET PROFIT MARGIN	EMPLOYEES
06/16	358	(0)	—	1,100
06/15	340	0	0.1%	—
Annual Growth	5.3%	—	—	—

2016 Year-End Financials

Return on assets: 18.7% Cash ($ mil.): 29
Return on equity: (-0.1%)
Current ratio: 1.30

GEORGIA TRANSMISSION CORPORATION

EXECUTIVES

Pres-Ceo, Jerry Donovan
Cfo, Barbara Hampton
SEC, Otis P Jones
SEC, Roy Tollerson Jr
Human Resources, Sharon N Williamson

LOCATIONS

HQ: GEORGIA TRANSMISSION CORPORATION
2100 E EXCHANGE PL, TUCKER, GA 300845342
Phone: 770 270-7400
Web: WWW.GATRANS.COM

HISTORICAL FINANCIALS
Company Type: Private

Income Statement — FYE: December 31

	REVENUE ($ mil.)	NET INCOME ($ mil.)	NET PROFIT MARGIN	EMPLOYEES
12/17	292	14	4.9%	285
12/09	229	14	6.3%	—
12/08	225	13	6.0%	—
Annual Growth	3.0%	0.7%	—	—

2017 Year-End Financials

Return on assets: 9.6% Cash ($ mil.): 32
Return on equity: 4.9%
Current ratio: 0.10

GHA TECHNOLOGIES, INC.

EXECUTIVES

Pres-SEC, George Hertzberg
Vice President, Steven Nevins
Manager, Hugo Del Castillo
Regional Sales Manager, James Welsh
Regional Sales Manager, Kent Kerslake
Accounting Staff, Linda Sanchez
Regional Sales Manager, Timothy Hesselgren
Regional Sales Manager, Aj Matheson
Vice-President Sales, Cory Reyman
Regional Sales Manager, Gregg Waller
Regional Sales Manager, Jim Lottig
Auditors: JOHNSON LAWDAHL ENDRES PLLC

LOCATIONS

HQ: GHA TECHNOLOGIES, INC.
8998 E RAINTREE DR, SCOTTSDALE, AZ 852607024
Phone: 480 951-6865
Web: WWW.GHA-ASSOCIATES.COM

HISTORICAL FINANCIALS
Company Type: Private

Income Statement				FYE: December 31
	REVENUE ($ mil.)	NET INCOME ($ mil.)	NET PROFIT MARGIN	EMPLOYEES
12/17	363	7	2.0%	165
12/15	138	0	0.7%	—
12/14	118	1	0.9%	—
12/13	103	1	1.1%	—
Annual Growth	36.8%	59.2%	—	—

2017 Year-End Financials
Return on assets: 2.8%
Return on equity: 2.0%
Current ratio: 1.50
Cash ($ mil.): 5

GILBANE BUILDING COMPANY

Gilbane Building Company has built a big business constructing for equally large customers. The firm provides construction services consulting subcontracting and facilities management to commercial institutional and governmental markets. Operating as the construction arm of Gilbane the company builds schools hospitals laboratories and prisons serving both the public and private sectors. Its completed projects include the Stroh Center at Bowling Green State University and the National WWII Memorial in Washington DC. Founded in 1873 as a carpentry and general contracting shop the family-owned Gilbane Building Company operates from more than 50 offices around the world.

Operations
The company has worked on a wide range of projects including: the Worcester Recovery Center & Hospital El Paso Corporation Building Renovation New York State Capital Restoration Georgia Tech Carbon Neutral Energy Solutions Laboratory University of North Florida Student Wellness and Sports Albert Einstein Health Network Elmhurst Memorial Healthcare and the University of Puerto Rico Molecular Sciences Building.

As part of its business Gilbane Building Company operates ITSI Gilbane a major provider of engineering and construction services to the US federal government including the Department of Defense Environmental Protection Agency and Department of Energy.

Geographic Reach
With more than 50 offices and 1000 projects underway around the world Gilbane Building Company enjoys a geographic footprint that extends from the US to Japan the United Arab Emirates Ireland South Korea and Afghanistan.

Sales and Marketing
Gilbane Building Company serves several sectors such as healthcare higher education K-12 schools federal and public entities mission critical corporate and sports and recreation. In 2014 the company boasted a 98.4% client satisfaction rate and reported that 65% of its work comes from repeat clients.

Some of its clients have included: Einstein Healthcare Network Google Inc. Operations Mane Inc Wilmington Public School Uihlein Wilson Architects City of Phoenix Crime Lab and the Operating Forces D&C Division.

Strategy

Gilbane Building Company has been busy working on projects in all parts of the country. In 2014 Gilbane secured a $43 million contract for historical renovation work on Pomerene and Oxley Halls on the Ohio State University campus. The firm's 2013 projects included the 131000-sq.-ft. Bergen County Justice Center in Hackensack New Jersey; the Columbus Regional Airport Authority's modernization of concourses B and C at Port Columbus international airports; and Miami University's Kreger Hall Rehabilitation & Addition Project which included the reorganization of 33372 sq. ft. of interior spaces and upgrades to the building's infrastructure as well as a major rehabilitation.

The company also continues to be recognized for its environment-conscious building designs particularly with schools. In early 2015 the company's completed Dunbar High School project — equipped with an advanced geothermal system a 482 kW array of photovoltaic panels and 20000-gallon cisterns — was awarded the LEED for Schools v2009 Platinum certification taking home the highest LEED score on record worldwide. Also in early 2015 the company was awarded the #1 ranking for Education K-12 Building Design and Construction and ranked within the top 5 of green contractor engineers.

It has also extended its reach in Europe in recent years. In 2012 the company formed a joint venture with Ed. ZA?blinAG known as ZA?blin Gilbane to pursue and execute projects in Europe.

EXECUTIVES

President And Ceo, Michael C. (Mike) McKelvy, age 58
Vice Chairman, William J. (Bill) Gilbane, age 71
Chairman, Thomas F. (Tom) Gilbane, age 70
Auditors: RSM US LLP BOSTON MASSACHUSE

LOCATIONS

HQ: GILBANE BUILDING COMPANY
7 JACKSON WALKWAY STE 2, PROVIDENCE, RI 029033694
Phone: 401 456-5800
Web: WWW.GILBANECO.COM

PRODUCTS/OPERATIONS

Selected Markets
Convention/cultural
Corporate
Criminal justice
Federal/public
Health care
  Children's hospitals
  Women's centers
  Cardiac-care centers
  Cancer centers
  Clinical and research facilities
Higher education
  Research laboratories
  Academic facilities
  Admissions buildings
  Residence halls
  Performing arts centers
  Sports and recreational centers
  Libraries and technology centers
  Student unions
K-12 schools
Life sciences
Mission critical
Sports/recreation
Transportation
Water/wastewater

Selected Services
Pre-construction
  Transition planning and management
  Building information modeling
  Conceptual cost modeling
  High-performance building & energy modeling
  Interdisciplinary document coordination
Consulting
  CAT-response

Facilities management services
Schedule & risk analysis
Transition planning & management
Construction
  Construction management at risk
  Construction management as agent
  Lump sum general contracting
  Integrated project delivery

COMPETITORS

Barton Malow	McCarthy Building
Batson-Cook	Peter Kiewit Sons'
Bechtel	Skanska USA Building
Bernards Brothers	Swinerton
Clark Construction Group	The Pike Company
Dimeo Construction	Thos. S. Byrne
Fluor	Turner Construction
KBR	Turner Corporation
L.F. Driscoll	Tutor Perini
MEDCO Construction	Walbridge Aldinger
	Whiting-Turner

HISTORICAL FINANCIALS
Company Type: Private

Income Statement				FYE: December 31
	REVENUE ($ mil.)	NET INCOME ($ mil.)	NET PROFIT MARGIN	EMPLOYEES
12/17	4,899	63	1.3%	2,500
12/14	3,840	0	—	—
12/13	4,100	0	—	—
12/12	3,386	0	—	—
Annual Growth	7.7%	—	—	—

2017 Year-End Financials
Return on assets: 19.5%
Return on equity: 1.3%
Current ratio: 1.00
Cash ($ mil.): 252

GILBERT UNIFIED SCHOOL DISTRICT 41

EXECUTIVES

Supt, Bradley K Barrett
Asst Supt, Clyde R Dangerfield
Executive of Information Techn, John Maas
Information, Mario Orona
Director, Jack Blanchard
Administrative Secretary, Laura Anderson
Coordinator, Damon Carvalho
Teacher, Rachel Ciccarone
Transportation Associate, Brian Fett
Director, Lorie Miller
Coordinator, Scott Lymer

LOCATIONS

HQ: GILBERT UNIFIED SCHOOL DISTRICT 41
140 S GILBERT RD, GILBERT, AZ 852961016
Phone: 480 497-3452
Web: WWW.GILBERTSCHOOLS.NET

HISTORICAL FINANCIALS
Company Type: Private

Income Statement   FYE: June 30

	REVENUE ($ mil.)	NET INCOME ($ mil.)	NET PROFIT MARGIN	EMPLOYEES
06/17	296	(6)	—	4,800
06/06	262	14	5.5%	—
06/05	262	14	5.5%	—
06/04	1,933	0	0.0%	—
Annual Growth	(13.4%)	—	—	—

GLENS FALLS HOSPITAL

EXECUTIVES

Pres, Dianne Shugrue
President, David G Kruczlnicki
V Pres-Cfo, D Michael Niles
Chief Operating Officer, James W Connolly
Cfo-Vice President, Mitchell J Amado III
Vice President, Kyle Brock
Vice President, Edward Hanchett
Senior Vice-President, Jeffrey Treasure
Coordinator, Donna Morgan
Information Technology Manager, Scott Williams
Technical Specialist, Chris Kopf

LOCATIONS

HQ: GLENS FALLS HOSPITAL
100 PARK ST, GLENS FALLS, NY 128014447
Phone: 518 926-1000
Web: WWW.GLENSFALLSHOSPITAL.ORG

HISTORICAL FINANCIALS
Company Type: Private

Income Statement   FYE: December 31

	REVENUE ($ mil.)	NET INCOME ($ mil.)	NET PROFIT MARGIN	EMPLOYEES
12/15	316	(3)	—	2,726
12/14	289	5	1.7%	—
12/13	308	1	0.5%	—
12/09	286	(0)	—	—
Annual Growth	1.7%	—	—	—

2015 Year-End Financials

Return on assets: 7.5%   Cash ($ mil.): 20
Return on equity: (-1.0%)
Current ratio: 1.00

GLOBAL HEALTH SOLUTIONS INC

EXECUTIVES

Vice President, T Rosenberger
V Pres, Thomas Rosenberger

LOCATIONS

HQ: GLOBAL HEALTH SOLUTIONS INC
325 SWANTON WAY, DECATUR, GA 300303001
Phone: 404 592-1430
Web: WWW.TASKFORCE.ORG

HISTORICAL FINANCIALS
Company Type: Private

Income Statement   FYE: August 31

	REVENUE ($ mil.)	NET INCOME ($ mil.)	NET PROFIT MARGIN	EMPLOYEES
08/15	1,609	0	—	2
08/14	1,790	0	—	—
08/13	1,574	0	—	—
08/10	1,120	0	0.0%	—
Annual Growth	7.5%	—	—	—

GOLD-EAGLE COOPERATIVE

EXECUTIVES

Board Member, Bill Cruise

LOCATIONS

HQ: GOLD-EAGLE COOPERATIVE
415 LOCUST ST, GOLDFIELD, IA 505425092
Phone: 515 825-3161
Web: WWW.GOLDEAGLECOOP.COM

COMPETITORS

ADM	GROWMARK
Ag Processing Inc.	Heartland Co-op
Bunge Limited	JR Simplot
CHS	NEW Cooperative
Cargill	West Central Co-op
DeBruce Grain	Wilbur-Ellis
Farmers Cooperative Society	

HISTORICAL FINANCIALS
Company Type: Private

Income Statement   FYE: September 30

	REVENUE ($ mil.)	NET INCOME ($ mil.)	NET PROFIT MARGIN	EMPLOYEES
09/17	284	8	3.0%	215
09/16	309	10	3.2%	—
09/09	302	10	3.3%	—
09/08	304	9	3.2%	—
Annual Growth	(0.8%)	(1.2%)	—	—

2017 Year-End Financials

Return on assets: 2.0%   Cash ($ mil.): 11
Return on equity: 3.0%
Current ratio: 0.50

GOOD SAMARITAN HOSPITAL

Good Samaritan Hospital provides a full slate of healthcare services to both southwest Indiana and southeast Illinois. Its services include cardiology emergency care orthopedics women's health and pediatrics among others. The 230-bed hospital is located a few blocks from the Wabash River which forms the border between the Hoosier and Prairies states. Good Samaritan operates specialty units as well including same-day surgery breast care be-

---

havioral health radiology sleep cancer care and rehabilitation centers. It also provides home health and hospice services. Established in 1908 with 25 beds Good Samaritan was Indiana's first county hospital.

Operations
Busy regional hospital Good Samaritan logs more than 458000 outpatient visits each year as well as an additional 35950 visits to its emergency room. It boasts an Imaging Center Dayson Heart Center and Cancer Pavilion with a 25000-sq.-ft. comprehensive oncology care center.

Good Samaritan is a member of the Voluntary Hospital Association Indiana Hospital Association and Genesis Health.

Geographic Reach
Located in Vincennes Indiana Good Samaritan serves residents along the neighboring southern borders of both Indiana and Illinois.

Sales and Marketing
The hospital uses TV advertising to market its services.

Strategy
While Good Samaritan is focused on serving patients as an outpatient facility the regional hospital is nearing completion of a new inpatient tower. It's building a 200000-sq.-ft. five-story 120-bed inpatient tower at the cost of $109 million. As part of this BEACON project Good Samaritan is redesigning key healthcare service areas and upgrading its critical engineering systems. Project completion dates span 2014 to late 2016 for the BEACON project.

To make information more readily available to its patients Good Samaritan in 2012 rolled out an Indiana Health Information Exchange clinical messaging service called DOCS4DOCS. The service provides a portal for accessing lab results radiology reports transcripts pathology and hospital admissions reports and discharge and transfer reports. Good Samaritan is one of several thousand participating hospitals along with physician practices labs and radiology centers.

EXECUTIVES

Medical Records Director, Wendy Mangin
Medical Librarian, Carmon Graves
Vice President Of Human Resources, Emily A Heineke
Ambulatory Services Director, Brenda Winkler
Ambulatory Services Dir, DEBBIE STEVENS
Occupational Therapy Director, Tammy Klein
Vice President Professional Support Services, Scott Kaminski
Vice President Operations, Matthew Schuckman
Physical Therapy Director, Clara Biehl
Physical Therapy Director, STEVE WISSEL
Secretary, Valerie Turpin
Auditors: BKD LLP INDIANAPOLIS IN

LOCATIONS

HQ: GOOD SAMARITAN HOSPITAL
520 S 7TH ST, VINCENNES, IN 475911038
Phone: 812 882-5220
Web: WWW.GSHVIN.ORG

PRODUCTS/OPERATIONS

Selected Centers
Dayson Heart Center
Cancer Pavilion
Imaging Center

COMPETITORS

Daviess Community Hospital	St. John's Hospital (Illinois)
Deaconess Health System	St. Mary's Medical Center of Evansville
IU Health	Wabash County Hospital
Southern Illinois Healthcare	

HISTORICAL FINANCIALS
Company Type: Private

Income Statement   FYE: December 31

	REVENUE ($ mil.)	NET INCOME ($ mil.)	NET PROFIT MARGIN	EMPLOYEES
12/17	322	(5)	—	1,900
12/16	315	0	0.1%	—
12/15	291	(4)	—	—
12/14	537	9	1.8%	—
Annual Growth	(15.6%)	—	—	—

2017 Year-End Financials

Return on assets: 4.7%   Cash ($ mil.): 36
Return on equity: (-1.6%)
Current ratio: 2.10

GOOD SAMARITAN HOSPITAL

LOCATIONS

HQ: GOOD SAMARITAN HOSPITAL
   2222 PHILADELPHIA DR, DAYTON, OH 454061891
Phone: 937 278-2612
Web: WWW.MONTORTHO.NET

COMPETITORS

Kettering Health   OhioHealth
   Network   TriHealth

HISTORICAL FINANCIALS
Company Type: Private

Income Statement   FYE: December 31

	REVENUE ($ mil.)	NET INCOME ($ mil.)	NET PROFIT MARGIN	EMPLOYEES
12/15	321	7	2.2%	2,000
12/06	307	11	3.9%	—
12/05	274	(5)	—	—
12/03	282	20	7.3%	—
Annual Growth	1.1%	(8.5%)	—	—

2015 Year-End Financials

Return on assets: 3.9%   Cash ($ mil.): 11
Return on equity: 2.2%
Current ratio: 1.70

GOOD SAMARITAN HOSPITAL

EXECUTIVES

Vice President Finance, Susan Dries
Vice President, Susan Harlow
Vice President Of Business Development, Samuel
   Feuerlicht
Medical Director, Harry Rosen
Vice President, Campbell Dean
Managing Director, Jigar Kadakia

LOCATIONS

HQ: GOOD SAMARITAN HOSPITAL
   1225 WILSHIRE BLVD, LOS ANGELES, CA 900171901
Phone: 213 977-2121
Web: WWW.GOODSAM.ORG

PRODUCTS/OPERATIONS

Selected Services
Clinical Services
Cardiology
Cardiac Surgery
Comprehensive Sleep Center
Diagnostic Imaging (Radiology)
Emergency Services
ENT (Ear Nose & Throat)
Gamma Knife
Gastroenterology
Laboratory
Neurosciences
Oncology (Cancer)
Ophthalmology and Retinal Medicine
Orthopedics
Physical Medicine
Podiatry
Pulmonary Medicine and Respiratory Care
Radiation Oncology
Surgery
Women's Health and Newborn Services
Urology

COMPETITORS

Aptium Oncology   Hoag Memorial Hospital
   Brotman Medical Center   Hollywood Presbyterian
   Cedars-Sinai Medical   Medical Center
      Center   Methodist Hospital of
   Childrens Hospital Los   Southern California
      Angeles   Newhall Memorial
   Glendale Adventist   Hospital
      Medical Center   Tenet Healthcare
   HCA

HISTORICAL FINANCIALS
Company Type: Private

Income Statement   FYE: August 31

	REVENUE ($ mil.)	NET INCOME ($ mil.)	NET PROFIT MARGIN	EMPLOYEES
08/16	319	19	6.1%	1,500
08/15	351	38	11.0%	—
08/03	219	0	0.0%	—
08/02	205	0	—	—
Annual Growth	3.2%	—	—	—

2016 Year-End Financials

Return on assets: 10.0%   Cash ($ mil.): 5
Return on equity: 6.1%
Current ratio: 0.50

GOOD SAMARITAN HOSPITAL CORVALLIS

EXECUTIVES

Pres, Becky Rose
V Pres-Fin, Ronald S Stevens
Prin, Larry Mullins
Director, Jana Kay Slater
Coordinator, Gloria Nordyke
Coordinator, Kim Dowe
Coordinator, Teena Graham
General Vascular Surgeon, Toshio Nagamoto
Information Technology Support, Beth Lackey
Physical Therapist, Daren Schell
Information Technology Directo, Manuel Amaez

LOCATIONS

HQ: GOOD SAMARITAN HOSPITAL CORVALLIS
   3600 NW SAMARITAN DR, CORVALLIS, OR
   973303700
Phone: 541 768-5069
Web: WWW.GOODSAMHOSP.ORG

HISTORICAL FINANCIALS
Company Type: Private

Income Statement   FYE: December 31

	REVENUE ($ mil.)	NET INCOME ($ mil.)	NET PROFIT MARGIN	EMPLOYEES
12/16	382	(9)	—	900
12/15	356	9	2.7%	—
12/14	312	(6)	—	—
12/08	231	5	2.3%	—
Annual Growth	6.5%	—	—	—

2016 Year-End Financials

Return on assets: 3.4%   Cash ($ mil.): —
Return on equity: (-2.4%)
Current ratio: 0.70

GOOD SAMARITAN HOSPITAL MEDICAL CENTER

The folks at Good Samaritan Hospital Medical Center have plenty of reasons to feel good about their efforts. The hospital is part of Catholic Health Services of Long Island (CHS) and serves the south shore community of West Islip New York. The full-service medical center boasts 900 physicians and 440 acute care beds offering a complete range of health care counseling and rehabilitation services. Good Samaritan provides emergency medicine and trauma care in addition to oncology cardiology pediatric woman's health diagnostic and surgical care. It also operates the Good Samaritan Nursing Home a 100-bed skilled nursing facility as well as satellite clinics and a home health care agency.

Operations

Good Samaritan which contributes about 28% of its parent's revenue logged more than 95000 emergency department visits in 2012. Its ambulatory surgery department treats an average of nearly 300 patients weekly as part of its focus on same-day procedures. Additionally the medical facility in 2012 admitted 27615 patients and logged 2820 births 66000 rehabilitation inpatient visits and 49640 dialysis treatments.

The hospital's outpatient services include same day surgeries pulmonary rehabilitation pediatric specialty visits and physical occupational and speech therapy sessions; it also has satellite locations that provide dialysis treatment. Good Samaritan's palliative care program offers an 11-bed dedicated acute palliative care inpatient unit.

Geographic Reach

Good Samaritan Hospital Medical Center serves those in and around West Islip New York.

Financial Performance

Net patient revenue dragged down Good Samaritan's revenue increases in fiscal 2012 vs. 2011. During the reporting period the medical center posted $579 million in revenue representing a marginal $260000 rise. Net income dropped some

77% to \$8.3 million in 2012 vs. 2011 thanks to rising operating expenses from increases in CHS Services.

Strategy

Good Samaritan is recognized for its cancer care and radiology programs as well as its cardiac pediatric and women's health services all of which it has been expanding and enhancing in recent years. For instance the hospital added a nephrology unit in 2011 within its pediatric division to evaluate and treat children with kidney disease. It expanded its pediatric nephrology unit in 2012 by opening a new 16-bed surgical intensive care unit (SICU). Good Samaritan also added a new diagnostic imaging center in 2012 that provides radiology services including breast imaging.

In addition Good Samaritan is working to add an open-heart surgery program to its cardiology division through a partnership with St. Francis Hospital another member of the CHS organization also known as The Heart Center. In 2013 Good Samaritan became the first facility in the New York metropolitan region to install and offer the GE Innova IGS 530 digital cardiovascular and interventional imaging system in its cardiac catheterization laboratory.

The not-for-profit facility's growth measures are supported in part by its charitable organization The Guilds of Good Samaritan Hospital Medical Center. The Good Samaritan hospital provides some \$50 million in community service and charity care each year.

Company Background

Founded in 1959 Good Samaritan became part of the CHS organization in 1997.

EXECUTIVES

Physical Therapy Director, Jill Bocchieri
Vice President, Stephen Trapani

LOCATIONS

HQ: GOOD SAMARITAN HOSPITAL MEDICAL CENTER
1000 MONTAUK HWY, WEST ISLIP, NY 117954927
Phone: 631 376-3000
Web: WWW.GOODSAM.ORG

PRODUCTS/OPERATIONS

Selected Premier Services
Cancer Care
Cardiac Care
Children's Care
Emergency Services
Satellites
Surgery
Women's Care

Selected Services
Ambulatory Surgery Unit
Audiology/Hearing Aids
BirthPlace
Breast Health Center
Cancer Care
Cancer Surgery
Cardiac Rehabilitation
Cardiology Services
Center for Pediatric Specialty Care
Care Management and Social Work
Child Life Services
da Vinci Surgery
Dentistry
Dermatology
Dialysis Services
Ear Nose and Throat
Emergency Department
Endocrinology
Family Practice
Gastroenterology
Good Samaritan Hospital Foundation
Good Samaritan Nursing Home
Hematology and Oncology
Imaging Services
Infectious Diseases
Inpatient Dialysis

Internal Medicine
Laboratory
Long Term Home Health Care
Managed Care
Martin Luther King Jr. Community Health Center
Maternal Fetal Medicine
Medical Education
Neonatology
Nephrology
Neurosurgery
Nursing at Good Sam
Nutrition and Food Services
Obstetrics and Gynecology
Oncology
Ophthalmology
Oral Surgery
Orthopaedics
Osteoporosis
Palliative Care
Pain Management
Pastoral/Spiritual Care Department
Pathology
Pediatric Services
Perinatal Education
Plastic and Reconstructive Services
Podiatry
Pre-Surgical Testing
Psychiatry
Pulmonary Rehabilitation
Radiation Oncology Center
Rehabilitation Services
Respiratory Care
Safe Haven Program
Sleep Apnea Center
Special Care
Support Groups
Surgery
Thoracic Surgery
Trauma Services
Urology
Vascular Suite
Vascular Surgery
Weight Loss Surgery/Bariatric Surgery
Women's Imaging Center

COMPETITORS

Brookhaven Memorial Hospital Medical Center
CSH
Catholic Healthcare System
Continuum Health Partners
Mather Memorial Hospital
Memorial Sloan-Kettering
New York City Health and Hospitals
NewYork-Presbyterian Healthcare
Northwell Health
Winthrop-University Hospital

HISTORICAL FINANCIALS

Company Type: Private

Income Statement   FYE: December 31

	REVENUE ($ mil.)	NET INCOME ($ mil.)	NET PROFIT MARGIN	EMPLOYEES
12/15	505	28	5.7%	3,774
12/14	488	36	7.5%	—
12/13*	534	(28)	—	—
06/05	118	(1)	—	—
Annual Growth	14.1%	—	—	—

*Fiscal year change

2015 Year-End Financials

Return on assets: 7.7%   Cash ($ mil.): 72
Return on equity: 5.7%
Current ratio: 1.20

GOOD SAMARITAN HOSPITAL OF CINCINNATI

EXECUTIVES

Pres, John S Prout
Chm, Robert L Walker
Sr Vice President, John R Robinson
Cfo, Craig Rucker
Coo, Gerald Oliphant
Internal Medicine Practitioner, Aleksandr Yultyev
Internal Medicine Practitioner, Ashirf Al-Ghanoudi
Internal Medicine Practitioner, Hiro Kawata
Internal Medicine Practitioner, Irina Gagua
Health Professional, Jiang Wu
Health Professional, Michelle Sotos
Auditors: BKD LLP CINCINNATI OH

LOCATIONS

HQ: GOOD SAMARITAN HOSPITAL OF CINCINNATI
375 DIXMYTH AVE, CINCINNATI, OH 452202489
Phone: 513 569-6251

HISTORICAL FINANCIALS

Company Type: Private

Income Statement   FYE: June 30

	REVENUE ($ mil.)	NET INCOME ($ mil.)	NET PROFIT MARGIN	EMPLOYEES
06/18	579	48	8.3%	3,452
06/15	578	81	14.0%	—
06/13	483	60	12.4%	—
06/10	479	43	9.1%	—
Annual Growth	2.4%	1.2%	—	—

2018 Year-End Financials

Return on assets: 4.5%   Cash ($ mil.): —
Return on equity: 8.3%
Current ratio: 1.10

GOOD SAMARITAN HOSPITAL, L.P.

Good Samaritan Hospital lends a hand to help Silicon Valley'sA techies and their neighbors stay healthy. The facility part of the HCA family of for-profit hospitalsA administers careA throughA campusesA inA San JoseA (the main campus) and Los Gatos California. Good Samaritan Hospital provides general acute care as well as a host of tertiary services that includeA cardiology and cardiovascular surgery; oncology; obstetrics and gynecology; and psychiatry (both inpatient and outpatient care). The main campus hospital has some 408 patient beds and 600 physicians and the Los Gatos outpatient and short-stay facilityA houses approximately 100 beds.

Operations

Each year Good Samaritan admitsA 17000 patients (excluding newborns) and handles more than 93500 outpatient visits. More than 4000 deliveries and 8000 surgeries are performed annually in 18 surgical suites.

Strategy

In additionA to being aA community hospital Good Samaritan is a world-class academic medical center affiliated with both USC and UCLA Schools of Medicine. To cater to theA diverse urban population the hospital system servesA Good Samaritan'sA medical staff and employees speak more than 54 languages/dialects.

Company Background

Good Samaritan Hospital opened its doors in 1965 as an acute care hospital with a staff of about 400.

EXECUTIVES

Vice President Of Operations, Jim Lamar

LOCATIONS

HQ: GOOD SAMARITAN HOSPITAL, L.P.
2425 SAMARITAN DR, SAN JOSE, CA 951243985
Phone: 408 559-2011
Web: WWW.GOODSAMSANJOSE.COM

PRODUCTS/OPERATIONS

Selected Services and Departments
Cardiology
Cardiac Surgery
Comprehensive Sleep Center
Diagnostic Imaging (Radiology)
ENT (Ear Nose & Throat)
Emergency Services
Gamma Knife
Gastroenterology
Laboratory
Neurosciences
Oncology (Cancer)
Opthalmology & Retinal Medicine
Orthopedics
Podiatry
Physical Medicine
Pulmonary Medicine & Respiratory Care
Radiation Oncology
Surgery
Women's Health & Newborn Services
Urology

COMPETITORS

Dignity Health
Mills-Peninsula Health Services
Sequoia Healthcare District
Stanford Health Care
The Palo Alto Medical Foundation
ValleyCare Health System

HISTORICAL FINANCIALS

Company Type: Private

Income Statement				FYE: January 31
	REVENUE ($ mil.)	NET INCOME ($ mil.)	NET PROFIT MARGIN	EMPLOYEES
01/17	618	141	22.8%	1,800
01/09*	413	30	7.3%	—
05/05	170	0	—	—
12/03	0	0	—	—
Annual Growth	—	—	—	—

*Fiscal year change

2017 Year-End Financials

Return on assets: 2.0%   Cash ($ mil.): —
Return on equity: 22.8%
Current ratio: 1.90

GOOD SAMARITAN REGIONAL MEDICAL CENTER

EXECUTIVES

Ceo, Philip Patterson
Ceo, Mary Leahy
Ceo, Dominick Stanzione
Sr Vice President, Jeff Reilly
Internal Medicine Practitioner, Emil Fernando
Director of Psychiatric Srvs, Bhupinder Gill
Cardiology Director, Richard Cantor

LOCATIONS

HQ: GOOD SAMARITAN REGIONAL MEDICAL CENTER
255 LAFAYETTE AVE, SUFFERN, NY 109014812
Phone: 845 368-5000
Web: WWW.GOODSAMHOSP.ORG

HISTORICAL FINANCIALS

Company Type: Private

Income Statement				FYE: December 31
	REVENUE ($ mil.)	NET INCOME ($ mil.)	NET PROFIT MARGIN	EMPLOYEES
12/15	286	36	12.8%	1,600
12/14	283	4	1.5%	—
12/08*	254	(12)	—	—
06/05	118	(1)	—	—
Annual Growth	8.3%	—	—	—

*Fiscal year change

2015 Year-End Financials

Return on assets: 5.6%   Cash ($ mil.): —
Return on equity: 12.8%
Current ratio: 1.30

GOOD360

EXECUTIVES

Pres-Ceo, Cindy Hallberlin
Chb, Carly Fiorina
V Pres, Kevin Hagan
V Pres, Melissa Trumpower
Coo, Don Miller
Cfo, Gerald Borenstein
Chief Financial Officer, David Maland
Officer, Elie Hollander
Manager, Lena Douglas
Auditors: BDO USA LLP BETHESDA MD

LOCATIONS

HQ: GOOD360
675 N WASHINGTON ST # 330, ALEXANDRIA, VA 223141939
Phone: 703 836-2121
Web: WWW.GOOD360.ORG

HISTORICAL FINANCIALS

Company Type: Private

Income Statement				FYE: December 31
	REVENUE ($ mil.)	NET INCOME ($ mil.)	NET PROFIT MARGIN	EMPLOYEES
12/15	382	4	1.1%	36
12/14	314	2	0.8%	—
12/13	310	(12)	—	—
12/08	426	0	—	—
Annual Growth	(1.5%)	—	—	—

2015 Year-End Financials

Return on assets: 0.3%   Cash ($ mil.): —
Return on equity: 1.1%
Current ratio: 0.20

GOODWILL INDUSTRIES OF SOUTHEASTERN WISCONSIN, INC.

EXECUTIVES

Pres-Ceo, Jacqueline Hallberg
Vice President, Mike Boelter
Vice President, Pat Boelter
Vice President, Timothy Christian
Vice President, Dan Depies
Vice-President Business Develo, Dwight Ferguson
Director, Betty Geren
Project Manager, Larry Champion
Human Resources Manager, Jennifer Nelson
Auditors: GRANT THORNTON LLP APPLETON

LOCATIONS

HQ: GOODWILL INDUSTRIES OF SOUTHEASTERN WISCONSIN, INC.
5400 S 60TH ST, GREENDALE, WI 531291404
Phone: 414 847-4200
Web: WWW.GOODWILLCHICAGO.COM

HISTORICAL FINANCIALS

Company Type: Private

Income Statement				FYE: December 31
	REVENUE ($ mil.)	NET INCOME ($ mil.)	NET PROFIT MARGIN	EMPLOYEES
12/17	414	5	1.4%	3,391
12/16	392	6	1.7%	—
12/15	306	10	3.3%	—
12/14	282	8	3.0%	—
Annual Growth	13.5%	(11.2%)	—	—

2017 Year-End Financials

Return on assets: 2.4%   Cash ($ mil.): 42
Return on equity: 1.4%
Current ratio: 1.70

GORDON E. AND BETTY I. MOORE FOUNDATION

EXECUTIVES

Pres, Lewis W Coleman
Cao, Chris McCrum
Chief Investment Officer, Denise Strack
Senior Administrative Assistan, Daniela Murcio

LOCATIONS

HQ: GORDON E. AND BETTY I. MOORE FOUNDATION
1661 PAGE MILL RD, PALO ALTO, CA 943041209
Phone: 650 213-3000
Web: WWW.MOORE.ORG

HISTORICAL FINANCIALS
Company Type: Private

Income Statement				FYE: December 31
	REVENUE ($ mil.)	NET INCOME ($ mil.)	NET PROFIT MARGIN	EMPLOYEES
12/15	284	(46)	—	75
12/14	423	154	36.4%	—
12/09	150	(50)	—	—
Annual Growth	11.2%	—	—	—

2015 Year-End Financials
Return on assets: 4.8% Cash ($ mil.): 296
Return on equity: (-16.4%)
Current ratio: 8.90

GORDON RESEARCH CONFERENCES INC

EXECUTIVES
Director, Nancy Ryan Gray
Operations Manager, Taryn Groves
Scientist, Bruce Demple
Treasurer, Taryn G Moran
Coordinator, Michelle Knapp
Conference Operations and Gran, Darlene Armstrong
Chief Operating Officer, Sarah Blendermann
Auditors: KPMG LLP BOSTON MA

LOCATIONS
HQ: GORDON RESEARCH CONFERENCES INC
512 LIBERTY LN, WEST KINGSTON, RI 028921502
Phone: 401 783-7644
Web: WWW.GRC.ORG

HISTORICAL FINANCIALS
Company Type: Private

Income Statement				FYE: October 31
	REVENUE ($ mil.)	NET INCOME ($ mil.)	NET PROFIT MARGIN	EMPLOYEES
10/16	410	371	90.7%	39
10/15	40	2	6.4%	—
10/14	40	4	11.1%	—
10/13	37	5	15.4%	—
Annual Growth	121.2%	299.7%	—	—

2016 Year-End Financials
Return on assets: — Cash ($ mil.): 7
Return on equity: 90.7%
Current ratio: 4.80

GRADY MEMORIAL HOSPITAL CORPORATION

EXECUTIVES
Pres-Ceo, John M Haupert

Cfo, Mark Meyer
Exec Vice President, Christopher R Mosley
Exec Vice President, Timothy Jefferson
Exec Vice President, Curtis Lewis
Vp of Fin, Ozzie Gilbert
Senior Vice-President, Calvin Thomas IV
Grants Manager, David Noble
Security Staff, Donise Musheno
Psychologist, Christopher Hill
Information Technology/Interne, David Butler
Auditors: KPMG LLP GREENSBORO NC

LOCATIONS
HQ: GRADY MEMORIAL HOSPITAL CORPORATION
80 JESSE HILL JR DR SE, ATLANTA, GA 303033050
Phone: 404 616-4360
Web: WWW.GRADYHEALTH.ORG

HISTORICAL FINANCIALS
Company Type: Private

Income Statement				FYE: December 31
	REVENUE ($ mil.)	NET INCOME ($ mil.)	NET PROFIT MARGIN	EMPLOYEES
12/16	1,444	47	3.3%	4,500
12/15	1,230	47	3.9%	—
12/08	358	(56)	—	—
Annual Growth	19.1%	—	—	—

2016 Year-End Financials
Return on assets: 10.7% Cash ($ mil.): 192
Return on equity: 3.3%
Current ratio: 1.90

GRAHAM ENTERPRISE, INC.

EXECUTIVES
Pres, John C Graham
V Pres, Eugene W Graham III
SEC, Matthew X Graham
Treas, Patrick T Graham
Personnel Executive, Marleen Finedore
Marketing Director, Suresh Bhatia
Director, Richard Byham
Auditors: FGMK LLC BANNOCKBURN ILLINO

LOCATIONS
HQ: GRAHAM ENTERPRISE, INC.
750 BUNKER CT STE 100, VERNON HILLS, IL 600611864
Phone: 847 837-0777
Web: WWW.GRAHAMEI.COM

HISTORICAL FINANCIALS
Company Type: Private

Income Statement				FYE: December 31
	REVENUE ($ mil.)	NET INCOME ($ mil.)	NET PROFIT MARGIN	EMPLOYEES
12/17	638	12	2.0%	350
12/16	596	6	1.1%	—
12/15	662	11	1.7%	—
12/14	866	8	0.9%	—
Annual Growth	(9.7%)	16.5%	—	—

2017 Year-End Financials
Return on assets: 0.4% Cash ($ mil.): 6
Return on equity: 2.0%
Current ratio: 0.80

GRAND RIVER DAM AUTHORITY

It took the dam authority of the State of Oklahoma to create the body that would dam the Grand River. The resulting power provider the Grand River Dam Authority is responsible for supplying wholesale electricity to municipal and cooperative utilities and industrial customers in its service territory which encompasses 24 counties in northeastern Oklahoma. It also sells excess power to customers across a four-state region. The state-owned utility has 1480 MW of generating capacity from hydroelectric and fossil-fueled power plants and operates a 2090-mile transmission system. Grand River Dam Authority also manages two lakes and a total of 70000 surface acres of water in Northeast Oklahoma.

Sales and Marketing

The company sells power to sixteen municipal customers in Oklahoma (serving 500000 homes) as well as customers in Arkansas Kansas and Missouri.

Financial Performance

In 2012 the Grand River Dam Authority's revenues increased by 4% due to improved sales (thanks to an improving economy pushing up demand) and higher electricity rates. Sales increases were led by growth in the industrial and off-system segments

The company's net income decreased by 7% in 2012 due to higher operating costs.

Strategy

The Grand River Dam Authority's long-term strategy is to balance ensuring low-cost supply with maintaining reliable electrical service (through infrastructure maintenance and upgrades) while delivering financial stability.

Honoring a promise to keep rates low and competitive while addressing environmental needs in 2013 the Authority lowered rates to 2009 levels.

Company Background

The Grand River Dam Authority was created by state legislation in 1935. It began construction on the Pensacola Dam across the Grand River in 1938. The dam was inaugurated in 1940. A second smaller dam (Robert S. Kerr Dam) downstream was completed in 1962.

EXECUTIVES
Secretary To The General Manager, Donna Jones
Auditors: DELOITTE & TOUCHE LLP TULSA

LOCATIONS
HQ: GRAND RIVER DAM AUTHORITY
226 W DWAIN WILLIS AVE, VINITA, OK 743014654
Phone: 918 256-5545
Web: WWW.GRDA.COM

COMPETITORS
AEP	OGE Energy
Empire District Electric	PG&E Corporation
Entergy	Westar Energy
Great Plains Energy	Western Farmers Electric

HISTORICAL FINANCIALS
Company Type: Private

Income Statement				FYE: December 31
	REVENUE ($ mil.)	NET INCOME ($ mil.)	NET PROFIT MARGIN	EMPLOYEES
12/17	436	7	1.6%	468
12/16	421	3	0.8%	—
12/12	411	53	13.0%	—
12/10	382	63	16.5%	—
Annual Growth	1.9%	(26.8%)	—	—

2017 Year-End Financials
Return on assets: 10.2% Cash ($ mil.): 41
Return on equity: 1.6%
Current ratio: 1.30

GRAND STRAND REGIONAL MEDICAL CENTER, LLC

EXECUTIVES

Infection Control Director, Winona McLamb
Medical Records Director, Gina Trahey-Romanuk
Vice President Of Operations, David Brooks
Ambulatory Services Director Operating Room Director, Kathy Hottois

LOCATIONS

HQ: GRAND STRAND REGIONAL MEDICAL CENTER, LLC
 809 82ND PKWY, MYRTLE BEACH, SC 295724607
Phone: 843 692-1000
Web: WWW.GRANDSTRANDMED.COM

COMPETITORS

Carolinas HealthCare System
Carolinas Hospital System
Conway Medical Center
Georgetown Hospital System
Laurens County Hospital
McLeod Health
Medical University of South Carolina
Palmetto Health
Roper St. Francis Healthcare
Soliant Health
Upstate Affiliate

HISTORICAL FINANCIALS
Company Type: Private

Income Statement				FYE: April 30
	REVENUE ($ mil.)	NET INCOME ($ mil.)	NET PROFIT MARGIN	EMPLOYEES
04/15	331	107	32.3%	1,000
04/13	265	65	24.6%	—
04/09	0	0	38.0%	—
Annual Growth	294.8%	284.3%	—	—

2015 Year-End Financials
Return on assets: 2.4% Cash ($ mil.): —
Return on equity: 32.3%
Current ratio: 2.70

GRAND VALLEY STATE UNIVERSITY

Even the most average student can get a grand education at Grand Valley State University. The school operates five campuses in western Michigan. The main one is in Allendale; it has additional facilities in Grand Rapids Holland Muskegon and Traverse City. Classes at the latter two locations are offered in conjunction with local community colleges. A public university with a liberal arts emphasis Grand Valley State offers more than 200 fields of study including about 80 undergraduate majors and more than 30 graduate programs. It has an enrollment of roughly 25000 students and approximately 835 regular faculty members. Its student-teacher ratio is about 27:1.

Operations

Grand Valley State is NCAA Division II and competes in the Great Lakes Intercollegiate Athletic Conference 20 varsity sports (11 womens and 9 mens). Its library has more than 1 million electronic journals and books and more than 518450 paper volumes. The university has a $74.1 million endowment.

Geographic Reach

Grand Valley State enrolls students from more than 8 countries. Some 807 of its students studied abroad in the 2011-2012 academic year.

The university's 1304 acre main campus is situated in Allendale some 12 miles west of Grand Rapids. It also has the 38-acre Robert C. Pew Campus in the heart of Grand Rapids which houses the Cook-DeVos Center for Health Sciences John C. Kennedy Hall of Engineering and the L. William Seidman Center. The school also offers classes at the Meijer Campus in Holland and in Muskegon and Traverse City.

Financial Performance

The school reported an 8% increase in revenues in 2012 was due to higher tuition rates and a growth in upper division credit hours.

Grand Valley State's net income decreased by 75% in 2012 due to an increase in operating expenses and decline in non-operating revenues (due to a drop in state funding government grants gifts and investment income).

The university saw an increase in revenues from 2010-12 due to higher student tuition and fees and a growth in auxiliary revenues.

Company Background

Grand Valley State was established in 1960 in response to the need for a public four-year college in Michigan's second largest metropolitan area.

EXECUTIVES

Vice President And General Counsel, Thomas Butcher
Associate Vice President Business Finance, Briand Copeland
Vice President, Jessica MacVane
Assistant Vice President For Business And Finance, Brian Copeland
Vice President, Audrey Tarbutton
Vice President, Anne Moore
Department Chair And Assistant Professor, Andrew Booth
Assistant Vice President Facilities Services, Timothy Thimmesch
Assistant Vice President Academic Affairs, Jean Nagelkerk
Assistant Vice President For Compliance, Donna Markus
Vice President, Corinne Farleigh
Vice President, Daniel Aday

Executive Vice President, Terrell Couch
Vice President Of Operations, Jenna Pizarek
Vice President Portfolio Management, Ryan Bowles
Vice President Of Operations, MarisaE Koltz
Assistant Vice President Of Facilities, Tim Thimmesch
Treasurer, Jonathan Cook
Secretary, Shelby Fullington
Secretary, Pat Waring
Secretary, Kay Hart
Treasurer, Maureen McBride
Secretary, Colin Schoen
Secretary, Michael Zingaretti
Treasurer, Tyler Joyce
Secretary, Alex Radner
Secretary, Bev Nyhuis
Secretary, Clyde Woods
Auditors: PLANTE & MORAN PLLC GRAND RA

LOCATIONS

HQ: GRAND VALLEY STATE UNIVERSITY
 1 CAMPUS DR, ALLENDALE, MI 494019403
Phone: 616 331-5000
Web: WWW.GVSU.EDU

HISTORICAL FINANCIALS
Company Type: Private

Income Statement				FYE: June 30
	REVENUE ($ mil.)	NET INCOME ($ mil.)	NET PROFIT MARGIN	EMPLOYEES
06/17	370	54	14.6%	3,630
06/16	355	26	7.5%	—
06/15	342	37	10.9%	—
Annual Growth	4.1%	20.3%	—	—

2017 Year-End Financials
Return on assets: 24.4% Cash ($ mil.): 34
Return on equity: 14.6%
Current ratio: 0.40

GRANITE SCHOOL DISTRICT

EXECUTIVES

Supt, Martin W Bates
SEC, Mary Lynn
SEC, Kathy Goodfellow
Information, Anjanette Anderson
Coordinator, Cindy Dunn
Director of Information Techno, Dale Roberts
Director, Jane Lindsay
Network Engineer, Dale Pitkin
Network Engineer, Jim Henderson
Data Processing Executive, Teresa Bruin
Programmer Analyst, Chui Chung
Auditors: SQUIRE & COMPANY PC OREM UT

LOCATIONS

HQ: GRANITE SCHOOL DISTRICT
 2500 S STATE ST, SALT LAKE CITY, UT 841153166
Phone: 385 646-5000
Web: WWW.GRANITESCHOOLS.ORG

HISTORICAL FINANCIALS

Company Type: Private

Income Statement   FYE: June 30

	REVENUE ($ mil.)	NET INCOME ($ mil.)	NET PROFIT MARGIN	EMPLOYEES
06/17	571	9	1.7%	8,000
06/16	561	16	3.0%	—
06/09	528	14	2.7%	—
06/08	510	18	3.6%	—
Annual Growth	1.3%	(6.5%)	—	—

GREAT RIVER ENERGY

Great River Energy powers up cooperatives along the Great River Road. The utility provides wholesale electricity to 1.7 million people (at 660000 homes businesses and farms) through 28 distribution cooperatives in Minnesota and Wisconsin. It operates more than 4600 miles of transmission lines and has more than 3500 MW of capacity from 12 fossil-fueled hydroelectric and renewable power generation facilities. The company also owns or partially owns more than 100 transmission substations. Great River Energy is the #2 electric utility in Minnesota in terms of generating capacity and one of the top five largest generation and transmission cooperatives in the US (based on assets).

Operations

Great River Energy's 28 co-ops have 88000 miles of distribution line and 555 substations. Its largest distribution co-op member serves more than 125000 consumers while its smallest serves about 2500 end users. Most of the company's power comes from coal with hydro renewable and natural gas making up the rest.

As part of its efforts to increase its green energy output Great River owns Blue Flint Ethanol which includes a 65-million gallon ethanol refinery that uses process steam produced at Great River Energy Coal Creek Station.

Geographic Reach

The company provides power to cooperatives which in turn serve customers in Minnesota and Wisconsin.

Financial Performance

Great River Energy's revenues increased by 4% due to a rise in all segments particularly in electric revenues.

Electric revenues increased due to a drop in member revenues driven by higher member energy and demand unit sales of 1.5% and 0.8% respectively.

The company's net income increased by 21% due to higher net revenues and a decrease in fuel expense related to lower repairs and maintenance of the coal handling system.

Great River Energy's operating cash inflow increased by 33%.

Strategy

The company has a plan to add about 1800 MW of generating resources (including renewable energy) by 2025 to satisfy increasing member demand for electricity. (The State of Minnesota requires utilities to generate 25% of their power from renewable sources by 2025). To support this push Great River Energy has a 30-year power purchase agreement with NextEra Energy Resources to buy 51 MW of output from a wind farm in North Dakota.

In 2014 Manitoba Hydro and Great River Energy also agreed to investigate the sale of up to 600MW) of electricity from Manitoba Hydro to Great River Energy commencing in 2020. An eventual agreement could take advantage of a new Manitoba to Minnesota transmission line also proposed as part of Manitoba Hydro's preferred development plan.

That year Great River Energy announced plans to construct 650 kW of new solar energy installations by mid-2015. The first construction project is a 250 kW solar array slated for land south of Great River Energy's headquarters facility and will include a mix of technologies to help determine how solar energy installations can be integrated into cooperative systems. The remaining 400 kW may include up to 20 individual projects located in its member cooperatives' systems across the state.

In 2014 the company announced plans to undertake the largest transmission refurbishment project with the overhaul and upgrade of the converter stations at either end of the 436-mile high-voltage direct-current transmission line which delivers power to Minnesota from the company's largest power plant located in central North Dakota.

Company Background

In 2013 the company signed a deal with Tangshan Shenzhou Manufacturing Company to make Great River Energy's DryFining technology (for more efficient coal use in power stations) available to utilities in China.

It is also cut costs and increasing efficiency at its own power plants. In 2012 these measures saved Great River Energy more than $8 million.

In 2012 Great River bought the remaining 51% of Blue Flint Ethanol it didn't already own. The move added to its production capabilities and helped push the company to record production that year.

The utility was formed in 1999 through the combination of two Minnesota utilities Cooperative Power and United Power Association.

EXECUTIVES

Vp Generation, Rick Lancaster
Ceo And President, David Saggau
Vp And Cfo, Larry Schmid
Vp Transmission, Will Kaul
Vp And Cio, Jim Jones
Vice President Power Marketing And Asset Utilitzation, Laureen Rossmccalib
Vice President, Geno Eddy
Vice Chairman, Sherman Liimatainen
Chairman, Michael Thorson
Board Of Directors, Scott Hughes
Auditors: DELOITTE & TOUCHE LLP MINNEA

LOCATIONS

HQ: GREAT RIVER ENERGY
12300 ELM CREEK BLVD N, MAPLE GROVE, MN 553694718
Phone: 763 445-5000
Web: WWW.GREATRIVERENERGY.COM

PRODUCTS/OPERATIONS

2014 Sales

	% of total
Member	83
Non-member	7
Other	7
Nonutility operations Excluding non-controlling Interest	3
Total	**100**

2014 Sales

	$mil.
% of total	
Electric revenue	93
Other operating revenue	7
Total	**100**

COMPETITORS

AEP	Entergy
Basin Electric Power	Southern Company
Black Hills	Xcel Energy
DTE	

HISTORICAL FINANCIALS

Company Type: Private

Income Statement   FYE: December 31

	REVENUE ($ mil.)	NET INCOME ($ mil.)	NET PROFIT MARGIN	EMPLOYEES
12/17	1,270	18	1.4%	850
12/16	1,022	21	2.1%	—
12/15	983	15	1.5%	—
12/14	0	44	—	—
Annual Growth	—	(25.7%)	—	—

2017 Year-End Financials

Return on assets: 5.3%   Cash ($ mil.): 322
Return on equity: 1.4%
Current ratio: 1.10

GREATER BALTIMORE MEDICAL CENTER LAND CORPORATION

EXECUTIVES

President, John Chessare
Anesthesiologist, Harold Goll
Auditors: DELOITTE TAX LLP ATLANTA GA

LOCATIONS

HQ: GREATER BALTIMORE MEDICAL CENTER LAND CORPORATION
6701 N CHARLES ST, BALTIMORE, MD 212046881
Phone: 443 849-2000
Web: WWW.GBMC.ORG

HISTORICAL FINANCIALS

Company Type: Private

Income Statement   FYE: June 30

	ASSETS ($ mil.)	NET INCOME ($ mil.)	INCOME AS % OF ASSETS	EMPLOYEES
06/16	642	27	4.3%	14
06/15	622	22	3.6%	—
06/14	536	28	5.3%	—
06/13	1	(0)	—	—
Annual Growth	588.1%	—	—	—

2016 Year-End Financials

Return on assets: 16.4%   Sales ($ mil): 433
Return on equity: 6.4%

GREATER HOUSTON COMMUNITY FOUNDATION

EXECUTIVES

President, Stephen Maislin
V Pres, Robert W Paddock
V Pres, Emelda J Douglas
Manager, Bridgette Wilkins
Director, Charlene Slack
Director, Judy Everett
Associate, Victoria Wallace
Executive Director, Carol Shattuck
Director, Jennifer Touchet
Director of Operations, Linda Gardner
Auditors: HARPER & PEARSON HOUSTON TX

LOCATIONS

HQ: GREATER HOUSTON COMMUNITY FOUNDATION
5120 WOODWAY DR STE 6000, HOUSTON, TX
770561791
Phone: 713 333-2200
Web: WWW.GHCF.ORG

HISTORICAL FINANCIALS
Company Type: Private

Income Statement
FYE: December 31

	REVENUE ($ mil.)	NET INCOME ($ mil.)	NET PROFIT MARGIN	EMPLOYEES
12/17	305	53	17.6%	9
12/16	177	65	36.8%	—
12/14	225	124	55.1%	—
12/13	125	11	9.2%	—
Annual Growth	25.0%	47.1%	—	—

2017 Year-End Financials
Return on assets: 0.9%   Cash ($ mil.): 157
Return on equity: 17.6%
Current ratio: 9.30

GREATER ORLANDO AVIATION AUTHORITY

Auditors: MOORE STEPHENS LOVELACE PA

LOCATIONS

HQ: GREATER ORLANDO AVIATION AUTHORITY
1 JEFF FUQUA BLVD, ORLANDO, FL 328274392
Phone: 407 825-2001
Web: WWW.GOAA.ORG

HISTORICAL FINANCIALS
Company Type: Private

Income Statement
FYE: December 31

	REVENUE ($ mil.)	NET INCOME ($ mil.)	NET PROFIT MARGIN	EMPLOYEES
12/15*	430	101	23.6%	670
09/15	430	101	23.6%	—
09/14	399	90	22.7%	—
09/13	380	86	22.8%	—
Annual Growth	6.4%	8.2%	—	—

*Fiscal year change

2015 Year-End Financials
Return on assets: 7.0%   Cash ($ mil.): 189
Return on equity: 23.6%
Current ratio: 0.80

GREEN BAY AREA PUBLIC SCHOOL DISTRICT

EXECUTIVES

Supt, Greg Mass
Supt, Michelle Lagenfeld
President, Jean Marsch
Vice President, Katie Maloney
District Treas, Judy Decleene
President, Brenda Warren
Staff, Kim Younkle
Staff, Barbara Parkman
Staff, Karen Boerst
Staff, Lynn Lemmens
Staff, Kathleen Wallen
Auditors: SCHENCK SC GREENBAY WISCONSI

LOCATIONS

HQ: GREEN BAY AREA PUBLIC SCHOOL DISTRICT
200 S BROADWAY, GREEN BAY, WI 543031516
Phone: 920 448-2101
Web: WWW.GBAPS.ORG

HISTORICAL FINANCIALS
Company Type: Private

Income Statement
FYE: June 30

	REVENUE ($ mil.)	NET INCOME ($ mil.)	NET PROFIT MARGIN	EMPLOYEES
06/17	300	6	2.3%	3,000
06/16	280	(21)	—	—
06/07	226	(1)	—	—
06/06	0	0	—	—
Annual Growth	—	—	—	—

GREEN MOUNTAIN POWER CORPORATION

Public utility Green Mountain Power (GMP) lights up the hills of Vermont supplying electricity to more than 250000 customers in the state. The utility also markets wholesale electricity in New England. The company operates several thousand miles of transmission and distribution lines and owns a minority stake in high-voltage transmission operator Vermont Electric Power (VELCO). About half of the generation capacity GMP taps is from hydroelectric and other renewable energy sources. GMP is an indirect subsidiary of Canada's GazMetro. The company absorbed Central Vermont Public Service's assets in 2012.

Operations

GMP produces transmits distributes and sells electricity in Vermont and is a leader in the production of wind and solar energy in that state.

Strategy

In a move to boost its Vermont assets in 2012 parent company GazMetro bought Central Vermont Public Service (CVPS) and is merging it with its GMP operations. CVPS is Vermont's largest electric utility and provides power to more than 159000 customers in 163 communities across the state.

The company is also pursuing a long term initiative to generate power from renewable sources as a way to cut carbon emissions and comply with strict federal clean air requirements. GMP has a preliminary deal to boost green energy sources with Hydro-Quebec as well as plans to to build a wind farm in Lowell make investments in solar power and upgrade its hydroelectric facilities.

While wind and solar only accounted for about 1% of the company's fuel mix for its power stations in 2011 it plans to boost that amount to almost 10% by the end of 2013.

Company Background

GazMetro acquired the company in 2007. The deal boosted Gaz Metro's presence in the Vermont energy market where it has owned Vermont Gas Systems for more than 20 years.

EXECUTIVES

Vice President Of Information Technology, Dawn Bugbee
Vice President Of Field Engineering, Greg White
Vice President Strategic Planning, Don Rendall
Auditors: MCSOLEY MCCOY & CO SOUTH BURL

LOCATIONS

HQ: GREEN MOUNTAIN POWER CORPORATION
163 ACORN LN, COLCHESTER, VT 054466611
Phone: 888 835-4672
Web: WWW.GREENMOUNTAINPOWER.COM

COMPETITORS

Avangrid	Maine & Maritimes
Bangor Hydro-Electric	NSTAR
Con Edison	Unitil
DPL	Vermont Gas
Eversource Energy	

HISTORICAL FINANCIALS
Company Type: Private

Income Statement
FYE: December 31

	REVENUE ($ mil.)	NET INCOME ($ mil.)	NET PROFIT MARGIN	EMPLOYEES
12/16	652	69	10.6%	190
12/15	0	0	74.2%	—
Annual Growth	1052891.9%	150965.2%	—	—

2016 Year-End Financials
Return on assets: 7.6%   Cash ($ mil.): 3
Return on equity: 10.6%
Current ratio: 0.30

GREENWICH HOSPITAL

EXECUTIVES

Pres-Ceo, Frank A Corvino
V Pres-Fin, Eugene Colucci
Exec Vice President, Brian J Doran
Vice President, Christine Beechner
Sr Vice President, Susan Brown
Manager, Valerie Mc Guire
Legal Staff, Amy Rozmus
Program Manager, Cara Giacomo

Office Manager, Maryann Conti
Manager, Luis Ortiz
Director, Mark Larobina

LOCATIONS

HQ: GREENWICH HOSPITAL
5 PERRYRIDGE RD, GREENWICH, CT 068304697
Phone: 203 863-3000
Web: WWW.GREENWICHHOSPITAL.ORG

HISTORICAL FINANCIALS

Company Type: Private

Income Statement				FYE: September 30
	REVENUE ($ mil.)	NET INCOME ($ mil.)	NET PROFIT MARGIN	EMPLOYEES
09/17	359	24	6.9%	1,600
09/16	353	34	9.8%	—
09/15	340	26	7.9%	—
09/14	0	0	—	—
Annual Growth	—	—	—	—

2017 Year-End Financials

Return on assets: 3.1%   Cash ($ mil.): 35
Return on equity: 6.9%
Current ratio: 1.30

GROSSMONT HOSPITAL FOUNDATION

EXECUTIVES

Ex Dir, Elizabeth Morgante
Registered Nurse Pcu, Brittany Campbell
Wound Healing Hyperbaric Cente, Koye Durmick
Administrative Assistant, Kristina Walker
Rn, Magda Angel
Rn, Michelle Lescault
Auditors: ERNST & YOUNG US LLP SAN DIEG

LOCATIONS

HQ: GROSSMONT HOSPITAL FOUNDATION
5555 GROSSMONT CENTER DR, LA MESA, CA
919423077
Phone: 619 740-4200
Web: WWW.GROSSMONTHEALTHCARE.ORG

HISTORICAL FINANCIALS

Company Type: Private

Income Statement				FYE: September 30
	REVENUE ($ mil.)	NET INCOME ($ mil.)	NET PROFIT MARGIN	EMPLOYEES
09/16	738	65	8.9%	6
09/09	5	0	8.5%	—
09/08	5	0	16.8%	—
09/01	1	3	314.9%	—
Annual Growth	54.5%	21.8%	—	—

2016 Year-End Financials

Return on assets: 7.6%   Cash ($ mil.): 43
Return on equity: 8.9%
Current ratio: 2.10

GROVE ELK UNIFIED SCHOOL DISTRICT

EXECUTIVES

Supt, Steven Ladd
Assc Supt, Richard Odegaard
Auditors: CROWE HORWATH LLP SACRAMENTO

LOCATIONS

HQ: GROVE ELK UNIFIED SCHOOL DISTRICT
9510 ELK GROVE FLORIN RD, ELK GROVE, CA
956241801
Phone: 916 686-5085
Web: WWW.EGUSD.NET

HISTORICAL FINANCIALS

Company Type: Private

Income Statement				FYE: June 30
	REVENUE ($ mil.)	NET INCOME ($ mil.)	NET PROFIT MARGIN	EMPLOYEES
06/17	741	65	8.8%	5,600
06/07	560	(30)	—	—
06/06	0	0	—	—
06/03	454	19	4.4%	—
Annual Growth	3.6%	8.9%	—	—

GROWMARK, INC.

Retail farm-supply and grain-marketing cooperative GROWMARK can mark its growth by the grain. A member-owed agricultural co-op GROWMARK has more than 100000 members. Under the FAST STOP name the co-op runs more than 250 fuel stations and convenience stores in the Midwest. Its Seedway subsidiary sells commercial vegetable seed and farm seed for turf and grains including alfalfa corn wheat and soybeans. GROWMARK also offers fertilizer seeds ethanol biodiesel and farm financing. Its MID-CO COMMODITIES subsidiary trades grain and offers advice regarding futures and options.

Geographic Reach

GROWMARK is headquartered in Bloomington Illinois and serves customers in more than 40 states and Ontario Canada. SEEDWAY maintains eight office and warehouse locations in Vermont New York Pennsylvania and Florida.

Strategy

Cooperation is important within and among agricultural cooperatives. A strong believer in the latter part of this principle GROWMARK has marketing agreements and alliances with among others fertilizer maker and distributor CF Industries pet-food producer PRO-PET agribusiness company Syngenta and rural financial services provider CoBank.

Mergers and Acquisitions

GROWMARK acquires fertilizer storage terminals and transportation infrastructure on a regular basis.

EXECUTIVES

Vice Chairman, John Reifsteck
Ceo, Jeff Solberg
Vp And General Counsel, Brent Bostrom
Vp Eastern Retail Operations, Steve Buckalew
Vp And Cfo, Marshall Bohbrink
Vp Energy, Kevin Carroll

Vp Midwest Retail And Acquisitions, Shelly Kruse
Vp Grain, Brent Ericson
Vice President Human Resources & Compliance, Gary Swango
Vp Agronomy, Mark Orr
Vp Financial And Risk Management, Mike Woods
Vp Member Services, Denny Worth
Vice President Systems, George Key
Vice President, Ron Milby
Vice President Of Information Technology, Rick Norton
Vice President Member Services, Dennis Farmer
Vice Presidnet Of Finance, Jeffrey Solberg
Vice Chairman, Rick Nelson
Vice Chairman, Chet Esther
Board Member Administration Executive, Bob Phelps
Auditors: ERNST & YOUNG LLP CHICAGO I

LOCATIONS

HQ: GROWMARK, INC.
1701 TOWANDA AVE, BLOOMINGTON, IL 617012057
Phone: 309 557-6000
Web: WWW.GROWMARK.COM

PRODUCTS/OPERATIONS

Selected Retail Products and Operations
COMFORT PRO (propane heating oil)
FAST STOP (fuel facilities)
FS (farm supplies)
Green Yard (turf seed fertilizer)
Seedway (farm turf and vegetable seed)

Selected Member Cooperatives and Subsidiaries
AgVantage FS Inc.
AgView Grain LLC
Evergreen FS Inc.
GROWMARK FS LLC
MID-CO COMMODITIES
Northern Grain Marketing LLC
Seedway LLC
Total Grain Marketing LLC
Western Grain Marketing LLC

COMPETITORS

ADM	Marathon Oil
AGRI Industries	NC Hybrids
Ag Processing Inc.	Orscheln Farm and Home
BP	Pfister Hybrid Corn
Barkley Seed	Pioneer Hi-Bred
Bayer CropScience	Rabo AgriFinance
CHS	Sakata Seed
Cargill	Seed Enterprises
Chevron	Southern States
Costco Wholesale	Terra Nitrogen
DeBruce Grain	Wal-Mart
Exxon Mobil	Wilbur-Ellis

HISTORICAL FINANCIALS

Company Type: Private

Income Statement				FYE: August 31
	REVENUE ($ mil.)	NET INCOME ($ mil.)	NET PROFIT MARGIN	EMPLOYEES
08/18	8,522	65	0.8%	7,000
08/17	7,291	115	1.6%	—
08/16	7,031	101	1.4%	—
08/15	8,727	113	1.3%	—
Annual Growth	(0.8%)	(16.6%)	—	—

2018 Year-End Financials

Return on assets: 5.9%   Cash ($ mil.): 99
Return on equity: 0.8%
Current ratio: 0.70

GRUMA CORPORATION

Gruma Corporation has its business all wrapped up. With operations in the US and Europe the company manufactures and distributes more than 20 varieties of corn flour corn tortillas and related products such as tortilla chips and flatbreads the likes of pita and naan. Gruma's brand name offerings include Mission Calidad and Guerrero tortillas and Maseca corn flour. The company is a wholly owned subsidiary of the giant Mexican food company Gruma S.A.B. de C.V. and is its largest revenue producer. Gruma produces about 1.4 million metric tons of corn flour and tortillas every year and its products are available in 30000 retail food outlets in the US.

Operations

Gruma Corporation which generates nearly half of its parent's total revenue operates through two divisions — Mission Foods and Azteca Milling. Through its several plants the company has the capacity to process 1 million metric tons of product per year.

Geographic Reach

Gruma Corporation maintains more than 20 plants in the US and about a handful in Europe (in the UK the Netherlands and in Russia) that produce tortillas and tortilla chips. In the UK the company also makes flatbreads such as pita naan chapatti and piadinas. US plants are located mainly in the western and southwestern US.

Financial Performance

Revenue increased some 12% for Gruma Corporation in 2011 as compared to 2010 thanks to sales growth volume and price increases spurred by higher raw-material costs.

Strategy

The corn products company is chasing after the growing US Hispanic population which is expected to increase approximately 3.5% per year. It's banking on tortilla product consumption not only by Hispanics but by non-Hispanic communities living in the US. Besides its direct-to-consumer business Gruma Corporation grows its market share by selling its corn flower to other manufacturers of tortillas and tortilla chips.

EXECUTIVES

President And Ceo, Javier Velez Bautista

LOCATIONS

HQ: GRUMA CORPORATION
5601 EXECUTIVE DR STE 800, IRVING, TX 750382508
Phone: 972 232-5000
Web: WWW.MISSIONFOODS.COM

PRODUCTS/OPERATIONS

Selected Brands and Products
Guerrero
   Chicharron de Cerdo
   Tortillas de Harina (Original and Butter)
   Tortillas de Maíz Blanco
   Tostadas Norte?as Clásicas
   Tostadas Caseras Doraditas
Mission Foods
   96% Fat Free Heart Healthy tortillas
   All Natural Spicy Bean dip
   Caramel Twists
   Carb Balance tortillas
   Cheddar Cheese dip
   Chicharrones (Original BBQ Habanero and Picante)
   Cinnamon Twists
   Chunky Salsa Medium
   Corn tortilla
   Flour tortillas
   Guacamole dip
   Jumbo Taco shells
   Life Balance tortillas
   Multi-Grain Flour tortillas
   Organic Stone-Ground tortilla chips
   Pork Cracklins Plain Tenders
   Restaurant Style Tortilla Triangles (Cilantro Lime Premium White Corn and Salsa Roja)
   Restaurant Style Tortilla Rounds
   Salsa Con Queso
   Salsa Verde Medium
   Sliced Nacho Jalape?o Peppers
   Taco and tostada shells
   Wraps (Original Garden Spinach Jalapeno Cheddar Multi-Grain Sun-dried Tomato Basil and Zesty Garlic Herb)

COMPETITORS

Azteca Foods	Horizon Milling
Bimbo Bakeries	La Gloria Foods
Bob's Red Mill Natural Foods	La Reina
	La Tortilla Factory
Bunge Milling	Minsa
C.H. Guenther & Son	Ole' Mexican Foods
Casa de Oro Foods	Organic Milling
Don Pancho Authentic Mexican Foods	Ruiz Mexican Foods
	Star of the West
Flowers Foods	Taco Bell
Frito-Lay	Tumaro's Gourmet Tortillas
General Mills	
Grupo Bimbo	Tyson Foods
Hodgson Mill	

HISTORICAL FINANCIALS
Company Type: Private

Income Statement				FYE: December 31
	REVENUE ($ mil.)	NET INCOME ($ mil.)	NET PROFIT MARGIN	EMPLOYEES
12/17	2,050	215	10.5%	7,000
12/16	2,023	179	8.9%	—
12/15	2,086	152	7.3%	—
12/14	2,018	132	6.6%	—
Annual Growth	0.5%	17.5%	—	—

2017 Year-End Financials

Return on assets: 3.8%   Cash ($ mil.): 47
Return on equity: 10.5%
Current ratio: 1.20

GRUNLEY CONSTRUCTION CO., INC.

EXECUTIVES

Pres/Ceo, Kenneth M Grunley
SEC, Virginia Grunley
Sr V Pres/Opr Mgr, Bh Scott II
V Pres of Preconstr Srvc, Tom Walker
C Pres of Mktg & Bus Dev't, Sonya Brown
Vp-Purchasing, George Rusk
Pres, Gregory M Druga
Actg Sprvr, Gina Corcione
Auditors: BAKER TILLY VIRCHOW KRAUSE LL

LOCATIONS

HQ: GRUNLEY CONSTRUCTION CO., INC.
15020 SHADY GROVE RD # 500, ROCKVILLE, MD 208503390
Phone: 240 399-2000
Web: WWW.GRUNLEY.COM

COMPETITORS

Hega Construction Company	Parsons Transportation
	S. W. Rodgers

HISTORICAL FINANCIALS
Company Type: Private

Income Statement				FYE: December 31
	REVENUE ($ mil.)	NET INCOME ($ mil.)	NET PROFIT MARGIN	EMPLOYEES
12/17	399	9	2.5%	310
12/16	425	6	1.5%	—
12/15	403	0	—	—
12/11	323	0	—	—
Annual Growth	3.5%	—	—	—

2017 Year-End Financials

Return on assets: 15.1%   Cash ($ mil.): 13
Return on equity: 2.5%
Current ratio: 0.90

GRUPO ANTOLIN KENTUCKY, INC.

EXECUTIVES

Chm, Ernesto Antolin Arribas
Ceo, Jess Pascual Santos
SEC-Treas, Pablo Ruiz
Finance Manager, Mike Sewell
Manager, Judith Tyner
Engineer, Nelson Holzapfel
Human Resources Manager, Kim Byard
Engineering Manager, Mark Jorgensen
Engineer, William Copeland

LOCATIONS

HQ: GRUPO ANTOLIN KENTUCKY, INC.
208 COMMERCE CT, HOPKINSVILLE, KY 422406806
Phone: 270 885-2703
Web: WWW.GRUPOANTOLIN.COM

HISTORICAL FINANCIALS
Company Type: Private

Income Statement				FYE: December 31
	REVENUE ($ mil.)	NET INCOME ($ mil.)	NET PROFIT MARGIN	EMPLOYEES
12/17	294	1	0.6%	502
12/16	237	12	5.3%	—
12/15	222	19	8.6%	—
12/06	96	4	4.9%	—
Annual Growth	10.7%	(8.3%)	—	—

2017 Year-End Financials

Return on assets: 14.1%   Cash ($ mil.): —
Return on equity: 0.6%
Current ratio: 0.30

GUEST SERVICES, INC.

Guest Services satisfies hungry and sleepy patrons. The company provides contract food services and hospitality-management services nationwide. It operates cafeterias and onsite restaurants and offers catering to businesses hotels hospitals conference centers and government operations including the US Supreme Court the US House of Representatives and the National Park Service. For leisure and resort facilities Guest Services also provides special-event catering and offers management services such as marketing human resources procurement quality-assurance and information technology services. Guest Services was founded in 1917 as a private company to serve governmental agencies.

Operations

Guest Services serves some 250 facilities across the US and more than 25 million guests each year. The company also owns Lancaster Foods one of the largest wholesale produce companies in the mid-Atlantic region.

Additional offerings include corporate accounting systems and food safety and health support.

Geographic Reach

Based in Fairfax Virginia Guest Services serves a variety of customers nationwide.

Sales and Marketing

Guest Services serves several clients including government and business dining facilities museums hotels resorts conference centers luxury condominiums senior living centers health care systems state and national park recreation school and university dining facilities specialty retail stores and full-service restaurants.

Customers have included Washington DC's National Mall and Memorial Park. Guest Services also manages food lodging and recreation services at state parks in West Virginia New York and California.

Strategy

Guest Services has been expanding its portfolio of premium properties. For example it owns and manages the DoubleTree Suites by Hilton Naples. In 2013 Guest Services acquired The Lodge and Spa at Breckenridge which overlooks Colorado's Breckenridge Village. With 45 rooms the property is a popular destination for weddings and corporate events. It's adding food and beverage service in-house catering and event planning to the property's services.

EXECUTIVES

Ceo, Gerard T. Gabrys
President And Coo, Jeffrey A. Marquis
President Lancaster Foods, John Gates
Vp Hotel Division South, Barry G. Trice
Vp Sales And Marketing, Jerry Chadwich
Vp And Cfo, Nico Foris
Vice President Operations Division, Soterios Louvis
Auditors: PRICEWATERHOUSECOOPERS LLP MC

LOCATIONS

HQ: GUEST SERVICES, INC.
3055 PROSPERITY AVE, FAIRFAX, VA 220312290
Phone: 703 849-9300
Web: WWW.GUESTSERVICES.COM

PRODUCTS/OPERATIONS

Selected Services
Audits
Corporate Support Services
Financial Accounting Systems
Food Safety and Health
Human Resources
IT
Maintenance Support
Management Information Systems
Marketing
Onsite Test Kitchen
PeopleSoft Processing
Procurement
Quality Assurance
Safety
Security
Test Kitchen
Training

COMPETITORS

ARAMARK	Delaware North
Centerplate	Sodexo USA
Compass Group USA	Valley Services

HISTORICAL FINANCIALS

Company Type: Private

Income Statement | | | | FYE: December 31

	REVENUE ($ mil.)	NET INCOME ($ mil.)	NET PROFIT MARGIN	EMPLOYEES
12/17	459	(2)	—	99
12/16	442	1	0.4%	—
12/15	396	3	0.9%	—
12/14	375	0	0.3%	—
Annual Growth	7.0%	—	—	

2017 Year-End Financials

Return on assets: 4.7%   Cash ($ mil.): 24
Return on equity: (-0.6%)
Current ratio: 0.90

GUILDNET, INC.

EXECUTIVES

Ceo, Alan R Morse
Chairman, James M Dubin
Treasurer, Lawrence E Goldschmidt
Secretary, Robert B Okun
V Pres Admin, Larry Carr
Corporate Communications Staff, Pete Williamson
Admin Assistant, Angela Rosario
Staff Supervisor, Janet Corbin
Optometrist, Susan Weinstein
Nurse Case Manager, Mary McDermott
Supervisor, Bonita Blake
Auditors: KPMG LLP NEW YORK NY

LOCATIONS

HQ: GUILDNET, INC.
15 W 65TH ST, NEW YORK, NY 100236601
Phone: 212 769-6200
Web: WWW.JGB.ORG

HISTORICAL FINANCIALS

Company Type: Private

Income Statement | | | | FYE: December 31

	REVENUE ($ mil.)	NET INCOME ($ mil.)	NET PROFIT MARGIN	EMPLOYEES
12/15	950	(24)	—	377
12/14	826	1	0.1%	—
12/13	672	45	6.8%	—
12/12	433	42	9.8%	—
Annual Growth	29.9%	—	—	

2015 Year-End Financials

Return on assets: 0.4%   Cash ($ mil.): 12
Return on equity: (-2.5%)
Current ratio: 0.10

GULF COAST MEDICAL CENTRE LTD

EXECUTIVES

Prin, Jeffrey R Green
Senior Manager, Elain Paddock

LOCATIONS

HQ: GULF COAST MEDICAL CENTRE LTD
13691 METRO PKWY STE 110, FORT MYERS, FL 339124348
Phone: 239 343-1000
Web: WWW.LEEMEMORIAL.ORG

HISTORICAL FINANCIALS

Company Type: Private

Income Statement | | | | FYE: September 30

	REVENUE ($ mil.)	NET INCOME ($ mil.)	NET PROFIT MARGIN	EMPLOYEES
09/15	318	21	6.8%	268
09/13	284	13	4.6%	—
09/12	279	52	18.8%	—
Annual Growth	4.5%	(25.7%)	—	—

GUNDERSEN LUTHERAN HEALTH SYSTEM, INC.

EXECUTIVES

Ceo, Jeffrey E Thompson
Pres, Daniel J Lilly
Cfo, Michael Allen
V Pres, Bryan Erdmann
V Pres, Jan Dehaan
V Pres, Deb Rislow
Pediatric Dentistry Specialist, Mark Moeller
Information Specialist, Suzanne Severson
Secretary, Anne Rutz
Manager Pharmacy Information S, Denise Kachel
Epic Project Manager, Jared Wickus

LOCATIONS

HQ: GUNDERSEN LUTHERAN HEALTH SYSTEM, INC.
1900 SOUTH AVE, LA CROSSE, WI 546015467
Phone: 608 782-7300
Web: WWW.GUNDERSENHEALTH.ORG

HISTORICAL FINANCIALS

Company Type: Private

Income Statement | | | | FYE: December 31

	REVENUE ($ mil.)	NET INCOME ($ mil.)	NET PROFIT MARGIN	EMPLOYEES
12/16	1,015	77	7.7%	6,000
12/15	980	60	6.1%	—
12/14	0	0	—	—
Annual Growth	—	—	—	

2016 Year-End Financials

Return on assets: 1.7%   Cash ($ mil.): 187
Return on equity: 7.7%
Current ratio: 1.60

GUNDERSEN LUTHERAN MEDICAL CENTER, INC.

At the heart of the Gundersen Lutheran health system Gundersen Lutheran Medical Center serves residents of nearly 20 counties that stretch across the upper Midwest. The clinical campus for the University of Wisconsin's medical and nursing schools operates a 325-bed teaching hospital with a Level II Trauma and Emergency Center. Focused on caring for patients in western Wisconsin the hospital boasts several specialty services such as bariatrics behavioral health cancer care orthopedics palliative care pediatrics rehabilitation and women's health. The physician-led not-for-profit medical center is affiliated with a group of regional clinics and specialty centers.

Operations
Gundersen Lutheran Medical Center has a staff of some 800 doctors dentists and other professionals. As part of Gundersen Lutheran (also known as Gundersen Health System) the hospital's sister entities include the Gundersen Clinic and the Gundersen Lutheran Administrative Services entity.

In 2013 the Gundersen Health System reported 1437 births 17000 surgeries and 278000 outpatient hospital visits.

Geographic Reach
From its main campus in La Crosse Wisconsin as well as a satellite outpatient center in Onalaska the hospital serves communities located in 19 counties throughout western Wisconsin northeastern Iowa and southeastern Minnesota.

Strategy
The Gundersen Lutheran organization expands though partnerships such as an alliance with the Allen Hospital in Iowa to enhance regional cardiovascular services in 2013. The medical center is also working to upgrade its infrastructure to enable 100% energy independence in 2014.

To offer advanced training to residents and physicians Gundersen Lutheran Medical Center developed and opened a high-tech training center in 2012. The Cleary Kumm Simulation and Training Labs offer mock operating rooms and simulation labs for use by local doctors and nationwide medical professionals for training or conferences. Gundersen Lutheran Medical Center is banking on the simulation and training facility to draw interest talent and outside funds.

Company Background
Gundersen Lutheran Medical Center was founded in 1995 through the merger of Gunderson Clinic and Lutheran Hospital-La Crosse. The Lutheran Hospital opened in 1902.

EXECUTIVES

Medical Director Emergency Services, Eric Voter
Medical Director, Jackie Yaeger
Auditors: KPMG LLP MINNEAPOLIS MN

LOCATIONS

HQ: GUNDERSEN LUTHERAN MEDICAL CENTER, INC.
1900 SOUTH AVE, LA CROSSE, WI 546015467
Phone: 608 782-7300
Web: WWW.GUNDERSENHEALTH.ORG

PRODUCTS/OPERATIONS

Selected Services
Advance care planning
Apnea
Audiology
Autism Spectrum Disorder
BioBank
Brain disorders
Cardiac services
Children's health
Cleft Lip & Palate Clinic
Endocrinology
Hospice
Eye care
Gynecology
Hand surgery
Heart Institute
LASIK eye surgery
Massage
Neck surgery
Neurosciences
Oral and maxillofacial surgery
Pediatrics
Radiation oncology
Rehabilitation
Urgent care
Urology
Weight management
Wound care

COMPETITORS

Dean Health Systems Inc.
Franciscan Skemp Healthcare
Luther Midelfort
Mayo Clinic
Meriter Health Services
Ministry Health Care
Olmsted Medical
Sacred Heart Hospital
Tomah Memorial Hospital
University of Wisconsin Hospital and Clinics

HISTORICAL FINANCIALS
Company Type: Private

Income Statement				FYE: December 31
	REVENUE ($ mil.)	NET INCOME ($ mil.)	NET PROFIT MARGIN	EMPLOYEES
12/17	1,071	112	10.5%	4,500
12/15	980	60	6.1%	—
12/14	894	94	10.6%	—
12/11	431	49	11.5%	—
Annual Growth	16.3%	14.6%	—	—

2017 Year-End Financials
Return on assets: 1.4%   Cash ($ mil.): 205
Return on equity: 10.5%
Current ratio: 1.90

GWINNETT COUNTY BOARD OF EDUCATION

EXECUTIVES

Chairperson, Robert McClure
Accounting Staff, Kathy Stillwell
Coordinator, Bryan Yancey
Business Manager, Gwen Strabala
Payroll Staff, Lori Swilley
Administrative Assistant, Margie Morgenthal
Payroll Staff, Sherry Dudish
Administrative Assistant, Tammi Herring
Special Education Paraprofessi, Lisa Stansell
Teacher, Adam Hunter
Special Education Teacher, Caitlin Cohen

LOCATIONS

HQ: GWINNETT COUNTY BOARD OF EDUCATION
437 OLD PEACHTREE RD NW, SUWANEE, GA
300242978
Phone: 678 301-6000
Web: WWW.GCPS-FOUNDATION.ORG

HISTORICAL FINANCIALS
Company Type: Private

Income Statement				FYE: June 30
	REVENUE ($ mil.)	NET INCOME ($ mil.)	NET PROFIT MARGIN	EMPLOYEES
06/17	1,868	(2)	—	168
06/16*	1,791	349	19.5%	—
07/10	0	0	11.5%	—
08/09	0	0	18.4%	—
Annual Growth	247.9%	—	—	—
*Fiscal year change

2017 Year-End Financials
Return on assets: 1.6%   Cash ($ mil.): 126
Return on equity: (-0.1%)
Current ratio: 0.40

GWINNETT HOSPITAL SYSTEM, INC.

EXECUTIVES

Ceo, Philip R Wolfe
President, Franklin M Rinker
Sr V Pres-Cfo, Thomas Y Mc Bride III
Vice President, Georgia P Brogdon
V Pres-Coo, Thomas Karr
SEC, Gayle Delucia
President, Lea Bay
Exec Vice President, Alan Bier
Sr Vice President, Ed Brown
President, Jason Chandler
Sr Vice President, Patty Lavely
Auditors: KPMG LLP ATLANTA GA

LOCATIONS

HQ: GWINNETT HOSPITAL SYSTEM, INC.
1000 MEDICAL CENTER BLVD, LAWRENCEVILLE,
GA 300467694
Phone: 678 343-3428
Web: WWW.GWINNETTMEDICALCENTER.ORG

HISTORICAL FINANCIALS
Company Type: Private

Income Statement				FYE: June 30
	REVENUE ($ mil.)	NET INCOME ($ mil.)	NET PROFIT MARGIN	EMPLOYEES
06/18	731	12	1.7%	2,050
06/17	729	29	4.1%	—
06/16	735	(31)	—	—
06/15	698	15	2.2%	—
Annual Growth	1.5%	(6.3%)	—	—

2018 Year-End Financials
Return on assets: 5.8%   Cash ($ mil.): 54
Return on equity: 1.7%
Current ratio: 1.70

H. LEE MOFFITT CANCER CENTER AND RESEARCH INSTITUTE, INC.

EXECUTIVES

Pres, William Dalton
Project Coordinator, Donna Cosenzo
Scientist, Thinh Cao
Information Technology Manager, Terry Smith
Assistant Professor, Alfredo A Santillan
Manager, Lee Anne Corbin
Health Professional, Amber Shrewsbury
Assistant Professor, Andrew W Carroll
Scientist, Bin Fang
Scientist, Dawn Ruge
Pathologist, Santo V Nicosia
Auditors: ERNST & YOUNG LLP TAMPA FLORI

LOCATIONS

HQ: H. LEE MOFFITT CANCER CENTER AND
RESEARCH INSTITUTE, INC.
12902 USF MAGNOLIA DR, TAMPA, FL 336129416
Phone: 813 745-4673
Web: WWW.MOFFITT.ORG

HISTORICAL FINANCIALS
Company Type: Private

Income Statement — FYE: June 30

	REVENUE ($ mil.)	NET INCOME ($ mil.)	NET PROFIT MARGIN	EMPLOYEES
06/18	1,310	178	13.6%	5,500
06/17	1,132	76	6.8%	—
06/15	951	61	6.5%	—
Annual Growth	11.3%	42.7%	—	—

2018 Year-End Financials
Return on assets: 6.5%
Return on equity: 13.6%
Current ratio: 2.10
Cash ($ mil.): 258

HACIENDA-LA PUENTE UNIFIED SCHOOL DISTRICT

EXECUTIVES

Supt, Norman Kirschenbaum
Personnel Assistant, Carol Kelly
Technology/Computer Coordinato, Michael Gonzalez
Purchasing Coordinator, Vicki Cobos
Teacher, Chris Coleman
Personnel Specialist, Jeanette Raygoza
Assistant Superintendent, Judy Fancher
Secretary, Marcia Sainz
Manager, Desiree Apodaca
Psychologist, Diana Ayala
Assistant, Fernando Sanchez
Auditors: NIGRO & NIGRO PC MURRIETA CA

LOCATIONS

HQ: HACIENDA-LA PUENTE UNIFIED SCHOOL
DISTRICT
15959 GALE AVE, CITY OF INDUSTRY, CA 917451604
Phone: 626 933-1000
Web: WWW.HLPUSDJOBS.ORG

HISTORICAL FINANCIALS
Company Type: Private

Income Statement — FYE: June 30

	REVENUE ($ mil.)	NET INCOME ($ mil.)	NET PROFIT MARGIN	EMPLOYEES
06/17	292	3	1.1%	2,500
06/16	308	3	1.3%	—
06/05	0	0	14.7%	—
06/01	219	20	9.3%	—
Annual Growth	1.8%	(10.9%)	—	—

2017 Year-End Financials
Return on assets: 9.1%
Return on equity: 1.1%
Current ratio: —
Cash ($ mil.): 212

HALL COUNTY BOARD OF EDUCATION

EXECUTIVES

Chmn, Nath Morris
Executive Assitant, Penny Jordan
Tech Prep Coordinator, Rhonda Samples
Teacher, Carlene Walker
Assistant Director, Kathy Kelley
Teacher, Kristy Grizzle
Teacher, Lynn Johnson
Director, Lesley Congdon
Auditors: RUSSELL W HINTON CPA CGFM

LOCATIONS

HQ: HALL COUNTY BOARD OF EDUCATION
711 GREEN ST NW STE 100, GAINESVILLE, GA
305013368
Phone: 770 534-1080
Web: WWW.HALLCOUNTY.ORG

HISTORICAL FINANCIALS
Company Type: Private

Income Statement — FYE: June 30

	REVENUE ($ mil.)	NET INCOME ($ mil.)	NET PROFIT MARGIN	EMPLOYEES
06/17	285	17	6.2%	3,600
06/16	277	9	3.3%	—
06/08	256	(10)	—	—
06/07	241	15	6.3%	—
Annual Growth	1.7%	1.5%	—	—

2017 Year-End Financials
Return on assets: —
Return on equity: 6.2%
Current ratio: —
Cash ($ mil.): 75

HAMILTON CHATTANOOGA COUNTY HOSPITAL AUTHORITY

The Chattanooga-Hamilton County Hospital Authority (dba Erlanger Health System) offers a broad range of health service operations including the T.C. Thompson Children's Hospital a cancer treatment facility and centers devoted to heart treatment trauma and eye care. The system comprises five hospital campuses in Tennessee with some 810 acute care beds as well as 50 long-term care beds. A teaching center for the University of Tennessee College of Medicine Erlanger provides tertiary care for a region that includes southeastern Tennessee northern Georgia northern Alabama and western North Carolina.

Operations

Erlanger is the tri-state region's only Level One Trauma Center providing the highest level of trauma care for adults. The Children's Hospital at Erlanger houses the region's only Level III Neonatal Intensive Care Unit as well as a pediatric trauma team Emergency Center and Pediatric Intensive Care Unit

The hospital system treats more than 300000 patients every year. In 2014 Erlanger had 30394 inpatient admissions 230765 outpatient visits to physician practices and 28810 surgical patients. Some 3067 children were admitted to Children's Hospital and 43192 received treatment in the Emergency Department and outpatient surgery.

The LIFE FORCE air ambulance service is is equipped with two EC-135 aircraft capable of single pilot IFR and two Bell 407 aircraft. LIFE FORCE transported 1419 patients in 2014.

Geographic Reach

The Erlanger Health System is a multi-hospital system with five hospitals based in Chattanooga: the University Hospital Children's Hospital at Erlanger Erlanger North Hospital Erlanger East Hospital and Erlanger Bledsoe Hospital located in Pikeville Tennessee. Its LIFE FORCE air ambulance service is stationed in Chattanooga and Sparta in Tennessee and in Calhoun and Blue Ridge in Georgia.

Financial Performance

Medicare accounted for 33% of Erlanger's net patient revenues in fiscal 2014; Commercial insurance 31%; and Medicaid 22%.

Company Background

To extend its patient reach Erlanger entered into a management contract with Hutcheson Hospital located in North Georgia in 2011.

Erlanger was founded in 1889 through the generosity of French nobleman Baron Frederic Emile d'Erlanger who held financial interests in a number of railroads in the region. He donated $5000 (more than $4 million in today's dollars) for a new hospital. It opened with 72 beds in 1899.

EXECUTIVES

Senior Vice President Physician Services, Steven Burkett
Senior Vice President Planning And Business Development, Joseph Winick Fache
Infection Control Director, Susan Berry
Senior Vice President, Joseph Winick
Director Of Him, Jim Brown
Vice President, Bruce Komiske
Medical Director Of Quality And Safety, Woods Blake
Clinic Manager, Sue Cyphers
Medical Director, Jenny Mahaffey

Vice President Public Relations And Marketing,
Jed Mescon
Senior Vice President Chief Information Officer,
David Peterson
Assistant Vice President Of The Heart Institute,
Joscelyn Ccrn

LOCATIONS

HQ: HAMILTON CHATTANOOGA COUNTY HOSPITAL
AUTHORITY
975 E 3RD ST, CHATTANOOGA, TN 374032147
Phone: 423 778-7000
Web: WWW.ERLANGER.ORG

PRODUCTS/OPERATIONS

Selected Campuses
Dodson Avenue Community Health Center
Erlanger Bledsoe Campus
Erlanger East Campus
Erlanger Medical Center
Erlanger North Campus
Southside Community Health Center
T.C. Thompson Children's Hospital

Selected Medical Services
Breast Imaging
Cancer Services
Cardiology
Chattanooga Lifestyle Center
Community Health Centers
Craniofacial Center
Erlanger Metabolic and Bariatric Surgery Center
Erlanger Pharmacy
Gastroenterology
Heart
Home Health (ContinuCare)
HouseCalls
Hypertension Management Center
Imaging Services
LIFE FORCE
Neurobehavioral and Memory Services
Orthopedics
Radiology
Respiratory Services
Rheumatology
Robotic Surgery
Sleep Disorders Center
Stroke
The Weight Loss Program
Trauma Services
Urgent Care - Adult
Urology
UT Erlanger Kidney Transplant Center
Weight Management
Women's Services
WorkForce Corporate Health
Wound Care and Hyperbaric Oxygen center

COMPETITORS

Catholic Health	Saint Thomas
Initiatives	Rutherford Hospital
Community Health	Southern Hills
Systems	Vanderbilt University
Hutcheson Medical	Medical Center
Parkridge Medical	
Center	

HISTORICAL FINANCIALS

Company Type: Private

Income Statement				FYE: June 30
	REVENUE ($ mil.)	NET INCOME ($ mil.)	NET PROFIT MARGIN	EMPLOYEES
06/18	973	26	2.8%	4,700
06/17	888	13	1.6%	—
06/07	499	13	2.7%	—
06/06	439	17	4.0%	—
Annual Growth	6.9%	3.7%	—	—

2018 Year-End Financials

Return on assets: 11.8%   Cash ($ mil.): 43
Return on equity: 2.8%
Current ratio: 1.40

HARBOR-UCLA MEDICAL CENTER

EXECUTIVES

Ceo, Miguel Ortiz
Director, Darrell Harrington
Coordinator, Gail Grate
Pathologist, Shi K Peng
Chief Financial Officer, Jody Nakasuji
Information Specialist, Benjamin Wade
Chief Information Officer, Sandy Mungovan
Hematology Supervisor, Alev Brown
Research Scientist, Amiya Hikim
Research Scientist, David Martin
Project Manager, Helen Casey

LOCATIONS

HQ: HARBOR-UCLA MEDICAL CENTER
1000 W CARSON ST 2, TORRANCE, CA 905022059
Phone: 310 222-2345
Web: WWW.EMEDHARBOR.EDU

HISTORICAL FINANCIALS

Company Type: Private

Income Statement				FYE: June 30
	REVENUE ($ mil.)	NET INCOME ($ mil.)	NET PROFIT MARGIN	EMPLOYEES
06/16	637	(268)	—	3,000
06/15	607	(287)	—	—
Annual Growth	5.0%	—	—	—

2016 Year-End Financials

Return on assets: 13.5%   Cash ($ mil.): 9
Return on equity: (-42.2%)
Current ratio: 1.00

HARMONY PUBLIC SCHOOLS

EXECUTIVES

Pres, Oner Ulvi Celepcikay
Supt, Soner Tarim
V Pres, Cengizhan Keskin
V Pres, Ellen A Macdonald
SEC, Bilal Akin
Treas, Mustafa Ata Atik
Prin, Mehmet Basoglu
Prin, Serkan Kilic
Secondary, Ugur Demircan
Accounting Staff, Dana Hodgin
Librarian, Juana Diaz
Auditors: GOMEZ & COMPANY HOUSTON TEXA

LOCATIONS

HQ: HARMONY PUBLIC SCHOOLS
9321 W SAM HOUSTON PKWY S, HOUSTON, TX
770995204
Phone: 281 888-9764
Web: WWW.HARMONYTX.ORG

HISTORICAL FINANCIALS

Company Type: Private

Income Statement				FYE: June 30
	REVENUE ($ mil.)	NET INCOME ($ mil.)	NET PROFIT MARGIN	EMPLOYEES
06/17	314	3	1.0%	3,262
06/16	265	(8)	—	—
06/15	265	22	8.7%	—
06/14	239	7	3.1%	—
Annual Growth	9.6%	(23.9%)	—	—

2017 Year-End Financials

Return on assets: 2.6%   Cash ($ mil.): 56
Return on equity: 1.0%
Current ratio: 2.10

HARRIS COUNTY HOSPITAL DISTRICT

EXECUTIVES

Pres-Ceo, John Guest
Chb, J Evans Attwell
Chm, Stephen H Doncarlos
SEC, E Dale Wortham
Asst SEC, Daniel D Louie DDS
Cfo, Liz Alhand
Operations Manager, William Puder
Coordinator, Sheterra Jenkins
Information, Danin Kemp
Administrator, David Dungan
Coordinator, Jeffrey Benavides

LOCATIONS

HQ: HARRIS COUNTY HOSPITAL DISTRICT
2525 HOLLY HALL ST, HOUSTON, TX 770544124
Phone: 713 566-6400
Web: WWW.HARRISHEALTH.ORG

HISTORICAL FINANCIALS

Company Type: Private

Income Statement				FYE: February 28
	REVENUE ($ mil.)	NET INCOME ($ mil.)	NET PROFIT MARGIN	EMPLOYEES
02/17	1,731	4	0.2%	5,532
02/09	602	57	9.5%	—
02/08	983	126	12.8%	—
02/07	918	84	9.2%	—
Annual Growth	6.5%	(25.7%)	—	—

2017 Year-End Financials

Return on assets: 5.3%   Cash ($ mil.): 265
Return on equity: 0.2%
Current ratio: 0.90

HARRISON MEDICAL CENTER

EXECUTIVES

Pres-Ceo, Scott Bosch

Exec Vice President, Adar Palis
Sr Vice President, Patty Cochrell
Sr Vice President, Forrest G Ehlinger
Sr Vice President, Mariel S Kagan
SEC, James Smalley
Chief Officer, Michael R Anderson
Payroll Staff, Charlie Sanchez
Director, Rick Smith
Manager, Troy Perkins
Certified Pharmacy Technician, Julia Marks

LOCATIONS

HQ: HARRISON MEDICAL CENTER
2520 CHERRY AVE, BREMERTON, WA 983104229
Phone: 360 744-6510

HISTORICAL FINANCIALS

Company Type: Private

Income Statement   FYE: June 30

	REVENUE ($ mil.)	NET INCOME ($ mil.)	NET PROFIT MARGIN	EMPLOYEES
06/16	433	45	10.6%	2,400
06/15*	398	56	14.1%	—
04/12	345	(22)	—	—
04/11	363	15	4.2%	—
Annual Growth	3.6%	24.9%	—	—

*Fiscal year change

2016 Year-End Financials

Return on assets: 6.5%   Cash ($ mil.): 33
Return on equity: 10.6%
Current ratio: 1.20

HARTFORD HEALTHCARE CORPORATION

Hartford Health Care provides a variety of health services to the descendants of our founding fathers. Founded in 1854 the health care system operates a network of hospitals behavioral health centers nursing and rehabilitation facilities medical labs and numerous community programs for residents in northern Connecticut. Medical specialties range from orthopedics and women's health to cancer and heart care. Hartford Health Care's flagship facility is the Hartford Hospital an 870-bed teaching hospital affiliated with the University of Connecticut Medical School. Its network also includes MidState Medical Center (some 155 beds) Windham Hospital (145 beds) and The Hospital of Central Connecticut (415 beds).

Operations

Hartford Health Care provides primary and specialty care services through partnerships with several physician practice organizations and specialist facilities including diagnostic imaging centers and mental health facilities. The company provides medical laboratory services including pathology genetic testing and other diagnostic services through its Clinical Laboratory Partners affiliate. It also provides long-term care through Central Connecticut Senior Health Services as well as home health services through VNA HealthCare.

Financial Performance

In 2013 Hartford Health Care reported a 2% rise in revenue from $1.7 million to $2.1 million due to increased patient service revenue.

Strategy

As it becomes increasingly challenging for hospitals to remain independently profitable in an unstable economic climate especially as health reform

changes take effect Hartford has been working to expand its footprint in the Connecticut health care market. In 2012 Hartford Health Care formed an alliance with Backus Corporation which operates the Backus Hospital and other medical care centers in eastern Connecticut. Backus gained access to Hartford's broader resources but continues to manage its own day-to-day operations.

In 2014 Hartford Health Care broke ground on a new 90000-square-foot cancer center at The Hospital of Central Connecticut.

EXECUTIVES

Vice President Medical Director, Kent Stahl
Senior Vice President Finance, Richard Stys
Senior Vice President And Chief Human Resources Officer, Tracy Church
Vice President Marketing And Branding, Keith Fontaine
Vice President Governmental Affairs, Kimberly Harrison
Vice President Of Financial Services, Dan Lohr
Managing Director, Robert Hagberg
Vice Chair Department Of Radiology, Barry Stein
Auditors: ERNST & YOUNG LLP HARTFORD C

LOCATIONS

HQ: HARTFORD HEALTHCARE CORPORATION
1 STATE ST FL 19, HARTFORD, CT 061033102
Phone: 860 696-6248
Web: WWW.HARTFORDHEALTHCARE.ORG

PRODUCTS/OPERATIONS

2013 Sales

	% of total
Net patient revenue	90
Other operating revenue	10
Net asets released from restrctions for operations	-
Total	**100**

Selected Facilities

Alliance Occupational Health
Central Connecticut Senior Health Services
Clinical Laboratory Partners
Eastern Rehabilitation Network
Hartford Hospital (acute care)
Hartford Medical Group (primary care)
The Hospital of Central Connecticut (acute care)
Institute of Living (research and psychiatric care)
MidState Medical Center (acute care)
Natchaug Hospital (mental health facility)
Rushford (mental health treatment centers)
VNA HealthCare (home health)
Windham Hospital (acute care)

COMPETITORS

Baystate Medical Center
Berkshire Health Systems
Bristol Hospital
Connecticut Children's Medical Center
Griffin Health
Lawrence & Memorial Hospital
Saint Francis Hospital and Medical Center
St. Vincent's Health Services
University of Connecticut Health Center
Waterbury Hospital
Western Connecticut Health Network
Yale New Haven Health System
Yale-New Haven Hospital Saint Raphael Campus

HISTORICAL FINANCIALS

Company Type: Private

Income Statement   FYE: September 30

	REVENUE ($ mil.)	NET INCOME ($ mil.)	NET PROFIT MARGIN	EMPLOYEES
09/17	2,678	440	16.4%	5,100
09/15	297	(37)	—	—
09/12	2,090	63	3.1%	—
09/11	1,803	138	7.7%	—
Annual Growth	6.8%	21.2%	—	—

2017 Year-End Financials

Return on assets: 3.3%   Cash ($ mil.): 215
Return on equity: 16.4%
Current ratio: 1.30

HARTFORD HOSPITAL

EXECUTIVES

Pres-Ceo, Jeffrey A Flaks
V Pres, Gerry J Boisvert
Sr V Pres, Luis Tavares
Cfo, Tom Marchozzi
Coordinator, Betsy Centeno
Scientist, Michal Assaf
Health Professional, Gada M Abdelhafiz
Scientist, Pamela Tessier
Regional Vice-President, Barry Kriesberg
Coordinator, David Bailey
Assistant Chief, David Chung

LOCATIONS

HQ: HARTFORD HOSPITAL
80 SEYMOUR ST, HARTFORD, CT 061028000
Phone: 860 545-5000
Web: WWW.HARTFORDHOSPITAL.COM

HISTORICAL FINANCIALS

Company Type: Private

Income Statement   FYE: September 30

	REVENUE ($ mil.)	NET INCOME ($ mil.)	NET PROFIT MARGIN	EMPLOYEES
09/17	1,283	96	7.6%	7,500
09/16	1,031	76	7.5%	—
09/15	993	64	6.5%	—
09/14	986	62	6.3%	—
Annual Growth	9.2%	16.0%	—	—

2017 Year-End Financials

Return on assets: 3.2%   Cash ($ mil.): 39
Return on equity: 7.6%
Current ratio: 1.10

HARVARD MEDICAL FACULTY PHYSICIANS AT BETH ISRAEL DEACONESS MEDICAL CENTER, INC.

EXECUTIVES

Ceo, Stuart A Rosenberg
Vice President, Edward L Grab
Administrative Assistant III, Kishan Mahase
Director, Mary Leupold
Manager Technical, Carl Doebler
Auditors: LB DELOITTE TAX LLP JERICHO

LOCATIONS

HQ: HARVARD MEDICAL FACULTY PHYSICIANS AT
   BETH ISRAEL DEACONESS MEDICAL CENTER, INC.
   375 LONGWOOD AVE STE 3, BOSTON, MA
   022155395
Phone: 617 632-9755
Web: WWW.HMFPHYSICIANS.ORG

HISTORICAL FINANCIALS

Company Type: Private

Income Statement				FYE: September 30
	REVENUE ($ mil.)	NET INCOME ($ mil.)	NET PROFIT MARGIN	EMPLOYEES
09/15	487	1	0.3%	800
09/14	460	14	3.2%	—
09/08	22	2	11.6%	—
Annual Growth	55.3%	(6.4%)	—	—

2015 Year-End Financials

Return on assets: 7.2%   Cash ($ mil.): 26
Return on equity: 0.3%
Current ratio: 1.40

HARVARD PRIVATE CAPITAL REALTY, INC.

EXECUTIVES

Pres, Jane Mendillo
Dir, Robert Ettl
Sr V Pres, Karen Rimon

LOCATIONS

HQ: HARVARD PRIVATE CAPITAL REALTY, INC.
   600 ATLANTIC AVE, BOSTON, MA 022102211
Phone: 617 720-6859

HISTORICAL FINANCIALS

Company Type: Private

Income Statement				FYE: June 30
	REVENUE ($ mil.)	NET INCOME ($ mil.)	NET PROFIT MARGIN	EMPLOYEES
06/17	337	282	83.7%	3
06/10	632	202	32.1%	—
Annual Growth	(8.6%)	4.8%	—	—

HCL AMERICA INC.

EXECUTIVES

Chm, Shiv Nadar
Ceo, Manish Anand
Director, Abhishek Mendiratta
Director Marketing, Abhishek Vanamali
General Manager, Amit Varma
Sales Director, Anil Balwanti
Associate Vice President, Anil Verma
Vice President Marketing, Anubhav Saxena
Director Sales, Atul Athavale
Technical Lead, Bagavathy Mahendran
Technical Manager, Brian Song
Auditors: SR BATLIBOI & CO LLP HARYA

LOCATIONS

HQ: HCL AMERICA INC.
   330 POTRERO AVE, SUNNYVALE, CA 940854194
Phone: 408 733-0480
Web: WWW.HCLTECH.COM

HISTORICAL FINANCIALS

Company Type: Private

Income Statement				FYE: March 31
	REVENUE ($ mil.)	NET INCOME ($ mil.)	NET PROFIT MARGIN	EMPLOYEES
03/17*	3,559	130	3.7%	11,993
06/15	2,815	53	1.9%	—
06/14	2,353	0	0.0%	—
06/13	2,075	35	1.7%	—
Annual Growth	14.4%	37.9%	—	—

*Fiscal year change

2017 Year-End Financials

Return on assets: 9.8%   Cash ($ mil.): 4
Return on equity: 3.7%
Current ratio: 0.70

HDR ARCHITECTURE, INC.

EXECUTIVES

Ceo, George A Little
President, Eric L Keen
President, Douglas Wignall
SEC, Mary E Peters
SEC, Louis Pachman
Treas, Chad Hartnett
Cfo, Terence C Cox
Fin Mgr, Jennifer Wik
Director, Michaella Wright
Mgr, Robyn Pope
Vice-President, Hank Adams
Auditors: ERNST & YOUNG LLP OMAHA NE

LOCATIONS

HQ: HDR ARCHITECTURE, INC.
   1917 S 67TH ST, OMAHA, NE 681062973
Phone: 402 399-1000
Web: WWW.HDRINC.COM

HISTORICAL FINANCIALS

Company Type: Private

Income Statement				FYE: December 30
	REVENUE ($ mil.)	NET INCOME ($ mil.)	NET PROFIT MARGIN	EMPLOYEES
12/17	400	9	2.3%	1,472
12/16	408	6	1.7%	—
12/15	241	(6)	—	—
12/14	237	(18)	—	—
Annual Growth	19.0%	—	—	—

2017 Year-End Financials

Return on assets: 4.0%   Cash ($ mil.): 24
Return on equity: 2.3%
Current ratio: 0.50

HDR ENGINEERING, INC.

EXECUTIVES

Ceo, George A Little
Pres, Eric L Keen
Coo, George Little
Cfo, Terence C Cox
Exec V Pres, Terry Cox
Treas, Chad M Hartnett
SEC, Louis J Pachman
SEC, Patty Diggins
Mgr, Gerald T Holmes
Manager, Denis P Gilbert
Director, Kelly Vincent
Auditors: ERNST & YOUNG LLP OMAHA NE

LOCATIONS

HQ: HDR ENGINEERING, INC.
   1917 S 67TH ST, OMAHA, NE 681062973
Phone: 402 399-1000
Web: WWW.HDRINC.COM

HISTORICAL FINANCIALS

Company Type: Private

Income Statement				FYE: December 30
	REVENUE ($ mil.)	NET INCOME ($ mil.)	NET PROFIT MARGIN	EMPLOYEES
12/17	1,707	73	4.3%	6,111
12/16	1,748	89	5.1%	—
12/15	1,218	100	8.2%	—
12/14	1,115	74	6.7%	—
Annual Growth	15.2%	(0.4%)	—	—

2017 Year-End Financials

Return on assets: 4.3%   Cash ($ mil.): 12
Return on equity: 4.3%
Current ratio: 1.30

HDR, INC.

With projects ranging from restoring the Pentagon and the Everglades to working on the Hoover Dam Bypass project HDR has left its mark on the US. HDR is an architecture engineering and consulting firm that specializes in such projects as bridges water- and wastewater-treatment plants and hospitals. The company also provides mechanical and plumbing services construction and project management and utilities planning. It has completed projects nationwide and in some 60 countries through its more than 225 global locations. The employee-owned company was founded as Henningson Engineering in 1917 to build municipal plants in the rural Midwest.

Geographic Reach

Headquartered in Omaha Nebraska HDR has completed projects in 60 countries and maintains some 225 offices worldwide. It operates in the Americas (US and Canada) Asia (China and Mongolia) Australia Europe (Germany and the UK) and the Middle East.

Sales and Marketing

HDR's has performed design and engineering work for a number of clients including: Seattle Public Utilities DEXUS Property Group the Pirbright Institute SeaPort-e TXMAS and Xcel Energy.

Strategy

With the goal of cutting its client costs by 10% through smarter delivery processes in its designed and constructed facilities HDR has spent the past few years expanding its service capabilities through strategic acquisitions. To this end in early 2015 the company purchased Tennessee-based Infrastructure Corporation of America (ICA) which specializes in transport engineering and asset maintenance and management. Additionally it bought the assets of Georgia-based liquid natural gas firm MEI LLC.

The acquisition of architectural practice Rice Daubney in late 2013 enhanced the company's position in the Australian market while purchases in 2012 (Wyoming's Stetson Engineering) and 2011 (New Jersey's HydroQual) extended its water capabilities.

The company also continues to design and engineer big infrastructure projects for city and state governments. In late 2014 Seattle Public Utilities selected HDR develop and evaluate site plan concepts for the South Transfer Station Phase 2 project to create nearly a dozen facilities for recycling and waste-reuse to help the utility reach its goal of 70% solid waste diversion by 2025. Also in late 2014 HDR partnered with Jacobs Engineering Group to lead the engineering for the I-4 Mobility Partners group and will deliver final designs for roadway/traffic control draining structure and intelligent traffic systems for the I-4 Ultimate Project in Florida.

Mergers and Acquisitions

In January 2015 the company acquired both the Infrastructure Corporation of America (ICA) which specializes in transport engineering and asset maintenance and management along with the Georgia-based liquid natural gas firm MEI LLC to broaden its service capabilities.

In 2013 HDR purchased architecture firm Rice Daubney to bolster its design expertise and extend its reach in the Australian market.

In 2012 the company bought Wyoming's Stetson Engineering to broaden its water services.

EXECUTIVES

Chairman And Ceo, George A. Little
Cfo, Terence C. (Terry) Cox
Evp And Director Environmental Resource Management, Elwin Larson
Evp And Director Water Program, Gary L. Bleeker
Vice Chairman; President Hdr Engineering Inc., Eric L. Keen
President Manager, Kevin Keller
President Hdr Architecture Inc., Doug S. Wignall
Cio, Michael Geppert
Evp And Director Transportation, Charles O'Reilly
President Manager Richmond Hill Traffic Practice, David Argue
Auditors: ERNST & YOUNG LLP OMAHA NE

LOCATIONS

HQ: HDR, INC.
1917 S 67TH ST, OMAHA, NE 681062973
Phone: 402 399-1000
Web: WWW.HDRINC.COM

PRODUCTS/OPERATIONS

Selected Mergers and Acquisitions
FY2015
Brentwood Tennessee-based Infrastructure Corporation of America (ICA)
FY2103
    Rice Daubney (Australia architecture design for healthcare retail defense markets)
FY2012
    Stetson Engineering (Wyoming projects in water sewer storm water hydrology and transportation)
FY2011
    Amnis Engineering (Canada)
    Cooper Medical (Healthcare design/build specialist)
    HydroQual (New Jersey water resource management)
    Schiff Associates (California engineering)
FY2009

Devine Tarbell & Associates (Maine now named HDR|DTA)
iTrans Consulting (Toronto-based engineering firm)

Selected Markets
Architecture
    Academic
    Civic
    Corporate
    Healthcare
    Justice
    Science and Technology
Energy
    Oil and Gas
    Power Delivery
    Power Generation
    Renewable Energy
Federal
    Federal Architecture
    Federal Engineering
    Federal Planning
    Federal Environmental
    Federal Energy
    Federal Construction
    HDR SeaPort-e
Private Land Development
    Commercial
    Industrial
    Institutional
    Residential
    Resorts and Hotels
Resource Management
    Community Planning & Consulting
    Environmental Sciences & Permitting
    Fisheries Science & Design
    Mining
    Natural Resource Management
    Waste Management and Industrial
Transportation
    Aviation
    Freight Rail
    Highways and Local Roads
    Maritime
    Transit
Water
    Water
    Wastewater
    Water Planning
    Industrial

Selected Services
Analytical consulting
Architectural design
Coastal engineering and restoration
Consulting
Design/build
Environmental monitoring
Finished water storage facility services
Interior design
Landscape architecture
Master planning
Power facility engineering
Pump stations and flow control
Security services
Utility master planning and modeling
Water resources
Water treatment systems

COMPETITORS
AECOM
Black & Veatch
Brown and Caldwell
CH2M HILL
Epstein
Fuscoe Engineering
Gensler
Geotechnics
HBE Corporation
HKS Inc.
Interior Architects
Jacobs Engineering
KPA Associates
Kimley-Horn and Associates
Lee Burkhart Liu
Leo A Daly
MCG Architects
MWH Global
Michael Baker
Nasland Engineering

Perkowitz + Ruth
RMJM
RTKL Associates
SAIC Energy Environment & Infrastructure
STV
Tetra Tech
The Austin Company
Western Summit Constructors
Willdan Group

HISTORICAL FINANCIALS
Company Type: Private

Income Statement				FYE: December 30
	REVENUE ($ mil.)	NET INCOME ($ mil.)	NET PROFIT MARGIN	EMPLOYEES
12/17	2,362	82	3.5%	10,000
12/16	2,230	90	4.0%	—
12/15	2,132	74	3.5%	—
12/14	1,421	64	4.5%	—
Annual Growth	18.4%	8.8%	—	—

2017 Year-End Financials
Return on assets: 5.2%   Cash ($ mil.): 243
Return on equity: 3.5%
Current ratio: 1.10

HEALTH FIRST, INC.

Health First works to keep Florida's Space Coast denizens in tip-top shape. The not-for-profit health system operates four hospitals in Brevard County. Health First's biggest hospital is Holmes Regional Medical Center in Melbourne with more than 500 beds. Its Cape Canaveral Hospital and Palm Bay Community Hospital have 150 and 60 beds respectively. Its Viera Hospital is a 100-bed acute-care hospital. The system also runs outpatient clinics a home health service and a physicians group. Its for-profit subsidiary Health First Health Plans is the county's largest insurer with about 60000 commercial members and 23000 Medicare members.

Operations
The company operates four hospitals (Holmes Regional Medical Center Palm Bay Hospital Cape Canaveral Hospital and Viera Hospital) and offers a wide variety of health insurance plan options for patients in Brevard and Indian River Counties. Health First is the largest multi-specialty physician group on Florida's Space Coast. It also operates to Brevard County's only trauma center and a number of outpatient and wellness services including four pro-health and fitness centers.

Geographic Reach
Health First operates four hospitals and a health insurance company in Brevard County Florida.

Strategy
To expand its capacity Health First makes complementary acquisitions and pursues organic growth.

In 2103 Health First opened of a new center for fracture care at Health First Holmes Regional Medical Center and the center for joint replacement at Health First Viera Hospital. That year it formed a new Small Group Preferred Provider Organization (PPO) Plan offering increased flexibility when it comes to out-of-network coverage and fulfilling the needs of employer groups in its service area.

Mergers and Acquisitions
In 2012 the company acquired Melbourne Internal Medicine Associates (250 physician providers based in Melbourne) to increase patient quality safety and the patient experience. The entity

was renamed the Health First Medical Group in 2013.

Company Background

In 2011 Health First partnered with Nemours to expand pediatric care in Brevard County. That year Health First Health Plans opened a new Vero Beach office to serve residents of Indian River County and launch its Medicare Advantage plans to the rest of Indian River County.

Despite an ongoing lawsuit with Wuesthoff Health System (which claims that Health First has an unfair monopoly of hospital services in Brevard County) the company forged ahead with construction of its fourth hospital in the county the Viera hospital campus. The Medical Plaza at Viera Health Park which will includes offices for multi-specialty physicians and a diagnostic/imaging center opened in 2010. And the park's centerpiece Viera Hospital a 100-bed acute-care hospital opened in 2011.

Health First was founded in 1995 through a merger of regional hospitals. The Brevard Hospital (now Holmes Regional Medical Center) first opened in 1937.

EXECUTIVES

Chief Physician Executive, Jeffrey C. Stalnaker
Evp And Coo, J. Stuart Mitchell
Evp Chief Strategy Officer; Ceo Health First Health Plans, Drew Rector
Evp And Cfo, Joseph (Joe) Felkner
President Health First Medical Group, Travis L Douglass
President And Ceo, Steven P. Johnson
Ceo Community Hospitals, Aaron Robinson
Svp And Cio, Alex Popowycz
President Hospital Operations, Bill Calhoun
Chief Nursing Officer, Constance (Connie) Bradley
Vice President Marketing And Communications, Matthew Gerrell
Chairman, Pamela A. Gatto
Vice Chairman, Kevin B. Steele

LOCATIONS

HQ: HEALTH FIRST, INC.
6450 US HIGHWAY 1, ROCKLEDGE, FL 329555747
Phone: 321 434-4300
Web: WWW.HEALTH-FIRST.ORG

Selected facilities

Cape Canaveral Hospital (Cocoa Beach)
Holmes Regional Medical Center (Melbourne)
Palm Bay Community Hospital (Palm Bay)
Viera Hospital (Viera)

COMPETITORS

Adventist Health System Sunbelt Healthcare
Aetna
CIGNA
Florida Blue
HCA
Orlando Health
Osceola Regional Medical Center
Tenet Healthcare
Wuesthoff Health System

HISTORICAL FINANCIALS

Company Type: Private

Income Statement
FYE: September 30

	REVENUE ($ mil.)	NET INCOME ($ mil.)	NET PROFIT MARGIN	EMPLOYEES
09/15	1,255	19	1.6%	6,900
09/14	1,136	90	7.9%	—
09/13	1,059	51	4.8%	—
09/11	129	(0)	—	—
Annual Growth	76.5%	—	—	—

2015 Year-End Financials

Return on assets: 12.8%
Return on equity: 1.6%
Current ratio: 1.40

Cash ($ mil.): 152

HEALTH PARTNERS PLANS, INC.

Health Partners wants to partner up with Pennsylvanians in need of health care. The company is a not-for-profit health plan that provides health benefits to some 210000 Medicaid recipients in the Philadelphia area. Its HealthChoices plans for Medicaid participants cover medical dental prescription and vision costs. Its KidzPartners program is provided in partnership with the state of Pennsylvania's Children's Health Insurance Program (CHIP). Its provider network includes about 6000 primary and specialty care doctors and 30 hospitals in the region. The company also provides community outreach and wellness programs. Health Partners was founded in 1985 by a group of hospitals in the Philadelphia area.

Geographic Reach

Health Partners' plans cover members in Philadelphia and in Chester Delaware Bucks and Montgomery counties outside the city.

Strategy

Health Partners signed a provider contract with the University of Pennsylvania Health System that will increase access to care in Philadelphia for Health Partners Medicare members. The agreement increases Health Partners' network to include more than 1300 additional physicians from the Health System's network of practices and four hospitals.

Health Partners has been working to enhance its community health programs in recent years. It launched its Computer Health Care Management Education program to provide free monthly computer lessons combined with tutorials about healthy lifestyle programs.

It also teamed up with the Norcom Community Center to offer HealthChoices and KidzPartners members fitness benefits at the facility; the company has a total of more than 20 fitness centers in its expanding provider network. The KidzPartners program provides free or affordable insurance coverage to children and teens who don't qualify for Medicaid.

Company Background

The area hospitals that own Health Partners are Albert Einstein Medical Center Aria Health Temple University Hospital Episcopal Hospital and two Tenet Healthcare facilities (Hahnemann University Hospital and St. Christopher's Hospital for Children).

EXECUTIVES

President And Ceo, William S. George
Svp Healthcare Management And Chief Medical Officer, Steven E. Szebenyi
Svp Operations And Coo, Lisa Getzfrid
Government Relations, Kearline Jones
Vice President Of Marketing, Caroline Russell
Vice President Government Relations And Compliance, Kearline Mckellar-Jones
Vice President Finance And Chief Financi, John Sehi
Senior Vice President Of Strategic Planning And Initiatives, Tom Montanaro
Vice President, Johnna Baker
Vice President Medical Management, Michelle Mattiace
Auditors: KPMG LLP PHILADELPHIA PENNSY

LOCATIONS

HQ: HEALTH PARTNERS PLANS, INC.
901 MARKET ST STE 500, PHILADELPHIA, PA 191074496
Phone: 215 849-9606
Web: WWW.HEALTHPARTNERSPLANS.COM

COMPETITORS

Aetna
CIGNA
Coventry Health Care
Gateway Health Plan
Health Net
Highmark
Independence Blue Cross
Keystone Mercy
UnitedHealth Group

HISTORICAL FINANCIALS

Company Type: Private

Income Statement
FYE: December 31

	REVENUE ($ mil.)	NET INCOME ($ mil.)	NET PROFIT MARGIN	EMPLOYEES
12/15	1,502	(2)	—	620
12/14	910	(8)	—	—
12/13	1,000	(0)	—	—
12/12	1,034	(1)	—	—
Annual Growth	13.2%	—	—	—

2015 Year-End Financials

Return on assets: 1.3%
Return on equity: (-0.2%)
Current ratio: 1.00

Cash ($ mil.): 174

HEALTH QUEST SYSTEMS, INC.

EXECUTIVES

Ceo, Denise George
V Pres, Mary Ann Keppel
Sr V Pres, Ron Tatelbaumm
Sr V Pres, David Ping
Cfo, Yann Kepple
Sr V Pres, Ann Armater
Coordinator, Cheryl Mathieu
Project Manager, Deborah Driscoll
Chief Financial Officer, Gary Zmrhal
Information Specialist, Lew Hulse
Director, Norma Kurtz
Auditors: PRICEWATERHOUSECOOPERS LLP N

LOCATIONS

HQ: HEALTH QUEST SYSTEMS, INC.
1351 ROUTE 55 STE 200, LAGRANGEVILLE, NY 125405144
Phone: 845 475-9500
Web: WWW.HEALTH-QUEST.ORG

HISTORICAL FINANCIALS

Company Type: Private

Income Statement
FYE: December 31

	REVENUE ($ mil.)	NET INCOME ($ mil.)	NET PROFIT MARGIN	EMPLOYEES
12/15	870	39	4.6%	2,000
12/14	796	5	0.6%	—
12/13	706	103	14.6%	—
12/12	692	8	1.2%	—
Annual Growth	7.9%	69.7%	—	—

2015 Year-End Financials
Return on assets: 13.4%   Cash ($ mil.): 109
Return on equity: 4.6%
Current ratio: 1.30

HEALTH RESEARCH, INC.

EXECUTIVES

Exec Dir, Barbara Ryan
Exec Dir, Cheryl Mattox
Director of Operations, Tammy Young
Law Specialist, Nicole McMillin
Scientist, Vincent Escuyer
Manager, Donna Deluca
Associate, James Lieberman
Director of Information Techno, John Bintz
Co Director, Keith Cheung
Auditors: BONADIO & CO LLP ALBANY NE

LOCATIONS

HQ: HEALTH RESEARCH, INC.
  150 BROADWAY STE 560, MENANDS, NY 122042726
Phone: 518 431-1200
Web: WWW.HEALTHRESEARCH.ORG

HISTORICAL FINANCIALS
Company Type: Private

| Income Statement | | | FYE: March 31 | |
	REVENUE ($ mil.)	NET INCOME ($ mil.)	NET PROFIT MARGIN	EMPLOYEES
03/15	677	22	3.3%	1,400
03/14	703	13	1.9%	—
03/13	665	25	3.9%	—
03/12	661	(10)	—	—
Annual Growth	0.8%	—	—	—

2015 Year-End Financials
Return on assets: 3.7%   Cash ($ mil.): 187
Return on equity: 3.3%
Current ratio: —

HEALTHNOTES LLC

EXECUTIVES

Ceo, Dan Miller
Cfo, Bill Voloch
Coo, Ryan Simpson
Anesthesiology, Cynthia V Kruger
Health Care Director, Amy Guerra
Director of Infection Control, Sheila Huynh
Chief of Radiology, William Grande
Scientist, Catherine Serio
Chief of Cardiology, David Rogers
Human Resource Director, Donna Greeley
Coordinator, Janine Lafrankcis

LOCATIONS

HQ: HEALTHNOTES LLC
  1501 S POTOMAC ST, AURORA, CO 800125411
Phone: 303 695-2600
Web: WWW.HEALTHONECARES.COM

HISTORICAL FINANCIALS
Company Type: Private

| Income Statement | | | FYE: December 31 | |
	REVENUE ($ mil.)	NET INCOME ($ mil.)	NET PROFIT MARGIN	EMPLOYEES
12/17	346	108	31.2%	1,500
12/16	319	90	28.3%	—
12/15	322	90	28.0%	—
12/08	335	30	9.1%	—
Annual Growth	0.4%	15.1%	—	

2017 Year-End Financials
Return on assets: 3.0%   Cash ($ mil.): —
Return on equity: 31.2%
Current ratio: 1.90

HEARTLAND CO-OP

EXECUTIVES

Pres, Arthur L Churchill
Human Resources Administrator, Katherine
  Thompson
Manager, Gary Orstad
Information Technology Manager, Kami Snider
Staff, Terry Frahm
Accountant, Angela Harlow
Coordinator, Cathy Miller
Manager, Deak Pinegar
Director, Eric Finch
Manager, Jeff Jones
Staff, Jonathan Lewis
Auditors: BERGAN PAULSEN & COMPANY PC

LOCATIONS

HQ: HEARTLAND CO-OP
  2829 WESTOWN PKWY STE 350, WEST DES
  MOINES, IA 502661340
Phone: 515 225-1334
Web: WWW.HEARTLANDCOOP.COM

HISTORICAL FINANCIALS
Company Type: Private

| Income Statement | | | FYE: June 30 | |
	REVENUE ($ mil.)	NET INCOME ($ mil.)	NET PROFIT MARGIN	EMPLOYEES
06/18	901	20	2.2%	678
06/17	932	17	1.9%	—
06/16	854	15	1.9%	—
Annual Growth	2.7%	12.2%	—	—

2018 Year-End Financials
Return on assets: 1.6%   Cash ($ mil.): —
Return on equity: 2.2%
Current ratio: 0.10

HEARTLAND HEALTH

Heartland Health provides medical care in the heart of the Midwest. The integrated health care system serves residents of northwest Missouri as well as bordering areas of Kansas and Nebraska. Its flagship facility is Heartland Regional Medical Center a 350-bed acute-care hospital that features an emergency room and Level II trauma center as well as specialty care programs in heart disease cancer and obstetrics. Heartland Health also provides primary care through a multi-specialty medical practice (Heartland Clinic) and it offers home health hospice and long-term care services from the primary medical center facility. The company's Community Health Improvement Solutions unit is an HMO health insurer.

Strategy

In 2012 Heartland Health joined the Mayo Clinic Care Network which will enable to it to tap the knowledge and expertise of Mayo Clinic physicians to better serve its patients.

Company Background

Heartland Health was formed in 1984 through the merger of two St. Joseph Missouri hospital: Methodist Medical Center and St. Joseph's Hospital. The two facilities trace their roots back to 1924 and 1861 respectively.

EXECUTIVES

Ceo, Mark Laney
President, Lowell Kruse
V Pres-Cfo, John Wilson
Chairman*, Alfred L Purcell
Asst SEC, Karen Dittemore
Asst Treas-Contrl, Douglas Brandt
Cmo, Robert Permet
Chm, David Solanski
Coo, Cut Kretzinger
Staff, C R Shumann III
Staff, Monica Ray
Auditors: RSM US LLP DAVENPORT IOWA

LOCATIONS

HQ: HEARTLAND HEALTH
  5325 FARAON ST, SAINT JOSEPH, MO 645063488
Phone: 816 271-6000
Web: WWW.HEARTLAND-HEALTH.COM

PRODUCTS/OPERATIONS

Selected Affiliates
Atchison Hospital (Atchison KS)
Community Hospital (Fairfax MO)
Community Medical Center (Falls City NE)
Dental Clinic (St. Joseph MO)
Laser Cosmedic Center (Platte City MO)
North Kansas City Hospital (North Kansas City MO)
The Surgery Center (St. Joseph MO)

COMPETITORS

Ascension Health
BJC HealthCare
Blue Cross and Blue Shield of Kansas City
Catholic Health Initiatives
Children's Mercy Hospital
CoxHealth
HCA
Mercy Health
Mercy Hospital Springfield
Saint Luke's Health System
Shawnee Mission Medical Center
Sisters of Charity of Leavenworth
Truman Medical Centers
University of Kansas Medical Center

HISTORICAL FINANCIALS
Company Type: Private

| Income Statement | | | FYE: June 30 | |
	REVENUE ($ mil.)	NET INCOME ($ mil.)	NET PROFIT MARGIN	EMPLOYEES
06/18	667	64	9.6%	32,000
06/16	584	(6)	—	—
06/15	577	22	3.9%	—
06/14	560	64	11.4%	—
Annual Growth	4.5%	(0.0%)	—	—

2018 Year-End Financials
Return on assets: 3.0%   Cash ($ mil.): 26
Return on equity: 9.6%
Current ratio: 0.90

HEARTLAND PAYMENT SYSTEMS, LLC

Heartland Payment Systems (HPS) a wholly owned subsidiary of Global Payments Inc. makes sure plastic-card transactions don't get lost along their way. The company performs credit debit and prepaid card processing services at some 300000 locations nationwide. Its client list includes restaurants retailers convenience stores and professional service providers. The Heartland Payroll Solutions segment provides payroll processing such as check printing and direct deposit for more than 10000 customers. Other markets for the firm include K-12 school nutrition programs and payment processing for colleges and universities. Global Payments bought Heartland for $4.3 billion in 2016.

Change in Company Type

Atlanta-based payment technology firm Global Payments acquired Heartland Payment Systems in its largest acquisition to-date in 2016. Through that purchase it expanded its presence in the US small and mid-sized commercial customer market and added new merchant customers. Operating results of HPS are now reported as part of the Global Payments? North American segment.

Operations

Heartland primarily offers card payment processing and related services to small and midsized merchants and network services merchants. Its Campus Solutions unit provides payment processing integrated commerce solutions higher education loan services and open/closed loop payment solutions. Heartland School Solutions provides school nutrition and point-of-sale and related payment services to K-12 schools while Heartland Payroll Solutions provides payroll processing and related tax filing services. Other activities include electronic check processing gift card marketing and processing online payments and the sale and rental of point-of-sale processing equipment.

Geographic Reach

Princeton NJ-based Heartland Payment Systems serves customers throughout the US. The largest centers of its small and medium-sized business merchants are in California Texas Florida New York and Pennsylvania which together represent more than 30% of card processing volume. Its network services merchants are predominantly gas stations located throughout the US.

Sales and Marketing

The company serves small and midsized customers in a variety of businesses including restaurant hospitality education parking and retail. The network service segment primarily serves gas station merchants.

The firm employs sales professionals and relationship managers to build and maintain direct customer relationships.

Strategy

HPS is addressing the fast growth of mobile payments launching a variety of mobile applications in recent years to take advantage of the opportunity. The firm continues to nurture its Heartland Mobile and Online Ordering platform which allows smaller restaurants to accept mobile orders and payments. It also tends to the growth of its OneCard Mobile application which serves as a

?one-for-all? card for university students. The card is issued by campus administrators and serves as a virtual ID card and payment system for all campus services and activities and for permission-based access to events buildings rooms libraries and other facilities.

EXECUTIVES

Ceo, Robert O Carr
Co-President, Michael A Lawler
Co-President, David Gilbert
Cfo, Samir Zabaneh
Clo-Gen Counsel, Charles Kallenbach
Coo, Conan Lane
Cbo, Michael McMillan
Cso, Marty Moretti
Cso, John R South
Cao, Joseph E White
Cto, Bryan Thompson
Auditors: DELOITTE & TOUCHE LLP PHILADE

LOCATIONS

HQ: HEARTLAND PAYMENT SYSTEMS, LLC
10 GLENLAKE PKWY STE 324, ATLANTA, GA
303283495
Phone: 609 683-3831
Web: WWW.HEARTLANDPAYMENTSYSTEMS.COM

PRODUCTS/OPERATIONS

Products:
Billing Solutions
E-Commerce
Gift Cards
Internet of Things
Lending
Loyalty Program
Mobile Ordering
Mobile Payment
Payroll Services
Point of Sale
Processing
School Nutrition
School Payment

COMPETITORS

Banc of America Merchant Services	Fifth Third
Cardtronics	First Data
Chase Paymentech Solutions	Fiserv
	Fujitsu America
Comdata	Total System Services
Deluxe Corporation	Vantiv
ECHO Inc.	Wells Fargo
Elavon	iPayment
Fidelity National Information Services	

HISTORICAL FINANCIALS
Company Type: Private

Income Statement   FYE: December 31

	REVENUE ($ mil.)	NET INCOME ($ mil.)	NET PROFIT MARGIN	EMPLOYEES
12/15	2,682	84	3.2%	3,734
12/14	2,311	31	1.4%	—
12/13	2,135	78	3.7%	—
12/12	2,013	66	3.3%	—
Annual Growth	10.0%	8.4%	—	—

2015 Year-End Financials
Return on assets: 2.6%   Cash ($ mil.): 56
Return on equity: 3.2%
Current ratio: 0.50

HEARTLAND REGIONAL MEDICAL CENTER

Heartland Regional Medical Center strives for healthy hearts minds and bodies in the US heartland. The acute care hospital a subsidiary of Heartland Health provides medical services to residents of St. Joseph Missouri and some 20 surrounding counties in northwest Missouri southeast Nebraska and northeast Kansas. Heartland Regional Medical Center encompasses specialty centers for trauma and long-term care acute rehabilitation cancer heart disease and birthing. As part of the services provided by the medical center Heartland Regional Medical Center offers services such as arthritis pain and wound treatments as well as home health and hospice care.

Geographic Reach

Operating in Missouri Heartland Regional Medical Center serves the residents and visitors of its home state as well as those in Nebraska and Kansas. Altogether the medical center caters to a more than 20-county area.

Financial Performance

In fiscal 2012 as compared to 2011 Heartland Regional Medical Center's revenue rose some 8% and its net income saw a 31% boost.

Strategy

As part of its operations Heartland Regional Medical Center partners with several managed care organizations such as Aetna CCN Managed Care Coventry Healthcare and Blue Cross Blue Shield of Kansas City to give its patients payment options for its health services. In 2012 Heartland Regional Medical Center developed an accountable care organization. It's a participant in the Medicare Shared Savings Program and enters into other similar shared savings arrangements with commercial self-insured or other third-party payors.

In recent years the medical facility has been investing in growing its footprint. Heartland Regional Medical Center is funding a $55-million expansion project that includes adding a handful of new operating rooms and renovating 10 more.

EXECUTIVES

Chm, Alfred L Purcell
Ceo, Mark Laney
SEC, John Wilson
Project Manager, Chris Bennett
Marketing Staff, Diane R Smith
Director, Karen Baker
Auditors: BLD LLP KANSAS CITY MISSOUR

LOCATIONS

HQ: HEARTLAND REGIONAL MEDICAL CENTER
5325 FARAON ST, SAINT JOSEPH, MO 645063488
Phone: 816 271-6000
Web: WWW.MYMOSAICLIFECARE.ORG

PRODUCTS/OPERATIONS

Selected Services
Appendectomy
Cholecystectomy
Colon Resection
Hernia Repair
Nephrectomy
Assisted Vaginal Hysterectomy
Peritoneal Dialysis Catheter Placement
Pyloromyotomy
Tubal Ligation
Abdominal Perineal Resection
Adrenalectomy
Colostomy
Gastric Banding
Gastric Bypass

Gastric Sleeve
Gastrostomy Tube Placement
Laser Lysis of Adhesions/Endometriosis
Nissan Fundoplication
Salpingo-Oophorectomy
Prostatectomy

COMPETITORS

Ascension Health	Shawnee Mission
BJC HealthCare	Medical Center
Catholic Health	Sisters of Charity of
Initiatives	Leavenworth
Children's Mercy	Truman Medical Centers
Hospital	University of Kansas
CoxHealth	Medical Center
Mercy Health	
Saint Luke's Health	
System	

HISTORICAL FINANCIALS

Company Type: Private

Income Statement   FYE: June 30

	REVENUE ($ mil.)	NET INCOME ($ mil.)	NET PROFIT MARGIN	EMPLOYEES
06/18	639	64	10.1%	2,600
06/17	605	26	4.4%	—
06/16	562	(5)	—	—
06/15	563	20	3.7%	—
Annual Growth	4.3%	46.0%	—	—

2018 Year-End Financials

Return on assets: 3.0%   Cash ($ mil.): 22
Return on equity: 10.1%
Current ratio: 0.80

HEMET UNIFIED SCHOOL DISTRICT

EXECUTIVES

Supt, Christi Barrett
Business Official, Vincent Christekos
Assistant Supt, Darel Hansen
Accountant, Julie Shepherd
Psychologist, Terri Foster
Computer Technician, Bob Anderson
Facilities Specialist, Roxanne Estavillo
Teacher, Elizabeth Fiorito
Director, Pam Buckhout
Administrative Assistant, Debra Nagel
Consultant, Francina Kelly
Auditors: VANRINEK TRINE DAY & CO LL

LOCATIONS

HQ: HEMET UNIFIED SCHOOL DISTRICT
1791 W ACACIA AVE, HEMET, CA 925453797
Phone: 951 765-5100
Web: WWW.HEMETUSD.ORG

HISTORICAL FINANCIALS

Company Type: Private

Income Statement   FYE: June 30

	REVENUE ($ mil.)	NET INCOME ($ mil.)	NET PROFIT MARGIN	EMPLOYEES
06/17	299	(13)	—	2,989
06/16	280	3	1.3%	—
06/15	3	0	1.7%	—
06/06	141	47	33.6%	—
Annual Growth	7.0%	—	—	—

HENDRICK MEDICAL CENTER

EXECUTIVES

Ceo, Tim Lancaster
Sr Vice President, Joe Pearson
Vice President, Norm Archibald
Vice President, Stephen T Faehnle
Cfo, Jeremy Walker
Coordinator, Allen Rector
Customer Representativ, Amanda Runne
Internal Medicine Practitioner, Kirtan Patel
Cardiovascular Disease, Gorman M Thorp
Director, Sherri Bowden
Obstetrician Gynecologist, Whitney V Mascorro
Auditors: CONDLEY AND COMPANY LLP ABILE

LOCATIONS

HQ: HENDRICK MEDICAL CENTER
1900 PINE ST, ABILENE, TX 796012432
Phone: 325 670-2000
Web: WWW.HENDRICKHEALTH.ORG

HISTORICAL FINANCIALS

Company Type: Private

Income Statement   FYE: August 31

	REVENUE ($ mil.)	NET INCOME ($ mil.)	NET PROFIT MARGIN	EMPLOYEES
08/17	408	40	9.8%	2,900
08/16	419	44	10.6%	—
08/15	325	15	4.6%	—
08/14	394	55	14.2%	—
Annual Growth	1.2%	(10.5%)	—	—

2017 Year-End Financials

Return on assets: 9.7%   Cash ($ mil.): 20
Return on equity: 9.8%
Current ratio: 1.10

HENDRICKS COUNTY HOSPITAL

EXECUTIVES

Jd, Ceo, Kevin P Speer
Cfo, Isadore Rivas
Database Administrator, Laura Long
Director, Lynn Turner
Contractor, Steve Dewey
Assistant, Anita Dieckmann
Director, Matthew Browning
Registered Nurse, Beth Gephart
Coordinator, Stephanie Jones
Information Specialist, Tracy Day
Materials Manager, Brian Sheets
Auditors: BLUE & CO LLC INDIANAPOLIS

LOCATIONS

HQ: HENDRICKS COUNTY HOSPITAL
1000 E MAIN ST, DANVILLE, IN 461221991
Phone: 317 745-4451
Web: WWW.HENDRICKS.ORG

HISTORICAL FINANCIALS

Company Type: Private

Income Statement   FYE: December 31

	REVENUE ($ mil.)	NET INCOME ($ mil.)	NET PROFIT MARGIN	EMPLOYEES
12/17	550	39	7.1%	1,700
12/16	530	43	8.2%	—
12/15	235	9	4.1%	—
12/14	211	9	4.3%	—
Annual Growth	37.5%	62.5%	—	—

2017 Year-End Financials

Return on assets: 4.9%   Cash ($ mil.): 15
Return on equity: 7.1%
Current ratio: 0.50

HENRY AVOCADO CORPORATION

EXECUTIVES

Pres-Ceo, Philip Henry
Stock Holder, Richard Opel
Stock Holder, Donald Hoey
Stock Holder, Victor Varvel
Accounting Staff, Cheryl Pritchard
Office Manager, Lori Deaver
Information Specialist, Bill Panky
Accounting Staff, Diane Brownell
Vice-President, Rick Opel
Sales Manager, Chris Varvel
Manager, Jim Deaver
Auditors: WHITE NELSON DIEHL EVANS LLP

LOCATIONS

HQ: HENRY AVOCADO CORPORATION
2208 HARMONY GROVE RD, ESCONDIDO, CA 920292054
Phone: 760 745-6632
Web: WWW.HENRYAVOCADO.COM

HISTORICAL FINANCIALS

Company Type: Private

Income Statement   FYE: September 30

	REVENUE ($ mil.)	NET INCOME ($ mil.)	NET PROFIT MARGIN	EMPLOYEES
09/17	301	4	1.4%	88
09/16	212	4	2.2%	—
09/15	180	4	2.6%	—
09/14	169	3	2.1%	—
Annual Growth	21.3%	4.8%	—	—

2017 Year-End Financials

Return on assets: 6.9%   Cash ($ mil.): 6
Return on equity: 1.4%
Current ratio: 1.20

HENRY COUNTY BOARD OF EDUCATION

EXECUTIVES

Chair, Pam Nutt
Supt, Rodney M Bowler
V Chair, Mike Griffin
Certified Occupational Therapy, Diana Parden
Coordinator, Jane Cantrell
Coordinator of Learning Suppor, Kent Morrow
Network Coordinator, Chris Davis
Chief Financial Officer, Marc Nicholas

LOCATIONS

HQ: HENRY COUNTY BOARD OF EDUCATION
33 N ZACK HINTON PKWY, MCDONOUGH, GA
302532344
Phone: 770 957-6601
Web: WWW.HENRY.K12.GA.US

HISTORICAL FINANCIALS

Company Type: Private

Income Statement

FYE: June 30

	REVENUE ($ mil.)	NET INCOME ($ mil.)	NET PROFIT MARGIN	EMPLOYEES
06/17	466	(51)	—	3,071
06/16	449	254	56.7%	—
06/05	295	(31)	—	—
06/04	266	135	50.8%	—
Annual Growth	4.4%	—	—	—

2017 Year-End Financials

Return on assets: 2.3% Cash ($ mil.): 37
Return on equity: (-11.1%)
Current ratio: —

HENRY FORD HEALTH SYSTEM

Built around a hospital founded by Detroit's favorite son the not-for-profit Henry Ford Health System (HFHS) is a hospital network that is also involved in medical research and education. The system's half-dozen hospitals — including the flagship Henry Ford Hospital as well as Henry Ford Wyandotte Hospital and mental health facility Kingswood Hospital — are home to roughly 2200 beds. HFHS also operates a 1200-doctor-strong medical group (with more than 40 specialties) as well as nursing homes hospice and a home health care network. The system's Health Alliance Plan of Michigan provides managed care and health insurance to more than half a million members.

Operations

Along with its hospitals large and small the system also operates more than 30 medical centers and maintains partnerships with community health services. About 20% of ambulatory care and 10% of acute care services in the region are provided by HFHS. In 2013 its hospitals took in more than 89000 patients and delivered more than 7900 babies. It also had 3.2 million outpatient visits and performed more than 88000 surgical procedures. HFHS conducts more than 285000 home health care visits annually.

For patients who need more than an ambulance to get them to the hospital the Henry Ford Hospital provides air ambulance transportation. The flagship hospital provides transport for critically ill and trauma patients within a 150-mile radius of Detroit (in Michigan Ohio and Ontario) via its Air Med 1 aeromedical helicopter.

Affiliated with Wayne State University's School of Medicine the health system is a leading education and research center with ongoing research in areas such as stroke heart disease cancer and diabetes. Wayne State and HFHS have agreed to expand their affiliation by increasing the number of medical students who train at Henry Ford working together on research projects and opening a new research center. HFHS trains more than 1500 future physicians every year. Henry Ford Hospital is responsible for many of those providing about 45 accredited programs to medical students.

Flagship facility Henry Ford Hospital is an 877-bed tertiary care hospital education and research complex. Kingswood Hospital is a 100-bed hospital offering inpatient care for individuals with acute episodes of mental illness. Henry Ford Macomb Hospital has 349 beds while Henry Ford West Bloomfield Hospital has 191 beds. Henry Ford Wyandotte Hospital is 401-bed acute care facility.

Geographic Reach

HFHS serves patients in Detroit and southeastern Michigan.

Sales and Marketing

Medicare accounted for 45% of payors in 2014 followed by Blue Cross (23%) Medicaid (17%) and self-pay and other (15%).

Financial Performance

Revenue increased 4% to $4.7 billion in 2014 as net patient services and health care premiums rose. However the system reported a net loss of $54.6 million that year as it used cash in pension and other post-retirement net adjustments and lost money on investments.

Cash flow from operations more than doubled to $142 million due to a decline in pension and health care premium receivables and changes in trading securities and accounts payable.

Strategy

HFHS grows organically and through partnerships. In 2012 it teamed up with Presbyterian Villages of Michigan forming a joint venture to operate the Center for Senior Independence. The Center is now a separate not-for-profit organization expected to increase the number of seniors it serves from 230 to nearly 1000 by 2016.

HFHS has increased its physician base by launching a subsidiary the Henry Ford Physician Network which is composed of private practice and hospital-employed physicians as well as the existing Henry Ford Medical Group.

In 2014 the system launched a clinical trial to investigate a new drug to treat tinnitus a chronic ringing of the head or ears.

Company Background

Automaker Henry Ford founded Henry Ford Hospital in 1915.

EXECUTIVES

Evp; President And Ceo Health Alliance Plan, James M. Connelly
Ceo, Nancy M. Schlichting
Coo, Robert G. (Bob) Riney
President, Wright L. Lassiter, age 55
Evp And Chief Medical Officer; President And Ceo Henry Ford Hospital, John Popovich
President And Ceo Community Care Services, John J. Polanski
Evp And Cfo, Edward G. (Ed) Chadwick
Evp; Ceo Henry Ford Medical Group, William A. Conway
President And Ceo Henry Ford West Bloomfield Hospital, Lynn M. Torossian

President And Ceo Henry Ford Wyandotte Hospital, Denise Brooks-Williams
Chief Nursing Officer; Coo Henry Ford Hospital, Veronica M. Hall
President And Ceo Henry Ford Macomb Hospitals, Barbara W. Rossmann
Svp Community Health And Equity; Chief Wellness Officer, Kimberlydawn Wisdom
Svp And Cio, Mary Alice Annecharico
Director Of Radiology, Mark C Diamond
Director Of Radiology, Xia Wang
Senior Vice President Is Clinical Integration And Transformation, Michelle Schreiber
Director Of Radiology, Scott G Sturza
Director Of Radiology, John W Bonnett
Vice President Corporate Strategic Planning, Joel Keiper
Vice President, Mary Whitbread
Vice President Clinical Transformation And Information Technology Integration, Matt Walsh
Director Of Radiology, Jay Pearlberg
Director Of Radiology, Manuel L Brown
Director Of Radiology, Peter J Feczko
Director Of Radiology, Randall R Walter
Director Of Radiology, Riffat K Ahmed
Director Of Radiology, Sampath Ramachandran
Director Of Radiology, Suresh C Patel
Director Of Radiology, Todd R Aho
Vice President Information Technology, Veeresh Nama
System Vice President Risk Finance And Insurance Services, John Mucha
Medical Director Of Perioperative Services, Gaylord Alexander
Vp Of It Applications, Josephine Molle
Director Of Radiology, Daniel Croteau
Vice President, Gregory Solecki
Senior Vice President, Henry W Lim
Medical Records Director, SUSAN GLEASON
Vice President Finance, Paul Kolpasky
Vice President Physician Development, Timothy Ryan
Executive Vice President And Chief Strategy Officer, Seth Frazier
Chair Department Of Anesthesiology, Michael Lewis
Director Of Radiology, Zachary Delpropoto
Vice President Revenue Cycle, Kevin Oneill
Vice Chair Radiology, William Sanders
Secretary, Barbara Paul
Auditors: DELOITTE & TOUCHE LLP DETROI

LOCATIONS

HQ: HENRY FORD HEALTH SYSTEM
1 FORD PL, DETROIT, MI 482023450
Phone: 313 916-2600
Web: WWW.HFHS.ORG

HOSPITAL LOCATIONS

Henry Ford Allegiance Health
Henry Ford Hospital
Henry Ford Kingswood Hospital
Henry Ford Macomb Hospital - Clinton Township
Henry Ford West Bloomfield Hospital
Henry Ford Wyandotte Hospital

PRODUCTS/OPERATIONS

SELECTED SERVICES

Bariatric Surgery
Cancer
Heart & Vascular
Neurology & Neurosurgery
OptimEyes
Orthopedic Surgery
Primary Care
Transplant Services

COMPETITORS

Ascension Health	Mount Clemens Regional
Beaumont Health System	Medical Center
Blue Cross Blue Shield	OmniCare Health Plan
of Michigan	St. John Health

Crittenton Hospital
Detroit Medical Center
Garden City Hospital
Harper-Hutzel Hospital
McLaren Health Care

Total Health Care
Trinity Health (Novi)
University of Michigan
 Health System

HISTORICAL FINANCIALS
Company Type: Private

Income Statement   FYE: December 31

	REVENUE ($ mil.)	NET INCOME ($ mil.)	NET PROFIT MARGIN	EMPLOYEES
12/17	5,977	203	3.4%	23,000
12/14	1,513	(13)	—	—
12/13	4,517	135	3.0%	—
12/09	2,118	26	1.3%	—
Annual Growth	13.8%	28.8%	—	—

2017 Year-End Financials
Return on assets: 4.5%   Cash ($ mil.): 774
Return on equity: 3.4%
Current ratio: 1.20

HENRY FORD MACOMB HOSPITALS

EXECUTIVES

Pres, Stephen J Hathaway
Internal Medicine Practitioner, Dale Scarlett
Director of Patient Accounts, Alicia Letson
Director, Melissa Allen

LOCATIONS

HQ: HENRY FORD MACOMB HOSPITALS
 215 NORTH AVE, MOUNT CLEMENS, MI 480431716
Phone: 586 466-9310
Web: WWW.MEDSEEK.COM

HISTORICAL FINANCIALS
Company Type: Private

Income Statement   FYE: December 31

	REVENUE ($ mil.)	NET INCOME ($ mil.)	NET PROFIT MARGIN	EMPLOYEES
12/17	455	3	0.7%	1,287
12/16	438	9	2.1%	—
12/15	411	(0)	—	—
12/08	328	12	3.9%	—
Annual Growth	3.7%	(13.9%)	—	—

2017 Year-End Financials
Return on assets: 5.1%   Cash ($ mil.): 3
Return on equity: 0.7%
Current ratio: 1.10

HENRY FORD WYANDOTTE HOSPITAL

EXECUTIVES

Ceo, Denise Brooks-Williams
President, Annette S Phillips
Ceo, Nancy M Schlichting

Internal Medicine Practitioner, Mohammad Amir
Internal Medicine Practitioner, Wendy Manzon
Director, Desiree Blake
Emergency Medicine Specialist, Agata Dow
Emergency Medicine Specialist, Christopher J Budziak
Emergency Medicine Specialist, Elizabeth Plemmons
Trustee, Jerry Griffith
Chief of Obstetrics Gynecology, Grace Engler

LOCATIONS

HQ: HENRY FORD WYANDOTTE HOSPITAL
 2333 BIDDLE AVE, WYANDOTTE, MI 481924668
Phone: 734 246-6000
Web:
 WWW.HENRYFORD.COM/LOCATIONS/WYANDOTTE

HISTORICAL FINANCIALS
Company Type: Private

Income Statement   FYE: December 31

	REVENUE ($ mil.)	NET INCOME ($ mil.)	NET PROFIT MARGIN	EMPLOYEES
12/17	297	(5)	—	1,600
12/16	278	(15)	—	—
12/15	267	(9)	—	—
12/14	259	(3)	—	—
Annual Growth	4.7%	—	—	—

HENRY MAYO NEWHALL MEMORIAL HOSPITAL

EXECUTIVES

Senior Vice President And Director Business Development, Terry Stone
Director Of Nursing, Sue Galvin
Director Of Him, Kelly Torrance
Vice President Nursing, Diane Lynch
Vice President Of Marketing And Communications, Marlee Lauffer
Managing Director, Reuel Asinas
Auditors: BDO USA LLP LOS ANGELES CA

LOCATIONS

HQ: HENRY MAYO NEWHALL MEMORIAL HOSPITAL
 23845 MCBEAN PKWY, VALENCIA, CA 913552001
Phone: 661 253-8000
Web: WWW.HENRYMAYO.COM

COMPETITORS

Aptium Oncology
 Brotman Medical Center
 Cedars-Sinai Medical Center
 Childrens Hospital Los Angeles
 Glendale Adventist Medical Center
 Good Samaritan Hospital (Los Angeles)
 HCA
 Hoag Memorial Hospital
 Hollywood Presbyterian Medical Center
 Marin General Hospital
 Methodist Hospital of Southern California
 Tenet Healthcare
 United Surgical Partners

HISTORICAL FINANCIALS
Company Type: Private

Income Statement   FYE: September 30

	REVENUE ($ mil.)	NET INCOME ($ mil.)	NET PROFIT MARGIN	EMPLOYEES
09/17	320	11	3.6%	1,600
09/16	321	29	9.1%	—
09/15	307	23	7.5%	—
09/14	249	(7)	—	—
Annual Growth	8.6%	—	—	—

2017 Year-End Financials
Return on assets: 12.3%   Cash ($ mil.): 34
Return on equity: 3.6%
Current ratio: 1.20

HENSEL PHELPS CONSTRUCTION CO.

EXECUTIVES

President Phelps Development, Eric L. Wilson
Cfo, Stephen J. (Steve) Carrico
Evp, Wayne S. Lindholm
Evp, Jon W. Ball
President And Ceo, Jeffrey K. (Jeff) Wenaas
Evp, Michael J. Choutka
Evp, Richard G. Tucker
President Hensel Phelps Services, Edwin (Glen) Miller
Auditors: KPMG LLP DENVER CO

LOCATIONS

HQ: HENSEL PHELPS CONSTRUCTION CO.
 420 6TH AVE, GREELEY, CO 806312332
Phone: 970 352-6565
Web: WWW.HENSELPHELPS.COM

PRODUCTS/OPERATIONS

Selected Projects
Hilton Hok
Aegis Asho
Regional O
Guam NAVFAC Bachelor Enlisted Quarters (BEQ)
Mamizu Utilities and Site Improvements Phase I
Samaritan MOB and Parking Structure
Santa Clara Valley Medical Center Receiving and Support Center
Santa Clara Family Justice Center
Santa Clara Valley Medical Center Receiving and Support Center
Rotary PlayGarden
Norman Y. Mineta San José International Airport Terminal Area Improvement Program (TAIP)
Vantage Data Center V2
Vantage Data Center V1

Selected Services
Construction
 Change management
 Construction waste management
 LEED project registration
 Quality control
 Safety management
 Scheduling
 Self-perfoming concrete
 Status reporting
 Subcontractor management
 Sustainability audits
 Quality control
Development
 Feasibility studies
 Financing

Green building planning/education
Land acquisition
Leasing
Pro forma review
Post-construction
As-built documentation
Building operations
Certificate of occupancy
Commissioning and warranty programs
LEED project certification
Moving services
Preconstruction
Bid packaging
Budgeting/cost modeling
Design management
Estimating
Green building and planning/education
Phasing plans
Regulatory investigation
Scheduling
Status reporting
Subcontractor prequalification
Value engineering

Selected Markets

Commercial
Education
High technology
Industrial
International
Justice
Leisure
Medical
Multiresidence
Public
Transportation

COMPETITORS

Balfour Beatty Construction	M. A. Mortenson McCarthy Building
C.F. Jordan	PCL Employees Holdings
CH2M HILL	Rooney Holdings
Clark Construction Group	Skanska USA Building Turner Corporation
Fluor	Tutor Perini
Gilbane	Walbridge Aldinger
Hunt Construction	Walsh Group
Jacobs Engineering	Whiting-Turner
KBR	

HISTORICAL FINANCIALS

Company Type: Private

Income Statement   FYE: December 31

	REVENUE ($ mil.)	NET INCOME ($ mil.)	NET PROFIT MARGIN	EMPLOYEES
12/17	3,360	80	2.4%	2,000
12/16	3,540	76	2.2%	—
12/15	3,142	70	2.2%	—
12/14	2,507	38	1.5%	—
Annual Growth	10.2%	27.7%	—	—

2017 Year-End Financials

Return on assets: 11.9%   Cash ($ mil.): 281
Return on equity: 2.4%
Current ratio: 0.70

HEWLETT, WILLIAM AND FLORA FOUNDATION (INC)

The Hewlett Foundation is dedicated to helping solve the world's social and environmental problems. One of the nation's largest charitable institu-

tions it has some $8.6 billion in assets and it disbursed approximately $240 million in grants and gifts in 2013. It provides grants in a diverse areas including education reform environmental protection in the West and population growth. The private foundation also promotes the performing arts in the San Francisco Bay Area and has funded conflict resolution and international relations programs in the past. The late Bill Hewlett co-founder of Hewlett-Packard founded the Hewlett Foundation with his wife and eldest son in 1967.

Financial Performance

The non-profit charitable organization reported $8.6 billion in unrestricted net assets in 2013 compared with about $7.7 billion in 2012. Net investment revenue rose to $1.17 billion in 2013 versus $801.5 million in 2012. The foundation awarded 634 grants in 2013 in the average amount of $354287.

Strategy

Broadening its scope in 2014 the Hewlett Foundation created a new initiative designed to help address the problem of cyber threats against governments businesses and individuals. The foundation plans to invest $20 million over the next five years in what it calls its Cyber Initiative to build a field of expertise to help better understand and address the wide array of issues posed by the Internet.

EXECUTIVES

Pres, Paul Brest
Officer, Eli Sugarman
Officer, Sabrina Coleman
Officer, Sarah Staats
Officer, David Sasaki
Officer, Heath Wickline
General Counsel, Kristy Tsadick
Officer, Liz Judge
Officer, Lindsay A Louie
Fellow, Prithi Trivedi
Benefits Manager, Christine Nishimura

LOCATIONS

HQ: HEWLETT, WILLIAM AND FLORA FOUNDATION (INC)
2121 SAND HILL RD, MENLO PARK, CA 940256909
Phone: 650 234-4500
Web: WWW.HEWLETT.ORG

HISTORICAL FINANCIALS

Company Type: Private

Income Statement   FYE: December 31

	REVENUE ($ mil.)	NET INCOME ($ mil.)	NET PROFIT MARGIN	EMPLOYEES
12/16	317	(164)	—	60
12/14	624	204	32.8%	—
12/05	0	0	—	—
12/02	94	426	453.1%	—
Annual Growth	9.1%	—	—	—

2016 Year-End Financials

Return on assets: 3.2%   Cash ($ mil.): 132
Return on equity: (-51.9%)
Current ratio: 0.60

HEXAWARE TECHNOLOGIES, INC.

EXECUTIVES

Ceo, Ramakarthikeyan Srikrishna
R V Pres-SEC, Kalpesh Bhatt
Staff, Michael Greulich
Business Manager, Mayank Shah
Auditors: PRICE WATERHOUSE CHARTERED ACC

LOCATIONS

HQ: HEXAWARE TECHNOLOGIES, INC.
101 WOOD AVE S STE 600, ISELIN, NJ 088302767
Phone: 609 409-6950
Web: WWW.HEXAWARE.COM

HISTORICAL FINANCIALS

Company Type: Private

Income Statement   FYE: December 31

	REVENUE ($ mil.)	NET INCOME ($ mil.)	NET PROFIT MARGIN	EMPLOYEES
12/17	444	8	1.9%	1,600
12/16	371	8	2.2%	—
12/15	328	7	2.1%	—
12/11	137	0	0.3%	—
Annual Growth	21.6%	70.3%	—	—

2017 Year-End Financials

Return on assets: 17.5%   Cash ($ mil.): 54
Return on equity: 1.9%
Current ratio: 0.50

HILL PHYSICIANS MEDICAL GROUP, INC.

Hill Physicians Medical Group is the doctors' answer to HMOs. The company is an independent practice association (IPA) serving some 300000 health plan members in northern California. The company contracts with managed care organizations throughout the region — including HMOs belonging to Aetna CIGNA and Health Net— to provide care to health plan members through its provider affiliates. Its network includes about 3800 primary care and specialty physicians 38 hospitals and 24 urgent care centers. The company also provides administrative services for doctors and patients. PriMed a management services organization created Hill Physicians Medical Group in 1984 and still runs the company.

Geographic Reach

Hill Physicians Medical Group's member facilities are located in Alameda Contra Costa El Dorado Placer Sacramento San Francisco San Joaquin San Mateo Solano and Yolo counties in northern California.

Financial Performance

Hill Physicians Medical Group reported a 3% increase in 2013 to about $455 million due to higher health plan revenues and investment income. Net income grew by 15% to some $13.6 million that year due to higher revenues and cost savings programs.

Strategy

Hill Physicians Medical Group has been working to enhance its technology systems to improve coordination of care including installing electronic prescription and referral management systems. It is also forming partnerships with area insurers and hospitals to improve communication among regional providers as well as to control overall health care costs. For instance the company teamed up with Dignity Health and Blue Shield of California to form an accountable care organization (ACO).

EXECUTIVES

President, Steve McDermott
Director, Harpreet S Grewal
Chief Officer and Dire, Thomas Long
Marketing Director, Michael Crawford
Supervisor, Brenda Schmiegel
Technology, Dean Burrill
Technician, Hai Pham
Consultant, Jennifer Chen
Manager, Luis Castaneda
Manager, Sheronica Josey
Auditors: KPMG LLP SAN FRANCISCO CALIF

LOCATIONS

HQ: HILL PHYSICIANS MEDICAL GROUP, INC.
2409 CAMINO RAMON, SAN RAMON, CA 945834285
Phone: 800 445-5747
Web: WWW.HILLPHYSICIANS.COM

PRODUCTS/OPERATIONS

Selected Health Plan Partners
Aetna of California
Alliance CompleteCare
Anthem/Blue Cross of California
Blue Shield of California
Blue Shield 65 Plus
CIGNA Healthcare of California
Health Net of California
Health Net Medicare
United Healthcare West (formerly Pacificare)
SCAN
Secure Horizons by United Healthcare
Western Healthcare Advantage

COMPETITORS

Alta Bates Summit Medical Center	Orion HealthCorp
	Prospect Medical
Beaver Medical Group	The Palo Alto Medical
HealthCare Partners	Foundation

HISTORICAL FINANCIALS

Company Type: Private

Income Statement			FYE: December 31
	REVENUE ($ mil.)	NET INCOME ($ mil.)	NET PROFIT MARGIN	EMPLOYEES
---	---	---	---	---
12/15	504	6	1.3%	488
12/10	427	5	1.2%	—
12/06	427	5	1.2%	—
12/05	414	7	1.9%	—
Annual Growth	2.0%	(1.3%)	—	—

2015 Year-End Financials
Return on assets: 1.5%   Cash ($ mil.): 46
Return on equity: 1.3%
Current ratio: 0.90

HILLSBOROUGH COUNTY SCHOOL DISTRICT

EXECUTIVES

Chm, April Griffin
Superintendent, Maryellen Elia
V Chm, Cindy Stuart
MBR, Susan L Valdes
MBR, Sally Harris
MBR, Melissa Snively
Building and Grounds Director, Chris Farkas
Information Specialist, Rafy Velez
Secretary, Dawn Diaz
Director, Dennis Holt
Manager, David Borisenko
Auditors: KPMG LLP TAMPA FL

LOCATIONS

HQ: HILLSBOROUGH COUNTY SCHOOL DISTRICT
901 E KENNEDY BLVD, TAMPA, FL 336023502
Phone: 813 272-4000
Web: WWW.SDHC.K12.FL.US

HISTORICAL FINANCIALS

Company Type: Private

Income Statement			FYE: June 30
	REVENUE ($ mil.)	NET INCOME ($ mil.)	NET PROFIT MARGIN	EMPLOYEES
---	---	---	---	---
06/16	2,133	(59)	—	25,000
06/15	2,042	(110)	—	—
06/14	1,984	(45)	—	—
06/13	1,878	(44)	—	—
Annual Growth	4.3%	—	—	—

2016 Year-End Financials
Return on assets: 2.3%   Cash ($ mil.): 113
Return on equity: (-2.8%)
Current ratio: —

HMH HOSPITALS CORPORATION

Hackensack University Medical Center (HUMC) is an acute care teaching and research hospital that serves northern New Jersey and parts of New York. The hospital has about 775 beds and staffs more than 2200 medical professionals. HUMC administers general medical surgical emergency and diagnostic care. The center also includes specialized treatment centers including a children's hospital a women's hospital a cancer center and a heart and vascular hospital. HUMC is part of the Hackensack University Health Network which also includes a physician practice group and a joint venture that operates two community hospitals. In 2016 the network merged with Meridian Health to create Hackensack Meridian Health.

Operations

HUMC helps train future dentists and doctors through its affiliation with the University of Medicine and Dentistry of New Jersey. It expanded its education programs in 2012 by partnering with the Stevens Institute of Technology to offer joint biomedical training programs.

The hospital also performs research through the David Joseph Jurist Research Center for Tomorrow's Children. The center has roughly 475 research programs in operation at any given time.

Financial Performance

Medicare accounts for 29.5% of HUMC's funding; HMOs 28%; and Blue Cross 28%.

Strategy

The company grows organically and through acquisitions partnerships and affiliations.

To expand its services HUMC broke ground on a $35 million project to expand and renovate its trauma and emergency facilities in 2012 (scheduled to open in 2015).

Hackensack University Health Network is increasing its partnerships and affiliations with other regional care providers following the trend of US hospitals seeking to improve and lower the cost of health care through shared services and resources. The network partnered up with Texas-based LPH Hospital Group in 2012 to reenovate the Pascack Valley Hospital (now HackensackUMC Pascack) in Westwood New Jersey. Hackensack took over the bankrupt facility's ER back in 2007 and in 2012 the joint venture launched a $90 million project to revamp the rest of the 130-bed acute-care community hospital. It reopened in 2013.

Hackensack University Health Network also formed a joint venture with an area physician group to open two ambulatory surgery centers in 2012 and it entered a collaboration with CVS Health's MinuteClinic to open new urgent care centers.

That year HUMC formed a joint venture partnership with community physicians and United Surgical Partners International to buy and operate ambulatory surgery centers in Bergen County: Hackensack Endoscopy Center and the Endoscopy Center of Bergen County.

Mergers and Acquisitions

In 2015 the Hackensack University Health Network agreed to merge with fellow New Jersey care provider Meridian Health. The combined system to be named Hackensack Meridian Health will have 11 hospitals and two children's hospitals. The deal which is one of a number of consolidation efforts by hospitals in the state is pending regulatory approval.

Company Background

To simplify its operations HUMC sold its hospice operations to Amedisys in 2011. The health provider previously sold its home health agency to Amedisys in 2009 to generate revenue and control costs after struggling with financial losses throughout the year due to declining admissions.

HUMC completed construction of its new John Theurer Cancer Center in late 2010 giving it one of the largest comprehensive cancer centers in the US. The center includes diagnostic and treatment units that focus on specific types of cancers.

HUMC was founded as a hospital in 1888 with 12 beds.

EXECUTIVES

Chairman Department Of Ophthamology, Michael Rosenberg
Auditors: PRICEWATERHOUSECOOPERS LLP NE

LOCATIONS

HQ: HMH HOSPITALS CORPORATION
343 THORNALL ST, EDISON, NJ 088372206
Phone: 201 996-2000
Web: WWW.HACKENSACKUMC.ORG

PRODUCTS/OPERATIONS

Selected Services
Donna A. Sanzari Women's Hospital
Emergency Services
Heart & Vascular Hospital

Hospital Services
John Theurer Cancer Center
Joseph M. Sanzari Children's Hospital
Medical
Specialized
Surgical
Tackle Kids Cancer

Selected Facilities
Donna A. Sanzari Women's Hospital
Hackensack University Medical Center Mountainside
Hackensack University Medical Center Pascack
Heart & Vascular Hospital
John Theurer Cancer Center
Joseph M. Sanzari Children's Hospital
  Tomorrows Children's Institute for Cancer and Blood
  Disorders

COMPETITORS

Bergen Regional	Lenox Hill Hospital
Medical	Montefiore Medical
Bronx-Lebanon Hospital	NewYork-Presbyterian
Continuum Health	Healthcare
Partners	Newark Beth Israel
Englewood Hospital and	Medical Center
Medical Center	St. Joseph's
Hospital for Special	Healthcare System
Surgery	Valley Health System

HISTORICAL FINANCIALS
Company Type: Private

Income Statement   FYE: December 31

	REVENUE ($ mil.)	NET INCOME ($ mil.)	NET PROFIT MARGIN	EMPLOYEES
12/15	1,357	83	6.1%	1,100
12/14	1,309	106	8.1%	—
12/08	1,037	(86)	—	—
12/07	1,183	48	4.1%	—
Annual Growth	1.7%	7.0%	—	—

2015 Year-End Financials
Return on assets: 9.0%   Cash ($ mil.): 155
Return on equity: 6.1%
Current ratio: 0.80

HMO MINNESOTA

EXECUTIVES

Eo, Andrew Czajkowski
Chb, Jonathon Killmer
Cfo, Tim Peterson
Director, Ben Field
Director, Deborah Madson
Director, Gerald Etesse
Director, Jan Lysen
Director, John Orner
Director, Kathy Mock
Director, Kathy Richardson
Director, Lonnie Nichols

LOCATIONS

HQ: HMO MINNESOTA
  3535 BLUE CROSS RD, SAINT PAUL, MN 551221154
Phone: 952 456-8434
Web: WWW.BLUECROSSMN.COM

HISTORICAL FINANCIALS
Company Type: Private

Income Statement   FYE: December 31

	REVENUE ($ mil.)	NET INCOME ($ mil.)	NET PROFIT MARGIN	EMPLOYEES
12/16	1,839	(156)	—	40
12/15	918	52	5.7%	—
12/14	850	85	10.1%	—
12/09	978	30	3.1%	—
Annual Growth	9.4%	—	—	—

2016 Year-End Financials
Return on assets: 1.2%   Cash ($ mil.): 108
Return on equity: (-8.5%)
Current ratio: —

HOAG MEMORIAL HOSPITAL PRESBYTERIAN

EXECUTIVES

President And Ceo, Robert Braithwaite
Svp And Cfo, Jennifer Mitzner
Executive Vice President Chief Operating Officer,
  Michael Ricks
Operating Room Director, Carole Metcalf
Vice President Centers Of Excellence, Trish Bartel
Senior Vice President President, Flynn Andrizzi
Medical Records Director, Leslie Scarborough
Director Of Radiology, Bob Marco
Vice President, Joanne Tucker
**Vice President Marketing And Corporate
  Communications,** Nina B Robinson
Medical Director, Katie Love
Board Member, Richard Taketa
Board Member, Kris Iyer

LOCATIONS

HQ: HOAG MEMORIAL HOSPITAL PRESBYTERIAN
  1 HOAG DR, NEWPORT BEACH, CA 926634162
Phone: 949 764-4624
Web: WWW.HOAG.ORG

COMPETITORS

Adventist Health	Saddleback Memorial
System West	Medical Center
Anaheim Regional	St. Joseph Hospital of
Medical Center	Orange
Children's Hospital of	St. Jude Medical
Orange County	Center
Citrus Valley Health	Tenet Healthcare
Partners	Torrance Memorial
Dignity Health	Medical Center
Long Beach Memorial	Trinity Health (Novi)
Memorial Health	Western Medical Center
Services	- Santa Ana
Pasadena Hospital	
Association	

HISTORICAL FINANCIALS
Company Type: Private

Income Statement   FYE: June 30

	REVENUE ($ mil.)	NET INCOME ($ mil.)	NET PROFIT MARGIN	EMPLOYEES
06/16	894	100	11.2%	3,800
06/15	822	107	13.1%	—
/* 0	0	—	—	—
Annual Growth	—	—	—	—
*Fiscal year change				

2016 Year-End Financials
Return on assets: 3.1%   Cash ($ mil.): 189
Return on equity: 11.2%
Current ratio: 0.30

HOBBY LOBBY STORES, INC.

If something wicker this way comes Hobby Lobby Stores may be the source. Across more than 45 states the company operates more than 600 stores that sell arts and crafts supplies baskets beads candles frames home-decorating accessories and silk flowers. It also operates in China Hong Kong and the Philippines. The #3 craft and fabric retailer (behind Michaels Stores and Jo-Ann Stores) boasts sister companies: Mardel a seller of Christian and educational products and Hemispheres a supplier of home furnishings and other merchandise to Hobby Lobby stores. CEO David Green who owns the company founded Hobby Lobby in 1972 and operates it according to biblical principles including closing shop on Sunday.

Operations

Hobby Lobby operates about 600 stores in 45-plus US states. Its portfolio of 67000 products spans needle art to jewelry and scrapbooking supplies.

The company's operations are supported by a sole Oklahoma manufacturing and distribution center that measures some 3.4 million sq. ft. Affiliate Mardel Christian and Education Stores run by Green's son Mart is also based there. Mardel operates about 35 stores in Arkansas Colorado Kansas Oklahoma and Texas. Hemispheres imports and sells high-end furniture and home dA©cor accessories from Europe and Asia. In addition to supplying Hobby Lobby with select imports Hemispheres operates a store in Oklahoma and a handful in Texas. Its other affiliated companies include Ethno-Graphic Media a non-profit ministry that develops interactive learning materials and Every Tribe Entertainment. Every Tribe founded in 2003 produced the motion picture End of the Spear in 2006.

Geographic Reach

Based in Oklahoma City Oklahoma Hobby Lobby operates retail shops nationwide under the banners Hobby Lobby Mardel and Hemispheres. It sources some of its 67000 products from Europe and Asia. The company maintains an onsite manufacturing plant in Oklahoma that makes store fixtures candles scented products art canvases and picture frames. The facility also features product-packaging capabilities.

Strategy

One of America's largest private companies fast-growing Hobby Lobby has been busy expanding its network of stores which average 55000 sq. ft.

The company has plans to reach a stores count of about 625 by the end of 2014. It's extending its reach in Oregon Vermont and Minnesota to supplement recently added stores in Virginia Wisconsin Kansas California and New York in 2013.

President Steven Green the son of founder David Green is typically the executive who is tasked with scouting new locations for the company. In general Hobby Lobby sets up shop in second-generation retail sites such as vacated supermarkets and superstores.

EXECUTIVES

Executive Vice President Assistant, Bill Owens
Asst Vp Advertising, John Schumacher
Ceo, David Green
Cfo, Jon Cargill
President, Steve Green
Executive Vice President, Stan Lett
Assistant Vice President Construction, Bob Mackey
Assistant Vice President, Deloris Miller
Department Head, Andrea Bruner
Department Head, Christi Claxon
Assistant Vice President Risk Management, Becky Robinson
Vice President Finance, Mandy Rodriguez
Seniorvice President Distribution, Bill Woody
Vice President Finance, Jerry Ballard
Vice President Art And Creative Department Greens Daughter, Darsee Green-Lett
Vice President Marketing And Advertising, Dolois Smith
Assistant Vice President Controller, Barbara Walke
Assistant Vice President Risk Manager, Rebecca Robinson
Department Head, JEAN STEPHENSON
Regional Vice President Region 2, Eddy McLaughlin
Regional Vice President Region 9, Joe Guerra
Vice President International Relations, Allen Quine
Assistant Vice President Of Accounting, Barbara A Walke
Administrative Assitant To Vice President Of Information And Interactive Sys, Sherri R Fisher
Executive; Sec Treas; Treasurer, Mart Green

LOCATIONS

HQ: HOBBY LOBBY STORES, INC.
 7707 SW 44TH ST, OKLAHOMA CITY, OK 731794899
Phone: 405 745-1100
Web: WWW.HOBBYLOBBY.COM

PRODUCTS/OPERATIONS

Selected Products
Arts and crafts supplies
Baskets
Candles
Cards
Furniture
Home accent pieces
Jewelry-making supplies
Needlework
Party supplies
Picture frames and framing
Scrapbooking supplies
Seasonal items
Sewing materials (fabric patterns notions)
Silk flowers
Toys
Wearable art

Selected Affiliates
Hemispheres (home furnishings and accessories stores)
Mardel Christian Office & Educational Supply (Christian materials office supplies and educational products)

COMPETITORS

A.C. Moore	Kirkland's
Burnes Home Accents	Michaels Companies
Garden Ridge	Old Time Pottery
Hancock Fabrics	Target Corporation
Jo-Ann Stores	Wal-Mart

HISTORICAL FINANCIALS
Company Type: Private

Income Statement   FYE: December 31

	REVENUE ($ mil.)	NET INCOME ($ mil.)	NET PROFIT MARGIN	EMPLOYEES
12/17	4,544	352	7.8%	30,218
12/06	196	58	29.5%	—
12/04	1,363	88	6.5%	—
12/03	150	58	39.0%	—
Annual Growth	27.5%	13.7%	—	—

2017 Year-End Financials
Return on assets: 6.9%   Cash ($ mil.): —
Return on equity: 7.8%
Current ratio: 0.10

HOLLINGSWORTH OIL CO. INC.

EXECUTIVES

Chb-Treas, Glenn Hollingsworth
President, Ronnie H Hollingsworth
Vice President, Jennifer Johnston
Accounting Staff, Penny Fulcher
Customer Staff, Sherry Grogan
Human Resources, Alice Palmer
Compliance Manager, Clint Sweatt
Director of Maintenance, Jeff Benton
Manager, Jeremy Baldwin
Csr, Tammy Palmore
Administrative Assistant, Tomilynn Herndon
Auditors: ROBINSON HUGHES & CHRISTOPHER

LOCATIONS

HQ: HOLLINGSWORTH OIL CO. INC.
 1503 MEMORIAL BLVD STE B, SPRINGFIELD, TN 371723269
Phone: 615 242-8466
Web: WWW.HOLLINGSWORTHTIREPROS.COM

COMPETITORS

American Buildings	Gladstone Commercial
Belz	Highwoods Properties
Childress Klein	Varco Pruden Buildings
Crescent Resources	

HISTORICAL FINANCIALS
Company Type: Private

Income Statement   FYE: December 31

	REVENUE ($ mil.)	NET INCOME ($ mil.)	NET PROFIT MARGIN	EMPLOYEES
12/17	408	2	0.6%	300
12/16	380	1	0.3%	—
12/14	547	0	0.2%	—
12/13	564	0	0.1%	—
Annual Growth	(7.8%)	47.5%	—	—

2017 Year-End Financials
Return on assets: 4.0%   Cash ($ mil.): —
Return on equity: 0.6%
Current ratio: 0.30

HOLY NAME MEDICAL CENTER, INC.

EXECUTIVES

Pres-Ceo, Michael Maron
Vice President, Adam Jarrett
Exec Vice President, Sheryl Slonim
V Pres Asian Health Services*, Kyung Hee Choi
V Pres Hr, Manny Gonzalez
V Pres CIO, SAI Kandamangalam
V Pres-Cfo, Ryan Kennedy
V Pres Admin, Sean O'Rourke
Vp of Finance, Gregory Adams
Director, Susan Milnes
Vice-President Human Resources, Anthony Pellicano
Auditors: ERNST & YOUNG LLP ISELIN NJ

LOCATIONS

HQ: HOLY NAME MEDICAL CENTER, INC.
 718 TEANECK RD, TEANECK, NJ 076664245
Phone: 201 833-3000
Web: WWW.HOLYNAME.ORG

HISTORICAL FINANCIALS
Company Type: Private

Income Statement   FYE: December 31

	REVENUE ($ mil.)	NET INCOME ($ mil.)	NET PROFIT MARGIN	EMPLOYEES
12/16	376	9	2.4%	1,800
12/15	351	30	8.6%	—
12/14	320	21	6.8%	—
12/13	313	27	8.9%	—
Annual Growth	6.4%	(31.3%)	—	—

2016 Year-End Financials
Return on assets: 8.2%   Cash ($ mil.): 22
Return on equity: 2.4%
Current ratio: 1.10

HOLZER HEALTH SYSTEM

EXECUTIVES

Pres, Brent Saundrs
Rn, Winter Branham
Recruiting Coordinator, Julie Howell
Financial Analyst, Linda Stanley
Vice President of Human Resour, Lisa Halley
Operations Manager, Tomma Shuler
Auditors: PLANTE & MORAN PLLC COLUMBUS

LOCATIONS

HQ: HOLZER HEALTH SYSTEM
 100 JACKSON PIKE, GALLIPOLIS, OH 456311560
Phone: 740 446-5060
Web: WWW.HOLZER.ORG

HISTORICAL FINANCIALS
Company Type: Private

Income Statement
FYE: June 30

	REVENUE ($ mil.)	NET INCOME ($ mil.)	NET PROFIT MARGIN	EMPLOYEES
06/17	323	(1)	—	1,500
06/10	4	1	34.5%	—
06/08	2	0	14.0%	—
Annual Growth	70.5%	—	—	—

2017 Year-End Financials
Return on assets: 8.3% Cash ($ mil.): 37
Return on equity: (-0.4%)
Current ratio: 1.10

HOMETOWN HEALTH PLAN INC

LOCATIONS
HQ: HOMETOWN HEALTH PLAN INC
1155 MILL ST, RENO, NV 895021576
Phone: 775 982-3000

HISTORICAL FINANCIALS
Company Type: Private

Income Statement
FYE: June 30

	REVENUE ($ mil.)	NET INCOME ($ mil.)	NET PROFIT MARGIN	EMPLOYEES
06/17	372	9	2.6%	4
06/16	352	2	0.8%	—
06/15	333	(9)	—	—
06/14	296	(10)	—	—
Annual Growth	8.0%	—	—	—

2017 Year-End Financials
Return on assets: 16.7% Cash ($ mil.): 53
Return on equity: 2.6%
Current ratio: 0.90

HORRY COUNTY SCHOOL DISTRICT

EXECUTIVES
Supt, Dr Rick Maxey
Accounting Staff, Patsy Johnson
Accounting Staff, Ruthenia Johnson
Health Professional, Marti Graves
Auditors: MCGREGOR & COMPANY LLP COLUM

LOCATIONS
HQ: HORRY COUNTY SCHOOL DISTRICT
335 FOUR MILE RD, CONWAY, SC 295264506
Phone: 843 488-6700
Web: WWW.HORRYCOUNTY.ORG

HISTORICAL FINANCIALS
Company Type: Private

Income Statement
FYE: June 30

	REVENUE ($ mil.)	NET INCOME ($ mil.)	NET PROFIT MARGIN	EMPLOYEES
06/18	548	(42)	—	5,000
06/17	520	(140)	—	—
06/16	494	218	44.2%	—
06/15	472	9	2.0%	—
Annual Growth	5.1%	—	—	—

2018 Year-End Financials
Return on assets: 10.8% Cash ($ mil.): 271
Return on equity: (-7.8%)
Current ratio: —

HOSPITAL AUTHORITY OF VALDOSTA AND LOWNDES COUNTY, GEORGIA

Hospital Authority of Valdosta and Lowndes County Georgia oversees South Georgia Medical Center (SGMC) a 335-bed regional hospital serving southern Georgia and northern Florida. The hospital offers a range of services focusing on such specialties as diabetes management pulmonary care pediatrics and women's health. SGMC's Pearlman Cancer Center is devoted to a holistic approach to cancer care. The medical center also operates a specialized wound healing center and orthopedic and spine centers. The public hospital was founded as Pineview General Hospital in 1955. Its governing board is appointed by the local city council and county commissioners.

Operations
SGMC serves as a regional referral hospital meaning it handles major medical cases for smaller community hospitals in the area. The medical center employs 2700 staff members including more than 300 physicians.

SGMC operates several satellite campuses including SGMC Outpatient Plaza Smith Northview Hospital SGMC Lanier and SGMC Berrien. Together the facilities are known as South Georgia Health System.

Sales and Marketing
Medicare payments accounted for 32% of net patient revenue in 2014; Medicaid accounted for 4% of net patient revenue that year.

Strategy
The medical center added a new facility in 2013 — the community facility in Berrien County. In 2015 SGMC Lakeland Villa broke ground on an adjacent replacement nursing home which will offer private rooms two courtyards a rehabilitation and therapy room and a spa room.

EXECUTIVES
Ceo, Randy Sauls
Chief of Psychiatric, Livingstone Rasalam
Administrative Assistant, Mary Jane Davis
Chief of Radiology, W Cameron Wright
Chief of Ob/Gyn, T Hank Moseley
Accounting Staff, Donna Baker
Chief of Medicine, Thomas W Hobby
Crna, Randall H Walker

LOCATIONS
HQ: HOSPITAL AUTHORITY OF VALDOSTA AND LOWNDES COUNTY, GEORGIA
2501 N PATTERSON ST, VALDOSTA, GA 316021735
Phone: 229 333-1000
Web: WWW.LOWNDESCOUNTY.COM

PRODUCTS/OPERATIONS

2014 Sales

	% of total
Net patients service revenue	96
Other revenue	4
Total	100

COMPETITORS
Appling
Doctors Hospital of Augusta
Liberty Regional Medical Center
Memorial Health University Medical Center
St. Joseph's/Candler Health System
Tallahassee Memorial HealthCare
Tift Regional Medical Center

HISTORICAL FINANCIALS
Company Type: Private

Income Statement
FYE: September 30

	REVENUE ($ mil.)	NET INCOME ($ mil.)	NET PROFIT MARGIN	EMPLOYEES
09/17	314	11	3.7%	3,000
09/16	305	28	9.3%	—
09/15*	310	(2)	—	—
06/08	0	0	42.1%	—
Annual Growth	90.3%	45.4%	—	—

*Fiscal year change

2017 Year-End Financials
Return on assets: 5.7% Cash ($ mil.): 5
Return on equity: 3.7%
Current ratio: 0.70

HOSPITAL OF CENTRAL CONNECTICUT

The Hospital of Central Connecticut an acute care facility serves the communities of central Connecticut from two campuses. With approximately 415 beds and more than 400 physicians the hospital offers a full range of diagnostic and treatment services as well as education and prevention programs. Its diabetes treatment program is an affiliate of the Boston-based Joslin Diabetes Center; the hospital is also affiliated with the University of Connecticut School of Medicine and other universities. Central Connecticut Health Alliance (CCHA) is the parent company of The Hospital of Central Connecticut and is part of the Hartford Health Care network.

Operations
In addition to its 415 acute-care beds the two Hospital of Central Connecticut campuses have about 30 bassinets. Through its university affiliations the hospital facilities provide residency and training programs in fields including critical care internal medicine gastroenterology general surgery and pulmonary medicine. It also conducts medical research including clinical trials in fields such as diabetes mental health and cancer treatment.

Affiliates that are part of the CCHA organization include Alliance Occupational Health Central Connecticut Senior Health Services Central Connecticut Physical Medicine and Central Connecticut VNA. CCHA affiliates provide a wide range of whole-life services throughout the region.

Geographic Reach

The Hospital of Central Connecticut's two Connecticut locations are the Bradley Memorial Campus in Southington and the New Britain General Campus in New Britain.

Strategy

In 2015 the hospital system opened a 75000-sq. ft. cancer center at the Hartford HealthCare Cancer Institute. Services include prevention and detection; treatments including chemotherapy radiation therapy and radiosurgery; ongoing support; and clinical trials.

Hospital of Central Connecticut also recently opened a Family Health Center including a primary care medical office outpatient lab radiology center and wound care center. The center which opened in 2013 also offers hyperbaric services such as hyperbaric oxygen therapy.

Company Background

The Hospital of Central Connecticut was formed through the merger of New Britain General Hospital and Bradley Memorial Hospital.

EXECUTIVES

Pres-Ceo, Clarence J Silvia
Cfo, Ralph Becker
Chief of Emergency, Jeffery A Finkelstein
Chief Staff, Robert A Lapkin
Radiology, Wanda M Kirejczyk
Project Manager, Beatriz Heredia
Coordinator, Harmony Hadlock
Coordinator, Catherine Denuzzio
Chief of Medicine, Robert Lapkin
Legal Secretary, Kimberly Paulakos
Oncologist, Neal B Goldberg

LOCATIONS

HQ: HOSPITAL OF CENTRAL CONNECTICUT
100 GRAND ST, NEW BRITAIN, CT 060522016
Phone: 860 224-5011
Web: WWW.THOCC.ORG

PRODUCTS/OPERATIONS

Selected Centers and Services
Bariatric surgery
Breast care
Cancer Center
Cardiovascular
Clinical research
Diabetes care
Emergency services
Endocrine and bone health
Family Enrichment Center
Healthy Aging Center
Joint and Spine Center
Laboratory
Lifeline
Maternity
Medical services
Nursing
Occupational health
Occupational therapy
Outpatient services
Pain management
Palliative care
Pediatrics
Physical medicine
Primary care and specialty practices
Psychiatry
Radiology
Sleep disorders
Speech therapy
Stroke Center
Surgical services
Vascular Center
Weigh Your Options
Wellness programs
Wound care

COMPETITORS

Bristol Hospital
Lawrence & Memorial Hospital
Saint Francis Hospital and Medical Center
Waterbury Hospital
Western Connecticut Health Network
Yale New Haven Health System

HISTORICAL FINANCIALS

Company Type: Private

Income Statement   FYE: September 30

	REVENUE ($ mil.)	NET INCOME ($ mil.)	NET PROFIT MARGIN	EMPLOYEES
09/17	366	23	6.3%	2,500
09/15	338	(4)	—	—
09/14	360	24	6.8%	—
09/13	403	26	6.7%	—
Annual Growth	(2.4%)	(3.6%)	—	—

2017 Year-End Financials

Return on assets: 2.6%   Cash ($ mil.): 12
Return on equity: 6.3%
Current ratio: 1.30

HOSPITAL OF THE UNIVERSITY OF PENNSYLVANIA

EXECUTIVES

Director, Pamela Mack-Brooks
Vice-Chairman, Larry Kricka
Coordinator, Alvaro Talavera
Coordinator, Cherlyn Bynum
Coordinator, Denise Amaro
Coordinator, Patricia Josaphouitch
Coordinator, Pete Caldwell
Assistant Professor, Rajat Deo
Research and Staff, Alexander Wright
Assistant Professor, Dennis Hadjiliadis
Nurse Practitioner, Diana Van Houten

LOCATIONS

HQ: HOSPITAL OF THE UNIVERSITY OF PENNSYLVANIA
3400 SPRUCE ST OFC, PHILADELPHIA, PA 191044208
Phone: 215 301-3776
Web: WWW.PENNMEDICINE.ORG

HISTORICAL FINANCIALS

Company Type: Private

Income Statement   FYE: June 30

	REVENUE ($ mil.)	NET INCOME ($ mil.)	NET PROFIT MARGIN	EMPLOYEES
06/16	2,236	283	12.7%	25
06/15	2,164	320	14.8%	—
Annual Growth	3.3%	(11.5%)	—	—

2016 Year-End Financials

Return on assets: —   Cash ($ mil.): 1,091
Return on equity: 12.7%
Current ratio: 9.60

HOSPITAL SERVICE DISTRICT 1 OF TANGIPAHOA PARISH

EXECUTIVES

Prin, Shirley Hsing

LOCATIONS

HQ: HOSPITAL SERVICE DISTRICT 1 OF TANGIPAHOA PARISH
155 S 5TH ST, PONCHATOULA, LA 704542609
Phone: 985 386-5161

HISTORICAL FINANCIALS

Company Type: Private

Income Statement   FYE: June 30

	REVENUE ($ mil.)	NET INCOME ($ mil.)	NET PROFIT MARGIN	EMPLOYEES
06/18	313	5	1.6%	1
06/17	298	(5)	—	—
Annual Growth	5.3%	—	—	—

2018 Year-End Financials

Return on assets: 5.0%   Cash ($ mil.): 9
Return on equity: 1.6%
Current ratio: 0.80

HOUSING AUTHORITY OF THE COUNTY OF SANTA CLARA

EXECUTIVES

Exec Dir, Alex Sanchez
Information Technology Manager, Amy Ramos

LOCATIONS

HQ: HOUSING AUTHORITY OF THE COUNTY OF SANTA CLARA
505 W JULIAN ST, SAN JOSE, CA 951102300
Phone: 408 275-8770
Web: WWW.HACSC.ORG

HISTORICAL FINANCIALS

Company Type: Private

Income Statement   FYE: June 30

	ASSETS ($ mil.)	NET INCOME ($ mil.)	INCOME AS % OF ASSETS	EMPLOYEES
06/15	656	55	8.5%	4
06/14	581	22	3.9%	—
Annual Growth	12.9%	145.6%	—	—

2015 Year-End Financials

Return on assets: 0.8%   Sales ($ mil): 315
Return on equity: 17.6%

HOUSING FINANCE AND DEVELOPMENT CORP

EXECUTIVES

Prin, Patti Miyamoto
Manager, Stephanie Aveiro

LOCATIONS

HQ: HOUSING FINANCE AND DEVELOPMENT CORP
1002 N SCHOOL ST, HONOLULU, HI 968176912
Phone: 808 587-0641

HISTORICAL FINANCIALS

Company Type: Private

Income Statement   FYE: June 30

	ASSETS ($ mil.)	NET INCOME ($ mil.)	INCOME AS % OF ASSETS	EMPLOYEES
06/17	1,232	70	5.7%	2
06/16	1,098	30	2.8%	—
Annual Growth	12.2%	128.6%	—	—

2017 Year-End Financials

Return on assets: 0.2%   Sales ($ mil.): 76
Return on equity: 92.0%

HOUSTON COUNTY BOARD OF EDUCATION

EXECUTIVES

Chairperson, Fred Wilson
Procurement Staff, Becky Daniel
Manager, Leslie Grimes
Director, Jason Smith
Teacher, Monique Vickers
Teacher, Barbara Green
Teacher, Matthew Boone
Teacher, Melanie Bratcher
Teacher, Melanie Jones
Teacher, Melanie Lockhart
Teacher, Melanie Turcotte
Auditors: GREG S GRIFFIN ATLANTA GEORG

LOCATIONS

HQ: HOUSTON COUNTY BOARD OF EDUCATION
1100 MAIN ST, PERRY, GA 310693531
Phone: 478 988-6200
Web: WWW.HCBE.NET

HISTORICAL FINANCIALS

Company Type: Private

Income Statement   FYE: June 30

	REVENUE ($ mil.)	NET INCOME ($ mil.)	NET PROFIT MARGIN	EMPLOYEES
06/17	312	38	12.2%	3,856
06/16	302	1	0.6%	—
06/15	292	0	0.3%	—
06/14	281	(9)	—	—
Annual Growth	3.5%	—	—	—

2017 Year-End Financials

Return on assets: —   Cash ($ mil.): 113
Return on equity: 12.2%
Current ratio: —

HOUSTON COUNTY HEALTHCARE AUTHORITY

The Houston County Health Authority is the governing body for Southeast Alabama Medical Center (SAMC) a not-for-profit acute-care hospital that serves Southeastern Alabama and adjacent parts of Georgia and Florida. In addition to providing comprehensive medical surgical and emergency care the 420-bed SAMC provides specialty services including heart cancer and women's health care. The health system also operates primary care physician offices and clinics specializing in neurology pain management and cardiovascular care as well as a home health agency. SAMC offers residency programs for medical students most of whom attend the Alabama College of Osteopathic Medicine.

Operations

SAMC serves the tri-state area with the help of approximately 50 physicians. Aside from its primary hospital in Dothan Alabama SAMC boasts primary care physician offices a home health agency and about 10 specialty centers.

Geographic Reach

SAMC serves some 600000 residents spanning not only Southeast Alabama but Southwest Georgia and the Florida Panhandle.

Strategy

To expand and improve the health care services it offers in its community SAMC looks for opportunities to open new clinics or specialty centers. For example it recently acquired a former retail development near the hospital in late 2017; the system has not revealed any plans for the property yet.

In mid-2017 SAMC implemented a restructuring which included some layoffs. Through the efforts it hopes to save some $30 million annually on purchasing goods and services as well as on labor costs.

Company Background

SAMC was founded in 1957.

EXECUTIVES

Svp And Cfo, Derek Miller
Svp And Coo, Charlie Brannen
Ceo, Richard O. Sutton
Director Information Services, Eric Daffron
Vp Patient Care Services And Chief Nursing Officer, Diane Buntyn
Vp Medical Affairs, Charles L. Harkness
Vp Marketing And Public Relations, Claudia Hall
Vice President Operations, Ronald E Dean
Vice President Of Information Technology, Karen Loftin
Chairman, Chester Sowell
Vice Chairman, John McDaniel
Auditors: DRAFFIN & TUCKER LLP ATLANTA

LOCATIONS

HQ: HOUSTON COUNTY HEALTHCARE AUTHORITY
1108 ROSS CLARK CIR, DOTHAN, AL 363013022
Phone: 334 793-8111
Web: WWW.SAMC.ORG

PRODUCTS/OPERATIONS

Selected Services

Behavioral Health
Diabetes
Endoscopy
Endovascular Surgery
Family Services
Heart & Vascular
Lithotripsy
Living Well Fitness
Neurology Associates
NeuroSpine Center
Orthopedic Services
Pain Management Center
Rehabilitation Services
Sleep Center
Southeast Cancer Center
Women's Services
Wound Care Center

COMPETITORS

Baptist Health (AL)
Bay Medical Center
East Alabama Medical Center
Encompass Health
Jackson County Hospital of Florida
Jackson Hospital & Clinic of Alabama
Phoebe Putney Memorial Hospital

HISTORICAL FINANCIALS

Company Type: Private

Income Statement   FYE: September 30

	REVENUE ($ mil.)	NET INCOME ($ mil.)	NET PROFIT MARGIN	EMPLOYEES
09/17	381	16	4.3%	2,500
09/16	364	9	2.5%	—
09/15	311	0	0.3%	—
09/14	290	1	0.4%	—
Annual Growth	9.6%	143.4%	—	—

2017 Year-End Financials

Return on assets: 6.0%   Cash ($ mil.): 43
Return on equity: 4.3%
Current ratio: 1.50

HOUSTON INDEPENDENT SCHOOL DISTRICT

EXECUTIVES

Supt, Grenita Lathan
Cfo, Melinda Garrett
SEC-Treas, Diana Davila
Accounting Staff, Glenn Reed
Accounting Staff, Stephanie Matlock
Executive Officer, Manuel Rodriguez
Accounting Staff, David Clardy
Site Manager, Christina Johnson
Auditors: DELOITTE & TOUCHE LLP HOUSTO

LOCATIONS

HQ: HOUSTON INDEPENDENT SCHOOL DISTRICT
4400 W 18TH ST, HOUSTON, TX 770928501
Phone: 713 556-6000
Web: WWW.HOUSTONISD.ORG

HISTORICAL FINANCIALS

Company Type: Private

Income Statement   FYE: June 30

	REVENUE ($ mil.)	NET INCOME ($ mil.)	NET PROFIT MARGIN	EMPLOYEES
06/18	2,695	(250)	—	22,440
06/17	2	(0)	—	—
06/16	2,333	266	11.4%	—
06/13	1,876	117	6.3%	—
Annual Growth	7.5%	—	—	—

2018 Year-End Financials
Return on assets: 5.3%   Cash ($ mil.): 7
Return on equity: (-9.3%)
Current ratio: —

HOUSTON METHODIST HOSPITAL

EXECUTIVES

Ceo, Marc L Boom
Chm, Ewing Werlein Jr
Treas, Carlton E Baucum
SEC, Gregory V Nelson
Senior Project Manager, Hosea Lee
Senior Project Manager, Randy Leonard
Director, Trey Jones
Manager, Enrica De Rosa
Assistant Professor, Joshua Swan
Staff, Michael Deavers
Staff, Claudia Molina

LOCATIONS

HQ: HOUSTON METHODIST HOSPITAL
  1213 HERMANN DR STE 300, HOUSTON, TX
  770046671
Phone: 713 790-3311
Web: WWW.HOUSTONMETHODIST.ORG

HISTORICAL FINANCIALS
Company Type: Private

Income Statement			FYE: December 31	
	REVENUE ($ mil.)	NET INCOME ($ mil.)	NET PROFIT MARGIN	EMPLOYEES
12/17	3,887	681	17.5%	656
12/16	3,746	338	9.0%	—
Annual Growth	3.8%	101.7%	—	—

2017 Year-End Financials
Return on assets: 15.9%   Cash ($ mil.): 102
Return on equity: 17.5%
Current ratio: 0.30

HOWARD UNIVERSITY (INC)

EXECUTIVES

Pres, Dwayne Frederick
Vp Communications-Chief Commun, Crystal Brown
Cntlr, Rosoloc Henderson
Staff, Claude Williams
Assistant Professor, Debra White-Coleman
Assistant Professor, Ella Carter
Coordinator, Gaelle Amazan
Health Professional, Philip Lucas
Staff, Quito Swan
Information Specialist, Raven Smith
Assistant Professor, Yin Germaschewski

LOCATIONS

HQ: HOWARD UNIVERSITY (INC)
  2400 6TH ST NW, WASHINGTON, DC 200590002
Phone: 202 806-6100
Web: WWW.HOWARD.EDU

PRODUCTS/OPERATIONS

Selected Schools and Colleges
Arts and Sciences
Business
Communications
Dentistry
Divinity
Education
Engineering Architecture and Computer Sciences
Graduate School
Law
Medicine
Nursing and Allied Health Sciences
Pharmacy
Social Work

HISTORICAL FINANCIALS
Company Type: Private

Income Statement				FYE: June 30
	REVENUE ($ mil.)	NET INCOME ($ mil.)	NET PROFIT MARGIN	EMPLOYEES
06/15*	970	(41)	—	5,600
12/14	398	(79)	—	—
06/13	843	202	24.0%	—
06/12	1,000	(148)	—	—
Annual Growth	(1.0%)	—	—	—
*Fiscal year change

2015 Year-End Financials
Return on assets: 21.3%   Cash ($ mil.): 22
Return on equity: (-4.3%)
Current ratio: —

HPS LLC

EXECUTIVES

Mng MBR, Matt Thompson
Cfo-MBR, Thomas J La Pres
Tres-MBR, Joseph Schodde
Treas-MBR, Dwith Gascho
Information Technology Manager, Brian McKinley
Marketing Manager, Kendra Tossava
Senior Director, Kevin Crampton
Customer Representativ, Tracy Keeler
Regional Manager, Jami Markle
Member Specialist, Patty Stephenson
Direct Source Int Design Assis, Robin Tagg
Auditors: MEYNARD TOLMAN & VENLET PC

LOCATIONS

HQ: HPS LLC
  3275 N M 37 HWY, MIDDLEVILLE, MI 493339126
Phone: 269 795-3308
Web: WWW.HPSNET.COM

HISTORICAL FINANCIALS
Company Type: Private

Income Statement				FYE: June 30
	REVENUE ($ mil.)	NET INCOME ($ mil.)	NET PROFIT MARGIN	EMPLOYEES
06/18	782	0	0.1%	38
06/16	1,032	0	0.1%	—
06/15	960	0	0.1%	—
06/14	862	0	0.1%	—
Annual Growth	(2.4%)	2.0%	—	—

2018 Year-End Financials
Return on assets: 0.1%   Cash ($ mil.): 4
Return on equity: 0.1%
Current ratio: 1.90

HUMAX USA, INC

EXECUTIVES

Ceo, Keehyuk Sung
Corp SEC, Chong Hong
Sales Manager, Rich Tudanger

LOCATIONS

HQ: HUMAX USA, INC
  15641 RED HILL AVE # 150, TUSTIN, CA 927807327
Phone: 714 389-1924
Web: WWW.HUMAXDIGITAL.COM

COMPETITORS

DIRECTV   Sony USA
SANYO   Tivo Solutions
Samsung Electronics

HISTORICAL FINANCIALS
Company Type: Private

Income Statement				FYE: December 31
	REVENUE ($ mil.)	NET INCOME ($ mil.)	NET PROFIT MARGIN	EMPLOYEES
12/17	482	(4)	—	29
12/16	360	(0)	—	—
12/15	373	0	0.1%	—
12/14	448	0	0.1%	—
Annual Growth	2.5%	—	—	—

2017 Year-End Financials
Return on assets: 58.1%   Cash ($ mil.): 3
Return on equity: (-1.0%)
Current ratio: 0.40

HUMBLE INDEPENDENT SCHOOL DISTRICT

EXECUTIVES

Supt, Guy M Sconzo
Human Resources Manager, Lorrie Dabbs
Food Director, Shirley Parker
Information Specialist, Janice Johnson
Nurse, Amanda Stewart
Nurse, Lorraine Cano
Psychologist, Carol Reiner
Public Relations Director, Robin McAdams
Teacher, Beverly Wells
Accountant, Ginger Ramer
Administrative Assistant, Ken Hair
Auditors: WHITLEY PENN LLP HOUSTON TEX

LOCATIONS

HQ: HUMBLE INDEPENDENT SCHOOL DISTRICT
  20200 EASTWAY VILLAGE DR, HUMBLE, TX
  773382405
Phone: 281 641-1000
Web: WWW.HUMBLE.K12.TX.US

HISTORICAL FINANCIALS
Company Type: Private

Income Statement   FYE: June 30

	REVENUE ($ mil.)	NET INCOME ($ mil.)	NET PROFIT MARGIN	EMPLOYEES
06/17	462	(11)	—	5,000
06/16	458	11	2.4%	—
06/13	365	(8)	—	—
06/12	354	2	0.7%	—
Annual Growth	5.4%	—	—	—

HUNTINGTON HOSPITAL

EXECUTIVES

Prin, Peter W Corrigan
Information Specialist, Marcia Etcheverry
Executive Officer, John Mangoni
Payroll Staff, Amanda Lewis
Project Coordinator, Tracy Hetherington
Infectious Disease Specialist, Kimberly Shriner

LOCATIONS

HQ: HUNTINGTON HOSPITAL
  100 W CALIFORNIA BLVD, PASADENA, CA 911053010
Phone: 626 397-5000
Web: WWW.HUNTINGTONHOSPITAL.COM

HISTORICAL FINANCIALS
Company Type: Private

Income Statement   FYE: December 31

	REVENUE ($ mil.)	NET INCOME ($ mil.)	NET PROFIT MARGIN	EMPLOYEES
12/17	654	15	2.3%	3,500
12/16	646	6	0.9%	—
12/15	551	3	0.7%	—
12/14	513	1	0.4%	—
Annual Growth	8.4%	102.0%	—	—

2017 Year-End Financials
Return on assets: 4.0%   Cash ($ mil.): 11
Return on equity: 2.3%
Current ratio: 0.10

HUNTINGTON HOSPITAL DOLAN FAMILY HEALTH CENTER, INC.

When residents of the Gold Coast feel poorly Huntington Hospital is there to help. Part of the North Shore-Long Island Jewish Health System Huntington Hospital is a 410-bed not-for-profit tertiary care center providing a comprehensive range of medical services to residents of Huntington New York and surrounding communities. Along with general surgical services the hospital provides specialty cardiac cancer maternity pediatric and psychiatric care. Huntington also operates a number of outpatient diagnostic and community clinics where patients can turn for primary care physical rehabilitation or specialized care for other ailments.

Operations
In addition to a full range of general and specialist medical services Huntington Hospital provides medical training services. The facility is a clinical campus for the Hofstra North Shore-LIJ School of Medicine a partnership between the parent organization and Hofstra University. As a not-for-profit organization the hospital also provides community outreach and charity care services.

In 2013 Huntington Hospital had 15159 inpatient discharges (including the delivery of 1383 babies); 49702 emergency department visits; and 9064 ambulatory surgeries.

Geographic Reach
Located in Huntington New York Huntington Hospital serves residents along much of Long Island's North Shore.

Strategy
Huntington Hospital continues to expand its range of medical services. The medical center has added pain management and electrophysiology capabilities in recent years. It also provides expanded peripheral cardiac procedures including elective angioplasties and has added a second cardiac catheterization lab. In 2014 the hospital broke ground on a $50 million expansion that will add nearly 24000 sq. ft. of space to its emergency department.

In 2015 Huntington Hospital partnered with Ob Hospitalist Group to provide onsite obstetrician/gynecology hospitalist services at all times.

Company Background
The hospital was established in 1916. It has been part of the North Shore-LIJ Health System since 1994.

EXECUTIVES

Pres-Ceo, Michael J Dowling
Chb, Irving Klein
Exec V Pres-Cfo-Ceo, Kevin Lawlor
Treas, Gordon Hargraves
SEC, Harry Mariani
Vice President, Michael J Alesandro
Secretary, Fred J Buckholtz
Health Professional, Danielle Conahan
Registered Nurse, Amy McConnell
Laboratory Outreach Coordinato, Crystal Salazar
Pharmacist, Fred Mock

LOCATIONS

HQ: HUNTINGTON HOSPITAL DOLAN FAMILY
  HEALTH CENTER, INC.
  270 PARK AVE, HUNTINGTON, NY 117432799
Phone: 631 351-2000
Web: WWW.HUNTHOSP.ORG

PRODUCTS/OPERATIONS

Selected Centers and Services
Cardiac Intervention and Electrophysiology
Center for Orthopedics and Joint Replacement Surgery
Comprehensive Laboratory Services
Comprehensive Women's Health Center
Critical Care Services
Designated Comprehensive Cancer Center
Designated Emergency and Elective Angioplasty Program
Designated Level II Trauma Center
Designated Stroke Center
Dolan Family Center
Dolan Family Health Center
Epilepsy Program
Healthier Tomorrow Pediatric Weight Management Program
Internal Medicine - Hospitalist Program
Interventional Radiology
Intracranial Neurosurgery
Joint Replacement Program
Level II Neonatal Critical Care Center

Palliative Medicine
Pediatric Emergency Care Center
Pediatric Medicine
Perinatal Services
Psychiatric Services
Surgical Services
Thoracic Surgery

COMPETITORS

Calvary Hospital
Catholic Health Services of Long Island
Catholic Healthcare System
Encompass Health
Mather Memorial Hospital
Montefiore Medical
New York City Health and Hospitals
New York Health Care
NewYork-Presbyterian Healthcare
NewYork-Presbyterian Hospital
Stamford Health

HISTORICAL FINANCIALS
Company Type: Private

Income Statement   FYE: December 31

	REVENUE ($ mil.)	NET INCOME ($ mil.)	NET PROFIT MARGIN	EMPLOYEES
12/17	336	19	5.7%	2,000
12/16	339	25	7.5%	—
12/15	302	2	0.9%	—
12/14	283	14	5.3%	—
Annual Growth	5.9%	9.0%	—	—

2017 Year-End Financials
Return on assets: 6.4%   Cash ($ mil.): —
Return on equity: 5.7%
Current ratio: 0.70

HUNTSVILLE HOSPITAL HEALTH SYSTEM

EXECUTIVES

Ceo, David Spillers
Coo, Jeff Samz

LOCATIONS

HQ: HUNTSVILLE HOSPITAL HEALTH SYSTEM
  101 SIVLEY RD SW, HUNTSVILLE, AL 358014470
Phone: 256 265-1000
Web: WWW.HUNTSVILLEHOSPITAL.ORG

HISTORICAL FINANCIALS
Company Type: Private

Income Statement   FYE: June 30

	REVENUE ($ mil.)	NET INCOME ($ mil.)	NET PROFIT MARGIN	EMPLOYEES
06/16	864	98	11.4%	28
06/15	799	100	12.6%	—
Annual Growth	8.1%	(2.4%)	—	—

2016 Year-End Financials
Return on assets: 3.9%   Cash ($ mil.): 186
Return on equity: 11.4%
Current ratio: 0.90

HURLEY MEDICAL CENTER

A community hospital owned by the City of Flint Hurley Medical Center is a teaching hospital serving Genesee Lapeer and Shiawassee counties in eastern Michigan. The 440-bed acute care facility is affiliated with the medical schools of Michigan State University and The University of Michigan. It provides care in areas such as cancer mental health rehabilitation surgery and women's health and it is a regional center for pediatrics. Hurley Medical Center also offers advanced specialty care such as trauma care neonatal intensive care kidney transplantation burn medicine and bariatric (weight loss) surgery. The center was founded in 1908 and is owned by the state of Michigan.

Operations

Hurley Medical Center has a physician health organization (PHO) partnership with the Professional Medical Corporation. The Hurley PHO of Mid-Michigan is a multi-specialty physician group that contracts with managed care organizations to provide care.

The hospital has an affiliation partnership with the Henry Ford Health System; the two health care providers offer a joint kidney transplantation program. Hurley Medical Center also operates the Genesys Hurley Cancer Institute in partnership with the Genesys Regional Medical Center.

Financial Performance

Hurley's revenue increased 3% in 2013 as it took in more patient payments. It reported a net loss of $2.3 million due to increased expenses including salaries unrealized losses on investments.

Strategy

The medical center works to update and expand its services on a regular basis. In 2012 it doubled in size with the opening of the Paul F. Reinhart Emergency Trauma Center.

EXECUTIVES

Vice President Human Resources, Beth Brophy
Vice President Of Operations, Melanie Gavulic
Vice Chair Marilyn Fuller, Chris Flores

LOCATIONS

HQ: HURLEY MEDICAL CENTER
1 HURLEY PLZ, FLINT, MI 485035902
Phone: 810 262-9000
Web: WWW.HURLEYMC.COM

COMPETITORS

Covenant HealthCare	McLaren Health Care
Crittenton Hospital	Munson Healthcare
Detroit Medical Center	Sparrow Health System
Genesys Regional Medical Center	St. John Health
Henry Ford Health System	Trinity Health (Novi)

HISTORICAL FINANCIALS

Company Type: Private

Income Statement				FYE: June 30
	REVENUE ($ mil.)	NET INCOME ($ mil.)	NET PROFIT MARGIN	EMPLOYEES
06/16	422	44	10.6%	2,884
06/15	378	24	6.4%	—
06/08*	350	3	1.1%	—
03/08	250	0	0.1%	—
Annual Growth	6.8%	97.7%	—	—

*Fiscal year change

2016 Year-End Financials

Return on assets: 10.7%   Cash ($ mil.): 71
Return on equity: 10.6%
Current ratio: 1.30

ICREST INTERNATIONAL LLC

EXECUTIVES

Mng MBR, Naoki Ibata
Evp Chief Strategic Officer, Naoti Tsoshima
Cfo, James Katayama
Board of Director, Makoto Sawanoi
Asst Acct Mgr, Christine Tokunaga
Auditors: DELOITTE & TOUCHE LLP LOS AN

LOCATIONS

HQ: ICREST INTERNATIONAL LLC
200 N PACIFIC COAST HWY # 925, EL SEGUNDO, CA 902454340
Phone: 310 760-3200
Web: WWW.ICRESTJCP.COM

HISTORICAL FINANCIALS

Company Type: Private

Income Statement				FYE: March 31
	REVENUE ($ mil.)	NET INCOME ($ mil.)	NET PROFIT MARGIN	EMPLOYEES
03/17	516	9	1.9%	35
03/13*	433	8	1.9%	—
12/10	309	9	3.0%	—
12/09	1,396	0	—	—
Annual Growth	(13.2%)	715.2%	—	—

*Fiscal year change

2017 Year-End Financials

Return on assets: 1.9%   Cash ($ mil.): 4
Return on equity: 1.9%
Current ratio: 0.50

IDEA PUBLIC SCHOOLS

EXECUTIVES

Chm, Mike Rhodes
President, Thomas E Torkelson
V Pres-Fin, Carlo Hershberger
Cfo, Wyatt Truscheit
SEC, Gabriel Puente
Exec SEC, Rose Marquez
Treas, Bill Carrera
Human Resource, Vernice Carino
Director Shareholder, Alberto Castillo
Coordinator, Linn Collins
Federal Program Director, Dolores Gonzalez
Auditors: RSM US LLP SAN ANTONIO TEXAS

LOCATIONS

HQ: IDEA PUBLIC SCHOOLS
2115 W PIKE BLVD, WESLACO, TX 785960054
Phone: 956 377-8000
Web: WWW.IDEAPUBLICSCHOOLS.ORG

HISTORICAL FINANCIALS

Company Type: Private

Income Statement				FYE: June 30
	REVENUE ($ mil.)	NET INCOME ($ mil.)	NET PROFIT MARGIN	EMPLOYEES
06/18	422	31	7.6%	2,381
06/17	332	18	5.6%	—
06/16	269	20	7.7%	—
06/15	208	14	6.8%	—
Annual Growth	26.6%	31.2%	—	—

2018 Year-End Financials

Return on assets: 6.5%   Cash ($ mil.): 118
Return on equity: 7.6%
Current ratio: 1.00

IDEMIA IDENTITY & SECURITY USA LLC

MorphoTrust USA builds trust with its credentials and biometrics-based recognition systems. MorphoTrust provides driver's licenses passports voter and other government and corporate-issued IDs as well as related data verification systems. Its biometrics products include face finger and iris recognition scanners. The company which operates in all 50 states serves US federal state and local governments and commercial entities; government contracts represent about 95% of revenues. In addition to its contract-based services MorphoTrust operates a network of more than 1200 ID service centers. It is a subsidiary of Paris-based aerospace components maker SAFRAN.

Geographic Reach

MorphoTrust has 1100 service centers located in Illinois Iowa Indiana Minnesota Massachusetts New Jersey Tennessee Virginia and the District of Columbia.

Sales and Marketing

MorphoTrust caters to more than 3 million customers each year including the Department of Defense the State Department and the Department of Homeland Security.

Financial Performance

The company claims to generate $400 million in annual revenue.

Strategy

MorphoTrust has enjoyed growth from its US federal government activities primarily its FBI products and services involving universal enrollment and weapons permits. However like most companies servicing the public sector it is at the mercy of its clients' budgetary cuts and restrictions.

In 2014 the company won new contracts to provide fingerprint-based background checks for the Massachusetts Executive Office of Public Safety and Security the New Jersey Department of Public Safety the Division of State Police and fingerprint channeling services in Nevada for the Department of Public Safety. It believes these agreements could yield up to $25 million in revenue over the next six years.

EXECUTIVES

President And Ceo, Robert A. (Bob) Eckel
Vice President, Ben Mallen

HQ: IDEMIA IDENTITY & SECURITY USA LLC
296 CONCORD RD STE 300, BILLERICA, MA
018213487
Phone: 978 215-2400
Web: WWW.MORPHOTRUST.COM

PRODUCTS/OPERATIONS

Selected Products and Services
Biometric-based access control to buildings and
restricted areas
Biometric recognition technologies that accurately
identify individuals
Enrollment centers for processing pre-employment
background checks
Secure credentials that serve as proof of identity
Solving critical issues facing US intelligence and
national security

COMPETITORS

3M Cogent	Edentify
Acsys Biometrics	Entrust DataCard
Allied Security	ImageWare Systems
Innovations	SecuGen
CSSN	Security First
Cross Match	Ultra-Scan
Technologies	Verint Systems
De La Rue	

HISTORICAL FINANCIALS

Company Type: Private

Income Statement   FYE: December 31

	REVENUE ($ mil.)	NET INCOME ($ mil.)	NET PROFIT MARGIN	EMPLOYEES
12/16	708	(7)	—	1,400
12/15	604	0	—	
Annual Growth	17.1%	—	—	—

2016 Year-End Financials
Return on assets: 2.4%   Cash ($ mil.): 73
Return on equity: (-1.0%)
Current ratio: 1.20

IHC HEALTH SERVICES, INC.

EXECUTIVES

Pres-Ceo, William Nelson
Svp-Cfo, Bert Zimmerli
V Pres-Pres, Charles Sorenson
Orthopedist, Zachary Leitze
Doctor, April Larson
Human Resources Consultant, Gail Burns
Emergency Medicine, Gerald Rowland
Diagnostic Radiologist, Steven Davis
Chief Staff, Steven Vannorman
Auditors: KPMG LLP SALT LAKE CITY UT

LOCATIONS

HQ: IHC HEALTH SERVICES, INC.
1380 E MEDICAL CENTER DR, ST GEORGE, UT
847902123
Phone: 435 251-2992
Web: WWW.SELECTHEALTH.ORG

HISTORICAL FINANCIALS

Company Type: Private

Income Statement   FYE: December 31

	REVENUE ($ mil.)	NET INCOME ($ mil.)	NET PROFIT MARGIN	EMPLOYEES
12/17	5,483	884	16.1%	4,000
12/16	5,275	564	10.7%	—
12/14	394	55	14.2%	—
Annual Growth	140.5%	150.9%	—	—

2017 Year-End Financials
Return on assets: 6.6%   Cash ($ mil.): 164
Return on equity: 16.1%
Current ratio: 0.50

ILLINOIS MUNICIPAL ELECTRIC AGENCY

EXECUTIVES

Pres-Ceo, Kevin M Gaden
Sr Vice President, Phillip Doc Mueller
Vice President, Troy Fodor
Vice-President Engineering, Kevin Wagner
Cfo, Robert Childers
Cfo, Bob Childers
Sr Acct, Cindy Evans
Manager, Ed Cobau
Administrative Assistant, Rodd Whelpley
Administrator, Tammy Hall
Manager, Amanda Ripperda
Auditors: BAKER TILLY VIRCHOW KRAUSE LL

LOCATIONS

HQ: ILLINOIS MUNICIPAL ELECTRIC AGENCY
3400 CONIFER DR, SPRINGFIELD, IL 627118301
Phone: 217 789-4632
Web: WWW.IMEA.ORG

HISTORICAL FINANCIALS

Company Type: Private

Income Statement   FYE: April 30

	REVENUE ($ mil.)	NET INCOME ($ mil.)	NET PROFIT MARGIN	EMPLOYEES
04/17	320	21	6.5%	28
04/16	318	26	8.2%	—
04/14	327	17	5.4%	—
04/13	304	15	5.1%	—
Annual Growth	1.3%	7.9%	—	—

2017 Year-End Financials
Return on assets: 5.7%   Cash ($ mil.): 41
Return on equity: 6.5%
Current ratio: 0.90

ILWU-PMA WELFARE TRUST

EXECUTIVES

Prin, Michael Ouchida
Auditors: PRICEWATERHOUSECOOPERS LLP WA

LOCATIONS

HQ: ILWU-PMA WELFARE TRUST
1188 FRANKLIN ST STE 101, SAN FRANCISCO, CA
941096852
Phone: 415 673-8500
Web: WWW.ILWU.ORG

HISTORICAL FINANCIALS

Company Type: Private

Income Statement   FYE: June 30

	REVENUE ($ mil.)	NET INCOME ($ mil.)	NET PROFIT MARGIN	EMPLOYEES
06/17	738	5	0.8%	3
06/15	676	27	4.1%	—
06/14	624	(21)	—	—
06/10	585	18	3.1%	—
Annual Growth	3.4%	(15.5%)	—	—

2017 Year-End Financials
Return on assets: 13.8%   Cash ($ mil.): 3
Return on equity: 0.8%
Current ratio: 1.60

IMPERIAL IRRIGATION DISTRICT

Imperial Irrigation District (IID) keeps the lights
on and the water flowing. A public agency IID is
the six largest public power utility in the state of
California providing generation transmission and
distribution services to more than 145000 residential commercial and industrial customers. It is
also the largest irrigation district in the US with
more than 3000 miles of canals and drains delivering water to active farmland and providing
wholesale water to local municipalities primarily
in the Southern California desert corridors of Imperial Valley and Coachella Valley. The district is
governed by a five-member board of directors
elected by district residents.

Financial Performance
IID saw its revenues increase 6% from $530 mil-
lion in 2011 to $562 million in 2012. The growth
was driven by a 12% surge in water revenue; this
was due to a rise in water transfer rates and a volume increase in water transferred to the San Diego
County Water Authority and the Coachella Valley
Water District of about $5 million. Power revenues
also climbed 4% in 2012 due to a spike in energy
sales mainly from residential customers.

Strategy
In the area of renewable energy IID is part of a
statewide effort to significantly increase solar energy development and production by the year
2017. In 2011 it announced a public-private partnership with renewable energy generators. The
partnership involves the signing of interconnection
and transmission service agreements among IID
CalEnergy Generation 8minuteenergy Ormat
Technologies and the Los Angeles Department of
Water and Power. It's the first step in a renewable
energy transmission expansion plan to increase
capacity enough to support more than a dozen renewable energy construction projects.

In addition IID offers a variety of programs to
assist its customers in reducing their personal energy consumption including rebates for buying select energy efficient products online home energy
audits and funding for residential projects that in-
volve installing solar technologies such as photovoltaic (PV) systems.

Company Background
Founded in 1911 IID acquired properties from the financially struggling California Development Company and its Mexican subsidiary. By 1922 it had purchased 13 mutual water companies each of which had developed and operated distribution canals in the Imperial Valley. Principal water customers today include farm operators and municipalities that treat the water and resell it to their residential and business customers. The district entered the power business in 1936 to utilize the hydroelectric generation of the All-American Canal. Since that time IID has added geothermal natural gas coal and solar to its energy generation portfolio. Its electric services account for majority of IID's annual revenues.

EXECUTIVES

Secretary Admin, Angelita Alvarado
Secretary Admin, Angelica Velasquez

LOCATIONS

HQ: IMPERIAL IRRIGATION DISTRICT
3027 E BARIONI BLVD, IMPERIAL, CA 922511773
Phone: 800 303-7756
Web: WWW.IID.COM

HISTORICAL FINANCIALS
Company Type: Private

Income Statement				FYE: December 31
	REVENUE ($ mil.)	NET INCOME ($ mil.)	NET PROFIT MARGIN	EMPLOYEES
12/17	634	3	0.5%	1,300
12/16	631	(16)	—	—
12/07	524	151	29.0%	—
12/06	503	108	21.5%	—
Annual Growth	2.1%	(27.3%)	—	—

2017 Year-End Financials
Return on assets: 9.9%   Cash ($ mil.): 68
Return on equity: 0.5%
Current ratio: 1.00

INDEPENDENT PHARMACY COOPERATIVE

EXECUTIVES

Pres, Don Anderson
Marketing Director, Linda Reedy Sr
Director, Peggy Manning
Sales and Marketing Staff, Jake Lewis
Sales Director, Tim Knight
Sales Associate, Lisa Hawkins
Staff, Vickie Miller
Purchasing Coordinator, Stacy Geiger
Member, Carrie Brooks
Marketing Director, Mindy Herrmann
Human Resources Executive, Michelle R Johnson
Auditors: GRANT THORNTON LLP APPLETON

LOCATIONS

HQ: INDEPENDENT PHARMACY COOPERATIVE
1550 COLUMBUS ST, SUN PRAIRIE, WI 535903901
Phone: 800 755-1531
Web: WWW.IPCRX.COM

HISTORICAL FINANCIALS
Company Type: Private

Income Statement				FYE: December 31
	REVENUE ($ mil.)	NET INCOME ($ mil.)	NET PROFIT MARGIN	EMPLOYEES
12/16	1,427	30	2.1%	160
12/14	1,052	2	0.2%	—
12/13	1,058	2	0.2%	—
12/11	806	1	0.2%	—
Annual Growth	12.1%	73.9%	—	—

2016 Year-End Financials
Return on assets: 8.1%   Cash ($ mil.): 40
Return on equity: 2.1%
Current ratio: 0.50

INDEPENDENT SCHOOL DIST 625

EXECUTIVES

Spdt, Joe Gothard
Mgmt Specialist, Andrew Mosca
Executive of Information Techn, Cathy Bloomquist
Executive of Information Techn, Jim Litwin
Accounting Staff, Shirley Davis
Accounting Staff, Patty Kelly
Accounting Staff, Gloria Thompson
Project Coordinator, Deb Campobasso
Information Technology Manager, Mary Engel
Chief Information Officer, Julie Huppertz
Nurse, Michelle Durand
Auditors: MALLOY MONTAGUE KARNOWSKI R

LOCATIONS

HQ: INDEPENDENT SCHOOL DIST 625
360 COLBORNE ST, SAINT PAUL, MN 551023228
Phone: 651 767-8100
Web: WWW.SPPS.ORG

HISTORICAL FINANCIALS
Company Type: Private

Income Statement				FYE: June 30
	REVENUE ($ mil.)	NET INCOME ($ mil.)	NET PROFIT MARGIN	EMPLOYEES
06/17	706	49	7.0%	6,500
06/16	693	(37)	—	—
06/08	608	(1)	—	—
06/07	589	(14)	—	—
Annual Growth	1.8%	—	—	—

INDEPENDENT SCHOOL DISTRICT 1 OF TULSA COUNTY

EXECUTIVES

Pres, Mr Gary Percefull
Vice President, Ms Anna America
Treas, Joe Stoeptelwerth
Supt, Dr Keith Ballard
Supt, Deborah Gift
Treasurer, Mark A Poole
Director of Information Techno, Blaine Young
Human Resources Manager, Carolyn McClure
Manager, Bob Labass
Athletic Director, Jon Rabovsky
Teacher, Karen Sullivan

LOCATIONS

HQ: INDEPENDENT SCHOOL DISTRICT 1 OF TULSA COUNTY
3027 S NEW HAVEN AVE, TULSA, OK 741146131
Phone: 918 746-6800
Web: WWW.TULSASCHOOLS.ORG

HISTORICAL FINANCIALS
Company Type: Private

Income Statement				FYE: June 30
	REVENUE ($ mil.)	NET INCOME ($ mil.)	NET PROFIT MARGIN	EMPLOYEES
06/17	415	18	4.4%	6,115
06/11	403	(10)	—	—
06/08	388	9	2.4%	—
06/07	373	(17)	—	—
Annual Growth	1.1%	—	—	—

2017 Year-End Financials
Return on assets: —   Cash ($ mil.): 65
Return on equity: 4.4%
Current ratio: 2.10

INDEPENDENT SCHOOL DISTRICT 279

EXECUTIVES

Supt, Kate Maguire
Supt, Susan Hinz
Chm, Dean G Henke
Dir, Linda Etim
Executive Officer, Barbara Tonn
Director, Julie Bocock
Teacher Personnel Director, Judy McDonald
Assistant Superintendent, Kim Hiel
Purchasing Agent, Dale Carlstrom
Auditors: MALLOY MONTAGUE KARNOWSKI R

LOCATIONS

HQ: INDEPENDENT SCHOOL DISTRICT 279
11200 93RD AVE N, MAPLE GROVE, MN 553693669
Phone: 763 391-7000
Web: WWW.ISD279.NET

HISTORICAL FINANCIALS
Company Type: Private

Income Statement				FYE: June 30
	REVENUE ($ mil.)	NET INCOME ($ mil.)	NET PROFIT MARGIN	EMPLOYEES
06/17	319	(47)	—	2,700
06/16	319	(47)	—	—
06/13	281	(2)	—	—
06/12	280	(48)	—	—
Annual Growth	2.7%	—	—	—

2017 Year-End Financials
Return on assets: 2.8%   Cash ($ mil.): 1
Return on equity: (-14.8%)
Current ratio: —

INDIANA FCC INC

EXECUTIVES

Pres, Yoshitaka Saito
V Pres-Admin, Jeff Bailey
Account Manager, Joe Rotman
Purchasing Manager, Cecil Edwards

LOCATIONS

HQ: INDIANA FCC INC
555 INDUSTRIAL PARK DR, PORTLAND, IN
473719399
Phone: 260 726-8023

HISTORICAL FINANCIALS

Company Type: Private

Income Statement — FYE: March 31

	REVENUE ($ mil.)	NET INCOME ($ mil.)	NET PROFIT MARGIN	EMPLOYEES
03/17	313	6	2.2%	742
03/04	185	9	5.4%	—
03/03	178	21	12.3%	—
03/02	136	22	16.8%	—
Annual Growth	5.7%	(7.6%)	—	—

2017 Year-End Financials

Return on assets: 7.5%   Cash ($ mil.): 18
Return on equity: 2.2%
Current ratio: 1.90

INDIANA UNIVERSITY HEALTH BLOOMINGTON, INC.

Indiana University Health Bloomington wants to put a bloom back in patients' cheeks. The facility operating as IU Health Bloomington provides care in a ten-county region in south central Indiana. The not-for-profit hospital — which includes a 350-bed main campus in Bloomington and a 25-bed rural hospital in Paoli — provides care in a number of medical specialties including cardiovascular disease cancer orthopedics and neuroscience. It also runs home health and hospice urgent care lab and specialty care facilities as well as physician practices under the name Southern Indiana Physicians. IU Health Bloomington is part of the Indiana University Health (IU Health) system.

Operations

The company's operations include Indiana University Health Paoli (Paoli) Indiana University Health Morgan Hospital (Morgan) and Indiana University Health White Memorial Hospital (White).

Geographic Reach

IU Health Bloomington has a customer base of about 415000 patients in a 10-county area in south central Indiana. The hospital serves as a regional referral center for other hospitals in the area.

Strategy

Like most hospitals IU Health Bloomington enters partnerships to extend its patient reach. In 2012 IU Health Bloomington and a Monroe County YMCA collaborated to provide a new space in a new northwest YMCA dedicated to IU Health for physical therapy orthopedic services sports medicine and health and wellness services.

Company Background

After several years of negotiations IU Health Bloomington officially became an integrated part of the Clarian network at the start of 2010. Then at the beginning of 2011 Clarian changed its name to IU Health to clarify its relationship with Indiana University and to provide a unified brand to connect all of its facilities.

EXECUTIVES

Vice President Revenue Cycle Services And Treasurer, Jennifer Alvey

LOCATIONS

HQ: INDIANA UNIVERSITY HEALTH BLOOMINGTON, INC.
601 W 2ND ST, BLOOMINGTON, IN 474032317
Phone: 812 353-5252
Web: WWW.IUHEALTH.ORG

PRODUCTS/OPERATIONS

Selected Services

Anticoagulation Center
Assisted Medical Transportation
Behavioral Health
Cancer
Cardiovascular
Children's Therapy Center
Diabetes Center
Emergency
Home Care
Home Medical Equipment
Hospice
Laboratory
Neuroscience
Occupational
Orthopedics
Pain Center
Primary Care
Radiology
Rehabilitation
Sleep Lab
Surgical
Urgent Care Centers
Women and Children's
Wound Center

COMPETITORS

Ascension Health	Memorial Hospital
Community Health Network	(Logansport)
Daviess Community Hospital	Riverview Hospital
Franciscan Alliance	St. Vincent Health
Henry County Memorial Hospital	Union Hospital (Indiana)
	Wabash County Hospital

HISTORICAL FINANCIALS

Company Type: Private

Income Statement — FYE: December 31

	REVENUE ($ mil.)	NET INCOME ($ mil.)	NET PROFIT MARGIN	EMPLOYEES
12/15	359	71	19.9%	3,200
12/14	382	92	24.1%	—
12/12	355	64	18.1%	—
12/11	391	22	5.7%	—
Annual Growth	(2.1%)	33.8%	—	—

2015 Year-End Financials

Return on assets: 5.7%   Cash ($ mil.): 173
Return on equity: 19.9%
Current ratio: 5.50

INFINITE COMPUTER SOLUTIONS, INC.

EXECUTIVES

Chb, Sanjay Govil
Ceo, Upinder Zutshi
Sr V Pres Fin and Ops, Ashoka Tankala
Exec V Pres, Sanjeev Gulati
Sr V Pres, Sheppard Lyngdoh
Exec V Pres, K S RAO
Programmer Analyst, Barbara Demosthenous
Senior Software Engineer, Krzysztof Pakula
Assistant Vice-President, Lokesh RAO
Information Technology Project, Thomas Hoffman
Vice-President, Anju Abel

LOCATIONS

HQ: INFINITE COMPUTER SOLUTIONS, INC.
15201 DIAMONDBACK DR # 125, ROCKVILLE, MD
208503312
Phone: 301 355-7760
Web: WWW.INFINITE.COM

HISTORICAL FINANCIALS

Company Type: Private

Income Statement — FYE: March 31

	REVENUE ($ mil.)	NET INCOME ($ mil.)	NET PROFIT MARGIN	EMPLOYEES
03/18	347	1	0.5%	650
03/17	325	2	0.6%	—
03/16	278	1	0.7%	—
03/15	248	0	0.3%	—
Annual Growth	11.9%	36.1%	—	—

2018 Year-End Financials

Return on assets: 14.9%   Cash ($ mil.): —
Return on equity: 0.5%
Current ratio: 0.80

INFIRMARY HEALTH SYSTEM, INC.

EXECUTIVES

Ceo, D Mark Nix
President, E Chandler Bramlett
Contrl, Jim Mitchell
Human Resources Information MA, Stephanie Andrews
Controller, Becky Michels
Information Technology/Interne, Curtis Rye
Administrative Assistant, Dana Thomas
Vice-President, Harry Brislin
Coordinator, Shannon Pavel
Executive Vice-President, Alan Whaley
Technical Staff, David Smith

LOCATIONS

HQ: INFIRMARY HEALTH SYSTEM, INC.
5 MOBILE INFIRMARY CIR, MOBILE, AL 366073513
Phone: 251 435-3030
Web: WWW.DEBAKEYDRUGEDUCATION.COM

HISTORICAL FINANCIALS
Company Type: Private

Income Statement				FYE: March 31
	REVENUE ($ mil.)	NET INCOME ($ mil.)	NET PROFIT MARGIN	EMPLOYEES
03/18	727	35	4.8%	5,000
03/17	696	70	10.2%	—
03/15	58	(4)	—	—
03/14	51	(4)	—	—
Annual Growth	93.6%	—	—	—

2018 Year-End Financials
Return on assets: 8.3%   Cash ($ mil.): 68
Return on equity: 4.8%
Current ratio: 1.80

INGHAM REGIONAL MEDICAL CENTER

EXECUTIVES

Ceo, Philip Incarnati
President, Dennis Litos
Cfo, Dale Thompson
Phlebotomist, Ladosha Washington
Internal Medicine Practitioner, Amit Ghose
Physician, John Flood

LOCATIONS

HQ: INGHAM REGIONAL MEDICAL CENTER
   401 W GREENLAWN AVE, LANSING, MI 489100899
Phone: 517 975-7800
Web: WWW.IRMC.ORG

HISTORICAL FINANCIALS
Company Type: Private

Income Statement				FYE: September 30
	REVENUE ($ mil.)	NET INCOME ($ mil.)	NET PROFIT MARGIN	EMPLOYEES
09/17	344	21	6.2%	2,500
09/16	340	13	4.0%	—
09/15	312	(11)	—	—
09/14	254	6	2.5%	—
Annual Growth	10.6%	50.3%	—	—

2017 Year-End Financials
Return on assets: 6.5%   Cash ($ mil.): 22
Return on equity: 6.2%
Current ratio: 1.10

INLAND COUNTIES REGIONAL CENTER, INC.

EXECUTIVES

Ceo, Carol A Fitzgibbons
Exec Dir, Carol Fitzgibbons
Psychologist, Brad Onomura
Psychologist, Harry Zhang
Manager, Gigi Thompson
Psychologist, Guadalupe Hernandez

Psychologist, Tom Young
Controller, Kaye Quintero
Manager, Mary Hernandez
Manager, Elizabeth Stroh
Psychologist, Carmela Aquino
Auditors: WINDES INC LONG BEACH CA

LOCATIONS

HQ: INLAND COUNTIES REGIONAL CENTER, INC.
   1365 S WATERMAN AVE, SAN BERNARDINO, CA
   924082804
Phone: 909 890-3000
Web: WWW.INLANDRC.ORG

HISTORICAL FINANCIALS
Company Type: Private

Income Statement				FYE: June 30
	REVENUE ($ mil.)	NET INCOME ($ mil.)	NET PROFIT MARGIN	EMPLOYEES
06/16	402	(7)	—	586
06/15	378	4	1.1%	—
06/14	335	(2)	—	—
06/13	314	(2)	—	—
Annual Growth	8.6%	—	—	—

2016 Year-End Financials
Return on assets: 8.6%   Cash ($ mil.): 24
Return on equity: (-1.9%)
Current ratio: 0.40

INNOVATIVE AG SERVICES CO.

EXECUTIVES

Ceo, Rick Vaughan
President, Randy Blake
1st Vp, Paul Cook
Cfo, Brenda Hoefler
Director of Information Techno, Drew Dunkel
Human Resources Staff, Marilyn E Ewing
Manager, Mike Bachman
Human Resources Representative, Susan Walsh
Auditors: MERIWETHER WILSON & COMPANY

LOCATIONS

HQ: INNOVATIVE AG SERVICES CO.
   2010 S MAIN ST, MONTICELLO, IA 523107707
Phone: 319 465-3501
Web: WWW.INNOVATIVEAG.COM

HISTORICAL FINANCIALS
Company Type: Private

Income Statement				FYE: August 31
	REVENUE ($ mil.)	NET INCOME ($ mil.)	NET PROFIT MARGIN	EMPLOYEES
08/17	615	15	2.6%	500
08/16	682	10	1.6%	—
08/15	657	18	2.8%	—
08/14	855	23	2.8%	—
Annual Growth	(10.4%)	(12.6%)	—	—

2017 Year-End Financials
Return on assets: 3.7%   Cash ($ mil.): 9
Return on equity: 2.6%
Current ratio: 0.30

INNOVIS HEALTH, LLC

EXECUTIVES

Ceo, Greg Glasner
Cfo, Bert Norman
Chief Operating Officer, Kevin Pitzer
Ceo, Peter Person
Coo, John Smylie
Engineering Manager, Brent Aasland
Optometrists, Lori Y Scheel
Urology Specialist, Steven Strinden
Neurology Specialist, Curtis W Penney
Health Care Director, Becky Kirsch
Health Professional, Bessant Parker

LOCATIONS

HQ: INNOVIS HEALTH, LLC
   1702 UNIVERSITY DR S, FARGO, ND 581034940
Phone: 701 364-8900

HISTORICAL FINANCIALS
Company Type: Private

Income Statement				FYE: June 30
	REVENUE ($ mil.)	NET INCOME ($ mil.)	NET PROFIT MARGIN	EMPLOYEES
06/16	363	0	0.3%	2,000
06/12	272	(12)	—	—
/*	0	0	—	—
Annual Growth	—	—	—	—

*Fiscal year change

2016 Year-End Financials
Return on assets: 11.4%   Cash ($ mil.): 3
Return on equity: 0.3%
Current ratio: 0.20

INTEGRIS BAPTIST MEDICAL CENTER, INC.

EXECUTIVES

Pres, Chris Hammes
Cfo, Wentz J Miller
Human Resources Manager, Patricia Barrett
Coordinator, Dorothy Welcome
Coordinator, Claudia Hampton
Coordinator, Owen Thompson
Coordinator, Roberto Gonzalez
Internal Medicine Practitioner, Kristopher Lepere
Director, Carl Frownfelter
Diagnostic Radiologist, Annette Kezbers
Maintenance Supervisor, Keith Rush

LOCATIONS

HQ: INTEGRIS BAPTIST MEDICAL CENTER, INC.
   3300 NW EXPRESSWAY, OKLAHOMA CITY, OK
   731124418
Phone: 405 949-3011
Web: WWW.INTEGRISOK.COM

PRODUCTS/OPERATIONS

Selected Centers and Services
Advanced Cardiac Care
Anticoagulation Clinics
Bariatrics
Bennett Fertility Institute
Bones and Joints
Breast Care
Burn Center
Cancer Care

Cardiology
Case Management
Children's Health
Comprehensive Breast Center of Oklahoma
Continuing Medical Education
Corporate Assistance Program
Diabetes
Diagnostic Services
Digestive Health
Emergency Department
Fertility
General Heart Care
General Pediatrics
Home Care
Hospice
Hospitalist Program
Hough Ear Institute
Hyperbaric Medicine and Wound Care
James R. Daniel Cerebrovascular and Stroke Center
Jim Thorpe Rehabilitation Center
Labor and Delivery
Men's Health
Nazih Zuhdi Transplant Institute
Neonatal Intensive Care Unit (NICU)
Orthopedics
PACER Fitness Center
Pastoral Care
Pediatric Intensive Care Unit (PICU)
Pediatric Neurology
Pharmacy
Radiology Services
Senior Health
Sleep Disorders Center of Oklahoma
Stroke Center
Surgical Services
TeleHealth
Urogynecology
Weight Loss

COMPETITORS

Deaconess Health Care	Norman Regional Health
Hillcrest Medical Center	SSM Health Care
Jackson County Memorial Hospital	Saint Francis Health System
Marian Health System	Texas Health Denton
Mercy Health	Universal Health Services

HISTORICAL FINANCIALS

Company Type: Private

Income Statement   FYE: June 30

	REVENUE ($ mil.)	NET INCOME ($ mil.)	NET PROFIT MARGIN	EMPLOYEES
06/18	814	67	8.3%	2,700
06/16	701	6	1.0%	—
06/09*	582	22	3.9%	—
12/08	0	0	—	—
Annual Growth	—	—	—	—

*Fiscal year change

2018 Year-End Financials

Return on assets: —   Cash ($ mil.): 339
Return on equity: 8.3%
Current ratio: 2.30

INTEGRIS HEALTH, INC.

INTEGRIS Health provides a range of health services to residents throughout the Sooner state. The company one of Oklahoma's largest not-for-profit health care organization operates 16 hospitals with some 1500 combined beds in both urban and rural communities. The hospitals provide services including primary diagnostic emergency surgical behavioral therapeutic and rehabilitative care. INTEGRIS also operates specialty facilities for the treatment of hearing disorders and neuromuscular ailments and for rehabilitation care. The company operates assisted living centers and a home health agency plus a network of physician clinics and ambulatory care centers.

Operations

Operations include INTEGRIS Baptist Medical Center (the system's largest with 629 beds) INTEGRIS South Oklahoma City (dba INTEGRIS Southwest Medical Center 389 beds) and INTEGRIS Rural Health facilities INTEGRIS Baptist Regional Health Center INTEGRIS Bass Baptist Health Center and INTEGRIS Grove Hospital.

INTEGRIS Health has approximately 1400 physicians in its system.

Sales and Marketing

Managed care payments account for more than half of net patient service revenue; Medicare and Medicaid combined account for around a third.

INTEGRIS Health offers community residents with more life experience such services as senior seminars and classes health screenings support groups and technology classes to help stay up-to-date on computer use. The idea is to help keep the elderly as independent as possible for as long as possible.

Financial Performance

The company's revenue increased slightly in fiscal 2015 rising 1% to $1.4 billion. This was due to growth in net patient service revenues. However INTEGRIS Health reported a net loss of $150 million (versus a net gain in 2014) due to factors that included higher operating expenses (salaries supplies) and higher pension liability adjustments. This in turn led to a 60% drop in cash flow from operations which totaled $49 million.

EXECUTIVES

President Integris Southwest Medical Center, James D. Moore
Chief Medical Officer, James White
Evp And Coo, Chris Hammes
President And Ceo, Bruce Lawrence
Cfo, David Hadley
President Integris Baptist Medical Center, Tim Johnsen
President Integris Bass Baptist Health Center Enid, Eddie Herrman
President Integris Baptist Regional Health Center Miami, Jordan Cash
President Integris Canadian Valley Hospital Yukon, Rex Van Meter
President Integris Cancer Institute Of Oklahoma, Phil Lance
President Integris Health Edmond, Avilla Williams
President Integris Health Partners, Carl Raczkowski
President Integris Heart Hospital, R. Mel Clark
President Integris Medical Group, Jeff Cruzan
President Lakeside Women's Hospital, Kelley Brewer
President And Coo Integris Mental Health And James L. Hall Jr. Center For Mind Body And Spirit, R. Murali Krishna
Vp Integris Nazih Zuhdi Transplant Insitute Integris Advanced Cardiac Care, Kathie Calbone
President Integris Grove Hospital, Tim Bowen, age 35
Director Of Radiology, Amy Brown
Clinical Director, Anne Gates
Vice President, Jeff Brown
Clinical Director, John Needham
Medical Director Pediatric Intensive Care Unit, Johnny Griggs
Medical Director, Derek Irwin
Clinical Director, Nada Cain
Vice President, Anne Clouse
Clinic Manager, Jennifer Gomez
Clinic Supervisor, Shelia Pendergraft
Clinic Supervisor, Tammie Johnston

Clinical Director, Lisa Aishman
Director Of Pharmacy, Larry Anderson
Auditors: KPMG LLP OKLAHOMA CITY OKLAH

LOCATIONS

HQ: INTEGRIS HEALTH, INC.
3300 NW EXPRESSWAY, OKLAHOMA CITY, OK 731124418
Phone: 405 949-6066
Web: WWW.INTEGRISOK.COM

PRODUCTS/OPERATIONS

2015 Sales

	% of total
INTEGRIS Baptist Medical Center Inc.	39
INTEGRIS South Oklahoma City Hospital Corporation	15
INTEGRIS Rural Health Inc.	14
INTEGRIS Health Edmond	3
All others	29
Eliminations	-
Total	**100**

Selected Facilities

Baptist Medical Center
Baptist Regional Health Center
Bass Baptist Health Center
Blackwell Regional Hospital
Canadian Valley Regional Hospital
Cancer Institute of Oklahoma
Clinton Regional Hospital
Grove General Hospital
Health Edmond
Hospice House
Jim Thorpe Rehabilitation
Marshall County Medical Center
Mayes County Medical Center
Mental Health Spencer
Seminole Medical Center
Southwest Medical Center

COMPETITORS

Ardent Health Services	Marian Health System
Deaconess Health Care	Mercy Health
Fairview Health	Norman Regional Health
HealthEast Care System	Saint Francis Health System
Hillcrest Medical Center	St. John Health System

HISTORICAL FINANCIALS

Company Type: Private

Income Statement   FYE: June 30

	REVENUE ($ mil.)	NET INCOME ($ mil.)	NET PROFIT MARGIN	EMPLOYEES
06/18	1,673	53	3.2%	9,500
06/17	1,558	111	7.2%	—
06/15	1,384	(90)	—	—
06/06	1,067	89	8.4%	—
Annual Growth	3.8%	(4.2%)	—	—

2018 Year-End Financials

Return on assets: —   Cash ($ mil.): 76
Return on equity: 3.2%
Current ratio: 0.90

INTERMOUNTAIN HEALTH CARE INC

If you whoosh down the side of one of Idaho's majestic mountains and take a nasty spill Intermountain Health Care (dba Intermountain Healthcare) can pick you up and put you back together. From air ambulance services to urgent care clinics and general hospitals Intermountain has all the tools to mend skiers (and non-skiers alike) in Utah and southern Idaho. With about 1600 physicians the not-for-profit health system operates 22 hospitals and some 180 clinics as well as urgent care centers and rehabilitation centers. Intermountain also has an insurance arm named SelectHealth.

Operations

Intermountain Healthcare's hospitals range from general surgical to specialty care including orthopedic and pediatric facilities. Along with the full spectrum of physical health care services Intermountain also offers comprehensive mental health and substance abuse programs for patients of all ages. The organization's spectrum of care includes acute inpatient residential treatment day treatment chemical dependency inpatient/detoxification and intensive outpatient programs.

The system conducts cancer research through its partnership with Huntsman Cancer Institute at the University of Utah. The two share data best practices funding and co-conduct clinical trials. They also operate a number of cancer-specific treatment centers including multi-disciplinary tumor-specific clinics designed to provide one-stop service for cancer patients to meet with different cancer specialists on the same day for a more comprehensive treatment plan. Other areas of research include cardiovascular intensive medicine surgical care and behavioral health.

On the physician side the Intermountain Medical Group administers multi-specialty health care services in clinics located throughout the region. The group also operates urgent care clinics under the InstaCare and KidsCare banners.

Entering itself into the "what doesn't Intermountain do?" category the health system also provides health and dental insurance plans through its SelectHealth division.

Geographic Reach

Intermountain Healthcare serves the health care needs of Utah and Idaho residents.

Financial Performance

In 2016 Intermountain Healthcare's revenue grew 14% to $7.6 billion in fiscal 2016. This was due to increases in net patient services income non-patient activity income and investment income. Net patient services accounted for 63% of the system's total revenue that year.

The company used $7 billion of that revenue towards operating expenses including salaries and benefits medical supplies and facilities maintenance and other business services as well as towards funds dedicated to future needs.

Strategy

Intermountain Healthcare uses its dedicated supply chain organization to continuously improve system efficiency. In addition to delivering medical supplies the unit also oversees hospital vehicles.

The system partners with several leading IT companies (including Xi3 Intel Dell and NetApp) to operate its Healthcare Transformation Lab on the campus of its flagship hospital Intermountain Medical Center in Murray Utah. The lab researches develops and measures new ideas to improve patient care.

In 2016 the system launched Navican Genomics its genomics research and testing arm. Also that year it partnered with the Stanford Genome Technology Center to establish a collaborative research program.

Intermountain has a number of projects underway to add expand or replace existing facilities.

Company Background

Intermountain was formed in 1975 when the Church of Jesus Christ of Latter Day Saints donated 15 hospitals to local communities.

EXECUTIVES

Senior Vice President, Greg Poulsen
Ceo Intermountain Medical Group And Vp Physician Division, Linda C. Leckman
President And Ceo Selecthealth, Patricia R. Richards
Evp And Cfo, Bert R. Zimmerli
Evp And Coo, Laura S. Kaiser
Regional Vp Central Region, Moody L. Chisholm
Vp And Cio, Marc Probst
President And Ceo, A. Marc Harrison, age 54
Regional Vp Soutwest Region, Terri Kane
Ceo Park City Medical Center, Robert Allen
Vp Clinical Operations And Chief Nursing Officer, Kim Henrichsen
Ceo Urban North Region And Mckay-dee Hospital Center, Timothy T. Pehrson
Chief Medical Officer, Brent E. Wallace
Ceo Primary Childrenâ's Medical Center, Katherine A. (Katy) Welkie
Regional Vp South Region, Steve Smoot
Vp Supply Chain And Support Services, Joe Walsh
Assistant Vice President Of Risk Management Services, Harlan Hammond
Vice President Management, Jim Darrington
Vice President Marketing And Communication, Todd Frehse
Director Media Relations, Daron Cowley
Medical Director, Scott Whittle
Assistant Vice President Research, Raj Srivastava
Medical Director Epilepsy Program, Tawnya Constantino
Medical Director, Kristian Kemp
Vice President Business Ethics And Compliance, Suzie Draper
Vice President Human Resources, Dan Zuhlke
Vice President And General Counsel, Doug Hammer
Vice President Rural Region, Rob Allen
Pharmacy Manager, Robb Dengg
Cota L, Celeste Marsh
Assistant Vice President Telehealth Services, Brian Wayling
Medical Director Clinical Genetics Institute, Steven Bleyl
Clinical Director Primary Children's Pediatric Behavioral Health Clinic, Nancy Cantor
Vice President Of Underwriting, Mike Brown
Occupational Therapy Director, Andrew Bracken
Medical Director Information Technology, Ed Clark
Medical Director Informatics, Farukh Usmani
Operating Room Dir, DEBRA ESPLIN
Vice Chairman, Bruce T. Reese
Chairman, A. Scott Anderson
Secretary, Nicole Houghton
Secretary, Jeri Lay
Secretary, Stephanie Stromberg
Secretary, Jodi Simmons
Auditors: KPMG LLP SALT LAKE CITY UT

LOCATIONS

HQ: INTERMOUNTAIN HEALTH CARE INC
36 S STATE ST STE 1600, SALT LAKE CITY, UT 841111633
Phone: 801 442-2000
Web: WWW.INTERMOUNTAINHEALTHCARE.ORG

PRODUCTS/OPERATIONS

2016 Sales

	$ mil.	% of total
Net patient services	4,368	57
Non-patient activities	3,010	40
Non-operating income	237	3
Total	**7,617**	**100**

Selected Hospitals

Alta View Hospital (Sandy UT)
American Fork Hospital (Utah)
Bear River Valley Hospital (Tremonton UT)

Cassia Regional Medical Center (Burley ID)
Delta Community Medical Center (Utah)
Dixie Regional Medical Center (St. George UT)
Fillmore Community Medical Center (Utah)
Garfield Memorial Hospital (Panguitch UT)
Heber Valley Medical Center (Heber City UT)
Intermountain Medical Center (Murray UT)
LDS Hospital (Salt Lake City)
Logan Regional Hospital (Orem UT)
McKay-Dee Hospital Center (Ogden UT)
McKay-Dee Behavioral Health Institute
Orem Community Hospital (Utah)
Park City Medical Center (Park City UT)
Primary Children's Medical Center (Salt Lake City)
Riverton Hospital (Riverton UT)
Sanpete Valley Hospital (Mt. Pleasant UT)
Sevier Valley Hospital (Richfield UT)
TOSH - The Orthopedic Specialty Hospital (Murray UT)
Utah Valley Regional Medical Center (Provo UT)
Valley View Medical Center (Cedar City UT)

COMPETITORS

CHRISTUS Health
Encompass Health
HCA
LifePoint Health
Ogden Regional Medical Center

Regence BlueCross BlueShield of Utah
St. Mark's
University of Utah Hospitals & Clinics

HISTORICAL FINANCIALS

Company Type: Private

Income Statement

FYE: December 31

	REVENUE ($ mil.)	NET INCOME ($ mil.)	NET PROFIT MARGIN	EMPLOYEES
12/17	6,940	1,061	15.3%	35,000
12/16	6,716	606	9.0%	—
12/15	6,058	155	2.6%	—
12/14	5,573	(156)	—	—
Annual Growth	7.6%	—	—	—

2017 Year-End Financials

Return on assets: 6.0%   Cash ($ mil.): 204
Return on equity: 15.3%
Current ratio: 0.40

INTERNATIONAL RESCUE COMMITTEE, INC.

EXECUTIVES

Pres-Ceo, David Miliband
General Counsel, Ricardo Castro
Cfo, Danusia Dzierzbinski
Project Coordinator, Emelina Cesheshyan
Programmer Analyst, Adnan Suvalic
General Counsel, Carrie Simon
Director, Debi Wheeler
Director, Amanya Michael
Senior Vice-President, Carrie Welch
Director, Nicola Smith
Computer Specialist, Paul Amendola
Auditors: KPMG LLP NEW YORK NY

LOCATIONS

HQ: INTERNATIONAL RESCUE COMMITTEE, INC.
122 E 42ND ST, NEW YORK, NY 101680002
Phone: 212 551-3000
Web: WWW.RESCUE.ORG

HISTORICAL FINANCIALS

Company Type: Private

Income Statement | | | | FYE: September 30

	REVENUE ($ mil.)	NET INCOME ($ mil.)	NET PROFIT MARGIN	EMPLOYEES
09/17	753	44	5.9%	8,000
09/14	562	9	1.7%	—
09/11	397	11	2.9%	—
09/10	316	10	3.3%	—
Annual Growth	13.2%	22.9%	—	—

2017 Year-End Financials

Return on assets: 5.2% Cash ($ mil.): 105
Return on equity: 5.9%
Current ratio: —

INTERNATIONAL TRANSMISSION COMPANY

EXECUTIVES

Pres-Ceo, Joseph L Welch
Cfo, Edward Rahill
Exe Vice President, Linda H Blair
Exe Vice President, Cameron M Bready
Exe Vice President, Jon E Jipping
Exe Vice President, Daniel J Oginsky
Prod, Charles V Waits
Benefits Manager, Judy Michaels
Designer, Spenser Williams
Senior Technician, Carlos Wentworth
Senior Engineer In Plan, Dan Barr

LOCATIONS

HQ: INTERNATIONAL TRANSMISSION COMPANY
27175 ENERGY WAY, NOVI, MI 483773639
Phone: 248 374-7100
Web: WWW.ITCTRANSCO.COM

HISTORICAL FINANCIALS

Company Type: Private

Income Statement | | | | FYE: December 31

	REVENUE ($ mil.)	NET INCOME ($ mil.)	NET PROFIT MARGIN	EMPLOYEES
12/17	391	116	29.9%	100
12/16	373	108	29.0%	—
12/05	205	34	16.9%	—
12/03	102	8	8.7%	—
Annual Growth	10.1%	20.2%	—	—

2017 Year-End Financials

Return on assets: 8.6% Cash ($ mil.): —
Return on equity: 29.9%
Current ratio: —

IOWA FINANCE AUTHORITY

EXECUTIVES

Eo, David Jamison
Coo, Steven Harvey
Coordinator, Amber Lewis
General Counsel, Mark Thompson
Accounting Manager, Michelle Thomas
General Manager, Carolann Jensen
Government Relations Director, Wes Peterson
Director, Janet Phipps
Officer, Samantha Day
Clerk, Amanda Jenkins
Investment Manager, Mark Fairley
Auditors: KPMG LLP DES MOINES IA

LOCATIONS

HQ: IOWA FINANCE AUTHORITY
2015 GRAND AVE STE 200, DES MOINES, IA
503124903
Phone: 515 725-4900
Web: WWW.IOWAFINANCEAUTHORITY.GOV

HISTORICAL FINANCIALS

Company Type: Private

Income Statement | | | | FYE: June 30

	ASSETS ($ mil.)	NET INCOME ($ mil.)	INCOME AS % OF ASSETS	EMPLOYEES
06/16	2,565	42	1.7%	89
06/10	2,914	63	2.2%	—
06/09	2,519	85	3.4%	—
06/08	0	80	—	—
Annual Growth	—	(7.7%)	—	—

2016 Year-End Financials

Return on assets: 6.8% Sales ($ mil): 85
Return on equity: 49.6%

IOWA HEALTH SYSTEM

The land where the tall corn grows is also the land of Iowa Health System (IHS) which does business as UnityPoint. The integrated health care system operates some 15 acute care hospitals that serve large communities throughout Iowa as well as parts of western Illinois and Madison Wisconsin. UnityPoint also supports about a dozen rural hospitals and it manages about 300 physician clinics located in rural and suburban areas. The system's hospitals provide general medical-surgical care as well as care in a number of medical specialties such as cardiovascular disease and home health services. Founded in 1993 UnityPoint has about 3700 licensed beds.

Operations

In 2014 the system had about 155000 patient admissions facilitated 20000 births and saw a total of some 4.5 million patients.

Geographic Reach

UnityPoint Health includes a dozen hospitals in 10 Iowa cities four in Illinois and another in Wisconsin. Its largest geographic markets served are Anamosa Cedar Rapids Des Moines Dubuque Fort Dodge Sioux City and Waterloo Iowa; the Quad Cities/Muscatine region in Iowa and Illinois; Peoria Illinois; and Madison Wisconsin.

Strategy

In early 2013 Iowa Health System rebranded itself UnityPoint to showcase its mission to be a point of unity for patient care. It probably also helped that the company was expanding and including health care facilities in other states. That same year it picked up new affiliates in Illinois expanded its broadband Internet access program across Iowa and added Meriter Health Services of Madison Wisconsin. The health system operates many of its member hospitals through similar affiliation agreements where it provides administration contracting billing legal recruitment information technology and other central services. In 2015 the system built a new primary care facility in Cedar Falls Iowa.

The system is also expanding in areas beyond its physical locations. In 2015 it partnered with MDLive to begin offering telehealth services in Iowa and it added a plane to its air ambulance fleet. UnityPoint also plans to launch a new insurance firm with not-for-profit organization Health-Partners.

EXECUTIVES

President And Ceo Unitypoint Health -des Moines, Eric Crowell
Vp And Cio, Joy M. Grosser
Ceo, Kevin Vermeer
Vp Supply Chain Management, Katie Marchik
Svp And Cfo, Mark Johnson
Evp And Coo; President And Ceo Meriter-unitypoint Health Madison, Arthur Nizza
Vp Payor Innovation; Ceo Unitypoint At Work, Brian Jones
Ceo Unitypoint Health -st. Luke's -sioux City, Lynn Wold
Ceo Jones Regional Medical Center Anamosa, Eric Briesemeister
President And Ceo Unitypoint Health -dubuque, David Brandon
President And Ceo Unitypoint Health -peoria, Debbie Simon
President And Ceo Unitypoint Health -trinity (quad Cities Muscatine), Rick Seidler
President And Ceo Unitypoint Health -waterloo, Pam Delagardelle
President And Ceo St. Luke's -cedar Rapids, Ted Townsend
Ceo Unitypoint Health Partners, David Williams
Svp Insurance Division And Ceo Physicians Plus Insurance Corporation (ppic), Troy Caraway
Evp And Coo Unitypoint Health Des Moines And Interim Ceo Unitypoint Clinic, Steve Stephenson
Svp Integration And Optimization And Interim Ceo Unitypoint At Home, Susan K. Thompson
President And Ceo Unitypoint Health Fort Dodge, Mike Dewerff
Vice President People Excellence, Emily Porter
Vice President Patient Services, Pam Askew
Medical Director, Samir Y Alabsi
Vice President Of Practice Operations, Matt Behrens
Vice President And Chief Nurse Executive, Mary E Hagen
Associate Medical Director, Julia Jenkins
Vice President Operations, Joe Linn
Vice President Surgical And Diagnostic Services, Jeanette Murray
Vice President Network Business Services Development, Lori Weih
Vice President Business Development, Todd Burchill
Chairman, Mike Williams
Vice Chair, Mike Stone
Secretary, Lucinda Barnes
Auditors: BKD LLP KANSAS CITY MO

LOCATIONS

HQ: IOWA HEALTH SYSTEM
1776 WEST LAKES PKWY # 400, WEST DES
MOINES, IA 502668377
Phone: 515 241-6161
Web: WWW.IHS.ORG

PRODUCTS/OPERATIONS

Selected Facilities
Metropolitan Hospitals
  Allen Memorial Hospital Corporation (Waterloo Iowa)
  Iowa Lutheran Hospital (Des Moines Iowa)
  Iowa Methodist Medical Center (Des Moines Iowa)
  Blank Children's Hospital (Des Moines Iowa)
  Methodist Medical Center of Illinois (Peoria Illinois)
  Methodist West Hospital (West Des Moines Iowa)
  St. Luke's Hospital (Cedar Rapids Iowa)
  St. Luke's Regional Medical Center (Sioux City Iowa)
  Jones Regional Medical Center (Anamosa Iowa)
  The Finley Hospital (Dubuque Iowa)
  Trinity Bettendorf (Bettendorf Iowa)
  Trinity Moline (Moline Illinois)
  Trinity Muscatine (Muscatine Iowa)
  Trinity Regional Medical Center (Fort Dodge Iowa)
  Trinity Rock Island (Rock Island Illinois)
Rural Hospitals
  Buena Vista Regional Medical Center (Storm Lake Iowa)
  Clarke County Hospital (Osceola Iowa)
  Community Memorial Hospital (Sumner Iowa)
  Greater Regional Medical Center (Creston Iowa)
  Greene County Medical Center (Jefferson Iowa)
  Grundy County Memorial Hospital (Grundy Center Iowa)
  Guthrie County Hospital (Guthrie Center Iowa)
  Guttenberg Municipal Hospital (Guttenberg Iowa)
  Humboldt County Memorial Hospital (Humboldt Iowa)
  Loring Hospital (Sac City Iowa)
  Pocahontas Community Hospital (Pocahantas Iowa)

COMPETITORS

Avera Health	Mercy Health Network
Blessing Hospital	Methodist Health
CHI Health	System
Genesis Health System	OSF Healthcare System
McDonough District	
Hospital	

HISTORICAL FINANCIALS

Company Type: Private

Income Statement				FYE: December 31
	REVENUE ($ mil.)	NET INCOME ($ mil.)	NET PROFIT MARGIN	EMPLOYEES
12/17	4,157	229	5.5%	18,923
12/16	4,054	148	3.7%	—
Annual Growth	2.5%	54.4%	—	—

2017 Year-End Financials
Return on assets: 4.3%   Cash ($ mil.): 251
Return on equity: 5.5%
Current ratio: 1.20

IOWA STATE UNIVERSITY OF SCIENCE AND TECHNOLOGY

Home to the Cyclones athletics teams Iowa State University of Science and Technology (ISU) can be a whirlwind experience for some. ISU is a public land-grant institution offering higher education courses and programs with an emphasis on science technology and related areas. ISU's eight colleges offer more than 100 undergraduate degrees and nearly 200 fields of study leading to graduate and professional degrees. The university has an enrollment of more than 31000 students and charges more than $7720 in tuition and fees for resident students for two semesters.

Operations
In fiscal 2012 Iowa State received $360.2 million in grants contracts co-operative agreements and gifts of which about 60% is utilized for research purpose. The university's research park has about 20000 square feet of incubators space including office and laboratories.

Geographic Reach
The university enrolls students from 50 states and more than 100 countries.

Financial Performance
The 6% increase in revenues in 2012 was due to higher tuition and fees sales and services of educational activities and auxiliary enterprise revenues. The tuition revenue increase was to a 5% hike in the resident tuition rate coupled with record enrollments. The increase in sales and services of educational activities was due to large one-time events ISU farms and the Vet Diagnostic Lab. ISU's auxiliary enterprises reported revenue growth thanks to new revenue sources and a record number of students in the residence system.

ISU's net income increased by 47% in 2012 thanks to higher operating expenses and a decline in non-operating revenues. Non-operating revenues decreased $24.4 million thanks to an $11 million decrease in funding from education appropriations. Investment income also dropped $16.3 million or 49% mainly due to an unrealized loss in the value of investments.

Company Background
Chartered as Iowa Agriculture College in 1858 the school first officially opened for classes in 1869. Among ISU's notable alumni is scientist and inventor George Washington Carver.

EXECUTIVES

Vice President, Atalie Ruhnke
Auditors: MARY MOSIMAN CPA DES MOINES

LOCATIONS

HQ: IOWA STATE UNIVERSITY OF SCIENCE AND TECHNOLOGY
1350 BEARDSHEAR HALL, AMES, IA 500112025
Phone: 515 294-6162
Web: WWW.IASTATE.EDU

PRODUCTS/OPERATIONS

Colleges
Agriculture and Life Sciences
Business
Design
Engineering
Graduate
Human Sciences
Liberal Arts and Sciences
Veterinary Medicine

HISTORICAL FINANCIALS

Company Type: Private

Income Statement				FYE: June 30
	REVENUE ($ mil.)	NET INCOME ($ mil.)	NET PROFIT MARGIN	EMPLOYEES
06/17	920	77	8.4%	5,800
06/16	902	67	7.5%	—
06/15	858	67	7.8%	—
06/14	806	118	14.8%	—
Annual Growth	4.5%	(13.3%)	—	—

2017 Year-End Financials
Return on assets: 5.3%   Cash ($ mil.): 20
Return on equity: 8.4%
Current ratio: 0.20

IOWA STUDENT LOAN LIQUIDITY CORPORATION

EXECUTIVES

Pres, Steven W McCullough
SEC, Mary Kay Debolt
Treas, Erin Lacey
Auditors: KPMG LLP DES MOINES IOWA

LOCATIONS

HQ: IOWA STUDENT LOAN LIQUIDITY CORPORATION
6775 VISTA DR, WEST DES MOINES, IA 502669305
Phone: 515 243-5626
Web: WWW.STUDENTLOAN.ORG

HISTORICAL FINANCIALS

Company Type: Private

Income Statement				FYE: June 30
	ASSETS ($ mil.)	NET INCOME ($ mil.)	INCOME AS % OF ASSETS	EMPLOYEES
06/17	1,675	29	1.8%	214
06/16	1,659	7	0.5%	—
06/10	3,748	(28)	—	—
06/09	4,046	17	0.4%	—
Annual Growth	(10.4%)	7.1%	—	—

2017 Year-End Financials
Return on assets: 15.4%   Sales ($ mil.): 83
Return on equity: 35.9%

IRC RETAIL CENTERS LLC

IRC Retail Centers (formerly Inland Real Estate Corporation) buys leases and operates retail properties mainly in the Midwest with a concentration in the Chicago and Minneapolis/St. Paul metropolitan markets. The self-managed real estate investment trust (REIT) owns about 150 properties most of which are strip shopping centers anchored by a grocery or big-box store. It also invests in single-tenant retail properties and develops properties usually through joint ventures. The REIT's portfolio totals about 14 million sq. ft. of leasable space in a dozen states. IRC Retail Centers was acquired by DRA Advisors in early 2015.

Operations
As a REIT IRC Retail Centers is exempt from paying federal income tax so long as it distributes quarterly dividends to shareholders. Most tenants of its investment properties are responsible for paying real estate taxes as insurance as well as maintaining the properties.

Financial Performance

Overall revenues fell 4% in 2012 to $160 million. That year the company had decreased income across the board from rent property fees and joint venture fees despite buying 20 new properties and divesting eight. However it posted profits of almost $18 million in 2012 thanks to one-time earnings on continuing operations and a gain on equity in joint ventures.

Strategy

In 2013 the company announced plans for a new joint venture with an affiliate of Australia-based MAB Corporation. The project calls for developing about 20 grocery-anchored shopping centers that would include a 50000-sq.-ft. supermarket with another 20000 sq. ft. of retail space. The JV will extend IRC Retail's reach to the eastern US namely Florida Georgia North and South Carolina Virginia and Washington DC.

Another joint venture with Dutch pension fund administrator PGGM (established 2010) calls for acquiring grocery-anchored and community retail centers in the Midwest. In 2013 the JV bought three Wal-Mart shopping centers in the Milwaukee area for $24.2 million a 139000-sq.-ft. Whole Foods/CVS shopping center in Cleveland for $25 million and is building a 92000-sq.-ft. shopping center in Evergreen Park Illinois.

EXECUTIVES

Senior Vice President, William Anderson
Auditors: KPMG LLP CHICAGO ILLINOIS

LOCATIONS

HQ: IRC RETAIL CENTERS LLC
814 COMMERCE DR STE 300, OAK BROOK, IL 605238823
Phone: 877 206-5656
Web: WWW.IRCRETAILCENTERS.COM

2015 Properties (excluding joint ventures)

	No.
Illinois	62
Minnesota	16
Wisconsin	7
Indiana	5
Ohio	2
Alabama	1
Florida	1
Nebraska	1
North Carolina	1
Total	**96**

PRODUCTS/OPERATIONS

2015 Sales

	$ mil.	% of total
Rents	135	66
Tenant recoveries	57	28
Other property income	5	3
Fee income from unconsolidated joint ventures	5	3
Total	**203**	**100**

COMPETITORS

Brixmor	Noddle Development
CBL & Associates Properties	Pennsylvania Real Estate
Canal Capital	Ramco-Gershenson
DDR	Realty Income
Federal Realty Investment	Retail Properties of America
Horizon Group Properties	Rubloff Development Schottenstein
Kimco Realty	Taubman Centers
Macerich	Weingarten Realty

HISTORICAL FINANCIALS

Company Type: Private

Income Statement   FYE: December 31

	ASSETS ($ mil.)	NET INCOME ($ mil.)	INCOME AS % OF ASSETS	EMPLOYEES
12/15	1,521	25	1.7%	129
12/14	1,572	39	2.5%	—
12/13	1,529	111	7.3%	—
12/12	1,243	17	1.4%	—
Annual Growth	**7.0%**	**13.0%**		

2015 Year-End Financials

Return on assets: 31.2%   Sales ($ mil.): 203
Return on equity: 12.5%

IRVINE UNIFIED SCHOOL DISTICT

EXECUTIVES

Superintendent, Terry Walker
Ceo, Michael B Regele
Teacher, Michael Gerakos
Assistant, Robert Valdez
Internal Medicine Practitioner, Justin LI
Administrative Assistant, Nancy Albers
Auditors: VAVRINEK TRINE DAY & CO LL

LOCATIONS

HQ: IRVINE UNIFIED SCHOOL DISTICT
5050 BARRANCA PKWY, IRVINE, CA 926044698
Phone: 949 936-5000
Web: WWW.IUSD.ORG

HISTORICAL FINANCIALS

Company Type: Private

Income Statement   FYE: June 30

	REVENUE ($ mil.)	NET INCOME ($ mil.)	NET PROFIT MARGIN	EMPLOYEES
06/17	380	138	36.5%	2,212
06/16	360	(61)	—	—
06/09	278	19	7.0%	—
06/08	260	(30)	—	—
Annual Growth	**4.3%**	—	—	—

IRVING INDEPENDENT SCHOOL DISTRICT INC

EXECUTIVES

Upt, Jose L Parra
President, Larry Stipes
Vice President, Randy Randal
Cfo, Gary Micinski
Dir of Purchasing, Jerome Pilgrim
Teacher, Irene Van Alstine
Staff, Marisela Arredondo
Teacher, Brian Riley
Staff, Rachael Bauman
Coordinator, Matt Macveigh
Director of Information Techno, John Mynatt
Auditors: WEAVER AND TIDWELL LLP DALLA

LOCATIONS

HQ: IRVING INDEPENDENT SCHOOL DISTRICT INC
2621 W AIRPORT FWY, IRVING, TX 750626020
Phone: 972 600-5000
Web: WWW.IRVINGISD.NET

HISTORICAL FINANCIALS

Company Type: Private

Income Statement   FYE: August 31

	REVENUE ($ mil.)	NET INCOME ($ mil.)	NET PROFIT MARGIN	EMPLOYEES
08/17	417	9	2.2%	3,934
08/16	395	(17)	—	—
08/10	340	(8)	—	—
08/09	317	20	6.4%	—
Annual Growth	**3.5%**	**(9.6%)**	—	—

2017 Year-End Financials

Return on assets: 1.8%   Cash ($ mil.): 133
Return on equity: 2.2%
Current ratio: —

ISEC, INCORPORATED

EXECUTIVES

Pres, Dusty Morgan
Vp, Joan Norblom
Vp, Mike Polanchyck
Sr Vp, Tim McCoy
Sr Vp, Michael Polanchyck
Sr Vp, Brent Paden
Sr Vp, Greg Timmerman
Vp, David Herzel
Contrl, Mark Lane
Cfo, Charlie Dietrich
Vp, Branden Derks
Auditors: MARTIN VEJVODA AND ASSOCIATES

LOCATIONS

HQ: ISEC, INCORPORATED
6000 GREENWOOD PLAZA BLVD # 200, GREENWOOD VILLAGE, CO 801114818
Phone: 410 381-6049
Web: WWW.ISECINC.COM

HISTORICAL FINANCIALS

Company Type: Private

Income Statement   FYE: June 30

	REVENUE ($ mil.)	NET INCOME ($ mil.)	NET PROFIT MARGIN	EMPLOYEES
06/16	295	3	1.2%	1,150
06/15	235	1	0.7%	—
06/14	248	2	1.2%	—
06/11	252	2	0.9%	—
Annual Growth	**3.2%**	**9.7%**	—	—

2016 Year-End Financials

Return on assets: 8.7%   Cash ($ mil.): 8
Return on equity: 1.2%
Current ratio: 1.00

ISSAQUAH SCHOOL DISTRICT 411

EXECUTIVES

Supt, Ron Thiele
Cfo, Jacob Kuper
Coordinator, Debbie Romano
Administrator, Mary Parnell
Manager, Robert Miller
Secretary, Barbara Hell
Technical Staff, Foster Dan
Education Specialist, Klopfenstine Terri
Director, Longman Doug
Personnel Specialist, Scammon Carleena
Teacher, Dunn Kathy

LOCATIONS

HQ: ISSAQUAH SCHOOL DISTRICT 411
565 NW HOLLY ST, ISSAQUAH, WA 980272899
Phone: 425 837-7000
Web: WWW.ISSAQUAH.WEDNET.EDU

HISTORICAL FINANCIALS
Company Type: Private

Income Statement				FYE: August 31
	REVENUE ($ mil.)	NET INCOME ($ mil.)	NET PROFIT MARGIN	EMPLOYEES
08/17	289	64	22.1%	1,700
08/16	270	86	32.2%	—
08/15	246	9	3.8%	—
08/14	284	22	7.9%	—
Annual Growth	0.6%	42.0%	—	—

2017 Year-End Financials

Return on assets: 5.3%
Return on equity: 22.1%
Current ratio: —
Cash ($ mil.): 329

IVIE & ASSOCIATES, LLC

EXECUTIVES

Pres, Warren Ivie
Treas, Sharon Renee Rawlings
Vice-President Business Develo, Brandon Ivie
V Pres-Fin, Gary Long
Creative Director, Anthony Woolridge
Vice-President, David Bailey
Analyst, John Ackley
Vice-President, Osye Pritchett
Director of Operations, Sandra Ogden
Coordinator, Julie Pritchett
Account Manager, Ty Hernandez

LOCATIONS

HQ: IVIE & ASSOCIATES, LLC
601 SILVERON STE 200, FLOWER MOUND, TX
750284030
Phone: 972 899-5000
Web: WWW.IVIEINC.COM

HISTORICAL FINANCIALS
Company Type: Private

Income Statement				FYE: December 31
	REVENUE ($ mil.)	NET INCOME ($ mil.)	NET PROFIT MARGIN	EMPLOYEES
12/17	297	0	—	242
12/15	259	0	—	—
12/14	216	0	—	—
12/13	781	0	—	—
Annual Growth	(21.5%)	—	—	—

2017 Year-End Financials

Return on assets: 4.4%
Return on equity: —
Current ratio: 1.00
Cash ($ mil.): 5

J M SMITH CORPORATION

J M Smith Corporation has gone from corner drugstore to supplying drugstores and more. The family-owned holding company's primary subsidiary is Smith Drug which provides purchasing and distribution services for more than 1000 independent pharmacies in more than 20 US states. It also operates through QS/1 Data Systems and Integral Solutions both of which offer data management software and services for pharmacies care providers and government agencies. Smith Premier provides prescription benefit management while other divisions offer automated dispensing systems for pharmacies and marketing services for drugmakers. Other units include Norgenix and RxMedic Systems.

Operations

The company operates through six business units: Smith Drug Company QS/1 Smith Premier Services Integral Solutions Group Norgenix and RxMedic Systems.

In addition to being its oldest subsidiary J M Smith's core Smith Drug unit is one of the top private wholesale drug distributors in the US. The company's Smith Premier unit also has a nationwide presence providing prescription management services through some 57000 contracted pharmacies.

Meanwhile the growing QS/1 division has installed more than 12000 health care and pharmacy automation systems and has more than 20 service offices across the US. The Integral Solutions unit which has about 15 offices scattered across the nation offers communication networking systems for universities banks and manufacturers in addition to health care customers.

J M Smith newest subsidiary Norgenix is a specialty pharmaceutical medical device and biotech company that engages in the development commercialization and sales of pharmaceutical products that serve the unmet needs within women's health. It acquires or licenses rights for select pharmaceuticals which it then markets through its direct sales force in North America. Norgenix is focused on the women's health markets and began marketing its first hormone replacement therapy in 2009.

RxMedic Systems provides leading-edge dispensing technology to pharmacies.

Geographic Reach

Smith Drug serves customers in 21 states primarily in the southern US as well as Washington DC and the Virgin Islands.

Sales and Marketing

The company supplies products services and technologies to pharmacies institutions local government agencies and businesses across the US.

Strategy

J M Smith's cornerstone Smith Drug subsidiary continues to be a key growth component doubling the number of states in which it operates over the last decade. However the company is also extolling its energies towards developing and introducing innovative data management and technology solutions through other subsidiaries to meet the rising demand for such solutions in the health care market.

Smith Premier is working to help customers go paperless by offering electronic prescription processing while RxMedic's dispensing systems allow pharmacies to increase productivity with its robotic counting and dispensing equipment.

The company's QS/1 subsidiary has experienced rapid growth in recent years as pharmacies and care providers increasingly look to automate processes and the Integral Solutions unit also benefits from recent trends in the health care market to improve electronic communication systems.

Partnerships are also key to J M Smith's growth. In 2014 Norgenix partnered with CrossBay Medical for the co-promotion of the SonoSure a device for use to access the uterine cavity for saline infusion sonohysterography and to obtain an endometrial biopsy if needed using the same device.

Mergers and Acquisitions

In late 2016 the company agreed to buy Vermont-based Burlington Drug Company which serves community pharmacies in New England and New York as well as certain assets of Pharmacy Health Services. The moves will broaden J M Smith's presence in the Northeast a target market for the company.

Company Background

In 2010 Smith expanded by acquiring health equipment manufacturing firm RxMedic. Through the purchase the company entered the automated dispensing system market.

J M Smith was founded in 1943 by drugstore proprietor James Smith and is run by the Smith family.

EXECUTIVES

President Integral Solutions Group (isg), Joe Strayer
President Smith Drug Company, Jeff Foreman
President Integra Ltc Solutions Llc, Kevin Welch
Chairman And Ceo, A. Alan Turfe
President Qs/1, Saul Factor
Cfo And Treasurer, Philip J. Ryan
Senior Vice President Business Development, Rick Simerly

LOCATIONS

HQ: J M SMITH CORPORATION
101 W SAINT JOHN ST # 305, SPARTANBURG, SC
293065150
Phone: 864 542-9419
Web: WWW.JMSMITH.COM

Selected Office Locations
Altamonte Springs FL
Brandon MS
Columbia SC
Dallas TX
Fairmont WV
Gray ME
Hermitage PA
Houston TX
Indianapolis IN
Lexington KY
Mechanicsburg PA

Miami FL
Morrisville GA
Paragould AR
Perry GA
Pleasant Hill MO
Richmond VA
Seattle WA
Spartanburg SC
St. Paul MN
Sturbridge MA
Valdosta GA
Valencia CA
Wake Forest NC

PRODUCTS/OPERATIONS

Selected Divisions
Integral Solutions Group
Norgenix Pharmaceuticals
QS/1
RxMedic
Smith Drug Company
Smith Premier Services

COMPETITORS

AmerisourceBergen	HP Enterprise Services
CVS	Kinray
Cardinal Health	McKesson
Express Scripts	PharMerica
Fiserv	
H. D. Smith Wholesale	
Drug	

HISTORICAL FINANCIALS
Company Type: Private

Income Statement   FYE: February 28

	REVENUE ($ mil.)	NET INCOME ($ mil.)	NET PROFIT MARGIN	EMPLOYEES
02/15	2,566	47	1.8%	235
02/14	2,370	38	1.6%	—
02/13	2,362	26	1.1%	—
Annual Growth	4.2%	33.8%	—	—

2015 Year-End Financials
Return on assets: 8.9%   Cash ($ mil.): 142
Return on equity: 1.8%
Current ratio: 1.20

J.E. DUNN CONSTRUCTION COMPANY

From first building designs to the last brick J.E. Dunn Construction helps make building plans a done deal. The contractor offers general construction services construction management and design/build services nationwide. It's known for its work on campus health care and commercial projects including the Mizzou Arena at the University of Missouri the H&R Block headquarters the Topfer Theatre at ZACH and the National Nuclear Security Administration campus. Founded in 1924 the company is one of Kansas City's top commercial construction firms and has been listed as one of the nation's top 10 general building companies. It operates as a subsidiary of J.E. Dunn Construction Group.

Operations
JE Dunn has ranked as one of the top 15 largest general building companies in the US in recent years. It counts several noteworthy projects among its portfolio such as CyrusOne Phoenix Data Center Tucson Medical Center West Campus CCA La Palma Correctional Center Lone Butte Casino Oasis Hospital Mountain Vista Medical Center and West Valley Medical Center Hospital.

Geographic Reach
Based in Kansas City Missouri JE Dunn operates about 20 offices throughout the US.

Sales and Marketing
JE Dunn works on projects for clients in several sectors including projects related to: science and technology corporate environments healthcare hospitality government and military energy and utility education and multifamily residential properties among others.

Financial Performance
While full financial information of the privately-held company were not available the company reported that it brings in annual revenue of $2.7 billion as of early 2015.

Strategy
J.E. Dunn Construction Company has been busy working on a variety of different projects in recent years. As of early 2015 JE Dunn's project portfolio included: the Health Care Patient Tower at the University of Missouri the Jennie Smoly Caruthers Biotechnology Building at the University of Colorado at Boulder the National Renewable Energy Laboratory (NREL) Energy System Integration Facility (Phase I) the Outpatient Cancer Center and parking garage for the Georgia Regents Health System and the new headquarters for the school-improvement group AdvancED. In 2013 JE Dunn completed a $300-million-plus renovation of the Kansas Capitol Building which involved renovating underground areas previously occupied by storage and maintenance areas into new space with improved ventilation technology and security.

JE Dunn is also adding offices to position itself near new target growth areas. To this end in early 2013 it opened an office in Williston North Dakota.

Company Background
In the past JE Dunn grew through acquisitions purchasing RJ Griffin & Co. (Atlanta) in 2000 Witcher Construction (Minneapolis) in 1990 and Drake Construction (Portland Oregon) in 1992.

EXECUTIVES

Evp And Cfo, Gordon E. Lansford
Midwest Regional President, Dirk Schafer
Evp And Chief Risk Officer, Casey S. Halsey
Evp And Chief Legal Officer, Thomas F. (Tom) Whittaker
President Je Dunn Rocky Mountain, Steve Hamline
East Regional President, Dan Kaufman
Cio, John Jacobs
South Central Regional President, Greg Lorei
Cfo, Beth Soukup
Evp And Chief Marketing Officer, Greg Nook
Vice President Of Preconstruction For The Southwest Division, Curt Campbell
Senior Vice President, Tom Raney
Dbia Vice President, Ryan Price
Vice President, Mike Cloud
Vice President, Andy McGarrity
Senior Vice President, Bill Edwards
Senior Vice President, Randall Bredar
Vice President Of Audit, John Conley
Vice President Group Manager, Dustin Liljehorn
Vice President Preconstruction, Justin Griffin
Vice President, John Johnston
Vp Operations, Marc Hutson
Vice President Marketing, Diane Miller
Vice President, Chris Cole
Vice President, Chris Sorenson
Vice President, Eric Peterson
Vice President Healthcare, Bill Igel
Vice President, Donnie Lindstrom
Senior Vice President, Paul Neidlein

Vice President, Jim Ray
Vice President, Scott Sharp
Vice President Industrial Group, Brent Strength
Senior Vice President Dallas Office Leader, Chris Peck
Vice President, Angela Talbot
Vice President Of Education And Aviation Group Manager, Paul Fenzl
Vice President, Patrick Oaks
Vice President, Todd Freed
Vice President Division Manager, Paul Fenzel
Vice President, Dave Perez
Senior Vice President Business Development, Thomas Raney
Vice President Project Executive, Michael Blakemore
Vice President Preconstruction, Monty Everson
Vice President, Inna Tassada
Vice President Business Development, Keith Knight
Vice President Of Business Development And Small Business Programs, Jose Amaya
Vice Chair, William H Dunn
Chairman, Steve Dunn
Auditors: KPMG LLP KANSAS CITY MISSOU

LOCATIONS

HQ: J.E. DUNN CONSTRUCTION COMPANY
   1001 LOCUST ST, KANSAS CITY, MO 641061904
Phone: 816 474-8600
Web: WWW.JEDUNN.COM

PRODUCTS/OPERATIONS

Selected Project Delivery Methods
Competitive Bid
Construction Management (Agency)
Design-Build
General Contracting/CM At Risk
Integrated Project Delivery
Project Management

COMPETITORS

Adolfson & Peterson Inc.	H.J. Russell Hensel Phelps
Barnhart	Construction
Boran Craig Barber Engel	Korte M. A. Mortenson
C.F. Jordan	MEDCO Construction
CORE Construction	Skanska USA Building
Clarkson Construction	Turner Corporation
Flintco	Weitz

HISTORICAL FINANCIALS
Company Type: Private

Income Statement   FYE: December 31

	REVENUE ($ mil.)	NET INCOME ($ mil.)	NET PROFIT MARGIN	EMPLOYEES
12/17	2,945	0	—	1,635
12/16	2,909	0	—	—
12/15	2,909	0	—	—
12/14	2,242	0	—	—
Annual Growth	9.5%	—	—	—

2017 Year-End Financials
Return on assets: 13.4%   Cash ($ mil.): 29
Return on equity: —
Current ratio: 0.50

J.E. DUNN CONSTRUCTION GROUP, INC.

Owned by descendants of founder John Ernest Dunn J.E. Dunn Construction Group operates as the holding company for a group of construction firms that includes flagship J.E. Dunn Construction and Atlanta-based R.J. Griffin & Company. Founded in 1924 it builds institutional commercial and industrial structures nationwide. It also provides construction and program management and design/build services. J.E. Dunn Construction which is among the largest US general builders was one of the first contractors to offer the construction management delivery method. Some of its major projects have included an IRS facility and the world headquarters for H&R Block both located in Kansas City Missouri.

Operations

Besides its primary operations of J.E. Dunn Construction and R.J. Griffin & Company the construction company runs Dunn Project Solutions a construction services unit that tackles projects ranging in size from $50000 to $5 million. The business focuses on projects related to corporate interiors retail improvements historic rehabilitation additions fixtures and equipment building upgrades maintenance work and small office projects.

The company's ranked as the 10th largest general building company in the US in 2015.

Geographic Reach

Headquartered in Kansas City Missouri J.E. Dunn operates some 20 offices across the nation. It has offices in Georgia Texas North Carolina Colorado Iowa Missouri Minnesota Tennessee Oklahoma Nebraska Arizona Oregon Kansas and North Dakota.

Sales and Marketing

The company works on corporate environments mission critical correctional/justice and mixed use/retail projects among others.

Financial Performance

J.E. Dunn Construction last reported annual revenues of more than $2.6 billion in 2014.

Strategy

Some of the group's more recent projects projects include work on the North Dakota governor's residence and the new Bank of North Dakota Financial Center in Bismark (2016); the Harold Newman Arena in Jamestown (2016); the Trinity High School reconstruction and expansion project (2016); the building of the 378000 sq. ft. Cambridge North Tower at The University of Kansas Hospital (September 2017); the 92000 sq. ft. entertainment of the arts at the University of Colorado; the 151000 sq. ft. expansion project on an inpatient pavilion at the UCHealth University of Colorado Hospital (May 2015); the 92000 sq. ft. Fallen Fire Fighter Memorial in Colorado Springs (June 2015); and the 160000 sq. ft. CHI St. Joseph's Hospital and Health Center (October 2014).

Past projects include work on the Charles R. Drew Charter School Senior Academy the Kauffman Center for the Performing Arts the Topfer Theatre at ZACH the Energy Systems Integration Facility (ESIF) the Collaborative Life Sciences Building & Skourtes Tower and the Georgia Regents Health System Outpatient Cancer. Other past projects have included Baylor Scott & White Cancer Center Hotel Sorella GSA National Nuclear Security Administration City of Houston Bethel Park Renovation and the B.E. Smith Corporate Headquarters Renovation.

Company Background

A bigwig particularly in the Midwest the group regularly bids on federal government projects. J.E. Dunn won a major contract from the US Army Corps of Engineers to build a regional correctional facility at Fort Leavenworth Kansas that replaced smaller prisons in Texas Kentucky and Oklahoma.

In 2012 the company earned the designation of having the first ever LEED Gold Certified building in downtown Kansas City.

The descendants of John Ernest Dunn hold a majority stake in the company.

EXECUTIVES

Evp And Cfo, Gordon E. Lansford
President Midwest Region, Dirk Schafer
Evp, William H. (Bill) Dunn
Evp General Counsel And Secretary, Casey S. Halsey
President West Region, Steve Hamline
Evp Marketing, Gregory E. (Greg) Nook
President East Region, Dan Kaufman
Evp And Chief Legal Officer, Tom Whittaker
Cio, John Jacobs
President South Central, Greg Lorei
Cfo, Beth Soukup
Senior Vice President, Tom Raney
Chairman, Stephen D. (Steve) Dunn
Auditors: KPMG LLP KANSAS CITY MISSOUR

LOCATIONS

HQ: J.E. DUNN CONSTRUCTION GROUP, INC.
1001 LOCUST ST, KANSAS CITY, MO 641061904
Phone: 816 474-8600
Web: WWW.JEDUNN.COM

PRODUCTS/OPERATIONS

Selected Group Companies
JE Dunn Midwest
JE Dunn North Central
JE Dunn Northwest
JE Dunn Rocky Mountain
JE Dunn South Central
R.J. Griffin & Company

Selected Services
Preconstruction
  Constructability review
  Feasibility studies
  Market analysis
  Mechanical electrical plumbing review
  Preconstruction estimating
  Quality control
  Risk management
  Scheduling
Construction
  Change order management
  Labor relations
  Progress monitoring
  Quality control and testing
Post Construction
  Commissioning
  Final closeout
  Lien releases
  One-year walkthrough
  Operations and maintenance manuals

COMPETITORS

Alberici	Skanska USA Building
Clark Enterprises	Sundt
Hensel Phelps	Turner Corporation
Construction	Tutor Perini
Hunt Construction	Weitz
McCarthy Building	Whiting-Turner

HISTORICAL FINANCIALS
Company Type: Private

Income Statement   FYE: December 31

	REVENUE ($ mil.)	NET INCOME ($ mil.)	NET PROFIT MARGIN	EMPLOYEES
12/17	2,947	0	—	2,080
12/15	2,910	0	—	—
12/14	2,243	0	—	—
12/13	2,243	0	—	—
Annual Growth	7.1%	—	—	—

JACKSON COUNTY SCHNECK MEMORIAL HOSPITAL

EXECUTIVES

Mha, Ceo-Pres, Gary A Meyer
Cfo, Warren Forgey
Director, Peggy Findley
Chief of Obstetrics/Gynecology, Eric Fish
Director, Holly Wischmeier
Customer Representativ, Kathy Nelson
Accounting Director, Debbie Ridlen
Information Technology Manager, Charlene Mellencamp
Supervisor, George Weir
Manager, Tyler Wessel
Director, Vicky Gilbert

LOCATIONS

HQ: JACKSON COUNTY SCHNECK MEMORIAL HOSPITAL
411 W TIPTON ST, SEYMOUR, IN 472742363
Phone: 812 522-2349
Web: WWW.SCHNECKMEDICAL.ORG

HISTORICAL FINANCIALS
Company Type: Private

Income Statement   FYE: December 31

	REVENUE ($ mil.)	NET INCOME ($ mil.)	NET PROFIT MARGIN	EMPLOYEES
12/17	286	32	11.3%	700
12/15	132	17	13.2%	—
12/14	114	(12)	—	—
12/13	0	0	70.9%	—
Annual Growth	313.3%	161.2%	—	—

2017 Year-End Financials
Return on assets: 7.1%   Cash ($ mil.): 76
Return on equity: 11.3%
Current ratio: 3.10

JACKSON ELECTRIC MEMBERSHIP CORPORATION

Jackson EMC distributes electricity to more than 197800 individual customers (more than 210200 meters) in 10 counties around Atlanta and in northeastern Georgia. The majority of customers are residential with commercial and industrial customers accounting for 42% of fiscal year 2013 revenues. One of the largest nonprofit power cooperatives in the US and the largest electric cooperative in Georgia Jackson EMC is owned by its members. The cooperative's generation and transmission partners include Oglethorpe Power Corp. Georgia Systems Operation and Georgia Transmission Corp.

Operations
Jackson EMC operates 86 substations and more than 13550 miles of power line.

Financial Performance
In fiscal 2013 the coop reported a revenue increased of 1%. Net income declined slightly by 0.3%. That year the non-profit coop returned $5.5 million in margin refunds to nearly 201000 members.

Strategy
Among other initiatives Jackson EMC is promoting conservation and green energy options as a way to slow energy growth and reduce greenhouse gas emissions. Initiatives include advocating the use of more efficient light bulbs and the widespread use of solar panels for power generation.

Company Background
Although the county of Jackson is named after a Georgia statesman from the Revolutionary War era Jackson Electric Membership Corporation (Jackson EMC) can trace its roots more directly to US president Franklin Roosevelt whose frequent trips to Warm Springs alerted him to the shortage of affordable electric power outside of major cities. Jackson EMC was founded in 1938 as part of the Roosevelt government's national rural electrification drive.

EXECUTIVES

Ceo, Randall Pugh
Cfo, Greg Keith
Coo, Roy Stowe
Executive Officer, Douglas Smith
Auditors: MCNAIR MCLEMORE MIDDLEBROOKS &

LOCATIONS

HQ: JACKSON ELECTRIC MEMBERSHIP CORPORATION
850 COMMERCE RD, JEFFERSON, GA 305493329
Phone: 706 367-5281
Web: WWW.JACKSONEMC.COM

HISTORICAL FINANCIALS
Company Type: Private

Income Statement				FYE: May 31
	REVENUE ($ mil.)	NET INCOME ($ mil.)	NET PROFIT MARGIN	EMPLOYEES
05/17*	518	28	5.5%	445
12/15	541	0	—	—
12/14	527	0	—	—
12/13	472	0	—	—
Annual Growth	3.2%	—	—	—

*Fiscal year change

JACKSON HEALTHCARE, LLC

Jackson Healthcare can help find physicians to work at hospitals and help keep track of patients as they enter and leave hospitals. Its staffing businesses offer job search recruiting and placement services for physicians and other health care professionals; provide anesthesiologists; and coordinate the work of traveling nurses. Jackson Healthcare's physician job boards attract thousands of visitors per month giving it a reputation for filling openings quickly. Subsidiary Patient Placement Systems manages patient flow through the medical system and Care Logistics provides patient tracking software. Richard Jackson formed the company in 1978.

Operations
Jackson Healthcare operates more than a dozen subsidiaries and operations units and serves more than 7 million patients spread throughout 1300 health care facilities.

Subsidiaries and divisions include Premier Anesthesia Jackson Therapy Partners LucumTenens.com Jackson Nurse Professionals and Jackson & Coker. Other operations include AdvancedPractice.com Jackson Surgical Assistants Jackson Pharmacy Professionals Tyler & Company and Parker HealthcareIT.

Its health care software and technology portfolio is managed by Care Logistics and Patient Placement Systems.

Mergers and Acquisitions
Jackson Healthcare's growth strategy involves acquiring other staffing businesses to augment its geographical reach. In 2014 it purchased Sullivan Healthcare Consulting (SHC) a Michigan-based firm focused on improving the performance of the hospital's perioperative suite.

EXECUTIVES

Managing Director Jackson Healthcare, Paul D. Foster
Ceo Jackson Therapy Partners And President Jackson Nurse Professionals, Scott L'Heureux
Chairman And Ceo, Richard L. Jackson
President Jackson Healthcare And Locumtenens.com, R. Shane Jackson
Evp Human Resources, Michael Hiffa
Cto, Tim Aligheri
Cfo, Douglas B. Kline
President Care Logistics, Karl Straub
President Premier Anesthesia, Kerry Teel
President Advancedpractice.com, Susan Mesa
President Jackson & Coker Permanent Placement, Tony Stajduhar
President And Ceo Parker Health Care It, Debbie Crandall
President Healthit Project Managers, Jack Williams
Vp And General Manager Healthcare Staffing Technologies, Karyn Mullins
Vp Advancedpractice.com And Jackson Pharmacy Professionals, David McAnally
Vp And General Manager Patient Placement Systems, Doug Walker
Cio, Ryan Esparza
Vice Chairman, William H. Franklin

LOCATIONS

HQ: JACKSON HEALTHCARE, LLC
2655 NORTHWINDS PKWY, ALPHARETTA, GA 300092280
Phone: 770 643-5500
Web: WWW.JACKSONHEALTHCARE.COM

PRODUCTS/OPERATIONS

Selected Subsidiaries and Operating Units
Jackson Healthcare Staffing
 AdvancedPractice.com (a full-service locum tenens agency dedicated to physician assistants and nurse practitioners)
 Healthcare Staffing Technologies (provider of career concierge sites in the healthcare market)
 HealthIT Project Managers (provider of experienced IT project management contractors to hospitals)
 Jackson & Coker (locum tenens and permanent recruitment firm for physicians)
 Jackson Nurse Professionals (specializes in the placement of registered nurses in healthcare settings nationwide)
 Jackson Pharmacy Professionals (national pharmacy-only staffing and recruiting company)
 Jackson Surgical Assistants (staffing of certified surgical assistants to surgeons and hospitals)
 Jackson Therapy Partners (staffing of rehabilitation therapists and other allied healthcare professionals)
 LocumTenens.com (locum tenens physician recruitment agency)
 Parker HealthcareIT (provider of supplemental IT staffing)
 Premier Anesthesia (anesthesia department management company)
Jackson Healthcare Technology
 Care Logistics (firm that helps hospitals transform their operations to deliver hospital efficiency)
 Patient Placement Systems (supplier of continuing care provider software)

COMPETITORS

AMN Healthcare	Gentiva
ATC Healthcare	Kelly Services
Adecco	ManpowerGroup
CHG Healthcare	On Assignment
CompHealth	RehabCare
Cross Country Healthcare	TeamStaff
	inVentiv Health

HISTORICAL FINANCIALS
Company Type: Private

Income Statement				FYE: December 31
	REVENUE ($ mil.)	NET INCOME ($ mil.)	NET PROFIT MARGIN	EMPLOYEES
12/17	949	99	10.5%	949
12/16	838	93	11.1%	—
12/15	696	70	10.2%	—
Annual Growth	16.7%	18.4%	—	—

2017 Year-End Financials
Return on assets: 3.2%   Cash ($ mil.): 65
Return on equity: 10.5%
Current ratio: 4.00

2017 Year-End Financials
Return on assets: 6.6%   Cash ($ mil.): 13
Return on equity: 5.5%
Current ratio: 0.40

JACKSON-MADISON COUNTY GENERAL HOSPITAL DISTRICT

EXECUTIVES

Pres-Ceo, James Ross
Chm, Phil Bryant
Cfo, Jeffrey Blankenship

Chief Staff, Richard Wagner
Coordinator, Trisha Ross
Executive Director, Bart Teague
Materials Director, Tom Fendley
Director, Mary Bryant
Director, Carolyn Hill
Doctor, Christopher Mitchell
Manager, Shana Taylor

LOCATIONS

HQ: JACKSON-MADISON COUNTY GENERAL
HOSPITAL DISTRICT
620 SKYLINE DR, JACKSON, TN 383013923
Phone: 731 541-5000
Web: WWW.WTH.ORG

HISTORICAL FINANCIALS

Company Type: Private

Income Statement   FYE: June 30

	REVENUE ($ mil.)	NET INCOME ($ mil.)	NET PROFIT MARGIN	EMPLOYEES
06/16	597	10	1.8%	6,000
06/15	554	20	3.7%	—
06/04	429	37	8.6%	—
06/03	307	247	80.4%	—
Annual Growth	5.3%	(21.4%)	—	—

2016 Year-End Financials

Return on assets: 3.1%   Cash ($ mil.): 20
Return on equity: 1.8%
Current ratio: 2.90

JACO OIL COMPANY

Jaco Oil Company is jockeying for its piece of the convenience store pie. The company's Fastrip Food Stores subsidiary operates more than 50 convenience stores and gas stations primarily in and around Bakersfield California but also in Arizona. Besides offering customers traditional convenience-store fare which includes coffee milk beer snacks tobacco and the like the Fastrip chain stocks a full range of grocery items and provides in-store financial service centers. Financial services include check cashing payday loans wire transfer services via The Western Union Company refund anticipation loans and other services at many locations. Jaco Oil Company was founded in 1970.

Operations

The company operates nearly 50 stores in Bakersfield and Kern counties as well as in Fresno Sacramento and the Chico area. It also has four stores in Arizona located in Bullhead Casa Grande and Nogales. As part of its business Jaco Oil offers food beverages and financial services such as payday loans wire transfer services and tax preparation services.

Geographic Reach

Jaco Oil owns and operates gasoline service stations and convenience stores in the Western US.

Strategy

Fastrip works to distinguish itself from other convenience store chains by stocking a complete assortment of grocery items including such staples as sugar flour salt cake mix and even green beans. The chain bills itself as a Mini Grocery Store a strategy that other retailers including Dollar General and drugstore-giant Walgreen have adopted. It's also always open (24/7/365).

EXECUTIVES

Ceo, T J Jamieson
Vice President, Charles Mc Can
SEC-Treas, Lee Jamieson

Cfo, Brian Busacca
Controller, Cynthia Salazar
Area Supervisor, Ron Jonas
Marketing Staff, Brittney Guiniling
Human Resources Director, Dan Sproat
Auditors: MOSS ADAMS LLP LOS ANGELES C

LOCATIONS

HQ: JACO OIL COMPANY
3101 STATE RD, BAKERSFIELD, CA 933084931
Phone: 661 393-7000
Web: WWW.JACO.COM

2013 Stores

	No.
California	49
Arizona	4
Total	**53**

PRODUCTS/OPERATIONS

Selected Services
Check cashing
EBT
Ice
Liquor
Lottery
Money orders
Money transfers
Phone cards
Quick serve restaurant
Restrooms
WIC

Selected Products
Alcoholic beverages
Beverages
Coffee
Dairy
Food
Fountain drinks
Groceries
Snacks
Tobacco products

COMPETITORS

7-Eleven	Ralphs Grocery
Chevron	Stater Bros.
Couche-Tard	Vons
Dollar General	Walgreen
Exxon Mobil	

HISTORICAL FINANCIALS

Company Type: Private

Income Statement   FYE: December 31

	REVENUE ($ mil.)	NET INCOME ($ mil.)	NET PROFIT MARGIN	EMPLOYEES
12/17	506	13	2.7%	350
12/16	429	17	4.0%	—
12/15	442	17	3.9%	—
12/14	542	14	2.7%	—
Annual Growth	(2.2%)	(2.2%)	—	—

2017 Year-End Financials

Return on assets: 3.5%   Cash ($ mil.): 62
Return on equity: 2.7%
Current ratio: 2.10

JARDEN CORPORATION

EXECUTIVES

Ceo, Michael B Polk
Information Specialist, Gragg Miller
Auditors: PRICEWATERHOUSECOOPERS LLP NE

LOCATIONS

HQ: JARDEN CORPORATION
221 RIVER ST, HOBOKEN, NJ 070305989
Phone: 201 610-6600
Web: WWW.JARDENCS.COM

COMPETITORS

AZZ	Johnson Outdoors
Academy Sports	Kaz
Amazon.com	Kellwood
Amer Sports	Lasko Products
Andis	Lifetime Brands
BWAY	Lowe's
Bass Pro Shops	MEGA Brands
Bauer Hockey	Mattel
Bed Bath & Beyond	Mayborn Group
Burton	Mizuno
Cabela's	NACCO Industries
CalCedar	NIKE
Canadian Tire	New Balance
Carrefour	Newell Rubbermaid
Church & Dwight	Owens-Illinois
Conair Consumer	Patch Products
Products	Philips Avent
Costco Wholesale	Procter & Gamble
Crayola	Quiksilver
Daiwa	REI
De'Longhi	Richco
Deswell	Rollerblade
Dick's Sporting Goods	Rossignol
EBSCO	Russell Hobbs
Easton-Bell Sports	SEB
Elmer's Products	Sealy
Energizer Holdings	Simmons
Evenflo	Spectrum Brands
Female Health	Suncast
Gaming Partners	Target Corporation
International	Tecnica
Gerber Products	Tegrant
Habasit America	UTC Climate Controls
Hamilton Beach	& Security
Hanesbrands	Universal Security
Head N.V.	Instruments
Hillerich &	VF Corporation
Bradsby	W.C. Bradley Co.
HoMedics	Wahl Clipper
Home Depot	West Pharmaceutical
Honeywell ACS	Services
Igloo Products	Whirlpool
Intex DIY	Worthington Industries
Invensys	adidas
Johnson & Johnson	

HISTORICAL FINANCIALS

Company Type: Private

Income Statement   FYE: December 31

	REVENUE ($ mil.)	NET INCOME ($ mil.)	NET PROFIT MARGIN	EMPLOYEES
12/15	8,603	146	1.7%	17,000
12/14	8,287	242	2.9%	—
12/13	7,355	203	2.8%	—
12/12	6,696	243	3.6%	—
Annual Growth	8.7%	(15.6%)	—	—

2015 Year-End Financials

Return on assets: 9.5%   Cash ($ mil.): 1,298
Return on equity: 1.7%
Current ratio: 1.10

JEA

As long as sparks are flying in Jacksonville everything is A-OK with JEA. The community-owned not-for-profit utility provides electricity to 438000 customers in Jacksonville and surrounding areas in northeastern Florida. Managing an electric system that dates back to 1895 JEA has a net generating capacity of 3747 MW. It owns an electric system with five primarily fossil-fueled generating plants. JEA also gets 12.8 MW of generating capacity from two methane-fueled landfill plants. The company resells electricity to other utilities including NextEra Energy. JEA also provides water and wastewater services; it serves 321600 water customers and 247500 wastewater customers.

Operations

JEA is the largest community-owned utility in Florida and the eighth largest in the US.

The company operates in four segments: the Electric System and Bulk Power Supply System; the St. Johns River Power Park System System; the Water and Sewer System; and the District Energy System.

The Electric System operates five generating plants in Florida (and holds a stake in a power plant in Georgia) and all transmission and distribution facilities including more than 745 miles of transmission lines and more than 6500 miles of distribution lines. It purchases power locally from a solar field and a landfill gas facility. This segment accounted for 77% of the company's 2014 revenues.

JEA's Water System consists of 134 artesian wells that tap into the Floridan aquifer. Water is distributed through 37 water treatment plants and more than 4300 miles of water lines. Wastewater is collected through more than 3800 miles of wastewater collection lines and treated at seven regional treatment plants.

The company's operations are funded by three enterprise funds: the Electric Enterprise Fund the Water and Sewer Fund and the District Energy System The Electric Enterprise Fund is comprised of the JEA Electric System Bulk Power Supply System and St. Johns River Power Park System.

Geographic Reach

The cooperative serves customers in Northeast Florida.

Financial Performance

In 2014 JEA's revenues increased by 3% due to a 3% growth in electric sales as the result of higher consumption (primarily 4.3% in residential sales). Water and sewer sales increased by 1% related to a rise in customers and District Energy System sales increased by 2%. Approximately 47% of JEA's electric 2014 revenues came from its 375000 residential customers 50% from 48000 commercial and industrial customers and 3% from one wholesale customer.

The company's net income increased by 97% due to higher investment returns and a decline in loss from interest on debt.

JEA's operating cash flow decreased by 4% due to higher payments to suppliers.

Strategy

To help meet state regulations for carbon emission control JEA plans to get 10% of its energy requirements from nuclear energy by 2018 and 30% by 2030. In this regard JEA has signed a purchase power agreement to get 206 MW from a nuclear plant beginning in 2016 and is pursuing additional purchased power contracts.

JEA is also building out more fossil fuel capacity.

Company Background

The electric utility grew from a department of city of Jacksonville into an independent authority created by city and county government consolidation in 1967. In 1997 the water and sewer systems (which had been operated by the city since 1880) were also placed under JEA management.

In 2011 it completed the Greenland Energy Center which included two 175-MW natural gas-fired combustion turbines.

EXECUTIVES

Ceo, Paul McElroy
Vice President, Mike Brost
Vice President, Brian Roche
Exec President, James Chancellor
Exec Vice President, James Dickenson
Mng Dir, Walter Bussells
CIO, Ron Baker
Cfo, Melissa Dykes
Foreman/Supervisor, Henry Papa
Staff, William Adams
Project Coordinator, Bradley W Collier

LOCATIONS

HQ: JEA
21 W CHURCH ST FL 1, JACKSONVILLE, FL 322023158
Phone: 904 665-6000
Web: WWW.JEA.COM

PRODUCTS/OPERATIONS

2014 Sales

	$ mil.	% of total
Electric	1,431	77
Water & wastewater	383	21
District Energy System	8	-
Other	38	2
Total	**1,861**	**100**

COMPETITORS

Chesapeake Utilities	Seminole Electric
Florida Power & Light	Southern Company
Florida Public Utilities	TECO Energy
NextEra Energy	United Water Inc.
Progress Energy	Utilities Inc.

HISTORICAL FINANCIALS

Company Type: Private

Income Statement				FYE: September 30
	REVENUE ($ mil.)	NET INCOME ($ mil.)	NET PROFIT MARGIN	EMPLOYEES
09/17	1,875	254	13.6%	2,356
09/16*	1,782	210	11.8%	—
06/09	1,319	71	5.4%	—
03/09	857	45	5.4%	—
Annual Growth	**9.1%**	**21.0%**	—	—

*Fiscal year change

2017 Year-End Financials

Return on assets: 7.0%   Cash ($ mil.): 489
Return on equity: 13.6%
Current ratio: 1.20

JEFFERSON COUNTY BOARD OF EDUCATION

EXECUTIVES

Supt, Donna Hargenes
Supt, Donna Hargens
Supt, Steven Daeschner PHD
Coordinator, Linda Spencer
Coordinator, Sue Carmouche
Auditors: STROTHMAN & COMPANY PSC LOUI

LOCATIONS

HQ: JEFFERSON COUNTY BOARD OF EDUCATION
3332 NEWBURG RD, LOUISVILLE, KY 402182414
Phone: 502 485-3011
Web: WWW.JEFFERSON.K12.KY.US

HISTORICAL FINANCIALS

Company Type: Private

Income Statement				FYE: June 30
	REVENUE ($ mil.)	NET INCOME ($ mil.)	NET PROFIT MARGIN	EMPLOYEES
06/17	1,274	18	1.4%	14,000
06/16	1,251	31	2.5%	—
06/14	1,158	24	2.1%	—
06/13	1,179	(26)	—	—
Annual Growth	**2.0%**	—	—	—

2017 Year-End Financials

Return on assets: —   Cash ($ mil.): 315
Return on equity: 1.4%
Current ratio: —

JEFFERSON COUNTY BOARD OF EDUCATION

EXECUTIVES

Pres, Jennifer Parsons
Supt, Bobby G Neighbors
Vice President, Ronald Rhodes
SEC, Jerrylane McLandon
Business Marketing Coordinator, Dawn Davis
Business Marketing Coordinator, Jan Nicholson
Secretary, Diana Wojdula
Staff Accountant, Gayle Brandt
Staff Accountant, Teresa Smith
Auditors: RONALD L JONES

LOCATIONS

HQ: JEFFERSON COUNTY BOARD OF EDUCATION
2100 RICHARD ARRINGTON JR, BIRMINGHAM, AL 352091298
Phone: 205 379-2000
Web: WWW.JEFCOED.COM

HISTORICAL FINANCIALS

Company Type: Private

Income Statement				FYE: September 30
	REVENUE ($ mil.)	NET INCOME ($ mil.)	NET PROFIT MARGIN	EMPLOYEES
09/17*	381	121	31.9%	5,000
12/08	1	0	—	—
06/06	243	0	—	—
09/05	243	11	4.6%	—
Annual Growth	**3.8%**	**21.9%**	—	—

*Fiscal year change

2017 Year-End Financials

Return on assets: 1.9%   Cash ($ mil.): 152
Return on equity: 31.9%
Current ratio: —

JEFFERSON COUNTY SCHOOL DISTRICT NO. R-1

EXECUTIVES

Supt, Dan McMinimee
Supt, Cindy Stevenson
Office Aid, Grease Butte
Manager, Anne Scott
Administrative Assistant, Alicia Strasheim
Coordinator, Kay Bridges
Coordinator, Mary J Abbott
Executive Director, Amy Weber
Manager, Ezra Paddock
Coordinator, Stacy Oryshchyn
Administrative Assistant, Shelly Watanabe
Auditors: CLIFTONLARSONALLEN LLP BROOMF

LOCATIONS

HQ: JEFFERSON COUNTY SCHOOL DISTRICT NO. R-1
1829 DENVER WEST DR # 27, GOLDEN, CO
804013120
Phone: 303 982-6500
Web: WWW.JEFFCOPUBLICSCHOOLS.ORG

HISTORICAL FINANCIALS
Company Type: Private

Income Statement				FYE: June 30
	REVENUE ($ mil.)	NET INCOME ($ mil.)	NET PROFIT MARGIN	EMPLOYEES
06/17	808	(40)	—	12,000
06/15	801	(18)	—	—
06/14	785	(14)	—	—
06/13	759	97	12.8%	—
Annual Growth	1.6%	—	—	—

2017 Year-End Financials
Return on assets: 1.9%   Cash ($ mil.): 5
Return on equity: (-5.0%)
Current ratio: —

JERSEY CENTRAL POWER & LIGHT COMPANY

New Jersey native son Bruce Springsteen may be The Boss but Jersey Central Power & Light (JCP&L) electrifies more fans than he does every day. The company a subsidiary of multi-utility holding company FirstEnergy transmits and distributes electricity to 1.1 million homes and businesses in 13 counties in central and northern New Jersey. JCP&L operates 22670 miles of distribution lines; its 2550-mile transmission system is overseen by regional transmission organization (RTO) PJM Interconnection. The utility also has some power plant interests.

Operations
The company provides regulated electric transmission and distribution services. JCP&L also has an ownership interest in a hydroelectric generating facility.

Geographic Reach

JCP&L conducts business in 3200 square miles of east central northern and western New Jersey. The area it serves has a population of approximately 2.7 million.

Financial Performance
Revenues decreased by 18% in 2011 due to a rate adjustment for all customer classes and lower power deliveries. The lower power delivery to residential customers was the result of decreased weather-related usage in 2011. Lower distribution deliveries to commercial and industrial customers that year reflected the impact of economic conditions in JCP&L's service territory. A decrease in retail generation revenues was due to lower generation power sales in all customer classes primarily due to an increase in customers shopping around for alternative providers. Wholesale generation revenues decreased due to a drop in PJM spot market energy sales.

JCP&L's net income decreased by 39% in 2011 due to lower revenues offset by reductions in purchased power costs and amortization of regulatory assets.

Company Background
The utility was organized under the laws of the State of New Jersey in 1925.

EXECUTIVES

Pres-Ceo, Donald M Lynch
Cfo-Cao-Controller, Marlene A Barwood
Director, Ernest J Novak Jr
Director, Jesse T Williams Sr
Vp Corporate Risk and Chief R, William D Byrd
V Pres External Affairs, Mark A Jones
Assistant, Rachel Greer
Customer Staff, Sandra Rudolph
Vp-Operations, Alex Patton
General Manager, Chad Hampson
Director President, Charles E Jones
Auditors: PRICEWATERHOUSECOOPERS LLP C

LOCATIONS

HQ: JERSEY CENTRAL POWER & LIGHT COMPANY
76 S MAIN ST, AKRON, OH 443081812
Phone: 800 736-3402
Web: WWW.FIRSTENERGYCORP.COM

PRODUCTS/OPERATIONS

Selected Services
Electrical services
Outdoor lighting
Professional tree services

COMPETITORS

Conectiv Power Delivery	Public Service Electric and Gas
New Jersey Natural Gas	South Jersey Gas
Orange & Rockland Utilities	Southern Company Gas

HISTORICAL FINANCIALS
Company Type: Private

Income Statement				FYE: December 31
	REVENUE ($ mil.)	NET INCOME ($ mil.)	NET PROFIT MARGIN	EMPLOYEES
12/17	1,801	115	6.4%	1,413
12/16	1,787	80	4.5%	—
12/11	2,495	144	5.8%	—
12/10	3,027	192	6.3%	—
Annual Growth	(7.1%)	(7.1%)	—	—

2017 Year-End Financials
Return on assets: 6.9%   Cash ($ mil.): 251
Return on equity: 6.4%
Current ratio: 1.30

JERSEY CITY MEDICAL CENTER (INC)

With roots extending back to 1882 Jersey City Medical Center (JCMC) may have history but it's not stuck in the past. The 350-bed acute-care hospital serves residents of New Jersey's Hudson County area. Operated by Liberty Healthcare the hospital includes a trauma center a perinatal center and a heart institute. JCMC also offers pediatric women's health rehabilitation and ambulatory care and it is a teaching affiliate for the Mount Sinai School of Medicine. JCMC's modern incarnation came about in the Great Depression when it was constructed by a political ally of Franklin Roosevelt.

Operations
JCMC operates as a regional referral center meaning that it takes on complicated cases from smaller community hospitals in the area. As an area teaching hospital the hospital offers medical residency programs in internal medicine and nursing. It also offers continuing education courses to keep its medical residents up on the latest medical developments.

JCMC's mobile outreach program provides health and wellness screenings dispense care and offer health education. It is funded through a grant provided by The New Jersey Department of Health and Senior Services. Among other things the van will provide diabetes HIV and mental health screenings as well as perform blood pressure checks offer preventive care and educate people on the streets of Hudson County and Jersey City. The van travels to health fairs and regularly scheduled outreach events such as at schools and senior centers.

Geographic Reach
The 15-acre JCMC campus which overlooks the New York Harbor and the Liberty State Park is also home to the Wilzig Hospital and the Provident Bank Ambulatory Center. JCMC offers a Mobile Health Screening Unit that will travel to underserved areas throughout Hudson County. The hospital is the primary medical facility serving New York's Hudson Essex and Union counties.

Strategy
In mid-2013 JCMC announced that it has entered an agreement to become part of the Barnabas Health system. The merger was expected to close by the end of 2013 following regulatory approval.

JCMC focuses on expanding and improving services for area residents. The hospital opened a hand and upper extremity unit in 2013 to address the needs of patients with pain and functional difficulties related to arthritis carpal tunnel syndrome injuries and other conditions. It also added about 200 new physicians during 2012 to enhance patient access to general and specialty care. It opened a new gastrointestinal disorder center on the main campus in 2012 and it expanded its cardiac care services with the opening of a new electrophysiology lab.

In 2012 it announced plans to renovate and reopen the former Greenville Hospital campus in Jersey City as an outpatient facility to meet the rising needs for ambulatory care in the area.

EXECUTIVES

Radiology Medical Director, Anthony Tramontana
Medical Director, Chalapathy Narisety
Director Of Nursing, Irene Ondieki

LOCATIONS

HQ: JERSEY CITY MEDICAL CENTER (INC)
355 GRAND ST, JERSEY CITY, NJ 073024321
Phone: 201 915-2000
Web: WWW.LIBERTYHEALTH.ORG

PRODUCTS/OPERATIONS

Selected Locations
Emergency Services at JCMC
Family Regional Perinatal Center
Fannie E. Rippel Foundation Heart Institute
General Pediatrics at JCMC
Nursing at JCMC
Provident Bank Ambulatory Center
Port Authority Heroes of Sept 11 Trauma Center
The Rehabilitation Services Department
Volunteer Services at JCMC
Wilzig Hospital

COMPETITORS

Bergen Regional Medical
Bronx-Lebanon Hospital
Continuum Health Partners
Englewood Hospital and Medical Center
Hackensack University Medical Center
Hospital for Special Surgery
Lenox Hill Hospital
Montefiore Medical
Newark Beth Israel Medical Center
Robert Wood Johnson University Hospital at Rahway
St. Joseph's Healthcare System
The Valley Hospital
Valley Health System

HISTORICAL FINANCIALS
Company Type: Private

Income Statement				FYE: December 31
	REVENUE ($ mil.)	NET INCOME ($ mil.)	NET PROFIT MARGIN	EMPLOYEES
12/17	385	26	6.8%	1,942
12/16	354	(2)	—	—
12/15	375	37	10.1%	—
12/14	341	6	1.8%	—
Annual Growth	4.1%	62.2%	—	—

2017 Year-End Financials
Return on assets: 4.6%   Cash ($ mil.): —
Return on equity: 6.8%
Current ratio: 0.60

JEWISH COMMUNAL FUND

EXECUTIVES

Pres, Zoya Raynes
V Pres, Susan F Dickman
Sr V Pres, Jose Virella
Offc Mgr, Wanda Gutierrez
Manager, Hilda Beck
Associate Director, Igor Musayev
Coordinator, Claudia Pinto
Chief Operations Officer, Beth Wohlgelernter
Director of Grants, Karla Floris
Freelance Journalist, Tamar Snyder
Auditors: EISNERAMPER LLP NEW YORK NY

LOCATIONS

HQ: JEWISH COMMUNAL FUND
575 MADISON AVE STE 703, NEW YORK, NY
100228591
Phone: 212 752-8277
Web: WWW.JEWISHCOMMUNALFUND.ORG

HISTORICAL FINANCIALS
Company Type: Private

Income Statement				FYE: June 30
	ASSETS ($ mil.)	NET INCOME ($ mil.)	INCOME AS % OF ASSETS	EMPLOYEES
06/17	1,558	55	3.6%	14
06/13	1,179	110	9.3%	—
06/12	1,012	(57)	—	—
06/11	1,086	42	3.9%	—
Annual Growth	6.2%	4.6%		

2017 Year-End Financials
Return on assets: 0.1%   Sales ($ mil): 461
Return on equity: 12.0%

JOHN D ARCHBOLD MEMORIAL HOSPITAL

EXECUTIVES

Pres, Perry Mustian
Sr Vice President, John A Fischer
Cfo, Skip Hightower
SEC, Delora Harris
Chb, Daniel Autry
Manager, Pamela Tucker
Director of Risk Management, Kellie Odom
Information Technology/Interne, Martin Slusher
Purchasing Director, Pryor Connell
Chief Information Officer, Tracy Gray
Information Specialist, Andrea Jackson
Auditors: DRAFFIN & TUCKER LLP ALBANY

LOCATIONS

HQ: JOHN D ARCHBOLD MEMORIAL HOSPITAL
GORDON AVE AT MIMOSA DR, THOMASVILLE, GA
31792
Phone: 229 228-2000
Web: WWW.ARCHBOLD.ORG

HISTORICAL FINANCIALS
Company Type: Private

Income Statement				FYE: September 30
	REVENUE ($ mil.)	NET INCOME ($ mil.)	NET PROFIT MARGIN	EMPLOYEES
09/17	337	25	7.6%	2,700
09/16	262	28	10.9%	—
09/15	251	30	12.0%	—
09/14	233	22	9.5%	—
Annual Growth	13.1%	4.7%		—

2017 Year-End Financials
Return on assets: 1.2%   Cash ($ mil.): 26
Return on equity: 7.6%
Current ratio: 2.20

JOHN MUIR HEALTH

Named after famed naturalist and champion of wilderness preservation John Muir John Muir Health provides health care throughout the scenic San Francisco Bay area. The not-for-profit system operates three hospitals eight outpatient and urgent care centers two surgery centers a physician practice organization and several community health foundations. The John Muir Medical Center Walnut Creek Campus has more than 570 beds and specializes in neurological and obstetrics care. The Concord Campus has about 315 beds and specializes in cardiac and cancer care. The John Muir Behavioral Health Center is a 70-bed psychiatric hospital. John Muir Health also offers home health rehabilitation and wellness programs.

Operations
John Muir Health's network of outpatient facilities include physical therapy and occupational therapy centers as well as specialty pediatric women's health and diabetes centers. The system also includes medical imaging centers and the MuirLab division which performs a full range of clinical and anatomic pathology laboratory testing at more than a dozen locations.

The system has 900 physicians associated with the John Muir Physician Network which owns and operates two dozen locations.

John Muir Health partners include Aetna Anthem Blue Cross Blue Shield of California and CIGNA.

Geographic Reach
The company's hospitals are located in California's Contra Costa County (Concord and Walnut Creek); outpatient centers are located in Brentwood Concord Walnut Creek and Walnut Creek gated community Rossmoor.

Financial Performance
John Muir Health reported $1.41 billion in revenues for 2012 a total that was slightly down from the $1.44 billion it reported in 2011.

Strategy
To better serve residents of the growing San Francisco Bay area John Muir Health has made additions to its existing facilities including increasing bed counts and upgrading its IT infrastructure. Other initiatives that aim to improve patient care — and ultimately to lower the overall cost of care and meet federal reform guidelines — include upgrading medical equipment coordinating regional care establishing joint ventures and attracting and retaining skilled physicians. In 2015 the system partnered with Stanford Children's Health to open a new pediatric intensive care unit at its Walnut Creek medical center.

Also that year John Muir Health joined together with Health Net of California to form an Accountable Care Organization (ACO) serving Health Net's members from the system's medical centers.

In 2013 John Muir Health established a joint venture with Tenet Healthcare Corporation that created a partnership with San Ramon Regional Medical Center. Through this partnership John Muir Health is spending $100 million to acquire a 49% ownership interest in San Ramon Regional Medical Center. Together the two organizations will expand and improve the efficiency and coordination of care in the TriValley area and nearby communities including San Ramon. The new partnership will also increase patient access to a stronger network of services and align outpatient and physician-focused health care in the region. In 2014 the partnership invested in a 92000 sq. ft. building slated to become a new outpatient center in Pleasanton California.

Company Background

John Muir Health was formed from the 1997 merger of the John Muir Medical Center (the Walnut Creek Campus which dates back to 1965) and the Mt. Diablo Medical Center (now the Concord Campus dating back to 1930 as the Concord Hospital).

EXECUTIVES

Director Of Pharmacy, Martin Iyoya
President And Ceo, Calvin (Cal) Knight
President And Chief Administrative Officer John Muir Medical Center Walnut Creek Campus, Jane A. Willemsen
President And Chief Administrative Officer John Muir Medical Center Concord Campus, Michael S. Thomas
President Cao Of John Muir, Lee Huskins
President John Muir Health Foundation, Patrick J. Carew
Interim Cfo, Chris Pass
Svp And Cio, Jon Russell
Clinical Director, Jeanette Moore
Chairman, David L. Goldsmith
Vice Chairman, Thomas Rundall
Auditors: KPMG LLP SAN FRANCISCO CALIF

LOCATIONS

HQ: JOHN MUIR HEALTH
1601 YGNACIO VALLEY RD, WALNUT CREEK, CA 945983122
Phone: 925 947-4449
Web: WWW.JOHNMUIRHEALTH.COM

PRODUCTS/OPERATIONS

Selected California Locations
Behavioral Health Center (Concord)
Breast Health Center (Walnut Creek)
Caring Hands Volunteer Program (Walnut Creek)
Clinical Research Centers (Concord)
Diabetes Center (Walnut Creek)
Garret Thrift Shop (Walnut Creek)
John Muir Medical Center (Concord)
John Muir Medical Center (Walnut Creek)
John Muir Outpatient Center (Brentwood Tice Valley/Rossmoor)
Medical Imaging (Brentwood Concord San Ramon Walnut Creek)
MuirLab (Regional)
Occupational Medicine (Brentwood Concord Walnut Creek)
Physical Rehabilitation Center (Concord Pleasant Hill)
Urgent Care Centers (Brentwood Concord San Ramon Walnut Creek)
Women's Health Center (Walnut Creek)
Wound Care Center (Walnut Creek)

Selected Services
Behavioral Health
Cancer
Cardiovascular Services
Chemical Dependency
Children's Services
Emergency Services
Lab Services
Medical Imaging
Orthopedics
Neurosciences
Physical Rehabilitation
Pregnancy & New Parent
Primary Care
Urgent Care

COMPETITORS

Alta Bates Summit Medical Center
California Pacific Medical Center
Children's Hospital & Research Center at Oakland
Community Hospital of the Monterey Peninsula
Dignity Health
Healdsburg District Hospital
Hill Physicians Medical Group
Marin General Hospital
Mills-Peninsula Health Services
Sequoia Healthcare District
Stanford Health Care
Sutter Health
Tenet Healthcare
The Palo Alto Medical Foundation
UCSF Medical
ValleyCare Health System

HISTORICAL FINANCIALS
Company Type: Private

Income Statement   FYE: December 31

	REVENUE ($ mil.)	NET INCOME ($ mil.)	NET PROFIT MARGIN	EMPLOYEES
12/17	1,831	92	5.0%	2,200
12/16	1,734	107	6.2%	—
Annual Growth	5.6%	(14.0%)	—	—

2017 Year-End Financials
Return on assets: 6.5%   Cash ($ mil.): 72
Return on equity: 5.0%
Current ratio: 0.80

JOHN MUIR PHYSICIAN NETWORK

EXECUTIVES

Prin, Cal Knight
Administrative Assistant, Laura Kazaglis
Internal Medicine Practitioner, Moizah Saad
Chief Operating Officer, Richard Kamrath
Internist, Lisa Hudson
General Surgeon, Andreas Kamlot
Internist, Rebecca A Parish
Vascular Surgeon, Tanveer A Khan

LOCATIONS

HQ: JOHN MUIR PHYSICIAN NETWORK
1450 TREAT BLVD, WALNUT CREEK, CA 945972168
Phone: 925 296-9700
Web: WWW.JOHNMUIRHEALTH.COM

HISTORICAL FINANCIALS
Company Type: Private

Income Statement   FYE: December 31

	REVENUE ($ mil.)	NET INCOME ($ mil.)	NET PROFIT MARGIN	EMPLOYEES
12/17	322	(30)	—	3,612
12/02	658	48	7.3%	—
12/01	1,747	17	1.0%	—
Annual Growth	(10.0%)	—	—	—

2017 Year-End Financials
Return on assets: 1.6%   Cash ($ mil.): 3
Return on equity: (-9.5%)
Current ratio: 1.00

JOHN T. MATHER MEMORIAL HOSPITAL OF PORT JEFFERSON, NEW YORK, INC.

Shipbuilder John T. Mather envisioned a legacy that would keep his community of Port Jefferson in good health and John T. Mather Memorial Hospital came to fruition in 1929 one year after it's namesake's death. The not-for-profit hospital has some 250 beds and provides a variety of health care services to the residents of Port Jefferson New York and surrounding areas of Suffolk County. Services include emergency care occupational therapy psychiatry and radiology. Mather Hospital is a member of Long Island Health Network an association of about a dozen affiliated hospitals all serving Long Island. It is also MagnetA® recognized hospital by the American Nurses Credentialing Center.

Operations

Mather Hospital has some 600 physicians both full-time employees and affiliates who serve some 12000 inpatient customers annually. The emergency room handles about 44000 visits per year. It provides more than 18000 diagnostic breast health screenings annually. The hospital's specialty service units include the Fortunato Breast Health Center which provides outpatient diagnostics as well as centers for sleep disorder treatment bariatrics wound care and stroke management.

In addition to its membership in the Long Island Health Alliance Mather Hospital has formed a partnership with nearby St. Charles Hospital and Rehabilitation Center to provide tandem services in some areas including cancer and pediatric care.

Financial Performance

The hospital reported a 6% increase in revenues in 2012 thanks to higher patient services revenue and other non-patient care services. It saw net loss of $2 million year (compared to net income in 2011) due to an increase in expenses (salaries benefits supplies and other) and depreciation.

Strategy

The company grows through organic initiatives.

In 2013 Mather Hospital broke ground on a new patient care pavilion. The expansion the first at the hospital in more than ten years will house a 35-single-bedded patient care unit; offices and teaching facilities for a Graduate Medical Education Program with residencies in Internal Medicine Family Practice Medicine Psychiatry and Transitional Year; and a conference center. The new facility which adds more than 28400 sq. ft. of space to the existing hospital will be known as the Arthur & Linda Calace Family Pavilion.

In 2012 the hospital began using an electronic health records system to improve patient safety and care. Other 2012 initiatives included a cardiac computed tomography angiography program which uses digital imaging to diagnose heart disease. Mather also launched a Palliative Medicine program for patients with a serious or chronic illness.

Looking to green resources to cut its carbon emissions and costs Mather Hospital is using lower cost hydropower to reduce its energy costs by $2.5 million over seven years through the ReCharge NY award from the New York Power Authority. It also has a solar power unit.

Company Background

In 2011 Mather Hospital became the first Long Island hospital to use solar power via a federally funded state energy grant. It built a 50 KW photovoltaic ground-mounted solar panel bank on its campus.

The hospital was founded in 1929 as the first not-for-profit community hospital in the Town of Brookhaven.

EXECUTIVES

Ambulatory Services Director, Karen Tuzzolo
Vice President Operations, Tamara Weiss
Infection Control Director, Raymond Luttinger
Respiratory Therapy Director, Ted Nilsson

LOCATIONS

HQ: JOHN T. MATHER MEMORIAL HOSPITAL OF PORT JEFFERSON, NEW YORK, INC.
75 N COUNTRY RD, PORT JEFFERSON, NY 117772119
Phone: 631 476-2738
Web: WWW.MATHERHOSPITAL.ORG

PRODUCTS/OPERATIONS

Selected Centers and Services
Bariatric Surgery Center of Excellence
Behavioral Health Services
Breast Health Center
Critical Care
Emergency Department
Hospitalists
Hyperbaric Oxygen Therapy Unit
Imaging Services/Radiology
Infusion Center
Intensivists
Joint Replacement Program
Laboratory
Lithotripsy
Lymphedema Program
Pain Management Program
Palliative Medicine
Physical Therapy
Prostate Health Program
Respiratory Therapy
Transitional Care Unit
Sleep Disorders Center
Surgical Services
Wound Treatment Center

COMPETITORS

CSH
Catholic Health Services of Long Island
Catholic Healthcare System
Long Island College Hospital
New York City Health and Hospitals
NewYork-Presbyterian Healthcare
Northwell Health

HISTORICAL FINANCIALS

Company Type: Private

Income Statement   FYE: December 31

	REVENUE ($ mil.)	NET INCOME ($ mil.)	NET PROFIT MARGIN	EMPLOYEES
12/17	320	0	0.1%	1,700
12/16	305	2	0.8%	—
12/15	279	(1)	—	—
12/14	292	(28)	—	—
Annual Growth	3.1%	—	—	—

2017 Year-End Financials

Return on assets: 10.0%   Cash ($ mil.): 14
Return on equity: 0.1%
Current ratio: 1.00

JOHNS HOPKINS ALL CHILDREN'S HOSPITAL, INC.

Johns Hopkins All Children's Hospital has about 260 beds all dedicated to the health of west-central Florida's children. With roughly 200 pediatric physician specialists on board the hospital offers its young patients (infants children and teens) a variety of services including a Neonatal Intensive Care Unit for premature and "at-risk" infants. Its heart bone marrow and kidney transplant programs are nationally renowned. The teaching hospital is also affiliated with the University of South Florida College of Medicine. All Children's Hospital is a member of the Johns Hopkins Medicine network.

Operations

The hospital handles about 8000 inpatient visits each year as well as 45000 emergency room and 400000 outpatient visits. All Children's Hospital has expanded its services over the years to include specialty cancer cystic fibrosis cardiology neurology and cleft palate programs. The organization also includes several satellite outpatient care centers; its All Children's Specialty Physicians group practice organization includes 100 doctors with 15 general and specialist programs.

Geographic Reach

As a referral center for children All Children's draws patients from throughout Florida all 50 states and 36 foreign countries. Most of its patients come from the Florida counties of Hillsborough Manatee Pinellas Pasco and Sarasota.

Outpatient facilities are located in towns including Aquatics Brandon East Lake Fort Myers Lakeland Lakewood Ranch Pasco Sertoma Sarasota South Tampa and Tampa.

Financial Performance

All Children's Hospital revenue increased 7% to $425 million in 2014 as patient service income and investment earnings rose.Net income slipped 4% to $33 million that year on higher contributions to affiliates and increased operating expenses including salaries and benefits.

Cash flow from operations fell 14% to $39 million that year.

Strategy

All Children's has focused on strengthening and expanding services including new pediatric stroke and thrombosis (clotting disorder) programs launched in 2013. The following year it opened its 11th outpatient care center (in South Tampa Florida). Through its affiliation with other Johns Hopkins entities the pediatric facility is also increasing its research activities.

Company Background

The hospital became a fully integrated part of the Johns Hopkins Health System (the operating health organization of Johns Hopkins Medicine) through a non-cash transaction in 2011. Under terms of the agreement Florida residents remained a majority of the All Children's governing board thereby ensuring local control and staffing and day-to-day operations would not change drastically. The deal gave All Children's access to the Johns Hopkins extensive educational and research resources. It also gave Johns Hopkins a dedicated pediatric facility something it previously lacked.

The hospital traces its roots to the American Legion Hospital for Crippled Children which was opened in 1927 in St. Petersburg to treat children suffering from polio and other diseases.

EXECUTIVES

President; Vice Dean All Children's Hospital Johns Hopkins University School Of Medicine, Jonathan M. Ellen
Ctro Director, Neil Goldenberg
Assistant Dean Administration Office Of The Vice Dean For All Children's Hospital, Sylvia Powell
Vice Chairman, J. Mark Stroud
Chairman, Joseph (Jay) Fleece

LOCATIONS

HQ: JOHNS HOPKINS ALL CHILDREN'S HOSPITAL, INC.
501 6TH AVE S, SAINT PETERSBURG, FL 337014634
Phone: 727 898-7451
Web: WWW.ALLKIDS.ORG

PRODUCTS/OPERATIONS

Selected Affiliates
ACHPOB Inc.
All Children's Hospital Foundation Inc.
All Children's Research Institute Inc. (ACRI)
Kids Home Care Inc.
Pediatric Physician Services Inc.
SurgiKid of Florida Inc.
West Coast Neonatology Inc.

Selected Services
Acute Care Rehabilitation
Allergy/ Immunology
Anesthesiology
Applied Behavior Analysis (ABA)
Asthma Coalition
Audiology: Hearing and Hearing Aid Services
Autism Center
Blood and Marrow Transplant (BMT)
Cancer and Blood Disorders
CanSurvive Clinic
Cardiology and Cardiovascular Surgery
Child Life Services
Craniofacial and Craniomaxillofacial
Critical Care
Early Steps
Emergency Medicine
Endocrinology & Diabetes
Fit4AllKids
Fit4AllMoms
Gastroenterology Nutrition and Hepatology
General Pediatrics
Genetics
Healthy Start
Hematology/ Oncology
Hospitalists
Infectious Disease
Kids Home Care
Minimally Invasive Surgery
Music Therapy at All Children's Hospital
Neonatal Surgery
Neonatology
Nephrology
Neurology
Neuropsychiatry
Neuroscience Institute
Nutrition
Obstetrics/ Gynecology
Occupational Therapy Services
Ophthalmology
Orthopaedic and Scoliosis Surgery
Otolaryngology and Cochlear Implant Program
Pathology and Laboratory Medicine
Pediatric Developmental Medicine
Pediatric General Surgery
Perinatology
Physical Therapy Services
Plastic and Reconstructive Surgery
Psychiatry
Pulmonology
Radiology and Neuroradiology
Rehabilitation Services
Retail Pharmacy
Rheumatology
SAFE KIDS
Safe Routes to School
Speech-Language Pathology Services
Sports Medicine
STEPS to a Healthier Florida
Stroke Program

Thoracic Surgery
Thrombosis Program
Transport Team
Trauma Services
Urology

COMPETITORS

BayCare Health System
Bayfront Health
Florida Hospital Tampa Bay Division
Florida Hospital Waterman
H. Lee Moffitt Cancer Center & Research Institute
Kindred Healthcare
Manatee Memorial Hospital
Mayo Clinic Jacksonville
Miami Children's Hospital
Northside Hospital and Heart Institute
Shriners Hospitals For Children
St. Anthony's Hospital
Tampa General Hospital

HISTORICAL FINANCIALS

Company Type: Private

Income Statement   FYE: June 30

	REVENUE ($ mil.)	NET INCOME ($ mil.)	NET PROFIT MARGIN	EMPLOYEES
06/16	400	21	5.4%	2,325
06/15	408	(1)	—	—
Annual Growth	(1.8%)	—	—	—

2016 Year-End Financials

Return on assets: 9.7%   Cash ($ mil.): 29
Return on equity: 5.4%
Current ratio: 1.00

JOHNS HOPKINS BAYVIEW MEDICAL CENTER, INC.

If you've just been pulled from the bay like an old emptyA crab trap Johns Hopkins Bayview might be the first place you're taken. One of five member institutions in the Johns Hopkins Health System Johns Hopkins Bayview Medical Center is a community teaching hospital. Its Baltimore-based operations include a neonatal intensive care unit as well as centers devoted to trauma geriatrics sleep disorders and weight management. It also features the state's onlyA regional burn center.A The facilityA includes a meditation labyrinth for patients families and staff to walk. Established in 1773 the medical center has more than 560 beds.

Operations

As an academic teaching hospital all of the physicians at Johns Hopkins Bayview are also full-time faculty at the Johns Hopkins School of Medicine. Students from TheA Johns Hopkins University School of Nursing also come to the medical center for hospital-based instruction in acute and long term care.

EXECUTIVES

Vice President Support Services, Cheryl Koch
Vice President Clinical Operations, Charles Reuland
Auditors: PRICEWATERHOUSECOOPERS LLP BA

LOCATIONS

HQ: JOHNS HOPKINS BAYVIEW MEDICAL CENTER, INC.
4940 EASTERN AVE, BALTIMORE, MD 212242735
Phone: 410 550-0100
Web: WWW.JHMI.EDU

PRODUCTS/OPERATIONS

Selected services

Primary Care Services
  General Internal Medicine
  Obstetrics/Gynecology
  Pediatrics
Specialty Services
  Bariatrics
  Burn
  Cardiology
  Clinical Nutrition
  Dermatology
  Endocrinology
  Gastroenterology
  General Surgery
  Hematology/Oncology
  Imaging (X-ray mammography ultrasound etc)
  Minor Surgery
  Neurodiagnostic Lab
  Neurology
  Ophthalmology
  Otolaryngology (ear nose and throat)
  Orthopaedics
  Plastic Surgery
  Podiatry
  Urology
  Vascular Lab

COMPETITORS

Franklin Square Hospital Center
GBMC
Good Samaritan Hospital of Maryland
Harbor Hospital
Levindale Hospital
LifeBridge Health
Sinai Hospital of Baltimore
St. Agnes HealthCare
St. Joseph Medical Center
University of Maryland Medical System

HISTORICAL FINANCIALS

Company Type: Private

Income Statement   FYE: June 30

	REVENUE ($ mil.)	NET INCOME ($ mil.)	NET PROFIT MARGIN	EMPLOYEES
06/18	628	12	1.9%	3,300
06/16	544	11	2.1%	—
06/15	507	16	3.2%	—
06/14	541	11	2.2%	—
Annual Growth	3.8%	0.7%	—	—

2018 Year-End Financials

Return on assets: 7.5%   Cash ($ mil.): 20
Return on equity: 1.9%
Current ratio: 0.90

JOHNS HOPKINS HEALTH SYS CORP

Named after philanthropist Johns Hopkins the Johns Hopkins Health System (JHHS) gifts Baltimore residents with an array of health care services. The health system is an affiliate of world-renowned Johns Hopkins Medicine and oversees six hospitals: All Children's Hospital Johns Hopkins Hospital Bayview Medical Center Howard County General Hospital Sibley Memorial Hospital and Suburban Hospital. The not-for-profit teaching hospitals offer inpatient and outpatient health services that include general medicine emergency/trauma care pediatrics maternity care senior care and numerous specialized areas of medicine. JHHS also operates community health and satellite care facilities.

Operations

JHHS facilities handle 2.8 million patient encounters each year including 115000 inpatient admissions and 350000 emergency room visits. In addition to the six Johns Hopkins Medicine hospitals (which combined house more than 2600 beds) the JHHS organization includes four surgery centers two dozen primary care clinics associated with the Johns Hopkins Community Physicians practice organization and a home health care services agency. JHHS offers unified shared services to its members including advertising purchasing finance legal and other administrative functions.

The Johns Hopkins name is well-known for health care but is probably equally as well-known for its medical education and research initiatives. The health system's hospitals are affiliated with Johns Hopkins University offering physicians-in-training a whole host of residency options.

Geographic Reach

The JHHS inpatient and outpatient facilities are located throughout Maryland and the Washington DC-area as well as in Florida. The system operates a handful of outpatient surgery and imaging centers as well. The group's hospitals serve visitors from all over the world.

Strategy

The organization regularly expands through small to large construction efforts as well as through acquisitions. For example it has acquired two hospitals (All Children's Hospital in Florida and Sibley Memorial Hospital in Washington DC) since 2010.

EXECUTIVES

Pres, Ronald R Peterson
Chb, C Micheal Amstrong
V Pres Fin-Cfo, Ronald J Werthman
V Pres-Medical Affairs, Beryl Rosenstein
Corp SEC, Hannah Jones
Accountant, Donna Deinish
Assistant Director, Renee Genco
Programmer Analyst, Keith Haggard
Manager, Bridget Carver
Coordinator, Matthew Trojanowski
Senior Vice-President, Bertrand M Emerson
Auditors: PRICEWATERHOUSECOOPERS LLP BA

LOCATIONS

HQ: JOHNS HOPKINS HEALTH SYS CORP
600 N WOLFE ST, BALTIMORE, MD 212870005
Phone: 410 955-5000
Web: WWW.JINHEMD.COM

PRODUCTS/OPERATIONS

Selected Facilities

All Children's Hospital (St. Petersburg FL)
Bayview Medical Center (Baltimore MD)
Howard County General Hospital (Columbia MD)
Johns Hopkins at Cedar Lane (Columbia MD)
Johns Hopkins at Greenspring Station (Lutherville MD)
Johns Hopkins at Odenton (Odenton MD)
Johns Hopkins at White Marsh (White Marsh MD)
Johns Hopkins Hospital (Baltimore MD)
Johns Hopkins Outpatient Center (Baltimore MD)
Sibley Memorial Hospital (Washington DC)
Suburban Hospital (Bethesda MD)

COMPETITORS

Anne Arundel Medical Center
Ascension Health
Bon Secours Health
Carilion Clinic
LifeBridge Health
MedStar Health
MedStar Union Memorial Hospital
Sinai Hospital of

Christiana Care
Dimensions Healthcare
Franklin Square
  Hospital Center
GBMC
Good Samaritan
  Hospital of Maryland
Harbor Hospital
Levindale Hospital

Baltimore
St. Agnes HealthCare
St. Joseph Medical
  Center
University of Maryland
  Medical System
Upper Chesapeake
  Health

HISTORICAL FINANCIALS

Company Type: Private

Income Statement

FYE: June 30

	REVENUE ($ mil.)	NET INCOME ($ mil.)	NET PROFIT MARGIN	EMPLOYEES
06/18	6,558	308	4.7%	13,000
06/17	6,153	412	6.7%	—
06/07	2,438	163	6.7%	—
06/06	0	0	2.5%	—
Annual Growth	122.9%	134.8%	—	—

2018 Year-End Financials

Return on assets: 9.9%
Return on equity: 4.7%
Current ratio: 1.00
Cash ($ mil.): 579

JOHNS HOPKINS HOSPITAL

EXECUTIVES

Pres, Ronald Peterson
Cfo, Ronald Werthman
Doctor, Rafael Tamargo
Ophthalmologist, Albert Jun
Health Professional, Tonya Bradley
Diagnostic Radiologist, Bruce Wasserman
Oncologist, Christian F Meyer
Radiation Oncologist, Daniel Song
Gynecologic Oncologist, Edward Tanner III
Psychiatry, Paul Nestadt
Assistant, Christine White

LOCATIONS

HQ: JOHNS HOPKINS HOSPITAL
  1800 ORLEANS ST, BALTIMORE, MD 212870010
Phone: 410 550-0730
Web: WWW.HOPKINSMEDICINE.ORG

HISTORICAL FINANCIALS

Company Type: Private

Income Statement

FYE: June 30

	REVENUE ($ mil.)	NET INCOME ($ mil.)	NET PROFIT MARGIN	EMPLOYEES
06/18	2,422	98	4.1%	12,000
06/16	1,968	80	4.1%	—
06/15	1,879	68	3.6%	—
06/12	1,791	(238)	—	—
Annual Growth	5.2%	—	—	—

2018 Year-End Financials

Return on assets: 7.8%
Return on equity: 4.1%
Current ratio: 1.00
Cash ($ mil.): 80

JOHNS HOPKINS UNIVERSITY

Founded in 1876 with a $7 million bequest from its namesake The Johns Hopkins University has established its reputation by molding itself in the image of a European research institution. While renowned for its School of Medicine the private university offers 260 academic programs spanning fields of study including arts and sciences business and international studies. The university enrolls more than 24000 full- and part-time students. Johns Hopkins has about a half-dozen campuses in Maryland and Washington DC as well as facilities in China and Italy. The student-teacher ratio is 13:1. The affiliated Johns Hopkins Health System provides health care from its three Baltimore-area hospitals.

Operations

Johns Hopkins University a private and non-profit institution with 1700 non-medical and 2800 medical faculty members offers education research and professional medical services. Its research and related services are offered through about 1800 government and private sponsors.

Keenly focused on research Johns Hopkins is engaged in a range of disciplines including health and medicine social sciences humanities the arts natural sciences engineering and technology. Projects include researching alternatives to animal testing disease treatments and chemical and biomolecular engineering topics among others.

The Johns Hopkins University offers graduate programs in business finance and real estate through its relatively new Carey Business School. Trustee emeritus William Polk Carey chairman of W. P. Carey & Co. partially funded the $100 million development of the school with $50 million which was completed in 2007.

Notable alumni of the school include 28th US president Woodrow Wilson Michael Bloomberg and horror film director Wesley Craven.

Geographic Reach

The university boasts three major campuses in Baltimore as well as single campus locations in (Montgomery County) Maryland and Washington DC. Johns Hopkins also operates facilities in the Baltimore-Washington area and abroad in China and Italy.

Strategy

Johns Hopkins is mid-way through its Ten By Twenty program — comprising 10 goals to achieve by 2020 — launched in 2013. The 10 goals are divided into four categories: One University (forging collaboration across disciplines); Individual Excellence (supporting faculty students and staff); Commitment to Our Communities (enriching ties to Baltimore the US and the world); and Institution Building (building a stronger university). In its 2017 progress report some of the achievements listed are more robust mental health resources; smaller class sizes; around 25 (out of a goal of 50) hires of interdisciplinary scholars; improved diversity and inclusion; and raised $4.6 billion in donations.

EXECUTIVES

Cio And Vice Provost Information Technology, Stephanie L. Reel
President, Ronald J. (Ron) Daniels
Svp Finance And Administration, Daniel G. Ennis
Svp Academic Affairs And Provost, Sunil Kumar
Vice President, Thomas Lewis
Vice President, Joseph Zolenas
Vice President Finance, Debbie Palmerino

Medical Director, Haig Kazazian
Senior Vice President Patient Care Services, Laura Wood
Vice President, Ben Myers
Medical Director Wilmer Eye Instructor At Columbia, Dean Glaros
Medical Director, Jeanette Nazarian
Clinical Director, Peter Hill
Vice President Chief Strategy Officer, Jackie Crain
Medical Director Of Care Coordination, Joseph Perno
Vice President For Population Health And Advancement, Elizabeth Kromm
Vice President And Chief Administrator, Sowell Ashlyn
Vice President Human Resources, Marcos Deleon
Director Of Nursing, Laurie Saletnik
Medical Director, Ekaterina Stepanova
Vice President Human Resources, Jon Oravec
Senior Vice President Health Care Transformation And Strategic Planning, John Colmers
Medical Director, Anne Ruble
Secretary, Beth Six
Assistant Secretary, Judith Moss
Secretary, Laura Cornelius
Secretary, Keisha Guice

LOCATIONS

HQ: JOHNS HOPKINS UNIVERSITY
  3400 N CHARLES ST, BALTIMORE, MD 212182680
Phone: 410 516-8000
Web: WWW.JHU.EDU

PRODUCTS/OPERATIONS

Selected Schools and Colleges

Bloomberg School of Public Health
Carey Business School
Krieger School of Arts and Sciences
Peabody Institute
School of Advanced International Studies
School of Education
School of Medicine
School of Nursing
Whiting School of Engineering

Selected Centers and Institutes

American Institute for Contemporary German Studies
Bloomberg School of Public Health Department of
  Health Policy and Management Fall Institute in
  Barcelona Spain
Bloomberg School of Public Health Research Centers
Center for Africana Studies
Center for Communication Programs
Center for Constitutional Studies and Democratic
  Development
Center for Clinical Global Health Education
Center for Global Health
Center for International Business and Public Policy
Center for Language Education
Center for Talented Youth
Center for Transatlantic Relations
Central Asia Caucasus Institute
Foreign Policy Institute
Hopkins Nanjing Center
Institute for Global Studies in Culture Power and
  History
Institute for Policy Studies
Johns Hopkins SAIS Bologna Center
Office of Global Nursing
SAIS Research Centers
Summer Language Institute
The Institute for Johns Hopkins Nursing
Yeung Center for Collaborative China Studies

Selected Campuses

Columbia Center - Columbia Maryland
East Baltimore Campus - Baltimore
Harbor East - Downtown Baltimore
Homewood Campus - Baltimore
Hopkins-Nanjing Center - Nanjing Jiangsu Province
  People's Republic of China
Johns Hopkins University Applied Physics Laboratory -
  Laurel MD; Baltimore and Washington

Johns Hopkins University Zanvyl Krieger School of Arts
  & Sciences Advanced Academic Programs -
  Washington DC
Montgomery County Center - Rockville Maryland
Nitze School of Advanced International Studies (SAIS) -
  Washington D.C
Peabody Campus - Baltimore
School of Advanced International Studies - Bologna Italy

HISTORICAL FINANCIALS
Company Type: Private

Income Statement				FYE: June 30
	REVENUE ($ mil.)	NET INCOME ($ mil.)	NET PROFIT MARGIN	EMPLOYEES
06/18	6,020	705	11.7%	37,600
06/13	4,793	526	11.0%	—
06/11	4,369	826	18.9%	—
Annual Growth	4.7%	(2.2%)	—	—

2018 Year-End Financials
Return on assets: 10.6%   Cash ($ mil.): 262
Return on equity: 11.7%
Current ratio: —

JOHNSON & WALES UNIVERSITY INC

Things are a little upside-down at Johnson &
Wales University and that's just the way the school
likes it. The private not-for-profit accredited institution provides what it calls an upside-down curriculum allowing students to take courses in their
major during the first year so they learn right away
if their career choice is right for them. At the end
of two years of study students earn an associate's
degree and the opportunity to go on to earn a
bachelor's degree. Founded in 1914 the school
enrolls more than 14000 graduate undergraduate
and online students across its four campuses in
Colorado Florida North Carolina and Rhode Island
instructed by more than 600 faculty members.

Operations
Johnson & Wales University offers degrees in
business education foodservice hospitality culinary
arts and technology. Student-faculty ratio is 20:1.
The university has alumni from some 120 countries. It offers 40 study abroad programs and independent exchanges. More than 92% of the students receive institutional scholarships or grants
from the university

Undergraduate tuition at Johnson & Wales University runs more than $29000 a year.

Geographic Reach
Johnson & Wales University has campuses in
Providence Rhode Island North Miami Florida Den-
ver Colorado and Charlotte North Carolina.

Sales and Marketing
Johnson & Wales University attracts students
from nearly 100 countries. Its top 10 international
populations (among its more than 1800 international students) hail from China South Korea Taiwan Saudi Arabia India Morocco Turkey the Bahamas the Netherlands and Malaysia.

Financial Performance
Johnson & Wales University's revenues fell
slightly to $345 million in 2017 (ended June) from
$346 million 2016. While most sources of revenue
including tuition rose for the year the school increased financial aid and scholarship money by
about $11 million.

Strategy

Johnson & Wales University adds areas of study
at a fast clip to keep up with market demands. In
the past few years the school has opened studies
in biology political science psychology and information security at the undergraduate and master's
degree levels. It also added master's programs in
physician assistant studies and health and wellness.

EXECUTIVES
Chancellor, John J. Bowen
Provost And Vice Chancellor, Thomas L. G. Dwyer
Coo And President Providence Campus, Mim L.
  Runey
Treasurer And Cfo, Joseph J. Greene
President Charlotte Campus, Robert C. Mock, age
  52
President North Miami Campus, Larry Rice
**Senior Vice President Planning And Human
  Resources,** William McArdle
**Vice President Student Affairs And Dean
  Students,** Ron Martel
Chairman, James H. (Jim) Hance, age 73
Auditors: MCGLADREY LLP CHARLESTOWN MA

LOCATIONS
HQ: JOHNSON & WALES UNIVERSITY INC
  8 ABBOTT PARK PL, PROVIDENCE, RI 029033775
Phone: 401 598-1000
Web: WWW.JWUATHLETICS.COM

PRODUCTS/OPERATIONS

2017 Sales
	% of total
Net student fees	90
Practicum properties	3
Investment return appropriated for operations	3
Private gifts grants and federal aid to students	1
Other sources	2
Net Assets Released from Restriction	1
Total	100

Selected Programs
Accounting
Advertising and marketing communications
Baking & pastry arts
Baking & pastry arts and food service management
Beverage industry operations and retail management
Biology
Business administration
Business studies
Computer programming
Computerized drafting
Corporate accounting and financial analysis
Counseling
Counseling psychology
Criminal justice
Culinary arts

Selected Colleges and Schools
The Alan Shawn Feinstein Graduate School
College of Business
College of Culinary Arts
The Hospitality College
School of Technology

Selected Operations
CAFE LLC
Griffin Realty Enterprises Inc.
Griffin Realty of Rhode Island-Florida Inc.
Harborside Enterprises Inc.
J.W.C. Corporation
J&W Corporation
Johnson & Wales Alumni Services Corporation
Johnson & Wales University
Johnson & Wales University Club

HISTORICAL FINANCIALS
Company Type: Private

Income Statement				FYE: June 30
	REVENUE ($ mil.)	NET INCOME ($ mil.)	NET PROFIT MARGIN	EMPLOYEES
06/17	344	24	7.0%	1,400
06/16	346	(11)	—	—
06/15	503	26	5.4%	—
06/13	349	37	10.6%	—
Annual Growth	(0.3%)	(10.2%)	—	—

2017 Year-End Financials
Return on assets: 12.8%   Cash ($ mil.): 16
Return on equity: 7.0%
Current ratio: 0.40

JOHNSON CONTROLS FIRE PROTECTION LP

SimplexGrinnell handles emergencies well. The
company provides integrated security alarm fire
suppression healthcare communications and emergency lighting systems. SimplexGrinnell reaches
some 1 million customers in the US and Canada
through more than 150 district offices located in
the Americas Europe Asia and other regions. In
addition to providing security and fire related products SimplexGrinnell operates a service division
devoted to test and inspection preventive maintenance central station monitoring and emergency
services. The company's clients include members
of local state and federal government agencies corporations oil and gas companies hospitals and educational facilities.

Operations
The company's communications segment provides mass notification and commercial paging as
well as intercom and other sound systems. The
company also provides healthcare communications
such as infant security nurse call and emergency
alert units.

Strategy
SimplexGrinnell launched a new website to give
its customers a fast and convenient way to purchase many of its products that do not require installation support.

EXECUTIVES
Vp And Cfo, Robert F. (Bob) Chauvin
Ceo, George Oliver

LOCATIONS
HQ: JOHNSON CONTROLS FIRE PROTECTION LP
  4700 EXCHANGE CT STE 300, BOCA RATON, FL
  334314450
Phone: 561 988-7200
Web: WWW.TYCOSIMPLEXGRINNELL.COM

PRODUCTS/OPERATIONS

Selected Products and Services
Fire Detection and Alarm
Control Panels
Notification
Network Solutions
Smoke Detector and Carbon Monoxide Detection
Sound and Communication
Healthcare Communications
Emergency Communications
Public Address and Intercom
Sound Reinforcement
Telephone Networks

Integrated Security
Access Control
Intrusion Detection
Property Surveillance
Mass Notification
Fire Sprinkler and Suppression
Fire Extinguisher
Special Hazards
Sprinkler

COMPETITORS

APi Group
Brink's
COSCO Fire Protection
Honeywell International
Ingersoll-Rand Security Technologies
Protection One

HISTORICAL FINANCIALS

Company Type: Private

Income Statement				FYE: September 30
	REVENUE ($ mil.)	NET INCOME ($ mil.)	NET PROFIT MARGIN	EMPLOYEES
09/16	1,871	182	9.7%	9,500
09/09	1,750	0	—	—
Annual Growth	1.0%	—	—	—

JOHNSON CONTROLS, INC.

EXECUTIVES

Pres-Coo, George R Oliver
Exec V Pres-Cfo, Brian Stief
V Pres-Gen Counsel-Sec, Brian J Cadwallader
V Pres-Corp Contrl, Suzanne M Vincent
Cpo-V Pres of Controls Operati, Michael Bartschat
Coordinator, Bob Anders
Designer, Ed Stevens
Coordinator, Debra Morley
Coordinator, Mary Moore
Compliance Staff, Melissa Goetz-Krummel
Coordinator, Patricia Kettner
Auditors: PRICEWATERHOUSECOOPERS LLP MI

LOCATIONS

HQ: JOHNSON CONTROLS, INC.
5757 N GREEN BAY AVE, MILWAUKEE, WI 532094408
Phone: 414 524-1200
Web: WWW.JCI.COM

COMPETITORS

3M	Honeywell
A123 Systems	International
Addison	Illinois Tool Works
Alcoa	Inci Aku
Building Technologies	International Paper
Caterpillar	Invensys
Comfort Systems USA	Lear Corp
DENSO	Lennox
Deere	Lockheed Martin
Delphi Automotive	Magna International
Systems	Northrop Grumman
Dow Chemical	Paloma Group
DuPont	Raytheon
Eagle-Picher	Rieter Automotive
East Penn	North America
Manufacturing	Robert Bosch
Eaton	SPX
Emerson Electric	Trane Inc.
Exide	United Technologies
Faurecia	Valeo

GS Yuasa
General Dynamics
General Motors
Goodman Global
Goodyear Tire & Rubber
Visteon
Whirlpool
Yazaki North America

HISTORICAL FINANCIALS

Company Type: Private

Income Statement				FYE: September 30
	REVENUE ($ mil.)	NET INCOME ($ mil.)	NET PROFIT MARGIN	EMPLOYEES
09/15	37,179	1,679	4.5%	139,000
09/14	42,828	1,335	3.1%	—
09/13	42,730	1,297	3.0%	—
Annual Growth	(6.7%)	13.8%	—	—

2015 Year-End Financials

Return on assets: 12.1%
Return on equity: 4.5%
Current ratio: 0.60
Cash ($ mil.): 597

JOINT SCHOOL DISTRICT 2

EXECUTIVES

Supt, Linda Clark
Asst Supt, Bruce Gestrin
Superintendent, Mary Ann Ranells
Security Staff, Alex Wells
Coordinator, Andrew Hunter
Teacher, Callie Pugel
Database Administrator, Gary Ackaret
Coordinator, Tobey Jossis
Security Staff, Travis Stuart
Auditors: EIDE BAILLY LLP BOISE IDAHO

LOCATIONS

HQ: JOINT SCHOOL DISTRICT 2
1303 E CENTRAL DR, MERIDIAN, ID 836427991
Phone: 208 855-4500
Web: WWW.WESTADA.ORG

HISTORICAL FINANCIALS

Company Type: Private

Income Statement				FYE: June 30
	REVENUE ($ mil.)	NET INCOME ($ mil.)	NET PROFIT MARGIN	EMPLOYEES
06/18	322	98	30.5%	4,000
06/17	300	(15)	—	—
06/16	278	(35)	—	—
06/15	257	97	37.9%	—
Annual Growth	7.8%	0.2%	—	—

2018 Year-End Financials

Return on assets: 12.0%
Return on equity: 30.5%
Current ratio: —
Cash ($ mil.): 36

JORDAN SCHOOL DISTRICT

EXECUTIVES

Supt, Patrice Johnson
Bus Admin, Burke Jolley
Vice President, Leah Voorhies
Prin, Richard S Osborn
Prin, Susan Pulsipher
Payroll Staff, Ladenea Jenkins
Director, Darby Cowles
Assistant, Amanda Hansen
Technology/Computer Coord, Mark Sowa
Secretary, Dianne Christensen
Secretary, Brenda Crockett
Auditors: SQUIRE & COMPANY PC OREM UT

LOCATIONS

HQ: JORDAN SCHOOL DISTRICT
7387 S CAMPUS VIEW DR, WEST JORDAN, UT 840845500
Phone: 801 280-3689
Web: WWW.JORDANDISTRICT.ORG

HISTORICAL FINANCIALS

Company Type: Private

Income Statement				FYE: June 30
	REVENUE ($ mil.)	NET INCOME ($ mil.)	NET PROFIT MARGIN	EMPLOYEES
06/16	415	27	6.6%	5,900
06/15	391	9	2.3%	—
06/14	378	(3)	—	—
06/13	366	5	1.6%	—
Annual Growth	4.2%	69.0%	—	—

JP ENERGY PARTNERS LP

EXECUTIVES

Pres-Ceo, J Patrick Barley
Evp-Cfo, Patrick J Welch
Sr Vp-Cao, Shiming Chen
Vp-Corp Controller-Cao, Michael Croney
Auditors: PRICEWATERHOUSECOOPERS LLP DA

LOCATIONS

HQ: JP ENERGY PARTNERS LP
600 LAS COLINAS BLVD E # 2000, IRVING, TX 750395607
Phone: 972 444-0300
Web: WWW.JPENERGYPARTNERS.COM

HISTORICAL FINANCIALS

Company Type: Private

Income Statement				FYE: December 31
	REVENUE ($ mil.)	NET INCOME ($ mil.)	NET PROFIT MARGIN	EMPLOYEES
12/16	493	(34)	—	737
12/14	1,693	(53)	—	—
Annual Growth	(46.0%)	—	—	—

2016 Year-End Financials

Return on assets: 8.7%
Return on equity: (-7.0%)
Current ratio: 0.90
Cash ($ mil.): 2

JSI RESEARCH AND TRAINING INSTITUTE, INC.

EXECUTIVES

Pres, Joel H Lamstein
Vice President, Theo Lippeveld
Coo, Alexander K Baker
Dir, Carolyn Hart
Dir, Ken Olivola
Information Technology Manager, Lori Kiel
Technical Manager, Wayne Zafft
Project Director, Debra Olesen
Vice-President, Pat Fairchild
Manager, Chet Shala
Project Director, Rachel Kohn
Auditors: NORMAN R FOUGERE JR CPA DU

LOCATIONS

HQ: JSI RESEARCH AND TRAINING INSTITUTE, INC.
44 FARNSWORTH ST FL 7, BOSTON, MA 022101206
Phone: 617 482-9485
Web: WWW.JSI.COM

HISTORICAL FINANCIALS

Company Type: Private

Income Statement				FYE: September 30
	REVENUE ($ mil.)	NET INCOME ($ mil.)	NET PROFIT MARGIN	EMPLOYEES
09/17	349	2	0.8%	135
09/16	321	14	4.6%	—
09/15	270	5	2.2%	—
09/14	196	5	2.6%	—
Annual Growth	21.2%	(18.0%)	—	—

2017 Year-End Financials

Return on assets: 3.3%   Cash ($ mil.): 74
Return on equity: 0.8%
Current ratio: 1.50

KADLEC REGIONAL MEDICAL CENTER

Kadlec Regional Medical Center is an acute care hospital facility serving southeastern Washington and northeastern Oregon. In addition to providing comprehensive medical surgical and emergency services the hospital provides neonatal intensive care cardiopulmonary rehabilitation interventional cardiology neurology cancer care and other specialist services. Not-for-profit Kadlec Regional has some 270 inpatient beds including pediatric intensive intermediate and critical care capacity. It also operates outpatient physician offices and clinics in surrounding areas.

Operations

Kadlec Regional's cardiovascular programs include open heart surgery and interventional cardiology. The hospital also operates an all-digital outpatient imaging center and the region's only level III neonatal intensive care unit (NICU). Kadlec was is also designated as a Level 1 Cardiac Center and a Level 2 Stroke Center. Area specialist practices include centers for dermatology colorectal surgery nephrology pediatrics women's health ENT (ear nose and throat) and foot and ankle practices. Kadlec Regional also operates satellite urgent care and family practice clinics.

The Kadlec Neuroscience Center offers a wide range of services to treat and diagnose conditions related to the brain spine spinal cord & peripheral nervous system.

In 2013 the hospital reported more than 2700 births 66000 emergency department visits and about 15000 admissions.

That year Kadlec Regional provided $27 million in charity care.

Geographic Reach

Kadlec Regional has hospital and clinic locations in Hermiston Kennewick Pasco Pendleton Prosser and Richland.

Financial Performance

The hospital reported revenue of $312 million in 2012 consisting of $305 million in net patient service earnings and other revenue of some $7.5 million. Kadlec Regional brought in profits of some $29 million.

Strategy

The hospital has undergone aggressive expansion efforts adding a new patient tower with diagnostic outpatient and intermediate care and surgery rooms. Kadlec Regional is enhancing its specialty service units in fields to attract specialists and increase revenue. The organization launched a $10 million project to expand its NICU unit in 2013. It will add 27 private and semi-private rooms and new observation gathering and lactation areas.

It is also expanding outpatient service facilities such as a new $19 million three-story specialty physician practice office that opened in Richland in 2013. The new building increases collaboration between various surgical and medical specialists in the Kadlec Regional clinic network.

The year the company also expanded its emergency room offerings through the opening of the Kadlec ER in Kennewick. The new 15-bed ER is the first in the region to operate as a freestanding facility like traditional hospital-based ERs.

Mergers and Acquisitions

Kadlec Regional also absorbs other area providers. In 2013 Inland Cardiology Associates become part of the Kadlec Regional health system. The region's largest independent group of experienced cardiologists Inland provides comprehensive invasive noninvasive and interventional services throughout southeast Washington and northeast Oregon.

Company Background

In 2011 it partnered with the nearby PMH Medical Center to increase collaboration and specialist referrals between the two hospitals. The partnership extends the reach of Kadlec Regional's medical specialists to additional communities and brings PMH online with Kadlec Regional's electronic health record system. Both hospitals remained independently run.

The hospital system was founded in 1944.

EXECUTIVES

Vice President Strategic Planning, Jeffrey Clark
Vice President Of Technical, Nathan Sheeran
Board Member, Jeff Clark

LOCATIONS

HQ: KADLEC REGIONAL MEDICAL CENTER
888 SWIFT BLVD, RICHLAND, WA 993523514
Phone: 509 946-4611
Web: WWW.KADLEC.ORG

PRODUCTS/OPERATIONS

Selected Services
The Birth Center
Bloodless Medicine and Surgery
Cancer Care
Cardiac Care
Cardiac Catheterization
CardioPulmonary Rehabilitation
Cardiovascular and Thoracic Surgery
CaringBridge
Clinical Decision Unit
Coumadin Clinic
Diabetes Learning Center
Diagnostic Imaging
Don and Lori Watts Pediatric Center
Emergency Department
Emergency Room-Kennewick
Home Health Care
Imaging
Inpatient Rehabilitation and Therapy
Intensive Care Unit
Joint Care Center
Kadlec Academy
Kadlec Healthy Ages
Kadlec Medical Associates
Neonatal Intensive Care Unit
Occupational Medicine
Occupational Therapy
Ostomy Support Group
Outpatient Imaging Center
Outpatient Procedures
Physical Therapy
Planetree
Rehabilitation and Therapy Services
Speech Therapy
Urgent Care
Water Therapy
Wound Healing Center

COMPETITORS

Adventist Health System West
Asante Health System
Legacy Health System
PeaceHealth
Providence Health & Services-Washington
Providence St. Joseph Health
Salem Hospital
Wenatchee Valley Medical Center
Yakima Valley Memorial

HISTORICAL FINANCIALS

Company Type: Private

Income Statement				FYE: December 31
	REVENUE ($ mil.)	NET INCOME ($ mil.)	NET PROFIT MARGIN	EMPLOYEES
12/17	595	87	14.7%	2,668
12/16	534	9	1.9%	—
12/15	504	(7)	—	—
12/14	417	190	45.7%	—
Annual Growth	12.6%	(23.0%)	—	—

2017 Year-End Financials

Return on assets: 2.8%   Cash ($ mil.): 139
Return on equity: 14.7%
Current ratio: 5.10

KALISPELL REGIONAL HEALTHCARE SYSTEM

EXECUTIVES

Pres-Ceo, Pamela Robertson
Pres, Velinda Stevens
Chb, Doug Nelson
Treas, Charles T Pearce
Manager Supply/Materials Mgmt, Dave Brabham
Network Engineer, Aaron Turner
Supervisor, Christl Stanwood
Phlebotomist, Doreen Hatcher
Manager, Cheryl Holland
Chief Pilot, Matthew Weller
Chief Policy Advisor Governmen, Rebecca Manna
Auditors: JORDAHL & SLITER PLLC KALISPE

LOCATIONS

HQ: KALISPELL REGIONAL HEALTHCARE SYSTEM
310 SUNNYVIEW LN, KALISPELL, MT 599013129
Phone: 406 752-8991
Web: WWW.KALISPELLREGIONAL.ORG

HISTORICAL FINANCIALS

Company Type: Private

Income Statement				FYE: March 31
	REVENUE ($ mil.)	NET INCOME ($ mil.)	NET PROFIT MARGIN	EMPLOYEES
03/18	571	(21)	—	3,100
03/14	2	(2)	—	—
03/12	2	(1)	—	—
03/11	1	(1)	—	—
Annual Growth	126.9%	—	—	—

2018 Year-End Financials

Return on assets: 8.7%
Return on equity: (-3.7%)
Current ratio: 0.80
Cash ($ mil.): 50

KANSAS STATE UNIVERSITY

K-State is a big deal in the Little Apple. Located in Manhattan Kansas (aka the Little Apple) Kansas State University (K-State) is a land grant institution that has an enrollment of some 24000 students. It offers more than 250 undergraduate majors 65A master's degrees 45 doctoral degrees and more than 20 graduate certificate programs. Major fields of study include agriculture technologyA and veterinary medicine.A Notable alumni include former White House press secretary Marlin Fitzwater and actor Gordon Jump. Along with the University of Kansas and other universities technical schools and community collegesA in the state K-State is governed byA TheA Kansas Board of Regents.

Operations

With a student-to-faculty ratio of 20:1 K-State ranks among top US colleges and has one of the highest levels of prestigious scholarship winners (including Rhodes Marshall and Truman scholars) in the US. The university also has several notable research organizations in fields including agriculture and genetic science.

K-State is also big on sports and is part of the Big 12 Conference of collegiate athletics.

Geographic Reach

K-State has its main campus on 670-acres in Manhattan Kansas. It also has satellite campuses in Salina and Olathe. It also hasA agricultural and researchA centersA at five KansasA locations.A The university's students come from all 50 US states and more than 90 countries.

Financial Performance

K-State increased revenues by 9% to $541 millionA in 2012 due toA higher income fromA student fees; government and non-government grants and contracts (for research and athletic activities); and auxiliary enterprises. Net income decreased 24% to $47 millionA due to higher operating expenses and lower non-operating revenues which was attributed to lower state appropriation levels and higher interest expenses.

Strategy

K-State is expanding its facilities and programs to meet the needs of its students. It completed the first $22 million phase of its National Bio and Agro-Defense Facility in 2012 as well as work on a new student recreational housing classroom and athletics facilities. In 2011 it added a new bachelor's degree program in social work. It also expanded its partnership with the Chinese scholarship council to allow additional students from China to study at K-State.

Company Background

K-State was established in 1858 as Bluemont Central College; five years later it was one of the firstA colleges in the USA to be designated a land-grant school.

EXECUTIVES

Pres, Richard B Myers
Provost and Senior Vice Presid, April Mason
Accounting Staff, Jenny Imhoff
Digital & Social Media Directo, Jay Alloway
Scientist, Christopher M Sorensen
Payroll Staff, Donnita Nelson
Scientist, George Marchin
Scientist, Marietta R White
Scientist, Maureen J Gorman
Scientist, Neena Kanwar
Scientist, Vijayalakshmi Iyer

LOCATIONS

HQ: KANSAS STATE UNIVERSITY
ANDERSON HALL 110 1301 MI, MANHATTAN, KS 66506
Phone: 785 532-6011
Web: WWW.OLATHE.K-STATE.EDU

PRODUCTS/OPERATIONS

Selected Colleges and Departments

College of Agriculture
  Agricultural Economics
  Agronomy
  Animal Sciences and Industry
  Entomology
  Food Science Institute
  Grain Science and Industry
  Plant Pathology
College of Architecture Planning and Design
  Architecture
  Interior Architecture and Product Design
  Landscape Architecture/Regional and Community Planning
College of Arts and Sciences
  Aerospace Studies
  American Ethnic Studies
  Art
  Biochemistry
  Chemistry
  Economics
  English
  Geography
  Geology
  History
  International and Area Studies
  Journalism and Mass Communications
  Kinesiology
  Mathematics
  Military Science
  Modern Languages
  Music
  Philosophy
  Physics
  Political Science
  Psychology
  Statistics
  Women's Studies
College of Business Administration
  Accounting
  Finance
  Management
  Marketing
College of Education
  Educational Leadership
  Elementary Education
  Secondary Education
  Special Education Counseling and Student Affairs
College of Engineering
  Architectural Engineering and Construction Science
  Biological and Agricultural Engineering
  Chemical Engineering
  Computing and Information Science
  Electrical and Computer Engineering
  Mechanical and Nuclear Engineering
College of Human Ecology
  Apparel Textiles and Interior Design
  Gerontology
  Human Nutrition
College of Technology and Aviation
  Arts Sciences and Business
  Aviation Technology
College of Veterinary Medicine
  Anatomy and Physiology
  Clinical Sciences

COMPETITORS

Baylor University	University of Colorado
Iowa State University	University of Missouri
Oklahoma State	University of Nebraska
Texas A&M	University of Oklahoma
Texas Tech	University of Texas
The University of Kansas	Wichita State University

HISTORICAL FINANCIALS

Company Type: Private

Income Statement				FYE: June 30
	REVENUE ($ mil.)	NET INCOME ($ mil.)	NET PROFIT MARGIN	EMPLOYEES
06/17	620	50	8.2%	5,168
06/10	459	50	11.0%	—
06/09	420	10	2.6%	—
Annual Growth	5.0%	21.4%	—	—

2017 Year-End Financials

Return on assets: 8.2%
Return on equity: 8.2%
Current ratio: 1.60
Cash ($ mil.): 150

KAPIOLANI MEDICAL CENTER FOR WOMEN AND CHILDREN

EXECUTIVES

Ceo, Martha Smith
Surgeon, Devin Puapong
Gynecology/Obstetrics Speclst, Angela M Pratt
Gynecology/Obstetrics Speclst, Donna Yamada
Gynecology/Obstetrics Speclst, Jon Morikawa
Gynecology/Obstetrics Speclst, Rosemarie Chang
Obstetrician, Christina Arnett
Psychiatrist, Roshni Koli
Pediatrician, Shelley Loui
Manager, Sneha Sood
Family Practitioner, Hisashima Zale

LOCATIONS

HQ: KAPIOLANI MEDICAL CENTER FOR WOMEN AND CHILDREN
1319 PUNAHOU ST STE 630, HONOLULU, HI 968261044
Phone: 808 535-7401
Web: WWW.KAPIOLANI.ORG

HISTORICAL FINANCIALS
Company Type: Private

Income Statement FYE: June 30

	REVENUE ($ mil.)	NET INCOME ($ mil.)	NET PROFIT MARGIN	EMPLOYEES
06/15	371	102	27.7%	1,378
06/09	218	23	10.6%	—
06/05*	187	13	6.9%	—
03/04	130	8	6.5%	—
Annual Growth	10.0%	25.3%	—	—

*Fiscal year change

KATY INDEPENDENT SCHOOL DISTRICT

EXECUTIVES

Pres, Bryan Michalsky
Pres-SEC, Rebecca Fox
Vice President, Henry Dibrell
Vice President, Joe M Adams
Supt, Alton Fraley
Treas, Charles Griffin
Cfo, William L Moore
Board of Directors, Neal Howard
Coordinator, Howard Grimet
Staff, Jacqui Fitzgerald
Board of Directors, Tom Law

LOCATIONS

HQ: KATY INDEPENDENT SCHOOL DISTRICT
6301 S STADIUM LN, KATY, TX 774941057
Phone: 281 396-6000
Web: WWW.KATYISD.ORG

HISTORICAL FINANCIALS
Company Type: Private

Income Statement FYE: August 31

	REVENUE ($ mil.)	NET INCOME ($ mil.)	NET PROFIT MARGIN	EMPLOYEES
08/16	841	15	1.9%	6,631
08/11*	601	123	20.5%	—
12/09	540	(2)	—	—
08/08	508	(3)	—	—
Annual Growth	6.5%	—	—	—

*Fiscal year change

KAWEAH DELTA HEALTH CARE DISTRICT

EXECUTIVES

Ceo, Donna Archer
Ceo, Lindsay K Mann
V Pres-Cfo, Gary Herbst
Vice-President Finance, Jennifer Stockton
Director, Thomas L Gray
Information Technology/Interne, Christine Muldoon
Information Technology/Interne, Danny Desimas

Human Resources Administrator, Jaime Thomason
Blood Bank Manager, Carol Young
Marketing Director, Dru Quesnoy
Controller, Bill Blair

LOCATIONS

HQ: KAWEAH DELTA HEALTH CARE DISTRICT
400 W MINERAL KING AVE, VISALIA, CA 932916237
Phone: 559 624-2000
Web: WWW.KAWEAHDELTA.ORG

HISTORICAL FINANCIALS
Company Type: Private

Income Statement FYE: June 30

	REVENUE ($ mil.)	NET INCOME ($ mil.)	NET PROFIT MARGIN	EMPLOYEES
06/18	710	28	4.1%	3,200
06/16	537	52	9.8%	—
06/15	475	26	5.7%	—
06/08	370	16	4.5%	—
Annual Growth	6.7%	5.7%	—	—

2018 Year-End Financials

Return on assets: 6.3%   Cash ($ mil.): 5
Return on equity: 4.1%
Current ratio: 1.40

KCP&L GREATER MISSOURI OPERATIONS COMPANY

EXECUTIVES

Ceo, Terry D Bassham
Sr Vice President, Paul Perkins
Vice President, Maria Jenks
Vice President, Marvin L Rollison
Vice President, Chuck Tickles
Vice President, Stephen T Easley
Vice President, Scott Heidtbrink
Vice President, Lori A Wright
Vice President, Jim Alberts
Vice President, Kevin E Bryant
Vice President, Lora C Cheatman

LOCATIONS

HQ: KCP&L GREATER MISSOURI OPERATIONS COMPANY
1200 MAIN ST FL 30, KANSAS CITY, MO 641052122
Phone: 816 556-2200
Web: WWW.KCPL.COM

HISTORICAL FINANCIALS
Company Type: Private

Income Statement FYE: December 31

	REVENUE ($ mil.)	NET INCOME ($ mil.)	NET PROFIT MARGIN	EMPLOYEES
12/17	818	(40)	—	2,213
12/16	801	60	7.6%	—
Annual Growth	2.1%	—	—	—

2017 Year-End Financials

Return on assets: 10.1%   Cash ($ mil.): —
Return on equity: (-5.0%)
Current ratio: —

KENDALL WEST BAPTIST HOSPITAL INC

EXECUTIVES

Ceo, Javier Hernandez Lichtl
Internal Medicine Practitioner, Teresa Cardoso
Internal Medicine Practitioner, Carmen Andux-Gonzalez
Emergency Medicine Specialist, Richard Rodriguez
Emergency Medicine Specialist, Armando Clift
Family Practitioner, Natasha A Fajardo

LOCATIONS

HQ: KENDALL WEST BAPTIST HOSPITAL INC
9555 SW 162ND AVE, MIAMI, FL 331966408
Phone: 786 467-2000

HISTORICAL FINANCIALS
Company Type: Private

Income Statement FYE: September 30

	REVENUE ($ mil.)	NET INCOME ($ mil.)	NET PROFIT MARGIN	EMPLOYEES
09/16	309	10	3.4%	138
09/15	201	14	7.1%	—
09/14	182	5	3.2%	—
Annual Growth	30.3%	33.7%	—	—

2016 Year-End Financials

Return on assets: 8.4%   Cash ($ mil.): —
Return on equity: 3.4%
Current ratio: 0.20

KENERGY CORP.

EXECUTIVES

Vice President Human Resources, Keith Ellis
Vice President Finance And Accounting, Steve Thompson

LOCATIONS

HQ: KENERGY CORP.
6402 OLD CORYDON RD, HENDERSON, KY 424209392
Phone: 270 926-4141
Web: WWW.KENERGYCORP.COM

COMPETITORS

Duke Energy Kentucky   Warren RECC
Kentucky Utilities

HISTORICAL FINANCIALS
Company Type: Private

Income Statement FYE: December 31

	REVENUE ($ mil.)	NET INCOME ($ mil.)	NET PROFIT MARGIN	EMPLOYEES
12/15	375	0	0.0%	155
12/14	474	0	0.0%	—
12/13	506	0	0.0%	—
12/12	495	0	0.0%	—
Annual Growth	(8.8%)	(0.0%)	—	—

2015 Year-End Financials

Return on assets: 10.0%   Cash ($ mil.): 1
Return on equity: —
Current ratio: 0.90

KENNESTONE HOSPITAL AT WINDY HILL, INC.

Kennestone cures kidney stones and other ailments for residents of Cobb County Georgia. WellStar Kennestone Hospital has more than 630 beds and a full range of specialty services. The hospital's physicians provide cardiac care inpatient and outpatient surgery and rehabilitation trauma diabetes care oncology dialysis and home health care. The hospital also operates centers specializing in women's health senior living facilities diagnostic clinics and a wellness and fitness center. WellStar Kennestone Hospital is part of the not-for-profit WellStar Health System which operates hospitals and other medical facilities throughout Georgia.

Operations

WellStar Kennestone Hospital is the anchor of the group's WellStar Kennestone Regional Medical Center division. WellStar Kennestone Hospital handles about 37000 inpatient admissions each year as well as more than 400000 outpatient appointments and 120000 emergency room visits. It also conducts about 23000 inpatient and outpatient surgeries and 9000 births annually and operates a level II regional trauma center. The hospital has been recognized in a number of specialist fields such as orthopedics neurology and gastroenterology.

Geographic Reach

Located in Marietta Georgia WellStar Kennestone Hospital primary serves northern and central Cobb County.

Strategy

The hospital is undergoing renovation and expansion efforts including construction of a new hospital tower with all private patient rooms; the tower was completed and opened in early 2013. Two years later the hospital opened a new inpatient pediatric unit. It also began renovations of its cancer center.

WellStar Kennestone also regularly upgrades its medical technology systems and tools such as robotic surgery systems and data management programs.

EXECUTIVES

Director Of Him, Beth Kost

LOCATIONS

HQ: KENNESTONE HOSPITAL AT WINDY HILL, INC.
677 CHURCH ST NE, MARIETTA, GA 300601101
Phone: 770 793-5000
Web: WWW.WELLSTAR.ORG

COMPETITORS

Adventist Health System Sunbelt Healthcare
Children's Healthcare of Atlanta
DeKalb Medical
Emory Healthcare
Grady Health System
Northside Hospital
Piedmont Healthcare
Redmond Regional Medical Center
Regency Hospital
Shepherd Center
SunLink Health Systems
The Fulton-DeKalb Hospital Authority
West Georgia Health System

HISTORICAL FINANCIALS

Company Type: Private

Income Statement   FYE: June 30

	REVENUE ($ mil.)	NET INCOME ($ mil.)	NET PROFIT MARGIN	EMPLOYEES
06/15	821	106	12.9%	2,950
06/05	481	54	11.2%	—
06/04	877	50	5.7%	—
06/03	792	24	3.1%	—
Annual Growth	0.3%	12.9%	—	—

2015 Year-End Financials

Return on assets: 0.1%   Cash ($ mil.): —
Return on equity: 12.9%
Current ratio: 8.00

KENNESTONE HOSPITAL INC

Auditors: PRICEWATERHOUSECOOPERS LLP PH

LOCATIONS

HQ: KENNESTONE HOSPITAL INC
805 SANDY PLAINS RD, MARIETTA, GA 300666340
Phone: 770 792-5023
Web: WWW.WELLSTAR.ORG

HISTORICAL FINANCIALS

Company Type: Private

Income Statement   FYE: June 30

	REVENUE ($ mil.)	NET INCOME ($ mil.)	NET PROFIT MARGIN	EMPLOYEES
06/15	948	182	19.2%	15
06/14	836	113	13.5%	—
06/13	791	123	15.6%	—
06/10	800	123	15.5%	—
Annual Growth	3.5%	8.0%	—	—

2015 Year-End Financials

Return on assets: 2.2%   Cash ($ mil.): —
Return on equity: 19.2%
Current ratio: 7.80

KENOSHA UNIFIED SCHOOL DISTRICT 1

EXECUTIVES

Pres, Rebecca Stevens
Up, Michele Hancock
Exec Dir, Ms Sheronda Glass
Cfo, Tina Schmitz
Financial, Val Dowe
Vice President, Jo Ann Taube
Treas, Carl Bryan
Staff, Paul Levonowich
Food Director, Cindy Gossett
Maintenance Supervisor, Kevin Christoun
Supervisor, Steve Mastronardi

LOCATIONS

HQ: KENOSHA UNIFIED SCHOOL DISTRICT 1
3600 52ND ST, KENOSHA, WI 531442664
Phone: 262 359-6300
Web: WWW.KUSD.EDU

HISTORICAL FINANCIALS

Company Type: Private

Income Statement   FYE: June 30

	REVENUE ($ mil.)	NET INCOME ($ mil.)	NET PROFIT MARGIN	EMPLOYEES
06/17	298	63	21.1%	2,093
06/16	291	11	4.0%	—
06/11	289	(23)	—	—
06/08	224	(2)	—	—
Annual Growth	3.2%	—	—	—

KENT COUNTY MEMORIAL HOSPITAL

As one of Rhode Island's largest hospitals Kent County Memorial Hospital offers Ocean Staters a sea of medical care options. The healthcare facility provides inpatient acute care as well as outpatient services (such as diagnostic imaging) and primary care. It also offers a range of specialties including cardiology orthopedics oncology surgery pediatrics and women's health. A member of the Care New England Health System Kent Hospital opened in 1951 with 90 beds; today the hospital has about 360 beds and a staff of some 600 doctors.

Operations

As a member of Care New England Kent Hospital is affiliated with the University of New England College of Osteopathic Medicine (UNECOM) for medical education. IT also has relationships with the University of Rhode Island Rhode Island College Northeastern University and medical training and research other organizations.

The Kent Hospital staff works in more than 30 specialty areas. The hospital's care team includes more than 2300 nurses technical professionals and support staff. Kent Hospital's ER is the second busiest in the state with some 67000 annual visits. Overall the hospital handles 15000 inpatient admissions each year including 1000 births and conducts about 15000 inpatient and outpatient surgeries annually.

Geographic Reach

Kent Hospital is located on a 60-acre campus in Warwick Rhode Island (11 miles south of Providence); it also operates satellite primary care and diagnostic centers in the area. The hospital provides care to about 300000 residents across central Rhode Island in communities including Coventry Cranston Exeter Greenwich North Kingstown and Warwick.

Financial Performance

The hospital brought in $315.3 million in revenue during fiscal 2011. Kent Hospital's net revenue was some $3.2 million as operating expenses totaled $312.1 million.

During fiscal 2011 Kent Hospital provided $13.9 million in community and charity health care services.

Strategy

Kent Hospital opened its newly constructed ambulatory surgery center in 2013. The center includes eight surgery suites including specialist facilities for endoscopic and interventional spine procedures. Other facility expansions have included the opening of a $2 million emergency cardiac angioplasty center in 2009. In addition Kent Hospital has expanded its outpatient care and clinical research programs in recent years.

EXECUTIVES

Director Of Respiratory Therapy, Nancy Roman
Auditors: PRICEWATERHOUSECOOPERS LLP BO

LOCATIONS

HQ: KENT COUNTY MEMORIAL HOSPITAL
455 TOLL GATE RD, WARWICK, RI 028862770
Phone: 401 737-7000
Web: WWW.KENTRI.ORG

PRODUCTS/OPERATIONS

Selected Centers and Services
Behavioral Health Unit
Breast Health
Cancer Care
Cardiology
Colonoscopy
Continuing Medical Education Program
Cosmetic Surgery
CT Scan (CAT Scan or Computerized Axial Tomography)
Dentistry
Diagnostic Imaging Services
Dialysis
Education
Emergency Medicine
Endocrinology
Endoscopy
Expresscare Service
Eye Care
Family Practice
Food and Nutrition Services
Gastroenterology
Gift Shop
Hearing Assessment/Newborns
Home Medical Equipment (HME)
Hypertension
INNOVATION CENTER
Intensive Care Unit
Internal Medicine
Interventional Radiology (Special Procedures Suite)
Kent Hospitalists
Kids Choose to be Healthy
Laboratory Services
Library
Magnetic Resonance Imaging (MRI)
Multiple Sclerosis Center
Neonatal I
Nephrology
Neurology/Neurosurgery
Nuclear Medicine
Occupational Therapy
Orthopedics
Outpatient Rehabilitation Services
Outpatient Surgery
Palliative Care
Parkinson's Information and Referral Center
Pastoral Care
Pediatric Emergency Services
Pediatrics
Physical Therapy
Physician Relations
Podiatry
Prolotherapy
Psychiatry
Pulmonary Medicine
Radiology
Rehabilitation Center
Rheumatology
Sleep Lab
Social Services
Speech-Language Pathology
Stroke Center
Support Groups
Thoracic Surgery
Ultrasound
Urology
Videostroboscopy
Women's Diagnostic Imaging Center
Wound Recovery and Hyperbaric Medicine Center

COMPETITORS

Baystate Health
Day Kimball Hospital
Memorial Hospital of Rhode Island
Partners HealthCare
Roger Williams Medical Center

Southcoast Health
Southcoast Hospitals Group
Sturdy Memorial
Yale New Haven Health System

HISTORICAL FINANCIALS

Company Type: Private

Income Statement FYE: September 30

	REVENUE ($ mil.)	NET INCOME ($ mil.)	NET PROFIT MARGIN	EMPLOYEES
09/16	380	8	2.1%	1,850
09/15	318	14	4.7%	—
09/14	323	4	1.4%	—
09/13	339	(0)	—	—
Annual Growth	3.9%	—	—	—

2016 Year-End Financials
Return on assets: 11.0%   Cash ($ mil.): 6
Return on equity: 2.1%
Current ratio: 0.70

KENT SCHOOL DISTRICT

EXECUTIVES

Supt, Dr Calvin J Watts
Dir of Fin Svc, Ralph Fortunato
Administrative Assistant, Kathy Hiatt
Business Analyst, Cole Grubbs
K12 Teacher, Anna Whalen
Supervisor of Purchasing, Hal Nourse
Lead Business Analyst, Joelle Bejarano
K12 Teacher, Zina Rodriguez

LOCATIONS

HQ: KENT SCHOOL DISTRICT
12033 SE 256TH ST, KENT, WA 980306643
Phone: 253 373-7000
Web: WWW.KENT.K12.WA.US

HISTORICAL FINANCIALS

Company Type: Private

Income Statement FYE: August 31

	REVENUE ($ mil.)	NET INCOME ($ mil.)	NET PROFIT MARGIN	EMPLOYEES
08/17	368	66	18.2%	3,505
08/16	355	(20)	—	—
08/12	290	(2)	—	—
08/11	289	(2)	—	—
Annual Growth	4.1%	—	—	—

2017 Year-End Financials
Return on assets: 0.3%   Cash ($ mil.): 98
Return on equity: 18.2%
Current ratio: —

KENTUCKY MEDICAL SERVICES FOUNDATION, INC.

EXECUTIVES

Pres, Marc Randall
Exec Dir, Darrell Griffith
Vice President, Raleigh Jones
Dir, David Moliterno
Dir, Edwin Bowe
Dir, Joseph N Zwischenberger
Customer Representativ, Heather Taylor
Director, Brenda Nichols
Director, Julie Floyd
Auditors: DEAN DORTON ALLEN FORD PLLC L

LOCATIONS

HQ: KENTUCKY MEDICAL SERVICES FOUNDATION, INC.
2333 ALUMNI PARK PLZ # 200, LEXINGTON, KY 405174012
Phone: 859 257-7910
Web: WWW.KMSF.COM

COMPETITORS

Appalachian Regional Healthcare
Baptist Health
Catholic Health Initiatives

Jewish Hospital & St. Mary's HealthCare
Norton Healthcare

HISTORICAL FINANCIALS

Company Type: Private

Income Statement FYE: June 30

	REVENUE ($ mil.)	NET INCOME ($ mil.)	NET PROFIT MARGIN	EMPLOYEES
06/15	306	10	3.6%	150
06/14	236	1	0.7%	—
06/13	225	(0)	—	—
06/10	196	(4)	—	—
Annual Growth	9.3%	—	—	—

2015 Year-End Financials
Return on assets: 2.2%   Cash ($ mil.): 59
Return on equity: 3.6%
Current ratio: 14.40

KERN HIGH SCHOOL DST

EXECUTIVES

Supt, Donald E Carter
Principal, Robert Schneider
Principal, Jim Caswell
Payroll Staff, Gregory Vasquez
Superintendent, Don Carter
Auditors: MAYER HOFFMAN MCCANN PC BAK

LOCATIONS

HQ: KERN HIGH SCHOOL DST
5801 SUNDALE AVE, BAKERSFIELD, CA 933097908
Phone: 661 827-3100
Web: WWW.KERNHIGH.ORG

HISTORICAL FINANCIALS

Company Type: Private

Income Statement

FYE: June 30

	REVENUE ($ mil.)	NET INCOME ($ mil.)	NET PROFIT MARGIN	EMPLOYEES
06/17	518	40	7.8%	2,000
06/16	507	44	8.7%	—
06/13	405	(11)	—	—
06/08	482	31	6.4%	—
Annual Growth	0.8%	3.0%	—	—

2017 Year-End Financials

Return on assets: 7.6%   Cash ($ mil.): 317
Return on equity: 7.8%
Current ratio: —

KERN RIVER GAS TRANSMISSION COMPANY

EXECUTIVES

Pres, Gary W Hoogeveen
Vice President, Micheal Dunn
Vice President, Richard Stapler
Vice President, Bret W Reich
Vice President, Robert S Checketts
Vice President, John T Dushinske
Vice President, Mary Kay Miller
Vice President, J Gregory Porter
Senior Analyst, Jacob Daniel
Manager, Glen Bancroft
Administrative Assistant, Michael Farmer

LOCATIONS

HQ: KERN RIVER GAS TRANSMISSION COMPANY
2755 E COTTONWOOD PKWY # 300, SALT LAKE CITY, UT 841216949
Phone: 801 937-6000
Web: WWW.KERNRIVERGAS.COM

HISTORICAL FINANCIALS

Company Type: Private

Income Statement

FYE: December 31

	REVENUE ($ mil.)	NET INCOME ($ mil.)	NET PROFIT MARGIN	EMPLOYEES
12/17	301	103	34.2%	160
12/16	342	92	27.0%	—
Annual Growth	(11.8%)	11.6%	—	—

2017 Year-End Financials

Return on assets: 1.4%   Cash ($ mil.): 7
Return on equity: 34.2%
Current ratio: 1.00

KETTERING ADVENTIST HEALTHCARE

Kettering Adventist Healthcare dba Kettering Health Network and named for famed inventor Charles F. Kettering is an Ohio-based health care system. It comprises about 120 outpatient facilities including seven acute care hospitals: Kettering Medical Center Grandview Medical Center Sycamore Medical Center Southview Medical Center Fort Hamilton Hospital Greene Memorial Hospital and Soin Medical Center. Other facilities include Kettering Behavioral Hospital and multiple outpatient diagnostic senior care and urgent care clinics. Among its specialized services are heart care rehabilitation orthopedics women's health and emergency medicine.

Operations

Several times in recent years Kettering Health has been named by Thomson Reuters as one of the Top 10 US Healthcare Systems.

The system operates nine radiology centers 10 pharmacies eight outpatient rehab centers seven sleep centers 13 sports medicine centers and five wound centers.

Kettering Health provides community care benefits including health screenings education programs charity care for uninsured patients and coverage of Medicare/Medicaid shortfalls for under-insured patients.

Geographic Reach

Kettering Health's facilities are located in Dayton Ohio and the surrounding towns of Beavercreek Centerville Hamilton Kettering Miamisburg and Xenia.

Financial Performance

Revenue totaled $1.4 billion in 2014.

Strategy

Kettering makes capital investments in its medical centers to better serve its communities. It works to improve specialty units and equipment at its existing inpatient hospitals as well as technologically advanced hospitals tend to attract better physicians (and therefore patients). Kettering is adding new freestanding emergency room facilities in Franklin and in Eaton to the tune of $19 million. In 2015 it broke ground on a $49 million five-story cancer center at Kettering Medical Center.

The health network is also intent on expanding its outpatient facility network.

It's expanding in Ohio as well through a 2014 collaboration with Health Innovations of Ohio. To keep its database up to date Kettering in 2014 enlisted the help of ProVation Order Sets to oversee its clinical content management system.

EXECUTIVES

Medical Director Ccu And Respiratory Services, Hemant Shah
Vice President Medical Affairs Chief Medical Officer, Robert Smith

LOCATIONS

HQ: KETTERING ADVENTIST HEALTHCARE
3535 SOUTHERN BLVD, DAYTON, OH 454291221
Phone: 937 298-4331
Web: WWW.KHNETWORK.ORG

PRODUCTS/OPERATIONS

Selected Ohio Facilities

Acute Care Hospitals
Fort Hamilton Hospital (Hamilton)
Grandview Medical Center (Dayton)
Greene Memorial Hospital (Xenia)
Kettering Medical Center (Kettering)
Soin Medical Center (Beavercreek)
Southview Medical Center (Dayton)
Sycamore Medical Center (Miamisburg)
Other
Adolescent Recovery Center of Hope
Beavercreek Health Center
Beavercreek Health Park
Charles H. Huber Health Center
Corwin M. Nixon Health Center
Englewood Community Medical Center
Kettering Behavioral Hospital (Dayton)
Sugarcreek Health Center
Sycamore Glen Health Center
Sycamore Glen Retirement Center
Sycamore Primary Care Center
Urgent Care Centers (regional)

Selected Services

Assisted Living
Back Pain
Bariatric
Behavioral Health
Bladder Confidence
Breast Health
Cancer Care
Cardiovascular
Corporate Wellness
Community Outreach
Counseling
Diabetes
Emergency
Epilepsy
Executive Health
Fertility
Gamma Knife
Heart Care
Home Care
Hyperbaric Medicine
Imaging
Independent Living
Mammography
Maternity
Mental Health
Minimally Invasive Surgery
Neonatal Care
Neuroscience
NeuroRehab
Nutrition Counseling
Obstetrics
Oncology
Orthopedics
Pain Management
Palliative Care
Pastoral Care
Pelvic Control
Physical Therapy
Pulmonary Rehab
Radiology
Rehab Therapy
Reproductive
Robotic Surgery
Senior Living
Short-term Rehab
Skilled Nursing
Sleep
Spine
Spiritual Services
Sports Medicine
Stroke
Surgery
Urgent Care
Weight Loss
Wound Care

COMPETITORS

AdCare
Adena Health System
Cincinnati Children's Hospital
Fairfield Medical Center
Licking Memorial Health Systems
MetroHealth System
Mount Carmel Health
OhioHealth
Premier Health Partners
Regency Hospital
Select Medical
TriHealth
UC Health
University Hospitals Health System

HISTORICAL FINANCIALS

Company Type: Private

Income Statement
FYE: December 31

	REVENUE ($ mil.)	NET INCOME ($ mil.)	NET PROFIT MARGIN	EMPLOYEES
12/17	1,753	171	9.8%	6,800
12/16	1,577	98	6.2%	—
Annual Growth	11.2%	74.6%	—	—

2017 Year-End Financials

Return on assets: 5.5%
Return on equity: 9.8%
Current ratio: 1.40

Cash ($ mil.): 243

KEY FOOD STORES CO-OPERATIVE, INC.

Key Food Stores Co-Operative is a friend to independent New York area grocers. The co-op provides retail support and other services to 150 independently owned food retailers in the New York City area. Key Food's member-owners run stores mainly in Brooklyn and Queens but also in the other boroughs and surrounding counties. It operates stores primarily under the Key Food banner but it also has Key Food Marketplace locations that feature expanded meat deli and produce departments. In addition the co-op supplies Key Foods-branded products to member stores. Among its members are Pick Quick Foods Dan's Supreme Super Markets Gemstone Supermarkets and Queens Supe rmarkets. Key Foods was founded in 1937.

Geographic Reach

Staten Island-based Key Food Stores Co-Operative operates supermarkets across the five boroughs and on Long Island in upstate New York and in New Jersey and Pennsylvania.

Financial Performance

Key Foods Stores has annual sales of about $1.5 billion.

Strategy

Key Food has been expanding in Queens and Brooklyn and on Long Island after scaling back in Manhattan — where many of its stores were converted to Duane Reade drugstores as the pharmacy chain expanded and took over individual locations. To that end in late 2013 the regional grocer launched a new banner called Urban Market in Brooklyn. The 16000-square foot store in Williamsburg was the co-op's 150th location. The cooperative is expanding aggressively adding more than 30 locations under the Key Food Key Fresh & Natural and Food Dynasty banners including stores in Harlem and the Bronx. It also recently reopened a store in Coney Island that was destroyed by Hurricane Sandy in 2012.

EXECUTIVES

Ceo, Dean Janeway
Chb, Lawrence Mandel
Pres, Richard Grobman
V Pres, Salvatore Bonavita
SEC, Sam Obeid
Treas, Anthony Bileddo
Asst SEC, Benjamin Levine
Coordinator, Marnique Ortiz
Executive Office Manager, Madeline Donohue
Information Technology Project, Michaele Domnisch
Vice President Finance, Sharon Konzelman
Auditors: ANCHIN BLOCK & ANCHIN LLP N

LOCATIONS

HQ: KEY FOOD STORES CO-OPERATIVE, INC.
1200 SOUTH AVE, STATEN ISLAND, NY 103143413
Phone: 718 370-4200
Web: WWW.KEYFOODSTORES.COM

PRODUCTS/OPERATIONS

Selected Banners
Food Dynasty
Food World
Holiday Farms
Key Food
Key Food Marketplace
Key Fresh & Natural
Locust Valley
Milford Farms
Urban Market
Vitelio's Marketplace

COMPETITORS

A&P	Fresh Direct
D'Agostino	Gristede's Foods
Supermarkets	King Kullen Grocery
Food Emporium	Walgreen

HISTORICAL FINANCIALS

Company Type: Private

Income Statement
FYE: April 25

	REVENUE ($ mil.)	NET INCOME ($ mil.)	NET PROFIT MARGIN	EMPLOYEES
04/15	893	(0)	—	84
04/14	753	0	0.0%	—
04/11	537	(0)	—	—
04/10	0	0	—	—
Annual Growth	—	—	—	—

2015 Year-End Financials

Return on assets: 4.9%
Return on equity: (-0.1%)
Current ratio: 0.80

Cash ($ mil.): 4

KEYSTOPS, LLC

EXECUTIVES

Mmbr, Lester Key
MBR, Rex Hazelip
MBR, Richard Shepherd
MBR, Kent Pyle
MBR, Charles Key
Distribution Shipping Transpor, George Cole
Auditors: BKD LLP BOWLING GREEN KENTUC

LOCATIONS

HQ: KEYSTOPS, LLC
376 REASONOVER AVE, FRANKLIN, KY 421344003
Phone: 270 586-8283
Web: WWW.KEYSTOPS.COM

HISTORICAL FINANCIALS

Company Type: Private

Income Statement
FYE: September 30

	REVENUE ($ mil.)	NET INCOME ($ mil.)	NET PROFIT MARGIN	EMPLOYEES
09/17	500	2	0.5%	200
09/16	430	4	1.0%	—
09/15	584	6	1.2%	—
09/14	900	3	0.3%	—
Annual Growth	(17.8%)	(4.0%)	—	—

2017 Year-End Financials

Return on assets: 3.5%
Return on equity: 0.5%
Current ratio: 0.70

Cash ($ mil.): 1

KILLEEN INDEPENDENT SCHOOL DISTRICT

EXECUTIVES

Supt, John Craft
Pres, Carlos Cole Jr
V Pres, Joshua Ayers
Dir, Tia Perry
Dir, Javoris Jordan
Dir, Jamal Wright
Cfo, Megan Bradley
Tech Prep Coordinator, Marvin Rainwater
Secretary, Angela Inman
Administrator, Larry Stegall
Manager of Management Informat, Anna Campos
Auditors: LOTT VERNON & COMPANY PC K

LOCATIONS

HQ: KILLEEN INDEPENDENT SCHOOL DISTRICT
200 N W S YOUNG DR, KILLEEN, TX 765434025
Phone: 254 336-0000
Web: WWW.KILLEENISD.ORG

HISTORICAL FINANCIALS

Company Type: Private

Income Statement
FYE: August 31

	REVENUE ($ mil.)	NET INCOME ($ mil.)	NET PROFIT MARGIN	EMPLOYEES
08/17	436	(30)	—	6,200
08/16	438	7	1.7%	—
08/15	418	21	5.2%	—
08/14	392	(3)	—	—
Annual Growth	3.7%	—	—	—

2017 Year-End Financials

Return on assets: 2.0%
Return on equity: (-6.9%)
Current ratio: —

Cash ($ mil.): 48

KING COUNTY PUBLIC HOSPITAL DISTRICT 2

EXECUTIVES

Ceo, Bob Malte
Sr Vice President, Neil Johnson
Vice President, Jack Handley
Scientist, Deanne Gilbert
Chief of Medicine, James D Brown
Project Manager, Brian Kenkman
Analyst, Cheryl Riley
Information Specialist, Dana Tran
Project Coordinator, Denise Peterson
Director, Gregg Aoyama
Physician, Aileen Mickey

LOCATIONS

HQ: KING COUNTY PUBLIC HOSPITAL DISTRICT 2
12040 NE 128TH ST, KIRKLAND, WA 980343013
Phone: 425 899-2769
Web: WWW.EVERGREENHEALTHCARE.ORG

HISTORICAL FINANCIALS
Company Type: Private

Income Statement				FYE: December 31
	REVENUE ($ mil.)	NET INCOME ($ mil.)	NET PROFIT MARGIN	EMPLOYEES
12/17	713	14	2.0%	2,400
12/16	597	(3)	—	—
12/15	565	3	0.7%	—
12/06	273	16	6.2%	—
Annual Growth	9.1%	(1.4%)	—	—

2017 Year-End Financials
Return on assets: 4.5%   Cash ($ mil.): 44
Return on equity: 2.0%
Current ratio: 1.40

KING'S DAUGHTERS HEALTH SYSTEM, INC.

EXECUTIVES

Ceo, Fred Jackson
SEC, Sheryl Mahaney
Treasurer, Jeff Treasure
Director, Ray Mecca
Directors, Charlie Borders
Assistant Chief Office, Charbel Salem
Administrator, David McDonald
Network Engineer, Dennis Knudson
Human Resources Business Partn, Earnie Duty
Network Engineer, Greggory Howard
Analyst, Jason Addis
Auditors: BAKER TILLY VIRCHOW KRAUSE LLP

LOCATIONS

HQ: KING'S DAUGHTERS HEALTH SYSTEM, INC.
2201 LEXINGTON AVE, ASHLAND, KY 411012843
Phone: 606 408-4000
Web: WWW.KINGSDAUGHTERSHEALTH.COM

HISTORICAL FINANCIALS
Company Type: Private

Income Statement				FYE: September 30
	REVENUE ($ mil.)	NET INCOME ($ mil.)	NET PROFIT MARGIN	EMPLOYEES
09/17	475	3	0.8%	4,200
09/16	459	(8)	—	—
09/14	0	0	—	—
09/13	0	0	—	—
Annual Growth	—	—	—	—

2017 Year-End Financials
Return on assets: 5.2%   Cash ($ mil.): 15
Return on equity: 0.8%
Current ratio: 1.60

KINGMAN HOSPITAL, INC.

EXECUTIVES

Ceo, Brian Turney
Prin, David French
Family Medicine Program Direct, Deborah Bennet
Information Specialist, Stephanie Lomax
Controller, Kevin Keener
Chief Financial Officer, Larry Lewis
Coordinator, Wendy Lankford
Coordinator, Bridget Sipilovic
Chief of Medicine, Garry Forkosh
Hospitalist, Lisa Yamamoto
Director of Plant Operations, Mike Van
Auditors: BKD LLP COLORADO SPRINGS CO

LOCATIONS

HQ: KINGMAN HOSPITAL, INC.
3269 N STOCKTON HILL RD, KINGMAN, AZ
864093619
Phone: 928 757-2101
Web: WWW.AZKRMC.COM

HISTORICAL FINANCIALS
Company Type: Private

Income Statement				FYE: June 30
	REVENUE ($ mil.)	NET INCOME ($ mil.)	NET PROFIT MARGIN	EMPLOYEES
06/17	283	9	3.3%	1,300
06/16	277	8	3.1%	—
Annual Growth	2.3%	9.2%	—	—

2017 Year-End Financials
Return on assets: 3.4%   Cash ($ mil.): 17
Return on equity: 3.3%
Current ratio: 1.90

KIRBY - SMITH MACHINERY, INC.

EXECUTIVES

Pres, Ed Kirby
Coordinator, Alan Soab
Manager, Dewayne McDaris
Auditors: EIDE BAILLY OKLAHOMA CITY OK

LOCATIONS

HQ: KIRBY - SMITH MACHINERY, INC.
6715 W RENO AVE, OKLAHOMA CITY, OK 731276590
Phone: 888 861-0219
Web: WWW.KIRBY-SMITH.COM

HISTORICAL FINANCIALS
Company Type: Private

Income Statement				FYE: December 31
	REVENUE ($ mil.)	NET INCOME ($ mil.)	NET PROFIT MARGIN	EMPLOYEES
12/17	421	36	8.6%	516
12/16	312	25	8.2%	—
12/15	321	33	10.5%	—
12/14	353	29	8.2%	—
Annual Growth	6.0%	7.4%	—	—

2017 Year-End Financials
Return on assets: —   Cash ($ mil.): —
Return on equity: 8.6%
Current ratio: 0.40

KLEIN INDEPENDENT SCHOOL DISTRICT

EXECUTIVES

Supt, Bret A Champion
Pres, Steven E Smith
V Pres, Ronnie K Anderson
SEC, Stephen J Szymczak
Building) Instructional Office, Pat Braunagel
Accounting Staff, Heather Cummings
Coordinator, Karri Clark
Coordinator, Kim Huseman
Superintendent, Bret Champion
Auditors: HEREFORD LYNCH SELLARS & KIR

LOCATIONS

HQ: KLEIN INDEPENDENT SCHOOL DISTRICT
7200 SPRING CYPRESS RD, SPRING, TX 773793215
Phone: 832 249-4000
Web: WWW.KLEINISD.NET

HISTORICAL FINANCIALS
Company Type: Private

Income Statement				FYE: August 31
	REVENUE ($ mil.)	NET INCOME ($ mil.)	NET PROFIT MARGIN	EMPLOYEES
08/17	548	8	1.5%	5,691
08/16	539	(135)	—	—
08/15	511	186	36.5%	—
08/14	474	6	1.4%	—
Annual Growth	5.0%	6.6%	—	—

2017 Year-End Financials
Return on assets: 6.1%   Cash ($ mil.): 234
Return on equity: 1.5%
Current ratio: 3.60

KNOUSE FOODS COOPERATIVE, INC.

Is there a Knouse in the house? Might be. With retail brand names such as Apple Time Lucky Leaf Musselman's Lincoln and Speas Farm Knouse Foods Cooperative's apple products are in many a pantry. The company is a growers' co-op made up of some 150 Appalachian Mountain and Midwestern grower/members. It processes its members' apples for sale as canned and bottled applesauce juice cider vinegar apple butter pie fillings and snack packs all of which are available nationwide. In addition to stocking supermarket shelves Knouse founded in 1949 supplies foodservice operators and industrial-ingredient companies with bulk apple and other fruit products. It also offers private-label and co-packing services.

Operations

The company's business segments include: retail; foodservice which supplies restaurants cafeterias healthcare facilities and other institutional customers; an industrial/ingredient division that provides customized products for industrial clients; and co-packing.

Knouse gets an A for all things Apple but also makes the grade with foodservice cheese sauces dessert toppings and fillings and puddings. And along with apple its pie fillings include apricot blackberry blueberry cherry lemon peach pineapple raisin raspberry and strawberry.

Geographic Reach

The company operates half a dozen processing plants in Pennsylvannia — covering nearly 2.4 million sq. ft. on about 300000 acres — and a single plant in Paw Paw Michigan.

Strategy

In recent years companies like Knouse have been focused on packaging to make its products more portable. To this end Knouse in 2014 introduced Musselman's Squeezables single-serve apple sauce.

EXECUTIVES

Pres, Kenneth E Guise Jr
Vice President, Emery C Etter Jr
Vice President, Richard W Esser
Vice President, Eugene Kelly
Vice President, Linda Kelly
Vice President, Thomas M Denisco
SEC, John L Rice
Treas, Craig M Hinkle
Executive Officer, Douglas Lott
Executive Officer, William Lower
Manager, Eric Hoover

LOCATIONS

HQ: KNOUSE FOODS COOPERATIVE, INC.
800 PACH GLEN IDAVILLE RD, PEACH GLEN, PA 173750001
Phone: 717 677-8181
Web: WWW.KNOUSE.COM

PRODUCTS/OPERATIONS

Selected Products
Apple butter
Apple juice & cider
Apple sauce
Pie filling
Specialty fruit (cherries sliced apples)

COMPETITORS

BakeMark	Odwalla
Big Heart Pet Brands	Old Orchard
Birds Eye	Seneca Foods
Chelan Fruit Company	Shamrock Foods
Chiquita Brands	Smucker
Dole Food	Snapple
Eagle Family Foods	Sun-Rype
H. J. Heinz Limited	Tree Top
Monster Beverage	TreeHouse
Mott's	Tropicana
Naked Juice	Wet Planet Beverages
Ocean Spray	

HISTORICAL FINANCIALS

Company Type: Private

Income Statement				FYE: June 30
	REVENUE ($ mil.)	NET INCOME ($ mil.)	NET PROFIT MARGIN	EMPLOYEES
06/17	281	0	0.2%	1,200
06/16	296	2	0.7%	—
Annual Growth	(5.1%)	(72.5%)	—	—

2017 Year-End Financials
Return on assets: 4.9%   Cash ($ mil.): —
Return on equity: 0.2%
Current ratio: 0.40

KOOTENAI HOSPITAL DISTRICT

EXECUTIVES

Prin, Jon Ness
Cfo, Kim Webb
Vice President, Jeremy S Evans
Accounting Staff, Jenny Lea
Chief Staff, Thomas Nickol
Chief Information Officer, Steve Garske
Executive Assistant, Mitzi Wilkes
Manager, Brian S Jerome
Manager, Charlie Linder
Phlebotomist, Daphne Kaiser
Administrative Assistant, Kali Singleton

LOCATIONS

HQ: KOOTENAI HOSPITAL DISTRICT
2003 KOOTENAI HEALTH WAY, COEUR D ALENE, ID 838146051
Phone: 208 625-4000
Web: WWW.KH.ORG

HISTORICAL FINANCIALS

Company Type: Private

Income Statement				FYE: December 31
	REVENUE ($ mil.)	NET INCOME ($ mil.)	NET PROFIT MARGIN	EMPLOYEES
12/17	506	35	6.9%	2,776
12/16	467	15	3.4%	—
12/15	398	35	9.0%	—
12/14	368	30	8.3%	—
Annual Growth	11.1%	4.6%	—	—

2017 Year-End Financials
Return on assets: 5.4%   Cash ($ mil.): 80
Return on equity: 6.9%
Current ratio: 2.40

KORTE CONSTRUCTION COMPANY

EXECUTIVES

Vice President Of Healthcare, Chris Gilliam
Auditors: RUBIN BROWN LLP SAINT LOUIS

LOCATIONS

HQ: KORTE CONSTRUCTION COMPANY
5700 OAKLAND AVE STE 275, SAINT LOUIS, MO 631101375
Phone: 314 231-3700
Web: WWW.KORTECO.COM

COMPETITORS

Berglund Construction	J.E. Dunn Construction
Bulley & Andrews	Leopardo
Clarkson Construction	Ragnar Benson
George Sollitt Construction	West Coast Contractors of Nevada
HOK	

HISTORICAL FINANCIALS

Company Type: Private

Income Statement				FYE: December 31
	REVENUE ($ mil.)	NET INCOME ($ mil.)	NET PROFIT MARGIN	EMPLOYEES
12/17	341	(3)	—	170
12/16	268	0	0.3%	—
12/15	119	(2)	—	—
12/13	106	(2)	—	—
Annual Growth	33.8%	—	—	—

2017 Year-End Financials
Return on assets: 15.6%   Cash ($ mil.): 3
Return on equity: (-1.2%)
Current ratio: 0.10

KRUEGER INTERNATIONAL, INC.

Krueger International can be found in cubicles classrooms cafeterias and college dorms. The company which does business as KI makes ergonomic seating cabinets and other furniture used by businesses healthcare organizations government agencies and educational institutions. The company offers everything from benches and beds to desks and tables not to mention shelving filing systems movable walls and trash bins. KI markets its products through sales representatives furniture dealers architects and interior designers worldwide. Founded in 1941 KI was purchased in the 1980s by its managers who later allowed employees to buy stock. Today KI is 100% employee owned.

Operations

Boasting $700 million in sales and the title of sixth-largest contract furniture manufacturer in the industry KI operates a variety of subsidiaries including KI UK Ltd. KI East Asia Sdn. Bhd KI Nova Scotia KI Canada KI-Sebel and KI India.

KI also owns three subsidiaries: AWP Wood Products Pallas Textiles and Spacesaver. Quebec-based AWP Wood Products makes architectural wood doors for the office partition industry. Pallas Textiles which operates out of Wisconsin creates textile products for contract upholstery panel systems and wall-coverings healthcare environments and casements. Spacesaver Corporation also located in Wisconsin makes high-density mobile storage systems for office institutional and industrial applications and is a major supplier of steel shelving systems rotary storage systems and storage accessories.

The company maintains nine manufacturing sites around the globe. Besides its four locations in Wisconsin (in Bonduel Fort Atkinson Green Bay and Manitowoc) KI operates production facilities in High Point North Carolina; Penmroke Ontario Canada; and Tupelo Mississippi. In 2012 KI expanded its Green Bay Wisconsin plant (at the tune of $3.3 million) by more than 100000 sq. ft. for additional elbow room devoted to manufacturing shipping receiving and warehousing.

Geographic Reach

Based in Wisconsin KI sells its products worldwide and operates manufacturing facilities and sales offices in the US Canada China and India as well as throughout Europe Latin America and Asia. It has subsidiaries based in the UK Canada India and Malaysia. Its showrooms are in several metropolitan areas across the US Toronto and London.

Sales and Marketing

KI sells products globally through furniture dealers sales representatives architects and interior designers. It primarily serves the educational university healthcare business and government markets.

The company staffs direct sales offices around the world. It also boasts showrooms in metropolitan areas to display its products to potential business and individual customers.

Strategy

KI is well regarded in the classroom furniture market and is a leading supplier for both K-12 schools and universities. The company has outfitted classrooms lecture halls administrative offices computer labs media centers residence halls and student unions. KI has been a government vendor for more than six decades providing furnishings for an assortment of federal agencies including all branches of the military. KI's corporate products are ergonomically designed to help individuals work more comfortably and efficiently. In addition to these corporate customer groups KI has also installed its furnishings in outdoor public spaces sports arenas conference centers and airports.

It regularly rolls out new products. In 2013 KI launched the Grazie Seating Collection through a collaboration between renowned designer Giancarlo Piretti and in 2012 introduced the elegant and sophisticated Affina Collection an expansive seating and table line designed by Paul James and Dan Cramer. KI also expanded its existing product licensing agreement with UK seating industry leader Boss Design in 2013 to give Boss Design an extended reach into the US market and KI a broader portfolio of lounge task seating and occasional table items.

Company Background

The company has expanded its network of showrooms in the US and abroad over the years. KI added a showroom in Houston in 2010 to boost its US presence which includes about 10 locations in half a dozen states. To better serve its Asian and European customers the company operates through a showroom in Shanghai China. KI has international showrooms in London Malaysia Mexico Puerto Rico and Toronto. To support its growth KI completed a $3.3-million 100000-sq.-ft. plant expansion in 2012 to reduce costs and streamline its business. The move boosts its manufacturing shipping receiving and warehousing space.

As its showroom presence grew KI also formed new sales partnerships. The company tapped Heartland Furniture Group a contract furniture representative in 2011 to take care of existing customer accounts and broker sales in Kansas Missouri and southern Illinois.

It's also looked to acquisitions to extend the reach of its business. In 2011 KI purchased Sebel Furniture Limited from GWA Group Ltd. a top supplier of building fixtures in Australia. The $24 million deal has given KI a foothold in the commercial furniture business in Australia New Zealand the UK and Hong Kong.

EXECUTIVES

Chairman And Ceo, Richard J. (Dick) Resch
President, Brian Krenke
Vice President Architectural Wall Operations, Ryan Usiak
Vice President Marketing, Tom Abrahamson
Auditors: BAKER TILLY VIRCHOW KRAUSE LL

LOCATIONS

HQ: KRUEGER INTERNATIONAL, INC.
  1330 BELLEVUE ST, GREEN BAY, WI 543022197
Phone: 920 468-8100
Web: WWW.KI.COM

PRODUCTS/OPERATIONS

Selected Products
Auditorium seating
Beds
Benches
Bookcases
Carrels
Chairs
Desks
File cabinets
Lecterns
Movable walls
Planters
Power and data connections
Receptacles
Recliners
Residence hall furniture
Sleepers
Special events seating
Stools
Tables

COMPETITORS

ABCO Office Furniture	Kewaunee Scientific
Allsteel	Kimball International
Bretford	Knoll Inc.
CFGroup	La-Z-Boy
Columbia Manufacturing	Norstar Office
Edsal Manufacturing	Products
Global Group	Sagus
HNI	Steelcase
Haworth Inc.	Trendway
Herman Miller	Virco Mfg.
Inscape corp	

HISTORICAL FINANCIALS

Company Type: Private

Income Statement				FYE: December 31
	REVENUE ($ mil.)	NET INCOME ($ mil.)	NET PROFIT MARGIN	EMPLOYEES
12/16	616	46	7.5%	2,300
12/15	617	53	8.6%	—
12/11	649	56	8.8%	—
12/10	615	59	9.6%	—
Annual Growth	0.0%	(4.0%)		

2016 Year-End Financials

Return on assets: 4.5%   Cash ($ mil.): 5
Return on equity: 7.5%
Current ratio: 0.60

L & M DEVELOPMENT PARTNERS INC.

EXECUTIVES

Ceo, Ron Moelis
Chm-Founding Ptnr, Sanford Loewentheil
V Chm-Sen Ptnr, Debra Kenyon
V Chm-Sen Ptnr, Richard Weinstock
Cfo-Founding Ptnr, Lenny Rueben
Coordinator, Alexander Eney
Information Specialist, Robert Merejo

LOCATIONS

HQ: L & M DEVELOPMENT PARTNERS INC.
  1865 PALMER AVE STE 203, LARCHMONT, NY
  105383037
Phone: 914 833-3000
Web: WWW.LMDEVPARTNERS.COM

HISTORICAL FINANCIALS

Company Type: Private

Income Statement				FYE: December 31
	ASSETS ($ mil.)	NET INCOME ($ mil.)	INCOME AS % OF ASSETS	EMPLOYEES
12/16	205	63	31.0%	15
12/01	1	1	79.3%	—
12/00	2	1	62.0%	—
12/99	2	6	305.1%	—
Annual Growth	30.9%	14.4%	—	—

2016 Year-End Financials

Return on assets: 9.3%   Sales ($ mil): 311
Return on equity: 20.4%

LA JOYA INDEPENDENT SCHOOL DISTRICT

EXECUTIVES

Supt, Dr Alda T Benavides
President, Juan Jos Jj Pea Jr
SEC, Joel Garca
Public Relations Offc, Blanca Cantu
Coordinator, Abel Zamora
Coordinator, Sandra Villarreal
Coordinator, Tommy Garcia
Senior Purchasing Buyer, Juan Pena
Teacher, Lisa Navarro
Counselor, Marybel Uresti
Auditors: REYNA & GARZA PLLC CPA'S TX

LOCATIONS

HQ: LA JOYA INDEPENDENT SCHOOL DISTRICT
  201 E EXPRESSWAY 83, LA JOYA, TX 785604001
Phone: 956 580-2000
Web: WWW.LAJOYAISD.COM

HISTORICAL FINANCIALS

Company Type: Private

Income Statement				FYE: August 31
	REVENUE ($ mil.)	NET INCOME ($ mil.)	NET PROFIT MARGIN	EMPLOYEES
08/17	337	(21)	—	2,800
08/16	342	1	0.3%	—
08/07	211	18	8.7%	—
08/06	175	0	—	—
Annual Growth	6.1%	—	—	—

2017 Year-End Financials

Return on assets: 2.4%   Cash ($ mil.): 14
Return on equity: (-6.5%)
Current ratio: —

LAFAYETTE GENERAL HEALTH SYSTEM, INC.

EXECUTIVES

Chb, Clay M Allen
Pres-Ceo, David Callecod
Dir of Finance, Lana Adams
Senior Manager, Diana Motty

LOCATIONS

HQ: LAFAYETTE GENERAL HEALTH SYSTEM, INC.
 1214 COOLIDGE BLVD, LAFAYETTE, LA 705032621
Phone: 337 289-8125

HISTORICAL FINANCIALS

Company Type: Private

Income Statement				FYE: September 30
	REVENUE ($ mil.)	NET INCOME ($ mil.)	NET PROFIT MARGIN	EMPLOYEES
09/16	700	13	1.9%	2,600
09/15	585	18	3.2%	—
09/14	495	24	5.0%	—
09/13	31	25	79.5%	—
Annual Growth	180.6%	(19.6%)	—	—

2016 Year-End Financials

Return on assets: 8.8%   Cash ($ mil.): 68
Return on equity: 1.9%
Current ratio: 1.40

LAFAYETTE GENERAL MEDICAL CENTER, INC.

EXECUTIVES

Exec Dir, Caroline Huval
Svp-Coo, Al Patin
Assistant Vice President Human, Wendy Alexander
Human Resources Director, Sheena Mitchell
Chief Crna, Cameron Chappuis

LOCATIONS

HQ: LAFAYETTE GENERAL MEDICAL CENTER, INC.
 1214 COOLIDGE BLVD, LAFAYETTE, LA 705032621
Phone: 337 289-7991
Web: WWW.LAFAYETTEGENERAL.COM

COMPETITORS

Baton Rouge General	LifePoint Health
CHRISTUS St. Frances	Our Lady of Lourdes
Cabrini Hospital	Women & Children's
HCA	Hospital

HISTORICAL FINANCIALS

Company Type: Private

Income Statement				FYE: September 30
	REVENUE ($ mil.)	NET INCOME ($ mil.)	NET PROFIT MARGIN	EMPLOYEES
09/17	465	44	9.5%	1,626
09/16	454	50	11.2%	—
09/15	428	55	12.9%	—
09/14	357	58	16.5%	—
Annual Growth	9.1%	(9.2%)	—	—

2017 Year-End Financials

Return on assets: 4.5%   Cash ($ mil.): 13
Return on equity: 9.5%
Current ratio: 2.90

LAFAYETTE PARISH SCHOOL BOARD

EXECUTIVES

Pres, Tommy Angelle
Supt, Pat Cooper
President, Hunter Beasley
Education Specialist, Sylvia Richard
Education Specialist, Terry Auzenne
Accounting Staff, Yvonne Menard
Accounting Staff, Eva Broussard
Accountant, Suzanna Boyd
Director, Jennifer Morrow
Special Education, Pam Dehm
Auditors: KOLDER CHAMPAGNE SLAVEN & CO

LOCATIONS

HQ: LAFAYETTE PARISH SCHOOL BOARD
 113 CHAPLIN DR, LAFAYETTE, LA 705082101
Phone: 337 521-7000
Web: WWW.LPSSONLINE.COM

HISTORICAL FINANCIALS

Company Type: Private

Income Statement				FYE: June 30
	REVENUE ($ mil.)	NET INCOME ($ mil.)	NET PROFIT MARGIN	EMPLOYEES
06/17	358	18	5.1%	3,400
06/16	342	(2)	—	—
06/15	345	(6)	—	—
06/14	346	0	0.1%	—
Annual Growth	1.2%	251.8%	—	—

LAHEY CLINIC HOSPITAL, INC.

EXECUTIVES

Ceo, Howard R Grant JD
Ceo, David Barrett
Chm, Bernard Gordon
V Chm, John Libertino
V Pres, Donna Cameron
Director of Comm & Mktg, Scott V Hartman
Information Technology Manager, Elizabeth Gardner
Manager, Anupindi Sharma
Director of Laboratory, Linda Capone
Internal Medicine Practitioner, Anu Diddee
Ophthalmologist, Paul R Cotran

LOCATIONS

HQ: LAHEY CLINIC HOSPITAL, INC.
 41 MALL RD, BURLINGTON, MA 018050002
Phone: 781 273-5100
Web: WWW.LAHEY.ORG

HISTORICAL FINANCIALS

Company Type: Private

Income Statement				FYE: September 30
	REVENUE ($ mil.)	NET INCOME ($ mil.)	NET PROFIT MARGIN	EMPLOYEES
09/15	816	(17)	—	1
09/14	800	(0)	—	—
09/13	774	228	29.5%	—
09/12	796	192	24.1%	—
Annual Growth	0.8%	—	—	—

2015 Year-End Financials

Return on assets: 4.2%   Cash ($ mil.): 105
Return on equity: (-2.1%)
Current ratio: 0.70

LAHEY CLINIC, INC.

EXECUTIVES

Ceo, Joanne Conroy
President, Howard R Grant JD
Cfo-Treas, Timothy P Oconnor
Neurologist, Caitlin E Macaulay
Managing Director, Christine Diedwardo
Information Technology Manager, Christine Scott
Injury Prevention Coordinator, Darlene Bourgeois
Plastic Surgery, David J Bryan
Radiation Oncology, Eileen Cirino
Senior Benefits Administrator, Janice Johnson
Manager of Financial Web Appli, Jay Lewis

LOCATIONS

HQ: LAHEY CLINIC, INC.
 41 MALL RD, BURLINGTON, MA 018050002
Phone: 781 744-5100
Web: WWW.LAHEY.ORG

HISTORICAL FINANCIALS

Company Type: Private

Income Statement				FYE: September 30
	REVENUE ($ mil.)	NET INCOME ($ mil.)	NET PROFIT MARGIN	EMPLOYEES
09/15	816	(17)	—	5,000
09/09	227	(16)	—	—
09/05	679	57	8.4%	—
Annual Growth	1.9%	—	—	—

2015 Year-End Financials

Return on assets: 4.2%   Cash ($ mil.): 105
Return on equity: (-2.1%)
Current ratio: 0.70

LAKE HOSPITAL SYSTEM, INC.

The aptly named Lake Hospital System (doing business as Lake Health) serves several northeast Ohio communities located along Lake Erie and throughout Lake County. The not-for-profit health system comprises two main hospital campuses (TriPoint Medical Center and West Medical Center) which together house more than 350 beds as well as numerous ancillary facilities offering rehabilitative care outpatient surgery urgent care services primary care and specialist doctors' offices and diagnostic imaging. The system's Lake Health Physician Group includes physicians ranging from family practitioners to vascular surgeons.

Operations
Lake Health has 600 physicians 2600 health care professionals and nearly 1000 volunteers.

The system is the largest private employer in Lake County Ohio.

Geographic Reach
Lake Health has 16 facilities throughout Lake Geauga Ashtabula and Cuyahoga counties in Ohio.

Strategy
Throughout its history Lake Health has expanded by opening new facilities to broaden its care offerings. In 2018 it opened its Mentor Wellness Campus in Mentor Ohio. That campus features a fitness center with three pools in addition to urgent care primary care integrative care and other medical specialties. In 2017 the system opened a continuing care campus in Concord Township a foot specialty hospital in Beachwood and the Perrico Health Campus in Mentor. The year before that it opened its SOM Center Campus in Willoughby.

Also in 2016 Lake Health reintroduced home visits for housebound patients.

In looking at the health needs of Lake Health's service community the system has named its key priorities. These include improving access to preventative screenings reducing the occurrence of congestive heart failure and heart disease and fighting high blood pressure and diabetes.

In 2015 and 2016 Lake Health reported losses for the first time since 2000. The $300 million total deficit was attributed to an IT upgrade to its financial administration and billing department.

Company Background
Lake Health was founded in 1902 by the Daughters of the American Revolution.

EXECUTIVES

President And Ceo, Cynthia Moore-Hardy
Svp Administrative Services, Steven R. Karns
Vp Information Technologies And Cio, Jerry Peters
Svp Patient Care Services And Chief Nursing Officer, Mary L. Ogrinc
Svp Business Development, Richard Cicero
Vp Quality And Chief Quality Officer, Joyce Taylor
Svp Finance And Cfo, Michael E. Kittoe
Svp Medical Affairs And Chief Medical Officer, Michael R. Goler
President Medical Staff, David Rollins
Vp Perioperative Care Critical Care Emergency Nursing Resources And Pharmacy, Andrea Wasdovich
Executive Director Lake Health Foundation, Greg Sanders
Director Of Surgery Services, Mary Gallik
Auditors: LANTE & MORAN PLLC COLUMBUS

LOCATIONS

HQ: LAKE HOSPITAL SYSTEM, INC.
7590 AUBURN RD, PAINESVILLE, OH 440779176
Phone: 440 375-8100
Web: WWW.LHS.NET

Selected Facilities
Lyndhurst Diagnostics
Madison Campus
Madison Emergency Room
Mentor Campus
Mentor Diagnostics
Mentor Physical Therapy
Painesville Quick Care Center
The Clinic At Madison
The Clinic At Middlefield
Tyler Urgent Care Center
TriPoint Medical Center

West Medical Center
Willoughby Hills Diagnostics
Willoughby Physical Therapy
Chardon Campus
Willowick Campus

PRODUCTS/OPERATIONS

Selected Services
Anti-Coagulation Clinic
Cancer Services
Cardiac Services
Chronic Kidney Disease Clinic
Congestive Heart Failure Clinic
Diabetes Care Center
Emergency Services
Family Birthing Center
Geriatric Psychiatry
Home Health
Imaging Services
Integrated Medicine
Men's Health
Occupational Health
Orthopedics/Sports Medicine
Pain Management
Senior Services
Sleep Center
Surgical Services
Women's Services
Wound Care Center

COMPETITORS

Akron Children's Hospital	ProMedica
Akron General Health System	Robinson Memorial Hospital
Akron General Medical Center	Summa Health System
MetroHealth System	The Cleveland Clinic
Ohio State University	University Hospitals Health System
Parma Community General Hospital	

HISTORICAL FINANCIALS
Company Type: Private

Income Statement				FYE: December 31
	REVENUE ($ mil.)	NET INCOME ($ mil.)	NET PROFIT MARGIN	EMPLOYEES
12/17	356	33	9.3%	2,200
12/16	334	(13)	—	—
Annual Growth	6.8%	—	—	—

2017 Year-End Financials
Return on assets: 6.1%   Cash ($ mil.): 4
Return on equity: 9.3%
Current ratio: 0.90

LAKELAND REGIONAL MEDICAL CENTER, INC.

Lakeland Regional Medical Center (LRMC) serves Florida's Polk County (roughly between Kissimmee and Tampa) through an acute care hospital with approximately 850 beds. Among its specialty services are cardiac care cancer treatment senior care urology emergency medicine orthopedics women's and children's health care and surgery. LRMC also operates general care and specialty outpatient clinics. Additionally the hospital provides medical training programs for radiology specialists. Its LRMC Foundation offers financial support for indigent patients facing ongoing treatment.

Operations

LRMC is part of Lakeland Regional Health System a not-for-profit organization that also includes Lakeland Regional Cancer Center Lakeland Regional Family Health Center and Lakeland Regional Health Medical Group.

Annually LRMC has more than 41000 admissions and performs more than 15000 surgeries. Its emergency department treats more than 200000 patients each year.

Financial Performance
Revenue in 2014 totaled $633 million (representing 92% of Lakeland Regional Health System's revenue) while net income totaled $67 million.

LRMC funds its activities through charges to patients for inpatient and outpatient services as well as from non-hospital activities such as its cafeteria gift and uniform shops and physicians' answering service. Although the hospital also receives payment from federal agencies such as Medicaid and Medicare they along with other managed care entities have cut their reimbursement levels causing LRMC's charity care levels to increase.

Strategy
The hospital has been undergoing facility and data systems improvement efforts to enhance care and increase efficiencies. It recently expanded its intensive care department and upgraded technology in areas including radiology orthopedics and chemotherapy.

In 2014 Lakeland Regional Health System announced plans to build an eight-story women and children pavilion at LRMC. The $250 million addition will include 300000 sq. ft. of space including 32 private rooms for mothers and newborns a 30-bed neonatal intensive care unit 64 private rooms for women's surgical and medical care three surgical suites and 12 private suites for labor delivery and recovery. It will also have an education and conference center. The pavilion is expected to open in 2017.

EXECUTIVES

President And Chief Medical Officer, Mack Reavis
Auditors: PERSHING YOAKLEY & ASSOCIATES

LOCATIONS

HQ: LAKELAND REGIONAL MEDICAL CENTER, INC.
1324 LAKELAND HILLS BLVD, LAKELAND, FL 338054500
Phone: 863 687-1100
Web: WWW.LRMC.COM

PRODUCTS/OPERATIONS

Selected Facilities
Lakeland Regional Cancer Center
Lakeland Regional Medical Center (LRMC) Foundation
Lakeland Regional Orthopedics Associates
Lakeland Regional Rehabilitation and Sports Medicine Clinic

Selected Services and Centers
Emergency
Family health center
Gastroenterology
Heart center
Mental health & addictions
Neurosurgery
Nursing
Oncology care
Orthopedic care
Palliative care
Pharmacy
Rehabilitation and sports medicine clinic
Robotic surgery
School of radiologic technology
Stroke center
Surgery
Trauma services
Women and children
Wound center

COMPETITORS

Adventist Health System Sunbelt Healthcare
All Children's Hospital
Baptist Health South Florida
BayCare Health System
Bayfront Health
DeSoto Memorial
Florida Hospital Tampa Bay Division
HCA
Manatee Memorial Hospital
Sarasota Memorial Health Care
Tampa General Hospital
Winter Haven Hospital

HISTORICAL FINANCIALS

Company Type: Private

Income Statement				FYE: September 30
	REVENUE ($ mil.)	NET INCOME ($ mil.)	NET PROFIT MARGIN	EMPLOYEES
09/16	790	84	10.7%	3,100
09/15	674	68	10.2%	—
09/14	618	66	10.8%	—
09/13	584	55	9.4%	—
Annual Growth	10.6%	15.3%	—	—

2016 Year-End Financials

Return on assets: 2.7%   Cash ($ mil.): 1
Return on equity: 10.7%
Current ratio: —

LAKEVIEW CENTER, INC

EXECUTIVES

Pres-Ceo, Gary L Bembry
Vp-Chief Financial Officer, Xan Smith
Chief Financial Officer, Allison Hill
Vice President, Rich Gilmartin
Vice President, Dennis Goodspeed
Vice President, Shawn Salamida
Vice President/Corporate Devel, Sandy Whitaker
Chief Operating Officer, Tra Williams
Manager, Nancy Kirton
Finance Manager, Angela Brewton
Controller, Doreen Drimmie
Auditors: ERNST & YOUNG LLP

LOCATIONS

HQ: LAKEVIEW CENTER, INC
   1221 W LAKEVIEW AVE, PENSACOLA, FL 325011836
Phone: 850 432-1222
Web: WWW.ELAKEVIEWCENTER.ORG

HISTORICAL FINANCIALS

Company Type: Private

Income Statement				FYE: September 30
	REVENUE ($ mil.)	NET INCOME ($ mil.)	NET PROFIT MARGIN	EMPLOYEES
09/17	281	33	11.9%	1,900
09/16	257	23	9.1%	—
09/15	231	11	4.9%	—
09/14	217	17	8.1%	—
Annual Growth	9.0%	24.0%	—	—

2017 Year-End Financials

Return on assets: 4.7%   Cash ($ mil.): 55
Return on equity: 11.9%
Current ratio: 2.00

LAMAR CONSOLIDATED INDEPENDENT SCHOOL DISTRICT (INC)

EXECUTIVES

Supt, Thomas Randle
President, Julie Thompson
Vice President, Rhonda Zacharias
SEC, Kay Danziger
Prin-MBR, Sam Hopkins
Security Staff, Colleen Martin
Staff, Jason Bothe
Building and Grounds Director, Aaron Morgan
Teacher, Adam Frenzel
Administrative Assistant, Barbara Lucero
Teacher, Catherine Barth
Auditors: NULL-LAIRSON PC HOUSTON TX

LOCATIONS

HQ: LAMAR CONSOLIDATED INDEPENDENT SCHOOL
   DISTRICT (INC)
   3911 AVENUE I, ROSENBERG, TX 774713901
Phone: 832 223-0000
Web: WWW.LCISD.ORG

HISTORICAL FINANCIALS

Company Type: Private

Income Statement				FYE: August 31
	REVENUE ($ mil.)	NET INCOME ($ mil.)	NET PROFIT MARGIN	EMPLOYEES
08/17	332	37	11.4%	4,200
08/16	320	(77)	—	—
08/06*	169	(57)	—	—
12/05	0	0	—	—
Annual Growth	—	—	—	—

*Fiscal year change

LAMEX FOODS INC.

EXECUTIVES

Ceo, Phillip O Wallace
President, Steven Anderson
Vice President, Mark Barrett
Sr Dir, Mark Ryder
Coordinator, Danielle Waterhouse
Logistics Coordinator, Gary Welsh
Accounting Manager, Lisa Henkel
Director, Paul Wallace
Latin America Trade Manager, Robert Preska
Controller, Marianne Dove

LOCATIONS

HQ: LAMEX FOODS INC.
   8500 NORMANDALE, BLOOMINGTON, MN 55437
Phone: 952 844-0585
Web: WWW.LAMEXFOODS.US

HISTORICAL FINANCIALS

Company Type: Private

Income Statement				FYE: March 31
	REVENUE ($ mil.)	NET INCOME ($ mil.)	NET PROFIT MARGIN	EMPLOYEES
03/16	501	7	1.6%	60
03/15	592	7	1.3%	—
03/05	103	1	1.0%	—
03/04	76	0	0.9%	—
Annual Growth	16.9%	22.7%	—	—

2016 Year-End Financials

Return on assets: 3.5%   Cash ($ mil.): 1
Return on equity: 1.6%
Current ratio: 0.80

LANDMARK SERVICES COOPERATIVE

EXECUTIVES

Ceo, Bob Carlson
President, John Blaska
Board of Directors, Junior Manthe
Exec V Pres-Coo, Mike Elder
Exec Vice President, Doug Cropp
Credit Mgr, Tom Hanes
Customer Staff, Martin Newhouse
Sales Staff, Bill Weisensel
Sales Staff, Dan Peterson
Customer Staff, Janet Klug
Safety Manager, Matt Solymossy
Auditors: BAKER TILLY VIRCHOW KRAUSE LL

LOCATIONS

HQ: LANDMARK SERVICES COOPERATIVE
   1401 LANDMARK DR, COTTAGE GROVE, WI
   535278984
Phone: 608 819-3115
Web: WWW.LANDMARK.COOP

HISTORICAL FINANCIALS

Company Type: Private

Income Statement				FYE: September 30
	REVENUE ($ mil.)	NET INCOME ($ mil.)	NET PROFIT MARGIN	EMPLOYEES
09/16	383	3	1.0%	400
09/15	418	13	3.2%	—
09/03	76	1	2.0%	—
09/02	56	2	4.9%	—
Annual Growth	14.7%	2.1%	—	—

2016 Year-End Financials

Return on assets: 2.6%   Cash ($ mil.): 32
Return on equity: 1.0%
Current ratio: 1.10

LANE INDUSTRIES INCORPORATED

EXECUTIVES

Pres-Ceo, Robert Alger
Treas-Asst SEC, Vincent Caiola
Exec V Pres, Kirk Junco
V Pres, David Benton
Exec V Pres, Mike Cote
Administrator, Cynthia Lango
Auditors: KPMG LLP HARTFORD CT

LOCATIONS

HQ: LANE INDUSTRIES INCORPORATED
   90 FIELDSTONE CT, CHESHIRE, CT 064101212
Phone: 203 235-3351
Web: WWW.LII.COM

HISTORICAL FINANCIALS
Company Type: Private

Income Statement				FYE: December 31
	REVENUE ($ mil.)	NET INCOME ($ mil.)	NET PROFIT MARGIN	EMPLOYEES
12/17	1,592	14	0.9%	4,500
12/16	1,292	36	2.8%	—
12/15	1,197	(13)	—	—
Annual Growth	15.3%	—	—	—

2017 Year-End Financials
Return on assets: 12.2%   Cash ($ mil.): 121
Return on equity: 0.9%
Current ratio: 0.90

LANSING BOARD OF WATER AND LIGHT

EXECUTIVES

Ceo, J Peter Lark
Chief Operating Officer, Susan Devon
Executive Officer, Wendy Bradley
Coordinator, Annie Rzepecki

LOCATIONS

HQ: LANSING BOARD OF WATER AND LIGHT
   1201 S WASHINGTON AVE, LANSING, MI 489101650
Phone: 517 702-6714
Web: WWW.LBWL.COM

HISTORICAL FINANCIALS
Company Type: Private

Income Statement				FYE: June 30
	REVENUE ($ mil.)	NET INCOME ($ mil.)	NET PROFIT MARGIN	EMPLOYEES
06/17	371	4	1.2%	740
06/14	21	11	52.1%	—
06/11	306	7	2.5%	—
06/10	18	17	97.3%	—
Annual Growth	53.7%	(18.3%)	—	—

LARGO MEDICAL CENTER, INC.

EXECUTIVES

Ceo, Anthony Degina
President, Richard H Satcher
Cfo, Robert Billings
SEC, Karen H Chack
Treas, Vicky A Chiszar
Coordinator, Lorie Jennings
Marketing Manager, Holly Borota
Information Technology Manager, Joe Parise
Family Practitioner, Jamie Melichar
Dermatologist, Kelly Reed
Human Resources Manager, Denise Ford

LOCATIONS

HQ: LARGO MEDICAL CENTER, INC.
   201 14TH ST SW, LARGO, FL 337703199
Phone: 727 588-5200
Web: WWW.LARGOMEDICAL.COM

HISTORICAL FINANCIALS
Company Type: Private

Income Statement				FYE: February 28
	REVENUE ($ mil.)	NET INCOME ($ mil.)	NET PROFIT MARGIN	EMPLOYEES
02/17	291	43	14.8%	755
02/09	241	17	7.2%	—
Annual Growth	2.4%	12.0%	—	—

2017 Year-End Financials
Return on assets: 3.1%   Cash ($ mil.): —
Return on equity: 14.8%
Current ratio: 1.60

LARSEN & TOUBRO INFOTECH LIMITED

EXECUTIVES

Ceo, Sanjay Jalona
Cfo, Ashok Sonthalia
Exec Vp, Sunil Pande
Business Director, Gaurav Ranjan
Business Manager, Nitin Jain
Vice President, Harsh Naidu
Project Manager, Singaravelu Arumugam
Auditors: RAMESH SARVA CPA PC FOR

LOCATIONS

HQ: LARSEN & TOUBRO INFOTECH LIMITED
   2035 STATE ROUTE 27 # 3000, EDISON, NJ
   088173351
Phone: 732 248-6111
Web: WWW.LNTINFOTECH.COM

HISTORICAL FINANCIALS
Company Type: Private

Income Statement				FYE: March 31
	REVENUE ($ mil.)	NET INCOME ($ mil.)	NET PROFIT MARGIN	EMPLOYEES
03/15	478	8	1.7%	20,000
03/13	398	7	1.8%	—
Annual Growth	9.6%	8.6%	—	—

2015 Year-End Financials
Return on assets: 0.3%   Cash ($ mil.): 6
Return on equity: 1.7%
Current ratio: 1.30

LAS VEGAS CONVENTION & VISITORS AUTHORITY

EXECUTIVES

Pres-Ceo, Rossi Ralenkotter
Sr V Pres Oprs, Terry Jicinsky
V Pres Fin, Brenda Siddall
Pres-Coo, Steve Hill
Project Manager, Todd Messett
Manager, Kelly Sawyer
Purchasing Agent, Joni Doubenmier
Administrator, Milan Marovich
Public Relations Manager, Heidi Hayes
Supervisor, Blane Blood
Senior Manager, Bob Naugle
Auditors: PIERCY BOWLER TAYLOR & KERN L

LOCATIONS

HQ: LAS VEGAS CONVENTION & VISITORS
   AUTHORITY
   3150 PARADISE RD, LAS VEGAS, NV 891099096
Phone: 702 892-0711
Web: WWW.LVCVA.COM

HISTORICAL FINANCIALS
Company Type: Private

Income Statement				FYE: June 30
	REVENUE ($ mil.)	NET INCOME ($ mil.)	NET PROFIT MARGIN	EMPLOYEES
06/17	369	13	3.6%	1,100
06/16	329	(3)	—	—
06/15	298	15	5.1%	—
06/14	291	42	14.7%	—
Annual Growth	8.2%	(32.3%)	—	—

LAWNWOOD MEDICAL CENTER, INC.

EXECUTIVES

Ceo, Rodney Smith
Cfo, Robert Dunwoody Jr
Coordinator, Helen Benson
Food Director, Michael Montemurro
Director, Tommie Smith

Safety Director, Ashley Raymond
Director of Security, Jim Tobin
Staff Manager, Patricia Rochedieu
Nurse Recruiter, Tina Ankeny
Case Management Director, Andrea Mulligan
Pharmacy Director, Leiser Hicks

LOCATIONS

HQ: LAWNWOOD MEDICAL CENTER, INC.
1700 S 23RD ST, FORT PIERCE, FL 349504899
Phone: 772 461-4000
Web: WWW.LAWNWOODMED.COM

COMPETITORS

Broward Health	Mayo Clinic
Heart & Family Health	Jacksonville
Institute	Orlando Health
Holy Cross Hospital	South Broward Hospital
Fort Lauderdale	District
Jupiter Medical Center	Tenet Healthcare

HISTORICAL FINANCIALS

Company Type: Private

Income Statement   FYE: September 30

	REVENUE ($ mil.)	NET INCOME ($ mil.)	NET PROFIT MARGIN	EMPLOYEES
09/15	300	54	18.1%	1,200
09/14*	283	59	20.9%	—
03/09	0	0	0.8%	—
Annual Growth	347.5%	658.3%	—	—

*Fiscal year change

2015 Year-End Financials

Return on assets: 3.1%   Cash ($ mil.): —
Return on equity: 18.1%
Current ratio: —

LAWRENCE + MEMORIAL HOSPITAL, INC.

Lawrence & Memorial Hospital (L + M) connects residents of Connecticut with health care whether they're near the Rhode Island border or enjoying the Connecticut River. The not-for-profit hospital founded in 1912 provides services to a 10-town region on the Connecticut shoreline and neighboring areas in the Northeast. L + M has roughly 280 beds and provides general acute care including medical surgical rehabilitative pediatric psychiatric and obstetrical services. The hospital also runs about a dozen community physician practices and specialty clinics.L + M is owned by Yale New Haven Health Services.

Operations

Each year L + M sees some 86000 patients in its emergency room. In all it sees tens of thousands of patients annually. The hospital's specialty programs include a cardiac rehabilitation program a sleep disorder unit and a the region's only neonatal ICU.

Affiliates of the L + M system include Joslin Diabetes Center the Visiting Nurse Association of Southeastern Connecticut and various community organizations with which the hospital advances wellness for the area's population.

Geographic Reach

L + M serves patients in eastern Connecticut as well as Washington County in Rhode Island and the Fishers Island region of New York State.

Strategy

The changing economy and health care landscape in the US has prompted many independent hospitals to seek affiliations with other medical providers as a means of controlling spending and enhancing care and L + M is no exception. It became affiliated with Yale New Haven Health System in 2016 after suffering from operating losses in 2013 2014 and 2015. Yale New Haven has been investing in L + M's growth since the acquisition.

EXECUTIVES

President Ceo And Director, Bruce D. Cummings
Vice President And Chief Medical And Clinical Operations Officer, Daniel Rissi
Vp And Cio, Kimberly Kalajainen
Vp And Chief Financial And Support Services Officer, Lou Inzana
Vice President General Counsel, Maureen Anderson
Medical Director, Sheldon Robbins
Vice President Patient Care Services Cno, Lauren Williams
Chairman, Ulysses B. Hammond
Vice Chairman, Granville Morris
Secretary, Jillian Sferrazza
Auditors: PRICEWATERHOUSECOOPERS LLP HA

LOCATIONS

HQ: LAWRENCE + MEMORIAL HOSPITAL, INC.
365 MONTAUK AVE, NEW LONDON, CT 063204769
Phone: 860 442-0711
Web: WWW.LMHOSPITAL.ORG

PRODUCTS/OPERATIONS

Selected Services
Core Services
   Cardiac Care
   Maternity Care
   Cancer Care
   Surgery
   Occupational Health Care
Other Services
   Behavioral Medicine
   Chronic Pain
   Diagnostic Imaging
   Emergency Services
   Gastroenterology
   Hand Center
   Infectious Diseases
   Joint Replacement Center
   Joslin Diabetes Center
   Laboratory
   Neurosurgery
   Pulmonary Disorders
   Pulmonary Rehabilitation
   Rehabilitation - Acute Inpatient
   Rehabilitation - Signature Outpatient
   Sleep Center
   Social Work
   Women's and Infants Services
   Wound and Hyperbaric Center

COMPETITORS

Backus
Care New England
Connecticut Children's Medical Center
Day Kimball Hospital
Harrington Memorial Hospital
Hartford Health Care
Hospital of Central Connecticut
Kent Hospital
Roger Williams Medical Center
Saint Francis Hospital and Medical Center
Sturdy Memorial
University of Connecticut Health Center
Waterbury Hospital

HISTORICAL FINANCIALS

Company Type: Private

Income Statement   FYE: September 30

	REVENUE ($ mil.)	NET INCOME ($ mil.)	NET PROFIT MARGIN	EMPLOYEES
09/16	346	(17)	—	2,200
09/15	339	14	4.3%	—
09/14	337	5	1.8%	—
09/13	315	10	3.4%	—
Annual Growth	3.2%	—	—	—

2016 Year-End Financials

Return on assets: 9.2%   Cash ($ mil.): 3
Return on equity: (-5.1%)
Current ratio: 0.60

LAWRENCE NEWYORK-PRESBYTERIAN HOSPITAL

EXECUTIVES

Pres, Michael J Fosina
Cmo, Anthony L Pucillo
Vice-President, James Keogh
Director of Pharmacy, Lisa Oronzio
Quality Assurance Director, Nora Mulcahy
Purchasing Manager, William Follen
Cardiac Physician, Mitchell Fishbach
Pharmacist, Derrick Stone
Director of Case Management, Eileen Mullaney
Pharmacist, Michelle Guiliano
Nurse Manager, Missy Paolicelli
Auditors: ERNST & YOUNG LLP NEW YORK N

LOCATIONS

HQ: LAWRENCE NEWYORK-PRESBYTERIAN HOSPITAL
55 PALMER AVE, BRONXVILLE, NY 107083403
Phone: 914 787-1000
Web: WWW.NYPLAWRENCE.ORG

HISTORICAL FINANCIALS

Company Type: Private

Income Statement   FYE: December 31

	REVENUE ($ mil.)	NET INCOME ($ mil.)	NET PROFIT MARGIN	EMPLOYEES
12/17	313	4	1.3%	2,000
12/16	230	(9)	—	—
12/15	212	(7)	—	—
12/14	194	16	8.3%	—
Annual Growth	17.4%	(35.8%)	—	—

2017 Year-End Financials

Return on assets: 8.4%   Cash ($ mil.): 24
Return on equity: 1.3%
Current ratio: 0.70

LAWRENCE TOWNSHIP SCHOOL DISTRICT INC

EXECUTIVES

Spdt, Crystal Edwards
Bus Admin, Thomas Eldridge
Food Director, Marybeth Dilorenzo
Teacher, Rosemary Sorensen
Auditors: SAMUEL A DELP JR VINELAND

LOCATIONS

HQ: LAWRENCE TOWNSHIP SCHOOL DISTRICT INC
2565 PRINCETON PIKE, LAWRENCEVILLE, NJ
086483631
Phone: 609 671-5500
Web: WWW.LTPS.ORG

HISTORICAL FINANCIALS
Company Type: Private

Income Statement				FYE: June 30
	REVENUE ($ mil.)	NET INCOME ($ mil.)	NET PROFIT MARGIN	EMPLOYEES
06/17	10,232	53	0.5%	475
06/16	10	0	0.4%	—
Annual Growth	101401.6%	147352.8%	—	—

2017 Year-End Financials
Return on assets: 1.8% Cash ($ mil.): 2,410
Return on equity: 0.5%
Current ratio: —

LAWRENCE WHOLESALE, LLC

EXECUTIVES

Mng MBR, Mark Liszt
MBR-Cfo, Robert Francis
MBR, Max Liszt
Accounting Staff, Anna Vela
Buyer, Billy Lu
Sales Team Member, Darryl Merlino
Sales Team Member, Adam Rappoport
Auditors: MOSS ADAMS LLP LOS ANGELES C

LOCATIONS

HQ: LAWRENCE WHOLESALE, LLC
4353 EXCHANGE AVE, VERNON, CA 900582619
Phone: 323 235-7525
Web: WWW.LAWRENCEWHOLESALE.COM

HISTORICAL FINANCIALS
Company Type: Private

Income Statement				FYE: December 31
	REVENUE ($ mil.)	NET INCOME ($ mil.)	NET PROFIT MARGIN	EMPLOYEES
12/17	810	8	1.0%	30
12/16	741	9	1.2%	—
Annual Growth	9.4%	(11.2%)	—	—

2017 Year-End Financials
Return on assets: 3.5% Cash ($ mil.): 1
Return on equity: 1.0%
Current ratio: 0.60

LEANDER INDEPENDENT SCHOOL DISTRICT

EXECUTIVES

Supt, Bret A Champion
Acct, Dana Paulson
Manager, Dale Walker
Social Worker, Julie Rocha
Director, Tony Cacciola
Academic Advisor, Cathy Neely
Food Director, Kathy Bell
Coordinator, Eva Guardiola
Executive Director, Nancy Scott
Assistant Director, Gina Mitschke
Administrative Assistant, Marie Cook

LOCATIONS

HQ: LEANDER INDEPENDENT SCHOOL DISTRICT
204 W SOUTH ST, LEANDER, TX 786411719
Phone: 512 570-0000
Web: WWW.LEANDERISD.ORG

HISTORICAL FINANCIALS
Company Type: Private

Income Statement				FYE: August 31
	REVENUE ($ mil.)	NET INCOME ($ mil.)	NET PROFIT MARGIN	EMPLOYEES
08/17	440	(29)	—	2,700
08/16	414	(36)	—	—
08/07	239	9	3.8%	—
08/06	197	98	49.9%	—
Annual Growth	7.6%	—	—	—

2017 Year-End Financials
Return on assets: 1.3% Cash ($ mil.): 14
Return on equity: (-6.6%)
Current ratio: 0.60

LEE COUNTY ELECTRIC COOPERATIVE, INC.

If you are a Floridian who is a really early riser or a night owl Lee County Electric Cooperative (LCEC) may help light your way. The electric cooperative provides power to more than 198880 residential and commercial customers across five counties in southwestern Florida (Lee County and parts of Collier Hendry Charlotte and Broward counties. The member-owned non-profit electric utility operates more than 8000 miles of transmission and distribution lines and more than 20 substations. Tampa-based Seminole Electric Cooperative serves as LCEC's wholesale power supplier.

Geographic Reach

The company's service territory includes Cape Coral North Fort Myers Marco Island Sanibel and Captiva Islands Pine Island Everglades City Immokalee and parts of Lehigh Acres.

Financial Performance

In 2012 LCEC's revenues declined by 0.3% as the result of abnormally mild weather and conservation efforts by customers coupled with ongoing economic uncertainty all of which trimmed demand. Net income decreased by 11% in 2012 as the drop in net sales outpaced only slightly lower operating costs for the year.

As part of its non-profit charter LCEC returns surplus equity to its current and former members. In 2012 its Board of Trustees approved $12.9 million in equity distribution.

Strategy

The cooperative is working on a number of strategic initiatives in order to keep up with the demands of the growing population in its service area: maintain power quality enhance disaster recovery competency keep up with regulatory compliance requirements implement mobile workforce technology and keep employees engaged.

To better support its customers that year LCEC upgraded its website with improved navigation and additional energy management tips and tools.

Company Background

Under the leadership of Homer Welch (and as part of a nationwide rural electrification drive) LCEC began operations with 15 miles of distribution line and 158 members or about 1% of Lee County's 1940 population of 17500.

EXECUTIVES

Ceo, Dennie Hamilton
Cfo, Donald Schleicher
SEC, Joann Costallos
Supervisor, Cheryl Fuoss
Supervisor, Tina Matyja
Computer Technician, David Rhodes
Information Specialist, Kayon Walters
Staff, Bob Tomlin
Human Resources, Bonnie Tate
Manager, Karen Sherman
Information Technology Manager, Susan Crisafulli

LOCATIONS

HQ: LEE COUNTY ELECTRIC COOPERATIVE, INC.
4980 BAYLINE DR, FORT MYERS, FL 339173998
Phone: 800 599-2356
Web: WWW.LCEC.NET

HISTORICAL FINANCIALS
Company Type: Private

Income Statement				FYE: December 31
	REVENUE ($ mil.)	NET INCOME ($ mil.)	NET PROFIT MARGIN	EMPLOYEES
12/15	413	(0)	—	400
12/12	404	2	0.6%	—
Annual Growth	0.8%	—	—	—

2015 Year-End Financials
Return on assets: 11.5% Cash ($ mil.): 2
Return on equity: (-0.1%)
Current ratio: 0.90

LEGACY EMANUEL HOSPITAL & HEALTH CENTER

Legacy Emanuel Hospital and Health Center part of the Legacy Health System provides acute and specialized health care to residents of Portland Oregon and surrounding communities. The 420-bed teaching hospital's operations include centers devoted to trauma treatment burn care oncology birthing neurosurgery orthopedics and cardiology. It also houses a pediatric hospital and operates the region's Life Flight Network service which is owned by a consortium of local hospitals. Legacy Emanuel's emergency department handles more than 15600 visits every year.

Operations

Legacy Emanuel's trauma and burn centers are level I designated facilities meaning they receive severe trauma and burn cases from other area hospitals. The hospital's burn center is the only one of its kind in an area stretching from Seattle to Sacramento and Salt Lake City. Other specialist facilities at Legacy Emanuel include its maternity center and its diagnostic imaging and screening units.

The medical center sees more than 18000 inpatients each year. Its staff includes about 140 full-time doctors and dentists as well as 700 full-time registered nurses. The Randall Children's Hospital located within Legacy Emanuel has about 600 affiliated pediatricians and specialists on its staff and handles about 100000 patient encounters each year including 20000 emergency room visits.

Strategy

The hospital has undergone massive expansion efforts. The hospital has completed construction of the new Randall Children's Hospital facilities making it one of the largest pediatric facilities in the state. The new pediatric center is four times as large as the past facilities. Other expansion efforts in recent years include new acute and intensive care capacity.

Company Background

To expand its medical transportation services Legacy Emanuel and other owners of LFN teamed up to purchase 15 new helicopters in 2012.

Legacy Emanuel Hospital was established in 1912 by the Lutheran Church.

EXECUTIVES

Ceo-Pres, George J Brown
Administrative Assistant, Mary Ann McNulty
Chief of Cardiology, Amanda Kopra
Project Manager, Barri Stiber
Executive Director, Lisa Harris
Coordinator, Amy Lyons
Hematologist, Jason Glover
Occupational Therapist, Terezia Hazen

LOCATIONS

HQ: LEGACY EMANUEL HOSPITAL & HEALTH CENTER
2801 N GANTENBEIN AVE, PORTLAND, OR 972271623
Phone: 503 413-2200
Web: WWW.LHS.ORG

PRODUCTS/OPERATIONS

Selected Centers and Services

Burn care
Cancer care
Children's care
Diabetes and nutrition
Emergency services
Family birth center
Gardens
High-risk obstetrics
Imaging
Injury prevention
Intensive care
Interventional and diagnostic cardiology
Level I trauma center
Life flight network
Maternal-fetal medicine
Neurology and neurosurgery including spine surgery
Orthopedics
Pediatrics
Rehabilitation (inpatient and outpatient)
Radiation oncology
Stroke
Surgery (including minimally invasive surgery)
Vascular clinic
Wound and ostomy clinic
Wound care and outpatient burn clinic

COMPETITORS

Adventist Health System West	PeaceHealth
Asante Health System	PeaceHealth Southwest Medical Center
Dignity Health	Providence St. Joseph
Kadlec Regional Medical Center	Health
	Salem Hospital

HISTORICAL FINANCIALS

Company Type: Private

Income Statement   FYE: March 31

	REVENUE ($ mil.)	NET INCOME ($ mil.)	NET PROFIT MARGIN	EMPLOYEES
03/15	705	29	4.2%	3,619
03/14	649	30	4.8%	—
03/13	566	6	1.1%	—
03/12	571	(6)	—	—
Annual Growth	7.3%	—	—	—

LEGACY HEALTH

Legacy Health strives to promote positive health in the Portland/Vancouver metropolitan area. A not-for-profit provider of health care services in Oregon and Washington the health system operates half a dozen hospitals including Legacy Emanuel Medical Center and Legacy Good Samaritan Medical Center as well as the Randall Children's Hospital at Legacy Emanuel. Legacy Health has more than 1200 total beds and its facilities provide such services as acute and critical care behavioral health and outpatient and health education programs. It also operates home health hospice and research facilities; emergency transportation helicopters; and a number of regional clinics and labs.

Operations

Legacy Health's hospitals include Legacy Emanuel Medical Center Randall Children's Hospital Legacy Good Samaritan Medical Center Legacy Meridian Park Medical Center Legacy Mount Hood Medical Center and Legacy Salmon Creek Medical Center in Washington.

Legacy Medical Group includes more than 300 affiliated physicians operating nearly 30 primary care clinics in the region as well as a number of specialty care centers in fields such as obstetrics pediatrics cardiology neurology and orthopedics.

In addition to providing medical care Legacy Health partners with government and commercial entities to conduct medical research studies.

Geographic Reach

Legacy Health System operates six hospitals some 70 outpatient clinics and a number of hospice research and diagnostic facilities in the Portland/Vancouver metropolitan area. It has three hospitals located in Portland as well as one each in Gresham Oregon; Tualatin Oregon; and Vancouver Washington.

Financial Performance

Legacy Health had an 8% increase in net operating revenue to some $2.1 billion in fiscal 2018 (ended March) marking several straight years of rising revenues due to organic growth.

However revenues in excess of expenses declined 20% to $100.2 million that year as operating income and non-operating gains fell significantly. Part of that decline was due to costs related to providing services to patients unable to pay for health care.

Strategy

Legacy Health is focused on improving its existing hospitals. It is also opening new general care and specialty clinics partly through partnerships with area physicians. The addition of new clinics is designed not only to service the needs of small communities but also to ensure that referrals from area doctors help to sustain its nearby hospitals. New facilities also allow Legacy to broaden its Portland-area offerings by providing pediatric orthopedic diagnostic and sports medicine services among others.

In 2017 the system joined together with OHSU Kaiser Permanente Northwest and Adventist Health to open the first comprehensive full-time behavioral health care center in the area. Unity Center for Behavioral Health offers psychiatric emergency care for adults and operates a 107-bed inpatient facility for adults and adolescents. The state of Portland began investigating complaints from the center's employees in 2018 which led the facility to temporarily close its doors to new patients.

Company Background

Legacy Health was founded through the 1989 merger of HealthLink and Good Samaritan Hospital.

EXECUTIVES

Vice President Human Resources, Sonya Steves
Svp And Chief Nursing Officer, Carol Bradley
President And Ceo, George J. Brown
Chief Administrative Officer Legacy Meridian Park Medical Center, Allyson Anderson
Chief Administrative Officer Legacy Salmon Creek Medical Center, Jonathan Avery
Svp And Cio, John Kenagy
Interim Chief Administrative Officer The Children's Hospital At Legacy Emanuel, Bronwyn Houston, age 49
Svp And Coo, Mike Newcomb
Svp And Chief Medical Officer, Lewis Low
Chief Administrative Officer Legacy Mount Hood Medical Center, Gretchen Nichols
Svp And Cfo, Linda Hoff
Chief Administrative Officer, Bryce Helgerson
Vice President Finance, Gordon Edwards
Clinical Vice President Womens Services And Surgical Services, Duncan Neilson
Medical Director Behavioral Health, Judith Marcus
Auditors: KPMG LLP PORTLAND OREGON

LOCATIONS

HQ: LEGACY HEALTH
1919 NW LOVEJOY ST, PORTLAND, OR 972091503
Phone: 503 415-5600
Web: WWW.LEGACYHEALTH.ORG

PRODUCTS/OPERATIONS

Selected Facilities

Hospitals
Legacy Emanuel Medical Center (Portland Oregon)
Legacy Good Samaritan Medical Center (Portland Oregon)
Legacy Meridian Park Medical Center (Tualatin Oregon)
Legacy Mount Hood Medical Center (Gresham Oregon)
Legacy Salmon Creek Medical Center (Vancouver Washington)
Randall Children's Hospital At Legacy Emanuel (Portland Oregon)
Clinics
Legacy Med
Legacy Med
Legacy Med
Legacy Med
Legacy Med
Legacy Medical Group - Fisher's Landing
Legacy Medical Group - Good Samaritan
Legacy Medical Group - Lake Oswego
Legacy Med
Legacy Med

Legacy Medical Group - Salmon Creek Family
Medicine (Vancouver Washington)
Legacy Medical Group - Salmon Creek Internal
Medicine (Vancouver Washington)
Legacy Med
Legacy Medical Group - West Linn
Legacy Med

COMPETITORS

Adventist Health
  System West
Asante Health System
Kadlec Regional
  Medical Center
Kaiser Foundation
  Hospitals

Oregon Health &
  Science University
PeaceHealth
Providence St. Joseph
  Health
Salem Hospital

HISTORICAL FINANCIALS

Company Type: Private

Income Statement				FYE: March 31
	REVENUE ($ mil.)	NET INCOME ($ mil.)	NET PROFIT MARGIN	EMPLOYEES
03/18	2,117	100	4.7%	10,675
03/17	1,965	172	8.8%	—
03/15	1,658	156	9.4%	—
03/14	183	9	5.2%	—
Annual Growth	84.4%	80.0%	—	—

2018 Year-End Financials

Return on assets: 2.5%   Cash ($ mil.): 67
Return on equity: 4.7%
Current ratio: 1.20

LEGAL SERVICES CORPORATION

EXECUTIVES

Pres, James Sandman
Treas, David Richardson
CIO, Peter Campbell
Vp For Grants Management, Lynn A Jennings
Gen Counsel-Vp For Legal Affai, Ronald Flagg
Dir of Gov Relations & Pub Aff, Carol A Bergman
Editor, Eliot Sasaki
Coordinator, Betty Balderston
Auditors: WITHUM SMITH & BROWN PC PHILA

LOCATIONS

HQ: LEGAL SERVICES CORPORATION
  3333 K ST NW STE 1, WASHINGTON, DC 200073522
Phone: 202 295-1500
Web: WWW.LSC.GOV

HISTORICAL FINANCIALS

Company Type: Private

Income Statement				FYE: September 30
	ASSETS ($ mil.)	NET INCOME ($ mil.)	INCOME AS % OF ASSETS	EMPLOYEES
09/16	91	(0)	—	130
09/15	91	0	1.0%	—
09/14	82	0	0.7%	—
09/13	71	0	0.4%	—
Annual Growth	8.3%	—	—	—

2016 Year-End Financials

Return on assets: 0.4%   Sales ($ mil): 387
Return on equity: (-0.1%)

LEHIGH UNIVERSITY

Lehigh University (LU) nestled in eastern Pennsylvania's Lehigh Valley offers about 90 undergraduate programs and majors at colleges of arts and sciences business and economics engineering and applied sciences and education. It also offers more than 40 masters and doctoral degree programs as well as certificate programs. Tuition is more than $40000 per year; more than half of students receive financial aid. LU has an enrollment of nearly 7000 undergraduate and graduate students. The university was founded in 1865 by entrepreneur and philanthropist Asa Packer.

Operations
The student to faculty ratio is 10:1 and the average class size is 27. The students are instructed by about 700 faculty memebrs.

Geographic Reach
One of the most selective schools in the nation it accepts about 3600 students per year out of the more than 12000 who apply; about a third of those accepted matriculate at LU.

EXECUTIVES

Executive Vice President, John D Simon
Associate Vice President Marketing And C, Ira Rubien
Vice President Finance And Administration, Patricia Johnson
Associate Vice President For Government Relations, William Michalerya
Vice President And Associate Provost For Research And Graduate Studies, Alan Snyder
Vice President Internal Programming, Toni Isreal
Vice President, Will Kuehne
Vice President Internal Programming, Maryam Khan
Vice President, James Carrigan
Assistant Vice President Alumni Engagement, Jennifer Cunningham
Assistant Vice President Community And Regional Affairs, Adrienne Washington
Associate Vice President Human Resources, Chris Halladay
Vice President Internal Programming, Klaudia Jazwinska
Vice President For Club Relations, Kaung Myat
Assistant Treasurer Finance And Administration, David Hammer
Secretary Controllers Office, Marlene Peltz
Secretary, Daniele Holland
Secretary, Mary K Wagner
Secretary Health Center, Christina Finley
Auditors: KPMG LLP PHILADELPHIA PENNSY

LOCATIONS

HQ: LEHIGH UNIVERSITY
  27 MEMORIAL DR W UNIT 8, BETHLEHEM, PA 180153005
Phone: 610 758-3000
Web: WWW.LEHIGH.EDU

HISTORICAL FINANCIALS

Company Type: Private

Income Statement				FYE: June 30
	REVENUE ($ mil.)	NET INCOME ($ mil.)	NET PROFIT MARGIN	EMPLOYEES
06/18	416	110	26.5%	4,000
06/17	396	171	43.3%	—
06/14	367	156	42.6%	—
06/13	357	114	32.0%	—
Annual Growth	3.1%	(0.8%)	—	—

2018 Year-End Financials

Return on assets: 11.2%   Cash ($ mil.): 58
Return on equity: 26.5%
Current ratio: —

LEHIGH VALLEY HEALTH NETWORK, INC.

Residents of the Lehigh Valley seeking medical care head uptown to facilities operated by the Lehigh Valley Health Network (LVHN). The not-for-profit health care provider operates through four full-service hospital campuses housing a total of about 1000 licensed beds. The medical center serves as a regional referral center for trauma and burn care and organ transplantation as well as specialty care in numerous areas such as cardiology women's health and pediatric surgery. LVHN also boasts a network of physician practices and community health centers as well as home health and hospice units.

Operations
The company's hospitals provide care in about 95 specialist fields including pediatric care burn treatment trauma care organ transplant cardiovascular care oncology and neurology. Its children's hospital includes inpatient emergency and specialist units. LVHN also conducts medical training programs and performs research in a range of different areas including cancer cardiovascular and infectious disease; a number of these programs are conducted through partnerships with entities including the H. Lee Moffitt Cancer Center and the University of South Florida's Morsani College of Medicine.

In addition to its core hospital operations the health organization has an alliance with the Sacred Heart Hospital of Allentown through which it provides Sacred Heart with certain services in the areas of cardiac care primary care telehealth services and mental health care. The two hospitals discussed but ultimately dismissed the possibility of a formal merger settling on being affiliated instead.

LVHN's 40 community clinics administer primary and specialty care for area residents including facilities for low-income patients. For patients (insured or not) who need care for minor ailments and routine tests LVHN operates a handful of retail health clinics under the Careworks brand. In addition the network includes a system of medical laboratories (Health Network Laboratories).

Geographic Reach
The LVHN system's main facilities are located in Allentown Bethlehem and Hazleton. With more than a dozen additional health centers the network provides services to residents of a five-county territory in Pennsylvania.

Financial Performance
Revenues increased 8% to $1.7 billion in 2014 on higher patient service and supporting operations revenues as well as higher investment earnings. Net income increased 59% to $95.5 million that year.

Strategy
LVHN opened the region's first pediatric emergency department at its Cedar Crest campus in 2011. The center houses about a dozen beds and is staffed by pediatric emergency physicians and nurses as well as a child life specialist. To further expand its emergency capabilities in 2013 the organization added emergency transportation services to its offerings.

In early 2014 LVHN merged with Greater Hazleton Health Alliance adding Hazleton General Hospital (now Lehigh Valley Hospital-Hazleton) to its network of facilities. The merger also added a physician group a hospital-based home health agency and a health and wellness center all in Hazleton

To promote care coordination and communication LVHN entered into a clinical affiliation with CVS Health in 2015. Through the partnership information on patient visits and prescriptions is accessible to care providers through secure electronic health record (EHR) systems.

EXECUTIVES

President And Ceo, Brian A. Nester
Coo, Terry Capuano
Evp And Chief Medical Officer, Thomas V. Whalen
Svp And Cfo, Edward O'Dea
Acting President Lehigh Valley Hospital Pocono, Elizabeth Wise
President Lehigh Valley Health Network Medical Staff And Trustee, Joseph Patruno
President Lehigh Valley Hospital-hazleton Medical Staff And Trustee, Anthony P. Veglia
Svp Patient Care Services And Chief Nursing Officer, Marie K. (Kim) Jordan
Vice Chair, William F. Hecht, age 75
Chairman, John D. Stanley, age 61
Vice Chair, Jefferson K. (Jeff) Aiken
Auditors: KPMG LLP PHILADELPHIA PENNSY

LOCATIONS

HQ: LEHIGH VALLEY HEALTH NETWORK, INC.
1247 S CEDAR CREST BLVD, ALLENTOWN, PA 181036298
Phone: 610 402-8000
Web: WWW.LVH.COM

PRODUCTS/OPERATIONS

Selected Facilities
Community Health Centers
  Hamburg Community Health Center
  Lehigh Valley Health Center at Bath
  Lehigh Valley Health Center at Bethlehem Township
  Lehigh Valley Health Center at Hellertown
  Lehigh Valley Health Center at Kutztown
  Lehigh Valley Health Center at Saucon Valley
  Lehigh Valley Health Center at Trexlertown
  Upper Bucks Health & Diagnostic Center (in partnership with Grand View Hospital Quakertown)
Hospitals
  Lehigh Valley Hospital - 17th St. (short-stay hospital Salisbury Township in Allentown)
  Lehigh Valley Hospital - Cedar Crest (Allentown)
  Lehigh Valley Hospital - Muhlenberg (Bethlehem)

COMPETITORS

Abington Memorial Hospital
Ascension Health
Community Health Systems
Doylestown Hospital
Grand View
Main Line Health System
Mercy Health System
Moses Taylor Hospital
North Philadelphia Health System
Pennsylvania Hospital
Reading Hospital and Medical Center
Sacred Heart Hospital of Allentown
Shore Memorial Hospital
St. Luke's University Health Network
Tenet Healthcare
University of Pennsylvania Health System
Wyoming Valley Health Care System

HISTORICAL FINANCIALS

Company Type: Private

Income Statement   FYE: June 30

	REVENUE ($ mil.)	NET INCOME ($ mil.)	NET PROFIT MARGIN	EMPLOYEES
06/18	2,739	106	3.9%	12,000
06/17	2,432	409	16.8%	—
06/12	1,620	(63)	—	—
06/11	1,524	314	20.6%	—
Annual Growth	8.7%	(14.3%)	—	—

2018 Year-End Financials

Return on assets: —
Return on equity: 3.9%
Current ratio: 1.30
Cash ($ mil.): 109

LELAND STANFORD JUNIOR UNIVERSITY

Prospectors panning for gold in higher education can strike it rich at The Leland Stanford Junior University. The school known as Stanford University is one of the premier educational institutions in the US boasting respected programs in business engineering law and medicine among others. Stanford serves more than 16300 students (taught by 2180 faculty members) and a student-teacher ratio of about 4:1. A private institution Stanford is supported through an endowment of some $22.4 billion one of the largest in the US. The university was established in 1885 by Leland Stanford Sr. who made his fortune selling provisions to California gold miners; it was named after his son Leland Stanford Jr.

Operations

Stanford University is widely recognized as one of the top US research universities and sports a host of laboratories and research centers including the Stanford Institute for Economic Policy Research and the Stanford Linear Accelerator Center. Its faculty members include around 20 Nobel Prize winners a handful of Pulitzer Prize winners and more than 20 MacArthur fellows.

The university also offers 35 varsity sports and 20 club sports; it boasts more than 110 NCAA team championships.

Geographic Reach

Stanford is located in the heart of California's Silicon Valley known worldwide as an epicenter for technology and research ventures. Google (headquartered in Silicon Valley) got its start at Stanford when Sergey Brin and Larry Page developed the page-rank algorithm while they were still computer science graduate students.

The university is located on 8180 contiguous acres and has almost 700 major buildings.

Financial Performance

Stanford University reported revenues of some $9.8 billion in fiscal 2016 up from $9.1 billion in 2015 due to an increase in student income higher patient service revenues (from the Stanford Hospitals and Clinics organization) sponsored research funding and increased returns on its investment portfolio assets.

Net income fell to $490 million in 2016 (versus $700 million in 2015) as expenses including salaries and benefits rose especially within the medical school. Other expenditures that year such as facilities and infrastructure maintenance and higher depreciation also impacted net income.

The university has received sizable donations from notable alumni such as Jerry Yang (co-founder of Yahoo!) Charles Schwab Texas billionaire Robert Bass and William Hewlett (of Hewlett-Packard who has since died).

Strategy

To further widen its student resources Stanford has recently completed renovation and construction efforts on some 40 campus buildings and added a number of new faculty and fellowship positions. The university is also exploring options to establish a satellite-applied science and engineering campus in another US city. In addition Stanford is examining whether it might begin to offer courses through an online platform.

In 2017 Stanford launched a new major in aeronautics and astronautics (allowing students to work with unmanned aerial vehicles satellites autonomous systems and other flight technologies).

HISTORY

In 1885 Leland Stanford Sr. and his wife Jane established Leland Stanford Junior University in memory of their son Leland Jr. who had died of typhoid at age 15. Stanford made his fortune selling provisions to California gold miners and as a major investor in the Central Pacific Railroad one of the two companies that built the first transcontinental railway. It was Stanford who connected the tracks laid eastward by Central Pacific and westward by Union Pacific with a gold railway spike in 1869. He also served as California's governor and as a US senator.

The Stanfords donated more than 8000 acres of land from their own estate to establish an unconventional university one that was coeducational and nondenominational with a focus on preparing students for a profession. Stanford opened its doors in 1891 to a freshman class of 559 students. It awarded its first degrees four years later and among the graduates was future US president Herbert Hoover.

Leland Stanford Sr. died in 1893 and in 1903 Jane Stanford turned the university over to the board of trustees. After weathering significant damage in 1906 from the Great San Francisco Earthquake the university established a law school in 1908 and its medical school five years later.

During WWI the university mobilized half of its students into the Students' Army Training Corps. The School of Education was established in 1917 followed by the School of Engineering and Graduate School of Business eight years later. In 1933 a rule limiting the number of women admitted to Stanford was abolished.

Wallace Sterling who became president of the university after WWII initiated the transformation of Stanford into a world-class institution with a reputation for teaching and research. Under Sterling the university initiated development on the Stanford Research Park.

In 1958 Stanford opened its first overseas campus (near Stuttgart Germany) and the Stanford Medical Center was completed the following year. The university created a computer science department in 1965 and two years later opened the Stanford Linear Accelerator Center dedicated to physics research.

Donald Kennedy became president in 1980. The next year students voted to abandon the university's official mascot the "Indians" in response to concerns raised by Native American students. The nickname "Cardinal" was adopted in its place. The term refers to the school's color cardinal red.

Also during Kennedy's tenure it was revealed that Stanford had overcharged the Office of Naval Research for indirect costs associated with research. The scandal led to Kennedy's resignation in 1992 and in 1994 the Office of Naval Research and the university settled a related lawsuit for $1.2 million and a stipulation that Stanford had not committed any wrongdoing. Gerhard Casper succeeded Kennedy as president.

In 1997 Stanford and the University of California at San Francisco combined their teaching hospitals in a public/private merger. Two years later after the controversial experiment had harmed both hospitals' financial pictures the merger was terminated and the two hospitals agreed to go their separate ways.

In 1999 Casper announced his intention to resign as president. The school tapped provost John Hennessy as his replacement. Soon after his appointment in 2000 Hennessey launched a campaign to raise $1 billion. Former Stanford professor and Netscape co-founder Jim Clark donated $150 million later that year to support Stanford's biomedical engineering and sciences program. The school also launched a new company SKOLAR which developed an online search engine for the medical industry.

EXECUTIVES

President, John L. Hennessy
Provost, John W. Etchemendy
Dean School Of Humanities And Science, Richard P. Saller
Vp Business Affairs And Cfo, Randall S. (Randy) Livingston
Dean School Of Earth Energy And Environmental Sciences, Pamela Matson
Associate Vp It Services, Bill Clebsch
President And Ceo Stanford Health Care, Amir Dan Rubin
Vice Provost And Dean Of Research, Ann Margaret Arvin
Dean Graduate School Of Business, Garth Saloner
Dean Graduate School Of Education, Deborah Stipek
Dean School Of Engineering, Persis S. Drell
Dean Law School, M. Elizabeth Magill
Dean School Of Medicine, Lloyd Minor
President And Ceo Stanford Children's Health, Christopher Dawes
Assistant Vice President And Chief Information Security Officer, Michael Duff
Associate Vice President Benefits, Les Schlaegel
Vice President Human Resources, David Jones
Vice President, Britt Hedman
Associate Vice President, Anne Hannigan
Vice President Information Technology, Stephen Wong
M.s. Candidate In Computer Science Audit Intern Vice President Of Board Games, Hana Lee
Associate Vice President Of Sponsored Research, Russell Brewer
Medical Director Performance Improvement, Terry Platchek
Medical Director, Catherine Forest
Medical Director, Kirsti Weng
Associate Medical Director, Susan Galel
David Starr Jordan Professor And Chair Department Of Psychology, Ian Gotlib
Vice President For Academic Life, Jared Crum
Medical Director Emergency Medicine, Sam Shen
Vice President Of External Relations, Tina Jiang
External Relations Vice President, Udai Baisiwala
Vice President Of Account Management, Meg Avery
Medical Director Vaden Health Center, Robyn Tepper
Secretary Of The Board Of Trustees, Jeffrey Wachtel
Auditors: PRICEWATERHOUSECOOPERS LLP SA

LOCATIONS

HQ: LELAND STANFORD JUNIOR UNIVERSITY
450 SERRA MALL, STANFORD, CA 943052004
Phone: 650 723-2300
Web: WWW.STANFORD.EDU

PRODUCTS/OPERATIONS

2014 Sales

	% of total
Healthcare services	50
Sponsored reseach support	16
Investment income	15
Student income	7
Special program fee and other income	7
Gifts	3
Net assets released from restrictions	2
Total	**100**

Selected Schools

Undergraduate
  School of Earth Sciences
  School of Engineering
  School of Humanities and Sciences
Graduate
  School of Business
  School of Earth Sciences
  School of Education
  School of Engineering
  School of Humanities and Sciences
  School of Law
  School of Medicine

Selected Interdisciplinary Research Centers

Alliance for Innovative Manufacturing at Stanford
Center for Computer Research in Music and Acoustics
Center for Integrated Facility Engineering
Center for Integrated Systems

Selected Laboratories Centers and Institutes

Center for Research on Information Storage Materials
Center for the Study of Language and Information
Edward L. Ginzton Laboratory
Institute for International Studies
Institute for Research on Women and Gender
John and Terry Levin Center for Public Service and
  Public Interest Law
Stanford Center for Buddhist Studies
Stanford Humanities Center
Stanford Institute for Economic Policy Research
W.W. Hansen Experimental Physics Laboratory

Selected Medical Research Facilities

Center for Biomedical Ethics
Center for Research in Disease Prevention
Human Genome Center
Richard M. Lucas Center for Magnetic Resonance
  Spectroscopy & Imaging
Sleep Disorders Center
Other Selected Research Facilities
Hoover Institution on War Revolution and Peace
Hopkins Marine Station
Martin Luther King Jr. Papers Project
Stanford Linear Accelerator Center

HISTORICAL FINANCIALS
Company Type: Private

Income Statement				FYE: August 31
	REVENUE ($ mil.)	NET INCOME ($ mil.)	NET PROFIT MARGIN	EMPLOYEES
08/17	5,604	2,972	53.0%	15,000
08/06	4,511	3,007	66.7%	—
08/05	4,162	2,896	69.6%	—
08/04	3,743	1,739	46.5%	—
Annual Growth	3.2%	4.2%	—	—

2017 Year-End Financials

Return on assets: 15.4%   Cash ($ mil.): 260
Return on equity: 53.0%
Current ratio: —

LENOX HILL HOSPITAL

LOCATIONS

HQ: LENOX HILL HOSPITAL
210 E 64TH ST FL 4, NEW YORK, NY 100657471
Phone: 212 472-8872
Web: WWW.LENOXHILL.ORG

HISTORICAL FINANCIALS
Company Type: Private

Income Statement				FYE: December 31
	REVENUE ($ mil.)	NET INCOME ($ mil.)	NET PROFIT MARGIN	EMPLOYEES
12/16	960	21	2.3%	41
12/15	885	6	0.7%	—
Annual Growth	8.5%	244.8%	—	—

2016 Year-End Financials

Return on assets: 6.7%   Cash ($ mil.): —
Return on equity: 2.3%
Current ratio: 0.50

LETTIE PATE EVANS FOUNDATION

EXECUTIVES

President, Charles H McTier
V Pres, P Russell Harding
Treasurer, J Lee Tribble
Secretary, Erik S Johnson
Officer, Elizabeth A Smith
Vice-Chairman, James M Sibley
Executive Director, Antone Callaway
Manager, Amy Todd
Vice President, Susan Shows
Vice President Marketing, John Cooper

LOCATIONS

HQ: LETTIE PATE EVANS FOUNDATION
191 PEACHTREE ST NE # 3540, ATLANTA, GA 303031740
Phone: 404 522-6755
Web: WWW.LPEVANS.ORG

HISTORICAL FINANCIALS
Company Type: Private

Income Statement				FYE: December 31
	ASSETS ($ mil.)	NET INCOME ($ mil.)	INCOME AS % OF ASSETS	EMPLOYEES
12/16	2,694	90	3.3%	12
12/15	44	11	25.0%	—
12/14	33	0	—	—
12/12	33	0	0.3%	—
Annual Growth	198.4%	444.0%	—	—

LEXINGTON COUNTY SCHOOL DISTRICT NO. 1.

EXECUTIVES

Supt, Gregory D Little
Cfo, John Butler
Director*, Deena Bishop
Executive Secretary, Ashley Summers
Assistant, Sherry Walters
Assistant, Luke Clamp
Executive Secretary, Teresa Blankenship
Teacher, Marion Mason
Teacher, Catherine Lazenby
Information Specialist, Deb Huggins
Information Technology/Interne, Melanie Bennett
Auditors: BURKETT BURKETT & BURKETT CPA

LOCATIONS

HQ: LEXINGTON COUNTY SCHOOL DISTRICT NO. 1.
100 TARRAR SPRINGS RD, LEXINGTON, SC
290723835
Phone: 803 821-1000
Web: WWW.LEXINGTON1.NET

HISTORICAL FINANCIALS
Company Type: Private

Income Statement   FYE: June 30

	REVENUE ($ mil.)	NET INCOME ($ mil.)	NET PROFIT MARGIN	EMPLOYEES
06/18	356	(10)	—	3,500
06/17	327	46	14.2%	—
06/15	0	0	15.7%	—
06/13	254	(55)	—	—
Annual Growth	**6.9%**	—	—	—

2018 Year-End Financials
Return on assets: 11.2%   Cash ($ mil.): 98
Return on equity: (-2.9%)
Current ratio: —

LEXINGTON MEDICAL CENTER

Lexington Medical Center is a not-for-profit health care organization serving the residents of South Carolina's Lexington County. Established in 1971 the medical center has some 415 beds and provides general emergency surgical and diagnostic services. Specialty services include cancer treatment cardiovascular care women's health and rehabilitation. Lexington Medical Center also operates a skilled nursing center as well as a network of affiliated community health centers urgent care clinics and affiliated physician practices. The hospital is managed by the Lexington County Health Service District.

Operations
The 414-bed facility is home to the largest extended-care facility in the Carolinas. It sees about 100000 emergency department visits each year.

Altogether the Lexington Medical Center's network of facilities — which includes six community clinics an occupational health center an Alzheimer's care center and 60 doctors' offices — employs some 5900 health professionals.

Strategy
Lexington Medical Center is expanding its facilities to better serve the growing population in its service territory. In 2015 it opened a new cardiac rehabilitation program at its Irmo Medical Park campus. The program — the first of its kind in the area — provides services to patients with a history of heart attack angioplasty heart failure heart transplant bypass surgery or the like.

In 2014 Lexington's physician practice opened a third sleep lab where clinicians can diagnose such conditions as hypersomnia insomnia narcolepsy restless leg syndrome snoring and sleep apnea.

EXECUTIVES

Vice President Pateint Care Services, Cindy Rhoman
Vice President, Harriet Horton
Vice President Physician Network Services, Donna Lyles
Vice President Patient Care, Cindy Rohman
Vice President Of Finance, DK Walker
Vice President Physician Network, Matthew Cogdill
Auditors: KPMG LLP ATLANTA GA

LOCATIONS

HQ: LEXINGTON MEDICAL CENTER
2720 SUNSET BLVD, WEST COLUMBIA, SC
291694810
Phone: 803 791-2000
Web: WWW.LEXMED.COM

PRODUCTS/OPERATIONS

Selected Services
Patient Care
Alzheimer's Care
Birth Center
Extended Care
Family Medicine
General Surgery
Imaging
Laboratory & Pathology
Occupational Health
Weight-Loss Surgery
Health & Wellness
Community Health Screenings
Health Directions Wellness Center
Nutrition Therapy
Sleep Solutions

Selected Facilities
Community Medical Centers
  LMC Batesburg-Leesville
  LMC Chapin
  LMC Gilbert
  LMC Irmo
  LMC Lexington
  LMC Swansea
Hospital Units
  Alzheimers Care Center
  Birth Center
  Cancer Center
  Emergency Care
  Extended Care
  Heart Center
  Obesity Surgery Center
  Urgent Care
  Women's Services

COMPETITORS

Carolinas HealthCare System	Laurens County Hospital
Carolinas Hospital System	McLeod Health
Georgetown Hospital System	Palmetto Health
Grand Strand Regional Medical Center	Upstate Affiliate

Company Type: Private

Income Statement   FYE: September 30

	REVENUE ($ mil.)	NET INCOME ($ mil.)	NET PROFIT MARGIN	EMPLOYEES
09/17	953	(9)	—	5,616
09/16	906	21	2.3%	—
09/15	863	86	10.0%	—
09/14	781	95	12.2%	—
Annual Growth	**6.8%**	—	—	—

2017 Year-End Financials
Return on assets: 7.9%   Cash ($ mil.): 173
Return on equity: (-1.0%)
Current ratio: 2.00

LHH CORPORATION

When Manhattanites are looking for health care many of them head for the hill: Lenox Hill Hospital to be exact. The 650-bed facility provides care to patients on Manhattan's Upper East Side — about 45% of its patient base is from Manhattan the rest from surrounding boroughs. Services include cardiac care high-risk obstetrics pediatrics and orthopedics and sports medicine. Lenox Hill serves as a teaching affiliate for NYU Medical Center and also owns Manhattan Eye Ear and Throat Hospital a provider of specialty care for vision hearing and speech disorders. Today it's part of North Shore-Long Island Jewish Health System.

Operations
As part of the North Shore-LIJ system Lenox Hill has access to the larger organization's resources. North Shore-LIJ one of the largest health care providers in New York State; Lenox Hill is its first hospital in the New York metropolitan area.

Lenox Hill Hospital operates a handful of outpatient locations that provide medical surgical and specialized services. Its center for mental health administers a wide range of inpatient and ambulatory psychiatric services for adults and children. To provide quality services to a diverse population Lenox Hill provides multi-lingual translators.

The hospital treats more than 325000 patients a year.

Geographic Reach
The hospital serves patients from Manhattan and surrounding neighborhoods from two campuses in New York City and one in Westchester County.

Financial Performance
In 2012 Lenox Hill reported revenues of $729 million and a net loss of $37 million.

Strategy
Lenox Hill Hospital has also expanded in recent years by opening primary care center and urgent care centers in Manhattan and upgrading and enhancing some of its existing facilities such as its emergency care center to accommodate a growing number of patients. In 2012 it opened a new pediatric inpatient care unit for general and surgical care as well as new head and neck and cranial base surgery centers. In 2013 it opened a new reproduction clinic for fertility services.

Expanding its medical services outside of North Shore-LIJ system's 16 hospitals and into community settings in 2013 Lenox Hill opened the 3200-sq.-ft. Heart and Vascular Institute in Yorktown Heights — the first facility for the hospital system in Westchester County.

In 2012 Lenox Hill became the first in the New York area to perform minimally invasive heart valve replacement.

Company Background

US News & World Report has ranked Lenox Hill as one the top 50 in Cardiology and Heart Surgery and Ear Nose and Throat facilities in the US and among the top 10 hospitals in New York state.

In 2010 the hospital expanded its service offerings by adding palliative care to its medical roster. The services are aimed at relieving pain symptoms and stress related to serious illness. In many cases palliative care specialists provide care to patients who are not eligible for or don't want hospice care when facing a fatal illness.

It performed the first coronary angioplasty in the US (in 1978) and the first angiocardiogram (in 1938).

The hospital was established in 1857 as the German Dispensary.

EXECUTIVES

Exec Dir, Franck Danza
R&a, Paul Zabetakis
Scientist, V A Subramanian
Nephrology, Maria V Devita
Information Specialist, Tony Karran
Pathologist, Adnan Hasanovic
Pathologist, Alyssa Yurovitsky
Nursing Director, Cathy Fogarty
Pathologist, Christopher Des Jean
Pathologist, John Pearson
Qa Qc Manager, Lynda Hartman

LOCATIONS

HQ: LHH CORPORATION
100 E 77TH ST, NEW YORK, NY 100751850
Phone: 212 434-2000
Web: WWW.LHHNETWORK.ORG

PRODUCTS/OPERATIONS

Selected Services
Bariatric surgery
Cardiothoracic surgery
Cardiovascular care
Colorectal surgery
Critical care
Maternal and child health
Manhattan Ear Eye and Throat Institute
Mental health
Neurosurgery
Palliative care
Pathology
Plastic and reconstructive surgery
Primary care
Radiology
Rehabilitation
Robotic surgery

COMPETITORS

Beth Israel Medical Center
Bronx-Lebanon Hospital
Catholic Health Services of Long Island
Catholic Healthcare System
Lutheran HealthCare
Maimonides Medical Center
Memorial Sloan-Kettering
Montefiore Medical
New York City Health and Hospitals
NewYork-Presbyterian Hospital

HISTORICAL FINANCIALS
Company Type: Private

Income Statement
FYE: December 31

	REVENUE ($ mil.)	NET INCOME ($ mil.)	NET PROFIT MARGIN	EMPLOYEES
12/17	993	24	2.4%	2,955
12/16	960	21	2.3%	—
12/14	790	3	0.4%	—
Annual Growth	7.9%	96.4%	—	—

2017 Year-End Financials
Return on assets: 6.3%   Cash ($ mil.): —
Return on equity: 2.4%
Current ratio: 0.50

LIBERTY UNIVERSITY, INC.

EXECUTIVES

Pres, Jerry Lamon Falwell Jr
Sr Vice President, Mark Hine
Cfo, Don Moon
Cao, Ronald E Hawkins
Coo, Randy Smith Randy Smith
SEC, David M Corry
Project Coordinator, William Mailand
Assistant Professor, Bruce M Kirk
Assistant Professor, Danielle E Scholten
Assistant Professor, Michael R Mitchell
Accounting Staff, Michael Ohemeng-Dapaah
Auditors: DIXON HUGHES GOODMAN LLP RICH

LOCATIONS

HQ: LIBERTY UNIVERSITY, INC.
1971 UNIVERSITY BLVD, LYNCHBURG, VA 245150002
Phone: 434 582-2000
Web: WWW.LIBERTY.EDU

HISTORICAL FINANCIALS
Company Type: Private

Income Statement
FYE: June 30

	REVENUE ($ mil.)	NET INCOME ($ mil.)	NET PROFIT MARGIN	EMPLOYEES
06/18	896	276	30.8%	7,200
06/17	961	289	30.1%	—
06/15	1,001	223	22.3%	—
06/11	628	203	32.4%	—
Annual Growth	5.2%	4.5%	—	—

2018 Year-End Financials
Return on assets: 4.8%   Cash ($ mil.): 267
Return on equity: 30.8%
Current ratio: —

LIFEBRIDGE HEALTH, INC.

LifeBridge Health links patients to healthcare. Serving the Baltimore region the not-for-profit company operates two general hospitals — Sinai Hospital of Baltimore and Northwest Hospital — with specialties including oncology neurology pe-

diatrics and sports medicine. The LifeBridge Health network also provides long-term care at the Levindale Hebrew Geriatric Center and Hospital (nursing subacute and adult day care services) and the Courtland Gardens Nursing & Rehabilitation Center. Altogether the health system boasts some 1190 beds. LifeBridge's Health Wellness division includes a health and fitness program and community fitness center.

Operations

Sinai Hospital is a teaching hospital with residency programs for medical students training at Johns Hopkins University and University of Maryland. Levindale also serves as a teaching facility for medical dental nursing and social work students pursuing training to serve geriatric populations.

EXECUTIVES

Ceo, Neil M Meltzer
Chb, Howard Weiss
Sr Vice President, Aric Spitulnik
Cfo, David Krajewski
Dir of Fin, Michelle Durham
Doctor, Benjamin Dubois
Neurology, Braeme Glaun
Executive Assistant, Darlene Sicca
Anesthesiology, Mark Coleman
Doctor, Mark Deitch
Anesthesiology, Sukhjit Sandhu
Auditors: KPMG LLP BALTIMORE MD

LOCATIONS

HQ: LIFEBRIDGE HEALTH, INC.
2401 W BELVEDERE AVE, BALTIMORE, MD
212155216
Phone: 410 601-5653
Web: WWW.LIFEBRIDGEHEALTHWEIGHTLOSS.ORG

PRODUCTS/OPERATIONS

Selected Locations
Courtland Gardens Nursing & Rehabilitation Center
Levindale Hebrew Geriatric Center and Hospital
Northwest Hospital
Sinai Hospital

Selected Services
Bariatric and Minimally Invasive Surgery
Brain & Spine Institute
Cancer Institute
Hospitalist Program
Rubin Institute for Advanced Orthopedics
Vascular Institute

COMPETITORS

Anne Arundel Medical Center	Johns Hopkins Health System
Ascension Health	MedStar Health
Bon Secours Health	MedStar Union Memorial Hospital
Franklin Square Hospital Center	University of Maryland Medical System
GBMC	

HISTORICAL FINANCIALS
Company Type: Private

Income Statement
FYE: June 30

	REVENUE ($ mil.)	NET INCOME ($ mil.)	NET PROFIT MARGIN	EMPLOYEES
06/17	1,527	111	7.3%	6,000
06/15	145	0	0.5%	—
06/13	1,033	53	5.2%	—
06/11	99	(3)	—	—
Annual Growth	57.5%	—	—	—

2017 Year-End Financials
Return on assets: 8.4%   Cash ($ mil.): 356
Return on equity: 7.3%
Current ratio: 1.80

LIFEMARK HOSPITALS OF FLORIDA, INC.

EXECUTIVES

Ceo, Ana Mederos
Cfo, Oscar Vicente
Coo, Gina C Diaz
Coordinator, Dinia Turner
Director of Information Techno, Pedro Nevarez
Controller, Hopeton English
Chief of Radiology, Jose Becerra
Doctor, Agustin Martinez
Director, Arturo Muniz
Director of Risk Management, Maria Hincapie
Internal Medicine Practitioner, Vincenzo Barbato

LOCATIONS

HQ: LIFEMARK HOSPITALS OF FLORIDA, INC.
2001 W 68TH ST, HIALEAH, FL 330161801
Phone: 305 823-5000
Web: WWW.PALMETTOGENERAL.COM

HISTORICAL FINANCIALS
Company Type: Private

Income Statement				FYE: December 31
	REVENUE ($ mil.)	NET INCOME ($ mil.)	NET PROFIT MARGIN	EMPLOYEES
12/16	293	24	8.5%	1,400
12/15	279	18	6.5%	—
12/14*	262	13	5.0%	—
09/05	0	0	—	—
Annual Growth	—	—	—	—

*Fiscal year change

2016 Year-End Financials
Return on assets: 3.6%
Return on equity: 8.5%
Current ratio: 1.60

Cash ($ mil.): —

LIFENET HEALTH

EXECUTIVES

Ceo, Rony Thomas
Coordinator, Patti Dean
Facilities Manager, Mike Bliley
Information Specialist, Troy Bell
Manager, Uzair Rajput
Director, Raymond Pinto
Vice-President, Michael Plew
Security Staff, Ron Jackson
Vice-President, Richard Flores
Accounting Manager, Ashley Walter
Vice-President, Patrick Thompson
Auditors: LB KPMG LLP MC LEAN VA

LOCATIONS

HQ: LIFENET HEALTH
1864 CONCERT DR, VIRGINIA BEACH, VA 234531903
Phone: 757 464-4761
Web: WWW.LIFENETHEALTH.ORG

HISTORICAL FINANCIALS
Company Type: Private

Income Statement				FYE: December 31
	REVENUE ($ mil.)	NET INCOME ($ mil.)	NET PROFIT MARGIN	EMPLOYEES
12/16	355	63	17.8%	500
12/15	260	19	7.5%	—
12/14	210	0	0.4%	—
12/13	210	7	3.4%	—
Annual Growth	19.0%	106.4%	—	—

2016 Year-End Financials
Return on assets: 21.6%
Return on equity: 17.8%
Current ratio: 1.20

Cash ($ mil.): 55

LIFEWAY CHRISTIAN RESOURCES OF THE SOUTHERN BAPTIST CONVENTION

LifeWay Christian Resources of the Southern Baptist Convention helps to spread the teachings of Jesus. The company is a not-for-profit Christian publisher. It also sells Bibles CDs gifts software church furniture signs and other supplies. In addition to its roughly 200 LifeWay Christian Stores located in more than 25 states the retailer sells products online and through its catalog. LifeWay operates two of the nation's largest Christian conference facilities and summer camps. LifeWay Ridgecrest Conference Center in North Carolina and LifeWay Glorieta Conference Center in New Mexico together welcome some 2000 conference and overnight guests each year. LifeWay was founded in 1891 by Dr. J.M. Frost.

Operations

The B&H Publishing Group produces Bibles books Sunday school teaching materials and audio and video products which are sold to bookstores and other retailers. Its Holman Christian Standard Bible is one of the best-selling versions in the US. As part of its digital outreach efforts Lifeway provides ministry services-related Digital Church which can be accessed through Lifeway's website and offers an array of resources for ministries including downloadable worship music and a video publishing utility.

Its Executive Communications and Relations division produces LifeWay's news and information services directs corporate events builds corporate relations and supports the office of the president. It works with state conventions and other evangelical organizations as well. The Technology division offers strategic retail enterprise and Internet services. The company's Research and Ministry Development division is where LifeWay conducts its research and explores new ministry ventures it calls "blue oceans." LifeWay's Finance and Business Services division which runs a conference center in Ridgecrest North Carolina oversees the company's financial policies and general accounting as well as directs business services such as legal investment purchasing real estate strategic planning corporate services and human resources.

Geographic Reach

Based in Nashville LifeWay boasts offices and conference centers in three states: Tennessee New Mexico and North Carolina. In Nashville the company has more than 1.3 million sq. ft. of office retail parking conference and warehouse space that covers 14.6 acres. As part of its operations LifeWay has a 350000-sq.-ft. warehouse on 44 acres in Lebanon Tennessee that supports the LifeWay Christian Stores the company operates nationwide in more than 25 states and extends its reach globally through its website and catalogs.

EXECUTIVES

Vp Lifeway Christian Stores, Tim Vineyard
Vp Finance And Business Services; Cfo, Jerry Rhyne
President And Ceo, Thom S. Rainer
Evp, Brad Waggoner
Vp Insights Division, Ed Stetzer
Vp Church Resources Division, Eric Geiger
Vp And Cio, Tim Hill
Vice President Marketing And Sales, Jim Baird
Auditors: LBMC BRENTWOOD TENNESSEE

LOCATIONS

HQ: LIFEWAY CHRISTIAN RESOURCES OF THE SOUTHERN BAPTIST CONVENTION
1 LIFEWAY PLZ, NASHVILLE, TN 372341001
Phone: 615 251-2000
Web: WWW.LIFEWAY.COM

2013 Stores

	No.
Texas	26
Tennessee	21
North Carolina	14
Alabama	11
Georgia	11
Virginia	9
Florida	8
Kentucky	8
Arkansas	6
Mississippi	6
South Carolina	6
Louisiana	5
Minnesota	5
Missouri	5
Ohio	4
Pennsylvania	3
California	2
Illinois	2
Kansas	2
Maryland	2
Oklahoma	2
Washington	2
Colorado	1
Indiana	1
New Mexico	1
Oregon	1
Utah	1
Total	**165**

PRODUCTS/OPERATIONS

Selected Divisions
B&H Publishing Group
Church Resources
Executive Communications and Relations
Finance and Business Services
LifeWay Christian Stores
Research and Ministry Development
Technology

Selected Products
Apparel
Audio
Bibles
Books
Church supplies
Curriculum
eBooks
Events
Gifts
Magazines
Movies
Music
Video

COMPETITORS

Amazon.com
Baker Publishing
Barnes & Noble
Deseret Management
United Methodist Publishing
Wal-Mart

HISTORICAL FINANCIALS
Company Type: Private

Income Statement				FYE: September 30
	REVENUE ($ mil.)	NET INCOME ($ mil.)	NET PROFIT MARGIN	EMPLOYEES
09/17	476	43	9.2%	5,000
09/16	502	8	1.6%	—
09/15	487	(67)	—	—
09/14	500	(25)	—	—
Annual Growth	(1.6%)	—	—	—

2017 Year-End Financials

Return on assets: 9.6%
Return on equity: 9.2%
Current ratio: 0.60

Cash ($ mil.): 1

LIGHTHOUSE GUILD INTERNATIONAL, INC.

EXECUTIVES

Chb, James M Dubin
Ceo, Alan R Morse
Treas, Sarah Smith
Cfo, Christina Wong
Program Director, Alexandra Henzel
Assistant Vice President, Anne Becker
Chief Low Vision Clinic, Bruce Rosenthal
Nurse Case Manager, Casandra Dowling
Senior Accountant, James Vosilla
Media, Jennifer Drue
Referral Coordinator, Kathy Gonzalez
Auditors: KPMG LLP NEW YORK NY

LOCATIONS

HQ: LIGHTHOUSE GUILD INTERNATIONAL, INC.
250 W 64TH ST, NEW YORK, NY 100236402
Phone: 800 284-4422
Web: WWW.LIGHTHOUSEGUILD.ORG

HISTORICAL FINANCIALS
Company Type: Private

Income Statement				FYE: December 31
	REVENUE ($ mil.)	NET INCOME ($ mil.)	NET PROFIT MARGIN	EMPLOYEES
12/15	972	118	12.2%	29
12/14	849	(9)	—	—
Annual Growth	14.5%	—	—	—

2015 Year-End Financials

Return on assets: 0.8%
Return on equity: 12.2%
Current ratio: 0.20

Cash ($ mil.): 18

LINCOLN MEDICAL AND MENTAL HEALTH CENTER

EXECUTIVES

Exec Dir, Milton Nunez
Gastroenterologist, Sulaiman Azeez
Director of Pharmacy, Michael Thomas
Pediatrician, Paola A Carugno
Marketing Director, Cheryl Simmons-Oliver
Pediatrician, Shafi Choudhury
Oncologist, Aubrey Freiberg
Internal Medicine Practitioner, Matsuko Takeshige
Internal Medicine Practitioner, Pooja Singh
Director, Angela Buchanan
Anesthesiologist, Jean R Maurice

LOCATIONS

HQ: LINCOLN MEDICAL AND MENTAL HEALTH CENTER
234 E 149TH ST, BRONX, NY 104515504
Phone: 718 579-5000
Web: WWW.NYCHHC.ORG

HISTORICAL FINANCIALS
Company Type: Private

Income Statement				FYE: June 30
	REVENUE ($ mil.)	NET INCOME ($ mil.)	NET PROFIT MARGIN	EMPLOYEES
06/16	616	120	19.6%	78
06/15	530	20	3.9%	—
Annual Growth	16.2%	488.5%	—	—

2016 Year-End Financials

Return on assets: 6.9%
Return on equity: 19.6%
Current ratio: 0.10

Cash ($ mil.): —

LINNEA BASEY CANCER RESOURCE CENTER

EXECUTIVES

Director, Karen Shanks
Nursing Director, Linda Goodwin
Anesthesiologist, Eugene Prokopyschyn
Anesthesiologist, Paul Gutowski
Anesthesiologist, Sarah Kadhim
Internist, Sujata Fretz
Psychiatrist, Alfred Richter
General Surgeon, Daniel Cornelius
Emergency Medicine Specialist, Khoshal Latifzai

LOCATIONS

HQ: LINNEA BASEY CANCER RESOURCE CENTER
11600 W 2ND PL, LAKEWOOD, CO 802281527
Phone: 773 484-1000
Web: WWW.STANTHONYHOSPITAL.ORG

HISTORICAL FINANCIALS
Company Type: Private

Income Statement				FYE: June 30
	REVENUE ($ mil.)	NET INCOME ($ mil.)	NET PROFIT MARGIN	EMPLOYEES
06/16	409	43	10.6%	1
06/15	388	39	10.3%	—
Annual Growth	5.5%	8.8%	—	—

LITTLE ROCK SCHOOL DISTRICT

EXECUTIVES

Cfo, Kelsey Bailey
Spdt, Dexter Suggs Sr
Cfo, Christopher Prowse
Superintendent, Mike Poore
Manager, Kevin Crawford
Administrative Assistant, Joyce Jacobs
Assistant, Karen Greenlee
Teacher, Benita Browning
Teacher, Beth Davis
Teacher, Darlene Little
Technology/Computer Coordinato, Swayzine Horton
Auditors: HUDSON CISNE & CO LLP LITTL

LOCATIONS

HQ: LITTLE ROCK SCHOOL DISTRICT
810 W MARKHAM ST, LITTLE ROCK, AR 722011306
Phone: 501 447-1000
Web: WWW.LRSD.ORG

HISTORICAL FINANCIALS
Company Type: Private

Income Statement				FYE: June 30
	REVENUE ($ mil.)	NET INCOME ($ mil.)	NET PROFIT MARGIN	EMPLOYEES
06/16	344	9	2.8%	4,000
06/12	349	16	4.6%	—
06/11	337	(9)	—	—
06/10	314	4	1.5%	—
Annual Growth	1.5%	12.3%	—	—

2016 Year-End Financials

Return on assets: 8.1%
Return on equity: 2.8%
Current ratio: —

Cash ($ mil.): 72

LIVE OAK BANKING COMPANY

EXECUTIVES

Ceo, Chip Mahan
Chb, James S Mahan III
Coo, Neil L Underwood
Cfo, Brett Caines
Pres, Scott Custer
Manager, Catie Laflamme

Associate, Kaelin Stone
Internal Medicine Practitioner, Shayla Long
Manager, Stephen Hayes
Loan Officer, Angus McDonald
Associate, Brandon Bolen

LOCATIONS

HQ: LIVE OAK BANKING COMPANY
1741 TIBURON DR, WILMINGTON, NC 284036244
Phone: 910 790-5867
Web: WWW.LIVEOAKBANK.COM

HISTORICAL FINANCIALS

Company Type: Private

Income Statement   FYE: December 31

	ASSETS ($ mil.)	NET INCOME ($ mil.)	INCOME AS % OF ASSETS	EMPLOYEES
12/17	2,666	114	4.3%	30
12/16	1,700	21	1.3%	—
12/15	1,008	22	2.2%	—
12/14	634	21	3.5%	—
Annual Growth	61.4%	73.3%	—	—

2017 Year-End Financials

Return on assets: —
Return on equity: 42.7%
Sales ($ mil.): 266

LODI UNIFIED SCHOOL DISTRICT

EXECUTIVES

Supt, Dr Cathy Washer
VPresident, Mr Joe Nava
President, Mr Ron Heberle
Administrative Secretary, Desiree Wise
Network Technician, Jared Shippy
Administrative Secretary, Jennifer Molina
Administrative Secretary, Lisa Ruby
Administrative Secretary, Nadine Gallegos
Supervisor, Cindy Oliver
Analyst, I Frazier
Administrative Secretary, Lori Lott
Auditors: GILBERT ASSOCIATES INC SACR

LOCATIONS

HQ: LODI UNIFIED SCHOOL DISTRICT
1305 E VINE ST, LODI, CA 952403179
Phone: 209 331-7000
Web: WWW.LODIUSD.NET

HISTORICAL FINANCIALS

Company Type: Private

Income Statement   FYE: June 30

	REVENUE ($ mil.)	NET INCOME ($ mil.)	NET PROFIT MARGIN	EMPLOYEES
06/18	387	23	6.0%	3,516
06/17	360	92	25.8%	—
06/16	353	9	2.6%	—
06/15	297	(12)	—	—
Annual Growth	9.2%		—	—

2018 Year-End Financials

Return on assets: 6.3%
Return on equity: 6.0%
Current ratio: —
Cash ($ mil.): 305

LOGICALIS US HOLDINGS, INC.

EXECUTIVES

Ceo, Vince Deluca
Sr V Pres, Dan Sytsma
Exec V Pres, Eric Tilds
Cfo, Rich Pirrotta
Coo, Michael Souders
Cso, Mike Houghton
Marketing Specialist, Chad Oda
Engineer, Dean Peirce
Sr Delivery Consultant, Rockwell Malave
Account Executive, Stan Barr
Account Manager, Thomas Marthens
Auditors: DELOITTE & TOUCHE LLP DETROIT

LOCATIONS

HQ: LOGICALIS US HOLDINGS, INC.
1 PENN PLZ, NEW YORK, NY 101190002
Phone: 212 596-7160
Web: WWW.LOGICALIS.COM

HISTORICAL FINANCIALS

Company Type: Private

Income Statement   FYE: February 28

	REVENUE ($ mil.)	NET INCOME ($ mil.)	NET PROFIT MARGIN	EMPLOYEES
02/17	452	9	2.2%	702
02/16	465	6	1.4%	—
Annual Growth	(2.8%)	47.4%	—	—

2017 Year-End Financials

Return on assets: 17.5%
Return on equity: 2.2%
Current ratio: 0.50
Cash ($ mil.): 1

LOGISTICARE SOLUTIONS, LLC

LogistiCare is a go-between for getting from your house to the doctor's office and back. The company brokers non-emergency transportation services for commercial health plans government entities (such as state Medicaid agencies) and hospitals throughout the US. Using its nearly 20 call centers and a network of some 1500 independent contracted transportation providers the company coordinates the medical-related travel arrangements of its clients' members. In addition it contracts with local school boards to coordinate transportation for special needs students. The company provides more than 26 million trips each year for clients in some 40 states. LogistiCare is a subsidiary of Providence Service.

Operations

LogistiCare also known as Charter LCI has contracts with clients including metro transit authorities HMOs and commercial insurance firms. OtherA services include finance and consulting to help companies with billing management and claims adjudication customer reimbursement risk management and discount programs for patients requesting noncovered services. LogistiCare's eligibility and authorization services include call screening to determine client-provided benefit criteria as well as screening to determine type of transport needed.

The company operates more than a dozen regional call centers that match incoming requests with subcontracted transportation providers including local taxi and ambulance companies. Transportation customers often include the elderly or those with disabilities that prevent self-transportation.

Strategy

A major part of LogistiCare's growth strategy is to secure contracts with state and local authorities to become the sole Medicaid or Medicare transportation provider. It scored one such contract in late 2010 with Sussex County Delaware. Under terms of that agreement LogistiCare became the statewide broker for all Medicaid medical transportation.

EXECUTIVES

Ceo, Jeff Felton
Chief Administrative Officer, Albert Cortina
Vp Finance, Ken Shepard
Cto, Neil Singer
Coo, Richard Boland Jr
Cfo, Kevin Dotts
Chief Financial Officer, Thomas E Oram
Corporate Information Technolo, Eric Lorne
Director of Operations, Joe Kukura
Director, Namon Huddleston
Svp-Program & Prod Mgmnt, Andres Salinas

LOCATIONS

HQ: LOGISTICARE SOLUTIONS, LLC
1275 PEACHTREE ST NE FL 6, ATLANTA, GA 303093580
Phone: 404 888-5831
Web: WWW.LOGISTICARE.COM

PRODUCTS/OPERATIONS

Selected Services
Billing and claims management
Call center management
Credentialing
Data management and reporting
Eligibility and authorization services
Logistics
Non-emergency transportation management
(ambulatory/livery vans wheel chair vans stretcher vans)
Provider payment
Quality assurance

COMPETITORS

AMR	National Express Group
Coach USA	Safe Ride Services
FirstGroup America	Veolia Transportation
MV Transportation	

HISTORICAL FINANCIALS

Company Type: Private

Income Statement   FYE: December 31

	REVENUE ($ mil.)	NET INCOME ($ mil.)	NET PROFIT MARGIN	EMPLOYEES
12/17*	1,318	35	2.7%	2,000
04/17	1,234	44	3.6%	—
12/15	1,083	40	3.7%	—
12/14	884	71	8.1%	—
Annual Growth	14.2%	(21.0%)	—	—

*Fiscal year change

2017 Year-End Financials

Return on assets: —
Return on equity: 2.7%
Current ratio: 1.00
Cash ($ mil.): 26

LOGISTICS HOLLINGSWORTH GROUP LLC

EXECUTIVES

Chm-Ceo, Stephen Barr
Pres, Michael T McNamara
Manager, Deb Rodriguez
V Pres of Hr, Martha Chalifoux

LOCATIONS

HQ: LOGISTICS HOLLINGSWORTH GROUP LLC
14225 W WARREN AVE, DEARBORN, MI 481261456
Phone: 313 768-1400
Web: WWW.HOLLINGSWORTHLLC.COM

HISTORICAL FINANCIALS
Company Type: Private

Income Statement				FYE: December 31
	REVENUE ($ mil.)	NET INCOME ($ mil.)	NET PROFIT MARGIN	EMPLOYEES
12/17	293	0	—	700
12/15	196	0	—	—
12/14	183	0	—	—
12/13	183	0	—	—
Annual Growth	12.5%	—	—	—

2017 Year-End Financials
Return on assets: 11.1%   Cash ($ mil.): —
Return on equity: —
Current ratio: 1.20

LOMA LINDA UNIVERSITY MEDICAL CENTER

As a teaching research hospital Loma Linda University Medical Center (LLUMC) knows the lay of the health care landscape in California's Inland Empire. Affiliated with Loma Linda University the 1000-bed healthcare network includes the main acute care LLUMC hospital which contains the system's Children's Hospital and offers general acute care and specialized services such as oncology neurology transplants and rehabilitation. The system also includes the LLUMC East Campus the LLUMC Marietta Campus a Behavioral Health Center and a Heart and Surgery Hospital as well as various regional clinics. Founded in 1905 the not-for-profit medical center is supported by the Seventh-day Adventist Church.

Operations
Among LLUMC's staff are some 400 physicians that belong to physician management organization Loma Linda University Health Care. These physicians practice at the main campus facilities the satellite hospitals and more than a dozen regional clinics that provide general practice and specialty care.

In 2013 the hospital treated more than 46000 inpatients and 1620000 outpatients delivered 4000 babies and handled 98000 emergency room visits.

Geographic Reach
LLUMC's Level I trauma center located on the main LLUMC campus is the designated regional trauma center for a territory that includes about a fourth of the state including Inyo Mono Riverside and San Bernardino counties. All of the company's main hospital facilities are located in the town of Loma Linda with the exception of its satellite hospital campus in Marietta.

Strategy
Increasing its services and locations to better serve the region are top priorities for LLUMC. In 2013 the hospital expanded its emergency department and opened a new women's oncology center. It also announced plans for a new children's tower next to its existing children's hospital.

EXECUTIVES

Vice Chairman And President, Richard H. Hart
Ceo, Ruthita J. Fike
Svp Finance And Cfo, Steven Mohr
Vp Graduate Medical Education, Daniel W. Giang
Svp And Chief Nursing Officer, Judith Storfjell
Vp Institutes, Mark Reeves
Vp And Administrator Llumc East Campus Llu Heart And Surgical Hospital, Lyndon Edwards
Ceo Loma Linda University Medical Center, Kerry Heinrich
Director Of Pharmacy, Kyle Miller
Physical Therapy, Sondra Caposio
Assistant Vice President Risk Manager, Raul Castillo
Physical Therapy, Barbara Cassimy
Secretary, Tina Huerta
Auditors: ERNST & YOUNG LLP IRVINE CA

LOCATIONS

HQ: LOMA LINDA UNIVERSITY MEDICAL CENTER
11234 ANDERSON ST, LOMA LINDA, CA 923542871
Phone: 909 558-4000
Web: WWW.UROLOGYSEMINAR.COM

Selected Facilities
Beaumont California
  Highland Springs Medical Plaza (in collaboration with Redlands Community Hospital and Beaver Medical Group)
Loma Linda California
  Loma Linda University Children's Hospital
  Loma Linda University Health Care
  Loma Linda University Medical Center
  Loma Linda University Medical Center East Campus Hospital
  Loma Linda University Outpatient Rehabilitation Center
  Loma Linda University Outpatient Surgery Center
Redlands California
  Loma Linda University Behavioral Medicine Center
  Loma Linda University Heart & Surgical Hospital

PRODUCTS/OPERATIONS

Selected Facilities
University Hospital
Loma Linda University Children's Hospital
Loma Linda University East Campus
Loma Linda University Heart & Surgical Hospital
Loma Linda University Behavioral Medicine Center

Selected Services and Centers
Allergy Asthma and Immunology
Allergy Laboratory
Cancer Center
Clinical Trial Center
Dentistry
Diabetes Treatment Center
Ears Nose and Throat (ENT)
Emergency and Trauma Services
Family Medicine
Fertility and In Vitro Fertilization
Gastroenterology
Heart and Vascular
Home Care
Metabolic and Bariatric Surgery
Nephrology
Neurology
Neurosurgery
Obstetrics and Gynecology
Ophthalmology
Orthopedics
Pediatrics
Perinatal Institute
Pharmacy
Plastic Surgery
Pulmonology
Radiology
Transplantation Institute and Liver Center
Urogynecology
Urology

COMPETITORS

Adventist Health System West	Childrens Hospital Los Angeles
Arrowhead Medical Center	Dignity Health
Beaver Medical Group	Memorial Health Services
Children's Hospital of Orange County	Tenet Healthcare

HISTORICAL FINANCIALS
Company Type: Private

Income Statement				FYE: December 31
	REVENUE ($ mil.)	NET INCOME ($ mil.)	NET PROFIT MARGIN	EMPLOYEES
12/16	1,776	128	7.3%	4,676
12/15	846	(413)	—	—
12/06*	848	64	7.6%	—
06/05	879	39	4.5%	—
Annual Growth	6.0%	10.3%	—	—

*Fiscal year change

2016 Year-End Financials
Return on assets: 5.6%   Cash ($ mil.): 415
Return on equity: 7.3%
Current ratio: 2.30

LONE STAR NGL PIPELINE LP

EXECUTIVES

Ptnr-Ceo, Kelcy L Warren
Ptnr-Pres-Coo, Marshall S McCrea III
Ptnr-Cfo, Martin Salinas Jr
Sr Dir, Josie Castrejana
Vice-President, Brad Burmaster

LOCATIONS

HQ: LONE STAR NGL PIPELINE LP
1300 MAIN ST 10, HOUSTON, TX 770026803
Phone: 210 403-7300

HISTORICAL FINANCIALS
Company Type: Private

Income Statement				FYE: December 31
	REVENUE ($ mil.)	NET INCOME ($ mil.)	NET PROFIT MARGIN	EMPLOYEES
12/17	471	366	77.7%	200
12/16	360	302	83.8%	—
Annual Growth	30.7%	21.2%	—	—

LONESTAR FREIGHTLINER GROUP, LLC

EXECUTIVES

Coo, Dan Steven
Pres, Vic Corley
Ptnr, Clay Corley
Ptnr, Jay Simmons
MBR-Cfo, James Bennie
Executive Officer, Dan Chase
Customer Staff, Dennis Hill
Coordinator, Morgan Bailey
Coordinator, Wesley Aulds
Sales Manager, Lance Robelia
Executive Vice President of SA, Adam Arrington
Auditors: LANE GORMAN TRUBITT PLLC DAL

LOCATIONS

HQ: LONESTAR FREIGHTLINER GROUP, LLC
2051 HUGHES RD, GRAPEVINE, TX 760517317
Phone: 817 428-9736
Web: WWW.LONESTARTRUCKGROUP.COM

HISTORICAL FINANCIALS
Company Type: Private

Income Statement				FYE: December 31
	REVENUE ($ mil.)	NET INCOME ($ mil.)	NET PROFIT MARGIN	EMPLOYEES
12/17	420	14	3.3%	580
12/15	420	11	2.8%	—
12/14	374	11	3.0%	—
12/11	117	3	3.1%	—
Annual Growth	23.6%	25.1%	—	—

2017 Year-End Financials
Return on assets: 2.6%   Cash ($ mil.): 28
Return on equity: 3.3%
Current ratio: 0.40

LONG BEACH MEMORIAL MEDICAL CENTER

Long Beach Memorial Medical Center (LBMMC) is an old-timer in the Long Beach health care market. A subsidiary of Memorial Health Services LBMMC provides a full range of health services to residents of the Long Beach California area. The medical center a 420-bed acute-care hospital was founded in 1907 and is one of the largest private hospitals on the West Coast. Services include primary emergency diagnostic surgical therapeutic and rehabilitative care. The hospital is home to centers for treatment of cancer heart stroke and women's and children's health concerns. It also provides home and hospice care programs as well as occupational health services.

Operations
LBMMC comprises a breast center cancer institute center for women heart and vascular institute imaging center joint replacement center rehabilitation institute and stroke center. The medical center is a 420-bed acute-care hospital.

Geographic Reach

Long Beach Memorial Medical Center (LBMMC) is one of the nation's largest private hospitals on the West Coast.

Strategy
LBMMC boasts an electronic medical record (EMR) system that connects the hospital and all of its affiliated physicians and pharmacies so that they can transfer patient information electronically between different care providers and locations. Hospitals that use an EMR are eligible for incentives and higher reimbursements from the federal government. Additionally EMRs help to reduce medical errors and increase patient safety by eliminating things like medication interactions and duplicate patient records.

LBMMC expanded its cancer services by building a new $31 million dedicated outpatient cancer facility. The MemorialCare Todd Cancer Institute at Long Beach Memorial which was completed in mid-2013 serves to supplement its current center which had reached capacity. With the new 65000-sq.-ft. MemorialCare Todd Cancer Institute pavilion LBMMC enhances its cancer care technology and capacity.

LBMMC has also expanded its robotics program beyond cardiology. The hospital recently established a new intensivist program in the Intensive Care Unit (ICU). The ICU program integrates teaching from the University of California Irvine residents and interns.

EXECUTIVES

Cio, Scott Joslyn
Cfo, Wendy Dorchester
President And Ceo, Barry Arbuckle
Vice President Of Quality, Donna Hartman
Vice President Material Resources, Gerald Olson
Medical Director Ed, Gary Moreau
Secretary Executive, Donna Reyes
Secretary Department Medical, Elvera Barycki
Secretary Executive, Barbara Steinhauser
Secretary Executive, Kelly Ambrose
Secretary Department Medical, Heather Lawrence
Secretary Executive, Evelyn Satele
Secretary Admin, Carmencita De Jesus
Secretary Department Medical, Deborah Ruman

LOCATIONS

HQ: LONG BEACH MEMORIAL MEDICAL CENTER
2801 ATLANTIC AVE FL 2, LONG BEACH, CA 908061701
Phone: 562 933-2000
Web: WWW.MEMORIALCARE.ORG

PRODUCTS/OPERATIONS

Selected Institutes and Centers
Certified Comprehensive Stroke Center
Long Beach Adult & Pediatric Sleep Center
MemorialCare Breast Center at Long Beach Medical Center
MemorialCare Heart & Vascular Institute
MemorialCare Imaging Center
MemorialCare Joint Replacement Center
MemorialCare Rehabilitation Institute
MemorialCare Todd Cancer Institute
Spine Center at Long Beach Memorial
Trauma Center at Long Beach Medical Center

Selected Services
Blood Donation Center
Diabetes Care
Digestive Care
Emergency Department
Gynecological Care at Long Beach Medical Center
Lung & Respiratory Care
Minimally Invasive Surgery at Long Beach Memorial
Palliative Care Program at Long Beach Medical Center
Pharmacy at Long Beach Medical Center
Robotic-Assisted Surgery at Long Beach Memorial
Surgical Care
Wound Healing & Hyperbaric Medicine at Long Beach Medical Center

COMPETITORS

Adventist Health System West
Aptium Oncology
Brotman Medical Center
Cedars-Sinai Medical Center
Dignity Health
Good Samaritan Hospital (Los Angeles)
HCA
Hoag Memorial Hospital
Hollywood Presbyterian Medical Center
Methodist Hospital of Southern California
Newhall Memorial Hospital
Pasadena Hospital Association
Providence Health System Southern California
Sutter Health
Tenet Healthcare
Torrance Memorial Medical Center
Trinity Health (Novi)
Western Medical Center - Santa Ana

HISTORICAL FINANCIALS
Company Type: Private

Income Statement				FYE: June 30
	REVENUE ($ mil.)	NET INCOME ($ mil.)	NET PROFIT MARGIN	EMPLOYEES
06/16	618	88	14.4%	6,000
06/15	624	93	15.0%	—
06/11	1,083	63	5.9%	—
06/09	446	53	12.0%	—
Annual Growth	4.8%	7.5%	—	—

2016 Year-End Financials
Return on assets: 2.3%   Cash ($ mil.): —
Return on equity: 14.4%
Current ratio: 2.00

LONG ISLAND JEWISH MEDICAL CENTER

Just off the Grand Central Parkway you'll find Long Island Jewish Medical Center. The medicalA center servesA the western edge of Long IslandA and the eastern edge of theA greater metropolitan New York area. The 890-bed medical center campus includesA Long Island Jewish Hospital aA general acute careA hospital; Cohen Children's Medical Center of New York Hospital which provides a full range of pediatric care services; and The Zucker Hillside Hospital a psychiatric hospital for patients of all ages.A The medicalA center'sA staffA includes 500 physicians.A Long Island Jewish Medical Center is the primary clinical andA medical trainingA facility of the North Shore-Long Island Jewish Health System.

Operations
The Long Island Jewish Medical Center's main activities are centered at the 490-bed Long Island Jewish Hospital which provides emergency diagnostic surgical inpatient and outpatientA services. The hospitalA has centers for cancer treatment cardiac surgery and women's health as well as units specializing in hearing loss stroke recovery sleep disorders and hemophilia treatment. As an affiliate of Hofstra University's medical school and Yeshiva University'sA Albert Einstein College of Medicine the Long Island Jewish Hospital also provides graduate medical education programs.

Altogether the hospitals of the Long Island Jewish Medical Center serve some 47000 patients per year conduct 22000 surgeriesA and handle more than 100000 emergency room visits per year.

Geographic Reach

Long Island Jewish Medical Center is located on a 48-acre campus on the border of New York's Queens and Nassau counties about 15 miles east of Manhattan.

Strategy

To enhance services provided to residents of the growing New York City metropolitan area Long Island Jewish Medical Center is conducting expansion efforts on its facilities. In 2012 itA openedA a new $300 million 10-story inpatient tower (containing 160 private patient rooms) at the Long Island Jewish Hospital. The project increased the hospital's overall capacity and added women's health cardiovascular careA and wellness centers.

EXECUTIVES

Medical Records Director, Patricia Hennelly

LOCATIONS

HQ: LONG ISLAND JEWISH MEDICAL CENTER
27005 76TH AVE, NEW HYDE PARK, NY 110401496
Phone: 516 465-2600
Web: WWW.LIJ.EDU

PRODUCTS/OPERATIONS

Selected Facilities
Long Island Jewish Hospital (490 beds)
The Steven and Alexandra Cohen Children's Medical Center (160 beds)
The Zucker Hillside Hospital (240 beds)

Selected Services
Anesthesiology
Cardiac Services
Center for Maternal-Fetal Health
Dental Medicine
Emergency Medicine
Medicine
Neurosciences
Obstetrics
Ophthalmology
Orthopaedic Surgery
Otolaryngology
Pathology
Radiation Oncology
Radiology
Rehabilitation
Surgery
Thoracic Surgery
Urogynecology
Urology: The Arthur Smith Insitute for Urology

COMPETITORS

Catholic Health Services of Long Island
Mercy Medical Center (NY)
North Shore University Hospital
NuHealth
St. Francis Hospital Roslyn
Winthrop-University Hospital

HISTORICAL FINANCIALS

Company Type: Private

Income Statement				FYE: December 31
	REVENUE ($ mil.)	NET INCOME ($ mil.)	NET PROFIT MARGIN	EMPLOYEES
12/17	2,222	154	6.9%	1,214
12/16	2,093	162	7.8%	—
12/15	1,524	44	2.9%	—
12/14	1,446	96	6.7%	—
Annual Growth	15.4%	16.9%	—	—

2017 Year-End Financials
Return on assets: 5.4%
Return on equity: 6.9%
Current ratio: 0.80
Cash ($ mil.): 61

LONG ISLAND POWER AUTHORITY

EXECUTIVES

Ceo-Coo, Michael D Hervey
Gen Counsel-Sec, Lynda Nicolino
V Pres-Envrnm Affrs, Michael Deering
V Pres-Cfo, Herbert L Hogue
Vice President, Kenneth Kane
It Software Manager, Meena Malhotra
Manager, Paul Oberting
Buyer, Ronald Filosa
Assistant General Counsel, Joseph S Wiener
Procurement Director, Maria Gomes
Auditors: KPMG LLP NEW YORK NEW YORK

LOCATIONS

HQ: LONG ISLAND POWER AUTHORITY
333 EARLE OVINGTON BLVD # 403, UNIONDALE, NY 115533606
Phone: 516 222-7700

PRODUCTS/OPERATIONS

Energy Conservation Products and Services
Commercial energy analysis
Construction and renovation incentives
Energy Star labeled homes program
Geothermal rebates
HVAC upgrades
Lighting and appliance solutions
Peak demand reduction programs
Residential energy affordability program
Residential energy audit
Solar Pioneer program
Wind energy development initiatives

COMPETITORS

Avangrid
CH Energy
Con Edison
New York Power Authority

HISTORICAL FINANCIALS

Company Type: Private

Income Statement				FYE: December 31
	REVENUE ($ mil.)	NET INCOME ($ mil.)	NET PROFIT MARGIN	EMPLOYEES
12/16	3,399	(26)	—	100
12/09	3,312	40	1.2%	—
Annual Growth	0.4%	—	—	—

2016 Year-End Financials
Return on assets: 13.1%
Return on equity: (-0.8%)
Current ratio: 0.80
Cash ($ mil.): 562

LONG ISLAND UNIVERSITY

EXECUTIVES

Assistant Vice President Sponsored Research, Kathryn Rockett
Associate Vice President Controller, Mark Schmotzer
Vp Of It, Stuart Alleyne
Vice President Of University Advancement, Charles Rasberry
Department Chair And Professor, Bryan Diffley
Department Chair And Professor, Sara Dierks
Secretary, Kathleen Prince
Secretary Special Collections Department, Heather Hesse
Bds Mphc Treasurer, Sagar Patel
Secretary, Jane Janas
Secretary Service Corporate, Beth Raptis
Auditors: KPMG LLP MELVILLE NY

LOCATIONS

HQ: LONG ISLAND UNIVERSITY
700 NORTHERN BLVD, GREENVALE, NY 115481327
Phone: 516 299-2535
Web: WWW.LIU.EDU

HISTORICAL FINANCIALS

Company Type: Private

Income Statement				FYE: August 31
	REVENUE ($ mil.)	NET INCOME ($ mil.)	NET PROFIT MARGIN	EMPLOYEES
08/16	388	28	7.4%	3,300
08/15	396	33	8.5%	—
08/14	501	41	8.2%	—
08/11	468	2	0.5%	—
Annual Growth	(3.7%)	63.1%	—	—

2016 Year-End Financials
Return on assets: 4.1%
Return on equity: 7.4%
Current ratio: —
Cash ($ mil.): 110

LOS ANGELES COUNTY OFFICE OF EDUCATION

EXECUTIVES

Ceo, Rudell S Freer
President, Rebecca J Turrentine
Vice President, Katie Braude
E-Business Point of Contact, Roberta Gerarde
Executive Officer, Ronald Reynolds
Buyer, Joel Duarte
Consultant, Carolina Alvarez
Board of Directors, Maria Yepes
Program Manager, Anna Whalen
Programmer Analyst, Gregory Brignoni
Bus/Finance/Purchasing Directo, Scott Price
Auditors: VAVRINEK TRINE DAY & CO LL

LOCATIONS

HQ: LOS ANGELES COUNTY OFFICE OF EDUCATION
9300 IMPERIAL HWY, DOWNEY, CA 902422813
Phone: 562 922-6111
Web: WWW.LACOE.EDU

HISTORICAL FINANCIALS

Company Type: Private

Income Statement				FYE: June 30
	REVENUE ($ mil.)	NET INCOME ($ mil.)	NET PROFIT MARGIN	EMPLOYEES
06/17	646	17	2.6%	4,000
06/16	661	7	1.2%	—
06/08	6	0	1.4%	—
Annual Growth	65.4%	77.4%	—	—

LOS ANGELES DEPARTMENT OF WATER AND POWER

The Los Angeles Department of Water and Power (LADWP) keeps the movie cameras running and the swimming pools full. The largest municipally owned utility in the US LADWP provides electricity to 1.4 million residential and business customers and water to 674000 customers. The company has power plant interests that give it more than 7220 MW of generating capacity; it also buys and sells wholesale power. Most of the city's water supply is transported through two aqueduct systems from the Sierra Nevada Mountains; other water sources include wells and local groundwater basins. Because LADWP is city-owned its retail monopoly status has been unaffected by utility deregulation in California.

Operations

The department has 114 tanks and reservoirs 78 pump stations a distribution main of 7263 miles of pipe and storage capacity of 315245 acre-feet.

It has a budget of $1.5 billion of which $422 million is for operations and maintenance; $722 million for capital projects; and $343 million for purchased water.

Financial Performance

LADWP's operations are entirely financed by the sale of water and electric services. The multi-utility transfers about 7% of its annual electric revenues and 5% of its water revenues to the City of Los Angeles general fund.

Strategy

Residential customers form the largest client group of the utility's water service unit; commercial customers the largest customer class of the power segment. To enhance operating efficiencies and conserve energy the department has launched a 10-year $1 billion Smart Grid program to automate and upgrade the City's grid.

It is also pushing to increase the amount of energy it generates from renewable sources (mainly wind and solar power) to meet state and federal clean air goals. LADWP got only 5% of it power from renewables in 2005 but has upped that amount to more than 20% by 2014. LADWP sold ts Navajo Generating Station in Arizona in 2015 which cut carbon emissions by a further 26%.

In 2013 LADWP signed a decade-long power purchase agreement to purchase renewable geothermal power (about 34 MW) from the Imperial Valley (enough to provide enough clean energy to serve 47600 Los Angeles homes).

In addition as the Western US states battle a prolonged drought the utility is negotiating with water agencies across the region to ensure a reliable future supply for its citizens.

Proposed rate changes for residential customers see an increase of about 3% for water and power on bills each year for five years. This reflects an average monthly bill increase of $4.20 each year from 2016 through 2020.

Company Background

LADWP was founded in 1902.

EXECUTIVES

Chief Administrative Officer, David H. Wiggs
Senior Assistant General Manager Power System, David H. (Dave) Wright
General Manager, Marcie L. Edwards
Senior Assistant General Manager Water System, Martin L. Adams
Chief Sustainability And Economic Development Officer, Nancy Sutley
Cfo, Phil Leiber
Fac Vice President, Kevin Brown
Vice President Of Information Technology, Eduardo Cartagena
Legal Secretary, Patricia Stanard
First Vice President, Demarlo Sims
Vice President Of Market Strategy, John Poplawski
Medical Director, Leslie Israel
President Board Of Commissioners, Mel Levine
Vp Board Of Commissioners, William W. Funderburk
Secretary To Executive Vice President, Javier Romero
Secretary, Mar'ja Garcia
Auditors: KPMG LLP LOS ANGELES CA

LOCATIONS

HQ: LOS ANGELES DEPARTMENT OF WATER AND POWER
111 N HOPE ST, LOS ANGELES, CA 900122607
Phone: 213 367-4211
Web: WWW.LADWP.COM

COMPETITORS

AES	Edison International
American States Water	PG&E Corporation
Avista	Sacramento Municipal
California Water Service	Utility
Calpine	Sempra Energy
Duke Energy	SouthWest Water

HISTORICAL FINANCIALS

Company Type: Private

Income Statement — FYE: June 30

	REVENUE ($ mil.)	NET INCOME ($ mil.)	NET PROFIT MARGIN	EMPLOYEES
06/17	1,118	140	12.6%	9,500
06/11	3,125	57	1.8%	—
06/10	812	67	8.3%	—
Annual Growth	4.7%	11.1%	—	—

2017 Year-End Financials

Return on assets: 10.3% Cash ($ mil.): 320
Return on equity: 12.6%
Current ratio: 0.50

LOS ROBLES HOSPITAL & MEDICAL CENTER

EXECUTIVES

Ceo, Greg Angle
Director of Mis/Is, Alex Bryar
Chief of Radiology, Barry Klein
Director of Information Techno, Alex Brier
Dermatologist, Michael Bodnar
Respiratory Therapy Director, Pam Whitener
Dermatologist, Ralph Kamell
Surgeon, Alan Mintz
Associate, Craig Corley
Director, Michael McDonald
Internal Medicine Practitioner, Anna Stewart

LOCATIONS

HQ: LOS ROBLES HOSPITAL & MEDICAL CENTER
215 W JANSS RD, THOUSAND OAKS, CA 913601899
Phone: 805 497-2727
Web: WWW.LOSROBLESHOSPITAL.COM

HISTORICAL FINANCIALS

Company Type: Private

Income Statement — FYE: December 31

	REVENUE ($ mil.)	NET INCOME ($ mil.)	NET PROFIT MARGIN	EMPLOYEES
12/16	474	107	22.7%	1,700
12/15	465	97	20.9%	—
12/08	276	25	9.3%	—
12/04	0	0	7.8%	—
Annual Growth	103.1%	122.0%	—	—

2016 Year-End Financials

Return on assets: 2.8% Cash ($ mil.): —
Return on equity: 22.7%
Current ratio: 2.70

LOTUS INTERNATIONAL COMPANY

EXECUTIVES

Pres, Madan M Sharma
Cfo, Sam Venkat
Human Resources Manager, Geralyn Venkat
Executive of Sales, Prasad Koppolu
Shipping, Joe Hannah
Srmanager Corporate Quality, Palani Masilamani

LOCATIONS

HQ: LOTUS INTERNATIONAL COMPANY
6880 COMMERCE BLVD, CANTON, MI 481874457
Phone: 734 245-0140
Web: WWW.LICUS.COM

HISTORICAL FINANCIALS

Company Type: Private

Income Statement — FYE: December 31

	REVENUE ($ mil.)	NET INCOME ($ mil.)	NET PROFIT MARGIN	EMPLOYEES
12/17	373	23	6.4%	520
12/16	361	22	6.1%	—
12/14	281	0	—	—
12/13	245	14	6.1%	—
Annual Growth	11.0%	12.4%	—	—

2017 Year-End Financials

Return on assets: 3.9% Cash ($ mil.): 21
Return on equity: 6.4%
Current ratio: 3.50

LOUDOUN COUNTY PUBLIC SCHOOL DISTRICT

EXECUTIVES

Supt, Eric Williams
Coordinator, Mark Taylor
Assistant Superintendent, Mary V Kealy

Coordinator, Paige Neeley
Finance Assistant, Diane Aaronson
Sergeant, Linda Cerniglia
Economist, Doug Kinney
Legal Assistant, Kelley A Watt
Information Technology Manager, Andrew Leith
Auditors: CHERRY BEKAERT LLP TYSONS COR

LOCATIONS

HQ: LOUDOUN COUNTY PUBLIC SCHOOL DISTRICT
21000 EDUCATION CT, BROADLANDS, VA 201485526
Phone: 571 252-1000
Web: WWW.LCPS.ORG

HISTORICAL FINANCIALS
Company Type: Private

Income Statement   FYE: June 30

	REVENUE ($ mil.)	NET INCOME ($ mil.)	NET PROFIT MARGIN	EMPLOYEES
06/16	1,130	14	1.3%	9,822
06/15	1,080	19	1.8%	—
06/05	0	0	25.6%	—
Annual Growth	110.2%	59.7%	—	—

LOUDOUN HOSPITAL CENTER

EXECUTIVES

Pres-Ceo, Randall Kelley
President, J Knox Singleton
Cfo, Glenn Zirbser
Principal, Rhonda Kohnen
SEC, Susan Jane Stack
Chief of Pediatrics, Sunil Gupta
Manager, Ellen Carter
Manager, Nicole Bascope
Materials Manager, Lance Greene
Chief of Cardiology, David Reich
Director, Marissa Jamarik

LOCATIONS

HQ: LOUDOUN HOSPITAL CENTER
44045 RIVERSIDE PKWY, LEESBURG, VA 201765101
Phone: 703 858-6000
Web: WWW.INOVA.ORG

HISTORICAL FINANCIALS
Company Type: Private

Income Statement   FYE: December 31

	REVENUE ($ mil.)	NET INCOME ($ mil.)	NET PROFIT MARGIN	EMPLOYEES
12/17	343	66	19.4%	1,000
12/15	302	48	15.9%	—
Annual Growth	6.5%	17.8%	—	—

2017 Year-End Financials
Return on assets: 4.8%
Return on equity: 19.4%
Current ratio: 1.40
Cash ($ mil.): 9

LOWELL GENERAL HOSPITAL

EXECUTIVES

Ceo, Joseph White III
Cfo, Susan Green
Vice President, Amy Hoey
Director, William J Galvin II
Director, Elizabeth Lydstone
Director, Lisa Breen
Human Resources, Nancy Dale
Chief of Anesthesiology, Vijay Channamsetty
Cardiac Physician, Deirdre Proudman
Director of Risk Management, Tatiana Schultz
Director of Quality Improvemen, Gina O'Connor
Auditors: DELOITTE & TOUCHE LLP BOSTON

LOCATIONS

HQ: LOWELL GENERAL HOSPITAL
295 VARNUM AVE, LOWELL, MA 018542193
Phone: 978 937-6000
Web: WWW.LOWELLGENERAL.ORG

HISTORICAL FINANCIALS
Company Type: Private

Income Statement   FYE: September 30

	REVENUE ($ mil.)	NET INCOME ($ mil.)	NET PROFIT MARGIN	EMPLOYEES
09/16	441	1	0.3%	3,000
09/15	419	10	2.6%	—
09/14	405	17	4.3%	—
09/13	0	0	—	—
Annual Growth	—	—	—	—

2016 Year-End Financials
Return on assets: 16.8%
Return on equity: 0.3%
Current ratio: 1.00
Cash ($ mil.): 49

LOWER COLORADO RIVER AUTHORITY

The stars at night may be big and bright but more than 1 million people deep in the heart of Texas still need electricity from the Lower Colorado River Authority (LCRA). Serving 80 counties along the lower Colorado River between Central Texas and the Gulf of Mexico the not-for profit state-run entity supplies wholesale electricity to more than 40 retail utilities (primarily municipalities and cooperatives). It operates three fossil-fuel powered plants and six hydroelectric dams that give it a production capacity of about 3800 megawatts; it also purchases electricity from Texas wind farms. The LCRA provides water and wastewater utility services to more than 30 communities as well.

Operations

Founded by the Texas Legislature in 1934 the LCRA has pursued two complementary goals — providing reliable low-cost utility and public services and ensuring the protection of the area's natural resources. In the latter role the LCRA owns or operates more than 40 public recreation areas comprising more than 16400 acres; it also monitors the water quality and levels of the lakes formed by its dams.

Sales and Marketing

Sales of electricity to one major customer represented 25% of its total electric revenue for 2014.

Financial Performance

LCRA receives no state tax revenues but operates by selling electricity electric transmission and water services at cost. It does not levy taxes or receive specific appropriations from any government. Its net income for fiscal year 2014 increased 1% over 2013 while its revenues remained flat.

Strategy

LCRA's capital improvement and expansion programs from fiscal year 2015 through 2019 totals at $1.2 billion with $0.8 billion or 67% to be debt funded. The majority of the forecasted capital costs will go toward expansion of transmission services dam improvements and the construction of a new water reservoir. LCRA continues to increase its transmission system investment due to the need for additional electric transmission capability statewide.

EXECUTIVES

Deputy General Manager, Ross Phillips
General Manager And Ceo, Phil Wilson
Cfo, Brady Edwards
Manager Information Services And Strategy, Debbie Dunn-Krause
Chairman, Timothy T. Timmerman, age 57
Vice Chairman, John C. Dickerson
Auditors: BAKER TILLY VIRCHOW KRAUSE LLP

LOCATIONS

HQ: LOWER COLORADO RIVER AUTHORITY
3700 LAKE AUSTIN BLVD, AUSTIN, TX 787033504
Phone: 512 473-3200
Web: WWW.LCRA.ORG

PRODUCTS/OPERATIONS

Selected Subsidiaries and Affiliates

Fayette Power Project (coal-fired power generating units)
GenTex Power Corporation (power generation)
LCRA Transmission Services Corporation (power transmission services)

HISTORICAL FINANCIALS
Company Type: Private

Income Statement   FYE: June 30

	REVENUE ($ mil.)	NET INCOME ($ mil.)	NET PROFIT MARGIN	EMPLOYEES
06/15	1,021	15	1.5%	1,800
06/12	1,261	101	8.0%	—
06/11	1,185	48	4.1%	—
06/10	1,244	110	8.9%	—
Annual Growth	(3.9%)	(32.5%)	—	—

2015 Year-End Financials
Return on assets: 5.7%
Return on equity: 1.5%
Current ratio: 0.70
Cash ($ mil.): 182

LOYOLA MARYMOUNT UNIVERSITY

Loyola Marymount University (LMU) in Los Angeles is a Jesuit (Catholic) institution with an enrollment of more than 9500 students. It offers more than 115 graduate and undergraduate programs through four colleges: Bellarmine College of Liberal Arts College of Business Administration College of Communication and Fine Arts and Seaver College of Science and Engineering. There is also the School of Education and School of Film and Television. Other programs include the Graduate Division Continuing Education Program and Loyola Law School. LMU has an 11:1 student-to-faculty ratio. The university was formed in 1973 by the merger of Loyola College (founded in 1911) and Marymount Junior College.

Operations

The university offers about 60 majors and 55 minor study programs to its undergraduate students. LMU also offers more than 40 master's degrees two doctorates and a dozen certification programs. In total it employs about 2000 faculty and staff members.

LMU has partnerships with about a dozen public and private elementary and secondary schools in the Los Angeles area. Through the LMU Family of Schools model school demonstration program the university provides professional development and educational resources to the schools.

Geographic Reach

LMU is located on a 140-acre campus in Los Angeles.

Financial Performance

The university experienced a 3% increase in revenues from $320 million to $328 million due to higher net tuition and fee income auxiliary enterprise revenue and investment returns designated for operations. Tuition runs at some $40000 annually plus some $13000 in room and board. LMU reported net income of $63 million over a net loss in 2012 due to increased investment returns and gains on interest rate swaps. Cash from operations dropped by $6 million to $20 as the university used cash in account receivable and contributions for long-term investments.

Strategy

In 2013 LMU broke ground on a $110 million life sciences complex that will become Pereira Hall (for engineering) and Seaver Hall (for physics and math).

To increase student access to its programs LMU launched a new scholarship initiative in 2012. Through the program the university seeks to raise some $100 million for new scholarships through donations and endowment returns over a three-year period.

EXECUTIVES

Senior Vice President For Administration, Lynne Scarboro
Provost And Executive Vice President, Joseph Hellige
Senior Vice President For University Relations, Dennis Slon
Vice President Vice President For Student Affairs, Lane Bove
Budget Analyst Enrollment Management Vice President Office, Gabriela De Anda
Associate Vice President Of Administration Services, Michael Wong
Senior Vice President Administration, Evelynne Scarboro
Executive Vice President International And Insurance Group, David Zuercher
Auditors: PRICEWATERHOUSECOOPERS LLP L

LOCATIONS

HQ: LOYOLA MARYMOUNT UNIVERSITY
1 LMU DR UHALL STE 4900, LOS ANGELES, CA 90045
Phone: 310 338-2700
Web: WWW.LMU.EDU

PRODUCTS/OPERATIONS

Colleges and Schools
Bellarmine College of Liberal Arts
College of Business Administration
College of Communication and Fine Arts
Graduate Division
LMU Extension
Loyola Law School
School of Education
School of Film and Television
Seaver College of Science and Engineering

HISTORICAL FINANCIALS
Company Type: Private

Income Statement
FYE: May 31

	REVENUE ($ mil.)	NET INCOME ($ mil.)	NET PROFIT MARGIN	EMPLOYEES
05/18	393	51	13.1%	1,449
05/14	338	70	20.9%	—
05/13	328	62	19.1%	—
Annual Growth	3.7%	(3.9%)	—	—

2018 Year-End Financials
Return on assets: 11.7%   Cash ($ mil.): 44
Return on equity: 13.1%
Current ratio: —

LOYOLA UNIVERSITY OF CHICAGO INC

Loyola University is a Jesuit Catholic university with a reach that extends far beyond the Windy City. In addition to its three Chicago-area campuses the university also maintains an undergraduate campus in Italy and a study center in Beijing China. Loyola University's nearly 16000 students can choose from about 80 undergraduate 85 master's 30 doctoral and about two dozen graduate-level certificate programs. With about 1550 full-time staff members the not-for-profit school has a 14:1 student-teacher ratio. Notable alumni include actor Bob Newhart and writer Sandra Cisneros. Established in 1870 by a group of Jesuit priests the university turned its medical center into a separate subsidiary in 1995.

Geographic Reach

Loyola University three Chicago campuses include Lake Shore Water Tower and Health Sciences as well as the John Felice Rome Center in Italy. It is home to 10 schools and colleges that include arts and sciences business administration communication education graduate studies law medicine nursing continuing and professional studies and social work.

Loyola also features course locations in Beijing China and Saigon-Ho Chi Minh City Vietnam.

Strategy

In 2013 Loyola University Chicago broke ground on a new $137 million medical research and education building at its Health Sciences Campus. Named the Loyola University Chicago Center for Translational Research and Education the building will include laboratory space and a 250-seat auditorium. It is scheduled to open in mid-2016.

In 2011 the Loyola University Health System (LUHS) was sold to Trinity Health one of the largest Catholic health care systems in the US. LUHS and its half-dozen hospitals had not been profitable and the sale allowed it to pay less in subsidies to Loyola University's medical school in exchange for the university getting out from underneath the health system's debt.

EXECUTIVES

President And Ceo, Michael J. Garanzini
Provost, John Pelissero
Government Relations, Philip Hale
Vice President Spence And Elster, Nanette Elster
Vice President Of Resolutions Systems Institute, Terry Moritz
Vice President Strategic Capital Planning, Wayne F Magdziarz
Chairman, Robert L. Parkinson
Vice Chairman, Mary Ann Zollmann
Board Member, Carolyn Saari
Auditors: DELOITTE & TOUCHE LLP CHICAG

LOCATIONS

HQ: LOYOLA UNIVERSITY OF CHICAGO INC
1032 W SHERIDAN RD, CHICAGO, IL 606601537
Phone: 773 274-3000
Web: WWW.LUC.EDU

PRODUCTS/OPERATIONS

Selected Schools & Colleges
College of Arts and Sciences
Graduate School of Business
Institute of Pastoral Studies
Marcella Niehoff School of Nursing
Quinlan School of Business
School of Communication
School of Continuing and Professional Studies
School of Education
School of Law
School of Social Work
Stritch School of Medicine
The Graduate School

HISTORICAL FINANCIALS
Company Type: Private

Income Statement
FYE: June 30

	REVENUE ($ mil.)	NET INCOME ($ mil.)	NET PROFIT MARGIN	EMPLOYEES
06/18	594	109	18.4%	10,500
06/17	582	109	18.7%	—
06/13	509	87	17.2%	—
06/12	490	74	15.3%	—
Annual Growth	3.3%	6.5%	—	—

2018 Year-End Financials
Return on assets: 9.8%   Cash ($ mil.): 70
Return on equity: 18.4%
Current ratio: —

LUBBOCK COUNTY HOSPITAL DISTRICT

EXECUTIVES

Pres-Ceo, David Allison
Coordinator, Carol Cloud
Coordinator, Ace Garcia
Coordinator, Jayton Zachary
Coordinator, Jillian Edge
Coordinator, Kelsey Thrasher
Chief of Medicine, Werner De Riese
Staff, Elsie Foli
Coordinator, Jeffrey Fuerstenberg
Vice President, Terrell Thrasher

LOCATIONS

HQ: LUBBOCK COUNTY HOSPITAL DISTRICT
602 INDIANA AVE, LUBBOCK, TX 794153364
Phone: 806 775-8200
Web: WWW.UMCHEALTHSYSTEM.COM

HISTORICAL FINANCIALS

Company Type: Private

Income Statement   FYE: December 31

	REVENUE ($ mil.)	NET INCOME ($ mil.)	NET PROFIT MARGIN	EMPLOYEES
12/16	463	57	12.4%	2,000
12/15	444	49	11.2%	—
12/14*	473	33	7.0%	—
05/05	0	(0)	—	—
Annual Growth	**77.6%**	—	—	—

*Fiscal year change

2016 Year-End Financials

Return on assets: 7.3%   Cash ($ mil.): 141
Return on equity: 12.4%
Current ratio: 3.10

LUBBOCK INDEPENDENT SCHOOL DISTRICT

EXECUTIVES

Supt, Cathy Rollo
Cntrl, Nina Waller
Academic Advisor, Christie Stewart
Administrator, Amy Carroll
1st Grade Teacher, Cory Davis
Teacher Coach, Darrell Baldwin
Band Director Atkins Middle SC, Derrek Eldredge
Special Education Teacher, Jacqueline Malone
Teacher, Jane Berta
Assistant, Linda Landin
Teacher, Lisa Gilbert
Auditors: BOLINGER SEGARS GILBERT & MO

LOCATIONS

HQ: LUBBOCK INDEPENDENT SCHOOL DISTRICT
1628 19TH ST, LUBBOCK, TX 794014832
Phone: 806 766-1000
Web: WWW.LUBBOCKISD.ORG

HISTORICAL FINANCIALS

Company Type: Private

Income Statement   FYE: June 30

	REVENUE ($ mil.)	NET INCOME ($ mil.)	NET PROFIT MARGIN	EMPLOYEES
06/17	309	(5)	—	3,300
06/16	307	(0)	—	—
06/15	295	(8)	—	—
06/14	284	12	4.3%	—
Annual Growth	**2.9%**	—	—	—

LUCILE SALTER PACKARD CHILDREN'S HOSPITAL AT STANFORD

EXECUTIVES

Pres-Ceo, Christopher Dawes
Cfo, Timothy W Carmack
Coordinator, Arlene Sheehan
Coordinator, Sonja Avery
Chief Information Security Off, Auston Davis
Chief of Medicine, Dennis Lund
Programmer Analyst, Irene Todd
Coordinator, Carrie Johnson
Coordinator, Erin Murphy
Coordinator, Jennifer Cctc
Occupational Specia, Quiara Smith
Auditors: PRICEWATERHOUSECOOPERS LLP BO

LOCATIONS

HQ: LUCILE SALTER PACKARD CHILDREN'S
HOSPITAL AT STANFORD
725 WELCH RD, PALO ALTO, CA 943041601
Phone: 650 497-8000
Web: WWW.LPCH.ORG

HISTORICAL FINANCIALS

Company Type: Private

Income Statement   FYE: August 31

	REVENUE ($ mil.)	NET INCOME ($ mil.)	NET PROFIT MARGIN	EMPLOYEES
08/18	1,637	22	1.4%	1,100
08/17	1,486	227	15.3%	—
08/16	1,402	157	11.2%	—
08/14	1,135	98	8.7%	—
Annual Growth	**9.6%**	**(30.7%)**	—	—

2018 Year-End Financials

Return on assets: 12.0%   Cash ($ mil.): 288
Return on equity: 1.4%
Current ratio: 1.60

M. F. A. OIL COMPANY

Many farmers appreciate MFA Oil. The energy cooperative controlled by its 40000 farmer-members produces fuel and lubrication products and manages bulk petroleum and propane plants in the Central and Western US. Operating 140 propane plants the company sells more propane for farm use and home heating than any other company in Missouri. It also operates nearly 100 oil and lubricant bulk plants and serves customers in Arkansas Iowa Kansas and Oklahoma. Additionally the company operates 76 convenience stores under the Break Time brand (in Arkansas and Missouri) more than 160 Petro-Card 24 fueling locations and owns 10 Jiffy Lube and a dozen Big O Tire franchises.

Geographic Reach

MFA Oil serves customers in Arkansas Colorado Kansas Kentucky Indiana Iowa Missouri Nebraska Oklahoma Virginia and Wyoming.

Strategy

While not a pure vertically integrated enterprise over time the cooperative has developed multiple complementary business lines to enable it to respond to a wide range of its members' fuel transportation and food service needs. In this tradition in 2011 MFA Oil teamed up with biofuel developer Aloterra Energy to form MFA Oil Biomass LLC. The partnership aims to help farmers to produce a renewable energy crop that can be used as biomass for an alternative cleaner burning energy supply for use in power generation plants as well as a liquid fuel. In 2011 about 250 farmers had signed letters of intent to grow miscanthus (a perennial grass) on more than 21000 acres as part of this initiative.

Mergers and Acquisitions

Expanding its geographic network in 2013 MFA Oil acquired Kansas-based American Petroleum Marketers which distributes fuel to more than 60 Cenex branded sites along with unbranded fuel in six states.

Company Background

MFA Oil has grown well beyond its Missouri roots where it was founded by farmers in 1929. The company's first bulk plant was located at Wright City Missouri.

EXECUTIVES

Ceo, Jerry Taylor
Chb, Benny Farrell
SEC, Beverly Twellman
Cfo, Robert Condron
Admin, Joy Page
Accounts Receivable, Kari Evans
Vice President of Logistics, Larry Ehrman
Operations, Scott Watson
Auditors: WILLIAMS-KEEPERS LLC COLUMBIA

LOCATIONS

HQ: M. F. A. OIL COMPANY
1 RAY YOUNG DR, COLUMBIA, MO 652013506
Phone: 573 442-0171
Web: WWW.BIGOTIRES.COM

COMPETITORS

Ag Processing Inc.	Lykins
Green Brick Partners	Shell Oil Products
Green Plains	Valero Energy
Jordan Oil Company	WilcoHess

HISTORICAL FINANCIALS

Company Type: Private

Income Statement   FYE: August 31

	REVENUE ($ mil.)	NET INCOME ($ mil.)	NET PROFIT MARGIN	EMPLOYEES
08/17	900	8	0.9%	1,500
08/16	800	24	3.1%	—
08/15	1,045	48	4.6%	—
08/14	1,471	40	2.8%	—
Annual Growth	**(15.1%)**	**(41.1%)**	—	—

2017 Year-End Financials

Return on assets: 1.7%   Cash ($ mil.): 22
Return on equity: 0.9%
Current ratio: 1.20

M.A. PATOUT & SON LIMITED, L.L.C.

EXECUTIVES

Chb-Pres, Frank W Patout
Ceo, Craig Caillier
SEC, Thomas G Duhe

Cfo, Randall K Romero
Treas, J Jared Patout
Gen Mgr, Robert B Patout
Chief Financial Officer, Ashlee Gary
General Manager, Lance Weber
Auditors: BROUSSARD POCHE LLP LAFAYETT

LOCATIONS

HQ: M.A. PATOUT & SON LIMITED, L.L.C.
   3512 J PATOUT BURNS RD, JEANERETTE, LA
   705447122
Phone: 337 276-4592
Web: WWW.MAPATOUT.COM

COMPETITORS

ADM
   Amalgamated Sugar
   American Crystal Sugar
   Associated British Foods
   C&H Sugar
   Eurosugar
   Imperial Sugar
   Ingredion
   Michigan Sugar Company
   Nordzucker
   SMBSC
   Seaboard
   Sugar Cane Growers Cooperative of Florida
   S dzucker
   Tate & Lyle
   Tereos
   U.S. Sugar
   Western Sugar Cooperative

HISTORICAL FINANCIALS

Company Type: Private

Income Statement   FYE: July 31

	REVENUE ($ mil.)	NET INCOME ($ mil.)	NET PROFIT MARGIN	EMPLOYEES
07/18	305	27	9.0%	413
07/16	288	11	4.0%	—
/ 0	0	0	—	—
Annual Growth	—	—	—	—

2018 Year-End Financials

Return on assets: 1.0%   Cash ($ mil.): 22
Return on equity: 9.0%
Current ratio: 0.30

MADISON METROPOLITAN SCHOOL DISTRICT

EXECUTIVES

Pres, James Howard
Supt, Jane Belmore
Vice President, Marj Passman
Treas, Beth Moss
Staff, Ann Wersal
Facilities Manager, Joseph Anderson
Administrative Assistant, Jennifer Trendel
Coordinator, Kevin Blackmore
Accountant, Ross Macpherson
Coordinator, Samuel Espich
Assistant Director, Joanne Grassman

LOCATIONS

HQ: MADISON METROPOLITAN SCHOOL DISTRICT
   545 W DAYTON ST, MADISON, WI 537031995
Phone: 608 663-1879
Web: WWW.MADISON.K12.WI.US

HISTORICAL FINANCIALS

Company Type: Private

Income Statement   FYE: June 30

	REVENUE ($ mil.)	NET INCOME ($ mil.)	NET PROFIT MARGIN	EMPLOYEES
06/17	426	(2)	—	4,006
06/16	414	28	6.8%	—
06/11	374	3	1.0%	—
06/08	349	(4)	—	—
Annual Growth	2.2%	—	—	—

2017 Year-End Financials

Return on assets: 1.4%   Cash ($ mil.): 114
Return on equity: (-0.7%)
Current ratio: —

MAGEE-WOMENS HOSPITAL OF UPMC

EXECUTIVES

Pres, Leslie C Davis
Chb, William Pietragallo
Treas, Peter Eisenbrandt
SEC, Claire Williams
Oncology, Margaret V Ragni
Project Coordinator, Meredith Colaizzi
Information Specialist, Michele King
Administrative Assistant, Nancy Cupps

LOCATIONS

HQ: MAGEE-WOMENS HOSPITAL OF UPMC
   300 HALKET ST, PITTSBURGH, PA 152133108
Phone: 412 641-1000
Web: WWW.MAGEE.UPMC.COM

HISTORICAL FINANCIALS

Company Type: Private

Income Statement   FYE: June 30

	REVENUE ($ mil.)	NET INCOME ($ mil.)	NET PROFIT MARGIN	EMPLOYEES
06/16	838	92	11.1%	2,300
06/15	823	62	7.6%	—
06/00	7	7	98.8%	—
Annual Growth	33.9%	16.8%	—	—

2016 Year-End Financials

Return on assets: 0.4%   Cash ($ mil.): 1
Return on equity: 11.1%
Current ratio: 3.00

MAGELLAN PIPELINE COMPANY, L.P.

EXECUTIVES

Ptnr-Pres-Ceo, Don Wellendorf
Ptnr-V Pres-Tres,, Jeff Holman
Accounting Staff, Dana Taylor
Director, Doug Chabino
Manager, Destiny Stephens
Marketing Staff, Garland Tackett
Analyst, Tj Simmons
Land Supervisor, Bob Miller
Area Supervisor, James Bacon
Senior Engineering Project Man, Josh Fidler
Project Manager, Stein Haakenstad

LOCATIONS

HQ: MAGELLAN PIPELINE COMPANY, L.P.
   1 WILLIAMS CTR, TULSA, OK 741720140
Phone: 918 574-7000
Web: WWW.MAGELLANLP.COM

HISTORICAL FINANCIALS

Company Type: Private

Income Statement   FYE: December 31

	REVENUE ($ mil.)	NET INCOME ($ mil.)	NET PROFIT MARGIN	EMPLOYEES
12/17	828	396	47.9%	435
12/16	911	339	37.2%	—
Annual Growth	(9.1%)	17.0%	—	—

2017 Year-End Financials

Return on assets: 7.5%   Cash ($ mil.): 15
Return on equity: 47.9%
Current ratio: 0.30

MAIMONIDES MEDICAL CENTER

Maimonides Medical Center a not-for-profit hospital offers emergency medicine surgical procedures psychiatric treatment and other traditional hospital services to patients in Brooklyn New York. It has more than 710 beds and more than 70 subspecialty treatment programs for a range of conditions including cancer cardiac stroke neurological pediatric and women's health ailments. It also operates outpatient family health and specialty clinics. Maimonides Medical Center is an independent teaching hospital that serves as a training facility for SUNY-Brooklyn St. George's University and other schools.

Financial Performance

In fiscal 2015 revenue remained flat at $1.1 billion compared to 2014. Although net patient service revenue rose 1% the hospital saw a 23% decline in "other" revenue. Net income fell 78% to $11 million that year as expenses rose; the center also reported accrued benefits liabilities to be recognized in future periods.

Despite the decline in profits operating cash flow increased 203% to $33 million primarily due to a change in receivables for patient fare.

Strategy

Maimonides Medical Center works to keep its utilization rates up (the number of patients it sees) and make itself attractive to doctors by making capital investments in its facilities and technology systems on a regular basis. In 2015 it established a partnership with North Shore-LIJ Health System (now Northwell) through which the systems will share services infrastructure and expertise; Northshore will also provide Maimonides with funding.

The hospital uses a fully-implemented electronic health record (EHR) system that includes a computerized physician order entry system (CPOE) that reduces prescription errors and a picture archival communications system (PACS) to store digital radiology images. The use of such technology is becoming increasingly tied to how the government reimburses hospitals for the services they provide especially in the new health care reform laws.

Company Background

Maimonides Medical Center traces its roots to the New Utrecht Dispensary which opened in 1911. The medical center later merged with Beth Moses and United Israel Zion hospitals in 1947. It is named after 12th-century philosopher Rabbi Moshe Ben Maimon.

EXECUTIVES

Evp And Cfo, Robert Naldi
Vp Management Information Systems And Cio, Walter J. Fahey
Executive Vice President Clinical Affairs & Affiliations, David I. Cohen
Evp And Coo, Dominick Stanzione
Chairman, Kenneth Gibbs
Blood Bank Director Laboratory Director, Robert Kalter
Vice President Finance, Wade Wilson
Avp Mis, Nancy Daurio
Vice President For Legal Affairs, Anthony Mancuso
Vice President, Martin Cammer
Chairman, Eugene J. Keilin
Vice Chairman Of Academic Affairs, Dennis Feierman

LOCATIONS

HQ: MAIMONIDES MEDICAL CENTER
  4802 10TH AVE, BROOKLYN, NY 112192916
Phone: 718 581-0598
Web: WWW.MAIMONIDESMED.ORG

PRODUCTS/OPERATIONS

2014 Sales

	% of total
Net patient revenue less provision for bad debts	95
Net assets released from restrictions	
Other revenue	5
Total	**100**

Selected Services

Adult Primary Care
Ambulatory Health Services
Bay Parkway Multi-Specialty
Manfredi Family Health Center
Newkirk Family Health Center
Outpatient Eye Clinic
Pediatric Primary Care
Primary Health Services
Sheepshead Bay
Women's Primary Care Services

COMPETITORS

Beth Israel Medical Center
Bronx-Lebanon Hospital
Brookdale University Hospital
Brooklyn Hospital Center
Catholic Healthcare System
Continuum Health Partners
Lutheran HealthCare
Montefiore Medical
New York City Health and Hospitals
New York Methodist Hospital
NewYork-Presbyterian Hospital
North Shore University Hospital
SUNY Downstate

Jamaica Hospital Medical Center
Kingsbrook Jewish Medical Center
Long Island College Hospital
Staten Island University Hospital
Wyckoff Heights Medical Center

HISTORICAL FINANCIALS
Company Type: Private

Income Statement				FYE: December 31
	REVENUE ($ mil.)	NET INCOME ($ mil.)	NET PROFIT MARGIN	EMPLOYEES
12/17	958	19	2.0%	6,382
12/16	940	20	2.2%	—
12/15	890	(2)	—	—
12/14	884	10	1.2%	—
Annual Growth	**2.7%**	**23.2%**	**—**	**—**

2017 Year-End Financials
Return on assets: 8.5%   Cash ($ mil.): 16
Return on equity: 2.0%
Current ratio: 0.50

MAIN LINE HEALTH SYSTEM

EXECUTIVES

Pres-Ceo, Jack Lynch
Sr Vice President, Thomas Mendicino
Assistant Manager, Laura Armstrong
Hris Analyst, Michelle Massaro
Senior Recruiter, Andrew Miller
Manager, Annemarie Cellucci
Research, Daisy Romero
Disability, Donna Monaco
Senior Recruiter, Douglas Clautics
Recruiter, Katie Kealey
Benefits Administrator, Mark Wallace

LOCATIONS

HQ: MAIN LINE HEALTH SYSTEM
  240 N RADNOR CHESTER RD, RADNOR, PA 190875170
Phone: 610 225-6200

COMPETITORS

Abington Memorial Hospital
Albert Einstein Healthcare Network
Crozer-Keystone Health System
LVHN
Lancaster General
Memorial Hospital (PA)
Mercy Health System
North Philadelphia Health System
TUHS
University of Pennsylvania Health System
Virtua Health

HISTORICAL FINANCIALS
Company Type: Private

Income Statement				FYE: June 30
	REVENUE ($ mil.)	NET INCOME ($ mil.)	NET PROFIT MARGIN	EMPLOYEES
06/18	1,742	267	15.4%	17,485
06/17	1,695	51	3.0%	—
06/16	1,660	(130)	—	—
06/15	1,586	121	7.6%	—
Annual Growth	**3.2%**	**30.2%**	**—**	**—**

2018 Year-End Financials
Return on assets: 5.2%   Cash ($ mil.): 113
Return on equity: 15.4%
Current ratio: 1.30

MAIN LINE HOSPITALS, INC.

EXECUTIVES

Vice President Material Management, Chris Torres
Vice President Operations, Jim Paradis
Vice President Of Finance And Treasurer, Michael Bouongiono
Vice President And Chief Medical Information Officer, Harm Scherpbier

LOCATIONS

HQ: MAIN LINE HOSPITALS, INC.
  130 S BRYN MAWR AVE, BRYN MAWR, PA 190103121
Phone: 610 526-3000
Web: WWW.BRYNMAWRUROLOGY.COM

COMPETITORS

Abington Memorial Hospital
Albert Einstein Healthcare Network
Christiana Care
Crozer-Keystone Health System
Doylestown Hospital
Memorial Hospital (PA)
Moses Taylor Hospital
North Philadelphia Health System
Tenet Healthcare
University of Pennsylvania Health System
Virtua Memorial

HISTORICAL FINANCIALS
Company Type: Private

Income Statement				FYE: June 30
	REVENUE ($ mil.)	NET INCOME ($ mil.)	NET PROFIT MARGIN	EMPLOYEES
06/18	1,193	100	8.4%	5,840
06/16	327	36	11.0%	—
Annual Growth	**90.9%**	**67.0%**	**—**	**—**

2018 Year-End Financials
Return on assets: 4.2%   Cash ($ mil.): 68
Return on equity: 8.4%
Current ratio: 1.90

MAINE MEDICAL CENTER

Maine Medical Center (MMC) makes healing happen for the residents of northern New England. Part of MaineHealth the not-for-profit medical center consists of a tertiary care community hospital The Barbara Bush Children's Hospital and outpatient clinics. Specialty services include cancer care geriatrics emergency medicine cardiovascular care rehabilitation neurology orthopedics and women's health. Through its partnership with the Tufts University School of Medicine the 640-bed teaching hospital provides a variety of medical education and training programs. MMC also conducts research through the Maine Medical Center Research Institute. The medical center was founded in 1874 with 40 beds.

Operations

MMC boasts a large ever-expanding outpatient segment that provides day surgery cardiac catheterization laboratory services and rehabilitation services. It also operates about three dozen outpatient clinics. MMC provides preventive and consultation services including the MMC Diabetes Center the AIDS Consultation Service and the Center for Lipids and Cardiovascular Health.

MMC is expanding the surgical facilities at its main campus. Due for completion in 2015 the medical center embarked on a $40-million expansion plan that will add five modern operating rooms including a cardiac hybrid operating room and 20 perioperative spaces for patient prep and recovery.

The medical center is one of the largest employers in its service territory with a workforce of some 6500. Its Maine Medical Partners physician organization maintains about 175 doctors who provide care at some 30 primary and specialty care centers. MMC also provides more than 20% of charity care for uninsured or underinsured patients in the state.

Geographic Reach

Located in Portland the MMC serves the northern New England area.

Strategy

In keeping with its reputation of being technologically forward the hospital operates a Telestroke Network that provides area residents with around-the-clock access to MMC's neurology and ER physicians. The Telestroke Network is a form of telemedicine an increasingly popular way of expanding access to care by allowing patients to "visit" physicians either telephonically or via streaming web and video. MMC is also one of a growing number of teaching hospitals to use high-tech simulation rooms to train medical students.

To improve the quality of care MMC is enacting evidence-based medicine programs. Through such programs hospitals seek to lower medical expenses and improve patient outcomes through data exchange systems that allow physicians to review best practices in specific medical fields. The hospital is also looking to expand its research programs by partnering with other area medical R&D firms.

EXECUTIVES

Evp And Coo, Richard W. (Rich) Petersen
Senior Vice President Chief Information Officer, Barry Blumenfeld
Svp Planning And Marketing Maine Medical Center And Mainehealth, Mark A. Harris
Vp Medical And Academic Affairs; Chief Medical Officer And Academic Dean Tufts University School Of Medicine Medical School Program, Peter W. Bates
Evp And Coo, Jeffrey D. (Jeff) Sanders
President Medical Staff, M. Parker Roberts
President And A Principal Of Cbre|boulos Property Management, Morris Fisher
President Mainehealth, William L. Caron
Vice President Of Strategy And Business Development, Edward Farrell
Senior Vice President Of Finance, Lugene Inzana
Senior Vice President Clinical Services, Maureen Van Benthuysen
Nursing Director, Deborah Bachand
Assistant Vice President Research And Director Maine Medical Center Research Institute, Donald Germain
Vice President Revenue Cycle, Chausse Paul
Vice President System Planning, Sue Cobb
Medical Director, Tammi Schaeffer
Vice President Cardiovascular Services, Tim Kafer

Medical Director, Mark Fulton
Chairman, Christopher W. Emmons
Board Director And District, Aaron Weiss

LOCATIONS

HQ: MAINE MEDICAL CENTER
22 BRAMHALL ST, PORTLAND, ME 041023175
Phone: 207 662-0111
Web: WWW.MMC.ORG

PRODUCTS/OPERATIONS

Selected Specialty Centers
Cancer Institute
Cardiovascular Institute
Emergency Medicine
Family Birth Center
Joint Replacement Center
Neuroscience Institute
The Barbara Bush Children's Hospital

COMPETITORS

Eastern Maine Healthcare Systems	MaineGeneral Health
Franklin Community Health Network	Mercy Health System of Maine
Maine Coast Memorial Hospital	St. Joseph Healthcare

HISTORICAL FINANCIALS
Company Type: Private

Income Statement				FYE: September 30
	REVENUE ($ mil.)	NET INCOME ($ mil.)	NET PROFIT MARGIN	EMPLOYEES
09/17	1,236	152	12.4%	2,000
09/16	1,126	3	0.3%	—
09/15	1,023	(39)	—	—
09/14	905	53	5.9%	—
Annual Growth	11.0%	41.9%	—	—

2017 Year-End Financials
Return on assets: 5.5%   Cash ($ mil.): 146
Return on equity: 12.4%
Current ratio: 0.90

MAINE MUNICIPAL BOND BANK

EXECUTIVES

President, Robert Lenna
Chief Information Officer, Michele Sucy

LOCATIONS

HQ: MAINE MUNICIPAL BOND BANK
127 COMMUNITY DR 101, AUGUSTA, ME 043308010
Phone: 207 622-9386
Web: WWW.MAINEBONDBANK.COM

HISTORICAL FINANCIALS
Company Type: Private

Income Statement				FYE: June 30
	ASSETS ($ mil.)	NET INCOME ($ mil.)	INCOME AS % OF ASSETS	EMPLOYEES
06/18	2,443	14	0.6%	18
06/17	2,410	12	0.5%	—
Annual Growth	1.3%	15.5%	—	—

MAINEGENERAL MEDICAL CENTER

EXECUTIVES

Ceo, Chuck Hays
Princ, Paul Stein
Officer, Charles Hays
Communications Manager, Barbara Martin
Supervisor, Joy Leach
Cardiac Physician, Kevin White
Senior Vice-President, Gail Evans
Director, John Bielecki
Director, Kevin Ward
Data Administrator, Linda Allen
Administrative Assistant, Chris Hoffman
Auditors: BAKER NEWMAN & NOYES PORTLAN

LOCATIONS

HQ: MAINEGENERAL MEDICAL CENTER
35 MEDICAL CENTER PKWY, AUGUSTA, ME 043308160
Phone: 207 626-1289
Web: WWW.MAINEGENERAL.ORG

HISTORICAL FINANCIALS
Company Type: Private

Income Statement				FYE: June 30
	REVENUE ($ mil.)	NET INCOME ($ mil.)	NET PROFIT MARGIN	EMPLOYEES
06/18	476	13	2.8%	2,200
06/13	378	40	10.6%	—
06/11	372	39	10.7%	—
06/10	336	10	3.2%	—
Annual Growth	4.5%	3.0%	—	—

2018 Year-End Financials
Return on assets: 2.5%   Cash ($ mil.): 20
Return on equity: 2.8%
Current ratio: 1.70

MANAGEMENT & TRAINING CORPORATION

Management & Training Corporation (MTC) prepares prison inmates for re-entry into society. It provides a variety of academic vocational and social-skills training in rehabilitation-oriented private prisons. Its holistic education model offers programs to help inmates avoid substance abuse as they also boost their engagement in community service find work and increase their cognitive skills. As part of its services MTC operates about two dozen correctional facilities in eight states through a contract with the Department of Labor. The company also operates Job Corps centers and provides healthcare-related services to correctional facilities.

Operations

MTC operates through four divisions: Correctional Education & Training MTC Medical and Economic & Social Development. Its correctional division operates facilities that house more than 31100 inmates and is one of the largest US correctional contractors for the Department of Labor. The Education & Training division trains some

14000 young adults each year at 23 Job Corps centers.

The company's MTC Medical unit provides subcontracted healthcare services to correctional facilities by employing a range of medical providers including dentists optometrists psychiatrists and psychologists and physicians. The Economic & Social Development division which offers research retraining and vocational training through contracts with other organizations has provided vocational training to citizens in Iraq and research and retraining efforts in China Haiti Mongolia Southern Sudan Tunisia Pakistan Indonesia Jordan and Palestine.

The company trains its supervisors senior managers and executives through its MTC Corporate University while its MTC Institute performs research into forming best practices related to addressing issues facing those who work with Job Corps youth and prison inmates.

Geographic Reach

The company's main offices are located in Centerville Utah and it has satellite centers in Georgia Texas and Washington DC. MTC operates through more than 60 contracts in about 20 states including correctional facility contracts in Arizona California Florida Idaho Ohio New Mexico Mississippi and Texas.

MTC operates internationally providing governments NGOs ministries and private entities with customized training programs designed to help develop workforces. Its international unit has assisted clients in Africa Asia Australia the Middle East and North America.

Sales and Marketing

In addition to the Department of Labor the company has held contracts with the US Agency for International Development the African Development Bank UNICEF and other organizations. It also serves state agencies such as the Texas Department of Criminal Justice.

Strategy

MTC expands by recruiting and retaining quality educators health professionals and international consultants. To maximize its employees' potential the company conducts leadership development programs for all of its employees. MTC also expands by adding new contracts with state correctional agencies.

Working with MTC in 2014 Georgia's Wilkinson County Correctional Facility started a new program to help inmates deal with anger issues. The following year MTC was granted a contract to operate the Polk Secure Adult Detention Center in Livingston Texas.

Company Background

MRC was founded in 1981.

EXECUTIVES

Senior Vice President Of Training Programs, John Pedersen
President And Ceo, R. Scott Marquardt
Director Marketing Corrections, Mike Murphy
Vice President Operations, Janae Panagoplos
Vice President And General Counsel, Dawn Call
Vice President, Lowder Korey
Chairman, Robert Marquardt
Auditors: KPMG LLP SALT LAKE CITY UTAH

LOCATIONS

HQ: MANAGEMENT & TRAINING CORPORATION
500 N MARKET PLACE DR # 100, CENTERVILLE, UT 840141711
Phone: 801 693-2600
Web: WWW.MTCTRAINS.COM

PRODUCTS/OPERATIONS

Selected Services
Communicate through formal and informal channels
Develop custom training for students clients & offenders
Manage facilities
Provide community connections
Provide data solutions

COMPETITORS

Avalon Correctional Services
Community Education Centers
Conmed Healthcare
Corizon
Corrections Corporation of America
G4S
GEO Group
MHM Services
Res-Care
Wexford Health

HISTORICAL FINANCIALS

Company Type: Private

Income Statement   FYE: December 31

	REVENUE ($ mil.)	NET INCOME ($ mil.)	NET PROFIT MARGIN	EMPLOYEES
12/17	667	49	7.5%	9,500
12/15	753	30	4.0%	—
12/13	735	50	6.9%	—
12/12	704	45	6.5%	—
Annual Growth	(1.1%)	1.8%	—	—

2017 Year-End Financials

Return on assets: 2.6%   Cash ($ mil.): 2
Return on equity: 7.5%
Current ratio: 1.30

MANAGEMENT SCIENCES FOR HEALTH, INC.

EXECUTIVES

Ceo-Pres, Jonathan Quick
Cfo, Vickie Barrow Klein
Coo, Paul Auxila
Sr Acct, Fernado Joves
Executive Officer, Abid Ansari
Associate, Moushumi Sur
Auditors: BDO USA LLP MC LEAN VA

LOCATIONS

HQ: MANAGEMENT SCIENCES FOR HEALTH, INC.
200 RIVERS EDGE DR, MEDFORD, MA 021555479
Phone: 617 250-9500
Web: WWW.MSH.ORG

HISTORICAL FINANCIALS

Company Type: Private

Income Statement   FYE: June 30

	REVENUE ($ mil.)	NET INCOME ($ mil.)	NET PROFIT MARGIN	EMPLOYEES
06/16	288	8	3.0%	400
06/15	303	2	0.9%	—
06/10	247	1	0.6%	—
06/08	134	1	0.9%	—
Annual Growth	9.9%	28.6%	—	—

2016 Year-End Financials

Return on assets: 9.7%   Cash ($ mil.): 28
Return on equity: 3.0%
Current ratio: 2.00

MANATEE MEMORIAL HOSPITAL, L.P.

EXECUTIVES

Vice President Of Marketing And Business Development, Vernon Desear
Nursing Director, Candace Smith

LOCATIONS

HQ: MANATEE MEMORIAL HOSPITAL, L.P.
206 2ND ST E, BRADENTON, FL 342081000
Phone: 941 746-5111
Web: WWW.MANATEEMEMORIAL.COM

PRODUCTS/OPERATIONS

Selected Services
Adult Partial Hospitalization Program
Behavioral Health
Breast Care Center
Cancer/Oncology
Critical Limb Care Services
Emergency Services
Family BirthPlace
Heart & Vascular Center
Hospitalist Program
MOMM's Place
Orthopedic/Spine Center
Outpatient Imaging Center
Pediatric Center
Rehabilitation Services
Respiratory Care Services
Robotic Surgery
Sleep Center
Stroke/Cerebrovascular Center
Surgery Center
Surgical Weight-Loss
The Valve Institute
Women's Services
Wound Care Center

COMPETITORS

BayCare Health System
Bayfront Health
DeSoto Memorial
Englewood Community Hospital
Florida Hospital Tampa Bay Division
H. Lee Moffitt Cancer Center & Research Institute
Northside Hospital and Heart Institute
Sarasota Memorial Health Care
Shriners Hospitals For Children
St. Anthony's Hospital
Tampa General Hospital

HISTORICAL FINANCIALS

Company Type: Private

Income Statement   FYE: December 31

	REVENUE ($ mil.)	NET INCOME ($ mil.)	NET PROFIT MARGIN	EMPLOYEES
12/17	299	33	11.1%	1,450
12/16	268	7	2.7%	—
12/15	249	2	1.0%	—
12/14	244	11	4.7%	—
Annual Growth	7.0%	42.4%	—	—

2017 Year-End Financials

Return on assets: 4.2%   Cash ($ mil.): —
Return on equity: 11.1%
Current ratio: 1.40

MANN+HUMMEL FILTRATION TECHNOLOGY INTERMEDIATE HOLDINGS INC.

Affinia Group Intermediate Holdings caters to car drivers with a natural affinity for parts. The company is a leading designer manufacturer and distributor of aftermarket vehicular components. Affinia's slew of products — primarily oil and air filters ball joints idler arms steering components and suspension parts — are made for passenger cars; SUVs; light medium and heavy trucks; and off-highway vehicles. Its well-known brand names including McQuay-Norris Nakata ecoLAST Raybestos and WIX are sold in 70 countries. It primarily serves the US and South American markets.

Geographic Reach

Affinia has operations in North and South America Europe and Asia spanning nearly 12 countries. It manufactures and distributes products in 11 countries and sells into more than 70 countries. The US accounts for 42% of the company's sales; Brazil is its second-largest market generating 30%.

Sales and Marketing

Affinia's largest customers include aftermarket distributors NAPA (22% of total sales) and CARQUEST (6%). Other customers include AutoZone O'Reilly Auto Parts and Canadian Tire. The company derived 97% of its 2013 net sales from the on and off-highway replacement products and services industry.

Financial Performance

The company saw its revenues jump 8% from 2012 to 2013. The growth for 2013 was driven by a 9% increase in its filtration segment due to increased sales in its North American and Asia operations driven by increased volume as a result of market growth and new business with existing customers. European sales increased in 2013 due to higher sales in Poland along with favorable currency translation effects in Poland. Increased Venezuela filter sales were the main contributor to the increase in South America sales.

Affinia posted net income of $10 million in 2013 after posting net losses in 2011 and 2012. The positive net income for 2013 was attributed to the absence of losses from discontinued operations as opposed to other years.

Strategy

With the sale of its Brake North America and Asia group in 2012 and the announced signing of an agreement to sell its Chassis group in 2014 the company is focused on operating strictly as a Filtration segment and Affinia South America segment company. (Affinia agreed to sell its chassis operations to Federal-Mogul in January 2014.)

Company Background

Affinia got its start in 2004. Private-equity firm Cypress and OMERS (Ontario Municipal Employees Retirement System) a Canadian pension fund bought the auto replacement parts business of Dana Holding Corporation to form Affinia. In mid-2010 Affinia filed to go public but remains privately owned.

EXECUTIVES

Pres-Ceo, Keith A Wilson
Chb, James S McElya
Sr V Pres-Cfo-Treas, Steven P Klueg
CIO, Karl J Westrick
Sr V Pres Hr, Kay Teixeira
Sr Vpres-General Counsel-Sec, David E Sturgess
Svp, Sales and Marketing, Dave McColley
CIO, Karl Westrick
Purchasing Manager, Bobbie Howe
Senior Vice President, Secreta, Dave Sturgess
Manager, Monty Gibson
Auditors: DELOITTE & TOUCHE LLP CHARLOT

LOCATIONS

HQ: MANN+HUMMEL FILTRATION TECHNOLOGY INTERMEDIATE HOLDINGS INC.
1 WIX WAY, GASTONIA, NC 280546142
Phone: 704 869-3300
Web: WWW.AFFINIAGROUP.COM

2013 Sales

	% of total
US	42
Brazil	30
Poland	12
Venezuela	6
Canada	3
Other	7
Total	**100**

PRODUCTS/OPERATIONS

2013 Sales

	$ mil.	% of total
Filteration	902	66
South America	459	34
Total	**1,361**	**100**

Selected Products and Services

Filteration
Air FiltersCabin Air FiltersCoolant System FiltrationFuel FiltersHeavy DutyHydraulic FiltersLight DutyOil FiltersRacing
Steering/Suspension
Alignment ProductsBall JointsControl Arm AssembliesIdler ArmsSway Bar LinkTie Rod EndsSelected Brands
McQuay-Norris
Nakata
Raybestos Chassis
WIX-Filtron
WIX ecoLAST
WIX Filters

Selected Markets

Agriculture
Construction equipment
Heavy-duty trucks
Light-duty cars and trucks
Marine
Mass transit
Mining
Power generation
Recreational vehicles
Small engine
Stationary equipment
Water filtration

COMPETITORS

CLARCOR
  Cardone Industries
  Cummins
  Donaldson Company
  Federal-Mogul
Genuine Parts
Honeywell
  International
UCI International

HISTORICAL FINANCIALS

Company Type: Private

Income Statement

FYE: December 31

	REVENUE ($ mil.)	NET INCOME ($ mil.)	NET PROFIT MARGIN	EMPLOYEES
12/15	899	(72)	—	5,575
12/14	1,396	82	5.9%	—
12/13	1,361	10	0.7%	—
12/12	1,453	(102)	—	—
Annual Growth	(14.8%)	—	—	—

2015 Year-End Financials

Return on assets: 9.6%
Return on equity: (-8.0%)
Current ratio: 0.30
Cash ($ mil.): 28

MANTECA UNIFIED SCHOOL DISTRICT

EXECUTIVES

Supt, Jason Messer
Assistant, Donald Halseth
Prin, Frank Gonzales
Administrative Assistant, Karen King
Administrative Assistant, Lisa Sotelo
Supervisor, Ben Cadile
Director of Information Techno, Colby Clark
Clerk, Marlana Bakmas
Telecommunications Analyst, Dave Snitchler
Bus Finance Purchasing Directo, Dawn Everson
Payroll Technician, Kiani Goodwin
Auditors: VAVRINEK TRINE DAY & CO LL

LOCATIONS

HQ: MANTECA UNIFIED SCHOOL DISTRICT
2271 W LOUISE AVE, MANTECA, CA 953378381
Phone: 209 825-3200
Web: WWW.MANTECAUSD.NET

HISTORICAL FINANCIALS

Company Type: Private

Income Statement

FYE: June 30

	REVENUE ($ mil.)	NET INCOME ($ mil.)	NET PROFIT MARGIN	EMPLOYEES
06/17	288	(6)	—	1,400
06/16	282	67	24.0%	—
06/09	203	(6)	—	—
06/08	213	(25)	—	—
Annual Growth	3.4%	—	—	—

MAP INTERNATIONAL (INC.)

EXECUTIVES

Pres/Ceo, Steve Stirling
Int Pres-Ceo, Chok-Pin Foo
Cfo, Daniel C Reed
Chm, Immanuel Phangaraj

VCM, Edwin G Corr
SEC, Ingrid M Mail
Asst SEC, Carrene G Rosser
Coordinator, Connie Reed
Senior Philanthropy Officer, Jennifer Hardie
Auditors: CAPINCROUSE LLP ATLANTA GEO

LOCATIONS

HQ: MAP INTERNATIONAL (INC.)
   4700 GLYNCO PKWY, BRUNSWICK, GA 315256901
Phone: 912 265-6010
Web: WWW.MAP.ORG

HISTORICAL FINANCIALS

Company Type: Private

Income Statement				FYE: September 30
	REVENUE ($ mil.)	NET INCOME ($ mil.)	NET PROFIT MARGIN	EMPLOYEES
09/17	598	(40)	—	200
09/16	606	87	14.5%	—
09/15	547	60	11.1%	—
09/14	320	15	4.9%	—
Annual Growth	23.2%	—	—	—

2017 Year-End Financials
Return on assets: —   Cash ($ mil.): 2
Return on equity: (-6.8%)
Current ratio: 1.80

MARCUM LLP

Marcum LLP (formerly MarcumStonefield) is making a mark on the world of accounting and consulting. With more than 20 offices in the US China and the Caribbean Marcum offers a full range of business and personal financial services including accounting auditing and tax and investment consulting. It also offers professional services such as mergers and acquisitions planning family office services forensic accounting and litigation support. The firm serves multiple industries such as construction health care real estate media and entertainment and financial services. Founded in 1951 Marcum is a member of the Marcum Group.

Operations
Marcum also provides international services through The Leading Edge Alliance.

Geographic Reach
New York-headquartered Marcum has more than 20 offices throughout New York New Jersey Massachusetts Connecticut Pennsylvania California Florida Grand Cayman and China (Beijing Guangzhou Hangzhou and Shanghai).

Sales and Marketing
Marcum serves a variety of clients With its staff of 160 partners and 1300 professionals including: broker dealers; employee benefit plan providers (ERISA); manufacturers; contractors; healthcare professionals; financial institutions; transaction services companies; and high-net-worth individuals among others.

Marcum has also entered several niche markets serving private equity partnerships; hedge funds; SEC registrants; real estate; public and not-for-profit sectors; and bankruptcies and receiverships; as well as a China specialty practice.

Strategy
Marcum has been pursuing a nationwide growth strategy in recent years mostly through mergers and acquisitions. In 2014 for example the firm acquired small accounting firms to expand its reach into Massachusetts Rhode Island and Connecticut. In 2013 and 2012 it similarly purchased four more accounting firms to broaden its expertise and ex-

tend its reach into southern California New York City and Boston regions.

Mergers and Acquisitions
In 2014 Marcum took over two small accounting firms Braver PC and Thomas E. Finn P.C. Braver PC has offices in Needham MA and Providence RI; while Thomas E. Finn P.C. is located in Greenwich CT.

In 2013 it added three more firms under the Marcum banner — WilsonMorgan LLP Cornerstone Accounting Group and Parent McLaughlin & Nagle CPAs Inc. WilsonMorgan is located in Irvine CA while Cornerstone Accounting Group which focuses on the real estate industry is in New York City. Parent McLaughlin & Nagle CPAs Inc. came with deep roots in the Boston financial services community.

In 2012 Marcum acquired the Boston firm Robert Finnegan & Lynah PC.

Company Background
Marcum is a member of the Marcum Group a collection of companies that offer services such as technology solutions (Marcum Technology) job recruitment (Marcum Search) and wealth management (Marcum Financial Services).

EXECUTIVES

Mng Ptnr, Jeffrey M Weiner
Ptnr, Lawrence Schienthal
Ptnr, James T Ashe
Ptnr, David Bukzin
Ptnr, James Smart
Cfo, Edward Scicchitano
Prin, Lisa Mackell
Internal Medicine Practitioner, John Han
Administrative Assistant, Luz Guillen
Accountant, Stacy Messina
Information Specialist, Yazhou Hu

LOCATIONS

HQ: MARCUM LLP
   750 3RD AVE FL 11, NEW YORK, NY 100172716
Phone: 212 485-5500
Web: WWW.MARCUMTECHNOLOGY.COM

PRODUCTS/OPERATIONS

Selected Industry Specializations
Construction
Entertainment
Financial services
Health care
Hedge funds
High-net-worth individuals
High-tech and software
Independent grocers
Insurance
Manufacturing and distribution
Maritime
Real estate
Talent and literary agencies

Selected Products and Services
Alternative investments
Accounting services
Assurance and audit
Business management services
Business valuation
Cost segregation
Family office services
Forensic accounting
Hedge funds and investment partnerships
Information technology consulting
Litigation services
Mergers and acquisitions
Personal financial management
Sales and use tax recovery
SEC-related services
Staffing
State and local tax consulting
Tax advisory and compliance services
Tax controversy resolution
Trust and estate planning
Wealth management

COMPETITORS

Anchin Block & Anchin	KPMG L.L.P.
CohnReznick	Marks Paneth & Shron
Deloitte & Touche	PricewaterhouseCoopers
EisnerAmper	US
Ernst & Young LLP	Rothstein Kass
Grassi & CO.	

HISTORICAL FINANCIALS

Company Type: Private

Income Statement				FYE: December 31
	REVENUE ($ mil.)	NET INCOME ($ mil.)	NET PROFIT MARGIN	EMPLOYEES
12/17	341	14	4.2%	1,434
12/16	320	11	3.5%	—
12/15	273	15	5.8%	—
12/14	251	15	6.1%	—
Annual Growth	10.7%	(2.3%)	—	—

2017 Year-End Financials
Return on assets: 0.3%   Cash ($ mil.): —
Return on equity: 4.2%
Current ratio: 1.40

MARIETTA AREA HEALTH CARE INC

EXECUTIVES

Exec Dir-Pres, Larry Unroe
Administrator, Susan Crozier

LOCATIONS

HQ: MARIETTA AREA HEALTH CARE INC
   401 MATTHEW ST, MARIETTA, OH 457501635
Phone: 740 374-1400

HISTORICAL FINANCIALS

Company Type: Private

Income Statement				FYE: September 30
	REVENUE ($ mil.)	NET INCOME ($ mil.)	NET PROFIT MARGIN	EMPLOYEES
09/17	448	5	1.1%	15
09/12	267	(0)	—	—
09/11	271	1	0.6%	—
09/10	230	(0)	—	—
Annual Growth	10.0%	—	—	—

2017 Year-End Financials
Return on assets: 10.5%   Cash ($ mil.): 21
Return on equity: 1.1%
Current ratio: 1.20

MARIETTA MEMORIAL HOSPITAL INC

EXECUTIVES

Chb, Tom Tucker
President, J Stott Cantley
Vice President, Orive E Fischer

Cfo, Eric Young
SEC, Colleen Cook
Treas, Glen Hale
Chief of Medicine, David Casto
Information Specialist, Tamara Moore
General Manager, Diana Chapman
General Manager, Inge Chenoweth
Coordinator, Crissenda Brewer
Auditors: BLUE & CO LLC COLUMBUS OH

LOCATIONS

HQ: MARIETTA MEMORIAL HOSPITAL INC
  401 MATTHEW ST, MARIETTA, OH 457501699
Phone: 740 374-1400

HISTORICAL FINANCIALS
Company Type: Private

Income Statement   FYE: September 30

	REVENUE ($ mil.)	NET INCOME ($ mil.)	NET PROFIT MARGIN	EMPLOYEES
09/16	400	7	1.8%	1,100
09/15	378	12	3.4%	—
09/14	307	(0)	—	—
09/13	303	(1)	—	—
Annual Growth	9.7%	—	—	—

2016 Year-End Financials

Return on assets: 8.3%   Cash ($ mil.): 33
Return on equity: 1.8%
Current ratio: 1.80

MARIN GENERAL HOSPITAL

EXECUTIVES

Director Of Him And Patient Access, Celia Lenson
Director Of Pharmacy, Michael Sillman
Medical Director, Adrienne Fratini
Director Of Nursing, Karin Reese

LOCATIONS

HQ: MARIN GENERAL HOSPITAL
  250 BON AIR RD, KENTFIELD, CA 949041784
Phone: 415 925-7000
Web: WWW.MARINGENERAL.ORG

COMPETITORS

California Pacific	The Palo Alto Medical
Medical Center	Foundation
Dignity Health	UCSF Medical

HISTORICAL FINANCIALS
Company Type: Private

Income Statement   FYE: December 31

	REVENUE ($ mil.)	NET INCOME ($ mil.)	NET PROFIT MARGIN	EMPLOYEES
12/17	370	17	4.8%	1,100
12/16	350	6	1.8%	—
12/15	342	20	6.1%	—
12/14	320	10	3.2%	—
Annual Growth	5.0%	19.7%	—	—

2017 Year-End Financials

Return on assets: 5.4%   Cash ($ mil.): 67
Return on equity: 4.8%
Current ratio: 2.30

MARION COMMUNITY HOSPITAL INC

EXECUTIVES

Blood Bank Director, Brad Mason

LOCATIONS

HQ: MARION COMMUNITY HOSPITAL INC
  1431 SW 1ST AVE, OCALA, FL 344716500
Phone: 352 401-1000
Web: WWW.OCALAREGIONAL.COM

PRODUCTS/OPERATIONS

Selected Services
Bariatrics Center
Cancer Center
Cardiovascular Services
Emergency Services
Imaging & Diagnostics
Neuroscience Center
Orthopedic Joint Care Center
Rehabilitation Services
Robotic Surgery
Senior Wellness
Women's Center
Wound and Hyperbaric Center

COMPETITORS

Adventist Health	System Sunbelt Healthcare
Baptist Health South	Florida
Baptist Health System	
Florida Hospital	Heartland
Florida Hospital	Waterman
Mount Sinai Medical	Center of Florida
Munroe Regional Health	System
Orlando Health	
Putnam Community	Medical Center
Shands at the	University of Florida

HISTORICAL FINANCIALS
Company Type: Private

Income Statement   FYE: August 31

	REVENUE ($ mil.)	NET INCOME ($ mil.)	NET PROFIT MARGIN	EMPLOYEES
08/15*	301	50	16.6%	1,100
09/05	0	0	0.8%	—
Annual Growth	81.0%	145.5%	—	—

*Fiscal year change

2015 Year-End Financials

Return on assets: 2.8%   Cash ($ mil.): —
Return on equity: 16.6%
Current ratio: 2.10

MARITZ HOLDINGS INC.

Maritz may not send your employees on business trips but it will motivate them to go. The company's mission is to understand enable and motivate people to unleash their hidden potential enabling people to do things differently by developing their strengths knowledge and confidence. The Steve Maritz-owned company designs employee incentive and reward programs (including incentive travel rewards) and customer loyalty programs. It also plans corporate trade shows and events and offers traditional market research services such as the creation of product launch cam-

paigns. Its programs are designed to help its clients improve workforce quality and customer satisfaction.

Operations
Maritz's subsidiaries and segments include Maritz Canada Maritz Dealer Solutions The Maritz Institute Maritz Journeys Maritz Loyalty Maritz Motivation Solutions Maritz Research and Maritz Travel.

Geographic Reach
A global player Maritz has offices in Canada Germany the UK and the US.

Sales and Marketing
Its customers include a majority of the Forbes 500 including businesses in the automotive financial services health care retail pharmaceutical telecommunications and professional and business services industries. Maritz has worked with such high-profile clients as AT&T Bank of America General Motors and Procter & Gamble.

Strategy
One of Maritz's competitive strengths is its widely diversified customer base which makes it less susceptible to regional or industry-specific economic downturns. It also makes acquisitions to strengthen its offerings in order to keep its competitive edge.

EXECUTIVES

Chairman And Ceo, W. Stephen (Steve) Maritz, age 61
Vp Sales, Dennis Hummel
Cfo, Rick Ramos
President Of Maritz Travel Company, David Peckinpaugh
Vice President, Mike Kopec
Vice President Of Sales And Marketing, Carrie Nolan
Division Vice President, Kari Mcgraw
Vice President Group Business Manager, Terry Erwin
Vice President Corporate Infrastructure Team Solutions, Jason Hampton
Vice President, Stuart Bowling
Vice President Global Business Manager, Chris Haenni
Director Finance Assistant Treasurer, Thomas Sizemore
Auditors: KPMG LLP ST LOUIS MO

LOCATIONS

HQ: MARITZ HOLDINGS INC.
  1375 N HIGHWAY DR, FENTON, MO 630990001
Phone: 636 827-4000
Web: WWW.MARITZ.COM

PRODUCTS/OPERATIONS

Selected Services
Marketing Research
  Custom marketing research
  Customer satisfaction and customer value analysis
  Data collection (focus groups telephone interviews)
  Maritz Polls and Maritz Research Reports
  Syndicated buyer research
  Telecommunications research
Performance Improvement
  Communications
  e-Learning
  Fulfillment
  Internet consulting
  Loyalty marketing
  Measurement and feedback
  Rewards and recognition
Travel
  Consulting services
  Corporate travel management
  Group travel services
  Travel award programs

COMPETITORS

Franklin Covey	J.D. Power
Gallup	JTB Corp.
GiftCertificates.com	Kantar Group
Harris Interactive	Motivcom
IMS Health	Nielsen
Information Resources Inc.	ORC International

HISTORICAL FINANCIALS

Company Type: Private

Income Statement — FYE: March 31

	REVENUE ($ mil.)	NET INCOME ($ mil.)	NET PROFIT MARGIN	EMPLOYEES
03/17	1,217	(30)	—	4,646
03/16	1,274	(16)	—	—
03/13	1,256	42	3.3%	—
03/12	1,155	47	4.1%	—
Annual Growth	1.1%	—	—	—

2017 Year-End Financials

Return on assets: 10.6%   Cash ($ mil.): 139
Return on equity: (-2.5%)
Current ratio: 0.60

MARJAM SUPPLY CO., INC.

EXECUTIVES

Pres-Chb, Mark Buller
Vice President, James Buller
Contrl, Bruce Respler
Mgr, Glenn Thoven
Sales Associate, Jeff Pauley
Sales Manager, Bob Kephart
Operations Manager, Hugh Higgins
Operations Manager, Lake Gilliland
Account Manager, Keith Walton
Sales Staff, Martin Secofsky
Sales and Marketing Staff, Terence Schaefer

LOCATIONS

HQ: MARJAM SUPPLY CO., INC.
885 CONKLIN ST, FARMINGDALE, NY 117352400
Phone: 631 249-4900
Web: WWW.MARJAM.COM

HISTORICAL FINANCIALS

Company Type: Private

Income Statement — FYE: December 31

	REVENUE ($ mil.)	NET INCOME ($ mil.)	NET PROFIT MARGIN	EMPLOYEES
12/16	433	12	2.8%	614
12/15	400	10	2.7%	—
12/14	386	9	2.4%	—
Annual Growth	6.0%	14.7%	—	—

2016 Year-End Financials

Return on assets: 11.4%   Cash ($ mil.): 5
Return on equity: 2.8%
Current ratio: 0.80

MARKET AMERICA WORLDWIDE, INC.

EXECUTIVES

President, James H Ridinger
Exec Vice President, Dennis Franks
Sr Vice President, Loren Ridinger
Exec Vice President, Martin Weissman
Coo, Marc Ashley
Exec Vice President, Joseph Bolyard
Auditors: DIXON HUGHES GOODMAN LLP WIN

LOCATIONS

HQ: MARKET AMERICA WORLDWIDE, INC.
1302 PLEASANT RIDGE RD, GREENSBORO, NC
274099415
Phone: 336 605-0040
Web: WWW.MARKETAMERICA.COM

HISTORICAL FINANCIALS

Company Type: Private

Income Statement — FYE: December 31

	REVENUE ($ mil.)	NET INCOME ($ mil.)	NET PROFIT MARGIN	EMPLOYEES
12/16	400	17	4.4%	875
12/09	284	27	9.7%	—
12/08	275	37	13.7%	—
12/07	1,794	0	—	—
Annual Growth	—	394.9%	—	—

2016 Year-End Financials

Return on assets: 1.2%   Cash ($ mil.): 69
Return on equity: 4.4%
Current ratio: 1.70

MARKET AMERICA, INC.

Calling itself a cross between Amazon and QVC Market America is an Internet marketer and broker of products and services from a variety of categories including apparel beauty and personal care electronics entertainment nutrition and sports. Market America sells more than 2500 of its own branded products (such as Isotonix Motives and Snap) and spotlights the offerings of more than 3000 other retailers (including Sears Staples and Wal-Mart) on its SHOP.COM web site (acquired in 2010). In addition the company manages UnFranchise a network marketing business with more than 180000 independent shopping consultants. The company was founded in 1992 by president and CEO James "JR" Ridinger.

Operations

Market America's independent shopping consultants operate under the company's UnFranchise business model also referred to as "one-to-one marketing." The UnFranchise platform comes complete with a business plan customizable Web portal merchandising materials and management system. To develop community relations consultants can provide online assistance to shoppers in their areas and recruit potential UnFranchise consultants. Consultants earn commissions when shoppers purchase products and services through their Market America shopping portals. In 2010 Market America opened its UnFranchise business model to nonprofits. The company said individuals following its business model have netted more than

$2 billion in commissions and retail profits since it was established.

Geographic Reach

Based in North Carolina the company has a presence in several global markets including the US Canada Australia Hong Kong Taiwan the UK and Mexico. It's expanding into Latin America. Through its website Market America provides access to its brands to consumers in 200-plus countries.

Financial Performance

Market American rings up $500 million in sales annually. Since its founding the product brokerage and Internet marketing company boasts more than $5.3 billion in accumulated retail sales.

Strategy

Operating in seven global markets Market America looks to expand into Spain Colombia Costa Rica Ecuador and the Dominican Republic. It's working to extend the reach of its UnFranchise business model to Latino entrepreneurs. The move marks the company's largest expansion in its history.

To bolster its position in Internet retailing Market America has been expanding its operations outside the US. The company has international branches in Canada Australia Hong Kong Taiwan and the Philippines. It plans to extend its reach to the UK Mexico Latin America and other markets where it does not yet have a presence.

Mergers and Acquisitions

Market America acquired e-tailer SHOP.COM in late 2010 to blend its marketing and brokering expertise with SHOP.COM's strength in technology and merchandising. The result creates a "social shopping" movement capable of challenging some of the Internet's leading shopping destinations. As part of the deal the two firms agreed to operate their websites separately.

EXECUTIVES

Exec V Pres, Dennis Franks
Sr V Pres, Loren Ridinger
Coo, Marc Ashley
Exec V Pres, Marty Weismann
Executive Vice President, Joseph Bolyard
Chief of Medicine, Julian Blumenfeld
Sourcing Manager Motives Cosme, Connie Thornton
Administrative Assistant, Terri Cox

LOCATIONS

HQ: MARKET AMERICA, INC.
1302 PLEASANT RIDGE RD, GREENSBORO, NC
274099415
Phone: 336 605-0040

PRODUCTS/OPERATIONS

Selected Brands

Cellular Laboratories
Custom Cocktail
Fixx
Gene SNP DNA Analysis
Heart Health
Isotonix
MA Capital Resources
MA Webcenters
Matriskin
Motives
NutriClean
Pentaxyl
Pet Health
Prime
Royal Spa
Snap
Timeless Prescriptions
TLS Weight Loss Solution
Ultimate Aloe

Selected Product Categories

Anti-aging
Apparel jewelry and shoes

Automotive and tools
Baby products
Beauty products cosmetics
Books movies and video games
Cameras
Cell phones and communications
Computers
Consumer electronics
Crafts
Grocery
Health and nutrition
Home and Garden
Jewelry
Music
Party supplies
Pet supplies
Tickets
Toys

COMPETITORS

AMS Health Sciences	Overstock.com
Amazon.com	PriceGrabber.com
Amway	QVC
Astral Brands	Shaklee
Avon	Shopzilla
Buy.com	USANA Health Sciences
HSN	ViSalus
Mannatech	Yahoo!
Melaleuca	eBay
NexTag	

HISTORICAL FINANCIALS

Company Type: Private

Income Statement   FYE: October 31

	REVENUE ($ mil.)	NET INCOME ($ mil.)	NET PROFIT MARGIN	EMPLOYEES
10/16*	412	23	5.7%	650
12/09	224	15	7.0%	—
12/08	228	3	1.5%	—
12/07	218	0	0.0%	—
Annual Growth	7.3%	391.3%	—	—

*Fiscal year change

2016 Year-End Financials

Return on assets: 1.2%   Cash ($ mil.): 73
Return on equity: 5.7%
Current ratio: 2.00

MARLIN BUSINESS BANK

EXECUTIVES

Pres, Raymond Dardano
Vp-Chief Lending Officer, George F Coburn

LOCATIONS

HQ: MARLIN BUSINESS BANK
2795 E COTTONWOOD PKWY # 120, SALT LAKE CITY, UT 841217092
Phone: 888 479-9111
Web: WWW.MARLINBANK.COM

HISTORICAL FINANCIALS

Company Type: Private

Income Statement   FYE: December 31

	ASSETS ($ mil.)	NET INCOME ($ mil.)	INCOME AS % OF ASSETS	EMPLOYEES
12/17	1,011	20	2.0%	25
12/16	871	14	1.7%	—
12/15	754	20	2.7%	—
12/14	704	20	2.9%	—
Annual Growth	12.8%	0.1%	—	—

2017 Year-End Financials

Return on assets: —   Sales ($ mil.): 107
Return on equity: 19.2%

MARQUETTE UNIVERSITY

A member of the Association of Jesuit Colleges and Universities Marquette University provides undergraduate graduate and professional courses and programs. It specializes in business engineering arts and sciences nursing law dentistry and other fields. The university offers undergraduates some 75 majors and 65 minors and post-graduate students about 50 doctoral and master's degree programs. With an enrollment of more than 11700 students Marquette University boasts a student/faculty ratio of 14:1. Its student population consists of students from all 50 US states and nearly 70 countries. Founded in 1881 the university is named after French missionary explorer Father Jacques Marquette.

Operations
Marquette University an independent coeducational and not-for-profit institution of higher learning and research consists of a dozen separate colleges and schools.

Geographic Reach
Based in Milwaukee Wisconsin the Marquette University campus attracts students across the nation and from nearly 70 countries worldwide.

Financial Performance
The educational institution logged a marginal 1% increase in revenue in fiscal 2012 as compared to 2011 due to rising tuition and fees contributions government and private grants and endowment income used in operations. Net income during the same reporting period dropped some 90% thanks to increases in operating expenses and declines in endowment gains in excess of the amount designated for current operations (net other).

Strategy
To boost its healthcare presence the Marquette University College of Nursing opened the Wheaton Franciscan Healthcare Center for Clinical Simulation in late 2012. The facility features a six-bed hospital suite with a pair of intensive care rooms two medical surgical rooms one pediatrics room and one labor and delivery suite.

EXECUTIVES

Vp Finance, John Lamb
Executive Vice President Learning And Development, Christopher Longstreet
Vice President Technology, Alice Gormley
Associate Vice President For Research And Innovation, Carmel Ruffolo
Vice President, Sally Sutko
Secretary, Joe Foti

Secretary, Greg Merkel
Auditors: KPMG LLP MILWAUKEE WI

LOCATIONS

HQ: MARQUETTE UNIVERSITY
1250 W WISCONSIN AVE, MILWAUKEE, WI 532332225
Phone: 414 288-7250
Web: WWW.MARQUETTE.EDU

PRODUCTS/OPERATIONS

Selected Schools and Colleges
College of Business Administration
College of Education
College of Engineering
College of Health Sciences
College of Nursing
College of Professional Studies
Graduate School
Graduate School of Management
Helen Way Klingler College of Arts and Sciences
J. William and Mary Diederich College of Communications
Law School
School of Dentistry

HISTORICAL FINANCIALS

Company Type: Private

Income Statement   FYE: June 30

	REVENUE ($ mil.)	NET INCOME ($ mil.)	NET PROFIT MARGIN	EMPLOYEES
06/17	434	67	15.4%	3,000
06/15	548	48	8.8%	—
06/13	391	37	9.5%	—
06/12	385	9	2.4%	—
Annual Growth	2.4%	48.0%	—	—

2017 Year-End Financials

Return on assets: 12.0%   Cash ($ mil.): 69
Return on equity: 15.4%
Current ratio: —

MARSHFIELD CLINIC, INC.

EXECUTIVES

Pres, Brian H Ewert
V Pres, Douglas Reding
Cfo, Gary Jankowski
V Pres, C Todd Stewart
Treas, Mark A Lepage
Urology Specialist, Gregory A Anderson
Neurology Specialist, Loren A Rolak
Ophthalmologist, Richard B Patchett
Director, Robert Gribble
Physical Medicine Specialist, Jill R Meilahn
Manager, Teri Herr-Wilczek
Auditors: KPMG LLP MINNEAPOLIS MN

LOCATIONS

HQ: MARSHFIELD CLINIC, INC.
1000 N OAK AVE, MARSHFIELD, WI 544495702
Phone: 715 387-5511
Web: WWW.MARSHFIELDRESEARCH.ORG

HISTORICAL FINANCIALS
Company Type: Private

Income Statement				FYE: September 30
	REVENUE ($ mil.)	NET INCOME ($ mil.)	NET PROFIT MARGIN	EMPLOYEES
09/15	1,211	24	2.0%	363
09/09	1,062	78	7.4%	—
09/08*	102	6	5.9%	—
06/06	813	23	2.9%	—
Annual Growth	4.5%	0.5%	—	—

*Fiscal year change

2015 Year-End Financials
Return on assets: 9.9%   Cash ($ mil.): 96
Return on equity: 2.0%
Current ratio: 0.60

MARTHA JEFFERSON HOSPITAL

EXECUTIVES

Ceo, James E Haden
Vp-Cfo, Joseph Burris
SEC, Elliot Kuida
Treas, J Michael Burris
Pathologist, Hunt M Lll
Coordinator, James Patterson
Diagnostic Radiologist, Christopher D Cook
Health Professional, Mark Mandichak
Neurology Specialist, Sandeep S Teja
Chief of Cardiology, Ashley Jones
Coordinator, Courtney Lambert
Auditors: KPMG LLP NORFOLK VIRGINIA

LOCATIONS

HQ: MARTHA JEFFERSON HOSPITAL
  500 MARTHA JEFFERSON DR, CHARLOTTESVILLE,
  VA 229114668
Phone: 434 982-7000
Web: WWW.MJHFOUNDATION.ORG

HISTORICAL FINANCIALS
Company Type: Private

Income Statement				FYE: December 31
	REVENUE ($ mil.)	NET INCOME ($ mil.)	NET PROFIT MARGIN	EMPLOYEES
12/17	293	8	3.0%	3,277
12/15	258	12	4.9%	—
12/13	252	9	3.8%	—
Annual Growth	3.9%	(2.4%)	—	—

2017 Year-End Financials
Return on assets: 2.0%   Cash ($ mil.): 7
Return on equity: 3.0%
Current ratio: 3.40

MARTIN & BAYLEY, INC.

Martin & Bayley (dba Huck's Food and Fuel) operates 115 Huck's convenience stores and a number travel centers in mostly in Illinois and Indiana but also in Missouri Kentucky and Tennessee. Half of its outlets are in Illinois. The company operates a commissary at its warehouse in Carmi Illinois to supply sandwiches chicken and other food items to its stores. Some stores sell Godfather's Pizza. Family-owned since its inception Martin & Bayley became a 100% employee-owned firm when the Martin and Bayley families sold their stakes in the company.

Geographic Reach
Martin & Bayley owns and operates convenience stores in Illinois Indiana Missouri Kentucky and Tennessee.

Sales and Marketing
The company's vendor includes Fritolay Jack Link's Kraft MillerCoors Nestle Pepsi Red Bull and Wonka.

The convenience store operator is growing in the south with new Hucks locations opening in Huntingdon Tennessee and Paducah and Hopkinson Kentucky.

Company Background
Founders Bob Martin and Frank Bayley formed a partnership in 1960. In 1974 they opened the first Huck's convenience store in Illinois. The Martins and the Bayleys sold the company to its employees in 2001.

EXECUTIVES

Vice President Marketing, Tim Tilford
Vice President Of Operations, Mark Mckinney
Auditors: HARDING SHYMANSKI & COMPANY

LOCATIONS

HQ: MARTIN & BAYLEY, INC.
  1311A W MAIN ST, CARMI, IL 628211389
Phone: 618 382-2334
Web: WWW.MARTINANDBAYLEY.COM

PRODUCTS/OPERATIONS

2013 Stores

	No.
Illinois	55
Indiana	26
Kentucky	18
Missouri	14
Tennessee	2
Total	115

Selected Product Lines
Godfathers Pizza
5 Buck Huck
Bigg Swigg
Coffee
Deli Express
Fresh Brewed Ice Tea
Hot to Go at Huck's
Sweet Street

COMPETITORS

7-Eleven	Exxon Mobil
Casey's General Stores	Krause Gentle
Chevron	TravelCenters of
Couche-Tard	America

HISTORICAL FINANCIALS
Company Type: Private

Income Statement				FYE: March 27
	REVENUE ($ mil.)	NET INCOME ($ mil.)	NET PROFIT MARGIN	EMPLOYEES
03/18	523	8	1.6%	1,500
03/11	528	7	1.4%	—
03/10	466	5	1.1%	—
03/09	1,579	0		—
Annual Growth	—	193.4%	—	—

2018 Year-End Financials
Return on assets: 3.2%   Cash ($ mil.): 11
Return on equity: 1.6%
Current ratio: 0.40

MARTIN MEMORIAL HEALTH SYSTEMS, INC.

EXECUTIVES

Pres-Ceo, Mark E Robitaille
Vice President, Amy Barry
Vice President, John Tagliareni
Sr Vice President, L Mark Cocorullo
Sr Vice President, Karen Ripper
Sr Vice President, Michael Skehan
Sr Vice President, Donna H Griffith
Sr VPresident, Robert L Lord Jr
Vp-Clo, Ramona Thomas
Coordinator, Micaela Wolfe
Director of Facilities Enginee, Brandon Bardowsky

LOCATIONS

HQ: MARTIN MEMORIAL HEALTH SYSTEMS, INC.
  200 SE HOSPITAL AVE, STUART, FL 349942346
Phone: 772 287-5200
Web: WWW.MMHS.COM

HISTORICAL FINANCIALS
Company Type: Private

Income Statement				FYE: September 30
	REVENUE ($ mil.)	NET INCOME ($ mil.)	NET PROFIT MARGIN	EMPLOYEES
09/18	586	16	2.8%	2,972
09/17	559	30	5.4%	—
09/16	542	25	4.6%	—
Annual Growth	4.0%	(19.5%)	—	—

2018 Year-End Financials
Return on assets: 2.5%   Cash ($ mil.): 27
Return on equity: 2.8%
Current ratio: 1.20

MARTIN MEMORIAL MEDICAL CENTER, INC

EXECUTIVES

Pres, Mark Robitaille
V Pres-Cfo, L Mark Cocorullo
Treas, John Lowenberg
Secr, James Orr III
Sr Vice President, Donna H Griffith
Vice President, Craig Chindemi
Cfo, Chuck Cleaver
Chief of Pediatric, Kristen Walker
Executive Officer, Cindy Pingolt
Assistant Vice-President, Sharon Andre
Consultant, Stacey Rhodewalt

LOCATIONS

HQ: MARTIN MEMORIAL MEDICAL CENTER, INC
  200 SE HOSPITAL AVE, STUART, FL 349942346
Phone: 772 287-5200
Web: WWW.MARTINHEALTH.ORG

MARTIN RESOURCE MANAGEMENT CORPORATION

Martin Resource Management likes to push around petroleum products. The employee-owned company's flagship affiliate Martin Midstream Partners offers transportation storage marketing and logistics management services for petroleum products including sulfur sulfur derivatives fuel oil liquefied petroleum gas asphalt and other bulk tank liquids primarily in the southern US. Martin Resource also manufactures and markets fertilizer and other processed sulfur products. Through its Martin Energy Services unit the company offers inland marine fuel supply and offshore support services. Other units include The Brimrock Group (sulfur) Cross Oil Refining & Marketing and Martin Asphalt.

Operations
Each year the company markets more than 250 million gallons of diesel fuel and lubricants along the Gulf Coast and 1.5 million barrels of naphthenic lubricants and base oils across the US. In addition Martin Resource also provides surface transportation services for products such as molten sulfur sulfuric acid fuel oil natural gas liquids (NGLs) asphalt paper mill liquids and other bulk tank liquids.

The company's more than $550 million of assets include a fleet of truck trailers and tractors. Its Martin Transport subsidiary has about 25 terminals in the Southeast and Southern US with more than 850 trucks and 1200 trailers. Martin Product Sales LLC markets and distributes petroleum-based products including asphalt fuel oil and sulfuric acid.

Martin Resource owns a 28.0% limited partnership interest and a 2% general partnership interest in its flagship operating company Martin Midstream Partners. Its Martin Energy Services subsidiary offers marine fuel supply and offshore support services.

Sales and Marketing
The company's customers include agriculture petrochemical petroleum and utility companies.

Strategy
Martin Resource markets oil and gas and by-products through facilities located throughout the Gulf Coast region. It acquires other companies or forms joint ventures to develop its portfolio. It also redistributes operating assets to its major subsidiaries to improve their performance.

In 2013 Canadian subsidiary Brimrock signed an engineering service agreement with Keyera to act as the engineering management and technology provider for Keyera's planned sulphur forming and materials handling facilities upgrade.

That year Martin Resource sold a 49% voting interest in MMGP Holdings LLC a newly-formed sole member of Martin Midstream GP LLC the general partner of Martin Midstream Partners to Alinda Capital Partners.

In 2012 Martin Midstream Partners also sold its East Texas and Northwest Louisiana natural gas gathering and processing assets to CenterPoint Energy Field Services for $275 million.

Streamlining its businesses in 2012 the company formed Martin Energy Services LLC combining the entities of Midstream Fuel Service LLC L & L Oil and Gas Services L.L.C. and PEPCO into one entity for improved service and growth.

Mergers and Acquisitions
In 2013 Martin Midstream Partners' subsidiary Martin Operating Partnership L.P bought Kansas City Missouri-based NL Grease LLC a grease manufacturer that specializes in private-label packaging of commercial and industrial greases.

Boosting its NGL handling capabilities that year Martin Midstream Partners purchased six liquefied petroleum gas pressure barges and two commercial push boats from affiliates of Florida Marine Transporters for $51 million.

In 2012 Martin Midstream Partners acquired Gulf Coast fuels and lubricants provider Talen's Marine & Fuel LLC. The transactions boosted the company's marine terminal infrastructure adding ten marine terminals between Houston/Galveston and Port Fourchon in Louisiana with total tankage of 300000 barrels and an additional 4000 feet of water-accessible bulkhead.

In 2012 Martin Midstream Partners bought the remaining equity interests in Redbird Gas Storage LLC for $150 million. (In 2011 Martin Resource and Martin Midstream Partners formed the Redbird Gas Storage natural gas storage joint venture to invest in Cardinal Gas Storage Partners a joint venture between Redbird and Energy Capital Partners focused on the development of natural gas storage facilities across North America).

Company Background
The acquisition of L & L Oil and Gas L.L.C. by Midstream Fuel Service in 2011 increased Martin Resources' capability along the U.S. Gulf Coast to 31 facilities for offshore fuels lubricants and logistical services including land based commercial and industrial fuels and lubricants.

In 2011 Martin Resource and Martin Midstream Partners formed the Redbird Gas Storage natural gas storage joint venture to invest in Cardinal Gas Storage Partners. Cardinal is a joint venture between Redbird and Energy Capital Partners that is focused on the development construction operation and management of natural gas storage facilities across North America.

To raise cash and boost the Martin Midstream Partners' storage segment in 2011 Martin Resource sold 13 terminals to that unit for $36.5 million.

Founded in 1951 by R. S. Martin Jr. Martin Resource also holds a stake in Ican Energy an LPG distributor. To raise cash and increase its financial flexibility in 2002 the company spun off a portion of its assets.

EXECUTIVES

Senior Vice President Of Roddey Engineering Services, Michael Newton
Vp Operations, Scot Shoup
Auditors: KPMG LLP DALLAS TEXAS

LOCATIONS

HQ: MARTIN RESOURCE MANAGEMENT CORPORATION
4200 STONE RD, KILGORE, TX 756626935
Phone: 903 983-6200
Web: WWW.MARTIN-GAS.COM

PRODUCTS/OPERATIONS

Selected Companies
Altec Environmental Consulting
Commercial & Industrial Fuels & Lubricants
Commercial & Industrial Tanks & Equipment
Cross Oil Refining & Marketing Inc.
Marine Lubricants & Specialty Products
Martin Crude Marketing Company
Martin Energy Services LLC
Martin Product Sales LLC
Martin Transport Inc
Roddey engineering services Inc.

COMPETITORS

Enterprise Products	Penn Octane
George Warren	Sun Coast Resources
Global Partners	Williams Companies
Gulf Oil	

MARTIN'S POINT HEALTH CARE, INC.

EXECUTIVES

Ceo-Pres, David Howes
Chb, Robert Moore
Cfo, Daniel Chojnowski
Coordinator, Elizabeth Chadbourne
Coordinator, INA Levasseur
Coordinator, Jeanne Richards
Coordinator, Sheryl Fossett
Chief of Medicine, Steven Hess
Manager, David Stearns
Vice-President, Jeffry Bland
Nurse Practitioner, Robin Baier
Auditors: BAKER NEWMAN & NOYES LLC POR

LOCATIONS

HQ: MARTIN'S POINT HEALTH CARE, INC.
331 VERANDA ST STE 1, PORTLAND, ME 041035544
Phone: 207 774-5801
Web: WWW.MARTINSPOINT.ORG

HISTORICAL FINANCIALS
Company Type: Private

Income Statement
FYE: December 31

	ASSETS ($ mil.)	NET INCOME ($ mil.)	INCOME AS % OF ASSETS	EMPLOYEES
12/16	386	17	4.6%	839
12/14	351	3	1.0%	—
12/13	345	10	3.0%	—
12/09	247	30	12.2%	—
Annual Growth	6.6%	(7.2%)	—	—

2016 Year-End Financials
Return on assets: 4.8%   Sales ($ mil.): 704
Return on equity: 2.5%

MARYLAND DEPARTMENT OF TRANSPORTATION

EXECUTIVES

SEC, Pete K Rahn
SEC, John Porcari
Prin, Donald A Halligan
Prin, Robert Ehrlich
Bay Bridge Facility Administra, Richard Jaramillo
Coordinator, Cathy Kahl
Coordinator, Colleen Johnson
Auditors: SB & COMPANY LLC HUNT VALLEY

LOCATIONS

HQ: MARYLAND DEPARTMENT OF TRANSPORTATION
7201 CORPORATE CENTER DR, HANOVER, MD
210761415
Phone: 410 865-1037
Web: WWW.MDOT.STATE.MD.US

HISTORICAL FINANCIALS
Company Type: Private

Income Statement
FYE: June 30

	REVENUE ($ mil.)	NET INCOME ($ mil.)	NET PROFIT MARGIN	EMPLOYEES
06/17	4,490	85	1.9%	1,000
06/16	4,170	(232)	—	—
06/14	3,890	58	1.5%	—
06/13	3,719	81	2.2%	—
Annual Growth	4.8%	1.1%	—	—

2017 Year-End Financials
Return on assets: 10.6%   Cash ($ mil.): 68
Return on equity: 1.9%
Current ratio: 0.20

MARYLAND SOUTHERN ELECTRIC COOPERATIVE INC

Historic Southern Maryland gets it power via the South Maryland Electric Cooperative (SMECO) which distributes electricity to about 154000 residential commercial and industrial customers in four counties via about 11360 miles of power line and 54 electric substations. One of the ten largest electric cooperatives in the US the member-owned enterprise gets its wholesale power supply through its membership in wholesale energy trading and risk management service company ACES Power Marketing. Overseen by a board of directors SMECO's single mission is to provide reliable competitively priced energy and related services to its members.

Geographic Reach

SMECO's 1150 sq. ml. service area includes all of Charles and St. Mary's counties and parts of of Calvert and Prince George's counties. Cities covered include Hughesville Leonardtown Prince Frederick and White Plains.

Financial Performance

In 2012 SMECO revenues decreased by 7% due to weaker residential power demand and lower costs paid for third-party purchased power. The coop's net income decreased by 15%.

Strategy

Like other coops SMECO is pushing conservation the use of green energy and smart technology to reduce power costs. It is also promoting the development of solar and wind energy and integrating it into the power supply it makes available to its members.

In addition SMECO is constructing the Southern Maryland Reliability Project which aims to upgrade SEMCOs existing 69000-volt transmission line to 230000 volts by 2015. The Project's expanded capacity will ensure a more reliable supply.

Company Background

In 1937 as part of the national rural electrification drive of the Roosevelt government a local committee in St. Mary's county and one representing Charles and Prince George's counties merged to form the Southern Maryland Tri-County Cooperative Association. The members converted this association into a non-profit membership cooperative in 1942 and changed its name to Southern Maryland Electric Cooperative.

In 2011 the coop's service areas felt the full brunt of Hurricane Irene which knocked out 11 transmission circuits and cut power 108000 customers and caused $7 million of damage to the coop's electric system.

EXECUTIVES

Sr. Vice President And Cfo, Sonja Cox
Vice President And Chief Information Officer, Andrew Yeskie
Auditors: I ADAMS JENKINS CHEATHAM PC

LOCATIONS

HQ: MARYLAND SOUTHERN ELECTRIC COOPERATIVE INC
15035 BURNT STORE RD, HUGHESVILLE, MD
206372699
Phone: 301 274-3111
Web: WWW.SMECO.COOP

HISTORICAL FINANCIALS
Company Type: Private

Income Statement
FYE: December 31

	REVENUE ($ mil.)	NET INCOME ($ mil.)	NET PROFIT MARGIN	EMPLOYEES
12/15	451	4	1.0%	375
12/14	490	1	0.3%	—
12/10	492	17	3.5%	—
12/09	462	3	0.7%	—
Annual Growth	(0.4%)	5.6%	—	—

2015 Year-End Financials
Return on assets: 6.2%   Cash ($ mil.): 4
Return on equity: 1.0%
Current ratio: 1.50

MASSACHUSETTS HOUSING FINANCE AGENCY PROPERTY ACQUISITION AND DISPOSITION CORPORATION

EXECUTIVES

Chb, Michael J Dirrane
Chm, Ronald A Homer
Exec Dir, Thomas R Gleason
Treas, Andris J Silins
Prin, Tom O'Brien
Cfo, Michael Fitzmaurice
Staff, Tyrone Reed
Real Estate Conultant, Kristin Olsen
Executive Secretary, Christine Bond
Manager, Kevin Mello
Vp-Homeownership Programs, Mounzer M Aylouche

LOCATIONS

HQ: MASSACHUSETTS HOUSING FINANCE AGENCY PROPERTY ACQUISITION AND DISPOSITION CORPORATION
1 BEACON ST, BOSTON, MA 021083107
Phone: 617 854-1000
Web: WWW.MYMASSMORTGAGE.ORG

HISTORICAL FINANCIALS
Company Type: Private

Income Statement
FYE: June 30

	ASSETS ($ mil.)	NET INCOME ($ mil.)	INCOME AS % OF ASSETS	EMPLOYEES
06/18	5,460	6	0.1%	325
06/07*	5,457	80	1.5%	—
12/06	1	0	0.8%	—
06/05	0	(21)	—	—
Annual Growth	—	—	—	—

*Fiscal year change

MASSACHUSETTS INSTITUTE OF TECHNOLOGY

Massachusetts Institute of Technology (MIT) takes the prize for breeding ingenuity. A leading research institution the school is typically granted more patents annually than any other university and about 90 people associated with MIT are Nobel Prize recipients. Blending that science and engineering acumen with top business programs (including the Sloan School of Management) MIT graduates have started more than 30000 active companies. MIT has more than 11000 students more than 60% of whom attend graduate school. The faculty of the nearly three dozen academic departments includes more than 1000 professors. The school's student teacher ratio is 3:1 (undergraduates). Founded in 1865 MIT is privately endowed.

Operations

MIT's research is conducted both through its academic facilities which employ more than 3700 researchers and engage some 2500 graduate students and through its Lincoln Laboratory in Lexington Massachusetts. The Lincoln Laboratory has approximately 3200 workers focused on federally funded research programs in areas of national security such as information communication and decision making. Lincoln Laboratory specialized in sensors signal processing and embedded computer systems.

The university offers 46 major and 49 minor undergraduate programs. Its undergraduate tuition for academic year 2016-2017 was about $48000. MIT's libraries have more than 5 million items in print and digital formats.

MIT is one of a growing number of universities to begin offering OpenCourseWare which makes teaching materials used in MIT undergraduate and graduate courses available on the internet free of charge to any user anywhere in the world for uses ranging from curriculum development to self-learning.

Geographic Reach

MIT is located on 168 acres in Cambridge Massachusetts and includes 18 student residences and 26 acres of athletic fields.

MIT enrolled students from all 50 states and the District of Columbia three territories and about 100 foreign nations in the academic year ending 2017.

Financial Performance

MIT clearly has a strong emphasis on procuring funding for its technology research programs. The institute receives grants from a variety of commercial and non-commercial entities bringing in a total of $1.7 billion in sponsored funding each year. The Department of Defense and Department of Health and Human Services the largest sponsors. Other sponsors include the Department of Energy National Science Foundation NASA local government agencies and not-for-profit entities. MIT also conducts $100 million in contracted general industry research each year.

Annual revenue for MIT in fiscal 2017 was $3.5 billion up from about $3.4 billion in 2016. About 50% of revenue comes from research funding. About 10% comes from tuition.

Strategy

MIT's primary goal is to advance science and technology both among its students and on a worldwide scale. It aims to make discoveries in areas including energy economics and medicine. To take its efforts to the broader population MIT licenses more technologies to startups than any other university. Its licensing office enters about 100 licensing and option agreements each year with about a quarter of those going to startup technology firms.

While MIT is well-known for students and graduates who create businesses the university has created a fund to help early stage enterprises along. The Engine as the fund is called invests in university-related startups in their early stages. It steps in where venture capital funds usually don't go technologies that require time to commercialize. Main areas of investment include robotics biotechnology manufacturing and materials and energy. The fund has about $200 billion for investment.

Company Background

MIT has some extraordinary alumni who include former chairman of the Federal Reserve Ben Bernanke former US Representative Pete Stark former National Economic Council chairman Lawrence H. Summers and former Council of Economic Advisors chairwoman Christina Romer. Outside of politics MIT alumni founded or co-founded several notable companies such as Intel Hewlett-Packard Texas Instruments Qualcomm Bose and Campbell Soup.

EXECUTIVES

Dean Digital Learning, Sanjay Sarma
President, L. Rafael Reif
Dean Sloan School Of Management, David C. Schmittlein
Evp And Treasurer, Israel Ruiz
Dean School Of Engineering, Ian A. Waitz
Dean Graduate Education, Christine Ortiz
Dean Undergraduate Education, Dennis M. Freeman
Dean Student Life, Costantino (Chris) Colombo
Chancellor, Cynthia Barnhart
Provost, Martin A. Schmidt
Dean School Of Architecture And Planning, Hashim Sarkis
Dean School Of Humanities Arts And Social Sciences, Melissa Nobles
Dean School Of Science, Michael Sipser
Vp Information Systems And Technology, John Charles
Director Of Pharmacy, Ratna Bhojani
Executive Vice President Marketing, Donald Rosenfield
Associate Vice President For Human Resources, Meg Regan
Vice President Supply Chain Management, Lalitendu Panda
Vice President, Susan Hockfield
Vice President Resource Development, Julie Lucas
Associate Vice President And Chief Operating Officer, David Woodruff
Vice President, Richard Molnar
Vice President, Ann Drumm
Vice President Of Sales, Lawrence Krakauer
Vice President Of Engineer, Anthony Johnson
Senior Advisor Office Of The Vice President For Research, Tom Kiley
Senior Vice President Member Services, Kim Mandola
Vice President And Dean For Student Life, Suzy Nelson
Vice President Of The Undergraduate Association, Alexa Martin

Vice President Of Membership, Shang Chou
Department Head, Gerald Banner
Vice President, Catelin Bonvie
Chairman, Robert B. Millard, age 68
Secretary, Debra Blanchard
Board Member, Tenley Albright
Board Member, Noor Sweid
Secretary Class Of 84, Pam Gannon

LOCATIONS

HQ: MASSACHUSETTS INSTITUTE OF TECHNOLOGY
77 MASSACHUSETTS AVE, CAMBRIDGE, MA
021394307
Phone: 617 253-1000
Web: WWW.WWW-MATH.MIT.EDU

PRODUCTS/OPERATIONS

2014 Sales

	% of total
Reseach revenue	49
Support from investment	20
Tuition and similar revenue	10
Fee and services	6
Gifts	5
Auxiliary enterprises	4
Other program	4
Net asset reclassification	2
Total	**100**

Schools and Areas of Study

Schools and Areas of Study
School of Architecture and Planning
 Architecture
 Media Arts and Sciences
 Urban Studies and Planning
School of Engineering
 Aeronautics and Astronautics
 Biological Engineering
 Chemical Engineering
 Civil and Environmental Engineering
 Electrical Engineering and Computer Science
 Engineering Systems Division
 Materials Science and Engineering
 Mechanical Engineering
 Nuclear Science and Engineering
School of Humanities Arts and Social Sciences
 Anthropology
 Comparative Media Studies
 Economics
 Foreign Languages and Literatures
 History
 Humanities
 Linguistics and Philosophy
 Literature
 Music and Theater Arts
 Political Science
 Science Technology and Society
 Writing and Humanistic Studies
Sloan School of Management
 Management
School of Science
 Biology
 Brain and Cognitive Sciences
 Chemistry
 Earth Atmospheric and Planetary Sciences
 Mathematics
 Physics
Whitaker College of Health Sciences and Technology
 Harvard-MIT Division of Health Sciences and Technology
MIT-WHOI Joint Program in Oceanography and Applied Ocean Science and Engineering
Degrees Offered
Bachelor of Science (SB)
Master of Architecture (MArch)
Master of Business Administration (MBA)
Master in City Planning (MCP)
Master of Engineering (MEng)
Master of Finance (MFin)
Master of Science (SM)
Engineer (degree designates the field)
Doctor of Philosophy (PhD)
Doctor of Science (ScD)

HISTORICAL FINANCIALS
Company Type: Private

Income Statement
FYE: June 30

	REVENUE ($ mil.)	NET INCOME ($ mil.)	NET PROFIT MARGIN	EMPLOYEES
06/18	3,626	2,391	65.9%	12,000
06/17	3,551	2,195	61.8%	—
06/10	2,727	(199)	—	—
Annual Growth	3.6%	—	—	—

2018 Year-End Financials
Return on assets: 13.4%
Return on equity: 65.9%
Current ratio: —

Cash ($ mil.): 428

MASSACHUSETTS PORT AUTHORITY

Massachusetts Port Authority (Massport) operates three airports: Boston Logan International Hanscom Field and Worcester Regional. Logan is home to 50 airlines and is New England's largest airport and the first port of call for many international flights entering the US. (It accounts for the majority of Massport's revenues.) Hanscom Field operates as the region's main aviation airport and offers niche commercial services while Worcester Regional primarily supports commercial flight services. Massport also oversees various waterfront properties of the Port of Boston. The agency was created by the Commonwealth of Massachusetts in 1956. The governor of Massachusetts appoints the agency's board members.

Operations

Massport's business consists of two distinct operating departments: Aviation and the Port. Logan airport catered to 29.4 million aviation passengers and 369000 cruise passengers in 2013. Its shipping operations serviced more than 110000 containers of products at its port.

Financial Performance

Massport's net revenues have steadily climbed over the years. Revenues jumped 2% from $1.78 billion in 2012 to $1.83 billion in 2013 thanks mainly to parking concession ground services and other revenue from nearly 125000 more passengers at Logan. The overall revenue increase for 2013 was generated by operating revenues exceeding operating expenses by $2.4 million.

EXECUTIVES

Secretary, Rita Hannon

LOCATIONS

HQ: MASSACHUSETTS PORT AUTHORITY
1 HARBORSIDE DR STE 200S, BOSTON, MA 021282905
Phone: 617 561-1600
Web: WWW.MASSPORT.COM

HISTORICAL FINANCIALS
Company Type: Private

Income Statement
FYE: June 30

	REVENUE ($ mil.)	NET INCOME ($ mil.)	NET PROFIT MARGIN	EMPLOYEES
06/16	699	105	15.1%	1,102
06/07	526	49	9.3%	—
06/06*	497	74	15.0%	—
12/05	0	0	11.5%	—
Annual Growth	108.0%	113.7%	—	—

*Fiscal year change

2016 Year-End Financials
Return on assets: 21.3%
Return on equity: 15.1%
Current ratio: 0.60

Cash ($ mil.): 63

MASSACHUSETTS SCHOOL BUILDING AUTHORITY

EXECUTIVES

Exec Director, Katherine Craven
Accounting Staff, Audrey Cushman
Executive Board Member, Matthew Deninger
Associate General Counsel, Brian Kelley

LOCATIONS

HQ: MASSACHUSETTS SCHOOL BUILDING AUTHORITY
40 BROAD ST STE 500, BOSTON, MA 021094371
Phone: 617 720-4466
Web: WWW.MASSSCHOOLBUILDINGS.ORG

HISTORICAL FINANCIALS
Company Type: Private

Income Statement
FYE: June 30

	REVENUE ($ mil.)	NET INCOME ($ mil.)	NET PROFIT MARGIN	EMPLOYEES
06/17	828	148	17.9%	8
06/16	908	237	26.1%	—
Annual Growth	(8.9%)	(37.6%)	—	—

MATER MISERICORDIAE HOSPITAL

EXECUTIVES

Ceo, David Dunham
Manager of Information, Cheryl Baijnauth
Chief Operating Officer, Chuck Kassis
Pharmacist, Harwinder Sharma
Chief Financial Officer, Michael Strasser
Chief of Medicine, Robert Streeter
Emergency Medicine Specialist, Kevin M Jones
Director of Marketing, Paul Feltz
Emergency Medicine Specialist, Gary Tamkin
Family Practitioner, Jacqueline Craig
Emergency Medicine Specialist, Jason Antunez

LOCATIONS

HQ: MATER MISERICORDIAE HOSPITAL
333 MERCY AVE, MERCED, CA 953408319
Phone: 209 564-5000

HISTORICAL FINANCIALS
Company Type: Private

Income Statement
FYE: June 30

	REVENUE ($ mil.)	NET INCOME ($ mil.)	NET PROFIT MARGIN	EMPLOYEES
06/16	298	18	6.3%	1,200
06/15	305	31	10.4%	—
Annual Growth	(2.2%)	(40.3%)	—	—

MAURY REGIONAL HOSPITAL

EXECUTIVES

Ceo, Alan Watson
Coo, Paul Betz
Chief Financial Officer, Nick Swift
Information Technology Manager, Warren Robinson
Chief Information Officer, Jim Parcel
Facilities Specialist, John Collier
Physician Recruiter, Melissa Bates
Public Relations Director, Rita Williams
Director, Charles Ball
Internal Medicine Practitioner, Christopher Turner
Plant Manager, Paul Corvin

LOCATIONS

HQ: MAURY REGIONAL HOSPITAL
1224 TROTWOOD AVE, COLUMBIA, TN 384014802
Phone: 931 381-1111
Web: WWW.MAURYREGIONAL.COM

HISTORICAL FINANCIALS
Company Type: Private

Income Statement
FYE: June 30

	REVENUE ($ mil.)	NET INCOME ($ mil.)	NET PROFIT MARGIN	EMPLOYEES
06/16	336	16	4.8%	2,100
06/15	232	9	4.0%	—
06/10	257	6	2.6%	—
06/09	192	(9)	—	—
Annual Growth	8.3%	—	—	—

2016 Year-End Financials
Return on assets: 2.6%
Return on equity: 4.8%
Current ratio: 2.80

Cash ($ mil.): 49

MAXIM HEALTHCARE SERVICES, INC.

Maxim Healthcare Services aims to promote good health by offering medical staffing and home health care as well as immunizations and other wellness services to clients nationwide. The company provides medical and administrative personnel for hospitals school systems nursing homes and correctional facilities. The company's staffing division offers contract per diem and travel assignments. Maxim Healthcare's consultants are available 24 hours a day seven days a week to provide assistance for clients. The company which operates from more than 360 locations nationwide was established in 1988.

Operations

The company's Maxim Health Systems division established in 1996 provides immunizations health screenings and health fairs. Each year the division's immunization program is responsible for vaccinating millions of people across more than 40000 clinics.

Other major Maxim Healthcare divisions include Maxim Staffing Solutions (Nurse Allied Health and Administrative Staffing) Maxim Government Services Maxim Physician Resources Timeline Recruiting Maxim Coders Maxim Pediatric Services; Logix Healthcare Search Partners and StaffAssist.

EXECUTIVES

Cio, Kevin Apperson
Coo Maxim Staffing Solutions, Chris Powell
Ceo, W. Bradley (Brad) Bennett
Vp Chief Medical Officer And Chief Quality Officer, W. John Langley
Cfo, Raymond (Ray) Carbone
Director Of Clinical Services, Ann Lopez
Director Of Clinical Services, Jolinda Jackson
Vice President Of Finance, Dave Kowalczyk
Area Vice President Southeast, Matt Rozelle
Area Vice President, Jeremy Markewicz
Director Of Clinical Services, Debra Ruggieri
Area Vice President Of Clinical Operations, Kathy Mandeville
Vice President Of Finance, Steve Walsh
Vice President Human Resources, Kelly Bart
Director Of Clinical Services, Stephanie Blanchard
Director Of Clinical Services, Melissa Geiselman
Director Of Clinical Services, Joan Rn
Auditors: PRICEWATERHOUSECOOPERS LLP BA

LOCATIONS

HQ: MAXIM HEALTHCARE SERVICES, INC.
7227 LEE DEFOREST DR, COLUMBIA, MD 210463236
Phone: 410 910-1500
Web: WWW.MAXIMHEALTHCARE.COM

PRODUCTS/OPERATIONS

Selected Services

Allied Health staffing
Facility nurse staffing
Flu and wellness services
Government services
Health information services
International nursing
Home healthcare
HME/pharmacy services
Habilitation services
Physician services
Travel nursing

Selected Divisions

CareFocus
CareFocus Companion Services
Centrus Premier Homecare
Logix Healthcare Search Partners
Maxim Coders
Maxim Government Services
Maxim Health Information Services
Maxim Health Systems
Maxim Healthcare Services (Homecare)
Maxim Home Health Resources
Maxim Pediatric Services
Maxim Physician Resources
Maxim Staffing Solutions - Administrative Staffing
Maxim Staffing Solutions - Allied Health
Maxim Staffing Solutions - Nurse Staffing
Orbis Clinical
Reflectx Services
StaffAssist
TimeLine Recruiting
TravelMax

COMPETITORS

American HomePatient
Apria Healthcare
Cross Country Healthcare
MedStaff
Medsearch Staffing Services
PHS Correctional Healthcare
Team Health
TeamStaff

HISTORICAL FINANCIALS

Company Type: Private

Income Statement   FYE: December 31

	REVENUE ($ mil.)	NET INCOME ($ mil.)	NET PROFIT MARGIN	EMPLOYEES
12/17	1,510	38	2.5%	35,000
12/15	1,382	11	0.8%	—
12/14	1,269	4	0.4%	—
12/13	1,226	(1)	—	—
Annual Growth	5.3%	—	—	—

2017 Year-End Financials

Return on assets: 0.3%   Cash ($ mil.): 8
Return on equity: 2.5%
Current ratio: 1.30

MAYER ELECTRIC SUPPLY COMPANY, INC.

Mayer Electric Supply helps to light up those southern nights. The company is one of the nation's largest distributors of electrical supplies with about 50 branch locations in the southeastern US. It offers some 40000 items made by leading manufacturers such as 3M GE Littelfuse and Schneider Electric. Products include conduit circuit breakers controls and switches fire and safety products LED and low-voltage lighting systems motors power tools transformers and wire and cable. Mayer Electric supplies customers in the construction datacomm government industrial and utility industries. The Collat family including CEO Nancy Collat Goedecke owns Mayer Electric.

Operations

Besides distributing electrical supplies Mayer Electric offers several services. Its Mayer Project Management group works to lower cost for construction contractors by providing on-site storage and inventory management. Other services include lamp and battery recycling conduit bending and threading and wire and cable cutting. The company also specializes in factory automation energy efficiency and datacomm systems.

Geographic Reach

Mayer Electric serves customers through locations in Alabama Florida Georgia Mississippi the Carolinas Texas Tennessee and Virginia.

Sales and Marketing

The electrical supplies distributor serves multiple customer segments including those in the construction government industrial datacomm and utility industries through about 51 branch locations across US Southeast.

Strategy

Growing its geographic presence in 2013 Mayer Electric opened a branch location in the Houston area.

Mergers and Acquisitions

Looking to expand further in the southeastern US Mayer Electric in 2012 acquired Mustang Electric Supply based outside Dallas in Lewisville

Texas. Established in 1998 Mustang Electric serves commercial and residential contractors across the Dallas and Fort Worth area allowing Mayer Electric to expand to the dynamic and lucrative Dallas market. The purchase included Mustang Electric's 40000-sq.-ft. facility in Lewisville.

Company Background

The recession hit companies like Mayer Electric hard as residential and commercial construction efforts were backburnered. Sales for Mayer Electric dropped by about 21% in 2009 compared to the prior year. Rather than responding by laying off employees or shuttering branches the company planned for break-even results or a small loss for the year. Indeed the company made a small profit in 2009.

Mayer Electric was founded in 1930.

EXECUTIVES

Chb-Ceo, Nancy Collat Goedecke
President, Wes Smith
Exec V Pres-Coo, Charles A Collat Jr
Exec Vice President, Glenn Goedecke
Executive Officer, Mike Dunaway
Staff, Steve Poremba
Human Resources, Melissa Hill
Quotations Manager, Victor Fraga
Interior Designer, Abby Crider
Project Manager, Grace Christino
Outside Account Manager, Jake Gray

LOCATIONS

HQ: MAYER ELECTRIC SUPPLY COMPANY, INC.
3405 4TH AVE S, BIRMINGHAM, AL 352222300
Phone: 205 583-3500
Web: WWW.MAYERELECTRIC.COM

PRODUCTS/OPERATIONS

Selected Services

Basic distributor services
Construction partner
Maintenance repair and operations

Selected Products

Ballasts
Batteries
Cable and wire
Circuit breakers
Conduit
Factory automation products
Fan boxes
Fasteners
Fuses
LED lighting systems
Lenses
Lighting fixtures
Locks
Low-voltage lighting systems
Meters
Motors
Panelboards
Power supplies
Relays
Switches
Surge protection devices
Terminal blocks
Tools
Transformers
Voltage regulators

COMPETITORS

Anixter International
Consolidated Electrical
Crescent Electric Supply
Gexpro
Graybar Electric
Independent Electric Supply
Rexel Inc.
W.W. Grainger
WESCO International
Wholesale Supply Group

HISTORICAL FINANCIALS

Company Type: Private

Income Statement   FYE: December 30

	REVENUE ($ mil.)	NET INCOME ($ mil.)	NET PROFIT MARGIN	EMPLOYEES
12/17	911	11	1.2%	900
12/16	812	5	0.7%	—
12/15	811	7	0.9%	—
12/14	737	6	0.9%	—
Annual Growth	7.3%	18.5%	—	—

2017 Year-End Financials

Return on assets: 7.8%   Cash ($ mil.): 4
Return on equity: 1.2%
Current ratio: 1.60

MAYO CLINIC HEALTH SYSTEM-SOUTHWEST MINNESOTA REGION

EXECUTIVES

Pres, Gregory R Kutcher
V Pres, Jerome Crest
V Pres, Richard Grace
Interim Cfo, Ryan Ashlando
Audiologist, Jenne Tunnell
Internal Medicine Practitioner, John C Wagonlander
Internal Medicine Practitioner, Vishal Sekhri
Doctor of Medicine, Carroll Galvin
Director, Julie Oliver
Director, Shawn M Severson

LOCATIONS

HQ: MAYO CLINIC HEALTH SYSTEM-SOUTHWEST
 MINNESOTA REGION
 1025 MARSH ST, MANKATO, MN 560014752
Phone: 507 625-4031
Web: WWW.MAYOCLINICHEALTHSYSTEM.ORG

HISTORICAL FINANCIALS

Company Type: Private

Income Statement   FYE: December 31

	REVENUE ($ mil.)	NET INCOME ($ mil.)	NET PROFIT MARGIN	EMPLOYEES
12/17	354	0	0.2%	2,830
12/12	293	16	5.6%	—
12/02	127	(6)	—	—
12/01	1,198	0	—	—
Annual Growth	—	64.8%	—	—

2017 Year-End Financials

Return on assets: 0.7%   Cash ($ mil.): —
Return on equity: 0.2%
Current ratio: 0.70

MAYO CLINIC HOSPITAL-ROCHESTER

Multidisciplinary teamwork with coordinated care is Mayo Clinic's secret sauce. The not-for-profit Mayo Clinic provides health care most notably for complex medical conditions through its clinics in Rochester Minnesota Arizona and Florida. The clinics' multidisciplinary approach to care attracts more than a million patients a year from around the globe. For less specialized care the Mayo Clinic Health System operates a regional network of affiliated community hospitals and clinics in Minnesota Iowa and Wisconsin. Mayo Clinic also conducts research and trains physicians nurses and other health professionals. The Mayo Clinic is named for Dr. William Worrall Mayo who settled in Rochester in 1863.

Operations

Mayo Clinic Health System's regional network operates more than a dozen hospitals that combined are home to about 1000 beds and 3800 staff physicians medical scientists and clinical and research associates. The system also includes roughly 70 clinics in northern Iowa western Wisconsin and southeastern Minnesota. To manage its patient load Mayo forms referral alliances with other hospital groups HMOs and other organizations.

The clinic's education programs include the Mayo Medical School Mayo Graduate School and the Mayo School of Health Sciences; some medical training programs are conducted through partnerships with universities including the University of Minnesota. It also provides continuing education programs to medical professionals.

Financial Performance

The Mayo Clinic's revenue increased by nearly 7% in 2011 vs. 2010 while net income declined 18% over the same period. Indeed revenue gains and other support has steadily increased in recent years to nearly $8.5 billion in 2011. Sales of medical services (which account for about 85% of the Mayo Clinic's total) grew by 6% vs. the prior year. The Mayo Clinic list more than $10 billion in total assets.

Strategy

Already a giant in health care in the Midwest the Mayo Clinic continues to grow in other regions. In 2018 it announced plans to invest some $648 million in its Phoenix campus over the next five years. The project will roughly double the size of the campus allowing the system to meet growing demand for complex health care services in the Southwest. Similarly Mayo Clinic is investing some $144 million in its Jacksonville Florida campus.

Mayo Clinic strives to accommodate patients who travel to get to its facilities and will schedule multiple appointments and tests tightly together to make the most of patient's time. Rather than paying physicians based upon the quantity of patients seen the clinic's doctors are paid salaries as an incentive to quality care. These and other innovations have drawn attention to the clinic's patient-centered model of care. It has created a Center for the Science of Health Care Delivery and collaborates with other innovators including Cleveland Clinic and Intermountain Healthcare.

To reach remote areas Mayo Clinic in Arizona pioneered a telemedicine program that places robots in rural hospitals allowing local doctors and hospital staff to communicate with Mayo doctors in real time as they treat patients with such conditions as stroke or collapsed lungs.

EXECUTIVES

Regional Vice President, Annie Sadosty
Chair Department Of Medicine, Morie Gertz
Senior Vice President, Andrew Moore
Vice President, Victoria Hanson
Vice President, Brian Arendt
Medical Director, Jerry Swanson
Director Patient Care Nursing, Bonny Young
Vice President, BOBBIE S GOSTOUT
Regional Vice President Bus Development And Marketing, Peter Hughes
Secretary Treasurer, Paul Mueller
Board Member, John Dilger
Internal Audit Vice Chair, Carrie Graunke
Treasurer, Daniel Van Dyke
Secretary, Luanne Wussow
Secretary, Lisa Jurrens
Auditors: RSM US LLP MINNEAPOLIS MINNE

LOCATIONS

HQ: MAYO CLINIC HOSPITAL-ROCHESTER
 200 1ST ST SW, ROCHESTER, MN 559050002
Phone: 507 284-2511
Web: WWW.MAYOCLINIC.ORG

Selected Locations and Affiliates

Direct subsidiaries
 Arizona
  Mayo Clinic Hospital (Phoenix)
  Mayo Clinic Scottsdale
 Florida
  Mayo Clinic Hospital (Jacksonville)
  Mayo Clinic Jacksonville
 Minnesota
  Mayo Clinic Rochester
  Rochester Methodist Hospital
  Saint Marys Hospital (Rochester)
  Mayo Eugenio Litta Children's Hospital
Mayo Health System affiliates
 Iowa
  Armstrong Clinic
  Decorah Clinic
  Lake Mills Clinic
 Franciscan
  Swea City Clinic
 Minnesota
  Fountain Centers in Fairmont
  Fountain Centers in Waseca
 FamilyHeal
  FamilyHealth Medical Clinic - Northfield Hospital
  Franciscan Healthcare in Caledonia
  Franciscan Healthcare La Crescent Clinic
  Mayo Clinic Health System - Albert Lea
 Mayo Clini
 Mayo Clini
 Mayo Clini
 Mayo Clini
 Wisconsin
  Chippewa Valley in Bloomer
  Chippewa Valley in Chippewa Falls
  Chippewa Valley in Colfax
  Eau Claire Home Health & Hospice
  Franciscan Healthcare Arcadia Campus
  Franciscan Healthcare Holmen Clinic
  Franciscan Healthcare Lake Tomah Clinic
  Franciscan Healthcare Onalaska Clinic
  Franciscan Healthcare Prairie du Chien Clinic
  Franciscan Healthcare Sparta Campus
  Northland in Barron
  Red Cedar in Elmwood
  Red Cedar in Glenwood
  Red Cedar in Menomonie

PRODUCTS/OPERATIONS

2015 Revenues

	$ mil.	% of total
Medical services	8,620	84
Grants & contracts	386	4
Investment return	233	2
Contributions	211	2
Premiums	144	1
Other	721	6
Total	**8,476**	**100**

COMPETITORS

Allina Hospitals
Ascension Health
Beth Israel Deaconess Medical Center
CentraCare Health
Children's Hospitals and Clinics of Minnesota
Dana-Farber
Fairview Health
Fox Chase Cancer Center
Gundersen Lutheran
HCA
Henry Ford Health System
Intermountain Health Care
Johns Hopkins Medicine
MD Anderson Cancer Center
Memorial Sloan-Kettering
North Memorial Health Care
Olmsted Medical
Park Nicollet Health Services
Roswell Park Cancer Institute
Scottsdale Healthcare
Tenet Healthcare
The Cleveland Clinic
Wistar Institute

HISTORICAL FINANCIALS

Company Type: Private

Income Statement   FYE: December 31

	REVENUE ($ mil.)	NET INCOME ($ mil.)	NET PROFIT MARGIN	EMPLOYEES
12/17	11,993	856	7.1%	82,000
12/16	10,998	(480)	—	—
Annual Growth	9.0%	—	—	—

2017 Year-End Financials

Return on assets: 3.7%   Cash ($ mil.): 66
Return on equity: 7.1%
Current ratio: 0.80

MAYO CLINIC JACKSONVILLE (A NONPROFIT CORPORATION)

With more than 370 doctors and scientists on staff Mayo Clinic Jacksonville offers a broad range of medical surgical and research services. The clinic part of the larger Mayo Clinic network and one of its four major campuses offers specialty services such as organ transplantation neurology and oncology therapy. Most patients provided care from the clinic are treated on an outpatient basis; those who require hospitalization are admitted to the adjacent Mayo Clinic Hospital a 214-bed acute care facility. The Jacksonville campus also includes the Birdsall Medical Research center and the Griffin Cancer Research building.

Geographic Reach

While it draws heavily from the local population Mayo Clinic Jacksonville is also a destination for interregional and international patients seeking the coordinated treatment services that are ingrained in the Mayo approach to care.

Strategy

In recent years May Clinic Jacksonville has boosted its presence across the Northeast Florida region. The move includes its $80-million capital improvement of the hospital off San Pablo Road which added two floors and 90 beds in 2013.

Mayo Clinic Jacksonville has also been busy in 2014 opening primary care centers throughout the region including those on the city's Southside Jacksonville Beach and St. Augustine areas.

Since its opening in 1986 the Jacksonville campus has steadily added new facilities. It built and opened the Mayo Clinic Hospital building in 2008 on its current campus. In 2011 it opened a sleep disorder center and a simulation training center where physicians can improve their skills in risk-free environment. Because so many patients travel to receive treatment at Mayo Clinic Jacksonville the clinic also houses two hotels on its campus as well as the extended-stay Gabriel House of Care.

Company Background

The Jacksonville clinic originally provided acute care services at St. Luke's Hospital. The clinic sold St. Luke's to St. Vincent's Medical Center (one of the members of Jacksonville's St. Vincent's Health System) in 2005. The Mayo Clinic leased back the St. Luke's hospital until its new facility was completed in 2008.

EXECUTIVES

Chb, Marilyn Carlson Nelson
Ceo, William C Rupp
Cfo, Mary J Hoffman
ADM Asst, Leslie Carraway
Professor, William Tatum

LOCATIONS

HQ: MAYO CLINIC JACKSONVILLE (A NONPROFIT CORPORATION)
4500 SAN PABLO RD S, JACKSONVILLE, FL 322241865
Phone: 904 953-2000

PRODUCTS/OPERATIONS

Selected Facilities

Birdsall Medical Research Building
Cannaday Building
Gabriel House of Care
Griffin Cancer Research Building
Mayo Clinic Hospital
The Inn at Mayo Clinic

COMPETITORS

Baptist Health System
Florida Hospital Tampa Bay Division
H. Lee Moffitt Cancer Center & Research Institute
Lawnwood Medical Center
Nemours Foundation
North Florida Regional Medical Center
Ocala Regional Medical Center
Palms West Hospital
St. Vincent's Health System
UF Health Jacksonville
UF&Shands

HISTORICAL FINANCIALS

Company Type: Private

Income Statement   FYE: December 31

	REVENUE ($ mil.)	NET INCOME ($ mil.)	NET PROFIT MARGIN	EMPLOYEES
12/16	520	94	18.2%	5,500
12/15	457	65	14.3%	—
12/13	657	(0)	—	—
12/09	340	(4)	—	—
Annual Growth	6.2%	—	—	—

2016 Year-End Financials

Return on assets: 0.8%   Cash ($ mil.): —
Return on equity: 18.2%
Current ratio: 0.40

MCCARTHY BUILDING COMPANIES, INC.

A company that was in construction before Reconstruction McCarthy Building Companies is one of the oldest and largest privately-held builders in the US. The general contractor and construction manager ranks among the top builders of health care education and green building facilities in the country. Contracts include heavy construction projects (bridges and water- and waste-treatment plants) commercial projects (retail and office buildings) and institutional projects (airports schools and prisons). Subsidiary MC Industrial handles energy auto and other manufacturing projects. Founded by Timothy McCarthy in 1864 the company is 100% employee owned and generates $3 billion in annual revenues.

Operations

As of 2016 nearly half of the builder's project portfolio was made up of Construction Manager at Risk projects while around a quarter of the portfolio consisted of Hard Bid projects. The rest was made up of Design/Build Construction Manager Owner Agent and Negotiated General Contracting projects. About 70% of its work came from repeat clients.

That year the company reported that it had 1600 full-time salaried and 1200 weekly payroll employees.

Geographic Reach

Headquartered in Saint Louis McCarthy Building Companies has worked on projects in 44 US states. Its offices are in Newport Beach San Francisco Sacramento and San Diego California; Albuquerque New Mexico; Las Vegas; Phoenix; St. Louis; Atlanta; Dallas; Houston; and Illinois. It does business in about 45 states.

Sales and Marketing

The firm gets more than 70% of its work from repeat clients which have included Kaiser Permanente California State University and Bally's Casino Resort.

Financial Performance

Ranked among the Top 10 commercial builders in the US McCarthy generates about $3 billion in annual revenues (as of 2016).

Strategy

McCarthy Building Companies has been steadily building its presence with new office openings in strong building markets across the US over the past few years with one of its most recent being an office in Lakewood Colorado in mid 2015. The company has also been growing through acquisitions of smaller companies that complement its existing service lines.

Some of the company's more recent contracts (around early 2016) include: the Genome Lab for J. Craig Venter Institute; the Chino Valley Solar project for Arizona Public Service; the Dallas City Performance Hall for the City of Dallas; the McCarran International Airport for Clark County; the Sacramento Recreation & Wellness Center for California State University; the San Diego and Paramount Unified School Districts in California; and the Lake Pleasant Water Treatment Plant for the City of Phoenix among others.

Some of its past projects include The Platinum condominium/hotel tower in Las Vegas expansion at M.D. Anderson Cancer Center and renovation and expansion of the National Baseball Hall of Fame and Museum in Cooperstown New York.

Mergers and Acquisitions

In October 2014 McCarthy bought St. Louis-based Castle Contracting and its subsidiary

CastleGPS. Castle provided turnkey civil services utilities earthwork and trenchless technology directly to owners general contractors and mechinncal electrical and plumbing contractors. Castle's GPS technology provides "industry-leading" subsurface 3-Dimensional utility mapping. The acquired company would continue using the Castle brand name.

EXECUTIVES

Ceo, Michael D. (Mike) Bolen
President And Coo, Derek W. Glanvill
President Northern Pacific Division, Richard A. (Rich) Henry
President Southwest Region, Robert (Bo) Calbert
President Texas Region, Michael J. McWay
President Southeast Division, Kevin Kuntz
President Mc Industrial, Tom Felton
Corporate President And Coo, Scott Wittkop
Evp, Ray Sedey
Evp Operations, Robert Betz
Vp And Cio, Mike Oster
Cfo, Doug Audiffred
President Central Division, John Buescher
Vice President Mep Services, Jaime Perera
Vice President, Drew Jackson
Vice President, Mike Myers
Vice President Operations, Mark Heit
Vice President Business Development Dallas, Charles Buescher
Vice President Engineering Procurement And Construction Phoenix, Dhruv Patel
Senior Vice President General Counsel, Matt Lawson
Senior Vice President And Retail Division Manager, Dazarene Randall
Vice President Business Development Houston, Wendell Rychlik
Executive Vice President Operations Newport Beach, John McRitchie
Vice President Business Development San Francisco, Tuyet Le
Senior Vice President Atlanta, Bobby Campbell
Auditors: RUBINBROWN LLP SAINT LOUIS M

LOCATIONS

HQ: MCCARTHY BUILDING COMPANIES, INC.
 1341 N ROCK HILL RD, SAINT LOUIS, MO 631241441
Phone: 314 968-3300
Web: WWW.MCCARTHY.COM

PRODUCTS/OPERATIONS

Selected Markets
Commercial
Education K-12
Health care
Heavy/civil/transportation
Higher education
High performance/green
Hospitality/entertainment
Industrial
Native American
Parking structures
Science and technology
Water/wastewater

Selected Services
Negotiated general contracting
Construction management
Hard bid (lump sum contract for services)
Design/build
Construction management/general contracting

COMPETITORS

Alberici	Korte
Barton Malow	Peter Kiewit Sons'
Bechtel	Primus Builders
Clayco	S. M. Wilson
DPR Construction	Skanska
Gilbane	Swinerton
HBE Corporation	Turner Corporation
Hensel Phelps Construction	Tutor Perini

HISTORICAL FINANCIALS

Company Type: Private

Income Statement   FYE: December 31

	REVENUE ($ mil.)	NET INCOME ($ mil.)	NET PROFIT MARGIN	EMPLOYEES
12/17	3,574	0	—	3,102
12/16	3,265	0	—	—
12/15	2,719	0	—	—
Annual Growth	14.6%	—	—	—

2017 Year-End Financials

Return on assets: 15.6%   Cash ($ mil.): 370
Return on equity: —
Current ratio: 1.30

MCCARTHY HOLDINGS, INC.

EXECUTIVES

Chb-Ceo, Michael D Bolen
Pres-Coo, Scott Wittkop
Exec V Pres-Cfo-Sec, J Douglas Audiffred
Sr V Pres-Gen Counsel, Matthew Lawson
Treas-Asst SEC, Danel Dillon
Engineer, Amanda Morgan
Controller, Lisa Vaglio
Project Engineer, Mitch Nissen
Quality Control Manager, Paul Tonner
Project Engineer, Andrew K Short
Coordinator of Marketing, Cassie Bustos
Auditors: RUBINBROWN LLP SAINT LOUIS M

LOCATIONS

HQ: MCCARTHY HOLDINGS, INC.
 1341 N ROCK HILL RD, SAINT LOUIS, MO 631241441
Phone: 314 968-3300
Web: WWW.MCCARTHY.COM

HISTORICAL FINANCIALS

Company Type: Private

Income Statement   FYE: December 31

	REVENUE ($ mil.)	NET INCOME ($ mil.)	NET PROFIT MARGIN	EMPLOYEES
12/17	3,666	0	—	3,650
12/16	3,481	0	—	—
12/15	2,837	0	—	—
12/14	2,696	0	—	—
Annual Growth	10.8%	—	—	—

2017 Year-End Financials

Return on assets: 18.0%   Cash ($ mil.): 67
Return on equity: —
Current ratio: 0.70

MCKINNEY INDEPENDENT SCHOOL DISTRICT

EXECUTIVES

Supt, Dr J D Kennedy
Supt, David Anthony
Coordinator, Cecil Fueston
Coordinator, DOT Leach
Coordinator, Suzanne Ellis
Technology/Computer Coord, David Span
Coordinator, Gwen Arnold
Director, James Shoemake
Assistant, Jennifer Frazier
Assistant, Michael Demakas
Education Specialist, Tiffany Collett
Auditors: EVANS PINGLETON AND HOWARD P

LOCATIONS

HQ: MCKINNEY INDEPENDENT SCHOOL DISTRICT
 1 DUVALL ST, MCKINNEY, TX 750693210
Phone: 469 302-4000
Web: WWW.MCKINNEYISD.NET

HISTORICAL FINANCIALS

Company Type: Private

Income Statement   FYE: June 30

	REVENUE ($ mil.)	NET INCOME ($ mil.)	NET PROFIT MARGIN	EMPLOYEES
06/18	326	40	12.4%	1,130
06/17	303	40	13.4%	—
06/16	299	18	6.2%	—
06/15	280	15	5.4%	—
Annual Growth	5.1%	38.8%	—	—

2018 Year-End Financials

Return on assets: 1.1%   Cash ($ mil.): 248
Return on equity: 12.4%
Current ratio: —

MCLANE COMPANY, INC.

You could say this company makes it convenient for stores and restaurants to get food. McLane Company is one of the largest wholesale suppliers of food products in the US serving more than 45000 retail stores and food service operators from more than 40 distribution centers. Its grocery and retail distribution division serves convenience stores drugstores and mass merchants including Wal-Mart. The company's McLane Foodservice division delivers food paper products and other supplies to chain restaurants and other food service providers. McLane also distributes alcoholic beverages in the southeastern US. The company is owned by Warren Buffett's Berkshire Hathaway.

Operations

McLane distributes grocery and non-food products to retailers convenience stores and restaurants. The company's McLane Grocery Distribution unit supplies more than 46000 retail grocery locations including drug stores mass merchants warehouse clubs convenience stores and more from 23 distribution centers across the US. McLane Foodservice supplies restaurants and food service providers from distribution centers in the US. Its McLane Beverage Distribution division provides alcoholic beverage distribution in select states. Another subsidiary Empire Distributors is a leading supplier of spirits wine beer and non-alcoholic beverages in Georgia North Carolina and Tennessee to more than 8000 accounts.

In 2014 the grocery and foodservice units accounted for 99% of the company's total revenues.

Geographic Reach

Texas-based McLane Co. does business in all 50 US states. McLane Foodservice's distribution unit based in Carrollton Texas focuses on serving the quick service restaurant industry. This division's operations are conducted through 18 facilities in 16 states. The foodservice distribution unit services 21000 chain restaurants across the country.

Sales and Marketing

McLane provides wholesale distribution services to its former parent company Wal-Mart Stores which contributed about 24% of its 2014 revenue versus 25% in 2013. Other important customers include 7-Eleven and Yum! Brands.

Financial Performance

The company's revenues increased by 1.5% in 2014 reflecting increased foodservice and beverage revenues. Grocery revenues were relatively flat.

Strategy

Changing trends in the grocery business have presented McLane with new opportunities. As a dominant player in the wholesale supply business McLane's grocery division competes in a league of giants including C & S Wholesale Nash-Finch and Core-Mark while its foodservice unit fights for business with such industry leaders as SYSCO U.S. Foodservice and Performance Food Group. Wholesale distribution continues to be a highly fragmented industry however meaning the company must also compete with a patchwork of regional and local suppliers. As the company's grocery and foodservice businesses are characterized by high sales volume and very low profit margins scale is immensely important to its financial performance.

In 2014 McLane was on track to open its newest grocery distribution center (its 22nd) in 2016. The $38-million distribution center is being built in northern Findlay Ohio to supply convenience stores mass merchants drugstores and restaurants.

In 2014 Kangaroo Express convenience stores signed a deal to continue to do business with McLane. The chain's parent company The Pantry signed a new distribution service agreement to continue to purchase food and non-food general merchandise including cigarettes and tobacco products from McLane.

Company Background

McLane bought North Carolina-based Meadowbrook Meat Company (MBM) in August 2012. With $6 billion in sales MBM is one of the largest food service distributors for national restaurant chains. Its customers include Arby's Burger King and Darden Restaurants. The deal will substantially increase McLane's size by adding to its food service unit which already serves more than 20000 chain restaurants.

As dollar stores have moved forcefully into food retailing McLane in 2012 entered into a partnership with one of the nation's largest dollar store operators Family Dollar Stores to supply a variety of merchandise including refrigerated and frozen food to the chain's 7200-plus locations across 45 states.

McLane has been expanding in recent years building up an alcohol distribution business with a series of acquisitions beginning in 2010. It purchased Kahn Ventures whose holdings included Empire Distributors (serving Georgia) and Empire Distributors of North Carolina. According to Buffet the acquisition is part of the shared vision of Berkshire McLane and Kahn to develop innovation opportunities and to grow and lead the beverage in-

dustry. McLane added to its Empire operations by acquiring Tennessee-based distributor Horizon Wine and Spirits later in the year. Gaining access to resources and operational best practices in the beverage distribution arena McLane is positioned for further growth in the sector

Starting as a family-owned grocery store in 1894 McLane expanded into wholesale distribution in the early 1900s. The McLane family including Houston Astros owner Drayton McLane sold the business to Wal-Mart Stores in the 1990s. Conglomerate Berkshire Hathaway acquired McLane Company in 2003 for about $1.5 billion.

EXECUTIVES

President Mclane Grocery, Mike Youngblood
Evp Administration, James L. (Jim) Kent
President And Ceo, W. Grady Rosier
President Southeast Southern And Dothan Divisions, Ron Clark
President Mclane Carolina And Mid-atlantic Divisions, George Bolts
Svp And Chief Marketing Officer, Tom Sicola
Vice President Of Information Technology, Mona Huffman
Vice President Of Sales, Jimmy Morales
Senior Vice President, Charles Freeman
Vice President Of Logistics, Robbie Wainwright
Vice President Of Distribution, Mark Hermacinski
Vice President Of Sales Convenience And Military Executive, Vito Maurici

LOCATIONS

HQ: MCLANE COMPANY, INC.
4747 MCLANE PKWY, TEMPLE, TX 765044854
Phone: 254 771-7500
Web: WWW.MCLANECO.COM

PRODUCTS/OPERATIONS

Selected Subsidiaries

C.D. Hartnett Company (grocery distribution)
Empire Distributors Inc. (beverages)
First American Carriers (third-party distribution)
McCarty-Hull Inc. (convenience store distribution)
Meadowbrook Meat Company Inc.
Professional Datasolutions Inc. (technology support services)
Salado Sales (private-label products)
Vantix Logistics (third-party logistics)

COMPETITORS

AMCON Distributing	H. T. Hackney
Associated Wholesale Grocers	MAINES
	Reinhart FoodService
Ben E. Keith	SUPERVALU
C&S Wholesale	Southern Glazer's Wine
Core-Mark	and Spirits
Eby-Brown	Sysco
GSC Enterprises	US Foods
Golden State Foods	Wakefern Food
Gordon Food Service	

HISTORICAL FINANCIALS

Company Type: Private

Income Statement   FYE: December 30

	REVENUE ($ mil.)	NET INCOME ($ mil.)	NET PROFIT MARGIN	EMPLOYEES
12/16*	48,016	0	—	20,128
01/16	48,144	0	—	—
12/12	37,389	0	—	—
01/09	29,800	0	—	—
Annual Growth	6.1%	—	—	—

*Fiscal year change

2016 Year-End Financials

Return on assets: 4.0%   Cash ($ mil.): 122
Return on equity: —
Current ratio: 0.60

MCLAREN REGIONAL MEDICAL CENTER

EXECUTIVES

Ceo, Donald Kooy
Ophthalmology, Edward Stack
Oncology, Brett Wheeler
Pathologist, Ernesto Quiachon
Director, Gayle Consiglio
Oncology, Hesham Gayar
Director of Radiology, Mark Camens
Director of Laboratory, James M Nielsen
Pathologist, Julio Badin
Pathologist, Nader B Hanna
Ophthalmology, Walter Cukrowski

LOCATIONS

HQ: MCLAREN REGIONAL MEDICAL CENTER
401 S BALLENGER HWY, FLINT, MI 485323638
Phone: 810 342-2000
Web: WWW.MCLAREN.ORG

HISTORICAL FINANCIALS

Company Type: Private

Income Statement   FYE: September 30

	REVENUE ($ mil.)	NET INCOME ($ mil.)	NET PROFIT MARGIN	EMPLOYEES
09/17	408	35	8.8%	2,250
09/16	415	26	6.4%	—
09/15	410	(6)	—	—
09/14	403	29	7.2%	—
Annual Growth	0.4%	7.1%	—	—

2017 Year-End Financials

Return on assets: 6.7%   Cash ($ mil.): 18
Return on equity: 8.8%
Current ratio: 0.80

MCLEOD REGIONAL MEDICAL CENTER OF THE PEE DEE, INC.

EXECUTIVES

Chb, Ronnie Ward
Ceo, Robert L Colones
Procurement Staff, George Nixon
Executive Officer, Brad Willbanks
Sam Poc, David Anderson
Internal Medicine Practitioner, Mahendrabhai Patel
Internal Medicine Practitioner, Worku Wondafrash

LOCATIONS

HQ: MCLEOD REGIONAL MEDICAL CENTER OF THE PEE DEE, INC.
555 E CHEVES ST, FLORENCE, SC 295062617
Phone: 843 777-2000
Web: WWW.MCLEODHEALTH.ORG

HISTORICAL FINANCIALS

Company Type: Private

Income Statement   FYE: September 30

	REVENUE ($ mil.)	NET INCOME ($ mil.)	NET PROFIT MARGIN	EMPLOYEES
09/15	607	72	11.8%	5,000
09/09	537	24	4.5%	—
09/08	577	49	8.5%	—
Annual Growth	0.7%	5.6%	—	—

2015 Year-End Financials

Return on assets: 3.4%   Cash ($ mil.): 13
Return on equity: 11.8%
Current ratio: 1.00

MCNAUGHTON-MCKAY ELECTRIC CO.

Getting connected at work has a completely different meaning at McNaughton-McKay. Its more than 10000 customers can buy electrical supplies sensors and controls and automation and security software online or through 23 branches in five US states and two offices in Germany and Brazil. One of the largest employee-owned companies in the US McNaughton-McKay distributes some 300 product lines from manufacturers such as Hubbell GE Brady Belden Coleman Cable Leviton Thomas & Betts Cognex Specter Instruments and Rockwell Automation. It sells to the construction commercial government and industrial automation markets.

Geographic Reach

The company serves more than 10000 customers through 23 branches in the US Germany and Brazil.

Sales and Marketing

The company sells its products from its sales offices and as well as eSales Centers. In addition to the industrial automation commercial and construction markets McNaughton-McKay supports government customers on a Federal State and Local level by providing hundreds of electrical products and MRO supplies with local support and inventory. McNaughton-McKay's customers include supplyFORCE Vanguard National Alliance and Vantage Group.

Strategy

McNaughton-McKay — informally known as Mc-Mc — has grown by expanding its product lineup and increasing its purchasing power through buying and marketing groups such as Affiliated Distributors supplyFORCE and Vantage Group. The distributor has also added a group dedicated to green products primarily energy-efficient lighting and power distribution products along with an Engineered Solutions Group that sells and installs solar and wind energy through partnerships with companies that include Schletter and Ohio Green Wind.

Company Background

Founded in 1910 the Bull and McNaughton families ran McNaughton-McKay until 2006. It established a sales office in Germany in 2004.

EXECUTIVES

Evp And, Donald D. (Don) Slominski
Evp Sales And Marketing, Richard (Rick) Dahlstrom
Vp Information Technology, Gregory H. (Greg) Chun
Vice President Human Resources, John D. Kuczmanski
Corporate Purchasing Manager, Maridee Curry
Auditors: KPMG LLP

LOCATIONS

HQ: MCNAUGHTON-MCKAY ELECTRIC CO.
1357 E LINCOLN AVE, MADISON HEIGHTS, MI 480714126
Phone: 248 399-7500
Web: WWW.MC-MC.COM

PRODUCTS/OPERATIONS

Selected Products

Bar code scanners and systems
Communication input/output (I/O) networks
Computers and peripherals
Convenience panels (cables and equipment)
Cordsets
Data-collection terminals and software
Drives and motor controllers
Engineered products
I/O products (AC/DC modules)
Motion-control products
  CNC controls
  Servos
  Spindles
Motors (AC)
PLC processors
Radio-frequency identification (RFID) products
Safety products
  Gate switches
  Light curtains
  Mats
  Relays
Sensors
Software
Vision products (inspection equipment)

COMPETITORS

Anixter International	Kendall Electric
Border States Electric	Madison Electric
Consolidated	Medler Electric
Electrical	OneSource Distributors
Crescent Electric	Rexel Inc.
Supply	SUMMIT Electric Supply
Dealers Electrical	Steiner Electric
Electrocomponents	Stuart C. Irby
Graybar Electric	W.W. Grainger
Hite Company	WESCO International

HISTORICAL FINANCIALS

Company Type: Private

Income Statement   FYE: December 31

	REVENUE ($ mil.)	NET INCOME ($ mil.)	NET PROFIT MARGIN	EMPLOYEES
12/17	822	0	—	854
12/16	724	0	—	—
12/15	702	0	—	—
12/14	689	0	—	—
Annual Growth	6.1%	—	—	—

2017 Year-End Financials

Return on assets: 6.9%   Cash ($ mil.): 26
Return on equity: —
Current ratio: 1.60

MCV ASSOCIATED PHYSICIANS

EXECUTIVES

President, John Ward
Administrative Assistant, S Brooks
Director of Human Resources, Qnne Pbuchren
Director, Greg Strickland
General Manager, Keith Purcell
Auditors: KPMG LLP MC LEAN VA

LOCATIONS

HQ: MCV ASSOCIATED PHYSICIANS
830 E MAIN ST STE 2400, RICHMOND, VA 232192703
Phone: 804 358-6100

HISTORICAL FINANCIALS

Company Type: Private

Income Statement   FYE: June 30

	REVENUE ($ mil.)	NET INCOME ($ mil.)	NET PROFIT MARGIN	EMPLOYEES
06/18	358	(21)	—	1,337
06/17	412	(0)	—	—
06/14	292	(6)	—	—
06/12	247	5	2.2%	—
Annual Growth	6.4%	—	—	—

2018 Year-End Financials

Return on assets: 0.3%   Cash ($ mil.): 19
Return on equity: (-6.0%)
Current ratio: 0.80

MEASE COUNTRYSIDE AMBULATORY CARE CENTER

EXECUTIVES

Principal, Lou Galdieri
Qa Qc Manager, Glenn Simpson
Manager, Kathleen Johnson

LOCATIONS

HQ: MEASE COUNTRYSIDE AMBULATORY CARE CENTER
3231 MCMULLEN BOOTH RD, SAFETY HARBOR, FL 346956607
Phone: 727 725-6111
Web: WWW.BAYCARE.ORG

HISTORICAL FINANCIALS

Company Type: Private

Income Statement   FYE: December 31

	REVENUE ($ mil.)	NET INCOME ($ mil.)	NET PROFIT MARGIN	EMPLOYEES
12/15	325	83	25.7%	28
12/14	298	69	23.4%	—
Annual Growth	9.2%	20.2%	—	—

2015 Year-End Financials

Return on assets: 1.6%   Cash ($ mil.): —
Return on equity: 25.7%
Current ratio: 3.30

MEDECINS SANS FRONTIERES U.S.A., INC

EXECUTIVES

Pres, Deane Marchbein
Cfo, Maureen Burnley
Exec Dir, Sophie Delaunay

Vice President, Aditya Nadimpalli
Office Manager, Beth Golden
Editor, Jason Cone
Officer, Lauren Ford
Manager, Michael Goldfarb
Director, Michelle Childs
Direct Marketing Associate, Nadine Ahrabi-Nejad
Auditors: TAIT WELLER & BAKER LLP PHILA

LOCATIONS

HQ: MEDECINS SANS FRONTIERES U.S.A., INC
   40 RECTOR ST FL 16, NEW YORK, NY 100061751
Phone: 212 679-6800
Web: WWW.DOCTORSWITHOUTBORDERS.ORG

HISTORICAL FINANCIALS

Company Type: Private

Income Statement				FYE: December 31
	REVENUE ($ mil.)	NET INCOME ($ mil.)	NET PROFIT MARGIN	EMPLOYEES
12/16	374	10	2.9%	100
12/13	221	4	2.1%	—
12/11	193	12	6.5%	—
12/09	144	(1)	—	—
Annual Growth	14.5%	—	—	—

2016 Year-End Financials

Return on assets: 2.0%   Cash ($ mil.): 58
Return on equity: 2.9%
Current ratio: —

MEDICAL CENTER OF THE ROCKIES

EXECUTIVES

Ceo, George Hayes
Exec Dir, Laurie Tuka
Asst Gen Council, Emily Weber
Director, Kyra Knapp
Case Manager, Kathy Kimball

LOCATIONS

HQ: MEDICAL CENTER OF THE ROCKIES
   2500 ROCKY MOUNTAIN AVE, LOVELAND, CO
   805389004
Phone: 970 624-2500
Web: WWW.UCHEALTH.ORG

HISTORICAL FINANCIALS

Company Type: Private

Income Statement				FYE: June 30
	REVENUE ($ mil.)	NET INCOME ($ mil.)	NET PROFIT MARGIN	EMPLOYEES
06/16	421	61	14.6%	4,000
06/15	403	68	16.9%	—
/*	0	0	—	—
Annual Growth	—	—	—	—

*Fiscal year change

2016 Year-End Financials

Return on assets: 2.4%   Cash ($ mil.): 4
Return on equity: 14.6%
Current ratio: 2.00

MEDICAL FACULTY ASSOCIATES, INC.

EXECUTIVES

Ceo, Stephen L Badger
Pres, Alan Waserman
SEC, Joseph Giordano
Cfo, Kenneth W Marter
Obstetrician/Gynecologist, Anna Maria Gray
Pathologist, Robert V Jones
Optometrists, Stanley Tempchin
Internal Medicine Practitioner, Cristina Amado
Internal Medicine Practitioner, Amanda Rudman
Ophthalmologist, Janet Leath
Internal Medicine Practitioner, Jehan El-Bayoumi

LOCATIONS

HQ: MEDICAL FACULTY ASSOCIATES, INC.
   2150 PENNSYLVANIA AVE NW, WASHINGTON, DC
   200373201
Phone: 202 741-3000
Web: WWW.GWDOCS.COM

HISTORICAL FINANCIALS

Company Type: Private

Income Statement				FYE: June 30
	REVENUE ($ mil.)	NET INCOME ($ mil.)	NET PROFIT MARGIN	EMPLOYEES
06/16	404	(18)	—	1,600
06/15	363	2	0.7%	—
06/13	329	0	0.1%	—
06/12	337	11	3.4%	—
Annual Growth	4.6%	—	—	—

MEDSTAR HEALTH, INC.

Whether you're seeing stars or are just plain sickly MedStar Health can cater to you. The not-for-profit organization runs 10 hospitals and about 20 other health-related businesses across Maryland and the Washington DC area including Union Memorial and Georgetown University Hospital. With more than 3000 beds and 6000 affiliated physicians MedStar has a comprehensive service offering including acute and long-term sub-acute care emergency services home health care and rehabilitation. It also operates emergency clinics and assisted living and nursing homes maintains a primary care and specialist physician network (MedStar Physician Partners) and conducts research and medical education activities.

Operations

Along with its 10 hospitals and a dizzying array of inpatient and outpatient services MedStar Health also operates a Medicaid managed care program called MedStar Family Choice.

Its Nascott Orthotics and Prosthetics division provides adult and pediatric prosthetic services and devices to patients in Washington DC and Baltimore. The company provides a continuum of care from initial measurement to fabrication of the device and maintenance through four locations scattered throughout the service areas.

MedStar Health's Visiting Nurse Association (VNA) administers home health care infusion services private duty nursing and hospice as well as immunizations. The VNA also uses telemonitoring services to keep tabs on home care patients without having to physically visit each patient's home.

In 2014 the system had 148685 inpatient admissions and nearly 4 million outpatient visits.

Financial Performance

In fiscal 2014 MedStar Health's net operating revenue totaled $4.6 billion.

Strategy

Despite its already hefty size MedStar Health is not adverse to getting bigger. It grows usually through acquisitions of existing facilities but also through alliances with other health care providers. MedStar Health has acquired several hospitals in recent years including St. Mary's Hospital with 100 beds in southern Maryland and Montgomery General Hospital a 150-bed general acute care facility located in Montgomery County Maryland.

The company also grows by establishing new facilities. In 2014 it opened an integrated multi-specialty care center in downtown Baltimore as well as four new PromptCare locations in Maryland and Virginia. That year it began work on a new ambulatory care center at the 16-acre MedStar Health Bel Air Medical Campus. MedStar is also developing a new ambulatory care center at Lafayette Centre in northwest Washington DC.

MedStar Health has also entered the growing quick-care and urgent care market by partnering with Rite Aid to establish walk-in health clinics in a number of Rite Aid pharmacies throughout the Baltimore and Washington DC markets.

In 2015 the system expanded its Medicare Choice plan into Baltimore City and Anne Arundel Baltimore Charles Prince George's and St. Mary's counties.

EXECUTIVES

Evp Insurance And Diversified Operations, Eric R. Wagner
Evp And Chief Administrative Officer, Michael J. Curran
Evp And Coo, M. Joy Drass
President Medstar Ambulatory Services, Bob Gilbert
Svp And President Medstar Good Samaritan Hospital And Medstar Union Memorial Hospital, Bradley S. Chambers
Svp And Chief Nursing Officer, Maureen P. McCausland
President Medstar Medical Group, Richard Goldberg
President Ceo And Director, Kenneth A. Samet
President Medstar Visiting Nurse Association, Traci K. Anderson
Evp Medical Affairs And Chief Medical Officer, Stephen R. T. Evans
Svp And President Medstar National Rehabilitation Network, John D. Rockwood
President Medstar Health Research Institute, Neil J. Weissman
Svp And President Medstar Southern Maryland Hospital Center And St. Mary's Hospital, Christine R. Wray
Svp And President Medstar Franklin Square Medical Center, Samuel E. Moskowitz
Evp And General Counsel, Oliver M. Johnson
Svp And President Medstar Washington Hospital Center, John Sullivan
Svp Marketing And Strategy, Kevin P. Kowalski
Vp Applications And Interim Cio, Mark K. Schneider
Svp And President Medstar Georgetown University Hospital, Michael C. Sachtleben
Svp And President Medstar Montgomery Medical Center, T. J. Senker
Assistant Vice President Infrastructure And Operations, Charles Burchinal
Director Of Nursing, Diana Langhauser
Chairman, William R. Roberts
Vice Chairman, William J. Oetgen

LOCATIONS

HQ: MEDSTAR HEALTH, INC.
10980 GRANTCHESTER WAY, COLUMBIA, MD
210446097
Phone: 410 772-6500
Web: WWW.MEDSTARHEALTH.ORG

Selected Facilities
Maryland
Franklin Square Hospital Center (Baltimore)
Good Samaritan Hospital (Baltimore)
Harbor Hospital (Baltimore)
Montgomery General Hospital (Olney)
St. Mary's Hospital (Leonardtown)
Union Memorial Hospital (Baltimore)
Washington DC
Georgetown University Hospital
National Rehabilitation Hospital
Washington Hospital Center

PRODUCTS/OPERATIONS

Selected Affiliates/Operations
Clinical Research
Georgetown University Medical Center (Washington DC)
MedStar Research Institute (Hyattsville Maryland)
Home Health Care
MedStar Health VNA (Washington DC)
MedStar Health Infusion (Elkridge Maryland)
MGH Community Health (Olney Maryland)
Managed Care
MedStar Family Choice (Baltimore Maryland)
Nursing Homes/Senior Living
Franklin Woods (Rosedale Maryland)
Good Samaritan Nursing Center (Baltimore Maryland)
Belvedere Green (Baltimore Maryland)
Woodbourne Woods (Baltimore Maryland)
Primary Care
MedStar Physician Partners (Washington DC)
Outpatient Surgery Centers
MedStar Surgery Center (Washington DC)
Harbor Hospital HealthPark (Pasadena Maryland)
SurgiCenter at Pasadena (Pasadena Maryland)

COMPETITORS

Adventist HealthCare
Anne Arundel Medical Center
Ascension Health
Bon Secours Health
Carilion Clinic
Children's National Medical Center
Christiana Care
Civista Health
Franklin Square Hospital Center
GBMC
Harbor Hospital
Inova
Johns Hopkins Health System
Johns Hopkins Medicine
Kaiser Foundation Health Plan of the Mid-Atlantic
Levindale Hospital
LifeBridge Health
MedStar Union Memorial Hospital
Sinai Hospital of Baltimore
Suburban Hospital
Trinity Health (Novi)
University of Maryland Medical System
Valley Health
Virginia Hospital Center

HISTORICAL FINANCIALS
Company Type: Private

Income Statement				FYE: June 30
	REVENUE ($ mil.)	NET INCOME ($ mil.)	NET PROFIT MARGIN	EMPLOYEES
06/18	5,604	324	5.8%	33,000
06/13	4,217	311	7.4%	—
06/11*	4,011	271	6.8%	—
12/09	1,936	200	10.4%	—
Annual Growth	14.2%	6.2%	—	—

*Fiscal year change

2018 Year-End Financials

Return on assets: 8.4%   Cash ($ mil.): 692
Return on equity: 5.8%
Current ratio: 1.00

MEDSTAR-GEORGETOWN MEDICAL CENTER, INC.

Medstar-Georgetown Medical Center (dba as Medstar Georgetown University Hospital as a part of MedStar Health) is a 609-bed acute care teaching hospital serving residents of the greater Washington DC area including Maryland and Virginia. The hospital's staff of more than 1100 physicians represents a wide range of medical specializations including cardiology oncology neurology/neurosurgery and surgical transplantation. Medstar Georgetown provides a comprehensive array of inpatient outpatient surgical and rehabilitative care services. The hospital is part of a local network of affiliated primary care providers.

Operations
Medstar Georgetown's Transplant Institute is one of a handful of centers in the US that offers living-donor liver transplants; it opened a new medical space in 2014. Also Georgetown Neurosciences is the sixth unit nationwide to provide CyberKnife stereotactic radiosurgery for the treatment of tumors and lesions of the brain neck and spine.

Strategy
In 2015 Medstar Georgetown submitted a letter of intent with the District of Columbia State Health Planning and Development Agency seeking approval to modernize its existing medical facility by constructing a new state-of-the-art medical surgical pavilion. The pavilion will house surgical critical care and emergency departments as well as related administrative functions.

In 2014 MedStar Georgetown became the first center in Washington DC to perform a two-level artificial disc replacement in a patient's neck.

Company Background
In 2011 Medstar Georgetown became the first health system in the area to offer bloodless surgery to patients who prefer not to receive someone else's blood usually for religious reasons. There are three primary approaches to performing bloodless surgeries: before during and after surgery. Before surgery the hospital gives the patient medications such as iron supplements or epoprotein to boost the blood's hemoglobin level. During surgery the hospital is precise as it can be with its surgical techniques to limit blood loss and there are anesthesia techniques to lower blood pressure so patients bleed less. There is also a machine called Cell Saver that is used during surgery that collects blood lost suctions it into a canister washes and filters it and then returns it directly into the patient as a product that is about 60-percent pure red blood cells. After surgery medications are used to raise blood levels and medical providers avoid taking multiple blood draws for blood tests.

The hospital was founded in 1898 to promote health through education research and patient care. The current hospital/medical center was opened in 1947.

EXECUTIVES

Assistant Vice President Perioperative S, Frances Baldwin
Vice President Of Marketing And Public Affairs, Karen Alcorn
Medical Director, Maral Skelsey

LOCATIONS

HQ: MEDSTAR-GEORGETOWN MEDICAL CENTER, INC.
3800 RESERVOIR RD NW, WASHINGTON, DC
200072113
Phone: 202 444-2000
Web: WWW.MEDSTARGEORGETOWN.ORG

PRODUCTS/OPERATIONS

Selected Services
Anesthesiology
Audiology
Bloodless Medicine and Surgery Program
Bone Marrow Transplant
Breast Cancer
Breast Health Program
Cancer Care
Cardiology
Cerebrovascular Center
Colon and Rectal Surgery
Ear Nose and Throat (ENT)
Emergency Urgent Care and Trauma
Endocrinology
Epilepsy
Family Medicine
Fracture Liaison
Head and Neck Cancer
Headache Center
Hematology
Hospital Medicine
Huntington Disease Center
Hyperbaric Oxygen Therapy
Ophthalmology
Orthopaedics
Ostomy Clinic
Otolaryngology
Pastoral Care
Pediatrics
Pharmacy
Physical Medicine
Plastic Surgery
Primary Care
Prostate Cancer

COMPETITORS

Adventist HealthCare
Bon Secours Health
Calvert Memorial Hospital
Children's National Medical Center
Chindex International
Dimensions Healthcare
Doctors Community Hospital
Inova Alexandria Hospital
Providence St. Joseph Health
Suburban Hospital
Upper Chesapeake Health

HISTORICAL FINANCIALS
Company Type: Private

Income Statement				FYE: June 30
	REVENUE ($ mil.)	NET INCOME ($ mil.)	NET PROFIT MARGIN	EMPLOYEES
06/16	801	104	13.1%	4,000
06/15	774	98	12.7%	—
06/11	809	43	5.4%	—
06/10	782	45	5.8%	—
Annual Growth	0.4%	15.0%	—	—

2016 Year-End Financials

Return on assets: 7.8%   Cash ($ mil.): 5
Return on equity: 13.1%
Current ratio: 1.70

MEMORIAL HEALTH CARE SYSTEM, INC.

EXECUTIVES

Pres, James M Hobson
President, Shawn Morrow
Sr Vice President, Debra L Moore
Cfo, Cheryl A Sadro
Vice President, Leigh Bertholf
Vice President, Diona Brown
Auditors: CATHOLIC HEALTH INITIATIVES E

LOCATIONS

HQ: MEMORIAL HEALTH CARE SYSTEM, INC.
2525 DESALES AVE, CHATTANOOGA, TN 374041161
Phone: 423 495-2525
Web: WWW.MEMORIAL.ORG

HISTORICAL FINANCIALS
Company Type: Private

Income Statement				FYE: June 30
	REVENUE ($ mil.)	NET INCOME ($ mil.)	NET PROFIT MARGIN	EMPLOYEES
06/16	545	22	4.1%	8,800
06/15	527	34	6.6%	—
06/14	557	25	4.6%	—
Annual Growth	(1.1%)	(6.0%)	—	—

2016 Year-End Financials
Return on assets: 13.9%   Cash ($ mil.): 238
Return on equity: 4.1%
Current ratio: 3.00

MEMORIAL HEALTH SERVICES

Where do you go after you get sick riding the tea cups at Disneyland? Not-for-profit Memorial Health Services (known as MemorialCare) owns six hospitals in Southern California including Long Beach Memorial Medical Center Miller Children's Hospital Orange Coast Memorial Medical Center and Saddleback Memorial Medical Center. The facilities have a total of more than 1500 beds and offer a full spectrum of medical services including rehabilitation diagnostic/radiology and emergency services. MemorialCare also operates women's health facilities and other specialty and general practice clinics as well as home health and hospice programs. The organization was founded in 1907.

Operations
MemorialCare's outpatient facilities include the physician practices of the MemorialCare Medical Group the Memorial Prompt Care urgent care centers and the MemorialCare HealthExpress clinics. The network also includes the affiliated practices of the Greater Newport Physicians organization. In addition to inpatient outpatient and home medical care the organization provides clinical training and graduate medical education programs.

Altogether the system's facilities employ 2600 physicians and serve 70000 inpatients each year. They also handle some 35000 surgeries 10000 births 200000 emergency room visits and 40000 home health visits.

Geographic Reach
MemorialCare's facilities are located in Los Angeles County and Orange County in Southern California.

Financial Performance
MemorialCare reported $1.9 billion in revenues and $83 million in net income in 2012. Most of the organization's revenues come from patient services.

Strategy
MemorialCare is expanding to meet continued demand throughout its service area. It has several projects either going on or recently completed that have added operating rooms neonatal beds more advanced technology and centers of excellence in imaging cardiac cancer and obesity at several of its hospitals. In 2014 it opened the new Lung Nodule Center at The MemorialCare Todd Cancer Institute part of Long Beach Memorial.

The organization is also expanding its outpatient care facilities. For instance MemorialCare has joined the growing trend of hospitals partnering with retailers to open in-store retail clinics (under the HealthExpress brand) that offer basic after-hours medical care through physicians and nurse practitioners. It has recently opened four new outpatient surgery centers and launched a couple of new physician locations in affiliation with UC Irvine Health.

EXECUTIVES

Senior Vice President Chief Financial Officer, Cheryl Sadro
President Ceo, James Hobson
Information Technology Vice President, Steven Beal
Medical Librarian, Veena Vyas
Medical Director Of Breast Surgery, Jane Kakkis
Chairman, Keith Nelson
Auditors: PRICEWATERHOUSECOOPERS LLP LO

LOCATIONS

HQ: MEMORIAL HEALTH SERVICES
17360 BROOKHURST ST # 160, FOUNTAIN VALLEY, CA 927088003
Phone: 714 377-6748
Web: WWW.MEMORIALCARE.ORG

Selected Facilities
Long Beach Memorial Medical Center (Long Beach California)
Miller Children's Hospital (Long Beach California)
Community Hospital (Long Beach California)
Orange Coast Memorial Medical Center (Fountain Valley California)
Saddleback Memorial Medical Center (San Clemente California)
Saddleback Memorial Medical Center (Laguna Hills California)
MemorialCare Medical Group (regional)
MemorialCare HealthExpress (regional)
MemorialCare Imaging Centers (regional)
Memorial Prompt Care (regional)

PRODUCTS/OPERATIONS

Selected Services
Blood Donation
Diabetes Care
Heart and Vascular Care
Joint Replacement
Neonatal Intensive Care
Rehabilitation and Therapy
Wellness Care
Cancer Care
Gynecological Care
Imaging and Radiology
Maternity Care
Orthopedic Care
Stroke Care
Wound Healing
Breast Care
Express Care
Hyperbaric Medicine
Laboratory Services
Pediatric Care
Surgical Care
Women's Care

COMPETITORS

Adventist Health System West
Cedars-Sinai Medical Center
Childrens Hospital Los Angeles
Community Health Systems
Dignity Health
Good Samaritan Hospital (IN)
Good Samaritan Hospital (Los Angeles)
HCA
HealthCare Partners
Hollywood Presbyterian Medical Center
LifePoint Health
Methodist Hospital of Southern California
Pasadena Hospital Association
Prospect Medical
Providence St. Joseph Health
St. Jude Medical Center
Sutter Health
Tenet Healthcare
Trinity Health (Novi)
Western Medical Center - Santa Ana

HISTORICAL FINANCIALS
Company Type: Private

Income Statement				FYE: June 30
	REVENUE ($ mil.)	NET INCOME ($ mil.)	NET PROFIT MARGIN	EMPLOYEES
06/18	2,232	101	4.5%	6,000
06/15	215	26	12.3%	—
Annual Growth	117.8%	56.3%	—	—

2018 Year-End Financials
Return on assets: 5.7%   Cash ($ mil.): 122
Return on equity: 4.5%
Current ratio: 0.50

MEMORIAL HEALTH SYSTEMS, INC.

EXECUTIVES

Pres, Daryl Tol
Coo, Darwinda Copeland
Cfo, Debbie Thomas
Cmo, Michelle Goeb-Burkett
Accountant, Tim W
Administrative Assistant, Henry Miller
Nurse Manager, Denise Duty
Nurse Manager, Denise Halligan
Director Anesthesiolog, Michael Longfellow
Infection Control Director, April Pojero
Case Management Director, Denise McDowell

LOCATIONS

HQ: MEMORIAL HEALTH SYSTEMS, INC.
301 MEMORIAL MEDICAL PKWY, DAYTONA BEACH, FL 321175167
Phone: 386 231-6000
Web: WWW.FHMMC.ORG

HISTORICAL FINANCIALS
Company Type: Private

Income Statement				FYE: December 31
	REVENUE ($ mil.)	NET INCOME ($ mil.)	NET PROFIT MARGIN	EMPLOYEES
12/15*	295	23	7.9%	1,500
09/12	754	47	6.3%	—
03/11	364	40	11.0%	—
Annual Growth	(4.1%)	(10.2%)	—	—

2015 Year-End Financials

Return on assets: 4.7%	Cash ($ mil.): 148
Return on equity: 7.9%	
Current ratio: 3.40	

MEMORIAL HEALTH, INC.

EXECUTIVES

Pres, Margaret Gill
Administrative Secretary, Barbara Roundtree
Auditors: DIXON HUGHES GOODMAN LLP ASHE

LOCATIONS

HQ: MEMORIAL HEALTH, INC.
4700 WATERS AVE, SAVANNAH, GA 314046220
Phone: 912 350-8000
Web: WWW.MEMORIALHEALTH.COM

HISTORICAL FINANCIALS

Company Type: Private

Income Statement				FYE: December 31
	REVENUE ($ mil.)	NET INCOME ($ mil.)	NET PROFIT MARGIN	EMPLOYEES
12/16	581	(38)	—	4,500
12/14	42	(11)	—	—
12/13	24	0	—	—
Annual Growth	185.6%	—	—	—

2016 Year-End Financials

Return on assets: 11.2%	Cash ($ mil.): 16
Return on equity: (-6.6%)	
Current ratio: 1.10	

MEMORIAL HERMANN HEALTH SYSTEM

EXECUTIVES

Ceo, Charles Stokes
Cfo, Dennis Laraway
Chief of Medicine, Todd M Price
Information Technology Manager, Joe Dickson
Coordinator, Melissa Aing
Director of Radiology, Alla Vargo
Secretary, Aida Guerra
Lead Project Manager, Chuck Dickson
Director of Nursing, Daniel Kelly
Neurologist, Joanne Y Kim
Educator, Linda Whitson
Auditors: ERNST & YOUNG LLP HOUSTON TX

LOCATIONS

HQ: MEMORIAL HERMANN HEALTH SYSTEM
929 GESSNER RD STE 1900, HOUSTON, TX
770242317
Phone: 713 242-3000
Web: WWW.MEMORIALHERMANN.ORG

HISTORICAL FINANCIALS

Company Type: Private

Income Statement				FYE: June 30
	REVENUE ($ mil.)	NET INCOME ($ mil.)	NET PROFIT MARGIN	EMPLOYEES
06/18	5,258	318	6.1%	14,000
06/17	5,061	313	6.2%	—
06/14	3,741	454	12.1%	—
06/13	3,285	230	7.0%	—
Annual Growth	9.9%	6.6%	—	—

2018 Year-End Financials

Return on assets: 5.7%	Cash ($ mil.): 371
Return on equity: 6.1%	
Current ratio: 0.80	

MEMORIAL HOSPITAL CORPORATION

EXECUTIVES

Vp Of Physician Services, Vivek Abhyankar

LOCATIONS

HQ: MEMORIAL HOSPITAL CORPORATION
1400 E BOULDER ST, COLORADO SPRINGS, CO
809095599
Phone: 719 365-5000
Web: WWW.MEMORIALHEALTHSYSTEM.COM

COMPETITORS

Banner Health	The Memorial Hospital
Centura Health	University of Colorado
Exempla Healthcare	Hospital
HealthONE	Valley View Hospital
Poudre Valley Health	
System	

HISTORICAL FINANCIALS

Company Type: Private

Income Statement				FYE: June 30
	REVENUE ($ mil.)	NET INCOME ($ mil.)	NET PROFIT MARGIN	EMPLOYEES
06/16	693	25	3.7%	2,438
06/15	612	34	5.6%	—
/*	0	0	—	—
Annual Growth	—	—	—	—

*Fiscal year change

2016 Year-End Financials

Return on assets: 3.1%	Cash ($ mil.): 4
Return on equity: 3.7%	
Current ratio: 0.60	

MEMORIAL HOSPITAL OF LARAMIE COUNTY

EXECUTIVES

Ceo, John Lucas
Cfo, Kerry Warburton
Vice President, Ashutosh Goel
Vice-President, Debbie Nunley
Public Relations Manager, Kathy Baker
Office Manager, Leonard Geringer
Pharmacist, William Harrison
Interim Manager, Arlene Flood
Manager, Bonnie Raner
Information Technology Manager, Jody Siltzer
Information Technology Manager, Mark Bohm

LOCATIONS

HQ: MEMORIAL HOSPITAL OF LARAMIE COUNTY
214 E 23RD ST, CHEYENNE, WY 820013748
Phone: 307 633-7667
Web: WWW.CHEYENNEREGIONAL.ORG

HISTORICAL FINANCIALS

Company Type: Private

Income Statement				FYE: June 30
	REVENUE ($ mil.)	NET INCOME ($ mil.)	NET PROFIT MARGIN	EMPLOYEES
06/18	344	7	2.3%	1,270
06/17	338	18	5.5%	—
06/16	297	12	4.4%	—
06/15	279	9	3.5%	—
Annual Growth	7.2%	(6.9%)	—	—

2018 Year-End Financials

Return on assets: 1.9%	Cash ($ mil.): 38
Return on equity: 2.3%	
Current ratio: 3.00	

MEMORIAL MEDICAL CENTER

EXECUTIVES

Physical Therapy Director, Jason Beeler
Medical Director, David Gelber
Auditors: ERNST & YOUNG LLP ST LOUIS

LOCATIONS

HQ: MEMORIAL MEDICAL CENTER
701 N 1ST ST, SPRINGFIELD, IL 627810001
Phone: 217 788-3000
Web: WWW.MEMORIALMEDICAL.COM

PRODUCTS/OPERATIONS

Selected Services
Bariatric Services
Behavioral Health
Regional Burn Center
Regional Cancer Center
Da Vinci Robotic Surgery
EEG
Emergency Department
Express Care
Family Maternity
Food Nutrition Counseling
Healthcare Psychology
Hearing Center
Heart and Vascular Services
Intensive Care Unit
Industrial Rehab
JointWorks
Lab Services
Medical Imaging Services
Neurosciences
Orthopedic Services
Palliative Care
Rehab Services
Sleep Disorder Center
SpineWorks
SportsCare
Stroke Center

Surgical Services
Transplant Services
Would Healing Center

COMPETITORS

Decatur Memorial
  Hospital
Hospital Sisters
  Health System
OSF Healthcare System

Sarah Bush Lincoln
  Health Center
St. John's Hospital
  (Illinois)

HISTORICAL FINANCIALS

Company Type: Private

Income Statement   FYE: September 30

	REVENUE ($ mil.)	NET INCOME ($ mil.)	NET PROFIT MARGIN	EMPLOYEES
09/17	682	63	9.3%	2,849
09/16	699	12	1.8%	
09/15	667	(28)	—	
09/14	1,850	78	4.3%	
Annual Growth	(28.3%)	(6.9%)	—	—

2017 Year-End Financials

Return on assets: 5.5%   Cash ($ mil.): 61
Return on equity: 9.3%
Current ratio: 1.60

MEMORIAL SLOAN-KETTERING CANCER CENTER

Memorial Sloan-Kettering Cancer Center (MSKCC) leads the way in cancer research and treatment. The center includes the 470-bed Memorial Hospital for Cancer and Allied Diseases providing pediatric and adult cancer care and the Sloan-Kettering Institute for cancer research activities. Memorial Hospital specializes in bone-marrow transplants radiation therapy and chemotherapy and it offers programs in cancer prevention diagnosis treatment research and education. The Sloan-Kettering Institute conducts medical and clinical laboratory research on cancer genetics and therapeutics.The hospital was founded in 1884 as the New York Cancer Center by a group that included John Astor and his wife Charlotte.

Operations

MSKCC includes the 470-bed Memorial Hospital for Cancer and Allied Diseases and the Sloan-Kettering Institute for cancer research activities. It has more than 20 surgical suites and the Center for Image-Guided Interventions.

MSKCC also provides cancer care through partnerships with some acute-care hospitals in the region such as Phelps Memorial Hospital Center and Mercy Medical Center. The health care organization also has partnerships with Rockefeller University and Cornell University through which it provides medical training to oncology professionals.

The hospital's clinical staff is made up of more than 900 attending physicians and over 2200 registered nurses. MSKCC also has over 140 senior laboratory investigators 320-plus research fellows more than 540 postdoctoral researchers and nearly 250 PhD- and MD/PhD- graduate students.

MSKCC's physicians treat more than 400 different subtypes of cancer each year. In 2013 the network saw nearly 137000 patients and admitted nearly a sixth of them to Memorial Hospital.

Geographic Reach

Memorial Hospital is located in New York City. Memorial Sloan-Kettering Cancer Center (MSKCC) offers outpatient services from about a dozen Manhattan Long Island and New Jersey clinic locations.

Financial Performance

To keep its various projects and clinical trials funded MSKCC counts on grants from a number of biomedical research institutions including the National Institutes of Health and the National Cancer Institute. It also receives a good portion of its cash through fundraising efforts and philanthropic donations.

MSKCC's revenue grew by 8% to $3 billion in 2013 mostly thanks to higher patient care revenue but also thanks to increased grants and contracts contributions allocated to operations and royalty income. Higher revenue and tight control on operating expense growth also helped net income jump by 95% to $178 million in 2013.

Strategy

To provide the most comprehensive and effective care for cancer patients MSKCC's Sloan-Kettering Institute researchers work with physicians to research cancer care techniques. The institute also conducts clinical trials to develop new cancer pharmaceuticals. At any given time Sloan-Kettering Institute is engaged in hundreds of clinical trials for pediatric and adult cancers.

MSKCC has expanded over the years by renovating existing centers and adding new outpatient facilities. In late 2014 for example it opened its sixth outpatient treatment center in the suburbs of West Harrison New York and also announced that it would begin building a new facility in Middletown New Jersey.

Using generous contributions the health network has been investing in research centers designed to further next-generation medical treatments. In 2014 MSKCC opened the Center for Molecular Imaging and Nanotechnology (CMINT) to accelerate research on the biology of cancers and further the development of new diagnostic and prognostic tools and treatments which include molecularity-based image-guided therapies. In 2013 it opened several new research centers aimed at capturing genetic information from tumors and exploiting its full potential to the medical field including the $100 million Marie Josee and Henry R. Kravis Center for Molecular Oncology (CMO).

In 2012 the center spent $2.2 billion on a clinical expansion aimed at treating blood head and neck and thoracic cancers while providing an outpatient bone marrow transplant facility and a place for early stage clinical trials among other things. It also announced a collaboration with IBM to build a tool that gives doctors access to more and better cancer data.

Company Background

The institute was founded in 1945 by Alfred Sloan and Charles Kettering to research new cancer cures; it merged with Memorial Hospital in 1980.

EXECUTIVES

Svp Information Systems And Cio, Patricia C. Skarulis
Evp And Cfo, Michael P. Gutnick
Coo, Kathryn Martin
Vp Facilities Management, Edward J. Mahoney
Vp International Programs And Benno C. Schmidt Chair In Clinical Oncology, Murray F. Brennan, age 77
President And Ceo, Craig B. Thompson, age 65
Vice President Research And Technology Management, Eric M. Cottington

Svp And Chief Investment Officer, Jason Klein
Physician-in-chief And Chief Medical Officer Memorial Hospital, José Baselga
Chairman Department Of Surgery, Jeffrey A. Drebin
Evp And Hospital Administrator, Ned Groves
Evp And General Counsel, Jorge Lopez
Vice President Human Resources, Kerry Bessey
Vice President Human Resources Operations And Information Systems, Bill Morgan
Vice President, Tomya Ryans
Vice President Systems Development Information Systems, Janet Mak
Senior Vice President Patient Revenues, Ruth Lande
Director Of Radiology, Linda Aboody
Senior Vice President And Chief Information Technology Officer, Anna A Spitzer
Senior Vice President Strategic Partnerships, James Harden
Vice President And Chief Information Security Officer, Michael Czumak
Operating Room Director, Tuhin Das
Secretary Iv, Sorita Alvarez
Secretary V, Lucy Jacobino
Secretary Iv, Carol Bencivenga
Secretary V, Noila Johnson
Secretary, Simone Joseph
Secretary Iv, Michele Black
Board Member, J Stewart
Secretary, Maire Brennan
Secretary, Gnana Krishnamoorthy

LOCATIONS

HQ: MEMORIAL SLOAN-KETTERING CANCER CENTER
  1275 YORK AVE, NEW YORK, NY 100656007
Phone: 212 639-2000
Web: WWW.MSKCC.ORG

PRODUCTS/OPERATIONS

2013 Sales

	$ mil.	% of total
Patient care	2,367	78
Grants and contracts	202	7
Other	455	15
Total	3,025	100

COMPETITORS

Aptium Oncology
City of Hope
Columbia University Continuum Health Partners
Dana-Farber
Fox Chase Cancer Center
Johns Hopkins Medicine
MD Anderson Cancer Center
Mayo Clinic
New York City Health and Hospitals

NewYork-Presbyterian Healthcare
Northwell Health
Partners HealthCare
Roswell Park Cancer Institute
Sandford Burnham Institute
St. Jude Children's Research Hospital
Wistar Institute

HISTORICAL FINANCIALS

Company Type: Private

Income Statement   FYE: December 31

	REVENUE ($ mil.)	NET INCOME ($ mil.)	NET PROFIT MARGIN	EMPLOYEES
12/15	2,220	190	8.6%	9,325
12/13	582	0	0.2%	—
12/09	2,105	(195)	—	—
12/06	1,622	320	19.8%	—
Annual Growth	3.5%	(5.6%)	—	—

2015 Year-End Financials

Return on assets: 6.9%   Cash ($ mil.): —
Return on equity: 8.6%
Current ratio: 0.70

MENTOR GRAPHICS CORPORATION

Mentor Graphics lends a hand to guide engineers who design electronic components. The company is a leading global developer of electronic design automation (EDA) software and systems used by engineers to design simulate and test electronic components such as integrated circuits (IC's) wire harness systems and printed circuit boards (PCBs). Products include PADS (PCB design) Nucleus (operating system) and Calibre (IC design). Its software is used to design components for such products as computers and wireless handsets. Clients come from the aerospace IT telecommunications and increasingly transportation industries. Mentor Graphics was acquired by Siemens for $4.5 billion in 2017.

Change in Company Type
Mentor Graphics supplies a crucial set of software products to help Siemens fill out its portfolio. The companies agreed to the $4.5billion deal in 2016 and it was finalized in 2017. Mentor Graphics became part of the Siemens PLM Software business in the Siemens Digital Factory division. Mentor?s system design product portfolio adds to Siemens? Digital Enterprise strategy bolstering model-driven design methodologies with Mentor?s electronic system design expertise.

Operations
Mentor Graphics creates system and software products most of which are sold through term software license contracts. It also provides service and support including professional services consulting training and other services.

Geographic Reach
Based in Wilsonville Oregon Mentor Graphics has US research and development operations in Colorado Washington Alabama and Massachusetts. It also conducts R&D in Armenia Egypt France Germany Hungary India Israel Pakistan Poland Russia Taiwan and the UK.

Financial Performance
Mentor Graphics reported increases in revenue and profit in 2017 (ended January). The company?s sales rose 9% to $1.3 billion in 2017 from 2016 and profit shot up 60% to $155 million for the year. The company had robust growth in all geographic markets except for the US its biggest market with about 40% of sales. Japan was particularly strong in 2017 with sales jumping more than 35% while sales rose about 15% each in the Pacific Rim and Europe. The company credited the overseas growth to the timing of contract renewals and blamed the North America decline of 3% on weaker sales of emulation hardware systems and a slower rate of contract renewals for the year.

The 60% rise in profit to $1.3 billion in 2017 resulted from higher sales combined with lower special charges in 2017 from 2016. The higher profit helped boost cash flow from operations to $322 million in 2017 from $228 million in 2016.

Strategy
Mentor Graphics is moving to apply its processes to new businesses. The automotive business is one example. It has grown to 20% of Mentor Graphics' revenue in several years. The company is keen on driving its products into other transportation areas such as the design of electronic components in airplanes and trains.

HISTORY

Mentor Graphics was founded in 1981 by a group from instrument maker Tektronix to market desktop computers to design engineers. Throughout the 1980s the company was a leader in electronic design automation (EDA) software but the early 1990s found it in trouble. Revenues fell because of delays in upgrade releases and a worldwide recession.

In 1992 Mentor Graphics began phasing out hardware sales further disrupting operations. Texas Instruments veteran Walden Rhines became CEO in 1993. That year the company acquired CheckLogic a maker of testing software for integrated circuit (IC) design. By 1994 cost-cutting and product line restructuring returned Mentor to profitability.

The company bought ANACAD which developed design software for analog and mixed-signal ICs and Model Technology a very-high-density logic simulation tool firm in 1994. It acquired 14 more companies in 1995 and 1996 including embedded software tool developer Microtec Research (1996) which moved Mentor into the market for software development tools.

EXECUTIVES

Vice President, Henry Potts
Vice President Global Accounts, Don Cantow
President, Gregory K. (Greg) Hinckley, $619,000 total compensation
Chairman And Ceo, Walden C. (Wally) Rhines, $761,000 total compensation
Vp And General Manager Deep Submicron Division, Robert Hum, $319,725 total compensation
Vp Corporate Marketing, Brian Derrick, $350,000 total compensation
Vp Europe And India, Hanns Windele
Vp And General Manager Design-to-silicon, Joseph D. (Joe) Sawicki, $345,000 total compensation
Vp And General Manager Mentor Emulation, Eric Selosse
General Manager System-level Engineering, Serge Leef
Vp And General Manager Embedded Software Division, Glenn Perry
General Manager China Region, Danny Perng
Vp Worldwide Consulting, Paul Hofstadler
Vp And Cio, Ananthan Thandri
Vp Focus Products Organization, Erich Buergel
President And Managing Director Mentor Graphics Japan Co. Ltd., Yukio Tsuchida
Vp And General Manager Board Systems Division, A.J. Incorvaia
Vp And General Manager Integrated Electrical Systems Division, Martin OÅ'Brien
Vice President Manager Director, Matthew Miller
Vice President Manager Diretor, Subba Somanchi
Executive Vice President Of Human Resources, Susan Evans
Vice President Of Engineering, Guy Insley
Vice President Engineering, Juan Rey
Vice President, Dean Freed
Vice President Of Engineering, Nafees Qureshy
Board Member, Kurt Takara
Treasurer, Ethan Manuel
Auditors: KPMG LLP PORTLAND OREGON

LOCATIONS

HQ: MENTOR GRAPHICS CORPORATION
8005 SW BOECKMAN RD, WILSONVILLE, OR 970707777
Phone: 503 685-7000
Web: WWW.MENTORG.COM

2016 Sales

	$ mil.	% of total
United States	488	41
Europe	254	22
Japan	87	7
Pacific Rim	335	29
Other	15	1
Total	**1,181**	**100**

PRODUCTS/OPERATIONS

2017 Sales

	$ mil.	% of total
System and software	794	62
Service & support	488	38
Total	**1,282**	**100**

Selected Products
Embedded software development
  Compilers
  Debugger
  Real-time operating system
Integrated circuit (IC) design and verification
  Analog/mixed signal
  Custom design
  Design-for-test
  Field-programmable gate array/application-specific IC design
  Formal verification
  High-capacity circuit simulation
  Interconnect modeling
  Physical optimization
  Physical verification & manufacturability
  Resolution enhancement technologies
  Static timing
  Synthesis
Printed circuit board design and analysis
  Design tools
  Digital high-speed
  Integration interfaces and viewers
  Layout
  Library management
  Radio-frequency/mixed-signal
  Simulation and analysis
System-level design and verification
  Accelerated system verification
  Cabling design and analysis
  Design creation
  Digital simulation
  Hardware emulation and simulation
  Intellectual property
  Process management
  System-on-a-chip
  Web-based development system

COMPETITORS

ANSYS	Interra Systems
AXIOM Design	Intrinsix
Altium	PDF Solutions
Autodesk	QNX Software Systems
Blue Ridge Numerics	Silvaco
Cadence Design	Synopsys
CollabNet	Wind River Systems
Green Hills Software	Zuken

HISTORICAL FINANCIALS
Company Type: Private

Income Statement
FYE: January 31

	REVENUE ($ mil.)	NET INCOME ($ mil.)	NET PROFIT MARGIN	EMPLOYEES
01/17	1,282	154	12.1%	5,700
01/16	1,180	94	8.0%	—
01/15	1,244	145	11.7%	—
01/14	1,156	153	13.3%	—
Annual Growth	**3.5%**	**0.3%**	**—**	**—**

2017 Year-End Financials
Return on assets: 1.3%
Return on equity: 12.1%
Current ratio: 1.30
Cash ($ mil.): 441

MERCY CHILDREN'S HOSPITAL

Children's Mercy Kansas City is a not-for-profit health system providing care services for youngsters in and around Kansas City Missouri. The system has two hospitals three urgent care facilities and five campuses featuring primary care offices and more than 25 specialty clinics. Among its specialized services are diabetes and endocrinology genetics heart surgery neonatology and rehabilitation. Children's Mercy also offers medical training and research facilities. Founded in 1897 the system today has some 500000 patient visits annually.

Operations

Children's Mercy has a medical staff of roughly 750 pediatric specialists. Its main campus Children's Mercy Adele Hall has 355 beds; there are an additional 53 at the Children's Mercy Hospital Kansas suburban campus.

The system performs roughly 20000 surgeries annually; it has around 200000 emergency room visits each year.

Geographic Reach

Children's Mercy Adele Hall is the only Level I pediatric trauma center between St. Louis Missouri and Denver Colorado.

It is a teaching hospital affiliated with University of Missouri-Kansas City School of Medicine University of Kansas School of Medicine and the Kansas City University of Medicine and Biosciences among others.

Sales and Marketing

Children's Mercy has recently begun advertising for the first time. It uses its marketing campaign in part to solicit donations as it relies heavily on philanthropy to manage operating costs.

Financial Performance

In 2017 Children's Mercy had revenue of $1.3 billion about 95% of which came from patient care services.

Strategy

Children's Mercy is in the midst of a multi-year $800 million expansion plan designed to more than double the size of the main hospital increase the number of patient beds by 50% add a new emergency room six new operating rooms new heart catheterization labs new educational buildings clinics and doctors' offices. A nine-story research tower will also be built atop an existing parking garage at the hospital's campus.

A large part of the funding for the expansion comes from philanthropic donations. Since the project began growth at the health system has included new urgent and specialty care centers a Pediatric Research Center new primary care centers and additional patient units and beds. The hospital has also undergone remodeling and expansion of certain existing facilities.

Children's Mercy has been expanding its research activities. It recently launched the Children's Research Institute to manage its research portfolio which includes gene therapy trials for leukemia and a cancer research partnership.

The system is vulnerable to potential reimbursement cutbacks that could result from the termination or reduction of the federal Children's Health Insurance Program (CHIP). Funding for the program temporarily ran out in 2017 as Congress deliberated on CHIPs future. Other public health care programs could also be shut down which would impact the system's ability to provide services to low-income families.

Company Background

Children's Mercy is a not-for-profit free-standing pediatric health system that offers low-income families a low- or no-cost health plan through the Take CARE benefit plans.

EXECUTIVES

President Ceo And Director, Randall L. O'Donnell
Svp Patient Care Services, Karen Cox
Evp And Co-coo, Jo Stueve
Evp And Cfo, Sandra A. J. Lawrence
Vp And Chief Nursing Officer, Cheri Hunt
Vp Market Development And Outreach, Warren Dudley
Surgeon-in-chief, George W. Holcomb
Pediatrician-in-chief, Michael Artman
Medical Director, Ashley Daly
Vice President General Counsel, Sally B Surridge
Senior Vice President And General Counsel, Robin Foster
Medical Director, Melissa Miller
Vice President Of Supply Chain, Laurisa Jackson
Chairman, Jack Ovel
Board Member, Kristi Canty
Assistant Treasurer Honorary Directors, David White

LOCATIONS

HQ: MERCY CHILDREN'S HOSPITAL
2401 GILLHAM RD, KANSAS CITY, MO 641084619
Phone: 816 234-3000
Web: WWW.CHILDRENSMERCY.ORG

Selected locations
Children's Mercy Adele Hall Campus (Kansas City MO)
Children's Mercy Blue Valley (Overland Park KS)
Children's Mercy Broadway (Kansas City)
Children's Mercy College Boulevard (Overland Park KS)
Children's Mercy East (Independence MO)
Children's Mercy Hospital Kansas (Overland Park KS)
Children's Mercy Northland (Kansas City MO)
Children's Mercy Olathe (Olathe KS)
Children's Mercy West (Kansas City KS)
Children's Mercy Sports Medicine Center at Village West (Kansas City KS)

COMPETITORS

Ascension Health
CoxHealth
Liberty Hospital
Saint Luke's Health System
Shawnee Mission Medical Center
Shriners Hospitals For Children
Sisters of Charity of Leavenworth
Truman Medical Centers
University of Kansas Medical Center

HISTORICAL FINANCIALS
Company Type: Private

Income Statement				FYE: June 30
	REVENUE ($ mil.)	NET INCOME ($ mil.)	NET PROFIT MARGIN	EMPLOYEES
06/16	1,020	35	3.5%	7,000
06/15	978	79	8.1%	—
06/13	9	(0)	—	—
06/11	816	13	1.6%	—
Annual Growth	4.5%	22.3%	—	—

2016 Year-End Financials
Return on assets: 7.0%
Return on equity: 3.5%
Current ratio: 1.90
Cash ($ mil.): 63

MERCY CORPS

EXECUTIVES

Interim Vice President Senior Director Policy And Advocacy, Ann Vaughan
Global Treasurer, Jay Price

LOCATIONS

HQ: MERCY CORPS
45 SW ANKENY ST, PORTLAND, OR 972043500
Phone: 503 796-6800
Web: WWW.MERCYCORPSNW.ORG

HISTORICAL FINANCIALS
Company Type: Private

Income Statement				FYE: June 30
	REVENUE ($ mil.)	NET INCOME ($ mil.)	NET PROFIT MARGIN	EMPLOYEES
06/15	329	2	0.9%	450
06/14	275	(3)	—	—
06/13	236	(4)	—	—
06/12	232	(7)	—	—
Annual Growth	12.2%	—	—	—

2015 Year-End Financials
Return on assets: 10.7%
Return on equity: 0.9%
Current ratio: 0.60
Cash ($ mil.): 52

MERCY HEALTH

Mercy Health formerly known as the Sisters of Mercy Health System provides a range of health care and social services through its network of facilities and service organizations. The organization operates some 35 acute care hospitals (including four specialty heart hospitals and two children's hospitals) with more than 4200 licensed beds as well as 700 clinics and outpatient facilities in four Midwestern states. Its hospital groups include facilities for nursing homes medical practices and outpatient centers. Mercy Health also operates Resource Optimization & Innovation (ROi) its industry-leading health care supply chain organization and health outreach organizations in Louisiana Mississippi and Texas.

Operations

Mercy Health also operates three rehabilitation hospitals and two orthopedic hospitals. The system has more than 2000 Mercy Clinic physicians.

In 2014 Mercy Health had 150696 acute inpatient discharges; 158911 inpatient and outpatient surgeries; 631444 emergency department visits; 23213 births; and nearly 8.4 million outpatient visits.

Geographic Reach

The system operates in Arkansas Kansas Missouri and Oklahoma.

Mercy Health's outreach efforts include Mercy Ministries of Laredo a group providing primary health care and social services to residents of Laredo Texas. In New Orleans Mercy Health sponsors Mercy Family Center which provides mental health services; in Mississippi it funds a health care advocacy group.

Sales and Marketing

Commercial and other third-party payments accounted for 44% of net patient service revenue while Medicare and Medicaid combined accounted for 51%.

Financial Performance

Mercy Health's operating revenue increased 14% to $4.5 billion in 2014 as net patient and other revenues grew. However the system reported a net loss of $6.5 million that year (versus net income in 2013) as a result of interest rate swap agreement losses and higher expenses as well as lower investment earnings.

Cash flow from operations fell 46% to $354 million in 2014.

Strategy

In 2013 Mercy Health opened new facilities in Missouri (St. Charles and Wentzville) as well as a new heart and vascular center that centralized its outpatient heart and vascular offerings. The following year it opened a new orthopedic hospital in Fort Smith and a 60-bed rehabilitation hospital.

The system acquired Lincoln County Medical Center (renamed Mercy Hospital Lincoln) and its eight affiliated clinics in 2015 expanding its presence in eastern Missouri.

Despite its various expansions the Mercy system experienced the same industry challenges as its health care brethren including escalating medical and pharmaceutical costs and increasing self-pay bad debts (uninsured patients who leave their medical bills unpaid). Several of the health system's facilities have seen a decline in discharges.

Company Background

The organization was founded by the Sisters of Mercy of the St. Louis Regional Community in 1986 and operated under that model until 2008 when its sponsorship was transferred from the Sisters of Mercy of the St. Louis Regional Community to a new entity Mercy Health Ministry. The shift to the new sponsorship organization was made to allow lay members to join the Sisters of Mercy in sponsoring the ministry. It also reflected the growing number of lay people holding executive positions at the system's hospitals and on the board of directors.

EXECUTIVES

Vice President Performance Management, Fred Ford
Senior Vice President, Vance Moore
Auditors: ERNST & YOUNG LLP ST LOUIS

LOCATIONS

HQ: MERCY HEALTH
14528 SOUTH OUTER 40 RD # 100, CHESTERFIELD, MO 630175743
Phone: 314 579-6100
Web: WWW.MERCY.COM

Selected Locations

Arkansas
  Berryville
  Fort Smith
  Hot Springs
  Ozark
  Paris
  Rogers
  Waldron
Kansas
  Columbus
  Fort Scott
  Independence
Missouri
  Aurora
  Cassville
  Joplin
  Lebanon
  Mountain View
  St. Louis
  Springfield
  Washington
Oklahoma
  Ada
  Ardmore
  El Reno
  Guthrie
  Healdton
  Kingfisher
  Marietta
  Oklahoma City
  Tishomingo
  Watonga

PRODUCTS/OPERATIONS

2014 Sales

	% of total
Net patient service revenue less provision for bad debts	85
Member revenue	11
Other revenue	4
Total	**100**

Selected Facilities

Arkansas
  Mercy Hospital Berryville
  Mercy Hospital Fort Smith
  Mercy Hospital Hot Springs
  Mercy Hospital Northwest Arkansas
  Mercy Hospital of Scott County
  Mercy Hospital Ozark
  Mercy Hospital Paris
  Mercy Hospital Waldron
Kansas
  Mercy Health Center
  Mercy Hospital Fort Scott
  Mercy Hospital Independence
  Mercy Maude Norton Hospital Columbus
Missouri
  Mercy Hospital Aurora
  Mercy Hospital Cassville
  Mercy Hospital Joplin
  Mercy Hospital Lebanon
  Mercy Hospital St. Louis
  Mercy Children's Hospital St. Louis
  Mercy Heart and Vascular Hospital St. Louis
  Mercy Heart Hospital St. Louis
  Mercy Rehabilitation Hospital St. Louis
  Mercy Hospital Springfield
  Mercy Children's Hospital Springfield
  Mercy Hospital Washington
  Mercy McCune-Brooks Hospital
  Mercy St. Francis Hospital
Oklahoma
  Arbuckle Memorial Hospital
  Mercy Health Love County
  Mercy Hospital Ardmore
  Mercy Hospital El Reno
  Mercy Hospital Healdton
  Mercy Hospital Logan County
  Mercy Hospital Oklahoma City
  Mercy Hospital - Tishomingo
  Valley View Regional Hospital
  Watonga Municipal Hospital

COMPETITORS

Ascension Health	SSM Health Care
BJC HealthCare	Saint Luke's Health
Baptist Health	System
(Arkansas)	Shawnee Mission
Barnes-Jewish Hospital	Medical Center
CHRISTUS Health	Sisters of Charity of
Christian Hospital	Leavenworth
Community Health	St. Anthony's Medical
Systems	Center
CoxHealth	St. Vincent Health
HCA	System
INTEGRIS Health	Tenet Healthcare
Memorial Hospital	Universal Health
(Illinois)	Services
RehabCare	

HISTORICAL FINANCIALS

Company Type: Private

Income Statement

FYE: June 30

	REVENUE ($ mil.)	NET INCOME ($ mil.)	NET PROFIT MARGIN	EMPLOYEES
06/18	6,254	243	3.9%	8,800
06/17	5,527	558	10.1%	—
06/10*	18	7	38.4%	—
03/09	2,936	(196)	—	—
Annual Growth	**8.8%**	—	—	—

*Fiscal year change

2018 Year-End Financials

Return on assets: 4.5%
Return on equity: 3.9%
Current ratio: 1.20
Cash ($ mil.): 481

MERCY HEALTH

EXECUTIVES

Ceo-Pres, Michael D Connelly
Coordinator, Fiona McCloy
Chief Officer and Pres, Randy Curnow
Scientist, Larry Jackson
Information Technology Manager, Dave Hedgespeth
Health Care Director, Angela Price
Executive Vice President, David A Catalano
Senior Vice President Operatio, Rebecca Sykes
Director Information Technolog, Shawn Kent
Director, Tom Ramsey
Purchasing Agent, William Mueller
Auditors: ERNST & YOUNG LLP CINCINNATI

LOCATIONS

HQ: MERCY HEALTH
1701 MERCY HEALTH PL, CINCINNATI, OH 452376147
Phone: 513 639-2800
Web: WWW.HEALTH-PARTNERS.ORG

HISTORICAL FINANCIALS

Company Type: Private

Income Statement

FYE: December 31

	REVENUE ($ mil.)	NET INCOME ($ mil.)	NET PROFIT MARGIN	EMPLOYEES
12/17	4,737	456	9.6%	35,000
12/14	4,510	130	2.9%	—
12/08	4,044	(657)	—	—
Annual Growth	**1.8%**	—	—	—

2017 Year-End Financials

Return on assets: 4.8%
Return on equity: 9.6%
Current ratio: 0.70
Cash ($ mil.): 146

MERCY HEALTH - ST. RITA'S MEDICAL CENTER, LLC

St. Rita's Medical Center is all about healing. The general medical-surgical hospital serves west central Ohio. The not-for-profit facility provides health care services in a number of medical specialties including trauma and emergency care orthopedics cancer pediatrics women's health and cardiovascular disease. It also has physical rehabilitation mental health and outpatient care facilities and works to improve community health through disease screenings smoking cessation programs and other outreach initiatives. Established in 1918 by the Sisters of Mercy the hospital is a member of Catholic Healthcare Partners.

Operations
Community outreach efforts are conducted at the main hospital facility as well as at its MEDCARE health clinic which provides care for low-income and uninsured patients. The hospital also operates a dental clinic and a Neighborhood Nurse program to conduct some of its community screenings and health programs. St. Rita's Medical Center provides some $46 million in community services (including charity care and educational programs) each year.

Geographic Reach
St. Rita's Medical Center provides acute care to residents in a 70-mile area around Lima Ohio that includes about 10 counties. The hospital has additional outpatient treatment facilities in and around the city including an occupational health clinic in Lima and additional centers in Delphos Glandorf and Wapakoneta.

Financial Performance
St. Rita's Medical Center increased revenues by 7% to $454 million in 2012 due to higher patient revenues and lower bad debt provisions. As a result net income rose more than 200% that year to some $49 million.

Strategy
In 2012 St. Rita's Medical Center completed the implementation of the region's first hospital-based EPIC electronic health record (EHR) system known as CarePATH. The system allows for improved communication and patient care coordination among caregivers and facilities. As part of parent CHS' program to go digital St. Rita's was the 11th hospital in the system to transition to EHRs; the St. Rita's Professional Services physician practice group launched the CarePATH system in 2011.

EXECUTIVES

Chb, Steve Walter
Cfo, John Renner
Doctor, Kenneth E Patick
Gastroenterology, Howard J Solomon
Administrator, Kathy Moline
Pediatrics, Susan R Savich
Personnel Director, Gwen Taulbee
Director, Al Gay
Administrator, Lara Hayes

LOCATIONS

HQ: MERCY HEALTH - ST. RITA'S MEDICAL CENTER, LLC
730 W MARKET ST, LIMA, OH 458014602
Phone: 419 227-3361
Web: WWW.EHEALTHCONNECTION.COM

PRODUCTS/OPERATIONS

Selected Centers
Cancer Network of West Central Ohio
Institute for Orthopaedic Surgery
Kidney Services of West Central Ohio
New Vision Medical Laboratory
North Central Ohio Physician Services - Neurosurgery & Neurological Services
Occupational Health Center
St. Rita's Health Management Group
St. Rita's Professional Services (physician offices)
Surgery & Endoscopy Center of West Central Ohio

COMPETITORS

AdCare	OhioHealth
Adena Health System	Premier Health
Fairfield Medical	Partners
Center	ProMedica
Kettering Health	Regency Hospital
Network	TriHealth
Licking Memorial	UC Health
Health Systems	University Hospitals
MetroHealth System	Health System
Mount Carmel Health	

HISTORICAL FINANCIALS
Company Type: Private

Income Statement   FYE: December 31

	REVENUE ($ mil.)	NET INCOME ($ mil.)	NET PROFIT MARGIN	EMPLOYEES
12/17	427	120	28.1%	2,850
12/16	408	91	22.4%	—
12/06	3,505	143	4.1%	—
12/04	272	22	8.3%	—
Annual Growth	3.5%	13.7%	—	—

2017 Year-End Financials
Return on assets: 7.2%   Cash ($ mil.): 175
Return on equity: 28.1%
Current ratio: 4.30

MERCY HEALTH SERVICES, INC.

EXECUTIVES

Pres, Thomas Mullen
MD, Jay S Goodman
Vice President Finance, John Lepley
Senior Vice President of Medic, Scott Spier
Manager of Comp, Tammy Janus
Auditors: DIXON HUGHES GOODMAN LLP TYSO

LOCATIONS

HQ: MERCY HEALTH SERVICES, INC.
301 SAINT PAUL ST, BALTIMORE, MD 212022102
Phone: 410 332-9000

HISTORICAL FINANCIALS
Company Type: Private

Income Statement   FYE: June 30

	REVENUE ($ mil.)	NET INCOME ($ mil.)	NET PROFIT MARGIN	EMPLOYEES
06/18	737	31	4.2%	1
06/17	705	50	7.1%	—
06/14	9	1	16.3%	—
06/13	602	15	2.6%	—
Annual Growth	4.1%	14.9%	—	—

2018 Year-End Financials
Return on assets: 14.0%   Cash ($ mil.): 110
Return on equity: 4.2%
Current ratio: 1.30

MERCY HEALTH ST VINCENT MED LLC

EXECUTIVES

President, Tim Koder
President, Steven Mickus
Chb, Beverly J McBride
SEC, Julie Higgins
Treas, Robert A Sullivan
Occupational Specia, Amy M Smith
Clinical Coordinator Pharmacy, Andrea Decker
Clinical Coordinator, Colleen Harrell
Health Professional, Mandasmitha Sowmarpet
Family Practitioner, Tracey Hooker
Internal Medicine Practitioner, Vandana Gambhir

LOCATIONS

HQ: MERCY HEALTH ST VINCENT MED LLC
2213 CHERRY ST, TOLEDO, OH 436082603
Phone: 419 251-3232
Web: WWW.MERCY.COM

HISTORICAL FINANCIALS
Company Type: Private

Income Statement   FYE: December 31

	REVENUE ($ mil.)	NET INCOME ($ mil.)	NET PROFIT MARGIN	EMPLOYEES
12/16	478	24	5.1%	6,000
12/15	467	22	4.8%	—
12/00	333	5	1.5%	—
12/99	327	(7)	—	—
Annual Growth	2.3%	—	—	—

MERCY HEALTH SYSTEM CORPORATION

EXECUTIVES

Ceo, Javon R Bea
V Pres-Cfo, Joseph Nemeth
Optometrists, Kevin Walter
Optometrists, Becky Trujillo
Public Relations Director, Ronald Del Ciello
Procurement Staff, Steve Walker
Training and Direc, Wynn Biedermann
Coordinator, Kristin Hansberry
Coordinator, Karen Ellis
Chief of Medicine, David Pittenger
Coordinator, Lisa Whitcomb
Auditors: WIPFLI LLP MILWAUKEE WISCONS

LOCATIONS

HQ: MERCY HEALTH SYSTEM CORPORATION
1000 MINERAL POINT AVE, JANESVILLE, WI 535482940
Phone: 608 741-6891
Web: WWW.MERCYHEALTHSYSTEM.ORG

HISTORICAL FINANCIALS
Company Type: Private

Income Statement
FYE: June 30

	REVENUE ($ mil.)	NET INCOME ($ mil.)	NET PROFIT MARGIN	EMPLOYEES
06/16	559	19	3.5%	2,200
06/15	523	12	2.3%	—
06/14	478	39	8.2%	—
06/13	473	21	4.5%	—
Annual Growth	5.7%	(2.5%)	—	—

2016 Year-End Financials
Return on assets: 8.6%
Return on equity: 3.5%
Current ratio: 0.50
Cash ($ mil.): 66

MERCY HOME SERVICES A CALIFORNIA LIMITED PARTNERSHIP

EXECUTIVES

Ceo, George A Govier
Director of Operations, Roger Page
Analyst, Alexis Ross
Buyer, Peggy Podliska
or Manager, Kirk Williams
Data Coordinator, Mary Sanders
Supervisor, Tina Trabold
Director of Human Resources, Denise Little
Safety Manager, George Knight
Chemistry Supervisor, Jeff Hodges

LOCATIONS

HQ: MERCY HOME SERVICES A CALIFORNIA LIMITED PARTNERSHIP
2175 ROSALINE AVE STE A, REDDING, CA 960012549
Phone: 530 225-6000

HISTORICAL FINANCIALS
Company Type: Private

Income Statement
FYE: June 30

	REVENUE ($ mil.)	NET INCOME ($ mil.)	NET PROFIT MARGIN	EMPLOYEES
06/15	446	54	12.1%	1,200
06/09	283	8	3.0%	—
Annual Growth	7.8%	36.2%	—	—

2015 Year-End Financials
Return on assets: 2.9%
Return on equity: 12.1%
Current ratio: 2.70
Cash ($ mil.): 62

MERCY HOSPITAL OF BUFFALO

EXECUTIVES

Ceo, Charles J Urlaub
Coo, Mark A Sullivan
Sr Vice President, John Stavros
Management Vice-President, Nancy Sheehan
Sr Vice President, Richard J Ruh
Prin, James R Boldt
Treas, William K Buscaglia Jr
SEC, Sr Margaret Tuley D C
Coordinator Infection Control, Karen Calaiacova
Management Vice-President, Karen Burger
Coordinator, Mary Graham

LOCATIONS

HQ: MERCY HOSPITAL OF BUFFALO
565 ABBOTT RD, BUFFALO, NY 142202095
Phone: 716 826-7000
Web: WWW.MERCYMOOSELAKE.ORG

HISTORICAL FINANCIALS
Company Type: Private

Income Statement
FYE: December 31

	REVENUE ($ mil.)	NET INCOME ($ mil.)	NET PROFIT MARGIN	EMPLOYEES
12/15	391	3	0.8%	2,000
12/14	381	20	5.4%	—
12/08	249	6	2.6%	—
12/05	205	6	3.2%	—
Annual Growth	6.7%	(7.5%)	—	—

2015 Year-End Financials
Return on assets: 4.4%
Return on equity: 0.8%
Current ratio: 2.00
Cash ($ mil.): 94

MERCY HOSPITAL SPRINGFIELD

Mercy Hospital Springfield is an 890-bed acute-care hospital in the Mercy Health system. The facility provides health care to southwestern Missouri and northwestern Arkansas and includes the Mercy Children's Hospital Springfield. Other hospital specialties include cardiology and stroke care as well as women's and seniors' health cancer emergency trauma burn neuroscience rehabilitation and sports medicine. In addition to its hospital in Springfield Mercy Hospital Springfield operates a number of community clinics and specialty care centers in the area.

Operations

Mercy Hospital Springfield has about 700 doctors on its medical staff. The center sees some 441000 outpatient visits per year as well as 94000 emergency room visits and 37000 surgeries. It also enables more than 3000 births Specialty units feature a level I trauma and burn center (the highest ranking in the US) a neonatal intensive care unit a nationally certified stroke center and high-tech surgery suites (including da Vinci robotic surgery and CyberKnife radiosurgery centers). It also operates an air ambulance service.

Geographic Reach

The hospital serves patients in southwest Missouri and northwest Arkansas.

Financial Performance

The hospital's revenues decreased by 1% in 2014 due to 1% drop in net patient service revenue (which contributed 98% of the revenue) and a 11% decrease in revenues from other sources.

In 2014 the company provided charity care of about $26 million along with unreimbursed Medicaid expenses of around $17 million.

Strategy

That year Mercy Hospital Springfield opened the 60-bed Mercy Rehabilitation Hospital Springfield which is spread across a 63000-square-feet facility. The new $28 million building allows for more options for patient rehabilitation and will also serve as the region's only burn unit.

In 2014 the company also opened Phase II of its Betty and Bobby Allison Neonatal Intensive Care Unit (NICU) which expands the number of beds under NICU to 46. With this final phase complete Mercy permanently closed its former NICU.

Company Background

Formerly St. John's Regional Health Center the hospital's name changed to Mercy Hospital Springfield in 2012; the move coincided with the parent organization's efforts to unify its brand identity. (The parent group's named changed as well from Sisters of Mercy Health System to Mercy Health.)

The hospital was founded in 1891 by the Sisters of Mercy.

EXECUTIVES

Ceo, Lynn Britton
Ceo, Kim Day
Pres, John Swope
Exec V Pres, Michael McCurry
Exec V Pres, Shannon Sock
Emergency Medicine Specialist, Jeffrey Spencer
Nurse, Paula Gallegos

LOCATIONS

HQ: MERCY HOSPITAL SPRINGFIELD
1235 E CHEROKEE ST, SPRINGFIELD, MO 658042203
Phone: 417 820-2000
Web: WWW.GOODNEIGHBORPHARMACY.COM

PRODUCTS/OPERATIONS

Selected Services
Bariatric Surgery
Cancer Care
Children's Care
Heart Care
Integrative Medicine
Mother and Baby Care
Neurosciences
Orthopedic and Sport Care
Palliative Care
Pastoral Care
Senior Care
Trauma and Burn Care
Women's Care

COMPETITORS

Ascension Health	HCA
BJC HealthCare	Heartland Health
Boone Hospital Center	Liberty Hospital
Catholic Health Initiatives	Tenet Healthcare
Christian Hospital	Truman Medical Centers
CoxHealth	University of Kansas Medical Center

	REVENUE ($ mil.)	NET INCOME ($ mil.)	NET PROFIT MARGIN	EMPLOYEES
06/16	1,024	104	10.2%	4,400
06/15	948	93	9.9%	—
06/14	964	42	4.4%	—
06/13	965	87	9.1%	—
Annual Growth	2.0%	6.1%	—	—

Income Statement — FYE: June 30

2016 Year-End Financials

Return on assets: 1.4%
Return on equity: 10.2%
Current ratio: 3.60
Cash ($ mil.): 25

MERCY HOSPITAL, CEDAR RAPIDS, IOWA

EXECUTIVES

Pres, Timothy L Charles
Cfo, Phil Peterson
Oncology, Wook Lee
Chief Nursing Officer, James V Guliano
Graphic Designer, Kelly Michael
Director, Marilyn Ward
Director of Security, Rod McCool
Director, David Carter
Physical Therapy Director, Bill Grudzinski
Vice-President, Diane Stefani
Oncologist, Janet Merfeld
Auditors: RSM US LLP DAVENPORT IOWA

LOCATIONS

HQ: MERCY HOSPITAL, CEDAR RAPIDS, IOWA
701 10TH ST SE, CEDAR RAPIDS, IA 524031251
Phone: 319 398-6011
Web: WWW.MERCYCARE.ORG

HISTORICAL FINANCIALS
Company Type: Private

Income Statement — FYE: June 30

	REVENUE ($ mil.)	NET INCOME ($ mil.)	NET PROFIT MARGIN	EMPLOYEES
06/18	334	22	6.8%	2,375
06/16	314	(6)	—	—
06/15	303	(6)	—	—
06/14	269	15	5.9%	—
Annual Growth	5.5%	9.6%	—	—

2018 Year-End Financials

Return on assets: 4.8%
Return on equity: 6.8%
Current ratio: 1.10
Cash ($ mil.): 6

MERCY HOSPITALS EAST COMMUNITIES

EXECUTIVES

President, Jeffrey Johnston
Vice President, Paul Hintze
Attorney, Melissa Jackson
Dermatologist, Brooke Shadel
Obstetrician, Christina L Byron
Director, Mary Burton

LOCATIONS

HQ: MERCY HOSPITALS EAST COMMUNITIES
615 S NEW BALLAS RD, SAINT LOUIS, MO
631418221
Phone: 417 820-2000

COMPETITORS

BJC HealthCare
Memorial Hospital (Illinois)
SSM Health Care
St. Anthony's Medical Center
St. Luke's Hospital (MO)

HISTORICAL FINANCIALS
Company Type: Private

Income Statement — FYE: June 30

	REVENUE ($ mil.)	NET INCOME ($ mil.)	NET PROFIT MARGIN	EMPLOYEES
06/16	1,023	184	18.0%	10,000
06/15	940	132	14.1%	—
06/14	1,177	118	10.1%	—
06/13	840	82	9.8%	—
Annual Growth	6.8%	30.9%	—	—

2016 Year-End Financials

Return on assets: 2.0%
Return on equity: 18.0%
Current ratio: 4.00
Cash ($ mil.): 22

MERCY HOUSING, INC.

EXECUTIVES

Pres, Jane Graf
V Pres-Fin, Vince Dodds
Vice President, Michele Mamet
Sr Vice President, L Steven Spears
Sr Vice President, Cindy Holler
Sr Vice President, Carol Breslau
Compliance Staff, Shana Morgan
Senior Vice-President, Christy Richardson
Property Manager, Denise Rankin
Coordinator, Elaine Rudolph
Director of Information Techno, Gunnar Tande

LOCATIONS

HQ: MERCY HOUSING, INC.
1999 BROADWAY STE 1000, DENVER, CO 802025704
Phone: 303 830-3300
Web: WWW.MERCYHOUSING.ORG

Income Statement — FYE: December 31

	REVENUE ($ mil.)	NET INCOME ($ mil.)	NET PROFIT MARGIN	EMPLOYEES
12/17	322	42	13.2%	1,200
12/16	495	(109)	—	—
12/15	16	(1)	—	—
12/14	13	5	44.9%	—
Annual Growth	191.6%	93.9%	—	—

2017 Year-End Financials

Return on assets: 24.8%
Return on equity: 13.2%
Current ratio: 0.40
Cash ($ mil.): 104

MERCY MEDICAL CENTER, INC.

EXECUTIVES

Chb, Sister Helen Amos
Ceo, Thomas R Mullen
Exec V Pres-Cfo, John E Topper
Exec Vice President, Amy Freeman
Sr V Pres Medical Affairs, Dr Scott Spier
Coordinator, Rona Kassem
Scientist, Ruth Bates
Analyst, John Goldbeck
Internal Medicine Practitioner, Robert G Davidson
Director, Deb Lightcap
Coordinator, Eric Barbieri
Auditors: DIXON HUGHES GOODMAN LLP ROCK

LOCATIONS

HQ: MERCY MEDICAL CENTER, INC.
345 SAINT PAUL ST, BALTIMORE, MD 212022123
Phone: 410 332-9000
Web: WWW.MERCYRESIDENCY.ORG

HISTORICAL FINANCIALS
Company Type: Private

Income Statement — FYE: June 30

	REVENUE ($ mil.)	NET INCOME ($ mil.)	NET PROFIT MARGIN	EMPLOYEES
06/18	502	25	5.1%	2,139
06/16	446	(16)	—	—
06/10	387	36	9.3%	—
Annual Growth	3.3%	(4.3%)	—	—

2018 Year-End Financials

Return on assets: 16.4%
Return on equity: 5.1%
Current ratio: 1.20
Cash ($ mil.): 95

MERCY MEDICAL CENTER, INC.

Mercy Medical Center keeps patients doing the cancan in Canton. The facility is a 480-bed acute care hospital serving residents of five counties in southeastern Ohio. The Catholic medical center has 700 physicians and provides a comprehensive range of care including inpatient outpatient and rehabilitative services. It operates specialty care centers for cardiac vascular stroke and cancer treatment as well as trauma chest pain and rehabilitation units. Mercy Medical Center also operates outpatient health centers in the communities surrounding Canton Ohio. The facility is part of the Sisters of Charity Health System (SCHS) a not-for-profit ministry of the Sisters of Charity of St. Augustine.

Operations
Mercy Medical's center of excellence includes Mercy Heart Center Emergency Services/Trauma Center Emergency Chest Pain Center Mercy Cancer Center Mercy Rehabilitation Services Mercy Stroke Center and Mercy Vascular Center.

Geographic Reach
Mercy Medical Center serves patients living in the Southeastern Ohio counties of Carroll Holmes Stark Tuscarawas and Wayne. In addition to the main hospital in Canton the health care provider operates outpatient centers in Carrollton Jackson Township Lake Township Louisville North Canton and Plain Township as well as Tuscarawas County.

Sales and Marketing
The medical facility markets its services through social media and via TV commercials.

Financial Performance
Mercy Medical's total operating revenues were $275.1 million in fiscal 2012.

Strategy
Mercy Medical Center is focused on increasing operational efficiencies and pursuing growth opportunities including expanding services to patients. To that end the hospital in 2014 began to offer adult and pediatric therapy services in Western Stark County. It also launched an $80-million program in 2010 to invest in capital projects including facility improvements and equipment upgrades. The care provider also opened a new primary care office in Canton in 2012.

Company Background
Mercy Medical Center traces its roots to Mercy Hospital founded in 1908 in the former home of President William McKinley. The hospital was opened by the Sisters of Charity of St. Augustine which established SCHS as the parent company for its hospital operations in 1982. Between 1999 and 2009 SCHS operated the Mercy Medical Center and several other Ohio facilities through a joint venture with the University Hospitals Health System; however after 10 years full control of the facilities was reverted back to SCHS.

EXECUTIVES

Vice President Of Revenue Cycle, Michael Rieger
Vice President Chief Nursing Officer, James Williams
Nursing Director, Allison Goshay
Cio Chief Technology Officer Vice President Information Technology, Jim Carroll
Vice President, Lorraine Washington
Vice President Fund Development And Government Relations, Thomas Turner
Vice President Finance, John Lepley
Medical Director, Douglas Lyle Blocker
Respiratory Therapy Director, Jason Robinson
Ambulatory Services Director, Jamie Carbone
Medical Director, Bruce Hensley
Auditors: PLANTE & MORAN PLLC COLUMBUS

LOCATIONS

HQ: MERCY MEDICAL CENTER, INC.
1320 MERCY DR NW, CANTON, OH 447082641
Phone: 330 489-1000
Web: WWW.CANTONMERCY.ORG

Selected Facilities
Mercy Medical Center - Canton Ohio
Mercy Health Center of Alliance - Alliance Ohio
Mercy Health Center of Carroll County - Carrollton OH
Mercy Health Center of Lake - Uniontown OH
Mercy Health Center of Louisville - Louisville OH
Mercy Health Center of Jackson - Massillon OH
Mercy Health Center of North Canton - North Canton OH
Mercy Health Center of Plain - Canton OH
Mercy Health Center of Tuscarawas County - New Philadelphia OH
Mercy Medical Center at St. Paul Square - Canton Ohio

COMPETITORS

Akron Children's Hospital	Robinson Memorial Hospital
Akron General Health System	Summa Health System
Aultman Health Foundation	The Cleveland Clinic
Lake Health	Trinity Health System
OhioHealth	University Hospitals Health System
Parma Community General Hospital	

HISTORICAL FINANCIALS
Company Type: Private

Income Statement
FYE: December 31

	REVENUE ($ mil.)	NET INCOME ($ mil.)	NET PROFIT MARGIN	EMPLOYEES
12/16	309	(1)	—	80
12/15	298	2	0.9%	—
12/14	301	5	1.7%	—
12/13	283	10	3.6%	—
Annual Growth	3.0%	—	—	—

2016 Year-End Financials
Return on assets: 5.2%
Return on equity: (-0.3%)
Current ratio: 1.50
Cash ($ mil.): 29

MERCY SCRIPPS HOSPITAL

EXECUTIVES

Prin, Andrew C Ping
Coordinator, Callie Huza
Chief Financial Officer, Nina Galvan
Materials Manager Purchasing D, Eddye Coates
General Surgery, Alan Wittgrove
Security Manager, Anthony Roman
Ophthalmologist, Brian Chang
Surgeon, Dennis Mayer
Manager Surgical, Dorothea Meyers
Radiologist, Douglas Bates
Internist, Erin Whitaker

LOCATIONS

HQ: MERCY SCRIPPS HOSPITAL
4077 5TH AVE MER35, SAN DIEGO, CA 921032105
Phone: 619 294-8111
Web: WWW.SCRIPPS.ORG

HISTORICAL FINANCIALS
Company Type: Private

Income Statement
FYE: September 30

	REVENUE ($ mil.)	NET INCOME ($ mil.)	NET PROFIT MARGIN	EMPLOYEES
09/15	750	44	5.9%	77
09/14	623	3	0.6%	—
09/13	700	41	5.9%	—
Annual Growth	3.5%	3.7%	—	—

MERCY UPMC

EXECUTIVES

Pres, Will Cook
Cfo, Eileen Simmons
Dir, Anthony J Pinevich
Urology Specialist, Tatum Tarin

LOCATIONS

HQ: MERCY UPMC
1400 LOCUST ST, PITTSBURGH, PA 152195114
Phone: 412 232-8111
Web: WWW.MERCY.PMHS.ORG

HISTORICAL FINANCIALS
Company Type: Private

Income Statement
FYE: June 30

	REVENUE ($ mil.)	NET INCOME ($ mil.)	NET PROFIT MARGIN	EMPLOYEES
06/16	378	1	0.5%	2,010
06/15	373	0	0.1%	—
Annual Growth	1.4%	337.7%	—	—

2016 Year-End Financials
Return on assets: 0.9%
Return on equity: 0.5%
Current ratio: 6.80
Cash ($ mil.): —

MERIDIAN HOSPITALS CORPORATION

Auditors: PRICEWATERHOUSECOOPERS LLP NE

LOCATIONS

HQ: MERIDIAN HOSPITALS CORPORATION
1945 ROUTE 33, NEPTUNE, NJ 077534859
Phone: 732 751-7500

HISTORICAL FINANCIALS
Company Type: Private

Income Statement
FYE: December 31

	REVENUE ($ mil.)	NET INCOME ($ mil.)	NET PROFIT MARGIN	EMPLOYEES
12/15	674	64	9.5%	5,200
12/09	929	94	10.2%	—
12/08	873	(140)	—	—
Annual Growth	(3.6%)	—	—	—

2015 Year-End Financials
Return on assets: 6.0%
Return on equity: 9.5%
Current ratio: 1.60
Cash ($ mil.): 300

MERITER HOSPITAL, INC.

EXECUTIVES

Ceo, James L Woodward
Pres, Robert Turngren
V Pres, Sue Erickson
Cfo, Kevin Boren
Chief of Medicine, Geoffrey Priest
Coordinator, Amy Schwarz
Program Director, Gary Robb
Internal Medicine Practitioner, Jeremy W Jaskunas
Payroll Staff, Marcia Virgil
Staff, Mussallem Matthew
Health Professional, Nicole Kemp

LOCATIONS

HQ: MERITER HOSPITAL, INC.
202 S PARK ST, MADISON, WI 537151596
Phone: 608 417-6000
Web: WWW.MERITER.COM

HISTORICAL FINANCIALS

Company Type: Private

Income Statement				FYE: December 31
	REVENUE ($ mil.)	NET INCOME ($ mil.)	NET PROFIT MARGIN	EMPLOYEES
12/15	402	52	13.0%	2,548
12/14	434	47	11.0%	—
12/13	454	56	12.5%	—
12/12	432	34	8.1%	—
Annual Growth	(2.3%)	14.5%	—	—

2015 Year-End Financials

Return on assets: 10.7%   Cash ($ mil.): 13
Return on equity: 13.0%
Current ratio: 1.10

MERITUS MEDICAL CENTER, INC.

EXECUTIVES

Ceo-Pres, Joseph Ross
Sr Vice President, Deborah Addo Samuels
Sr Vice President, Raymond Grahe
Vice President, Heather Lorenzo
Vice President, Carolyn Simonsen
Psychiatrist, Garry A Seligman
Internal Medicine Practitioner, Mark S Baran
Health Professional, Simon Iroha
Chief of Medicine, Vincent Cantone
Administrative Assistant, Donna Stewart
Health Professional, Mohammed S Aziz

LOCATIONS

HQ: MERITUS MEDICAL CENTER, INC.
11116 MEDICAL CAMPUS RD, HAGERSTOWN, MD 217426710
Phone: 301 797-2000
Web: WWW.MERITUSHEALTH.COM

HISTORICAL FINANCIALS

Company Type: Private

Income Statement				FYE: June 30
	REVENUE ($ mil.)	NET INCOME ($ mil.)	NET PROFIT MARGIN	EMPLOYEES
06/17	386	32	8.4%	2,400
06/15	361	25	7.1%	—
06/14	346	13	3.9%	—
06/12	288	3	1.4%	—
Annual Growth	6.0%	52.1%	—	—

2017 Year-End Financials

Return on assets: 6.1%   Cash ($ mil.): 50
Return on equity: 8.4%
Current ratio: 1.40

MERRILL CORPORATION

Document services company Merrill is no relation to financial services giant Merrill Lynch but the companies do share an interest in SEC paperwork. Merrill Corporation is a provider of outsourced document management branded marketing services and other information management services. It helps clients gather organize and manage confidential and time-sensitive information for legal and financial transactions. In addition the company provides marketing and communication services such as document composition printing fulfillment and digital delivery as well as technology integration.

Operations

Merrill's Legal and Financial Transaction Services (LFTS) offers legal financial and corporate professionals a suite of advanced services and web-based tools to gather organize and manage transactional information. The company's Marketing and Communication Solutions (MCS) segment specializes in technology-enabled marketing and compliance communications.

Geographic Reach

Merrill operates through more than 40 offices in the US and about 20 international locations. It also has an IT Technology Center in Chennai India and another IT-focused facility in Coimbatore India.

Strategy

While Merrill continues to print individual annual reports brochures catalogs and other publications it has diversified beyond its traditional printing business through numerous acquisitions and strategic alliances to position itself as a business process outsourcing company. It sees growth opportunities in its legal solutions offerings which include managing electronic data discovery and in Merrill Datasite which provides online hosting of documents related to mergers and acquisitions.

In addition to acquisitions Merrill also divests assets from time to time to support its ongoing strategic repositioning efforts in the business process outsourcing marketplace. In 2016 it sold its language services subsidiary Merrill Brink International to United Language Group Inc. The same year it divested its real Estate and Franchise Business selling it to direct marketing technologies firm Xpressdocs Holdings.

HISTORY

Kenneth Merrill founded K. F. Merrill with his wife Lorraine in 1968 and grew the company into a major regional printer. He turned over the reins in 1984 to John Castro who had worked his way up from production manager. The company went public two years later.

EXECUTIVES

Managing Director Asia, Nancy Yu
Chief Product Officer, Thomas Fredell, age 48
Evp And Chief Administrative Officer, Brenda J. Vale
Coo Marketing And Communications Solutions, Roy Gross
Coo Legal And Financial, Rodney D. Johnson
Regional Managing Director Europe Middle East Africa (emea), Alun Baker
Ceo, James (Rusty) Wiley
Cfo, Thomas Donnelly
Cio, Brad Smuland
Senior Vice President, James Garippa
Vice President Sales, Laura Lipani
Senior Vice President President, Thomas Killeen
Senior Vice President Sales, Osterman Steve
Senior Vice President Sales, Scott Taylor
Senior Vice President, Jean Gardner
Vice President Finance, John Gyurci
Vice President, Raul Varela
Senior Vice President Sales, Andrea Sparke
Senior Vice President, Nancy Skluth
Vice President Sales, Phillip Juett
Vice President Regional Sales Manager, Christy Vierzba
Senior Vice President, Mark Williams
Senior Vice President Sales, Michelle Fenley
Vice President Sales, Peter Snyder
Vice President Operations And Business Development, Raju Subramanyan
Vice President, Tony Bednar
Vice President Product Marketing, Axel Kirstetter
Senior Vice President, Jerry Long
Senior Vice President, Mike Sabutis
Senior Vice President Product Management, Christian Idiodi
Vice President Global Tax, Timothy Stoffel
Senior Vice President Sales, Steve Piccone
Senior Vice President, Neal Davies
Senior Vice President, Clark Graebner
Senior Vice President And Regional Director Sales Merrill Datasite Merrill Bridge, Mark Plaehn
Senior Vice President, Shannon Otwell
Vice President, Michael Keating
Chairman, James V. (Jim) Continenza, age 55
Auditors: PRICE WATER HOUSE COOPER LLP

LOCATIONS

HQ: MERRILL CORPORATION
1 MERRILL CIR, SAINT PAUL, MN 551085264
Phone: 651 646-4501
Web: WWW.MERRILLCORP.COM

PRODUCTS/OPERATIONS

SERVICES

Capital Transactions
Contract Management
Data Warehousing
Elections
Financial Services Marketing & Communications
Healthcare Member Communications
Intellectual Property Management
M&A Reorganizations & Exchange Offers
Merrill IFN
Portfolio Management
Regulatory Disclosure

COMPETITORS

Applied Discovery	Pitney Bowes
Diebold	R.R. Donnelley
Harte-Hanks	Ricoh USA
IntraLinks	St Ives
Kroll Ontrack	Williams Lea
Lionbridge	Xerox

HISTORICAL FINANCIALS
Company Type: Private

Income Statement
FYE: January 31

	REVENUE ($ mil.)	NET INCOME ($ mil.)	NET PROFIT MARGIN	EMPLOYEES
01/16	579	78	13.5%	5,418
01/15	691	64	9.3%	—
01/14	815	24	3.0%	—
01/13	851	(9)	—	—
Annual Growth	(12.0%)	—	—	—

2016 Year-End Financials
Return on assets: 4.6%
Return on equity: 13.5%
Current ratio: 1.40

Cash ($ mil.): 31

MESA UNIFIED SCHOOL DISTRICT 4

EXECUTIVES

Supt, Amber Conley
Site Manager, Theresa Chucri
Director of Bands, Roby Brooks
Director of Community Educatio, Tot Wallace
Director of Technology, David Sanders
Procurement Specialist Supervi, Gary Barkman
Exec Asst, Alice Swinehart
Auditors: HEINFELD MEECH & CO PC P

LOCATIONS

HQ: MESA UNIFIED SCHOOL DISTRICT 4
63 E MAIN ST STE 101, MESA, AZ 852017422
Phone: 480 472-0200
Web: WWW.MPSAZ.ORG

HISTORICAL FINANCIALS
Company Type: Private

Income Statement
FYE: June 30

	REVENUE ($ mil.)	NET INCOME ($ mil.)	NET PROFIT MARGIN	EMPLOYEES
06/16	549	(22)	—	9,621
06/15	531	(19)	—	—
06/14	520	(25)	—	—
06/13	514	31	6.0%	—
Annual Growth	2.2%	—	—	—

MESQUITE INDEPENDENT SCHOOL DISTRICT

EXECUTIVES

RES, Robert Seward
Supt, David Vroonland
Vp, Greg Everett
SEC, Archimedes Faulkner
Exec Drt, Mandy Burns

Coordinator, Betty Wisdom
Coordinator, Bob Ankrum
Coordinator, Carolyn Pyles
Coordinator, Ella Wilcox
Coordinator, Leigh Farley
Coordinator, Nancy Gray
Auditors: WEAVER AND TIDWELL LLP DA

LOCATIONS

HQ: MESQUITE INDEPENDENT SCHOOL DISTRICT
3819 TOWNE CROSSING BLVD, MESQUITE, TX
751502799
Phone: 972 288-6411
Web: WWW.MESQUITEISD.ORG

HISTORICAL FINANCIALS
Company Type: Private

Income Statement
FYE: August 31

	REVENUE ($ mil.)	NET INCOME ($ mil.)	NET PROFIT MARGIN	EMPLOYEES
08/17	447	115	25.8%	4,200
08/16	432	52	12.1%	—
08/15	414	9	2.2%	—
08/14	396	21	5.4%	—
Annual Growth	4.2%	75.4%	—	—

2017 Year-End Financials
Return on assets: 5.0%
Return on equity: 25.8%
Current ratio: —

Cash ($ mil.): 123

MESSER CONSTRUCTION CO.

From casinos and courthouses to laboratories and dormitories Messer Construction has built them all. The builder provides commercial construction services (including design/build and project management) for projects in Indiana Kentucky Ohio North Carolina and Tennessee. Messer completes over $830 million worth of projects each year for clients in the life sciences higher education senior living commercial manufacturing/industrial public and health care sectors among others. Its projects have included one of the US's only LEED-certified research buildings (at the University of Louisville) and the Newport Aquarium in Kentucky. Founded in 1932 employee-owned Messer boasts a return-customer rate of 80%.

Operations
Messer Construction offers a range of commercial construction services including building information modeling cost planning and estimating integrated project delivery lean construction and safety programs. It also offers prefabrication services such as mechanical/electrical/plumbing services bathroom pods and health care headwall assemblies.

Geographic Reach
Based in Cincinnati Ohio Messer operates regional offices in North Carolina (Charlotte) Ohio (Cincinnati Columbus and Dayton) Indiana (Indianapolis) Tennessee (Knoxville and Nashville) and Kentucky (Lexington and Louisville).

Sales and Marketing
Messer Construction has served customers from a variety of industries including clients such as: Aisin Automotive Casting Cummins DHL Express Dow AgroSciences Forest Pharmaceuticals Gannett Co General Motors Honda of America Praxair Procter & Gamble Sonoco and Worthington Steel.

Strategy
Messer continues to work on high-value projects across a wide range of industries in the Midwest particularly in secure industries such as healthcare government and education.

During 2015 for example it worked on the 70000-square-foot expansion to Cincinnati Children's Hospital Medical Center (CCHMC) adding a fourth floor 30 beds kitchen full-service cafeteria expanded medical and surgery specialty clinics a gift shop and more. That year it also worked on the $24.1 million- expansion at the National Air and Space Intelligence Center's (NASIC) Foreign Materials Exploitation Laboratory in Dayton for the US Department of Defense as well as the University of Kentucky's $175 million- Student Center Transformation Project (to be completed in 2017) which will span 360000 square feet and include updated student activity and study spaces dining and retail outlets parking a bookstore and more.

Company Background
Formerly known as Frank Messer & Sons Inc. the company changed its name to Messer Construction Co. in March 2002.

EXECUTIVES

Sr Vp, Bernard Suer
Vice President Columbus Office, Robert Verst
Operations Vice President, Mark Hill
Senior Vice President, Mark R Gillming
President And Ceo, Thomas M. (Tom) Keckeis
Svp And Cfo, E. Paul Hitter
Vp And Cio, Richard A. Hensley
Vice President Finance, Paul Hitter
Vice President, Karen Pawsat
Vice President, John Megibben
Operations Vice President, Steve Jones
Finance Vice President, Brian Doyle
Vice President Building Systems Group, Michael Hann
Vice President, Kevin M Cozart
Vice President Leed Ap, Robert Williams
Operations Vice President, Tim Gusler
Operations Vice President, Richard Zoller
Vice President And Chief Information Officer, John Carder
Senior Vice President, Jim Hess
Rental Division Vice President, Tom Wall
Auditors: DELOITTE & TOUCHE LLP CINCINN

LOCATIONS

HQ: MESSER CONSTRUCTION CO.
643 W COURT ST, CINCINNATI, OH 452031511
Phone: 513 242-1541
Web: WWW.MESSER.COM

PRODUCTS/OPERATIONS

Selected Projects
Health Care
  Norton Healthcare
  Knoxville Orthopedic Clinic
Life Sciences
  Indiana University
  University of Kentucky
Higher Education
  Xavier University
  Western Kentucky University
Senior Living
  Graceworks Lutheran Services
  Episcopal Retirement Homes
Commercial
  IGS Energy
  Penn National Gaming
Manufacturing & Industrial
  Aisin Automotive Casting Tennessee Inc.
  DHL Express Inc.
Public/Institutional
  The Ohio Building Authority
  Commonwealth of Kentucky

COMPETITORS

Albert M. Higley	Shook National
Danis	Skanska USA Building
F.A. Wilhelm	The Austin Company
Gray Construction	Turner Corporation
Hunt Construction	Tutor Perini
Pepper Construction	

HISTORICAL FINANCIALS

Company Type: Private

Income Statement   FYE: September 30

	REVENUE ($ mil.)	NET INCOME ($ mil.)	NET PROFIT MARGIN	EMPLOYEES
09/17	1,092	0	—	900
09/15	1,167	0	—	—
09/14	1,029	0	—	—
09/13	831	0	—	—
Annual Growth	7.0%	—	—	—

2017 Year-End Financials

Return on assets: 20.9%
Return on equity: —
Current ratio: 1.10
Cash ($ mil.): 83

METALDYNE PERFORMANCE GROUP INC.

EXECUTIVES

Ceo, George Thanopoulos
Chb, Kevin Penn
Pres-Coo, Douglas Grimm
Cfo, Mark Blaufuss
Exec V Pres-Gen Counsel-Sec, Thomas M Dono Jr
Exec V Pres Sls, Russell Bradley
V Pres-Cao-Controller, Gary Ford
Plant Manager, Carl Koerschner
Auditors: DELOITTE & TOUCHE LLP DETROIT

LOCATIONS

HQ: METALDYNE PERFORMANCE GROUP INC.
1 TOWNE SQ STE 550, SOUTHFIELD, MI 480763710
Phone: 248 727-1800
Web: WWW.AAM.COM

HISTORICAL FINANCIALS

Company Type: Private

Income Statement   FYE: December 31

	REVENUE ($ mil.)	NET INCOME ($ mil.)	NET PROFIT MARGIN	EMPLOYEES
12/16	2,790	96	3.5%	12,000
12/15	3,047	125	4.1%	—
12/14	2,717	73	2.7%	—
Annual Growth	1.3%	15.0%	—	—

2016 Year-End Financials

Return on assets: 9.3%
Return on equity: 3.5%
Current ratio: 1.30
Cash ($ mil.): 209

METHODIST HEALTH CARE SYSTEM

EXECUTIVES

Pres, Larry L Mathis
President, Mauro Ferrari
Vice President, S Jeffrey Atcherman
Operations Administrator, Laura Espinosa PHD Rn
Chief of Medicine, Bruce Kennedy
Staff, Korsh Jafarnia
Health Professional, Sherrie Alexander
Scientist, David Raskin
Hpf Consultants, Annette Depauw
Consultant, Brian Schapper
Epic Boost Consultant, Deepak Gunasekaran
Auditors: GRANT THORNTON LLP DALLAS TX

LOCATIONS

HQ: METHODIST HEALTH CARE SYSTEM
6565 FANNIN ST D200, HOUSTON, TX 770302703
Phone: 713 793-1602
Web: WWW.HOUSTONMETHODIST.ORG

HISTORICAL FINANCIALS

Company Type: Private

Income Statement   FYE: September 30

	REVENUE ($ mil.)	NET INCOME ($ mil.)	NET PROFIT MARGIN	EMPLOYEES
09/17	1,536	161	10.5%	30
09/14*	1,199	151	12.6%	—
06/05	17	0	1.9%	—
Annual Growth	45.4%	67.8%	—	—

*Fiscal year change

2017 Year-End Financials

Return on assets: 8.3%
Return on equity: 10.5%
Current ratio: 2.20
Cash ($ mil.): 58

METHODIST HOSPITAL OF SOUTHERN CALIFORNIA

If you're dehydrated in the Valley Methodist Hospital of Southern California can help. The hospital provides medical care to the residents of California's central San Gabriel Valley. The healthcare facility boasts some 600 beds and is part of Southern California Healthcare Systems. The not-for-profit hospital provides comprehensive acute care including surgical pediatric and intensive care units. It also offers a wide range of specialty services such as cardiology oncology neurology bariatrics and orthopedics. The hospital opened its doors in 1903 with five beds.

Operations

Methodist Hospital serves Arcadia Azusa Baldwin Park Bradbury Duarte El Monte Monrovia Pasadena Rosemead San Gabriel Sierra Madre and Temple City.

In addition to typical acute care services Methodist Hospital's cardiac care center provides complete cardiovascular services including open-heart surgery. The medical facility's intensive care units boast both neonatal and adult centers. Its cardiovascular stroke and cancer centers are certified by various national medical specialist organizations. The hospital employs about 630 medical staff members.

It also operates a rehabilitation clinic and a long-term recovery facility for patients requiring transitional care.

Geographic Reach

Methodist Hospital is located in Arcadia California in the northeastern corner of the Los Angeles metropolitan area; it serves patients from surrounding communities as well.

Financial Performance

Methodist Hospital in fiscal 2013 boasted a $248 million total operating budget.

Strategy

A grant from the H.N. and Frances C. Berger Foundation in 2012 has allowed the hospital to install a state-of-the-art hyperbaric (high-pressure oxygen) chamber in the hospital's Wound Healing Center. The chamber helps to treat diabetic patients suffering from chronic wounds as well as wounds resulting from immune deficiencies and assists patients suffering from decompression sickness or the "bends" as a result of diving accidents.

In recent years Methodist Hospital has continued with its infrastructure expansion and improvement projects with a focus on expanding its emergency department in 2013 and opening a new GYN Oncology Institute in 2014.

Each year the hospital serves 47000 emergency department visits 16800 outpatient visits 16600 inpatient admissions 5100 surgeries and 1800 deliveries.

EXECUTIVES

Director Of Medical Records, Bridgett Didier
Vice President, Bobbie Mccaffrey
Auditors: KPMG LLP LOS ANGELES CA

LOCATIONS

HQ: METHODIST HOSPITAL OF SOUTHERN CALIFORNIA
300 W HUNTINGTON DR, ARCADIA, CA 910073402
Phone: 626 898-8000
Web: WWW.METHODISTHOSPITAL.ORG

PRODUCTS/OPERATIONS

Selected Services
Cardiology
Diabetes Services
Emergency Services
Gynecology
Maternal Child Health
Neurology
Oncology
Orthopedics
Outpatient Services
Rehabilitation Services
Senior Services
Surgical Services
Stroke
Transitional Care Unit
Weight Loss Surgery
Wound Healing Center

COMPETITORS

Citrus Valley Health Partners
Dignity Health
Glendale Adventist Medical Center
Good Samaritan Hospital (Los Angeles)
HCA
Hollywood Presbyterian Medical Center
Memorial Health Services
Newhall Memorial Hospital
Tenet Healthcare

HISTORICAL FINANCIALS

Company Type: Private

Income Statement				FYE: December 31
	REVENUE ($ mil.)	NET INCOME ($ mil.)	NET PROFIT MARGIN	EMPLOYEES
12/16	297	13	4.7%	2,200
12/15	300	11	3.9%	—
12/12	281	0	0.3%	—
12/11	245	(4)	—	—
Annual Growth	3.9%	—	—	—

2016 Year-End Financials

Return on assets: 5.2%   Cash ($ mil.): 15
Return on equity: 4.7%
Current ratio: 1.20

METHODIST HOSPITALS OF DALLAS INC

Methodist Hospitals of Dallas serves the health care needs of North Texas — from Mansfield to McKinney. The church-affiliated organization which does business as Methodist Health System operates 10 hospitalsand more than two dozen family health centers and medical facilities in and around the area deemed by locals as Big D. The original hospital Methodist Dallas Medical Center opened in 1927. The 585-bed teaching and referral hospital boasts a Level I trauma center and an organ transplant program. Other facilities include the 317-bed Methodist Charlton Medical Center the 254-bed Methodist Mansfield Medical Center and the 334-bed Methodist Richardson Medical Center.

Operations

Each year Methodist Health System handles more than 80000 inpatient visits and more than 350000 emergency department and other outpatient visits. It has more than 2700 physicians.

The Methodist Dallas Transplant Institute is one of the largest and most active transplant centers in the southwestern part of the country performing dozens of adult kidney pancreas and liver transplants each year.

Other facilities include the Methodist Campus for Continuing Care Methodist McKinney Hospital Methodist Hospital for Surgery and Methodist Rehabilitation Hospital.

Geographic Reach

Methodist Hospitals of Dallas serves the residents of several communities located in and around the North Dallas area such as Midlothian Grand Prairie Cedar Hill Richardson Plano Garland Wylie and McKinney.

Strategy

In recent years Methodist Health System has grown through a series of acquisitions as well as through organic expansion efforts such as the construction of about 50 rooms and new surgery suites in the Methodist Charlton hospital.In 2017 its Mansfield Medical Center opened the Alexander Medical Pavilion (including a center for diagnostic imaging) and the specialty Black and Blue Sports Injury Clinic. The hospital is also undergoing an $85 million expansion which will add 150 private patient rooms a surgery room and a parking garage.

EXECUTIVES

President Methodist Mansfield Medical Center, John E. Phillips
President And Ceo, Stephen L. (Steve) Mansfield
Evp And Cfo, Michael J. Schaefer, age 67, $370,759 total compensation
Evp And Chief Legal Officer, Michael O. (Mickey) Price, $219,359 total compensation
Svp External Affairs; President And Ceo Methodist Health System Foundation, April B. Chamberlain
Svp And Cio, Pamela G. McNutt
President Methodist Dallas Medical Center, Laura Irvine
Vp And Chief Medical Informatics Officer, Sam Bagchi
Evp And Coo, Pamela (Pam) Stoyanoff
Evp System Alignment And Integration, Tim B. Kirby
President Methodist Charlton Medical Center, Jonathan S. Davis
President Methodist Richardson Medical Center, E. Kenneth Hutchenrider
Svp And Chief Medical Officer, Adam L. Myers
Vice President Of Managed Care, Shannon Huggins

LOCATIONS

HQ: METHODIST HOSPITALS OF DALLAS INC
1441 N BECKLEY AVE, DALLAS, TX 752031201
Phone: 877 637-4297

PRODUCTS/OPERATIONS

Selected Services

Back and Spine
Behavioral Health and Addiction Recovery
Cancer Services
Cardiovascular
da Vinci Surgical System
Diabetes
Digestive Diseases
Ear Nose & Throat (ENT) Services & Allergy Treatments
Emergency and Trauma Care
Fitness Programs
Home Health
Imaging and Radiology
The Liver Institute
Neurosurgery and Neurology
Ophthalmology
Orthopedics
Pain Management
Palliative Care
Physical Therapy and Rehabilitation
Prostate Screening and Awareness Program
Sleep Disorders
Transplant
Urology
Weight Management
Women and Children's Services
Women's Imaging and Mammography
Wound Care and Hyperbaric Center

Selected Facilities

Golden Cross Academic Clinic
Methodist Dallas Medical Center
Methodist Charlton Medical Center
Methodist Family Health Centers
  Cedar Hill
  Central Grand Prairie
  Dallas
  Midlothian
  South Grand Prairie
Methodist Hospital for Surgery
Methodist Mansfield Medical Center
Methodist McKinney Hospital
Methodist Richardson Medical Center
Methodist Rehabilitation Hospital

COMPETITORS

CHRISTUS Health
Children's Medical Center of Dallas
Community Health Systems
Cook Children's Health
JPS Health Network
Parkland Health & Hospital System
Presbyterian Hospital of Dallas
Southwestern Medical

Care System
HCA
Harris Methodist Fort Worth Hospital
Hunt Memorial
Center
Tenet Healthcare
Texas Health Denton
Texas Health Resources

HISTORICAL FINANCIALS

Company Type: Private

Income Statement				FYE: June 30
	REVENUE ($ mil.)	NET INCOME ($ mil.)	NET PROFIT MARGIN	EMPLOYEES
06/16	431	35	8.2%	4,804
06/15*	411	21	5.3%	—
09/14	1,096	137	12.5%	—
09/12	969	165	17.1%	—
Annual Growth	(18.3%)	(31.9%)	—	—

*Fiscal year change

2016 Year-End Financials

Return on assets: 2.2%   Cash ($ mil.): 1
Return on equity: 8.2%
Current ratio: 5.00

METROHEALTH MEDICAL CENTER

EXECUTIVES

Ceo, Ekran Boutros
Pres, Akram Boutros
Cfo, Nancy Fisher
Prin, J B Silvers PHD
Prin, Sharon Sobol Jordan
Cfo, Craig Richmond
Admin Coordinator, Jane Knowles

LOCATIONS

HQ: METROHEALTH MEDICAL CENTER
2500 METROHEALTH DR, CLEVELAND, OH 441091900
Phone: 216 778-7800
Web: WWW.METROHEALTH.ORG

HISTORICAL FINANCIALS

Company Type: Private

Income Statement				FYE: December 31
	REVENUE ($ mil.)	NET INCOME ($ mil.)	NET PROFIT MARGIN	EMPLOYEES
12/16	883	(8)	—	6,000
12/15	795	35	4.5%	—
12/14	782	32	4.2%	—
Annual Growth	6.3%	—	—	—

2016 Year-End Financials

Return on assets: 6.0%   Cash ($ mil.): 11
Return on equity: (-0.9%)
Current ratio: 0.70

METROPOLITAN AIRPORTS COMMISSION

EXECUTIVES

Ceo, Brian Ryks
Chm, Daniel Boivin
Coo, Roy Fuhrmann
Coordinator, Timothy Blaylark
Purchasing Manager, Brad Johnson
Human Resources, Cindy Ketola
Director, Mike Everson
Director of Finance, Steve Busch
Marketing Director, Mitchell Kilian
Assistant Chief, Jeffrey Klawiter
General Manager, Patricia Anderson
Auditors: BKD LLP INDIANAPOLIS INDIAN

LOCATIONS

HQ: METROPOLITAN AIRPORTS COMMISSION
   6040 28TH AVE S, MINNEAPOLIS, MN 554502701
Phone: 612 726-8100
Web: WWW.METROAIRPORTS.ORG

HISTORICAL FINANCIALS

Company Type: Private

Income Statement				FYE: December 31
	REVENUE ($ mil.)	NET INCOME ($ mil.)	NET PROFIT MARGIN	EMPLOYEES
12/17	353	59	16.9%	575
12/16	338	44	13.0%	—
12/15	307	46	15.1%	—
12/14	298	25	8.5%	—
Annual Growth	5.9%	33.1%	—	—

2017 Year-End Financials

Return on assets: 20.6%   Cash ($ mil.): 8
Return on equity: 16.9%
Current ratio: 0.10

METROPOLITAN EDISON COMPANY

EXECUTIVES

Pres, Charles E Jones
Exec V Pres-Cfo, Mark T Clark
V Pres-Controller-Cao, Harvey L Wagner
Exec V Pres-Gen Counsel, Leila L Vespoli
V Pres-Treas, James F Pearson
Real Estate Conultant, Craig Correll
Clerk, Michelle Frey
Supervisor Engineering, Alfred Nerino
Customer Associate, Matthew Kemp
Auditors: PRICEWATERHOUSECOOPERS LLP CL

LOCATIONS

HQ: METROPOLITAN EDISON COMPANY
   76 S MAIN ST, AKRON, OH 443081812
Phone: 800 736-3402
Web: WWW.FIRSTENERGYCORP.COM

COMPETITORS

Columbia Gas of   PECO Energy
   Pennsylvania   PPL Electric
Direct Energy

HISTORICAL FINANCIALS

Company Type: Private

Income Statement				FYE: December 31
	REVENUE ($ mil.)	NET INCOME ($ mil.)	NET PROFIT MARGIN	EMPLOYEES
12/17	837	97	11.6%	678
12/16	865	87	10.1%	—
12/10	1,818	58	3.2%	—
12/09	1,688	55	3.3%	—
Annual Growth	(8.4%)	7.3%	—	—

2017 Year-End Financials

Return on assets: 6.3%   Cash ($ mil.): —
Return on equity: 11.6%
Current ratio: 0.60

METROPOLITAN OPERA ASSOCIATION, INC.

Italians and Germans alike desire an American debut at the Met. Well their operas do anyway. The Metropolitan Opera Association manages The Metropolitan Opera company which presents more than 200 performances every year in its residence at the Lincoln Center for the Performing Arts. The Met is known for performing most works in their original languages and for producing regular Saturday radio broadcasts which are aired throughout North America and in South America Europe and the Asia/Pacific region. In association with sponsors the Met makes video and CD recordings of the performances and distributes them worldwide. The Met was founded in 1883.

Operations
The opera house has 3800 seats and 195 standing room places for a total capacity of 3975. The facility employs more than 860 people.

Geographic Reach
The Metropolitan Opera is is part of the Lincoln Center complex located in the Midtown Manhattan section of New York City.

Financial Performance
The Met's endowment has been cut in recent years. Donations and ticket sales have been down slightly although the Met is still on solid financial ground.

EXECUTIVES

Managing Director Information Technology, John Pennino
Department Head, William Malloy
Vice President, Richard Wagner

LOCATIONS

HQ: METROPOLITAN OPERA ASSOCIATION, INC.
   LINCOLN CTR, NEW YORK, NY 10023
Phone: 212 799-3100
Web: WWW.METOPERA.ORG

METROPOLITAN ST. LOUIS SEWER DISTRICT

Business is draining for The Metropolitan St. Louis Sewer District (MSD) which provides wastewater collection and treatment services for a population of about 1.3 million in the St. Louis area. The district operates nearly 10000 miles of sewer lines and seven wastewater treatment plants that process an average of 370 million gallons of sewage per day. MSD serves about 425000 residential and commercial/industrial customers. It has a budget of more than $470 million and is governed by a six-member board divided equally between appointees of the mayor of St. Louis and of the St. Louis County executive. The district was created by voters in 1954 and began operations two years later.

Financial Performance
MSD reported operating revenue in 2012 of $226 million up about 3% from the prior year. Operating income also rose to nearly $10 million from a loss of $25 million in 2011 as the district saw a decrease in expenses particularly engineering and asset management. It also saw a drop in water backup claims.

EXECUTIVES

Chief Sales Officer, Ken Lucas
Secretary Treasurer, Tim Snoke
Assistant Secretary Treasurer, John Strahlman
Board Member, Bob Meppiel
Auditors: RUBINBROWN LLP SAINT LOUIS M

LOCATIONS

HQ: METROPOLITAN ST. LOUIS SEWER DISTRICT
   2350 MARKET ST STE 300, SAINT LOUIS, MO
   631032555
Phone: 314 768-6200
Web: WWW.STLMSD.COM

HISTORICAL FINANCIALS

Company Type: Private

Income Statement				FYE: July 31
	REVENUE ($ mil.)	NET INCOME ($ mil.)	NET PROFIT MARGIN	EMPLOYEES
07/15	335	26	7.8%	1,500
07/09	223	(71)	—	—
07/08	309	34	11.3%	—
07/05	286	0	—	—
Annual Growth	1.6%	—	—	—

2015 Year-End Financials

Return on assets: 7.7%   Cash ($ mil.): 4
Return on equity: 7.8%
Current ratio: 0.10

HISTORICAL FINANCIALS

Company Type: Private

Income Statement				FYE: June 30
	REVENUE ($ mil.)	NET INCOME ($ mil.)	NET PROFIT MARGIN	EMPLOYEES
06/16	319	48	15.3%	976
06/12	226	21	9.4%	—
06/11	219	(10)	—	—
06/09	249	68	27.6%	—
Annual Growth	3.6%	(4.8%)	—	—

2016 Year-End Financials
Return on assets: 11.7%   Cash ($ mil.): 26
Return on equity: 15.3%
Current ratio: 0.20

METROPOLITAN TRANSPORTATION COMMISSION

EXECUTIVES

Exec Dir, Steve Hieminger
Vice Chb, Jake Mackenzie
Exec Dir-Policy, Therese McMillan
Dep Exec Dir-Oprs, Ann Flemer
Treas-Cfo, Brian Mayhew
Deputy Director*, Andrew B Fremier
Coordinator, Shauna Callow
Law Specialist, Alice Truong
Project Coordinator, Jeffrey Nazareno
Program Manager, Kenneth KAO
Information Technology Manager, Mark Dinh
Auditors: PRICEWATERHOUSECOOPERS LLP SA

LOCATIONS

HQ: METROPOLITAN TRANSPORTATION
COMMISSION
375 BEALE ST STE 800, SAN FRANCISCO, CA
941052179
Phone: 415 778-6700
Web: WWW.CLIPPERCARD.COM

HISTORICAL FINANCIALS

Company Type: Private

Income Statement				FYE: June 30
	REVENUE ($ mil.)	NET INCOME ($ mil.)	NET PROFIT MARGIN	EMPLOYEES
06/18	313	49	15.8%	115
06/17	251	(31)	—	—
06/16	237	21	8.9%	—
06/15	305	44	14.5%	—
Annual Growth	0.8%	3.7%	—	—

2018 Year-End Financials

Return on assets: 0.1%   Cash ($ mil.): —
Return on equity: 15.8%
Current ratio: 1.30

METROPOLITAN UTILITIES DISTRICT

The Metropolitan Utilities District (MUD) distributes natural gas and water in the Omaha Nebraska metropolitan area. The company serves some 220000 natural gas customers and more than 200000 water customers. It also collects sewer and trash fees for municipalities. Customer-owned MUD which claims to be the fifth-largest public gas utility in the nation is a political subdivision of the State of Nebraska. Its board members are elected by residents of its service territory.

Geographic Reach

MUD provides natural gas to customers in Omaha Bennington Fort Calhoun Springfield Yutan and Bellevue; its water operations cover Omaha Bellevue Bennington Carter Lake LaVista Ralston Waterloo and the Papio-Missouri Natural Resources District (which supplies water to Fort Calhoun).

Financial Performance

Overall revenue was down 6% in 2012 to about $293 million. A nearly 30% increase in water sales because of record-breaking demand during an unusually hot dry summer was not enough to offset a nearly 20% drop in natural gas sales. MUD's net income rose from $15 million to about $46 million that year however as operating expenses declined particularly the cost of natural gas.

Company Background

The Metropolitan Water District was created by the Nebraska Legislature in 1913. In 1918 state legislators authorized the City of Omaha to take charge of the gas system and the Metropolitan Water District subsequently was renamed as the Metropolitan Utilities District.

EXECUTIVES

Senior Vice President Chief Financial Officer, Debra Schneider
Vice President Marketing, Jeff Breci
Vice President Information Technology Business Systems, Raied Stanley
Vice President Safety And Security, Steve Ausdemore
Auditors: RSM US LLP OMAHA NEBRASKA

LOCATIONS

HQ: METROPOLITAN UTILITIES DISTRICT
1723 HARNEY ST, OMAHA, NE 681021960
Phone: 402 554-6666
Web: WWW.MUDOMAHA.COM

HISTORICAL FINANCIALS

Company Type: Private

Income Statement				FYE: December 31
	REVENUE ($ mil.)	NET INCOME ($ mil.)	NET PROFIT MARGIN	EMPLOYEES
12/16	291	31	10.9%	852
12/12	292	46	15.8%	—
12/11	311	15	4.9%	—
Annual Growth	(1.3%)	15.8%	—	—

2016 Year-End Financials

Return on assets: 11.3%   Cash ($ mil.): 151
Return on equity: 10.9%
Current ratio: 1.80

METROPOLITAN WATER RECLAMATION DISTRICT OF GREATER CHICAGO

EXECUTIVES

President, Terrence J Obrien
V Pres, Kathleen Meany
Chief of Mno, Thomas O Conner
Principal, Jeff Weber
Actng Public Info Coordinat, Mary Carroll
Information Technology/Interne, Vitaliy Bunimovich
Information Technology Manager, Eileen McElligott

Acting Director, Ellen Barry
Accounting Staff, Marilyn Torres
Scientist, Weizhe An
Executive Officer, Joe Cannici
Auditors: RSM US LLP CHICAGO ILLINOIS

LOCATIONS

HQ: METROPOLITAN WATER RECLAMATION
DISTRICT OF GREATER CHICAGO
100 E ERIE ST, CHICAGO, IL 606112829
Phone: 312 751-5600
Web: WWW.MWRDECU.ORG

HISTORICAL FINANCIALS

Company Type: Private

Income Statement				FYE: December 31
	REVENUE ($ mil.)	NET INCOME ($ mil.)	NET PROFIT MARGIN	EMPLOYEES
12/17	719	76	10.6%	2,259
12/16	703	10	1.5%	—
12/15	679	37	5.6%	—
12/14	670	63	9.5%	—
Annual Growth	2.4%	6.2%	—	—

2017 Year-End Financials

Return on assets: 11.4%   Cash ($ mil.): 49
Return on equity: 10.6%
Current ratio: —

MFA INCORPORATED

Agricultural cooperative MFA brings together 45000 farmers in Missouri and adjacent states. One of the US' oldest regional co-ops supplying its member/owners with agronomy distribution financing and purchasing services it runs more than 145 retail farm supply centers and works with independent dealers. MFA supplies animal feeds seed fertilizer and crop protection products. The co-op also provides its members with agronomy services animal-health products and farm supplies. It also offers marketing services and is the publisher of Today's Farmer. Agmo Corporation MFA's finance company provides co-op members longer credit terms for purchases made through MFA's retail outlets.

Operations

MFA's plant food sales exceed 1 million tons each year.

Geographic Reach

The coop has fertilizer terminals on the Mississippi River as well as on the Missouri and Arkansas rivers.

Sales and Marketing

The coop sells through 400 independent dealers.

Strategy

Part of MFA's strategy is to focus on growth initiatives and find opportunistic products and services to provide to its customers. Strategic river terminals and other bulk facilities give it capacity to deliver bulk quantities of plant food. It also invests in rolling stock trucks and application equipment to ensure bulk products are efficiently delivered to retail customers.

In 2016 the coop formed a joint venture with MFA Oil Company a farmer-owned energy supply cooperative to build a shuttle-loader facility on the Union Pacific Railroad line about 5 miles east of Hamilton Missouri. The grain-handling facility will consist of 2 million bushels of permanent storage and 1.5 million bushels of temporary storage along with a loop rail siding to accommodate a 110-railroad-car 'shuttle' unit. Once completed the structure will allow farmers in north central Missouri and southern Iowa to deliver crops to a modern high-speed grain facility.

Company Background

Expanding its assets in 2013 MFA acquired Producers Grain Company's assets in El Dorado Springs Walker Bronaugh and Nevada in Missouri.

The co-op was established in 1914 when seven Missouri farmers got together to buy binder twine.

EXECUTIVES

Svp Corporate And Member Services, Janice Schuerman
Svp Corporate Operations, J. Brian Griffith
President And Ceo, Bill Streeter
Vp Feed Division, Alan Wessler
Svp And Cfo, Ernie Verslues
Vp Plant Foods And Transportation, Bill Coen
Vp Crop Protection Seed And Farm Supply, Don Houston
Vp Agri Services, Craig Childs
Senior Vice President Corporate Operations, Brian Griffith
Vice President Mill Operations, Tom Staudt
Second Vice President Finance, David Moore
Vice President And General Manager, Cassy Landewee
Vice Chairman, John Moffitt
Chairman, Don Mills
Auditors: WILLIAMS KEEPERS LLC COLUMBIA

LOCATIONS

HQ: MFA INCORPORATED
  201 RAY YOUNG DR, COLUMBIA, MO 652013599
Phone: 573 874-5111
Web: WWW.MFAINCORPORATED.COM

COMPETITORS

ADM	GROWMARK
Andersons	Heartland Co-op
Cargill	Missouri Farm Bureau
Farm Service Cooperative	Orscheln Farm and Home
Farmers Cooperative Company	Tennessee Farmers Co-op
	United Producers

HISTORICAL FINANCIALS

Company Type: Private

Income Statement				FYE: August 31
	REVENUE ($ mil.)	NET INCOME ($ mil.)	NET PROFIT MARGIN	EMPLOYEES
08/18	1,367	6	0.5%	1,393
08/17	1,373	14	1.0%	—
08/16	1,192	4	0.3%	—
08/15	1,434	10	0.8%	—
Annual Growth	(1.6%)	(14.0%)	—	—

MGM HOLDINGS INC.

EXECUTIVES

Ceo, Gary Barber
Pres, Mark Burnett
Head of Administration, Bill Lopatto
Executive Vice President and D, Cheryl Rodman
Manager, Elaine Kojima
Executive Assistant, John Harding
Manager, Mary Yang
Manager, Megan Bradford
Vice President, Mike Murashko
Auditors: ERNST & YOUNG LLP LOS ANGELES

LOCATIONS

HQ: MGM HOLDINGS INC.
  245 N BEVERLY DR, BEVERLY HILLS, CA 902105319
Phone: 310 449-3000
Web: WWW.MGM.COM

HISTORICAL FINANCIALS

Company Type: Private

Income Statement				FYE: December 31
	REVENUE ($ mil.)	NET INCOME ($ mil.)	NET PROFIT MARGIN	EMPLOYEES
12/16	1,184	155	13.1%	4
12/15	1,158	252	21.8%	—
Annual Growth	2.2%	(38.5%)	—	—

MIAMI UNIVERSITY

Not that Miami the other one. Named for the Miami Indian Tribe that inhabited the area now known as the Miami Valley Region of Ohio Miami University emphasizes undergraduate study at its main campus in Oxford (35 miles north of Cincinnati) as well as at commuter campuses in Hamilton Middletown and West Chester Ohio and a European Center in Luxembourg. The school offers bachelors masters and doctoral programs in areas including business administration arts and sciences engineering and education. Its student body includes more than 15000 undergraduates on the Oxford campus; 2500 graduate students; and another 5700 students attending satellite campuses. Miami University was established in 1809.

Financial Performance

Miami University's 2011 revenue increased 3% vs. 2010 due to a correspondingA increase in undergraduate tuition on its three campuses and a rising rates for room and board. Net income at the public universityA rose 25% over the same period on higher revenue and lower operating expenses due primarily to a reduction in the number of positions and no salary increases. The rise in tuition for Ohio residentsA in 2011 was the first in four years. Also investment income rose in 2011 for the second consecutive year.

Company Background

Miami University celebrated its bicentennial in 2009. The school was chartered inA February ofA 1809 by the State of Ohio but the first classses were not held untilA 1824.

EXECUTIVES

Vice President, Beck Parker
Vice President, Brenden Clinton
Chief Information Officer And Vice President Information Technology, Peter Natale
Assistant Vice President For Auxiliary Services, Peter C Miller
Vice President For Student Affairs, Jayne Brownell
Assistant Vice President And Information Security Officer, Joe Bazeley
Senior Vice President Information Technology Programmer, Valerie Garnett
Vice President For Student Affairs, Barbara Jones
Program Associate Vice President Of Finance, Agnes A Shea
Associate Vice President For Finance And Associate Treasurer, Beverly Thomas
Interim Vice President For Information Technology, Debra Allison
Assistant Vice President For Student Affairs, Scott Walter
Assistant Vice President Enterprise Operations Information Technology Services, Troy Travis
Vice President Of Human Resource, Eric White
Vice President Information Technology Technical Support, Carolyn Ledford
Executive Manager, Susan Clark
Assistant Vice President, Jen Franchak
Vice President Of Public Relations, Matt Steward
Economics Major Entrepreneurship Minor Theta Chi Treasurer, Michael Beresford
Auditors: MCGLADREY LLP CLEVELAND OHIO

LOCATIONS

HQ: MIAMI UNIVERSITY
  501 E HIGH ST, OXFORD, OH 450561846
Phone: 513 529-1809
Web: WWW.MIAMIOH.EDU

HISTORICAL FINANCIALS

Company Type: Private

Income Statement				FYE: June 30
	REVENUE ($ mil.)	NET INCOME ($ mil.)	NET PROFIT MARGIN	EMPLOYEES
06/17	544	83	15.4%	4,925
06/16	522	65	12.5%	—
06/12	440	32	7.5%	—
06/11	418	120	28.8%	—
Annual Growth	4.5%	(5.9%)	—	—

2017 Year-End Financials

Return on assets: 7.6%   Cash ($ mil.): 77
Return on equity: 15.4%
Current ratio: 1.00

MIAMI VALLEY HOSPITAL

Don't go to Florida looking for this hospital! Miami Valley Hospital (MVH) is an acute care facility serving the residents of Dayton Ohio and surrounding areas through two campuses. MVH and MVH South have roughly 950 beds and offer 50 primary and specialty care practices through its Regional Adult Burn Center the MVH Cancer Center MVH Sports Medicine Center and behavioral health units for outpatient and inpatient chemical dependency therapy and other psychiatric services. MVH also offers Level I trauma services Level III-B NICU adult burn center an air ambulance program and blood marrow and kidney transplant services. The hospital is part of the Premier Health Partners network.

Operations

In addition to MVH the Premier Health Partners network consists of Good Samaritan Hospital (also stationed in Dayton Ohio) Atrium Medical Center in nearby Middletown and Upper Valley Medical Center in Troy. Collectively the multi-hospital health system houses about 1800 inpatient beds and around 65 facilities.

MVH have more than 1100 physicians in more than 70 primary and specialty medical practice areas. It was a 2012 recipient of the HealthGrades Distinguished Hospital Award for Clinical Excellence placing it among the top 5% of hospitals in the US.

In 2012 it had 41555 inpatient admissions; 164140 outpatient visits; 125622 emergency department visits; and oversaw 4000 births.

Financial Performance

Medicare accounted for 40% of the company's 2012 revenues; Medicaid 20%.

Strategy

Over the past few years MVH has focused on upgrading its infrastructure. It has built a $135 million 440000-sq. ft. 11-story heart tower on the south side of the campus and spent $19 million on renovating and expanding its neonatal intensive care unit.

In 2013 it opened its new $6 million 24-hour Emergency Center in Jamestown Ohio to meet the growing demand for emergency care.

In 2013 MVH South opened a $20 million Comprehensive Cancer Center and (in 2012) a new maternity center which includes five labor and delivery suites two surgical suites for c-section deliveries and 16 private after-birthing suites.

Company Background

MVH was formed in 1890.

EXECUTIVES

Pres-Ceo, Bobbie Gerhart
President, Mark Shaker
Vice President, Makkie Clancy
Cfo, Lisa Bishop
V Pres-Coo, Barbara Johnson
Staff, Ed Graham
Coordinator, Carrie Clark
Health Professional, Jon D Girard
Coordinator, Carmen Young
Human Resources, Gretchen Long MBA
Coordinator, Melissa Brook

LOCATIONS

HQ: MIAMI VALLEY HOSPITAL
  1 WYOMING ST, DAYTON, OH 454092711
Phone: 937 208-8000
Web: WWW.MIAMIVALLEYHOSPITAL.ORG

PRODUCTS/OPERATIONS

Campus Locations
Miami Valley Hospital - Dayton OH
Miami Valley Hospital South - Centerville Ohio

Selected Services and Specialties
Ablation (Cardiology)
Access and Transfer Center (physicians)
Alcoholism Drug Dependency and Addiction Treatment
Aneurysm (Neurosciences)
Ankle Surgery
Arterial Interventions
Audiology
Bariatrics/Weight Loss Surgery
Behavioral Services
Biotherapy/Targeted Therapy
Blood and Marrow Transplant Program
Brachytherapy
Brain Conditions and Treatments
Brain Injury Rehabilitation
Breast Cancer Navigators
Breast Center
Breast Center
Brethen Center for Surgical Advancement (physicians)
Bull Family Diabetes Center
Burn Center
Cancer Care
Cancer Care (Oncology)
Cardiac Electrophysiology Lab
Cardiac Rehabilitation
Cardiology
Cardiology
Cardiothoracic Surgery
CareFlight - Medical Transportation
Catheterization Lab Procedures
Center for Sleep and Wake Disorders
Chemoembolization
Chemotherapy and Infusion Therapy
Childbirth Education
Colon Cancer
Colorectal Cancer
Complementary Medicine (Cancer)
Comprehensive Outpatient Rehab Program (CORP)
Counseling/Pastoral Care
Craniectomy (Neuroscience)
Craniotomy (Neuroscience)
Cryoablation
CT scan (Imaging)
Dental Center
Depression/Anxiety Treatment
Diabetes
Dialysis Services
Discectomy
Drug Addiction Treatment
Elder Care
Emergency & Trauma Center (ETC)
Foot Surgery
Fractures (Athletes)
Fusion (spinal treatment)
Gastric Bypass
Genetic Testing
Gynecologic Cancer
Gynecology
Hand Therapy
Head and Neck Cancer
Heart Care
Heart Surgery
High Risk Breast Cancer Center
Hip Surgery
Hormone Therapy
Hospitalists/Medical Professionals
Hyperbaric Oxygen Therapy Center
Image Guided Radiation Therapy (IGRT)
Injury Prevention Center
Inpatient Rehabilitation
Intensity Modulated Radiation Therapy (IMRT)
Intensive Care Unit (ICU)
Interventional Radiology
Joint replacements
Kidney Transplant
Knee Surgery
Kyphoplasty
Leukemia
Lung Cancer
Lymphoma
Mammography Screenings
Maternal-Fetal Medicine
Maternity
Maternity
Medical Professionals/Hospitalists
Medical Transportation - CareFlight
Mental Health Services
Minimally Invasive Surgery
Mother and Baby Services
MRI (Imaging)
Nanoknife
Neonatal Intensive Care
Neuro Rehabilitation
NeuroInterventional Center
Neuroscience
Neurosciences
Nutrition Services
OB-GYN
Obstetrics
Occupational Rehabilitation
Occupational Therapy
Oncology
Organ Transplant
Orthopedics
Orthopedics
Outpatient Physical Therapy
Pain Management
Palliative Care
Pancreatic Cancer
Perinatal Intensive Care
PET Scan (Imaging)
Pharmacy
Physiatry
Physical Therapy
Pre-Admission Testing
Premier HeartWorks
Preventive Cardiology
Prostate Cancer
Pulmonary Services
Radiofrequency ablation
Radiology
Radionuclide scan
Rehabilitation
Rehabilitation Institute of Ohio
Respiratory Care
Robotic Surgery
Shoulder Surgery
Shunt (Neuroscience)
Skin Cancer
Sleep Center
Solitaire Revascularization Device (Neurosciences)
Speech-Language Pathology
Spinal decompression surgery
Spinal disc replacement
Spinal fracture treatment
Spinal tumor surgery
Spine and back injuries (Orthopedics)
Spine Conditions and Treatments (Neuroscience)
Sports Medicine
Sports Medicine
Stereotaxis
Stomach Cancer
Stroke Treatments
Surgery Center
Surgical Oncology
Thoracic Surgery
Throat Cancer
Trauma
Ultrasound (Imaging)
Urological Cancer
Urology
Vascular Services
Venous Interventions
Vertebroplasty
Weight Loss Surgery (Bariatrics)
Weight Loss Surgery/Bariatrics
Wheelchair Clinic
Women's Health
Women's Heart Services
Women's Services
Wound Therapy
X-rays (Imaging)
Y-90 Radioembolization

COMPETITORS

Cincinnati Children's Hospital
Deaconess Associations
Encompass Health
Good Samaritan Hospital (IN)
Kettering Health Network
OhioHealth
The Christ Hospital Corporation
TriHealth
UC Health

HISTORICAL FINANCIALS

Company Type: Private

Income Statement				FYE: December 31
	REVENUE ($ mil.)	NET INCOME ($ mil.)	NET PROFIT MARGIN	EMPLOYEES
12/16	809	35	4.4%	6,000
12/15	827	37	4.5%	—
12/14	785	37	4.8%	—
12/07	622	44	7.1%	—
Annual Growth	3.0%	(2.3%)	—	—

2016 Year-End Financials

Return on assets: 2.9%
Return on equity: 4.4%
Current ratio: 2.00
Cash ($ mil.): 42

MICHIGAN ELECTRIC TRANSMISSION COMPANY, LLC

EXECUTIVES

MBR, Joseph L Welch
MBR, Edward Rayhil
Acct Mgr, Patricia Wenzel
Senior Vice-President, Cameron M Bready
Vice-President Finance, Rejji Hayes
Vice-President, Terry Harvill
Vice-President Operations, Elizabeth Howell

HQ: MICHIGAN ELECTRIC TRANSMISSION COMPANY, LLC
27175 ENERGY WAY, NOVI, MI 483773639
Phone: 248 946-3000
Web: WWW.ITC-HOLDINGS.COM

HISTORICAL FINANCIALS
Company Type: Private

Income Statement — FYE: December 31

	REVENUE ($ mil.)	NET INCOME ($ mil.)	NET PROFIT MARGIN	EMPLOYEES
12/17	325	89	27.4%	90
12/16	295	87	29.5%	—
Annual Growth	10.2%	2.4%	—	—

2017 Year-End Financials
Return on assets: 5.9%   Cash ($ mil.): —
Return on equity: 27.4%
Current ratio: —

MICHIGAN STATE UNIVERSITY

Remember the Spartans? You should if you graduated from a land-grant university in the US. Founded in 1855 Michigan State University (MSU) was the model of a land-grant institution made into law in 1862. Today MSU and its 50000 students cover a lot of land in East Lansing. The university offers more than 200 programs of study through 17 colleges. It has extensive programs in core fields including education physics psychology medicine and communications. It is also a leading research university with top-ranked international studies programs. As a highly ranked research university MSU is awarded millions of dollars in research grants each year from public and private entities.

Operations
Each year MSU receives about $600 million in research grants from entities including the National Science Foundation the US Department of Health and Human Services US Department of Energy and the US Department of Agriculture.

With 5100 faculty and academic staff members and a student-teacher ratio of about 16:1 MSU is noted by U.S. News & World Report for its programs in graduate-level elementary and secondary education nuclear physics and industrial and organizational psychology. It is the only university in the country with three on-campus medical schools graduating allopathic (MD) and osteopathic (DO) physicians as well as veterinarians (DVMs).

Geographic Reach
MSU's 5200-acre main campus is in East Lansing three miles east of Lansing (the capital city of Michigan). The campus includes about 560 buildings (100 of which are academic). The university also has another 20000 acres-some used for animal agricultural and forestry research.

MSU's students hail from all 50 US states as well as more than 130 other countries. It also has one of the largest study abroad programs in the US including about 280 partnerships with international institutions.

Financial Performance
MSU's had budgeted revenues of $1.3 billion in 2017-18. Tuition and fees accounted for about 70% of this and state appropriations about 20%. Higher student tuition and fees have contributed to MSU's revenue growth over the last few years.Academics and related services take about two-thirds of the university's expenditures annually.

Strategy
Expanding facilities is a core growth initiative at MSU. Recent construction projects include a new art museum new science labs and residence halls and a new nursing education building. MSU is also constructing the Facility for Rare Isotope Beams a $680 million center supported by grants from the US Department of Energy to advance understanding of rare nuclear isotopes as well as the evolution of the cosmos. It has also partnered with University of Wisconsin-Madison to establish a $125 million bioenergy research center (also funded by the US Department of Energy).

Company Background
MSU was founded in 1855 a forerunner of the land-grant college concept under the name Agricultural College of the State of Michigan. The Morrill Act which codified land-grant institutions became law in 1862. MSU became a full university in 1955 as Michigan State University of Agriculture and Applied Science. It changed its name to Michigan State University in 1964.

EXECUTIVES

Provost And Vp Academic Affairs, Lou Anna K. Simon
Evp For Academic Affairs And Provost, June Youatt
Evp For Administrative Services, Satish Udpa
Dean James Madison College, Sherman W. Garnett
Dean Lyman Briggs College, Elizabeth H. Simmons
Dean College Of Law, Joan W. Howarth
Dean College Of Music, James (Jim) Forger
Dean College Of Natural Science, R. James Kirkpatrick
Dean College Of Osteopathic Medicine, William D. Strampel
Dean Residential College In The Arts And Humanities, Stephen L. (Steve) Esquith
Dean Honors College, Cynthia Jackson-Elmoore
Vp Information Technology And Cio, Joanna Young
Dean College Of Education, Donald E. Heller
Vp Finance And Treasurer, Mark P. Haas
Dean College Of Veterinary Medicine, John Baker
Dean College Of Communication Arts And Sciences, Prabu David
Vice President Human Resources, Lauren Marinez
Chairman, Joel I. Ferguson, age 79
Vice Chairman, Mitch Lyons
Secretary, Shawna Prater
Auditors: PLANTE & MORAN PLLC EAST LANS

LOCATIONS

HQ: MICHIGAN STATE UNIVERSITY
426 AUDITORIUM RD, EAST LANSING, MI 488242600
Phone: 517 355-1855
Web: WWW.MSU.EDU

PRODUCTS/OPERATIONS

Selected Colleges and Divisions
College of Agriculture and Natural Resources
College of Arts and Letters
College of Communication Arts and Sciences
College of Education
College of Engineering
College of Human Medicine
College of Law (affiliated)
College of Music
College of Natural Science
College of Nursing
College of Osteopathic Medicine
College of Social Science
College of Veterinary Medicine
Eli Broad College of Business and Eli Broad Graduate School of Management
Honors College
James Madison College
Lyman Briggs College
Residential College in the Arts and Humanities
Undergraduate University Division

HISTORICAL FINANCIALS
Company Type: Private

Income Statement — FYE: June 30

	REVENUE ($ mil.)	NET INCOME ($ mil.)	NET PROFIT MARGIN	EMPLOYEES
06/17	1,931	481	25.0%	11,100
06/16	1,811	71	3.9%	—
06/13	1,578	148	9.4%	—
06/11	1,389	256	18.5%	—
Annual Growth	5.6%	11.1%	—	—

2017 Year-End Financials
Return on assets: 5.8%   Cash ($ mil.): 20
Return on equity: 25.0%
Current ratio: 0.40

MID-AMERICA PIPELINE COMPANY, LLC

EXECUTIVES

Mng MBR-Pres, J M Collingsworth
MBR, W Randall Fowler
MBR-Sr V Pres, Michael J Knesek
MBR-Treas, Bryan F Bulawa
MBR-SEC, Raymond P Albrecht
Credit Mgr, Charles Kaufman
Human Resources, Andy Tomasik
Manager, David West

LOCATIONS

HQ: MID-AMERICA PIPELINE COMPANY, LLC
1100 LA ST STE 1000, HOUSTON, TX 77002
Phone: 713 880-6500
Web: WWW.EPROD.COM

HISTORICAL FINANCIALS
Company Type: Private

Income Statement — FYE: December 31

	REVENUE ($ mil.)	NET INCOME ($ mil.)	NET PROFIT MARGIN	EMPLOYEES
12/17	591	361	61.1%	250
12/16	591	366	62.0%	—
Annual Growth	0.0%	(1.4%)	—	—

MID-KANSAS COOPERATIVE ASSOCIATION

EXECUTIVES

Pres, Dave Christiansen
Cfo, Danny Posch

Information Technology Manager, David Sell
Coordinator, Hilary Worcester
Manager, Jonathan Reazin
Manager, Nick Mazouch
Communications Specialist, Nichole Gouldie
Inventory Manager, Kandee Prieb
Specialist, Kevin Whitehair
Seed Logistics Coordinator, Lane Allison
Linsborg Location Manager, Shane Eck
Auditors: LINDBURG VOGEL PIERCE FARIS CE

LOCATIONS

HQ: MID-KANSAS COOPERATIVE ASSOCIATION
307 W COLE ST, MOUNDRIDGE, KS 671077533
Phone: 620 345-6328
Web: WWW.MKCOOP.COM

HISTORICAL FINANCIALS

Company Type: Private

Income Statement				FYE: February 29
	REVENUE ($ mil.)	NET INCOME ($ mil.)	NET PROFIT MARGIN	EMPLOYEES
02/16	458	7	1.7%	250
02/15	403	14	3.7%	—
02/14	120	9	7.6%	—
02/13	125	14	11.1%	—
Annual Growth	53.9%	(17.2%)	—	—

2016 Year-End Financials
Return on assets: 9.5%   Cash ($ mil.): 3
Return on equity: 1.7%
Current ratio: 0.10

MIDCOAST ENERGY PARTNERS, L.P.

EXECUTIVES

Pres, Laura Sayavedra
Sr V Pres, Mark A Maki
L.L.C., Gen Ptnr, Midcoast Holdings
Vice President, Stephen J Neyland
Auditors: PRICEWATERHOUSECOOPERS LLP HO

LOCATIONS

HQ: MIDCOAST ENERGY PARTNERS, L.P.
1100 LA ST STE 3300, HOUSTON, TX 77002
Phone: 713 821-2000
Web: WWW.MIDCOASTPARTNERS.COM

COMPETITORS

Buckeye Partners
DCP Midstream Partners
Duke Energy
Koch Industries Inc.
Magellan Midstream
Martin Midstream
  Partners

ONEOK
Sunoco Logistics
TransCanada
Williams Companies

HISTORICAL FINANCIALS

Company Type: Private

Income Statement				FYE: December 31
	REVENUE ($ mil.)	NET INCOME ($ mil.)	NET PROFIT MARGIN	EMPLOYEES
12/16	1,966	(157)	—	11
12/15	2,842	(284)	—	—
12/14	5,894	144	2.4%	—
12/13	5,593	53	1.0%	—
Annual Growth	(29.4%)	—	—	—

2016 Year-End Financials
Return on assets: 3.7%   Cash ($ mil.): 7
Return on equity: (-8.0%)
Current ratio: 0.10

MIDCONTINENT INDEPENDENT SYSTEM OPERATOR, INC.

Midwest and more. Non-profit Midwest Independent Transmission System Operator (Midwest ISO) monitors and coordinates the operation of an electric transmission system with more than 49970 miles of transmission lines across 11 Midwestern states and Manitoba and more than 15810 miles across four southern US states. In 2012 it managed energy markets with $18.4 billion in gross energy transactions. The Regional Transmission Organization (RTO) ensures fair access to the grid and facilitates communication between its members which include investor-owned cooperative and municipal utilities as well as power marketers and independent transmission companies. Midwest ISO also provides wholesale electric service.

Operations
The company oversaw 131964 MW of generating capacity in 2012.

Financial Performance
The RTO's revenues dropped by 7% in 2012. About 83% of Midwest ISO's revenue is accounted from cost recovery and 14% from FERC assessments.

Strategy
Midwest ISO is looking to add new members in order to expand the range and efficiency of its network. Regional power player Entergy joined the RTO in 2013 adding a handful of southern US states to Midwest ISO'a portfolio. In 2011 Missouri River Energy Services (a municipal power agency servicing 60 municipal electric utilities in Iowa Minnesota North Dakota and South Dakota) became a member.

Power generators and utilities do have a choice about which RTO they participate with and in 2011 American Transmission and Duke Energy left the system.

Company Background
Midwest ISO was established in 2001 as the nation's first regional transmission organization.

After years of planning in 2009 Midwest ISO launched another market ancillary services (which integrates the purchase and use of regulated and contingency reserves). That year it also became the energy market area's overall Balancing Authority (maintaining the load/resource balance) responsible for North America's largest geographic region reaching from Montana to Missouri to Michigan and beyond.

In 2010 it teamed up with fellow RTO PJM Interconnection (East Coast) to coordinate their introduction of smart grid technology in order to upgrade the reliability of their power transmission systems. The companies are coordinating the introduction of phasor measurement units to improve their operators' visibility of the grid.

EXECUTIVES

President Yent And Ceo, John R. Bear
Evp Transmission And Technology, Clair J. Moeller

Cfo, Melissa A. Brown
Evp Operations And Corporate Services, Richard Doying
Vp Transmission, Jennifer Curran
Vp Forward Markets And Operations Services, Joseph J. Gardner
Vp Miso South, Todd Hillman
Vp System Operations And Market Services, Todd Ramey
Vp Strategy And Business Development, Wayne Schug
Vice President Information Technology, Makumba Mulenga
Vice President Of Government And Regulatory Affairs, David Boyd
Vice President And Chief Information Security Officer, Keri Glitch
Chairman, Michael J. Curran
Member Board Of Directors, Phyllis Currie
Auditors: ERNST & YOUNG LLP INDIANAPOLI

LOCATIONS

HQ: MIDCONTINENT INDEPENDENT SYSTEM
OPERATOR, INC.
720 CITY CENTER DR, CARMEL, IN 460323826
Phone: 317 249-5400
Web: WWW.MISOENERGY.ORG

PRODUCTS/OPERATIONS

2012 Sales

	$ mil.	% of total
Cost recovery adders	233	83
FERC Assessment	39	14
Contract revenue	4	1
Engineering studies income	1	1
Grant revenue	0	-
Other tariff services revenue	2	1
Other	0	-
Total	282	100

HISTORICAL FINANCIALS

Company Type: Private

Income Statement				FYE: December 31
	REVENUE ($ mil.)	NET INCOME ($ mil.)	NET PROFIT MARGIN	EMPLOYEES
12/17	356	0	—	700
12/16	337	0	—	—
12/14	305	(3)	—	—
12/13	296	(10)	—	—
Annual Growth	4.7%	—	—	—

2017 Year-End Financials
Return on assets: 1.6%   Cash ($ mil.): 708
Return on equity: —
Current ratio: 0.70

MIDFLORIDA FEDERAL CREDIT UNION

EXECUTIVES

Pres, Kevin Jones
Cao, Gail O'Brien
Coo, Dennis Pershing
Clo, Sandra Gibson
Vice-President Human Resources, Nancy Irvin
Human Resources Director, Brian Palmer
Vice-President, John King
Vice-President, Nancy I Irvin
Member Officer, Amanda Jones
Associate Manager, Amber Kelly
Assistant Vice President Datab, Eric Jensen

LOCATIONS

HQ: MIDFLORIDA FEDERAL CREDIT UNION
129 S KENTUCKY AVE # 100, LAKELAND, FL
338015073
Phone: 866 913-3733
Web: WWW.MIDFLORIDA.COM

HISTORICAL FINANCIALS

Company Type: Private

Income Statement				FYE: December 31
	ASSETS ($ mil.)	NET INCOME ($ mil.)	INCOME AS % OF ASSETS	EMPLOYEES
12/17	3,055	35	1.2%	278
12/16	2,640	28	1.1%	—
Annual Growth	15.7%	24.5%	—	—

2017 Year-End Financials

Return on assets: 52.4% Sales ($ mil.): 95
Return on equity: 37.4%

MIDMICHIGAN MEDICAL CENTER-MIDLAND

EXECUTIVES

Pres, Currie Scott
Vice President, Sandy Hermann
Vice President, Greg Rogers
Vice President, Francine Padgett
Cfo, Scott Currie
Chief of Medicine, Jay C Hough
Chief of Medicine, Jim Bicknell
Chief Information Security Off, T Moore
Chief of Emergency Room, Jesse Walker
Chief of Radiology, Jeff Herman
Pathologist, Daniel Wunderlich
Auditors: ANDREWS HOOPER PAVLIK PLC SAG

LOCATIONS

HQ: MIDMICHIGAN MEDICAL CENTER-MIDLAND
4000 WELLNESS DR, MIDLAND, MI 486702000
Phone: 989 839-3000
Web: WWW.MIDMICHIGAN.ORG

HISTORICAL FINANCIALS

Company Type: Private

Income Statement				FYE: June 30
	REVENUE ($ mil.)	NET INCOME ($ mil.)	NET PROFIT MARGIN	EMPLOYEES
06/18	427	37	8.7%	1,404
06/15	377	34	9.1%	—
Annual Growth	4.2%	2.8%	—	—

2018 Year-End Financials

Return on assets: 2.2% Cash ($ mil.): 8
Return on equity: 8.7%
Current ratio: 1.80

MIDWEST DIVISION - RMC, LLC

EXECUTIVES

MBR, Jackie Desouza
Director, Doris Seaton
General Practitioner, Shari Ommen
General Practitioner, Kyle Coffman
Oncologist, Kelly Pendergrass
General Practitioner, Gazala Parvin
General Practitioner, Jennifer Kelley
Coordinator, Marilyn Sample
Health Professional, McEnaney Denise
Program Director, Charlotte Haupt
Family Practice, Jon Welsh

LOCATIONS

HQ: MIDWEST DIVISION - RMC, LLC
2316 E MEYER BLVD, KANSAS CITY, MO 641321136
Phone: 816 276-4000
Web: WWW.RESEARCHMEDICALCENTER.COM

HISTORICAL FINANCIALS

Company Type: Private

Income Statement				FYE: December 31
	REVENUE ($ mil.)	NET INCOME ($ mil.)	NET PROFIT MARGIN	EMPLOYEES
12/17	403	(21)	—	2,400
12/16	385	(13)	—	—
12/15	354	(9)	—	—
12/14	338	(0)	—	—
Annual Growth	6.1%	—	—	—

2017 Year-End Financials

Return on assets: 3.3% Cash ($ mil.): —
Return on equity: (-5.3%)
Current ratio: 2.10

MIDWESTERN UNIVERSITY

EXECUTIVES

Pres-Ceo, Kathleen H Goeppinger
Sr V Pres-Cfo, Gregory J Gaus
Vice President, Dean Malone
Vice President, Karen D Johnson
Vice President, Dean P Malone
Vice President, Mary Lee
Vice President, Angela Marty
Sr Exec Vice President, Arthur G Dobbelaere
Assistant Professor, Reji Mathew
Director, Carol Van Dijk
Program Director, Timothy J Todd
Auditors: ERNST & YOUNG LLP CHICAGO IL

LOCATIONS

HQ: MIDWESTERN UNIVERSITY
555 31ST ST, DOWNERS GROVE, IL 605151235
Phone: 630 515-7300
Web: WWW.MIDWESTERN.EDU

HISTORICAL FINANCIALS

Company Type: Private

Income Statement				FYE: June 30
	REVENUE ($ mil.)	NET INCOME ($ mil.)	NET PROFIT MARGIN	EMPLOYEES
06/18	450	121	27.1%	1,300
06/17	414	118	28.6%	—
06/16	380	69	18.4%	—
06/15	358	86	24.0%	—
Annual Growth	7.9%	12.2%	—	—

2018 Year-End Financials

Return on assets: 1.5% Cash ($ mil.): 383
Return on equity: 27.1%
Current ratio: 3.60

MILLER ELECTRIC COMPANY

EXECUTIVES

Ceo, Henry K Brown
Prin, David Long
Sr V Pres, Ed Witt Jr
V Pres, Daniel Brown
Cfo-Sec-Treas, Susan A Walden
Pres, Thomas D Long
Project Manager, Kevin Hebert
Project Manager, Keith Riordan
Project Manager, Kevin Flanigan
Director, Mike Oliver
Accounting Staff, Pat Lewis
Auditors: BISHOP AND DRAPER JACKSONVILL

LOCATIONS

HQ: MILLER ELECTRIC COMPANY
2251 ROSSELLE ST, JACKSONVILLE, FL 322043125
Phone: 904 388-8000
Web: WWW.MECOJAX.COM

COMPETITORS

Dycom	Megatran
Edd Helms	Pike Corporation
Honshy Electric	Tri-City Electrical
Johnson Contractors	Contractors

HISTORICAL FINANCIALS

Company Type: Private

Income Statement				FYE: September 30
	REVENUE ($ mil.)	NET INCOME ($ mil.)	NET PROFIT MARGIN	EMPLOYEES
09/17	296	11	3.9%	691
09/16	249	8	3.3%	—
09/15	260	7	2.9%	—
09/14	216	6	3.0%	—
Annual Growth	11.1%	22.1%	—	—

2017 Year-End Financials

Return on assets: 8.5% Cash ($ mil.): —
Return on equity: 3.9%
Current ratio: 1.40

MILLMAN LUMBER COMPANY

EXECUTIVES

Chb, Robert L Millman
Pres, Richard G Millman
Treas, Kenneth G Mains
SEC, Thomas Corbett
General Manager, Justin Dunlavy
Sales and Marketing Staff, Brian Judy
Manager, Dean Hendrix
Sales Associate, Denny Bush
Manager, Rob Sparger
Sales and Marketing Staff, Tom Shaul
Sales, Barry Goodwin

LOCATIONS

HQ: MILLMAN LUMBER COMPANY
9264 MANCHESTER RD, SAINT LOUIS, MO
631442636
Phone: 314 968-1700
Web: WWW.MILLMANLUMBER.COM

HISTORICAL FINANCIALS

Company Type: Private

Income Statement   FYE: October 31

	REVENUE ($ mil.)	NET INCOME ($ mil.)	NET PROFIT MARGIN	EMPLOYEES
10/16	287	6	2.3%	80
10/15	258	3	1.4%	—
10/14	255	2	1.0%	—
10/13	245	2	0.9%	—
Annual Growth	5.4%	43.3%	—	—

2016 Year-End Financials

Return on assets: —   Cash ($ mil.): 1
Return on equity: 2.3%
Current ratio: 0.70

MILTON HERSHEY SCHOOL & SCHOOL TRUST

EXECUTIVES

Owner, Milton Hershey
Auditors: PRICEWATERHOUSECOOPERS LLP PH

LOCATIONS

HQ: MILTON HERSHEY SCHOOL & SCHOOL TRUST
711 CREST LN, HERSHEY, PA 170338903
Phone: 717 520-1100
Web: WWW.MHSKIDS.ORG

HISTORICAL FINANCIALS

Company Type: Private

Income Statement   FYE: July 31

	REVENUE ($ mil.)	NET INCOME ($ mil.)	NET PROFIT MARGIN	EMPLOYEES
07/17	469	198	42.2%	13
07/12	386	180	46.7%	—
07/10	211	3	1.6%	—
Annual Growth	12.1%	79.2%	—	—

2017 Year-End Financials

Return on assets: 49.1%   Cash ($ mil.): 59
Return on equity: 42.2%
Current ratio: 0.40

MILWAUKEE PUBLIC SCHOOLS (INC)

EXECUTIVES

Supt, Darienne Driver
Cfo, Gerald Pace
Personnel Dir, Daniel Chanen
Comptroller, Lawanda Baldwin
Principal, Deborah Bell
Principal, Martha Wheeler-Fair
Principal, Jewell Riano
Principal, Daniel J Donder
Social Worker, Cathy Klein
SEC, Tracy Harris
Food Dir, Tina Barkstrom
Auditors: BAKER TILLY VIRCHOW KRAUSE LL

LOCATIONS

HQ: MILWAUKEE PUBLIC SCHOOLS (INC)
5225 W VLIET ST, MILWAUKEE, WI 532082698
Phone: 414 475-8393
Web: WWW.MILWAUKEE.K12.WI.US

HISTORICAL FINANCIALS

Company Type: Private

Income Statement   FYE: June 30

	REVENUE ($ mil.)	NET INCOME ($ mil.)	NET PROFIT MARGIN	EMPLOYEES
06/17	1,182	9	0.8%	14,154
06/16	1,178	(0)	—	—
06/11	1,292	(2)	—	—
06/09	1,237	(5)	—	—
Annual Growth	(0.6%)	—	—	—

MINERS INCORPORATED

Miner's is a family-owned chain of about 30 grocery stores in Michigan North Dakota northern Minnesota and Wisconsin. Most of the company's stores fly the Super One Foods banner but there are a few under the U-Save Foods and Marketplace Foods names. Following the acquisition of seven Jubilee and Festival Foods stores in Minnesota from Plaza Holding Co. Miner's converted the stores to its Super One Foods banner most of which are located in Minnesota. Miner's also has a wholesale grocery operation in Duluth. Miner's was founded by Anton and Ida Miner who started out selling groceries out of their tavern in Grand Rapids Michigan in the 1930s. In 1943 they built the family's first store Miner's Market.

Geographic Reach

Minnesota is the regional grocery chain's largest market home to 21 of its 31 stores. Wisconsin and Michigan are each home to about five locations. The grocery chain has a single store North Dakota.

Financial Performance

Miner's rang up an estimated $437 million in sales in fiscal 2013 (ended June).

Strategy

Miner's takes a measured approach to growth combining occasional acquisitions with organic growth. Its newest location is a 59000-square-foot Super One Foods store slated to open in 2014 in Superior Wisconsin.

Mergers and Acquisitions

In May 2011 Miner's upped its store count with the acquisition of four family-owned Paulson's Super Valu grocery stores in northern Minnesota and Wisconsin.

Prevented by Minnesota law from selling alcohol in grocery stores the company recently bought two liquor stores in Cloquet and Duluth.

EXECUTIVES

Vice President Operations, Bob Halvorson
Vice President, Jim Miner
Auditors: RSM US LLP DULUTH MINNESOTA

LOCATIONS

HQ: MINERS INCORPORATED
5065 MILLER TRUNK HWY, HERMANTOWN, MN
558111442
Phone: 218 729-5882
Web: WWW.SUPERONEFOODS.COM

2014 Stores

	No.
Minnesota	21
Michigan	5
Wisconsin	4
North Dakota	1
Total	**31**

PRODUCTS/OPERATIONS

2014 Stores

	No.
Super One Foods	27
U-Save Foods	2
Country Market	1
Marketplace Foods	1
Total	**31**

COMPETITORS

Cub Foods	Roundy's
IGA	SpartanNash
Kroger	Target Corporation
Meijer	Wal-Mart

HISTORICAL FINANCIALS

Company Type: Private

Income Statement   FYE: June 24

	REVENUE ($ mil.)	NET INCOME ($ mil.)	NET PROFIT MARGIN	EMPLOYEES
06/17	548	26	4.8%	2,300
06/12	501	31	6.3%	—
06/11	475	30	6.4%	—
06/10	463	27	5.8%	—
Annual Growth	2.4%	(0.5%)	—	—

2017 Year-End Financials

Return on assets: 0.5%   Cash ($ mil.): 7
Return on equity: 4.8%
Current ratio: 0.20

MINNEAPOLIS PUBLIC SCHOOL DISTRICT

EXECUTIVES

Suptd, Michael Goar
Supt, Bernadeia Johnson
Payroll Staff, Diane Woolridge
Occupational Specia, Laura Wilcox
Information Technology/Interne, Pravesh Khadka
Payroll Staff, Stacy Swain
Information Technology/Interne, Tim Davis
Coordinator, Ben Mulhern
Administrator, Kristi Ward
Research/Development Director, Eric Moore
Transportation Director, Scott James
Auditors: BERGAN KDV LTD MINNEAPOLIS

LOCATIONS

HQ: MINNEAPOLIS PUBLIC SCHOOL DISTRICT
1250 W BROADWAY AVE, MINNEAPOLIS, MN
554112533
Phone: 612 668-0200
Web: WWW.MPLS.K12.MN.US

HISTORICAL FINANCIALS
Company Type: Private

Income Statement   FYE: June 30

	REVENUE ($ mil.)	NET INCOME ($ mil.)	NET PROFIT MARGIN	EMPLOYEES
06/16	709	(25)	—	9,000
06/15	685	116	17.1%	—
06/05	441	18	4.2%	—
06/04	632	(42)	—	—
Annual Growth	1.0%	—	—	—

MINNKOTA POWER COOPERATIVE, INC.

EXECUTIVES

Ceo, Robert McLennan
Vice President, Russell Okeson
SEC-Treas, Jeffrey Folland
Substation Mgr, Dale Thompson
Coordinator, Miles Mettler
Administrative Assistant, Brian Buchholtz
Coordinator, Callie Wagner
Staff, Jason Uhlir
Coordinator, Rocky Schlosser
Telecommunications Staff, Todd Bommersbach
Manager, Wayne Lembke

LOCATIONS

HQ: MINNKOTA POWER COOPERATIVE, INC.
5301 32ND AVE S, GRAND FORKS, ND 582013312
Phone: 701 795-4000
Web: WWW.MINNKOTA.COM

COMPETITORS

Basin Electric Power   Great River Energy
Black Hills Power

HISTORICAL FINANCIALS
Company Type: Private

Income Statement   FYE: December 31

	REVENUE ($ mil.)	NET INCOME ($ mil.)	NET PROFIT MARGIN	EMPLOYEES
12/17	415	29	7.1%	355
12/16	149	2	1.9%	—
12/15	159	2	1.6%	—
12/14	145	2	1.7%	—
Annual Growth	41.8%	129.6%	—	—

MISSION HEALTH SYSTEM, INC.

EXECUTIVES

Ceo, Ronald A Paulus
Technician, Don Davis
General Practitioner, Rebecca Brooks
General Practitioner, Steven Johnson
Svp-Innovation, Marc B Westle
Cmo-Mission Hospital, William R Hathaway
Sr V Pres Operations, Sonya B Greck
Auditors: KPMG LLP CHARLOTTE NC

LOCATIONS

HQ: MISSION HEALTH SYSTEM, INC.
509 BILTM AVE AKA HWY 25, ASHEVILLE, NC 28801
Phone: 828 213-1111

HISTORICAL FINANCIALS
Company Type: Private

Income Statement   FYE: September 30

	REVENUE ($ mil.)	NET INCOME ($ mil.)	NET PROFIT MARGIN	EMPLOYEES
09/17	1,753	161	9.2%	12,000
09/16	1,632	90	5.5%	—
09/08	17	7	42.3%	—
09/06	773	101	13.2%	—
Annual Growth	7.7%	4.3%	—	—

2017 Year-End Financials
Return on assets: 3.1%   Cash ($ mil.): 97
Return on equity: 9.2%
Current ratio: 1.30

MISSION HOSPITAL REGIONAL MEDICAL CENTER INC

EXECUTIVES

Ceo, Kenn Nicfaralnd
Financial Executive, Kenn Mc Farland
Director of Laboratory, Don White
Manager, Laura Salem
Manager, Franco Petruzzella
Emergency Medicine Specialist, Michael Ritter
Emergency Medicine Specialist, James Keany
Manager, Melissa Arnold
Health Care Director, Carol Blanchard
Coordinator, Maryann Hubbard
Director of Security, Scott Odonnell
Auditors: ERNST & YOUNG US LLP SAN DIEG

LOCATIONS

HQ: MISSION HOSPITAL REGIONAL MEDICAL CENTER INC
27700 MEDICAL CENTER RD, MISSION VIEJO, CA
926916426
Phone: 949 364-1400
Web: WWW.MISSION4HEALTH.COM

HISTORICAL FINANCIALS
Company Type: Private

Income Statement   FYE: June 30

	REVENUE ($ mil.)	NET INCOME ($ mil.)	NET PROFIT MARGIN	EMPLOYEES
06/16	547	28	5.3%	2,600
06/15	516	23	4.5%	—
06/10	500	50	10.1%	—
06/09	355	12	3.5%	—
Annual Growth	6.4%	13.0%	—	—

2016 Year-End Financials
Return on assets: 0.5%   Cash ($ mil.): 38
Return on equity: 5.3%
Current ratio: 1.30

MISSION HOSPITAL, INC.

Its mission is clear and bold: Improve the health of all in western North Carolina. Mission Hospital is a 760-bed regional referral center serving the western quarter of North Carolina and portions of adjoining states. A not-for-profit community hospital system Mission is located in Asheville on two adjoining campuses: Memorial and St. Joseph's. It provides tertiary-level services in neurosciences cardiac care trauma care surgery pediatric medicine and women's services and has a medical staff of more than 540. It also includes the Mission Children's Hospital. Mission Hospital is the flagship hospital of Mission Health System which is being acquired by HCA Healthcare for $1.5 billion.

Change in Company Type
In 2018 hospital operator HCA Healthcare agreed to buy Mission Health System which includes Mission Hospital and six smaller hospitals in Asheville North Carolina for $1.5 billion. As part of the deal HCA will keep all rehab and acute-care hospitals open for at least 10 years. It will also invest several hundreds of millions of dollars in various expenditures.

Geographic Reach
Mission Health System serves patients in western North Carolina.

Strategy
Mission Hospital has been actively expanding and modernizing its facilities in recent years. It built a surgery registration and waiting area to ease patient comfort as they wait to be seen at the Memorial Campus. It also opened a four-story facility to provide more surgery suites and patient beds for Mission Hospital. In order to increase patient satisfaction the hospital opened a new surgery registration and waiting area at its Memorial Campus.

Mission Hospital places great focus on genetic medicine. It has an entire department dedicated to the study of genetics genetic therapy and the study of fetal alcohol spectrum disorders.

Mission Health partnered with Western Carolina University to provide a graduate certification program in Healthcare Innovation Management. The program which began in 2013 is a component of Mission Health's budding Center for Innovation established to foster a spirit of advancement in healthcare throughout western North Carolina. The program consists of four courses over a period of 21 months and is open to all Mission Health employees. Students who complete the program which is fully funded by Mission Health will earn credit towards bachelor's and master's degrees.

Company Background

Mission Hospital was formed in 1996 from the partnership (and eventual merger) of Memorial and St. Joseph's hospitals.

EXECUTIVES

Pres, Joseph Damore
Ceo, Ronald A Paulus
Sr Vice President, Charles F Ayscue
Human Resources Representative, Dan McFatter
Human Resources Representative, Teresa McCarthy
Chief Staff, Alan S Baumgarten
Credentialing Coordinator, Brittany Thompson
Allergy and Immunology, John Van Wye
Rheumatology Specialist, Christopher Meyer
Anesthesiologist, David M Stanley
General Practice, David A Wells

LOCATIONS

HQ: MISSION HOSPITAL, INC.
   509 BILTMORE AVE, ASHEVILLE, NC 288014601
Phone: 828 213-1111
Web: WWW.MISSION-HEALTH.ORG

PRODUCTS/OPERATIONS

Surgical Services
General Surgery
Minimally Invasive Surgery
Outpatient Surgery
Prepare for Surgery
Robotic Surgery
Surgery at Mission Hospital
Surgery Guide
Programs of Service
Endoscopy
Genetics
Integrative Healthcare
Mother and Baby
Outpatient Care Centers
Sleep Center
Urology
Weight Management Center
Wound Healing and Hyperbarics
Support Services
Chronic Medical Conditions
Long-Term Acute Care
Laboratory
Pastoral Care Services
Pharmacy
Psychiatric Services
Radiology (Imaging) Services
Rehabilitation Services
Research Institute
Respiratory Therapy
Senior Services and Geriatrics

COMPETITORS

Blue Ridge HealthCare
CaroMont
Carolinas HealthCare System
Duke University Health System
Haywood Regional Presbyterian Healthcare
UNC Hospitals

HISTORICAL FINANCIALS

Company Type: Private

Income Statement

FYE: September 30

	REVENUE ($ mil.)	NET INCOME ($ mil.)	NET PROFIT MARGIN	EMPLOYEES
09/15	1,019	91	9.0%	10,000
09/14	936	64	6.9%	—
09/13	942	71	7.6%	—
09/12	861	86	10.0%	—
Annual Growth	5.8%	2.0%	—	—

MISSISSIPPI STATE UNIVERSITY

EXECUTIVES

Pres, Mark E Keenum
Executive Officer, Terry Kiser
Manager, Donna Buckelew
Assistant Professor, Heidi Renninger
Coordinator, Janice Pettus
Principal, Michael Murphy
Assistant Professor, Jun Liao
Coordinator, Anne Skinner
Public Relations Director, Anthony Craven
Assistant Professor, Jamie E Larson
Coordinator, John B Auel

LOCATIONS

HQ: MISSISSIPPI STATE UNIVERSITY
   245 BARR AVE MCRTHUR HL MCARTHUR HALL,
   MISSISSIPPI STATE, MS 39762
Phone: 662 325-2302
Web: WWW.MSSTATE.EDU

HISTORICAL FINANCIALS

Company Type: Private

Income Statement

FYE: June 30

	REVENUE ($ mil.)	NET INCOME ($ mil.)	NET PROFIT MARGIN	EMPLOYEES
06/17	461	18	4.0%	4,500
06/16	462	48	10.4%	—
06/14	392	64	16.4%	—
06/13	371	25	6.9%	—
Annual Growth	5.6%	(7.9%)	—	—

2017 Year-End Financials

Return on assets: 5.2%
Return on equity: 4.0%
Current ratio: 2.40
Cash ($ mil.): 113

MISSOURI BAPTIST MEDICAL CENTER

EXECUTIVES

Pres, Joan Magruder
V Pres-Cfo, Gary McLaughlin
VPresident, Timothy Ranney
VPresident, Douglas Black
VPresident, Sandra Young
VPresident, Tim Mislan

Pricipal*, John Antes
Director of Finance, Amy Desart
Health Professional, Anshu Jain
Supervisor, Patricia Burns
Diagnostic Radiologist, Geoffrey S Hamill

LOCATIONS

HQ: MISSOURI BAPTIST MEDICAL CENTER
   3015 N BALLAS RD, SAINT LOUIS, MO 631312374
Phone: 314 996-5000
Web: WWW.BJC.ORG

HISTORICAL FINANCIALS

Company Type: Private

Income Statement

FYE: December 31

	REVENUE ($ mil.)	NET INCOME ($ mil.)	NET PROFIT MARGIN	EMPLOYEES
12/17	600	18	3.0%	1,670
12/16	570	25	4.5%	—
12/15	511	15	3.0%	—
12/14	472	22	4.8%	—
Annual Growth	8.3%	(7.4%)	—	—

2017 Year-End Financials

Return on assets: 1.0%
Return on equity: 3.0%
Current ratio: 3.30
Cash ($ mil.): —

MISSOURI HIGHER EDUCATION LOAN AUTHORITY

EXECUTIVES

Finance Vice President, Scott Giles
Vice President Of Human Resources, Susan Crump
Auditors: ERNST & YOUNG LLP ST LOUIS

LOCATIONS

HQ: MISSOURI HIGHER EDUCATION LOAN AUTHORITY
   633 SPIRIT DR, CHESTERFIELD, MO 630051243
Phone: 636 733-3700
Web: WWW.MOHELA.COM

COMPETITORS

Bank of America
Brazos Higher Education Service Corp.
Great Lakes Higher Education
JPMorgan Chase
Nelnet
Pennsylvania Higher Education Assistance Agency
Sallie Mae
Texas Guaranteed

HISTORICAL FINANCIALS

Company Type: Private

Income Statement

FYE: June 30

	ASSETS ($ mil.)	NET INCOME ($ mil.)	INCOME AS % OF ASSETS	EMPLOYEES
06/17	1,971	20	1.0%	550
06/16	2,208	8	0.4%	—
06/03	3,344	24	0.7%	—
06/02	2,730	19	0.7%	—
Annual Growth	(2.1%)	0.3%	—	—

2017 Year-End Financials

Return on assets: —
Return on equity: 15.9%
Sales ($ mil): 128

MISSOURI JOINT MUNICIPAL ELECTRIC UTILITY COMMISSION

EXECUTIVES

Ceo, Duncan Kincheloe
Cfo, Michael Loethen
Acct Asst, Becky Gini
Accountant, Becky Class

LOCATIONS

HQ: MISSOURI JOINT MUNICIPAL ELECTRIC UTILITY COMMISSION
1808 INTERSTATE 70 DR SW, COLUMBIA, MO 652031032
Phone: 573 445-3279
Web: WWW.MPUA.ORG

HISTORICAL FINANCIALS

Company Type: Private

Income Statement				FYE: December 31
	REVENUE ($ mil.)	NET INCOME ($ mil.)	NET PROFIT MARGIN	EMPLOYEES
12/17	340	9	2.8%	29
12/16	340	9	2.7%	—
12/15	343	6	1.9%	—
12/05	84	1	1.6%	—
Annual Growth	12.4%	18.0%	—	—

2017 Year-End Financials

Return on assets: 5.7%
Return on equity: 2.8%
Current ratio: 0.70
Cash ($ mil.): 41

MMR CONSTRUCTORS, INC.

EXECUTIVES

Pres, James B Rutland
V Pres, Tom Welborn
Cfo, Donald Fairbanks
Dir, Gary Williams
SEC, Rodi F Rispone
V Pres, Thomas B Rutland
Human Resources, Christy Linder
Network Manager, Dustin Landry
Auditors: MADDOX & ASSOCIATES APC BATO

LOCATIONS

HQ: MMR CONSTRUCTORS, INC.
15961 AIRLINE HWY, BATON ROUGE, LA 708177412
Phone: 225 756-5090
Web: WWW.MMRGRP.COM

HISTORICAL FINANCIALS

Company Type: Private

Income Statement				FYE: December 31
	REVENUE ($ mil.)	NET INCOME ($ mil.)	NET PROFIT MARGIN	EMPLOYEES
12/17	581	16	2.9%	4,000
12/16	531	14	2.7%	—
12/15	513	16	3.1%	—
12/14	649	20	3.1%	—
Annual Growth	(3.6%)	(6.1%)	—	—

2017 Year-End Financials

Return on assets: 4.6%
Return on equity: 2.9%
Current ratio: 1.60
Cash ($ mil.): 2

MMR GROUP, INC.

That murmur you hear could be the gentle hum of a properly functioning power system. MMG Group provides electrical and instrumentation construction maintenance management and technical services for clients in the oil and gas manufacturing chemical and power generation industries around the world. It also offers services in offshore marine and platform environments. Its Power Solutions division constructs onsite power-generation systems in industrial plants and other facilities. The group primarily operates in the Gulf of New Mexico. Founded in 1990 MMG is 100% management owned and has served such clients as Chevron Shell BP Merck Air Liquide DuPont and 3M.

Operations

MMR Group's provides four main services: electrical and instrumentation contracting safety services panel fabrication and communications.

MMR's electrical and instrumentation contractors work on projects throughout the US and overseas. To ensure its projects are completed on time and within budget its personnel has support and management control systems and emphasizes planning scheduling progress tracking and labor analysis.

The MMR Offshore Safety Services division specializes in disaster prevention and safety helping with navigation fire and gas detection suppression products paging and alarm systems level one cathodic protection inspections and other related services.

For panel fabrication services MMR stages tests and designs control systems that best fit client needs.

The MMR ProCom division is in charge of pre-commissioning commissioning and start-Up activities for both MMR Group construction projects and for outside clients interested in turning their facilities construction into a safe and reliable operation seamlessly.

Geographic Reach

MMR operates out of some 20 offices spread across North and South America with most of its offices in Texas Louisiana and California. The company works on projects all over the world with foreign affiliate offices in Calgary Canada; Cartagena Colombia; Puerto la Cruz Venezuela; and Port of Spain Trinidad & Tobago.

Sales and Marketing

MMR serves a variety of markets including: alternative energy exploration and production chemical and petrochemical industrial and manufacturing oil and gas power generation and waste and water treatment among others.

Some of the company's panel fabrication clients have included Shell Pipeline Chevron Pipeline Enbridge Pipeline AGI Services Cimitation Engineering ExxonMobil Keystone Engineering W.S. Nelson Engineering and Entergy among others.

Depending on the project and client's preference MMR operates on all types of fixed-price and cost-plus contracts.

Strategy

The company continues to expand its operations to accommodate more projects. In 2014 the company built a 19-office administration building along with a 6000 square-foot warehouse facility to support the influx of new projects going on in the Golden Triangle area between Beaumont TX and Lake Charles LA.

EXECUTIVES

Pres, James B Rutland
Vice President, Thomas O Welborn
SEC-Treas, Donald W Fairbanks
Information Specialist, Meagan L Bourgeois
Internal Medicine Practitioner, Garrett Benoit
Coordinator, Brandon Legrange
Auditors: MADDOX & ASSOCIATES APC BATO

LOCATIONS

HQ: MMR GROUP, INC.
15961 AIRLINE HWY, BATON ROUGE, LA 708177412
Phone: 225 756-5090
Web: WWW.MMRGRP.COM

PRODUCTS/OPERATIONS

Selected Services

Instrumentation
  Air supply installation
  Control room equipment installation
  Instrument installation
  Process leads
  Panel fabrication
  Signal wiring
Electrical
  Controls
  Electrical equipment setting
  Grounding
  Lighting
  Power distribution
Technical
  Calibration
  Commissioning
  Detail design
  High voltage testing
  Instrument procurement
  Loop check
  Maintenance
  Start up assistance
  System analysis

Selected Divisions

MMR Constructors
MMR International
MMR Power Solutions
MMR Offshore Services
MMR Technical Services
Southwestern Power Group

COMPETITORS

Alberici	MYR Group
EMCOR	Matrix Service
Fisk Electric	Turner Industries
Industrial Specialty Contractors	

HISTORICAL FINANCIALS
Company Type: Private

Income Statement				FYE: December 31
	REVENUE ($ mil.)	NET INCOME ($ mil.)	NET PROFIT MARGIN	EMPLOYEES
12/17	618	9	1.5%	4,000
12/16	608	14	2.5%	—
12/15	585	24	4.3%	—
12/14	674	25	3.7%	—
Annual Growth	(2.9%)	(27.6%)	—	—

2017 Year-End Financials
Return on assets: 4.8%   Cash ($ mil.): 4
Return on equity: 1.5%
Current ratio: 1.50

MOBILE INFIRMARY ASSOCIATION

EXECUTIVES

Chb, David Cooper
Admin, Joe Stough
Coordinator, Fred Anderson
Director of Laboratory, Sandra Lozano
Diagnostic Radiologist, Daniel E Reimer
Manager, Beth Elkins
Director, Glenn Swanson
Director of Information Techno, Eddie Stevens
Diagnostic Radiologist, John T Renz
Internal Medicine, Samuel Hooks
Nursing Director, Ursula Lawrence

LOCATIONS

HQ: MOBILE INFIRMARY ASSOCIATION
 5 MOBILE INFIRMARY CIR, MOBILE, AL 366073513
Phone: 251 435-2400
Web: WWW.INFIRMARYHEALTH.ORG

HISTORICAL FINANCIALS
Company Type: Private

Income Statement				FYE: March 31
	REVENUE ($ mil.)	NET INCOME ($ mil.)	NET PROFIT MARGIN	EMPLOYEES
03/18	402	36	9.1%	2,938
03/17	387	13	3.4%	—
03/13	411	27	6.6%	—
03/11	394	24	6.3%	—
Annual Growth	0.3%	5.9%	—	—

2018 Year-End Financials
Return on assets: 6.3%   Cash ($ mil.): 27
Return on equity: 9.1%
Current ratio: 2.90

MODESTO CITY SCHOOL DISTRICT

EXECUTIVES

Supt-Ceo, Pamela Able
President, Cindy Marks
Vice President, Amy Elliott Neumann
Dir, Patti Pruett
Management Info Dir, Cindy Minter

Human Resources, Chad Stephens
Assistant, David Antinetti
Manager, Duane Wolterstorff
Administrative Assistant, Elsa Martinez
Coordinator, Kimbra Draper
Director, Marlin Sumpter
Auditors: VAVRINEK TRINE DAY & CO LL

LOCATIONS

HQ: MODESTO CITY SCHOOL DISTRICT
 426 LOCUST ST, MODESTO, CA 953512631
Phone: 209 576-4011
Web: WWW.MONET.K12.CA.US

HISTORICAL FINANCIALS
Company Type: Private

Income Statement				FYE: June 30
	REVENUE ($ mil.)	NET INCOME ($ mil.)	NET PROFIT MARGIN	EMPLOYEES
06/17	417	15	3.7%	3,000
06/16	387	25	6.6%	—
06/15	333	2	0.8%	—
06/14	306	1	0.6%	—
Annual Growth	10.9%	102.8%	—	—

MODESTO IRRIGATION DISTRICT (INC)

Modesty notwithstanding Modesto Irrigation District (MID) does much more than irrigate almost 58000 acres of land in and around Modesto California. The state-owned not-for-profit utility also generates transmits and distributes electricity. In 2012 the company reported that it distributed electricity in a 260-sq.-ml. area to about 94120 residential and 12265 commercial and industrial customers and some 7547 other customers. MID also markets wholesale power and treats and provides drinking water to the city of Modesto for distribution purposes. In 2012 the organization had 103733 irrigated acres (and more than 3100 customer accounts) in its service area.

Geographic Reach

MIS serves the greater Modesto area (north of the Tuolumne River Waterford Salida Mountain House and parts of Ripon Escalon Oakdale and Riverbank).

Financial Performance

In 2012 the company's revenue grew by 5% as the result of an increase in retail electric revenues due to a ate hike aimed at capturing costs related to capital improvement and greenhouse gas allowances.

Net income increased by 63% in 2012 thanks to higher net sales and a cut in the operating costs.

Strategy

In 2012 MID was exploring the possibility expanding its services by selling water to the City and County of San Francisco. The potential deal is seen as a way to increase revenues by opening up a new market without losing any significant water flow from the Tuolumne River one of MID's primary water sources.

Company Background

The company was formed by the government of Stanislaus County in 1887 to provide irrigation services in the Modesto region.

The utility began to provide irrigation water via an expanded canal system in 1904. It introduced electric services in 1923 and in 1978 MID merged with the Waterford Irrigation District.

EXECUTIVES

Vice President Marketing, Bob Root
Vice President Marketing, Tracy Herbeck
Secretary, Barbara Solarez
Assistant Treasurer, Ana Vigil
Auditors: BAKER TILLY VIRCHOW KRAUSE LL

LOCATIONS

HQ: MODESTO IRRIGATION DISTRICT (INC)
 1231 11TH ST, MODESTO, CA 953540701
Phone: 209 526-7337
Web: WWW.MID.ORG

COMPETITORS

Calpine   Turlock Irrigation
 PG&E Corporation   District
Sempra Energy

HISTORICAL FINANCIALS
Company Type: Private

Income Statement				FYE: December 31
	REVENUE ($ mil.)	NET INCOME ($ mil.)	NET PROFIT MARGIN	EMPLOYEES
12/17	384	18	4.8%	440
12/16	413	36	8.8%	—
12/15	425	42	10.0%	—
12/14	416	43	10.5%	—
Annual Growth	(2.7%)	(25.3%)	—	—

2017 Year-End Financials
Return on assets: 8.3%   Cash ($ mil.): 63
Return on equity: 4.8%
Current ratio: 1.20

MOHEGAN TRIBAL GAMING AUTHORITY

The sun also rises at Mohegan Sun a gaming and entertainment complex run by the Mohegan Tribal Gaming Authority for the Mohegan Indian tribe of Connecticut. The Native American-themed Mohegan Sun complexA includes three casinosA (Casino of the Earth Casino of the Sky and Casino of the Wind) that featureA slot machinesA game tables horse race wagering an arena a cabaret stores restaurants andA a luxury hotel. The companyA also owns Pocono Downs a horse racetrack in Pennsylvania. Gambling revenues go to the Mohegan Tribe and are used for cultural and educational programs. The tribe has lived as a community for hundreds of years in what is today southeastern Connecticut and has about 1900 members.

Operations

In addition to operating casinos and hotels the Mohegan Tribal Gaming Authority also owns the Connecticut Sun WNBA basketball team. The companyA has an added benefitA from Connecticut Sun ticket sales as the team plays its home games in the Mohegan Sun Arena.

Mohegan Sun also owns the Mohegan Sun Country Club in Connecticut and it has formed a venture to pursue potential gaming opportunities in Massachusetts should that state pass legislation toA legalize gambling.A Other operations include subsidiaries that plan to assist the Cowlitz Indian Tribe of Washington and the Menominee Indian Tribe of Wisconsin to open and/or manageA casinos.

Financial Performance

The tribes' are still working on development ofA new casinos despite a weak tourism market.A It's no secret that the leisure industry has been hit hard as people pinch penniesA duringA the prolonged recession and as a result Mohegan Tribal's revenues and net income haveA been flatA in recent years. The company has claimed about $1.4 billion in revenue duringA fiscal 2009 2010 and 2011.

Strategy

Stagnant earnings have caused the company to put on holdA a renovation project at Mohegan Sun called Project Horizon — including hotel retail and new parking garage elements.

The company has been affected by increased competition in the area. Its Mohegan Sun targets visitors located within several hoursA driving distance. The property is approximately 125 miles from New York City and about 100 miles from Boston. TheA legalization or expansion of gaming in New England New York New Jersey and Pennsylvania gives area gamblersA a glut of options (such as the nearby Foxwoods owned by the Mashantucket Pequot and several Atlantic City casinosA including those from Trump Resorts).

EXECUTIVES

Vice President Casino Marketing (mohegan Sun), Lyndon Stockton

LOCATIONS

HQ: MOHEGAN TRIBAL GAMING AUTHORITY
1 MOHEGAN SUN BLVD, UNCASVILLE, CT 063821355
Phone: 860 862-8000
Web: WWW.MOHEGANSUN.COM

COMPETITORS

Boyd Gaming
Caesars Entertainment
Connecticut Lottery
Lake of the Torches
Mashantucket Pequot
Seminole Tribe of
 Florida
Trump Resorts

HISTORICAL FINANCIALS

Company Type: Private

Income Statement				FYE: September 30
	REVENUE ($ mil.)	NET INCOME ($ mil.)	NET PROFIT MARGIN	EMPLOYEES
09/18	1,355	131	9.7%	8,640
09/17	1,380	76	5.5%	—
09/16	1,334	133	10.0%	—
09/15	1,291	92	7.1%	
Annual Growth	1.6%	12.6%	—	—

2018 Year-End Financials

Return on assets: 1.1%   Cash ($ mil.): 103
Return on equity: 9.7%
Current ratio: 0.50

MONMOUTH MEDICAL CENTER INC.

Monmouth Medical Center is a 530-bed tertiary care teaching hospital providing comprehensive health care to residents of central New Jersey. The not-for-profit medical center offers services ranging from orthopedics diagnostics and obstetric care to surgery dentistry and geriatric services. The medical center campus also includes a children's hospital a cancer center a neuroscience institute an outpatient care clinic and hospice and home health facilities. Monmouth Medical Center is a major teaching affiliate of the Drexel University College of Medicine in Philadelphia. The hospital is an affiliate of the Saint Barnabas Healthcare System.

Operations

Monmouth Medical Center handles 19000 inpatient admissions each year as well as 49000 emergency room visits. Its outpatient clinic handles some 126000 appointments annually. The hospital has 700 doctors representing 60 specialties on its staff.

Geographic Reach

Monmouth Medical Center is located on about 20 acres in Long Branch New Jersey near the Atlantic Ocean. The campus includes the main 16-wing hospital and and about 16 other buildings including resident physician dwellings a day care center a medical education and training facility and a Ronald McDonald House.

The hospital serves a territory consisting of Monmouth Ocean and Middlesex counties with a total of about one million residents. It has outpatient locations in Colts Neck Howell Long Branch Ocean Township and Shrewsbury.

Strategy

The hospital has conducted recent expansion projects including additions of new a new cancer center surgical suites and a family center. In 2013 it opened a new postpartum wing and newborn nursery as well as a larger neonatal ICU. Monmouth Medical Center also extended its pediatric and oncology programs by forming partnerships with other area hospitals in 2012.

Company Background

Monmouth Medical Center was founded in 1887. It has expanded over the years to provide a number of specialist services including high-tech offerings such as robotic surgery.

EXECUTIVES

Vice President Of Patient Care Services, Diann Johnston
Vice President Quality Risk Management, Patricia Keating
Assistant Vice President Financial Services, James Alexander
Operational Vice President, Bill Arnold
Medical Records Director, Dianna Jankos
Vice President Of Supply Chain, Robert Carretta
Vice President Of Patient Care Services, Sari Kaplon
Auditors: KPMG LLP NEW YORK NY

LOCATIONS

HQ: MONMOUTH MEDICAL CENTER INC.
300 2ND AVE, LONG BRANCH, NJ 077406395
Phone: 732 222-5200
Web: WWW.MMCSURGERY.COM

PRODUCTS/OPERATIONS

Selected Centers and Services
Anesthesiology Services
Behavioral Health Network
Brain Tumor Center (David S. Zocchi)
The Breast Center (Jacqueline M. Wilentz Comprehensive)
Burn Center
Cancer Services
Cardiac Services
Cardiac Surgery
Children's Hospital at Monmouth (Pediatrics)
Cleft Palate Center
Cord Blood Banking Program
Cosmetic Surgery
Cranmer Ambulatory Surgery Center
Critical Care Services
Diabetes Education - Center for Diabetes Education
Dental Medicine
Diagnostic Imaging Services
The Eisenberg Family Center
Emergency Services
Epilepsy Monitoring Program

Extracorporeal Membrane Oxygenation Program (ECMO)
The Gamma Knife Center
Geriatric Emergency Medicine (GEM) Unit
Geriatric Health Center
Head & Neck Surgery
Hernias Repair Institute for the Treatment of Complex
HIV/AIDS Program
Home Health Care
Home Infusion Care
Hospice
Hyperbaric Oxygen Therapy
Integrative Medicine (Center for)
Joint Replacement and Spine Center
Medical Records
Medical Alert/Lifeline
Medicine (Department of)
Minimally Invasive Surgery
Monmouth Family Health Center
Neonatal Intensive Care Unit (Regional Newborn Center)
Neuroscience Institute
Nutritional Counseling
Obstetrics/Gynecological Services
Occupational Medicine
Orthopaedic Services
Outpatient Services Location
Pain Management Program
Palliative Care
Pastoral Care
Pathology & Laboratory Services
Pediatric Services
Pediatric Subspecialty Center at Toms River The
Pediatric Surgery
Pharmacy Department
Plastic Surgery
Podiatry Services
Pre-Admission Testing Services
Psychiatric Services
Pulmonary Services
Radiation Oncology
Rehabilitation Services
Renal Services
Renal Transplantation
Respiratory Services
Robotic Surgery
Senior Services Program
Sleep Disorders Center
Spine Center
Surgical Services
Urogynecology
Urology
Valerie Fund Cancer Center (Pediatrics)
Vascular Surgery
The Weight Loss Institute of New Jersey
Wound Treatment Center

COMPETITORS

Atlantic Health
Bergen Regional Medical
Capital Health System
CentraState Healthcare System
Hackensack Meridian Health
Princeton HealthCare
Saint Peter's University Hospital
Shore Memorial Hospital
St. Joseph's Healthcare System
Trinitas Regional Medical Center
Valley Health System

HISTORICAL FINANCIALS

Company Type: Private

Income Statement				FYE: December 31
	REVENUE ($ mil.)	NET INCOME ($ mil.)	NET PROFIT MARGIN	EMPLOYEES
12/17	529	52	10.0%	2,400
12/16	399	46	11.5%	—
12/14	375	38	10.2%	—
12/13	355	47	13.3%	—
Annual Growth	10.5%	3.0%	—	—

2017 Year-End Financials

Return on assets: 3.6%   Cash ($ mil.): —
Return on equity: 10.0%
Current ratio: 0.70

MONOGRAM FOOD SOLUTIONS, LLC

Monogram Food Solutions is focused on M E A and T. As a manufacturer of meat and meat snack products the company produces beef jerky sausage hot dogs bacon and other processed food items. Its brands include Circle B King Cotton and Trail's Best Meat Snacks. Through several special licensing agreements Monogram Food Solutions also sells Jeff Foxworthy Jerky Products NASCAR Jerky and Steak Strips and Bass Pro Uncle Buck's Licensed Products. The company which distributes its products nationwide operates facilities in Minnesota Indiana and Virginia. Founded in 2004 Monogram Food Solutions was formed through the merger of assets (King Cotton and Circle B) previously owned by Sara Lee Corp.

Geographic Reach

From its headquarters in Memphis Tennessee Monogram Food Solutions directs the operation of additional facilities in (Chandler) Minnesota (Muncie and Bristol) Indiana and (Martinsville) Virginia. The company distributes its products nationwide.

Strategy

Licensing agreements have helped Monogram Food Solutions build a firm foundation for its business. Aside from its deal with Bass Pro Shops and Jeff Foxworthy the company enjoys licensing partnerships with Johnsonville Sausage and Glory Foods. Its alliance with Johnsonville Sausage inked in 2012 gave Monogram Food Solutions the go-ahead to produce and market Johnsonville Deli Bites Bacon Jerky and other meat snacks innovations.

Beginning in 2010 the company began manufacturing and selling meat snacks for the energy drink maker DNA Beverages Corporation under the DNA brand. Geared toward a younger consumer the DNA beef products gives Monogram a larger demographic for its products.

Mergers and Acquisitions

Since its founding the company has quickly built itself up by buying established meat product manufacturers and processing plants. In 2009 it acquired three companies including beef jerky maker Wild Bill's Foods and Al Pete's Meats (and the Pete's Pride brand name). It also acquired the Hannah's Bull's O'Brien's and Dakota meat snack brands from meat processing company American Foods Group.

In late 2012 Monogram Food Solutions purchased Hinsdale Farms of Bristol Indiana. As one of the nation's largest makers of corn dogs Hinsdale also has a hand in serving retail private label customers and co-packing for other manufacturers. The deal added a fourth manufacturing plant for processing meat. As part of the acquisition Monogram Food Solutions is working to integrate the Hinsdale business into its manufacturing and sales systems.

EXECUTIVES

Vice President Human Resources, Richard Stewart
Vice President And General Manager, Brett Elliott
Corporate Vice President And Controller, Matt Arinder
Vice President And Product Development, Bill Southard
Auditors: MAYER HOFFMAN MCCANN PC MEM

LOCATIONS

HQ: MONOGRAM FOOD SOLUTIONS, LLC
530 OAK COURT DR STE 400, MEMPHIS, TN
381173735
Phone: 901 685-7167
Web: WWW.MONOGRAMFOODS.COM

PRODUCTS/OPERATIONS

Selected Brands
Circle B
Hannah's
King Cotton
O'Brien's Meat Snacks/Sausages
Wild Bill's

COMPETITORS

Bridgford Foods	Hormel
Carl Buddig	Jerky Snack Brands
Clemens Family	Link Snacks
Corporation	Oberto Sausage Company
ConAgra	Weaver Meats

HISTORICAL FINANCIALS

Company Type: Private

Income Statement   FYE: December 30

	REVENUE ($ mil.)	NET INCOME ($ mil.)	NET PROFIT MARGIN	EMPLOYEES
12/17	640	2	0.4%	790
12/16*	565	12	2.2%	—
01/16	419	0	0.2%	—
12/14	321	3	1.1%	—
Annual Growth	25.8%	(10.6%)	—	—

*Fiscal year change

2017 Year-End Financials
Return on assets: 8.8%   Cash ($ mil.): —
Return on equity: 0.4%
Current ratio: 0.50

MONONGAHELA POWER COMPANY

Electricity flows from Monongahela Power (Mon Power) just like the river the utility was named after. The company services approximately 388000 residential and commercial customers in a service area of 13000 sq. mi. in West Virginia. Mon Power along with West Penn Power and Potomac Edison comprise the Allegheny Power arm of Allegheny Energy which is now part of FirstEnergy. In 2013 Mon Power owned or controlled 3580 MW of generating capacity. The company is contractually obligated to supply Potomac Edison with sufficient power to meet that company's power load obligations in West Virginia.

Operations

Mon Power provides generation transmission and distribution services. Its infrastructure includes 25390 miles of distribution lines and more than 2125 miles of transmission lines.

Geographic Reach

The utility's service area includes Northern Central and Southeastern West Virginia.

Strategy

In 2013 the parent company invested about $131 million in Mon Power and planned to invest about $233 million more in 2014 to help Mon Power expand its operations.

In a transfer of assets within FirstEnergy's West Virginia-based operations to improve efficiencies in 2013 Mon Power sold its 8% share of the Pleas-

ants power plant at its fair market value of $73 million to Allegheny Energy Supply. In return Allegheny Energy Supply sold its 80% stake in the Harrison plant to Mon Power at its book value of $1.2 billion.

To lower carbon emissions in 2012 Mon Power shut down three aging coal-fired power plants in West Virginia: Albright Willow Island and Rivesville.

Company Background

The company is a subsidiary of Allegheny Energy which is owned by FirstEnergy.

Mon Power was incorporated in Ohio in 1924.

EXECUTIVES

Chb-Ceo, Paul J Evanson
Vice President, Philip L Goulding
President, David E Flitman
Contrl, Thomas R Gardner
V Pres-SEC, Hyun Park
Cfo, Jeffrey David Serkes
Manager- Cust Ser, Lannie Howell
Chief Technology Officer, Keith March
Chief Operating Officer, Arthur Erskine
Chief Information Officer, Gary Benz

LOCATIONS

HQ: MONONGAHELA POWER COMPANY
5001 NASA BLVD, FAIRMONT, WV 265548248
Phone: 800 686-0022
Web: WWW.ALLEGHENYPOWER.COM

COMPETITORS

Appalachian Power	Dominion Transmission
Buckeye Power	Ohio Edison
Dominion Hope	Ohio Valley Electric

HISTORICAL FINANCIALS

Company Type: Private

Income Statement   FYE: December 31

	REVENUE ($ mil.)	NET INCOME ($ mil.)	NET PROFIT MARGIN	EMPLOYEES
12/17	1,619	69	4.3%	4,000
12/16	1,613	66	4.1%	—
Annual Growth	0.3%	4.5%	—	—

2017 Year-End Financials
Return on assets: 1.1%   Cash ($ mil.): 76
Return on equity: 4.3%
Current ratio: 0.90

MONROE REGIONAL HEALTH SYSTEM

EXECUTIVES

Principle, R Cyrus Huffman
Coordinator, Paulette Beckford

LOCATIONS

HQ: MONROE REGIONAL HEALTH SYSTEM
131 SW 15TH ST, OCALA, FL 344716529
Phone: 352 351-7200
Web: WWW.MUNROEREGIONAL.COM

Income Statement   FYE: September 30

	REVENUE ($ mil.)	NET INCOME ($ mil.)	NET PROFIT MARGIN	EMPLOYEES
09/15*	340	(4)	—	2,500
12/08	0	(0)	—	
09/97	0	0	—	
Annual Growth	—	—	—	—

*Fiscal year change

MONSTER BEVERAGE 1990 CORPORATION

EXECUTIVES

Chb-Ceo, Rodney C Sacks
V Chb-Pres-Cfo-coo-sec, Hilton H Schlosberg
Sr V Pres Fin, Thomas J Kelly
Coo Monster Beverage Co, Nick R Gagliardi
Chief Marketing Officer, Mark J Hall

LOCATIONS

HQ: MONSTER BEVERAGE 1990 CORPORATION
1 MONSTER WAY, CORONA, CA 928797101
Phone: 951 739-6200

COMPETITORS

5-hour ENERGY	Mott's
Bazi	Naked Juice
Campbell Soup	National Beverage
Caribou Coffee	National Grape
Celsius Holdings	Cooperative
Chiquita Brands	Nestle
Cinnabon	Ocean Spray
Clearly Canadian	Odwalla
Coca-Cola	PepsiCo
Cott	Red Bull
Del Monte Foods	Reed's
Dole Food	Smucker
Dr Pepper Snapple	South Beach Beverage
Group	Starbucks
Energy Brands	Sunny Delight
Gatorade	Suntory Holdings
Godiva Chocolatier	Tree Top
Goya	Tropicana
Hornell Brewing	Unilever
IZZE	Welch's
Impulse Energy USA	Wet Planet Beverages
Jones Soda	illy
Mondelez International	

HISTORICAL FINANCIALS
Company Type: Private

Income Statement   FYE: December 31

	REVENUE ($ mil.)	NET INCOME ($ mil.)	NET PROFIT MARGIN	EMPLOYEES
12/17	3,369	820	24.4%	2,001
12/16	3,049	712	23.4%	—
12/15	2,722	546	20.1%	—
12/14	2,464	483	19.6%	—
Annual Growth	11.0%	19.3%	—	—

2017 Year-End Financials
Return on assets: 7.3%   Cash ($ mil.): 528
Return on equity: 24.4%
Current ratio: 1.70

MONTEFIORE MEDICAL CENTER

The primary teaching hospital of the Albert Einstein College of Medicine Montefiore Medical Center attends to the health care needs of residents of the Bronx and nearby Westchester County. The health system operates four main hospitals with about 1500 beds (and 93000 annual admissions) more than 100 ambulatory care offices a children's hospital and Centers of Excellence in cancer care cardiovascular services transplantation and neurosciences. Additionally it operates a home health care agency as well as outpatient facilities that provide ambulatory and diagnostic services. Montefiore also offers medical education programs in partnership with the Albert Einstein College of Medicine.

Operations

Montefiore provides medical services to more than 2.6 million people in the Bronx and Westchester County. With nearly 300000 visits per year Montefiore's emergency department is one of the busiest in the nation while the home health program provides over 500000 visits annually. As the teaching hospital for Albert Einstein College of Medicine Montefiore provides postgraduate training for nearly 100 accredited residency and fellowship programs at the Children's Hospital at Montefiore Moses Division and Weiler Division and eight residency and fellowship programs sponsored by New York Medical College.

Through Montefiore Care Management the company uses a global prepayment or similar strategies to manage care for 200000 individuals for hospital care rehabilitation outpatient care professional services home care mental health counseling community-based services remote patient monitoring and other programs.

Montefiore and Einstein are among about three dozen academic medical centers nationwide to be awarded the Clinical and Translational Science Award (CTSA) by the National Institutes of Health.

Geographic Reach

Montefiore is made up of four hospitals within three main campuses in the Bronx and more than 100 ambulatory care offices throughout the Bronx and Westchester County (and a total of 140 locations across its entire service area). It has nearly 50 primary care locations throughout the New York metropolitan area.

Strategy

The health center's strategy is to advance its partnership with the Einstein College of Medicine and to improve the health of the communities it serves. Montefiore has grown in scale through acquisitions and mergers in order to diversify its earning potential and increase its bargaining power with drug wholesalers. The system which treats a relatively high percentage of Medicaid patients also stands to benefit by serving a larger volume of patients. Medicaid is shifting to the managed care model which pays a set amount per patient or service. Therefore Montefiore and other providers are seeking growth by caring for more patients in a more efficient manner thereby reducing losses from providing patient care above the government payor's set payment. Additionally the system launched its own insurance coverage for small businesses in early 2015.

The health system is largely involved in the community and is one of the region's hospitals to participate in the Bronx Regional Health Information Organization (Bronx RHIO) a not-for-profit organization established to help the borough's vast number of health care providers share patient information. Participants include hospitals health systems ambulatory care centers individual physician offices long-term care and home care services. Collectively they deliver care to more than 1 million residents including more than 95% of the borough's annual hospital discharges.

Company Background

Founded in 1884 to treat tuberculosis patients Montefiore has a long history of responding to community health crises including lead poisoning and AIDS. In response to rising needs in the community Montefiore opened a community clinic with the aim of vaccinating young women for HPV a sexually transmitted disease that can cause cervical cancer.

EXECUTIVES

Evp Finance And Cfo, Joel A. Perlman
President And Ceo, Steven M. Safyer, age 70
Evp And Coo, Philip O. Ozuah
Svp And Chief Medical Officer, Andrew D. Racine

LOCATIONS

HQ: MONTEFIORE MEDICAL CENTER
111 E 210TH ST, BRONX, NY 104672401
Phone: 718 920-4321
Web: WWW.MONTEFIORE.ORG

PRODUCTS/OPERATIONS

Selected Services

Allergy & Immunology
Arthritis & Joint Disease (Rheumatology)
Blood (Hematology)
Bones Muscles & Joints Orthopaedics)
Brain (Neurology)
Centers of Excellence
Dentistry & Oral Surgery
Dermatology
Diabetes Hormones Metabolism (Endocrinology)
Diagnostics & Testing (Pathology)
Digestive & Liver Dieases (Gastroenterology)
Elder Care (Geriatrics)
Emergency Medicine
Eyes (Opthalmology and Visual Sciences)
Family and Social Medicine
General Internal Medicine
Headache Center
HIV/AIDS
Home Care
ICU (Critical Care Medicine)
Infectious Diseases
Internal Medicine
Kidney Disease (Nephrology)
Lungs (Pulmonary Medicine)
Neurosurgery
OB/GYN & Women's Health
Otorhinolaryngology - Head and Neck Surgery
Pain Management & Anesthesiology
Pediatrics
Pharmacy Services
Primary Care
Psychiatry and Behavioral Sciences
Radiology
Rehabilitation Medicine
Sleep-Wake Disorders Center
Surgery
Surgical Services (All)
Urology
Wound Care (Hyperbaric Medicine)

Selected Facilities

Greene Medical Arts Pavilion (outpatient care)
Mercy Community Care (outpatient care)
Montefiore Medical Group (23 Bronx and Westchester locations)
Montefiore Medical Park (outpatient care)
Moses Division Hospital (or Henry and Lucy Moses Division)
   The Children's Hospital at Montefiore
North Division (formerly Our Lady of Mercy Medical Center)
Weiler Division Hospital (or Jack D. Weiler Hospital)

COMPETITORS

Beth Israel Medical
  Center
Bronx-Lebanon Hospital
Brookdale University
  Hospital
Brooklyn Hospital
  Center
Catholic Healthcare
  System
Jamaica Hospital
  Medical Center
Kingsbrook Jewish
  Medical Center

Lenox Hill Hospital
Maimonides Medical
  Center
New York City Health
  and Hospitals
NewYork-Presbyterian
  Healthcare
Northwell Health
Phelps Memorial
  Hospital Center
SUNY Downstate
Winthrop-University
  Hospital

HISTORICAL FINANCIALS

Company Type: Private

Income Statement

	REVENUE ($ mil.)	NET INCOME ($ mil.)	NET PROFIT MARGIN	EMPLOYEES
				FYE: December 31
12/17	3,762	43	1.2%	11,000
12/16	2,690	42	1.6%	—
Annual Growth	39.9%	2.7%	—	—

2017 Year-End Financials

Return on assets: 7.4%   Cash ($ mil.): 253
Return on equity: 1.2%
Current ratio: 0.60

MOORE REGIONAL HOSPITAL, INC.

EXECUTIVES

Chb, Walker Morris
SEC, Judy Cox
Asst SEC, Charles T Frock
Treas, Norris L Hodgins Jr
Controller, Robert T Ward

LOCATIONS

HQ: MOORE REGIONAL HOSPITAL, INC.
  20 PAGE DR, PINEHURST, NC 283748847
Phone: 910 295-7888

HISTORICAL FINANCIALS

Company Type: Private

Income Statement

	REVENUE ($ mil.)	NET INCOME ($ mil.)	NET PROFIT MARGIN	EMPLOYEES
				FYE: September 30
09/15	468	55	11.9%	1,400
09/08	358	31	8.7%	—
09/05	326	45	13.9%	—
Annual Growth	3.7%	2.1%	—	—

2015 Year-End Financials

Return on assets: 3.9%   Cash ($ mil.): 25
Return on equity: 11.9%
Current ratio: 0.30

MORENO VALLEY UNIFIED SCHOOL DISTRICT

EXECUTIVES

V Pres, Cleveland Johnson
Supt, Judy D White
Coordinator, Karla Noonan
Director, Dan Reed
Human Resources Director, Maria Lawler
Teacher, Alexandra Enriquez
Teacher, Carla Legerton
Purchasing Director, Josie Ripoly
Teacher, Ana Myers
Clerk, Anita Bridges
Teacher, Armida Corral
Auditors: JEANETTE L GARCIA & ASSO FATE

LOCATIONS

HQ: MORENO VALLEY UNIFIED SCHOOL DISTRICT
  25634 ALESSANDRO BLVD, MORENO VALLEY, CA
  925534916
Phone: 951 571-7500
Web: WWW.MVUSD.K12.CA.US

HISTORICAL FINANCIALS

Company Type: Private

Income Statement

	REVENUE ($ mil.)	NET INCOME ($ mil.)	NET PROFIT MARGIN	EMPLOYEES
				FYE: June 30
06/17	486	4	1.0%	3,500
06/16	467	33	7.1%	—
06/05	2	0	0.1%	—
06/03	176	16	9.5%	—
Annual Growth	7.5%	(8.6%)	—	—

MORSE OPERATIONS, INC.

Morse Operations (dba Ed Morse Automotive Group) has been selling cars and trucks long enough to know the code of the road. It owns about a dozen new car dealerships across Florida most of them operating under the Ed Morse name. Dealerships house more than 15 franchises and 10 domestic and import car brands including Cadillac Fiat Chevrolet Buick GMC Scion Honda Mazda and Toyota. The company's Bayview Cadillac in Fort Lauderdale is one of the world's largest volume sellers of Cadillacs. Morse Operations also sells used cars provides parts and service and operates a fleet sales division. Founder and auto magnate the late Ed Morse entered the automobile business in 1946 with a 20-car rental fleet.

Operations

Ed Morse Fleet Sales offers vehicles from about 10 different brands including Honda Cadillac Fiat Chevrolet Buick GMC Scion Mazda and Toyota. To date annual fleet sales have reached 100000 vehicles.

Fleet customers include daily rental companies such as National Car Rental Avis and Alamo Rent A Car.

Geographic Reach

The dealership network serves customers throughout Florida along the East and West coasts and in Central Florida.

EXECUTIVES

Pres, Edward J Morse III
V Pres-Cfo, Carmine Colella
Ceo-Coo, Dennis M Macinnes
Vice President, Rany Hoffman
Financial Officer, Craig Davis
Director, Dennis Drucker
Advertising Staff, Howard Isaacs
Information Technology Interne, Patrick Werner
Executive Vice President, Randy Hoffman
Creative Director, Scott Reynolds
Auditors: CROWE HORWART LLP FORT LAUDER

LOCATIONS

HQ: MORSE OPERATIONS, INC.
  2850 S FEDERAL HWY, DELRAY BEACH, FL
  334833216
Phone: 561 276-5000
Web: WWW.EDMORSESAWGRASS.COM

PRODUCTS/OPERATIONS

Selected Dealerships

Brandon Auto Mall
Ed Morse Auto Plaza - Port Richey
Ed Morse Bayview Cadillac
Ed Morse Cadillac - Delray Beach
  Ed Morse C
  Ed Morse C
Ed Morse Delray Toyota/Scion
Ed Morse Honda Blue Heron
  Ed Morse M
Ed Morse Sawgrass

COMPETITORS

AutoNation
  Braman Management
  Buchanan Automotive
  Ferman Automotive
  Holman Enterprises
  Island Lincoln-Mercury

JM Family Enterprises
March/Hodge
Penske Automotive
  Group
Scott-McRae

HISTORICAL FINANCIALS

Company Type: Private

Income Statement

	REVENUE ($ mil.)	NET INCOME ($ mil.)	NET PROFIT MARGIN	EMPLOYEES
				FYE: December 31
12/17	1,019	4	0.4%	925
12/16	1,334	9	0.7%	—
12/15	1,095	14	1.3%	—
12/14	863	10	1.2%	—
Annual Growth	5.7%	(24.6%)	—	—

2017 Year-End Financials

Return on assets: 1.3%   Cash ($ mil.): 18
Return on equity: 0.4%
Current ratio: 0.40

MORTON PLANT HOSPITAL ASSOCIATION, INC.

EXECUTIVES

Pres, Phil Beauchant
V Pres-Oprs-Adm, Hal Ziecheck
Doctor, Margaret Ann Kelleher
Surgeon, Michael Rothberg
Doctor, Michael Starsiak

Internal Medicine Practitioner, Andrew Fink
Diagnostic Radiologist, Yair Safriel
Pathologist, Jason Savell
Nurse Manager Post Partum, Jennifer Wasilewski
Registered Nurse Cniii, Norma Kirk
Doctor, John C Dormois

LOCATIONS

HQ: MORTON PLANT HOSPITAL ASSOCIATION, INC.
   300 PINELLAS ST, CLEARWATER, FL 337563892
Phone: 727 462-7000
Web: WWW.MORTONPLANT.COM

HISTORICAL FINANCIALS

Company Type: Private

Income Statement   FYE: December 31

	REVENUE ($ mil.)	NET INCOME ($ mil.)	NET PROFIT MARGIN	EMPLOYEES
12/16	555	83	14.9%	3,000
12/15	107	(8)	—	—
12/13	598	49	8.3%	—
12/09	517	33	6.5%	—
Annual Growth	1.0%	13.8%		

2016 Year-End Financials

Return on assets: 3.7%   Cash ($ mil.): —
Return on equity: 14.9%
Current ratio: 1.90

MOTHER FRANCES HOSPITAL REGIONAL HEALTH CARE CENTER

EXECUTIVES

Pres, Lindsey Bradely Jr
Sr V Pres-Cfo, William Bellenfant
Vice President, Ray Thompson
V Pres-Cfo, Joyce Hester
SEC, Teresa Mika
Information Technology Manager, Robert Hilliard
Contrl, Shelly Rutherford
Auditors: BKD LLP HOUSTON TX

LOCATIONS

HQ: MOTHER FRANCES HOSPITAL REGIONAL
   HEALTH CARE CENTER
   800 E DAWSON ST, TYLER, TX 757012093
Phone: 903 593-8441
Web: WWW.TMFHS.ORG

HISTORICAL FINANCIALS

Company Type: Private

Income Statement   FYE: June 30

	REVENUE ($ mil.)	NET INCOME ($ mil.)	NET PROFIT MARGIN	EMPLOYEES
06/16*	618	63	10.2%	2,747
03/10	314	50	16.1%	—
/ 0	0	0	—	—
Annual Growth	—	—	—	—

*Fiscal year change

2016 Year-End Financials

Return on assets: 5.0%   Cash ($ mil.): 40
Return on equity: 10.2%
Current ratio: 1.10

MOUNT AUBURN HOSPITAL

EXECUTIVES

Ceo, Jeanette G Clough
Cfo, Peter Semaneza
Doctor, Carolyn Lamb
Marketing Director, Michael Oconnell
Director, Laure Campbell
General Counsel, Leslie Joseph
Director, Eileen Dillon
Pain Management Specialist, Erica J Bial
Chief of Emergency Room, Gary Setnik
Internal Medicine Practitioner, Tiffany A Kolniak
Internal Medicine Practitioner, Joseph G Omlor

LOCATIONS

HQ: MOUNT AUBURN HOSPITAL
   330 MOUNT AUBURN ST, CAMBRIDGE, MA
   021385597
Phone: 617 492-3500
Web: WWW.MOUNTAUBURNHOSPITAL.ORG

HISTORICAL FINANCIALS

Company Type: Private

Income Statement   FYE: September 30

	REVENUE ($ mil.)	NET INCOME ($ mil.)	NET PROFIT MARGIN	EMPLOYEES
09/17	411	(23)	—	1,700
09/16	415	4	1.2%	—
09/15	316	20	6.5%	—
09/14	321	21	6.8%	—
Annual Growth	8.6%	—	—	—

2017 Year-End Financials

Return on assets: 7.4%   Cash ($ mil.): 30
Return on equity: (-5.6%)
Current ratio: 1.40

MOUNT CARMEL HEALTH PLAN MEDIG

LOCATIONS

HQ: MOUNT CARMEL HEALTH PLAN MEDIG
   6150 E BROAD ST, COLUMBUS, OH 432131574
Phone: 614 546-3138
Web: WWW.MEDIGOLD.COM

HISTORICAL FINANCIALS

Company Type: Private

Income Statement   FYE: December 31

	REVENUE ($ mil.)	NET INCOME ($ mil.)	NET PROFIT MARGIN	EMPLOYEES
12/16	571	(20)	—	3
12/13	423	37	8.8%	—
Annual Growth	10.5%	—	—	—

2016 Year-End Financials

Return on assets: 3.1%   Cash ($ mil.): 55
Return on equity: (-3.5%)
Current ratio: 3.30

MOUNT CARMEL HEALTH SYSTEM

Mount Carmel Health System cares for the sick in the greater Columbus area and central Ohio. The health care system boasts 1500 physicians at three general hospitals and a specialty surgical hospital offering a comprehensive range of medical and surgical services including cardiovascular care. Mount Carmel Health also operates outpatient centers including primary care and specialty physicians' practices and it offers home health care services. The hospital group is part of Trinity Health one of the largest Catholic health care systems in the US.

Operations

Mount Carmel's facilities include the acute care Mount Carmel East Mount Carmel West and Mount Carmel St. Ann's hospitals as well as the Mount Carmel New Albany a surgical hospital specializing in orthopedic neurological and musculoskeletal treatments. The system also operates several freestanding emergency and surgery centers and other outpatient and community care centers. Its HealthProviders subsidiary manages about two dozen primary care and specialty practices with more than 100 physicians in central Ohio.

In the realm of education Mount Carmel Health operates six medical residency programs for physicians and its Mount Carmel College of Nursing is one of the largest in the state.

Strategy

In 2015 Mount Carmel announced that it was investing more than $700 million in a major expansion. The investment includes big projects at three Mount Carmel campuses: Mount Carmel East Mount Carmel Grove City and Mount Carmel West. Mount Carmel East will begin a $310 million modernization in 2015 to be completed in phases through 2019.

That year the company signed an agreement with HealthSouth to begin construction on a new inpatient rehabilitation hospital in Westerville Ohio. The 60-bed hospital will be a joint venture between HealthSouth and Mount Carmel and will provide specialized rehabilitative care to patients who have experienced stroke trauma brain and orthopedic injuries or other major illnesses or injuries. Construction on the 60000-square-foot hospital is expected to be completed in early 2017. When the new hospital opens Mount Carmel will relocate its existing 24-bed unit at Mount Carmel West to the new facility.

Company Background

In 2012 the company launched a $110 million facilities improvement project (Project GRACE) which includes the renovation of the St. Ann's hospital. Mount Carmel Health plans for the upgraded St. Ann's facility to serve as a regional medical center.

In 2010 Mount Carmel completed construction of a new freestanding emergency center in the town of Canal Winchester through a partnership with Fairfield Medical Center. The center features both general emergency and pediatric urgent care facilities. In time the center might expand into a larger hospital facility.

Mother M. Angela and Sister M. Rufina Dunn of the Congregation of the Sisters of the Holy Cross of Notre Dame founded Mount Carmel in 1886.

EXECUTIVES

Vice President Pfs, Karen Geisler
Vice President, Christine Aucreman

Vice President Managed Care Services, Lyn Flanagan
Vice President Patient Care Services And, Rachel Wright

LOCATIONS

HQ: MOUNT CARMEL HEALTH SYSTEM
6150 E BROAD ST, COLUMBUS, OH 432131574
Phone: 614 234-6000
Web: WWW.MOUNTCARMELHEALTH.COM

PRODUCTS/OPERATIONS

Selected Facilities
Hospitals
  Mount Carmel East
  Mount Carmel New Albany
  Mount Carmel St. Ann's
  Mount Carmel West
Other Facilities
  Anticoagulation Centers
  Atrial Fibrillation Center
  Cardiac Rehabilitation
  Diley Ridge Medical Center
  Mount Carmel Grove City Medical Center
  Geriatrics Center
  Health Centers
  Heart Failure Centers
  Home Medical Equipment
  Imaging Centers
  Mount Carmel Medical Group
  Occupational Health Centers
  Outpatient Cancer Treatment
  Outpatient Labs
  Physician Offices
  Rehab and Sports Medicine Services
  Sleep Medicine
  Surgery Centers
  Urgent Care Centers
  Women's Health Centers
  Wound Centers

COMPETITORS

Adena Health System
Fairfield Medical Center
Genesis HealthCare System (Ohio)
Licking Memorial Health Systems
Nationwide Children's Hospital
OhioHealth
Regency Hospital

HISTORICAL FINANCIALS
Company Type: Private

Income Statement   FYE: June 30

	REVENUE ($ mil.)	NET INCOME ($ mil.)	NET PROFIT MARGIN	EMPLOYEES
06/15	1,267	131	10.4%	8,000
06/14	1,223	94	7.7%	—
06/13	1,195	89	7.5%	—
06/10	198	2	1.2%	—
Annual Growth	44.9%	124.8%	—	—

2015 Year-End Financials
Return on assets: 9.9%
Return on equity: 10.4%
Current ratio: 1.60
Cash ($ mil.): 42

MOUNT CARMEL HEALTH SYSTEM

EXECUTIVES

Ceo, Jay Kasey
Manager, Brenda Austin

Director, Linda Atkinson
Consultant, Mary Buckley
Marketing Director, Robyn Morton
Marketing Staff, Steve Dunn
Administrative Assistant, Eric Woloschuk
Vascular Surgeon, Kenneth Wright
Senior Director, Joyce Bogan
Vice-President, Bruce Lucas
Customer Staff, Kelly Butler

LOCATIONS

HQ: MOUNT CARMEL HEALTH SYSTEM
793 W STATE ST, COLUMBUS, OH 432221551
Phone: 614 234-5000
Web: WWW.PW-HEALTH.COM

HISTORICAL FINANCIALS
Company Type: Private

Income Statement   FYE: June 30

	REVENUE ($ mil.)	NET INCOME ($ mil.)	NET PROFIT MARGIN	EMPLOYEES
06/16	743	33	4.5%	1
06/15	707	47	6.7%	—
Annual Growth	5.1%	(29.5%)	—	—

2016 Year-End Financials
Return on assets: 6.4%
Return on equity: 4.5%
Current ratio: 2.60
Cash ($ mil.): 39

MOUNT CLEMENS REGIONAL MEDICAL CENTER

Mount Clemens Regional Medical Center (doing business as McLaren Medical Center-Macomb) is an general acute care hospital serving the Macomb County area of suburban Detroit. With about 290 beds the hospital offers such specialties as cardiac and cancer care family practice services home and hospice care and emergency care. The McLaren Health Care-controlled company also operates three prompt care centers in nearby townships as well as a wound treatment clinic. Of the more than 420 physicians on staff at the hospital more than 100 are family medicine and internal medicine specialists who provide primary care.

Geographic Reach
The hospital system serves Michigan patients in the Macomb County area of suburban Detroit.

Strategy
Growing its geographic network of services in 2012 McLaren Medical Center-Macomb opened a new facility in Richmond-Lenox its offers includes physical therapy X-ray/diagnostic imaging and a laboratory blood draw station.

That year it also expanded its technological capabilities with the addition of the da VinciA® Si HD Surgical System robotic technology. The acquisition was part of a long history of adopting surgical advancements.

Company Background
The hospital was founded in 1944.

EXECUTIVES

Ceo, Thomas M Brisse
Pres, Mark O'Halla
Dir of Acct, Sherry Koshurba

Internal Medicine Practitioner, Ryan Malek
Executive Officer, Andrea Phillips
Coordinator, Lori Clanton

LOCATIONS

HQ: MOUNT CLEMENS REGIONAL MEDICAL CENTER
1000 HARRINGTON ST, MOUNT CLEMENS, MI 480432920
Phone: 586 493-8000
Web: WWW.MCLAREN.ORG

PRODUCTS/OPERATIONS

Selected Departments and Services
Bariatrics
Behavioral Health
Blood Conservation
Cancer Services
Cardiac
Diabetes
Diagnostic Imaging
Dialysis Services
Emergency Care
EMS
Family BirthPlace
Fitness Centers
Free Clinics
Health Insurance
Home Care
Hospice
Immunizations
Implantable Hearing Solutions
Infectious Disease
Infusion Center
Intensive Care
Internal Medicine
Laboratory and Pathology
Lifeline
Medical Library
Medical Supplies & Equipment
Neurosciences
Nutritional Counseling
Ophthalmology
Orthopedics
Pain Management
Pediatrics
Pharmacy Services
Primary Care
Proton Therapy
Pulmonary and Respiratory
Rehabilitaton and Therapy
Robotic Surgery
Sleep Medicine
Stroke Center
Surgical and Endoscopy Services
Trauma
Urology
Walk-in Clinics
Women's Services
Wound Care

COMPETITORS

Beaumont Health System
Crittenton Hospital
St. John Hospital & Medical Center
St. John Macomb-Oakland Hospital

HISTORICAL FINANCIALS
Company Type: Private

Income Statement   FYE: September 30

	REVENUE ($ mil.)	NET INCOME ($ mil.)	NET PROFIT MARGIN	EMPLOYEES
09/15	305	8	2.8%	2,249
09/14	312	18	6.0%	—
09/13	303	18	6.1%	—
09/09	277	11	4.2%	—
Annual Growth	1.6%	(4.9%)	—	—

2015 Year-End Financials
Return on assets: 7.5%
Return on equity: 2.8%
Current ratio: 1.60
Cash ($ mil.): 33

MOUNT NITTANY MEDICAL CENTER

EXECUTIVES

Int Pres-Ceo, Richard Wisniewski
Exec Vice President, David B Peterson
Sr Vice President, Janet Schachtner
Registered Nurse, Susan Foster
Research Analyst, Barbara Gutch
Administrator, Kathryn Witt
Chief of Cardiology, Scott Crisp
Nephrology Specialist, Stephen Donelan
Manager, Tina Kephart
Network Analyst, James Walker
Director of Pharmacy, John Rossi
Auditors: BAKER TILLY VIRCHOW KRAUSE LLP

LOCATIONS

HQ: MOUNT NITTANY MEDICAL CENTER
 1800 E PARK AVE, STATE COLLEGE, PA 168036797
Phone: 814 231-7000
Web: WWW.MOUNTNITTANY.ORG

HISTORICAL FINANCIALS
Company Type: Private

Income Statement				FYE: June 30
	REVENUE ($ mil.)	NET INCOME ($ mil.)	NET PROFIT MARGIN	EMPLOYEES
06/16	381	23	6.2%	902
06/15	331	21	6.5%	—
06/14	325	20	6.4%	—
06/12	260	(7)	—	—
Annual Growth	10.0%			

2016 Year-End Financials
Return on assets: 29.1%
Return on equity: 6.2%
Current ratio: 0.20
Cash ($ mil.): 21

MOUNT SINAI HOSPITALS GROUP, INC.

EXECUTIVES

Pres-Ceo, Kenneth L Davis
Emergency Medicine Specialist, Jacob Isserman
Doctor, Anthony Manasia
Doctor, Bruce Darrow
Doctor, Bryan Markinson
Doctor, Dov Kolker
Doctor, Eric Genden
Director, Albert Siu
Associate Professor, David Muller
Coordinator, Deborah Lehrer
Doctor, James Eisenkraft

LOCATIONS

HQ: MOUNT SINAI HOSPITALS GROUP, INC.
 1 GUSTAVE L LEVY PL, NEW YORK, NY 100296504
Phone: 212 241-6500
Web: WWW.MOUNTSINAI.ORG

HISTORICAL FINANCIALS
Company Type: Private

Income Statement				FYE: December 31
	REVENUE ($ mil.)	NET INCOME ($ mil.)	NET PROFIT MARGIN	EMPLOYEES
12/15*	2,025	70	3.5%	12,559
06/15	304	5	1.8%	—
Annual Growth	564.6%	1160.5%	—	—

*Fiscal year change

2015 Year-End Financials
Return on assets: 8.2%
Return on equity: 3.5%
Current ratio: 1.20
Cash ($ mil.): 194

MOUNT SINAI MEDICAL CENTER OF FLORIDA, INC.

Mount Sinai Medical Center of Florida is a not-for-profit acute care teaching hospital providing a wide range of health services to residents of South Florida. The medical center which boasts more than 670 beds provides general medical and surgical care as well as specialty care in cardiology (Mount Sinai Heart Institute) neuroscience oncology orthopedics pulmonology radiology and other fields. It also participates in clinical research studies and drug trials with an emphasis on cancer heart and lung conditions It maintains an inpatient behavioral health unit and houses the Wien Center for Alzheimer's disease and memory disorders diagnosis and research the largest such facillity in the region.

Operations
Mount Sinai Medical Center of Florida has 26 operating suites and more than 700 physicians. In 2012 it reported more than 63000 emergency visits 22000 patients admissions and 12000 surgeries.

Geographic Reach
Reaching beyond its main South Florida campus the Mount Sinai Medical Center of Florida also operates a multi-specialty physicians' clinic emergency care and diagnostic center in nearby Aventura. It also operates physicians' clinics in Key Biscayne and Hialeah and an outpatient center in Coral Gables.

Sales and Marketing
The Center markets its services through TV and radio commercials and via print media.

Financial Performance
The company's revenues grew by 3% to $497 million in 2012 due to higher patient service revenues (net of contractual allowances discounts and other revenue). Medicare accounted for 36% of patient service revenues; Medicaid 7%.

Mount Sinai Medical Center of Florida reported net income of $34 million in 2012 (compared to a net loss in 2011) thanks to the absence of impairment of long-lived assets partially offset by a loss on extinguishment of debt. Net income also improved due to change in the beneficial interest in the net assets of Mount Sinai Medical Center Foundation Inc.

Strategy
The company teams up with larger institutions to expand its reach and skill set. Its medical education programs include a cardiology partnership with Columbia University and resident programs for medical students from the University of Miami Florida International University and Nova Southeastern University. The center's partnership with Columbia University has created the Mount Sinai Heart Institute and the Columbia University Division of Urology at Mount Sinai the only Ivy League affiliated programs in South Florida.

Other programs support students entering such health care professions as nursing pharmacy and therapy.

Enhancing its standing in 2014 Mount Sinai Medical Center of Florida received full accreditation for percutaneous coronary intervention from the Society of Cardiovascular Patient Care an international body dedicated to preventing and treating heart disease.

Company Background
Mount Sinai Medical Center of Florida was founded in 1949 by a group of philanthropists and concerned citizens.

EXECUTIVES

President And Ceo, Steven D. Sonenreich
Evp Operations And Cfo, Alex Mendez
Chief Medical Officer, Robert C. Goldszer
President Medical Staff, Peter Segall
Senior Vice President Operations, Angel Pallin
Assistant Vice President Of Nursing, Maryse Dufresne
Senior Vice President And Chief Operating Officer, Amy Perry
Vice President Human Resources, Jennifer Foreman
Assistant Vice President Ambulatory Services And Network Development, Jim Gaton
Chairman, Michael M. Adler

LOCATIONS

HQ: MOUNT SINAI MEDICAL CENTER OF FLORIDA, INC.
 4300 ALTON RD, MIAMI BEACH, FL 331402948
Phone: 305 674-2121
Web: WWW.MSMC.COM

PRODUCTS/OPERATIONS

Florida Locations
MOUNT SINAI MEDICAL CENTER (MAIN CAMPUS): Miami Beach
MOUNT SINAI AVENTURA EMERGENCY ROOM PHYSICIAN OFFICES CANCER CENTER AND DIAGNOSTIC CENTER: Aventura
MOUNT SINAI KEY BISCAYNE PHYSICIAN OFFICES: Key Biscayne
MOUNT SINAI CORAL GABLES DIAGNOSTIC CATHETERIZATION LAB: Coral Gables
MOUNT SINAI PRIMARY & SPECIALTY CARE CORAL GABLES: Coral Gables
MOUNT SINAI HIALEAH: Hialeah

COMPETITORS

Baptist Health South Florida	Miami Children's Hospital
Broward Health	Tenet Healthcare
HCA	University of Miami Hospital
Jackson Health System	

HISTORICAL FINANCIALS
Company Type: Private

Income Statement				FYE: December 31
	REVENUE ($ mil.)	NET INCOME ($ mil.)	NET PROFIT MARGIN	EMPLOYEES
12/16	560	19	3.5%	3,225
12/15	533	38	7.2%	—
12/14	530	17	3.2%	—
12/13	584	42	7.3%	—
Annual Growth	(1.4%)	(22.9%)	—	—

MOUNTAIN STATES HEALTH ALLIANCE AUXILIARY, INC.

EXECUTIVES

Admin, Dennis Vonderfecht
Sr Vice President, Marvin Eichorn
Attorney, Walter Price
Compliance Director, Paige Carter
Information Specialist, Amy Williams
Health Care Director, Mellisa Johnson
Information Specialist, Robert Combs
Chemistry Manager, Brenda Minasian
Respiratory Therapy Director, Jennifer Pinnell
Performance Improvement Coordi, Lisa Davidson
Executive Assistant, Betty Cusick

LOCATIONS

HQ: MOUNTAIN STATES HEALTH ALLIANCE
AUXILIARY, INC.
400 N STATE OF FRNKLIN RD, JOHNSON CITY, TN
376046035
Phone: 423 431-6111
Web: WWW.MSHA.COM

HISTORICAL FINANCIALS

Company Type: Private

Income Statement				FYE: June 30
	REVENUE ($ mil.)	NET INCOME ($ mil.)	NET PROFIT MARGIN	EMPLOYEES
06/16	437	36	8.4%	2,300
06/15	433	43	10.0%	—
06/05	6	0	7.5%	—
06/03	436	9	2.2%	—
Annual Growth	0.0%	10.8%	—	—

2016 Year-End Financials

Return on assets: 6.4%   Cash ($ mil.): —
Return on equity: 8.4%
Current ratio: 1.30

MOZILLA FOUNDATION

EXECUTIVES

Ceo, Mark Surman
Manager, Benjamin Sternthal
Director, John Lilly
Senior Accountant, Angela Leung
Manager, Jennifer Bertsch
Committeeman, Mark Mayo
Web Developer, Rob Helmer
Manager, Al Billings
Strategic Partner Manager, Joanne Nagel
Director Hive City Strategy, Meghan McDermott
Senior Software Engineer, Laura Thomson
Auditors: DELOITTE TAX LLP SAN FRANCISC

LOCATIONS

HQ: MOZILLA FOUNDATION
331 E EVELYN AVE, MOUNTAIN VIEW, CA 940411550
Phone: 650 903-0800
Web: WWW.MOZILLA.ORG

COMPETITORS

Apple Inc.	Microsoft
Google	Opera Software

HISTORICAL FINANCIALS

Company Type: Private

Income Statement				FYE: December 31
	REVENUE ($ mil.)	NET INCOME ($ mil.)	NET PROFIT MARGIN	EMPLOYEES
12/15	421	57	13.6%	588
12/14	19	3	17.9%	—
Annual Growth	2081.7%	1553.4%	—	—

2015 Year-End Financials

Return on assets: 3.1%   Cash ($ mil.): 70
Return on equity: 13.6%
Current ratio: 2.30

MULESOFT, INC.

MuleSoft Inc.?s name describes what it does ? if you know that IT workers call the drudgery of connecting company networks ?donkey work.? The company replaced donkey with mule and began selling software that uses application programming interfaces (APIs) to connect applications data and devices into a network of applications. MuleSoft?s Anypoint Platform enables an infrastructure so companies can conduct business using mobile cloud software-as-a-service and Internet of Things technologies. When a purchase is made with a mobile app MuleSoft makes sure it is connected to a company?s supply chain software and other pertinent functions. MuleSoft raised about $120 million in a 2017 IPO. Then in 2018 it agreed to be bought by Salesforce.com for about $6.5 billion.

Change in Company Type

In 2017 Mulesoft agreed to Salesforce.com's offer to buy it for $6.5 billion. With the addition of Mulesoft's technologies Salesforce can help its customers connect information throughout their companies across public and private clouds and data sources. Mulesoft expects to get a boost from Salesforce's resources. The deal Salesforce's most expensive was expected to close in mid-2018.

IPO

MuleSoft Inc. raised about $220 million in its initial public offering in March 2017. The company intends to use the proceeds for general corporate purposes including working capital operating expenses and capital expenditures. It also could use the money to acquire complementary businesses products services or technologies.

Operations

MuleSoft Inc. makes all its revenue from the Anypoint Platform by selling subscriptions and support and providing professional services and training. About 80% of the company?s revenue comes from subscriptions (usually about a year in length but getting longer) and support with the rest generated by professional services.

The company runs its cloud-based software on Amazon.com?s Amazon Web Services.

Geographic Reach

MuleSoft Inc. is based in San Francisco California and has extensive research and development operations in Argentina. The company also has a significant portion of sales personnel and customer support operations in Europe Asia Australia and South America.

Sales and Marketing

MuleSoft Inc. reaches customers through a direct sales force which focuses on large companies with global operations. MuleSoft targets CIOs chief IT architects and line-of-business leaders. The company also works with systems integrators and value-added resellers to find sales prospects and provide integration services for installing the Anypoint Platform.

The company counts more than 1000 customers. Some 30 customers have about $1 million each in average annual contract value of subscription and support contracts. Customers include Citrix The Coca-Cola Company Dixons Carphone McDonald?s Office Depot Europe B.V. Salesforce ServiceNow Spotify the State of Colorado Toyota Motor Corporation Australia and Unilever.

Financial Performance

MuleSoft Inc.?s revenue has grown quickly but so have expenses. The company reported about $188 million in revenue in 2016 a 70% increase from 2015. Subscription and support revenue rose more than 70% in 2016 with 60% of the increase from sales to existing customers and the rest from subscriptions bought by new customers. Professional services and other revenue rose 58% from the company?s larger customer base.

MuleSoft reduced its net loss to about $50 million in 2016 from about $65 million the year before aided by higher revenue.

Besides narrowing its loss in 2016 MuleSoft slashed its negative cash flow from operations to about $3 million for the year down from about $50 million negative cash flow in 2015.

Strategy

MuleSoft Inc. has good timing. Its Anypoint Platform which connects applications across a company?s network addresses the needs of companies to plug more devices and applications into their networks. MuleSoft software helps its customers connect ERP systems to CRM systems and legacy systems to new systems.

The company quotes estimates that peg the market for making those connections at $29 billion and most of that money is spent by large multinational companies with big networks to manage — and those are MuleSoft?s sales targets. New customers include Bentley Motors Scotia Gas University of Pittsburgh and Veritas and customers buying more services include Airbnb Cox Automotive Harper Collins Hertz Northrop Grumman and Unilever.

The company aims to increase the amount of revenue from international customers who generate about 40% of sales. The company has put money into building its global sales and marketing staffs service delivery and customer support.

While MuleSoft is in a new enterprise software market there are competitors. Among them are IBM Oracle and TIBCO as well as newer players such as Apigee which was acquired by Google.

EXECUTIVES

Vp Marketing, Mahau Ma
Cto, Uri Sarid
Cfo, Matt Langdon
Chairman And Ceo, Greg Schott
Chief Product Officer, Mark Dao
Svp People Ops General Counsel And Secretary, Rob Horton
President Field Operations, Simon Parmett
Vice President Of Emea, David Wyatt
Vice President Asia Pacific, Will Bosma

Senior Vice President Global Sales, Matt Kilguss
Vice President Global Customer Success, Brent Grimes
Regional Vice President Sales, Chris Erickson-King
Vice President Global Services, Mike Randall
Vice President And Corporate Controller, Laura Merkl
Vice President Global Channels And Services, Brent Hayward
Vice President Business Development, Brian Miller
Vice President Of Corporate Marketing, Vidya Peters
Regional Vice President Alliances, Dan McAllister
Regional Vice President Federal, Chris Aherne
Vice President Finance And Sales Operations, Lou Dora
Auditors: KPMG LLP SANTA CLARA CALIFOR

LOCATIONS

HQ: MULESOFT, INC.
50 FREMONT ST STE 300, SAN FRANCISCO, CA 941052231
Phone: 415 229-2009
Web: WWW.MULESOFT.COM

COMPETITORS

Google	Oracle
IBM	TIBCO Software

HISTORICAL FINANCIALS

Company Type: Private

Income Statement				FYE: December 31
	REVENUE ($ mil.)	NET INCOME ($ mil.)	NET PROFIT MARGIN	EMPLOYEES
12/17	296	(79)	—	841
12/16	187	(49)	—	—
Annual Growth	57.9%	—	—	—

2017 Year-End Financials

Return on assets: 0.7%
Return on equity: (-27.0%)
Current ratio: 0.80
Cash ($ mil.): 79

MULTICARE HEALTH SYSTEM

MultiCare Health System is a not-for-profit health system that serves the residents of four counties in the southern Puget Sound region and southwestern Washington. Altogether the system's five hospitals have more than 1100 beds. The largest facility Tacoma General boasts about 440 beds and provides specialized cancer cardiac orthopedic and trauma care in addition to general medical and surgical care. Other medical centers include Good Samaritan Hospital (with 286 beds) Allenmore Hospital (130 beds) Auburn Regional Medical Center (195 beds) and Mary Bridge Children's Hospital (82 beds).

Operations

MultiCare has more than 1000 staff physician specialists. In addition to its five hospitals the health system also operates dozens of primary care specialty care and urgent care clinics in the region as well as home health and hospice care agencies. Tacoma General Hospital operates the MultiCare Regional Cancer Center an obstetrics and neonatal intensive care unit the MultiCare Neuroscience Center of Washington orthopedics the MultiCare Surgical Care Center and the MultiCare Regional Heart & Vascular Center. Tacoma General also of-

fers Level II Adult Trauma Center and Level IIIB neonatal intensive care unit. Mary Bridge Children's Hospital & Health Center operates a pediatric intensive care unit a pediatric heart center a Center for Childhood Safety child abuse intervention programs and outpatient specialty clinics.

In 2013 alone the company provided free and subsidized health care services at an estimated cost of $185 million.

In 2013 MultiCare reported 217590 emergency department visits; 47138 admissions; 9616 inpatient surgeries 23502 outpatient surgeries and 5817 live births.

Geographic Reach

MultiCare serves patients in more than 130 locations in Washington's Pierce South King Thurston and Kitsap counties.

Strategy

The company is expanding its infrastructure to keep up with demand.

In 2014 MultiCare opened the 115929-sq.-ft. Rainier Pavilion as part of a $192 million project to expand services for women newborns and children at Tacoma General Hospital and Mary Bridge Children's Hospital. When the final phase is completed in 2015 the project will add 133919 sq. ft. of new space and 144835 sq. ft. of renovated space.

Also that year MultiCare broke ground on a new hospital in Covington improving access to health care services in South King County. The new 24-bed three-story hospital (with the potential to expand to 58 beds) will open in 2016. Other new facilities that broke ground in 2013 and 2014 are a 120-bed psychiatric hospital in Tacoma (for which MultiCare is partnering up with CHI Franciscan Health to build) and a birth center at Tacoma General Hospital.

On the technology front MultiCare uses technologies such as digital mammography CyberKnife Radiosurgery technology and Da Vinci Robotic Surgery to provide better service to the patients. In 2013 MultiCare Auburn Medical Center upgraded its billing processes to an electronic health record system.

EXECUTIVES

Vice President Information Technology, Harold Moscho
President And Ceo, William G. (Bill) Robertson, age 58
Evp, Florence Chang
President East Pierce Region, Glenn Kasman
President West Pierce Region, Shelly Mullin
Chief Physician Officer, Claire Spain-Remy
Cfo, Anna Loomis
President South King Region, Hugh Kodama
Cio, Robert Biernbaum
Nursing Director, Linda Dean
Vice President Of Human Resources, Steven Bascom
Secretary, Debbie Day
Auditors: KPMG LLP SEATTLE WA

LOCATIONS

HQ: MULTICARE HEALTH SYSTEM
316 M L KING JR WAY # 314, TACOMA, WA 984054252
Phone: 253 403-1000
Web: WWW.MULTICARE.ORG

PRODUCTS/OPERATIONS

Selected Facilities
Hospitals
Allenmore Hospital (Tacoma)
Auburn Medical Center (Auburn)
Good Samaritan Hospital (Puyallup)
Mary Bridge Children's Hospital and Health Center (Tacoma)
Tacoma General Hospital (Tacoma)

Other facilities
Allenmore Medical Center
Auburn MultiCare Clinic
Covington MultiCare Clinic
Lakewood Urgent Care Clinic
Kent MultiCare Clinic
MultiCare Home Services
Spanaway MultiCare Clinic
Tacoma Family Medicine
University Place Urgent Care Clinic
Westgate Urgent Care Clinic
Selected Services
Adult Day Health
Behavioral Health
Boutique
Breast Health
Cancer Center
Center for Healthy Living
Children's Therapy Unit
Community Programs
CyberKnife Radiosurgery
Diabetes Services
Ear Nose and Throat
Emergency and Urgent Care
Family Birth Centers
Geriatric Psychiatric Center
Health Care Resource Center
Heart Care
Home Health and Hospice
Immunization Clinic
Infusion Center
Institute for Research & Innovation
Laboratories Northwest
Maternal-Fetal Medicine
Medical Imaging
Nephrology
Neonatal Intensive Care Unit
Neurosciences
Nutrition
OB/GYN
Occupational Medicine
Orthopedics
Pain Management
Palliative Medicine
Perinatal Outreach Program
Pharmacy
Physical Therapy
Podiatry
Primary Care Clinics
Pulmonary Care
Pulmonary Rehabilitation
Rehabilitation
Robotic Technology
Senior Services
Sexual Assault Services
Spa
Sports Medicine
Surgical Services
Tobacco Cessation
Transfusion Free Medical and Surgical Program
Urology
Weight Loss and Wellness
Wound Healing Center

COMPETITORS

Catholic Health Initiatives	Providence St. Joseph Health
Franciscan Health System	Seattle Children's Hospital
Harrison Medical Center	Swedish Health Services
Overlake Hospital	Yakima Valley Memorial
PeaceHealth	

HISTORICAL FINANCIALS

Company Type: Private

Income Statement				FYE: December 31
	REVENUE ($ mil.)	NET INCOME ($ mil.)	NET PROFIT MARGIN	EMPLOYEES
12/17	2,416	347	14.4%	6,510
12/16	1,927	180	9.4%	—
12/11	1,384	27	2.0%	—
12/10	1,384	146	10.6%	—
Annual Growth	8.3%	13.2%	—	—

Return on assets: 8.3%   Cash ($ mil.): 368
Return on equity: 14.4%
Current ratio: 1.60

MUNICIPAL ELECTRIC AUTHORITY OF GEORGIA

With more juice than a ripe Georgia peach the Municipal Electric Authority of Georgia (MEAG Power) supplies wholesale electric power. The authority has a generating capacity of 2069 MW through its interests in nuclear and fossil-fueled plants. Some 49% of the energy MEAG Power delivered in 2012 came from its nuclear plants. MEAG Power transmits electricity to 48 municipal and one county distribution systems across Georgia that in turn serve some 600000 consumers. It utilizes a transmission network that is co-owned by all the power suppliers in Georgia although it is considering joining a regional transmission organization (RTO) to further defray costs.

Operations

MEAG Power owns more than 1300 miles of high-voltage transmission lines and almost 200 substations. It also provides value-added services including management infrastructure and marketing support to its member municipalities energy marketers and other utilities.

The company generates most of its revenues from Project One (ownership stakes in nine generating units other owned transmission plants and working capital). Higher member billings for operating expenses related to fuel and nuclear operations lifted MEAG Power's revenues and net income in 2010.

Geographic Reach

The company serves 49 communities across Georgia.

Financial Performance

In 2012 MEAG Power's revenues increased by 8% thanks to higher participant billings related to a planned reduction in trust transfers as well as an increase in debt service related to environmental improvements to the coal operations and higher contract energy sales. These gains were partially offset by lower participant billings for maintenance and fuel expenses.

That year the company's net income increased by 351% as the result of higher net sales and decreased operating costs.

Strategy

With Georgia restricted in its natural potential for solar and wind power development MEAG Power is pushing hard for the expansion of nuclear power as a clean energy alternative to coal.

In a major breakthrough in 2012 the Nuclear Regulatory Commission approved a Combined Construction and Operating License for units 3 and 4 of the Vogtle plant (near Waynesboro Georgia) the first such license ever approved for a US nuclear plant and the first federal go-ahead for nuclear plant construction since 1978.

In 2013 MEAG Power completed a basemat of structural concrete for the nuclear island at the Vogtle Unit 4 nuclear expansion site the second of two units under construction at Plant Vogtle.

Company Background

In 2009 the Georgia Public Service Commission gave the go ahead for the expansion of the nuclear-powered Vogtle Electric Generating Plant which is co-owned by MEAG Power and in 2010 MEAP Power sold $2.7 billion in bonds to fund this expansion.

EXECUTIVES

Vice President Finance, Jim Fuller
Vice President And Chief Administrative Officer, Douglas Lego
Auditors: PRICEWATERHOUSECOOPERS LLP AT

LOCATIONS

HQ: MUNICIPAL ELECTRIC AUTHORITY OF GEORGIA
1470 RIVEREDGE PKWY, ATLANTA, GA 303284640
Phone: 770 563-0300
Web: WWW.MEAGPOWER.ORG

COMPETITORS

AEP	Progress Energy
Dominion Energy	Santee Cooper
Duke Energy	Southern Company
North Carolina	Southern Company Gas
Electric Membership	TVA
Oglethorpe Power	

HISTORICAL FINANCIALS

Company Type: Private

Income Statement   FYE: December 31

	REVENUE ($ mil.)	NET INCOME ($ mil.)	NET PROFIT MARGIN	EMPLOYEES
12/17	623	0	—	150
12/16	661	(110)	—	—
12/15	642	(131)	—	—
12/14	748	(36)	—	—
Annual Growth	(5.9%)	—	—	—

2017 Year-End Financials

Return on assets: 13.3%   Cash ($ mil.): 4
Return on equity: —
Current ratio: 0.10

MUNICIPAL GAS AUTHORITY OF GEORGIA

EXECUTIVES

Pres, Arthur C Corbin
Business Analyst, Rai Trippe
Auditors: ERNST & YOUNG LLP ATLANTA GA

LOCATIONS

HQ: MUNICIPAL GAS AUTHORITY OF GEORGIA
104 TOWNPARK DR NW, KENNESAW, GA 301445556
Phone: 770 590-1000
Web: WWW.PUBLICGAS.ORG

HISTORICAL FINANCIALS

Company Type: Private

Income Statement   FYE: December 31

	REVENUE ($ mil.)	NET INCOME ($ mil.)	NET PROFIT MARGIN	EMPLOYEES
12/17	331	(0)	—	50
12/16	317	0	0.0%	—
12/14	390	(0)	—	—
Annual Growth	(5.2%)	—	—	—

2017 Year-End Financials

Return on assets: 11.1%   Cash ($ mil.): 52
Return on equity: (-0.2%)
Current ratio: 0.40

MUNSON HEALTHCARE

Munson Healthcare is a not-for-profit health care system serving residents in northern Michigan. Its flagship facility is Munson Medical Center in Traverse City a regional referral hospital with about 390 beds offering specialty services including cancer treatment behavioral health cardiac care and orthopedics. Munson Healthcare also has management agreements and other types of affiliations with about a dozen other hospitals in the region. In addition Munson Healthcare operates urgent care and community clinics home health care and hospice agencies an ambulance service and the Northern Michigan Supply Alliance a supply chain management group co-owned with Trinity Health.

Operations

Munson Healthcare is composed of eight hospitals located throughout northern Michigan - Charlevoix Area Hospital (Charlevoix) Kalkaska Memorial Health Center (Kalkaska) Mercy Hospital Cadillac (Cadillac) Mercy Hospital Grayling (Grayling) Munson Medical Center (Traverse City) Otsego Memorial Hospital (Gaylord) Paul Oliver Memorial Hospital (Frankfort) and West Shore Medical Center (Manistee). Services are also available at Munson Community Health Center (Traverse City) and Mercy Community Health Center (Prudenville). Munson Healthcare also works closely with Alpena General Hospital in Alpena and War Memorial Hospital in Sault St. Marie.

In addition to its hospital operations Munson Healthcare also offers in-home care through Munson Home Health and Munson Hospice and Palliative Care. Other specialty services and resources include speech and hearing clinics physical rehabilitation CAT scans magnetic resonance imaging and cardiac catheterization.

Munson Healthcare provides direct access to nearly 800 physicians representing more than 50 specialties.

Eah year the system sees some 22500 admissions performs some 8000 inpatient and 7000 outpatient surgeries and has some 51000 emergency department visits.

Geographic Reach

The health care system offers a continuum of health care services to people in 24 Michigan counties.

Strategy

To better provide services to region residents Munson Healthcare partnered with critical access hospital Mackinac Straits Health System in 2015. The affiliation is focused on improving health care services in rural northern Michigan.

Munson Healthcare is also forming an air ambulance joint venture between its North Flight EMS Air Division and Spectrum Health's Aero Med. The venture to be named North Flight Aero Med will provide critical care air emergency transport services in northern Michigan. It will begin operating in 2016.

Company Background

Munson Healthcare was founded in 1915.

EXECUTIVES

Vice President Patient Care Service And Chief Nursing Officer Munson Medical Center, Jim Fischer
Vice President, Jeanne M Wolf
Vice President Physician Integration Munson Healthcare, Tim Binder
Medical Director Dialysis Centers, Ahmet Sevimli
Vice President View Biography, Lorraine Franklightfoot
Secretary, Robert Sprunk
Secretary Volunteer Services, Cathi Consolino
Vice Chair Kathy Ervin Secretary, Sonja Ganger

LOCATIONS

HQ: MUNSON HEALTHCARE
1105 SIXTH ST, TRAVERSE CITY, MI 496842345
Phone: 800 252-2065
Web: WWW.MUNSONHEALTHCARE.ORG/HOME-
HEALTH/MUNSON-HOME-HEALTH

PRODUCTS/OPERATIONS

Selected Michigan Facilities
Charlevoix
Kalkaska M
Mercy Hosp
Mercy Hosp
Munson Community Health Center - Traverse City
Munson Hospice House - Traverse City
Munson Manor Hospitality House - Traverse City
Munson Medical Center - Traverse City
Northwest Michigan Surgery Center - Traverse City
Otsego Mem
Paul Olive
Smith Family Breast Health Center - Traverse City
West Shore
Medical Specialties
Bariatric Surgery
Behavioral Health
Bleeding Disorders Center
Cancer Services
Diabetes
Dialysis
Emergency Services
Hearing Clinic
Heart and Vascular Services
Hospice and Palliative Care
Occupational Health and Medicine
Orthopedics
Senior's Health
Sleep Disorders Center
Stroke Care
Teen's Health
Urgent Care
Urology
Women and Children

COMPETITORS

Borgess Health	McLaren Health Care
Covenant HealthCare	Spectrum Health
Genesys Regional	Trinity Health (Novi)
Medical Center	Zeeland Community
Hurley Medical Center	Hospital

HISTORICAL FINANCIALS
Company Type: Private

Income Statement				FYE: June 30
	REVENUE ($ mil.)	NET INCOME ($ mil.)	NET PROFIT MARGIN	EMPLOYEES
06/18	1,039	142	13.7%	4,000
06/17	940	160	17.1%	—
06/15	8	(7)	—	—
06/13	6	(3)	—	—
Annual Growth	175.3%	—	—	—

2018 Year-End Financials
Return on assets: 4.8%   Cash ($ mil.): 106
Return on equity: 13.7%
Current ratio: 1.70

MUNSON MEDICAL CENTER

EXECUTIVES

Ceo, Edwin A Ness
Cfo, Edward Carlson
Coo, Derk Pronger

Director of Home, Sharri Mc Clennan
Occupational Specia, Kristine A Siemer
Chief Information Officer, Christopher Podges
Manager, Joe Dechow
Director of Mis/Is, William Chung
Pharmacist, Eric Davis
Manager, Eric Warren
Analyst, Lisa Robinson

LOCATIONS

HQ: MUNSON MEDICAL CENTER
1105 SIXTH ST, TRAVERSE CITY, MI 496842386
Phone: 231 935-6000
Web: WWW.MUNSONHEALTHCARE.ORG

HISTORICAL FINANCIALS
Company Type: Private

Income Statement				FYE: June 30
	REVENUE ($ mil.)	NET INCOME ($ mil.)	NET PROFIT MARGIN	EMPLOYEES
06/16	533	67	12.7%	3,100
06/15	509	60	11.9%	—
06/10	441	28	6.4%	—
06/09	394	(0)	—	—
Annual Growth	4.4%	—	—	—

2016 Year-End Financials
Return on assets: 3.4%   Cash ($ mil.): 189
Return on equity: 12.7%
Current ratio: 3.80

MUNSTER MEDICAL RESEARCH FOUNDATION, INC

EXECUTIVES

Pres-Ceo, Donald S Powers
Treas, George E Watson
Admin, Edward Robinson
SEC, Palmer C Singleton
Vice President, Joseph Morrow
Chm, Frankie L Fesko
Prin, James J Richards
SEC, William A Hasse III
Treas, David E Wickland
Coordinator, Linda Kosteba
Coordinator, Carol Hernandez
Auditors: ERNST & YOUNG LLP

LOCATIONS

HQ: MUNSTER MEDICAL RESEARCH FOUNDATION, INC
901 MACARTHUR BLVD, MUNSTER, IN 463212901
Phone: 219 836-1600
Web: WWW.COMHS.ORG

HISTORICAL FINANCIALS
Company Type: Private

Income Statement				FYE: June 30
	REVENUE ($ mil.)	NET INCOME ($ mil.)	NET PROFIT MARGIN	EMPLOYEES
06/18	548	74	13.5%	2,000
06/16	508	50	9.9%	—
06/15	495	58	11.8%	—
06/14	465	36	7.8%	—
Annual Growth	4.2%	19.5%	—	—

2018 Year-End Financials
Return on assets: 0.5%   Cash ($ mil.): —
Return on equity: 13.5%
Current ratio: 2.20

MUSCOGEE COUNTY SCHOOL DISTRICT

EXECUTIVES

Supt, Susan Andrews PHD
School Board President, Cathy Williams
MBR, Dr John Phillips Jr
MBR, John Wells
Teacher, Bernadette St Clair
Supervisor, Debra Van Pelt
Director of Information Techno, John Broom
Teacher, Donna Thomas
Human Resources, Linda McCardle
Teacher, Anna Mion
Teacher, Brooke Sheppard
Auditors: ROBINSON GRIMES & COMPANY P

LOCATIONS

HQ: MUSCOGEE COUNTY SCHOOL DISTRICT
2960 MACON RD, COLUMBUS, GA 319062204
Phone: 706 748-2000
Web: WWW.MUSCOGEE.K12.GA.US

HISTORICAL FINANCIALS
Company Type: Private

Income Statement				FYE: June 30
	REVENUE ($ mil.)	NET INCOME ($ mil.)	NET PROFIT MARGIN	EMPLOYEES
06/17	353	10	2.9%	6,000
06/16	351	52	15.1%	—
06/08	373	24	6.6%	—
06/06	340	19	5.6%	—
Annual Growth	0.3%	(5.5%)	—	—

2017 Year-End Financials
Return on assets: 17.1%   Cash ($ mil.): 112
Return on equity: 2.9%
Current ratio: —

MUTUALBANK

EXECUTIVES

Chb, Will Davis
Ceo, David Heeter
Pres-Coo, Pat Botts
SEC, Rosalee Petro
Cfo, Chris Cook
Director, R Don Roberts
Vice President, Ralph Spencer Jr
Regional President, Charles Viater
Administrative Assistant, Meleah Perkins
Customer Staff, Shari Ash
Manager, Todd Yarbrough

LOCATIONS

HQ: MUTUALBANK
110 E CHARLES ST, MUNCIE, IN 473052468
Phone: 765 747-2800
Web: WWW.BANKWITHMUTUAL.COM

HISTORICAL FINANCIALS
Company Type: Private

Income Statement				FYE: December 31
	ASSETS ($ mil.)	NET INCOME ($ mil.)	INCOME AS % OF ASSETS	EMPLOYEES
12/17	1,585	11	0.8%	309
12/16	1,551	12	0.8%	—
12/15	1,477	12	0.9%	—
12/14	1,423	11	0.8%	—
Annual Growth	3.7%	1.3%	—	—

2017 Year-End Financials
Return on assets: —
Return on equity: 15.6%
Sales ($ mil): 76

MVP HEALTH PLAN, INC.

MVP Health Plan also know as MVP Health Care provides health insurance and employee benefits to its more than 700000 members in upstate New York New Hampshire and Vermont. MVP a not-for-profit organization offers a variety of plans including HMO PPO and indemnity coverage as well as dental plans health accounts and Medicare Advantage plans. Subsidiary MVP Select Care provides third-party administration (TPA) services for self-insured employers. MVP Health Care was founded in 1983 as Mohawk Valley Physicians' Health Plan.

Geographic Reach
MVP Health Care operates regional service and support offices across New York Vermont and New Hampshire. New York State is its largest service area. The firm has offices in Binghamton Fishkill Schenectady Syracuse Rochester and Utica New York as well as in Manchester New Hampshire; and Williston Vermont.

The company's provider network includes 19000 doctors in its three-state service territory; the firm also provides its members with access to about 500000 providers in other states through a partnership with CIGNA.

Sales and Marketing
The company uses a direct sales force as well as brokerages and call centers to sell its products. Its customers include individuals Medicare and Medicaid participants and employer groups.

Financial Performance
MVP Health Care revenue increased 18% to $2.9 billion in 2014; that growth was bolstered by the integration of Hudson Health Plan (acquired in 2013) as well as commercial and government membership growth. Medicaid Managed Care membership grew 21% that year.

Despite that growth the company lost a net $13.6 million.

Strategy
In addition to acquiring other area providers MVP Health Care widens its product offerings to attract a diversified customer base adding new non-employer group options (individual and high-deductible plans) and new small employer group products. It is has also launched new financial and preventative care tools including flexible spending accounts and disease management programs. Cutting policy prices has helped boost membership numbers as well.

The company also partners with health care providers to provide better care for its members as well as developing programs to target specific segments of the population.

MVP Health Care utilizes new technologies to cut its own operating costs. Recent initiatives include launching an e-commerce/plan administration platform creating virtual medical records with area health information organizations and supporting the Taconic Health Information Network and Community (an independent physician practice association).

EXECUTIVES

Evp And Medical Affairs Officer, Allen J. Hinkle
Evp Government Programs, Patrick Glavey
President And Ceo, Denise V. Gonick
Evp Networks And Contracting, Karla Austen
Evp And Cfo, Mark Fish
Associate Medical Director, Clifford Elson
Pharmacy Manager, David Stitt
Medical Director, David Phelps
Medical Director, Jason Merola
Vice President Network Operations, Matt Mackinnon
Executive Vice President Strategy, Christopher Delvecchio
Vice Chairwoman, Karen Johnson
Auditors: PRICEWATERHOUSECOOPERS LLP HA

LOCATIONS
HQ: MVP HEALTH PLAN, INC.
  625 STATE ST, SCHENECTADY, NY 123052260
Phone: 518 370-4793
Web: WWW.MVPHEALTHCARE.COM

PRODUCTS/OPERATIONS

Selected Products
Alternative Funding Arrangements
Deferred Deductible Plans
Defined Contribution Plans
EPOs and PPOs
Health Spending Accounts
High-Deductible Health Plans
HMOs
Medicare Advantage Plans
Regional Plan Options

COMPETITORS
Affinity Health
Blue Cross and Blue Shield of Vermont
CIGNA
Capital District Physicians' Health Plan
EmblemHealth
Excellus BlueCross BlueShield
Fallon Community Health Plan
Fidelis Care New York
HealthPlus Amerigroup
Healthfirst
Independent Health
Lifetime Healthcare
UnitedHealth Group
healthnow new york inc

HISTORICAL FINANCIALS
Company Type: Private

Income Statement				FYE: December 31
	REVENUE ($ mil.)	NET INCOME ($ mil.)	NET PROFIT MARGIN	EMPLOYEES
12/15	1,573	11	0.7%	1,500
12/14	1,673	(26)	—	—
12/13	0	(1)	—	—
12/09	0	(3)	—	—
Annual Growth	535.0%	—	—	—

2015 Year-End Financials
Return on assets: 1.5%
Return on equity: 0.7%
Current ratio: —
Cash ($ mil.): 6

MWH GLOBAL, INC.

MWH Global is an environmental engineering construction and management firm that specializes in water-related projects or "wet infrastructure." The company's typical projects include building water treatment or desalination plants water transmission systems or storage facilitates. MWH also provides general building services for transportation energy mining ports and waterways and industrial projects. The company is active in some 35 countries and serves governments public utilities and private sector clients. Affiliates of the employee-owned company include software provider Innovyze and business and government relations firm mCapitol. Canadian Engineering firm Stantec acquired MWH Global for $795 million in May 2016.

Geographic Reach
When it comes to projects MWH Global lives up to its name. The Colorado-based firm operates from 180 offices in 35 countries on six continents in the Americas the Asia/Pacific region the Middle East Africa and Europe.

Sales and Marketing
MWH Global seeks projects in five main markets including: the energy and power; water and wastewater; natural resources and mining; ports waterways and coastal; industrial and commercial transportation; and oil and gas markets.

It also does work for local regional and federal governments; US federal clients; public and private utilities; financial institutions; and insurance companies.

Strategy
MWH Global has kept busy in recent years working on a series of high-profile design and construction projects around the globe.

In 2015 the company continued its design-build work on the $7 billion Panama Canal Third Set of Locks project which will double the canal's capacity by the time its completed at the end of the year. The company also continued working with international electricity and gas company National Grid on the largest energy infrastructure program in the UK.

In late-2014 through a joint venture with Costain MWH Global signed on to a A?200 million ($325 million) contract to provide design and build services for Southern Water's water and wastewater infrastructure and non-infrastructure assets program in Southeast England; part of Southern Waters' A?3 billion ($5 billion) business plan for 2015-2020. Around the same time MWH Global completed its nearly two-decade-long Huanza Hydroelectric project in the Andes Mountains which now provides 92 Megawatts of electricity to some 90000 households in Peru.

In mid-2014 the South Florida Water Management District awarded MWH Global with a master services agreement to help implement the $880 million Restoration Strategies Regional Water Quality Plan which is part of the state's long-term strategy to restore the Everglades. In 2012 the Qatar Public Works Authority appointed MWH to design a drainage master plan in Qatar which will provide a road map for future investment into water and wastewater treatment and other water-related infrastructure programs over the next 50 years.

EXECUTIVES

Cfo, David G. Barnes, age 55
President Energy And Industry, Joseph (Joe) Adams
President Natural Resources Industry & Infrastructure Mwh Americas, Alan J. Krause, age 64

President Innovyze, Paul F. Boulos
President Business Solutions, Dan McConville
President Mwh Constructors, Blair Lavoie
President Europe Africa Government And Infrastructure, Wim Drossaert
President Government And Infrastructure Americas And Asia Pacific, Marshall Davert
Cio, Claire Rutkowski
Managing Director United Kingdom, Catherine Schefer
Chief Strategy Officer, David A. Smith
Vice President Finance, David Harper
Vice President And Director Of Development, Charles Taylor
Vice President Of Information Technology, Greg Clark
Vice President, Sean Searles
Vice President, Joseph Jacangelo
Vice President, Kari Shively
Vice President And Business Development Director, Sandra L Shuster
Vice President, Kirk Sepulveda
Vice President, Geoffrey Carthew
Vice President, Charles Kahler
Vice President, Donald A Erpenbeck
Vice President, Jim Stahl
Vice President Location Manager Principal Geotechnical Engineer, Greg Rollins
Vice President, Jason Mumm
Vp Information Technology, John Guilfoyle
Vice President, Vincent Zipparro
Vice President Corporate Communications, Meg Vanderlaan
Vice President, Stephen Taylor
Senior Vice President, Donal J Bassett
Vice President, Philip Croessmann
Vice President Business Unit Leader, Beth Knackstedt
Vice President Director Of Business De, Norman Gadzinski
Senior Vice President, Mario Finis
Vice President, Jim Brennan
Vice President, Tauseef Choudry
Senior Vice President And Director Of Global Business Development, Paul Dekeyser
Vice President, Edward Cryer
Vice President, Roger Stephenson
Auditors: DELOITTE & TOUCHE LLP DENVER

LOCATIONS

HQ: MWH GLOBAL, INC.
370 INTERLOCKEN BLVD # 300, BROOMFIELD, CO 800218009
Phone: 303 533-1900
Web: WWW.MWHGLOBAL.COM

PRODUCTS/OPERATIONS

Selected Services
Construction
Airports
General building
Industrial
Highways bridges roads
Marine and port facilities
Engineering and technical services
Facilities development
Government relations
Program management and management consulting
Research and testing
Renewable energy and sustainability
Chemical and soil remediation
Hazardous waste
Hydroelectric power
Non-hydro renewable energy
Power distribution and transmission lines
Thermal power
Risk assessment
Specialized consulting services
Water and environment
Dams and reservoirs
Landfills biosolids
Sanitary/storm sewers conveyance pumping stations
Water resources planning management
Water treatment and desalination plants
Water transmission lines aqueducts
Waste water planning and management

COMPETITORS

AECOM	KBR
Bechtel	Peter Kiewit Sons'
Black & Veatch	Severn Trent
CH2M HILL	Siemens Water
Camp Dresser McKee	Technologies
EA Engineering	Tetra Tech
Engie	Veolia Environnement
Fluor	WS Atkins
Jacobs Engineering	Zachry Inc.

HISTORICAL FINANCIALS
Company Type: Private

Income Statement   FYE: January 1

	REVENUE ($ mil.)	NET INCOME ($ mil.)	NET PROFIT MARGIN	EMPLOYEES
01/16*	1,318	35	2.7%	6,700
12/05	946	0	—	—
01/03	975	942	96.6%	—
12/01	774	19	2.6%	—
Annual Growth	3.9%	4.3%	—	—

*Fiscal year change

2016 Year-End Financials
Return on assets: 12.0%   Cash ($ mil.): 68
Return on equity: 2.7%
Current ratio: 1.30

NAES CORPORATION

EXECUTIVES

Pres, Robert E Fishman
Pres-Coo, Tom Bartolomei
Sr V Pres, George Wackerhagen
Sr V Pres, Norman Escover
Sr V Pres, Andrew Gay
Sr V Pres, Glen Canavera
V Pres, Susan George
Mgr of Fin&crdt, Stephanie Sprouse
Vice President, Mark R Iraola
Auditors: PRICEWATERHOUSECOOPERS LLP SE

LOCATIONS

HQ: NAES CORPORATION
1180 NW MAPLE ST STE 200, ISSAQUAH, WA 980278106
Phone: 425 961-4700
Web: WWW.NAES.COM

HISTORICAL FINANCIALS
Company Type: Private

Income Statement   FYE: March 31

	REVENUE ($ mil.)	NET INCOME ($ mil.)	NET PROFIT MARGIN	EMPLOYEES
03/15	514	6	1.2%	2,534
03/14	472	3	0.8%	—
03/13	445	5	1.1%	—
Annual Growth	7.5%	8.7%	—	—

2015 Year-End Financials
Return on assets: 0.4%   Cash ($ mil.): 33
Return on equity: 1.2%
Current ratio: 0.70

NAPERVILLE COMMUNITY UNIT SCHOOL DISTRICT 203

EXECUTIVES

Superintendent, Mark Mitrovich
Bkpr, Kristine Roberts
Social Worker, Domenica Ottolino
Teacher, Ginny Mulholland
Assistant Secretary, Marybeth Zielinski
Manager, Kathleen Barak
Assistant Superintendent, Kitty Murphy
Education Specialist, Linda Parker
Information Technology Manager, Lisa Dalton
Computer Specialist, Terri Stevens
Nurse, Debbie Baker
Auditors: KLEIN HALL CPAS AURORA ILLIN

LOCATIONS

HQ: NAPERVILLE COMMUNITY UNIT SCHOOL DISTRICT 203
203 W HILLSIDE RD, NAPERVILLE, IL 605406500
Phone: 630 420-6300
Web: WWW.NAPERVILLE203.ORG

HISTORICAL FINANCIALS
Company Type: Private

Income Statement   FYE: June 30

	REVENUE ($ mil.)	NET INCOME ($ mil.)	NET PROFIT MARGIN	EMPLOYEES
06/17	324	11	3.4%	2,000
06/16	318	19	6.1%	—
06/15	309	16	5.4%	—
06/14	300	1	0.6%	—
Annual Growth	2.5%	79.7%	—	—

NAPLES COMMUNITY HOSPITAL INC

EXECUTIVES

Chm, Carl E Westman
Ceo-Pres, Allen S Weiss
V Chm, Joseph Perkovich
V Chm, John Morrison
SEC-Treas, Edwin Stedem
Cfo, Vicki Hale
Asst SEC, Beth Martin
Buyer, Alan Ipp
Regional Manager, Allison Zablo
Health Care Director, Annette Campbell
Vice-President, Dora Krauss

LOCATIONS

HQ: NAPLES COMMUNITY HOSPITAL INC
350 7TH ST N, NAPLES, FL 341025754
Phone: 239 436-5000
Web: WWW.NCHMD.ORG

HISTORICAL FINANCIALS
Company Type: Private

Income Statement   FYE: September 30

	REVENUE ($ mil.)	NET INCOME ($ mil.)	NET PROFIT MARGIN	EMPLOYEES
09/17	472	38	8.2%	3,300
09/15	443	38	8.6%	—
09/14	398	51	12.8%	—
09/13	383	9	2.4%	—
Annual Growth	5.3%	43.1%	—	—

2017 Year-End Financials
Return on assets: 5.3%   Cash ($ mil.): 45
Return on equity: 8.2%
Current ratio: 0.80

NARRAGANSETT ELECTRIC COMP

LOCATIONS
HQ: NARRAGANSETT ELECTRIC COMP
642 GEORGE WASHINGTON HWY, LINCOLN, RI
028654244
Phone: 401 335-6238

HISTORICAL FINANCIALS
Company Type: Private

Income Statement   FYE: December 31

	REVENUE ($ mil.)	NET INCOME ($ mil.)	NET PROFIT MARGIN	EMPLOYEES
12/17	1,387	121	8.8%	2
12/16	1,269	84	6.7%	—
Annual Growth	9.3%	43.0%	—	—

2017 Year-End Financials
Return on assets: 11.2%   Cash ($ mil.): 8
Return on equity: 8.8%
Current ratio: 0.30

NASSAU HEALTH CARE CORPORATION

Nassau Health Care (NuHealth) keeps residents healthy in the suburbs of the Big Apple. The health system operates Nassau University Medical Center which has some 530 beds as well as the A. Holly Patterson Extended Care Facility a skilled nursing center with 590 beds. Other operations include about a half-dozen community family health centers and a home health care agency serving the people of Long Island. Nassau University Medical Center's specialized services include trauma burn care orthopedics psychiatry and obstetrics. NuHealth is a public benefit company governed by a representative board appointed by state and county officials.

Operations
The Nassau University Medical Center is a teaching center affiliated with the SUNY-Stony Brook Health Sciences Center. It also provides some services in affiliation with the North Shore-Long Island Jewish Health System. NuHealth's Nassau Medical Associates affiliate has an interest in primary care and selected specialty practices in central to southern Nassau County.

In 2012 NuHealth reported 283172 outpatient visits; 75240 emergency visits; 22347 discharges and 1576 births.

Sales and Marketing
In 2012 NuHealth launched the Talking Well social media campaign on Facebook and Twitter in an attempt to more effectively communicate with the public.

Financial Performance
The company's revenues grew by 5% to $518 million in 2012 due to an 8% increase in net patient service revenues thanks to an acceleration of intergovernmental transfers and higher contractual rates with third-party insurance companies. Other operating revenues declined in 2012 due to the reduction of services provided to the Nassau County Correctional Facility. Revenues from Medicaid and Medicare accounted for 77% of 2012 net revenues for services provided to patients.

NuHealth's net loss decreased by 69% to $45 million in 2012 due to a decline in salaries and wages primarily as the result of a reduction in full-time employees; a decline in a loss from employee benefits expenses; and changes to Medicaid eligibility estimates.

Strategy
NuHealth is conducting a $240 million multi-year modernization program. Efforts completed or in progress include the rebuilding of the Patterson Extended Care Facility reconstruction and renovation efforts at the Nassau University Medical Center (including the completion of a new emergency room in 2010 and the remodeling of its maternity wing in 2012) improvements to community health centers and equipment and technology investments. In 2014 NuHealth opened new labor and delivery suites and a new catheterization laboratory.

NuHealth is also working to promote community care wellness initiatives access to specialists and integrated delivery methods. In 2013 Nassau University Medical Center teamed up with Advocates for Community Health on Project DOCC which will deliver chronic care and the Center for Civic Engagement at Hofstra University to improve the health of underserved Long Island families particularly those whose children have developmental disabilities and serious chronic conditions.

Towards this goal NuHealth also collaborates with other area providers such as North Shore-LIJ. It is also expanding its physician education programs; it launched a new osteopathic family medicine residency program to train doctors at its inpatient and outpatient facilities in 2012. It also introduced a hematology and oncology fellowship program that year.

Expanding its products in 2012 Nassau University Medical Center began to offer personalized travel medicine services to meet the needs of travelers going abroad for both business and pleasure.

Company Background
The Nassau University Medical Center opened in 1935 as Meadowbrook Hospital and joined the NuHealth organization in 1997. It was renamed Nassau University Medical Center in 2001.

EXECUTIVES
Pres, Arthur A Gianelli
President, Arthur Gianelli
Vice President, Ronald Tomo
Svp-Patient Care Svcs-Cno, Kathy Skarka
Chief Financial Officer, Richard Perrotti
Exec Vice President, Robert S Heatley
Cfo, John Maher
Exec Vice President, Larry I Slatky
Exec Vice President, Steven J Walerstein
Executive Assistant, Andrea Rivera
Coordinator, Lynore Dupiton

LOCATIONS
HQ: NASSAU HEALTH CARE CORPORATION
2201 HEMPSTEAD TPKE, EAST MEADOW, NY 115541859
Phone: 516 572-0123
Web: WWW.NUMC.EDU

PRODUCTS/OPERATIONS

Selected Services
Anesthesiology
Blood Bank
Brain & Nerves
Burn Center
Cardiac Care
Community Services
Dental Medicine
Diagnostic Imaging
Emergency Medicine
Eye Care
Family Medicine
Hypertension Diabetes & Vascular Disease
Internal Medicine
Mental Health & Addiction
Orthopedics & Rehabilitation
Pathology
Pediatrics
Primary & Preventive Care
Primary Care & Wellness
Radiology
Radiology & Laboratory
Senior Services
Shared Laboratory Services
Specialized Medicine
Specialty Services
Surgery
Surgical & Emergency Care
Trauma Center
Women's Health

COMPETITORS
Catholic Health Services of Long Island
Catholic Healthcare System
Continuum Health Partners
Lutheran HealthCare
MediSys Health Network
New York City Health and Hospitals
Northwell Health
Queens-Long Island Medical Group

HISTORICAL FINANCIALS
Company Type: Private

Income Statement   FYE: December 31

	REVENUE ($ mil.)	NET INCOME ($ mil.)	NET PROFIT MARGIN	EMPLOYEES
12/17	425	15	3.7%	3,500
12/16	375	(62)	—	—
12/15	363	(80)	—	—
12/14	391	5	1.4%	—
Annual Growth	2.8%	42.8%	—	—

2017 Year-End Financials
Return on assets: 23.2%   Cash ($ mil.): 21
Return on equity: 3.7%
Current ratio: 0.20

NATIONAL CHRISTIAN CHARITABLE

EXECUTIVES

Prin, Terra Parker
Treasurer, David D Johnson
Vice President, George Cox
Chief Information Officer., Amy Garrett
Vice President., Marsha Walker
Director, Maureen Starr
Gift Planning Team, Don Etheridge
Director of Giver, Mary Keating
Vice President, Paul Forbes
Director of Giver, Katie Kavehrad
Auditors: CAPIN CROUSE LLP ATLANTA GE

LOCATIONS

HQ: NATIONAL CHRISTIAN CHARITABLE
11625 RAINWATER DR # 500, ALPHARETTA, GA
300098678
Phone: 404 252-0100
Web: WWW.NATIONALCHRISTIAN.COM

HISTORICAL FINANCIALS

Company Type: Private

Income Statement				FYE: December 31
	REVENUE ($ mil.)	NET INCOME ($ mil.)	NET PROFIT MARGIN	EMPLOYEES
12/16	1,413	306	21.7%	2
12/11	665	141	21.3%	—
12/09	396	50	12.7%	—
Annual Growth	19.9%	29.4%	—	—

2016 Year-End Financials

Return on assets: 0.3%   Cash ($ mil.): 457
Return on equity: 21.7%
Current ratio: —

NATIONAL COLLEGIATE ATHLETIC ASSOCIATION

The National Collegiate Athletic Association (NCAA) supports the intercollegiate sports activities of around 1000 member colleges and universities. A not-for-profit organization the NCAA administers scholarship and grant programs enforces conduct and eligibility rules and works to support and promote the needs of student athletes. The association is known for its lucrative branding and television deals such as those surrounding the popular "March Madness" tournament for Division I men's basketball. Seeking reform of athletics rules and regulations officials from 13 schools formed the Intercollegiate Athletic Association of the United States in 1906. The organization took its current name in 1910.

Financial Performance

NCAA revenue in fiscal 2013 (ended August) was $913 million up 5% versus the prior year most of which came from the rights agreement with CBS Sports and Turner Broadcasting. Indeed about 80% of the NCAA's revenue come from television and marketing rights fees generated primarily from the Division I men's basketball championship. Another 12% comes from championships and NIT tournaments including ticket and merchandise sales.

About 96% of NCAA revenue is distributed directly to the Division I membership or to support championships or programs that benefit student-athletes. The remaining 4% goes for central services such as building operations and salaries not related to particular programs.

Strategy

The NCAA is coming under pressure to modify its rules on how student-athletes are compensated. In 2014 the National Labor Relations Board ruled that a group of Northwestern football players were employees of the univerisity and have the right to form a union and bargain collectively. The organization is also facing challenges regarding compensation for student-athletes whose likenesses are used in video games and broadcasts as well a lawsuits relating to its handling of head injuries.

EXECUTIVES

Pres, Mark A Emmert
Customer Staff, Melody Lawrence
Accounting Staff, Morgan Sanders
Project Coordinator, Reggie Krow
Information Technology Interne, Nathan Mallison
Auditors: DELOITTE & TOUCHE LLP INDIANA

LOCATIONS

HQ: NATIONAL COLLEGIATE ATHLETIC ASSOCIATION
700 W WASHINGTON ST, INDIANAPOLIS, IN
462042710
Phone: 317 917-6222
Web: WWW.NCAA.ORG

PRODUCTS/OPERATIONS

2013 Revenues

	% of total
Television & marketing rights fees	80
Championships & NIT tournaments	12
Investments	4
Sales & services	3
Contributions facilities & other	1
Total	100

HISTORICAL FINANCIALS

Company Type: Private

Income Statement				FYE: August 31
	REVENUE ($ mil.)	NET INCOME ($ mil.)	NET PROFIT MARGIN	EMPLOYEES
08/17	1,061	104	9.9%	508
08/16	995	(403)	—	—
08/15	952	43	4.5%	—
08/14	906	7	0.9%	—
Annual Growth	5.4%	138.6%	—	—

2017 Year-End Financials

Return on assets: 23.5%   Cash ($ mil.): 13
Return on equity: 9.9%
Current ratio: 0.20

NATIONAL GRID GENERATION LLC

EXECUTIVES

Pres, John Gregory Cochrane
MBR-Vp, Robert Teetz
MBR-Sr Vp-Cpo, Raymond C Schlaff
Mbr-Treasurer, Malcolm Charles Cooper
Asst SEC, Alfred C Bereche
Spokesperson, Howard Fichtel

Senior Engineer, Tony Mattia
Manager, Steve Trezza
Coordinator, Aaron Womble

LOCATIONS

HQ: NATIONAL GRID GENERATION LLC
175 E OLD COUNTRY RD, HICKSVILLE, NY
118014257
Phone: 631 755-6650

HISTORICAL FINANCIALS

Company Type: Private

Income Statement				FYE: December 31
	REVENUE ($ mil.)	NET INCOME ($ mil.)	NET PROFIT MARGIN	EMPLOYEES
12/17	471	75	16.0%	200
12/16	463	27	5.9%	—
Annual Growth	1.6%	175.6%	—	—

NATIONAL MARROW DONOR PROGRAM INC

EXECUTIVES

Ceo, C Randal Mills PHD
Director, Stephen Spellman
Accounting Manager, Lynn Anderson
Manager, Katy Engelby
Information Specialist, Mikhail Feynberg
Regional Director, Kim Allen
Manager, Pam Robinett
Manager, Merry Duffy
Technology, Jane Pollack
Assistant Controller, Gina Graves
Administrative Assistant, Kristi Van Pelt
Auditors: GRANT THORNTON LP MILWAUKEE

LOCATIONS

HQ: NATIONAL MARROW DONOR PROGRAM INC
500 N 5TH ST, MINNEAPOLIS, MN 554011206
Phone: 612 627-5800
Web: WWW.BETHEMATCH.ORG

HISTORICAL FINANCIALS

Company Type: Private

Income Statement				FYE: September 30
	REVENUE ($ mil.)	NET INCOME ($ mil.)	NET PROFIT MARGIN	EMPLOYEES
09/15	397	22	5.6%	975
09/05	143	0	0.6%	—
Annual Growth	10.8%	38.4%	—	—

2015 Year-End Financials

Return on assets: 15.3%   Cash ($ mil.): 38
Return on equity: 5.6%
Current ratio: 0.90

NATIONAL RAILROAD PASSENGER CORPORATION

National Railroad Passenger Corporation better known as Amtrak has been riding the rails for more than 40 years. Amtrak is the US' intercity passenger rail provider and its only high-speed rail operator. More than 30 million passengers travel on Amtrak every year on more than 300 daily trains. It connects 46 states Washington DC and three provinces in Canada. Its network consists of about 21000 route miles of track most of which is owned by freight railroads. Amtrak also operates commuter rail systems on behalf of several states and transit agencies. Owned by the US government through the US Department of Transportation Amtrak depends on subsidies from the federal government to operate.

HISTORY

US passenger train travel peaked in 1929 with 20000 trains in operation. But the spread of automobiles bus service and air travel cut into business and by the late 1960s only about 500 passenger trains remained running in the country. In 1970 the combined losses of all private train operations exceeded $1.8 billion in today's dollars. That year Congress passed the Rail Passenger Service Act which created Amtrak to preserve America's passenger rail system. Although railroads were offered stock in the corporation for their passenger equipment most just wrote off the loss.

Amtrak began operating in 1971 with 1200 cars most built in the 1950s. Although the company lost money from the outset ($153 million in 1972) it continued to be bankrolled by Uncle Sam despite much criticism. Amtrak ordered its first new equipment in 1973 the year it also began taking over stations yards and service staff. The company didn't own any track until 1976 when it purchased hundreds of miles of right-of-way track from Boston to Washington DC.

After a 1979 study showed Amtrak passengers to be by far the most heavily subsidized travelers in the US Congress ordered the company to better utilize its resources. The 1980s saw Amtrak leasing its rights-of-way along its tracks in the Northeast corridor to telecommunications companies which installed fiber-optic cables and beginning mail and freight services for extra revenue.

In the early 1990s Amtrak faced a number of challenges: Midwest flooding falling airfares and safety concerns over a number of rail accidents particularly the 1993 wreck of the Sunset Limited near Mobile Alabama in which 47 people were killed (the worst accident in Amtrak's history). In 1994 Amtrak's board of directors (at Congress' behest) adopted a plan to be free of federal support by 2002. In 1995 the company began planning high-speed trains for its heavily traveled East Coast routes.

In 1997 Amtrak finalized agreements to buy the high-speed cars and locomotives central to its self-sufficiency plan. It also began increasing its freight hauling and had its first profitable offering: the Metroliner route between New York and Washington DC.

Amtrak's board of directors was replaced by Congress in 1997 with a seven-member Reform Board appointed by President Clinton. Chairman and president Thomas Downs resigned that year and Tommy Thompson then governor of Wisconsin took over as chairman. Former Massachusetts governor Michael Dukakis was named vice chairman and George Warrington stepped in as Amtrak's president and CEO.

Technical problems in 1999 delayed Amtrak's introduction of the Acela high-speed train in the Northeast until late 2000 when service began in the Boston-Washington corridor. In 2001 Amtrak pitched a 20-year plan involving an annual outlay of $1.5 billion in federal funds for expanding and modernizing its passenger service to help alleviate highway and airport congestion nationwide.

Thompson left the Amtrak board in 2001 after he was named US secretary of health and human services.

Realizing Amtrak would not meet its end-of-the-year deadline to be self-sufficient in 2002 the Amtrak Reform Council sent a proposal to Congress that Amtrak be divided into three groups: one to oversee operations and funding a second to maintain certain Amtrak-owned tracks and properties and a third to operate trains. It also called for competition to be allowed on some passenger routes within two to three years.

Also in 2002 Warrington resigned and was replaced by David Gunn who formerly headed the metropolitan transit systems in New York and Toronto. Gunn began moving to cut costs and he worked to secure new federal money to avert a threatened shutdown of rail service in July 2002. In 2004 the company exited the mail-carrying business which had not been profitable.

Gunn was fired in November 2005 however and chief engineer David Hughes was named interim president and CEO. He left the company after Alexander Kummant was made president and CEO in September 2006.

The Passenger Rail Investment and Improvement Act of 2008 gives five annual grants to Amtrak amounting to $9.8 billion for fiscal years 2009 through 2013. Another boon came in the form of $1.3 billion of stimulus money earmarked for Amtrak by the American Recovery and Reinvestment Act (ARRA) of 2009 which authorizes the Federal Railroad Administration to make the funds available to Amtrak by grant agreement. About $446.8 million will be used for capital security grants including life safety improvements. Another $884 million will go toward the repair rehabilitation or upgrade of railroad assets and infrastructure and toward capital projects that expand rail capacity including the rehabilitation of rolling stock. The Obama administration promised an ongoing investment of about $1 billion annually for high-speed rail projects.

A record 28.7 million passengers rode on Amtrak in fiscal 2010. While impressive the company also has a history of recurring operating losses. Although total revenues increased about 7% in 2010 compared to 2009 Amtrak reported fairly comparable net losses in both years.

EXECUTIVES

Pres-Ceo, Joseph H Boardman
Chb, Anthony R Coscia
Vice Chb, Jeffrey R Moreland
Evp-Cfo, William Feidt
Chief Safety Officer-Evp, Ken Hylander
Law, Randolph Barton
Staff, Nikunj Patel
Senior Manager, Sriram Chellappan
Princ, Todd Stennis
Manager of Management Informat, Alyse Schwoyer
Corrections Officer, Brian Cozzolino

LOCATIONS

HQ: NATIONAL RAILROAD PASSENGER CORPORATION
60 MASSACHUSETTS AVE NW, WASHINGTON, DC 20001
Phone: 202 906-3000
Web: WWW.AMTRAK.COM

PRODUCTS/OPERATIONS

2014 Sales

	% of total
Passenger related	78
Commuter	4
Other	18
Total	**100**

2014 Sales

	% of total
Ticket	69
State Contribution	7
Food Beverage	4
Others	20
Total	**100**

COMPETITORS

AirTran Airways
American Airlines Group
Delta Air Lines
Frontier Airlines
Greyhound
JetBlue
Port Imperial Ferry Corp.
Southwest Airlines
Trailways Transportation System
United Continental

HISTORICAL FINANCIALS

Company Type: Private

Income Statement   FYE: September 30

	REVENUE ($ mil.)	NET INCOME ($ mil.)	NET PROFIT MARGIN	EMPLOYEES
09/17	3,305	(968)	—	18,650
09/16	3,240	(1,080)	—	—
09/14	0	0	—	—
09/08	2	(1)	—	—
Annual Growth	122.7%	—	—	—

2017 Year-End Financials

Return on assets: 14.3%   Cash ($ mil.): 1,101
Return on equity: (-29.3%)
Current ratio: 0.90

NATIONAL RIFLE ASSOCIATION OF AMERICA

The NRA believes in the right to bear arms. With more than 5 million members The National Rifle Association (NRA) is the staunch defender of Second Amendment rights. It's a major player in the political arena and stands firm in its resolve to protect the right to keep and bear arms. The NRA offers a variety of educational and gun safety programs and publishes magazines (America's 1st Freedom American Hunter Women's Outlook). It also caters to more than one million youth through its shooting sports events and affiliated programs with the likes of 4-H the Boy Scouts of America and others. It also sells NRA merchandise.

Union army veterans William Church and George Wingate founded the NRA in 1871.

Operations

The Institute for Legislative Action (ILA) established in 1975 is the lobbying arm of the NRA. With offices in Fairfax and Washington DC the ILA has a staff of more than 80 with a team of full-time lobbyists defending Second Amendment issues on Capitol Hill in state legislatures and in local government bodies. The NRA also operates the National Firearms Museum in Fairfax Virginia.

The NRA has made a commitment to training education and marksmanship. Its education and training department is supported by more than 65000 certified instructors who offer lessons to some 750000 gun owners each year. Through NRA's law enforcement division training program the NRA offers certified and standardized firearm instructor training and has trained over 50000 law enforcement firearm instructors.

Strategy

The NRA's membership ranks topped a record 5 million in 2013 as efforts to pass gun-control legislation following multiple mass shootings — including the Newtown Connecticut and Colorado movie theater tragedies — swelled the organization's ranks. About 500000 new members joined in 2013.

EXECUTIVES

Board Of Directors, Joseph Debergalis
Auditors: MCGLADREY LLP MC LEAN VA

LOCATIONS

HQ: NATIONAL RIFLE ASSOCIATION OF AMERICA
11250 WAPLES MILL RD # 1, FAIRFAX, VA 220309400
Phone: 703 267-1000
Web: WWW.NRAILA.ORG

PRODUCTS/OPERATIONS

Selected Programs
Business Alliance & Clubs
NRA Sports
Competitions & Matches
Eddie Eagle GunSafe
Firearm Training
Hunter Services
Law Enforcement Services
Range Services
Women's Programs
Friends of NRA Banquets
National Firearms Museum
NRA Headquarters Range
Gunsmithing Schools
NRA Recruiter
NRA Hunters Rights.
Youth
  National Youth Shooting Sports Cooperative Program
  Brownells/NRA Day Program
  Brownells/NRA Outstanding Achievement Youth Award
  Marksmanship Qualification Program
  Youth Hunter Education Challenge
  Brownells/NRA National Youth Shooting Sports
  Ambassador Program
  Youth Education Summit
  Resources & Information
  Youth Wildlife Art Contest
  Santioned Special Tournament
  Junior Membership
  InSights Magazine
  Email List Signup
  Youth Essay Contest
  Special Offers
  Volunteer State Coordinators
  NRA's Home Air Gun Program
  Request for Eagle Scout Certificate
  National Junior Shooting Camps

HISTORICAL FINANCIALS
Company Type: Private

Income Statement FYE: December 31

	REVENUE ($ mil.)	NET INCOME ($ mil.)	NET PROFIT MARGIN	EMPLOYEES
12/16	366	(45)	—	500
12/14	310	(35)	—	—
12/13	347	57	16.5%	—
12/09	237	1	0.5%	—
Annual Growth	6.4%	—	—	—

2016 Year-End Financials
Return on assets: 26.0%   Cash ($ mil.): 13
Return on equity: (-12.5%)
Current ratio: 0.70

NATIONWIDE CHILDREN'S HOSPITAL

Buckeye babies toddlers and teens don't have to travel the country to find pediatric care with Nationwide Children's Hospital at their disposal. The Columbus Ohio health care provider is one of the largest pediatric care centers in the US. The hospital has some 430 licensed beds and offers services in areas such as behavioral health cardiology hospice orthopedics and surgery. It has roughly 1100 health care providers on its medical staff and its emergency department treats more than 83000 patients each year. The hospital also operates outpatient and specialty clinics in the area and a research institute which is investigating gene therapy.

Operations
The hospital provides more than $122 million in charity care and community benefit services annually. It had more than 1 million patient visits and had more than 25000 surgery cases in 2014.

Geographic Reach
Nationwide Children's Hospital serves patients from 50 US states and 32 countries. The company is 68 facilities extending out across Ohio and beyond. The company's top ten outpatient visits counties are Franklin Delaware Fairfield Licking Clark Pickaway Madison Union Muskingum and Knox.

Sales and Marketing
Nationwide Children's Hospital payor mix in 2014 included commercial 43%; Medicaid managed care Cap 33%; and Medicaid 13%.

Strategy
In 2015 Nationwide Children's Hospital announced plans to adopt and integrate GenomeNext's genomic sequencing analysis platform for both clinical laboratory services and clinical research initiatives

In 2014 the company outlined numerous details of its $130 million campus expansion project. Its plans include an $85 million outpatient care building and a $45 million building to house faculty offices. The outpatient building called the Livingston Ambulatory Center will house primary care services dental services behavioral health dermatology adolescent medicine sports rehabilitation and various clinics. Both buildings will be six stories tall.

The hospital added helicopter medical transport service in 2013.

Company Background
The health system in 2012 completed a $740 million project to build a new main hospital and add 2 million sq. ft. of clinical research and support space. The expansion added about 100 new beds.

Also in 2012 it opened an ambulatory surgery center in Westerville Ohio and a Close To Home lab and clinic in Springfield. In 2014 it opened the Sharon Woods Primary Care Center in north Columbus.

Nationwide Children's Hospital opened its doors in 1892.

EXECUTIVES

Ambulatory Services Director, Olivia Thomas
Chairman The Center For Family Safety And Healing, Abigail S. Wexner
Evp And Cfo, Timothy C. Robinson
President And Coo, Rick Miller
Svp And Chief Nursing Officer, Linda Stoverock
Ceo, Steve Allen
President The Research Institute, John Barnard
President The Center For Family Safety And Healing, Karen Days
Chief Medical Officer, Richard J. Brilli
Surgeon-in-chief, R. Lawrence Moss
Physician-in-chief, J. Philip Saul
Chairman Nationwide Children's Hospital Foundation, Cheryl W. Lucks
Chairman The Research Institute, Donald P. McConnell
Medical Director, Garey Noritz
Medical Director, Grant Morrow
Medical Director, David Axelson
Vice President Administration Surgical Services, Michelle Mckissick
Vice President, Steve Testa
Medical Director, Desalegn Yacob
Chairman, Alex Fischer
Secretary, Tami King

LOCATIONS

HQ: NATIONWIDE CHILDREN'S HOSPITAL
700 CHILDRENS DR, COLUMBUS, OH 432052639
Phone: 614 722-2000
Web: WWW.NATIONWIDECHILDRENS.ORG

PRODUCTS/OPERATIONS

Selected Subsidiaries
Nationwide Children's Hospital
Nationwide Children's Behavioral Health
Nationwide Children's Educational Institute
Nationwide Children's Hospital Inc
Nationwide Children's Hospital Homecare
Children's Anesthesia Associates
Nationwide Children's Hospital Foundation
Pediatric Academic Associates
Children's Orthopedic Medical Center
Children's Radiological Institute
Children's Surgical Associates Corp.
The Research Institute at Nationwide Children's Hospital
Pediatric Pathology Associates of Columbus
The Center for Family Safety and Healing at Nationwide Children's Hospital

Selected Departments and Services
Adolescent Congenital Heart Disease
Adolescent Medicine
Adult Congenital Heart Disease
Adult Medicine and Hospital Pediatrics
Allergy/Immunology
Ambulatory Pediatrics
Anatomic Pathology
Anesthesiology & Pain Medicine
Asthma Program
Audiology
Bariatric Surgery
Battelle Center for Mathematical Medicine
Behavioral Health
Blood Conservation Program
Burn Program
Cancer
CAP4Kids
Cardiology
Cardiopulmonary Rehabilitation
Cardiothoracic Surgery

Center for Biobehavioral Health (Research)
Center for Cardiovascular and Pulmonary Research
Center for Childhood Cancer (Research)
Center for Clinical and Translational Research
Center for Colorectal and Pelvic Reconstruction
Center for Gene Therapy (Research)
Center for Healthy Weight and Nutrition
Center for Injury Research and Policy
Center for Innovation in Pediatric Practice
Center for Microbial Pathogenesis (Research)
Center for Molecular and Human Genetics (Research)
Center for Perinatal Research
Center for Vaccines and Immunity (Research)
Central Ohio Poison Center
Cerebral Palsy Program
Chest Wall Clinic
Child Development/Psychology
Child Life Specialists
ChildLab
Cleft Lip and Palate Center
Clinical Nutrition and Lactation
Clinical Services and Care Coordination
Clinical Studies
Clinical Therapies
Close To Home Centers
Community Relations
Congenital Heart Disease
Connecting Families
Critical Care
Cystic Fibrosis
Dentistry
Dermatology
Developmental/ Behavioral Pediatrics
Diabetes Clinic
Disorders of Sexual Development (DSD)
Ear Nose & Throat Services (Otolaryngology)
Early Childhood Development Program
Education Classes
Emergency Services
Endocrinology Metabolism & Diabetes
Family Advisory Council
Family AIDS Clinic and Educational Services (FACES)
Family Health Information Center
Family Practice
Family Resource Center
Fetal Diagnostics
Financial Matters
Gastroenterology Hepatology and Nutrition
Gender Concerns
General Pediatric Surgery
Genetics (Molecular and Human)
Gift Cards
Gift Shop
Government Relations
Health Info Library
Health Information Management (HIM)
Hearing Program
Heart Center
Hemangioma Vascular Anomalies
Hematology Oncology & BMT
HIV Program
Homecare
Hospice
Immunology
Infectious Diseases
Interdisciplinary Feeding Clinic
International Adoption Clinic
Interventional Radiology
Jeune's Syndrome
Laboratory Medicine/Reference Lab
Massage Therapy
Medical Records
Melanoma & Pigmented Lesion Clinic
Music Therapy
myChildren's
Neonatology
Nephrology
Neurodiagnostics/EEG
Neurology
Neuromuscular Disorders
Neurosciences Center
Neurosurgery
Nuclear Medicine
Nurse-Family Partnership
Occupational Therapy
Ophthalmology/Eye Clinic
Orthopedics
Outpatient Surgery
Pain Service Clinic
Palliative Care
Pastoral Care

Patient and Family Relations
Patient and Visitor Guide
Patient Financial Services
PediaCast: a pediatric podcast for parents
Pediatric and Adolescent Gynecology
Pediatric Psychiatry
Pediatric Psychology
Pharmacy Services (Outpatient)
Physical Medicine & Rehabilitation
Physical Therapy
Physical Therapy - Sports and Orthopedic
Plastic and Reconstructive Surgery
Prader-Willi Syndrome Clinic
Primary Care Centers
Pulmonary Medicine
Radiology
Reach Out and Read
Rehabilitation
Request an Appointment
Research at Children's
Resonance Disorders Program
Rheumatology
Robot-Assisted Surgery
Ronald McDonald House
School Program
Sibling Support (Children's Clubhouse)
Sleep Disorder Center
Social Work
Speech and Language Pathology
Spina Bifida Program
Sports Medicine
Surgical Services
Telehealth
The Center for Family Safety and Healing
Therapeutic Recreation
THRIVE Program (DSD & Complex Urological & Gender Concerns)
Toxicology
Transplant Program
Transport
Trauma
Urgent Care Services
Urology
Velopharyngeal Dysfunction Program
Weight Loss Surgery

COMPETITORS

Akron Children's Hospital	Licking Memorial Health Systems
Cincinnati Children's Hospital	Mount Carmel Health
Fairfield Medical Center	OhioHealth
Genesis HealthCare System (Ohio)	Select Medical
	Shriners Hospitals For Children

HISTORICAL FINANCIALS
Company Type: Private

Income Statement				FYE: December 31
	REVENUE ($ mil.)	NET INCOME ($ mil.)	NET PROFIT MARGIN	EMPLOYEES
12/17	2,317	647	27.9%	12,000
12/16	1,385	330	23.9%	—
12/15	1,386	285	20.6%	—
12/14	1,282	332	26.0%	—
Annual Growth	21.8%	24.8%	—	—

2017 Year-End Financials
Return on assets: 3.0%   Cash ($ mil.): 315
Return on equity: 27.9%
Current ratio: 1.50

NATURAL GAS PIPELINE COMPANY OF AMERICA LLC

EXECUTIVES

MBR-Pres, David Devine
Mng MBR, Richard D Kinder
MBR, Scott Parker
MBR-Cfo, Jim Saunders
MBR-Exec Vice President, Steve Kean
MBR, Charles Schwager
MBR, Joseph Listengart
SEC, Tracy Brewer
Plant Manager, William Allison

LOCATIONS

HQ: NATURAL GAS PIPELINE COMPANY OF AMERICA LLC
   1001 LOUISIANA ST, HOUSTON, TX 770025089
Phone: 713 369-9000
Web: WWW.KINDERMORGAN.COM

HISTORICAL FINANCIALS
Company Type: Private

Income Statement				FYE: December 31
	REVENUE ($ mil.)	NET INCOME ($ mil.)	NET PROFIT MARGIN	EMPLOYEES
12/17	679	130	19.2%	1,747
12/16	613	121	19.7%	—
Annual Growth	10.8%	8.0%	—	—

2017 Year-End Financials
Return on assets: 5.6%   Cash ($ mil.): 15
Return on equity: 19.2%
Current ratio: 1.00

NAVIGATE AFFORDABLE HOUSING PARTNERS, INC

EXECUTIVES

Exec Dir, Eric Strong
Coo, Julie Reynolds
Dir, Lisa McCarroll
Accounting Staff, Deanna Baker
Deputy Director, Rob McLaughlin
Auditors: CLIFTONLARSONALLEN LLP LAKELA

LOCATIONS

HQ: NAVIGATE AFFORDABLE HOUSING PARTNERS, INC
   1827 1ST AVE N STE 100, BIRMINGHAM, AL 352033137
Phone: 205 423-0801
Web: WWW.NAVIGATEHOUSING.COM

HISTORICAL FINANCIALS
Company Type: Private

Income Statement   FYE: December 31

	REVENUE ($ mil.)	NET INCOME ($ mil.)	NET PROFIT MARGIN	EMPLOYEES
12/16	540	(12)	—	53
12/13	498	(6)	—	—
12/09	407	6	1.7%	—
12/08	17	8	47.8%	—
Annual Growth	54.1%	—	—	—

2016 Year-End Financials

Return on assets: 0.2%   Cash ($ mil.): 16
Return on equity: (-2.2%)
Current ratio: —

NBL PERMIAN LLC

Former Texas gubernatorial candidate Clayton Williams once devoted his energy to politics. Now he's devoted to the independent oil and gas firm that he founded. Clayton Williams Energy explores for oil and gas deposits primarily in Louisiana New Mexico and Texas and exploits those resources. The company has estimated proved reserves of 75.4 million barrels of oil equivalent located mainly in the Permian Basin and South Texas. It has 951000 gross undeveloped acres. It also operates gas pipeline and a small natural gas processing infrastructure in Louisiana Mississippi New Mexico and Texas and offers contract drilling services. In 2017 the company was acquired by Noble Energy for $2.7 billion.

Operations
The company's two business segments are oil and gas exploration and production and contract drilling services. Its Desta Drilling subsidiary operates 14 drilling rigs 12 of which are company-owned and two of which are leased under long-term contracts.

It also owned an interest in and operate natural gas service facilities in the states of Texas and Louisiana. These natural gas service facilities consist of interests in 102 miles of pipeline three treating plants one dehydration facility and seven wellhead type treating and/or compression stations.

Geographic Reach
Clayton Williams Energy operates primarily in Louisiana New Mexico and Texas.

While the Permian Basin and the Austin Chalk/Eagle Ford Shale are the key focus of the company's drilling activities (84% and 13% respectively of proved reserves in 2012) the company also has activities in other areas.

Strategy
The company's strategy of aggressive exploration and complementary development drilling activities is shaped primarily by Clayton Williams himself (with more than 50 years of experience in the oil industry).

In 2012 to consolidate its holdings in the Permian Basin the company merged subsidiary Southwest Royalties (SWR) with the six partnerships of which SWR is the general partner.

To raise cash to pay down debt Clayton Williams sold its Wolfberry oil and gas reserves leasehold interests and facilities in Andrews County Texas for $215.2 million. In 2016 it sold all of its assets in the Giddings Area in East Central Texas for $400 million.

EXECUTIVES

Vp Gas Gathering And Marketing, Robert C. Lyon
Vp Acquisitions And New Ventures, Patrick C. Reesby, $229,577 total compensation
President, Mel G. Riggs, $482,295 total compensation
Chairman And Ceo, Clayton W. Williams, $735,075 total compensation
Vp Land, Gregory S. (Greg) Welborn, $343,035 total compensation
Vp Engineering, Ronald D. Gasser, $413,333 total compensation
Vp Exploration, Samuel L. (Sam) Lyssy, $441,045 total compensation
Vp Drilling, John F. Kennedy
Svp And Cfo, Jaime R. Casas
Auditors: KPMG LLP DALLAS TEXAS

LOCATIONS

HQ: NBL PERMIAN LLC
1001 NOBLE ENERGY WAY, HOUSTON, TX 770701435
Phone: 281 872-3100
Web: WWW.NBLENERGY.COM

PRODUCTS/OPERATIONS

2016 Sales

	% of total
Oil & Gas	100
Contract Drilling	-
Elimination	-
Total	**100**

2016 Sales

	in million
% of total	
Oil & gas shale	55
Midstream services	2
Other operating revenues	43
Total	**100**

COMPETITORS

Anadarko Petroleum	Pioneer Natural
Carrizo Oil & Gas	Resources
Chevron	Vanguard Natural
EOG	Resources
Exxon Mobil	XTO Energy
Occidental Permian	

HISTORICAL FINANCIALS
Company Type: Private

Income Statement   FYE: December 31

	REVENUE ($ mil.)	NET INCOME ($ mil.)	NET PROFIT MARGIN	EMPLOYEES
12/16	289	(292)	—	253
12/15	232	(98)	—	—
12/14	468	43	9.4%	—
12/13	429	(24)	—	—
Annual Growth	(12.3%)	—	—	—

2016 Year-End Financials

Return on assets: 22.8%   Cash ($ mil.): 573
Return on equity: (-100.9%)
Current ratio: 5.60

NC STATE INVESTMENT FUND INC

EXECUTIVES

General Manager, Libby George
Auditors: WILLIAMS OVERMAN PIERCE LLP R

LOCATIONS

HQ: NC STATE INVESTMENT FUND INC
NCSU, RALEIGH, NC 276950001
Phone: 919 513-7149

HISTORICAL FINANCIALS
Company Type: Private

Income Statement   FYE: June 30

	ASSETS ($ mil.)	NET INCOME ($ mil.)	INCOME AS % OF ASSETS	EMPLOYEES
06/17	1,059	126	12.0%	2
06/16	854	19	2.3%	—
06/15	848	203	24.0%	—
06/14	598	39	6.6%	—
Annual Growth	21.0%	47.6%	—	—

2017 Year-End Financials

Return on assets: 0.3%   Sales ($ mil): 157
Return on equity: 80.6%

NCH CORPORATION

NCH has been cleaning up for years and like everyone else it's been using soaps and detergents to do so. The company makes and sells about 450 chemical maintenance repair and supply products including all kinds of cleaners for customers in more than 50 countries throughout the world. NCH markets its products through a direct sales force to companies in the agricultural home-improvement industrial recreational and utility markets. Other products include fasteners welding supplies pet care supplies plumbing parts lubricants and metal-working fluids.

Operations
The company's major areas of focus include producing products for the industrial cleaning and maintenance pet care plumbing specialty industries supply and water treatment and remediation markets.

NCH's cleaning products include hand cleaners industrial cleaners and housekeeping supplies. Specialty chemical products including cleaning and water treatment chemicals deodorizers lubricants paints and paint strippers patching compounds and flooring and carpet treatments account for the majority of sales.

The company's divisions include: Water Treatment Solutions plumbing Pet Care (Simple SolutionsA® Bags on BoardA® Vet's BestA® and OUT! Pet Care) Specialty Industrial Supplies (operates through Partsmaster) industrial and institutional maintenance oil and gas Parts Washing lubrication and biologicals.

NCH operates more than 40 separate business units. Subsidiary Supply Line Direct offers safety and maintenance products such as janitorial supplies safety signs first aid kits spills kits storage cabinets for hazardous chemicals and protective apparel. Its plumbing products group has plumbing supplies for OEM and retail consumer markets. Other subsidiaries include Pure Solve a parts washing service TERRA Services (which reduces hazardous chemicals used in the hydraulic fracturing process) and X-Chem an oil field services division.

Subsidiary companies in NCH's Chemical Specialties division produce a diverse array of maintenance chemicals that includes cleaners degreasers lubricants grounds care housekeeping and water treatment products. Companies in the Partsmaster group offer a wide variety of items for maintenance and repair including welding supplies and fasteners. The Plumbing Products Group provides plumbing supplies for the do-it-yourself retail consumer and the OEM market. The Retail Products Group markets a wide range of pet supplies.

Geographic Reach

NCH has operations in Asia Europe North America and Latin America. The company has representatives in 30 countries on five continents. The company's sales and service teams serve customers in North America Latin America Europe Asia Australia and India. NCH has wholly owned subsidiaries in more than 50 countries.

Sales and Marketing

NCH sells its products directly through a number of wholly owned subsidiaries many of which are engaged in the maintenance products business. These include Bags on Board Partsmaster Chemsearch Chem-Aqua and Mantek.

The Plumbing Products group provides supplies for the do-it-yourself consumer and the OEM market. The Retail Products group markets pet supplies. Other subsidiaries include X-Chem an oil field services division and Pure Solve a parts-washing business.

Strategy

NCH continues to seek new opportunities in water treatment oil and gas and in driving innovation to help keep its facilities and equipment running in optimum condition while reducing costs.

Research product development quality control field testing and customized analysis are all part of the ongoing efforts at NCH to deliver market-driven innovative and high-performing products to their customers and this strategy allowed them to remain competitive with larger corporations.

Descendants of founder Milton Levy own the company.

EXECUTIVES

Vice President Of Information Technology Operations, Jim Marshal
President Nch Asia, Dong Eun Kim
Senior Vice President Sales And Marketing, Mark Ayers
Vice President Corporate Real Estate, Don Moulton
Senior Vice President Sales, Brenda Sanders
Senior Vice President, Roy Levin
Vice President, Randy Marsh
Vice President Global Travel Management, Ann Levy
Vice President Of Global Logistics, Shayne Mai
Vice President Of Finance, Pete Bocian
Executive Vice President Customer Relationship, Susan Staples
Executive Vice President Southwest Regional Manager, Farah Victoria
Senior Vice President, David Kuntschik
Vice President Organizational Development And Learning, Jed Davis
Vice President Finance, Debra Carter
Vice President Information Systems, Bruce Wineberger
Vice President Research And Development, John Roheim
Vice President Information Technology, Leonard Brown
Vice President Research And Development, Scott Boyette
Vice President, Andy Leslie
Board Member, Marga Tubb
Treasurer, Joe Farrier
Auditors: PRICEWATERHOUSECOOPERS LLP DA

LOCATIONS

HQ: NCH CORPORATION
2727 CHEMSEARCH BLVD, IRVING, TX 750626454
Phone: 972 438-0211
Web: WWW.NCH.COM

PRODUCTS/OPERATIONS

Selected Operations and Products

Chemical Specialties
  Cleaning chemicals
  Deodorizers
  Floor and carpet care products
  HVAC products
  Lubricants
  Oil production facility chemicals
  Paint
  Paint removers
  Water-treatment chemicals
Landmark Direct
  First-aid supplies
  Workplace signage and productivity products
Pet Care
Partsmaster Group
  Cutting tools
  Electrical products
  Fasteners
  Welding alloys
Plumbing Products Group
  Plumbing products for new construction
  Plumbing repair and replacement parts
Industrial and Institutional Maintenance
Industrial and commercial cleaning
Industrial Repair and maintenance
Drains Grease Traps and lift stations
Lubrication and coolants
Equipment and supplies
Parts washing
Grounds Care
Personal hygiene
Pet Care
Training pads
Stain and Odor Removers
Cleaners and Disinfectants
Allergy Relief and shed Control
Grooming products
Plumbing
Sinks, Faucets
Tub & Showers
Toilets, Drains
Specialty Industrial Supply
High Performance Cutting Tools
Welding
Abrasives
Compounds
Fasteners
Electrical and Automotive
Shop Supplies
Storage Hardware
Tools
Water Treatment Solutions
Boiler
Cooling Towers
Colsed Recirculation Systems
Biocides and Algaecides
Cleaner/Descalers
Equipment
Wastewater and Bio Remediation

COMPETITORS

Church & Dwight	H.B. Fuller
Cintas	Illinois Tool Works
Clariant	Pioneer Corporation
Danaher	Quaker Chemical
Detrex	Safety-Kleen
Ecolab	WD-40

HISTORICAL FINANCIALS

Company Type: Private

Income Statement

FYE: April 30

	REVENUE ($ mil.)	NET INCOME ($ mil.)	NET PROFIT MARGIN	EMPLOYEES
04/16	996	0	0.0%	8,500
04/12	1,045	6	0.6%	—
04/11	952	6	0.7%	—
Annual Growth	0.9%	(52.6%)	—	—

2016 Year-End Financials

Return on assets: 7.8%   Cash ($ mil.): 10
Return on equity: —
Current ratio: 1.30

NCMC VOLUNTEERS

EXECUTIVES

Ceo, Gene O'Hara
Executive Officer, William Hughes
Director, Dawn Olson
Doctor, Gary Bauerle
Supervisor, Doug Egloff
Health Professional, Matthew Measel
Manager, Regina Riecken
Internal Medicine Practitioner, Leo Soehnlen
Infectious Disease Specialist, Ronald Quenzer
Coordinator, Angela Solomonson
Account Manager, Christopher Kiser

LOCATIONS

HQ: NCMC VOLUNTEERS
1801 16TH ST, GREELEY, CO 806315154
Phone: 970 352-4121
Web: WWW.NCMCFOUNDATION.ORG

HISTORICAL FINANCIALS

Company Type: Private

Income Statement

FYE: December 31

	REVENUE ($ mil.)	NET INCOME ($ mil.)	NET PROFIT MARGIN	EMPLOYEES
12/16	354	23	6.7%	12
12/15	372	33	9.0%	—
12/14	353	46	13.1%	—
Annual Growth	0.1%	(28.6%)	—	—

2016 Year-End Financials

Return on assets: 0.9%   Cash ($ mil.): —
Return on equity: 6.7%
Current ratio: 1.00

NEBO SCHOOL DISTRICT.

EXECUTIVES

Supt, Chris S Sorensen
Dir of Hr, Almon Mosher
Bus ADM, Tracy Olsen
SEC, Kay Davis
Supt, Rick Nielsen
Supt, Dean Rowley
Vice President, Rod Oldroyd
MBR, Kl Tischner
MBR, Kristen Betts
Coordinator, Lori Catmull
Facilities Director, Matt Gledhill
Auditors: GILBERT & STEWART CPA PC PR

LOCATIONS

HQ: NEBO SCHOOL DISTRICT.
350 S MAIN ST, SPANISH FORK, UT 846602408
Phone: 801 354-7400
Web: WWW.NEBO.EDU

HISTORICAL FINANCIALS

Company Type: Private

Income Statement				FYE: June 30
	REVENUE ($ mil.)	NET INCOME ($ mil.)	NET PROFIT MARGIN	EMPLOYEES
06/17	283	7	2.6%	2,000
06/13	227	21	9.4%	—
06/08	207	4	2.1%	—
06/07	1,930	0	—	—
Annual Growth	—	164.7%	—	—

NEBRASKA METHODIST HOSPITAL INC

EXECUTIVES

Pres, John M Fraser
Vice President, Mark A Burmester
Cfo, Linda K Burt
Prin, Steven Zuber
Health Professional, Tamara Doehner
Pathologist, Gene N Herbek
Chief of Radiology, Kevin Nelson
Nurse, Rita White
Leader, Cheryl Bohacek
Director Volunteer, Linda Rajcevich
Director, Lori Groves

LOCATIONS

HQ: NEBRASKA METHODIST HOSPITAL INC
8303 DODGE ST, OMAHA, NE 681144108
Phone: 402 354-4540
Web: WWW.BESTCARE.ORG

HISTORICAL FINANCIALS

Company Type: Private

Income Statement				FYE: December 31
	REVENUE ($ mil.)	NET INCOME ($ mil.)	NET PROFIT MARGIN	EMPLOYEES
12/17	520	54	10.4%	2,635
12/16	510	63	12.4%	—
12/15	511	51	10.1%	—
12/14	449	55	12.3%	—
Annual Growth	5.0%	(0.8%)	—	—

2017 Year-End Financials

Return on assets: 3.1%
Return on equity: 10.4%
Current ratio: 1.90

Cash ($ mil.): 48

NEBRASKA PUBLIC POWER DISTRICT

Nebraska Public Power District (NPPD) electrifies the Cornhusker State. The government-owned electric utility the largest in the state provides power in 86 of the state's 93 counties. The firm has a generating capacity of about 3130 MW and operates more than 5200 miles of transmission lines. NPPD distributes electricity to about 89000 retail customers in 81 cities and towns; it also provides power to about 1 million customers through wholesale power contracts with more than 50 towns and 25 public power districts. In addition NPPD purchases electricity from the federally owned Western Area Power Administration and operates a surface water irrigation system.

Operations

The company uses multiple sources including nuclear steam mixed wind hydro and diesel to generate power.

NPPD's revenues comes from wholesale power supply agreements with 50 towns and 25 rural public power districts and rural cooperatives who rely totally or partially on NPPD's electrical system. NPPD also serves about 81 communities at the retail level.

Financial Performance

Revenues for 2013 increased by 2% due mostly to rate increases and sales to other utilities. Net income jumped 30% on the revenue increase and reduced costs. Cash from operations followed suit and rose nearly $100 million.

Strategy

Faced with growing long-term demand for electricity along with pressure to keep prices low NPPD has implemented plans to increase transmission capacity. With a goal of getting of 15% it energy from renewable sources by 2025 the company is exploring alternative fuel sources for future plants. With 45% of NPPD's energy supply coming from coal in 2011 the company was looking to cleaner alternatives such as wind power and biomass in order to meet stricter environmental regulations. In 2014 it signed a deal to purchase wind power from Sempra a move that put it within sight of its goal to have 10% of its power generation come from renewable sources.

Company Background

NPPD was formed in 1970 through the merger of three public utilities: Consumers Public Power District Platte Valley Public Power and Irrigation District and Nebraska Public Power System.

EXECUTIVES

Vice President, Mike Dixon
Auditors: PRICEWATERHOUSECOOPER LLP ST

LOCATIONS

HQ: NEBRASKA PUBLIC POWER DISTRICT
1414 15TH ST, COLUMBUS, NE 686015226
Phone: 877 275-6773
Web: WWW.NPPD.COM

PRODUCTS/OPERATIONS

2013 Sales

	$ mil.	% of total
Wholesale	584	53
Retail	294	27
Other	227	20
Total	**1,106**	**100**

COMPETITORS

Basin Electric Power	Omaha Public Power
Berkshire Hathaway Energy	Tri-State Generation and Transmission
NorthWestern	

HISTORICAL FINANCIALS

Company Type: Private

Income Statement				FYE: December 31
	REVENUE ($ mil.)	NET INCOME ($ mil.)	NET PROFIT MARGIN	EMPLOYEES
12/17	1,101	71	6.5%	1,900
12/16	1,154	82	7.2%	—
12/15	1,097	91	8.3%	—
12/14	1,122	62	5.6%	—
Annual Growth	(0.6%)	4.6%	—	—

2017 Year-End Financials

Return on assets: 5.9%
Return on equity: 6.5%
Current ratio: 0.40

Cash ($ mil.): 27

NEIGHBORHOOD HEALTH PLAN, INCORPORATED

Neighborhood Health Plan (NHP) is a not-for-profit health plan provider that offers health insurance products and related services to more than 300000 members in Massachusetts. The organization is a leading provider of managed health care for members of MassHealth the state's Medicaid program for low-income and disabled residents. But it also provides commercial health plans for small businesses as well as low-cost and no-cost family and individual plans for people who qualify for subsidized health coverage under Massachusetts' 2006 health care reform law. NHP maintains a provider network of more than 4300 primary care physicians 13000 specialists and dozens of hospitals. The company was founded in 1986.

Sales and Marketing

NHP markets its products to individuals families and employers.

Its care network includes primary care providers specialists and hospitals such as Massachusetts General Hospital and Boston Children's Hospital. It also includes community health centers across the state.

In 2015 NHP hired Mechanica to manage its marketing branding and advertising efforts.

Strategy

The company's Partnership for Community Health initiative with Partners HealthCare with the Massachusetts League of Community Health Centers announced $6 million in grants for community health centers throughout Massachusetts.

In 2013 NHP was granted approval to expand coverage into Greater Plymouth County.

EXECUTIVES

President And Ceo, David Segal
Chief Medical Officer, Paul Mendis
Vp Operations And Cio, Marilyn Daly
Chief Customer Officer, Katie Catlender
Interim Cfo, Doug Thompson
Vice President Of Clinical Operations, Deb Bonin
Vice President Business Development, Carla Bettano
Vice President Of Human Resources, Sabrina Williams
Chairman, Matthew E. Fishman

LOCATIONS

HQ: NEIGHBORHOOD HEALTH PLAN, INCORPORATED
399 REVOLUTION DR STE 810, SOMERVILLE, MA 021451444
Phone: 617 772-5500
Web: WWW.NHP.ORG

COMPETITORS

Aetna
Blue Cross and Blue Shield of Massachusetts
CIGNA
ConnectiCare
Fallon Community Health Plan
Harvard Pilgrim
Health New England
MVP Health Plan
Tufts Health Plan
UnitedHealth Group

HISTORICAL FINANCIALS

Company Type: Private

Income Statement				FYE: December 31
	REVENUE ($ mil.)	NET INCOME ($ mil.)	NET PROFIT MARGIN	EMPLOYEES
12/15	2,178	(22)	—	340
12/14	1,743	(108)	—	—
12/13	1,380	(68)	—	—
Annual Growth	25.6%	—	—	—

2015 Year-End Financials
Return on assets: 10.9%   Cash ($ mil.): 120
Return on equity: (-1.0%)
Current ratio: 0.90

NEMOURS FOUNDATION

Even if their offspring are fanatical about Finding Nemo parents of sick children may prefer finding Nemours. The Nemours Foundation operates the Nemours/Alfred I. duPont Hospital for Children in Wilmington Delaware; the Nemours Children's Hospital in Orlando Florida; and dozens of pediatric clinics in Delaware Florida New Jersey and Pennsylvania that treat acutely and chronically ill children. Specialties include orthopedics cardiology neurology and oncology. Nemours also has extensive research programs and it operates a clinic in Delaware that serves low-income elderly residents. The not-for-profit foundation was created in 1936 through the will of chemicals pioneer Alfred I. duPont.

Operations
Some of Nemours' facilities are operated in partnership with other health care providers. For example it runs pediatric programs with Bryn Mawr Hospital Lancaster General and Thomas Jefferson University Hospital in Pennsylvania as well as with AtlantiCare and Virtua Health in New Jersey.

Financial Performance
In 2013 Nemours posted a 14% increase in revenue from $861 million to $982 million mostly due to trust distributions and net assets released from restrictions but also from a bump in patient service revenue. Net income also rose from a loss of $71 million in 2012 to a positive $144 million from a pension liability adjustment. Cash from operations followed suit going from $5 million to $28 million.

Strategy
Nemours Foundation completed construction of a full-service children's hospital in Orlando Florida where it already operated a pediatric specialty clinic. The $400 million facility named Nemours Children's Hospital has 95 patient beds and emergency diagnostic specialty and outpatient units as well as educational and research centers. The foundation is also expanding the Nemours/Alfred I. duPont Hospital for Children in Delaware; the new patient tower a $256 million project is scheduled to open in 2014.

The Nemours Foundation has also invested in upgrading its information technology system. It uses a comprehensive electronic health record (EHR) system NemoursOne to connect all of its doctors and facilities with shared patient information. Some of the foundation's facilities participate in the state EHR network (Delaware Health Information Network).

EXECUTIVES

Medical Director, Eric Gibson
Medical Librarian, Kristina Flathers
Vice President Of Human Resources, Theresa Young
Auditors: KPMG LLP JACKSONVILLE FL

LOCATIONS

HQ: NEMOURS FOUNDATION
10140 CENTURION PKWY N, JACKSONVILLE, FL 322560532
Phone: 904 697-4100
Web: WWW.NEMOURS.ORG

PRODUCTS/OPERATIONS

2013 Sales

	% of total
Net patient revenue less provision for bad debts	75
Distribution from the Alfred I.duPont testamentary Trust	14
Net assets released from restrictions used for operations	5
Contract service revenue	2
Grant revenue	2
other income	2
Total	**100**

COMPETITORS

All Children's Hospital
Baptist Health System
Children's Hospital Boston
Children's Hospital of Philadelphia
Children's Hospital of Pittsburgh
Children's National Medical Center
Children's Specialized Hospital
Christiana Care
Cincinnati Children's Hospital
Florida Hospital Waterman
HCA
Mayo Clinic Jacksonville
Miami Children's Hospital
Orlando Health
Shriners Hospitals For Children
St. Jude Children's Research Hospital
UF&Shands

HISTORICAL FINANCIALS

Company Type: Private

Income Statement				FYE: December 31
	REVENUE ($ mil.)	NET INCOME ($ mil.)	NET PROFIT MARGIN	EMPLOYEES
12/17	1,317	36	2.8%	4,400
12/08	160	(80)		
12/07	635	53	8.5%	
12/06	578	29	5.1%	
Annual Growth	7.8%	2.1%	—	—

2017 Year-End Financials
Return on assets: 5.1%   Cash ($ mil.): 300
Return on equity: 2.8%
Current ratio: 2.40

NETWORK FOR GOOD, INC.

EXECUTIVES

Ceo, Bill Strathmann
Dir, Gordon Caylor
Customer Staff, Abby Watt

LOCATIONS

HQ: NETWORK FOR GOOD, INC.
1140 CONN AVE NW STE 700, WASHINGTON, DC 200364011
Phone: 202 627-1600
Web: WWW.NETWORKFORGOOD.COM

HISTORICAL FINANCIALS

Company Type: Private

Income Statement				FYE: December 31
	REVENUE ($ mil.)	NET INCOME ($ mil.)	NET PROFIT MARGIN	EMPLOYEES
12/16	305	0	0.0%	20
12/14	230	0	0.2%	—
12/13	195	(0)		
Annual Growth	15.9%	—	—	—

2016 Year-End Financials
Return on assets: 0.4%   Cash ($ mil.): 5
Return on equity: —
Current ratio: 0.10

NEVADA SYSTEM OF HIGHER EDUCATION

You can gamble on a solid academic foundation with The Nevada System of Higher Education (NSHE). The system oversees Nevada's public colleges and institutions. NSHE encompasses eight institutions: the University of Nevada Las Vegas; the University of Nevada Reno; Nevada State College; community colleges Truckee Meadows Great Basin College College of Southern Nevada and Western Nevada College; and environmental research arm Desert Research Institute (DRI). The system which enrolls some 106000 students is governed by the Nevada Board of Regents consisting of 13 members elected for six-year terms.

Financial Performance
Total operating revenue fell 4% in 2012 as an increase in NSHE's largest segment (student tuition and fees) was not enough to offset double-digit declines in federal state and local grants and contracts. The rise in tuition and fees resulted from an increase in tuition rates to offset an enrollment decrease.

Strategy
In late 2013 NSHE announced a partnership to establish medical schools at the University of Nevada Las Vegas and Reno campuses.

EXECUTIVES

Ceo, Daniel Klaich
Director, James McKinney
Dean, Stephen Rosenbaum
Administrative Assistant, Dennis Thieme
Professor, Robert Parker
Assistant Professor, Natalie Berman
Professor, Dmitri Shalin
Acting Pres Wstrnnevadacollege, P Mark Ghan

LOCATIONS

HQ: NEVADA SYSTEM OF HIGHER EDUCATION
2601 ENTERPRISE RD, RENO, NV 895121666
Phone: 775 784-4901
Web: WWW.NEVADA.EDU

HISTORICAL FINANCIALS

Company Type: Private

Income Statement				FYE: June 30
	REVENUE ($ mil.)	NET INCOME ($ mil.)	NET PROFIT MARGIN	EMPLOYEES
06/17	1,115	140	12.6%	8,000
06/16	1,055	48	4.6%	—
06/07	685	116	17.0%	—
06/06	660	252	38.2%	—
Annual Growth	4.9%	(5.2%)	—	—

2017 Year-End Financials

Return on assets: 4.7%   Cash ($ mil.): 283
Return on equity: 12.6%
Current ratio: 1.20

NEW ENGLAND POWER COMPANY

EXECUTIVES

Pres, Rudolph L Wynter

LOCATIONS

HQ: NEW ENGLAND POWER COMPANY
40 SYLVAN RD, WALTHAM, MA 024511120
Phone: 978 772-2903

HISTORICAL FINANCIALS

Company Type: Private

Income Statement				FYE: December 31
	REVENUE ($ mil.)	NET INCOME ($ mil.)	NET PROFIT MARGIN	EMPLOYEES
12/16	415	88	21.3%	1
12/14	443	106	24.0%	—
Annual Growth	(3.3%)	(8.9%)	—	—

2016 Year-End Financials

Return on assets: 5.4%   Cash ($ mil.): —
Return on equity: 21.3%
Current ratio: 0.10

NEW JERSEY TRANS-PORTATION TRUST FUND AUTHORITY

EXECUTIVES

Commissioner, James Weinstein
Scientist, Katie Lynch
Auditors: MERCADIEN PC PRINCETON NJ

LOCATIONS

HQ: NEW JERSEY TRANSPORTATION TRUST FUND AUTHORITY
1035 PARKWAY AVE, EWING, NJ 086182309
Phone: 609 530-2035

HISTORICAL FINANCIALS

Company Type: Private

Income Statement				FYE: June 30
	REVENUE ($ mil.)	NET INCOME ($ mil.)	NET PROFIT MARGIN	EMPLOYEES
06/17	1,338	(532)	—	138
06/16	1,261	(412)	—	—
06/09	934	(1,078)	—	—
Annual Growth	4.6%	—	—	—

2017 Year-End Financials

Return on assets: 4.1%   Cash ($ mil.): 2,626
Return on equity: (-39.7%)
Current ratio: —

NEW JERSEY TURNPIKE AUTHORITY INC

EXECUTIVES

Chb, Jamie Fox
Ceo, Ronald Gravino
Treas, Michael R Dupont
Commissioner, Frank X Mc Dermott
Coo, John F O Hern
Exec Dir, Veronique Hakim
Commissioner, Harold L Hodes
Commissioner, Raymond M Pocino
Commissioner, Ulises E Diaz
Comm Supervisor, David Horton
Safety Manager, Edward Marsh

LOCATIONS

HQ: NEW JERSEY TURNPIKE AUTHORITY INC
1 TURNPIKE PLZ, WOODBRIDGE, NJ 070955195
Phone: 732 750-5300
Web: WWW.STATE.NJ.US

HISTORICAL FINANCIALS

Company Type: Private

Income Statement				FYE: December 31
	REVENUE ($ mil.)	NET INCOME ($ mil.)	NET PROFIT MARGIN	EMPLOYEES
12/17	1,698	329	19.4%	2,400
12/16	1,689	260	15.4%	—
12/14	1,549	265	17.1%	—
Annual Growth	3.1%	7.5%	—	—

2017 Year-End Financials

Return on assets: 8.9%   Cash ($ mil.): 183
Return on equity: 19.4%
Current ratio: 0.30

NEW PRIME, INC.

Specialized carrier New Prime (which does business simply as Prime) provides refrigerated flatbed tanker and intermodal trucking services throughout North America through more than 10000 remotely monitored temperature-controlled trailers. The company operates in the US and Canada and serves Mexico through arrangements with other carriers. A subsidiary Prime Floral uses the parent company's refrigerated equipment and facilities to serve the flower industry. In addition to its freight-hauling operations Prime provides logistics services including freight brokerage.

Operations

Prime which has a fleet of more than 4700 trucks operates through three divisions.

Prime's liquid bulk fleet (Tanker Division) consists of more than 200 trucks and more than 400 6800-gallon Walker Stainless MC407 trailers with air ride suspensions. The company's Refrigerated Division has a fleet of remotely monitored temperature-controlled trailers and serves businesses whose needs include transportation of fresh produce fresh cut floral produce pharmaceuticals fresh or frozen meats or any other dry or temperature controlled freight. Prime also has a Flatbed Division.

Its affiliates include Amber Aleri Prime Floral Prime Intermodal Prime Logistics and Trailer Skirt.

Geographic Reach

The company serves customers in Canada Mexico and the US. Based in Springfield Missouri Prime operates two US terminals in Pennsylvania and Utah.

Sales and Marketing

Prime has hauled goods for such blue chip consumer goods makers as ConAgra Foods Kraft Foods and General Mills. It markets its products through independent contractors stores and online.

Strategy

Prime is shifting its strategy to align with customer preferences for shortening supply chain mileage and delivery time all of which is intended to offset lower consumer demand and volatile fuel costs.

It is also using technology to enhance its position as an industry leader in the safe cost-effective transport of temperature-sensitive goods. Its Prime Position Tracking software enables the company to locate tractors in real-time within a 600 foot radius at all times. Prime Mapping and Routing provides detailed Rand McNally and PC*Miler directions to driver associates to ensure that loads get to their destination in the quickest safest and most efficient manner.

Company Background

Prime was founded in 1970 by Robert Low who continues to serve as Prime's president.

EXECUTIVES

President And Ceo, Robert E. Low
Manager Of Success Leasing Program, Fred Ege
Director Of Logistics, Rick Gallagher
Director Of Operations, Pat Leonard
Director Of Flatbed And Tanker Operations, Jim Wilkins
Vp Sales And Marketing, Steve Wutke
Director Of Finance, Dean Hoedl
Director Of Technology, Rodney Rader
Manager Of Tanker Division, Brett Vonwiller

LOCATIONS

HQ: NEW PRIME, INC.
2740 N MAYFAIR AVE, SPRINGFIELD, MO 658035084
Phone: 800 321-4552
Web: WWW.PRIMEINC.COM

COMPETITORS

Boyd Bros. Transportation
C.H. Robinson Worldwide
C.R. England
Central Refrigerated Service
Comcar
Frozen Food Express
KLLM Transport Services
Marten Transport
Quality Distribution
Stevens Transport

HISTORICAL FINANCIALS

Company Type: Private

Income Statement

FYE: March 31

	REVENUE ($ mil.)	NET INCOME ($ mil.)	NET PROFIT MARGIN	EMPLOYEES
03/17*	1,653	116	7.1%	5,000
04/16	1,598	133	8.3%	—
03/12	1,022	60	6.0%	—
04/11	941	47	5.0%	—
Annual Growth	9.8%	16.2%	—	—

*Fiscal year change

2017 Year-End Financials

Return on assets: 2.2%
Return on equity: 7.1%
Current ratio: 0.70

Cash ($ mil.): —

NEW RIVER ELECTRICAL CORPORATION

EXECUTIVES

Pres, Thomas M Wolden
Sr Vice President, John E Swim
Exec Vice President, Richard C Furr II
Vice President, Frank R Miller
Vice President, John F Ney
Vice President, Terry M Garrett
Vice President, Barry S Murray
Vice President, John E Lanning
Sr Vice President, Robert B Arritt Jr
Auditors: KENNETT & KENNETT PC ROANOKE

LOCATIONS

HQ: NEW RIVER ELECTRICAL CORPORATION
15 CLOVERDALE PL, CLOVERDALE, VA 240773124
Phone: 540 966-1650
Web: WWW.NEWRIVERELECTRICAL.COM

HISTORICAL FINANCIALS

Company Type: Private

Income Statement

FYE: December 31

	REVENUE ($ mil.)	NET INCOME ($ mil.)	NET PROFIT MARGIN	EMPLOYEES
12/17	283	23	8.4%	900
12/16	241	16	6.8%	—
12/15	271	22	8.3%	—
12/14	242	19	8.2%	—
Annual Growth	5.3%	5.9%	—	—

2017 Year-End Financials

Return on assets: 1.6%
Return on equity: 8.4%
Current ratio: 5.20

Cash ($ mil.): 48

NEW YORK BLOOD CENTER, INC.

New York Blood Center (NYBC) holds a very literal interpretation of the meaning of life. It is a not-for-profit blood distribution and research organization serving New York City and its environs in New York State and New Jersey as well as parts of Connecticut and Pennsylvania. As one of the largest blood centers in the US NYBC provides nearly 1 million blood components to some 200 hospitals each year. The center's facilities collect blood from more than 2000 donors each day. It also operates the nation's oldest and largest public cord blood bank. In addition its Kimball Research Institute includes more than a dozen research laboratories which study the prevention and treatment of blood-related illnesses.

Operations

Areas of research in the Kimball Research Institute include virology molecular genetics cell biology and signaling viral immunology and infectious disease prevention. It has been responsible for the development and licensing of solvent and detergent technology used to deactivate the potency of viruses in blood and blood products (such as plasma and platelets used in transfusions).

NYBC's clinical services division acts as an adjunct and resource to hospitals throughout its service areas by providing expertise in transfusion medicine as well as delivering more than 8500 specialized procedures each year. In addition the center maintains a bone marrow donor registry for the New York area provides hemophilia services to some 1500 patients and offers screening and education programs for cholesterol high blood pressure and cardiovascular disease.

Geographic Reach

Based in New York NYBC offers its services throughout New York City Long Island the Hudson Valley and in Connecticut New Jersey and Pennsylvania.

Strategy

Seeking greater breadth and financial stability NYBC announced it will combine its operations with Community Blood Center of Greater Kansas City (CBC) to form one of the leading blood centers serving patients and hospitals in the Northeast and Midwest. The combination is expected to be completed in mid-2014. The union of NYBC and CBC is expected to bring synergies in blood and laboratory services medical programs cell therapies and research.

Mergers and Acquisitions

In October 2013 NYBC acquired Coral Blood Services a subsidiary of HemaCare Corp. to advance its mission of providing innovative blood products and medical services to hospitals and patients throughout the Northeast. Coral Blood Services provides more than 2500 therapeutic apheresis procedures annually in New York New Jersey Connecticut and Pennsylvania.

EXECUTIVES

Cio, Michele Scaggiante
Vp And Director Lindsley F. Kimball Research Institute, Mohandas Narla
Director National Cord Blood Program, Pablo Rubinstein
President And Ceo, Christopher D. Hillyer
Head Of The Viral Immunology Laboratory, Shibo Jiang
Svp And Cfo, Elizabeth C. Gibson
Senior Vice President, Paddy C Mullen
Medical Director, Patricia Shi
Vice President General Counsel Secretary, Jordana Schwartz
Senior Vice President Strategic Services And Facilities Administration, Jeffrey Jacob
Senior Vice President, Frederick W Hill
Senior Vice President, John R Mullen
Vice President Customer Service, Robert Purvis
Senior Vice President Human Resources, Ollie Cheatham
Auditors: KPMG LLP NEW YORK NY

LOCATIONS

HQ: NEW YORK BLOOD CENTER, INC.
310 E 67TH ST, NEW YORK, NY 100656273
Phone: 212 570-3010
Web: WWW.NYBLOODCENTER.ORG

PRODUCTS/OPERATIONS

Selected Services
Blood products
Clinical services
Hemochromatosis phlebotomy program
Hemophilia services
Laboratory services
Ordertrak
Transfusion medicine services

COMPETITORS

Blood Systems Inc.	Red Cross
CSL Behring	SeraCare Life Sciences
Daxor	

HISTORICAL FINANCIALS

Company Type: Private

Income Statement

FYE: March 31

	REVENUE ($ mil.)	NET INCOME ($ mil.)	NET PROFIT MARGIN	EMPLOYEES
03/18	466	48	10.4%	1,600
03/15	320	(0)	—	—
Annual Growth	13.4%	—	—	—

2018 Year-End Financials

Return on assets: 13.5%
Return on equity: 10.4%
Current ratio: 1.40

Cash ($ mil.): 42

NEW YORK CITY ECONOMIC DEVELOPMENT CORPORATION

EXECUTIVES

Pres-Ceo, Maria Torres-Springer
Cfo, Kim Vaccari
Coo, Euan Robertson
Evp, Seth Myers
Treas, Spencer Hobson
Asst Treas, Fred D'Ascoli
Administrative Assistant, Natalie Molina
Coordinator, Crissette Maxwell
Senior Vice-President, Elizabeth Verostek
Coordinator, Erin Layton
Facilities Manager, Kenyell Smalls
Auditors: ERNST & YOUNG LLP NEW YORK

LOCATIONS

HQ: NEW YORK CITY ECONOMIC DEVELOPMENT CORPORATION
110 WILLIAM ST FL 4, NEW YORK, NY 100383950
Phone: 212 619-5000
Web: WWW.EDC.NYC

HISTORICAL FINANCIALS

Company Type: Private

Income Statement FYE: June 30

	REVENUE ($ mil.)	NET INCOME ($ mil.)	NET PROFIT MARGIN	EMPLOYEES
06/18	761	14	1.9%	438
06/16	908	100	11.1%	—
Annual Growth	(8.5%)	(62.1%)	—	—

2018 Year-End Financials

Return on assets: 25.1% Cash ($ mil.): 92
Return on equity: 1.9%
Current ratio: 0.60

NEW YORK CITY HEALTH AND HOSPITALS CORPORATION

New York City Health and Hospitals Corporation (HHC) takes care of the Big Apple. HHC has facilities in all five boroughs of New York City. As one of the largest municipal health service systems in the US HHC serves 1.4 million New Yorkers and more than 475000 who are uninsured. It operates a network of 11 acute care hospitals (including Bellevue the nation's oldest public hospital) five large diagnostic and treatment centers five skilled nursing centers long-term care facilities and a home health care agency. HHC also operates more than 70 community-based clinics and provides medical services to New York City's correctional facilities. In addition it operates MetroPlus a managed health care plan.

Sales and Marketing
Medicaid accounted for 26% of net patient service revenue in fiscal 2014; Medicaid managed care accounted for 21%. Following those up were disproportionate share supplemental pool (16%) MetroPlus (13%) and Medicare (12%).

Financial Performance
Revenue increased 10% to $8 billion in fiscal 2014 (ended June) due to a 10% increase in net patient service revenue (which accounted for 62% of earnings). City appropriations also contributed to the rise. Net income fell 21% to $314 million as operating expenses including personal service fringe benefits and employer payroll taxes rose. Investment returns also declined that year which helped lead to lower net income.

Cash flow from operations grew 38% to $246 million on an absence of cash appropriations remitted to the city plus an increase of cash generated from receipts from grants and from patients and third-party payors.

Strategy
HHC has been struggling financially facing a $1.1 billion budget gap for 2018. In mid-2017 the system cut 476 positions including nearly 400 management positions. The move which is intended to stem inefficiencies by eliminating unnecessary layers of management is expected to save $60 million in 2018.

To keep up with increasing demand the company has been busy opening new medical facilities while phasing out older less efficient ones.

In a bid to train more doctors in its service area in 2012 HHC and St. George University teamed up to award scholarships worth more than $11 million over five years to New York City residents who aspire to become doctors.

HISTORY

The City of New York in 1929 created a department to manage its hospitals for the poor. During the Depression more than half of the city's residents were eligible for subsidized care and its public hospitals operated at full capacity.

Four new hospitals opened in the 1950s but the city was already having trouble maintaining existing facilities and attracting staff (young doctors preferred private insurance-supported hospitals catering to the middle class). Meanwhile technological advances and increased demand for skilled nurses made hospitals more expensive to operate. The advent of Medicaid in 1965 was a boon for the system because it brought in federal money.

In 1969 the city created the New York City Health and Hospitals Corporation (HHC) to manage its public health care system — and it was hoped to distance it from the political arena. But HHC was still dependent on the city for funds arousing criticism from those who had hoped for more autonomy. A 1973 state report claimed "the people of New York City are not materially better served by the Health and Hospitals Corporation than by its predecessor agencies."

City budget shortfalls in the mid-1970s led to cutbacks at HHC including nearly 20% of staff. Later in the decade several hospitals closed and some services were discontinued. Ed Koch became mayor in 1978 and gained more control over HHC's operations. Struggles between his administration and the system led three HHC presidents to resign by 1981. That year Koch crony Stanley Brezenoff assumed the post and helped transform HHC into a city pseudo-department.

The early 1980s brought greater prosperity to the system. Reimbursement rates and collections procedures improved allowing HHC to upgrade its record-keeping and its ambulatory and psychiatric care programs. In the late 1980s sharp increases in AIDS and crack addiction cases strained the system and a sluggish economy decreased city funding. Criticism mounted in the early 1990s with allegations of wrongful deaths dangerous facilities and lack of Medicaid payment controls. HHC lost patients to managed care providers and revenues plummeted. In 1995 a city panel recommended radically revamping the system.

Faced with declining revenues and criticism from Mayor Rudolph Giuliani that HHC was "a jobs program" the company began cutting jobs and consolidating facilities in 1996. Under Giuliani's direction HHC made plans to sell its Coney Island Elmhurst and Queens hospital centers. In 1997 the New York State Supreme Court struck down Giuliani's privatization efforts saying the city council had a right to review and approve each sale. In 1998 Giuliani continued to seek to restructure HHC and the agency itself contended it was making progress toward its restructuring goals which were aimed at giving HHC more autonomy as well as more fiscal responsibility. In anticipation of a budget shortfall that year the system laid off some 900 support staff employees. In 1999 the state court of appeals ruled HHC could not legally lease or sell its hospitals.

In 2000 HHC launched an effort to improve its physical infrastructure by beginning the rebuilding and renovation of facilities in Brooklyn Manhattan and Queens. The organization also began converting to an electronic (and thus more efficient) clinical information system. In 2001 HHC forged ahead with further restructuring initiatives. It introduced the Open Access plan a cost-cutting measure designed to expedite the processes involved in outpatient visits.

In 2006 Mayor Michael Bloomberg committed $16 million in funds toward the treatment of those affected by exposure to toxic fumes and dust from the 2001 attacks on the World Trade Center. Together with the city HHC established the WTC Environmental Health Center at Bellevue Hospital; treatment was made available at little or no charge to the patient.

EXECUTIVES

Svp And General Counsel, Alan D. Aviles
Acting Svp South Manhattan Health Network; Acting Executive Director Bellevue Hospital Center, Lynda D. Curtis
Svp North Bronx Healthcare Network; Executive Director Jacobi Medical Center, William P. Walsh
Svp Finance And Cfo, Marlene Zurack
Executive Director Queens Hospital Center, Antonio Martin
Executive Director Hhc Health And Home Care, Meryl Weinberg
Executive Director Elmhurst Hospital Center, Chris Constantino
Executive Director Gouverneur Healthcare Services, Mendel Hagler
Executive Director And President Metroplus Health Plan, Arnold Saperstein
Executive Director Sea View Hospital Rehabilitation Center And Home, Angelo Mascia
Svp Queens Healthcare Network, Anne Marie Sullivan
Executive Director Hhc Health And Home Care, Ann Frisch
Svp Information Technology And Cio, Norberto (Bert) Robles
Executive Director Dr. Susan Smith Mckinney Nursing And Rehabilitation Center, Michael Tartaglia
Executive Director Coler-goldwater Specialty Hospital And Nursing Facility, Robert K. Hughes
Svp Quality And Corporate Chief Medical Officer, Ross Wilson
Acting Svp Generations Plus Northern Manhattan Healthcare Network; Executive Director Lincoln Medical And Mental Health Center, Denise C. Soares
Executive Director Kings County Hospital Center, Ernest J. Baptiste
Executive Director Queens Hospital Center, Julius Wool
Assistant Vice President, Laura Free
Senior Assistant Vice President, Paul Albertson
Assistant Vice President, Peter Fragale
Assistant Vice President Data Science, Vijay Saradhi
Vice President Planning, Tom Scully
Chairman, Michael A. Stocker
Vice Chair, Diane E. Lacey
Auditors: KPMG LLP NEW YORK NY

LOCATIONS

HQ: NEW YORK CITY HEALTH AND HOSPITALS CORPORATION
125 WORTH ST RM 514, NEW YORK, NY 100134006
Phone: 212 788-3321
Web: WWW.NYCHEALTHANDHOSPITALS.ORG

HHC Networks
Central Brooklyn Family Health Network
  Dr. Susan Smith McKinney Nursing and Rehabilitation Center
  East New York Diagnostic & Treatment Center
  Kings County Hospital Center
Generations Plus Northern Manhattan Health Network
  Harlem Hospital Center
  Lincoln Medical and Mental Health Center
  Metropolitan Hospital Center
  Morrisania Diagnostic & Treatment Center
  Renaissance Health Care Network Diagnostic & Treatment Center
  Segundo Ruiz Belvis Diagnostic & Treatment Center
North Bronx Healthcare Network

Jacobi Medical Center
North Central Bronx Hospital
North Brooklyn Health Network
Cumberland Diagnostic & Treatment Center
Woodhull Medical and Mental Health Center
Queens Health Network
Elmhurst Hospital Center
Queens Hospital Center
South Brooklyn and Staten Island Health Network
Coney Island Hospital
Sea View Hospital Rehabilitation Center & Home
South Manhattan Healthcare Network
Bellevue Hospital Center
Coler-Goldwater Specialty Care and Nursing Facility
Gouverneur Healthcare Services

PRODUCTS/OPERATIONS

2014 Sales

	% of total
Net patient service	62
Premiums	29
Grants	5
Other	3
Appropriations from City of New York	1
Total	**100**

Selected Services

Adolescent Health Services
Alcohol/Drug Dependency
Asthma Care
Bariatric Services
Behavioral/Mental Health Services
Burn Care
Cancer Care
Cardiology
Child Health Service
Colon Cancer Screening
Dental Care
Diabetes Care
Farmers Market
Flu Vaccination
Geriatric Services
HIV/AIDS Care
HPV Vaccine
Language/Translation Services
LGBT Healthcare Services
Mammograms
Mobile Medical Office-Staten Island
Neonatal Intensive Care
Obstetrics & Gynecology
Palliative Care
Parkinson's Disease
Pediatrics
Quit Smoking
Rehab Services
Sexual Response Assault Teams
Sickle Cell Disease
Sleep Disorder Labs
Stroke Prevention and Care
Telehealth Initiatives
Trauma Centers
Vision Care
Women's Health
WTC Environmental Health Center

COMPETITORS

Beth Israel Medical
Center
Catholic Healthcare
System
Columbia University
Continuum Health
Partners
Cornell University

Lenox Hill Hospital
Memorial
Sloan-Kettering
Montefiore Medical
NYU
NewYork-Presbyterian
Healthcare
Northwell Health

HISTORICAL FINANCIALS

Company Type: Private

Income Statement

FYE: June 30

	REVENUE ($ mil.)	NET INCOME ($ mil.)	NET PROFIT MARGIN	EMPLOYEES
06/17	9,550	(193)	—	35,700
06/02	4,285	(118)	—	—
06/01	4,287	(71)	—	—
06/00	4,083	9	0.2%	—
Annual Growth	**5.1%**	—	—	—

2017 Year-End Financials

Return on assets: 9.8%   Cash ($ mil.): 1,184
Return on equity: (-2.0%)
Current ratio: 0.50

NEW YORK CITY TRANSIT AUTHORITY

New York City Transit Authority has your ticket to ride in the Big Apple. Known as MTA New York City Transit it provides subway and bus transportation throughout New York City's five boroughs. It is the primary agency of the MTA and the largest public transportation system in North America. Its subway system — which includes more than 6300 subway cars 468 stations and 660 miles of track — serves more than 5.5 million passengers a day day on 238 local six select bus service and 61 express routes in the five boroughs. Its more than 5700 buses transport some 2.6 million riders each day. The agency also operates the Staten Island Railway system.

Operations

New York City Subways and Buses is comprised of two agencies of the MTA regional transportation network - MTA New York City Transit Transit and MTA Bus. The regional network also includes MTA Staten Island Railway (part of NYC Transit's Department of Subways) MTA Long Island Rail Road MTA Metro-North Railroad MTA Bridges and Tunnels and MTA Capital Construction.

MTA New York City Transit and its subsidiary Manhattan and Bronx Surface Transit Operating Authority provide subway and public bus service within New York City's five boroughs.

In 2013 MTA New York City Transit's total ridership was 2.4 billion up 62 million or 2.7% from 2012. After including 44 million of lost ridership from Superstorm Sandy in 2012 the company's 2013 ridership increased by 0.8% with a subway ridership increase of 19 million or 1.1% and no change in bus ridership.

Geographic Reach

The company serves customers in Brooklyn the Bronx Manhattan and Queens and Staten Island

Financial Performance

Rebounding from the effects of Superstorm Sandy on ridership (which resulted in lost revenues of $52 million) in 2013 MTA New York City Transit's revenues from fares increased by 9%. In 2014 its operating budget was $10.1 billion.

Strategy

MTA New York City Transit's parent company the MTA has been plagued by operating losses. To mitigate its losses the MTA has in recent years raised fares cut jobs and decreased service on its buses and subway lines. It has also sought to raise its non-operating revenues by seeking increased government funding.

With the help of federal stimulus and other funding MTA New York City Transit has been making capital improvements to its systems. Projects have included the construction of the Second Avenue Subway and renovations at the Fulton Street Transit Center and other stations throughout the system.

In 2013 the company broke ground on a new MTA Staten Island Railway station. The 27-month construction project the first such project to include a parking lot will replace the existing Atlantic and Nassau Stations in the Tottenville section of the borough.

Company Background

New York City Transit Authority was formed in the 1950s by New York's legislature; the city's transit system dates back to the early 1900s.

EXECUTIVES

Prin, Thomas F Prendergast
President, Lawrence G Reuter
Exec Vice President, Barbara Spencer
Executive, Emily Morgan
Director, Karen Giordano
Executive Officer, Miguel Teixeira
Sys Dir, Timothy Thompson
Auditors: PRICEWATERHOUSECOOPERS LLP ST

LOCATIONS

HQ: NEW YORK CITY TRANSIT AUTHORITY
2 BROADWAY FL 18, NEW YORK, NY 100043357
Phone: 718 330-1234

HISTORICAL FINANCIALS

Company Type: Private

Income Statement

FYE: December 31

	REVENUE ($ mil.)	NET INCOME ($ mil.)	NET PROFIT MARGIN	EMPLOYEES
12/17	4,911	(287)	—	47,956
12/06	3,041	1,780	58.6%	—
12/05	2,907	0	—	—
Annual Growth	**4.5%**	—	—	—

2017 Year-End Financials

Return on assets: 3.8%   Cash ($ mil.): 55
Return on equity: (-5.9%)
Current ratio: 0.40

NEW YORK COMMUNITY TRUST AND COMMUNITY FUNDS INC

EXECUTIVES

Pres-Exec Dir, Lorie A Slutsky
Sr Vice President, Joyce Bove
V Pres Donor Rltns, Robert V Edgar
V Pres of ADM, Mercedes M Leon
Vice President Donor Relations, Robert Edgar
Auditors: GRANT THORNTON LLP NEW YORK

LOCATIONS

HQ: NEW YORK COMMUNITY TRUST AND
COMMUNITY FUNDS INC
909 3RD AVE FL 22, NEW YORK, NY 100224752
Phone: 212 686-0010
Web: WWW.NYCOMMUNITYTRUST.ORG

HISTORICAL FINANCIALS

Company Type: Private

Income Statement   FYE: December 31

	ASSETS ($ mil.)	NET INCOME ($ mil.)	INCOME AS % OF ASSETS	EMPLOYEES
12/17	2,806	(5)	—	65
12/16	2,552	(5)	—	—
12/15	2,473	(99)	—	—
12/14	2,570	130	5.1%	—
Annual Growth	3.0%	—	—	—

2017 Year-End Financials

Return on assets: 0.3%   Sales ($ mil.): 251
Return on equity: (-2.2%)

NEW YORK HOTEL TRADES COUNCIL AND HOTEL ASSOCIATION OF NEW YORK CITY HEALTH CENTER, INC.,

EXECUTIVES

Chb, Joseph E Spinnato
Ceo, Robert Greenstan
Pres, Peter Ward
Cfo, Harry Veras
Acct Mgr, Christine Cheung
Support, Lydia Ortizlugo
Chief of Medicine, Robert Greenspan
Manager, Serge Saadoun
Member, Suzette Warburton
Network Engineer, Luis Rincon
Payroll Staff, Karen Hargrove
Auditors: ARMAO LLP GARDEN CITY NY

LOCATIONS

HQ: NEW YORK HOTEL TRADES COUNCIL AND
HOTEL ASSOCIATION OF NEW YORK CITY HEALTH
CENTER, INC.,
305 W 44TH ST, NEW YORK, NY 100365407
Phone: 212 586-6400
Web: WWW.HOTELFUNDS.ORG

HISTORICAL FINANCIALS

Company Type: Private

Income Statement   FYE: December 31

	REVENUE ($ mil.)	NET INCOME ($ mil.)	NET PROFIT MARGIN	EMPLOYEES
12/16	565	121	21.5%	1,000
12/15	138	18	13.5%	—
12/14	114	0	0.9%	—
12/13	112	1	1.1%	—
Annual Growth	71.2%	362.7%	—	—

2016 Year-End Financials

Return on assets: 5.9%   Cash ($ mil.): 52
Return on equity: 21.5%
Current ratio: 3.30

NEW YORK POWER AUTHORITY

The hydropower generated by the mighty Niagara Falls is the real authority behind the New York Power Authority (NYPA). More than 70% of the power that NYPA produces is from hydropower resources. The company generates and transmits more than 20% of New York's electricity making it the largest state-owned public power provider in the US. It is also New York's only statewide electricity supplier. NYPA owns hydroelectric and fossil-fueled generating facilities (16 in total) that produce about 5700 MW of electricity and it operates more than 1400 circuit-miles of transmission lines. NYPA is owned by the State of New York.

Geographic Reach

The company serves customers throughout New York State various public corporations in Southeastern New York within the metropolitan area of New York City (SENY Governmental Customers) and certain out-of-state customers.

Sales and Marketing

NYPA services more than 500 businesses and industrial customers including manufacturing companies such as Anchor Glass of Elmira and General Motors of Tonawanda and non-manufacturing companies like GEICO of Amherst and Yahoo! of Lockport and 114 government entities in New York City and Westchester County including New York City government the Metropolitan Transportation Authority The Port Authority of New York and New Jersey the New York City Housing Authority Westchester County government and most Westchester municipalities school districts and other public entities.

The company provides electricity to 51 municipal and cooperative electric systems to sell to their customers.

Financial Performance

In 2014 the company's net revenues increased by 5% to $3.18 billion due to a higher volume of market energy and capacity sales and higher prices on those sales.

Net income grew by 9% due to higher net revenues and an increase in investment income.

In 2014 NYPA's operating cash inflow slightly decreased by 0.2% due to changes in working capital.

Strategy

NYPA receives no state funds or tax credits. Instead it finances new projects through bond sales.

Following its shift from a regulated monopoly to a competitor in an open power market NYPA is aiming to grow by reducing the cost of the energy it provides and by developing electric transportation (such as electric cars) and other energy-efficiency projects including installing emergency power generators in metropolitan buildings. It is also working to improve the state's transmission grid increase its generating capacity and help support the state's directive to get 45% of its power from clean energy sources (including 100 MW of power from solar arrays at buildings across the state). NYPA has been tagged as the lead agency to reduce energy use at state facilities by 20% by 2020.

In 2014 NYPA completed the installation of solar thermal hot water systems at five New York City firehouses in the Rockaways section of Queens. The $550000 investment will reduce operating costs and could lead to the wider use of the clean energy-transfer technology in other city government facilities. The company's energy efficiency projects have saved New Yorkers more than

$148 million a year cutting annual oil use by more than 2.7 million barrels and offsetting the release of approximately 890000 tons of greenhouse gases. Its clean transportation program has placed more than 1300 electric-drive vehicles into service.

To improve its delivery of power the company is pursuing the development of a new cross-Hudson transmission line that will connect New York City customers to the PJM Interconnection power grid.

HISTORY

The Power Authority of the State of New York (aka New York Power Authority or NYPA) was established in 1931 by Gov. Franklin Roosevelt to gain public control of New York's hydropower resources. The utility's major power plants came on line with the opening of the St. Lawrence-Franklin D. Roosevelt Power Project (1958) and the Niagara Power Project (1961). The Blenheim-Gilboa Pumped Storage Power Project opened in 1973.

In the mid-1970s NYPA shifted to nuclear power when it opened the James A. FitzPatrick Nuclear Power Plant (1975) and the Indian Point 3 Nuclear Power Plant (1976). The company then opened gas- and oil-powered plants: the Charles Poletti Power Project (1977) and the Richard M. Flynn Power Plant (1994).

In 1998 the authority allocated low-cost electricity to five companies that planned to invest $104 million in business expansions in western New York. The company suffered a loss in 1999 in part from reduced hydro generation and a drop in investment earnings. In 2000 NYPA sold its two nuclear plants (1800 MW of capacity) to utility holding company Entergy for $967 million.

The company completed the installation of 11 gas-powered turbines at various locations in New York City and on Long Island in 2001; the program was initiated to prevent expected energy shortages that summer but it also helped maintain power in areas of the city during the September 11 terrorist attacks.

In 2013 The Village of Lake Placid unveiled a new hybrid-electric shuttle bus that will make commuting on public transportation quieter and cleaner. Financing for the bus was made possible through NYPA's Municipal Electric-Drive Vehicle Program which provides financial assistance to New York municipal utilities to facilitate the replacement of less fuel-efficient vehicles in order to advance the state's clean energy goals. That year NYPA added seven more hybrids and one more EV to its fleet bringing the total number of electric drive vehicles to 79. It also purchased just over 40000 gallons of B20 biodiesel which earned the Power Authority 17 Alternative Fuel Vehicle credits under the Department of Energy's Energy Policy Act that will be used to purchase additional hybrid and plug-in hybrid vehicles.

EXECUTIVES

Coo, Edward A. (Ed) Welz
President And Ceo, Gil C. Quiniones
Evp And Cfo, Robert F. Lurie
Chairman Board Of Trustees, John R. Koelmel
Vice Chair Board Of Trustees, Joanne M. Mahoney
Auditors: KPMG LLP NEW YORK NY

LOCATIONS

HQ: NEW YORK POWER AUTHORITY
123 MAIN ST, WHITE PLAINS, NY 106013104
Phone: 914 681-6200
Web: WWW.NYPA.GOV

PRODUCTS/OPERATIONS

2014 Sales

	$ mil.	% of total
Power sales	2,396	76
Wheeling charges	614	19
Transmission charges	165	5
Total	**3,175**	**100**

Selected Operations

Transmission Control Facility
  Frederick R. Clark Energy Center (Oneida County)
Fossil-Fueled Plants
  Charles Poletti Power Project (New York City)
  Richard M. Flynn Power Plant (Suffolk County)
  PowerNow! Turbines (11 units in New York City and
  Long Island)
Hydropower Plants
  Blenheim-Gilboa Pumped Storage Power Project
  (Schoharie County)
  Niagara Power Project (Niagara County)
  St. Lawrence-Franklin D. Roosevelt Power Project (St.
  Lawrence County)
Small Hydropower Plants
  Ashokan Project (Ulster County)
  Crescent Plant (Albany and Saratoga Counties)
  Gregory B. Jarvis Plant (Oneida County)
  Kensico Project (Westchester County)
  Vischer Ferry Plant (Saratoga and Schenectady
  counties)

COMPETITORS

Avangrid	National Grid USA
CH Energy	Rochester Gas and
Con Edison	Electric
Enbridge	TransCanada
Entergy	

HISTORICAL FINANCIALS

Company Type: Private

Income Statement   FYE: December 31

	REVENUE ($ mil.)	NET INCOME ($ mil.)	NET PROFIT MARGIN	EMPLOYEES
12/17	2,573	119	4.6%	1,700
12/16	2,421	22	0.9%	—
12/15	2,625	74	2.8%	—
12/14	3,175	272	8.6%	—
Annual Growth	**(6.8%)**	**(24.1%)**	**—**	**—**

2017 Year-End Financials

Return on assets: 15.8%   Cash ($ mil.): 37
Return on equity: 4.6%
Current ratio: 0.20

NEW YORK PRESBYTERIAN HOSPITAL WEILL CORNELL UNIVERSITY MEDICAL CENTER

EXECUTIVES

Prin, Lewis Drusin
Branch/Division/Department Hea, Janet Parisi
Administrator, Eugene Chan
Payroll Manager, Nadine Sylvain
Director, Steven Herrmann

Vice-President, Anita R Golbey
Project Leader, Dale Wright
Administrative Assistant, Lynn Reynolds
Director of Operations, Owen Davis
Professor, Joseph Hayes
Administrator, David Weir

LOCATIONS

HQ: NEW YORK PRESBYTERIAN HOSPITAL WEILL
CORNELL UNIVERSITY MEDICAL CENTER
525 E 68TH ST, NEW YORK, NY 100654870
Phone: 212 746-1754
Web: WWW.MED.CORNELL.EDU

HISTORICAL FINANCIALS

Company Type: Private

Income Statement   FYE: December 31

	REVENUE ($ mil.)	NET INCOME ($ mil.)	NET PROFIT MARGIN	EMPLOYEES
12/15	4,505	265	5.9%	5
12/12	75	21	28.2%	—
Annual Growth	**290.4%**	**131.8%**	**—**	**—**

2015 Year-End Financials

Return on assets: 8.7%   Cash ($ mil.): 227
Return on equity: 5.9%
Current ratio: 0.80

NEW YORK SOCIETY FOR THE RELIEF OF THE RUPTURED AND CRIPPLED, MAINTAINING THE HOSPITAL FOR

EXECUTIVES

Ceo, Louis Shapiro
Exec Vice President, Lisa A Goldstein
Exec Vice President, Stacey L Malakof
Cso, Lionel B Ivashkiv
Cdo, Catherine Callagy
Engineer, Andrew Kraszewski
Research Assistant, Ashlee Reilly
Internal Medicine Practitioner, Branden Sosa
Family Practitioner, Brett Toresdahl
Assistant Vice-President, Brian Sweeney
Orthopedic Surgeon, Brian Ward

LOCATIONS

HQ: NEW YORK SOCIETY FOR THE RELIEF OF THE
RUPTURED AND CRIPPLED, MAINTAINING THE
HOSPITAL FOR
535 E 70TH ST, NEW YORK, NY 100214823
Phone: 212 606-1000
Web: WWW.HSS.EDU

HISTORICAL FINANCIALS

Company Type: Private

Income Statement   FYE: December 31

	REVENUE ($ mil.)	NET INCOME ($ mil.)	NET PROFIT MARGIN	EMPLOYEES
12/16	1,038	51	5.0%	3,350
12/15	811	79	9.8%	—
12/14	996	109	10.9%	—
12/07	441	(21)	—	—
Annual Growth	**10.0%**	**—**	**—**	**—**

2016 Year-End Financials

Return on assets: 7.5%   Cash ($ mil.): 95
Return on equity: 5.0%
Current ratio: 1.00

NEW YORK STATE HOUSING FINANCE AGENCY

EXECUTIVES

Pres-Ceo, Stephen J Hunt
Chb, Judd S Levy
Sr Vice President, Ralph J Madalena
Sr Vice President, Bernard H Abramowitz
Sr Vice President, Robert M Drillings
Sr Vice President, James Angley
Counsel, Jay Ticker
Senior Asset Manager, Roger Harry
Vice President of Information, Jose Dilan
Senior Project Manager, Joey Lindicy
Auditors: DELOITTE & TOUCHE LLP NEW YOR

LOCATIONS

HQ: NEW YORK STATE HOUSING FINANCE AGENCY
641 LEXINGTON AVE FL 4, NEW YORK, NY
100224503
Phone: 212 688-4069
Web: WWW.NYHOMES.ORG

HISTORICAL FINANCIALS

Company Type: Private

Income Statement   FYE: October 31

	REVENUE ($ mil.)	NET INCOME ($ mil.)	NET PROFIT MARGIN	EMPLOYEES
10/17	400	112	28.0%	131
10/16	279	77	27.7%	—
10/09	182	(31)	—	—
10/08	355	23	6.5%	—
Annual Growth	**1.3%**	**19.1%**	**—**	**—**

2017 Year-End Financials

Return on assets: 3.9%   Cash ($ mil.): 12
Return on equity: 28.0%
Current ratio: —

NEW YORK UNIVERSITY

Higher education is at the core of this Big Apple
institution. The setting and heritage of New York

University (NYU) make it one of the nation's most popular educational institutions. With more thanA 50000 students attending its 18 schools and colleges NYU is among the largest private schools in the US. Its Tisch School of the Arts is well-regarded and its law school and Leonard N. Stern School of Business are among theA foremost in the country. NYU occupies five major centers in Manhattan; its Washington Square campus is in the heart of Greenwich Village. The school wasA founded in 1831. Notable alumni include former Federal Reserve Chairman Alan Greenspan and film producer Oliver Stone.

Operations
The school confers about 12000 degrees annually. Of those roughly 4500 are bachelor's degrees nearly 5000 are master's degrees and about 400 are doctoral. Associate and professional degrees make up the rest. NYU alumni and faculty also boast several prestigious awards including more than a dozen Nobel and Crafoord prizes and another four Pulitzer prizes.

NYU is one of the largest employers in New York City with more than 16000 employees.

Geographic Reach
Along with its campuses in New YorkA NYU operates branch campus and research programs in other parts of theA US and abroad as well as study abroad programs in more than 25 countries. International students make up about 10% of the school's student body.

Financial Performance
Undergraduate tuition for the university runs more than $37000 per year.

Strategy
NYU has established itself as the first global network university with a comprehensive liberal arts campus in Abu DhabiA that opened in 2010.

HISTORY
New York University was founded by several prominent New Yorkers in 1831. The school held its first classes the following year in rented rooms on the corner of Beekman and Nassau streets then moved to a building in Washington Square in 1835. It established its law school that year. NYU started its school of medicine in 1841 followed by the school of engineering and science (1854). Postgraduate studies in arts and science (its first coeducational program) began in 1886.

NYU's enrollment jumped from fewer than 2000 in 1900 to 28000 in 1930. After a lull during the Depression and WWII the campus boomed again in the postwar years. During the 1950s the university began focusing on improving academics rather than on increasing enrollment. It created a school of the arts in 1965 and in the early 1970s it completed the Elmer Holmes Bobst Library. However a cash crunch during that decade almost forced the school into bankruptcy.

President Jay Oliva took the reins in 1981 and focused on transforming NYU from a largely commuter college into a global university. The school began a campaign to raise $1 billion in 1984 but earmarked the funds for campus improvements rather than swelling its endowment. During the late 1980s NYU opened several new dormitories and conference spaces. In 1994 British historian and collector Sir Harold Acton bequeathed to the school his Tuscany estate — five art-filled villas overlooking Florence Italy.

In 1996 NYU's Medical Center began talks with Mount Sinai Medical Center aimed at merging their hospitals and medical schools. The talks fell apart in early 1997 but the following year the two sides agreed to merge hospitals and keep their medical schools distinct. Also in 1998 NYU formed NYU On-Line Inc. a for-profit subsidiary to develop and sell specialized Internet courses to other schools

training centers and students; the venture was subsequently folded in late 2001. During 1999 contributions to the school approached $250 million. That year however two upper-level school officials were fired following allegations of improper use of university money.

Oliva retired as president in 2002 and was replaced by John Sexton former School of Law dean. In 2004 Sexton announced that NYU would give $1 million to New York City towards renovation of Washington Square Park (the school annually gives some $200000 for the park's ongoing maintenance).

EXECUTIVES

Vp Academic And Health Affairs, Robert (Bob) Berne
Vp Information Technology And Chief Information Technology Officer, Marilyn A. McMillan
Provost, David W. McLaughlin
Evp Finance And Information Technology, Martin S. Dorph
Director Global Institute Of Public Health; Dean Of Global Public Health, Cheryl G. Healton
Dean Libraries, Carol A. Mandel
Herman Robert Fox Dean College Of Dentistry, Charles N. Bertolami
Evp Operations, Alison Leary
Director Institute For The Study Of The Ancient World, Roger Bagnall
Director Courant Institute Of Mathematical Sciences, Gérard Ben Arous
Saul J. Farber Dean Nyu School Of Medicine; Ceo Nyu Hospitals Center, Robert I. Grossman
Dean Gallatin School Of Individualized Study, Susanne L. Wofford
Dean Polytechnic School Of Engineering, Katepalli R. (Sreeni) Sreenivasan
Dean Silver School Of Social Work, Lynn Videka
Dean Liberal Studies, Fred Schwarzbach
Judy And Michael Steinhardt Director Institute Of Fine Arts, Patricia Lee Rubin
Dean Leonard N. Stern School Of Business, Peter B. Henry, age 48
Vice Chancellor New York University Abu Dhabi, Alfred H. Bloom
Vp Global Technology And Chief Global Technology Officer, Thomas A. (Tom) Delaney
Dean For Science Faculty Of Arts And Science, Michael D. Purugganan
President, Andrew Hamilton
Gale And Ira Drukier Dean Steinhardt School For Culture Education And Human Development, Dominic Brewer
Anne And Joel Ehrenkranz Dean Faculty Of Arts And Sciences, Thomas J. Carew
Dean For Humanities Faculty Of Arts And Sciences, Joy Connolly
Harvey J. Stedman Dean School Of Professional Studies, Dennis DiLorenzo
Dean Robert F. Wagner Graduate School Of Public Service, Sherry A. Glied
Dean Tisch School Of The Arts, Allyson Green
Dean For Social Sciences Faculty Of Arts And Science, Michael Laver
Vice Chancellor Nyu Shanghai, Jeffrey S. Lehman
Dean Undergraduate College Leonard N. Stern School Of Business, Geeta Menon
Dean School Of Law, Trevor Morrison
Director Marron Institute Of Urban Management, Paul Romer
Seryl Kushner Dean College Of Arts And Science, G. Gabrielle Starr
Dean College Of Nursing, Eileen Sullivan-Marx
Chancellor Nyu Shanghai, Yu Lizhong
Interim Dean Graduate School Of Arts And Science, Anna L. Harvey
Vice President, Marc Wais

Vice President For Financial Operations And Treasurer, Stephanie Pianka
Senior Vice President Development And Alumni Relations, Debra LaMorte
Vice President Finance, Harold T Read
Vice President Administration, Robert Goldfeld
Assistant Vice President Information Systems, Keith Whiteman
Department Chair, Christina Reuterskiold
Senior Vice President, Lynne Brown
Associate Vice President For Stewardship And Events, Gustave Fleury
Medical Director, Marcy Ferdschneider
Chair Department Of Anthropology, Fred Myers
Vice President Human Resources, Robert White
Vice President For Budget And Planning, Anthony Jiga
Global Finance Chief Of Staff To Executive Vice President For Finance And Information Technology, Carolyn Wood
Vice President For Enrollment Management, Mj Knoll-finn
Vice President Rxr Realty Michael Aisner, Luis Rosa
Medical Director, Ryan Harper
Clinic Manager, Danielle Bartlett
Vice President Finance, Pamela Morris
Clinic Manager, Fredelyne Paris
Vice President For Student Affairs, Susan B Neuman
Vice President Director Engineering, Chris Pak
Assistant Vice President External Affairs And Protective Services, Carl Barchus
Vice President For Local History, Kate Feighery
Vice President Of Administration, Angel Yu
Senior Vice President Education And Diversity Solutions, Jim Jones
Director Of Admissions, Williams Cassandra
Chairman Board Of Trustees, William R. (Bill) Berkley, age 72
Board Director, Christine Trump
Secretary, John Leiva
Vice Chair President, Peter Romain
Treasurer, Peter Rajsingh
Assistant Treasurer, Elisa Cohen
Secretary, Jennifer Neuman
Ms Global Affairs Candidate Treasurer Energy Policy International Club, Jude Buenaseda
Secretary Athletic Development, Raffaela Ianniciello
Secretary And Marketing, August Morar
Auditors: PRICEWATERHOUSECOOPERS LLP NE

LOCATIONS
HQ: NEW YORK UNIVERSITY
70 WASHINGTON SQ S, NEW YORK, NY 100121019
Phone: 212 998-1212
Web: WWW.NYU.EDU

HISTORICAL FINANCIALS
Company Type: Private

Income Statement				FYE: August 31
	REVENUE ($ mil.)	NET INCOME ($ mil.)	NET PROFIT MARGIN	EMPLOYEES
08/16	8,500	177	2.1%	21,000
08/11	5,172	563	10.9%	—
08/06	2,148	195	9.1%	—
Annual Growth	14.7%	(1.0%)	—	—

2016 Year-End Financials
Return on assets: 15.9%   Cash ($ mil.): 1,033
Return on equity: 2.1%
Current ratio: —

NEWARK BETH ISRAEL MEDICAL CENTER INC.

Part of the Saint Barnabas Health Care System Newark Beth Israel Medical Center is a 670-bed acute-care regional referral hospital. The facility servesA residents of Newark and surrounding areas in northern New Jersey. The hospital offers services including primary diagnostic emergency surgical and rehabilitative care. It is home to specialized programs such as kidney transplantation cancer care dentistry sleep disordersA geriatrics and women's health services. Newark Beth Israel Medical Center also houses the Children's Hospital of New Jersey and the Saint Barnabas Heart Center. The research and teaching hospital has a medical staff of more than 800 physicians.

Operations

Newark Beth Israel Medical Center along with sister hospital Saint Barnabas Medical CenterA has a teaching and research affiliation with the New Jersey Medical School (part of the University of Medicine and Dentistry of New Jersey). The hospital also has training programs with other regional schools.

Newark Beth Israel Medical Center handles about 25000 inpatient visits annually while the hospital's outpatient centers see some 300000 patients each year.

EXECUTIVES

Medical Director Cardiologist, Chunguang Chen
Radiology Director, Michael Connely
Managing Director, John Cerritelli
Medical Director Center For Asian Health, Su Wang
Auditors: WITHUMSMITHBROWN PC MORRISTOW

LOCATIONS

HQ: NEWARK BETH ISRAEL MEDICAL CENTER INC.
201 LYONS AVE, NEWARK, NJ 071122027
Phone: 973 926-7000
Web: WWW.CPRTRAININGNJ.COM

PRODUCTS/OPERATIONS

Selected Departments and Centers

Barnabas Health Heart Center
Center for Geriatric Health Care
Center for Women's Health
Children's Hospital of New Jersey
Cohen Comprehensive Cancer and Blood Disorder Center
Lung Center
Pacemaker and Defibrillator Center
Palliative Care Program
Regional Perinatal Center
Radiology
Robotic Surgery Center
Renal Transplantation
Sleep Disorders Center

COMPETITORS

AtlantiCare
Atlantic Health
Bergen Regional Medical
CentraState Healthcare System
Children's Specialized Hospital
Chilton Medical Center
East Orange General Hospital
Englewood Hospital and Medical Center
Hackensack Meridian Health
Hackensack University Medical Center
Newton Medical Center
Robert Wood Johnson University Hospital
Robert Wood Johnson University Hospital at Rahway
St. Joseph's Healthcare System
The Valley Hospital

Virtua Health
Winthrop-University Hospital

HISTORICAL FINANCIALS

Company Type: Private

Income Statement
FYE: December 31

	REVENUE ($ mil.)	NET INCOME ($ mil.)	NET PROFIT MARGIN	EMPLOYEES
12/17	545	35	6.5%	3,000
12/16	539	27	5.2%	—
12/15	542	38	7.1%	—
12/14	591	32	5.5%	—
Annual Growth	(2.7%)	3.3%	—	—

2017 Year-End Financials

Return on assets: 5.5%
Return on equity: 6.5%
Current ratio: 0.50
Cash ($ mil.): —

NEWARK ELECTRONICS CORPORATION

EXECUTIVES

Pres, Dan Hill
Vice President, Steven Webb
Vice Pres-General Counsel & SE, Jospeh R Daprile
Treasurer & Asst Secretary, Paul M Barlak
Vice Pres, Thomas Mayfield
Sr V Pres, Susan Fischer
Operations Staff, Myron Robinson

LOCATIONS

HQ: NEWARK ELECTRONICS CORPORATION
300 S RIVERSIDE PLZ, CHICAGO, IL 606066613
Phone: 773 784-5100

HISTORICAL FINANCIALS

Company Type: Private

Income Statement
FYE: January 31

	REVENUE ($ mil.)	NET INCOME ($ mil.)	NET PROFIT MARGIN	EMPLOYEES
01/16*	525	8	1.7%	834
02/15	543	24	4.5%	—
02/14	541	23	4.4%	—
02/13	580	20	3.5%	—
Annual Growth	(3.3%)	(23.9%)	—	—

*Fiscal year change

2016 Year-End Financials

Return on assets: 6.9%
Return on equity: 1.7%
Current ratio: 1.70
Cash ($ mil.): 17

NEWBURGH CITY SCHOOL DISTRICT

EXECUTIVES

Pres, Dawn M Fucheck
Supt, Annette Saturnelli
Vice President, Pamela R Freeman-Resc
Asst Supt-Fin, Micheal Tacella
SEC, Kaye Gwithen
Superintendent, Mary E Limr
Superintendent, Russell Agostaro
Corporate Communications Staff, Charles J Houck
Office Manager, Dale Salisbury
Federal Program Director, Bruce Cohen
Producer, Robin Hastey

LOCATIONS

HQ: NEWBURGH CITY SCHOOL DISTRICT
124 GRAND ST, NEWBURGH, NY 125507301
Phone: 845 563-3400
Web: WWW.NEWBURGHSCHOOLS.ORG

HISTORICAL FINANCIALS

Company Type: Private

Income Statement
FYE: June 30

	REVENUE ($ mil.)	NET INCOME ($ mil.)	NET PROFIT MARGIN	EMPLOYEES
06/18	309	9	3.0%	3,356
06/17	293	7	2.6%	—
06/16	288	18	6.3%	—
06/07	0	0	—	—
Annual Growth	—	—	—	—

2018 Year-End Financials

Return on assets: 2.7%
Return on equity: 3.0%
Current ratio: 0.80
Cash ($ mil.): 25

NEWMARK & COMPANY REAL ESTATE, INC.

Whether you're talking cubicle cities or corner offices Newmark & Company Real Estate (dba Newmark Knight Frank or NKF) makes its mark on commercial real estate. As one of the world's top commercial real estate advisory firms it provides property brokerage development and management services to investors corporations and property owners. Newmark also offers facility management services overseeing a portfolio of properties across the globe. Together with its London-based partner Knight Frank NKF operates more than 370 offices across six continents. NKF comprises parent company BGC Partners' Real Estate Services segment which made up 40% of the parent company's total revenue in 2014.

Operations

NKF manages a broad range of properties including headquarters facilities and office space for a wide range of companies. It manages the day-to-day operations and maintenance for urban and suburban commercial properties of most types including office industrial data centers healthcare retail call centers urban towers suburban campuses and landmark buildings.

Property management services include building operations and maintenance leasing vendor and contract negotiation project oversight and value engineering labor relations property inspection/quality control property accounting and financial reporting cash flow analysis financial modeling lease administration due diligence and exit strategies. Newmark's facilities management services also include facility audits and reviews energy management services janitorial services mechanical services bill payment maintenance project management and moving management.

Its affiliates include Cantor Fitzgerald CCRE-Cantor Commercial Real Estate and Cantor Gaming.

Sales and Marketing

NKF serves clients across more than half a dozen sectors including advertising and marketing education healthcare media and entertainment financial services law firms real estate retail and food services and technology and telecom sectors. It counts several big names among its list of clients including AEG Live Apollo Global Management Deutsch CBS Corporation Cornell University and AmTrust Realty Corporation.

Financial Performance

As the Real Estate Services segment of BGC Partners Newmark Knight Frank's revenue jumped 23% to $708.8 million during 2014 thanks to its acquisition of Cornish & Carey stronger broker productivity and favorable trends in sales and leasing in the US commercial real estate market.

Strategy

The company is growing its business by adding new brokers making technological improvements and cultivating the company's relationships with clients in the US and abroad. It has also been growing its geographic reach and business lines by acquiring smaller real estate firms.

Mergers and Acquisitions

In January 2016 NKF bought Memphis-based Steffner Commercial Real Estate which was the "cornerstone" in NKF's plan to grow across the Mid-South region of Tennessee Kentucky Mississippi Alabama Arkansas and Louisiana.

December 2015 the real estate firm boosted its presence in the Midwest after it purchased Cincinnati Commercial Real Estate (CCR) which leases and invests in offices industrial facilities and retail space. The acquisition also added CCR's diversified client base of top Fortune 500 companies institutions and privately owned firms while also supporting growth opportunities for NKF's existing Ohio business in Cleveland and Columbus.

In August 2014 the company bought bought Cornish & Carey Commercial Inc. the leading full-service commercial real estate services company in the San Francisco Bay area and Silicon Valley. The company believes that this is a key strategic addition for Newmark in the key Northern California market.

In early 2013 it acquired commercial real estate developer Frederick Ross and brokerage Smith Mack.

EXECUTIVES

Managing Principal San Francisco, Michael Brown
Executive Managing Director, David Tilton
Senior Vice President, Jay Murtha
Executive Vice President Principal, Jeffrey Roseman
Vice President Brokerage Operations And Recruiting, Jeremy Bressman
Executive Vice President, Debora Mclachlan
First Vice President, Paul Graham
Vice President, Jesse Cardenas
Vice President, Collin Perkins
Executive Vice President, Bruce Moore
Assistant Vice President Of Development, Alison Cavanaugh
Executive Vice President Director Sales, Galvin Krysti

LOCATIONS

HQ: NEWMARK & COMPANY REAL ESTATE, INC.
125 PARK AVE, NEW YORK, NY 100175529
Phone: 212 372-2000
Web: WWW.NGKF.COM

Selected Locations
North America
US
Canada
Mexico
Europe
Asia-Pacific
Africa
Middle East

PRODUCTS/OPERATIONS

Selected Services
Leasing Advisory
Global Corporate Services
Investment Sales and Capital Markets
Retail
Industrial
Consulting
Program and Project Management
Facilities Management
Property Management
Landauer Valuation & Advisory
Residential Construction Services
Specialty Practice Groups
Data Center Consulting
Global Gaming Group
Global Healthcare
Government
Hotels
Law Firm Advisory
Loan Sale Advisory
Multi-Housing Group
Not-For-Profit Advisory
Retail Occupier Services
Self Storage Group

COMPETITORS

Breslin Realty Development Corp.	Eastdil Secured
CBRE Group	Greiner-Maltz
Colliers International	Jones Lang LaSalle
Cushman & Wakefield	Lend Lease
	Lincoln Property

HISTORICAL FINANCIALS

Company Type: Private

Income Statement   FYE: December 31

	ASSETS ($ mil.)	NET INCOME ($ mil.)	INCOME AS % OF ASSETS	EMPLOYEES
12/16	860	53	6.3%	2,250
12/15	694	139	20.1%	—
12/14	234	0	—	—
Annual Growth	91.7%	—	—	—

2016 Year-End Financials

Return on assets: 15.4%   Sales ($ mil): 1,058
Return on equity: 5.1%

NEWPORT CORPORATION

Newport helps all sorts of customers take a measured approach. The company makes lasers precision components and automated assembly measurement and test equipment. It makes products that are used around the world in such fields as fiber-optic communications health care life sciences military/aerospace scientific research and semiconductor manufacturing. Industrial and scientific components include lenses and other devices for vibration and motion control. Newport also offers automated systems used to make fiber-optic components and photonics. More than 60% of sales come from outside the US. In 2016 Newport was acquired by MKS Instruments.

Change in Company Type

With the acquisition Newport became a part of MKS. The companies expect $1.4 billion combined annual revenue. The $905 million price covered Newport's shares and about $93 million debt. The deal brings together companies with products in adjacent markets. They plan to cross-sell to each others' markets as well as to develop offerings for new customers.

Geographic Reach

Newport operates manufacturing plants stateside and abroad. US plants are located in California Connecticut Massachusetts Montana New York and Utah. Internationally its plants are located in developed and emerging markets in Austria China France Germany Israel and Romania.

The US is its largest single market accounting for about 38% of sales. Europe and Asia each are responsible for about a quarter of sales.

Sales and Marketing

Newport uses a direct sales force as well as an international network of independent distributors and sales representatives. It also uses e-commerce. Customers include OEMs and capital equipment makers.

Financial Performance

Sales for 2015 (ended January 2016) dropped 4% to $603 million from 2014. Photonics its biggest revenue generated managed a 1.5% revenue increase but Lasers and Optics both had less revenue in 2015. In terms of markets both microelectronics and life and health sciences sales were lower in 2015 while scientific research sales rose.

Newport's profit dropped 11% to $31 million in 2015 from 2014. While administrative and R&D costs were lower in 2015 the company recognized losses in selling a facility and software applications it no longer uses. The cost of eliminating some debt also reduced its profit.

Cash flow generated from operations was $52 million in 2015 down from $58 million in 2014.

Strategy

Newport has made several acquisitions to help it shift from a provider of research instruments to one that manufactures both components and integrated systems for research and commercial applications. The company's brands now consist of ILX Lightwave New Focus Newport Ophir Optimet Oriel Instruments Richardson Gratings Spiricon and Spectra-Physics.

The company also divests businesses that are not considered part of its core operations. In late 2013 it announced plans to sell its Micro Robotics Systems advanced packaging business (MRSI) to a private investment group. MRSI makes turn-key die bonding and dispensing systems while Newport is focused on lasers optics and photonics technologies.

EXECUTIVES

President Ceo And Director, Robert J. Phillippy, $529,000 total compensation
Svp Cfo And Treasurer, Charles F. (Chuck) Cargile, $377,577 total compensation
Svp And General Manager Lasers Group, David J. Allen, $300,192 total compensation
Svp And General Manager Photonics Group, Dennis L. Werth, $310,192 total compensation
Vp Asia Pacific, Wilson W. Lin
Evp General Counsel Corporate Secretary, Andrew Powell
Information Technology Vice President, Bernard Molinie
Vice President Corporate Finance, Michael Blajwas
Vice President Of Photonics Marketing And Technology, Christopher Palmer
Chairman, Kenneth F. Potashner
Auditors: DELOITTE & TOUCHE LLP COSTA M

LOCATIONS

HQ: NEWPORT CORPORATION
1791 DEERE AVE, IRVINE, CA 926064814
Phone: 949 863-3144
Web: WWW.NEWPORT.COM

2016 Sales

	$ mil.	% of total
US	231	38
Asia	170	28
Europe	157	26
Other regions	44	8
Total	**602**	**100**

PRODUCTS/OPERATIONS

2016 Sales

	$ mil.	% of total
Photonics & precision technologies	249	41
Lasers	192	32
Optics	160	27
Total	**602**	**100**

COMPETITORS

Adept Technology	Manz
Agilent Technologies	Nikon
Allied Motion	Nordson
Technologies	Oclaro
Anritsu	Palomar Technologies
Carl Zeiss	Parker-Hannifin
Coherent Inc.	Renishaw
Corning	Rockwell Automation
Danaher	Roper Technologies
EXFO	Spectris
HORIBA	TRUMPF
II-VI	Thermo Fisher
IPG Photonics	Scientific
Jenoptik	Viavi Solutions
Kinetic Systems	Zygo

HISTORICAL FINANCIALS
Company Type: Private

Income Statement
FYE: January 3

	REVENUE ($ mil.)	NET INCOME ($ mil.)	NET PROFIT MARGIN	EMPLOYEES
01/15*	605	35	5.8%	2,480
12/13	560	15	2.8%	—
12/12	595	(89)	—	—
Annual Growth	**0.8%**	**—**	**—**	**—**

*Fiscal year change

2015 Year-End Financials

Return on assets: 5.2% Cash ($ mil.): 46
Return on equity: 5.8%
Current ratio: 1.40

NEWTON WELLESLEY HOSPITAL CORP

Newton-Wellesley Hospital provides the Greater Boston area with a full range of medical surgical and diagnostic services. The hospital which boasts more than 260beds offers a variety of programs including a full-service diagnostic imaging department a multiple sclerosis clinic cancer center joint reconstruction surgery physical and occupational therapy and inpatient psychiatric care. In addition the Partners Reproductive Medicine Center offers infertility treatment in collaboration with two other area hospitals. Part of the Partners HealthCare family Newton-Wellesley is a teaching hospital for Tufts University's School of Medicine and the Mas-

sachusetts College of Pharmacy and Health Sciences..

Operations

Newton-Wellesley Hospital is a member of Partners HealthCare System a not-for-profit organization that includes acute care hospitals Massachusetts General Hospital Brigham and Women's/Faulkner Hospitals The North Shore Medical Center and specialty hospitals McLean Hospital and Spaulding Rehabilitation Hospital as well as the community-based Partners Community Physicians Organization.

Newton-Wellesley's patients have access to various centers of excellence such as the Vernon Cancer Center Kaplan Center for Joint Reconstruction Surgery the Spine Center the Auerbach Breast Center and the Center for Weight Loss Surgery. Newton-Wellesley also provides the latest diagnostic technology such as a 64-slice CT scanner MRI PET scans sleep studies and interventional radiology services. The Children's Corner established in 1978 and located on the hospital campus is a not-for-profit childcare program that provides quality care for the children of employees at Newton-Wellesley Hospital as well as care to local families in the community.

Geographic Reach

Based in Newton Massachusetts Newton-Wellesley collaborates with Massachusetts General Hospital MassGeneral Hospital for Children and Brigham and Women's Hospital to provide area residents and visitors a full range of medical surgical and specialty programs and services. It has more than 1000 affiliated physicians.

Strategy

Newton-Wellesley Hospital is focused on expanding its services and creating new programs to meet the needs of the community and its patients. In 2018 the hospital embarked on a new initiative — the Newton-Wellesley Collaborative for Healthy Families and Communities designed to address unmet medical and wellness needs in the area. The program will include educational and preventative interventions to improve the health of its community. The hospital's activities in this area have included providing Naloxone to emergency responders feeding children lunch during the summer break and bringing adolescent mental health programming to area high schools. New programs to launch will cover such needs as postpartum depression and palliative care.

EXECUTIVES

Vp Outpatient Services, Ellen Moloney
Svp And Cfo, Jeffrey P. (Jeff) Dion
Svp Patient Care Services And Chief Nursing Officer, Karen Conley
Director Of Health Information, Nancy Lafianza
Senior Vice President Administration, Patrick Jordan
Medical Director, James Macon
Director Of Radiology, Teresa Cahill
Medical Director, James Vernon
Vice President Of Marketing Communications And Public Affairs, John Looney
Director Of Pharmacy And Clinical Services, Steven Clark
Treasurer, Michael Jellinek

LOCATIONS

HQ: NEWTON WELLESLEY HOSPITAL CORP
2014 WASHINGTON ST, NEWTON, MA 024621607
Phone: 617 243-6000
Web: WWW.NWH.ORG

PRODUCTS/OPERATIONS

Selected Departments & Services
Anesthesiology
Anticoagulation Management Services

Auerbach Breast Center
Cardiovascular Health Programs
Center for Minimally Invasive Gynecologic Surgery
Center for Weight Loss Surgery
Diabetes Management Program
Emergency Medicine
Family Medicine
Kaplan Center for Joint Reconstruction Surgery
Laboratory Services/Pathology: For Lab Outreach Clients
Laboratory Services/Pathology: For Patients
Medical Emergency Department: Maxwell Blum Emergency Pavilion
Medicine
Multiple Sclerosis Clinic
Nursing
Nutrition Counseling
Obstetrics and Gynecology
Orthopaedic Surgery Service
Outpatient Surgery Center
Pain Management Service
Partners Reproductive Medicine Center
Pediatrics
Primary Stroke Service
Psychiatry
Radiology
Rehabilitation Services
Sleep Center
Spine Center
Surgery
Surgical Discharge Instructions
Transitional Year - Internship Program
Vernon Cancer Center
Waltham Urgent Care Center
Women's Imaging Center

Selected Clinical Centers
Auerbach Breast Center
Center for Minimally Invasive Gynecologic Surgery
Center for Weight Loss Surgery
Diabetes Management Program
Kaplan Center for Joint Reconstruction Surgery
Multiple Sclerosis Clinic
Outpatient Surgery Center
Pain Management Service
Partners Reproductive Medicine Center
Primary Stroke Service
Sleep Center
Spine Center
Vernon Cancer Center
Waltham Urgent Care Center
Women's Imaging Center

COMPETITORS

Beth Israel Deaconess	Emerson Hospital
Medical Center	Hallmark Health
Boston Medical Center	McLean Hospital
Children's Hospital	St. Elizabeth's
Boston	Medical Center

HISTORICAL FINANCIALS
Company Type: Private

Income Statement
FYE: September 30

	REVENUE ($ mil.)	NET INCOME ($ mil.)	NET PROFIT MARGIN	EMPLOYEES
09/17	435	(1)	—	2,500
09/16	414	(5)	—	—
09/15	422	21	5.2%	—
09/14	405	12	3.0%	—
Annual Growth	**2.4%**	**—**	**—**	**—**

2017 Year-End Financials

Return on assets: 2.6% Cash ($ mil.): 29
Return on equity: (-0.2%)
Current ratio: 1.30

NEWYORK-PRESBYTERIAN/BROOKLYN METHODIST

New York Methodist Hospital is a not-for-profit acute-care teaching hospital serving Brooklyn residents. Established in 1881 as the Methodist Episcopal Hospital the facility has more than 650 licensed beds. It offers a full range of medical services including primary and emergency care as well as specialty services such as women's health cancer cardiovascular pediatric geriatric and behavioral health. The hospital also operates satellite clinics in surrounding areas. A member of New York-Presbyterian Healthcare System New York Methodist is a teaching hospital affiliated with Cornell University's Weill Medical College.

Operations

New York Methodist Hospital handles about 40000 inpatient admissions and 100000 emergency department visits each year as well as 24000 surgeries and 5000 births. It also processes about 200000 laboratory sample processes annually.

New York Methodist Hospital includes specialty institutes in about 10 fields including pulmonary medicine cancer care and vascular health. In addition to providing inpatient care the organization operates some 10 primary and specialty outpatient centers. It also runs a number of graduate medical programs including programs affiliated with professional training schools in the areas of radiography medical technology radiation therapy and paramedics.

Geographic Reach

New York Methodist Hospital's main campus is in the Park Slope neighborhood of Brooklyn. It has several outpatient centers in other parts of Brooklyn as well.

Strategy

To expand care for area residents New York Methodist is adding new specialist programs and equipment. For instance in 2012 the hospital added a robotic-assisted surgery program for bariatric procedures. It also opened a new wound care and hyperbaric oxygen therapy center for hard-to-heal wounds. In addition in 2013 the hospital moved its sleep disorder center into a new facility.

EXECUTIVES

Chb, James Perkins
Vchb, Sharon Greenberger
President, Richard Liebowitz
Doctor, Izabella R Mullokandov
Coordinator, Maria Rivera
Internal Medicine Practitioner, Adnan Raza
Internal Medicine Practitioner, Ahmad Hakimzada
Internal Medicine Practitioner, Ahmer Ishtiaq
Internal Medicine Practitioner, Ajoke Bamisile
Internal Medicine Practitioner, Ali Mahjoub
Internal Medicine Practitioner, Michael Megally
Auditors: ERNST & YOUNG LLP NEW YORK N

LOCATIONS

HQ: NEWYORK-PRESBYTERIAN/BROOKLYN METHODIST
506 6TH ST, BROOKLYN, NY 112153609
Phone: 718 780-3000
Web: WWW.NYP.ORG

COMPETITORS

Beth Israel Medical Center	Lutheran HealthCare
	Maimonides Medical

Bronx-Lebanon Hospital Center
Brookdale University Hospital
Catholic Healthcare System
Kingsbrook Jewish Medical Center
New York City Health and Hospitals
Northwell Health
SUNY Downstate
Winthrop-University Hospital

HISTORICAL FINANCIALS
Company Type: Private

Income Statement
FYE: December 31

	REVENUE ($ mil.)	NET INCOME ($ mil.)	NET PROFIT MARGIN	EMPLOYEES
12/17	1,018	139	13.7%	4,929
12/16	788	145	18.5%	—
12/15	732	88	12.1%	—
12/14	687	68	10.0%	—
Annual Growth	14.0%	26.7%	—	—

2017 Year-End Financials
Return on assets: 8.4%
Return on equity: 13.7%
Current ratio: 1.00
Cash ($ mil.): 137

NEWYORK-PRESBYTERIAN/QUEENS

The New York Hospital Medical Center of Queens aims to provide care that's fit for royalty. Better known as the New York Hospital Queens the acute care hospital has about 520 beds and provides both primary and tertiary care. Specialist services include cancer cardiovascular pediatric obstetric surgical and dental care. The medical center also operates about a dozen outpatient clinics and care centers that offer such services as family health kidney dialysis rehabilitation and dental care as well as home health care services. New York Hospital Queens is part of the NewYork-Presbyterian Healthcare System.

EXECUTIVES

Pres-Ceo, Stephen S Mills
Sr V Pres-Cfo, Kevin Ward
Exec Vice President, John E Sciortino
Exec Vice President, Stephen Rimar
Sr Vice President, Kevin J Ward
Sr Vice President, Michaelle Williams
Procurement Staff, Jed Golden
Engineer, Pierre ROC
Project Manager, Debby Schem
Engineering Manager, Jeffrey Jordan
Manager, Jennifer Clem-Haniff
Auditors: ERNST & YOUNG LLP NEW YORK N

LOCATIONS

HQ: NEWYORK-PRESBYTERIAN/QUEENS
5645 MAIN ST, FLUSHING, NY 113555045
Phone: 718 670-2000
Web: WWW.NYHQ.ORG

PRODUCTS/OPERATIONS

Selected Services and Centers
Ambulatory Patient Care Facilities
Anesthesiology
Cancer Center
Cardiothoracic Surgery
Center for Dental and Oral Medicine
Children's Health (Pediatrics)
Emergency Medicine
Heart and Vascular Center

Neuroscience Institute
Obstetrics and Gynecology
Orthopaedics and Rehabilitation
Pathology and Laboratories
Primary Care and Specialties
Radiation Oncology
Radiology
Surgery
Women's Health

COMPETITORS

Catholic Healthcare System	NewYork-Presbyterian Hospital
Continuum Health Partners	Nyack Hospital
Jamaica Hospital Medical Center	Southside Hospital
	Winthrop-University Hospital

HISTORICAL FINANCIALS
Company Type: Private

Income Statement
FYE: December 31

	REVENUE ($ mil.)	NET INCOME ($ mil.)	NET PROFIT MARGIN	EMPLOYEES
12/17	846	5	0.6%	2,380
12/14	669	14	2.1%	—
12/05	457	10	2.3%	—
12/03	389	7	1.9%	—
Annual Growth	5.7%	(2.5%)	—	—

2017 Year-End Financials
Return on assets: 8.0%
Return on equity: 0.6%
Current ratio: 1.00
Cash ($ mil.): 16

NHK INTERNATIONAL CORPORATION

EXECUTIVES

Pres, Ko Masuda
Information Technology Manager, James Green
Project Manager, Jeff Schaad
Auditors: ERNST & YOUNG LLP LOUISVILLE

LOCATIONS

HQ: NHK INTERNATIONAL CORPORATION
46855 MAGELLAN DR STE 200, NOVI, MI 483772451
Phone: 248 926-0111
Web: WWW.NHKSEATING.COM

HISTORICAL FINANCIALS
Company Type: Private

Income Statement
FYE: March 31

	REVENUE ($ mil.)	NET INCOME ($ mil.)	NET PROFIT MARGIN	EMPLOYEES
03/16	894	12	1.4%	200
03/15	842	(13)	—	—
03/14	739	17	2.4%	—
03/13	688	14	2.1%	—
Annual Growth	9.1%	(4.4%)	—	—

2016 Year-End Financials
Return on assets: 9.0%
Return on equity: 1.4%
Current ratio: 0.60
Cash ($ mil.): 3

NIELSEN HOLDINGS PLC

EXECUTIVES

Ceo, Mitch Barns

LOCATIONS

HQ: NIELSEN HOLDINGS PLC
85 BROAD ST, NEW YORK, NY 100042434
Phone: 646 654-5000

HISTORICAL FINANCIALS

Company Type: Private

Income Statement | | | | FYE: December 31

	REVENUE ($ mil.)	NET INCOME ($ mil.)	NET PROFIT MARGIN	EMPLOYEES
12/15	6,172	575	9.3%	43,061
12/14	6,288	381	6.1%	—
12/13	5,703	736	12.9%	—
12/12	5,612	273	4.9%	—
Annual Growth	3.2%	28.2%	—	—

2015 Year-End Financials

Return on assets: 16.4%
Return on equity: 9.3%
Current ratio: 0.90
Cash ($ mil.): 357

NIMBLE STORAGE, INC.

In a mashup of Jack be nimble and Jumpin' Jack Flash Nimble Storage offers data storage systems that are a hybrid between a hard disk drive and a flash memory device. Its CS200 Series is designed for midsize IT organizations while its CS400 Series is geared for larger-scale deployments. The company even offers data analytics through its InfoSight service. Nimble Storage counts more than 2330 customers including cloud-based service providers government agencies and financial services health care manufacturing and technology companies. Nimble was bought by Hewlett Packard Enterprise for about $1.1 billion in April 2017.

Change in Company Type

With the acquisition by Hewlett Packard Enterprise Nimble's products and services will be supported by the new owner's sales and marketing operation as it tries to gain traction in the hybrid storage market. Further Nimble's InfoSight Predictive Analytics platform will be integrated into other HPE storage products. The Nimble operations were integrated into an HPE subsidiary and operate as a wholly owned subsidiary. The deal was completed in 2017.

Operations

Rather than make its own hardware Nimble Storage contracts with Flextronics to do the manufacturing.

Geographic Reach

Based in Silicon Valley the company's second US office is located in another tech hotspot - Research Triangle Park in Durham North Carolina. Though the company gets about 80% sales from the US its sales outside the US are growing. Nimble Storage has sales offices in Australia Canada Germany Singapore the UK and about 15 other countries. It has customers in about 50 countries.

Sales and Marketing

Nimble Storage primarily relies on distributors such as CDW Corporation to sell its products. Overall it works with about 1000 distributors. Customers include Ask.com Berkeley Research Group BlueTie Boulevard Brewing and Brightsource. The company doubled its budget for advertising to $3 million in 205.

Financial Performance

The company has been nimble in its revenue growth rapidly moving to new highs since 2010. The same can be said for its losses which also have grown year after year. In 2015 Nimble Storage's revenue rose 81% to $227 million from $125 million in 2014. It posted high double-digit and triple digit growth rates in products and service and across its geographies. The only exception was a geographic segment listed as other. Revenue there dropped 90%.

Seeking to gain customers and market share Nimble Storage increased spending on sales and marketing and research and development — costs that include salaries for more employees and stock-based compensation. As a result the company recorded a $98 million net loss in 2015 compared to a $43 million loss in 2014.

Nimble Storage has cash flow from operations of $5 million n 2015 recovering from an outflow of $6.7 million in 2014.

Strategy

The company's products are compatible with various servers software operating systems and hypervisors including those from Cisco Citrix CommVault Microsoft and VMware. It is working to expand product operability with additional alliance partners.

A focus on international sales is paying off with strong gains in the Asia Pacific region and in Europe. A distribution agreements with Ingram Micro helped boost sales in Europe and an agreement with Toshiba propelled sales in Japan.

EXECUTIVES

Cfo, Anup V. Singh, $300,000 total compensation
Ceo, Suresh Vasudevan, $375,000 total compensation
Cto, Umesh Maheshwari, $280,000 total compensation
Vp Engineering, Chetan Rai
Vp Operations, Stacey Cast
Vice President Sales East, Mike Wallerstedt
Auditors: ERNST & YOUNG LLP SAN JOSE C

LOCATIONS

HQ: NIMBLE STORAGE, INC.
211 RIVER OAKS PKWY, SAN JOSE, CA 951341913
Phone: 408 432-9600
Web: WWW.HPE.COM/US/EN/STORAGE/NIMBLE.HTML

2015 Sales

	% of total
US	73
Europe Middle East & Africa	12
Asia/Pacific	6
Total	**100**

PRODUCTS/OPERATIONS

2015 Sales

	% of total
Products	87
Support & service	13
Total	**100**

COMPETITORS

Dell	Oracle
EMC	SanDisk
Fusion-io	Seagate Technology
HP	Violin Memory
Hitachi Data Systems	Western Digital
NetApp	Xyratex

HISTORICAL FINANCIALS

Company Type: Private

Income Statement | | | | FYE: January 31

	REVENUE ($ mil.)	NET INCOME ($ mil.)	NET PROFIT MARGIN	EMPLOYEES
01/17	402	(158)	—	1,300
01/16	322	(120)	—	
01/15	227	(98)	—	
01/14	125	(43)	—	
Annual Growth	47.4%	—	—	—

2017 Year-End Financials

Return on assets: 8.2%
Return on equity: (-39.3%)
Current ratio: 1.70
Cash ($ mil.): 184

NJMHMC LLC

LOCATIONS

HQ: NJMHMC LLC
55 MEADOWLANDS PKWY, SECAUCUS, NJ 070942977
Phone: 201 392-3100
Web: WWW.MEADOWLANDSHOSPITAL.ORG

HISTORICAL FINANCIALS

Company Type: Private

Income Statement | | | | FYE: December 31

	REVENUE ($ mil.)	NET INCOME ($ mil.)	NET PROFIT MARGIN	EMPLOYEES
12/15	498	2	0.5%	650
12/14	468	2	0.5%	
Annual Growth	6.6%	(3.1%)	—	—

2015 Year-End Financials

Return on assets: 2.8%
Return on equity: 0.5%
Current ratio: 1.50
Cash ($ mil.): —

NOBLE HOLDING (U.S.) CORPORATION

EXECUTIVES

Prin, David W Williams
Corp Para Legal, Paul Stanford
Vice-President, John T Rynd
Vice-President, Ross W Gallup
Controller, Thomas F O'Rourke
Controller, Alan Middleton
Vice-President, Mike Lowther
Warehouse Manager, Pius Ajalla
Auditors: PRICEWATERHOUSECOOPERS LLP H

LOCATIONS

HQ: NOBLE HOLDING (U.S.) CORPORATION
3135 S DAIRY ASHFORD, SUGAR LAND, TX 77478
Phone: 281 276-6100
Web: WWW.NOBLECORP.COM

HISTORICAL FINANCIALS
Company Type: Private

Income Statement
FYE: December 31

	REVENUE ($ mil.)	NET INCOME ($ mil.)	NET PROFIT MARGIN	EMPLOYEES
12/15	3,352	607	18.1%	3,744
12/14	3,232	83	2.6%	—
12/13	4,234	935	22.1%	—
Annual Growth	(11.0%)	(19.4%)	—	—

2015 Year-End Financials
Return on assets: 6.6%
Return on equity: 18.1%
Current ratio: 1.20
Cash ($ mil.): 511

NOBLIS, INC.

Noblis' noble pursuit is through its offering of science-related strategic and technology consulting services. The not-for-profit company which pledges to serve the public interest helps various government entities and other clients evaluate technology options and vendors as well as solve complex technical problems. Noblis provides strategic planning decision analysis and acquisition support services. The company addresses problems in areas such as environment and energy intelligence health care homeland security public safety enterprise engineering and transportation. Noblis has worked with such clients as the US Air Force Army Navy and Departments of Commerce and Defense.

Geographic Reach
Noblis has more than half a dozen offices located in Maryland Texas Virginia West Virginia and Washington DC.

Sales and Marketing
The company's product suite includes RASMAS a Web-based service allowing health care providers and suppliers to respond more efficiently to product recalls and AcquTrak an acquisitions support tool aimed at helping government entities reduce costs and schedule times.

Company Background
The company was formed in 1996 as Mitretek Systems; it changed its name to Noblis in 2007.

EXECUTIVES

President And Ceo, Amr A. ElSawy
Svp Chief Financial And Administrative Officer And Treasurer, Mark A. Simione
Corporate Vp And Cto, H. Gilbert Miller
Vp And Cio, Gail Hogan
President Noblis Nsp, Ellen McCarthy
Business Development Vice President, Diana Fossett
Vice President Business Administration, Rick Dubois
Vice President, Jean Sphr
Chairman, Marion C. Blakey
Vice Chairman, Michael Chertoff
Assistant Treasurer, Pam Ware
Auditors: GRANT THORNTON LLP ARLINGTON

LOCATIONS

HQ: NOBLIS, INC.
2002 EDMUND HALLEY DR, RESTON, VA 201913436
Phone: 703 610-2000
Web: WWW.NOBLIS.ORG

COMPETITORS

Accenture	HP Enterprise Services
Bain & Company	IBM
Boston Consulting	McKinsey & Company
Deloitte Consulting	

HISTORICAL FINANCIALS
Company Type: Private

Income Statement
FYE: September 29

	REVENUE ($ mil.)	NET INCOME ($ mil.)	NET PROFIT MARGIN	EMPLOYEES
09/17	319	13	4.1%	1,000
09/16*	320	19	5.9%	—
10/15	314	12	3.8%	—
10/14	252	16	6.7%	—
Annual Growth	8.2%	(7.9%)	—	—

*Fiscal year change

2017 Year-End Financials
Return on assets: 5.0%
Return on equity: 4.1%
Current ratio: 0.80
Cash ($ mil.): —

NORDIC GROUP OF COMPANIES LTD.

EXECUTIVES

Chm, William R Sauey
SEC, Eric W Sauey
Treas, Todd L Sauey
Cfo, Bill Hans
Executive Offr, Alison Martin
Manager, Mike Maier
Auditors: BDO USA LLP MADISON WISCONS

LOCATIONS

HQ: NORDIC GROUP OF COMPANIES LTD.
715 LYNN AVE STE 100, BARABOO, WI 539132744
Phone: 608 356-7303
Web: WWW.FLAMBEAUPREMIUMS.COM

HISTORICAL FINANCIALS
Company Type: Private

Income Statement
FYE: June 24

	REVENUE ($ mil.)	NET INCOME ($ mil.)	NET PROFIT MARGIN	EMPLOYEES
06/17	320	11	3.6%	2,100
06/16	333	10	3.1%	—
06/15	342	14	4.3%	—
06/01	212	(7)	—	—
Annual Growth	2.6%	—	—	—

2017 Year-End Financials
Return on assets: 5.3%
Return on equity: 3.6%
Current ratio: 1.40
Cash ($ mil.): 4

NORMAN REGIONAL HOSPITAL AUTHORITY

NORM! Perhaps that's how locals refer to Norman Regional Health System when they are headed there for health care. The system operates in and around Norman Oklahoma through the full service 325-bed Norman Regional Hospital and affiliated health centers including Moore Medical Center Services and the HealthPlex a 136-bed specialty hospital focused on cardiology orthopedic and spine and women's and children's services. Moore Medical Center's services include include acute care and surgery diagnostic and outpatient health care services. The organization's programs include behavioral medicine rehabilitation a women's center and a sleep disorder clinic. The hospital which employs more than 350 physicians was established in 1946.

Geographic Reach
Norman Regional Health System serves Norman Oklahoma and its surrounding communities.

Financial Performance
In 2014 the system's revenues totaled $333 million while net income totaled $25 million. Cash flow from operations was $31 million.

Strategy
Norman Regional Health System broke ground on a new medical facility in Monroe Oklahoma in 2014. The $29 million complex is expected to open in 2016.

EXECUTIVES

Vice President Clinical Operations Cno, Nancy Brown
Auditors: BKD LLP TULSA OKLAHOMA

LOCATIONS

HQ: NORMAN REGIONAL HOSPITAL AUTHORITY
901 N PORTER AVE, NORMAN, OK 730716482
Phone: 405 307-1000
Web: WWW.NORMANREGIONAL.COM

Selected Locations (Oklahoma)
Brookhaven Medical Women's Center (Norman)
Doctors Park (Norman)
Family Medicine (Regional)
Findlay Medical Center (Norman)
HealthPlex (Norman)
Imaging Services (Regional)
Immediate Care of Oklahoma (Regional)
Moore Medical Center (Moore)
Norman Regional Hospital (Norman)
WaterView Medical Center (Oklahoma City)

PRODUCTS/OPERATIONS

Selected Services
Breast Care Center
Cancer Services
Cardiology Services
Diabetes Center
Emergency Services
Family Birth Center
Orthopedic Services
Stroke Center
Surgical Services
Weight Loss Surgery

COMPETITORS

Deaconess Health Care	Via Christi Health System
INTEGRIS Baptist Medical Center	

HISTORICAL FINANCIALS
Company Type: Private

Income Statement
FYE: June 30

	REVENUE ($ mil.)	NET INCOME ($ mil.)	NET PROFIT MARGIN	EMPLOYEES
06/17	382	18	4.9%	2,900
06/14	347	24	7.1%	—
06/12	324	8	2.5%	—
06/11	921	0	0.0%	—
Annual Growth	(13.6%)	476.1%	—	—

2017 Year-End Financials
Return on assets: 3.6%
Return on equity: 4.9%
Current ratio: 4.30
Cash ($ mil.): 124

NORTH ADVOCATE SIDE HEALTH NETWORK

EXECUTIVES

Chief Executive, Kenneth J Rojek
Supervisor, Alfonso Garza
Operations Manager, Paul Mangura
Endocrinologist, Renee Schickler
Director, Virginia Morse

LOCATIONS

HQ: NORTH ADVOCATE SIDE HEALTH NETWORK
836 W WELLINGTON AVE, CHICAGO, IL 606575147
Phone: 773 296-5699

HISTORICAL FINANCIALS
Company Type: Private

Income Statement — FYE: December 31

	REVENUE ($ mil.)	NET INCOME ($ mil.)	NET PROFIT MARGIN	EMPLOYEES
12/15	487	97	19.9%	1,600
12/08	317	29	9.3%	—
Annual Growth	6.3%	18.6%	—	—

2015 Year-End Financials

Return on assets: 10.9%
Return on equity: 19.9%
Current ratio: —
Cash ($ mil.): 30

NORTH AMERICAN LIGHTING, INC.

North American Lighting offers travelers a beacon of safety through the fog. The company is an independent manufacturer of vehicle lighting products in North America. Operating through four assembly plants and one technology center the company produces a line-up of headlamps signal lamps and fog lamps. Its forward-lighting products include mercury-free high intensity discharge (HID) headlamps and the Adaptive Front Lighting System (AFS). Among its signal lamps are rear-combo and license plate lamps. Its products are tailored to the designs of large auto makers and local Japanese automakers. Founded in 1983 North American Lighting is a subsidiary of Japan-based KOITO MANUFACTURING.

Geographic Reach

North American Lighting is stationed in Paris Illinois and has four manufacturing plants in Illinois and one in Alabama. Its technology research center resides in Michigan while a tool plan is located in Indiana.

Sales and Marketing

North American Lighting sells its products primarily to vehicle manufacturers in North America. It provides headlights and taillights to Toyota Nissan General Motors and Honda.

Financial Performance

The company generated 16% of its parent's revenue total in 2014. Revenues for the North American segment also skyrocketed by almost 20% in 2014 due to higher demand in the auto sector which resulted in increased automobile production.

Strategy

Like most players in the manufacturing sector North American Lighting's strategy for growth involves the expansion of its manufacturing capacity. It also attracts additional clients through new product launches. In 2013 the company invested $50 million to expand its plant in Edgar County Illinois by building a 200000 sq. ft. addition and purchasing new equipment for added production lines.

In 2014 the company also began production at its North American Lighting Mexico S.A. de C.V. (Mexican manufacturing plant) which was established in 2012 to expand automobile production throughout Mexico.

EXECUTIVES

Vice President Alabama Operations, Kem Cooley
Vice President, Kirk Gadberry

LOCATIONS

HQ: NORTH AMERICAN LIGHTING, INC.
2275 S MAIN ST, PARIS, IL 619442963
Phone: 217 465-6600
Web: WWW.NAL.COM

COMPETITORS

Delphi Automotive Systems	Robert Bosch
Hella	Valeo
	Visteon

HISTORICAL FINANCIALS
Company Type: Private

Income Statement — FYE: December 31

	REVENUE ($ mil.)	NET INCOME ($ mil.)	NET PROFIT MARGIN	EMPLOYEES
12/17	1,466	111	7.6%	2,200
12/11	297	13	4.4%	—
12/10	297	13	4.4%	—
Annual Growth	25.6%	35.6%		

2017 Year-End Financials

Return on assets: 4.8%
Return on equity: 7.6%
Current ratio: 1.30
Cash ($ mil.): 77

NORTH BROWARD HOSPITAL DISTRICT

North Broward Hospital District which operates as Broward Health takes care of shark bites and more. The taxpayer-supported not-for-profit health system serves the coastal city of Fort Lauderdale and the northern two-thirds of Broward County Florida with four acute care hospitals and a host of community-based centers. Flagship hospital Broward General Medical Center has more than 700 beds and features the Chris Evert Children's Hospital; all of the hospitals together have more than 1500 beds. Broward Health boasts about 30 additional facilities including family health and surgery centers and home health and hospice programs.

Operations

The Broward Health system also includes teaching hospital Broward Health Medical Center facilities such as Broward Health North and Broward Health Imperial Point Broward Health Community Services and Broward Health Physician Group. The company also operates urgent care clinics.

With more than 1200 physicians Broward Health typically sees some 62500 admissions 283000 emergency department visits 267000 outpatient visits and 17000 outpatient clinic visits each year. It also delivers some 6000 babies annually.

Broward Health is controlled by a seven-member board of commissioners appointed by Florida's governor. As a safety-net health provider in its service territory the system's hospitals receive property tax-based funding for the charity care they provide. The rest of Broward County is served by a second public hospital system South Broward Hospital District. (The county's dual structure goes back to the 1950s.)

Geographic Reach

The company has more than 50 locations across Broward County.

Sales and Marketing

Managed care accounts for more than half of Broward Health's net patient revenues; Medicare and Medicaid combined make up more than 20%.

Financial Performance

In fiscal 2014 revenue grew 2% to $971 million due to growth in net patient service revenues. Net income rose 20% that year on higher investment gains and a decline in interest expenses. The system reported an operating cash outflow to $80 million (versus $27 million in 2013) as less cash was generated from third-party payers and patients.

Strategy

Broward Health looks to improve services by adding new or renovating existing facilities in its system. For example in 2014 it opened a new Adult Cancer Infusion Center at Broward Health Medical Center (featuring an outdoor healing garden); it also opened AJ Acker Virtual Hospital with interactive patient simulators at Broward Health North for training purposes. It broke ground on a $70 million renovation of Broward Health North that will add more operating rooms and expand the emergency department. In 2015 it was given approval to expand Broward Health Coral Springs.

EXECUTIVES

Medical Director And Chief Pathologist, William D Williams
Vice President, Lori Perlman
Senior Vice President Business Development, Joseph Rogers
Director Of Pharmacy, Natalie Trach
Senior Vice President And Chief Medical Officer, Dan Westphal
Board Member, Ma James-Francis
Vice Chair, Christopher Ure

LOCATIONS

HQ: NORTH BROWARD HOSPITAL DISTRICT
1800 NW 49TH ST, FORT LAUDERDALE, FL 333093092
Phone: 954 473-7010
Web: WWW.BROWARDHEALTH.ORG

PRODUCTS/OPERATIONS

2014 Sales

	$ mil.	% of total
Patient care		
Broward Health Medical Center	432	44
Broward Health North	207	21
Broward Health Imperial Point	100	10
Broward Health Coral Springs	140	15
Other	96	10
Eliminations	(5.9)	7
Total	971	100

Selected Services

Bariatric Surgery
Barrett's Esophagus
Behavioral Health
Broward Health Complete
Cancer Services
Cardiac Services

Children's Diagnostic & Treatment Center
Clinical Trials
Colorectal Services
Concussion Care
Diabetes
Digestive Health
Dysphagia
Emergency Services
Endoscopic Sinus Surgery
Home Health & Hospice Services
International Services
Liver Transplant
Maternity Place
Men's Health
Neurology
Orthopedic Services
Ostomy
Outpatient Services
Pediatric Services
Pharmacy
Primary Care
Senior Services
Sickle Cell Day Unit
Single Incision Laparoscopic Surgery (SILS)

Selected Facilities
Hospitals
  Broward General Medical Center (Fort Lauderdale)
  Coral Springs Medical Center (Coral Springs)
  Imperial Point Medical Center (Fort Lauderdale)
  North Broward Medical Center (Deerfield Beach)
Other Facilities
  Chris Evert Children's Hospital (Fort Lauderdale)
  Broward Health Physician Group (Fort Lauderdale)
  Broward Health Weston (Weston)
  Gold Coast Home Health & Hospice Services (Fort Lauderdale)
  Seventh Avenue Family Health Center (Fort Lauderdale)

COMPETITORS

Baptist Health South Florida	Jupiter Medical Center
Boca Raton Regional Hospital	Larkin Community Hospital
Continucare	Mount Sinai Medical Center of Florida
HCA	South Broward Hospital District
Holy Cross Hospital Fort Lauderdale	University of Miami Hospital
Jackson Health System	

HISTORICAL FINANCIALS
Company Type: Private

Income Statement   FYE: June 30

	REVENUE ($ mil.)	NET INCOME ($ mil.)	NET PROFIT MARGIN	EMPLOYEES
06/18	1,035	120	11.6%	7,000
06/17	1,025	33	3.3%	—
06/16	1,014	(12)	—	—
06/08	1,335	67	5.0%	—
Annual Growth	(2.5%)	6.0%	—	—

2018 Year-End Financials
Return on assets: 11.8%   Cash ($ mil.): 121
Return on equity: 11.6%
Current ratio: 0.50

NORTH CAROLINA BAPTIST HOSPITAL

EXECUTIVES

Ceo, John D McConnell
CIO, Eric Tomlinson
Director Shareholder, Jana Newsome

Programmer Analyst, Jane Henderson
Physician Assistant, Jane McDaniel
Administrative Assistant, Kathy Clark
Administrative Assistant, Margie Troxler
Professor, Nancy Avis
Doctor, Pam Dean
Doctor, Pirouz Daeihagh
Pediatrician, Steven Block

LOCATIONS

HQ: NORTH CAROLINA BAPTIST HOSPITAL
  MEDICAL CENTER BLVD, WINSTON SALEM, NC
  271570001
Phone: 336 716-2011
Web: WWW.WFUBMC.EDU

HISTORICAL FINANCIALS
Company Type: Private

Income Statement   FYE: June 30

	REVENUE ($ mil.)	NET INCOME ($ mil.)	NET PROFIT MARGIN	EMPLOYEES
06/18	1,633	60	3.7%	12,563
06/11	1,084	195	18.1%	—
Annual Growth	6.0%	(15.4%)	—	—

2018 Year-End Financials
Return on assets: 6.0%   Cash ($ mil.): 43
Return on equity: 3.7%
Current ratio: 0.90

NORTH CAROLINA EASTERN MUNICIPAL POWER AGENCY

EXECUTIVES

Ceo, Jesse C Tilton III
Cfo, Al Conyers
Manager, Rebecca Agner
Manager, Andrew Fusco
Manager, Barbera Scheib
Coordinator, Sue Rubish
General and Operations Supervi, Kathy Moyer
Energy Management Eng, Marcus Freeman
Programmer Analyst, Nikki Taylor
Manager Marketing, Robert Tugwell
Engineer, Stuart Britt
Auditors: CHERRY BEKAERT LLP RALEIGH

LOCATIONS

HQ: NORTH CAROLINA EASTERN MUNICIPAL POWER AGENCY
  1427 MEADOW WOOD BLVD, RALEIGH, NC 276041532
Phone: 919 760-6000
Web: WWW.ELECTRICITIES.ORG

HISTORICAL FINANCIALS
Company Type: Private

Income Statement   FYE: December 31

	REVENUE ($ mil.)	NET INCOME ($ mil.)	NET PROFIT MARGIN	EMPLOYEES
12/17	531	(13)	—	100
12/16	552	52	9.4%	—
12/12	696	21	3.1%	—
12/10	729	10	1.5%	—
Annual Growth	(4.4%)	—	—	—

NORTH CAROLINA ELECTRIC MEMBERSHIP CORPORATION

EXECUTIVES

Vice President Research And Member Insights, Tom Laing
Vice President Manager Director, Joy Hart
Auditors: DELOITTE TAX LLP ATLANTA GA

LOCATIONS

HQ: NORTH CAROLINA ELECTRIC MEMBERSHIP CORPORATION
  3400 SUMNER BLVD, RALEIGH, NC 276162950
Phone: 919 872-0800
Web: WWW.NCEMCS.COM

PRODUCTS/OPERATIONS

Subsidiaries
North Carolina Association of Electric Cooperatives (NCAEC training programs)
The Tarheel Electric Membership Association Inc. (TEMA purchasing and materials supply)
North Carolina Cooperatives
Albemarle Electric Membership Corporation
Blue Ridge Electric Membership Corporation
Brunswick Electric Membership Corporation
Cape Hatteras Electric Cooperative
Carteret-Craven Electric Cooperative
Central Electric Membership Corporation
Edgecombe-Martin County Electric Membership Corporation
EnergyUnited
Four County Electric Membership Corporation
French Broad Electric Membership Corporation
Halifax Electric Membership Corporation
Haywood Electric Membership Corporation
Jones-Onslow Electric Membership Corporation
Lumbee River Electric Membership Corporation
Pee Dee Electric Membership Corporation
Piedmont Electric Membership Corporation
Pitt & Greene Electric Membership Corporation
Randolph Electric Membership Corporation
Roanoke Electric Cooperative
Rutherford Electric Membership Corporation
South River Electric Membership Corporation
Surry-Yadkin Electric Membership Corporation
Tideland Electric Membership Corporation
Tri-County Electric Membership Corporation
Union Power Cooperative
Wake Electric Membership Corporation

COMPETITORS

AEP	Progress Energy
Dominion Energy	SCANA
Duke Energy	Santee Cooper
MEAG Power	TVA

HISTORICAL FINANCIALS
Company Type: Private

Income Statement   FYE: December 31

	REVENUE ($ mil.)	NET INCOME ($ mil.)	NET PROFIT MARGIN	EMPLOYEES
12/17	1,017	23	2.3%	150
12/16	1,022	25	2.5%	—
12/08	1,006	6	0.6%	—
12/07	942	2	0.3%	—
Annual Growth	0.8%	22.7%	—	—

2017 Year-End Financials
Return on assets: 8.2%   Cash ($ mil.): 372
Return on equity: 2.3%
Current ratio: 2.20

NORTH DAKOTA UNIVERSITY SYSTEM

Auditors: ROBERT R PETERSON STATE AUDI

LOCATIONS

HQ: NORTH DAKOTA UNIVERSITY SYSTEM
  2000 44TH ST S STE 301, FARGO, ND 581037434
Phone: 701 231-6326
Web: WWW.NDUS.EDU

HISTORICAL FINANCIALS
Company Type: Private

Income Statement				FYE: June 30
	REVENUE ($ mil.)	NET INCOME ($ mil.)	NET PROFIT MARGIN	EMPLOYEES
06/17	702	66	9.5%	13
06/16	695	116	16.8%	—
06/15	676	163	24.1%	—
Annual Growth	1.9%	(36.2%)	—	—

2017 Year-End Financials
Return on assets: 4.8%   Cash ($ mil.): 185
Return on equity: 9.5%
Current ratio: 1.60

NORTH DAKOTA UNIVERSITY SYSTEM FOUNDATION

EXECUTIVES

Princ, Hamid Augustine Shirvani
Chancellor, William Goetz
Presi, Kirsten Diederich
V Pres, Terry Hjelmstad
Gis Coordinator, Subhro Mitra
Information Profession, Carol Tschakert
Scientist, Erin Koval
Scientist, Thomas Glass
Assistant Professor, Annie X Tangpong
Coordinator, David Dodds
Assistant Professor, David Newman
Auditors: ROBERT R PETERSON FARGO NORT

LOCATIONS

HQ: NORTH DAKOTA UNIVERSITY SYSTEM
  FOUNDATION
  600 E BOULEVARD AVE # 215, BISMARCK, ND
  585050601
Phone: 701 328-2960
Web: WWW.NDCHOOSE.COM

HISTORICAL FINANCIALS
Company Type: Private

Income Statement				FYE: June 30
	REVENUE ($ mil.)	NET INCOME ($ mil.)	NET PROFIT MARGIN	EMPLOYEES
06/17	1,252	66	5.3%	252
06/16	695	116	16.8%	—
06/15	676	163	24.1%	—
06/13	653	78	12.0%	—
Annual Growth	17.6%	(4.1%)	—	—

2017 Year-End Financials
Return on assets: 2.7%   Cash ($ mil.): 185
Return on equity: 5.3%
Current ratio: 1.60

NORTH EAST INDEPENDENT SCHOOL DISTRICT

EXECUTIVES

Supt, Brian G Gottardy
Board Pres, Beth Plummer
Board V Pres, Susan Galindo
Board SEC, Sandy Hughey
Occupational Specia, Gayla Aguilar
Corrections Officer, Andres De Leon
Occupational Specia, Katherine Farrimond
Executive of Information Techn, Betsy Williams
Executive of Information Techn, Dawn Gembler
Director of Operations, Juan De Losntos
Accounting Staff, Lori Garrison
Auditors: ABIP PC SAN ANTONIO TEXAS

LOCATIONS

HQ: NORTH EAST INDEPENDENT SCHOOL DISTRICT
  8961 TESORO DR, SAN ANTONIO, TX 782176209
Phone: 210 407-0359
Web: WWW.NEISD.NET

HISTORICAL FINANCIALS
Company Type: Private

Income Statement				FYE: June 30
	REVENUE ($ mil.)	NET INCOME ($ mil.)	NET PROFIT MARGIN	EMPLOYEES
06/18	759	23	3.0%	10,000
06/17	747	(2)	—	—
06/16	737	(53)	—	—
06/15	712	(143)	—	—
Annual Growth	2.1%	—	—	—

2018 Year-End Financials
Return on assets: 3.4%   Cash ($ mil.): 251
Return on equity: 3.0%
Current ratio: —

NORTH FLORIDA REGIONAL MEDICAL CENTER, INC.

North Florida Regional Medical Center (NFRMC) part of the HCA health services network is a 445-bed acute care community hospital serving Gainesville Florida and more than a dozen surrounding counties. The hospital boasts specialty centers for diabetes senior care obesity surgery and sleep disorders. It also provides emergency services cancer care heart care imaging services orthopedics neurological care physical therapy and wound therapy. NFRMC was founded in 1972 by HCA and a group of physicians. As part of HCA's North Florida Regional Healthcare network it has affiliates including physician practices and express care clinics.

Operations
The hospital has more than 480 physicians on staff practicing in 40 different specialties. It handles some 25000 inpatient admissions annually as well as 70000 emergency room visits and about 3000 births. In total NFRMC treats more than 190000 patients each year including Medicaid and Medicare patients and charity care (uninsured) patients.

Strategy
North Florida Regional Medical Center (NFRMC) completed a $62-million expansion project in 2013 that added a 100000 sq. ft. four-story patient tower with more than 90 beds. While the focus of the expansion is on cardiovascular care it also includes a Level II neonatal intensive care unit and more beds for neurosurgery care. At the conclusion of the expansion project NFRMC grew from a 350-bed facility to a 445-bed full-service medical and surgical acute care referral center.

The new patient tower was part of a multi-phase expansion program conducted over the past few years. Previously phases of expansion include the opening of a new cancer center in 2009 which added new radiation therapy systems. NFRMC also opened a new senior health care center to provide comprehensive geriatric heath care.

EXECUTIVES

Vice President Information Systems, Mathew Davis

LOCATIONS

HQ: NORTH FLORIDA REGIONAL MEDICAL CENTER,
  INC.
  6500 W NEWBERRY RD, GAINESVILLE, FL
  326054309
Phone: 352 333-4100
Web: WWW.NFRMC.COM

PRODUCTS/OPERATIONS

Selected Services
Cancer Center
Diabetes Center
Emergency Department
Endoscopy Center
Express Care
Heart Care
Imaging Services
Invision Imaging
Lung Screening Program
Neonatal Intensive Care Unit (NICU)
Neurosciences
Orthopedics
Pastoral Care Program
Physical Occupational and Speech Therapy
Robotic Surgery

Senior Health care Centers
Sleep Disorders Center
Surgical Pavilion
Weight Loss Procedures
Women's Center Services
Wound Therapy and Hyperbaric Services

COMPETITORS

Mayo Clinic Jacksonville	Putnam Community Medical Center
Munroe Regional Health System	St. Vincent's Health System
Orlando Health	UF&Shands

HISTORICAL FINANCIALS

Company Type: Private

Income Statement   FYE: February 28

	REVENUE ($ mil.)	NET INCOME ($ mil.)	NET PROFIT MARGIN	EMPLOYEES
02/17	443	110	24.9%	2,000
02/09*	331	61	18.7%	—
12/97	133	26	20.0%	—
Annual Growth	6.5%	7.8%	—	—

*Fiscal year change

2017 Year-End Financials

Return on assets: 2.7%   Cash ($ mil.): —
Return on equity: 24.9%
Current ratio: 1.80

NORTH KANSAS CITY HOSPITAL

EXECUTIVES

Ceo, Peggy Schmitt
Cfo, Jim McNey
Coo, Jody Abbott
Vice-President, Sarah Fields
Registered Nurse, Tamara Kettler
Infection Prevention, Becky Smith

LOCATIONS

HQ: NORTH KANSAS CITY HOSPITAL
2800 CLAY EDWARDS DR, NORTH KANSAS CITY, MO
641163220
Phone: 816 691-2000
Web: WWW.NKCH.ORG

HISTORICAL FINANCIALS

Company Type: Private

Income Statement   FYE: June 30

	REVENUE ($ mil.)	NET INCOME ($ mil.)	NET PROFIT MARGIN	EMPLOYEES
06/16	484	31	6.6%	6,200
06/15	462	35	7.6%	—
06/11	419	22	5.3%	—
06/09	370	36	9.9%	—
Annual Growth	3.9%	(2.0%)	—	—

2016 Year-End Financials

Return on assets: 3.1%   Cash ($ mil.): 11
Return on equity: 6.6%
Current ratio: 1.00

NORTH LA COUNTY REGIONAL CENTER INC

EXECUTIVES

Dir, George Stevens
Human Resources Director, Michele Marra
Human Resources Administrator, Felicia Nash
Board of Directors, K Jennifr
Executive Director, Thompson Kelly
Human Resources Director, Michel Marra
Chief Financial Officer, Kim Rolfes
Manager, Angela Rodriguez
Supervisor, Cristina Preuss
Administrative Assistant, June Maloy
Quality Assurance Director, Marianne Ross
Auditors: LAUTZE & LAUTZE SAN FRANCISCO

LOCATIONS

HQ: NORTH LA COUNTY REGIONAL CENTER INC
15400 SHERMAN WAY STE 170, VAN NUYS, CA
914064272
Phone: 818 778-1900
Web: WWW.NLACRC.ORG

HISTORICAL FINANCIALS

Company Type: Private

Income Statement   FYE: June 30

	REVENUE ($ mil.)	NET INCOME ($ mil.)	NET PROFIT MARGIN	EMPLOYEES
06/17	433	19	4.4%	350
06/16	375	1	0.4%	—
06/15	345	2	0.8%	—
06/14	318	(2)	—	—
Annual Growth	10.8%	—	—	—

2017 Year-End Financials

Return on assets: 9.5%   Cash ($ mil.): 33
Return on equity: 4.4%
Current ratio: 0.30

NORTH MEMORIAL HEALTH CARE

North Memorial Health Care fights illness in the Twin Cities. Established in 1939 as Victory Hospital the health care network is home to North Memorial Medical Center a 520-bed hospital that features a Level I trauma center and the Humphrey Cancer Center. The hospital also operates specialty centers for cardiovascular care orthopedics pediatrics and women's health as well as an emergency vehicle fleet of more than 125 ambulances and nearly 10 helicopters. The adjacent outpatient center provides oncology radiation and imaging services. North Memorial Health Care also has a network of primary and specialty care clinics in the Twin Cities region and it provides home health and hospice services.

Operations

As a regional trauma center North Memorial Medical Center must maintain a high level of technology resources and recruit skilled emergency room specialists. North Memorial's emergency fleet also adds to the facilities' capabilities as it is one of the largest hospital-based ambulance services in the country with eight helicopters and about 125 ground ambulances. Outpatient facilities include rehabilitation centers sleep diagnostic labs family practice offices imaging centers and mental health facilities.

The system's provider network includes more than 900 physicians including specialists and primary care providers.

Geographic Reach

North Memorial Health Care's primary facility (North Memorial Medical Center) is located in Robbinsdale Minnesota. In partnership with Fairview Health Services the company operates the 130-bed Maple Grove Hospital in nearby Maple Grove Minnesota. Its ambulance division serves the northwestern Twin Cities area as well other portions of Minnesota and Wisconsin.

Strategy

The health network is expanding its facilities to improve services for area residents. In 2015 it opened walk-in clinics in grocery stores located in the Minnesota cities of New Hope and Oakdale. The clinics offer primary health care services provided by North Memorial physician assistants and nurses.

North Memorial works to stay on top of the latest technological advances to enhance its care offerings. In 2015 North Memorial Medical Center became the first community hospital in Minnesota to use the da Vinci Xi robotic surgical system which provides more precision for minimally invasive procedures. The following year the system provided electronic tablets loaded with software designed to help caregivers calculate appropriate medication dosages for children. The tablets which are used by the company's ambulance EMTs and paramedics allow for first responders to adjust care while out in the field.

EXECUTIVES

Vp Emergency And Enterprise Operations, Mike Parrish
President North Memorial Medical Center, Gayle Mattson
Ceo Maple Grove Hospital, Andy Cochrane
Ceo, J. Kevin Croston
Vp Patient Care, Tracy Kirby
Chief Information Officer, Pat Taffe
Vp Operations, Jeff Wicklander
Chief Financial Officer, Todd Ostendorf

LOCATIONS

HQ: NORTH MEMORIAL HEALTH CARE
3300 OAKDALE AVE N, MINNEAPOLIS, MN
554222900
Phone: 763 520-5200
Web: WWW.NORTHMEMORIAL.COM

PRODUCTS/OPERATIONS

Selected Locations
Heart & Vascular Center - Maple Grove - Maple Grove Minnesota
Heart & Vascular Clinic - Buffalo - Buffalo Minnesota
Heart & Vascular Clinic - Monticello - Monticello Minnesota
Hope Chest Breast Center - Robbinsdale Minnesota
Humphrey Cancer Center - Robbinsdale Minnesota
Maple Grove Hospital - Maple Grove Minnesota
Maternal Fetal Medicine - Maple Grove - Maple Grove Minnesota
North Memorial Clinic Brooklyn Center - Brooklyn Center Minnesota
North Memorial Clinic Brooklyn Park - Brooklyn Park Minnesota
North Memorial Clinic Camden - Maple Grove - Maple Grove Minnesota
North Memorial Clinic Camden - Minneapolis - Minneapolis Minnesota
North Memorial Clinic Camden - Plymouth - Plymouth Minnesota
North Memorial Clinic Elk River - Elk River Minnesota
North Memorial Clinic Golden Valley - Golden Valley Minnesota

North Memorial Clinic Maple Grove - Maple Grove
  Minnesota
North Memorial Clinic Minnetonka - Minnetonka
  Minnesota
North Memorial Clinic Northeast - Minneapolis
  Minnesota
North Memorial Clinic Plymouth City Center -
  Plymouth Minnesota
North Memorial Clinic Silver Lake Clinic - St. Anthony -
  St. Anthony Minnesota
North Memorial Clinic Silver Lake Clinic - Blaine -
  Blaine Minnesota
North Memorial Medical Center - Robbinsdale Minnesota
North Memorial Urgent Care - Maple Grove - Maple
  Grove Minnesota
North Memorial Urgent Care - Roseville - Roseville
  Minnesota
Outpatient Imaging Center - Robbinsdale Minnesota
Outpatient Psychiatric Clinic - Robbinsdale Minnesota
Rehabilitation Services - Robbinsdale Minnesota
Rehabilitation Services - Maple Grove Minnesota
Rehabilitation Services - Elk River Minnesota
Residential Hospice - Brooklyn Center Minnesota
Sleep Health Center - Maple Grove Minnesota
Sleep Health Center - Robbinsdale Minnesota
Urgent Care - Blaine Minnesota

Selected Services

Acupuncture
Acute Concussion Clinic
Acute Inpatient Rehabilitation
Air Care
Ambulance Services
Anterior Hip Replacement
Balance Center
Breast Health
Breast Milk Depot
CACE Unit
Cancer Education & Support
Cancer Treatment
Cardiac Rehabilitation
Cardiology
Cardiology Clinic Services
Complex Heart Procedures and Interventional Services
Computed Tomography - CT
Dermatology
Diabetes Education
Domestic Abuse Victim Advocacy - SafeJourney
Emergency Department
EMS Education
Endovenous Laser Treatment (EVLT) for Varicose Veins
Family Birth Center
Family Medicine
Gastroenterology
General Radiology
Genetics Program
Geriatric Care
Gift Shop
Grief and Loss Support
Group Physical Therapy
Gynecology

COMPETITORS

Allina Hospitals
Bethesda Hospital
Catholic Health Initiatives
CentraCare Health
Children's Hospitals and Clinics of Minnesota
Fairview Health
First Care
HealthEast Care System
Mayo Clinic
Methodist Hospital (MN)
Park Nicollet Health Services
Regions Hospital
SCMC
St. John's Hospital (Minnesota)
St. Luke's Hospital (MN)
University of Minnesota Medical Center

HISTORICAL FINANCIALS
Company Type: Private

Income Statement | | | | FYE: December 31

	REVENUE ($ mil.)	NET INCOME ($ mil.)	NET PROFIT MARGIN	EMPLOYEES
12/17	651	(28)	—	5,180
12/16	721	(0)	—	—
12/13	735	51	7.0%	—
12/12	565	(4)	—	—
Annual Growth	2.8%	—	—	—

2017 Year-End Financials

Return on assets: 7.9%   Cash ($ mil.): —
Return on equity: (-4.4%)
Current ratio: 1.00

NORTH MISSISSIPPI HEALTH SERVICES, INC.

North Mississippi Health Services (NMHS) isn't contained by its name: The health system also provides health care to residents of northwestern Alabama. NMHS includes half a dozen community hospitals including its flagship North Mississippi Medical Center in Tupelo. North Mississippi Medical Clinics a regional network of more than 30 primary and specialty clinics; and nursing homes. Combined the facilities have nearly 1000 beds designated for acute long term and nursing care. Specialty services include home health and long-term care inpatient and outpatient behavioral health and treatment centers for cancer and digestive disorders. NMHS also operates outpatient care and wellness clinics in the region.

Operations

During 2014 NMHS handled about 30000 inpatient visits as well as more than 128000 emergency room visits and some 345000 outpatient care visits. It also conducted about 24000 surgeries at its various facilities. Its outpatient centers include more than 30 primary and specialty care clinics in Mississippi and Alabama operated through the North Mississippi Medical Clinics division as well as more than half a dozen wellness centers.

Geographic Reach

In all NMHS serves two dozen counties across the two states. In addition to its main hospital in Tupelo NMHS operates health centers in communities including Eupora Iuka Pontotoc and West Point Mississippi and in Hamilton Alabama. It also manages a center in Calhoun City Mississippi. Its Baldwyn Nursing Facility is located in Baldwyn Mississippi.

Financial Performance

Flagship North Mississippi Medical Center (NNMC)'s revenues increased by 6% due to a growth in net patient revenues. Medicare and Medicaid together accounted for about 50% of net patient revenues; managed care and commercial 25%; Blue Cross 14%; self-pay 10%; and Health Link 1%.

NNMC reported net loss of $14 million in 2014 over net income in 2013 due to pension-related changes.

NNMC's operating cash flow increased by 256% that year.

Mergers and Acquisitions

In 2018 North Mississippi Health Services agreed to buy Gilmore Memorial Hospital out of bankruptcy. It will pay $10.5 million for the Armory Mississippi hospital including the assumption of liabilities and financial commitments.

EXECUTIVES

Chb, Jim Kelley
Ceo, Shane Spees
Pres-Ceo, John Heer
Treas, Joe Reppert
SEC, Bruce Toppin
Cfo, Sharon Nobles
Doctor, Robert Stewart
Director of Nursing, Rodger Brown
Registered Nurse Fnpbc Pmhnpbc, Rebecca Cagle

LOCATIONS

HQ: NORTH MISSISSIPPI HEALTH SERVICES, INC.
  830 S GLOSTER ST, TUPELO, MS 388014934
Phone: 662 377-3000
Web: WWW.NMHS.NET

Selected Locations

Baldwyn Nursing Facility (Baldwyn Mississippi)
Calhoun County Medical Clinic (managed facility;
  Calhoun Mississippi)
NMMC-Eupora (Eupora Mississippi)
NMMC-Hamilton (Hamilton Alabama)
NMMC-Iuka (Iuka Mississippi)
NMMC-Pontotoc (Pontotoc Mississippi)
NMMC-Tupelo (Tupelo Mississippi)
NMMC-West Point (West Point Mississippi)
North Mississippi Medical Clinics (NMMCI regional)

PRODUCTS/OPERATIONS

Selected Facilities and Services

Acute Stroke Unit
Advanced Wound Center and Hyperbarics
Bariatric Center
Behavioral Health Center
Breast Care Center
Cancer Center
Center for Digestive Health
Community Health
Critical Care Unit
CRNA Program
Diabetes Treatment Center
Emergency Services
Family Medicine Residency Center
Heart Institute
Home Health and Hospice
Hospitalists
Joint Replacement Center
Le Bonheur Specialty Clinics
Medical Imaging
North Mississippi Surgery Center
Outpatient Infusion
Pain Management Center
Pastoral Care
Physician Specialties
Radiology
Rehabilitation Services
Respiratory Therapy
Skilled Nursing Facility
Sleep Disorders Center
Surgical Services
Tupelo Wellness Center
Vein Center
Volunteer Services
Women's Hospital
Women's and Children Services

COMPETITORS

Baptist Memorial Health Care
Community Health Systems
Delta Regional Medical Center
Forrest General Hospital
HCA
Memorial Hospital at Gulfport
Methodist Healthcare
Natchez Regional Medical Center
North Mississippi Medical
Shelby County Health Care
Southwest Mississippi Regional Medical Center

	REVENUE ($ mil.)	NET INCOME ($ mil.)	NET PROFIT MARGIN	EMPLOYEES
09/17	898	26	3.0%	6,000
09/16	893	30	3.4%	—
09/15	860	19	2.2%	—
09/14	779	(14)	—	—
Annual Growth	4.9%	—	—	—

Income Statement — FYE: September 30

2017 Year-End Financials
Return on assets: 4.4%   Cash ($ mil.): 36
Return on equity: 3.0%
Current ratio: 1.00

NORTH MISSISSIPPI MEDICAL CENTER, INC.

At North Mississippi Medical Center you might get some Mississippi Mud ice cream after your tonsils are removed. The full-service 650-bed regional referral hospital in Tupelo Mississippi is part of the North Mississippi Health Services system an affiliation of hospitals and clinics serving northern Mississippi northwestern Alabama and parts of Tennessee. It's the largest private not-for-profit hospital in Mississippi and the largest non-metropolitan hospital in America. Specialty services at the medical center include cancer treatment women's health care cardiology and behavioral health care. The hospital also operates a skilled-nursing facility and home health and hospice organizations.

Operations
Besides being a Mississippi State Department of Health-designated Level II trauma center North Mississippi Medical Center offers more than 40 specialties as well as centers for excellence in cardiac surgery cardiology research neurology neurosurgery pulmonology rehabilitation cancer treatment chemical dependency and neonatal programs.

The medical center's Home Health Agency canvases 17 counties in north Mississippi and provides complex and extremely high-tech procedures that can be performed in the home setting. It also operates Baldwyn Nursing Facility.

Geographic Reach
North Mississippi Medical Center serves more than 700000 people across 24 counties in north Mississippi northwestern Alabama and portions of Tennessee.

Strategy
In 2012 North Mississippi Medical Center - Hamilton opened a new pulmonary rehabilitation unit. Also the medical center's Outpatient Rehabilitation Center in 2012 became the first outpatient rehabilitation center in Mississippi to offer Fiberoptic Endoscopic Evaluation of Swallowing (FEES) to assess swallowing function.   Awards and Recognition

North Mississippi Medical Center's hospitalist program has been recognized by The American Journal of Medicine for providing cost-effective care to patients in the hospital. The program begun in 1997 serves hospitalized patients who do not have a primary care physician or whose primary care physicians do not have hospital practices.

EXECUTIVES
President, Steve Altmiller
Secretary, Bruce Toppin
Specialist, Lether Thornton
Pharmacy Purchasing, Memory Nowell
Pathologist, Sherry Okun

LOCATIONS
HQ: NORTH MISSISSIPPI MEDICAL CENTER, INC.
830 S GLOSTER ST, TUPELO, MS 388014934
Phone: 662 377-3000
Web: WWW.NMHS.NET

Selected Locations
Baldwyn Nursing Facility - Baldwyn Mississippi
NMMC - Eup
NMMC - Ham
NMMC - Iuk
NMMC - Pontotoc - Pontotoc Mississippi
NMMC - Tupelo - Tupelo Mississippi
NMMC - West Point - West Point Mississippi

PRODUCTS/OPERATIONS

Selected Programs & Services
Acute Stroke Unit
Advanced Wound Center and Hyperbarics
Bariatric Center
Behavioral Health Center
Breast Care Center
Cancer Center
Center for Digestive Health
Community Health
Critical Care Unit
CRNA Program
Diabetes Treatment Center
Emergency Services
Family Medicine Residency Center
Gift & Floral Shop
Heart Institute
Home Health and Hospice
Hospitalists
Joint Replacement Center
Le Bonheur Specialty Clinics
Medical Imaging
North Mississippi Surgery Center
Outpatient Infusion
Pain Management Center
Pastoral Care
Physician Specialties
Radiology
Rehabilitation Services
Respiratory Therapy
Skilled Nursing Facility
Sleep Disorders Center
Surgical Services
Tupelo Wellness Center
Vein Center
Volunteer Services
West Bedtower Project
Women's Hospital
Women's and Children Services

COMPETITORS

Community Health Systems
Delta Regional Medical Center
Forrest General Hospital
HCA
Memorial Hospital at Gulfport
Natchez Regional Medical Center
Southwest Mississippi Regional Medical Center

HISTORICAL FINANCIALS
Company Type: Private

	REVENUE ($ mil.)	NET INCOME ($ mil.)	NET PROFIT MARGIN	EMPLOYEES
09/15	627	45	7.3%	6,000
09/14	633	52	8.3%	—
09/13	537	2	0.5%	—
09/12	620	(6)	—	—
Annual Growth	0.4%	—	—	—

Income Statement — FYE: September 30

Return on assets: 5.2%   Cash ($ mil.): 18
Return on equity: 7.3%
Current ratio: 2.00

NORTH SHORE MEDICAL CENTER, INC.

This health systemA strives to cast a spell ofA salubriousness over Salem Massachusetts. The North Shore Medical Center (NSMC) provides medical care to the residents of several cities north of Boston including Salem (aka The Witch City) Lynn andA Peabody. The network is home toA two acute care hospitals children's and rehabilitation hospitals a heart institute a women's center and a number of community health centers. It also boasts more than 600 physicians and other health care professionals inA its North Shore Physician Group. Its flagship the NSMC Salem Hospital is a nearly 250-bed teaching hospital providing adult and pediatric services. The not-for-profit system is part of Partners HealthCare System.

Operations
With multiple hospitals ambulatory care sites and physician offices NSMCA provides comprehensive care. NSMC's staff includesA about 600 affiliated physicians representing primary care family practice and 50 additional subspecialties. Much of the staff isA part of the North Shore Physicians Group whichA provides multi-specialty and primary care through more than 15A North Shore locations.

NSMC collaborates with Massachusetts General Hospital on a number of clinical programs. The two started the Mass General/North Shore Center for Patient Care in 2009 to provide primary care and some surgical services to residents of the North Shore region. The center also serves as the home of a cancer center which is operated cooperatively by the two organizations.

Geographic Reach
North Shore Medical Center (NSMC) is the North Shore's largest healthcare provider one of its largest employers and the second largest community hospital system in Massachusetts.

Strategy
Mass General and NSMCA also partner to provide heart care pediatric care thoracic surgery and neurosurgery. By working together the two health care providers can effectively double the number of specialists available to perform these procedures at their respective hospitals.

EXECUTIVES

Secretary, Tracie Dudevoir

LOCATIONS

HQ: NORTH SHORE MEDICAL CENTER, INC.
81 HIGHLAND AVE, SALEM, MA 019702768
Phone: 978 741-1200
Web: WWW.NSMC.PARTNERS.ORG

Selected locations
NSMC Salem Hospital (Salem)
NSMC Union Hospital (Lynn)
Mass General/North Shore Cancer Center (Danvers)
Mass General/North Shore Center for Outpatient Care (Danvers)
NSMC Women's Center (Danvers)
NSMC North Shore Children's (Salem)
The Birthplace (Salem)
NSMC Wellness & Integrative Medicine Center (Salem)

Salem Family Health Center
Torigian Family Health Center (Peabody)
Lynn Community Health Center
Shaughnessy-Kaplan Rehabilitation Hospital (Salem)
Partners Home Care (Regional)

COMPETITORS

Beth Israel Deaconess	Children's Hospital
Medical Center	Boston
Boston Medical Center	Dana-Farber
Brigham and Women's	Elliot Health System
Hospital	Emerson Hospital
Cambridge Health	Exeter Health
Alliance	Resources
CareGroup	Hallmark Health
Caritas Holy Family	Lahey Health System
Hospital	McLean Hospital
Caritas Norwood	St. Elizabeth's
Hospital	Medical Center
Catholic Medical	Steward Health Care
Center	

HISTORICAL FINANCIALS

Company Type: Private

Income Statement   FYE: September 30

	REVENUE ($ mil.)	NET INCOME ($ mil.)	NET PROFIT MARGIN	EMPLOYEES
09/17	407	(57)	—	5,000
09/16	408	(48)	—	—
09/15	403	(35)	—	—
09/14	395	(21)	—	—
Annual Growth	1.0%	—	—	—

2017 Year-End Financials

Return on assets: 2.1%   Cash ($ mil.): 1
Return on equity: (-14.2%)
Current ratio: 0.40

NORTH SHORE UNIVERSITY HEALTH SYSTEM

EXECUTIVES

Prin, Steven Swiryn
Director, Tyler Bauer
Director, Michael Skonieczny
Vice-President, Nicole Fernandez
Associate, William Seiden
Manager, Barbara Eckert
Database Administrator, Lily Xu
Director, Phil Rozen
Assistant Vice President, Beverly Beine
Program Director, Brody Cmes
Lpn Clinical Administrative As, Georgia Jones

LOCATIONS

HQ: NORTH SHORE UNIVERSITY HEALTH SYSTEM
2650 RIDGE AVE, EVANSTON, IL 602011700
Phone: 847 570-2640
Web: WWW.NORTHSHORE.ORG

HISTORICAL FINANCIALS

Company Type: Private

Income Statement   FYE: September 30

	REVENUE ($ mil.)	NET INCOME ($ mil.)	NET PROFIT MARGIN	EMPLOYEES
09/15	1,419	55	3.9%	3
09/14	1,397	148	10.6%	—
09/13	1,815	238	13.1%	—
Annual Growth	(11.6%)	(51.7%)	—	—

2015 Year-End Financials

Return on assets: 4.3%   Cash ($ mil.): 62
Return on equity: 3.9%
Current ratio: 0.40

NORTH SHORE UNIVERSITY HOSPITAL

North Shore University Hospital (NSUH) knows you shouldn't have to leave the island for quality health care. The Long Island hospital has more than 800 beds devoted to adult and pediatric medicine rehabilitation stroke care women's health orthopedics urology wound healing dentistry and trauma emergency services among other areas. The hospital is home to specialist institutes for cancer care and cardiology. It also serves as a campus for the Hofstra Northwell Shool of Medicine. NSUH is part of Northwell Health.

Operations

The not-for-profit NSUH operates numerous satellite community health centers that provide primary surgery psychiatric dental and specialty care including the Schwartz Ambulatory Surgery Center. Its Stern Family Center for Extend Care and Rehabilitation has about 250 beds; NSUH also includes a Katz Women's Hospital (one of two in the system). The hospital provides comprehensive care in all health care specialties including organ transplant services. In addition the hospital operates mobile health vehicles and conducts educational and wellness programs for area residents.

NSUH has a staff of more than 6000 specialist and subspecialist physicians nurses and other medical workers. It handles about 50000 inpatient visits 90000 emergency room visits 20000 surgeries and 6000 births each year.

NSUH has medical health professional and nursing school affiliations with about 15 colleges and universities. Programs include residencies postgraduate training and fellowships.

Geographic Reach
Strategy

NSUH and the larger Northwell Health system tend to grow through the acquisitions of smaller campuses and mergers with other systems. This allows the hospital to gain operating efficiency through vertical integration bargaining power with vendors and a more diversified revenue stream.

In 2017 NSUH opened the Sandra Atlas Bass Heart Hospital for advanced cardiac care. The facility will be the first on Long Island to offer heart transplants and the sixth in New York State (which has a very high number of transplant candidates on its waiting list).

As part of its efforts to bring cutting-edge health care to the community it serves the hospital began offering 3D-printed titanium spinal implants in 2017.These synthetic implants approved in the US in 2016 are made with titanium powder rather than from a donor or from the patient's own body and manufactured using a 3D-printing process.

EXECUTIVES

Executive Vice President Chief Financial Officer, Robert S. (Bob) Shapiro
President North Shore-long Island Jewish Health System, Ralph A. Nappi
Senior Vice President Strategy And Business Informatics, Jeffrey A. Kraut
Executive Vice President Chief Operating Officer, Mark J. Solazzo
Regional Executive Director, Dennis Dowling
Executive Vice President And Physician-in-chief, Lawrence G. Smith
Executive Director, Susan Somerville
Senior Vice President And Chief Quality Officer, Mark Jarrett
Director Of Radiology, Edward S Wind
Chief Procurement Officer And Vice President, Phyllis McCready
Vice President Of Marketing, Don Simon
Vice President And Chief Talent Officer, Elaine Page
Medical Director, Rita Molina
Vice Chairman, Gary Giangola
Secretary, Rose Diaz

LOCATIONS

HQ: NORTH SHORE UNIVERSITY HOSPITAL
300 COMMUNITY DR, MANHASSET, NY 110303876
Phone: 516 562-0100
Web: WWW.NORTHWELL.EDU

PRODUCTS/OPERATIONS

Selected Centers and Services
Bariatric Services
Cancer Institute
Cardiovascular and Thoracic Services
Colorectal Surgery
Emergency Department / Trauma Services
Fertility and Reproductive Services
Geriatric and Palliative Medicine
Infectious Diseases / AIDS Research
Kidney Transplantation
Laparoendoscopic Single-Site Surgery
Military/Veterans Services
Minimally Invasive Robotic Surgery
Neuroscience
Obstetrics and Gynecology
Orthopaedics
Pain Management
Pediatric Services
Radiation Medicine
Travel Immunization
Urology Services
Wound Care

COMPETITORS

Brookhaven Memorial Hospital Medical Center
Catholic Health Services of Long Island
Catholic Healthcare System
Long Island College Hospital
Maimonides Medical Center
New York City Health and Hospitals
NewYork-Presbyterian Healthcare
Winthrop-University Hospital

HISTORICAL FINANCIALS

Company Type: Private

Income Statement   FYE: December 31

	REVENUE ($ mil.)	NET INCOME ($ mil.)	NET PROFIT MARGIN	EMPLOYEES
12/17	1,826	191	10.5%	5,000
12/16	1,795	171	9.6%	—
12/15	1,617	37	2.3%	—
12/14	1,495	84	5.7%	—
Annual Growth	6.9%	31.1%	—	—

2017 Year-End Financials

Return on assets: 7.9%   Cash ($ mil.): 64
Return on equity: 10.5%
Current ratio: 1.20

NORTH TEXAS MUNICIPAL WATER DISTRICT

EXECUTIVES

Pres, Darwin Whiteside
Vice President, Joe Joplin
SEC, Terry Sam Anderson
Exec Dir, Tom Kula
Officer, Russell Moody
Assistant, Jack Partain
Manager, Kelly Harden
Scientist, Rachel Blakey
Information Specialist, Shaya Hamilton
Program Inspector, Manual Rivas
Program Inspector, Richard Welsh
Auditors: WEAVER AND TIDWELL LLP DA

LOCATIONS

HQ: NORTH TEXAS MUNICIPAL WATER DISTRICT
501 E BROWN ST, WYLIE, TX 750984406
Phone: 972 442-5405
Web: WWW.NTMWD.COM

HISTORICAL FINANCIALS
Company Type: Private

Income Statement				FYE: September 30
	REVENUE ($ mil.)	NET INCOME ($ mil.)	NET PROFIT MARGIN	EMPLOYEES
09/17	439	129	29.4%	670
09/16	398	125	31.6%	—
09/15	338	86	25.7%	—
09/14	310	56	18.3%	—
Annual Growth	12.3%	31.4%	—	—

2017 Year-End Financials
Return on assets: 7.1%   Cash ($ mil.): 100
Return on equity: 29.4%
Current ratio: 0.70

NORTHBAY HEALTHCARE GROUP

EXECUTIVES

Ceo, Deborah Sugiyama
Director of Operating Room, Susan Gornall
Internal Medicine Practitioner, Olexander Barchan
Training and Direc, Becky Lessler
Internal Medicine Practitioner, Maria C Duran
Chief of Medicine, Tracy Johnson
Internal Medicine Practitioner, Girmay Gebremedhin
Urology Specialist, Kevin Rycyna
Internal Medicine Practitioner, Thanh Dang
Rn, Angela Serrano
Physician Director of Er, Fredric Gough

LOCATIONS

HQ: NORTHBAY HEALTHCARE GROUP
1200 B GALE WILSON BLVD, FAIRFIELD, CA
945333552
Phone: 707 646-5000
Web: WWW.NORTHBAY.ORG

HISTORICAL FINANCIALS
Company Type: Private

Income Statement				FYE: December 31
	REVENUE ($ mil.)	NET INCOME ($ mil.)	NET PROFIT MARGIN	EMPLOYEES
12/17	530	(4)	—	1,200
12/16	557	44	7.9%	—
12/15	460	15	3.3%	—
12/14	441	47	10.9%	—
Annual Growth	6.4%	—	—	—

2017 Year-End Financials
Return on assets: 6.1%   Cash ($ mil.): 9
Return on equity: (-0.9%)
Current ratio: 0.40

NORTHEAST GEORGIA MEDICAL CENTER, INC.

EXECUTIVES

Ceo, Carol Burrell
Vice President, Tracy Vardeman
Vice President, Anthony Williamson
Vice President, Paul Vervalin
Cfo, Anthony M Herdener
Oncology, Jack T Griffeth
Administrative Assistant, Elizabeth Winham
Director, Lawana Bryan
Operations Manager, Gail Wallace
Director, Deven Mattheus
Internal Medicine Practitioner, Ernest T Kamara

LOCATIONS

HQ: NORTHEAST GEORGIA MEDICAL CENTER, INC.
743 SPRING ST NE, GAINESVILLE, GA 305013715
Phone: 770 219-9000
Web: WWW.NGHS.COM

HISTORICAL FINANCIALS
Company Type: Private

Income Statement				FYE: September 30
	REVENUE ($ mil.)	NET INCOME ($ mil.)	NET PROFIT MARGIN	EMPLOYEES
09/17	1,152	7	0.7%	3,053
09/16	1,024	45	4.5%	—
09/15	892	51	5.8%	—
09/14	819	110	13.5%	—
Annual Growth	12.0%	(58.8%)	—	—

2017 Year-End Financials
Return on assets: 5.2%   Cash ($ mil.): 23
Return on equity: 0.7%
Current ratio: 0.90

NORTHEAST HOSPITAL CORPORATION

EXECUTIVES

Ceo, Philip M Cormier
Chief of Internal Medicine*, Robert Tufts
Cfo, Gary P Marlow
Vp, Cynthia Cafasso Donaldson

Vp, Althea Lyons
Vp, Lisa Neveling
Vice-President, Rebecca Imperiali
Bkpr, Joan Farrow
Doctor, Elise Campagnolo
Director of Pastoral Care, John Pearson
Executive Vice-President, Johnathan Wilhelm
Auditors: PRICEWATERHOUSECOOPERS LLP BO

LOCATIONS

HQ: NORTHEAST HOSPITAL CORPORATION
85 HERRICK ST, BEVERLY, MA 019151790
Phone: 978 922-3000
Web: WWW.BEVERLYHOSPITAL.ORG

HISTORICAL FINANCIALS
Company Type: Private

Income Statement				FYE: September 30
	REVENUE ($ mil.)	NET INCOME ($ mil.)	NET PROFIT MARGIN	EMPLOYEES
09/17	375	35	9.5%	2,800
09/16	372	(2)	—	—
09/15	341	13	4.1%	—
09/13	332	19	5.9%	—
Annual Growth	3.0%	15.9%	—	—

2017 Year-End Financials
Return on assets: 2.4%   Cash ($ mil.): 52
Return on equity: 9.5%
Current ratio: 1.40

NORTHEAST MEDICAL GROUP, INC.

EXECUTIVES

Prin, Alan Landau

LOCATIONS

HQ: NORTHEAST MEDICAL GROUP, INC.
99 HAWLEY LN, STRATFORD, CT 066141202
Phone: 203 688-2205
Web: WWW.NORTHEASTMEDICALGROUP.ORG

HISTORICAL FINANCIALS
Company Type: Private

Income Statement				FYE: September 30
	REVENUE ($ mil.)	NET INCOME ($ mil.)	NET PROFIT MARGIN	EMPLOYEES
09/17	398	2	0.6%	5
09/16	307	(40)	—	—
09/15	276	(51)	—	—
Annual Growth	20.0%	—	—	—

NORTHEAST OHIO REGIONAL SEWER DISTRICT

EXECUTIVES

Pres, Darnell Brown
Exec Dir, Julius Ciaccia
Vice President, Ronald D Sulik
Mgr, Robert First
Information Technology Manager, Frank Greenland
Security Staff, Brian Jasko
Planning Manager, Devona Marshall
Programmer Analyst, Jin Zhang
Manager, John Wasko
Manager, Thomas Lazio
Administrative Assistant, Jessica Shutty
Auditors: CIUNI & PANICHI INC CLEVELAN

LOCATIONS

HQ: NORTHEAST OHIO REGIONAL SEWER DISTRICT
3900 EUCLID AVE, CLEVELAND, OH 441152506
Phone: 216 881-6600
Web: WWW.NEORSD.ORG

HISTORICAL FINANCIALS
Company Type: Private

Income Statement				FYE: December 31
	REVENUE ($ mil.)	NET INCOME ($ mil.)	NET PROFIT MARGIN	EMPLOYEES
12/17	343	63	18.3%	623
12/16	313	68	21.9%	—
12/15	280	54	19.4%	—
12/14	239	20	8.7%	—
Annual Growth	12.9%	44.8%	—	—

2017 Year-End Financials

Return on assets: 2.8% Cash ($ mil.): 40
Return on equity: 18.3%
Current ratio: 1.50

NORTHEASTERN UNIVERSITY

Since 1898 Northeastern University has been educating students in Boston and beyond. The school enrolls roughly 24000 students and employs 1600 faculty members. Its nine colleges offer 100 undergraduate programs and 160 graduate programs in areas such as the arts business engineering and law. Northeastern has a student-to-teacher ratio of about 13:1. Its highly-regarded experiential education program integrates classroom learning with real-world experience; students typically alternate between school and paid full-time work and leave with up to two years of professional experience. Northeastern started out as a night school housed in a YMCA facility.

Operations

Roughly 90% of Northeastern's students participate in its cooperative learning program which is conducted over four or five years and can include overseas study programs. The idea behind the teaching strategy is to give students some professional experience before graduation putting them a step ahead of peers. Sectors include the arts and humanities (think Boston Symphony Orchestra) finance and insurance (Goldman Sachs in the UK) and communications (the White House offers a co-op opportunity in its media affairs office).

The school also boasts extensive research centers and institutes. Northeastern receives research funding from a number of outside sources that include the National Institutes of Health the Department of Energy and the Department of Defense and the Department of Homeland Security. Funded research areas include heart disease the link between preterm births and environmental contaminants new ways to detect explosives and renewable energy sources.

Geographic Reach

Northeastern's students hail from all 50 states and about 90 countries. The university has study abroad programs in locations including Argentina Costa Rica France China Germany and the UK (among many others).

In addition to its main campus in Boston Northeastern has satellite graduate schools in Charlotte North Carolina Seattle California and Toronto.

Financial Performance

Northeastern reported revenue of $1.16 billion in 2017 which was about the same as 2016. Tuition and fees account for about 98% of the university's revenue. Tuition and fees totaled $1.14 billion in 2017 from about $1 billion in 2016. The university paid about $316 million in financial aid in 2017 an increase from about $292 million the year before.

EXECUTIVES

Senior Vice President Administration And Finance, John McCarthy
Svp And Ceo Northeastern University Global Network, Philomena V. Mantella
Senior Vice President For External Affairs External Affairs, Michael Armini
President, Joseph E. Aoun
Svp Academinc Affairs And Provost, James C. Bean
Vp And Chief Marketing Officer, Brian Sullivan
Vice President, Kathy Spiegelman
Vice President Facilities, Nancy May
Vice President, Michael J Power
Assistant Vice President Of Communications, Renata Nyul
Special Assistant To The Senior Vice President, Maria Galarza
Vice President For Media And Membership, Christopher Cunningham
Assistant Vice President Student Affairs Residential Life, Marina Macomber
Vice President Of Student Affairs, John Obryant
Associate Vice President, Paul Zernicke
Vice President Of Media And Membership, Vijayeta Singh
Assistant Vice President, Lori Jacques
Vice President Online Experiential Learning, Chris Mallett
Vice President Of Media And Membership, Isha Srivastava
Vp Of Programs And Administration, Cristhy Mattos
First Vice President, Heather L Seligman
Vice President, Norton Julie
Executive Vice President, Angela Antoniello
Vice President, Harry Brodsky
Vice President Of Alumnae Relations, Sarah Nesti
Auditors: PRICEWATERHOUSECOOPERS LLP B

LOCATIONS

HQ: NORTHEASTERN UNIVERSITY
360 HUNTINGTON AVE, BOSTON, MA 021155000
Phone: 617 373-2000
Web: WWW.NORTHEASTERN.EDU

PRODUCTS/OPERATIONS

Selected Schools & Colleges
Bouvé College of Health Sciences
College of Arts Media and Design
College of Computer and Information Science
College of Engineering
College of Professional Studies
College of Science
College of Social Sciences and Humanities
D'Amore-McKim School of Business
School of Law

HISTORICAL FINANCIALS
Company Type: Private

Income Statement				FYE: June 30
	REVENUE ($ mil.)	NET INCOME ($ mil.)	NET PROFIT MARGIN	EMPLOYEES
06/18	1,306	163	12.5%	4,175
06/17	1,161	169	14.6%	—
06/16	1,106	3	0.3%	—
06/13	947	147	15.6%	—
Annual Growth	6.6%	2.0%	—	—

2018 Year-End Financials

Return on assets: 11.9% Cash ($ mil.): 239
Return on equity: 12.5%
Current ratio: —

NORTHERN ARIZONA UNIVERSITY

Located a stone's throw from the Grand Canyon Northern Arizona University (NAU) has been educating students to see forever for more than a century. About 20000 students attend the school which is dominated by a mountainous landscape. Founded in 1899 NAU offers roughly 100 baccalaureate about 50 master's and a handful of doctoral programs. Undergraduate majors include exercise science hotel and restaurant management and visual communication. It's home to the High Altitude Sports Training Complex a multi-sport training center used by athletes to prepare for different environments and enhance performance. NAU's Extended Campuses provide access to higher education for students in their own communities.

Operations

While the university has made several other locations available to its student body most of the activity at NAU is centered on its primary campus. About 15500 undergraduates and 2000 graduate students attend classes at the Flagstaff campus. About 6500 undergraduate students live on campus in more than 25 residence halls.

Aside from its bricks-and-mortar campuses NAU offers instruction to students virtually through 70 online degree programs. The university's in-state tuition fees run $8871 for fiscal 2013 and nonresident tuition comes in at more than $21000.

NAU's enrollment of about 20000 students is instructed by some 900 full-time faculty members with a student-to-faculty ratio of 17 to 1.

Geographic Reach

Based in Flagstaff Arizona NAU is a four-year public university boasts more than 35 additional campus locations throughout Arizona. Besides Phoenix satellite campuses are located in Prescott Scottsdale Tuba City Tucson Kingman Mesa Yuma Paradise Valley and Whiteriver.

Financial Performance

Board-approved tuition rate increases and higher student enrollment both helped the university to log a 4% rise in revenue in fiscal 2012 as compared to 2011. These gains were partially off-set however by decreases in grant and contracts.

Net income meanwhile dropped by 69% during the same reporting period due to declines in non-operating revenues resulting from drops in state appropriations and other non-operating revenues. Of note the educational institution received 23% of its revenue from state appropriations. NAU also points to increases in operating and non-operating expenses for the net income decreases. Non-operating expenses increased in 2012 due to rising interest expenses from capital asset-related debt.

EXECUTIVES

Pres, Dr Rita Cheng
Svp, University Advancement, Mary Ellen C Williams
Project Coordinator, Ceci Torres
Project Coordinator, Elena Arroyo
Coordinator, Erik Jaeke
Project Coordinator, Matt Hartman
Assistant Professor, Diane Stearns
Coordinator, Michael Rader
Staff, Steve De Pinet
Assistant Director, Barbara Soby
Scientist, Andrew Liguori
Auditors: DEBBIE DAVENPORT PHOENIX ARI

LOCATIONS

HQ: NORTHERN ARIZONA UNIVERSITY
601 S KNOLES DR ROOM 220, FLAGSTAFF, AZ 860110001
Phone: 928 523-9011
Web: WWW.NAUATHLETICS.COM

PRODUCTS/OPERATIONS

Selected Colleges
College of Arts & Letters
College of Education
College of Engineering Forestry & Natural Sciences
College of Health and Human Services
College of Social & Behavioral Sciences
Graduate College
The W.A. Franke College of Business

HISTORICAL FINANCIALS

Company Type: Private

Income Statement				FYE: June 30
	REVENUE ($ mil.)	NET INCOME ($ mil.)	NET PROFIT MARGIN	EMPLOYEES
06/17	351	5	1.5%	3,863
06/16	321	(8)	—	—
06/15	308	10	3.3%	—
06/14	282	4	1.5%	—
Annual Growth	7.5%	6.5%	—	—

2017 Year-End Financials
Return on assets: 3.5%
Return on equity: 1.5%
Current ratio: 2.40
Cash ($ mil.): 142

NORTHERN BORDER PIPELINE COMPANY

EXECUTIVES

V Pres-GM, Dean Ferguson
Human Resources Supervisor, Greg Tkaczyk
Auditors: KPMG LLP

LOCATIONS

HQ: NORTHERN BORDER PIPELINE COMPANY
700 LOUISIANA ST STE 700 # 700, HOUSTON, TX 770022873
Phone: 832 320-5000
Web: WWW.TRANSCANADA.COM

HISTORICAL FINANCIALS

Company Type: Private

Income Statement				FYE: December 31
	REVENUE ($ mil.)	NET INCOME ($ mil.)	NET PROFIT MARGIN	EMPLOYEES
12/17	291	80	27.8%	135
12/16*	291	86	29.6%	—
09/07	228	89	39.4%	—
Annual Growth	2.5%	(1.0%)	—	—

*Fiscal year change

2017 Year-End Financials
Return on assets: 1.3%
Return on equity: 27.8%
Current ratio: 0.70
Cash ($ mil.): 1

NORTHERN INDIANA PUBLIC SERVICE COMPANY

Northern Indiana Public Service Company (NIPSCO) can shine a little light on the topic of Hoosiers. The largest subsidiary of utility holding company NiSource NIPSCO has more than 457000 electricity customers and more than 786000 natural gas customers. The utility has three coal-fired power plants with 2540 MW of generating capacity. On the power side of the business NIPSCO generates transmits and distributes electricity to the northern part of Indiana and engages in electric wholesale and transmission transactions. The company operates approximately 13000 miles of electric transmission and distribution lines and 16000 miles of gas mains.

Operations

NIPSCO's three operating power facilities have a net capability of 2540 MW. It also owns and operates Sugar Creek a combined cycle gas turbine plant with a 535 MW capacity four gas-fired generating units with a net capability of 206 MW and two hydroelectric generating plants with a net capability of 10 MW. During 2012 NIPSCO generated 74.1% and purchased 25.9% of its electric requirements.

Geographic Reach

NIPSCO Gas is the largest natural gas distribution company in Indiana and NIPSCO Electric which serves customers in 20 counties is the state's #2 power distribution company behind Duke Energy Indiana.

Strategy

NIPSCO is promoting incentive plans to help customers save money through energy efficiency programs including appliance rebates for the installation of more energy efficient water heaters and other electric appliances and for automated air-conditioning cycling (cutting use for limited periods during peak loads). Other incentives are available for weatherizing energy audits and green construction projects.

In 2011 the company increased residential customer rates by 5%. The rate increase was in part a way to compensate for a decline in usage and revenues as a result of the global recession.

In 2011 NiSource companies Northern Indiana Fuel & Light and Kokomo Gas were consolidated with and into NIPSCO in order to improve operating efficiencies.

EXECUTIVES

Vice President Of Finance, William Omalley

LOCATIONS

HQ: NORTHERN INDIANA PUBLIC SERVICE COMPANY
801 E 86TH AVE, MERRILLVILLE, IN 464106271
Phone: 800 464-7726
Web: WWW.NIPSCO.COM

PRODUCTS/OPERATIONS

Selected Services
Call 811 Before You Dig
Commercial and Industrial Services
DependaBill
Dusk to Dawn Streetlights
Extra Service Protection
Green Power
IN-Charge Electric Vehicle Program
Meter Reading
NIPSCO Choice Program
NIPSCO Connect
Price Protection Service
Residential Builder and Developer Services
Selling Your Clean Energy
Smart Grid Technology
Start or Stop Gas and Electric Services
Trees and Power Lines
Wood Stove Changeout Program

COMPETITORS

AEP	IPALCO Enterprises
Citizens Energy	Indiana Michigan Power
Dominion Energy	Vectren
Duke Energy Indiana	

HISTORICAL FINANCIALS

Company Type: Private

Income Statement				FYE: December 31
	REVENUE ($ mil.)	NET INCOME ($ mil.)	NET PROFIT MARGIN	EMPLOYEES
12/17	2,418	226	9.3%	3,096
12/16	2,252	178	7.9%	—
Annual Growth	—	—	—	—

2017 Year-End Financials
Return on assets: 10.6%
Return on equity: 9.3%
Current ratio: —
Cash ($ mil.): 7

NORTHERN NATURAL GAS COMPANY

Northern Natural Gas (NNG) keeps the pipes gassed up. The company operates 14700 miles of natural gas pipeline (6300 miles of transmission line and 8400 miles of branch and lateral lines) stretching from the Permian Basin in Texas to the Great Lakes in the Midwest. It also provides transportation and storage services to almost 80 utilities and a number of other customers in the Upper Midwest. The company has a 5.5 billion cu. ft. per day market area peak capacity and its five natural gas storage facilities have a total capacity of 73 billion cu. ft. including 4 billion cu. ft. of liquefied natural gas (LNG). NNG which was formed in 1930 is an indirect subsidiary of Berkshire Hathaway Energy.

Operations

The company provides cross-haul and grid transportation between other interstate and intrastate pipelines in the Permian Anadarko Hugoton and Midwest areas.

Geographic Reach

NNG accesses natural gas supply in the Mid-Continent Rocky Mountain and Western Canadian basins. Its northern service unit (Market Area) delivers gas supply to customers in Illinois Iowa Michigan Minnesota Nebraska South Dakota and Wisconsin. Its southern system (Field Area) delivers to locations in Kansas New Mexico Oklahoma and Texas.

Sales and Marketing

The company offers its products for utilities municipalities gas marketing companies industrial and commercial users and other end-users.

In 2014 Northern Natural Gas had three customers including MidAmerican Energy that each accounted for greater than 10% of its transportation and storage revenue and its ten largest customers accounted for 63% of its system-wide transportation and storage revenue.

Financial Performance

The company's revenues increased by 22% due to higher gas & liquid and transportation sales.

NNG's net income was flat as the result of higher revenues being offset by higher operating cost and lower other income.

The company's operating cash flow increased by 12% due to a change in accounts payable and other accrued liabilities and a decline in cash used by accounts receivable and other assets.

Strategy

Growing its storage capacity since 2006 NNG has added 14 billion cu. ft. of storage cycle capacity through expansions and upgrades at its Cunningham Kansas and Redfield Iowa storage locations. In 2014 the company began working on a plan to add new pipelines compressor stations and meter stations between Nebraska and Iowa.

Company Background

NNG was established in 1930 in Omaha to serve 44 communities in Iowa Kansas and Nebraska. Its more recent history includes a takeover by Dynegy in 2002 from the pipeline unit's former parent bankrupt energy giant Enron. The deal was part of Dynegy's proposed acquisition of Enron which was subsequently called off. To strengthen its own balance sheet Dynegy ended up selling NNG to MidAmerican Energy (which later became Berkshire Hathaway Energy) that year.

In 2011 NNG brought in 13 billion cu. ft. of new gas supply to its northern system from tight sand formations in Oklahoma and Texas.

EXECUTIVES

President Ceo, Mark A. Hewett
Vp Operations, Royce Ramsay
Vp Information Technology, Paul Maakestad
Vp Marketing, Adam Wright

LOCATIONS

HQ: NORTHERN NATURAL GAS COMPANY
1111 S 103RD ST, OMAHA, NE 681241072
Phone: 877 654-0646
Web: WWW.NORTHERNNATURALGAS.COM

COMPETITORS

Enbridge	ONEOK Partners
Kinder Morgan Energy Partners	TransCanada
	Williams Companies

HISTORICAL FINANCIALS

Company Type: Private

Income Statement

FYE: December 31

	REVENUE ($ mil.)	NET INCOME ($ mil.)	NET PROFIT MARGIN	EMPLOYEES
12/17	693	170	24.6%	1,055
12/16	636	159	25.0%	—
12/07	663	161	24.3%	—
12/06	633	142	22.5%	—
Annual Growth	0.8%	1.7%	—	—

2017 Year-End Financials

Return on assets: 7.9%   Cash ($ mil.): 20
Return on equity: 24.6%
Current ratio: 0.30

NORTHERN UTAH HEALTHCARE CORPORATION

St. Mark's Hospital provides a variety of health care services in Salt Lake City and surrounding areas of northern Utah. The medical center has a capacity of some 320 beds and provides acute care and specialty services including cardiology orthopedics oncology women's services pain management general surgery and emergency care. It also offers family practice and specialist services. Established in 1872 St. Mark's Hospital is part of HCA's MountainStar Healthcare Network which operates hospitals and other health care facilities in Alaska Idaho and Utah.

Operations

St. Mark's employs about 600 physicians and handles about 15000 inpatient admissions each year. It also sees more than 80000 outpatients and manages 15000 surgeries and 3500 births. The hospital also operates a satellite emergency clinic the Lone Peak Emergency Center (Draper Utah) and it conducts a number of charity care programs.

Geographic Reach

In addition to its main facility and outpatient clinics in Salt Lake City St. Mark's has medical center locations in Draper Sandy and West Jordan Utah.

Strategy

To expand its service offerings and its geographic reach St. Mark's is expanding its facilities and its medical programs. In 2013 its trauma center was designed as a level III facility by the state department of health.

EXECUTIVES

Nursing Director, SANDY OSMOND

LOCATIONS

HQ: NORTHERN UTAH HEALTHCARE CORPORATION
1200 E 3900 S, SALT LAKE CITY, UT 841241300
Phone: 801 268-7111
Web: WWW.STMARKSHOSPITAL.COM

PRODUCTS/OPERATIONS

Selected Centers and Services
Cancer Support
Cardiovascular
Diabetes Center
Emergency Services
Imaging and Radiology
Interventional Pain Clinic
Orthopedic and Joint
Rehabilitation
Senior Health Center
Sleep Center
Stroke Care
Surgery
Weight Loss and Surgery
Women's Services

COMPETITORS

CHRISTUS Health	LifePoint Health
Intermountain Health Care	University of Utah Hospitals & Clinics

HISTORICAL FINANCIALS

Company Type: Private

Income Statement

FYE: June 30

	REVENUE ($ mil.)	NET INCOME ($ mil.)	NET PROFIT MARGIN	EMPLOYEES
06/16	352	103	29.4%	1,600
06/15*	341	110	32.3%	—
12/05	0	0	21.4%	—
05/00	140	17	12.4%	—
Annual Growth	5.9%	11.8%	—	—

*Fiscal year change

2016 Year-End Financials

Return on assets: 2.4%   Cash ($ mil.): —
Return on equity: 29.4%
Current ratio: 2.80

NORTHERN VIRGINIA ELECTRIC COOPERATIVE

NOVEC is no novice when it comes to electricity distribution. Northern Virginia Electric Cooperative (NOVEC) is a member-owned not-for profit utility that serves more than 150000 residential commercial industrial and government customers in a 651-sq. ml. service area in northern Virginia. NOVEC which has more than 6790 miles of power lines receives its power supply from the PJM Interconnection marketplace. The company also markets natural gas to retail customers in Virginia and Maryland through its NOVEC Energy Solutions unit. Subsidiary NOVEC Solutions sells gas and electric water heaters and other energy appliances and provides optical data networking service for large businesses and government agencies.

Geographic Reach

NOVEC distributes power to customers in Clarke Fairfax Fauquier Loudoun Prince William and Stafford counties and the City of Manassas Park.

Sales and Marketing

The utility company's large commercial customers include AT&T Doane Food Products Potomac Mills Outlet Mall NOAA's Mount Weather Facility and Vulcan Materials Company. NOVEC Energy Solutions supplies natural gas service to 20000 primarily residential customers.

Financial Performance
Due to the lower costs of generating power because of low natural gas prices NOVEC cut rates in 2011 and implemented a power cost adjustment credit in 2012 reducing the amount that customers paid for NOVEC-supplied power. Revenues decreased by 14% in 2012; net margin by 49%.

Strategy
In 2012 NOVEC received $10 million from the Department of Energy as a part of Smart Grid Investment Grant program. The company uses the proceeds to automate of 38 of its 53 substations; replaced 19 outdated line-protective devices; install 164 capacitor banks with automatic switching devices; and install 14 remote-controlled motor-operated switches to isolate problems and help restore power quickly.

Company Background
NOVEC was formed in 1983 through the merger of Prince William Electric Cooperative and Tri-County Electric Cooperative.

EXECUTIVES

Assistant Vice President Customer Service, Diane Johnson
Vice President And Corporate Counsel, Patrick Toulme
Senior Vice President Finance, Wilber Rollin

LOCATIONS

HQ: NORTHERN VIRGINIA ELECTRIC COOPERATIVE
10323 LOMOND DR, MANASSAS, VA 201093113
Phone: 703 335-0500
Web: WWW.NOVEC.COM
Northern Virginia Electric Cooperative operates in rural areas in Clarke Fairfax Fauquier Loudoun Prince William and Stafford counties as well as in the Town of Clifton and the City of Manassas Park in northern Virginia.

PRODUCTS/OPERATIONS

Subsidiaries and Affiliates
NOVEC Energy Solutions (formerly America's Energy Alliance retail gas marketing)
NOVEC Solutions (formerly NOVASTAR energy products and services)

COMPETITORS

AEP	FirstEnergy
Chesapeake Utilities	NiSource
Constellation Energy	Pepco Holdings
Group	Southern Company Gas
Delmarva Power	WGL Holdings
Dominion Energy	

HISTORICAL FINANCIALS
Company Type: Private

Income Statement   FYE: December 31

	REVENUE ($ mil.)	NET INCOME ($ mil.)	NET PROFIT MARGIN	EMPLOYEES
12/15	471	20	4.3%	275
12/14	433	20	4.7%	—
12/13	396	23	6.0%	—
12/09	419	50	12.2%	—
Annual Growth	2.0%	(14.2%)	—	—

2015 Year-End Financials
Return on assets: 7.3%   Cash ($ mil.): 45
Return on equity: 4.3%
Current ratio: 2.10

NORTHSHORE SCHOOL DISTRICT

EXECUTIVES

Supt, Larry Francois
Accounting Director*, Holly Burlingame
Coordinator, Jennifer Vitulli
Operations Manager, Jon Wiederspan
Accounting Staff, Rhonda Drew
Coordinator, Darren Donovan
Coordinator, David Kilpatrick
Coordinator, Kevin Lane
Security Staff, Mike Cook
Director, Damen Schuneman
Coordinator, Karen Cramer
Auditors: PAT MCCARTHY OLYMPIA WA

LOCATIONS

HQ: NORTHSHORE SCHOOL DISTRICT
3330 MONTE VILLA PKWY, BOTHELL, WA 980218972
Phone: 425 408-6000
Web: WWW.NSD.ORG

HISTORICAL FINANCIALS
Company Type: Private

Income Statement   FYE: August 31

	REVENUE ($ mil.)	NET INCOME ($ mil.)	NET PROFIT MARGIN	EMPLOYEES
08/16	291	(76)	—	2,312
08/15	266	23	8.7%	—
08/12	233	0	0.3%	—
08/11	241	(29)	—	—
Annual Growth	3.8%	—	—	—

2016 Year-End Financials
Return on assets: 4.3%   Cash ($ mil.): 145
Return on equity: (-26.3%)
Current ratio: —

NORTHSIDE HOSPITAL, INC.

Northside Hospital is no one-trick pony — it actually operates three hospitals serving Atlanta and surrounding areas. Also known as the Northside Healthcare Delivery System the Northside Hospital network includes some 840 licensed beds and more than 2500 physicians on multiple campuses with a host of outpatient health facilities including physician office parks and specialized cancer centers. All of Northside's hospitals are full-service acute-care facilities that provide specialty care including cancer care surgery radiology and women's health. Northside Hospital which opened in 1970 is merging with Gwinnett Health System.

Operations
In addition to its 537-bed hospital in Sandy Springs Northside has hospitals in Cherokee and Forsyth counties as well as more than 120 outpatient centers across Georgia.

Northside Hospital handles about 700000 patient visits annually at its facilities. The organization's cancer treatment division partners with the Cancer Support Community of Atlanta to provide mental health social and educational services to cancer patients and survivors as well as family members and friends.

Geographic Reach
Northside Hospital's three campuses are located in Atlanta Forsyth and Cherokee Georgia. It also operate about 40 outpatient clinics and physician practices scattered across the northern Atlanta metropolitan area.

Strategy
Northside Hospital is conducting expansion and renovation efforts to meet the needs of area residents. It recently completed an expansion and relocation of its Cherokee County Spine & Pain Center (near the Cherokee hospital campus). In 2015 it expanded its radiology offerings with a new outpatient imaging center in Jasper.

After two years of talks with fellow Georgia-based hospital system Gwinnett Health Northside and Gwinnett have agreed to merge operations. The combined system will have nearly 3500 physicians and 1480 beds.

EXECUTIVES

Cfo, Peggy Gatliff
Vp Administration And Ceo Northside Hospital-forsyth, Robert Putnam
Ceo Northside Hospital-cherokee, William (Billy) Hayes
Chair Department Of Obstetrics And Gynecology, Ceana Nezhat
Ceo Northside Hospital-forsyth, Skip Putnam
Coo, Peter Kennedy
Medical Director Of The Sleep Disorders Center, Lisa Johnston
Director Of Pharmacy Supervisor, Mike Tate
Director Of Radiology Services, Mary Shepherd
Director Icu Coronary Care Unit, Brandon Frady
Vice President Marketing And Communications, Lee Echols
Director Of Medical Records, Victoria WyllieAndrews
Vice President, Peter Singer
Managing Director, Scott Cooper
Clinic Manager, Rosemary Alexander
Secretary, Beth Keivani
Secretary, Kristen Ryan

LOCATIONS

HQ: NORTHSIDE HOSPITAL, INC.
1000 JOHNSON FERRY RD, ATLANTA, GA 303421611
Phone: 404 851-8000
Web: WWW.NORTHSIDE.COM

Selected Locations
Alpharetta Medical Campus
Dunwoody Cancer Center
Imaging at Peachtree Dunwoody
Medlock Bridge Imaging
Meridian Park Plaza
Northside Hospital Doctors Center
Northside Hospital-Atlanta
Northside Hospital-Cherokee
Northside Hospital-Forsyth
Northside-Forsyth Outpatient Surgery Center
Northside Sugar Hill Imaging (Buford)
Pediatric Center at Northside/Alpharetta
Roswell Cancer Center
Townelake Medical Office/Riverstone Imaging

COMPETITORS

Children's Healthcare of Atlanta	Piedmont Healthcare
DeKalb Medical	Regency Hospital
Emory Healthcare	Shepherd Center
Grady Health System	SunLink Health Systems
Gwinnett Health System	The Fulton-DeKalb
Northeast Georgia Health System	Hospital Authority
	WellStar Health System

HISTORICAL FINANCIALS
Company Type: Private

Income Statement
FYE: September 30

	REVENUE ($ mil.)	NET INCOME ($ mil.)	NET PROFIT MARGIN	EMPLOYEES
09/17	2,002	301	15.0%	8,000
09/16	1,897	157	8.3%	—
09/15	1,733	223	12.9%	—
09/13	1,253	109	8.7%	—
Annual Growth	12.4%	28.9%	—	—

2017 Year-End Financials
Return on assets: 4.8%
Return on equity: 15.0%
Current ratio: 2.60
Cash ($ mil.): 427

NORTHSIDE INDEPENDENT SCHOOL DISTRICT

EXECUTIVES

Supt, John Folks
Supt, Brian T Woods
President, Robert Blount Jr
Vice President, Katie N Reed
SEC, Bennie L Cole
Principal, Ellen Sutton
General, Lora Mathison
Coordinator, Dana Bickley
Assistant Superintendent, Donald Schmidt
Coordinator, Ana Turner
Information Technology Special, Esther Salazar
Auditors: RSM US LLP SAN ANTONIO TEXAS

LOCATIONS

HQ: NORTHSIDE INDEPENDENT SCHOOL DISTRICT
5900 EVERS RD, SAN ANTONIO, TX 782381606
Phone: 210 397-8770
Web: WWW.NISD.NET

HISTORICAL FINANCIALS
Company Type: Private

Income Statement
FYE: August 31

	REVENUE ($ mil.)	NET INCOME ($ mil.)	NET PROFIT MARGIN	EMPLOYEES
08/17	1,152	75	6.5%	13,698
08/16	1,119	16	1.5%	—
08/15	1,057	64	6.1%	—
08/14	1,011	125	12.4%	—
Annual Growth	4.4%	(15.6%)	—	—

2017 Year-End Financials
Return on assets: 2.8%
Return on equity: 6.5%
Current ratio: —
Cash ($ mil.): 577

NORTHWEST COMMUNITY HOSPITAL INC

Northwest Community Healthcare (NCH) has captured the hearts of northern Illinois. Located in Chicago's northwest suburbs the not-for-profit health system includes the not-for-profit Northwest Community Hospital a regional leader in providing all kinds of cardiac care including open-heart surgery cardiac catheterization and rehabilitation services. Along with cardiac care the nearly 500-bed hospital offers a comprehensive range of acute medical and surgical care. NCH also operates NCH Medical Group which has more than 150 primary and specialty physicians in more than 20 medical offices. Other offerings include an ambulatory surgery center a handful of urgent care centers and a behavioral health center. NCH has more than 1200 physicians on its staff.

Operations
NCH's Northwest Community Hospital is a Level II trauma center; it provides comprehensive medical and surgical care. It also provides a full range of outpatient infusion and injection services that include chemotherapy blood transfusions and treatments for blood and immunological disorders.

In 2016 Northwest Community Healthcare had 20000 inpatient and 350000 outpatient visits. It had more than 38000 home care visits and 2700 newborn deliveries as well as more than 17000 inpatient and outpatient surgeries (ranging from minimally invasive procedures to open-heart surgery).

Geographic Reach
Located in Arlington Heights Illinois NCH serves residents of Chicago's northwest suburbs.

Strategy
Like most integrated health care systems NCH works to broaden the spectrum of services it provides to better meet the needs of its service area. It often seeks partnership opportunities to expand its offerings. For example in 2017 Northwest Community Hospital added telemedicine capabilities to its pediatric emergency department and its neonatal intensive care unit. It partners with the Ann & Robert H. Lurie Children's Hospital to provide the service.

EXECUTIVES

President Medical Staff, Cynthia Valukas
President Ceo, Stephen O. Scogna
Cfo, Marsha Liu
Chief Technical Officer, Jack King
Vice President Facilities, Bob Klasek
Director Icu Coronary Care Unit Training Manager, Phyllis Cerone
Director Of Radiology, Peter Cormier
Director Of Pharmacy, Jason Alonzo
Director Of Radiology, Anthony J Malone
Vice President Hospital Operations, Melissa Smith
Vice President Facilities, Robert Klasek
Executive Vice President Patient Services Chief Nursing Officer, Kim Nagy
Vice Chairman, Max Brittain
Director, Daniel P. DiCaro

LOCATIONS

HQ: NORTHWEST COMMUNITY HOSPITAL INC
800 W CENTRAL RD, ARLINGTON HEIGHTS, IL 600052349
Phone: 847 618-1000
Web: WWW.NCH.ORG

PRODUCTS/OPERATIONS

Selected Facilities
Arlington Heights Medical Offices (Arlington Heights)
Buffalo Grove Fitness Center (Buffalo Grove)
Buffalo Grove Medical Offices (Buffalo Grove)
Buffalo Grove Treatment Center (Buffalo Grove)
Busse Center for Specialty Medicine (Arlington Heights)
Day Surgery Center (Arlington Heights)
Lake Zurich Treatment Center (Lake Zurich)
Northwest Community Hospital (Arlington Heights)
Palatine Medical Offices (Palatine)
Shaumburg Imaging Center (Schaumburg)
Shaumburg Medical Offices (Schaumburg)
Shaumburg Treatment Center (Schaumburg)
Youth Center Adolescent Substance Abuse Center (Arlington Heights)
Wellness Center (Arlington Heights)

COMPETITORS

Advocate Health Care
Alexian Brothers Health System
Central DuPage Hospital
Elmhurst Memorial Healthcare
Loyola University Health System
McDonough District Hospital
NorthShore University HealthSystem
Northwestern Lake Forest Hospital
Northwestern Memorial HealthCare
Rockford Health System
Rush System for Health
Silver Cross Hospital
St. Bernard Hospital and Health Care Center
University of Chicago Medical Center

HISTORICAL FINANCIALS
Company Type: Private

Income Statement
FYE: September 30

	REVENUE ($ mil.)	NET INCOME ($ mil.)	NET PROFIT MARGIN	EMPLOYEES
09/17	441	(7)	—	2,800
09/16	446	15	3.5%	—
09/15	432	24	5.6%	—
09/14	422	25	6.0%	—
Annual Growth	1.5%	—	—	—

2017 Year-End Financials
Return on assets: 4.4%
Return on equity: (-1.8%)
Current ratio: 0.70
Cash ($ mil.): 19

NORTHWEST HOSPITAL & MEDICAL CENTER

EXECUTIVES

Ceo, Cynthia Hecker
Pres-Ceo, Bill Schneider
Dir, Mark Green
Dir, Scott Hardman
Internal Medicine Practitioner, Anna Hagan
Internal Medicine Practitioner, David Ramenofsky
Internal Medicine Practitioner, Erich Koerner
Health Professional, Laura Quinnan-Hostein
Internal Medicine Practitioner, Naomi Lee

LOCATIONS

HQ: NORTHWEST HOSPITAL & MEDICAL CENTER
1550 N 115TH ST, SEATTLE, WA 981338498
Phone: 206 364-0500

HISTORICAL FINANCIALS

Company Type: Private

Income Statement   FYE: June 30

	REVENUE ($ mil.)	NET INCOME ($ mil.)	NET PROFIT MARGIN	EMPLOYEES
06/15	281	15	5.6%	1,600
06/10	5	0	16.3%	—
Annual Growth	—	—	—	—

*Fiscal year change

2015 Year-End Financials

Return on assets: 4.1%   Cash ($ mil.): 12
Return on equity: 5.6%
Current ratio: 1.00

NORTHWEST HOSPITAL, LLC

EXECUTIVES

Ceo, Kevin Stockton
Cfo, Gene Alexander
Dir, Kim Chimene
Coordinator, Elizabeth Gonzalez
Executive of Information Techn, David Bullock

LOCATIONS

HQ: NORTHWEST HOSPITAL, LLC
    6200 N LA CHOLLA BLVD, TUCSON, AZ 857413599
Phone: 520 742-9000
Web: WWW.NORTHWESTMEDICALCENTER.COM

HISTORICAL FINANCIALS

Company Type: Private

Income Statement   FYE: September 30

	REVENUE ($ mil.)	NET INCOME ($ mil.)	NET PROFIT MARGIN	EMPLOYEES
09/17	292	45	15.5%	1,100
09/16	283	36	13.0%	—
09/15	287	24	8.5%	—
09/14	0	0	—	—
Annual Growth	—	—	—	—

NORTHWESTERN MEMORIAL HOSPITAL

EXECUTIVES

Ceo, Dean Harrison
Pres, Richard J Gannotta
Cfo, Peter McCanna
Chb, William J Brodsky
Senior Client Coordin, Aaron J Powers
Director, Amy Galat
Nurse Practitioner, Amy Ochs
Pediatrician, Anjali S RAO
Property Operations Manager, Carol Koenig
Director Business, Christine Bonomo
Director, Cindy A Parker

LOCATIONS

HQ: NORTHWESTERN MEMORIAL HOSPITAL
    251 E HURON ST, CHICAGO, IL 606113055
Phone: 312 926-2000
Web: WWW.NM.ORG

HISTORICAL FINANCIALS

Company Type: Private

Income Statement   FYE: August 31

	REVENUE ($ mil.)	NET INCOME ($ mil.)	NET PROFIT MARGIN	EMPLOYEES
08/16	1,499	237	15.8%	5,800
08/15	1,337	198	14.8%	—
08/10	1,380	64	4.7%	—
08/09	1,304	4	0.3%	—
Annual Growth	2.0%	76.0%	—	—

NORTHWESTERN UNIVERSITY

With its main campus in the Chicago suburb of Evanston Northwestern University (NU) serves its 21000 students through about a dozen schools and colleges such as the Medill School of Journalism and the McCormick School of Engineering and Applied Sciences. Its Chicago campus houses the schools of law and medicine as well as several hospitals of the McGaw Medical Center. With a faculty of more than 3300 the school has a student-to-teacher ratio of about 6:1. NU is home to several research centers and community outreach programs; it also has a branch in Qatar. It is the only private member of the Big 10 conference; varsity sports include baseball football basketball and fencing.

Operations

Among NU's top-ranked programs are its law school medical school and its engineering program. Its Kellogg Graduate School of Management consistently ranks among the nation's top five business schools by Business Week and U.S. News & World Report. Its prestigious journalism and drama programs produced such alumni as Charlton Heston Gary Marshall and Julia Louis-Dreyfus. Retired US Supreme Court Justice John Paul Stevens is also a former Wildcat.

NU spends its $1.6 billion research budget (including about $620 million in sponsored funds) performing research at 24 university research centers (and nearly 100 other centers) in areas such as materials science biomedical engineering African studies performance studies and marketing. The school has earned recognition for its research in genetic medicine nanotechnology biochemistry neuroscience cancer research and materials sciences. NU partners have included the Argonne National Laboratory Fermilab and local universities.

Geographic Reach

NU's main campus in Chicago encompasses about 240 acres in Evanston. The university operates another 25-acre campus in Chicago as well as its education center in Qatar. NU was founded to serve the Northwest region of the US which includes parts or all of the states of Illinois Indiana Michigan Minnesota Ohio and Wisconsin.

Financial Performance

NU reported a 6% decrease in revenues to $2.1 billion in fiscal 2015 (ended August) a drop that was primarily driven by a decline in private gifts.

Net income plummeted 91% to $192 million that year and operating cash outflow totaled $91.4 million.

HISTORY

Northwestern University's Methodist founders met in 1850 to create an institution of higher learning serving the original Northwest Territory. The university was chartered in 1851 and two years later it acquired 379 acres of property north of Chicago on Lake Michigan. The town of Evanston was later named after John Evans one of the school's founders.

Classes began in the fall of 1855 with two professors and 10 students. By 1869 Northwestern had more than 100 students and began to admit women. In 1870 Northwestern signed an affiliation agreement with the Chicago Medical College (founded 1859) and three years later it joined with the original University of Chicago (no relation to the current institution) to create the Union College of Law. When the University of Chicago closed in 1886 due to financial difficulties Northwestern took control of the law school. The university reorganized in 1891 consolidating its affiliated professional schools (dentistry law medicine and pharmacy) into the university.

By 1900 Northwestern had become the third-largest university in the US (after Harvard and Michigan) with an enrollment of 2700. During the 1920s the university created the Medill School of Journalism named for Joseph Medill founder of the Chicago Tribune. In 1924 the school's athletic teams adopted the nickname Wildcats and two years later the university completed the primary buildings that form its Chicago campus. Northwestern suffered a drop in enrollment during the Depression but after WWII it saw student numbers swell as veterans took advantage of the GI Bill. Expansion continued throughout the 1960s and 1970s.

In 1985 the school and the City of Evanston began developing a research center to attract more high-tech industries to the area. The university's graduate school of business achieved national prominence in 1988 after it was ranked #1 in the US by Business Week. In 1995 Northwestern's football team forever the doormat of the Big 10 achieved national fame when it won the conference championship.

In 1998 faculty member Professor John Pople won the Nobel Prize in Chemistry the first Nobel Prize awarded to a faculty member while teaching at the university.

Northwestern won a significant legal battle in 1998 when a judge ruled that the university was not obligated to pay a faculty member simply because he had been granted tenure.

The university's dental school closed its doors in 2001 citing the difficulties posed for private schools in providing a competitive dental education.

EXECUTIVES

Vp Finance Operations And Treasurer, Ingrid S. Stafford, age 65
Vp Information Technology And Cio, Sean B. Reynolds
Dean Kellogg School Of Management, Sally E. Blount
Vp And Chief Investment Officer, William H. (Will) McLean
Dean School Of Communication, Barbara J. O'Keefe
Evp, Nim Chinniah
Provost, Daniel I. Linzer, age 65
Dean Libraries, Sarah M. Pritchard
President, Morton O. Shapiro

Vp Global Marketing And Cfhief Marketing Officer, Mary L. Baglivo
Dean Northwestern University In Qatar, Everette E. Dennis
Dean School Of Professional Studies, Thomas F. Gibbons
Dean Medill School Of Journalism Media And Integrated Marketing Communications, Bradley Hamm
Dean Graduate School, Dwight A. McBride
Dean Bienen School Of Music, Toni-Marie Montgomery
Dean Feinberg School Of Medicine, Eric G. Neilson
Dean School Of Education And Social Policy, Penelope L. Peterson
Dean Weinberg College Of Arts And Sciences, Adrian W. B. Randolph
Dean Mccormick School Of Engineering And Applied Science, Julio M. Ottino
Dean Pritzker School Of Law, Daniel B. Rodriguez
Vice President, Morteza Null Rahimi
Physical Therapy And Human Movement Sc, Julius Dewald
Vp Of It, Mylowe Wooley
Associate Vice President For Research, Fruma Yehiely
Vice President For Student Affairs, Margaret Sullivan
Assistant Vice President Marketing And Communications, Natasha DiPrima
Office Of The Vice President For Research, Erin Wallace
Associate Vice President Alumni Relations And Development, David Lively
Associate Vice President And Executive Director, Alicia Loffler
Medical Director, Linda Guthrie
Vice President For International Relations, Devora Grynspan
Assistant Vice President, Christopher Watson
Senior Vice President Global Human Resources Executive, Mikenzie Steffens
Associate Vice President Administrative Systems, Kristine O'Brien
Vice President And General Counsel, Phil Harris
Associate Vice President For Finance Financial Operations, Michael Szczepanek
Associate Vice President For Budget And Planning, Paul Castellucci
Associate Vice President Of Compliance, Marcia Isaacson
Director Of Admissions, Alex Schultes
Director Of Admissions Evening And Weekend Mba Program Kellogg School Of Management, Emily Haydon
Associate Vice President Human Resources, Dana Bradley
Director Of Clinical Services, David Shor
Executive Vice President Executive Director Senior Vice President Managing Director General Manager Vice President, Mike Null Monahan
Medical Director, Matthew Kippenhan
Vice President Of Medical Affairs, Michael Pelster
Chairman, William A. Osborn, age 70
Assistant Treasurer, Richard Emrich
Secretary, Debbie Robert
Secretary 1, Sheila Hodges
Board Member, Virginia Delancey
Board Member, Angela Y Lee
Treasurer, Spencer Carlson
Board Member, Leon Platanias
Auditors: PRICEWATERHOUSECOOPERS LLP

LOCATIONS

HQ: NORTHWESTERN UNIVERSITY
633 CLARK ST, EVANSTON, IL 602080001
Phone: 847 491-3741
Web: WWW.NORTHWESTERN.EDU

PRODUCTS/OPERATIONS

Selected Programs
Continuing and Professional Programs
Graduate Programs
Pre-Collegiate Programs
Undergraduate Programs

Selected Schools and Colleges
Bienen School of Music
Feinberg School of Medicine
The Graduate School
Kellogg School of Management
McCormick School of Engineering and Applied Science
Medill School of Journalism Media Integrated Marketing Communications
Northwestern in Qatar
School of Communication
School of Continuing Studies
School of Education and Social Policy
School of Law
Weinberg College of Arts and Science

HISTORICAL FINANCIALS

Company Type: Private

Income Statement | | | | FYE: August 31

	REVENUE ($ mil.)	NET INCOME ($ mil.)	NET PROFIT MARGIN	EMPLOYEES
08/16	2,200	221	10.1%	5,954
08/09	1,605	(1,388)	—	—
08/08	8	0	1.9%	—
Annual Growth	100.1%	146.8%	—	—

2016 Year-End Financials
Return on assets: —
Return on equity: 10.1%
Current ratio: —
Cash ($ mil.): 215

NORTON HOSPITALS, INC

EXECUTIVES

Pres, Steven A Williams
SEC, Robert B Azar
Treas, Michael W Gough
Vice President, Russell F Cox
SEC, Theodore T Myre Jr
Internal Medicine Practitioner, Deep Ajmani
Network Manager, Diana Wetterer
Manager of Management Informat, Joy Karrer
Human Resources Director, Judy Settle
Human Resources Director, Kevin Guthrie
Neurology Specialist, Roy Meckler

LOCATIONS

HQ: NORTON HOSPITALS, INC
200 E CHESTNUT ST, LOUISVILLE, KY 402021831
Phone: 502 629-8000
Web: WWW.NORTONHEALTHCARE.ORG

HISTORICAL FINANCIALS
Company Type: Private

Income Statement | | | | FYE: December 31

	REVENUE ($ mil.)	NET INCOME ($ mil.)	NET PROFIT MARGIN	EMPLOYEES
12/15	1,712	137	8.0%	1,500
12/14	1,577	187	11.9%	—
Annual Growth	8.6%	(26.7%)	—	—

2015 Year-End Financials
Return on assets: 4.7%
Return on equity: 8.0%
Current ratio: 1.80
Cash ($ mil.): —

NOVA SOUTHEASTERN UNIVERSITY, INC.

Nova Southeastern University (NSU) gives a whole new meaning to "school of sharks." NSU whose mascot is the deep sea predator has an enrollment of more than 27000 students and offers a variety of undergraduate graduate and professional academic programs. NSU offers degrees in several medical disciplines (osteopathic medicine pharmacy optometry nursing) marine biology business law education and computer sciences. The not-for-profit independent school operates four campuses in the Miami-Fort Lauderdale area several health centers and an oceanographic center. Founded in 1964 Nova University merged with Southeastern University of the Health Sciences in 1994 to become Nova Southeastern University.

Operations
In addition to its undergraduate and graduate programs NSU also operates The University School a pre-K through 12th grade college preparatory day school that draws part of its staff from NSU's School of Education and Human services. The university's Mailman Segal Institute for Early Childhood Studies serves the local community with programming for parents and educators.

Geographic Reach
NSU is a distance education pioneer (it was the first US university to offer graduate programs online) offering classes on the Internet as well as at six regional centers in Florida and Puerto Rico.

Financial Performance
Continuing a trend of earnings growth over the last five years from organic growth measures NSU reported a 4% rise in revenues in 2014 to some $640 million. The growth was attributed to increased tuition and fee income as well as revenues from auxiliary enterprises and government grants.

Strategy
As universities do NSU regularly invests in facility upgrades to meet the growing needs of its students. In 2014 it broke ground on the NSU Center for Collaborative Research (CCR) that will house an IBM supercomputer a tech incubator one of the state's largest wet labs and space for guest researchers. Other CCR facilities will include cancer and neuro-immune institutes an incubator for security businesses and an entire floor for the US Geological Survey which will partner with the university on research into Everglades restoration projects.

EXECUTIVES

Chancellor Health Professions Division, Frederick Lippman
Ceo President And Trustee, George L. Hanbury
Vp Finance, W. David Heron
Dean Student Affairs, Brad Williams
Director Alvin Sherman Library Research And Information Technology Center, Harriett MacDougall
Dean Shepard Broad Law Center, Athornia Steele
University Provost And Evp Academic Affairs, Frank DePiano
Dean University School, Jerome Chermak

Dean College Of Health Care Sciences, Richard E. Davis
Dean Oceanographic Center, Richard E. Dodge
Dean Center For Psychological Studies, Karen Grosby
Dean College Of Medical Sciences, Harold E. Laubach
Dean Mailman Segal Institute For Early Childhood Studies, Roni Leiderman
Dean College Of Optometry, David S. Loshin
Dean College Of Pharmacy, Andrés Malavé
Dean Farquhar College Of Arts And Sciences, Don Rosenblum
Dean College Of Osteopathic Medicine, Anthony J. Silvagni
Dean Fischler School Of Education, H. Wells Singleton
Dean College Of Dental Medicine, Robert A. Uchin
Dean Graduate School Of Humanities And Social Sciences, Honggang Yang
Evp And Coo, Jacqueline A. Travisano
Senior Executive Assistant President Manager, Shirley Naidoo
Ceo Health Clinics, Robert S. Oller
Vp Information Technology And Cio, Tom West
Executive Assistant Vice President, Katharine Perren
Pharmacy Manager, Todd Schmidt
Vice President Human Resources, Robert Pietrykowski
Provost And Executive Vice President For Academic Affairs, Ralph Rogers
Vice President Finance, Noel Oliveras
Clinical Director Restorative, Amir Farhangpour
Department Chair, Wilma Robles
Chair, Ronald G. Assaf
Vice Chair, Barry J. Silverman
Auditors: LB KPMG LLP GREENSBORO NC

LOCATIONS

HQ: NOVA SOUTHEASTERN UNIVERSITY, INC.
   3301 COLLEGE AVE, DAVIE, FL 333147796
Phone: 954 262-7300
Web: WWW.NOVA.EDU

COMPETITORS

Florida Atlantic
   University
Florida International
   University
University of Florida

HISTORICAL FINANCIALS
Company Type: Private

Income Statement				FYE: June 30
	REVENUE ($ mil.)	NET INCOME ($ mil.)	NET PROFIT MARGIN	EMPLOYEES
06/15	678	45	6.7%	2,500
06/12	689	48	7.1%	—
06/10	612	22	3.7%	—
Annual Growth	2.1%	15.2%	—	—

2015 Year-End Financials
Return on assets: 6.5%
Return on equity: 6.7%
Current ratio: 0.10
Cash ($ mil.): 35

NOVARTIS PHARMACEUTICALS CORPORATION

As the US pharmaceuticals unit of Swiss drug giant Novartis AG Novartis Pharmaceuticals Corporation (NPC) helps with the development manufacturing marketing and sales of its parent company's products in the US. Its product lines address a range of ailments including cardiovascular and respiratory diseases central nervous system disorders cancers bone and skin conditions infectious diseases and organ transplant complications. NPC's key products include tumor growth inhibitor Gleevec high blood pressure drug Diovan and attention deficit disorder therapies Focalin and Ritalin. NPC markets its products through an inhouse sales team.

Operations
NPC represents the best of both worlds for parent Novartis AG: It is part of the global Novartis Pharmaceuticals division which accounts for more than half of the parent company's annual revenues and it is also a major player in the US market which is Novartis' largest geographic segment.

In addition to its medicines for cancers cardiovascular diseases infectious diseases and organ transplant complications NPC offers treatments for endocrine disease inflammatory diseases and others.

Geographic Reach
Most of NPC's preclinical research efforts are conducted through US-based affiliate Novartis Institutes for BioMedical Research (NIBR) while clinical-stage development programs are conducted at Novartis sites around the globe.

Sales and Marketing
NPC markets its products through a dedicated force of sales representatives and specialists. Marketing initiatives are conducted online through partnerships with external web firms and an e-sales force.

Strategy
NPC widens its offerings in the US market through a number of methods including internal research programs licensing agreements and acquisitions. In 2015 the company received approval from the US FDA for its Cosentyx product for the treatment of moderate-to-severe plaque psoriasis in adults eligible for systemic therapy (drug absorbed through the bloodstream) or phototherapy (light therapy).

As part of its parent's efforts to focus on eye care generics and innovative pharmaceuticals NPC remains a vital part of Novartis' growth strategy. One area of growing interest is oncology; in 2015 Novartis acquired certain cancer-fighting products and pipeline compounds from GlaxoSmithKline.

Mergers and Acquisitions
In 2016 Novartis acquired the Oklahoma-based Selexys Pharmaceuticals which specializes in hematologic and inflammatory disorder treatments for some $665 million.

EXECUTIVES

President, Fabrice Chouraqui
Company President, Thomas (Tom) Kendris
Chief Financial And Administrative Officer, Paolo Tombesi
Us Country Head Information Technology, Ruth Thorpe
Evp Us Oncology, Bill Hinshaw
President Novartis Canada, Janice Murray

First Vice President, Robert Heinrich
Vp Purchase, Peter Carbone
Auditors: PRICEWATERHOUSECOOPERS LLP-BR

LOCATIONS

HQ: NOVARTIS PHARMACEUTICALS CORPORATION
   1 HEALTH PLZ, EAST HANOVER, NJ 079361016
Phone: 862 778-8300
Web: WWW.NOVARTIS.COM

PRODUCTS/OPERATIONS

2018 Sales by Segment

	% of total
Pharmaceutical Distribution	91
Insurance Pharmacy	5
Pharmaceutical Manufacturing	2
Healthcare-Related Services	2
Total	**100**

2018 Sales

	% of total
Ethical pharmaceuticals	91
Diagnostic reagents	4
Medical equipment & supplies	3
Other	2
Total	**100**

COMPETITORS

Alfresa
Takeda Pharmaceutical
Toho Pharmaceutical

HISTORICAL FINANCIALS
Company Type: Private

Income Statement				FYE: December 31
	REVENUE ($ mil.)	NET INCOME ($ mil.)	NET PROFIT MARGIN	EMPLOYEES
12/16	49,436	6,698	13.5%	7,000
12/15	49,440	17,794	36.0%	—
12/13	58,831	9,292	15.8%	—
Annual Growth	(5.6%)	(10.3%)	—	—

2016 Year-End Financials
Return on assets: 9.9%
Return on equity: 13.5%
Current ratio: 0.70
Cash ($ mil.): 7,007

NOVELART MANUFACTURING COMPANY

EXECUTIVES

President, Marvin H Schwartz
Chief Information Officer, Bob Reckers
Controller, Mike Fields
Buyer, Darlene Miller
Manager, Darrell Jump
Administrator, Nan Swain
Buyer, Angela Steinke
Vice President Sales, Dan Sunderuaus
Buyer, Mark Zimmer
Position In Business Developme, Adam Greenberg
Director Human Resources, Nancy Madden
Auditors: PITCHER ENDERS & DROHAN CINC

LOCATIONS

HQ: NOVELART MANUFACTURING COMPANY
 2121 SECTION RD, CINCINNATI, OH 452373509
Phone: 513 351-7700
Web: WWW.TOPICZINC.COM

HISTORICAL FINANCIALS

Company Type: Private

Income Statement   FYE: September 30

	REVENUE ($ mil.)	NET INCOME ($ mil.)	NET PROFIT MARGIN	EMPLOYEES
09/17	343	0	—	160
09/16	345	0	—	—
09/15	361	0	—	—
09/14	359	0	—	—
Annual Growth	(1.5%)	—	—	—

2017 Year-End Financials

Return on assets: 1.9%   Cash ($ mil.): 2
Return on equity: —
Current ratio: 1.50

NOVO CONSTRUCTION, INC.

EXECUTIVES

Ceo, James C Fowler
President, Jim Fowler
SEC, Robert Williamson
Project Manager, Scott Plummer
Project Engineer, Austin Stewart
Project Engineer, Caleb Silverman
Superintendent, Craig Butcher
Superintendent, Dave Fournier
Project Engineer, Jacob White
Superintendent, Todd Freeman
Executive Officer, Colin Stoner

LOCATIONS

HQ: NOVO CONSTRUCTION, INC.
 1460 OBRIEN DR, MENLO PARK, CA 940251432
Phone: 650 701-1500
Web: WWW.NOVOCONSTRUCTION.COM

HISTORICAL FINANCIALS

Company Type: Private

Income Statement   FYE: October 31

	REVENUE ($ mil.)	NET INCOME ($ mil.)	NET PROFIT MARGIN	EMPLOYEES
10/17	603	5	0.9%	155
10/16	577	6	1.1%	—
10/15	553	5	1.0%	—
10/14	463	4	1.0%	—
Annual Growth	9.2%	7.7%	—	—

2017 Year-End Financials

Return on assets: 17.0%   Cash ($ mil.): 54
Return on equity: 0.9%
Current ratio: 0.90

NPC RESTAURANT HOLDINGS, LLC

NPC International is the prince of pepperoni in a pizza empire. The world's largest franchisee of Pizza Hut restaurants NPC owns and operates more than 1275 pizza restaurants and delivery kitchens in about 30 states. The quick-service eateries located mostly in such southern states as Alabama Florida Georgia and Tennessee serve a variety of pizza styles as well as such items as buffalo wings and pasta. The pizza parlors are franchised from YUM! Brands the world's largest fast-food restaurant company. NPC was founded in 1962 by former chairman Gene Bicknell who was one of the first Pizza Hut franchisees. The company was acquired by private equity group NPC International Holdings in late 2011.

Operations

NPC runs more than 20 Wendys restaurants in addition to its large stable of pizza places. As a franchisee NPC gets the benefit of operating restaurants under a popular and well known name. It pays YUM! Brands royalties and fees in exchange for the right to use the Pizza Hut brand and other intellectual property. Typically local operators are also held to certain standards regarding food and service quality.

Strategy

NPC has grown to such a large size primarily through a series of acquisitions mostly corporate-run locations. In 2012 it snapped up 36 Pizza Hut units located primarily in Florida for roughly $19 million from Pizza Hut Inc. The deal enabled NPC to strengthen its position in its largest geographical market.

While NPC doesn't own the Pizza Hut chain as its largest franchisee the company can exert a certain amount of influence in how the fast-food business operates. It called upon YUM! Brands to improve its Pizza Hut marketing strategy while sales were slumping amid the economic downturn. The company spends 6% of its revenue on national and local advertising demonstrating its commitment to Pizza Hut operations and advertising strategy.

NPC's revenue improved in 2010 and 2011 partly as a result of promoting its value-priced menu items as a way to gain market share from competing chains including Domino's and Papa John's. (Within its local markets NPC competes against #1 Domino's franchisee RPM Pizza and Papa John's operator PJ United.)

EXECUTIVES

Chb-Pres-Coo, James K Schwartz
Exec V Pres Fin-Cfo, Troy D Cook
Sr V Pres-Head of Oprs, D Blayne Vaughn
Sr V Pres Mktg, Linda L Sheedy
Cao, Jason P Poenitske
Territory Vice President-South, Thomas D White
Territory Vice President-West, Tracy A Armentrout
Auditors: KPMG LLP KANSAS CITY MISSOUR

LOCATIONS

HQ: NPC RESTAURANT HOLDINGS, LLC
 7300 W 129TH ST, OVERLAND PARK, KS 662132631
Phone: 913 327-5555
Web: WWW.NPCINTERNATIONAL.COM

COMPETITORS

Boddie-Noell	PJ United
Burger King	Papa John's
Captain D's	RPM Pizza
Carrols	Sbarro

Chick-fil-A	Sonic Corp.
Domino's	Subway
Hardee's	Tacala
Interfoods	United States Beef
K-MAC	Valenti Management
Krystal	Wendy's
Little Caesar's	West Quality Foods
McDonald's	

HISTORICAL FINANCIALS

Company Type: Private

Income Statement   FYE: December 27

	REVENUE ($ mil.)	NET INCOME ($ mil.)	NET PROFIT MARGIN	EMPLOYEES
12/16	1,236	8	0.7%	29,000
12/15	1,223	6	0.5%	—
12/14	1,179	1	0.1%	—
12/13	1,094	29	2.7%	—
Annual Growth	4.2%	(33.5%)	—	—

2016 Year-End Financials

Return on assets: 2.9%   Cash ($ mil.): 13
Return on equity: 0.7%
Current ratio: 0.20

NTG INVESTMENT PARTNERS, INC

EXECUTIVES

Ceo, Kevin Nolan
President, Harold Baron
Cfo, Tyler Garell
Coo, Blake Malone
General Manager, Robert Burns
National Sales Manager, Adrian Ottens
National Sales Manager, Bascom Judy
Sales Staff, Bobby Burns
Operations Manager, Danny Sparks
Executive Officer, Harris Rainbow
National Sales Manager, Jessica Assil
Auditors: BARNETT & STEGALL LLC

LOCATIONS

HQ: NTG INVESTMENT PARTNERS, INC
 365 NORTHRIDGE RD STE 100, ATLANTA, GA 303506100
Phone: 770 509-9611
Web: WWW.NTGFREIGHT.COM

HISTORICAL FINANCIALS

Company Type: Private

Income Statement   FYE: December 31

	REVENUE ($ mil.)	NET INCOME ($ mil.)	NET PROFIT MARGIN	EMPLOYEES
12/17*	468	2	0.4%	881
09/16	199	(0)	—	—
12/14	114	0	0.4%	—
12/13	49	0	0.5%	—
Annual Growth	75.7%	66.6%	—	—

*Fiscal year change

2017 Year-End Financials

Return on assets: 9.1%   Cash ($ mil.): 2
Return on equity: 0.4%
Current ratio: 1.40

O'NEIL INDUSTRIES, INC.

A family of construction companies O'Neil Industries has also built W.E. O'Neil Construction Company. The employee-owned company operates in Arizona California Colorado and Illinois providing general contracting construction management design/build and structural concrete services for commercial projects in the US and Canada. O'Neil Industries has worked on corporate offices manufacturing and distribution facilities and mixed-use centers for clients in the education gaming health care hospitality and retail industries. The company also serves the residential and senior living sectors. Clients have included Boeing DePaul University and The Nature Conservancy.

Operations

Recent projects in Arizona include America West Airlines Flight Training Facility (in Phoenix) Arizona Cancer Center (in Tucson) and Air Center Scottsdale's McClain Street Facility (Scottsdale). In El Segundo California O'Neil Industries completed the Aerospace A6 PODS project.

The company transitioned its T.L. Roof & Associates business into its Tucson branch. Its O'Neil Construction Company unit serves as the company's concrete division. The company's Special Projects Group concentrates on small to midsized tenant improvement and facility- or campus-based projects.

Geographic Reach

While O'Neil Industries is primarily US-centric with a headquarters office in Chicago and five operating units in Illinois (Chicago) Arizona (Tucson and Phoenix) California (Los Angeles) and Colorado (Denver) the construction company also boasts a presence in Ontario Canada.

Sales and Marketing

O'Neil Industries works to maintain high customer satisfaction. More than 80% of O'Neil Industries' clients are repeat customers. Such clients include Dessert Bloom OB & Gyn Peter Palumbo Exton City of West Hollywood and The Boeing Company.

Strategy

O'Neil Industries is focused on environmentally-friendly construction projects. To this end it has devoted 80 full-time staff members who deemed LEED Accredited Professionals. The company has been involved in more than 4 million sq. ft. of LEED-certified projects including BRE Park Viridian Apartments Columbia College Media Production Center and Haworth Permanent Showroom at the Merchandise Mart.

One of the company's most recent projects include a new Chapel at Carondelet St. Joseph's Hospital in Tucson Arizona which it completed in 2013. The 3000-sq.-ft. addition to the hospital's existing courtyard was developed through a partnership with designer Swaim Associates.

In 2013 its W.E. O'Neil Construction Company began a renovation and addition project on the Sun City Oro Valley Fitness Center.

The construction firm is also upgrading its technology.

EXECUTIVES

Chb, William E O'Neil
Pres-Ceo, Brian Ramsay
Auditors: CROWE HORWATH LLP OAK BROOK

LOCATIONS

HQ: O'NEIL INDUSTRIES, INC.
1245 W WASHINGTON BLVD, CHICAGO, IL
606071929
Phone: 773 755-1611
Web: WWW.WEONEIL.COM

PRODUCTS/OPERATIONS

Selected Delivery Methods
Construction Management
General Contracting
Design/Build

Selected Markets
Aerospace
Education
Green
Healthcare
Hospitality & Restaurants
Industrial
Infrastructure
Municipal
Office
Gaming & Recreation
Retail
Religious
Residential
Senior Living
Special Projects
Tribal

COMPETITORS

Bulley & Andrews
Clark Construction Group
Gilbane Building Company
Graycor
Leopardo
McShane Construction
Pepper Construction
Sundt
The Austin Company
Walsh Group

HISTORICAL FINANCIALS
Company Type: Private

Income Statement				FYE: December 31
	REVENUE ($ mil.)	NET INCOME ($ mil.)	NET PROFIT MARGIN	EMPLOYEES
12/17	605	5	0.8%	400
12/16	605	5	0.8%	—
12/15	605	5	0.8%	—
12/14	605	5	0.8%	—
Annual Growth	(0.0%)	(0.0%)	—	—

2017 Year-End Financials
Return on assets: 25.0%
Return on equity: 0.8%
Current ratio: 0.90
Cash ($ mil.): 47

O-AT-KA MILK PRODUCTS COOPERATIVE, INCORPORATED

EXECUTIVES

Ceo, Robert Hall
Chb-President, Herbert Nobles
Vice President, Clyde Rutherford
SEC-Coo, Dan Wolf
Treas, Dudley Chaffee
Asst Treas-Cfo, Michael Patterson
Cntrl, Jerry Gefert
Production, Wasyl Puhacz
Auditors: DOPKINS & COMPANY BUFFALO NE

LOCATIONS

HQ: O-AT-KA MILK PRODUCTS COOPERATIVE, INCORPORATED
700 ELLICOTT ST, BATAVIA, NY 140203744
Phone: 585 343-0536
Web: WWW.OATKAMILK.COM

HISTORICAL FINANCIALS
Company Type: Private

Income Statement				FYE: December 31
	REVENUE ($ mil.)	NET INCOME ($ mil.)	NET PROFIT MARGIN	EMPLOYEES
12/17	319	11	3.6%	302
12/16	300	17	5.9%	—
12/15	295	18	6.4%	—
12/14	332	2	0.7%	—
Annual Growth	(1.3%)	72.9%	—	—

2017 Year-End Financials
Return on assets: 3.0%
Return on equity: 3.6%
Current ratio: 0.70
Cash ($ mil.): 7

O. C. TANNER COMPANY

O.C. Tanner recognizes that it's nice to be appreciated. The company designs and helps implement employee recognition programs for customers around the world. Related services intended to help customers take full advantage of their investment in employee recognition include communication consulting research leadership training and social programs. The company which operates from offices in the US Canada and the UK has shipped awards to clients in about 150 countries. Over the years O.C. Tanner has counted numerous Fortune 100 companies among its clients.

Operations

In addition to its recognition programs Tanner provides ancillary products and services such as recognition publication and lecture series engagement studies and leadership recognition training. Tanner's roster of authors and speakers are available to give presentations on topics such as delivering appreciation strategies and the company hosts an annual Executive Recognition Summit where industry leaders come together to share insights into their companies' employee recognition practices.

Geographic Reach

O.C. Tanner serves global customers from its locations in Salt Lake City Utah (US); Burlington Ontario (Canada); and Loughton Essex (UK). Outside of the US its main markets are Australia Brazil Canada China Europe Hong Kong Japan India Mexico and Singapore.

Sales and Marketing

O.C. Tanner has served some 8500 businesses including about 35 Fortune 100 companies such as American Express Caterpillar Abbott Labs Chevron FedEx and Wells Fargo.

Strategy

O.C. Tanner seeks to cater its recognition programs to each client applying insights into the employees brands and cultures present within each customer's operations. Its packages include blends of recognition awards coaching communication solutions social tools and management assistance components and its services are available for smaller customers as well as multi-national corporations.

Company Background

Namesake Obert C. Tanner founded the company in 1927 by selling class rings and pins for school graduates.

EXECUTIVES

Managing Director, Juan Field

LOCATIONS

HQ: O. C. TANNER COMPANY
1930 S STATE ST, SALT LAKE CITY, UT 841152383
Phone: 801 486-2430
Web: WWW.OCTANNER.COM

PRODUCTS/OPERATIONS

Selected Clients
Abbot
American Express
Bank of America
Caterpillar Inc.
Chevron Corporation
Comcast
ConocoPhillips
CVS
Dell
Dow Chemical
Express Scripts
FedEx
Freddie Mac
General Dynamics
HCA Corporate
Hess Corporation
Home Depot
Johnson Controls Inc.
JP Morgan Chase
Kraft Foods
The Kroger Co.
Marathon Petroleum
McKesson
Medco Health
Merck
Northrop Grumman
Raytheon
Safeway
State Farm Insurance
Sunoco Inc.
Sysco
Travelers
WellPoint
Wells Fargo

COMPETITORS

American Achievement
CA Short
ITAGroup
LoyaltyOne

Maritz Loyalty &
  Motivation
TharpeRobbins

HISTORICAL FINANCIALS

Company Type: Private

Income Statement				FYE: December 31
	REVENUE ($ mil.)	NET INCOME ($ mil.)	NET PROFIT MARGIN	EMPLOYEES
12/17	341	9	2.8%	1,700
12/16	351	16	4.8%	—
12/14	344	19	5.6%	—
12/13	327	27	8.5%	—
Annual Growth	1.1%	(23.5%)	—	—

O. C. TANNER RECOGNITION COMPANY

EXECUTIVES

Pres-Ceo, David Petersen
V Pres-Cfo, Scott Sperry
Vice-President, David Berg

Director of Information Techno, David Eghert
Manufacturing Manager, Drew Butler
Marketing Director, Leona Fox
Software Developer, Masoud Abbasi
Director of Information Techno, Nihar Nanda
Analyst, Russell Wilson
Personnel, Scott Christophe
Account Manager, Wayne Carlston

LOCATIONS

HQ: O. C. TANNER RECOGNITION COMPANY
1930 S STATE ST, SALT LAKE CITY, UT 841152311
Phone: 801 486-2430

HISTORICAL FINANCIALS

Company Type: Private

Income Statement				FYE: December 31
	REVENUE ($ mil.)	NET INCOME ($ mil.)	NET PROFIT MARGIN	EMPLOYEES
12/17	404	0	0.1%	1,700
12/14	401	(0)	—	—
12/13*	378	(2)	—	—
05/13	367	(2)	—	—
Annual Growth	1.9%	—	—	—

*Fiscal year change

OCEAN BEAUTY SEAFOODS LLC

Prefer your piscatory purchase to be fresh frozen or canned? Ocean Beauty Seafoods has it covered. Doing no fishing of its own the company buys seafood from commercial fishermen and then processes sells and distributes its seafood products in Alaska and across the continental US. Founded in 1910 the company also exports seafood to Mexico Europe Asia Africa and the Middle East. Ocean Beauty's specialty products include smoked salmon smoked salmon spreads pickled and marinated herring shrimp cocktail caviar and lobster pA?tA©. Nonprofit Bristol Bay Economic Development Corporation owns 50% of Ocean Beauty; individual investors own the rest.

Operations
Boasting offices or plants in eight US states plus overseas in Japan Ocean Beauty operates its own fleet of seafood delivery trucks across the Western US. The fleet makes regular stops at the seafood company's distribution facilities located in Oregon Idaho Texas Montana Utah and Washington. The company operates six production sites in Alaska in Alitak Cordova Excursion Inlet Kodiak Naknek and Petersburg as well as a pair of production sites in Seattle and Monroe Washington. Sales and administration offices are located in Seattle and Tokyo. Ocean Beauty exports its products to Mexico Europe Asia Africa and the Middle East.

Geographic Reach
Based in Washington Ocean Beauty enjoys a global reach.

Sales and Marketing
Ocean Beauty sells its fresh and frozen seafood products to both retail and foodservice customers. The company maintains sales offices in the states in Seattle and overseas in Tokyo.

Strategy
Ocean Beauty claims to be the first company to vacuum pack Alaskan seafood (in 1954). The company's products are primarily caught in the waters of the Pacific Northwest but Ocean Beauty also

purchases fish from harvesters worldwide. Its major manufacturing facilities are certified against the British Retail Consortium Audit Standards.

Ocean Beauty also voluntarily participates in the US Department of Commerce's Hazard Actions Critical Control Points (HACCP) Seafood Inspection Program for added assurance that its products are safe wholesome and properly labeled. The company's production and distribution operations are conducted in compliance with the US Food and Drug Administration's HACCP regulations.

EXECUTIVES

MBR, Howard Klein
Pres-Ceo, Mark Palmer
Cfo, Tony Ross
Finance Administrator, Johnathan Hanrahan
Sales Support Team Member, Taylor Chaffee

LOCATIONS

HQ: OCEAN BEAUTY SEAFOODS LLC
1100 W EWING ST, SEATTLE, WA 981191321
Phone: 206 285-6800
Web: WWW.OCEANBEAUTY.COM

PRODUCTS/OPERATIONS

Selected Brands
CircleSea
Commander
Deep Sea
Echo Falls
Icy Point
LASCCO
McGovern
Nathan's
Neptune
Ocean Beauty
Ocean Bonita
Pillar Rock
Pink Beauty
Pirate
Port Clyde
RITE
Royal Alaska
Sea Choice
Searchlight
Sound Beauty
St. Andrews
Surf King
Three Star
Tribe

Selected Products
Imported finfish
  Mahi mahi
  Sea Bass
  Shark
  Swordfish
  Tuna
North Pacific finfish
  Cod
  Farm-raised
  Flounder
  Halibut
  Perch
  Pollock
  Rockfish
  Salmon
  Sole
  Sturgeon
  Whiting
Shellfish
  Coldwater shrimp meat
  Clams
  Crab
  Mussels
  Oysters
  Prawns
Other products
  Milt
  Pickled herring
  Roe
  Surimi

COMPETITORS

Alaska Sausage	Maruha Nichiro
Alaska Seafood company	Orca Bay Seafoods
Alaskan Leader	Pacific Seafood Group
Fisheries	Peter Pan Seafoods
Arrowac Fisheries	Princes Limited
Banner Smoked Fish	Red Chamber Co.
Bumble Bee Foods	Salmolux
Chicken of the Sea	Santa's Smokehouse
Gorton's	Seafood Sales
High Liner Foods	StarKist
Icelandic Group	Trident Seafoods
Icicle Seafoods	

HISTORICAL FINANCIALS

Company Type: Private

Income Statement				FYE: December 31
	REVENUE ($ mil.)	NET INCOME ($ mil.)	NET PROFIT MARGIN	EMPLOYEES
12/16*	453	(27)	—	2,500
01/16	437	(4)	—	—
01/15	439	4	1.1%	—
12/13	425	11	2.6%	—
Annual Growth	2.1%	—	—	—

*Fiscal year change

2016 Year-End Financials

Return on assets: 4.2%
Return on equity: (-6.0%)
Current ratio: 0.40

Cash ($ mil.): 2

OCEAN SPRAY CRANBERRIES, INC.

Ocean Spray Cranberries has transformed that ubiquitous Thanksgiving side dish into a big business with beverages cereals and snacks. Known for its blue-and-white wave logo Ocean Spray is a top US maker of canned bottled and shelf-stable juice drinks. Formed in 1930 the cooperative is owned by more than 700 cranberry and grapefruit growers in North America. It produces juice drinks by blending the cranberries with other fruits typically ranging from apples to blueberries. Its other products include fresh and dried cranberries sauces trail mixes and instant oatmeal along with fresh citrus fruits. Ocean Spray sells its products through food retailers foodservice providers and food makers worldwide.

Operations

The food company operates its business through three divisions. Its Foodservice division supplies Ocean Spray products to restaurants bars cafeterias hospitals and hotels. The company's Ingredient Technology division sells cranberry products for use by global food and beverage makers. Ocean Spray's International division serves the Americas the Caribbean Africa Asia/Pacific Europe and the Middle East.

Geographic Reach

Ocean Spray boasts a global business. It supplies cranberry products to food and beverage manufacturers worldwide. The company serves customers in North America the Caribbean Central America South America Africa Asia/Pacific Europe and the Middle East.

The co-op has production facilities in Florida Massachusetts Nevada New Jersey Texas and Wisconsin. Its growers are located in British Columbia Florida Massachusetts New Jersey Oregon and Wisconsin.

Sales and Marketing

Juice remains the co-op's most lucrative product. Ocean Spray squeezes into the top three suppliers in the US juice market. Its namesake juices rank #3 behind #1 PepsiCo (with its Tropicana) and #2 Coca-Cola (with Minute Maid).

Strategy

Looking to diversify its products portfolio and further target health-conscious Baby Boomers Ocean Spray has worked to expand beyond the cranberry's traditional role on holiday tables. The company's promotional efforts have been aided by research showing that cranberry juice can reduce urinary tract infections and fight stomach ulcers.

To this end Ocean Spray has introduced a "white juice" made from pre-ripened cranberries that have a less tart taste as well as a line of pomegranate juice drinks (pomegranate being one of the superfruits touted for its antioxidant properties). It also has transformed dried cranberries into Craisins which now show up in co-branded cookies and cereals and expanded the line with the introduction of pomegranate- and blueberry-flavored Craisins.

HISTORY

Ocean Spray Cranberries traces its roots to Marcus Urann president of the Cape Cod Cranberry Company. In 1912 Urann who became known as the "Cranberry King" began marketing a cranberry sauce that was packaged in tins and could be served year-round. Inspired by the sea spray that drifted off the Atlantic and over his cranberry bogs Urann dubbed his concoction Ocean Spray Cape Cod Cranberry Sauce.

It didn't take long for other cranberry growers to make their own sauces and rather than compete the Cranberry King consolidated. In 1930 Urann merged his company with A.D. Makepeace Company and with Cranberry Products forming a national cooperative called Cranberry Canners. During the 1940s it added growers in Wisconsin Oregon and Washington and to reflect its new scope changed its name to National Cranberry Association.

Canadian growers were added to the fold in 1950. Urann retired in 1955 and two years later the co-op introduced its first frozen products. To take advantage of the popular Ocean Spray brand name in 1959 the company changed its name to Ocean Spray Cranberries.

EXECUTIVES

Vice President, David Williams
Vice President Global Innovation, Clark Reinhard
Assistant Treasurer, Suzy Lewis
Auditors: PRICEWATERHOUSECOOPERS LLP B

LOCATIONS

HQ: OCEAN SPRAY CRANBERRIES, INC.
1 OCEAN SPRAY DR, MIDDLEBORO, MA 023490001
Phone: 508 946-1000
Web: WWW.OCEANSPRAY.COM

PRODUCTS/OPERATIONS

Selected Brands & Products
Dried fruit
  Craisins Blueberry Juice Infused Dried Cranberries
  Craisins Cherry Juice Infused Dried Cranberries
  Craisins Original Dried Cranberries
  Craisins Pomegranate Juice Infused Dried Cranberries
  Craisins Snack Packs
  Craisins Trail Mix - Cranberry & Chocolate
  Craisins Trail Mix - Cranberry Fruit & Nut
Fresh Produce
  Clementines
  Cranberries
  Grapefruit
  Lemons
  Limes
  Oranges
  Tangerines
Instant oatmeal
  Cranberry
  Cranberry Honey Multigrain
  Cranberry Orange Muffin
  Cranberry Pomegranate
Juice
  100% Juice Blends
  Blueberry Juice Drinks
  Cran•Energy Energy Juice Drinks
  Cranberry Juice Cocktails
  Cranberry Juice Drink Blends
  Diet Juice Drinks
  Fruit & Veggie Juice
  Fruit & Veggie Juice Drinks
  Grapefruit Juice
  Grapefruit Juice Drinks
  Juice Drinks
  Light Juice Drinks
  On the Go Juice
  On the Go Juice Drinks
  Sugar-Free Drink Mixes
  White Cranberry Juice Drinks
Sauces
  Jellied cranberry sauce
  Whole berry cranberry sauce

COMPETITORS

A. Duda & Sons	Freshco
Arcade Industries	Jugos del Valle USA
Cherry Central	Mariani Packing
Cooperative Inc.	Meridian Nut Growers
Chiquita Brands	Naked Juice
Citrus World	National Grape
Coca-Cola	Cooperative
Coloma Frozen Foods	Nestlé USA
Cranberries Limited	Odwalla
Dole Food	Shoreline Fruit
Dundee Citrus Growers	Sunsweet Growers
Edinburg Citrus	Tampico Beverages
Fresh Del Monte	Tropicana
Produce	Wonderful Company

HISTORICAL FINANCIALS

Company Type: Private

Income Statement				FYE: August 31
	REVENUE ($ mil.)	NET INCOME ($ mil.)	NET PROFIT MARGIN	EMPLOYEES
08/15	1,719	317	18.5%	2,000
08/14	1,655	289	17.5%	—
08/13	1,658	389	23.5%	—
08/12	1,662	338	20.4%	—
Annual Growth	1.1%	(2.2%)	—	—

2015 Year-End Financials

Return on assets: 7.2%
Return on equity: 18.5%
Current ratio: 0.50

Cash ($ mil.): 38

OCHSNER HEALTH SYSTEM

EXECUTIVES

Dir, Pedro Cazabon M D
Dir, F Ralph Dauterive
Dir, William H Hines
Dir, R Paker Lecorgne
Accountant, Jessica George
Coordinator, John Cbet
Nurse Manager, Donna Jones
Coordinator, Lee Carrigan
Manager, Mimi Primeaux
Senior Marketing Specialist, Rachel Hymel
Editor, Connie Catha
Auditors: ERNST & YOUNG LLP NEW ORLEANS

LOCATIONS

HQ: OCHSNER HEALTH SYSTEM
  1516 JEFFERSON HWY, NEW ORLEANS, LA
  701212429
Phone: 504 842-3483
Web: WWW.OCHSNER.ORG

HISTORICAL FINANCIALS

Company Type: Private

Income Statement — FYE: December 31

	REVENUE ($ mil.)	NET INCOME ($ mil.)	NET PROFIT MARGIN	EMPLOYEES
12/16	2,812	55	2.0%	19,000
12/15	2,592	63	2.5%	—
Annual Growth	8.5%	(13.2%)	—	—

2016 Year-End Financials

Return on assets: 5.3%   Cash ($ mil.): 121
Return on equity: 2.0%
Current ratio: 0.90

OGDEN ARNOT MEDICAL CENTER

EXECUTIVES

Ceo, Robert Lambert
Cfo - Exec Vice President, Ronald Kintz
Exec SEC, Christine Bohart
Sr Acct, Terry Bellinger
Scientist, Alan Barton
Coordinator, Cheryl Marvel
Coordinator, Nicole Vanalstyne
Project Coordinator, Rosemary Anthony
Internal Medicine Practitioner, Elizabeth A
  Mendoza
Health Professional, Ranjan V Kumar
Information Specialist, Ronald May

LOCATIONS

HQ: OGDEN ARNOT MEDICAL CENTER
  600 ROE AVE, ELMIRA, NY 149051676
Phone: 607 737-4100
Web: WWW.AOMC.ORG

HISTORICAL FINANCIALS

Company Type: Private

Income Statement — FYE: December 31

	REVENUE ($ mil.)	NET INCOME ($ mil.)	NET PROFIT MARGIN	EMPLOYEES
12/16	286	(7)	—	2,400
12/15	211	(11)	—	—
12/14	212	4	2.0%	—
12/13	271	(7)	—	—
Annual Growth	1.9%	—	—	—

2016 Year-End Financials

Return on assets: 7.4%   Cash ($ mil.): 2
Return on equity: (-2.5%)
Current ratio: 0.80

OHIO EDISON COMPANY

Ohio Edison has taken a shine to the folks in the Buckeye state. The company distributes electricity to a population of about 2.3 million (more than 1 million customers) in a 7000 sq. ml. area of central and northeastern Ohio. Ohio Edison a unit of FirstEnergy also has 5955 MW of generating capacity from interests in primarily fossil-fueled and nuclear generation facilities and it sells excess power to wholesale customers. The utility's power plants are operated by sister companies FirstEnergy Nuclear and FirstEnergy Generation. Subsidiary Pennsylvania Power Company provides electric service to communities in a 1100 sq. ml. area of western Pennsylvania which has a population of approximately 400000.

Operations

Ohio Edison and Pennsylvania Power provide regulated electric distribution services and procure of generation services. Ohio Edison operates more than 30460 miles of distribution lines and 500 miles of transmission lines.

Geographic Reach

Ohio Edison and Pennsylvania Power conduct business in portions of Ohio and Pennsylvania.

Financial Performance

Revenues decreased by 11% in 2011 due to lower retail generation revenues partially offset by higher distribution and wholesale generation revenues. Retail generation revenues decreased primarily due to a drop in energy sales caused from an increase in customers shopping for alternative power providers and lower average prices across all customer classes.

Ohio Edison's net income decreased by 17% in 2011 due to lower revenues partially offset by lower purchased power costs.

Strategy

In 2011 parent FirstEnergy acquired Allegheny Energy in a $8.5 billion deal that grew FirstEnergy's generation capacity and dramatically boosted the company's position as a leading regional energy provider.

Company Background

FirstEnergy and Ohio Edison reached a settlement in 2005 with the federal government to reduce harmful emissions from its Ohio power generating plants; in addition to fines Ohio Edison has been mandated to pledge $25 million for wind power biomass and other alternative energy sources. In 2009 Ohio Edison began retrofitting two units at its Shadyside Ohio power plant to burn wood and other biomass materials in order to lower its greenhouse gas output.

EXECUTIVES

Pres, Charles E Jones Jr
Sr V Pres-Cfo, James F Pearson
V Pres-Controller, Harvey L Wagner
Supervisor, Monty Neel
Supervisor, Eric Umbel
Board Member, Ernest Novak
Supervisor Reg Operations Line, Jeffery Akers
Board Member, Paul Addison
Director of Operations Support, Tracy Mayse
Board Member, William Cottle
Engineer, Gregory Macmaster
Auditors: PRICEWATERHOUSECOOPES LP CLEV

LOCATIONS

HQ: OHIO EDISON COMPANY
  76 S MAIN ST BSMT, AKRON, OH 443081817
Phone: 800 736-3402
Web: WWW.FIRSTENERGYCORP.COM

COMPETITORS

Columbia Gas of Ohio   Ohio Power
DPL   Vectren Energy
Dominion East Ohio   Delivery of Ohio
Duke Energy Ohio

HISTORICAL FINANCIALS

Company Type: Private

Income Statement — FYE: December 31

	REVENUE ($ mil.)	NET INCOME ($ mil.)	NET PROFIT MARGIN	EMPLOYEES
12/16	1,394	150	10.8%	1,190
12/11	1,633	128	7.8%	—
12/10	1,836	157	8.6%	—
12/09	2,516	122	4.9%	—
Annual Growth	(8.1%)	3.0%	—	—

OHIO TURNPIKE AND INFRASTRUCTURE COMMISSION

EXECUTIVES

Ceo-Exec Dir, Randy Cole
SEC-Treas, Sandy Barber
Chm, Jerry N Hruby
Vice Chm, Joseph Balog
Brd Mgr, George Dixon
Brd MBR, Timothy J Paradiso
Cfo, Martin S Seekely
Manager, Diane Armstrong
Auditors: C&P ADVISORS LLC CLEVELAND

LOCATIONS

HQ: OHIO TURNPIKE AND INFRASTRUCTURE
  COMMISSION
  682 PROSPECT ST, BEREA, OH 440172711
Phone: 440 234-2081
Web: WWW.OHIOTURNPIKE.NET

HISTORICAL FINANCIALS

Company Type: Private

Income Statement — FYE: December 31

	REVENUE ($ mil.)	NET INCOME ($ mil.)	NET PROFIT MARGIN	EMPLOYEES
12/17	321	(66)	—	953
12/16	313	(230)	—	—
12/10	251	54	21.7%	—
12/09	205	9	4.7%	—
Annual Growth	5.7%	—	—	—

2017 Year-End Financials

Return on assets: 4.6%   Cash ($ mil.): 103
Return on equity: (-20.8%)
Current ratio: 1.10

OHIOHEALTH CORPORATION

Operating throughout the central part of the state OhioHealth aims to keep Buckeyes healthy. The not-for-profit system runs eight acute care hospitals and is affiliated with another 11 community hospitals and area health systems. All told OhioHealth has about 2000 staffed beds in and around Columbus. Additional facilities offer urgent care physical rehabilitation diagnostic imaging and sleep diagnostics services. Subsidiary HomeReach provides home health care and hospice care. Its WorkHealth program offers workers' compensation care management and occupational rehabilitation services. OhioHealth Group OhioHealth's joint venture with The Medical Group of Ohio operates the HealthReach PPO.

Operations
In addition to offering patient care OhioHealth also operates the The OhioHealth Research & Innovation Institute which coordinates research throughout the health system including conducting clinical trials of new drugs and medical devices. The system also operates The Center for Medical Education and Innovation a medical training facility that among other technologies offers human patient simulators on which medical professionals can practice new procedures in various clinical situations.

OhioHealth has some 28000 associates physicians and volunteers. Every year it facilitates approximately 2 million outpatient visits 95000 admissions 346000 emergency department visits 60000 surgeries and 13000 births.

Geographic Reach
OhioHealth operates in the Ohio communities of Athens Columbus Delaware Dublin Kenton Mansfield and Shelby.

Strategy
The company is focused on expanding geographically and capitalizing on opportunities due to population growth in the area. In 2013 it completed the construction of a new patient tower at its Riverside Methodist Hospital; the tower houses much of the company's Neuroscience Institute.

OhioHealth is now building an outpatient facility in Nelsonville which is expected to open sometime in 2017.

The system struck up a partnership with Berger Health System another Ohio-based health care network in 2014. The partners will explore ways to improve health care for the communities they serve.

Mergers and Acquisitions
In 2014 OhioHealth acquired O'Bleness Health System expanding its presence in southeastern Ohio. It also acquired MedCentral Health System.

Company Background
The health system traces its roots back to 1892 when Protestant Hospital (now known as Riverside Methodist Hospital) opened. The system initially organized as U.S. Health Corporation in 1984 later took on the OhioHealth name in 1997.

EXECUTIVES

President And Ceo, David P. Blom, age 64
Evp And Coo, Michael W. (Mike) Louge
President Marion General Hospital, Bruce Hagen
President Riverside Methodist Hospital, Brian D. Jepson
Chief Medical Officer, Bruce Vanderhoff
Svp And Cio, Michael Krouse
Svp External Affairs; President Ohiohealth Foundation, Karen Morrison
President Doctors Hospital, Mike Reichfield
President Ohiohealth Physician Group, Hugh Thornhill
President Ohiohealth Home Care, James P. Newbrough
President O'bleness Hospital, Mark Seckinger
President Mansfield Hospital And Shelby Hospital, Jean Halpin
Svp And Cfo, Vinson M. Yates
President Grant Medical Center, Michael Lawson
Svp And Chief Nursing Executive, Donna Hanly
President Dublin Methodist Hospital And Grady Memorial Hospital, Steve Bunyard
Medical Librarian, Susi Miller
Medical Director Cardiac Imaging Laboratory, Kanny Grewal
Vice Chairman, John P. McConnell, age 64
Chairman, Steve Rasmussen
Auditors: PLANTE & MORAN PLLC COLUMBUS

LOCATIONS
HQ: OHIOHEALTH CORPORATION
180 E BROAD ST, COLUMBUS, OH 432153707
Phone: 614 788-8860
Web: WWW.OHIOHEALTH.COM

PRODUCTS/OPERATIONS

Selected Facilities
Owned
Doctors Hospital (Columbus)
Doctors Hospital Nelsonville (Nelsonville)
Dublin Methodist Hospital (Dublin)
Grady Memorial Hospital (Delaware)
Grant Medical Center (Columbus)
Hardin Memorial Hospital (Kenton)
Marion General Hospital (Marion)
O'Bleness Memorial Hospital (Athens)
Riverside Methodist Hospital (Columbus)
Affiliated
Blanchard Valley Medical Center
Galion Community Hospital (Galion)
Genesis Healthcare System (Zanesville)
Knox Community Hospital
Morrow County Hospital (Mt. Gilead)
Samaritan Regional Health System (Ashland)
Southern Ohio Medical Center (Portsmouth)

COMPETITORS

Adena Health System	Mount Carmel Health
Fairfield Medical Center	Nationwide Children's Hospital
Licking Memorial Health Systems	Regency Hospital
	Select Medical

HISTORICAL FINANCIALS
Company Type: Private

Income Statement				FYE: June 30
	REVENUE ($ mil.)	NET INCOME ($ mil.)	NET PROFIT MARGIN	EMPLOYEES
06/18	4,045	519	12.8%	15,000
06/17	3,792	631	16.6%	—
06/14	2,179	354	16.3%	—
06/11	2,328	412	17.7%	—
Annual Growth	8.2%	3.3%	—	—

2018 Year-End Financials
Return on assets: 2.9%   Cash ($ mil.): 121
Return on equity: 12.8%
Current ratio: 0.70

OJIM, INC.

EXECUTIVES

Chb-Pres, Mijo Radocaj
President, Matt Radocaj
Vice President, Jerry Terwilliger
Manager, Tom Moretz

LOCATIONS
HQ: OJIM, INC.
1212 OBERLIN AVE SW, MASSILLON, OH 446477668
Phone: 330 832-9557
Web: WWW.OJIMINC.COM

HISTORICAL FINANCIALS
Company Type: Private

Income Statement				FYE: December 31
	REVENUE ($ mil.)	NET INCOME ($ mil.)	NET PROFIT MARGIN	EMPLOYEES
12/17	358	(13)	—	15
12/16	0	(0)	—	—
12/15	0	0	0.3%	—
12/14	0	0	13.4%	—
Annual Growth	863.6%	—	—	—

2017 Year-End Financials
Return on assets: 2.8%   Cash ($ mil.): 157
Return on equity: (-3.6%)
Current ratio: 20.60

OKAYA (U.S.A.), INC.

EXECUTIVES

Pres, Yoshitaka Honda
Depty Dir, Nobuo Tsukioka
SEC, Susan J Onuma
Dir, Kaifu Kaifu
Sales Manager, Daniel Yang
General Manager, Koichi Okochi
Auditors: EOS ACCOUNTANTS LLP SCHAUMBUR

LOCATIONS
HQ: OKAYA (U.S.A.), INC.
64 W SEEGERS RD, ARLINGTON HEIGHTS, IL 600053917
Phone: 847 621-5530
Web: WWW.OKAYAUSA.COM

HISTORICAL FINANCIALS
Company Type: Private

Income Statement				FYE: December 31
	REVENUE ($ mil.)	NET INCOME ($ mil.)	NET PROFIT MARGIN	EMPLOYEES
12/17	364	1	0.5%	71
12/06	205	0	0.4%	—
12/05	183	1	0.6%	—
12/04	963	0	—	—
Annual Growth	—	135.5%	—	—

2017 Year-End Financials
Return on assets: 3.7%   Cash ($ mil.): —
Return on equity: 0.5%
Current ratio: 0.50

OLATHE UNIFIED SCHOOL DISTRICT 233

EXECUTIVES

Supt, John Allison
Deputy Supt, John Hutchison
Business Manager, Kim Cross
Occupational Specia, Norma Cosgrove
Occupational Specia, Susan Culp
Occupational Specia, Wendy Nagel
Computer Specialist, Terri Clark
Auditors: MIZE HOUSER & COMPANY PA LAW

LOCATIONS

HQ: OLATHE UNIFIED SCHOOL DISTRICT 233
  14160 S BLACKBOB RD, OLATHE, KS 660622024
Phone: 913 780-7000
Web: WWW.OLATHESCHOOLS.COM

HISTORICAL FINANCIALS
Company Type: Private

Income Statement   FYE: June 30

	REVENUE ($ mil.)	NET INCOME ($ mil.)	NET PROFIT MARGIN	EMPLOYEES
06/18	413	12	3.1%	5,000
06/17	371	59	16.1%	—
06/16	361	(69)	—	—
06/15	357	(76)	—	—
Annual Growth	5.0%	—	—	—

OLD DOMINION UNIVERSITY

EXECUTIVES

Pres, John Broderick
President, John Browerick
Dir of Fin, Melanie O'Dell
Assistant Professor, Jelmer J Vos
Scientist, Andrew Gordon
Assistant Professor, Fred C Dobbs
Assistant Professor, Kaavonia Hinton-Johnson
Scientist, Daniel M Dauer
Scientist, Deborah A Waller
Scientist, Ian Bartol
Scientist, Koen A Vermeer

LOCATIONS

HQ: OLD DOMINION UNIVERSITY
  5115 HAMPTON BLVD, NORFOLK, VA 235290001
Phone: 757 683-3000
Web: WWW.ODU.EDU

HISTORICAL FINANCIALS
Company Type: Private

Income Statement   FYE: June 30

	REVENUE ($ mil.)	NET INCOME ($ mil.)	NET PROFIT MARGIN	EMPLOYEES
06/17	353	28	8.2%	4,390
06/16	275	50	18.3%	—
Annual Growth	28.2%	(42.6%)	—	—

2017 Year-End Financials
Return on assets: 12.5%   Cash ($ mil.): 138
Return on equity: 8.2%
Current ratio: 1.50

OMAHA PUBLIC POWER DISTRICT

Thirteen's the lucky number for Omaha Public Power District (OPPD). A subdivision of the Nebraska state government OPPD generates and distributes electricity to residents and businesses in 13 counties in southeastern Nebraska. It operates and maintains its facilities without tax revenues and raises money for major construction through bonds. OPPD serves more than 356000 customers in an area covering 5000 sq. mi. The utility has a generating capacity of more than 3235 MW which is powered by primarily nuclear coal oil and natural gas sources. It sells wholesale power to other utilities and offers energy consulting and management services.

Operations
OPPD is the 12th-largest publicly owned electric system in the US in terms of numbers of customers served. The power district provides retail service to about 50 towns and wholesale to five. OPPD operates more than 15500 miles of electric line.

The majority of OPPD's power comes from three baseload power plants: North Omaha Station and Nebraska City Station (both coal-fired) and the Fort Calhoun Station nuclear power plant.

Financial Performance
In 2013 OPPD's revenues grew by 4% primarily due to a jump in retail sales as the result of higher energy prices and an increase in the adjustment for the under-recovery of fuel and purchased power expenses. Retail sales growth was partially offset by a decrease in off-system sales and other electric sales.

The company's net income grew by 1% that year due to higher revenues.

In 2013 OPPD's operating cash inflow increased to $168.71 million (from $151.73 million in 2012) due to higher net income and a change in working capital as a result of an increase in cash received from retail customers and insurance companies. This was partially offset by higher cash paid to off-system parties for additional wind energy.

Strategy
Like other utilities OPPD is pushing conservation and green energy initiates to reduce carbon emissions with its customers as a service to help them control costs.

In 2015 OPPD approved the future generation resource plan created in June 2014 calling for the retirement of three of the district's oldest coal generation units and additional environmental controls. The plan includes a mixture of new programs and expansion of some existing programs aimed at reducing power demand.

The company is pursuing a goal of getting 30% of its retail energy from renewable sources. In 2013 it announced a wind farm deal (located northeast of O'Neill Nebraska). The 20-year agreement the largest wind power purchase to date for OPPD will increase its renewable energy generation capacity to 817 MW.

Company Background
It 2011 the utility announced that it was studying how to support the auto industry and customers regarding the larger numbers of electric cars being introduced into its service region.

OPPD was organized as a self-supporting subdivision of the State of Nebraska in 1946 although state power operations date back to 1917.

EXECUTIVES

President And Ceo, W. Gary Gates, age 67
Coo, Timothy J. (Tim) Burke
Vp And Cfo, Edward E. Easterlin
Vice President Of Finance, Leland Jacobsen
Vice President And Controller, Ronald K Bayer
Vice President, John Imig
Vice President, Tim Nissen
Senior Vice President Strategy And Corporate Development, Don Macisaac
Vice President Information Technology, Kathleen Brown
Vice Chair, Anne L. McGuire
Vice Chair, Michael A. (Mick) Mines

LOCATIONS

HQ: OMAHA PUBLIC POWER DISTRICT
  444 S 16TH ST, OMAHA, NE 681022247
Phone: 402 636-2000
Web: WWW.OPPD.COM

COMPETITORS

Basin Electric Power
  NorthWestern
  Preferred Energy
  Services
Tri-State Generation
  and Transmission

HISTORICAL FINANCIALS
Company Type: Private

Income Statement   FYE: December 31

	REVENUE ($ mil.)	NET INCOME ($ mil.)	NET PROFIT MARGIN	EMPLOYEES
12/17	1,104	77	7.0%	2,300
12/16	1,126	(933)	—	—
12/15*	1,131	34	3.1%	—
06/15	1,096	16	1.5%	—
Annual Growth	0.2%	67.4%	—	—
*Fiscal year change

2017 Year-End Financials
Return on assets: 7.7%   Cash ($ mil.): 10
Return on equity: 7.0%
Current ratio: 0.30

OMAHA PUBLIC SCHOOLS

EXECUTIVES

Fin Analyst, Ashley Bader
Controller, Dr Liz Standish
Assist Superintendent, Dr Dennis Pool
Coordinator, Suann Witt
Supervisor, Brenda Todd
Teacher, Brenda Larsen
Accounting Manager, Dan P Pruch
Teacher, Amy Williams
Teacher, Craig Hinson
Assistant, Jennifer Schlapia
Teacher, William Scarborough
Auditors: SEIM JOHNSON LLP OMAHA NEBR

LOCATIONS

HQ: OMAHA PUBLIC SCHOOLS
  3861 FARNAM ST, OMAHA, NE 681312024
Phone: 402 557-2120
Web: WWW.OPS.ORG

HISTORICAL FINANCIALS

Company Type: Private

Income Statement — FYE: August 31

	REVENUE ($ mil.)	NET INCOME ($ mil.)	NET PROFIT MARGIN	EMPLOYEES
08/17	720	33	4.7%	8,000
08/16	693	(41)	—	—
08/15	626	126	20.3%	—
08/14	633	9	1.5%	—
Annual Growth	4.4%	54.0%	—	—

2017 Year-End Financials

Return on assets: 5.1%
Return on equity: 4.7%
Current ratio: —
Cash ($ mil.): 326

ONEAMERICA FINANCIAL PARTNERS, INC.

EXECUTIVES

Chb-Pres-Ceo, J Scott Davison
Exec V Pres-Cfo, Jeffrey D Holley
Exec V Pres, Mark Roller
Exec V Pres-Sr Clo-SEC, Thomas M Zurek
Sr V Pres-CIO, Gene P Berry
Sr V Pres-Chief Hr Officer, Karin Sarratt
Pres Individual Insurance, Patrick M Foley
Vice President, Angela Trefethen
Consultant, Bartholomew Brown
Assistant Vice President, Brian Springer
Manager Public Relations Tax, Christina Cozzolino

LOCATIONS

HQ: ONEAMERICA FINANCIAL PARTNERS, INC.
1 AMERICAN SQ, INDIANAPOLIS, IN 462820020
Phone: 317 285-1877
Web: WWW.ONEAMERICA.COM

HISTORICAL FINANCIALS

Company Type: Private

Income Statement — FYE: December 31

	ASSETS ($ mil.)	NET INCOME ($ mil.)	INCOME AS % OF ASSETS	EMPLOYEES
12/16	19,921	88	0.4%	9,875
12/15	18,491	67	0.4%	—
12/14	0	0	—	—
12/04	15,028	56	0.4%	—
Annual Growth	2.4%	3.8%	—	—

2016 Year-End Financials

Return on assets: —
Return on equity: 8.0%
Sales ($ mil): 1,103

ONEOK PARTNERS, L.P.

For ONEOK Partners it's OK to have three businesses: natural gas pipelines; gas gathering and processing; and natural gas liquids (NGLs). Its pipelines include Midwestern Gas Transmission Guardian Pipeline Viking Gas Transmission and OkTex Pipeline. The ONEOK affiliate operates 17100 miles of gas-gathering pipeline and 7600 miles of transportation pipeline as well as gas processing plants and storage facilities (with 52 billion cu. ft. of capacity). It also owns one of the US's top natural NGL systems (more than 7200 miles of pipeline). In 2017 41%-owner ONEOK agreed to buy the stock of ONEOK Partners that it did not already own for $9.3 billion in a stock deal. Operations ONEOK Partners operates in three business segments: natural gas gathering and processing; natural gas pipelines; and natural gas liquids. Geographic Reach The company gathers and processes natural gas in the Mid-Continent region which includes the NGL-rich Cana-Woodford Shale and Granite Wash formations the Mississippian Lime formation of Oklahoma and Kansas and the Hugoton and Central Kansas Uplift Basins of Kansas. The Natural Gas Pipelines segment owns and operates regulated natural gas transmission pipelines natural gas storage facilities and natural gas gathering systems for nonprocessed gas. It also provide interstate natural gas transportation and storage service. The company's interstate natural gas pipeline assets transport natural gas through pipelines in North Dakota Minnesota Wisconsin Illinois Indiana Kentucky Tennessee Oklahoma Texas and New Mexico. Its Natural gas liquids assets provide nondiscretionary services to producers that consist of facilities that gather fractionate and treat NGLs and store NGL products primarily in Oklahoma Kansas and Texas. It also owns or has stakes in natural gas liquids gathering and distribution pipelines in Oklahoma Kansas Texas Wyoming and Colorado and terminal and storage facilities in Missouri Nebraska Iowa and Illinois. In addition it owns natural gas liquids distribution and refined petroleum products pipelines in Kansas Missouri Nebraska Iowa Illinois and Indiana that connect the company's Mid-Continent assets with Midwest markets including Chicago.

Financial Performance

Revenues decreased by 10% in 2012 due to lower net realized natural gas and NGL product prices offset partially by higher natural gas and NGL sales volumes from completed capital projects. The increase in natural gas supply resulting from the development of nonconventional resource areas in North America and a warmer than normal winter caused natural gas prices to drop. NGL prices particularly ethane and propane also decreased in 2012 due primarily to increased NGL production and an increase in available supply. Propane prices also were affected by a warmer than normal winter.

ONEOK Partners' net income grew by 7% in 2012 thanks to lower costs of sales and fuels and lower interest expenses.

Strategy

The company pursues a strategy of building up its fee-based earnings coupled with organic growth and complementary acquisitions in both conventional oil and gas and unconventional (shale plays). It is looking to increase NGL volumes gathered and fractionated in its NGL segment and natural gas volumes processed in its natural gas gathering and processing segment as producers continue to develop NGL-rich resource plays in the Mid-Continent and Rocky Mountain areas.

In 2012 ONEOK Partners announced plans to invest up to $360 million to grow its projects in the Woodford Shale formation.

Company Background

ONEOK Partners was formed in 2006 when ONEOK spun off its gathering and processing NGLs pipelines and storage businesses for $3 billion following that company's acquisition of Northern Border Partners (which was founded in 1993). Building out its assets in 2007 the company acquired an interstate pipeline system from Kinder Morgan Energy Partners for $300 million.

EXECUTIVES

Pres-Ceo, Terry K Spencer
Evp-Cfo, Walter S Hulse III
Svp,naturalgasgathering&procce, Michael A Fitzgibbons
Executive Vice President Opera, Robert F Martinovich

LOCATIONS

HQ: ONEOK PARTNERS, L.P.
100 W 5TH ST STE LL, TULSA, OK 741034298
Phone: 918 588-7000
Web: WWW.ONEOKPARTNERS.COM

PRODUCTS/OPERATIONS

Natural Gas Pipelines
Midwestern Gas Transmission Company
Viking Gas Transmission Company
Guardian Pipeline
OkTex Pipeline Company
ONEOK Gas Transportation
ONEOK Gas Gathering
ONEOK Gas Storage
ONEOK WesTex Transmission
ONEOK Texas Gas Storage
Mid Continent Market Center
ONEOK Transmission Company
Natural Gas Gathering & Processing
Crestone Energy Ventures
ONEOK Field Services
ONEOK Rockies Midstream

COMPETITORS

Enbridge	Panhandle Eastern Pipe
Kinder Morgan Energy	Line
Partners	TransCanada

HISTORICAL FINANCIALS

Company Type: Private

Income Statement — FYE: December 31

	REVENUE ($ mil.)	NET INCOME ($ mil.)	NET PROFIT MARGIN	EMPLOYEES
12/16	8,918	1,072	12.0%	2,364
12/15	7,761	597	7.7%	—
12/14	12,191	911	7.5%	—
Annual Growth	(14.5%)	8.5%	—	—

2016 Year-End Financials

Return on assets: 9.7%
Return on equity: 12.0%
Current ratio: 0.30
Cash ($ mil.): —

ONTARIO-MONTCLAIR SCHOOL DISTRICT

EXECUTIVES

Supt, James Q Hammond
Asst Supt, Dr Cyndy Byrd
Asst Supt, Karla Wells
Deputy Supt, Kim Stallings
Transportation Director, Martin Willis
Computer Specialist, Nelson Favela
Before/After School Coordinato, Justin Spencer
Personnel Specialist, Isabel Chavez
Director, Jennifer Clark
Director, Lizette Diaz
Auditors: VAVRINEK TRINE DAY & CO LL

LOCATIONS

HQ: ONTARIO-MONTCLAIR SCHOOL DISTRICT
950 W D ST, ONTARIO, CA 917623026
Phone: 909 459-2500
Web: WWW.OMSD.NET

HISTORICAL FINANCIALS

Company Type: Private

Income Statement | | | | FYE: June 30

	REVENUE ($ mil.)	NET INCOME ($ mil.)	NET PROFIT MARGIN	EMPLOYEES
06/17	283	56	19.9%	2,114
06/16	280	13	4.9%	—
06/02	205	19	9.3%	—
06/01	187	6	3.5%	—
Annual Growth	2.6%	14.5%	—	—

OPERATION BLESSING INTERNATIONAL RELIEF AND DEVELOPMENT CORPORATION

EXECUTIVES

Pres, William F Horan
Dir, Michael D Little
SEC, Randy J Morell
Coo, Robert W Fanning
Dir, A E Robertson
General Manager, David Andrews
Manager, Kathy Haines
Manager, Britni Capps
Vice-President, Steve O'Grady
Director, Britni Adkins
Vice-President Operations, Steven Ogrady
Auditors: KPMG LLP MC LEAN VA

LOCATIONS

HQ: OPERATION BLESSING INTERNATIONAL RELIEF AND DEVELOPMENT CORPORATION
977 CENTERVILLE TPKE, VIRGINIA BEACH, VA 234631001
Phone: 757 226-3401
Web: WWW.OB.ORG

HISTORICAL FINANCIALS

Company Type: Private

Income Statement | | | | FYE: March 31

	REVENUE ($ mil.)	NET INCOME ($ mil.)	NET PROFIT MARGIN	EMPLOYEES
03/17	346	1	0.3%	50
03/16	308	(0)	—	—
03/15	255	(1)	—	—
03/09	407	0	0.1%	—
Annual Growth	(2.0%)	9.6%	—	—

2017 Year-End Financials

Return on assets: 0.4%
Return on equity: 0.3%
Current ratio: —
Cash ($ mil.): 4

ORANGE AND ROCKLAND UTILITIES INC

EXECUTIVES

Pres, John McAvoy
President, William G Longhi
Vice President, Francis Peverly
Senior Engineer, Anthony Rainone

LOCATIONS

HQ: ORANGE AND ROCKLAND UTILITIES INC
1 BLUE HILL PLZ STE 20, PEARL RIVER, NY 109653100
Phone: 845 352-6000
Web: WWW.ORU.COM

PRODUCTS/OPERATIONS

2011 Sales

	$ mil.	% of total
Electric	641	75
Gas	214	25
Total	855	100

Subsidiaries

Subsidiaries
Pike County Light & Power Company
Rockland Electric Company

COMPETITORS

Avangrid	Niagara Mohawk
Delmarva Power	PPL Corporation
Enbridge	Public Service
National Fuel Gas	Enterprise Group
New Jersey Resources	

HISTORICAL FINANCIALS

Company Type: Private

Income Statement | | | | FYE: December 31

	REVENUE ($ mil.)	NET INCOME ($ mil.)	NET PROFIT MARGIN	EMPLOYEES
12/16	653	59	9.1%	1,060
12/05	824	50	6.1%	—
12/04	703	46	6.5%	—
12/03	727	45	6.2%	—
Annual Growth	(0.8%)	2.1%	—	—

2016 Year-End Financials

Return on assets: 6.2%
Return on equity: 9.1%
Current ratio: 0.10
Cash ($ mil.): —

ORANGE COUNTY SANITATION DISTRICT FINANCING CORPORATION

EXECUTIVES

Gen Mgr, James Herberg
Gen Mgr, James Ruth
Instrumentation & Controls Eng, Scott Wilcox
Auditors: MACIAS GINI & O'CONNELL LLP N

LOCATIONS

HQ: ORANGE COUNTY SANITATION DISTRICT FINANCING CORPORATION
10844 ELLIS AVE, FOUNTAIN VALLEY, CA 927087018
Phone: 714 962-2411
Web: WWW.OCSD.COM

HISTORICAL FINANCIALS

Company Type: Private

Income Statement | | | | FYE: June 30

	REVENUE ($ mil.)	NET INCOME ($ mil.)	NET PROFIT MARGIN	EMPLOYEES
06/16	315	163	51.9%	626
06/13	304	103	33.9%	—
06/12	260	95	36.6%	—
06/10	225	82	36.7%	—
Annual Growth	5.7%	12.0%	—	—

2016 Year-End Financials

Return on assets: 3.0%
Return on equity: 51.9%
Current ratio: 1.40
Cash ($ mil.): 125

ORANGE COUNTY SUPERINTENDENT OF SCHOOLS

EXECUTIVES

Ceo, Elizabeth Parker
Federal Program Director*, William Habermehl
Ph.d., Supt, Al Mijares
Coordinator, Ann Kantor
Coordinator, Jillian Johnson-Sharp
Supervisor, Kristin Lange
Legal Staff, Norma Garcia
Coordinator, Peggy Tunstall
Vice-President Legal, Trisha Martinez
Analyst, Cynthia Hutchinson
Administrative Assistant, Lujean Romero

LOCATIONS

HQ: ORANGE COUNTY SUPERINTENDENT OF SCHOOLS
200 KALMUS DR, COSTA MESA, CA 926265922
Phone: 714 966-4000
Web: WWW.OCDE.US

HISTORICAL FINANCIALS
Company Type: Private

Income Statement				FYE: June 30
	REVENUE ($ mil.)	NET INCOME ($ mil.)	NET PROFIT MARGIN	EMPLOYEES
06/16	284	25	8.9%	1,500
06/05	252	7	3.1%	—
06/04	110	(109)	—	—
06/03	242	0	0.3%	—
Annual Growth	1.2%	32.4%	—	—

2016 Year-End Financials
Return on assets: 14.8%
Return on equity: 8.9%
Current ratio: —
Cash ($ mil.): 225

ORANGE COUNTY TRANSPORTATION AUTHORITY

Public transportation in sunny Orange County California is overseen by the Orange County Transportation Authority (OCTA). The OCTA is the main provider of bus services in its 800-sq.-mi. territory which is home to more than 3 million people. In cooperation with the Southern California Regional Rail Authority the OCTA oversees Metrolink commuter rail service in Orange County. The agency also operates a 10-mile toll road and issues permits to taxi operators. Revenue from a half-cent local sales tax allows the agency to pay for road improvement and mass transit projects.

Operations
OCTA builds designs operates plans maintains and regulates the robust transportation network within Orange County. In addition to the four modes of transportation (transit driving bicycling and walking) OCTA oversees paratransit services taxi services light rail commuter rail and high?occupancy managed lanes.

It operates rail service for OCTA centers on Metrolink Southern California's commuter rail system linking residential communities to employment and activity centers. Metrolink is operated by the Southern California Regional Rail Authority- a joint powers authority of five member agencies representing the counties of Los Angeles Orange Riverside San Bernardino and Ventura. OCTA is one of the five member agencies that administers Orange County Metrolink activities.

The 91 Express Lanes is a four-lane 10-mile toll road built in the median of California's Riverside Freeway (SR-91) between the Orange/Riverside County line and the SR-55.

Geographic Reach
The company is located in Southern California - south of Los Angeles County north of San Diego County and west of Riverside and San Bernardino counties.

Financial Performance
OCTA's rail budget for fiscal year 2015-16 consists of both operating and capital expenses. Operating expenses in FY 2015-16 are budgeted at $31.6 million while capital expenditures are anticipated to reach $100.4 million. The FY 2015-16 rail capital projects. The organization saw a decline in its budget for FY 2015-16 due to drop in pas-

senger fares and state assistance federal capital assistance grants.

(OCTA uses its revenue primarily in salaries and benefits professional services and capital expenditure).

Strategy
The 2014 - 2019 OCTA Strategic Plan takes a comprehensive forward-looking approach to address Orange County's transportation needs during the next five years.(OCTA maintains a Long-Range Transportation Plan updated every four years to account for new planning efforts as well as changes in demographics economic conditions and available sources of transportation funding).

In the FY 2015-16 budget $6.9 million of Measure M funds deposited in the General Fund are being used to fund the final work on the West County Connectors project.

After four years in the making OCTA marked the completion of the $297 million West County Connector project in 2014 which will bring congestion relief where three major freeways (Interstate 405 Interstate 605 and State Route 22) converge.

In 2014 OCTA purchased 400 new buses for fixed-route and ACCESS services. This purchase combined with the in-process repainting of the existing fleet presents a cost-effective opportunity to explore new branding concepts for Orange County bus services.

Company Background
OCTA was formed in 1991 in a consolidation of seven transportation agencies.

EXECUTIVES
Ceo, Darrell Johnson
Dir, Don Hansen
Director, Charles V Smith
Auditors: VAVRINEK TRINE DAY & CO LL

LOCATIONS
HQ: ORANGE COUNTY TRANSPORTATION AUTHORITY
550 S MAIN ST, ORANGE, CA 928684506
Phone: 714 636-7433
Web: WWW.OCTA.NET

PRODUCTS/OPERATIONS

2014 Sales
	% of total
Sales taxes	93
Unrestricted investment earning	4
Property taxes	3
Other	-
Total	**100**

Selected Services
91 Express Lanes toll facility
Bus transit service
Freeway improvements funding
Freeway Service Patrol
Long-range planning
Measure M2 administration
Metrolink rail service
Rideshare options
Street and road improvements grants
Taxi administration program
Vanpool subsidies

HISTORICAL FINANCIALS
Company Type: Private

Income Statement				FYE: June 30
	REVENUE ($ mil.)	NET INCOME ($ mil.)	NET PROFIT MARGIN	EMPLOYEES
06/17	611	54	9.0%	1,050
06/16	600	67	11.2%	—
06/15	607	43	7.2%	—
06/12	609	23	3.8%	—
Annual Growth	0.1%	18.8%	—	—

ORANGE REGIONAL MEDICAL CENTER

EXECUTIVES
Ceo, Scott Batulis
Vice President, Joe Anesi
Vice President, Rosemary Baczewski
Chm, Rolland Peacock III
Vice President, Mitchell Amado
Director, Lisa A Fisher
Information Technology Project, Ken Sweeney
Executive Assistant, Nora Killeen
Vice-President Human Resources, Deborah Carr
Network Technician, Michael Petrulak
Director, Joseph Adonnino

LOCATIONS
HQ: ORANGE REGIONAL MEDICAL CENTER
707 E MAIN ST, MIDDLETOWN, NY 109402667
Phone: 845 343-2424
Web: WWW.ORMC.ORG

HISTORICAL FINANCIALS
Company Type: Private

Income Statement				FYE: December 31
	REVENUE ($ mil.)	NET INCOME ($ mil.)	NET PROFIT MARGIN	EMPLOYEES
12/16	442	6	1.5%	2,000
12/15	408	6	1.5%	—
12/14	374	4	1.3%	—
12/13	371	(8)	—	—
Annual Growth	6.0%	—	—	—

2016 Year-End Financials
Return on assets: 3.9%
Return on equity: 1.5%
Current ratio: 1.10
Cash ($ mil.): 26

OREGON HEALTH & SCIENCE UNIVERSITY

Oregon Health & Science University (OHSU) is the state's sole institution providing doctoral degrees in medicine dentistry and nursing. Its other two schools are science and engineering and in partnership with Oregon State University pharmacy. OHSU has about 2900 students. The university is also home to two hospitals (one a children's hospital) as well as specialty and primary care clinics research and interdisciplinary centers and community service programs. OHSU traces its roots to 1867 when members of the medical department at Willamette University began the first formal medical education program in Oregon.

Operations
OHSU's medical school has a small student-teacher ratio at just 4:1. The organization is renowned for its research initiatives. It has about 3000 active research projects and produced about 130 inventions in 2014. OHSU receives about $370 million in research funding each year. The school engages in an array of multidisciplinary research projects including diseases of the central nervous system weight regulation cancer rare genetic disorders and infectious disease.

Much of the university's medical research is performed at or in concert with clinical care operations at the University Hospital the Doernbecher Children's Hospital and other family care and specialty centers. The medical centers care for some 260000 patients each year.

Researchers at OHSU's Stem Cell Center worked with the Oregon National Primate Research Center to pioneer the first successful cloned nonhuman primate embryonic stem cells. Such cells could help stem cell research gain acceptance as the human element that causes such controversy has been removed.

Geographic Reach

OHSU's main campus includes about 40 buildings on 120 acres on Marquam Hill (overlooking downtown Portland). OHSU also operates two smaller research locations: The Schnitzer Campus in Portland and the West Campus in Hillsboro.

Financial Performance

The university's revenue totaled $2.5 billion in 2015 (versus less than $2 billion in 2012). The earnings primarily came from patient service revenue gifts grants and contracts. Net income increased 49% that year to $320 million thanks to the growing revenues.

OHSU has an operating budget of some $2.4 billion.

Strategy

OHSU completed construction of its collaborative life sciences building on the Schnitzer Campus in 2014. The 650000-sq.-ft. building features lecture halls classrooms specialty research centers offices simulation centers and serves as home to the School of Dentistry; it was built on land donated by the Schnitzer family in 2004. OHSU has purchased additional parcels of land in the area for future expansion efforts.

Also in 2014 OHSU partnered with the small hospital Mid-Columbia Medical Center (MCMC) to recruit medical professionals. Recruits will be employees of OHSU and their services will be leased to MCMC.

The system is working with Adventist Health Kaiser Permanente and Legacy Health to open up the Portland area's first comprehensive behavioral health center (to be named the Unity Center for Behavioral Health). It is expected to open in late 2016.

EXECUTIVES

Vice President, Amy Wayson
Executive Vice President Chief Financial Officer, Lawrence J. Furnstahl
Evp And Executive Director Ohsu Hospitals And Clinics, Peter F. Rapp
President And Director, Joseph (Joe) Robertson
Dean School Of Medicine, Mark Richardson
Executive Vice President And Provost, Jeanette Mladenovic
Medical Director Pediatric Bone Marrow Transplantation Program, Eneida Nemecek
Senior Vice President, Constance French
Director Of Admissions, Debbie Melton
Nursing Director, Irene Vetto
Senior Vice President For Public Affairs And Chief Of Staff, Connie Seeley
Vice President Finance And Administration, Lori Mueller
Vice President Oncology Services, Ann Raish
Senior Vice President, Jack Friedman
Vice President And Chief Integrity Officer, Jennifer Ruocco
Associate Vice President, Donald Lollar
Vice President Technology And Services, Nancy Goldschmidt
Medical Director, Zane Horowitz
Department Head Professor, Antonio Baptista
Vice President Technology Transfer And Business Development, Brendan Rauw
Medical Director, Jim Chesnutt

Clinic Manager, Mike Rennick
Associate Vice President Strategic Communications, Beth A Heinrich
Senior Vice President Human Resources, E F Keeling
Clinic Manager, Kimberly Harris
Medical Director, Scott Naugler
Chairman, Charles A. Wilhoite
Vice Chairman, Jay Waldron
Secretary, Diana Gernhart
Board Member, Sandra Gallagher
Auditors: KPMG LLP PORTLAND OR

LOCATIONS

HQ: OREGON HEALTH & SCIENCE UNIVERSITY
3181 SW SAM JACKSON PK RD, PORTLAND, OR 972393011
Phone: 503 494-8311
Web: WWW.OHSU.EDU

PRODUCTS/OPERATIONS

Selected schools
School of Dentistry
School of Medicine
School of Nursing
School of Pharmacy (with Oregon State University)
School of Science & Engineering

HISTORICAL FINANCIALS

Company Type: Private

Income Statement				FYE: June 30
	REVENUE ($ mil.)	NET INCOME ($ mil.)	NET PROFIT MARGIN	EMPLOYEES
06/18	3,050	259	8.5%	19,500
06/17	2,846	222	7.8%	—
06/13	2,169	221	10.2%	—
06/12	1,975	78	4.0%	—
Annual Growth	7.5%	22.0%	—	—

2018 Year-End Financials
Return on assets: 5.2%   Cash ($ mil.): 52
Return on equity: 8.5%
Current ratio: 0.90

ORLEANS INTERNATIONAL, INC.

EXECUTIVES

Ceo, Earl Tushman
SEC-Treas, Lawrence Tushman
V Pres, Larry Tushman
V Pres, Reed Tushman
V Pres, Marc Tushman
V Pres, Steve Sanger
Chief Financial Officer, Jerry Castellano
Coordinator, Andrea Thilmany
Executive Officer, Dave Archambeau
Executive Officer, Tim Stuart
Executive Officer, Pam Poma
Auditors: UHY LLP FARMINGTON HILLS MIC

LOCATIONS

HQ: ORLEANS INTERNATIONAL, INC.
30600 NORTHWESTERN HWY # 300, FARMINGTON HILLS, MI 483343172
Phone: 248 855-5556
Web: WWW.ORLEANSINTL.COM

HISTORICAL FINANCIALS

Company Type: Private

Income Statement				FYE: December 31
	REVENUE ($ mil.)	NET INCOME ($ mil.)	NET PROFIT MARGIN	EMPLOYEES
12/17	498	1	0.4%	32
12/16	610	1	0.3%	—
12/15*	856	1	0.2%	—
11/08	474	1	0.4%	—
Annual Growth	0.6%	0.1%	—	—

*Fiscal year change

ORLEANS PARISH SCHOOL DISTRICT

EXECUTIVES

Supt, Stanley Smith
Ceo-Supt, Alphonse G Davis
Coo, Roger Reese
Principal, Victor Gordon
Purchasing Coordinator, Lynn Dillon
Auditors: LA PORTE METAIRIE LA

LOCATIONS

HQ: ORLEANS PARISH SCHOOL DISTRICT
3520 GENERAL DE GAULLE DR # 5055, NEW ORLEANS, LA 701144000
Phone: 504 304-3520
Web: WWW.NOPS.K12.LA.US

HISTORICAL FINANCIALS

Company Type: Private

Income Statement				FYE: June 30
	REVENUE ($ mil.)	NET INCOME ($ mil.)	NET PROFIT MARGIN	EMPLOYEES
06/17	433	(0)	—	7,062
06/16	473	46	9.8%	—
06/05	419	19	4.7%	—
06/03	521	(18)	—	—
Annual Growth	(1.3%)	—	—	—

2017 Year-End Financials
Return on assets: 3.2%   Cash ($ mil.): 235
Return on equity: —
Current ratio: —

OROVILLE HOSPITAL

EXECUTIVES

Ceo, Robert J Wentz
Coo, Scott Chapple
Cfo, Ashok Khanchandani
Mgr, Peter M M Russo
Controller, Colleen Duncan
Quality Assurance Director, Debbie Jones
Information Technology Manager, Greg Bennett
Supervisor, John Glaspie
Operations Manager, James Campbell
Human Resources Manager, Jessica Montoya
Scientist, Darrin Kean
Auditors: ARMANINO LLP SAN RAMON CALIF

LOCATIONS

HQ: OROVILLE HOSPITAL
 2767 OLIVE HWY, OROVILLE, CA 959666118
Phone: 530 533-8500

HISTORICAL FINANCIALS
Company Type: Private

Income Statement				FYE: November 30
	REVENUE ($ mil.)	NET INCOME ($ mil.)	NET PROFIT MARGIN	EMPLOYEES
11/17	286	16	5.6%	1,400
11/16	251	9	3.8%	—
11/15	236	18	7.9%	—
11/14	217	14	6.7%	—
Annual Growth	9.7%	3.5%	—	—

2017 Year-End Financials
Return on assets: 4.4% Cash ($ mil.): 6
Return on equity: 5.6%
Current ratio: 0.60

OSF HEALTHCARE SYSTEM

OSF Healthcare helps patients who are feeling oh-so-frail in northern Illinois and southwestern Michigan. OSF Healthcare system includes 11 acute care hospitals and one long-term care facility that combined are home to more than 1500 beds and offer a full spectrum of inpatient and outpatient medical and surgical services. The system's primary care physician network consists of about 650 physicians at more than 105 locations throughout its service area. Subsidiary OSF Home Care provides hospice home visit and equipment services and OSF Saint Francis provides ambulance pharmacy and health care management services. The not-for-profit system is a subsidiary of the Sisters of The Third Order of St. Francis.

Operations
Along with its various acute care hospitals OSF Healthcare provides urgent care through its OSF PromptCare locations. PromptCare administers a range of services including labs MRI ultrasound and primary and specialty care.

The company also has two colleges of nursing — Saint Francis Medical Center College of Nursing in Peoria Illinois; and the Saint Anthony College of Nursing in Rockford Illinois.

The system had some 58000 inpatient admissions; 1.3 million outpatient visits; and 254000 emergency department visits in 2014.

Financial Performance
In 2014 gross patient services revenue totaled $6.9 billion.

Strategy
OSF Healthcare has an incubation collaboration with the University of Illinois College of Medicine at Peoria. The venture dubbed Jump Trading Simulation and Education Center was established in 2013 to focus on advances in education research and innovation. It has been involved in such activities as funding 3-D printing for surgical procedures and exposing high school students to medical training experiences.

EXECUTIVES

Ceo, Robert Sehring
Consultant, D Ick Brooks
Corporate Office Site Director, Mike Redd

Staff, Marc Matulis
Executive Officer, Judith Duva
Executive Officer, Ruth Clift
Senior Vice-President, Gerald J McShane
Senior Vice-President, Robert Sawicki
Auditors: KPMG LLP CHICAGO ILLINOIS

LOCATIONS

HQ: OSF HEALTHCARE SYSTEM
 800 NE GLEN OAK AVE, PEORIA, IL 616033200
Phone: 309 655-2850
Web: WWW.OSFHEALTHCARE.ORG

PRODUCTS/OPERATIONS

Selected Clinical Services
Cancer Care
Diabetes & Endocrinology
Emergency Services
Heart & Vascular
Home Health
Hospice
Neurosciences
Pediatrics
Primary Care
Rehabilitation
Surgery
Transplant Services
Weight Loss Management
Women's Health

Selected Support Services
Advance Care Planning
Clinical Research
Equipment Technology Services
Home Infusion Pharmacy
Home Medical Equipment
Mobile Medical Systems
OSF Life Flight
Retail Services
Skilled Nursing Network
System Laboratory
Telehealth

Selected Facilities
OSF Holy Family Medical Center (Monmouth IL)
OSF Saint Anthony Medical Center (Rockford IL)
OSF Saint Clare Home (Peoria Heights IL)
OSF Saint Elizabeth Medical Center (formerly Ottowa Regional Hospital Ottawa IL)
OSF Saint Francis Medical Center (Peoria IL)
OSF Saint James - John W. Albrecht Medical Center (Pontiac IL)
OSF St. Mary Medical Center (Galesburg IL)
OSF St. Francis Hospital (Escanaba MI)
OSF St. Joseph Medical Center (Bloomington IL)

COMPETITORS

Advocate BroMenn	Rush-Copley Medical
Centegra Health System	Center
Central DuPage	SwedishAmerican Health
Hospital	System
Covenant HealthCare	University of Chicago
Genesis Health System	Medical Center
McDonough District	University of Michigan
Hospital	Health System
Memorial Health System	Wheaton Franciscan
Northwestern Memorial	Services
HealthCare	

HISTORICAL FINANCIALS
Company Type: Private

Income Statement				FYE: September 30
	REVENUE ($ mil.)	NET INCOME ($ mil.)	NET PROFIT MARGIN	EMPLOYEES
09/17	2,561	144	5.7%	4,000
09/16	2,422	99	4.1%	—
09/15	86	19	22.3%	—
09/14	1,958	170	8.7%	—
Annual Growth	9.4%	(5.3%)	—	—

2017 Year-End Financials
Return on assets: 12.0% Cash ($ mil.): 195
Return on equity: 5.7%
Current ratio: 1.60

OUR LADY OF LOURDES MEDICAL CENTER, INC

Our Lady of Lourdes Medical Center tends to the sick of southern New Jersey. The hospital is a general acute care facility with about 325 inpatient beds. In addition to general medical emergency and surgical care the hospital specializes in organ transplantation joint replacement rehabilitation dialysis treatment cardiac care and birthing care. The hospital also offers nursing and other medical training programs and it operates area clinics and provides community health and outreach services. Our Lady of Lourdes Medical Center part of Catholic Health East's Lourdes Health System is sponsored by the Franciscan Sisters of Allegany New York.

Operations
The medical center's specialty units include the New Jersey Heart Institute at Lourdes the Regional Perinatal Center and the Lourdes Rehabilitation Center as well as regional dialysis and organ transplant clinics. Besides offering primary and specialty care services in a variety of fields Our Lady of Lourdes Medical Center is a teaching and research facility through affiliations with area universities and health professional schools. It also operates its own nursing school.

The hospital had a total of 13682 admissions on 2014. Its physicians performed 3184 inpatient and 2392 outpatient surgeries.

Strategy
Our Lady of Lourdes Medical Center has undergone expansion efforts over the years to attract and retain customers in the region by continually upgrading its technology. The hospital also strives to expand services and resources for doctors and health professionals. In 2014 it became one of only a few hospitals in the South Jersey region to implant subcutaneous implantable defibrillators. The cardiac device is the first and only one of its kind that provides defibrillator therapy without touching the heart.

Lourdes Health System has also expanded by opening new outpatient care centers in Camden and the greater Philadelphia metropolitan area. It is the only hospital in the tri-state area (New Jersey Pennsylvania and Delaware) to have been awarded the American Hospital Association's top honor for excellence in community outreach services.

Company Background
In 2012 Our Lady of Lourdes Medical Center relocated and expanded its birthing center to include all-private rooms with improved family accommodations. It has also updated some of its medical equipment and energy systems including the addition of a new MRI imaging system during 2012 to improve patient comfort and diagnostic capabilities.

That year it enriched its educational programs by forming partnerships with the Immaculata University and Camden Community College to offer nursing bachelor's and master's degrees through its Our Lady of Lourdes School of Nursing.

EXECUTIVES

Director Of Radiology, Glenn A Articolo
Director Of Medical Records, Octavia Gaston
Vice President, Kim Barnes

LOCATIONS

HQ: OUR LADY OF LOURDES MEDICAL CENTER, INC
1600 HADDON AVE, CAMDEN, NJ 081033101
Phone: 856 757-3500
Web: WWW.LOURDESNURSINGSCHOOL.ORG

PRODUCTS/OPERATIONS

Selected Services
Bariatric Surgery
Cardiac Services
Community Outreach
Dialysis
Emergency Services
Joint Replacement Center
Organ Transplantation
Rehabilitation Center
Senior Services
Stroke
Women and Children's Services

COMPETITORS

Abington Memorial Hospital
Albert Einstein Healthcare Network
Aria Health
Christiana Care
Fox Chase Cancer Center
Inspira Health Network
Main Line Health System
Mercy Health System
North Philadelphia Health System
TUHS
Tenet Healthcare
The Cooper Health System
University of Pennsylvania Health System
Virtua Health

HISTORICAL FINANCIALS

Company Type: Private

Income Statement				FYE: June 30
	REVENUE ($ mil.)	NET INCOME ($ mil.)	NET PROFIT MARGIN	EMPLOYEES
06/15	308	28	9.1%	3,000
06/14	298	14	4.7%	—
Annual Growth	3.5%	99.9%	—	—

2015 Year-End Financials
Return on assets: 9.5%
Return on equity: 9.1%
Current ratio: 1.50
Cash ($ mil.): 2

OUR LADY OF LOURDES MEMORIAL HOSPITAL, INC.

EXECUTIVES

Pres-Ceo, David Patak
Cfo, Michael Hammond
Chair Person, Thomas J Oven
Scientist, Kelly Cwikla
Senior Vice-President, Linda Miller
Chief Purchasing Officer, Dennis Mullen
Administrative Assistant, Lisa Schappert
Plastic Surgeon, Francisco Rilloraza
Manager, Shirley Simeck
Executive Director, Chris Baron
Auditors: P DELOITTE TAX LLP CINCINNAT

LOCATIONS

HQ: OUR LADY OF LOURDES MEMORIAL HOSPITAL, INC.
169 RIVERSIDE DR, BINGHAMTON, NY 139054198
Phone: 607 798-5111
Web: WWW.LOURDES.COM

HISTORICAL FINANCIALS

Company Type: Private

Income Statement				FYE: June 30
	REVENUE ($ mil.)	NET INCOME ($ mil.)	NET PROFIT MARGIN	EMPLOYEES
06/16	310	3	1.0%	1,500
06/15*	160	15	9.4%	—
12/14	286	25	9.0%	—
12/13	281	30	10.9%	—
Annual Growth	5.1%	(67.5%)	—	—

*Fiscal year change

2016 Year-End Financials
Return on assets: 6.0%
Return on equity: 1.0%
Current ratio: —
Cash ($ mil.): 5

OUR LADY OF LOURDES REGIONAL MEDICAL CENTER, INC.

EXECUTIVES

Vice President Finance Controller, Jennifer Clowers
Medical Director, Kemp Corell
Occupational Therapy Director, Holly Domingue
Vice President Medical Affairs, Anthony Blalock

LOCATIONS

HQ: OUR LADY OF LOURDES REGIONAL MEDICAL CENTER, INC.
4801 AMBSSDOR CFFERY PKWY, LAFAYETTE, LA 705086917
Phone: 337 470-2000
Web: WWW.LOURDESRMC.COM

COMPETITORS

Baton Rouge General
CHRISTUS St. Frances
   Cabrini Hospital
General Health System
LHC Group
LSU System
Lafayette General
   Medical Center
Lane Regional Medical
   Center
Our Lady of the Lake
   RMC
River Parishes
   Hospital
Terrebonne General
   Medical Center
Woman's Hospital

HISTORICAL FINANCIALS

Company Type: Private

Income Statement				FYE: June 30
	REVENUE ($ mil.)	NET INCOME ($ mil.)	NET PROFIT MARGIN	EMPLOYEES
06/18	294	2	1.0%	1,700
06/16	228	(24)	—	—
06/15	197	(38)	—	—
06/10	162	(9)	—	—
Annual Growth	7.7%	—	—	—

2018 Year-End Financials
Return on assets: 3.5%
Return on equity: 1.0%
Current ratio: 1.60
Cash ($ mil.): 20

OUR LADY OF THE LAKE HOSPITAL, INC.

Our Lady of the Lake Regional Medical Center reaches out to Baton Rouge residents with a helping hand. Participating in teaching programs for LSU and Tulane medical schools the medical center has some 800 inpatient beds and includes trauma emergency surgery general medical and specialty care centers for conditions including heart disease cancer orthopedics and ENT (ear nose and throat) disorders. Our Lady of the Lake also includes a Children's Hospital two nursing homes and an independent-living facility and it offers outpatient services at its main campus and at satellite facilities throughout the greater Baton Rouge area.

Operations

The hospital's family of services include an 800-bed Regional Medical Center; a dedicated Children's Hospital; a 350-provider Physician Group primary care network free-standing emergency room in Livingston Parish; an outpatient imaging and surgery centers; Assumption Community Hospital; a network of urgent care clinics; and Our Lady of the Lake College.

Our Lady of the Lake is a primary teaching site for graduate medical education programs and serves 45000 inpatients and 350000 outpatients a year.

The company has more than 850 doctors. Some 70% of its physicians and other professional medical staff members are board certified and in nearly one-third of the hospital system's medical specialty areas 100% of the physicians and other professionals are board certified.

Strategy

As a major facility in the Baton Rouge area Our Lady of the Lake has been expanding its services in the region in recent years. In 2015 Our Lady of the Lake Children's Hospital opened its first pediatric specialty clinic outside of the Baton Rouge area offering specialized outpatient care for pediatric gastroenterology patients.

In 2014 the company opened a new children's emergency room and expanded its adult emergency department.

Company Background

In 2012 the hospital constructed a freestanding emergency room facility in the suburban community of Livingston Louisiana. It is also building a new nine-story patient tower to the main hospital campus; the tower will house the heart and vascular center as well as an expanded ER and a new level 1 regional trauma center and will be completed in late 2013.

Our Lady of the Lake has also expanded its education programs. For instance it added a pediatric residency program in 2010. The hospital also moved to extend its relationship with LSU that year by agreeing to become the primary clinical site for the LSU medical school. The agreement came as LSU considered whether to build a replacement hospital for its aging teaching facility and coincides with the Our Lady of the Lake expansion projects. The partnership launched a new psychiatric residency program in 2012.

Our Lady of the Lake was founded in 1923 by the Franciscan Missionaries of Our Lady.

EXECUTIVES

Ceo-Pres, K Scott Wester
Chb, Charles Valluzzo
Staff, Griffith R Bryan Jr
Purchasing Coordinator, Pam Andrew
Director Comp, Hunter Richardson

LOCATIONS

HQ: OUR LADY OF THE LAKE HOSPITAL, INC.
7777 HENNESSY BLVD, BATON ROUGE, LA
708084300
Phone: 225 765-6565
Web: WWW.OLOLRMC.COM

PRODUCTS/OPERATIONS

Selected Services

Advanced Wound and Ostomy Clinic
Cancer
Children's Hospital
Critical Care
Diabetes & Nutrition Center
Emergency Services
Endoscopy Center
Hearing and Balance Center
Heart & Vascular Institute
Imaging Services
Laboratory and Diagnostics
Lake Express Check-In
LSU Health Baton Rouge
Mental and Behavioral Health
Neurology Neurosurgery and Stroke
Orthopedics
Palliative Care
Pharmacy
Rehabilitation Center
Respiratory Care
Senior Services
St. Anthony's Home
Surgery
Trauma Center
Urgent Care
Voice Center
Weight Loss

COMPETITORS

CHRISTUS St. Frances
  Cabrini Hospital
Dynacq Healthcare
General Health System
Lane Regional Medical
  Center

Our Lady of Lourdes
River Parishes
  Hospital
Woman's Hospital

HISTORICAL FINANCIALS

Company Type: Private

Income Statement   FYE: June 30

	REVENUE ($ mil.)	NET INCOME ($ mil.)	NET PROFIT MARGIN	EMPLOYEES
06/18	1,254	103	8.2%	1,800
06/16	895	(89)	—	—
06/15	984	21	2.1%	—
06/14	946	56	6.0%	—
Annual Growth	7.3%	16.0%	—	—

2018 Year-End Financials

Return on assets: 4.9%
Return on equity: 8.2%
Current ratio: 1.40

Cash ($ mil.): 118

OVERLAKE HOSPITAL ASSOCIATION

EXECUTIVES

Prin, Diane Sperry
Coordinator, Lisa Sato
Nurse Manager, Jody Burnell
Coordinator, Jennifer Fischer
Registered Nurse, Nancy Corbridge
Registered Nurse, Anastasia Samsonov
Recruiting Manager, Jan Malone

Coordinator, Jennifer Foskett
Physical Therapist, Magdalena Pertoldova
Coordinator, Alexis Merced
Director, Mark Forrest
Auditors: KPMG LLP SEATTLE WA

LOCATIONS

HQ: OVERLAKE HOSPITAL ASSOCIATION
1035 116TH AVE NE, BELLEVUE, WA 980044604
Phone: 425 688-5000
Web: WWW.OVERLAKEHOSPITAL.ORG

HISTORICAL FINANCIALS

Company Type: Private

Income Statement   FYE: June 30

	REVENUE ($ mil.)	NET INCOME ($ mil.)	NET PROFIT MARGIN	EMPLOYEES
06/18	559	41	7.4%	198
06/17	513	58	11.3%	—
06/16	511	8	1.6%	—
06/15	490	20	4.1%	—
Annual Growth	4.5%	27.3%	—	—

2018 Year-End Financials

Return on assets: 3.9%
Return on equity: 7.4%
Current ratio: 0.90

Cash ($ mil.): 29

OVERLAKE HOSPITAL MEDICAL CENTER

Over the lake and through the sound to Overlake Hospital Medical Center we go! The not-for-profit hospital provides health care services to residents of Bellevue Washington in the Puget Sound region. The nearly 350-bed facility provides comprehensive inpatient and outpatient services ranging from cancer care and surgery to specialized senior care. Overlake also operates a number of outpatient clinics providing primary care urgent care and specialty care such as weight loss surgery. The organization also provides patients with health and wellness programs addressing issues like women's and children's health.

Operations

The medical center has more than 1000 physicians on staff and runs Centers of Excellence in cardiac care cancer care surgical services women's and infants' care and emergency and Level III trauma care. The facility is home to a 24-hour urgent care clinic an anticoagulation clinic and a breast screening center. Overlake also operates numerous outpatient clinics providing primary care urgent care and specialty care.

Geographic Reach

Overlake provides health care services to residents of Bellevue Washington and the entire Puget Sound region. It operates clinics on its main campus in Bellevue as well as in Redmond and in Issaquah and on Mercer Island.

Sales and Marketing

In 2014 Medicare payments accounted for 27% of net patient revenues followed by group health organizations (17%) Premera (13%) and Regence (12%).

Financial Performance

Overlake's revenues increased by 2% to $433 million in 2014 as the result of higher net patient revenues and contribution revenues.

Net income rose 50% to $60 million that year primarily due to income from change in net unrealized gains on investments. Cash flow from oper-

ations fell 3% to $47 million as more cash was used in net clinic accounts receivable pledges receivable prepaid expenses and other long-term receivables.

Strategy

Increasing demand in the region has led the hospital to invest in expansions and equipment upgrades that include more emergency treatment capabilities and an on-campus helistop for trauma patients being airlifted to the area.

Along with its expansion and construction projects Overlake is investing in new technology to keep the health system in line with its competitors and to improve patient care. It is adding endoscopic video towers to its operating rooms to facilitate improved views of surgical procedures and is also moving to digitize all of its facilities with electronic health records.

In 2013 it opened the new $17.4 million David and Shelley Hovind Heart & Vascular center. The new 19200-sq.-ft. facility brings cardiac and vascular services together in one location.

Overlake has also focused on adding new primary care clinics and expanding its physician network to serve patients in locations closer to where they live and work.

Company Background

Overlake founded in 1960 is led by CEO Craig Hendrickson a veteran health care executive.

EXECUTIVES

Medical Director, Richard Clarfeld
Director Patient Care Nursing, Barbara Berkau
Ambulatory Services Director, Barbara Hein
  Murdock
Vice President Information Services And Cio, Jody
  Albright
Managing Director, Peter Kures
Vice President Of Strategy Marketing Pr And
  Network Development, Caitlin Hillary
Auditors: KPMG LLP SEATTLE WA

LOCATIONS

HQ: OVERLAKE HOSPITAL MEDICAL CENTER
1035 116TH AVE NE, BELLEVUE, WA 980044687
Phone: 425 688-5000
Web: WWW.OVERLAKEHOSPITAL.ORG

Selected Locations

Outpatient Rehabilitation Services
Outpatient Surgery (park in the West Garage; Outpatient Surgery is located on the first floor of the West Garage.)
Overlake Bellevue Campus and Overlake Medical Clinics Medical Tower
Overlake Medical Clinics Downtown Bellevue
Overlake Medical Clinics Issaquah
Overlake Medical Clinics Kirkland
Overlake Medical Clinics Redmond
Urgent Care Clinic in Issaquah
Urgent Care Clinic in Redmond

PRODUCTS/OPERATIONS

2014 Sales

	% of total
Net patient service revenue	97
Other operating revenue	3
Contribution revenue	-
Total	100

Selected Medical Services

Breast Health Services
Cancer Center at Overlake
Cardiac Center at Overlake
Clinical Trials
Emergency & Trauma Center
Medical Imaging
Overlake Medical Clinics
Surgical Services
Weight Loss Surgery
Women's & Infants' Center

HISTORICAL FINANCIALS

Company Type: Private

Income Statement				FYE: June 30
	REVENUE ($ mil.)	NET INCOME ($ mil.)	NET PROFIT MARGIN	EMPLOYEES
06/18	555	39	7.1%	2,450
06/16	502	21	4.3%	—
06/15	485	16	3.5%	—
06/14	450	59	13.3%	—
Annual Growth	5.4%	(10.0%)	—	—

2018 Year-End Financials

Return on assets: 3.9%
Return on equity: 7.1%
Current ratio: 1.00
Cash ($ mil.): 28

PACE UNIVERSITY

Students can learn at their own pace at Pace University which offers certificate programs as well as undergraduate graduate and doctoral degrees through half a dozen schools: arts and sciences business computer science and information systems education law and nursing. Altogether the school is home to 100 undergraduate majors offering roughly 30 undergraduate and graduate degrees 50 master's programs and four doctoral programs. Nearly 13000 students attend the university's three New York campuses (Lower Manhattan Pleasantville-Briarcliff and White Plains). Pace was founded in 1906 by the brothers Homer and Charles Pace as a co-educational business school called Pace Institute.

Operations

The school has an endowment of more than $100 million. Besides its three New York campuses the university also offers courses online and at a location in midtown Manhattan.

Geographic Reach

Pace boasts campus locations in New York City and in Westchester County.

Financial Performance

The university logged a 3% increase in revenue in 2012 as compared to 2011 due to a boost in contributions as well as tuition and fees net government grants and contracts. Net income meanwhile dropped by 160% during the same reporting period thanks to rises in expenses and unrealized depreciation in fair value of derivative instruments in 2012 vs. appreciation in 2011.

Company Background

In 1948 Pace began its transformation into its current incarnation as a liberal arts and sciences college.

EXECUTIVES

Pres, Stephen J Friedman
SEC-Legal Counsel, Stephen Brodsky
Cfo, Robert C Almon
Cfo, Toby Weiner

Programmer, Sarah Shamilov
Analyst, Stephen Salbod
Dean, Pforzheimer Honors Colle, Susan Dinan
Dean of Admissions, Todd E Heilman
Coordinator, Whitney Brown
Trustee, Barbara Ann Porceddu
Trustee, Charles N Jordan Jr
Auditors: PRICEWATERHOUSECOOPERS LLP NE

LOCATIONS

HQ: PACE UNIVERSITY
1 PACE PLZ, NEW YORK, NY 100381598
Phone: 212 346-1956
Web: WWW.PACE.EDU

HISTORICAL FINANCIALS

Company Type: Private

Income Statement				FYE: June 30
	REVENUE ($ mil.)	NET INCOME ($ mil.)	NET PROFIT MARGIN	EMPLOYEES
06/16	393	14	3.7%	1,862
06/14	492	26	5.4%	—
06/13	326	20	6.2%	—
06/12	310	(15)	—	—
Annual Growth	6.1%	—	—	—

2016 Year-End Financials

Return on assets: 14.3%
Return on equity: 3.7%
Current ratio: —
Cash ($ mil.): 9

PACIFIC COAST PRODUCERS

Fruits seafood sauces and organic tomato puree — rather than movies — are the creative output of this particular group of Pacific Coast Producers. The cooperative markets the apricots grapes peaches pears and tomatoes grown by its approximately 160 California-based members. It turns the produce into private-label canned fruit sauces and juices and sells them to the retail and foodservice industries. Pacific Coast Producers typically serves retailers the likes of Albertson's Aldi Kroger Safeway SUPERVALU Whole Foods and Wal-Mart as well as the US Department of Agriculture. The company founded in 1971 operates three production sites and one distribution center in California.

Operations

The cooperative boasts three food-processing facilities in California as well as distribution centers in California and Washington.

Geographic Reach

From its base in Lodi California Pacific Coast Producers grows its fruits in California and sells them nationwide.

Sales and Marketing

Pacific Coast Producers sells the products it grows and processes to retailers and foodservice operators nationwide as well as to the US Department of Agriculture.

Financial Performance

As one of California's premier private label packers Pacific Coast Producers has logged annual sales in excess of $535 million plus $100 million in alliance income.

Strategy

Pacific Coast Producers has expanded its warehouse space in Lodi to improve efficiency and boost capacity. The move cost the company $23 million. It expanded its distribution center by 50% to meet rising demand for canned food.

The cooperative serves tomato processor Morning Star through a sales and marketing alliance it formed with the company in 2009. As part of the collaboration Pacific Coast Producers provides canned tomatoes to the retail and foodservice industries.

EXECUTIVES

Vice President, Daniel Sroufe
Vice President Human Resources, Richard Ehrler
Auditors: KPMG LLP SACRAMENTO CALIFOR

LOCATIONS

HQ: PACIFIC COAST PRODUCERS
631 N CLUFF AVE, LODI, CA 952400756
Phone: 209 367-8800
Web: WWW.PACIFICCOASTPRODUCERS.COM

PRODUCTS/OPERATIONS

Selected Products

Apricots
Catsup
Chili Sauces
Chunky Mixed Fruit
Concentrated Crushed Tomatoes
Diced Style Tomatoes
Extra Heavy Concentrated Crushed Round Tomato Puree
Formulated Pizza Sauces
Fruit Cocktail
Fruit for Salad
Fruit Mix
Ground Tomatoes
Marinara Sauces
Non-Formulated Pizza Sauce
Organic Tomatoes
Peaches
Pears
Random Cut / Strip Style Tomatoes
Seafood Sauces
Stewed Style Tomatoes
Tomato Juice
Whole Peeled Tomatoes

COMPETITORS

Big Heart Pet Brands
Campbell Soup
Cento
ConAgra
Dole Food
General Mills
Glory Foods
Hain Celestial
Hanover Foods
Heinz
NORPAC
Pictsweet
Seneca Foods

HISTORICAL FINANCIALS

Company Type: Private

Income Statement				FYE: May 31
	REVENUE ($ mil.)	NET INCOME ($ mil.)	NET PROFIT MARGIN	EMPLOYEES
05/18	668	22	3.4%	1,000
05/17	607	26	4.4%	—
05/16	630	30	4.8%	—
05/15	623	30	4.9%	—
Annual Growth	2.3%	(9.4%)	—	—

2018 Year-End Financials

Return on assets: 6.1%
Return on equity: 3.4%
Current ratio: 0.30
Cash ($ mil.): 1

PACIFIC NORTHWEST FARMERS COOPERATIVE INC.

EXECUTIVES

Ceo, Bill Newbry
Chief Financial Officer, Don Himmelberger
Chief Operating Officer, Sam White
Consultant, Jacob Gisler
Auditors: JURGENS & CO PA LEWISTON I

LOCATIONS

HQ: PACIFIC NORTHWEST FARMERS COOPERATIVE INC.
117 W CHESTNUT, GENESEE, ID 83832
Phone: 208 285-1141
Web: WWW.PNW.COOP

HISTORICAL FINANCIALS

Company Type: Private

Income Statement FYE: May 31

	REVENUE ($ mil.)	NET INCOME ($ mil.)	NET PROFIT MARGIN	EMPLOYEES
05/18	280	5	1.8%	80
05/17	151	4	3.2%	—
05/16	118	2	1.7%	—
05/15	120	1	1.6%	—
Annual Growth	32.4%	39.4%	—	—

2018 Year-End Financials

Return on assets: 1.0%   Cash ($ mil.): —
Return on equity: 1.8%
Current ratio: 0.30

PACIFIC PREMIER BANK

EXECUTIVES

Pres-Ceo, Steven R Gardner
Chb, Jeff C Jones
Sr V Pres-Cfo, Kent Smith
Sr Exec Vpres-Cfo, Ronald J Nicolas Jr
Cro, Michael Karr
Evp-Cco, Donn Jakosky
Evp-Chief Acctg Officer, Lori Wright
General Counsel, Steve Arnold
Secretary, John Shindler
Customer Representativ, Leticia Rodriguez
Senior Vice President Director, Thomas Galindo

LOCATIONS

HQ: PACIFIC PREMIER BANK
17901 VON KARMAN AVE, IRVINE, CA 926146297
Phone: 714 431-4000
Web: WWW.PPBI.NET

HISTORICAL FINANCIALS

Company Type: Private

Income Statement FYE: December 31

	ASSETS ($ mil.)	NET INCOME ($ mil.)	INCOME AS % OF ASSETS	EMPLOYEES
12/17	8,022	68	0.9%	104
12/16	4,035	44	1.1%	—
12/15	2,782	29	1.1%	—
12/14	2,033	18	0.9%	—
Annual Growth	58.0%	54.0%	—	—

2017 Year-End Financials

Return on assets: —   Sales ($ mil): 298
Return on equity: 22.9%

PAJARO VALLEY UNIFIED SCHOOL DISTRICT

EXECUTIVES

Spdt, Michelle Rodriguez
Supt, Dorma Baker
Auditors: VAVRINEK TRINE DAY & CO LL

LOCATIONS

HQ: PAJARO VALLEY UNIFIED SCHOOL DISTRICT
294 GREEN VALLEY RD FL 1, WATSONVILLE, CA 950761382
Phone: 831 786-2100
Web: WWW.PVUSD.NET

HISTORICAL FINANCIALS

Company Type: Private

Income Statement FYE: June 30

	REVENUE ($ mil.)	NET INCOME ($ mil.)	NET PROFIT MARGIN	EMPLOYEES
06/17	285	(18)	—	2,139
06/16	279	47	16.9%	—
06/05	209	16	8.1%	—
06/04	92	34	37.9%	—
Annual Growth	9.1%	—	—	—

PALM SPRINGS UNIFIED SCHOOL DIST.

EXECUTIVES

Edd, Supt, Brian J Murray
Edd-Supt, Lorri S McCune
Edd, Asst Supt-Bus Srvcs, Dr Michael Swize
Director of Risk Management, Renee Brunelle
Psychologist, James Christopoulos
Communications Manager, Joan Boiko
Human Resources Administrator, Rosario Maloney
Teacher, Barbara Stanford
Technology/Computer Coordinato, Lee Grafton
Teacher, Jane Mills
Teacher, Jason Powell
Auditors: VAVRINEK TRINE DAY & CO LL

LOCATIONS

HQ: PALM SPRINGS UNIFIED SCHOOL DIST.
150 DISTRICT CENTER DR, PALM SPRINGS, CA 922643626
Phone: 760 883-2710
Web: WWW.PSUSD.US

HISTORICAL FINANCIALS

Company Type: Private

Income Statement FYE: June 30

	REVENUE ($ mil.)	NET INCOME ($ mil.)	NET PROFIT MARGIN	EMPLOYEES
06/17	345	79	22.9%	2,370
06/16	330	(105)	—	—
06/15	281	(28)	—	—
06/06	225	84	37.3%	—
Annual Growth	4.0%	(0.6%)	—	—

PALMDALE SCHOOL DISTRICT

EXECUTIVES

Pres, Juan Carrillo
Supt, Raul Maldonado
Board Member, Nancy Smith
Executive Director, Julie Ferebee
Superintendent, Julie Elliott
Information Specialist, Wendy Powell
Executive Assistant, Claudia Mejuto
Finance Staff, Roger Krause
Administrative Secretary, Susan McCormick
Coordinator, Mary Rees
Accounting Staff, Ana Herrera
Auditors: NIGRO NIGRO & WHITE PC SAN D

LOCATIONS

HQ: PALMDALE SCHOOL DISTRICT
39139 10TH ST E, PALMDALE, CA 935503419
Phone: 661 947-7191
Web: WWW.PALMDALESD.ORG

HISTORICAL FINANCIALS

Company Type: Private

Income Statement FYE: June 30

	REVENUE ($ mil.)	NET INCOME ($ mil.)	NET PROFIT MARGIN	EMPLOYEES
06/17	352	86	24.7%	1,800
06/16	307	8	2.8%	—
06/06	219	2	1.2%	—
06/04	242	25	10.5%	—
Annual Growth	2.9%	9.9%	—	—

PANDUIT CORP.

Panduit's got your cables covered connected and enclosed. The company's electrical components tie together the communications computing power and security systems of a building or physical location. Products include cabling connectors copper wire fiber-optic components cabinets and racks grounding systems outlets terminals and other electrical components. It also offers software used to integrate and manage separate building functions. The company partners with such companies as IBM Rockwell Automation EMC General Cable and Cisco Systems. Panduit introduced its first product in 1955.

Operations
Panduit organizes its products within its Unified Physical Infrastructure (UPI) approach. UPI is used to integrate the physical infrastructure and functions of a building using networks that control and automate building systems and connect with other locations. Panduit positions UPI to be used during the initial planning stages for new buildings as well as when existing buildings are retrofitted.

Geographic Reach
Based in Tinley Park Illinois Panduit has a manufacturing or sales and marketing presence in 112 countries.

Sales and Marketing
Panduit's markets include healthcare government education energy mining and metals shipbuilding food and beverage oil and gas heavy equipment and transportation. The company sells through a variety of channels that include its technology partners distributors system integrators architects engineers contractors and installers.

Customers have included the Vatican Apostolic Library Hertz Purdue University Carnegie Mellon BAE SYSTEMS Johns Hopkins Bloomberg School of Public Health Xerox and Union Pacific Railroad.

Financial Performance
Panduit claims to generate more than $1 billion in annual revenue.

Strategy
Panduit uses its global sales systems engineering and technical support teams to retain and add customers by helping solve their specific problems (from initial problem determination all the way to resolution).As companies have built out data centers Panduit has been in the thick of it supplying cables cabinets and rack enclosures. Most of the new products the company has introduced in recent years have concerned infrastructure that routes and connects miles of cable in data centers. In 2016 it unrolled the HD Flex 2.0 Fiber Cabling System for high-performance data centers.

Mergers and Acquisitions
Panduit makes acquisitions to expand it product line and reach new customers.

In 2019 Panduit acquired Atlona a maker of audio-visual equipment based in San Jose California. The deal will help Panduit round out its offerings with Atlona's networked AV signal distribution wireless collaboration and AV system automation technologies. Atlona became part of Atlona's enterprise group.

Company Background
Panduit was established in 1955 by Jack Caveney Sr.Its first product was the Panduct Wiring Duct.

EXECUTIVES

Ceo, John E. (Jack) Caveney
Vp Global Sales And Marketing, Ronald K. (Ron) Partridge
Cto, Jack Tison
President, Thomas C. (Tom) Donovan
Vice President Sls And Marketing, Bernard Westapher
Vice President Global Human Resources, Timothy Dee
National Account Manager, Michael Taylor
Vice President, Tom Donovan
Vice President Corporate Controller, Chris Allen
Svp Strategic Programs, Randall Woods
Vice President Of Business Operations, Deb Magee
Senior Vice President Human Resources, Tim Dee
Auditors: GRANT THORNTON

LOCATIONS

HQ: PANDUIT CORP.
  18900 PANDUIT DR, TINLEY PARK, IL 604873600
Phone: 708 532-1800
Web: WWW.PANDUIT.COM

PRODUCTS/OPERATIONS

PRODUCTS
Cabinets Thermal Management Racks and Enclosures
Cable and Wire Bundling
Cable Routing and Pathways
Copper Systems
Fiber Systems
Grounding
Identification
Japan Market Only Products
Power Distribution and Environmental Monitoring
Product Promotions
Safety and Security
Software and Hardware
Tools
Wire Routing Protection and Insulation
Wire Termination
SOFTWARE/INTELLIGENCE
DCIM
6 Zone™ Methodology
Data Center Management
Enterprise Management
Intelligent Hardware
Intelligent Software
SmartZone Overview
PROFESSIONAL SERVICES
Case Studies
Industrial Automation Services
Safety Services

COMPETITORS

Amphenol	Ortronics
Avaya	RiT Technologies
CommScope	Schneider Electric
Corning	Siemens AG
Molex	TE Connectivity
Optical Cable	

HISTORICAL FINANCIALS
Company Type: Private

Income Statement				FYE: December 31
	REVENUE ($ mil.)	NET INCOME ($ mil.)	NET PROFIT MARGIN	EMPLOYEES
12/16	937	0	—	5,050
12/15	924	0	—	—
12/14	973	0	—	—
Annual Growth	(1.9%)	—	—	—

PARADISE VALLEY UNIFIED SCHOOL DISTRICT

EXECUTIVES

Pres, Julie Bacon
Principal, North Ranch Element, Sarah Hartley
Reading Specialist, Lynn Halt
Reading Specialist, Ann Rachlin
Executive Assistant, Barbara Thompson
Administrative Assistant, Gina Squires
Director, Jodi McCarthy
Director, Michael Linn
Senior Buyer, Deana Castleberry
Director, Rafael Saragosa
Teacher, Rosanna Martinez
Auditors: HEINFELD MEECH & CO PC P

LOCATIONS

HQ: PARADISE VALLEY UNIFIED SCHOOL DISTRICT
  15002 N 32ND ST, PHOENIX, AZ 850324441
Phone: 602 867-5100
Web: WWW.PVSCHOOLS.NET

HISTORICAL FINANCIALS
Company Type: Private

Income Statement				FYE: June 30
	REVENUE ($ mil.)	NET INCOME ($ mil.)	NET PROFIT MARGIN	EMPLOYEES
06/17	324	2	0.8%	3,600
06/16	312	10	3.4%	—
06/06	283	25	9.1%	—
06/05	273	14	5.2%	—
Annual Growth	1.4%	(13.7%)	—	—

PAREXEL INTERNATIONAL CORPORATION

PAREXEL International excels in pharmaceutical development services. A top contract research organization (CRO) the firm counts among its clients some of the world's largest drug biotech diagnostics and medical device firms. Its core Clinical Research Services (CRS) segment provides clinical trial and data management study design patient recruitment biostatistical analysis clinical pharmacology and industry training and publishing. Its PAREXEL Consulting Services (PC) segment handles the non-clinical aspects of drug development regulatory affairs and new product launches. Finally the PAREXEL Informatics (PI) segment offers patient technology solutions and regulatory and clinical solutions. PAREXEL was taken private by Pamplona Capital Management for $4.5 billion in 2017.

Change in Company Type
In late 2017 PAREXEL was acquired by Pamplona Capital Management for some $4.5 billion. The deal was announced after pressure was placed on the company to sell itself due to lower-than-expected profit margins. The deal also followed a trend of consolidation in the CRO market.

Operations
PAREXEL's largest segment Clinical Research Services (CRS) accounts for more than half of total sales. Its core development business covers all phases of drug and device development from discovery research through clinical trials and post-marketing studies. The division has benefited from the market trend of increased R&D outsourcing by pharmaceutical and biotech drug companies particularly in the areas of Phase II Phase III and Early Phase development.

The PAREXEL Informatics (PI) segment's Perceptive Informatics and other units offer information technology systems and services that help manage clinical trials.

The PAREXEL Consulting Services (PC) segment provides product development and strategic compliance consulting as well as regulatory outsourcing services.

Geographic Reach
PAREXEL has some 85 facilities in more than 40 countries in Europe the Asia/Pacific region the Middle East North America South America and

Africa. More than half of PAREXEL's sales are generated outside of the Americas partly because of its core client base of large multinational corporations.

Sales and Marketing

PAREXEL's sales force directs custom marketing efforts towards niche market segments to match the appropriate services with each customer's needs. Its overall goal is to help clients reduce costs and risks related to product development and commercialization.

Strategy

PAREXEL stands to benefit from such industry factors as the virtualization of biopharmaceutical firms the trend to conduct smaller but more complex trials and advances in information technology. To best take advantage of these opportunities the company continues to serve its multinational clients while also expanding its offerings for small and mid-sized developers.

The company has a number of major customers such as Pfizer which has brought in more than 10% of total sales. PAREXEL is somewhat vulnerable to the loss of major customers which could occur due to a number of reasons ranging from budgetary concerns to corporate mergers to the completion of product launches. Losing a big customer could significantly impact the firm's sales.

Additionally the CRO market is very competitive with pharmaceuticals providing their own research in-house universities and teaching hospitals entering the fray and marketing and consulting firms providing product development advisory services. To stay competitive PAREXEL looks to establish and maintain long-term alliances with pharmaceutical companies.

In early 2019 the company established a division dedicated to serving the needs of emerging biotech companies. The unit offers customers expertise in operating in China's growing market genomic medicine services and other programs tailored to the sector. The timing coincides with rapid growth in the biotech sphere.

Mergers and Acquisitions

In early 2017 PAREXEL acquired The Medical Affairs Company which provides outsourced medical affairs services including consulting communications support and medical science liaison services to pharmaceutical biotech and medical device clients.

Company Background

Founders Josef von Rickenbach a health care and international products specialist and Anne Sayigh a chemist and regulatory affairs specialist started PAREXEL in 1982 to provide regulatory consulting services to pharmaceutical firms. Its name referred to 16th-century Swiss physician Theophrastus Bombastus von Hohenheim — better known as Paracelsus the father of empirical chemistry.

Through a series of acquisitions PAREXEL entered new markets including biostatistics and data management medical marketing and health consulting.

The company went public in 1995 and was taken private again in 2017.

HISTORY

Founders Josef von Rickenbach a health care and international products specialist and Anne Sayigh a chemist and regulatory affairs specialist started PAREXEL in 1982 to provide regulatory consulting services to pharmaceutical firms. Its name referred to 16th-century Swiss physician Theophrastus Bombastus von Hohenheim — better known as Paracelsus the father of empirical chemistry.

In 1988 PAREXEL bought Consulting Statisticians and moved into the biostatistics and data management market. The next year it went international with the purchase of the biostatistics and data management division of McDonnell Douglas Information Systems. In 1991 PAREXEL augmented its European operations with the acquisition of German contract researcher AFB Arzneimittelforschung — a move that paid off in rising sales.

PAREXEL went public in 1995. In the following two years it bought six health consulting firms including State and Federal Associates and medical marketing firm Rescon with the intention of boosting its ability to get its clients' products on the market. The company continued its acquisition spree in 1998; this time European marketing and research companies were on the shopping list. Competitor Covance was set to buy PAREXEL in 1999 then called off the deal when investors balked.

The company announced in 2000 that it would lay off more than 400 workers after Novartis cancelled a major contract. That year the company formed new alliances with such companies as NeuroRecovery Research Phenome Sciences and Prevention Concepts. PAREXEL also bought a full-service clinical pharmacology unit in the UK from GlaxoWellcome (now GlaxoSmithKline) as well as a majority stake in FARMOVS a clinical pharmacology research business and laboratory in South Africa.

In 2001 the company formed Perceptive Informatics a subsidiary focused on developing Internet-based information management systems. To strengthen its clinical trial management services PAREXEL bought software developer FW Pharma Systems in 2003. In 2006 it purchased US-based Behavioral and Medical Research LLC for $69 million to expand its research services.

EXECUTIVES

Chairman And Ceo, Josef H. von Rickenbach, $966,874 total compensation
President And Coo, Mark A. Goldberg, $622,263 total compensation
President Perceptive Informatics, Xavier Flinois
Svp And Cfo, Simon N. R. Harford
Svp And Worldwide Head Parexel Access, Joshua Schultz
Svp General Counsel And Secretary, Douglas A. Batt, $415,860 total compensation
Svp Clinical Research Services, Gadi Saarony, $455,051 total compensation
Vp And Worldwide Head Early Phase, Sy Pretorius
Senior Vice President Global Business Development, David Godwin
Vice President Worldwide Head Of Medcom, Susan Kammerman
Corporate Vice President, Janet Edwards
Medical Director, Lynn McRoy
Vice President Human Resources, Carl Weaver
Medical Director, Wayne Dankner
Vice President Human Resource Operations, Guy Schiller
Medical Director, Marina Bussel
Vice President Corporate Communications, Mark Stephenson
Corporate Vice President Head Global Medical Services, Dana Washburn
Vice President And Chief Scientific Officer For Medical Imaging, Peter Steiger
Vice President Global Monitoring Operations, Dennis Joseph
Auditors: ERNST & YOUNG LLP BOSTON MAS

LOCATIONS

HQ: PAREXEL INTERNATIONAL CORPORATION
195 WEST ST, WALTHAM, MA 024511146
Phone: 781 487-9900
Web: WWW.PAREXEL.COM

COMPETITORS

Albany Molecular Research
BioClinica
Charles River Laboratories
Covance
DATATRAK International
ICON
INC Research
IQVIA
PharmaNet Development Group
Pharmaceutical Product Development
ReSearch Pharmaceutical Services
WuXi PharmaTech
eResearchTechnology
inVentiv Health

HISTORICAL FINANCIALS
Company Type: Private

Income Statement — FYE: June 30

	REVENUE ($ mil.)	NET INCOME ($ mil.)	NET PROFIT MARGIN	EMPLOYEES
06/17	2,441	107	4.4%	18,900
06/16	2,426	154	6.4%	—
06/15	2,330	147	6.3%	—
06/14	2,266	129	5.7%	—
Annual Growth	2.5%	(6.0%)	—	—

2017 Year-End Financials

Return on assets: 4.2%   Cash ($ mil.): 302
Return on equity: 4.4%
Current ratio: 1.00

PARKER ADVENTIST HOSPITAL

EXECUTIVES

Pres/Ceo, Morre Dean
Cmo, Elizabeth Kincannon
Chief of Medicine, Stephanie Kraft
Health Professional, Jennifer Moroye-Young
Internal Medicine Practitioner, Maher Alami
Internal Medicine Practitioner, Lorette Johnson
Director Patient Care Nursing, Marie Bailey
Infection Prevention Director, Julie Duran
Business Manager, Tamera Ogren

LOCATIONS

HQ: PARKER ADVENTIST HOSPITAL
9395 CROWN CREST BLVD, PARKER, CO 801388573
Phone: 303 269-4000

HISTORICAL FINANCIALS
Company Type: Private

Income Statement — FYE: December 31

	REVENUE ($ mil.)	NET INCOME ($ mil.)	NET PROFIT MARGIN	EMPLOYEES
12/17*	308	43	14.2%	250
06/16	270	44	16.5%	—
06/15	241	31	13.2%	—
06/09	129	28	21.7%	—
Annual Growth	10.1%	5.0%	—	—

*Fiscal year change

2017 Year-End Financials

Return on assets: 3.9%   Cash ($ mil.): —
Return on equity: 14.2%
Current ratio: 2.00

PARKLAND COMMUNITY HEALTH PLAN, INC., A PROGRAM OF DALLAS COUNTY HOSPITAL

EXECUTIVES

Ceo, Rob Smith
Associate Director, Paula Keblar
Member, Joanne Tenery
Auditors: BRUCE E BERNSTEIN & ASSOC PC

LOCATIONS

HQ: PARKLAND COMMUNITY HEALTH PLAN, INC., A PROGRAM OF DALLAS COUNTY HOSPITAL
1341 W MOCKINGBIRD LN 1150E, DALLAS, TX 752474974
Phone: 214 266-2100

HISTORICAL FINANCIALS

Company Type: Private

Income Statement				FYE: December 31
	REVENUE ($ mil.)	NET INCOME ($ mil.)	NET PROFIT MARGIN	EMPLOYEES
12/15	527	(32)	—	2
12/13	519	27	5.2%	—
12/12	515	24	4.7%	—
12/11	470	39	8.4%	—
Annual Growth	2.9%	—	—	—

2015 Year-End Financials

Return on assets: 13.3%   Cash ($ mil.): 162
Return on equity: (-6.1%)
Current ratio: 2.40

PARKRIDGE MEDICAL CENTER, INC.

EXECUTIVES

Vice President Human Resources, Carole Hoffman

LOCATIONS

HQ: PARKRIDGE MEDICAL CENTER, INC.
2333 MCCALLIE AVE, CHATTANOOGA, TN 374043258
Phone: 423 698-6061
Web:
PARKRIDGEHEALTH.COM/LOCATIONS/PARKRIDGE-MEDICAL-CENTER/

COMPETITORS

Catholic Health Initiatives	LifePoint Health
Community Health Systems	Saint Thomas Rutherford Hospital
Covenant Health	Southern Hills
Encompass Health	Tennova Healthcare
Erlanger Health System	Vanderbilt University Medical Center
Hutcheson Medical	

HISTORICAL FINANCIALS

Company Type: Private

Income Statement				FYE: March 31
	REVENUE ($ mil.)	NET INCOME ($ mil.)	NET PROFIT MARGIN	EMPLOYEES
03/17	322	74	23.2%	1,364
03/09	215	24	11.4%	—
Annual Growth	5.1%	14.9%	—	—

2017 Year-End Financials

Return on assets: 2.4%   Cash ($ mil.): —
Return on equity: 23.2%
Current ratio: 2.60

PARKS XANTERRA & RESORTS INC

EXECUTIVES

Pres, Andrew N Todd
V Pres, Michael F Welch
SEC, Kirk Anderson
Assistant Vice President Finan, Lonnie Clark
Asst Cntlr, Linda K Zimmerman
Director, Daniel Borovsky
Director, Hector Garcia
Director, Paul Taillac
Director, Richard Rabinoff
Marketing Director, Andrew Heltzel
General Manager, Daisy Hobbs

LOCATIONS

HQ: PARKS XANTERRA & RESORTS INC
6312 S FIDDLERS GREEN CIR, GREENWOOD VILLAGE, CO 801114943
Phone: 303 600-3400
Web: WWW.XANTERRA.COM

HISTORICAL FINANCIALS

Company Type: Private

Income Statement				FYE: December 27
	REVENUE ($ mil.)	NET INCOME ($ mil.)	NET PROFIT MARGIN	EMPLOYEES
12/17	384	50	13.0%	3,500
12/16	376	29	7.9%	—
12/15	350	53	15.2%	—
12/14	358	79	22.2%	—
Annual Growth	2.4%	(14.3%)	—	—

2017 Year-End Financials

Return on assets: 25.8%   Cash ($ mil.): 20
Return on equity: 13.0%
Current ratio: 0.20

PARKWEST MEDICAL CENTER

EXECUTIVES

Nursing Director, Derek Dodson
Vice President Management, Linda Tillman
Infection Control Director, MARGARET CHAMBERS

LOCATIONS

HQ: PARKWEST MEDICAL CENTER
9352 PARK WEST BLVD, KNOXVILLE, TN 379234387
Phone: 865 373-1000
Web: WWW.TREATEDWELL.COM

PRODUCTS/OPERATIONS

Selected Adult Specialties
Cancer
Cardiology and heart surgery
Diabetes and endocrinology
Ear nose and throat
Gastroenterology
Geriatrics
Gynecology
Nephrology
Neurology and neurosurgery
Orthopedics
Pulmonology
Urology

Selected Outpatient Centers
Parkwest Comprehensive Breast Center
Parkwest Cardiac Rehabilitation
Rehabilitation Outpatient Program
Parkwest Therapy Center

COMPETITORS

Baptist Memorial Health Care	Saint Thomas Midtown Hospital
Baptist Memorial Hospital-Memphis	Saint Thomas Rutherford Hospital
Blount Memorial Hospital	Tennova Healthcare
East Tennessee Children's Hospital	University Health System Inc.
Erlanger Health System	Vanderbilt University Medical Center
Kindred Healthcare	Wellmont Health System
LifePoint Health	

HISTORICAL FINANCIALS

Company Type: Private

Income Statement				FYE: August 31
	REVENUE ($ mil.)	NET INCOME ($ mil.)	NET PROFIT MARGIN	EMPLOYEES
08/16	311	43	14.1%	1,300
08/15*	290	35	12.3%	—
12/13	337	29	8.8%	—
12/05	172	5	3.1%	—
Annual Growth	5.5%	21.0%	—	—

*Fiscal year change

PARTNERS HEALTHCARE SYSTEM, INC.

Partners HealthCare System is looking out for the health of the Bay State. Partners HealthCare includes two large acute-care medical centers — Brigham and Women's Hospital and Massachusetts General Hospital— and seven community hospitals. The not-for-profit system also provides primary and specialty care through clinics physician offices long-term care facilities and home health and hospice agencies. Its rehabilitation facilities include the Spaulding Rehabilitation Hospital Network. Partners HealthCare also provides medical training and research through an affiliation with Harvard. Other ventures include the Dana-Farber/Partners CancerCare clinic (a collaboration with Harvard and Dana-Farber Cancer Institute).
Operations

Partners HealthCare's Partners Community HealthCare division is a management services organization that provides support for a physician network encompassing some 6500 practitioners. Partners HealthCare also sponsors community health outreach programs. Community hospitals owned by or affiliated with Partners include McLean Hospital Newton-Wellesley Hospital North Shore Medical Center Nantucket Cottage Hospital and the Martha's Vineyard Hospital. Partners HealthCare also operates Faulkner Hospital as a subsidiary of the Brigham and Women's facility.

Brigham and Women's (a 777-bed facility) and Massachusetts General are both teaching hospitals for the Harvard Medical School. The Harvard Clinical Research Institute is a partnership between the Harvard Medical School Partners HealthCare and CareGroup (parent of Boston facilities including Beth Israel Deaconess Medical Center). Outside the US the system's Partners HealthCare International provides clinical advisory patient care research and educational programs with a number of global partners. With an annual research budget of $1.6 billion Partners HealthCare has a strong research funding base including awards of some $600 million annually from the National Institutes of Health.

The system serves 1.5 million patients annually.

Geographic Reach

Partners HealthCare provides services to patients in the Greater Boston area as well as New England and beyond. It also partners with health care systems and health-related academic institutions in more than 40 countries.

Strategy

Partners HealthCare strives to provide innovative yet affordable medical care to area residents. To keep its operations efficient as well as to comply with federal health reform incentive measures Partners HealthCare has put in place a health information system that requires all of its doctors to use electronic health records (EHRs). As one of the early adopters of EHR systems Partners HealthCare is upgrading its IT systems to install a new clinical information system across its facilities using new technologies from software maker Epic. The new system — which will enhance coordination of care reduce unnecessary health spending and simplify reporting and patient access features — will be implemented over 10 years and will cost between $600 and $700 million.

Other programs to meet new health care standards include reducing prices on certain procedures and renegotiating contracts with insurers as well as encouraging patients to participate in preventative care wellness and generic drug programs.

Mergers and Acquisitions

Partners HealthCare is buying Care New England as part of its bid to expand beyond Massachusetts. In 2018 the two companies approached Rhode Island-based Lifespan to also join forces but that proposal was subsequently dropped.

In another deal the organization has agreed to acquire specialty hospital Massachusetts Eye and Ear.

Company Background

Partners HealthCare has been recognized by the federal government and other organizations for its quality and efficiency programs. In 2012 the health network was selected by the Centers for Medicare and Medicaid Services to participate in the Pioneer ACO (accountable care organization) program which aims to slow cost growth in the Medicare market by enhancing care coordination.

Partners HealthCare was founded in 1994 through the merger of Brigham and Women's Hospital and Massachusetts General Hospital.

EXECUTIVES

Vice President Public Affairs Partners Community Benefit Programs, Lee Chelminiak
Vice President Of Finance, David Mcguire
Evp Administration And Finance Cfo And Treasurer, Peter K. Markell, age 62
President And Ceo Massachusetts General Hospital, Peter L. Slavin
Cio, James W. (Jim) Noga
President And Ceo North Shore Medical Center, Robert G. (Bob) Norton, age 68
President And Ceo Neighborhood Health Plan, Deborah C. Enos
President And Ceo Partners Continuing Care, David E. Storto
President And Ceo Brigham And Women's Hospital, Elizabeth G. (Betsy) Nabel
President And Chief Executive Officer, David F. Torchiana
President Of Partners Community, Thomas H. Lee
President And Ceo Spaulding Rehabilitation Network, Maureen Banks
President Mclean Hospital, Scott L. Rauch
President And Ceo Brigham And Women's Physicians Organization, Allen L. Smith
President And Ceo Martha's Vineyard Hospital, Timothy J. Walsh
President And Ceo Mgh Institute Of Health Professions, Janis P. Bellack
President And Ceo, David Torchiana
President And Ceo Nantucket Cottage Hospital, Margot Hartmann
President And Ceo Partners Healthcare At Home, Rod Carnifax
Medical Director, Judy A Nugent
Medical Director Of The Breast And Ovarian Cancer, Paula Ryan
Nursing Director, Elizabeth McGrath
Vice President Revenue Cycle Operations, Rosemary R Sheehan
Director Of Nursing, Deirdre Greene
Nursing Director, Janet Quigley
Nursing Director, Mary Sylvia-Reardon
Medical Director Of Quality Safey And Population Management, Adrienne Allen
Medical Director, Richard Kaufman
Project Manager To Senior Vice President Research, Angela Vail
Medical Director, Sharon Bober
Nursing Director, Judith Silva
Clinical Director, Jane Evans
Nursing Director, Michele Ohara
Clinical Director, Martha Kane
Vice President Of Operations, Hofmann Erika
Nursing Director, Peggy Settle
Vice President Of Systems, Meg Costello
Clinical Director, Scott Waugh
Assistant Vice President Regional Consultant, Viscomi Rudy
Assistant Vice President Regional Consultant, Vu Dung
Rsvp Team Leader, Jessica Grajeda
Vice President Of Information Technology, Karl Fitch
Chairman, Edward P. Lawrence, age 76
Secretary, Maria Sanchez
Board Member, Jonathan Katz
Treasurer, Xandra Breakefield
Board Member, Martha Pitman

LOCATIONS

HQ: PARTNERS HEALTHCARE SYSTEM, INC.
800 BOYLSTON ST STE 1150, BOSTON, MA 021998123
Phone: 617 278-1000
Web: WWW.PARTNERS.ORG

PRODUCTS/OPERATIONS

2014 Sales

	% of total
Net patient service revenue	65
Premium revenue	15
Direct academic and research	11
Indirect academic and research	3
Other revenue	6
Total	**100**

COMPETITORS

Baystate Health	Lahey Health System
Boston Medical Center	Milford Regional
Cambridge Health	Medical Center
Alliance	Northeast Health
Cape Cod Healthcare	System
Cape Cod Hospital	Southcoast Hospitals
Care New England	Group
CareGroup	Steward Health Care
Children's Hospital	Universal Health
Boston	Services

HISTORICAL FINANCIALS

Company Type: Private

Income Statement

FYE: September 30

	REVENUE ($ mil.)	NET INCOME ($ mil.)	NET PROFIT MARGIN	EMPLOYEES
09/15	11,665	(916)	—	67,000
09/10	8	(0)	—	—
09/08	551	(44)	—	—
Annual Growth	54.7%	—	—	—

2015 Year-End Financials

Return on assets: 15.4% Cash ($ mil.): 621
Return on equity: (-7.9%)
Current ratio: 0.70

PASADENA HOSPITAL ASSOCIATION, LTD.

No need to hunt for medical care if you're near Huntington Hospital. The not-for-profit Pasadena Hospital Association which does business as Huntington Hospital provides health care to residents of the San Gabriel Valley in Southern California. The hospital boasts some 625 beds and offers acute medical and surgical care and community services in a number of specialties including cardiology gastroenterology women's and children's health orthopedics and neurology. It engages in clinical cancer research (as well as diagnosis and treatment) through the Huntington Cancer Center. The hospital is also a teaching facility for the University of Southern California (USC) Keck School of Medicine.

Operations

As part of its operations the California hospital runs The Stroke Center Heart and Vascular Center Huntington Hospital Cancer Center Regional Neonatal Intensive Care Unit Prenatal High Risk Unit and Pediatric Intensive Care Unit. The hospital is the only level II trauma center and level III NICU in the San Gabriel Valley.

Through its partnership with USC Huntington Hospital offers graduate medical education in areas such as general surgery and internal medicine. Its Huntington Cancer Center partners with area physicians (including some affiliated with USC and UCLA) and the City of Hope medical center to provide comprehensive oncology services and research potential new cancer treatments.

The hospital has 900 physicians and more than 1200 nurses. In 2013 it had about 26000 inpatient admissions more than 216000 outpatient visits and helped deliver more than 3300 babies. Huntington Hospital provided a $92.9 million in community benefits that year.

Geographic Reach
Huntington Hospital serves the health care needs of those who reside in and around Southern California's San Gabriel Valley.

Sales and Marketing
The medical center is working to upgrade its information technology systems including the addition of an electronic health record (EHR) system.

Financial Performance
Huntington Hospital's revenues rose by 3% in 2013 thanks to an increase in patient services and revenues.

The hospital recorded a net loss of $10 million that year due to higher expenses (including salaries employees benefits and other costs).

Strategy
The company is pursuing infrastructure and services expansion and innovation to keep up with demand.

In 2014 Huntington Hospital collaborated with Anthem Blue Cross and six of its fellow leading hospitals in Los Angeles and Orange counties to form Anthem Blue Cross Vivity a new insurance entity.

In 2013 the hospital signed a deal with Shriners Hospitals for Children- Southern California to provide inpatient surgical services for its pediatric patients.

Huntington Hospital completed renovating its existing emergency facility in 2013. The project to increase patient capacity up to 80000 and increase diagnostic facilities came about in response to growing levels of ER visits.

Company Background
Huntington Hospital broke ground several years ago on an $80-million expansion effort to double the size of its emergency department. The project has included building a new portion that was completed in 2012.

Upgrading its technology to increase efficiency in 2012 Huntington Hospital launched a multi-year project to replace and upgrade its computer information system with new system (Huntington Access Network Knowledge) to manage the hospital's clinical and financial software.

In a medical innovation in 2012 the hospital became the first hospital in Southern California to offer an Ekso Bionics' technology enabling patients with lower-extremity paralysis or weakness to stand and walk.

Huntington Hospital was founded in 1892.

EXECUTIVES

Physical Therapy Director, Sunil Hegde
Vice President, James Luna
Auditors: ERNST & YOUNG US LLP IRVINE

LOCATIONS

HQ: PASADENA HOSPITAL ASSOCIATION, LTD.
100 W CALIFORNIA BLVD, PASADENA, CA 911053010
Phone: 626 397-5000
Web: WWW.HUNTINGTONHOSPITAL.COM

PRODUCTS/OPERATIONS

Selected Services
Ambulatory Care/Dispensary
Angiography
Anticoagulation Clinic
Asthma Education and Management
Bariatric Surgery
Breast Cancer Program
Cardiac Catheterization Lab
Cardiac Electrophysiology (EP)

Cardiac Rehabilitation
Cardiac Screening and Diagnostics
Cardiothoracic Surgery
Community Outreach
CT Scanning (Type 2) Diabetes Prevention and Management
Epilepsy and Brain Mapping
Gastroenterology
Genetic Counseling
Geriatric Assessment Clinic
Gynecological Cancer Program
Heart and Vascular Services
Neurophysiology
Neuroradiology
Neurosciences
Neurosurgery
Obstetrics
Orthopedics
Ostomy Clinic
Pediatric Obesity Prevention
Prenatal High Risk Unit
Prostate Cancer Program
Radiation Oncology
Urology
Uterine Artery Embolization (UAE)

COMPETITORS

Adventist Health System West	Dignity Health
Cedars-Sinai Medical Center	Glendale Adventist Medical Center
Citrus Valley Health Partners	Memorial Health Services
	Tenet Healthcare

HISTORICAL FINANCIALS
Company Type: Private

Income Statement
FYE: December 31

	REVENUE ($ mil.)	NET INCOME ($ mil.)	NET PROFIT MARGIN	EMPLOYEES
12/16	695	8	1.2%	2,800
12/15	593	0	0.0%	—
Annual Growth	17.2%	3278.7%	—	—

2016 Year-End Financials
Return on assets: 10.7%
Return on equity: 1.2%
Current ratio: 0.30
Cash ($ mil.): 12

PASADENA INDEPENDENT SCHOOL DISTRICT

EXECUTIVES

Pres, Mariselle Quijano-Lerma
Supt, Dr Kirk Lewis
Vice President, Vickie Morgan
SEC, Fred Roberts
Teacher, Annie Sargent
Administrative Secretary, Aurora Espinoza
Office Manager, Bibi Nunez-Mejia
Teacher, Brandon Ware
Administrator, Charlyn Jannasch
School Counselor, Cindy Resendez
Librarian, Dana Dimarco
Auditors: WHITLEY PENN LLP TEXAS CITY

LOCATIONS

HQ: PASADENA INDEPENDENT SCHOOL DISTRICT
1515 CHERRYBROOK LN, PASADENA, TX 775024099
Phone: 713 740-0000
Web: WWW.PASADENAISD.ORG

HISTORICAL FINANCIALS
Company Type: Private

Income Statement
FYE: August 31

	REVENUE ($ mil.)	NET INCOME ($ mil.)	NET PROFIT MARGIN	EMPLOYEES
08/17	606	(93)	—	5,000
08/16	611	(32)	—	—
08/13	522	98	18.9%	—
08/12	497	83	16.7%	—
Annual Growth	4.1%	—	—	—

2017 Year-End Financials
Return on assets: 3.8%
Return on equity: (-15.4%)
Current ratio: —
Cash ($ mil.): 20

PATERSON PUBLIC SCHOOL DISTRICT

EXECUTIVES

Supt, Jacqueline Jones
Supt, Donnie W Evans
Transportation Director, Gisela Aultmon
Research Director, Annalesa Barker
Assistant Superintendent, Elaine P Davis
Athletic Director, Nicholas Semeniuk
Director of Professional Devel, J Gordon-Scott
Auditors: LERCH VINCI & HIGGINS LLP F

LOCATIONS

HQ: PATERSON PUBLIC SCHOOL DISTRICT
90 DELAWARE AVE, PATERSON, NJ 075031804
Phone: 973 321-0980
Web: WWW.PATERSON.K12.NJ.US

HISTORICAL FINANCIALS
Company Type: Private

Income Statement
FYE: June 30

	REVENUE ($ mil.)	NET INCOME ($ mil.)	NET PROFIT MARGIN	EMPLOYEES
06/17	601	1	0.3%	3,055
06/11	541	7	1.3%	—
06/05*	0	0	—	—
12/00	300	2	0.7%	—
Annual Growth	4.4%	(1.3%)	—	—

*Fiscal year change

2017 Year-End Financials
Return on assets: 4.9%
Return on equity: 0.3%
Current ratio: —
Cash ($ mil.): 16

PATIENT ACCESS NETWORK FOUNDATION

EXECUTIVES

Dir of Ops, Svelana Durkovic
Prin, Julia E Reynes
Vice-President, Amy Niles
Marketing Staff, Megan Crout
Chief Operating Officer, Randy Crout
Auditors: CHERRY BEKAERT LLP CHARLOTTE

LOCATIONS

HQ: PATIENT ACCESS NETWORK FOUNDATION
805 15TH ST NW STE 500, WASHINGTON, DC
200052207
Phone: 202 347-9274
Web: WWW.PANFOUNDATION.ORG

HISTORICAL FINANCIALS

Company Type: Private

Income Statement				FYE: December 31
	REVENUE ($ mil.)	NET INCOME ($ mil.)	NET PROFIT MARGIN	EMPLOYEES
12/16	577	(243)	—	3
12/14	673	161	24.0%	—
Annual Growth	(7.4%)	—	—	—

2016 Year-End Financials

Return on assets: 1.6%   Cash ($ mil.): 86
Return on equity: (-42.2%)
Current ratio: 9.50

PAULDING COUNTY BOARD OF EDUCATION

EXECUTIVES

Superintendent, Mr Cliff Cole
Chairperson, Kim Curl
Vice Chair, Sammy McClure
MBR, Glen Albright
MBR, Nicholas Chester
Director, Tyre Rakestraw
Assistant Superintendent, Michelle Sayles

LOCATIONS

HQ: PAULDING COUNTY BOARD OF EDUCATION
3236 ATLANTA HWY, DALLAS, GA 301325725
Phone: 770 443-8000
Web: WWW.PAULDING.K12.GA.US

HISTORICAL FINANCIALS

Company Type: Private

Income Statement				FYE: June 30
	REVENUE ($ mil.)	NET INCOME ($ mil.)	NET PROFIT MARGIN	EMPLOYEES
06/17	294	(0)	—	4,200
06/16	282	(4)	—	—
06/08	284	(24)	—	—
06/07	246	42	17.1%	—
Annual Growth	1.8%	—	—	—

2017 Year-End Financials

Return on assets: 4.1%   Cash ($ mil.): 68
Return on equity: —
Current ratio: —

PAVILION HEALTH SERVICES, INC.

EXECUTIVES

Chm, A Hugh Green
President, Michael Lukaszewski
Dir, John F Wilbanks
Vice President, Christopher Durkin

SEC, Harvey Granger
Sls Mgr, Kenneth C Perry
Director Baptist B, Kerrie Slattery
Director of Nursing At Memoria, Tammy Daniel
Supervisor, John Cook

LOCATIONS

HQ: PAVILION HEALTH SERVICES, INC.
3563 PHILIPS HWY STE 106, JACKSONVILLE, FL
322075684
Phone: 904 202-5887

HISTORICAL FINANCIALS

Company Type: Private

Income Statement				FYE: September 30
	REVENUE ($ mil.)	NET INCOME ($ mil.)	NET PROFIT MARGIN	EMPLOYEES
09/17	305	(16)	—	785
09/09	41	2	6.3%	—
09/08	0	(0)	—	—
Annual Growth	90.3%	—	—	—

2017 Year-End Financials

Return on assets: 9.0%   Cash ($ mil.): 4
Return on equity: (-5.2%)
Current ratio: 0.80

PEARCE INDUSTRIES, INC.

EXECUTIVES

Chb, Louis M Pearce Jr
Pres-Ceo, Gary M Pearce
V Pres-Fncl Pl, Robert J Jesse
V Pres-Asst SEC, Louis Pearce III
V Pres-Treas, Stephen R Pearce
Evp-SEC Cfo, Richard E Bean
Director, Frank Pagura
Sales Representative, Brian Childress
Human Resources Generalist, Carmen Vargas
Executive Assistant, Jeri Craven
Operational Excellence Manager, Richard Underhill

LOCATIONS

HQ: PEARCE INDUSTRIES, INC.
12320 MAIN ST, HOUSTON, TX 770356206
Phone: 713 723-1050

HISTORICAL FINANCIALS

Company Type: Private

Income Statement				FYE: March 31
	REVENUE ($ mil.)	NET INCOME ($ mil.)	NET PROFIT MARGIN	EMPLOYEES
03/17	396	28	7.3%	750
03/16	511	2	0.5%	—
03/15	611	28	4.6%	—
03/14	515	16	3.3%	—
Annual Growth	(8.4%)	19.2%	—	—

2017 Year-End Financials

Return on assets: 8.8%   Cash ($ mil.): 5
Return on equity: 7.3%
Current ratio: 0.90

PENNSYLVANIA - AMERICAN WATER COMPANY

Pennsylvania-American Water distributes water and provides wastewater services to a population of more than 2 million people in some 390 communities across Pennsylvania. The company serves 635000 water customers and 17500 wastewater customers. It operates about 35 water treatment plants six wastewater facilities and 9800 miles of pipeline. Pennsylvania-American Water's service territory covers some three dozen Pennsylvania counties. The utility the largest regulated water and wastewater service provider in Pennsylvania is a subsidiary ofA New Jersey-based American Water Works.

Operations

Pennsylvania-American Water also has 85 well stations and treats and delivers about 216 millions of gallons of water each day. In addition itA operates 70 groundwater treatment facilities which process water sourced from more than 100 groundwater wells and maintains 250 treated water storage facilities 280 pumping stations and 60 dams.

Geographic Reach

The utility's primarily service areas include Mechanicsburg Mon Valley Norristown Pittsburgh Scranton Washington and Wilkes-Barre.

Financial Performance

Pennsylvania-American Water represents about a fifth of its parent company's sales; in 2011 it reported $516 million in revenue from Pennsylvania.

Mergers and Acquisitions

The utility expands its reach in Pennsylvania by picking up smaller water systems; in 2012 it completed six such acquisitions including a Monroe County system serving the Fernwood Resort and a Pike County system serving about 100 residents.

EXECUTIVES

Pres, Kathy Pape
Vice President, William C Kelvinton
SEC, Velma A Redmond
Treas, Stephen F Analdo
Support Manager, James P Oehling
Manager, David Derr
Director of Mis/Is, David Jerpe
Domino Administrator, Jill Breneman
Senior Developer, Richard Watts
Senior Manager, Charles Johnston
Counsel, Susan Simms

LOCATIONS

HQ: PENNSYLVANIA - AMERICAN WATER COMPANY
800 W HERSHEY PARK DR, HERSHEY, PA 170332400
Phone: 717 533-5000

COMPETITORS

Aqua America   Utilities Inc.
United Water Inc.

HISTORICAL FINANCIALS
Company Type: Private

Income Statement   FYE: December 31

	REVENUE ($ mil.)	NET INCOME ($ mil.)	NET PROFIT MARGIN	EMPLOYEES
12/17*	661	160	24.3%	1,007
06/14	589	127	21.7%	—
03/14	584	128	22.0%	—
12/13	571	122	21.4%	—
Annual Growth	3.7%	7.1%	—	—

*Fiscal year change

2017 Year-End Financials
Return on assets: 13.0%   Cash ($ mil.): 3
Return on equity: 24.3%
Current ratio: 0.10

PENNSYLVANIA ELECTRIC COMPANY

EXECUTIVES

Pres-Ceo, Charles E Jones
Exec V Pres-Cfo, Mark T Clark
Exec V Pres-Gen Counsel, Leila L Vespoli
V Pres-Controller-Cao, Harvey L Wagner
V Pres-Treas, James F Pearson
Director Generation and Fes In, Gunther Hehn
Vice President Human Resources, Josh Martin
Auditors: PRICEWATERHOUSECOOPERS LLP CL

LOCATIONS

HQ: PENNSYLVANIA ELECTRIC COMPANY
  76 S MAIN ST BSMT, AKRON, OH 443081817
Phone: 800 545-7741
Web: WWW.FIRSTENERGYCORP.COM

COMPETITORS

Columbia Gas of Pennsylvania	PECO Energy
	PPL Electric
Direct Energy	Peoples Natural Gas

HISTORICAL FINANCIALS
Company Type: Private

Income Statement   FYE: December 31

	REVENUE ($ mil.)	NET INCOME ($ mil.)	NET PROFIT MARGIN	EMPLOYEES
12/17	893	95	10.7%	896
12/16	904	88	9.8%	—
12/10	1,539	59	3.9%	—
12/09	1,448	65	4.5%	—
Annual Growth	(5.9%)	4.9%	—	—

2017 Year-End Financials
Return on assets: 6.0%   Cash ($ mil.): —
Return on equity: 10.7%
Current ratio: 0.60

PENNSYLVANIA HOUSING FINANCE AGENCY

EXECUTIVES

Chm, Robin Wiessmann
Vice President, Thomas B Hagen
Exec Dir, Craig H Alexander
Secretary, Carrie Barnes
Human Resources Representative, Arlene Frontz
Officer, Angela Kocher
Human Resources Executive, Jodi Hall
Finance Manager, John Zapotocky
Financial Officer, Kelly Wilson
Manager, Kevin Wike
Accountant, Laura Wildman

LOCATIONS

HQ: PENNSYLVANIA HOUSING FINANCE AGENCY
  211 N FRONT ST, HARRISBURG, PA 171011406
Phone: 717 780-3800
Web: WWW.PHFA.ORG

HISTORICAL FINANCIALS
Company Type: Private

Income Statement   FYE: June 30

	ASSETS ($ mil.)	NET INCOME ($ mil.)	INCOME AS % OF ASSETS	EMPLOYEES
06/18	4,366	20	0.5%	250
06/12	5,593	10	0.2%	—
06/11	6,051	39	0.7%	—
06/10	6,265	24	0.4%	—
Annual Growth	(4.4%)	(2.2%)	—	—

2018 Year-End Financials
Return on assets: 2.6%   Sales ($ mil): 192
Return on equity: 10.7%

PENNVEST

EXECUTIVES

Exec Director, Paul K Marchetti
Chb, Randolph Albright
Poc, Leeann Brown
Manager, Brion Johnson
Coordinator, Vickie Johnson

LOCATIONS

HQ: PENNVEST
  333 MARKET ST FL 8, HARRISBURG, PA 171012210
Phone: 717 787-8137

HISTORICAL FINANCIALS
Company Type: Private

Income Statement   FYE: June 30

	ASSETS ($ mil.)	NET INCOME ($ mil.)	INCOME AS % OF ASSETS	EMPLOYEES
06/18	4,143	125	3.0%	27
06/17	3,964	143	3.6%	—
06/93	742	0	0.1%	—
Annual Growth	7.1%	25.0%	—	—

2018 Year-End Financials
Return on assets: 1.6%   Sales ($ mil): 64
Return on equity: 193.4%

PEORIA UNIFIED SCHOOL DISTRICT NO.11

EXECUTIVES

Supt, Denton Santarelli
Director, Jill Thomas
Executive Director, Michelle R Myers
Director, Adriana Parsons
Teacher, Amanda Taylor
Teacher, Darcie Rose
Teacher, Erin Harper
Teacher, Gloria Nielsen
Teacher, Justina Carnahan
Administrative Assistant, Lissa Cuellar
Academic Advisor, Alesia Thomason
Auditors: HEINFELD MEECH & CO PC P

LOCATIONS

HQ: PEORIA UNIFIED SCHOOL DISTRICT NO.11
  6330 W THUNDERBIRD RD, GLENDALE, AZ
  853064002
Phone: 623 486-6000
Web: WWW.PEORIAUD.K12.AZ.US

HISTORICAL FINANCIALS
Company Type: Private

Income Statement   FYE: June 30

	REVENUE ($ mil.)	NET INCOME ($ mil.)	NET PROFIT MARGIN	EMPLOYEES
06/17	304	(4)	—	3,889
06/16	296	13	4.5%	—
06/09	300	(57)	—	—
06/08	327	3	1.0%	—
Annual Growth	(0.8%)	—	—	—

PEPPER CONSTRUCTION COMPANY

EXECUTIVES

Ceo, J David Pepper
President, Kenneth Egidi
Exec Pres, James A Nissen
Cfo, Chris Averill
Coordinator, Les Klemt
Manager, Atul Raj
Leader, Tom Gehrlich
Central Texas Regional Manager, Mike Watson
Project Administrator, Teresa Tropeano
Project Manager, John Robinson
Safety Manager, Justin Teague
Auditors: BDD LLP OAKBROOK TERRACE IL

LOCATIONS

HQ: PEPPER CONSTRUCTION COMPANY
  643 N ORLEANS ST, CHICAGO, IL 606543690
Phone: 312 266-4700
Web: WWW.PEPPERLAWSON.COM

HISTORICAL FINANCIALS
Company Type: Private

Income Statement				FYE: September 30
	REVENUE ($ mil.)	NET INCOME ($ mil.)	NET PROFIT MARGIN	EMPLOYEES
09/17	704	14	2.1%	900
09/16	805	20	2.5%	—
09/15	709	10	1.5%	—
09/11	668	4	0.6%	—
Annual Growth	0.9%	23.3%	—	—

2017 Year-End Financials
Return on assets: 19.9% Cash ($ mil.): 21
Return on equity: 2.1%
Current ratio: 1.10

PEPPER CONSTRUCTION COMPANY OF INDIANA, LLC

EXECUTIVES

Pres, Michael T McAnn
Manager, J David Pepper
Manager, Christopher Averill
Executive of Sales, Meg King
Auditors: DELOITTE & TOUCHE LLP CHICAG

LOCATIONS

HQ: PEPPER CONSTRUCTION COMPANY OF INDIANA, LLC
  1850 W 15TH ST, INDIANAPOLIS, IN 462022027
Phone: 317 681-1000
Web: WWW.PEPPERCONSTRUCTION.COM

HISTORICAL FINANCIALS
Company Type: Private

Income Statement				FYE: September 30
	REVENUE ($ mil.)	NET INCOME ($ mil.)	NET PROFIT MARGIN	EMPLOYEES
09/17	326	6	2.1%	120
09/16	147	3	2.1%	—
09/15	130	0	0.2%	—
09/11	245	4	1.9%	—
Annual Growth	4.8%	6.7%	—	—

2017 Year-End Financials
Return on assets: 16.7% Cash ($ mil.): 12
Return on equity: 2.1%
Current ratio: 0.90

PEPPER CONSTRUCTION GROUP, LLC

Pepper Construction GroupA spices up the construction business with a little of this and a pinch of that.A The company provides general contracting and construction management services for commercial office education entertainmentA health care and institutional clients as well as waterworks projects.A (Health care projects account for about 50% of Pepper's revenue.) ItsA client list includes UBS Northwestern University University of Notre DameA Texas Heart Institute Loyola University Medical CenterA and NASA. Pepper Construction Group has divisions in Illinois Indiana Ohio and Texas.A Stanley F. Pepper founded the company in Chicago in 1927. The group is owned by his family and employees of the firm.

Operations

The company's Pepper Environmental Technologies unitA provides environmental services. Green building has become a large part of Pepper Construction's operations. Its Green Team of certified professionals have helped construct more than 2.9 million sq. ft. of eco-friendly space. The GreenA Team has built the Apple Computer flagship store HSBC Chicago North and Kohl's Children's Museum.

The firm's Pepper-Lawson Waterworks groupA constructs water purification plants for municipal clients including Houston and Missouri City Texas.

Geographic Reach

Chicago-based Pepper Construction comprises four geographic divisions: Illinois; Indiana; Ohio; and Texas. Overall the company is active in about 20 states mostly in the central and northeastern states.

EXECUTIVES

Chm, Dave Pepper
V Pres-Assist SEC, Stephanie Vitner
Sr V Pres-Gen Counselor-Sec, Timothy F Sullivan
Chief Operating Officer, Chris Averill
Office Manager, Debbie Connolly
Auditors: DELOITTE & TOUCHE LLP CHICAG

LOCATIONS

HQ: PEPPER CONSTRUCTION GROUP, LLC
  643 N ORLEANS ST, CHICAGO, IL 606543690
Phone: 312 266-4700
Web: WWW.PEPPERCONSTRUCTION.COM

PRODUCTS/OPERATIONS

Selected Operations
Pepper Construction Group LLC (Chicago Illinois)
Pepper Construction Co. (Chicago Illinois)
Pepper Construction Co. of Indiana (Indianapolis Indiana)
Pepper Construction Co. of Ohio LLC (Dublin Ohio)
Pepper Environmental Technologies Inc. (Barrington Illinois)
Pepper-Lawson Construction LP (Houston Texas)
Pepper-Lawson Waterworks LLC (Houston Texas)

COMPETITORS

Barton Malow	Graycor
Bulley & Andrews	M. A. Mortenson
C. G. Schmidt	McCarthy Building
Charles Pankow Builders	Power Construction
	Turner Corporation
Clark Enterprises	Walbridge Aldinger
Gilbane	Walsh Group

HISTORICAL FINANCIALS
Company Type: Private

Income Statement				FYE: September 30
	REVENUE ($ mil.)	NET INCOME ($ mil.)	NET PROFIT MARGIN	EMPLOYEES
09/17	1,119	21	1.9%	1,100
09/16	1,179	23	2.0%	—
09/15	1,110	9	0.9%	—
09/11	911	15	1.7%	—
Annual Growth	3.5%	5.2%	—	—

2017 Year-End Financials
Return on assets: 18.3% Cash ($ mil.): 36
Return on equity: 1.9%
Current ratio: 1.10

PEPPERDINE UNIVERSITY

Pepperdine University offers undergraduate and graduate programs to some 7300 students. Affiliated with Churches of Christ the university boasts five colleges and schools: Seaver College of Letters Arts and Sciences; the Graziadio School of Business and Management; the School of Law; the School of Public Policy; and the Graduate School of Education and Psychology. Pepperdine whose 830-acre main campus overlooks the Pacific Ocean in Malibu California has half a dozen additional campuses in California as well as international campuses in Argentina Italy Germany and the UK. The university was founded in 1937 by Christian businessman George Pepperdine who also founded the Western Auto Supply Company.

Operations

Pepperdine has a 13:1 student-to-teacher ratio. Tuition and fees for academic year 2015-16 run at some $48000.

Supported by a $790 million endowment fund the educational institution boasts nearly 700 faculty members 91% of which have earned doctoral or terminal degrees.

Geographic Reach

Pepperdine University's campus in Malibu extends to six other California campuses as well as campuses established in Argentina Italy Germany and the UK. Specifically its permanent educational and residential facilities are located in Heidelberg Florence Buenos Aires Lausanne and London.

Financial Performance

The university's revenue totaled $317 million in 2014. Some 65% of those earnings came from net student tuition and fees while room and board private gifts and grants and endowment support each brought in about 10%. The remaining revenue came from government grants sales and other operations. Net income that year totaled $117 million.

EXECUTIVES

Vp And Cfo, Paul B. Lasiter, age 51
President And Ceo, Andrew K. Benton
Svp Investments And Chief Investment Officer, Jeff Pippin
Evp And Coo, Gary A. Hanson
Dean Graduate School Of Education And Psychology, Helen E. Williams
Dean School Of Public Policy, James R. Wilburn
Provost And Chief Academic Officer, Rick Marrs
Dean School Of Law, Deanell Reese Tacha
Cio, Jonathan See
Interim Dean Graziadio School Of Business And Management, David M. Smith
Dean Of Libraries, Mark S. Roosa
Dean Seaver College, Michael Feltner
Vice Chairman, James R. Porter, age 82
Chairman, Edwin Biggers
Auditors: PRICEWATERHOUSECOOPERS LLP L

LOCATIONS

HQ: PEPPERDINE UNIVERSITY
24255 PACIFIC COAST HWY # 5000, MALIBU, CA
902635000
Phone: 310 506-4000
Web: WWW.PEPPERDINE.EDU

Selected California Campuses
Encino
Irvine
Long Beach
Los Angeles
Malibu
Santa Clara
Westlake Village

PRODUCTS/OPERATIONS

2014 Sales

	% of total
Student tuition & fees	64
Room & board	11
Endowment support	11
Private gifts & grants	9
Sales & services	2
Government grants	1
Other	2
Total	**100**

Selected Courses
Accounting
Applied Behavioral Science
Business Law
Decision Sciences
Economics
Finance
Graziadio School of Business and Management
Information Systems and Technology Management
Marketing
Organization Theory and Management
Strategy

Selected Colleges and Schools
Frank R. Seaver College of Letters Arts and Sciences
The George L. Graziadio School of Business and
  Management
The Graduate School of Education and Psychology
The School of Law
The School of Public Policy

HISTORICAL FINANCIALS
Company Type: Private

Income Statement				FYE: July 31
	REVENUE ($ mil.)	NET INCOME ($ mil.)	NET PROFIT MARGIN	EMPLOYEES
07/18	383	70	18.4%	1,500
07/17	361	105	29.2%	—
07/15	437	31	7.3%	—
07/12	291	(8)	—	—
Annual Growth	4.7%	—	—	—

2018 Year-End Financials
Return on assets: 8.5%   Cash ($ mil.): 148
Return on equity: 18.4%
Current ratio: —

PERFUME CENTER OF AMERICA INC.

EXECUTIVES

Chm, Kanak R Golia
V-President, Prebha Golia
Vice President, Preeti Mehta
Auditors: RAICH ENDE MALTER & CO LLP M

LOCATIONS

HQ: PERFUME CENTER OF AMERICA INC.
2020 OCEAN AVE, RONKONKOMA, NY 117796536
Phone: 516 348-1110
Web: WWW.PERFUME-CENTER.COM

HISTORICAL FINANCIALS
Company Type: Private

Income Statement				FYE: December 31
	REVENUE ($ mil.)	NET INCOME ($ mil.)	NET PROFIT MARGIN	EMPLOYEES
12/16	315	5	1.8%	70
12/15	271	5	1.9%	—
12/14	286	10	3.6%	—
12/13	239	6	2.9%	—
Annual Growth	9.7%	(7.2%)	—	—

2016 Year-End Financials
Return on assets: 14.7%   Cash ($ mil.): —
Return on equity: 1.8%
Current ratio: 1.00

PERISHABLE DISTRIBUTORS OF IOWA, LTD.

EXECUTIVES

Pres, Dan Wampler
Exec Vice President, Linda Sharp
Executive of Information Techn, Gary Churchill
Human Resources Executive, Janel Jones
Management Information, Gary Barber
Maintenance Supervisor, Glen Sievers
Senior Vice-President, Kevin Gass
Manager, Randy Garvey
Engineer, Trent Maring
Human Resources Director, Leigh Walters
Director, Mark Kloberdanz

LOCATIONS

HQ: PERISHABLE DISTRIBUTORS OF IOWA, LTD.
2741 SE PDI PL, ANKENY, IA 500213958
Phone: 515 965-6300
Web: WWW.CONTACTPDI.COM

HISTORICAL FINANCIALS
Company Type: Private

Income Statement				FYE: October 1
	REVENUE ($ mil.)	NET INCOME ($ mil.)	NET PROFIT MARGIN	EMPLOYEES
10/17	1,343	35	2.6%	687
10/16*	1,307	33	2.6%	—
09/15	1,248	31	2.5%	—
09/14	1,153	27	2.4%	—
Annual Growth	5.2%	8.3%	—	—

*Fiscal year change

2017 Year-End Financials
Return on assets: 4.7%   Cash ($ mil.): 16
Return on equity: 2.6%
Current ratio: 0.60

PERMANENT UNIVERSITY FUND

LOCATIONS

HQ: PERMANENT UNIVERSITY FUND
221 W 6TH ST STE 1700, AUSTIN, TX 787013400
Phone: 512 225-1600

HISTORICAL FINANCIALS
Company Type: Private

Income Statement				FYE: August 31
	REVENUE ($ mil.)	NET INCOME ($ mil.)	NET PROFIT MARGIN	EMPLOYEES
08/18	1,906	1,964	103.0%	2
08/17	2,888	2,032	70.4%	—
Annual Growth	(34.0%)	(3.4%)	—	—

PETERSBURG MOTOR COMPANY INC

EXECUTIVES

Pres, Elizabeth M Borches
V Pres, Peter Borches
Exec Chmn, H Carter Myers III
SEC, Carolyn Kyger
CMA Payroll Administrator, Candra Gerrick
Vice President Operational Sup, Matt Walsh
Vice President, Pete Borches
Auditors: MITCHELL WIGGINS & COMPANY L

LOCATIONS

HQ: PETERSBURG MOTOR COMPANY INC
100 MYERS DR, CHARLOTTESVILLE, VA 229011166
Phone: 434 951-1000
Web: WWW.COLONIALAUTOCENTER.COM

HISTORICAL FINANCIALS
Company Type: Private

Income Statement				FYE: December 31
	REVENUE ($ mil.)	NET INCOME ($ mil.)	NET PROFIT MARGIN	EMPLOYEES
12/17	437	7	1.7%	388
12/16	406	7	1.8%	—
12/14	335	5	1.6%	—
12/13	319	4	1.4%	—
Annual Growth	8.2%	12.5%	—	—

2017 Year-End Financials
Return on assets: 0.7%   Cash ($ mil.): 26
Return on equity: 1.7%
Current ratio: 0.50

PETR-ALL PETROLEUM CONSULTING CORP.

EXECUTIVES

Ceo, Francis E Borer
Cfo, Daniel Twombly
Director of Information Techno, Timothy Gorman
Director, David Pasquale
Chief Operating Officer, Chris Sweeney
Manager, Pat Hyde
Controller, Chris Pirozzi
Human Resources Manager, Dan Twombly
Cfo, Pat Twombly
Auditors: DERMODY BURKE BROWN SYRACUSE

LOCATIONS

HQ: PETR-ALL PETROLEUM CONSULTING CORP.
7401 ROUND POND RD, SYRACUSE, NY 132122515
Phone: 315 446-0125
Web: WWW.EXPRESSMART.COM

HISTORICAL FINANCIALS
Company Type: Private

Income Statement				FYE: December 31
	REVENUE ($ mil.)	NET INCOME ($ mil.)	NET PROFIT MARGIN	EMPLOYEES
12/15	390	10	2.6%	600
12/13	482	0	0.0%	—
12/12	473	2	0.5%	—
12/11	471	2	0.6%	—
Annual Growth	(4.6%)	36.1%	—	—

2015 Year-End Financials
Return on assets: 3.5%   Cash ($ mil.): 5
Return on equity: 2.6%
Current ratio: 0.50

PETROLEUM TRADERS CORPORATION

Petroleum Traders Corporation barters with fuel. The company provides wholesale gasoline diesel fuel and heating oil to fuel distributors government agencies and other large consumers of fuel such as businesses with vehicle fleets. The largest pure wholesale fuel distributor in the country Petroleum Traders operates and trades in 44 US states. It supplies #1 and #2 low sulfur diesel fuels biodiesel high sulfur heating oil and kerosene and conventional ethanol and reformulated blends of gasoline in regular midgrade and premium octane ratings.

Operations
Petroleum Traders focuses on supplying wholesale diesel and gasoline exclusively in the US offering a range of turnkey wholesale diesel fuel and wholesale gasoline fuel services.

Sales and Marketing
The company provides discount fuel to commercial government and wholesale customers. In the commercial space it services the trucking construction railroad mining and manufacturing industries as well as utilities and private fleets.

Strategy
Petroleum Traders parlays its hedging experience in fuel cost management for its customers via firm pricing cap programs collars and fuel swaps.

Company Background
The company was founded in 1979.

EXECUTIVES

Pres-Ceo, Michael Himes
Asst Ceo, Vicki Himes
Chief Financial Officer, Linda Stephens
SEC, Glenn Moonen
Administrative Assistant, Michelle Beard
Sales and Marketing Staff, Gayle Newton
Account Manager, Linda Cambre
Human Resources, Jennifer Girardot
Vice President, Vicky Himes
Network Manager, Dan Espich
Information Technology Manager, John Bales
Auditors: BADEN GAGE & SCHROEDER LLC

LOCATIONS

HQ: PETROLEUM TRADERS CORPORATION
7120 POINTE INVERNESS WAY, FORT WAYNE, IN 468047928
Phone: 260 432-6622
Web: WWW.PETROLEUMTRADERS.COM

COMPETITORS

George Warren
Gulf Oil
Martin Resource Management
Petro Holdings
Sun Coast Resources

HISTORICAL FINANCIALS
Company Type: Private

Income Statement				FYE: June 30
	REVENUE ($ mil.)	NET INCOME ($ mil.)	NET PROFIT MARGIN	EMPLOYEES
06/18	1,815	11	0.6%	150
06/17	1,606	19	1.2%	—
06/16	1,667	38	2.3%	—
06/15	2,128	64	3.0%	—
Annual Growth	(5.2%)	(43.6%)	—	—

2018 Year-End Financials
Return on assets: 3.1%   Cash ($ mil.): 45
Return on equity: 0.6%
Current ratio: 1.60

PFLUGERVILLE INDEPENDENT SCHOOL DISTRICT

EXECUTIVES

Pres, Vernagene Mott
Vice President, Larry D Bradley
SEC, Mary Kimmins
SEC, Cynthia Graves
Cfo, Kenneth Adix
Spdt, Alex Etorrez
Payroll Staff, Kristin Baum
Superintendent, Charles E Dupre
Accounting Staff, Lisa Campbell
Accounting Staff, Lisa Casinelli
Building and Grounds Director, Kevin Myers
Auditors: NULL-LAIRSON PC HOUSTON T

LOCATIONS

HQ: PFLUGERVILLE INDEPENDENT SCHOOL DISTRICT
1401 W PECAN ST, PFLUGERVILLE, TX 786602518
Phone: 512 594-0000
Web: WWW.PFISD.NET

HISTORICAL FINANCIALS
Company Type: Private

Income Statement				FYE: August 31
	REVENUE ($ mil.)	NET INCOME ($ mil.)	NET PROFIT MARGIN	EMPLOYEES
08/17	285	(105)	—	2,631
08/16	278	(94)	—	—
08/08	192	115	59.8%	—
08/07	167	32	19.5%	—
Annual Growth	5.5%	—	—	—

2017 Year-End Financials
Return on assets: 6.1%   Cash ($ mil.): 12
Return on equity: (-37.0%)
Current ratio: —

PHALCON, LTD.

EXECUTIVES

Pres, Michael E McPhee
V Pres, Marcus W McPhee
SEC, Robert A Feiner
Cfo, John D Conroy
Information Technology Project, Mike Caron
Human Resources Director, Marie Popielarczyk
Executive Vice President, Marcus McPhee
Operations Manager, Mark Howard
Branch Manager, Thomas Lombardo
Auditors: BLUM SHAPIRO & COMPANY PC

LOCATIONS

HQ: PHALCON, LTD.
505 MAIN ST, FARMINGTON, CT 060322912
Phone: 860 677-9797
Web: WWW.PHALCON.US

HISTORICAL FINANCIALS
Company Type: Private

Income Statement				FYE: December 31
	REVENUE ($ mil.)	NET INCOME ($ mil.)	NET PROFIT MARGIN	EMPLOYEES
12/17	449	26	5.9%	1,000
12/16	373	21	5.8%	—
12/15	352	19	5.5%	—
12/14	276	22	8.3%	—
Annual Growth	17.6%	5.1%	—	—

2017 Year-End Financials
Return on assets: 5.0%   Cash ($ mil.): 50
Return on equity: 5.9%
Current ratio: 1.80

PHARR SAN JUAN-ALAMO INDEPENDENT SCHOOL DISTRICT

EXECUTIVES

Supt, Daniel King
President, Ronaldo Cantu
V-President, Jesus Vela Jr
SEC, Victor Perez
Assistant Supt For Finance, Janet C Robles
Auditors: OSAR R GONZALEZ CPA & ASSOCI

LOCATIONS

HQ: PHARR SAN JUAN-ALAMO INDEPENDENT
SCHOOL DISTRICT
601 E KELLY AVE, PHARR, TX 785774905
Phone: 956 354-2000
Web: WWW.PSJAISD.US

HISTORICAL FINANCIALS
Company Type: Private

Income Statement
FYE: August 31

	REVENUE ($ mil.)	NET INCOME ($ mil.)	NET PROFIT MARGIN	EMPLOYEES
08/17	383	(7)	—	3,500
08/16	382	9	2.4%	—
08/11	339	81	24.1%	—
08/07	269	80	29.9%	—
Annual Growth	3.6%	—	—	—

2017 Year-End Financials
Return on assets: 1.3%   Cash ($ mil.): 114
Return on equity: (-2.0%)
Current ratio: —

PHILADELPHIA CONSOLIDATED HOLDING CORP.

Because each industry has its own unique set of risks Philadelphia Insurance Companies and its subsidiaries specialize in designing and underwriting commercial property/casualty insurance. Its niche clients include rental car companies (for that insurance they always want to sell you at the counter) not-for-profits health and fitness centers and day-care facilities. Its specialty lines include loss-control policies and liability coverage for such professionals as lawyers doctors accountants dog groomers and even insurance claims adjusters. Philadelphia Insurance Companies is a subsidiary of Tokio Marine Holdings.

Geographic Reach

Philadelphia Insurance Companies' operating subsidiaries Philadelphia Insurance and Philadelphia Indemnity Insurance sell and service policies through a network of independent agents and about 50 regional offices that stretch across the US. With its new-found backing from Tokio Marine the insurer has access to broader distribution avenues in the US and overseas.

Sales and Marketing

In addition to commercial property and casualty insurance the company also sells personal coverage for collectible cars and homeowners flood insurance.

Strategy

Philadelphia Insurance Companies has been enhancing its information technology systems. The firm is working to upgrade its back-office infrastructure for more efficient handling of billing claims accounting and data management functions.

EXECUTIVES

Regional Vice President, Brent Kruse
Assistant Vice President And Pricing Actuary, John Ferraro
Executive Vice President Marketing, Robert OLeary
Senior Vice President Marketing, Brian O'Reilly
Assistant Vice President, Michael Henk
Assistant Vice President, Tsuyoshi Maeda
Assistant Vice President Human Resources, Laura Boylan
Vice President And Product Manager, Paul Siragusa
Senior Vice President, John Doyle
Regional Vice President, Bill Misita
Assistant Vice President, Liney Kevin
Executive Vice President, Sean Sweeney

LOCATIONS

HQ: PHILADELPHIA CONSOLIDATED HOLDING CORP.
1 BALA PLZ STE 100, BALA CYNWYD, PA 190041401
Phone: 610 617-7900
Web: WWW.PHLY.COM

PRODUCTS/OPERATIONS

Selected Products
Commercial and Personal Property/Casualty Insurance
  Adoption agencies
  Adult day care
  Amateur sports
  Antique collector car
  Apartments
  Auto leasing/rental program
  Boat dealers
  Bowling centers
  Builder's exchange
  Builders' risk
  Business auto fleet
  Camp operators
  Child care centers
  Consulting foresters
  Contractor environmental coverage
  Crime protection plus
  Entertainment
  Environmental
  Fairs and fairgrounds
  Festivals
  Film production
  Flood
  Golf and country clubs
  Health fitness and wellness
  Home health care
  Homeowners association
  Hospice
  Hotels
  Life and business coaches
  Loss control
  Medical facilities and hospitals
  Motorsports
  Museums
  Non-profit and social service organizations
  Nursing homes
  Office parks
  Outdoor recreation
  Performing arts
  Pest control services
  Professional sports
  Public entities
  Real rstate dchedules
  Religious organizations
  RV parks and campgrounds
  Schools
  Security services (The Guardian)
  Shopping centers
  Special events
  Substance abuse rehabilitation facilities
  Temporary staffing agencies
  Volunteer fire department
  Zoos
Liability
  Accountants professional liability
  Allied Health professional liability
  Business owners
  Cyber security liability
  Employed lawyers professional liability
  Employment practices stand alone
  Excess liability
  Miscellaneous professional liability (Affinity Pro)

COMPETITORS

AIG	Liberty Mutual
American Financial Group	Markel
	North Pointe
CNA Financial	RLI
Hagerty Insurance	State Farm
Hanover Insurance	Travelers Companies

HISTORICAL FINANCIALS
Company Type: Private

Income Statement
FYE: December 31

	ASSETS ($ mil.)	NET INCOME ($ mil.)	INCOME AS % OF ASSETS	EMPLOYEES
12/16	9,719	347	3.6%	1,374
12/15	9,047	323	3.6%	—
Annual Growth	7.4%	7.5%	—	—

PHILLIPS 66 CARRIER LLC

EXECUTIVES

Mng MBR, Greg C Garland

LOCATIONS

HQ: PHILLIPS 66 CARRIER LLC
3010 BRIARPARK DR, HOUSTON, TX 770423706
Phone: 855 283-9237
Web: WWW.PHILLIPS66PARTNERS.COM

HISTORICAL FINANCIALS
Company Type: Private

Income Statement
FYE: December 31

	REVENUE ($ mil.)	NET INCOME ($ mil.)	NET PROFIT MARGIN	EMPLOYEES
12/17	420	216	51.5%	538
12/16	213	143	67.0%	—
Annual Growth	96.8%	51.3%	—	—

PHILLIPS AND JORDAN, INCORPORATED

While some like to clear the air Phillips and Jordan (P&J) prefers to clear the land. Founded in 1952 as a small land clearing firm P&J is a general and specialty contractor that still provides land clearing services in addition to industrial commercial and residential site development and heavy civil construction on dams highways bridges railroads and waterways. P&J also performs reclamation landfill and disaster recovery services. The latter includes handling some of the nation's worst disaster cleanups including hurricanes floods toxic spills and land and rock slides. P&J operates about a dozen offices in eight states. The Phillips family owns and runs the company.

Operations
Phillips and Jordan operates a fleet of more than 850 pieces of heavy and specialized equipment including excavators graders loaders tractors and trucks. The firm performs projects across the US.

True to its roots the company has built a reputation for taking on difficult land clearing jobs. With a fleet of specialized equipment P&J clears and grubs swamp forest mountain and agricultural land to make way for reservoirs pipelines power transmission lines railways and roadways. Clients come from both the public and private sectors.

Geographic Reach
Knoxville Tennessee-based Phillips and Jordan has about a dozen offices in North Carolina and in California Florida North Dakota Tennessee and Wyoming.

Strategy
The booming oil and gas industry in Wyoming has drawn P&J to the state where in late 2013 it opened two rock pits in the Douglas area. The pits are managed from the firm's Douglas office. Also in 2013 P&J partnered with North Creek Energy to form a joint venture company Solar Jack LLC to market a system that offers oil and gas producers the opportunity to capture the regenerated energy from their pump jacks combined with solar energy to reduce energy consumption and costs. Previously the firm expanded its operations near Williston North Dakota opening an equipment maintenance shop and offices there in 2012.

EXECUTIVES

Ceo, William T Phillips Jr
President, J Patrick McMullen
Vice President, John D Lawrence
Sr V Pres-Sec-Dir, Connie H Nichols
Project Coordinator, Allyson Warren
Vice President, Steve Thompson
Auditors: RODGERS MOSS & CO PLLC KNOX

LOCATIONS

HQ: PHILLIPS AND JORDAN, INCORPORATED
10201 PARKSIDE DR STE 300, KNOXVILLE, TN 379221983
Phone: 865 688-8342
Web: WWW.PANDJ.COM

PRODUCTS/OPERATIONS

Selected Services
Apartment site development
Debris management
Disaster recovery
Earthmoving & erosion control
Heavy civil construction
Industrial and commercial site development
Land clearing
Landfill and liner design
Reclamation and mitigation
Storm drainage
Subdivision site development

COMPETITORS

Boh Bros Construction	McCarthy Building
Clarkson Construction	Peter Kiewit Sons'
Environmental Safety &	Rentenbach
Health	Constructors
Hardaway Construction	

HISTORICAL FINANCIALS
Company Type: Private

Income Statement				FYE: December 31
	REVENUE ($ mil.)	NET INCOME ($ mil.)	NET PROFIT MARGIN	EMPLOYEES
12/15	340	10	3.1%	650
12/14	340	14	4.3%	—
12/13	215	4	2.1%	—
12/12	284	11	4.0%	—
Annual Growth	6.1%	(2.6%)	—	—

2015 Year-End Financials
Return on assets: 4.0%   Cash ($ mil.): —
Return on equity: 3.1%
Current ratio: 1.50

PHOEBE PUTNEY MEMORIAL HOSPITAL, INC.

Phoebe Putney Memorial Hospital provides health care services to residents of southwest Georgia. With more than 650 beds and some 300 physicians the acute-care hospital provides emergency and inpatient services as well as cardiology oncology psychiatric women's health and pediatric specialty care. It's one of Georgia's largest comprehensive regional medical centers. Founded in 1911 it is part of the Phoebe Putney Health System which also includes the 25-bed Phoebe Worth Medical Center and several satellite community health centers that provide outpatient primary health laboratory and surgical services. The health system is governed by the Albany-Dougherty County Hospital Authority.

Operations
As part of its operations Phoebe Putney Memorial Hospital runs an ambulatory infusion center Carlton Breast Health Center and surgical weight loss/wellness center. Inpatient admissions average more than 21000 a year while clinic visits typically run about 711000 annually. With some 3800 employees payroll at Phoebe Putney Memorial Hospital is about $180 million on average.

Geographic Reach
The hospital serves a growing group of residents in 35 counties across southwest Georgia.

Sales and Marketing
Third-party payors accounted for 42% of net patient service revenues in 2014; Medicare and Medicaid accounted for 29% and 13% respectively.

Financial Performance
In 2014 revenue fell 5% to $488 million as net patient service revenues slipped. However the system returned to the black that year reporting $13 million in net income due to an absence of loss on impairment of goodwill. Cash flow from operation rose to $29 million (versus $9000 in 2013) due to changes in receivables supplies and estimated settlements. A decline in cash used for payments and expenses also contributed to the increase.

Strategy
To ensure that it can meet current and future demand for health care services Phoebe Putney Memorial Hospital has been focusing on building up its physician network.

EXECUTIVES

Vice President, Maureen Jackson
President Ceo And Director, Joel Wernick
Svp And Cfo, Kerry Loudermilk
Vp Information Systems Clinical Informatics, Jesse Diaz
Evp And Coo, Joe Austin
Vp Strategy And Marketing, Jackie Ryan
Vice President Internal Audits, Brad Hallford
Medical Director Chief Of Staff Chief Marketing Officer, Harry Dorsey
Vice Chairman, Mary H. Dykes
Chairman, John Culbreath

LOCATIONS

HQ: PHOEBE PUTNEY MEMORIAL HOSPITAL, INC.
417 W 3RD AVE, ALBANY, GA 317011943
Phone: 229 312-1000
Web: WWW.PHOEBEPUTNEY.COM

PRODUCTS/OPERATIONS

Selected Services
Ambulatory Infusion Center
Bariatric Surgery
Behavioral Health
Cardiac Rehabilitation
Carlton Breast Health Center
Corporate Health Services
Corporate Onsite Services
Da Vinci Robotic Surgery
Endoscopy Department
Hematology/Oncology
Hospice and Palliative Care
Hyperbaric Oxygen Therapy
Neurodiagnostics
Orthopedics
Pediatrics
Prostate Brachytherapy
Radiation Oncology
Rheumatology
Sickle Cell Clinic
Speech Therapy
Sports Medicine
Surgical Weight Loss/Wellness Center
Wound Care

COMPETITORS

Central Georgia Health Systems	Regency Hospital
HCA	WellStar Health System
Oconee Regional Health Systems	

HISTORICAL FINANCIALS
Company Type: Private

Income Statement				FYE: July 31
	REVENUE ($ mil.)	NET INCOME ($ mil.)	NET PROFIT MARGIN	EMPLOYEES
07/16	498	(13)	—	3,000
07/15	490	32	6.6%	—
07/09	513	19	3.8%	—
07/08	500	15	3.0%	—
Annual Growth	(0.0%)	—	—	—

2016 Year-End Financials
Return on assets: 2.6%   Cash ($ mil.): 49
Return on equity: (-2.7%)
Current ratio: 3.80

PHOEBE PUTNEY MEMORIAL HOSPITAL, INC.

EXECUTIVES

BR Mgr, Judy Clay
Vp Operations, Jeff Flowers

LOCATIONS

HQ: PHOEBE PUTNEY MEMORIAL HOSPITAL, INC.
2000 PALMYRA RD, ALBANY, GA 317011528
Phone: 229 434-2000
Web: WWW.PPMH.ORG

HISTORICAL FINANCIALS

Company Type: Private

Income Statement				FYE: July 31
	REVENUE ($ mil.)	NET INCOME ($ mil.)	NET PROFIT MARGIN	EMPLOYEES
07/15	490	32	6.6%	1
07/13	515	(4)	—	—
Annual Growth	(2.5%)	—	—	—

2015 Year-End Financials

Return on assets: 3.4%
Return on equity: 6.6%   Cash ($ mil.): 49
Current ratio: 3.10

PHOENIX UNION HIGH SCHOOL DISTRICT NO 210

EXECUTIVES

Supt, Raj Chopra
Supt, Dr Kent P Scribner
Purchasing Coordinator, Melody Bach
Information Specialist, Donald Sheldon
Teacher, Kim Padilla
Coordinator, Stephanie Newson
Athletic Director, Sarah Nix
Human Resources, Alexandra Harmon
Coordinator, Bolivia Gaytan
Teacher, Charles Almo
Psychologist, Dan Perez
Auditors: HEINFELD MEECH & CO PC P

LOCATIONS

HQ: PHOENIX UNION HIGH SCHOOL DISTRICT NO 210
4502 N CENTRAL AVE, PHOENIX, AZ 850121817
Phone: 602 271-3302
Web: WWW.PHOENIXUNION.ORG

HISTORICAL FINANCIALS

Company Type: Private

Income Statement				FYE: June 30
	REVENUE ($ mil.)	NET INCOME ($ mil.)	NET PROFIT MARGIN	EMPLOYEES
06/17	339	15	4.5%	2,704
06/16	327	(30)	—	—
06/13	291	35	12.2%	—
06/12	51	5	11.0%	—
Annual Growth	46.0%	21.9%	—	—

PIEDMONT HOSPITAL, INC.

Those feeling ill in Atlanta can count on Piedmont Healthcare for help. Founded in 1905 the not-for-profit organization's flagship facility is Piedmont Atlanta an acute care hospital with more than 485 beds. Piedmont Atlanta provides general and advanced medical-surgical care including open-heart surgery organ transplantation and neurosurgery. Also part of the Piedmont family are Piedmont Fayette Hospital with more than 170 beds; Piedmont Mountainside Hospital a 52-bed community hospital north of Atlanta; and the Piedmont Physicians Group a network of more than 150 primary care physicians operating in dozens of offices throughout metropolitan Atlanta.

Operations

Piedmont Healthcare also operates Piedmont Newnan Hospital a community hospital in Coweta County Georgia and the acute care community hospital Piedmont Henry Hospital.

Each year the system serves around 2 million patients performing some 44000 surgeries completing more than 200 organ transplants and handling more than 250000 emergency department visits. It also sees some 472000 outpatients and around 8000 infant deliveries annually.

Sales and Marketing

Medicare and Medicaid payments combined account for more than 40% of Piedmont's total net patient service revenue.

Financial Performance

Revenue increased 4% to $1.7 billion in fiscal 2014 (ended June) on higher net patient service revenues and other revenues. However net income fell 27% to $104.2 million as operating expenses and pension adjustments increased.

Cash flow from operations rose 66% to $150.1 million that year due primarily to a change in working capital.

Strategy

The health care system expands its offerings through investment and renovation as well as partnerships and acquisitions. In 2014 it partnered with WellStreet to launch Piedmont Urgent Care by WellStreet a network of urgent care centers offering extended-hour walk-in treatment for non-life threatening illnesses and injuries.

EXECUTIVES

Ceo Piedmont Physicians, Sid Kirschner
Chief Medical Officer, Leigh S. Hamby
Vice Chair, Harry M. McFarling
Coo, Gregory A. (Greg) Hurst
Chief Nurse Executive, Denise Ray
President And Ceo, Kevin Brown
Chief Strategy & Performance Improvement Officer, Michelle Fisher
Chief Consumer Officer, Matt Gove
Cfo, Michael McAnder
Cio, Geoff Brown
Vice President Of Ambulatory Services, Rob Simmons
Executive Assistant To Mark Cohen Medical Director Vpma, Kathie Alhadeff
Chair, Janine Brown

LOCATIONS

HQ: PIEDMONT HOSPITAL, INC.
1968 PEACHTREE RD NW, ATLANTA, GA 303091285
Phone: 404 605-5000
Web: WWW.PIEDMONT.ORG/LOCATIONS/PIEDMONT-ATLANTA/PAH-HOME

PRODUCTS/OPERATIONS

2014 Sales

	$ mil.	% of total
Net patient service revenue	1,595	96
Other revenue	62	4
Total	1,657	100

Selected Operations

Piedmont Atlanta
Piedmont Fayette Hospital (Fayetteville)
Piedmont Henry Hospital (Stockbridge)
Piedmont Mountainside Hospital (Jasper)
Piedmont Newnan Hospital (Newnan)
Piedmont Physicians Group (metropolitan Atlanta)

COMPETITORS

Children's Healthcare of Atlanta	Northside Hospital
DeKalb Medical	Shepherd Center
Emory Healthcare	Tenet Healthcare
Grady Health System	Universal Health Services

HISTORICAL FINANCIALS

Company Type: Private

Income Statement				FYE: June 30
	REVENUE ($ mil.)	NET INCOME ($ mil.)	NET PROFIT MARGIN	EMPLOYEES
06/16	918	60	6.5%	6,419
06/15	857	66	7.8%	—
06/10*	689	75	11.0%	—
12/09	1	(0)	—	—
Annual Growth	199.4%	—	—	—

*Fiscal year change

2016 Year-End Financials

Return on assets: 4.2%
Return on equity: 6.5%   Cash ($ mil.): 25
Current ratio: 1.80

PIKEVILLE MEDICAL CENTER, INC.

Taking a nasty fall while hiking the rugged Appalachians will likely land you at Pikeville Medical Center (PMC). Serving patients in eastern Kentucky the hospital boasts more than 260 beds and provides a full range of inpatient outpatient and surgical services. PMC's centers and departments handle a number of specialties such as diagnostic imaging echocardiogram neurosurgery cancer care and bariatric surgery. Employing some 350 physicians PMC also operates a rehabilitation hospital a home health agency and outpatient family practice and specialty clinics as well as a physician residency program. PMC first opened on Christmas Day in 1924.

Operations
Pikeville Kentucky-based PMC offers more than 400 services.

Strategy
PMC is rapidly expanding its services and facilities to keep pace with the needs of area residents. In recent years it has added such new services as pulmonary rehabilitation plastic surgery and orthopedic trauma. In addition the hospital launched a $150 million expansion project that will add an 11-story outpatient center (including physician practices and surgery suites) and a 10-story parking garage. Additional expansion efforts have included opening new outpatient cancer diagnostic pain management and primary care clinics.

An active participant in clinical trials and studies PMC works to expand its research opportunities for patients and physicians. In 2013 the hospital began new treatment for patients with Paroxysmal Atrial Fibrillation (Afib) using Medtronic's Arctic Front Advance Cardiac Cryoballoon System.

Since 2012 when it inked a Medicaid contract with Coventry PMC has contracts with all three providers: Coventry Wellcare and Kentucky Spirit. PMC become member of the Mayo Clinic Care Network in 2013. The agreement gives PMC providers access to Mayo Clinic resources including its online point-of-care information system and its electronic consulting process that connects physicians with Mayo Clinic specialists on questions of diagnosis therapy or care management.

EXECUTIVES

Vice President Of Physician Services, Peggy Justice
Auditors: PERSHING YOAKLEY & ASSOCIATES

LOCATIONS

HQ: PIKEVILLE MEDICAL CENTER, INC.
911 BYPASS RD, PIKEVILLE, KY 415011689
Phone: 606 218-3500
Web: WWW.PIKEVILLEHOSPITAL.ORG

PRODUCTS/OPERATIONS

Selected Services
Bariatric Surgery
Breast Care Center
Critical Care
Diagnostics
Diabetes Education
Ear Nose & Throat (Otolaryngology)
Emergency
Endocrinology
Family Practice
Gastroenterology
Gynecology/Obstetrics
Family Practice Clinic
Heart Institute
Heart Failure/Coumadin Clinic
Home Health
Home Medical Equipment
Inpatient
Infectious Disease
Laboratory Services
Leonard Lawson Cancer Center
Neonatology
Nephrology
Neurosurgery
Ophthalmology
Other Patient Services
Orthopedic Surgery
Palliative Care
Pediatrics
Pharmacy
Plastic & Reconstructive Surgery
Pulmonary Clinic
Radiology
Rehabilitation
Residency Program
Rheumatology
Sleep

Urology
Women and Childrens' Services
Wound Care Center

COMPETITORS

Appalachian Regional Healthcare
Clinch Valley Medical Center
Community Health Systems
Highlands Health
Norton Community Hospital
Norton Healthcare
Russell County Medical Center
University of Kentucky Chandler Hospital

HISTORICAL FINANCIALS
Company Type: Private

Income Statement   FYE: September 30

	REVENUE ($ mil.)	NET INCOME ($ mil.)	NET PROFIT MARGIN	EMPLOYEES
09/16	489	29	5.9%	2,527
09/15	381	9	2.5%	—
09/14	367	8	2.4%	—
09/13	394	2	0.7%	—
Annual Growth	7.4%	119.5%	—	—

2016 Year-End Financials
Return on assets: 4.4%   Cash ($ mil.): 170
Return on equity: 5.9%
Current ratio: 3.00

PIMA COUNTY

EXECUTIVES

Admin, Chuck Huckelberry
Senior Corporate Officer, Richard Elias
General Manager, Marilyn Hutzler
Information Specialist, Ed Sander
Legal Staff, Kelly Johnson
Customer Staff, Dana Moore
Manager, Allan Anthon
Coordinator, Anastasia Olander
Information Technology/Interne, Brian Barter
Manager, Daniel Riggs
Supervisor, David Adamovich
Auditors: STATE OF ARIZONA-DEBBIE DAVENP

LOCATIONS

HQ: PIMA COUNTY
201 N STONE AVE FL 9, TUCSON, AZ 857011215
Phone: 520 243-4600
Web: WWW.PIMA.GOV

HISTORICAL FINANCIALS
Company Type: Private

Income Statement   FYE: June 30

	REVENUE ($ mil.)	NET INCOME ($ mil.)	NET PROFIT MARGIN	EMPLOYEES
06/17	873	17	2.0%	7,500
06/16	863	2	0.3%	—
06/13	789	(13)	—	—
Annual Growth	2.6%	—	—	—

2017 Year-End Financials
Return on assets: 5.6%   Cash ($ mil.): 521
Return on equity: 2.0%
Current ratio: —

PITT COUNTY MEMORIAL HOSPITAL, INCORPORATED

Vidant Medical Center is an acute health services facility that serves the vibrant community of Greenville North Carolina and surrounding areas. The 909-bed regional referral hospital's specialty divisions include Vidant Children's Hospital East Carolina Heart Institute a rehabilitation center and the outpatient Vidant SurgiCenter. Other services include oncology transplant women's health orthopedic behavioral care and home health and hospice care units. The center also serves as a teaching facility for East Carolina University's Brody School of Medicine. Vidant Medical Center (formerly Pitt County Memorial Hospital) is a member of University Health Systems of Eastern Carolina (dba Vidant Health).

Operations
In addition to serving as a primary teaching facility for the Brody School of Medicine Vidant Medical Center provides clinical training for East Carolina University's allied health and nursing programs. About 2000 students complete clinical programs at the medical center and its affiliated Vidant Health facilities each year.

Its subsidiary PMI Inc. offers property management services.

Altogether Vidant Medical Center serves more than 1.4 million people across its 29-county service area. Boasting a clinical staff of more than 500 physicians and 1200 nurses the medical center in 2013 tended to more than 46000 inpatients and more than 275000 outpatients. Its emergency department visits reached 121000-plus in 2013.

Geographic Reach
Vidant Medical Center provides care to patients in a 29-county service territory in eastern North Carolina. It operates as a regional referral center for smaller community hospitals in the area taking on complex care cases in its specialized fields of medicine.

Strategy
To enhance its service offerings to area residents the Vidant Health organization regularly updates its facilities through capital improvement projects. In addition to basic equipment and infrastructure upgrades in 2011 the hospital completed phase one of an expansion project at the Vidant Medical Center that aims to improve the hospital's pediatric and cancer care capabilities.

To signify its mission to enhance the quality of life in its service territories in 2012 University Health Systems of Eastern Carolina began operating as Vidant Health and the Pitt County Memorial Hospital was renamed as Vidant Memorial Hospital.

EXECUTIVES

Vice President Financial Services Supply Chain Management, Preston Comeaux
Auditors: RSM US LLP MINNEAPOLIS MINNE

LOCATIONS

HQ: PITT COUNTY MEMORIAL HOSPITAL, INCORPORATED
2100 STANTONSBURG RD, GREENVILLE, NC 278342832
Phone: 252 847-4100
Web: WWW.VIDANTHEALTH.COM

PRODUCTS/OPERATIONS

Selected Services
Asthma Program (Pediatric)
Audiology
Behavioral & Mental Health
Cancer Care
Child Life
Children's Care
Children's Emergency Department
Children's Hospital
Community Health Programs
CyberKnife
Diagnostic Imaging
Diabetes
Emergency Services
Endoscopy Services
Gamma Knife

COMPETITORS

Adventist Health System Sunbelt Healthcare
 Bon Secours Health
 Carolinas HealthCare System
 Duke University Health System
 Novant Health
 Sentara Healthcare
 Tenet Healthcare
 UNC Hospitals
 Upstate Affiliate

HISTORICAL FINANCIALS

Company Type: Private

Income Statement				FYE: September 30
	REVENUE ($ mil.)	NET INCOME ($ mil.)	NET PROFIT MARGIN	EMPLOYEES
09/15	1,066	79	7.5%	15,000
09/14	1,025	79	7.8%	—
09/13*	1,031	91	8.9%	—
12/12	395	19	4.8%	—
Annual Growth	39.1%	61.1%	—	—

*Fiscal year change

2015 Year-End Financials
Return on assets: 3.3%   Cash ($ mil.): 23
Return on equity: 7.5%
Current ratio: 1.60

PITTSBURGH SCHOOL DISTRICT

EXECUTIVES

Supt, Linda Lane
Auditors: MAHER DUESSEL PITTSBURGH PEN

LOCATIONS

HQ: PITTSBURGH SCHOOL DISTRICT
  341 S BELLEFIELD AVE, PITTSBURGH, PA
  152133552
Phone: 412 622-3500
Web: WWW.PPS.K12.PA.US

HISTORICAL FINANCIALS

Company Type: Private

Income Statement				FYE: December 31
	REVENUE ($ mil.)	NET INCOME ($ mil.)	NET PROFIT MARGIN	EMPLOYEES
12/17	674	(4)	—	5,825
12/16	735	(2)	—	—
12/15	639	15	2.5%	—
Annual Growth	2.7%	—	—	—

2017 Year-End Financials
Return on assets: 2.1%   Cash ($ mil.): 67
Return on equity: (-0.7%)
Current ratio: 0.40

PLACENTIA-YORBA LINDA UNIFIED SCHOOL DISTRICT

EXECUTIVES

Supt, Doug Domene
Supt, Dennis Smith
SEC, Evelyn Kirk
Vice President, Carrie Buck
Administrator, Cindy Rex
Administrator, Keith Carmona
Administrator, Patrick Brown
Teacher, Rich Medellin
Information Technology Manager, Alex Marestaing
Teacher, Debbee Titov
Teacher, Susan Solomonson
Auditors: VAVRINEK TRINE DAY & CO LL

LOCATIONS

HQ: PLACENTIA-YORBA LINDA UNIFIED SCHOOL
  DISTRICT
  1301 E ORANGETHORPE AVE, PLACENTIA, CA
  928705302
Phone: 714 986-7000
Web: WWW.PYLUSD.ORG

HISTORICAL FINANCIALS

Company Type: Private

Income Statement				FYE: June 30
	REVENUE ($ mil.)	NET INCOME ($ mil.)	NET PROFIT MARGIN	EMPLOYEES
06/17	313	2	0.8%	1,500
06/16	308	7	2.4%	—
06/05	226	0	—	—
06/04	243	36	15.0%	—
Annual Growth	2.0%	(18.7%)	—	—

PLAINFIELD COMMUNITY CONSOLIDATED SCHOOL DISTRICT 202

EXECUTIVES

Spdt, Lane Abrell
Teacher, Robert Condon
Teacher, Samantha Lecrone
Purchasing Agent, Anna Rivera
Bookkeeper, Alma Esparza
Teacher, Denise Kusinski
Teacher, Emily Swistak
Teacher, Karyn Ward
Teacher, David Mannon
Teacher, Jay Patel
Teacher, Kristen Kovack
Auditors: KLEIN HALL CPAS AURORA IL

LOCATIONS

HQ: PLAINFIELD COMMUNITY CONSOLIDATED
  SCHOOL DISTRICT 202
  15732 S HOWARD ST, PLAINFIELD, IL 605442399
Phone: 815 439-5482
Web: WWW.PSD202.ORG

HISTORICAL FINANCIALS

Company Type: Private

Income Statement				FYE: June 30
	REVENUE ($ mil.)	NET INCOME ($ mil.)	NET PROFIT MARGIN	EMPLOYEES
06/17	353	15	4.5%	3,100
06/16	341	21	6.4%	—
06/10	306	(20)	—	—
06/09	301	(38)	—	—
Annual Growth	2.0%	—	—	—

PLAINS COTTON COOPERATIVE ASSOCIATION

EXECUTIVES

Pres-Ceo, Kevin Brinkley
Chm, Eddie Smith
Exec V Pres-Fin & Treas, Sam Hill
V Pres, Greg Bell
V Pres-Oprs, Jay Cowart
V Pres, Charley Triplett
V Pres, Joe Tubb
V Pres-Mkt, Lonnie Winters
Dir, John Johnson
V Chairman, David Pearson
Director of Tra, Rick Shepherd
Auditors: CROWE HORWATH LLP DALLAS TEX

LOCATIONS

HQ: PLAINS COTTON COOPERATIVE ASSOCIATION
  3301 E 50TH ST, LUBBOCK, TX 794044331
Phone: 806 763-8011
Web: WWW.PCCA.COM

PRODUCTS/OPERATIONS

Selected Sales and Services
Buying cotton
Cotton gins
  Gin bookkeeping
  Gin patronage
  Marketing and invoicing
  Scale ticket software
  Support and training
  Technology solutions
Cotton producers
  Agent gins
  Cash marketing
  marketing contracts
  Pool marketing
Warehousing

COMPETITORS

Alabama Farmers	J.G. Boswell Co.
Cooperative	Parkdale Mills
Calcot	Staplcotn
Dunavant Enterprises	Weil Brothers Cotton
Greenwood Mills	
International Cotton	
Marketing	

HISTORICAL FINANCIALS

Company Type: Private

Income Statement   FYE: June 30

	REVENUE ($ mil.)	NET INCOME ($ mil.)	NET PROFIT MARGIN	EMPLOYEES
06/17	1,373	45	3.3%	170
06/16	892	23	2.7%	—
06/15	975	25	2.6%	—
06/14	947	(36)	—	—
Annual Growth	13.2%	—	—	—

PLAINS PIPELINE, L.P.

EXECUTIVES

Ceo, Greg L Armstrong
V Pres, Harry N Pefanis
Exec V Pres, Al Swanson
Terminal Manager, Brad Dooley
District Manager, James Mount
Assistant Division Manager, Roddy Hughes

LOCATIONS

HQ: PLAINS PIPELINE, L.P.
  333 CLAY ST STE 1600, HOUSTON, TX 770024101
Phone: 713 646-4100
Web: WWW.PAALP.COM

HISTORICAL FINANCIALS

Company Type: Private

Income Statement   FYE: December 31

	REVENUE ($ mil.)	NET INCOME ($ mil.)	NET PROFIT MARGIN	EMPLOYEES
12/17	935	783	83.7%	200
12/16	780	621	79.6%	—
Annual Growth	19.9%	26.1%	—	—

2017 Year-End Financials

Return on assets: 29.0%   Cash ($ mil.): 8
Return on equity: 83.7%
Current ratio: 0.30

PLAN INTERNATIONAL, INC.

EXECUTIVES

Exec Dir, Thomas Miller
Human Resources Manager, Aboubacar O Diallo
Executive Personal Assistant, Ajima Jotivudh
Grants Data Officer, Alexandra Love
Education Field Officer For Ad, Alfred Ojok
Advocacy and Campaigns Officer, Andrew Small
Media Officer, Anil Bogati
Data Manager and Epidemiologis, Benjamin Dountio
Office Assistant, Christine Okello
Grants Management and Complian, David Tooke
Operation Coordinator, Heba Elbaghdady
Auditors: DYL & PERILLO INC PROVIDENCE

LOCATIONS

HQ: PLAN INTERNATIONAL, INC.
  155 PLAN WAY STE A, WARWICK, RI 028861099
Phone: 401 294-3693
Web: WWW.PLAN-INTERNATIONAL.ORG

HISTORICAL FINANCIALS

Company Type: Private

Income Statement   FYE: June 30

	REVENUE ($ mil.)	NET INCOME ($ mil.)	NET PROFIT MARGIN	EMPLOYEES
06/15	684	(5)	—	7
06/14	657	(5)	—	—
06/12	601	29	4.9%	—
06/10	531	93	17.6%	—
Annual Growth	5.2%	—	—	—

2015 Year-End Financials

Return on assets: 4.3%   Cash ($ mil.): 185
Return on equity: (-0.7%)
Current ratio: 6.40

PLANO INDEPENDENT SCHOOL DISTRICT

EXECUTIVES

Exec Dir, Mark Allen
Spdt, Richard Matkin
Deputy Supt, Jeff Bailey
Assoc Supt, Jim Hirsch
Accounting Staff, Brenda Lagerlef
Assistant, Mark De Hertogh
Coordinator, Suzana Spina
Instructional Media D, Mary L Skinner
Auditors: WEAVER AND TIDWELL LLP DA

LOCATIONS

HQ: PLANO INDEPENDENT SCHOOL DISTRICT
  2700 W 15TH ST, PLANO, TX 750757524
Phone: 469 752-8100
Web: WWW.PISD.EDU

HISTORICAL FINANCIALS

Company Type: Private

Income Statement   FYE: June 30

	REVENUE ($ mil.)	NET INCOME ($ mil.)	NET PROFIT MARGIN	EMPLOYEES
06/17	775	288	37.2%	5,610
06/16	712	19	2.8%	—
06/15	669	(18)	—	—
06/14	629	(32)	—	—
Annual Growth	7.2%	—	—	—

PLANTATION PIPE LINE COMPANY

EXECUTIVES

Pres, T A Bannigan
Treas-Cfo, Park Shaper
Asst Treas-Dir, Cheryl Beard
Asst Treas, Denise Martinez
V-President, Joe Listengardt
Engineer, Jeremy Nusum
Managing Director, Marcus Laube

LOCATIONS

HQ: PLANTATION PIPE LINE COMPANY
  1000 WINDWARD CONCOURSE # 250, ALPHARETTA, GA 300052072
Phone: 770 751-4000
Web: WWW.KINDERMORGAN.COM

COMPETITORS

Buckeye Pipe Line	NuStar Energy
Colonial Pipeline	

HISTORICAL FINANCIALS

Company Type: Private

Income Statement   FYE: December 31

	REVENUE ($ mil.)	NET INCOME ($ mil.)	NET PROFIT MARGIN	EMPLOYEES
12/17	281	82	29.2%	279
12/16	273	71	26.2%	—
12/06	174	15	8.8%	—
12/05	170	29	17.6%	—
Annual Growth	4.3%	8.8%	—	—

2017 Year-End Financials

Return on assets: 8.2%   Cash ($ mil.): 3
Return on equity: 29.2%
Current ratio: 0.40

PLUMAS LAKE ELEMENTARY SCHOOL DISTRICT

EXECUTIVES

Supt, Dione Beilby
Director, Brian Briggs
Teacher, Jenna Argetsinger

PLY GEM HOLDINGS, INC.

Ply Gem brings out a new side of homes. The company makes and supplies exterior building materials used in home construction and renovation primarily in the US. Its products — vinyl siding aluminum windows and doors stone veneer and fencing — are supplied to home center retailers distributors construction companies and contractors in North America. Subsidiaries include Variform (vinyl siding) Napco (vinyl and metal exterior siding and trim) Kroy Building Products (vinyl fencing) and Great Lakes Window (energy-efficient vinyl windows and patio doors). Ply Gem Holdings was founded in 2004; it was acquired by Clayton Dubilier & Rice in 2018.

Change in Company Type

In April 2018 building products manufacturer Clayton Dubilier & Rice (CD&R) completed the acquisition of Ply Gem for $2.4 billion along with another company Atrium Windows & Doors. The combined Ply Gem and Atrium companies are now a privately-held exterior products subsidiary of CD&R under the Ply Gem name. The new Ply Gem will continue to be headquartered in Cary NC.

Operations

Ply Gem divides its business into two segments: windows and doors; and siding fencing and stone.

The windows and doors segment which generates nearly 55% of the company's revenue sells its products under the Ply Gem Windows Simonton Windows Great Lakes Window and Ply Gem Canada brands.

The siding fencing and stone segment which accounts for more than 45% of total revenue sells siding and accessories (under brands such as Variform Napco and Mastic) vinyl fencing and railing and stone veneer products. The company also sells cellular PVC trim engineered slate and shake roofing and gutter protection products.

Geographic Reach

North Carolina-based Ply Gem maintains manufacturing operations in the US and Canada. The company operates about 90 facilities across both countries. The US accounts for nearly 90% of revenue with Canada and other foreign countries accounting for the remaining 10%.

Sales and Marketing

Ply Gem has a multi-channel distribution network that serves both the new construction and the home repair and remodeling sectors. The company sells its products to specialty and wholesale distributors and directly to independent building material dealers regional and national lumberyard chains retail home centers independent home improvement dealers and big box retail outlets. Its top ten customers account for more than 45% of the company's net sales. ABC Supply Co. Inc. the company's largest customer accounts for more than 10%.

Financial Performance

Ply Gem's net revenues have seen a steady increase in the past five years. Sales increased more than 7% to $2.0 billion in 2017 compared with the previous year. In the windows and doors segment a 6% increase was the result of improved market conditions in the US and Canada especially in the new construction business. Net sales for the siding fencing and stone segment saw a 9% increase with contributing factors being— higher demand for its products new business wins and higher average selling prices.

Net income fell by 9% to $68.3 million in 2017 mainly as a result of increased product costs and higher operating expenses. A 30% decrease in operating cash ($102 million compared with $145 million in 2016) was driven by higher working capital levels rising commodity costs and the company's early pay discount practices.

Strategy

Going forward Ply Gem aims to capitalize on the continued improvement in the new construction and home repair and remodeling markets. Current strategic initiatives include increasing brand equity with digital marketing initiatives and improving profitability.

With housing starts recovering and the current underinvestment in homes in the US Ply Gem believes there is significant opportunity for growth. It will focus on products targeting energy efficiency and potential cost savings for the customer.

The company has invested recently in digital marketing capabilities such as improved search engine optimization lead generation and website user experience in order to build brand equity and increase market penetration.

To boost profits Ply Gem launched a new profitability initiative entitled "2x20" during 2017 aimed at increasing net sales by at least $40 million by 2020. 2x20 activities include lean manufacturing vertical integration in its manufacturing facilities and consolidating purchases of key raw materials supplies and services. It has also centralized many back-office functions into its corporate office in Cary NC and has implemented more automation in its manufacturing processes.

EXECUTIVES

Chairman President And Ceo, Gary E. Robinette, age 69, $825,000 total compensation

Evp And Coo, John C. Wayne, age 56, $527,875 total compensation

Evp And Cfo, Shawn K. Poe, age 56, $420,000 total compensation

Svp Human Resources, David N. Schmoll, age 59, $285,700 total compensation

President U.s. Window And Door Group, Arthur W. (Art) Steinhafel, age 49

President Siding Fencing And Stone Group, John L. Buckley, age 53, $337,840 total compensation

National Sales Manager, Rick Rinshed

Vice President Sales, Steve Gore

Vice President Corporate Controller, Brian Boyle

Vice President Financial Planning And Analysis, Jennifer Ward

National Accounts Manager, Jim Ross

Auditors: KPMG LLP RALEIGH NORTH CAROL

LOCATIONS

HQ: PLY GEM HOLDINGS, INC.
5020 WESTON PKWY STE 400, CARY, NC 275132322
Phone: 919 677-3900
Web: WWW.PLYGEM.COM

2017 Sales

	$ mil.	% of total
United States	1,849	90
Canada	202	10
Other foreign countries	3	-
Total	2,056	100

PRODUCTS/OPERATIONS

2017 Sales

	$ mil.	% of total
Windows & Doors	1,086	53
Siding Fencing & Stone	970	47
Total	2,056	100

Selected Brands

Variform Siding
Napco Siding
Mastic Siding
Mitten Siding
Performance Siding
Georgia-Pacific
Canyon Stone
Simonton Windows
Great Lakes Window
Durabuilt
Leaf Relief
Leaf Relief Snap Tight
Leaf Smart
Leaf Logic
Ply Gem Shutters & Accents
Ply Gem Fence & Rail
Ply Gem Gutters
Ply Gem Roofing
Ply Gem Stone
Ply Gem Trim & Moulding
Ply Gem Windows & Doors

Selected Products

Fence & Rail
Gutters
Siding
Steel Siding
Stone Veneer
Trim
Windows and Doors

COMPETITORS

Alsco	Louisiana-Pacific
Andersen Corporation	MI Windows and Doors
Arconic	Masco
Armstrong World Industries	Owens Corning
Associated Materials	Pella
Atrium	Royal Group
CertainTeed	Simonton Windows Inc.
Harvey Industries	Therma-Tru
JELD-WEN	Trex Company

HISTORICAL FINANCIALS
Company Type: Private

Income Statement				FYE: December 31
	REVENUE ($ mil.)	NET INCOME ($ mil.)	NET PROFIT MARGIN	EMPLOYEES
12/17	2,056	68	3.3%	9,000
12/16	1,911	75	3.9%	—
12/15	1,839	32	1.8%	—
12/14	1,566	(31)	—	—
Annual Growth	9.5%	—	—	—

2017 Year-End Financials

Return on assets: 4.2%   Cash ($ mil.): 71
Return on equity: 3.3%
Current ratio: 1.00

POMONA UNIFIED SCHOOL DISTRICT

EXECUTIVES

Upt, Richard Martinez
Supt, Thelma Melendez
SEC, Bonita Madrid
Program Manager, David Jaramillo
Assistant, Robert Cook
Operations Manager, Jody Lopez
Assistant, Robert Rodarte
Assistant, Martha Olmos
Teacher, Jeanette Dehart
Auditors: ROGER PEARCE-PEARCE & ASSOCIAT

LOCATIONS

HQ: POMONA UNIFIED SCHOOL DISTRICT
800 S GAREY AVE, POMONA, CA 917663325
Phone: 909 397-4700
Web: WWW.PUSD.ORG

HISTORICAL FINANCIALS

Company Type: Private

Income Statement				FYE: June 30
	REVENUE ($ mil.)	NET INCOME ($ mil.)	NET PROFIT MARGIN	EMPLOYEES
06/16*	396	36	9.3%	2,764
07/09	0	0	20.2%	—
06/06	227	12	5.5%	—
06/05	344	0	—	—
Annual Growth	1.3%	—	—	—

*Fiscal year change

PORT OF HOUSTON AUTHORITY

EXECUTIVES

Director Of Health And Safety, Rich Galle
Chief People Officer, Jessica Shaver
Auditors: GRANT THORNTON LLP HOUSTON T

LOCATIONS

HQ: PORT OF HOUSTON AUTHORITY
111 EAST LOOP N, HOUSTON, TX 770294326
Phone: 713 670-2662

COMPETITORS

Alabama State Docks
Port of Corpus Christi
The Port of New Orleans

HISTORICAL FINANCIALS

Company Type: Private

Income Statement				FYE: December 31
	REVENUE ($ mil.)	NET INCOME ($ mil.)	NET PROFIT MARGIN	EMPLOYEES
12/17	332	103	31.0%	595
12/16	290	57	19.9%	—
12/15	293	85	29.1%	—
12/14	263	69	26.2%	—
Annual Growth	8.0%	14.2%	—	—

2017 Year-End Financials

Return on assets: 13.4%
Return on equity: 31.0%
Current ratio: 1.30
Cash ($ mil.): 75

PORT OF LOS ANGELES

EXECUTIVES

Exec Dir, Gene Seroka
Environmental Manager, Lisa Cloud Ochsner
Facilities Manager, Kosta Mallakis

LOCATIONS

HQ: PORT OF LOS ANGELES
425 S PALOS VERDES ST, SAN PEDRO, CA 907313309
Phone: 310 732-3508
Web: WWW.PORTOFLOSANGELES.ORG

HISTORICAL FINANCIALS

Company Type: Private

Income Statement				FYE: June 30
	REVENUE ($ mil.)	NET INCOME ($ mil.)	NET PROFIT MARGIN	EMPLOYEES
06/17	474	103	21.8%	47
06/16	441	99	22.4%	—
Annual Growth	7.5%	4.4%	—	—

2017 Year-End Financials

Return on assets: 6.7%
Return on equity: 21.8%
Current ratio: 3.60
Cash ($ mil.): 619

PORT OF PORTLAND (INC)

EXECUTIVES

Exec Dir, Bill Wyatt
Commission Pres, Jim Carter
Controller, Robert Burket
Cfo, Cynthia Nichol
Chief Financial Officer, E B Galligan
It Client Manager, Anthony Bonnett
Senior Human Resources Special, Brenda Patrick
Manager, Christine White
Human Resources Director, Carol Byers
Electrical Engineer, Jeff Nelson
Chief Information Security Off, John Rater
Auditors: MOSS ADAMS LLP PORTLAND OREG

LOCATIONS

HQ: PORT OF PORTLAND (INC)
7200 NE AIRPORT WAY, PORTLAND, OR 972181016
Phone: 503 944-7000
Web: WWW.PORTOFPORTLAND.COM

HISTORICAL FINANCIALS

Company Type: Private

Income Statement				FYE: June 30
	REVENUE ($ mil.)	NET INCOME ($ mil.)	NET PROFIT MARGIN	EMPLOYEES
06/17	341	95	27.9%	785
06/16	295	64	21.8%	—
06/15	263	57	21.9%	—
06/14	251	23	9.3%	—
Annual Growth	10.7%	59.8%	—	—

2017 Year-End Financials

Return on assets: 9.7%
Return on equity: 27.9%
Current ratio: 0.50
Cash ($ mil.): 36

PORT OF SEATTLE

The Port of Seattle oversees both an airport (Seattle-Tacoma International also known as Sea-Tac) and a seaport. The agency's aviation division sees more than 33.2 million passengers a year. The seaport division serves more than 18 container steamship lines that import and export container-ized and bulk cargo. It also handles calls from cruise ships. In addition the seaport division oversees commercial fishing marinas and portside commercial properties. Most of the agency's revenue comes from airport operations. The Port of Seattle is run by a five-member commission elected by King County voters.

Operations

One of the top landholders in King County the Port owns parks and public access areas cargo and container terminals and Sea-Tac airport. It also owns conference facilities at the airport and on the waterfront recreational boating marinas piers office space and storage and warehouse facilities.

Financial Performance

Operating revenues for fiscal 2013 were budgeted at $550.6 million 6% up on 2012 . Aeronautical revenues were $249.3 million (up 6%). Other operating revenues were budget for $301.3 million (7% higher than the 2012 budget) mainly due to Terminal 18 special bond refunding and higher concessions.

Strategy

Going forward the Port's projects are broadly aimed at preserving traffic to the Midwest via Seattle which other global gateways (the Panama and Suez canals and Prince Rupert's port British Columbia) threaten to divert. To this end it is pursuing cooperative opportunities between rail and highway infrastructure agencies. Concurrently the Port of Seattle is evaluating Sea-Tac airport's capacity needs. Its subsidy of Fisherman's Terminal which sustains jobs as well as the seaport's history and culture is on the table too given the cost to renovate and terminal's declining fish life. Most significant the Port is determined to continue to distinguish itself as the Green Gateway with the goal of minimizing the environmental consequences of its activities.

Company Background

In 2011 the Port marked its centennial year for moving people and cargo in and out of the Pacific Northwest.

EXECUTIVES

Cfo And Administrative Officer, Dan Thomas
Interim Ceo, Dave Soike
Managing Director Aviation Division, Lance Lyttle
Managing Director Economic Development Division, David McFadden
Managing Director Maritime Division, Lindsay Pulsifer
Government Relations Director, Pearse Edwards
Auditors: MOSS ADAMS LLP SEATTLE WASHI

LOCATIONS

HQ: PORT OF SEATTLE
2711 ALASKAN WAY PIER 69, SEATTLE, WA 981211107
Phone: 206 728-3000
Web: WWW.PORTSEATTLE.ORG

HISTORICAL FINANCIALS
Company Type: Private

Income Statement
FYE: December 31

	REVENUE ($ mil.)	NET INCOME ($ mil.)	NET PROFIT MARGIN	EMPLOYEES
12/17	632	199	31.6%	1,515
12/16	598	41	6.9%	—
12/15	558	19	3.6%	—
12/14	534	131	24.5%	—
Annual Growth	5.7%	15.1%	—	—

2017 Year-End Financials
Return on assets: 23.5% Cash ($ mil.): 39
Return on equity: 31.6%
Current ratio: 0.20

PORTLAND ADVENTIST MEDICAL CENTER

EXECUTIVES

Chb, Larry Dodds
Pres-Ceo, Scott Reiner
Exec V Pres-Coo, Bill Wing
Sr Vice President, Mark Ashlock
V Pres-Sr Fin Officer, John Beaman
Coordinator, Barbara Fulton
Coordinator, Sandy Montminy
Phlebotomy Supervisor, Alicia Quigley
Manager, Erin Flintjer
Director, Deb Pokorny
Director For Emergency, Erik Egsieker

LOCATIONS

HQ: PORTLAND ADVENTIST MEDICAL CENTER
10123 SE MARKET ST, PORTLAND, OR 972162599
Phone: 503 257-2500
Web: WWW.ADVENTISTHEALTHNW.COM

HISTORICAL FINANCIALS
Company Type: Private

Income Statement
FYE: December 31

	REVENUE ($ mil.)	NET INCOME ($ mil.)	NET PROFIT MARGIN	EMPLOYEES
12/15	347	7	2.1%	12,000
12/14	351	5	1.5%	—
12/13	317	3	0.9%	—
Annual Growth	4.7%	54.2%	—	—

2015 Year-End Financials
Return on assets: 4.5% Cash ($ mil.): 108
Return on equity: 2.1%
Current ratio: 8.80

PORTLAND GENERAL ELECTRIC COMP

LOCATIONS

HQ: PORTLAND GENERAL ELECTRIC COMP
33831 E FARADAY RD, ESTACADA, OR 970238432
Phone: 503 630-6821

HISTORICAL FINANCIALS
Company Type: Private

Income Statement
FYE: December 31

	REVENUE ($ mil.)	NET INCOME ($ mil.)	NET PROFIT MARGIN	EMPLOYEES
12/17	2,009	187	9.3%	2
12/16	1,923	193	10.0%	—
Annual Growth	4.5%	(3.1%)	—	—

2017 Year-End Financials
Return on assets: 6.6% Cash ($ mil.): 39
Return on equity: 9.3%
Current ratio: 0.50

PORTLAND PUBLIC SCHOOLS

EXECUTIVES

Superintendent, Carole Smith
Teacher, Richard McElroy
Teacher, Billy Fields
Teacher, Brian Valley
Teacher, Kathy Klein
Teacher, Megan O'Leary
Teacher, Richard Cherry
Auditors: TALBOT KORVOLA & WARWICK LLP

LOCATIONS

HQ: PORTLAND PUBLIC SCHOOLS
501 N DIXON ST, PORTLAND, OR 972271876
Phone: 503 916-2000
Web: WWW.PPS.NET

HISTORICAL FINANCIALS
Company Type: Private

Income Statement
FYE: June 30

	REVENUE ($ mil.)	NET INCOME ($ mil.)	NET PROFIT MARGIN	EMPLOYEES
06/15	691	255	36.9%	5,244
06/14	661	(0)	—	—
06/13	578	118	20.6%	—
06/12	574	(4)	—	—
Annual Growth	6.4%	—	—	—

2015 Year-End Financials
Return on assets: 4.0% Cash ($ mil.): 115
Return on equity: 36.9%
Current ratio: 1.40

PORTLAND STATE UNIVERSITY

Portland State University (PSU) is one of seven institutions of higher learning in the Oregon University System. It offers nearly 100 bachelor's 90 master's and 40 doctoral degrees as well as graduate certificates and continuing education programs. PSU has eight schools and colleges devoted to liberal arts and sciences; engineering and computer science; fine and performing arts; urban and public affairs; business administration; social work; and education. It also has a school dedicated to extended studies including distance learning continuing education and professional development. Student enrollment exceeds 29000 (80% undergrads) and the student to faculty ratio is 19:1. PSU was established in 1946.

Geographic Reach

About two thirds of the student body comes from PSU's backyard Clackamas Multnomah and Washington counties. Overall 79% of PSU students are from Oregon. Others come all over the US and more than 95 other countries with Saudi Arabia China India Japan and Vietnam garnering top representation.

PSU's 50-acre campus in downtown Portland holds 50 buildings and 10 student housing properties.

Financial Performance

For several decades PSU received close to half of its funding from state coffers. Legislation in 2011 however converted the state's public university system from a state agency to a free-standing public university system. The state now accounts for a lower percentage of PSU's total annual operating revenue. For its 2014-2015 year PSU plans to run a deficit of about $7 million which is down from the deficit of $10.7 million the previous year. Among the steps taken to reduce expenses was to stop using general fund money to support the PSU football team.

Strategy

PSU's strategic plan for growth is dependent on funding. To provide for that funding and its future the school is working to increase its visibility on a national level. It is developing staffing and compensation plans to ensure talent is in place to achieve its long-range goals. It is also developing an enrollment management plan to improve retention and graduation rates. PSU is looking to increase non-resident enrollment and establish an inclusive and diverse environment. It is also working to expand innovative research and graduate education by leveraging connections between application at the local level and relevance on a global basis.

Other priorities include upgrading its information technology systems fulfilling student needs for hybrid and fully online instruction and investing in research infrastructure human resource data management staff training and other management and communications systems.

The university is raising money to renovate and expand two structures. It has brought in 65% of the money needed to renovate the Peter W. Stott Educational Center and about 82% of the total needed to expand the School of Business Administration.

EXECUTIVES

Associate Vice President, Erin Flynn
Chair Department Of Psychology, Sherwin Davidson
Associate Vice President For Communications, Chris Broderick

Associate Vice President For Enrollment Management, Cindy Skaruppa
Auditors: CLIFTONLARSONALLEN LLP GREENW

LOCATIONS

HQ: PORTLAND STATE UNIVERSITY
  1600 SW 4TH AVE STE 730, PORTLAND, OR 972015519
Phone: 503 725-4444
Web: WWW.PDX.EDU

PRODUCTS/OPERATIONS

Selected Colleges and Schools
College of Liberal Arts and Sciences
College of Urban and Public Affairs
Graduate School of Education
Maseeh College of Engineering and Computer Science
School of Business Administration
School of Extended Studies
School of Fine and Performing Arts
School of Social Work

HISTORICAL FINANCIALS
Company Type: Private

Income Statement				FYE: June 30
	REVENUE ($ mil.)	NET INCOME ($ mil.)	NET PROFIT MARGIN	EMPLOYEES
06/17	353	47	13.4%	4,000
06/16	357	(4)	—	—
06/15	351	181	51.6%	—
06/14	350	36	10.4%	—
Annual Growth	0.3%	9.2%	—	—

2017 Year-End Financials
Return on assets: 8.3%   Cash ($ mil.): 61
Return on equity: 13.4%
Current ratio: 1.20

POTANDON PRODUCE L.L.C.

EXECUTIVES

Ceo, Mel Davenport
President, Steve Ottum
Vice President, Steve Elfering
Dir, Becky Thomas
Accountant, Geraldine Elizondo
Director of Operations, Kevin Flaherty
Supervisor, Jennifer Bjornlie
Coordinator, Jeri Carter
Production, Ben McWilliams
Transportation Associate, Gary Belknap
Production, Mike Boot
Auditors: RUDD & COMPANY PLLC IDAHO FAL

LOCATIONS

HQ: POTANDON PRODUCE L.L.C.
  1210 PIER VIEW DR, IDAHO FALLS, ID 834024966
Phone: 208 524-1900
Web: WWW.POTANDON.COM

HISTORICAL FINANCIALS
Company Type: Private

Income Statement				FYE: December 31
	REVENUE ($ mil.)	NET INCOME ($ mil.)	NET PROFIT MARGIN	EMPLOYEES
12/17	382	2	0.6%	110
12/16	384	1	0.5%	—
12/15	370	(1)	—	—
12/14	391	1	0.5%	—
Annual Growth	(0.7%)	3.5%	—	—

2017 Year-End Financials
Return on assets: 10.0%   Cash ($ mil.): —
Return on equity: 0.6%
Current ratio: 0.70

POUDRE SCHOOL DISTRICT

EXECUTIVES

President, Cathy Kipp
Vice President, David Trask
Director*, Nate Donovan
Director*, Christophe Febvre
Director*, Carolyn Reed
Executive Director, Vicki Thompson
Project Coordinator, Brad Knutson
Teacher, Gabe Vigil
Teacher, Richard Warren
Office Manager, Robin Herd
Teacher, Todd Matkin
Auditors: CLIFTONLARSONALLEN LLP BROOM

LOCATIONS

HQ: POUDRE SCHOOL DISTRICT
  2407 LAPORTE AVE, FORT COLLINS, CO 805212211
Phone: 970 482-7420
Web: WWW.PSDSCHOOLS.ORG

HISTORICAL FINANCIALS
Company Type: Private

Income Statement				FYE: June 30
	REVENUE ($ mil.)	NET INCOME ($ mil.)	NET PROFIT MARGIN	EMPLOYEES
06/17	330	(9)	—	907
06/16	320	20	6.4%	—
06/15	300	(19)	—	—
06/14	275	(15)	—	—
Annual Growth	6.2%	—	—	—

2017 Year-End Financials
Return on assets: 3.4%   Cash ($ mil.): 1
Return on equity: (-2.9%)
Current ratio: —

POUDRE VALLEY HEALTH CARE, INC.

Providing health care is what this Poudre Valley is all about. The not-for-profit Poudre Valley Health System (PVHS) cares for residents of Colorado western Nebraska and southern Wyoming through the Poudre Valley Hospital and the Medical Center of the Rockies. With a total of about 440 beds the two hospitals offer general medical and surgical services and trauma care. They also offer treatment centers for specialties including cancer heart brain and spine disorders. PVHS is home to the Mountain Crest Behavioral Healthcare Center which administers mental health and substance abuse treatment. PVHS is part of the Health District of Northern Larimer County; it is also part of University of Colorado Health.

Operations
The Poudre Valley Hospital features 270 patient beds while the Medical Center of the Rockies has a capacity of about 170 beds. Beyond its primary hospital campuses the health system also operates several outpatient clinics and a family medicine center that hosts a rural medicine residency program. Altogether PVHS has more than 550 physicians practicing in more than 40 specialty fields.

In addition to its joint operating agreement with the University of Colorado Hospital PVHS has formed collaborative care partnerships with local organizations including a local laser eye surgery center numerous outpatient centers for rehabilitation surgery and infusion therapy as well as home health care and home supply companies.

Geographic Reach
PVHS serves residents of Estes Park Fort Collins Greeley and Loveland Colorado as well as Larimer and Weld Counties. The system also serves customers from Cheyenne and Laramie Wyoming and Scottsbluff Nebraska.

Strategy
The organization has held a long tradition of partnering with numerous local organizations to expand its service offerings. To create a broader health organization for the Rocky Mountain region PVHS formed a joint operating agreement with University of Colorado Hospital in 2012. Together the systems are known as University of Colorado Health and are governed by a single board of directors. The hospitals continue to operate under their existing names.

Other growth efforts include the construction of a new $14.5 million emergency care center in 2012 and the opening of a new 12-bed women's and children's unit at Medical Center of the Rockies in 2013.

In 2013 it also opened the 36000-sq.-ft. Indian Peaks Medical Center in Frederick at an estimated cost of $20 million to $30 million. It includes cardiology and diagnostics departments.

Company Background
The organization was founded in 1925. Since 1995 when PVHS reorganized as a private not-for-profit health care organization local property taxes that used to go straight to PVHS have been paid to the Health District of Northern Larimer County which then uses them to fund PVHS' various activities.

EXECUTIVES

Ceo, Rulon Stacey
President, Keving Unger
Coordinator, Peter Nava
Coordinator, Brenda Nicholson
Manager, Paul Morris
Project Coordinator, Cindy Shultz
Emergency Medicine Specialist, Darlena D Leins
Trauma Program Director, Lori McDonald
Emergency Medicine Specialist, Laura Ivy
Obstetrician Gynecologist, Susan Haney
Emergency Medicine Specialist, Travis Brown

LOCATIONS

HQ: POUDRE VALLEY HEALTH CARE, INC.
2315 E HARMONY RD STE 200, FORT COLLINS, CO
805288620
Phone: 970 495-7000
Web: WWW.PVHS.ORG

PRODUCTS/OPERATIONS

Selected Services
Back Neck and Spine Care
Cancer Care
Diabetes and Endocrinology
Hyperbaric Medicine
Imaging and Radiology
Laboratory Services
Orthopedics
Pain Care and Management
Seniors' Health
Weight and Metabolism
Women's Health
Wound Care

COMPETITORS

Catholic Health
 Initiatives
Centura Health
Denver Health and
 Hospital Authority
Exempla Healthcare
HealthONE
Memorial Health System
 (Colorado)

North Colorado Medical
 Center
University of Colorado
 Hospital
Valley View Hospital
Wyoming Medical Center

HISTORICAL FINANCIALS

Company Type: Private

Income Statement   FYE: June 30

	REVENUE ($ mil.)	NET INCOME ($ mil.)	NET PROFIT MARGIN	EMPLOYEES
06/16	523	92	17.7%	2,800
06/15	480	98	20.6%	—
06/14	478	38	8.0%	—
Annual Growth	4.7%	56.2%	—	—

2016 Year-End Financials
Return on assets: 4.8%
Return on equity: 17.7%
Current ratio: 0.90
Cash ($ mil.): 25

POWER ENGINEERS, INCORPORATED

EXECUTIVES

Chb-Intl Evp, Jack Hand
Corp Secretary, Rachel Moore
Treasurer, Jan James
Evp, William Hansen
Evp, Gerry Murray
Evp, Timothy Ostermeier
Cao-Evp, Jim Haynes
Vp-Cfo, Chuck Kemp
Vp-Chro, Mark Mary
Svp, Holger Peller
Auditors: DELOITTE & TOUCHE LLP BOISE

LOCATIONS

HQ: POWER ENGINEERS, INCORPORATED
 3940 GLENBROOK DR, HAILEY, ID 833338446
Phone: 208 788-3456
Web: WWW.POWERENG.COM

HISTORICAL FINANCIALS

Company Type: Private

Income Statement   FYE: December 31

	REVENUE ($ mil.)	NET INCOME ($ mil.)	NET PROFIT MARGIN	EMPLOYEES
12/17	460	32	7.1%	2,400
12/16	398	15	3.9%	—
12/15	395	16	4.3%	—
Annual Growth	7.9%	38.8%	—	—

2017 Year-End Financials
Return on assets: 3.2%
Return on equity: 7.1%
Current ratio: 1.30
Cash ($ mil.): 15

POWERSOUTH ENERGY COOPERATIVE

Several hundred thousand Alabamans and Floridians get their electric power courtesy of the work of PowerSouth Energy Cooperative which provides wholesale power to its member-owners (16 electric cooperatives and four municipal distribution utilities). Its distribution members provide electric services to almost 417200 customer meters in central and southern Alabama and western Florida. PowerSouth operates a more than 2200-mile power transmission system and has more than 2000 MW of generating capacity from interests in six fossil-fueled and hydroelectric power plants.

Geographic Reach
PowerSouth serves customers in Alabama (39 counties) and Florida (10 counties).

Operations
The company owns and operates six generation facilities and holds ownership interest in an additional facility. Its diverse generating fuel mix includes natural gas coal and water (hydro). It also has compressed air energy storage technology and a disciplined fuel supply hedging program that minimizes the impact of fuel cost increases. In addition PowerSouth maintains long-term purchased power agreements to ensure economic and reliable power supply for its members.

PowerSouth serves the wholesale energy needs of electric cooperatives and municipal electric systems in Alabama and northwest Florida who in turn serve more than a million consumers. PowerSouth is dedicated to providing reliable energy at the lowest possible cost to its members.

Financial Performance
The company's revenues increased by 3% in 2013 primarily due to an increase in member revenues as a result of an increase in energy sales. The remaining increase was due to the surcharges added to the excess demand rate during 2013.

That year PowerSouth's net income decreased by 6% as the result of increased operating costs caused by higher distribution costs and administration and general expenses.

Its operating cash inflow increased to $63.5 million in 2013 (compared to $38.3 million in 2012) due to a rise in account receivables and inventories.

Strategy
To meet future demand and tightening environmental regulations the company is looking to diversify and expand its power production assets with an emphasis on cleaner energy plants. Pow-

erSouth's long-term energy plans include a 20-year contract for 125 MW of nuclear power from two Vogtle Units being built by the Municipal Energy Authority of Georgia near Augusta and due to come onstream in 2016 and 2017. The company is also investing in wind power and biomass-to-energy initiatives.

Company Background
PowerSouth is owned and managed by it 20 distribution members.

The company once provided propane but sold its Cooperative Propane unit in 2011 to focus on its core power businesses.

In 2008 Alabama Electric Cooperative changed its name to PowerSouth Energy Cooperative to better reflect its service territory (Alabama and Florida) and its opportunities for future growth.

Founded in 1941 as Alabama Electric Cooperative the coop promotes a strong economic development program aimed at bringing industry into both Alabama and Florida.

EXECUTIVES

Vice President Corporate Affairs, Beth Woodard
Vice President Information Technology, Lewis Jeffers
Vice President Administration, Elizabeth Woodard
Vice President, Tim Thomas
Auditors: BKD LLP OKLAHOMA CITY OKLAH

LOCATIONS

HQ: POWERSOUTH ENERGY COOPERATIVE
 2027 E THREE NOTCH ST, ANDALUSIA, AL
 364212427
Phone: 334 427-3000
Web: WWW.POWERSOUTH.COM

PRODUCTS/OPERATIONS

2013 Sales

	% of total
Electric	
Cooperatives	93
Municipalities	6
Other	1
Total	100

HISTORICAL FINANCIALS

Company Type: Private

Income Statement   FYE: December 31

	REVENUE ($ mil.)	NET INCOME ($ mil.)	NET PROFIT MARGIN	EMPLOYEES
12/17	588	9	1.6%	640
12/16	596	13	2.2%	—
12/15	622	17	2.7%	—
12/14	675	16	2.5%	—
Annual Growth	(4.5%)	(17.0%)	—	—

2017 Year-End Financials
Return on assets: 6.5%
Return on equity: 1.6%
Current ratio: 0.60
Cash ($ mil.): 49

POWERTECH AMERICA SALES, LLC

EXECUTIVES

Mmbr, Seongho Baek
Auditors: PK LLP OPELIKA ALABAMA

LOCATIONS

HQ: POWERTECH AMERICA SALES, LLC
6801 KIA PKWY, WEST POINT, GA 318334937
Phone: 706 902-6800
Web: WWW.POWERTECH.CO.KR

HISTORICAL FINANCIALS

Company Type: Private

Income Statement				FYE: December 31
	REVENUE ($ mil.)	NET INCOME ($ mil.)	NET PROFIT MARGIN	EMPLOYEES
12/16	313	(0)	—	19
12/15	401	5	1.3%	—
12/14	411	(8)	—	—
Annual Growth	(12.8%)	—	—	—

2016 Year-End Financials

Return on assets: 8.8% Cash ($ mil.): 2
Return on equity: (-0.3%)
Current ratio: 0.10

POWERTECH AMERICA, INC.

EXECUTIVES

Ceo, Sam Ho Cha
SEC, Taeeuk Kim
Cfo, Changyoung Kim
Purchasing Agent, Darren Wiker
Fin & Acct Specialist, Do Hyun Lee
Human Resources, Stephanie Moore
Director, Darren Lucas
Assistant Manager General Affa, Jinho Kim
Quality Assistant Manager Powe, Dan Kleiber
Auditors: PK LLP OPELIKA ALABAMA

LOCATIONS

HQ: POWERTECH AMERICA, INC.
6801 KIA PKWY, WEST POINT, GA 318334937
Phone: 706 902-6800
Web: WWW.POWERTECH.CO.KR

HISTORICAL FINANCIALS

Company Type: Private

Income Statement				FYE: December 31
	REVENUE ($ mil.)	NET INCOME ($ mil.)	NET PROFIT MARGIN	EMPLOYEES
12/16	1,134	7	0.6%	500
12/15	1,230	12	1.0%	—
12/14	1,250	11	0.9%	—
12/13	1,220	11	0.9%	—
Annual Growth	(2.4%)	(14.3%)	—	—

2016 Year-End Financials

Return on assets: 8.8% Cash ($ mil.): 22
Return on equity: 0.6%
Current ratio: 0.60

PRATT CORRUGATED HOLDINGS, INC.

LOCATIONS

HQ: PRATT CORRUGATED HOLDINGS, INC.
1800 SARASOT BUS PKWY NE C, CONYERS, GA
300135775
Phone: 770 918-5678

HISTORICAL FINANCIALS

Company Type: Private

Income Statement				FYE: June 30
	REVENUE ($ mil.)	NET INCOME ($ mil.)	NET PROFIT MARGIN	EMPLOYEES
06/18	2,518	87	3.5%	105
06/17	2,360	65	2.8%	—
Annual Growth	6.7%	33.4%	—	—

2018 Year-End Financials

Return on assets: 5.1% Cash ($ mil.): 86
Return on equity: 3.5%
Current ratio: 0.90

PRATT INDUSTRIES, INC.

Pratt Industries (USA) doesn't mill around when it comes to recycling and caring for the environment. The company rivals the world's largest manufacturers of recycled paper and packaging and claims to be the 5th largest box manufacturer in the US and the world's largest privately-held 100% recycled paper and packaging company. Pratt has a handful of operating divisions: recycling mills corrugating converting displays packaging systems and national accounts. Its products which include container board and corrugated sheets are sold to clients such as Rubbermaid and Pringles.

Operations

The company operates 32 sheet plants 18 recycling centers 16 corrugating plants seven distribution centers seven displaying facilities four recycled paper mills and one clean energy plant. It operates through the main divisions of Clean Energy Converting Corrugating Display Paper Mills Recycling Logistics Specialty and Strategic Services.

Geographic Reach

Pratt operates some 50 plants in more than 20 US states and Mexico.

Strategy

Pratt has strategically located its manufacturing facilities to reduce freight time and cost and to provide regional design and account management support. The locations enable it to react quickly and decisively to meet the needs of customers.

In 2015 Pratt Industries broke ground on its new $52 million corrugated box factory in Beloit Wisconsin. The 350000 sq. ft. facility due for start-up in early 2016 will sit on a 56-acre site and produce 600 tons of recycled boxes a day at capacity.

Mergers and Acquisitions

In 2015 the company improved its footprint through the purchase of California-based food and agricultural packaging company Robert Mann Packaging (RMP). Pratt paid $60 million for the privately-owned RMP group which has $150 million in annual sales and more than a dozen facilities in the western US and Mexico including a 350000 square-foot box-making plant in Salinas California. The deal gave the company a nation-wide footprint throughout the US with manufacturing sites stretching from New York to the West Coast.

Company Background

The company was founded in 1948 by Leon Pratt grandfather of Anthony Pratt.

EXECUTIVES

Executive Vice President, John Day
Vice President Tax, Dennis McNeely
Vice President Purchasing And Logistics, Danielle Roszko
Vice President Industry Relations And Supply Chain, Cathy Foley
Vice President General Manager Recycling Division Sales Engineer, Kurt Schmitz
Treasurer, Tom Stoskopf

LOCATIONS

HQ: PRATT INDUSTRIES, INC.
1800 SARASOTA BUSIN STE C, CONYERS, GA
300135775
Phone: 770 918-5678
Web: WWW.PRATTINDUSTRIES.COM

PRODUCTS/OPERATIONS

Selected Divisions
Converting
Corrugating
Displays
Mills
National Accounts
Packaging Systems
Recycling

Selected Products and Services
Bagging
  Merchandise bags
  Polypropylene bags
  Poly-tubing
  Seal-top bags
  Static shielded bags
Carton Closure/Sealing
  Adhesives
  Double coated tape
  Duct tape
  Filament tape
  Foam tape
  Foil tape
  Masking tape
  Poly-strapping
  Pressure sensitive carton sealing tape
  Staples
  Steel Strapping
  Teflon tape
  Water activate carton sealing tape
Cushioning/Void Fill
  Air dunnage bags
  Bubble wrap
  Cellulose wadding
  Foam-N-Place
  Honeycomb
  Kraft wrap
  Loose fill foam
  Newsprint
  Polyethylene foam
  Polypropylene foam
Edge/Corner Protection
  Angleboard
  Anglewrap
  Cornerboard
  Form-A-Board
  Protect-A-Board
  Protect-A-Wrap
  Stackmaster
  Strap protectors
Labeling and Coding
  Cleaners
  Inks
  Labels
  Ribbons
Mailing and Shipping
  Mailers
  Packing list envelopes
  Shipping tubes and tags
Unitization

Poly pallet covers
Poly pallet shrink bags
Poly top sheets
Poly-strapping
Shrink bundling
Steel strapping
Stretch film
Visual Packaging
  Blister packaging
  Clamshells
  Polyolefin shrinkfilm
  PVC shrink bands
  Skin packaging
  Skin packaging film

COMPETITORS

Georgia-Pacific	Packaging Corp. of
Green Bay Packaging	America
International Paper	Southern Container
Interstate Resources	Weyerhaeuser
Inc.	

HISTORICAL FINANCIALS

Company Type: Private

Income Statement				FYE: June 30
	REVENUE ($ mil.)	NET INCOME ($ mil.)	NET PROFIT MARGIN	EMPLOYEES
06/18	2,498	200	8.0%	5,890
06/06	713	(4)	—	—
06/05	0	(0)	—	—
06/04	446	(15)	—	—
Annual Growth	13.1%	—	—	—

2018 Year-End Financials

Return on assets: 8.6%   Cash ($ mil.): 339
Return on equity: 8.0%
Current ratio: 1.60

PRECISION CASTPARTS CORP.

Precision Castparts Corp. (PCC) is a maker of investment castings used in jet aircraft satellite launches aerostructures armaments and medical applications (prostheses). Its Investment Cast products segment makes jet engine parts fluid management valves and deep-hole boring tools. Forged Products and Airframe Products round out PCC's three segments and cover the power generation and paper and pulp industries as well as general industry. The aerospace sector accounts for the majority of PCC's sales. In January 2016 the company was acquired by Berkshire Hathaway in a mega-deal valued at $37 billion.

HISTORY

The history of Precision Castparts Corp. (PCC) is not as precise as its castings. The Oregon Saw Company was founded in 1949 and sold in 1953; its buyer wanted neither the future PCC nor a power tools unit so the two became Omark Industries. In 1956 a buyer purchased the power tool business but wasn't interested in castings; that operation was spun off as Precision Castparts Corp.

In the early 1950s a group of Oregon Saw's casting employees developed a process for producing parts as large as 60 inches by use of investment casting making products that rivaled the strength of forged and machined parts at a fraction of the cost. After a two-year search they landed their first aerospace customer — Air Research Corp. — with many to follow. The higher operating

temperatures generated by aircraft engines led the company to buy a vacuum furnace in 1959 to fabricate parts that could tolerate greater heat; two more vacuum furnaces were added and sales vaulted toward $10 million by 1967. PCC went public in 1968 and continued to grow. In 1976 the company acquired Centaur Cast Alloys (small investment castings UK) to make parts for the European aerospace industry. By that time General Electric (GE) and Pratt & Whitney accounted for most of PCC's business. Edward Cooley who had masterminded the company's growth since incorporation forged ahead with plans to double production capacity.

In 1980 the airline industry crashed but PCC's sales held at about $90 million. Structural airplane products soon picked up and in 1984 the company bought two titanium foundries in France. To diversify it added TRW's cast airfoils (used in aircraft engines and industrial gas turbines) division in 1986. That acquisition renamed PCC Airfoils increased PCC's annual sales by about 80%; sales reached $443 million by 1989.

The company broadened its offerings again in 1991 when it acquired Advanced Forming Technology which made small complex metal-injection molded parts used in everything from adding machines to military ordnance. The early 1990s recession hit the airline industry and sales dropped. Cooley retired as chairman in 1994 and GE veteran William McCormick replaced him. The next year PCC acquired Quamco Inc. (industrial tools and machines). In 1996 PCC flowed into the fluid management market with the acquisition of NEWFLO for about $300 million.

In 1997 PCC spent $437 million to acquire seven more companies that helped boost sales 75% from 1996 levels. The next year it purchased four metalworking companies that served industries other than aerospace. Having reduced dependence on sales to the aerospace industry to just over 50% PCC began consolidating operations and closing plants to reduce costs.

The company continued to diversify through acquisitions in 1999 but it also expanded its aerospace operations with the purchase of Wyman-Gordon a leading maker of advanced metal forgings for the aerospace market. PCC's 2000 acquisitions included the aerospace division of United Engineering Forgings and Germany-based Convey Engineering (heavy-duty valves). The next year the company bought the assets of Netherlands-based Wouter Witzel and the US's Drop Dies and Forgings Company (renamed Wyman-Gordon Cleveland). In 2002 PCC bought the rest of Western Australian Specialty Alloys (casting and forging alloys) for $27.6 million in cash and PCC shares.

In 2003 Precision Castparts' PCC Structurals unit reached a $400 million agreement with Rolls-Royce to supply large titanium and steel castings. That year the company acquired SPS Technologies a producer of fasteners and other metal components for the aerospace automotive and industrial markets. In 2004 subsidiary SPS Aerospace Fasteners signed a four-year deal with Airbus worth about $72 million to supply collars nuts studs and titanium pins to Airbus plants across Europe.

PCC acquired Air Industries Corporation in early 2005. In 2006 PCC bought Special Metals Corporation (SMC) a maker of nickel alloys and super alloys for $295 million in cash and the assumption of $245 million in SMC debt. PCC intended to use SMC's product as raw materials for its own aircraft engine components. SMC also served the automotive chemical and power generation industries.

Later in 2006 PCC bought Shur-Lok Corporation a manufacturer of aerospace fasteners for about $110 million. The acquisition combined with the 2005 purchase of Air Industries Corporation

helped to further PCC's desire to grow its airframe fasteners business.

Early in 2007 PCC completed the purchase of GSC a leading maker of aluminum and steel structural investment casting for the aerospace energy and medical markets. It also acquired Cherry Aerospace which expanded its fastener products portfolio.

In 2009 the company acquired Carlton Forge Works which makes aircraft engines for Boeing and Airbus; California-based Arcturus Manufacturing (hammer forging operations) was included in the transaction. PCC also picked up Airdrome Holdings (fluid fittings) Fatigue Technology (cold expansion technology) and Hackney Ladish (forged pipe fittings) in 2009.

In late summer 2011 PPC purchased Primus International a maker of complex metal industrial parts and assemblies. Its products (machined aluminum and titanium components used in aircraft wings fuselages and engine-related assemblies) cater to Boeing Airbus and other aerospace OEMs. The $900 million deal furthered the company's commitment to the global aerospace industry. In a similar vein the company obtained Unison Engine Components (operating as Tru-Form Rings) from GE Aviation in mid-2011. Tru-Form made flash-welded and cold-rolled rings with jet engine as well as gas turbine applications.

PCC also acquired RathGibson which makes tubing for the oil and gas chemical/petrochemical power-generation and other markets in 2012.

To expand both its Fasteners and Forged Products segments PCC acquired the aerostructures and industrial products businesses of HA©roux-Devtek for about CAD$300 million (about $295.5 million) in 2012. Among other benefits the acquisition expanded the company's product line for such OEMs as Lockheed Bombardier and Gulfstream. PCC also inked a deal to purchase the Synchronous Aerospace Group business of private investment firm Littlejohn & Co. in late 2012.

EXECUTIVES

Evp And Cfo, Shawn R. Hagel, $687,500 total compensation
Chairman And Ceo, Mark Donegan, $1,585,000 total compensation
Svp And President Airframe Products, Alan J. (Al) Power
Evp And President Wyman-gordon, Andrew V. Masterman, $592,500 total compensation
Vp And Cio, Byron J. Gaddis
Evp, Steven G. (Steve) Hackett, $708,750 total compensation
Svp And General Counsel, Ruth A. Beyer, $569,000 total compensation
Svp And Coo Aerostructures Division, Joseph I. Snowden, $356,347 total compensation
Svp And President Pcc Airfoils, John P. O'Neill
Svp And President Timet And Special Metals, James R. Pieron
Auditors: DELOITTE & TOUCHE LLP PORTLAN

LOCATIONS

HQ: PRECISION CASTPARTS CORP.
  4650 SW MCDAM AVE STE 300, PORTLAND, OR 97239
Phone: 503 946-4800
Web: WWW.PRECAST.COM

PRODUCTS/OPERATIONS

Selected Products and Services
Fasteners
  Advanced forming technology
  E/One (for the disposal of residential sanitary waste)
  J&L fiber services (for pulp and paper industry)
  PCC Precision Tool Group
  SPS aerospace fasteners (for commercial/military aircraft)

SPS engineered fasteners (high strength for
automotive and construction applications)
Forged products
Special Metals Corporation
Wyman-Gordon Forgings
Investment Cast Products
PCC Airfoils (high-temperature blades and vanes)
PCC Structurals (structural investment castings)
Specialty materials and alloys (alloys waxes and metal
processing for investment casting)

COMPETITORS

ATI Ladish	Hitachi Metals
Allegheny Technologies	Kennametal
Arconic	LISI
Carpenter Technology	Mettis Aerospace
Chicago Rivet	SOURIAU PA&E
Crane Co.	Swagelok
Curtiss-Wright	Teleflex
ESCO	ThyssenKrupp
Farwest Steel	United Technologies
Corporation	Universal Stainless
Federal Screw Works	V & M Tubes (USA)
Georg Fischer	Volvo Aero
Haynes International	

HISTORICAL FINANCIALS

Company Type: Private

Income Statement   FYE: January 3

	REVENUE ($ mil.)	NET INCOME ($ mil.)	NET PROFIT MARGIN	EMPLOYEES
01/16*	7,002	817	11.7%	30,100
03/15	10,005	1,533	15.3%	—
03/14	9,616	1,784	18.6%	—
03/13	8,377	1,429	17.1%	—
Annual Growth	(5.8%)	(17.0%)	—	—

*Fiscal year change

2016 Year-End Financials

Return on assets: 12.8%   Cash ($ mil.): 343
Return on equity: 11.7%
Current ratio: 1.20

PREMIER HEALTH PARTNERS

EXECUTIVES

Ceo-Pres, James R Pancoast
Sr Vice President, Mark Shaker
Vice President, Mary H Boosalis
Vice President, William E Linesch
Cfo, Thomas M Duncan
Prin, Sharon Rector
Information Specialist, Leslie Lindsey
Information Specialist, Terri Manuel
Director, Jeffrey Haas
Production Administrator, Steve Haworth
Auditors: I ERNST & YOUNG US LLP COLUM

LOCATIONS

HQ: PREMIER HEALTH PARTNERS
110 N MAIN ST STE 450, DAYTON, OH 454023712
Phone: 937 499-9596
Web: WWW.PREMIERHEALTHPARTNERS.ORG

PRODUCTS/OPERATIONS

Selected Operations
Atrium Medical Center (Middleton)
Fidelity Health Care (home health care)
Good Samaritan Hospital (Dayton)

Good Samaritan North Health Center (outpatient facility
Englewood)
Miami Valley Hospital (Dayton)
Miami Valley South Health Center (outpatient facility
Centerville)
Premier Community Health (community health
outreach)
Premier HealthNet (primary care physicians group)
Upper Valley Medical Center (Troy)

COMPETITORS

AdCare	Mount Carmel Health
Cincinnati Children's Hospital	OhioHealth
Kettering Health Network	TriHealth
	UC Health
MetroHealth System	University Hospitals Health System

HISTORICAL FINANCIALS

Company Type: Private

Income Statement   FYE: December 31

	REVENUE ($ mil.)	NET INCOME ($ mil.)	NET PROFIT MARGIN	EMPLOYEES
12/15	354	15	4.4%	5,336
12/14	340	11	3.4%	—
Annual Growth	4.1%	37.5%	—	—

2015 Year-End Financials

Return on assets: 6.9%   Cash ($ mil.): 11
Return on equity: 4.4%
Current ratio: 2.40

PREMISE HEALTH HOLDING CORP.

EXECUTIVES

Ceo, Edward Stuart Clark
Coo, Trent Riley
Cfo, Shannon Farrington
Pres, Jami Doucette
Chief Information Officer, Haden McWhorter
Chief Human Resources Officer, Elizebeth Reimer
Chief Compliance Officer, Dana Fields
Chief Information Security Off, Joey Johnson
Exec V Pres, Peter Vasquez
Exec V Pres, Ed McNamara
Vice-President, Will Rice
Auditors: RSM US LLP CHICAGO ILLINOIS

LOCATIONS

HQ: PREMISE HEALTH HOLDING CORP.
5500 MARYLAND WAY STE 200, BRENTWOOD, TN
370274973
Phone: 615 468-6562
Web: WWW.PREMISEHEALTH.COM

HISTORICAL FINANCIALS

Company Type: Private

Income Statement   FYE: December 31

	REVENUE ($ mil.)	NET INCOME ($ mil.)	NET PROFIT MARGIN	EMPLOYEES
12/17	685	7	1.0%	4,500
12/16	630	(2)	—	—
12/15	581	0	0.0%	—
12/14	303	(14)	—	—
Annual Growth	31.2%	—	—	—

2017 Year-End Financials

Return on assets: 5.0%   Cash ($ mil.): 37
Return on equity: 1.0%
Current ratio: 2.00

PRESBYTERIAN HOMES AND SERVICES

EXECUTIVES

Ceo, Daniel A Lindh
Chm, Kenneth S Larson
Pres-Ceo, Daniel Lindh
SEC, Janna R Severance
Cfo, Mark T Meyer
Director, David Millett
Information Technology Manager, Mark Stabnow
Information Technology Manager, Martha Hurr
Director, Natalie Morland
Marketing Staff, Billie J Fox
Coordinator, Emily Hjelvik
Auditors: CLIFTONLARSONALLEN LLP MINNEA

LOCATIONS

HQ: PRESBYTERIAN HOMES AND SERVICES
2845 HAMLINE AVE N # 200, ROSEVILLE, MN
551137116
Phone: 651 631-6100
Web: WWW.PRESHOMES.COM

HISTORICAL FINANCIALS

Company Type: Private

Income Statement   FYE: September 30

	REVENUE ($ mil.)	NET INCOME ($ mil.)	NET PROFIT MARGIN	EMPLOYEES
09/17	383	21	5.7%	4,750
09/16	363	17	4.8%	—
09/15	334	17	5.2%	—
09/14	314	17	5.6%	—
Annual Growth	6.8%	7.3%	—	—

2017 Year-End Financials

Return on assets: 1.8%   Cash ($ mil.): 36
Return on equity: 5.7%
Current ratio: 0.60

PRESBYTERIAN MEDICAL CENTER OF THE UNIVERSITY OF PENNSYLVANIA HEALTH SYSTEM

EXECUTIVES

Exec Dir, Michele Volpe
Program Director, Jeanmarie Perch
Vice-President, Scott Tornek

Controller, William Owens
Operations Manager, Bob Russell
Executive Director Nurse, Diane Maccarone
Operations Manager, Karen Greenfield
Associate Professor of Clinica, Martin Bohnenkamp
Clinical Assistant Professor O, Michael Colucciello
Procurement Manager, Nancy McCoy
Staff Nurse, Rasheda Peoples

LOCATIONS

HQ: PRESBYTERIAN MEDICAL CENTER OF THE
UNIVERSITY OF PENNSYLVANIA HEALTH SYSTEM
51 N 39TH ST, PHILADELPHIA, PA 191042692
Phone: 215 662-8000
Web: WWW.PENNMEDICINE.ORG

HISTORICAL FINANCIALS

Company Type: Private

Income Statement				FYE: June 30
	REVENUE ($ mil.)	NET INCOME ($ mil.)	NET PROFIT MARGIN	EMPLOYEES
06/15	546	(0)	—	1,370
06/14	445	21	4.7%	—
06/13	429	7	1.7%	—
06/05	301	(1)	—	—
Annual Growth	6.2%	—	—	—

PRESENCE CHICAGO HOSPITALS NETWORK

EXECUTIVES

Title Ceo, Robert Dahl
Prin, Paul Brydon
Project Manager, Sue Ellen Schumacher
Manager, Gina Shell-Lamore
Project Manager, Brenda Wade
Gynecology/Obstetrics Speclst, Carmen Scarimbolo
Doctor, Diana Iwanik
Manager, Jim Murrell
Doctor, Larry Jankelowitz
Purchasing Director, Marwan Fakhoury
Director Radia, Rosa Perez-Cuevas

LOCATIONS

HQ: PRESENCE CHICAGO HOSPITALS NETWORK
7435 W TALCOTT AVE, CHICAGO, IL 606313707
Phone: 773 737-4636
Web: WWW.RESURRECTIONEM.COM

HISTORICAL FINANCIALS

Company Type: Private

Income Statement				FYE: December 31
	REVENUE ($ mil.)	NET INCOME ($ mil.)	NET PROFIT MARGIN	EMPLOYEES
12/17	291	8	3.0%	99
12/15	277	3	1.1%	—
12/14	238	(19)	—	—
12/13	266	(4)	—	—
Annual Growth	2.3%	—	—	—

PRESIDENT AND BOARD OF TRUSTEES OF SANTA CLARA COLLEGE

Santa Clara University wants its students to achieve clarity. The Jesuit Catholic school California's oldest higher-education institution offers degrees in more than 40 disciplines. Its variety of graduate programs include business engineering law pastoral ministries counseling psychology and education. With more than 8000 students Santa Clara University boasts a student/faculty ratio of 12:1 and support from a $760 million endowment. The university occupies a 106-acre campus and has more than 520 full-time and more than 360 part-time faculty members.

Operations

The educational institution is recognized as the having the fourth-highest graduation rate among all US master's universities. About 61% of students come from California. The remainder are from 33 US states and 19 other countries.

Financial Performance

Its budget reached $387.4 million in 2013-14. The school charges undergraduate students $42156 million per year in tuition and fees.

Company Background

Notable alumni include Oakland mayor and former governor of California Jerry Brown soccer player Brandi Chastain Cirrus Logic chairman Michael Hackworth and winemaker Sam Sebastiani.

Santa Clara University was founded as Santa Clara College in 1851 on the site of Mission Santa Clara de AsAs the eighth of the original 21 California missions. It became a university in 1925 when the schools of engineering and law were added and became a coeducational institution in 1961.

EXECUTIVES

Vice President, Robert Warren
Department Chair, Michael Calegari
Managing Director High Tech Law Institute Santa Clara Law, Tom Lavelle
Assistant Vice President Alumni Relations, Kathy Kale
Assistant Vice President Auxiliary Services, Jane Barrantes
Vice President, Carol Omahony
Auditors: MOSS ADAMS LLP STOCKTON CA

LOCATIONS

HQ: PRESIDENT AND BOARD OF TRUSTEES OF SANTA CLARA COLLEGE
500 EL CAMINO REAL, SANTA CLARA, CA 950504345
Phone: 408 554-4000
Web: WWW.SCU.EDU

PRODUCTS/OPERATIONS

Degrees Offered
Undergraduate Degrees
  Bachelor of Arts
  Bachelor of Science
  Bachelor of Science in Commerce
Graduate Degrees
  Business (MBA EMBA MSIS)
  Counseling Psychology (M.A.)
  Education (M.A.)
  Engineering (M.S. Ph.D.)
  Law (J.D. LL.M.)
  Pastoral Ministries (M.A.)

HISTORICAL FINANCIALS

Company Type: Private

Income Statement				FYE: June 30
	REVENUE ($ mil.)	NET INCOME ($ mil.)	NET PROFIT MARGIN	EMPLOYEES
06/17	362	104	28.9%	1,431
06/16	460	16	3.5%	—
06/14	457	65	14.3%	—
06/13	0	29	—	—
Annual Growth	—	37.8%	—	—

2017 Year-End Financials

Return on assets: 12.5%   Cash ($ mil.): 30
Return on equity: 28.9%
Current ratio: —

PRESIDENT AND TRUSTEES OF COLBY COLLEGE

EXECUTIVES

Prin, Bruce McDougal

LOCATIONS

HQ: PRESIDENT AND TRUSTEES OF COLBY COLLEGE
4120 MAYFLOWER HL, WATERVILLE, ME 049018841
Phone: 207 859-4127

HISTORICAL FINANCIALS

Company Type: Private

Income Statement				FYE: June 30
	ASSETS ($ mil.)	NET INCOME ($ mil.)	INCOME AS % OF ASSETS	EMPLOYEES
06/17	1,481	72	4.9%	5
06/15	1,382	50	3.6%	—
06/14	1,267	55	4.4%	—
06/13	1,126	30	2.7%	—
Annual Growth	7.1%	24.8%	—	—

2017 Year-End Financials

Return on assets: 8.8%   Sales ($ mil): 259
Return on equity: 28.1%

PRESIDIAN DESTINATIONS, LTD.

EXECUTIVES

Partner, H Drake Leddy
Cfo, Jeanette Mosley
Director of Management, Angie Mock
Corporate Director of Sales, Sergio Cardenas
Operations Analyst, Jared Bailey
Property Manager, Dixie McClelland
Senior Manager, Dustin Crouch
Vice-President Corporate Devel, Lily Ng
Vice-President, Stanton Leddy

LOCATIONS

HQ: PRESIDIAN DESTINATIONS, LTD.
9000 TESORO DR STE 300, SAN ANTONIO, TX 782176132
Phone: 210 646-8811
Web: WWW.PRESIDIAN.COM

HISTORICAL FINANCIALS

Company Type: Private

Income Statement

	ASSETS ($ mil.)	NET INCOME ($ mil.)	INCOME AS % OF ASSETS	EMPLOYEES
12/15	924	583	63.1%	10
12/14	1,916	799	41.7%	—
12/13	1	0	34.5%	—
12/12	1	0	27.8%	—
Annual Growth	789.3%	1069.0%	—	—

2015 Year-End Financials

Return on assets: 0.1%   Sales ($ mil): 1,338
Return on equity: 43.6%

PRESSURE VESSEL SERVICE, INC.

EXECUTIVES

Pres-Ceo-Chm, James B Nicholson
Vice President, James M Nicholson
Vice President, Allan Schlumberger
Vice President, David A Nicholson
V Pres-Cfo, Candee M Saferian
V Pres-Gen Coun-SEC, Jonathan S Taub
Asst SEC, James Devleeschouwer
Asst Treas, Milisav M Bulatovic
Minibulk Account Representativ, Bill Rivers
Administrative Assistant, Eileen McDonnell
Human Resources, Gwen Sounart

LOCATIONS

HQ: PRESSURE VESSEL SERVICE, INC.
10900 HARPER AVE, DETROIT, MI 482133364
Phone: 313 921-1200
Web: WWW.PVSCHEMICALS.COM

HISTORICAL FINANCIALS

Company Type: Private

Income Statement

FYE: December 31

	REVENUE ($ mil.)	NET INCOME ($ mil.)	NET PROFIT MARGIN	EMPLOYEES
12/15	497	6	1.4%	800
12/12	566	21	3.8%	—
12/11	461	12	2.6%	—
12/10	356	10	2.8%	—
Annual Growth	6.9%	(7.5%)	—	—

PRIDE INDUSTRIES

EXECUTIVES

Ceo, Michael Ziegler
Exe Vice President, Tim Yamauchi
Coo, Peter Berghuis
Sr Vice President, Tina Oliveira
President, Jeff Dern

Accounts Receivable, Barbara Doll
Vp of Facilities Operations, Don Nelson
Coordinator, David Martinez
Information Technology Manager, Daniel Monighetti
Law Specialist, Laurel Petersen
Director, Linda Gilbert
Auditors: MOSS ADAMS LLP SACRAMENTO CA

LOCATIONS

HQ: PRIDE INDUSTRIES
10030 FOOTHILLS BLVD, ROSEVILLE, CA 957477102
Phone: 916 788-2100
Web: WWW.PRIDEINDUSTRIES.COM

HISTORICAL FINANCIALS

Company Type: Private

Income Statement

FYE: June 30

	REVENUE ($ mil.)	NET INCOME ($ mil.)	NET PROFIT MARGIN	EMPLOYEES
06/18	326	1	0.3%	5,003
06/16	290	0	0.1%	—
06/15	279	1	0.6%	—
06/14	258	3	1.5%	—
Annual Growth	6.0%	(26.1%)	—	—

2018 Year-End Financials

Return on assets: 4.7%   Cash ($ mil.): 3
Return on equity: 0.3%
Current ratio: 0.80

PRO PETROLEUM, INC.

EXECUTIVES

Pres, Marcus Griffin
Treas-Cfo, Don Hayden
Stkhldr, B R Griffin
Cr Mgr, Mark Macha
Contrl, Betty Catherman
Sales and Marketing Assistant, Tammy Snyder
Auditors: GARRETT AND SWANN LLP LUBBOC

LOCATIONS

HQ: PRO PETROLEUM, INC.
4710 4TH ST, LUBBOCK, TX 794164900
Phone: 806 795-8785
Web: WWW.PROPETROLEUM.COM

HISTORICAL FINANCIALS

Company Type: Private

Income Statement

FYE: December 31

	REVENUE ($ mil.)	NET INCOME ($ mil.)	NET PROFIT MARGIN	EMPLOYEES
12/17	1,075	17	1.6%	150
12/15	1,063	5	0.5%	—
12/14	1,701	4	0.3%	—
12/13	1,815	12	0.7%	—
Annual Growth	(12.3%)	9.4%	—	—

2017 Year-End Financials

Return on assets: 3.3%   Cash ($ mil.): 21
Return on equity: 1.6%
Current ratio: 0.90

PRODUCE ALLIANCE, L.L.C.

EXECUTIVES

MBR, George Melshenker
MBR, Scott Weber
Exe V Pres, Mike Williams
Partner Executive Vice Preside, Joe Collier
V Pres, Melissa Melshenker Ackerman
Cfo, Rob Feldgreber
Accountant, Monty Mittelman
Administrative Assistant, Cassie Young
Sales Staff, Adam Kramer
Assistant, Kevin Bateman
Account Manager, Paula Perrone
Auditors: MILLER COOPER & CO LTD DE

LOCATIONS

HQ: PRODUCE ALLIANCE, L.L.C.
100 LEXINGTON DR STE 201, BUFFALO GROVE, IL 600896937
Phone: 847 808-3030
Web: WWW.PRODUCEALLIANCE.COM

HISTORICAL FINANCIALS

Company Type: Private

Income Statement

FYE: December 31

	REVENUE ($ mil.)	NET INCOME ($ mil.)	NET PROFIT MARGIN	EMPLOYEES
12/17	441	1	0.3%	75
12/16	381	2	0.7%	—
12/15	326	1	0.4%	—
12/14	253	0	0.2%	—
Annual Growth	20.3%	33.0%	—	—

PRODUCERS RICE MILL, INC.

These producers aren't just milling about they're about milling. Producers Rice Mill dries mills and markets more than 50 million bushels of rice each year which it sells both domestically and overseas. The growers' cooperative is one of the largest private-label producers of rice in the US packaging more than 100 brands for the foodservice retail private label export and industrial industries. Its brands include ParExcellence LeGourment Golden Harvest Classic Grains Granada Mandalay Bamboo 103 Calrose and Thai Orchard. It also processes rice for animal feeds such as Buck Grub deer feed and Equi-Jewel horse feed.

Operations

Along with bagged and bulk rice Producers also offers parboiled rice and seasoned rice mixes and processes rice for animal feed. During 2012-13 Producers' mills processed 64.3 million bushels of rice up 14% from the previous year.

Geographic Reach

In addition to its corporate headquarters and production facilities in Stuttgart Arkansas the cooperative has receiving operations in Arkansas Mississippi and Texas. It has plants in DeWitt Eudora Fair Oaks Pine Bluff Stuttgart Tyronza Wilmot Wilson and Wynne in Arkansas; Boyle and Greenville in Mississippi; and DeWitt in Texas. About 15% of US milled grains like rice are exported to countries such as Canada Mexico Japan Haiti and Iraq.

Sales and Marketing

The company serves foodservice retail private label export and industrial customers. Ahold U.S.A. Federated Nash Finch and SUPERVALU have been long-term customers.

Strategy

The USDA projects a demand in US rice exports over the next several years. Milled rice will have a higher demand which will directly benefit the US rice industry.

Company Background

The cooperative was founded in 1943.

EXECUTIVES

Vice President Operations, Ken Dryden
National Sales Manager Foodservice, John May
Auditors: ERWIN & COMPANY LITTLE ROCK

LOCATIONS

HQ: PRODUCERS RICE MILL, INC.
518 E HARRISON ST, STUTTGART, AR 721603700
Phone: 870 673-4444
Web: WWW.PRODUCERSRICE.COM

COMPETITORS

ADM	Goya
American Rice	Mars Incorporated
CHS	Mondelez International
Cargill	PepsiCo
Cereal Byproducts	RiceX
Farmers Rice Milling	Riceland Foods
Farmers' Rice	Specialty Rice
Cooperative	

HISTORICAL FINANCIALS

Company Type: Private

Income Statement   FYE: July 31

	REVENUE ($ mil.)	NET INCOME ($ mil.)	NET PROFIT MARGIN	EMPLOYEES
07/18	436	260	59.6%	650
07/17	420	276	65.8%	—
07/16	415	275	66.3%	—
07/15	488	354	72.7%	—
Annual Growth	(3.6%)	(9.8%)	—	—

2018 Year-End Financials

Return on assets: 4.6%   Cash ($ mil.): 2
Return on equity: 59.6%
Current ratio: 0.90

PRODUCTION TECHNOLOGIES, INC.

EXECUTIVES

Chm, John Maclennon
Ceo, Mark Utley
V Pres, Michael Lundequam
Sales and Marketing Staff, Martha Timmers
Manager, Martha Smith

LOCATIONS

HQ: PRODUCTION TECHNOLOGIES, INC.
7651 WASHINGTON AVE S, EDINA, MN 554392417
Phone: 952 944-1076
Web: WWW.PTIMN.COM

HISTORICAL FINANCIALS

Company Type: Private

Income Statement   FYE: December 31

	REVENUE ($ mil.)	NET INCOME ($ mil.)	NET PROFIT MARGIN	EMPLOYEES
12/16	3,289	580	17.6%	25
12/15	3,488	719	20.6%	—
12/14	3,880	348	9.0%	—
12/11	4	0	9.8%	—
Annual Growth	280.1%	327.2%	—	—

PROHEALTH CARE INC

That cheddar-and-beer diet take a toll on your health? Might be time to turn your health over to the pros. ProHealth Care provides health care services to southeastern Wisconsin through a network of three hospitals (Waukesha Memorial Oconomowoc Memorial and the Rehabilitation Hospital of Wisconsin) about two dozen clinics assisted living facilities (Regency Senior Communities) a rehabilitation partnership home health care services and a hospice facility. The community-based organization's specialized services include advanced cancer care cardiology orthopedic and obstetrical and neonatal intensive care.

Operations

ProHealth Care's total operations include Waukesha Memorial Hospital Oconomowoc Memorial Hospital Rehabilitation Hospital of Wisconsin (RHOW) ProHealth Care Medical Associates ProHealth Home Care and Hospice West Wood Health & Fitness Center and senior living facilities.

The RHOW is a 40-bed hospital that is the result of a partnership between ProHealth Care and Centerre Healthcare to meet the increased rehabilitation needs of the region.

Oconomowoc Memorial Hospital has 58 available beds and provides general acute care and support activities in Oconomowoc Wisconsin and surrounding communities.

Financial Performance

In 2014 ProHealth Care's net sales increased by 3% due to higher sales from net patient service revenues less provision for bad debts. Patient service revenues net of contractual allowances and discounts was comprised of $657.9 million from third party payors and $7.3 from self-pay payors.

Net income decreased by $107.1 million in 2014 due to lower excess of revenues over expenses (due to unrealized investment loss and change in interest rate swap value) and pension-related changes other than net periodic benefit cost partially offset by increased revenues.

Net cash provided by the operating activities increased by 16% due to changes in patient accounts receivable and accounts payable.

Company Background

ProHealth Care in 2012 merged the foundations serving its two hospitals in Waukesha County in an effort to optimize the efficiency of its operations. With the merger the Waukesha Memorial Hospital Foundation and Oconomowoc Memorial Hospital Foundation became the ProHealth Care Foundation. The integration combined the foundation boards donors and volunteers into one organization.

ProHealth Care was established as a not-for-profit corporation in 1998.

EXECUTIVES

President And Ceo, Susan Edwards
Cio, Christine Bessler
Vice President, Ken Price
Clinic Manager, Nicky Ott
Senior Vice President Marketing And Business Development, Randy Sparrow
Chairman, Janet Swandby
Auditors: PLANTE & MORAN PLLC GRAND RA

LOCATIONS

HQ: PROHEALTH CARE INC
725 AMERICAN AVE, WAUKESHA, WI 531885031
Phone: 262 928-1000

PRODUCTS/OPERATIONS

2014 Sales

	%	
Net patient service revenues	91	
Other operating revenues	9	
Total	0	100

Selected Medical Services

Allergies
Birthing
Bones Joints and Muscles
Brain and Nerves
Breast Health
Cancer
CyberKnife
Diabetes
Diagnostic Services
Digestive
Ear Nose and Throat
Emergency Services/Urgent Care
Eyes and Vision
Gastrointestinal Services
Hearing
Heart and Vascular
Home Care and Hospice
Integrative Medicine
Kidneys and Urinary System
MAKOplasty
Mammography
Men's Health
Mental Health
Multiple Sclerosis
Occupational Health Services
Orthopedic
Pain
Palliative Medicine
Primary Care
Physical Therapy and Rehabilitation Services
Senior Services
Sleep
Spine Care
Stroke
Travel Medicine
Weight Loss
Women's Health
Women's Sexual Health
Wound Care

COMPETITORS

Beaver Dam Community Hospitals
Children's Hospital and Health System
Columbia St. Mary's
FHN
Froedtert Hospital
Hospital Sisters Health System
KishHealth
Ministry Health Care
Rockford Health System
SwedishAmerican Health System
UW Medical Foundation
University of Wisconsin Hospital and Clinics

Company Type: Private

Income Statement				FYE: September 30
	REVENUE ($ mil.)	NET INCOME ($ mil.)	NET PROFIT MARGIN	EMPLOYEES
09/18	820	111	13.6%	3,000
09/17	765	127	16.6%	—
09/16	747	74	10.0%	—
09/15	748	(20)	—	—
Annual Growth	3.1%	—	—	—

2018 Year-End Financials

Return on assets: 6.1% Cash ($ mil.): 20
Return on equity: 13.6%
Current ratio: 0.90

PROMEGA CORPORATION

Promega provides tools to help researchers delve into the life sciences. The company sells more than 3500 products that allow scientists to conduct various experiments in gene protein and cellular research. Its offerings fall into more than two dozen categories including DNA and RNA purification genotype analysis protein expression and analysis and DNA sequencing. Promega has branches in 15 countries around the world. The firm sells its products directly and through about 50 distributors. Customers include academic pharmaceutical and clinical labs as well as government agencies and energy and chemical companies.

Operations

Manufacturing unit Promega Biosciences (PBI) combines research in chemistry and manufacturing to serve the scientific community while Promega BioSystems (PBS) designs and manufactures single-tube and microplate readers for fluorescent and luminescent biological assays. Shanghai Promega Biological Products manufactures reagents and packaging for the Chinese market.

Another unit Terso Solutions provides inventory management services to distributors hospitals laboratories and manufacturers. Its system uses radio frequency identification-enabled (RFID-enabled) cabinets freezers and refrigerators to help clients keep tabs on the whereabouts of sensitive inventory such as reagents pharmaceuticals and hazardous materials. RFID uses radio-wave communication technology to exchange data between a reader and an electronic tag attached to the item being tracked. The technology allows users to maintain close tabs on the supply management chain usually via web-based applications in effort to control costs.

Promega holds hundreds of patents in the areas of nucleic acid purification human identification and bioluminescence as well as in vitro transcription and translation and cell biology.

Geographic Reach

Promega has branches in 16 countries with more than 50 global distributors serving 100 countries. It operates its manufacturing facilities through PBI in San Luis Obispo California; PBS in Seoul; Promega BioSystems Sunnyvale in Sunnyvale California; Shanghai Promega Biological Products in Shanghai; and Terso Solutions in Madison Wisconsin.

The company distributes its products in North America Africa and the Middle East Europe Latin America and the Asia/Pacific region.

Sales and Marketing

Promega's clients predominantly use its products for life science research in the fields of genomics proteomics (the study of proteins) and cellular analysis with the ultimate goal of identifying targets for drug development. Additionally its products are used for forensic testing by state and federal agencies including the FBI for human identification. Promega also offers paternity testing kits and in vitro diagnostic test systems.

Financial Performance

The company's revenues grew from $350 million in 2013 to $360 million in 2014.

Strategy

Promega is continuously growing its product offerings through research and development efforts; R&D spending accounts for more than 10% of annual revenue expenditures. It focuses on expanding the uses of its current technologies as well as introducing new add-ons for existing systems and kits. The company also licenses its technologies to other biotech firms.

Promega sometimes partners with other companies to expand its service offerings. In 2014 it formed a partnership with Genetic Technologies Limited (GTG) a diagnostics company through which it received rights in relation to GTG's Intron Sequence Analysis and Genomic Mapping patents.

Growing its product portfolio in 2014 the company released a new touchscreen interface for the Helix smart on-site stocking program. The touchscreen enhances the Helix experience by providing researchers easy access to relevant information about Promega products including applications and protocols. It also launched GloMax Discover an integrated multi-mode detection plate reader system.

Company Background

Promega was founded in 1978 and is owned by investors and employees and led by founder and CEO William Linton.

EXECUTIVES

Chairman And Ceo, William A. (Bill) Linton
Vice President Of Research And Development, Gary Tarpley
Auditors: GRANT THORNTON LLP MILWAUKEE

LOCATIONS

HQ: PROMEGA CORPORATION
2800 WOODS HOLLOW RD, FITCHBURG, WI 537115399
Phone: 608 274-4330
Web: WWW.PROMEGA.IN

PRODUCTS/OPERATIONS

Selected Product Categories
Cellular analysis
  Apoptosis
  Automation-robotics
  Cell viability
  Drug discovery
  Gene expression and reporter assays
  Immunological detection
  In-vitro toxicology
  Signal transduction
  Transfection
Genetic identity
Genomics
  Automation-robotics
  Cloning
  DNA and RNA purification
  Electrophoresis
  Food and GMO testing
  Genotype analysis
  In-vitro transcription
  Microarrays
  Plant biotechnology
Reverse transcription and cDNA synthesis
RNA interference
Sequencing
Proteomics
  Electrophoresis
  Gene expression and reporter assays
  Mutagenesis
  Protein expression and analysis
  Protein interactions
  RNA interference
  Transfection

COMPETITORS

Beckman Coulter	Roche Diagnostics
Becton Dickinson	Sequenom
Life Technologies Corporation	Siemens Healthcare
	Sigma-Aldrich
Luminex	Transgenomic
QIAGEN	Vermillion

HISTORICAL FINANCIALS
Company Type: Private

Income Statement				FYE: March 31
	REVENUE ($ mil.)	NET INCOME ($ mil.)	NET PROFIT MARGIN	EMPLOYEES
03/18	420	69	16.4%	1,487
03/17	386	55	14.3%	—
03/16	370	44	12.1%	—
Annual Growth	6.6%	24.1%	—	—

2018 Year-End Financials

Return on assets: 3.8% Cash ($ mil.): 64
Return on equity: 16.4%
Current ratio: 1.90

PROTRANS INTERNATIONAL, INC.

EXECUTIVES

Pres, Craig Roeder
Vice President, Michael Kattawar
Director, Jim McCrary
Manager of Information, Sherry Wooldridge
Coordinator, Lynn Russell
Managing Director, Timr Gartner
Manager, Linda Perez
Operations Manager, Miguel Terrazas
Procurement Manager, Shawn Gaidis
Operations Supervisor, Bob Luker
Coordinator of Marketing, Claudia Contreras
Auditors: BGBC PARTNERS LLP INDIANAPOLI

LOCATIONS

HQ: PROTRANS INTERNATIONAL, INC.
8311 NORTH PERIMETER RD, INDIANAPOLIS, IN 462413628
Phone: 317 240-4100
Web: WWW.PROTRANS.COM

HISTORICAL FINANCIALS
Company Type: Private

Income Statement				FYE: December 31
	REVENUE ($ mil.)	NET INCOME ($ mil.)	NET PROFIT MARGIN	EMPLOYEES
12/16	297	0	0.0%	500
12/15	283	5	2.0%	—
12/14	292	4	1.4%	—
12/13	256	9	3.5%	—
Annual Growth	5.0%	(75.8%)	—	—

PROVIDENCE HEALTH & SERVICES

EXECUTIVES

Ceo, Rod Hochman
Pres- Chief Dev Officer, Laurie Kelley
Exec V Pres-Cfo, Todd Hofheins
Information Technology/Interne, Michael Antrim
Materials Manager, Mike Minnick
Training Specialist, Sheryl Regan
Technology, Henry Morgan
Database Administrator, Jack Hwang
Human Resources Analyst, Kay Barksdale
Customer Staff, Patricia M McConnell
Program Manager, Mark Sizemore
Auditors: CLARK NUBER PS BELLEVUE WA

LOCATIONS

HQ: PROVIDENCE HEALTH & SERVICES
  1801 LIND AVE SW, RENTON, WA 980573368
Phone: 425 525-3355
Web: WWW.PROVIDENCE.ORG

HISTORICAL FINANCIALS

Company Type: Private

Income Statement — FYE: December 31

	REVENUE ($ mil.)	NET INCOME ($ mil.)	NET PROFIT MARGIN	EMPLOYEES
12/15	14,433	49	0.3%	9,700
12/12	280	14	5.3%	—
12/08	7,026	(156)	—	—
12/07	6,348	434	6.8%	—
Annual Growth	10.8%	(23.8%)		

2015 Year-End Financials

Return on assets: 3.0% Cash ($ mil.): 729
Return on equity: 0.3%
Current ratio: 1.00

PROVIDENCE HEALTH AND SERVICES

EXECUTIVES

Pres, Rodney Hochman
SEC, Cindy Strauss
SEC, Tammy Teodosio
SEC, John Whipple
Treas, Todd Hofheins
Cfo, Thomas Risse
Chief Exec, Jim Leonard
Director, Kathleen Nurmi
Director, George Chappell
Manager, Craig Arneson
Manager, Deborah Shawver

LOCATIONS

HQ: PROVIDENCE HEALTH AND SERVICES
  413 LILLY RD NE, OLYMPIA, WA 985065133
Phone: 360 491-9480
Web: WWW.PROVIDENCE.ORG

HISTORICAL FINANCIALS

Company Type: Private

Income Statement — FYE: December 31

	REVENUE ($ mil.)	NET INCOME ($ mil.)	NET PROFIT MARGIN	EMPLOYEES
12/16	458	10	2.3%	2,400
12/05	3	0	7.5%	
12/02	211	5	2.6%	
12/01	910	0		
Annual Growth	—	95.6%		

2016 Year-End Financials

Return on assets: 2.0% Cash ($ mil.): —
Return on equity: 2.3%
Current ratio: 1.10

PROVIDENCE HEALTH SERVICES OF WACO

EXECUTIVES

Ceo, Brett Esrock
Sr V Pres-Fin, Philip E Halford
SEC, Dennis Michaelis
Treas, Hal Whitaker
Executive Officer, Joe Dan
Director, Patty Hawk
Administrative Assistant, Peggy Pustejovsky
Health Care Director, Royda Frazier
Administrative Assistant, Drew Dickenson
Coordinator, Angela Gutierrez
Microbiology Supervisor, Richard George

LOCATIONS

HQ: PROVIDENCE HEALTH SERVICES OF WACO
  6901 MEDICAL PKWY, WACO, TX 767127910
Phone: 254 751-4000
Web: WWW.PROVIDENCE.NET

HISTORICAL FINANCIALS

Company Type: Private

Income Statement — FYE: June 30

	REVENUE ($ mil.)	NET INCOME ($ mil.)	NET PROFIT MARGIN	EMPLOYEES
06/16	324	16	5.2%	2,000
06/15	277	8	3.1%	—
06/14	267	23	8.7%	—
06/10	236	15	6.4%	—
Annual Growth	5.4%	1.7%	—	—

2016 Year-End Financials

Return on assets: 2.7% Cash ($ mil.): —
Return on equity: 5.2%
Current ratio: 0.40

PROVIDENCE HOSPITAL

Providence Hospital and Medical Centers provides health care in the Motor City and surrounding areas. The main Providence Hospital is a 408-bed teaching facility that has been recognized for its cardiology program and clinical expertise in behavioral medicine. It offers a variety of other services ranging from cancer treatment and neurosurgery to orthopedics and women's health. The network also includes dozens of affiliated general practice and specialty health clinics. The not-for-profit medical center founded in 1845 as St. Vincent's Hospital in Detroit by the Daughters of Charity is part of Catholic health ministry St. John Health (itself a subsidiary of Ascension Health).

Operations

As part of its health care system Providence Hospital and Medical Centers operates a host of hospitals and medical centers across the metropolitan Detroit area. They include Providence Southfield and four namesake Providence Medical Center locations in Farmington Hills Livonia Dearborn Heights and South Lyon. Across its system the medical facilities employ some 1500 physicians and enlist the help of about 300 active volunteers.

Carroll Manor is a skilled nursing center that provides short- and long-term medical care and rehabilitation services. The system's behavioral health division Seton House provides alcohol and addiction treatment in Washington DC.

Providence Hospital and Medical Centers had more than 41600 emergency department visits in 2013.

Strategy

In order to provide better services the hospital renovated and expanded its emergency department in 2014. Also that year its family medicine division opened a new office in the Glenn Dale/Bowie area.

EXECUTIVES

Medical Records Director, Lynn Lewandowski
Occupational Therapy Director, Andrew Vosburgh
Auditors: DELOITTE TAX LP CINCINNATI O

LOCATIONS

HQ: PROVIDENCE HOSPITAL
  16001 W 9 MILE RD, SOUTHFIELD, MI 480754803
Phone: 248 849-3000
Web: WWW.PROVIDENCEOBGYNRESIDENCY.COM

Selected Hospitals and Medical Centers
Providence Southfield-Southfield
Providence Medical Center-Farmington Hills
Providence Medical Center-Livonia
Providence Medical Center-Dearborn Heights
Providence Medical Center-South Lyon

PRODUCTS/OPERATIONS

Selected Primary Services
Cancer clinical trials
Cardiac rehabilitation
Childbirth
Congenital heart disease clinic
Emergency
Oncology
Orthopedics
Senior services
Surgery
Women's health

COMPETITORS

Beaumont Health System	McLaren Health Care
Crittenton Hospital	Trinity Health (Novi)
Detroit Medical Center	University of Michigan
Henry Ford Health	Health System
System	

Income Statement — PBS

Income Statement   FYE: June 30

	REVENUE ($ mil.)	NET INCOME ($ mil.)	NET PROFIT MARGIN	EMPLOYEES
06/16	703	21	3.1%	4,700
06/15	654	25	3.9%	—
06/14	659	53	8.1%	—
06/11	706	27	3.9%	—
Annual Growth	(0.1%)	(4.9%)	—	—

2016 Year-End Financials

Return on assets: 0.6%
Return on equity: 3.1%
Current ratio: —

Cash ($ mil.): 3

PUBLIC BROADCASTING SERVICE

You might say these shows get a lot of public support. Public Broadcasting Service (PBS) is a non-profit organization that provides educational and public interest programming to more than 350 member public TV stations in the US. In addition to such programs as NOVA This Old House and Downton Abbey it provides related services such as distribution fundraising support and technology development. PBS gets its revenue from underwriting membership dues federal funding (including grants from the not-for-profit Corporation for Public Broadcasting) royalties license fees and product sales. The organization was founded in 1969 to provide cultural and educational programming.

Operations

PBS operates through more than 350 member public TV stations across the US.

Geographic Reach

PBS reaches almost 200 million people through television and nearly 28 million people online each month.

Strategy

While PBS — and its federal funding — regularly finds itself caught in the crossfire between liberal and conservative political groups supporters of the non-profit trumpet the benefits of publicly-funded television programming created to serve groups often overlooked by commercial broadcasters.

PBS' children's programming and news shows such as Frontline and PBS NewsHour (formerly The NewsHour with Jim Lehrer) are often touted as examples of how public broadcasting can fill voids left by the major networks.

The organization has also been looking to capitalize on new distribution channels to get its programming to the public. PBS sells its programs on DVD and through Apple's iTunes store. It has also ramped up its online video efforts.

EXECUTIVES

Svp And Cfo, Barbara L. Landes
Coo, Jonathan Barzilay
Svp And General Manager Pbs Digital, Ira Rubenstein
President Ceo And Director, Paula A. Kerger
Executive Director Pbs Foundation, Brian J. Reddington
Cto, Mario Vecchi
Chief Programming Executive And General Manager General Audience Programming, Beth Hoppe
Svp Marketing And Communications; General Manager Children's Programming, Lesli Rotenberg
Senior Vice President System Leadership, Juan Sepulveda
Senior Vice President Strategy And Operations, Jayme Swain
Vice President Station Services, Thomas Crockett
Vice President Education, Sara Schapiro
Vice President News And Public Affairs Pbs, Marie Nelson
Chairman, Donald A. (Don) Baer
Director, Tom Axtell
Auditors: BDO USA LLP BETHESDA MD

LOCATIONS

HQ: PUBLIC BROADCASTING SERVICE
2100 CRYSTAL DR STE 100, ARLINGTON, VA 222023784
Phone: 703 739-5000
Web: WWW.PBS.ORG

PRODUCTS/OPERATIONS

Selected Programming
Antiques Roadshow
Austin City Limits
Barney
Downton Abbey
Frontline
Juila Child: Lessons with Master Chefs
Live from Lincoln Center
Masterpiece Theatre
Mister Rogers' Neighborhood
MotorWeek
Mystery!
Nature
NOVA
NOW
P.O.V.
PBS NewsHour
Reading Rainbow
Sesame Street
Teletubbies
This Old House
Victory Garden
Washington Week
ZOOM

COMPETITORS

ABC Cable Networks	Discovery
ABC Inc.	HBO
AMC Networks	MTV Networks
BBC Worldwide	NBC
CBS	Scripps Networks
Current Media	Turner Broadcasting

HISTORICAL FINANCIALS
Company Type: Private

Income Statement   FYE: June 30

	REVENUE ($ mil.)	NET INCOME ($ mil.)	NET PROFIT MARGIN	EMPLOYEES
06/15	473	(46)	—	507
06/14	539	89	16.7%	—
06/10	505	28	5.6%	—
06/09	502	(80)	—	—
Annual Growth	(1.0%)	—	—	—

2015 Year-End Financials

Return on assets: 26.2%
Return on equity: (-9.9%)
Current ratio: 0.40

Cash ($ mil.): 39

PUBLIC CONSULTING GROUP, INC.

EXECUTIVES

Pres-Ceo, William S Mosakowski
V Pres-Prin, Tony McLean Brown
SEC-Prin, Stephen Skinner
Cfo- Treas, Dan Heaney
Asst SEC, Debra V Clark
Executive Officer, Justin M Cuyler
Information Specialist, Deepa Kadam
Compliance Staff, Jamie Demonbreun
Auditors: DICICCO GULMAN & COMPANY LLP

LOCATIONS

HQ: PUBLIC CONSULTING GROUP, INC.
148 STATE ST FL 10, BOSTON, MA 021092589
Phone: 617 426-2026
Web: WWW.PCGUS.COM

HISTORICAL FINANCIALS
Company Type: Private

Income Statement   FYE: June 30

	REVENUE ($ mil.)	NET INCOME ($ mil.)	NET PROFIT MARGIN	EMPLOYEES
06/17	379	19	5.2%	1,015
06/13	244	14	6.1%	—
06/12	193	8	4.3%	—
06/11	159	9	6.0%	—
Annual Growth	15.6%	13.0%	—	—

2017 Year-End Financials

Return on assets: 3.7%
Return on equity: 5.2%
Current ratio: 1.50

Cash ($ mil.): 106

PUBLIC HEALTH TRUST OF MIAMI DADE COUNTY

Jackson Memorial Hospital is the flagship facility of the Jackson Health System (JHS). It has roughly 2450 beds and offers a wide variety of services including burn treatment trauma pediatrics rehabilitation obstetrics and transplants. It is also a teaching facility for the University of Miami School of Medicine. JHS also operates Holtz Children's Hospital a rehabilitation hospital a mental health hospital primary and specialty care centers two long-term care nursing facilities six corrections health clinics and two community hospitals. Jackson Memorial Hospital and JHS are overseen by The Public Health Trust of Miami-Dade County.

Operations

Jackson Memorial Hospital's Ryder Trauma Center is Miami-Dade County's only adult and pediatric Level 1 trauma center.

JHS is its region's primary provider of charity care spending some $700 million annually to administer health care to Florida's uninsured and underinsured populations. Along with Jackson Memorial Hospital JHS delivers medical care to Floridians through the Jackson South Community Hospital (226 beds) and the Jackson North Medical Center (382 beds) which also serves as a teaching hospital for the Florida International University College of Medicine. Holtz Children's Hospital is one of the largest children's hospitals in the state and one of three in the US that specializes in pediatric multi-organ transplants.

Strategy

The system has acquired a site to build a new campus (Jackson West) that will include a children's outpatient center and a free-standing emergency department. JHS is also adding a new walk-in facility on South Beach. The company has invested in bringing new lab equipment and software to its facilities.

Other initiatives have included adjusting prices to be more competitive doing business with HMOs and drawing in more affluent patients through first-class offerings.

Company Background

The Public Health Trust was created in 1973 by the Board of County Commissioners as an independent governing body to provide leadership for joint planning between Jackson Health System the University of Miami Miller School of Medicine Miami-Dade County and other private and community organizations. Today the Public Health Trust is considered the hospital system's governing board picking its CEO and overseeing the system's operations.

EXECUTIVES

President And Ceo Jackson Health System, Carlos A. Migoya
Evp And Coo Jackson Health System, David R. Small
Chief Administrative Officer Jackson Memorial Hospital And Jackson Rehabilitation Hospital, Alex Contreras-Soto
Chief Administrative Officer Jackson Behavioral Health Hospital, R. John Repique
Medical Director, Nicolette Schreiber
Associate Vice President Human Resources Administration, Michelle Kligman
Vice President Managed Care, Karen Lang
Senior Vice President And Chief Operating Officer, Kathleen Mercogliano
Department Head, Walter Bradley
Medical Director, Diana Cardenas
Director Of Pharmacy, Paul Eger

LOCATIONS

HQ: PUBLIC HEALTH TRUST OF MIAMI DADE COUNTY
1611 NW 12TH AVE, MIAMI, FL 331361005
Phone: 305 585-1111
Web: WWW.JACKSONHEALTH.ORG

COMPETITORS

Baptist Health South Florida	Mount Sinai Medical Center of Florida
Broward Health	NCH Healthcare
Continucare	Plantation General
Encompass Health	South Broward Hospital District
HCA	
Larkin Community Hospital	South Miami Hospital
MJHHA	University of Miami Hospital
Miami Children's Hospital	

HISTORICAL FINANCIALS

Company Type: Private

Income Statement
FYE: September 30

	REVENUE ($ mil.)	NET INCOME ($ mil.)	NET PROFIT MARGIN	EMPLOYEES
09/17	1,160	184	15.9%	11,000
09/15*	883	200	22.7%	—
06/05	0	0	—	—
09/03	960	(26)	—	—
Annual Growth	1.4%	—	—	—

*Fiscal year change

2017 Year-End Financials

Return on assets: 11.9%   Cash ($ mil.): 304
Return on equity: 15.9%
Current ratio: 0.50

PUBLIC HOSPITAL DISTRICT 1 OF KING COUNTY

EXECUTIVES

Admin-Ceo, Richard D Roodman
Cfo, Michael Bernstein
Comm, Carole Anderson
Coo, Paul Hayes
Doctor, Olga V Khait-Palant
Doctor, Daniel Letinsky
Doctor, Shreeketa M Mehta
Internal Medicine Practitioner, Amit Joshi
Anesthesiology, Andrew O Smith
Doctor, Joyce V Gauthier
Anesthesiology, Sidney W Postma
Auditors: KPMG LLP SEATTLE WASHINGTON

LOCATIONS

HQ: PUBLIC HOSPITAL DISTRICT 1 OF KING COUNTY
400 S 43RD ST, RENTON, WA 980555714
Phone: 425 228-3440
Web: WWW.VALLEYMED.ORG

HISTORICAL FINANCIALS

Company Type: Private

Income Statement
FYE: June 30

	REVENUE ($ mil.)	NET INCOME ($ mil.)	NET PROFIT MARGIN	EMPLOYEES
06/18	653	40	6.2%	2,700
06/16*	519	11	2.2%	—
12/07	327	25	7.8%	—
Annual Growth	7.1%	4.7%	—	—

*Fiscal year change

2018 Year-End Financials

Return on assets: 3.1%   Cash ($ mil.): 48
Return on equity: 6.2%
Current ratio: 1.00

PUBLIC HOSPITAL DISTRICT 1 SKAGIT COUNTY

EXECUTIVES

Pres-Ceo, Brian Ivie
Cfo, Tom Litaker
Information Technology Manager, Cherrayl Harrsch
Director of Information Techno, Doug Reilly
Manager, Jessica Samora
Chief Marketing Officer, Kathleen Abhold
Materials Director, Bill Thomas
Technician, Dave Slater
Information Technology/Interne, Kristin Eldridge
Manager, Debbie Snyder
Manager, Sharon Hale
Auditors: MOSS ADAMS LLP EVERETT WASHI

LOCATIONS

HQ: PUBLIC HOSPITAL DISTRICT 1 SKAGIT COUNTY
1415 E KINCAID ST, MOUNT VERNON, WA 982744126
Phone: 360 424-4111
Web: WWW.SKAGITVALLEYHOSPITAL.ORG

HISTORICAL FINANCIALS

Company Type: Private

Income Statement
FYE: December 31

	REVENUE ($ mil.)	NET INCOME ($ mil.)	NET PROFIT MARGIN	EMPLOYEES
12/17	373	(0)	—	2,000
12/16	303	(3)	—	—
12/11	216	4	2.3%	—
12/10	186	0	0.4%	—
Annual Growth	10.4%	—	—	—

2017 Year-End Financials

Return on assets: 4.8%   Cash ($ mil.): 1
Return on equity: (-0.1%)
Current ratio: 0.90

PUBLIC UTILITY DISTRICT 1 OF CLARK COUNTY

EXECUTIVES

Vice President, Nancy Barnes
Auditors: MOSS ADAMS LLP PORTLAND ORE

LOCATIONS

HQ: PUBLIC UTILITY DISTRICT 1 OF CLARK COUNTY
1200 FORT VANCOUVER WAY, VANCOUVER, WA 986633527
Phone: 360 992-3000
Web: WWW.CLARKPUBLICUTILITIES.COM

COMPETITORS

PacifiCorp	Puget Energy
Portland General Electric	

Income Statement   FYE: December 31

	REVENUE ($ mil.)	NET INCOME ($ mil.)	NET PROFIT MARGIN	EMPLOYEES
12/17	502	45	9.1%	325
12/16	486	35	7.3%	—
12/05	463	2	0.5%	—
12/04	423	12	3.1%	—
Annual Growth	1.3%	10.2%	—	—

2017 Year-End Financials
Return on assets: 7.3%
Return on equity: 9.1%
Current ratio: 2.70
Cash ($ mil.): 270

PUBLIC UTILITY DISTRICT 1 OF SNOHOMISH COUNTY

Keeping its customers satisfied is priority No. 1 at Public Utility District No. 1 of Snohomish County Washington (Snohomish County PUD) which distributes electricity to 332516 commercial industrial and residential customers in Washington State. The utility the largest PUD in the state with a 2200 sq. ml. service area purchases most of its power supply from third parties (Bonneville Power Administration and other producers. It operates hydroelectric and fossil-fueled power plants and participates in wholesale power transactions to balance its supply load. Snohomish County PUD also serves more than 20000 water utility customers in a 205 sq. ml. service territory via about 375 miles of pipe.

Operations
Snohomish County PUD's operations consist of three systems: the Electric System the Generation System and the Water System.

The Electric System is made up of electric transmission and distribution system.

The Generation System is composed of the company's Jackson Hydroelectric Project and two smaller hydroelectric projects.

The Water System is made up of water distribution system.

Sales and Marketing
The PUD serves three categories of customers: Residential (301639) Commercial (30524) Industrial (76) and other (street lighting temporary lighting etc. - 277).

The company offers a wide range of energy-efficiency solutions for business customers.

Financial Performance
In 2014 the PUD's revenues grew by 3% due to an increase in retail sales as a result of a general and a power contract pass-through rate increase in 2013 and wholesale sales driven by a rise in Megawatt-Hours sold.

The company's net income decreased by 19% due to an increase in operating expenses driven by higher volume of power purchases from the wholesale power market and increased operations expenses due to higher transmission and ancillary costs and costs related to the PUD's effort to implement a new enterprise resource planning system.

In fiscal 2014 the company's operating cash inflow decreased by 10% due to lower net income and changes in working capital.

Strategy
To meet federal and state goals for reducing greenhouse gases the utility is exploring a range of green energy options conservation measures and new power generation activities including geothermal tidal wind and solar power.

In 2015 the PUD's solar program increased its total contribution to 3.7 MW an almost 150% increase over the previous year.

In 2014 the company spent $110 million on electric system capital expenditures up from $94 million in 2013. The company increased the capital programs over the past two years to maintain expand and enhance its electric distribution system.

Company Background
In 2013 solar energy capacity stood at two MW enough to serve 170 homes. More than 350 PUD customers cover part of their electricity needs through their own solar energy units. The PUD's Solar Express program offers financial incentives and technical assistance for solar photovoltaic and solar hot water systems.

In 2012 the company amended a power contract with Hampton Lumber (a fuel supplier since 2007) that will boost the level of biomass energy the utility will receive from the lumber company's Darrington plant. The new agreement will allow Snohomish County PUD to receive up to 2.5 MW of energy from Hampton Lumber enough energy to power about 2000 homes.

Supported by $15.8 million in matching federal stimulus dollars in 2011 Snohomish County PUD completed its first major project as part of a long-term upgrade of its electric grid with smart grid technology. The upgrade includes the installation of more than 160 miles of fiber optic cable and connecting them to 62 substations two radio sites and other utility buildings.

The company began providing water utility service to parts of Snohomish County in 1946. Public Utility District No. 1 of Snohomish County began operating as power utility in 1949 providing publicly owned electric and water utility service to the residents of Snohomish County and Camano Island.

EXECUTIVES

President Send An, Toni Olson
General Manager, Steve Klein
Assistant General Manager Water Resources Division, Kim Moore
Chief Information Officer, Benjamin Beberness
Secretary Of The Board Of Commissioners, Kathleen (Kathy) Vaughn
Auditors: BAKER TILLY MADISON WI

LOCATIONS

HQ: PUBLIC UTILITY DISTRICT 1 OF SNOHOMISH COUNTY
2320 CALIFORNIA ST, EVERETT, WA 982013750
Phone: 425 257-9288
Web: WWW.SNOPUD.COM

PRODUCTS/OPERATIONS

2014 Sales

	$ mil.	% of total
Retail sales	554	86
Wholesale sales	59	9
Other	30	5
Total	**645**	**100**

COMPETITORS

Avista
Chelan County PUD
Grant County Public Utility District
Public Utility District No. 1 of Clark County
Puget Energy
Tacoma Public Utilities

Income Statement   FYE: December 31

	REVENUE ($ mil.)	NET INCOME ($ mil.)	NET PROFIT MARGIN	EMPLOYEES
12/17	686	75	11.1%	879
12/16	657	60	9.2%	—
12/15	626	52	8.3%	—
12/14	645	56	8.7%	—
Annual Growth	2.1%	10.6%	—	—

PUBLIC UTILITY DISTRICT NO. 1 OF CHELAN COUNTY

It's Number One! Public Utility District No. 1 of Chelan County Washington (Chelan County PUD) provides power and water to residents of the county located in the middle of the Evergreen State. The utility operates three hydroelectric generation facilities on or near the Columbia River that have a combined capacity of 1988 MW. About 30% of the district's electricity goes to its more than 48000 residential commercial and industrial customers; the rest is sold wholesale to other utilities operating in the northwestern US. Chelan County PUD also provides water and wastewater services to about 5900 customers. The company's major power purchasers serve 7 million homes and businesses in the Northwest.

Operations
Chelan County PUD has 25000 power poles which support 1950 miles of electric line. Residential power customers pay about 3.2 cents a kilowatt hour and use about 48% of the local load.

The PUD also provides telecommunication services and has about 10700 fiber-optic customer connections.

In addition it has built 14 parks covering more than 700 acres. These parks welcome more than 3 million visitors each year.

Financial Performance
The company's revenues grew by 3% to $624.8 million in 2013 as a result of slightly higher customer consumption of power an Electric System 2% general rate increase effective and a 3% rate increase to pass-through a wholesale power cost increase in 2013 from Bonneville Power Administration (the PUD's largest power provider).

In 2013 Chelan County PUD's net income increased by 8% to $69 million (from $63.7 million in 2012) primarily due to higher sales and lower interest charges.

The PUD's operating cash inflow increased to $127 million in 2013 from $115.7 million in 2012 due to an increase in cash received from customers.

Strategy
The company's strategic plan calls for it to continue to reduce debt and maintain low rates and reliable service by maintaining and upgrading PUD assets and by increasing conservation and green energy activities. Complementing its core power business the utility is developing a distinct green edge. In addition to its hydro-power facilities it has solar panels installed at more than 30 locations including schools and nonprofit agencies and pro-

motes wind energy as well. The PUD is also responsible for 14 parks.

In 2013 Chelan County PUD took four of the 11 generating units at Rocky Reach Dam out of service after discovering one of the units had a deep crack in a stainless steel rod that delivers oil to a servo motor. After repairs the units are planned to be brought back into service during 2014 with long-term repairs to be completed by the end of 2016. A unique bypass system installed at the Rocky Reach Hydro Project collects young salmon and steelhead on the upstream side of the dam and channels them past the dam through a large pipe.

Company Background
Chelan County PUD was established in 1936 as part of a nationwide drive to bring affordable electricity to rural areas and began providing electric service in 1947.

EXECUTIVES

Gen Mgr, John Janney
Comm, Carnan Bergren
General Counsel, Carol Wardell
Director of Finance, Debra Litchfield
Production Team Member, Jim Gray

LOCATIONS

HQ: PUBLIC UTILITY DISTRICT NO. 1 OF CHELAN
COUNTY
327 N WENATCHEE AVE, WENATCHEE, WA
988012011
Phone: 509 663-8121
Web: WWW.CHELANPUD.ORG

PRODUCTS/OPERATIONS

Selected Services
Electric Services
Community Services
Emerson Acres Line Extension Backbone Project
Establish a New Service
Services for Business
Start or Stop Service
Wastewater Services
New Wastewater Service Application
Utility Service Regulations
Wastewater Availability Building Permit
Wastewater Rates
Water/Wastewater Service Connection Guide
Water Services
Automated Meter Reading
Cold-Weather Tips
Service for Snowbirds
Starting a New Water Service
Utility Service Regulations
Water Leaks
Water Rates
Water Standard Details
Water Use Efficiency Rule

COMPETITORS

Avista   Puget Energy
 PacifiCorp

HISTORICAL FINANCIALS
Company Type: Private

Income Statement   FYE: December 31

	REVENUE ($ mil.)	NET INCOME ($ mil.)	NET PROFIT MARGIN	EMPLOYEES
12/17	372	104	28.2%	841
12/16	362	95	26.4%	—
Annual Growth	2.8%	9.7%	—	—

2017 Year-End Financials
Return on assets: 12.5%   Cash ($ mil.): 20
Return on equity: 28.2%
Current ratio: 0.40

PUBLIX SUPER MARKETS, INC.

Publix Super Markets tops the list of privately owned grocery operators in the US. By emphasizing service and a family-friendly image over price Publix has outgrown and outperformed its regional rivals. Some two-thirds of its nearly 1200 stores are in Florida but it also operates in half a dozen other southeastern states. Publix makes some of its own bakery deli dairy goods and fresh prepared foods at its own manufacturing plants in Florida and Georgia. Many stores also house pharmacies and banks. Founder George Jenkins began offering stock to Publix employees in 1930; employees own more than a quarter of the company.

Operations
Publix stores sell grocery products (dairy produce deli baker meat and seafood) health and beauty care products general merchandise pharmacy products flowers and other products and services. Grocery activities account for some 85% of sales.

Geographic Reach
Publix has nearly 1200 supermarkets in Florida (about two-thirds of total) and Georgia (more than 15% of total) as well as Alabama South Carolina Tennessee North Carolina and Virginia.

It restocks store shelves from nine distribution centers — seven in Florida and one each in Georgia and Alabama. The grocer also operates half a dozen dairy bakery and deli facilities four in Florida and two in Georgia.

Financial Performance
Publix has shown solid sales growth over the past five years as it continues to expand and open new stores across the Southeast. Its revenue has risen some 20% since 2013. With profit margins higher than many (if not all) of its grocery competitors the company has also seen increases in its net income in recent years.

In 2017 Publix reported revenue of $34.8 billion up about 1.5% from the prior year. New store openings powered the growth along with a 1.7% increase in comparable-store sales which was helped by customers' stocking up and replenishing before and after Hurricane Irma hit Florida. This was more than enough to offset an additional week of operation in 2016 which was a 53-week fiscal year.

As the dominant grocer in its primary market Florida Publix regularly reports net profit margins of between 5.5%-6% much higher than other super market chains (Kroger for example is in the 1.5%-2% range). In 2017 it had net earnings of $2.3 billion up from $2 billion in 2016. In addition to the increased revenue net earnings were boosted some $224 million by the Tax Cut and Jobs Act of 2017.

Cash at the end of 2017 was $580 million an increase of about $140 million from the prior year. Cash from operations contributed $3.6 billion to the coffers while investing and financing activities used some $3.45 million mainly for expenditures used in new and remodeled stores and for dividends and stock buybacks.

Strategy
Publix's growth strategy is based on investing in its stores and enhancing its customer service.

It plans to spend more than $1.5 billion in 2018 to open new stores remodel existing stores and increase ownership of its store portfolio. The company opened 44 stores in 2017 including its first locations in Virginia. At year's end it had about 35 stores under construction. In addition Publix re-

modeled more than 130 locations in 2017. It also continues to invest in its real estate portfolio. At the end of 2017 the company owned nearly a third of its stores up from 29% in 2016 and 11% in 2007.

Publix is also focused on keeping up with customer demand for delivery and other advanced services. It began working with grocery delivery firm Instacart in 2016 and currently offers home delivery in more than 90% of its operating area. The company is also testing curbside pickup and its online ordering platform has been expanded with smokehouse meats fried chicken and other items. It has also enhanced its pharmacy offerings through a partnership with BayCare Health System and serves pharmacy patients with new web and mobile applications.

Lastly Publix has announced plans to relaunch its GreenWise Market concept in select locations in 2018. GreenWise Market targets the health-conscious consumer with specialty natural and organic selections.

EXECUTIVES

Evp And Cfo, David P. Phillips, age 58, $1,051,090 total compensation
General Counsel And Secretary, John A. Attaway, age 59, $690,310 total compensation
Svp, David E. Bornmann, age 60, $488,300 total compensation
President Ceo And Director, Randall T. (Todd) Jones, age 55, $1,688,750 total compensation
Svp And Cio, Laurie Z. Douglas, age 54, $890,255 total compensation
Manager Government Relations, Shane Kunze
Vice Chairman, Hoyt R. (Barney) Barnett, age 75
Chairman, William E. (Ed) Crenshaw, age 67

LOCATIONS

HQ: PUBLIX SUPER MARKETS, INC.
3300 PUBLIX CORP PKWY, LAKELAND, FL
338113311
Phone: 863 688-1188
Web: WWW.PUBLIX.COM

2017 Supermarkets

	No.
Florida	779
Georgia	186
Alabama	65
South Carolina	58
Tennessee	41
North Carolina	30
Virginia	8
Total	**1,167**

PRODUCTS/OPERATIONS

2017 Sales

	% of total
Grocery	84
Other	16
Total	**100**

Selected Supermarket Departments
Bakery
Dairy
Deli
Floral
Groceries
Health and beauty care
Meat
Pharmacy
Produce
Seafood
Foods Processed
Baked goods
Dairy products
Deli items

COMPETITORS

ALDI   Kroger
 ALDI   Rite Aid

CVS	Rite Aid
CVS	Sedano's
Costco Wholesale	Sedano's
Costco Wholesale	Southeastern Grocers
Food Lion	Southeastern Grocers
Food Lion	The Pantry
IGA	The Pantry
IGA	Wal-Mart
Ingles Markets	Wal-Mart
Ingles Markets	Walgreen
Kmart	Walgreen
Kmart	Whole Foods
Kroger	Whole Foods

HISTORICAL FINANCIALS

Company Type: Private

Income Statement   FYE: December 31

	REVENUE ($ mil.)	NET INCOME ($ mil.)	NET PROFIT MARGIN	EMPLOYEES
12/16	34,274	2,025	5.9%	193,000
12/15	32,618	1,965	6.0%	—
12/14	30,802	1,735	5.6%	—
12/12	27,706	1,552	5.6%	—
Annual Growth	5.5%	6.9%	—	—

2016 Year-End Financials

Return on assets: 4.7%   Cash ($ mil.): 438
Return on equity: 5.9%
Current ratio: 0.40

PURDUE UNIVERSITY

Purdue University enrolls more than 70000 undergraduate graduate and continuing education students at its flagship West Lafayette campus four regional campuses and 10 satellite College of Technology locations. The university offers undergraduate and graduate programs from about a dozen colleges including agriculture education nursing veterinary medicine and family sciences; its College of Technology provides industrial courses (applicable towards associate's or bachelor's degrees) in conjunction with Indiana communities. The student-faculty ratio is 12:1. Through the newly established Purdue University Global (formerly Kaplan University) the institution provides coursework for another 30000 students.

Operations

Purdue confers undergraduate degrees in more than 200 disciplines; it also offers about 70 graduate programs. The school is noted for its aviation technology and aeronautical engineering programs; about two dozen of its graduates have gone on to become astronauts (including Neil Armstrong). Purdue is also recognized for its agriculture and business administration programs. Additionally it is known as a research institution operating more than 400 research laboratories focused on a full spectrum of areas from agriculture and education to science and veterinary medicine.

The school's Global arm established in 2018 to coincide with the acquisition of Kaplan University grants associate's and bachelor's degrees in areas including business information technology nursing and criminal justice.

There are a total of 138 university-approved centers and institutes at Purdue.

Financial Performance

Purdue's primary sources of income include student tuition and fees. It also attracts more than $450 million in research funding each year from a variety of sources including government agencies foundations and corporate partners.

In 2017 revenue increased 3% to crest the $1.5 billion-mark for the first time in a couple of years. The increase was mostly in tuition and fees thanks to higher enrollment at the West Lafayette campus and increase in summer enrolment and modest increases at its regional campuses.

Net income increased 62% to $172.0 million as the university's endowment fund performed strongly in the year up 11% to $750 million. The increase more than compensated for an increase in operating loss. As a result of the net profit Purdue's net position grew to $4.6 billion.

The institute recorded a cash outflow from operations of $420.7 million an increase of 20% on the previous year.

Mergers and Acquisitions

Purdue sent shockwaves in the higher education community in 2017 when it agreed to buy the for-profit institution Kaplan University. The purchase which closed in 2018 is intended to bring education to a broader range of students as well as extend Purdue's reach in adult and online education. As part of the move Purdue has established Purdue Global a new public university comprising Kaplan's 15 campuses and online platforms. While for-profit institutions such as Kaplan come with heightened public scrutiny Purdue believes the purchase will benefit millions of older Americans who have not had access to traditional higher education.

Company Background

Purdue was founded in 1869 and named for local businessman John Purdue who donated $150000 toward its establishment. In 1895 Purdue president James Smart proposed an intercollegiate athletics conference the Big Ten. Purdue remains part of the Big Ten Conference which is now the oldest Division I college athletic conference in the US (though it now consists of 12 universities instead of 10).

EXECUTIVES

Chancellor Purdue University Indianapolis, Charles R. Bantz
Chancellor Purdue University North Central, James B. Dworkin, age 69
Vp Research, Richard O. Buckius
Cfo And Treasurer, William E. (Bill) Sullivan, age 63
President And Ceo, Mitchell E. (Mitch) Daniels
Vp Information Technology And Cio, William G. (Gerry) McCartney
Chancellor Purdue University Fort Wayne, Vicky L. Carwein
Chancellor Purdue Calumet, Thomas L Keon
Executive Vice President For Research And Partnerships, Suresh Garimella
Vice President, Sally F Mason
Vice President Business Development, June Foster
Vice President Production, Todd Wetzel
Vice President Technology, Susan Aufderheide
Executive Vice President Technology, Carl Wood
Vice President Of Finance And Human Resources, Lisa Stein
Senior Vice President For Advancement, Jackie Butram
Associate Vice President Governmental Relations, Timothy Sanders
Assistant Vice President Finance And Human Resources Manger, Terri Duncan
Vice President For Research Dean Of The Graduate School, Gary E Isom
Executive Vice President, Paul W Brennan
Trustee, Thomas E. Spurgeon
Secretary, Helen Terrell
Secretary, Laura Warner
Secretary, Denise Riley
Secretary, Karen Clymer
Secretary, Jean Ehrmann
Secretary, Roslynn A Bol
Secretary, Annette Bosworth-Deluca
Secretary, Leesa Houser
Secretary, Pam Chase
Secretary, Mary Wildman
Secretary, Mary Vandeveer
Secretary, Lori Carte
Secretary V, Rebeka Frakes
Secretary Receptionist, Susan Mccreery
Treasurer, Brandy Cavanagh
Secretary, Jill Vigar
Treasurer, Carol Holmes
Secretary, Liz Brundige
Treasurer, Jill Dorff
Treasurer, Jean Kendall
Treasurer, Wendy Cuiksa
Secretary, Hayley Chan
Auditors: PAUL D JOYCE CPA INDIANAPOL

LOCATIONS

HQ: PURDUE UNIVERSITY
401 S GRANT ST, WEST LAFAYETTE, IN 479072024
Phone: 765 494-8000
Web: WWW.PURDUESPORTS.COM

Selected Indiana Locations

Main Campus (West Lafayette)
Regional Campuses
　Indiana University-Purdue University Indianapolis (IUPUI Indianapolis)
　Indiana University-Purdue University Fort Wayne (IPFW Fort Wayne)
　Purdue Calumet (Hammond)
　Purdue North Central (PNC Westville)
College of Technology locations
　Anderson
　Columbus
　Greensburg
　Indianapolis
　Kokomo
　Lafayette
　New Albany
　Richmond
　South Bend/Elkhart
　Vincennes

PRODUCTS/OPERATIONS

2013 Sales

	% of total
Tuition and fees	50
Grants and contracts	25
Auxiliary enterprises	17
Other operating revenues	8
Total	**100**

Selected Schools

College of Agriculture
College of Education
College of Engineering
College of Health and Human Sciences
College of Liberal Arts
Krannert School of Management
College of Pharmacy Nursing and Health Sciences
College of Science
College of Technology
School of Veterinary Medicine
The Graduate School

HISTORICAL FINANCIALS

Company Type: Private

Income Statement   FYE: June 30

	REVENUE ($ mil.)	NET INCOME ($ mil.)	NET PROFIT MARGIN	EMPLOYEES
06/17	1,529	172	11.3%	18,715
06/13	1,450	227	15.7%	—
06/12	1,429	136	9.5%	—
06/07	1,038	302	29.1%	—
Annual Growth	3.9%	(5.5%)	—	—

2017 Year-End Financials

Return on assets: 7.8%   Cash ($ mil.): 282
Return on equity: 11.3%
Current ratio: 1.10

PUYALLUP SCHOOL DISTRICT

EXECUTIVES

Supt, Tim Yeomans
Supt, Tony Apostle
Asst Supt, Debra Aungst
Building and Grounds Director, Mario Casello
Maintenance Staff, Bryan Rose
Maintenance Staff, Douglas Scott
Auditors: PAT MCCARTHY STATE AUDITOR O

LOCATIONS

HQ: PUYALLUP SCHOOL DISTRICT
302 2ND ST SE, PUYALLUP, WA 983723220
Phone: 253 840-8971
Web: WWW.PUYALLUP.K12.WA.US

HISTORICAL FINANCIALS

Company Type: Private

Income Statement — FYE: August 31

	REVENUE ($ mil.)	NET INCOME ($ mil.)	NET PROFIT MARGIN	EMPLOYEES
08/17	295	209	70.8%	3,000
08/16	282	94	33.3%	—
08/15	252	10	4.2%	—
08/14	233	(5)	—	—
Annual Growth	8.3%	—	—	—

2017 Year-End Financials
Return on assets: 4.0%   Cash ($ mil.): 9
Return on equity: 70.8%
Current ratio: 0.70

QUINNIPIAC UNIVERSITY

At Quinnipiac University the first thing you may have to learn is how to pronounce it (for the record it's KWIN-uh-pe-ack). The private university offers a variety of liberal arts undergraduate programs as well as graduate programs in selected professional fields (business education health sciences communications arts and sciences nursing and law) to some 9000 students with a student-to-faculty ration of 16 to 1. It often appears on lists of top colleges including those published by U.S. News & World Report. The university known to political junkies and others for its polling operation includes eight schools and colleges across three Connecticut campuses (Mount Carmel York Hill and North Haven).

Operations
Quinnipiac offers more than 50 undergraduate majors and more than 20 graduate programs. For fiscal year 2015-2016 its tuition and fees are $42270.

Geographic Reach
The school's York Hill campus is home to the TD Bank Sports Center; its North Haven campus houses the Center for Medicine Nursing and Health Sciences which includes the School of Health Sciences the Frank H. Netter MD School of Medicine and the School of Nursing.

Strategy
In 2014 Quinnipiac launched an online graduate business program as well as a master's program in sports journalism. With the 2013 opening of the Frank H. Netter MD School of Medicine the university became one of fewer than 100 with both a law school and a medical school on campus.

Company Background
Originally named the Connecticut College of Commerce the school was founded in 1929 by Samuel W. Tator as a small business college awarding associate's degrees. The college changed its name in 1951 to Quinnipiac College commemorating the early Indian settlers who made their home in and around the New Haven Connecticut harbor area.

EXECUTIVES

Chm, Terry W Goodwim
President, John L Lahey
Vice President, Lucille Marottolo
Associate Vp-Chief Diversity O, Don C Sawyer III
Occupational Specia, Carolyn Brown
Occupational Specia, Iram Azam
Occupational Specia, Karen Crainich
Occupational Specia, Shannon Depodesta
Payroll Staff, Lynn Ruquist
Scientist, Jillian Giguere
Scientist, Lisa Cuchara

LOCATIONS

HQ: QUINNIPIAC UNIVERSITY
275 MOUNT CARMEL AVE, HAMDEN, CT 065181908
Phone: 203 582-8200
Web: WWW.QUINNIPIAC.EDU

PRODUCTS/OPERATIONS

Selected Schools
College of Arts and Sciences
Schools of Business and Engineering
School of Communications
School of Education
School of Law
School of Health Sciences
School of Nursing

HISTORICAL FINANCIALS

Company Type: Private

Income Statement — FYE: June 30

	REVENUE ($ mil.)	NET INCOME ($ mil.)	NET PROFIT MARGIN	EMPLOYEES
06/17	343	114	33.2%	900
06/15	416	29	7.1%	—
06/13	376	45	12.2%	—
06/10	290	45	15.6%	—
Annual Growth	2.4%	14.1%	—	—

2017 Year-End Financials
Return on assets: 6.3%   Cash ($ mil.): 6
Return on equity: 33.2%
Current ratio: —

R. M. PARKS, INC.

EXECUTIVES

Pres, R M Parks
V Pres, Tim Callison
SEC-Treas, Marilyn Callison
Information Technology Manager, Richard Tipton
Sales Staff, Bobby Rogers
Sales Staff, Bryan Holmes
Auditors: GUMBINER SAVETT INC SANTA MO

LOCATIONS

HQ: R. M. PARKS, INC.
1061 N MAIN ST, PORTERVILLE, CA 932571686
Phone: 559 784-2384
Web: WWW.RMPARKSINC.COM

HISTORICAL FINANCIALS

Company Type: Private

Income Statement — FYE: October 31

	REVENUE ($ mil.)	NET INCOME ($ mil.)	NET PROFIT MARGIN	EMPLOYEES
10/17	477	(0)	—	4
10/16	448	0	0.2%	—
10/15	534	0	0.2%	—
10/14	612	0	0.0%	—
Annual Growth	(8.0%)	—	—	—

2017 Year-End Financials
Return on assets: 1.9%   Cash ($ mil.): —
Return on equity: (-0.1%)
Current ratio: 0.50

R.C. WILLEY HOME FURNISHINGS

R.C. Willey Home Furnishings does its best to be top dog. The company drives traffic by giving away some 600000 hot dogs a year at about a dozen stores in Utah Nevada California and Idaho. Despite Sunday store closures and operations in only four states R.C. Willey is one of the nation's largest furniture retailers. It sells furniture (La-Z-Boy Flexsteel) appliances (GE Maytag) electronics (Sony Panasonic) and flooring. The company also sells mattresses (Serta Spring Air Simmons). In 1932 Rufus Call (R.C.) Willey sold appliances door-to-door; today the company he founded is run by his son-in-law chairman Bill Child and grandsons. Berkshire Hathaway purchased the company in 1995.

Operations
R.C. Willey is part of Berkshire Hathaway's home furnishings business alongside Nebraska Furniture Mart Star Furniture and Jordan's Furniture.

The Salt Lake City Utah-based company boasts some 1.7 million sq. ft. of retail space across its nearly a dozen retail stores a pair of retail clearance facilities and three distribution centers to support its entire operation. R.C. Willey is known for its large selection and reliable brand names. It carries General Electric Whirlpool LG Maytag Amana KitchenAid Broyhill Flexsteel Lane Natuzzi AICO Pluaski Schnadi Sony Mitsubishi Toshiba Samsung Serta Spring Air Simmons and Tempur Sealy.

Geographic Reach
R.C. Willey operates its furniture business nationwide primarily in a handful of states.

Sales and Marketing
A plus to R.C. Willey Home Furnishings customers the company offers financing through its R.C. Willey Credit Card.

EXECUTIVES

President, Jeffrey S. (Jeff) Child
Cfo, Curtis Child
Vice President Of Marketing, Jack De Mill
Chairman, William H. (Bill) Child

LOCATIONS

HQ: R.C. WILLEY HOME FURNISHINGS
2301 S 300 W, SALT LAKE CITY, UT 841152525
Phone: 801 461-3900
Web: WWW.RCWILLEY.COM

PRODUCTS/OPERATIONS

Selected Products
Appliances
Electronics
Fitness
Flooring
Furniture
Mattresses

COMPETITORS

Abbey Carpet	J. C. Penney Company
Best Buy	La-Z-Boy
Costco Wholesale	Lowe's
Ethan Allen	Pier 1 Imports
Fry's Electronics	RadioShack
Home Depot	Williams-Sonoma

HISTORICAL FINANCIALS

Company Type: Private

Income Statement				FYE: December 31
	REVENUE ($ mil.)	NET INCOME ($ mil.)	NET PROFIT MARGIN	EMPLOYEES
12/17	807	19	2.4%	2,700
12/16	800	26	3.3%	—
12/14	712	17	2.4%	—
12/13	664	15	2.3%	—
Annual Growth	5.0%	6.3%	—	—

2017 Year-End Financials
Return on assets: 6.2%
Return on equity: 2.4%
Current ratio: 2.70
Cash ($ mil.): 62

R.S. HUGHES COMPANY, INC.

EXECUTIVES

Pres-Ceo, Peter Biocini
Chb, Robert McCollum
Cfo, Gail Zimmerman
V Pres, Joseph Vargas
Secretary, Ken McCormick
V Pres-E Strategy, Michael Page
Business Manager, Stan Basnett
Controller, Thomas Smith
Auditors: MOSS ADAMS LLP CAMPBELL CAL

LOCATIONS

HQ: R.S. HUGHES COMPANY, INC.
1162 SONORA CT, SUNNYVALE, CA 940865378
Phone: 408 739-3211
Web: WWW.SAUNDERSCORP.COM

PRODUCTS/OPERATIONS

Selected Products
Adhesives
Abrasive power tools
Aerosol paints and lubricants
Coatings
Labels
Printers
Sealants
Tapes

COMPETITORS

DXP Enterprises	W.W. Grainger
HD Supply	
Industrial	
Distribution Group	

HISTORICAL FINANCIALS

Company Type: Private

Income Statement				FYE: October 1
	REVENUE ($ mil.)	NET INCOME ($ mil.)	NET PROFIT MARGIN	EMPLOYEES
10/17	351	17	4.9%	505
10/16*	329	16	5.0%	—
09/15	323	16	5.1%	—
09/14	302	15	5.1%	—
Annual Growth	5.2%	3.5%	—	—

*Fiscal year change

2017 Year-End Financials
Return on assets: 4.1%
Return on equity: 4.9%
Current ratio: 2.90
Cash ($ mil.): 12

RACINE UNIFIED SCHOOL DISTRICT

EXECUTIVES

Supt, Ann Laing
Supt, Jim Shaw
Cfo, Dave Hazen
Supt, Dr Lolli Haws
Academic Advisor, Angelica Valdivia
Coordinator, Doris Zimmerman
Staff, Irene Guardiola
Teacher, Aaron Eick
Coordinator, Elizabeth Sacher
Staff, Nicole Riendeau
Staff, Susan Ervin

LOCATIONS

HQ: RACINE UNIFIED SCHOOL DISTRICT
3109 MOUNT PLEASANT ST, RACINE, WI 534041511
Phone: 262 635-5600
Web: WWW.RACINE.K12.WI.US

HISTORICAL FINANCIALS

Company Type: Private

Income Statement				FYE: June 30
	REVENUE ($ mil.)	NET INCOME ($ mil.)	NET PROFIT MARGIN	EMPLOYEES
06/17	291	6	2.3%	2,500
06/16	283	0	0.3%	—
06/06	207	(1)	—	—
06/05	0	0	—	—
Annual Growth	—	—	—	—

RADY CHILDREN'S HOSPITAL AND HEALTH CENTER

EXECUTIVES

Pres-Ceo, Donald B Kearns
Cmo, Irvin A Kaufman
Exec Vice President, Margareta E Norton
Sr V Pres-Cfo, Roger G Roux
Coo, Nicholas Holmes
Network Administrator, Jim Ward
Analyst, Benjelyn Barrera
Coordinator, Giuseppe Principato
Scientist, Andrea Hazen
Supervisor, Ruth Felix
Coordinator, Carrie Arii
Auditors: LB KPMG LLP LOS ANGELES CA

LOCATIONS

HQ: RADY CHILDREN'S HOSPITAL AND HEALTH
CENTER
3020 CHILDRENS WAY, SAN DIEGO, CA 921234223
Phone: 858 576-1700
Web: WWW.RCHSD.ORG

HISTORICAL FINANCIALS

Company Type: Private

Income Statement				FYE: June 30
	REVENUE ($ mil.)	NET INCOME ($ mil.)	NET PROFIT MARGIN	EMPLOYEES
06/18	1,243	205	16.5%	4,033
06/17	1,092	220	20.2%	—
06/15	13	13	98.7%	—
06/14	3	2	87.7%	—
Annual Growth	338.9%	189.2%	—	—

2018 Year-End Financials
Return on assets: 7.9%
Return on equity: 16.5%
Current ratio: 0.80
Cash ($ mil.): 44

RADY CHILDREN'S HOSPITAL-SAN DIEGO

Rady Children's Hospital-San Diego handles the big injuries of pint-sized patients. Serving as the region's only pediatric trauma center the nonprofit hospital boasts more than 520 beds. As part of its services Rady Children's Hospital-San Diego offers comprehensive pediatric care including surgical services convalescent care a neonatal intensive care unit and orthopedic services. Across its service area the hospital also operates about 25 satellite centers that provide such primary and specialized care services as physical therapy and hearing diagnostics. Rady Children's Hospital a teaching hospital affiliated with the University of California San Diego Medical School was founded in 1954.

Operations

Rady Children's operates its own 36-bed emergency department — The Sam S. and Rose Stein Emergency Care Center — that each day sees up to 300 patients. It is the only regional emergency center solely dedicated and equipped to care for children. The hospital also operates California's only pediatric skilled nursing facility — The Helen Bernardy Center — to provide 24-hour care to disabled and medically fragile children in a homelike environment.

For treating non-life-or-limb-threatening injuries and illnesses the hospital operates neighborhood urgent care centers in Escondido La Mesa Oceanside and San Diego.

Through its medical school affiliation Rady Children's engages in nearly 500 clinical trials in all pediatric specialties. It collaborates with University of California San Diego the Sanford-Burnham Medical Research Institute The Scripps Research Institute the Salk Institute for Biological Studies and St. Jude Children's Research Hospital. Specialized research facilities on campus include the Autism Discovery Institute the Blair L. Sadler Center for Quality and the Child and Adolescent Services Research Center.

The hospital operates a LEED-certified Acute Care Pavilion which holds a neonatal intensive care unit the Peckham Center for Cancer and Blood Disorders and the Warren Family Surgical Center. It serves those suffering from eating disorders through its inpatient center to allow for intensive psychiatric therapy for patients with anorexia and bulimia and to aid families with home care.

In 2014 the hospital had 18782 inpatient admissions 230383 outpatient visits nearly 85000 emergency department visits and more than 54000 urgent care visits. It performed about 20000 surgeries.

Geographic Reach

Rady Children's Hospital serves as the pediatric medical center that caters to the California region of San Diego Imperial and southern Riverside counties. It has more than 30 offices throughout San Diego and southern Riverside counties with satellite locations in Chula Vista El Centro Encinitas Escondido La Jolla La Mesa Murrieta Oceanside San Diego and Solana Beach.

EXECUTIVES

Chairman Rady Pediatric Genomics And Systems Medicine Institute, David F. Hale, age 69
President And Ceo Rady Pediatric Genomics And Systems Medicine Institute, Stephen Kingsmore
Evp And Chief Administrative Officer, Margareta E. (Meg) Norton
President And Ceo, Donald Kearns
Vp And Cio, Albert Oriol
Vp And Chief Nursing Executive, Mary Fagan
Chief Medical Officer, Irvin A. Kaufman
Svp And Coo, Nicholas Holmes
Executive Director Rady Childrenâ's Hospital Foundation And Svp Rady Childrenâ's Hospital, Stephen Jennings
Physician-in-chief And Chief Scientific Officer And Chairman Of Pediatrics Uc San Diego, Gabriel G. Haddad
Svp Rady Childrenâ's Specialists Of San Diego, Herb Kimmons
Medical Director, Sara Marchese
Clinical Director, Carolina Schaber
Director Of Nursing, Lesley Carlson
Vice President Finance And Controller, Nish Ratnayake
Senior Vice President Major Gifts, Lauren Bergquist
Vice Chairman, Michael P. (Mike) Peckham
Chairman, Theodore D. (Ted) Roth, age 67

LOCATIONS

HQ: RADY CHILDREN'S HOSPITAL-SAN DIEGO
3020 CHILDRENS WAY, SAN DIEGO, CA 921234223
Phone: 858 576-1700
Web: WWW.RCHSD.ORG

Selected Satellite Locations
Chula Vista
El Centro
Encinitas
Escondido
La Jolla
La Mesa
Murrieta
Oceanside
San Diego
Solana Beach

PRODUCTS/OPERATIONS

Selected Services
Allergy/Immunology
Attention Deficit Hyperactivity Disorder
Audiology/Hearing
Autism Discovery Institute
Behavioral Health
Brachial Plexus Clinic
Cancer & Blood Disorders
Cardiology
Cardiovascular Surgery
Celiac Disease Clinic
Center for Healthier Communities
Cerebral Palsy Center
Chadwick Center For Children & Families
Child & Adolescent Psychiatry Services (CAPS)
Child & Adolescent Services Research Center (CASRC)
Child Life Services
Children's Care Connection (C3)
Children's Hospital Emergency Transport (CHET)
Cleft Palate Clinic
Craniofacial Disorders
Critical Care
Cystic Fibrosis Center
Dental Surgery
Dermatology
Developmental Evaluation Clinic
Developmental-Behavioral Pediatrics
Developmental Screening & Enhancement Program (DSEP)
Developmental Services
Down Syndrome Center
Eating Disorders/
Medical-Behavioral Disorders Unit
Emergency Medicine
Endocrinology/Diabetes
Fatty Liver Clinic
Feeding Team
Gastroenterology Hepatology & Nutrition
Genetics/Dysmorphology
Heart Institute
Helen Bernardy Center for Medically Fragile Children
Hematology/Oncology
HomeCare
Hospice
Infectious Diseases
Kawasaki Disease Clinic
Kidney/Liver Tranplant Program
Kidney Disease
Laboratory Services/Pathology
Liver Disease
Liver Transplant
Muscle Disease Clinic
Metabolic Medicine
Neonatology
Nephrology
Neurology
Neurosurgery
Newborn Screening Program
Nutrition Clinic
Occupational Therapy
Ophthalmology
Orthopedics
Otolaryngology/ENT
Pain Services
Palliative Care
Pediatric Surgery
Pediatrics & Hospital Medicine
Pharmacy Services
Physical Therapy
Prader-Willi Syndrome Clinic
Psychiatry
Pulmonary/Respiratory Medicine
Radiology
Rehabilitation Medicine
Rheumatology
Sleep Center

Speech/Language Pathology
Spiritual Care
Sports Medicine
Surgery
Toddler School (Alexa's PLAYC)
Trauma Center
Urgent Care
Urology
Weight & Wellness Center

COMPETITORS

All Children's Hospital
Children's Health System
Children's Hospital & Research Center at Oakland
Children's Hospital of Orange County
Children's Hospital of Philadelphia
Children's Hospital of Richmond
Children's Specialized Hospital
Childrens Hospital Los Angeles
Cook Children's Health Care System
Dell Children's Medical Center
Nationwide Children's Hospital
Palomar Health
Scripps Health
Seattle Children's Hospital
Sharp HealthCare
Shriners Hospitals For Children
St. Jude Children's Research Hospital
Sutter Health
Tri-City Healthcare District
UCSF Medical

HISTORICAL FINANCIALS
Company Type: Private

Income Statement | | | | FYE: June 30

	REVENUE ($ mil.)	NET INCOME ($ mil.)	NET PROFIT MARGIN	EMPLOYEES
06/15	522	104	20.1%	2,313
06/14	838	82	9.8%	—
06/10	619	42	6.9%	—
06/09	490	(56)	—	—
Annual Growth	1.0%	—	—	—

2015 Year-End Financials
Return on assets: 19.7%   Cash ($ mil.): 75
Return on equity: 20.1%
Current ratio: 1.20

RALPH L. WADSWORTH CONSTRUCTION COMPANY, LLC

EXECUTIVES

Pres, Con Wadsworth
Vice President, Tod Wadsworth
Coo, Brandon Squire
Gen Mgr, Doug Clements
Controller, Mike Rowberry
Project Manager, Brad Watson
Vice-President, Cole Wadsworth
Administrative Assistant, Kristie Freeland
Chief Operating Officer, Nate Ballard
Controller, Verna Askwig
Financial Analyst, Kade Wadsworth

LOCATIONS

HQ: RALPH L. WADSWORTH CONSTRUCTION
COMPANY, LLC
166 E 14000 S STE 200, DRAPER, UT 840205455
Phone: 801 553-1661
Web: WWW.WADSCO.COM

HISTORICAL FINANCIALS

Company Type: Private

Income Statement				FYE: December 31
	REVENUE ($ mil.)	NET INCOME ($ mil.)	NET PROFIT MARGIN	EMPLOYEES
12/17	290	18	6.2%	200
12/16	190	10	5.4%	—
12/15	155	5	3.8%	—
12/14	144	4	3.3%	—
Annual Growth	26.1%	55.9%	—	—

2017 Year-End Financials

Return on assets: 11.5%
Return on equity: 6.2%
Current ratio: 1.00

Cash ($ mil.): 16

RAPID CITY REGIONAL HOSPITAL, INC.

Mt. Rushmore sightseers bikers and locals alike can seek medical care at Rapid City Regional Hospital. The medical facility is a general and psychiatric hospital with some 330 acute care beds and 50 psychiatric beds located in the Black Hills region of western South Dakota. In addition to emergency and acute care the not-for-profit hospital also offers a behavioral health center a rehabilitation facility a cancer care institute and women's and children's departments. Rapid City Regional Hospital is part of Regional Health a network of regional hospitals medical clinics and senior care centers.

Operations

Regional Health is comprised of five hospitals 24 clinic locations and employs nearly 5000 physicians and caregivers. In addition to Rapid City Regional Hospital the Regional Health group includes the Custer Regional Lead-Deadwood Regional Spearfish Regional and Sturgis Regional hospitals. It also operates area clinics and doctors' offices including a family medicine clinic that manages a physician residency program as well as retirement communities and nursing homes. Altogether Regional Health has a total of about 40 facilities in South Dakota's Black Hills region.

Sales and Marketing

Rapid City Regional Hospital provides health care services to the 360000 people who live in the Black Hills of South Dakota and the surrounding region as well as thousands of visitors each year.

Company Background

The hospital was established in 1973.

EXECUTIVES

Ceo, Charles Hart
Vice President, Michael Keegan
Treas, Jim Sorensen
Doctor, Byran Den Hartog
General, Dick Latushie
Vp Affairs, Robert Allen Jr
Information Specialist, Brian Crown
Human Resources Information MA, Jeremy Weaver
Rn, Kimberley Jackson

LOCATIONS

HQ: RAPID CITY REGIONAL HOSPITAL, INC.
353 FAIRMONT BLVD, RAPID CITY, SD 577017393
Phone: 605 719-1000
Web: WWW.REGIONALHEALTH.COM

PRODUCTS/OPERATIONS

Selected Services

Bariatrics and Weight Management
Behavioral Health
Bones Muscles and Joints
Brain and Spine
Cancer Care
Clinics (Primary and Speciality)
Diabetes
Heart and Vascular Care
Home Care
Home Medical Equipment
Hospice Care
Hospitalist
Hyperbaric Oxygen Therapy
Infusion Services
Intensive Care
Laboratory Services
Labor and Delivery
Lactation Services
Medical Imaging
Digital Mammography
Neonatal Care
Neurology
Nutrition Services
Pain Management
Pediatrics
Physical Therapy and Rehabilitation
Regional Health Research
Senior Care
Sepsis
Sports Medicine
Stroke Care
Telemedicine
Wound Care

COMPETITORS

Avera Health	St. Alexius Medical
Mayo Clinic	Center
Sanford	St. Mary's Healthcare
Health-MeritCare	

HISTORICAL FINANCIALS

Company Type: Private

Income Statement				FYE: June 30
	REVENUE ($ mil.)	NET INCOME ($ mil.)	NET PROFIT MARGIN	EMPLOYEES
06/16	467	28	6.1%	4,200
06/15	437	39	9.0%	—
06/14	517	56	10.9%	—
06/13	489	49	10.2%	—
Annual Growth	(1.6%)	(17.2%)	—	—

2016 Year-End Financials

Return on assets: 3.9%
Return on equity: 6.1%
Current ratio: 0.90

Cash ($ mil.): 17

RAPPAHANNOCK ELECTRIC COOPERATIVE

Like the river it's named after the Rappahannock Electric Cooperative (REC) keeps the power running smoothly. The consumer-owned cooperative provides electricity to homes businesses and industries in parts of 22 counties from the Blue Ridge Mountains to the mouth of the Rappahannock River in eastern Virginia. REC supplies power to more than 157000 members over more than 16000 miles of power line. REC offers surge protection internet services and home security plans to entice customers as competition from other suppliers arrives. Once rural in nature the cooperative's territory has seen large pockets of suburban growth.

Geographic Reach

The company serve members in 22 Virginia counties: Albemarle Caroline Clarke Culpeper Essex Fauquier Frederick Goochland Greene Hanover King and Queen King William Louisa Madison Orange Page Rappahannock Rockingham Shenandoah Spotsylvania Stafford and Warren.

Sales and Marketing

REC's largest customer is Bear Island Paper Company the second largest power consumer in the state of Virginia. Other major customers include DuPont GE Kings Dominion Amusement Park and Merillat Industries.

Financial Performance

In 2012 the company reported revenues of $405.6 million (1% down on 2011). Residential customers accounted for more than half of the REC's total sales in 2012.

Strategy

REC is also pursuing ways to help its customers to become more energy efficient to help them save money and to help the cooperative trim its power capacity growth plans. Supported by a $16 million federal green energy grant the company has replaced customers' older meters with smart (automated efficient) ones.

In 2012 REC and Old Dominion Electric Cooperative offered a pilot energy efficiency program (energy retrofits) for REC's members in Albemarle Louisa Greene Madison and Orange counties.

Company Background

REC was formed when the Virginia Electric Cooperative in Bowling Green and the Northern Piedmont Electric Cooperative in Culpeper merged in 1980.

Dramatically growing its business in 2010 the company and fellow co-op Shenandoah Valley Electric Cooperatives acquired Potomac Edison (Allegheny Energy's electric distribution operations in Virginia) for about $340 million. The expansion increased REC's coverage from 16 counties to 22 and its customer base by about 50%.

EXECUTIVES

Vice President Of Customer Services, David Koogler
Vice President, Ron Harris
Secretary, Lisa Hodgkiss

LOCATIONS

HQ: RAPPAHANNOCK ELECTRIC COOPERATIVE
247 INDUSTRIAL CT, FREDERICKSBURG, VA 224082443
Phone: 540 898-8500
Web: WWW.MYREC.COOP

COMPETITORS

Dominion Virginia Power	Pepco Energy Services WGL Holdings

HISTORICAL FINANCIALS
Company Type: Private

Income Statement				FYE: December 31
	REVENUE ($ mil.)	NET INCOME ($ mil.)	NET PROFIT MARGIN	EMPLOYEES
12/17	373	17	4.8%	423
12/16	418	14	3.6%	—
12/15	461	15	3.3%	—
12/14	434	14	3.4%	—
Annual Growth	(4.9%)	5.9%	—	—

2017 Year-End Financials
Return on assets: 8.8% Cash ($ mil.): 2
Return on equity: 4.8%
Current ratio: 0.40

RAYMOND JAMES & ASSOCIATES INC

Does everybody love Raymond James & Associates (RJA)? Raymond James Financial hopes so. RJA is that company's primary subsidiary and one of the largest retail brokerages in the US. The unit provides brokerage financial planning investments and related services to consumers. It performs equity and fixed income sales trading and research for institutional clients in North America and Europe. Its investment banking group provides corporate and public finance debt underwriting and mergers and acquisitions advice. RJA also makes markets for approximately 1000 stocks including thinly traded issues. Planning Corporation of America a wholly-owned subsidiary of RJA sells insurance and annuities.

Operations
RJA is engaged in most aspects of securities distribution and investment banking.

Geographic Reach
The company has more than 200 branches and satellite offices concentrated in the Mid-Atlantic Midwest Southeast and Southwest portions of the US in addition to ten institutional sales offices in Europe.

Sales and Marketing
RJA has many big name clients across dozens of industries. In 2013 Titan Medical announced that it has retained RJA to provide advisory services and present options which could include a possible sale.

Strategy
In 2012 the company's parent completed its acquisition of Morgan Keegan & Co. and MK Holding Inc. from Regions Financial Corporation. Some of the equity capital markets and fixed income operations of were integrated into RJA.

EXECUTIVES

Vice President, William Wallace
Vice President, Scott Cutliff
Vice President Investments Financial Advisor, Aamsa Zuniga
Managing Director, Dan Horgan
Auditors: KPMG LLP TAMPA FL

LOCATIONS

HQ: RAYMOND JAMES & ASSOCIATES INC
880 CARILLON PKWY, SAINT PETERSBURG, FL 337161100
Phone: 727 567-1000
Web: WWW.RAYMONDJAMES.COM

COMPETITORS

Ameriprise	Janney Montgomery
Charles Schwab	Scott
E*TRADE Financial	Merrill Lynch
Edward D. Jones	Scottrade
Edward Jones	TD Ameritrade
FMR	Wells Fargo Advisors

HISTORICAL FINANCIALS
Company Type: Private

Income Statement				FYE: September 30
	ASSETS ($ mil.)	NET INCOME ($ mil.)	INCOME AS % OF ASSETS	EMPLOYEES
09/17	9,917	198	2.0%	10,000
09/16	10,689	145	1.4%	—
09/15	7,893	167	2.1%	—
09/14	6,955	182	2.6%	—
Annual Growth	12.6%	2.8%	—	—

2017 Year-End Financials
Return on assets: — Sales ($ mil.): 3,255
Return on equity: 6.1%

REDNER'S MARKETS, INC.

Redner's Markets operates about 45 warehouse club-style supermarkets under the Redner's Warehouse Markets banner and more than a dozen Quick Shoppe convenience stores. Most of the company's stores are located in eastern Pennsylvania but the regional grocer also operates several locations in Maryland and Delaware having closed its one New York supermarket. Redner's Warehouse Markets house bakery deli meat produce and seafood departments as well as in-store banks. The employee-owned company was founded by namesake Earl Redner in 1970. It is still operated by the Redner family including chairman and CEO Richard and COO Ryan Redner.

Financial Performance
Redner's Markets rang up an estimated $865 million in sales in fiscal 2012 (ends September) up from about $859 million in sales the previous year.

Strategy
Redner's has been tinkering with its store portfolio shuttering underperforming locations including several in its core Pennsylvania market while building new stores in existing and new markets. The regional chain has grown to four stores each in Delaware and Maryland since entering those markets in 2008 and 2005 respectively. Redner's is also growing its Web presence doubling its online traffic in the first year of a digiral shopper marketing program conducted in partnership with Google Shopping Network.

EXECUTIVES

Vice President Of Finance, Michael McNaney
Vice President Human Resources, Robert McDonough
Vice President Purchasing, Dan Eberhart
Vice President And General Counsel, Jason Hopp
Vice President Perishable Operations, Gary Obrien
Auditors: RKL LLP WYOMISSING PENNSYLV

LOCATIONS

HQ: REDNER'S MARKETS, INC.
3 QUARRY RD, READING, PA 196059787
Phone: 610 926-3700
Web: WWW.REDNERSMARKETS.COM

2012 Warehouse Market Stores

	No.
Pennsylvania	36
Delaware	4
Maryland	4
Total	**44**

PRODUCTS/OPERATIONS

2012 Stores

	No.
Redner's Warehouse Market	44
Quick Shoppe	14
Total	**58**

COMPETITORS

7-Eleven	Wal-Mart
A&P	Wawa Inc.
Cumberland Farms	Wegmans
Giant Food Stores	Weis Markets
Sheetz	

HISTORICAL FINANCIALS
Company Type: Private

Income Statement				FYE: October 1
	REVENUE ($ mil.)	NET INCOME ($ mil.)	NET PROFIT MARGIN	EMPLOYEES
10/16*	864	4	0.6%	4,800
09/15	884	6	0.7%	—
09/14	902	1	0.2%	—
09/13	892	4	0.5%	—
Annual Growth	(1.1%)	1.8%	—	—
*Fiscal year change				

2016 Year-End Financials
Return on assets: 3.2% Cash ($ mil.): 56
Return on equity: 0.6%
Current ratio: 1.70

REDWOOD CREDIT UNION

EXECUTIVES

Pres-Ceo, Brett Martinez
Sales and Marketing Executive, Robin McKenzie
Senior Vice-President, Ron Felder
Assistant Vice-President, Joe Peyton
Human Resources Administrator, Robert Browne
Programmer, Sky Walker
Legal Staff, Alyssa Noone
Consultant, Carrie Bruce
Assistant Manager, Earl Chavez
Loan Officer, Gina Unciano
Loan Officer, Kathryn Clickner
Auditors: CLIFTONLARSONALLEN LLP PHOENI

LOCATIONS

HQ: REDWOOD CREDIT UNION
3033 CLEVELAND AVE # 100, SANTA ROSA, CA 954032126
Phone: 707 545-4000
Web: WWW.REDWOODCU.ORG

HISTORICAL FINANCIALS

Company Type: Private

Income Statement				FYE: December 31
	ASSETS ($ mil.)	NET INCOME ($ mil.)	INCOME AS % OF ASSETS	EMPLOYEES
12/17	4,046	67	1.7%	390
12/16	3,287	57	1.7%	—
12/14	2,468	47	1.9%	—
12/13	2,271	48	2.1%	—
Annual Growth	15.5%	8.6%	—	—

2017 Year-End Financials

Return on assets: 32.6%   Sales ($ mil): 126
Return on equity: 53.4%

REGAL ENTERTAINMENT GROUP

Regal Entertainment Group hopes to create loyal subjects out of fickle movie-goers. The largest theater owner and exhibitor in the US has around 560 theaters with some 7300 screens in 40-plus states through its Regal Cinemas Edwards Theatres United Artists Theatre Company Great Escapes Theatres and Hollywood Theatres brands. Its theaters house an average of 12.9 screens and more than 75% of its screens are in theaters with stadium seating. Regal Entertainment co-owns National CineMedia a joint venture that sells in-theater ads and operates a video network that distributes digital content to theaters. Regal Entertainment Group was formed in 2002. It was acquired by UK-based Cineworld in a $3.6 billion reverse takeover in 2018.

Change in Company Type

Regal Entertainment was acquired by UK-based cinema chain Cineworld in a $3.4 billion reverse takeover. The deal which closed in spring 2018 makes Cineworld the second-largest cinema chain globally after AMC.

Operations

Regal Entertainment manages its business under one reportable segment: theater exhibition operations.

Geographic Reach

Tennessee-based Regal Entertainment operates in around 45 US states the District of Columbia Guam Saipan and American Samoa. The chain targets midsized metropolitan markets and suburban growth areas of larger cities. It has a large number of theaters in California Florida and New York; those three states together account for nearly a third of Regal Entertainment's locations.

Sales and Marketing

Regal Entertainment employs an interactive marketing program for specific films and concession items to increase attendance and consumption. Its Regal Crown Club loyalty program rewards frequent moviegoers with deals of concessions and more.

The company uses the internet mobile and social media print and multimedia advertising to promote its service. Regal Entertainment conducts special interactive marketing programs for specific films and concessions items.

Regal Entertainment spends $1.1 billion on film rental and advertising costs annually.

Financial Performance

Regal Entertainment's revenue has been growing slowly and unevenly over the last five years.

In fiscal 2017 sales decreased 1% to $3.2 billion amid a 2-3% decline across the industry in the US. Revenue from concessions was unchanged as the impact of lower attendance was mostly offset by higher revenue per customer thanks to higher beverage and popcorn sales and selective price increases. Regal's other revenue streams recorded a net 10% uptick which include sales from its vendor marketing programs internet ticketing surcharges theater access fees paid by National CineMedia and gift card and bulk-ticket purchase programs.

Net income fell 34% to $112.3 million due to lower revenue a higher cost of concessions and an increase in loss on disposals and asset impairments.

Cash from operations in 2017 was unchanged at $410 million.

Strategy

A major part of Regal Entertainment's strategy to get customers out of the living room (where they are more inclined to watch DVDs from fancy home theater systems) and into the movie theater is through digital cinema. The company has most of its screens outfitted with digital projection systems and stadium seating. The theater chain completed its 3D deployment a couple of years ago.

Regal announced a new pricing strategy in 2018 based on peaks and troughs in demand. This means customers will pay more to see popular films at peak times and less for unpopular films at awkward hours. The company hopes the strategy will maximize revenue from customers desperate to see tentpole releases such as Star Wars and Marvel films on their opening weekends while drawing more customers in for cheaper mid-week showings of less popular pictures.

EXECUTIVES

Chairman And Ceo, Amy E. Miles, $1,024,850 total compensation

Evp General Counsel And Secretary, Peter B. Brandow, $504,700 total compensation

President And Coo, Gregory W. (Greg) Dunn, $612,850 total compensation

Evp Cfo And Treasurer, David H. Ownby, $566,500 total compensation

Vice President Oj Operations Western Region, James Dubois

Vice President Operations Southern Region, Bill Koontz

Vice President Film Systems And Administration, Kelly Palmer

Vice President Information Technology, Rick Campbell

Vice President Of Technical Services, Matt Basford

Vp Senior Film Buyer, Bob Mccormick

Vice President Of Tax, Chris Frye

Vice President Film, Ken Rather

Vice President, Alan Davy

Vice President Finance, Joe Fuller

Vice President Of Information Technology, David Doyle

Vice President Real Estate, Jerry Grewe

Vice President Film Marketing, Ken Foreman

Executive Vice President Business Development, Raymond Nutt

Vice President Of Theater Equipment, Ray Dunlap

Treasurer, Chris Dzambo

Auditors: KPMG LLP KNOXVILLE TENNESSEE

LOCATIONS

HQ: REGAL ENTERTAINMENT GROUP
101 E BLOUNT AVE STE 100, KNOXVILLE, TN
379201605
Phone: 865 922-1123
Web: WWW.REGMOVIES.COM

PRODUCTS/OPERATIONS

2017 Sales

	% of total
Admissions	64
Concessions	29
Other	7
Total	**100**

Selected Operations

Cinemas
  Edwards Theatres
  Regal Cinemas
  United Artists Theatre Company
Theater advertising
  National CineMedia (20%)

COMPETITORS

AMC Entertainment	Marcus Corporation
Alamo Drafthouse	National Amusements
Carmike Cinemas	Netflix
Cinemark	Pacific Theatres
Cineplex	Reading International
Landmark Theatres	Redbox

HISTORICAL FINANCIALS

Company Type: Private

Income Statement				FYE: December 31
	REVENUE ($ mil.)	NET INCOME ($ mil.)	NET PROFIT MARGIN	EMPLOYEES
12/17	3,163	112	3.6%	25,359
12/16	3,197	170	5.3%	—
12/15*	3,127	153	4.9%	—
01/15	2,990	105	3.5%	—
Annual Growth	1.9%	2.2%	—	—

*Fiscal year change

2017 Year-End Financials

Return on assets: —   Cash ($ mil.): —
Return on equity: 3.6%
Current ratio: 0.70

REGENTS OF THE UNIVERSITY OF MICHIGAN

Michigan — it's shaped like a mitten and higher education fits the state like a glove. With nearly 60000 students and about 7000 faculty members scattered across three campuses in Ann Arbor Dearborn and Flint the university's diverse academic units span such areas of study as architecture education law medicine music and social work. Notable alumni include the late President Gerald Ford (the university is home to the Gerald R. Ford Library and the Ford School of Public Policy) actor James Earl Jones Google cofounder Larry Page and seven Nobel laureates. In addition to state funding the university is supported by a $6.6 billion endowment.

Operations

The university operates some 20 schools offering education in everything from dentistry and medicine to music theater and dance. About 70% of the students are enrolled in undergraduate programs while the rest are graduate students.

There are seven museums on campus — including the Museum of Art the Exhibit Museum of Natural History (with a planetarium) and the Kelsey Museum of Archaeology — as well as the

Nichols Arboretum and the Matthaei Botanical Gardens.

Through its Health System the university maintains one of the largest health care complexes in the world. It is made up of more than 50 health centers and 120 outpatient clinics around the state and is responsible for more than 40% of The University of Michigan's revenue.

Along with its various health centers and clinics the university operates the C.S. Mott Children's Hospital. The children's hospital is noted for its heart surgery neonatal care and respiratory disorders and ranks among the nation's best for all other pediatric specialties — cancer digestive disorders general pediatrics and neurology.

Geographic Reach

The University of Michigan was founded in Detroit in 1817 but moved to Ann Arbor in 1837.

Financial Performance

The university has enjoyed an upward trend in revenue during recent fiscal years as a result of increases in tuition rates and undergraduate enrollment. It claimed more than $5 billion in revenue for fiscal 2012 up more than 5% compared to the $4.77 billion the university reported in revenue for fiscal 2011. The school brought in about $453 billion during fiscal 2010.

EXECUTIVES

Vp Government Relations, Cynthia H. Wilbanks
Vp Development, Jerry A. May
Chancellor University Of Michigan-dearborn, Daniel Little
Evp And Cfo, Kevin P. Hegarty, age 62
Chairman Victors For Michigan, Stephen M. Ross
President, Mark S. Schlissel
Dean School Of Public Health, Martin Philbert
Vp Information Technology And Cio, Kelli Trosvig
Dean Stamps School Of Art And Design, Gunalan Nadarajan
Dean School Of Dentistry, Laurie McCauley
Dean Law School, Mark D. West
Chancellor University Of Michigan-flint, Susan E. Borrego
Interim Provost And Evp Academic Affairs, Paul N. Courant
Evp Medical Affairs; Dean Medical School; Ceo Michigan Medicine, Marschall S. Runge
Vp And General Counsel, Timothy G. Lynch
Vp Research, S. Jack Hu
Interim Dean Taubman College Of Architecture And Urban Planning, Robert Fishman
Edward J. Frey Dean Ross School Of Business, Scott DeRue
Dean School Of Education, Elizabeth Birr Moje
Dean School Of Engineering, Alec D. Gallimore
Dean School Of Information, Thomas A. Finholt
Dean School Of Kinesiology, Lori Ploutz-Snyder
Dean College Of Literature Science And The Arts, Andrew D. Martin
Dean College Of Music Theatre And Dance, Aaron Dworkin
Interim Dean School Of Natural Resources And Environment, Dan Brown
Dean School Of Nursing, Patricia D. Hurn
Dean College Of Pharmacy, James T. Dalton
Dean School Of Social Work, Lynn Videka
Dean Rackham Graduate School; Vice Provost Academic Affairs Graduate Studies, Carol A. Fierke
Vice President Research, Stephen Forrest
Associate Vice President And Executive Director For Research Administration, Marvin Parnes
Associate Vice President Development, Julie Sparkman
Vice President Marketing, Rachelle Caoagas
Assistant Vice President Estate, Diane Tracy
Associate Vice President Facilities And Operations, Henry Baier
Vice President, Marina Epelman

Senior Executive Secretary Office Of Vice President For Research Department, BettyL Cook
Provost And Executive Vice President For Academic Affairs, Teresa Sullivan
Vice President Of Security Systems, Michael Dillard
Vice President Of Technology, Trung Nguyen
Vice President Technology, Jamila Power
Vice President Technology, Mehra Rohit
Vice President Investment Banking, Raj Singhal
Vice President Of Finance, Ruohao Li
Vice President Student Government Budget Allocations Committee, Mackenzie Swart
Vice President Event Planning, Kendall Witmer
Vice Chairman, Michael J. Behm
Chairman, Mark J. Bernstein
Treasurer, Kevin Morrison
Secretary Iii Umh Mworks Employ Assistant Program Department, Angela Hurlbut
Secretary Iv Lsa Dean Deans Office Department, Sandra Petee
Secretary Iv Oral Med Path Oncology Department, Wendy M Carbary
Secretary Iii Academic Affairs Dentistry Department, Diane Pasma
Secretary Iv Umh Administration Department, Melody Bond
Secretary Iii Associate Dean Grad Pgm And Facilities Department, Krisden Romine
Secretary Iv Law School Department, CherylL Erdmann
Secretary Iv Law School Department, LauraA Shiltz
Secretary Intermediate, Marie Bien
Executive Board Member, Garrett Stephens
Secretary, Mary Burton
Treasurer, Eleonore Edgell
Secretary Ii Flint School Partnerships Department, Pamela Zemore
Secretary Iv, Allisssa Ebenhoeh
Auditors: PRICEWATERHOUSECOOPERS LLP DE

LOCATIONS

HQ: REGENTS OF THE UNIVERSITY OF MICHIGAN
503 THOMPSON ST RM 3040, ANN ARBOR, MI
481091340
Phone: 734 764-1817
Web: WWW.UMICH.EDU

PRODUCTS/OPERATIONS

Selected Academic Units
Architecture and urban planning
Art and design
Business administration
Dentistry
Education
Engineering
Kinesiology
Law
Literature science and the arts
Medicine
Music
Natural resources and environment
Nursing
Pharmacy
Public health
Public policy
Social work

HISTORICAL FINANCIALS

Company Type: Private

Income Statement				FYE: June 30
	REVENUE ($ mil.)	NET INCOME ($ mil.)	NET PROFIT MARGIN	EMPLOYEES
06/18	7,466	920	12.3%	34,624
06/17	7,079	1,275	18.0%	—
06/16	6,278	(294)	—	—
06/14	5,534	1,574	28.5%	—
Annual Growth	7.8%	(12.6%)	—	—

2018 Year-End Financials

Return on assets: 3.9%   Cash ($ mil.): 163
Return on equity: 12.3%
Current ratio: 0.50

REGIONAL HEALTH, INC.

EXECUTIVES

Chm, Tom Morrison
Ceo, Charles E Hart
Exec V Pres, Joseph Sluka
Treas, Roy Dishman
Coo, Timothy Sughrue
Prin, Dennis Nesbit
Information, Bill Stockmann
Staff, Clinton Oyler
Staff, Teresa Lemmer
Compliance Staff, Sabine Colton
Vice-President, Robert Allen

LOCATIONS

HQ: REGIONAL HEALTH, INC.
353 FAIRMONT BLVD, RAPID CITY, SD 577017375
Phone: 605 755-1000
Web: REGIONALHEALTH.ORG/LOCATION/HOME-PHARMACY-RAPID-CITY

HISTORICAL FINANCIALS

Company Type: Private

Income Statement				FYE: June 30
	REVENUE ($ mil.)	NET INCOME ($ mil.)	NET PROFIT MARGIN	EMPLOYEES
06/18	689	22	3.2%	4,258
06/09	0	0	—	—
Annual Growth	114.9%	—	—	—

2018 Year-End Financials

Return on assets: 4.1%   Cash ($ mil.): 26
Return on equity: 3.2%
Current ratio: 1.70

REGIONAL TRANSPORTATION AUTHORITY

EXECUTIVES

Exec Dir, Richard J Bacigalupo
Chb, Thomas J McCraken Jr
Dep Exec Dir-Cfo, Joseph G Costello
Treas, Allan Sharkey
Prin, Julie Gomez
Prin, Carole Brown
Manager, Roxann Galvan
Coordinator, Deane Rosen
Manager, Michael Vandekreke
Senior Financial Analyst, Alejandro Montero
Project Manager, Fluturi Demirovski
Auditors: RSM US LLP CHICAGO ILLINOIS

LOCATIONS

HQ: REGIONAL TRANSPORTATION AUTHORITY
175 W JACKSON BLVD # 1650, CHICAGO, IL
606042711
Phone: 312 913-3200
Web: WWW.RTACHICAGO.COM

HISTORICAL FINANCIALS
Company Type: Private

| Income Statement | | | | FYE: December 31 |
	REVENUE ($ mil.)	NET INCOME ($ mil.)	NET PROFIT MARGIN	EMPLOYEES
12/16	637	(99)	—	80
12/15	805	(77)	—	—
12/14	755	(3)	—	—
12/13	934	(102)	—	—
Annual Growth	(12.0%)	—	—	—

2016 Year-End Financials
Return on assets: —
Return on equity: (-15.7%)
Current ratio: 0.30
Cash ($ mil.): 109

REHABILITATION INSTITUTE OF CHICAGO

EXECUTIVES

Pres-Ceo, Joanne C Smith
Gen Counsel- Sr Vice President, Nancy Paridy
Dir, Elliot Roth
Cfo, Edward B Case
Chief Marketing, Betsy Owens
Acct Mgr, Lavette Jones
Senior Vp, Rick Lieber
Coo, Peggy Kirk
Nurse Practitioner, Diane Dudas Sheehan
Scientist, Dennis Tkach
Svp Research-Chief Scientist, Richard L Lieber
Auditors: DELOITTE & TOUCHE LLP CHICAGO

LOCATIONS

HQ: REHABILITATION INSTITUTE OF CHICAGO
355 E ERIE ST, CHICAGO, IL 606114805
Phone: 312 238-1000
Web: WWW.RIC.ORG

HISTORICAL FINANCIALS
Company Type: Private

| Income Statement | | | | FYE: August 31 |
	REVENUE ($ mil.)	NET INCOME ($ mil.)	NET PROFIT MARGIN	EMPLOYEES
08/18	297	24	8.3%	1,500
08/17	267	92	34.7%	—
08/16	249	66	26.6%	—
08/13	228	129	56.6%	—
Annual Growth	5.4%	(28.1%)	—	—

2018 Year-End Financials
Return on assets: 5.7%
Return on equity: 8.3%
Current ratio: 0.90
Cash ($ mil.): 15

REID HOSPITAL & HEALTH CARE SERVICES, INC.

EXECUTIVES

Pres, Craig C Kinyon
Coordinator, David C Lark
Vice President of Information, Christie Brewer
Director, Pat Esham
Assistant of Human Resources, Pat Williams
Auditors: BKD LLP INDIANAPOLIS INDIAN

LOCATIONS

HQ: REID HOSPITAL & HEALTH CARE SERVICES, INC.
1100 REID PKWY, RICHMOND, IN 473741157
Phone: 765 983-3000
Web: WWW.REIDHEALTH.ORG

HISTORICAL FINANCIALS
Company Type: Private

| Income Statement | | | | FYE: December 31 |
	REVENUE ($ mil.)	NET INCOME ($ mil.)	NET PROFIT MARGIN	EMPLOYEES
12/17	430	43	10.1%	1,800
12/14	359	8	2.4%	—
12/13	339	47	14.1%	—
12/12	351	22	6.4%	—
Annual Growth	4.1%	14.1%	—	—

2017 Year-End Financials
Return on assets: 3.9%
Return on equity: 10.1%
Current ratio: 1.50
Cash ($ mil.): 29

REID HOSPITAL MSO, LLC

EXECUTIVES

Pres, Craig Kinyon
V Pres, Jim Puffenberger
SEC, Bonita Washington Lacey
V Pres, Angie Dickman
V Pres, Kay Cartwright
Cardiology Director, Cheryl N Rudy
Information Technology Manager, Gary Vadakian
Staff Pharmacist, Joy Swonder
Cardiology Supervisor, Brenda McClure
Nurse Educator or, Teri Barley
Auditors: BKD LLP CINCINNATI OH

LOCATIONS

HQ: REID HOSPITAL MSO, LLC
1100 REID PKWY, RICHMOND, IN 473741157
Phone: 765 983-3000
Web: WWW.SECURE.REIDHOSPITAL.ORG

HISTORICAL FINANCIALS
Company Type: Private

| Income Statement | | | | FYE: December 31 |
	REVENUE ($ mil.)	NET INCOME ($ mil.)	NET PROFIT MARGIN	EMPLOYEES
12/16	408	16	4.0%	3
12/15	375	(33)	—	—
12/12	354	35	10.0%	—
Annual Growth	3.6%	(17.5%)	—	—

2016 Year-End Financials
Return on assets: 3.4%
Return on equity: 4.0%
Current ratio: 1.70
Cash ($ mil.): 31

RENESAS ELECTRONICS AMERICA INC.

Intersil makes transfer of power an orderly process at least in electronics. Its line of semiconductor devices for power management include power regulators converters and controllers power modules amplifiers and buffers proximity and light sensors data converters video decoders and interfaces. Its products are components in data centers computers smartphones autos and a range of other applications. Almost three-quarters of its sales are to customers in Asia. In 2017 Intersil was bought by Renesas Electronics for $3.2 billion.

Change in Company Type

Intersil's products should fit nicely with the microcontroller business of Renesas. Having Intersil technology on board should help Renesas further its penetration of the automotive market a growing area for semiconductor companies. Intersil became a wholly owned subsidiary of Renesas after the transaction closed in early 2017.

Operations

Intersil's industrial and infrastructure division which addresses power automotive aerospace and broad-line industrial applications accounted for 64% of sales in 2014. Products in the company's computing division 21% of sales provide power management functions for personal computers including ultrabooks notebooks and desktops. The consumer division 15% makes devices for gaming consoles and systems.

Geographic Reach

As a region Asia accounts for 73% of Intersil's sales. China by itself makes up 50% of sales. The next highest country is the US with about 18%. Countries in Europe generate about 8% of sales.

Based in Milpitas California Intersil has sales and design operations around the world. It has a manufacturing plant in Florida where it makes about 13% of its products. The rest of production is handled by contract manufacturers including Global Foundries Taiwan Semiconductor Manufacturing Company and United Microelectronics Corporation.

Sales and Marketing

About 60% of revenue comes through distributors and value-added resellers. Avnet Inc. accounted for about 18% of revenue and WPG Holdings Ltd. for just more than 10% in 2014.

Financial Performance

Intersil's revenue fell by about 2% to $562.5 million in 2014 from 2013. Sales in its industrial and infrastructure division rose 6% (nearly $19 million) in 2014 from 2013 but sales were off 1% ($1.2 million) in computing. Intersil's de-emphasis of lower-margin products in its consumer division was reflected in the 26% ($30 million) drop in sales the unit posted in 2014.

The company's net income on the other hand rocketed 1800% higher to $55 million in 2014 from $2.8 million in 2013. The main reason was that Intersil didn't carry the burden of a $28 million restructuring charge it took in 2013. Reductions in head count and other factors also reduced expenses in 2014. Cash flow from operations fell to $73 million in 2014 from about $107 million the year before.

Strategy

Intersil has made power management its focus shedding most of its connectors business. The restructuring began in 2013 and was largely completed by 2015.

The main focus of the refocusing is toward the company's industrial and infrastructure applications for growing markets such with power management needs. They include data centers communications infrastructure and industrial applications with a desire for better energy efficiency.

Another area is automotive and aerospace markets. For automotive the company makes video circuits for the growing use of cameras in autos and power products for the increasing demands of monitoring and managing power in hybrid and electric vehicles. For aerospace applications the company makes components for satellites bombarded by high radiation as they sail through space.

In 2014 Intersil expanded its line of radiation hardened (rad hard) devices to include the ISL71091SEH10 20 33 and 40. The product offers stable output voltage noise and a reference voltage providing better precision in data acquisition signal processing and power management.

The company introduced a Single-Chip Display Power and LED driver for smartphones in 2014. It incorporates display power and backlight LED driver functions in a single chip which improves efficiency and increases battery life.

A product that could improve efficiency for product such as battery powered drills are Intersil's First Half and Full-Bridge Drivers for multi-cell lithium-ion battery devices. They provide a safety feature that prevents voltage kickback a leading cause of damage and deterioration of lithium-ion batteries.

The company made no acquisitions in 2014 but maintains the possibility to do so in order to add to its power management product line.

EXECUTIVES

Cfo, Richard D. (Rick) Crowley
Svp Infrastructure Power Products, Mark A. Downing
Svp Specialty Products, Susan J. Hardman, $362,151 total compensation
Svp Worldwide Operations And Technology, Gerry Edwards
Svp Mobile Power Products, Andrew M. Cowell, $338,511 total compensation
Evp Renesas Electronics And President And Ceo Intersil, Necip Sayiner
Vp Precision Products, Philip Chesley
Vice President Of Sales For The Asia Pacific Region, Clifton Ho
Vice President Product Development, Diwakar Vishakhadatta
Vice President, Noel Lister
Senior Vice President And Chief Internal Auditor, Lan Tran
Executive Vice President, Ryan Roderick
Vp Research And Development, Carlos Garcia

Vice President Of Corporate Communications, Shannon Pleasant
Vice President, Jim Mccreary
Assistant Treasurer, Carol Hackney
Board Member, Malcolm Cambra
Auditors: KPMG LLP SANTA CLARA CALIFOR

LOCATIONS

HQ: RENESAS ELECTRONICS AMERICA INC.
1001 MURPHY RANCH RD, MILPITAS, CA 950357912
Phone: 408 432-8888
Web: WWW.INTERSIL.COM

2012 Sales

	% of total
Asia/Pacific	78
North America	15
Europe & other	7
Total	**100**

PRODUCTS/OPERATIONS

2012 Sales

	% of total
Industrial & infrastructure	57
Personal computing	23
Consumer	20
Total	**100**

Selected Products

Amplifiers
Audio integrated circuits (ICs)
Automotive ICs
Bridge driver power management products
Broadband and hot plug power management products
Buffers
Core power devices (computers)
Data converters
Display ICs
High speed converters
Interface ICs
Line driver
Military-qualified analog ICs
Modulator/demodulators
Multiplexers
Operational amplifiers
Optical sensors
Optical storage devices
Potentiometers
Power amplifiers
Power converters
Power management ICs
Power modules
Signal integrity
Switches
Timing circuits
Video ICs
Voltage references

COMPETITORS

ANADIGICS	Microchip Technology
Advanced Analogic Technologies	Monolithic Power Systems
Alpha and Omega	NXP Semiconductors
Analog Devices	ON Semiconductor
Fairchild Semiconductor	Qualcomm Atheros
Linear Technology	STMicroelectronics
Maxim Integrated Products	Semtech
	Siliconix
	Texas Instruments

HISTORICAL FINANCIALS

Company Type: Private

Income Statement

FYE: December 30

	REVENUE ($ mil.)	NET INCOME ($ mil.)	NET PROFIT MARGIN	EMPLOYEES
12/16*	542	48	8.9%	1,027
01/16	521	7	1.4%	—
01/15	562	54	9.7%	—
01/14	575	2	0.5%	—
Annual Growth	**(2.0%)**	**156.4%**	**—**	**—**

*Fiscal year change

Return on assets: 3.9%   Cash ($ mil.): 224
Return on equity: 8.9%
Current ratio: 1.60

RESEARCH TRIANGLE INSTITUTE INC

The scientists at Research Triangle Institute address the problems of a sphere (the planet). Operating mainly under its trade name RTI International (RTI) the not-for-profit enterprise conducts research in such areas as advanced technologies environmental resources and medicine. It provides such services as certification and materials testing as well as software used in laboratories and research projects. Serving the US federal government other governments nonprofits and for-profit companies RTI offers analytical perspectives on public policy and has researchers working in offices around the world.

Operations

The company offers analytical perspectives on public policy. Its staff members represent more than 80 nationalities and speak nearly 90 languages enabling RTI to communicate and collaborate effectively with peer researchers clients and stakeholders around the world.

Geographic Reach

RTI serves clients in more than 75 countries. It has eight US offices and offices in China El Salvador India Indonesia Kenya Spain Sweden the UAE and the UK.

Sales and Marketing

The organization works with clients in government industry academia and public service. RTI's main clients are the Department of Health and Human Services and the US Agency for International Development. RTI's private sector clients have included 3M Chevron Cisco Systems GE and Sanofi-Aventis.

Financial Performance

The institute reinvests its net income in programs facilities and new capabilities.

EXECUTIVES

Vice President, Jerry Rench
Evp And Coo, James J. (Jim) Gibson
Evp Rti Health Solutions, Allen W. Mangel
President And Ceo, E. Wayne Holden
Evp International Development Group, Aaron S. Williams
Evp Social Statistical And Environmental Sciences, Timothy J. (Tim) Gabel
Evp And Cfo, Michael H. (Mike) Kaelin
Chair Fellow Program And Distinguished Fellow Early Childhood Development, Don Bailey
Vice President And Assistant General Counsel, Christopher Buchholtz
Senior Vice President, Edward Story
Executive Vice President Of Human Resources, Lisa May
Senior Vice President Education And Workforce Development, Kimberly Omalley
Vice President, Justin Eiler
Vice President, Mark Strader
Vice Chairman, Peter M. Scott
Chairman, William M. Moore
Treasurer, Ward Sax
Auditors: DELOITTE & TOUCHE LLP CHARLOT

LOCATIONS

HQ: RESEARCH TRIANGLE INSTITUTE INC
  3040 CORNWALLIS RD, DURHAM, NC 277090155
Phone: 919 541-6000
Web: WWW.RTI.ORG

PRODUCTS/OPERATIONS

Selected Research Areas
Advanced technology research and development
Drug discovery and development
Economic and social
Education and training
Energy
Environmental
Health
International development
Laboratory and chemistry
Statistics
Survey

COMPETITORS

Battelle Memorial   Urban Institute
 QSS Group
 Sandford Burnham
  Institute

HISTORICAL FINANCIALS

Company Type: Private

Income Statement   FYE: September 30

	REVENUE ($ mil.)	NET INCOME ($ mil.)	NET PROFIT MARGIN	EMPLOYEES
09/17	972	22	2.4%	3,117
09/16	884	15	1.8%	—
09/15	831	40	4.9%	—
09/14	788	31	4.0%	—
Annual Growth	7.2%	(10.4%)	—	—

2017 Year-End Financials
Return on assets: 6.9%   Cash ($ mil.): 29
Return on equity: 2.4%
Current ratio: 0.50

REX HOSPITAL, INC.

EXECUTIVES

Pres, Steve Burriss
Vp Legal Affairs, Tate Bombard
Chief Officer, Linda Butler
Vp/Rex Healthcare Foundation, Sylvia Hackett
Vp Patient Care Services / Cno, Joel Ray
Vp Physician Services, Bob Ricker
Vp Heart & Vascular Services, Kirsten Riggs
Ccmo, Lisa Schiller
Vp, Tammie Stanton
Vp Regional Hospitalist Servic, Sean Tehrani
Vp Ambulatory Services, Tom Williams

LOCATIONS

HQ: REX HOSPITAL, INC.
  4420 LAKE BOONE TRL, RALEIGH, NC 276076599
Phone: 919 784-3100
Web: WWW.REXHEALTH.COM

HISTORICAL FINANCIALS

Company Type: Private

Income Statement   FYE: June 30

	REVENUE ($ mil.)	NET INCOME ($ mil.)	NET PROFIT MARGIN	EMPLOYEES
06/16	904	106	11.8%	3,500
06/15	813	4	0.5%	—
06/14	724	25	3.6%	—
06/13	701	7	1.0%	—
Annual Growth	8.9%	145.0%	—	—

2016 Year-End Financials
Return on assets: 4.9%   Cash ($ mil.): 91
Return on equity: 11.8%
Current ratio: 1.10

REXFORD INDUSTRIAL REALTY, INC.

Rexford Industrial Realty knows that there's more to business in Southern California than moviemaking and fashion. A real estate investment trust or REIT Rexford Industrial owns and manages a portfolio of nearly 70 industrial properties in Los Angeles County and surrounding areas. Its portfolio comprises about 7.6 million sq. ft. of warehouse distribution and light manufacturing space that's leased to small and midsized businesses. It manages 20 more properties — altogether comprising 1.2 million sq. ft. of rentable space. A self-administered and self-managed REIT Rexford Industrial was formed in 2013 from the assets of its predecessor. In mid-2013 the company went public.

IPO
Rexford Industrial intends to use a portion of the $224 million in proceeds to repay debt much of which is secured by various properties.

Operations
Rexford Industrial's portfolio spans several California counties including Los Angeles Orange Ventura San Bernadino Riverside and San Diego.

Financial Performance
Revenue rose for Rexford Industrial by 27% in fiscal 2012 to $34 million from 2011's $28 million thanks to increases in rental revenue and tenant reimbursements from rising occupancy rates and a boost in revenues from properties it acquired during both 2012 and 2011. Rexford Industrial logged 64% increases in revenue from management leasing and development services due to the additional third-party management fees.

Strategy
Rexford Industrial is seeking to acquire equity stakes and debt in stable and distressed industrial properties in infill markets (i.e. highly developed urban centers) in Los Angeles Orange San Diego and Ventura counties and the West Inland Empire to the east. The REIT is also looking to manage properties located in these same areas that are owned by third parties.

The REIT has been buying properties throughout Southern California particularly in the cities of Van Nuys and Tarzana as well as in Glenview Illinois. It looks to purchase both newer and older vintage properties as well as single (40% of its portfolio) and multi-tenant (60%) projects. The REIT invests in every category of industrial property. Tenants are typically small and medium-sized businesses that are tied to the Southern California

economy. Rexford Industrial boasts an average tenant size of about 9000 sq. ft. Nearly 70% of its tenants occupy fewer than 50000 sq. ft. apiece.

EXECUTIVES

Co-ceo And Director, Howard Schwimmer, $495,000 total compensation
Co-ceo And Director, Michael S. Frankel, age 55, $495,000 total compensation
Cfo, Adeel Khan, $315,000 total compensation
Vice President And Assistant General Counsel, Laura Mask
Chairman, Richard S. Ziman, age 75
Auditors: ERNST & YOUNG LLP LOS ANGELES

LOCATIONS

HQ: REXFORD INDUSTRIAL REALTY, INC.
  11620 WILSHIRE BLVD # 1000, LOS ANGELES, CA 900256821
Phone: 310 966-1680
Web: WWW.REXFORDINDUSTRIAL.COM

PRODUCTS/OPERATIONS

2015 Revenue

	$ mil.	% of total
Rental		
Rental Revenues	81	86
Tenant Reimbursements	10	11
Management Leasing & Development Services	0	1
Other Income	1	1
Interest Income	0	1
Total	**93**	**100**

Selected Property Categories
Core
Core Plus
First Mortgages Tied to Target Industrial Property
Value Add

COMPETITORS

Brandywine Realty   Prologis
 Brandywine Realty   Prologis
 PS Business Parks   Terreno Realty
 PS Business Parks   Terreno Realty

HISTORICAL FINANCIALS

Company Type: Private

Income Statement   FYE: December 31

	ASSETS ($ mil.)	NET INCOME ($ mil.)	INCOME AS % OF ASSETS	EMPLOYEES
12/16	1,515	25	1.7%	40
12/15	1,153	1	0.2%	—
12/14	932	0	0.1%	—
12/13	554	(0)	—	—
Annual Growth	39.8%	—	—	—

2016 Year-End Financials
Return on assets: 10.8%   Sales ($ mil): 126
Return on equity: 20.5%

RIALTO UNIFIED SCHOOL DISTRICT

EXECUTIVES

Pres, Joanne T Gilbert
Vice President, Joseph Ayala
SEC, Michele Joseph
SEC, Rosie Williams
Supt, Hearold L Cebrun
Clerk, Alma Garibay

Payroll Staff, Glissandia Watkins
Teacher, Mindy Montry
Personnel Specialist, Ricardo Carranza
Teacher, William Brown
Auditors: VAVRINEK TRINE DAY & CO LL

LOCATIONS

HQ: RIALTO UNIFIED SCHOOL DISTRICT
   182 E WALNUT AVE, RIALTO, CA 923763598
Phone: 909 820-7700
Web: WWW.RIALTO.K12.CA.US

HISTORICAL FINANCIALS

Company Type: Private

Income Statement				FYE: June 30
	REVENUE ($ mil.)	NET INCOME ($ mil.)	NET PROFIT MARGIN	EMPLOYEES
06/17	325	4	1.2%	2,833
06/16	314	25	8.0%	—
06/06	231	(8)	—	—
06/05	226	(22)	—	—
Annual Growth	3.1%	—	—	—

2017 Year-End Financials

Return on assets: 8.6%   Cash ($ mil.): 136
Return on equity: 1.2%
Current ratio: —

RICELAND FOODS, INC.

Handling more than 125 million bushels of grain a year Riceland Foods is ingrained in its business. The agricultural cooperative processes and markets the rice soybeans and wheat grown by its 9000 member/owners who farm in Arkansas Louisiana Mississippi Missouri and Texas. One of the world's largest rice millers it sells white and brown rice plus flavored rices and meal kits under the Riceland and private-label brands. The co-op sells to food retailers and food service and food manufacturing companies worldwide. Riceland also makes cooking oils and processes soybeans bran and lecithin and offers rice bran and hulls to pet food makers and livestock farmers as feed and bedding.

Operations

Riceland's Research and Technical Center (Stuttgart Arkansas) is staffed by scientists and technicians with experience in rice edible oil and lecithin chemistry applications and process engineering.

The facility houses separate soybean and rice research laboratories to conduct product development product and process improvement and customer support. Riceland's business lines are supported by on-site analytical food applications and regulatory compliance labs consumer and food-service test kitchens and a well-equipped pilot plant. An ongoing research program reinforces Riceland's position as a premier supplier of rice edible oils and lecithin.

In addition to being a leader in rice milling the cooperative is a major soybean processor. Indeed its soybean processing plant in Stuttgart provides high-protein soybean meal and soybean mill run to poultry catfish and other livestock producers in the Mississippi Delta region and southwestern US.

Geographic Reach

Arkansas-based Riceland provides marketing services to farmers in its home state as well as Louisiana Mississippi Missouri and Texas.

Riceland markets rice products under the Riceland label private labels as ingredients and in bulk.

Riceland's products are sold across the US and in more than 75 foreign destinations.

Sales and Marketing

A major rice exporter and edible oil producer Riceland markets its rice and oil products under the Riceland and Chefway (vegetable oil and shortening) labels. Its products are sold nationwide and to more than 75 foreign destinations.

Rice and oil products are supplied to many of America's leading restaurants fast-food chains cafeterias and military installations. Packaged and flavored rice products are marketed under the Riceland brand. Vegetable oil and shortening products are sold under Riceland and private label brands. Wheat is exported to Mexico and Egypt. Soybeans are sold to US buyers. Rough rice is sold to Mexico and Central America.

Financial Performance

In 2014 Riceland Foods' revenues topped more than $1 billion for the seventh consecutive year. However its net sales for the year were down about 12% due to a decline in prices for rice and soybeans.

Strategy

A key business objective for Riceland is to increase the number of value-added products (such as Riceland Rice 'N Easy flavored rice mixes Riceland Turkey Fry Oil and Fish Fry Oil) and the level of its value added marketing. In 2014 a new riceland.com website went online allowing Riceland customers worldwide access to product information and sales personnel. The website brings consumers face-to-face with some Riceland farmer-members discussing their farming operations. It also includes cooking videos by Georgia Pellegrini a celebrity chef and author of 'Modern Pioneering.' The website

In 2015 Sage V Foods of Boulder Colorado has sold its interest in an instant rice production facility in Little Rock to Best Rice LLC which is jointly owned by Riceland Foods and Producers Rice Mill both based in Stuttgart.

EXECUTIVES

Ceo, Danny Kennedy
Vice President Sales, Larry Sharp
Vice President Application Development, Todd Thompson
Secretary, Karen West
Auditors: BKD LLP LITTLE ROCK ARKANSA

LOCATIONS

HQ: RICELAND FOODS, INC.
   2120 S PARK AVE, STUTTGART, AR 721606822
Phone: 870 673-5500
Web: WWW.RICELAND.COM

PRODUCTS/OPERATIONS

Selected Products
Consumer
   Saffron Yellow Rice Mix
   Rice N Easy Mix Wild Rice
   Long Grain & Wild Mix Rice N Easy Mix
   Broccoli & Cheese Rice N Easy Mix
   Spanish Rice Mix Rice N Easy Mix
   Chicken Rice Mix Rice N Easy Mix
   Long Grain Rice Riceland Extra Long Grain Rice
   Riceland GOLD Perfected Rice
   Riceland Jasmine Rice
   Riceland Natural Brown Rice
   Riceland Plump & Tender Medium Grain Rice
Food Service
   Oil
   Rice
Food Ingredients
   Long grain milled rice
   Long grain brown rice
   Medium grain milled rice
   Parboiled rice
   Broken grains

COMPETITORS

AarhusKarlshamn	Goya
American Rice	JFC International
CHS	Lotus Foods
Cereal Byproducts	Louis Dreyfus Group
Connell Company	Producers Rice Mill
Ebro Foods	Riviana Foods
Farmers Rice Milling	Specialty Rice
Farmers' Rice Cooperative	

HISTORICAL FINANCIALS

Company Type: Private

Income Statement				FYE: July 31
	REVENUE ($ mil.)	NET INCOME ($ mil.)	NET PROFIT MARGIN	EMPLOYEES
07/17	941	0	0.0%	1,646
07/16	1,007	5	0.6%	—
07/15	1,122	9	0.9%	—
07/14	1,148	2	0.2%	—
Annual Growth	(6.4%)	(54.4%)	—	—

2017 Year-End Financials

Return on assets: 1.2%   Cash ($ mil.): 2
Return on equity: —
Current ratio: 0.70

RICHARDSON INDEPENDENT SCHOOL DISTRICT

EXECUTIVES

Pres, Kim Quirk
Vice President, Karen Holburn
Treas, Kim Caston
SEC, Kris Oliver
Secretary, Place 7, Karen Ellis
Principal, Vaughn Gross
Principal, Steve Lemons
Principal, Nikki Hamilton
Principal, Mike Savage
Principal, Karin Holacka
Principal, Kirk Beard
Auditors: HANKINS EASTUP DEATON TONN

LOCATIONS

HQ: RICHARDSON INDEPENDENT SCHOOL DISTRICT
   400 S GREENVILLE AVE # 205, RICHARDSON, TX 750814100
Phone: 469 593-0000
Web: WWW.RISD.ORG

HISTORICAL FINANCIALS

Company Type: Private

Income Statement				FYE: June 30
	REVENUE ($ mil.)	NET INCOME ($ mil.)	NET PROFIT MARGIN	EMPLOYEES
06/16	406	(13)	—	4,500
06/15	388	(3)	—	—
06/14	376	(22)	—	—
Annual Growth	4.0%	—	—	—

RICHLAND COUNTY SCHOOL DISTRICT 1

EXECUTIVES

Coo, Michael Bobby
Commisioner, Jamie Devine
Supt, Allen Coles
Deputy Supt, Richard Moniuskzo
Principal, Jacpb Holmes
Project Manager, Charles Thompson
Board of Directors, Cheryl Harris
Manager, James Montgomery
Auditors: MAULDIN & JENKINS LLC COLUMB

LOCATIONS

HQ: RICHLAND COUNTY SCHOOL DISTRICT 1
1616 RICHLAND ST, COLUMBIA, SC 292012634
Phone: 803 231-7000
Web: WWW.RICHLANDONE.ORG

HISTORICAL FINANCIALS

Company Type: Private

Income Statement
FYE: June 30

	REVENUE ($ mil.)	NET INCOME ($ mil.)	NET PROFIT MARGIN	EMPLOYEES
06/17	388	(4)	—	5,200
06/16	373	(34)	—	—
06/15	363	50	14.0%	—
06/14	358	3	1.0%	—
Annual Growth	2.7%	—	—	—

RICHMOND MEDICAL CENTER

EXECUTIVES

Pres-Ceo, Daniel J Messina
Internal Medicine, Sharon M Clarke
Coordinator, Jean Gordon
Controller, Mou Lee
Internal Medicine Practitioner, Haruka Badger
Trustee, James Molinaro
Project Coordinator, Sandra McGoff
Nurse Practitioner, Barbara Gattullo
Administrative Director, Joe Earl
Administrative Director, Kathy Giovinazzo
Anesthesiologist, Paul Dadic

LOCATIONS

HQ: RICHMOND MEDICAL CENTER
355 BARD AVE, STATEN ISLAND, NY 103101664
Phone: 718 818-1234
Web: WWW.RUMCSI.ORG

HISTORICAL FINANCIALS

Company Type: Private

Income Statement
FYE: December 31

	REVENUE ($ mil.)	NET INCOME ($ mil.)	NET PROFIT MARGIN	EMPLOYEES
12/17	302	1	0.5%	2,555
12/16	300	7	2.6%	—
12/15	285	4	1.6%	—
12/14	274	7	2.7%	—
Annual Growth	3.4%	(40.3%)	—	—

2017 Year-End Financials

Return on assets: 9.6%   Cash ($ mil.): 33
Return on equity: 0.5%
Current ratio: 1.30

RIDEOUT MEMORIAL HOSPITAL

EXECUTIVES

Chm, Ronald M Sweeney
Ceo, Theresa Hamilton
Chprsn, John Wright
SEC, Lisa Del Pero
Treas, John Cary
Chief of Pulmonology, Michael Olsen

LOCATIONS

HQ: RIDEOUT MEMORIAL HOSPITAL
726 4TH ST, MARYSVILLE, CA 959015656
Phone: 530 749-4416

HISTORICAL FINANCIALS

Company Type: Private

Income Statement
FYE: June 30

	REVENUE ($ mil.)	NET INCOME ($ mil.)	NET PROFIT MARGIN	EMPLOYEES
06/16	335	(13)	—	775
06/15	324	(3)	—	—
06/09	245	(10)	—	—
06/05	134	5	4.1%	—
Annual Growth	8.6%	—	—	—

2016 Year-End Financials

Return on assets: 15.3%   Cash ($ mil.): 8
Return on equity: (-4.2%)
Current ratio: 0.70

RIVERSIDE HEALTHCARE ASSOCIATION, INC.

Extra! Extra! Read all about it! Residents of Newport News (and about a dozen other cities in Eastern Virginia) Turn to Riverside Health for Medical Care. The not-for-profit health care provider administers general emergency and specialty medical services from five hospitals Riverside Regional Medical Center Riverside Walter Reed Hospital Riverside Tappahannock Hospital and Riverside Shore Memorial Hospital and Riverside Doctors Hospital as well as a psychiatric hospital a physical rehabilitation facility and retirement communities. Riverside also operates physician offices and medical training facilities. Specialty centers provide home and hospice care cancer treatment and dialysis.

Operations

Combined Riverside's hospitals (including rehabilitation and psychiatric) are home to nearly 1000 beds. Its major hospitals include Riverside Regional Medical Center (450-bed flagship hospital); Riverside Walter Reed Hospital (67-bed acute care facility); Riverside Tappahannock Hospital (67-bed serving the Northern Neck rural area); Riverside

Shore Memorial Hospital (143-bed facility); and Riverside Doctors' Hospital Williamsburg (40 private rooms). It also operates specialty medical facilities including a psychiatric hospital a physical rehabilitation facility and retirement communities.

Geographic Reach

It serves Eastern Virginia including cities of Gloucester Hampton Newport News Poquoson Richmond Tappahannock West Point Williamsburg and Yorktown; Eastern Shore Area of Virginia; Counties of Essex Gloucester Isle of Wight James City King and Queen King William Lancaster Mathews Middlesex New Kent Northumberland Richmond and Surry.

Strategy

To keep up with demand Riverside Health has been upgrading its older facilities and building new ones.

In 2013 the company opened a new hospital the Doctors Hospital in Williamsburg. The 40 room hospital provides acute and emergency care as well as specialty services including cardiology neurology and pulmonary care.

That year Riverside broke ground on the new Riverside Shore Memorial Hospital in Onley which is expected to be completed in late 2015. It will have 57 private inpatient rooms with the ability to add 12 more in the future.

In 2012 Riverside Walter Reed Hospital opened a new intensive care unit.

It is also investing in technology physician expertise and patient services. In 2013 Riverside Shore Medical Center at Metompkin converted to digital mammography equipment offering patients a superior diagnostic tool to film mammograms.

Company Background

The original charter for Riverside dates back to 1915 when the company began as one hospital founded by the community. In 1962 the hospital was relocated to the present site in central Newport News.

EXECUTIVES

Senior Vice President And Chief Financial Officer, William Austin
Vice President Legal Affairs, Jason Houser
Director Of Nursing, Gaynor Callis
Auditors: ERNST & YOUNG LLP RICHMOND V

LOCATIONS

HQ: RIVERSIDE HEALTHCARE ASSOCIATION, INC.
701 TOWN CENTER DR # 1000, NEWPORT NEWS, VA 236064283
Phone: 757 534-7000
Web: WWW.RIVHS.COM

Selected Facilities – Virginia

HOSPITALS
Riverside Behavioral Health Center (Hampton)
Riverside Doctors' Hospital (Williamsburg)
Riverside Regional Medical Center (Newport News)
Riverside Rehabilitation Institute (Williamsburg)
Riverside Tappahannock Hospital (Tappahannock)
Riverside Shore Memorial Hospital (Nassawadox)
Riverside Walter Reed Hospital (Gloucester)

RETIREMENT COMMUNITIES
Patriots Colony (Williamsburg)
Sanders (Gloucester)
Warwick Forest (Newport News)

SURGERY CENTERS
Doctors Surgery Center (Williamsburg)
Peninsula Surgery Center (Newport News)
Riverside Hampton Surgery Center (Hampton)

COMPETITORS

Alleghany Regional Hospital	Franklin Hospital Corp.
Bon Secours Health	Novant Health
Carilion Clinic	Sentara Healthcare
Centra Health Inc.	
Children's Hospital of The King's Daughters	

RIVERSIDE HOSPITAL, INC.

Riverside Hospital operates as Riverside Regional Medical Center a 450-bed acute-care facility that serves the residents of Newport News Virginia. Founded in 1916 the hospital moved to its current 72-acre campus in 1963 providing more than 30 medical specialties including cancer treatment cardiology birthing and diagnostic imaging. It specializes in cardiovascular and neurological surgeries and provides radiosurgery (radiation surgery) through a partnership with the University of Virginia Health System. Its emergency department is a 42-room Level II Trauma Center that treats more than 57000 patients each year. Riverside Hospital is part of the Riverside Health System.

Operations

As part of its operations Riverside Hospital operates a heart center neonatal center 18-bed neonatal intensive care unit cancer care center and radiosurgery center through a partnership with Chesapeake Regional and the University of Virginia Health System. Riverside Hospital works to prevent diagnose and treat diseases of the stomach intestines esophagus pancreas gall bladder liver and biliary tract through its Peninsula Gastroenterology & Riverside Endoscopy Center.

Geographic Reach

Riverside Hospital serves the health care needs of those who reside in and around Newport News Virginia.

EXECUTIVES

Ceo-Pres, William B Downey
SEC, Wade D Broughman
Vice President, Mike J Doucette
Treas, Walter W Austin Jr
Mgr, Robin Brady
Chief of Medicine, Edward Chu
Chief of Medicine, James Mullins
Director, Michelle Wooten
Chief of Medicine, Paul Micale
Doctor, Brian Moylan
Office Manager, Cindy Hogge
Auditors: ERNST YOUNG RICHMOND VA

LOCATIONS

HQ: RIVERSIDE HOSPITAL, INC.
500 J CLYDE MORRIS BLVD, NEWPORT NEWS, VA 236011929
Phone: 757 594-2000
Web: WWW.RIVERSIDEONLINE.COM

PRODUCTS/OPERATIONS

Selected Services

Diagnostic Services
 Cardiac testing
 CT
 Digital mammography
 Electrocardiography
 Magnetic resonance imaging
 Nuclear medicine
 PET
 Ultrasound
Nutrition Services
 Radiosurgery Center
 Leksell Gamma Knife Synergy S Radiosurgery
 Gastroenterology Procedures
 Colonoscopy and polypectomy
 Flexible sigmoidoscopy
 Upper endoscopic exams and therapy
 Endoscopic retrograde cholangiopancreatography (ERCP)
 Percutaneous endoscopic gastrostomy (PEG)
 Capsule/Cam (M2A) study of the small intestine
 Esophageal dilation
 Esophageal and anal manometry
 BRAVO pH study of the esophagus
Pulmonary Rehabilitation
Surgical Services

COMPETITORS

Alleghany Regional Hospital
Bon Secours Health
Carilion Clinic
Centra Health Inc.
Children's Hospital of The King's Daughters
Franklin Hospital Corp.
Novant Health
Sentara Healthcare

RIVERSIDE MEDICAL CENTER

EXECUTIVES

Pres-Ceo, Phillip Kambik
SEC, Pamela Hull
Vice President, Bill W Douglas
Sr Vice President, David A Duda
Pharmacist, Steven Jackson
Customer Representativ, Lenise Mulvihill
Director, Nives Bernardi
Auditing Manager, Richard Schiltz
Administrator, Scott Schroeder
Coordinator, Teresa Ciaccio
Assistant, Samantha Oconnor

LOCATIONS

HQ: RIVERSIDE MEDICAL CENTER
350 N WALL ST, KANKAKEE, IL 609012991
Phone: 815 933-1671
Web: WWW.RIVERSIDEHEALTHCARE.ORG

RIVERSIDE UNIFIED SCHOOL DISTRICT

EXECUTIVES

Supt, Dr David Hansen
Supt, Michael H Fine
President, Lynn Carmen Day
Vice President, Charles L Beaty PHD
Staff, Brian Caldwell
Analyst, Aaron Lindsay
Analyst, Don Kramer
Trustee, Kathy Allavie
Information Technology Manager, Kitty Smith
Superintendent, Paulette Jones
Assistant Director, Kevin Hauser
Auditors: NIGRO & NIGRO PC MURRIETA C

LOCATIONS

HQ: RIVERSIDE UNIFIED SCHOOL DISTRICT
3380 14TH ST, RIVERSIDE, CA 925013810
Phone: 951 788-7135
Web: WWW.RUSDLINK.ORG

ROBINSON OIL CORPORATION

EXECUTIVES

Pres, Thomas L Robinson
Cfo, Stephen F White
2nd Vp, Erin Graziosi
2nd Vp, Reilly Musser

LOCATIONS

HQ: ROBINSON OIL CORPORATION
955 MARTIN AVE, SANTA CLARA, CA 950502608
Phone: 408 327-4300
Web: WWW.ROTTENROBBIE.COM

PRODUCTS/OPERATIONS

Selected Products
BioDiesel
Commercial fleet fueling
   CFN (Commercial Fueling Network)
   FleetWide Corp.
   Pacific Pride (PacPride)
Convenience store
Diesel
Kerosene
Lotto
Propane
   Blue Rhino
   Bulk

COMPETITORS

7-Eleven	Couche-Tard
Chevron	Flyers Energy

HISTORICAL FINANCIALS

Company Type: Private

Income Statement   FYE: December 31

	REVENUE ($ mil.)	NET INCOME ($ mil.)	NET PROFIT MARGIN	EMPLOYEES
12/16	339	20	6.1%	250
12/12	464	10	2.3%	—
12/09	292	8	2.8%	—
12/08	2,048	0	0.0%	—
Annual Growth	(20.1%)	352.3%	—	—

2016 Year-End Financials
Return on assets: 2.1%   Cash ($ mil.): 18
Return on equity: 6.1%
Current ratio: 1.80

ROCHESTER GAS AND ELECTRIC CORPORATION

Upstate New York residents count on Rochester Gas and Electric (RG&E) to keep the lights turned on. The regulated utility provides electricity to about 370000 customers and natural gas to 306000 customers. RG&E operates 22500 miles of power transmission and distribution lines and has a generating capacity of approximately 400 MW from interests in fossil-fueled and hydroelectric power plants. RG&E and sister utility company New York State Electric & Gas (NYSEG) are subsidiaries of regional power and gas distribution player Avangrid).

Change in Company Type
In 2012 ultimate parent company IBERDROLA reorganized consolidating Iberdrola Renewables Holdings and IBERDROLA USA under a new Avangrid holding company. Intermediate holding company Iberdrola USA Networks was then created to hold all of IBERDROLA's regulated US electric and gas utilities including RG&E.

Geographic Reach
RG&E's service territory contains a substantial suburban area and a large agricultural area in parts of nine counties including and surrounding the city of Rochester New York with a population of 1 million.

Financial Performance

The company operates under the Network business of IBERDROLA. The Network business accounted for 25% of IBERDROLA's 2013 revenues; some 28% of Network sales came from US operations. IBERDROLA generated 10% of its total revenues from the US in 2013.

Strategy
To reduce its carbon emissions RG&E along with affiliate NYSEG is pushing green energy options including a wind energy power program whereby residents can choose to have their power supply from wind generated sources.

In 2013 the company announced plans to retire its 18-MW Rochester 9 natural gas-fired combustion turbine as it would be too expensive to repair the equipment failures that forced the unit offline that year.

Company Background
Between 2008 and the end of 2010 NYSEG or RG&E interconnected six landfill gas plants with a total of 26MW of generating capacity three wind farms with 209 wind turbines (381 MW of generating capacity) in Wyoming and Steuben counties a new 30 MW combined heat and power facility for Cornell University and a lithium-ion battery energy storage facility for AES Corporation.

EXECUTIVES

Executive Vice President, Mike Dorfner
Auditors: KPMG LLP NEW YORK NEW YORK

LOCATIONS

HQ: ROCHESTER GAS AND ELECTRIC CORPORATION
89 EAST AVE, ROCHESTER, NY 146490002
Phone: 800 295-7323
Web: WWW.RGE.COM

COMPETITORS

CH Energy	New York Power
Con Edison	Authority
National Fuel Gas	Niagara Mohawk

HISTORICAL FINANCIALS

Company Type: Private

Income Statement   FYE: December 31

	REVENUE ($ mil.)	NET INCOME ($ mil.)	NET PROFIT MARGIN	EMPLOYEES
12/17	850	83	9.8%	865
12/16	1,042	80	7.7%	—
12/10	982	54	5.5%	—
Annual Growth	(2.0%)	6.3%	—	—

2017 Year-End Financials
Return on assets: 19.5%   Cash ($ mil.): —
Return on equity: 9.8%
Current ratio: 0.50

ROCHESTER GENERAL HOSPITAL INC

EXECUTIVES

Ceo, Mark Clement
Cfo, Robert Nesselbush
Clinical Director, Timothy Van Vassem
Information Specialist, Emily Wishart
Information Specialist, Heidi Mix
Coordinator, Nancy Latacki
Coordinator, Rank James
Accounting Staff, Stephanie Beiter

Buyer, Deann Osborne
Histology Supervisor, Hal James
Director, Roberto Vargas

LOCATIONS

HQ: ROCHESTER GENERAL HOSPITAL INC
1425 PORTLAND AVE, ROCHESTER, NY 146213095
Phone: 585 922-4101
Web: WWW.ROCHESTERGENERAL.ORG

HISTORICAL FINANCIALS

Company Type: Private

Income Statement   FYE: December 31

	REVENUE ($ mil.)	NET INCOME ($ mil.)	NET PROFIT MARGIN	EMPLOYEES
12/17	899	32	3.6%	3,100
12/16	858	24	2.9%	—
12/15	847	27	3.3%	—
12/14	810	32	4.0%	—
Annual Growth	3.5%	(0.6%)	—	—

2017 Year-End Financials
Return on assets: 5.7%   Cash ($ mil.): 36
Return on equity: 3.6%
Current ratio: 0.50

ROCHESTER INSTITUTE OF TECHNOLOGY (INC)

The Rochester Institute of Technology (RIT) is a privately endowed university with nine colleges focused on providing career-oriented education to about 18600 students. The school which has a student-faculty ratio of about 14:1 offers more than 90 bachelor's degree programs in art and design business engineering science and hotel management. RIT also confers master's and doctorate degrees. The university's National Technical Institute for the Deaf is the first and largest technological college for learners who suffer from hearing loss. RIT which traces its roots back to 1829 counts among its alumni the CEOs of Kodak and The Associated Press.

Operations
Spanning some 1300 acres in Rochester New York RIT's campus serves 15400 undergraduate and 3200 graduate students with help from its faculty and staff of more than 3850. Approximately 1300 deaf and hard-of-hearing students live study and work alongside hearing students on the RIT campus. Tuition runs nearly $33000 for general students and more than $12000 for deaf and hard-of-hearing students.

RIT operates a campus in Dubai's Silicon Oasis a government-owned high tech complex. The campus serves the university's goal of growing its reputation worldwide and expanding international opportunities for students. RIT Dubai offers undergraduate and graduate degree programs in engineering business information technology and leadership.

Geographic Reach
RIT is based in Rochester New York; it has locations abroad in Eastern Europe the Middle East and Asia.

Sales and Marketing
The university's students come from all 50 states and more than 100 nations around the world.

Financial Performance
Net revenue increased 4% to $523.9 million in fiscal 2015 as the school generated more income

from tuition and fees auxiliary services and government grants and contracts. However net income dropped 79% to $18.5 million largely due to a drop in investment earnings as well as higher operating expenses including salaries and benefits.

Cash flow from operations remained flat that year dropping 1% to $35.9 million mainly due to changes in working capital.

Strategy

To boost investment returns the university has adjusted its asset allocation to include more equities and alternative investments.

EXECUTIVES

Svp Finance And Administration, James H. Watters
Dean Kate Gleason College Of Engineering, Harvey Palmer
President, William W. (Bill) Destler
Dean College Of Applied Science And Technology, H. Fred Walker
Svp Academic Affairs And Provost, Jeremy A. Haefner
Vp And Dean Institute Of Health Sciences And Technology, Daniel B. Ornt
Dean College Of Imaging Arts & Sciences, Lorraine Justice
Dean College Of Liberal Arts, James J. Winebrake
Dean College Of Science, Sophia Maggelakis
Dean And President National Technical Institute For The Deaf, Gerard J. Buckley
Svp Enrollment Management And Career Services, James Miller
Dean B. Thomas Golisano College Of Computing And Information Sciences, Anne Haake
Dean Saunders College Of Business, Jacqueline Mozrall
Dean Graduate Studies, Hector Flores
Svp Student Affairs, Sandra Johnson
Secretary Of The Institute And Chief Of Staff, Karen Barrows
President Kosovo Campus, Sharon Y. Hart
Associate Vice President Development And Alumni Relations, Heather Engel
Assistant Vice President And Director Fin Aid And Scholarship, Verna Hazen
Department Head, Risa Robinson
Associate Vice President For Academic Affairs, Stephen Aldersley
Vice President For Academic Affairs, Katherine Mayberry
Assistant Vice President Human Resources, Judy Bender
Assistant Vice President For Student Affairs, David Bagley
Assistant Vice President Of Student Wellness Student Affairs, Donna Rubin
Associate Vice President Of Academic Affairs And Registrar, Joe Loffredo
Assistant Vice President For Institutional Research, Richard Dirmyer
Vice President Of The Association Of Computing, Vicki Hanson
Department Chair, Todd Dunn
Department Chair Of Photojournalism Program, Doug Rea
Associate Vice President For Student Health, Wendy Gelbard
Delta Sigma Pi Vice President Of Community Service, Anika Wright
Department Chair, Rebecca Edwards
Assistant Vice President Finance And Administration, Saleh Yammout
Department Chair And Associate Professor, Shal Khazanchi
Board Member, Thomas Kausch
Auditors: PRICEWATERHOUSECOOPERS LLP RO

LOCATIONS

HQ: ROCHESTER INSTITUTE OF TECHNOLOGY (INC)
1 LOMB MEMORIAL DR, ROCHESTER, NY 146235698
Phone: 585 475-2411
Web: WWW.RIT.EDU

PRODUCTS/OPERATIONS

Selected Colleges
College of Applied Science and Technology
    School of Engineering Technology
    School of International Hospitality and Service Innovation
E. Philip Saunders College of Business
B. Thomas Golisano College of Computing and Information Sciences
Kate Gleason College of Engineering
College of Health Sciences and Technology
College of Imaging Arts and Sciences
    School for American Crafts
    School of Art
    School of Design
    School of Film and Animation
    School of Media Sciences
    School of Photographic Arts and Sciences
College of Liberal Arts
National Technical Institute for the Deaf
College of Science

Selected Graduate & Undergraduate Programs
Accounting
Applied Networking & Systems Administration
Applied Statistics
Biochemistry
Business
Civil Engineering Technology
Clinical Chemistry
Computer Integrated Machining Technology
Computer Science
Digital Imaging & Publishing Technology
Electrical/Mechanical Engineering Technology
Environmental Science
Finance
Glass & Glass Sculpture
Health Systems Administration
Healthcare Billing & Coding Technology
Imaging Arts: Photography
Industrial & Systems Engineering
Instruction Technology
Management
Medical Illustration
Metals/Jewelry Design
Ophthalmic Optical Finishing Technology
Print Media
Psychology
Service Leadership and Innovation
Voice Communication
Woodworking and Furniture Design

HISTORICAL FINANCIALS
Company Type: Private

Income Statement				FYE: June 30
	REVENUE ($ mil.)	NET INCOME ($ mil.)	NET PROFIT MARGIN	EMPLOYEES
06/18	579	203	35.2%	3,300
06/17	560	74	13.2%	—
06/12	490	16	3.4%	—
06/06	370	45	12.2%	—
Annual Growth	3.8%	13.4%	—	—

2018 Year-End Financials
Return on assets: 8.8%
Return on equity: 35.2%
Current ratio: —
Cash ($ mil.): 62

ROCKFORD, BOARD OF EDUCATION

EXECUTIVES

Pres, Kenneth Serivano
Supt, Dr Ehren Jarrett
President, Harmon Mitchell
Vice President, Jude Makulec
SEC, Lisa Jackson
Supt, Linda Hernandez
Teacher, Melissa Wolf
Teacher, Nicole Adams
Manager, Breanna Johansen
Manager, Chrystine Harned
Project Coordinator, Emily Tropp
Auditors: SIKICH LLP ROCK ILLINOIS

LOCATIONS

HQ: ROCKFORD, BOARD OF EDUCATION
501 7TH ST, ROCKFORD, IL 611041242
Phone: 815 966-3000
Web: WWW.RPS205.COM

HISTORICAL FINANCIALS
Company Type: Private

Income Statement				FYE: June 30
	REVENUE ($ mil.)	NET INCOME ($ mil.)	NET PROFIT MARGIN	EMPLOYEES
06/17	509	(23)	—	4,200
06/16	445	(15)	—	—
06/15	446	19	4.4%	—
06/14	398	(54)	—	—
Annual Growth	8.5%	—	—	—

ROCKIES EXPRESS PIPELINE LLC

LOCATIONS

HQ: ROCKIES EXPRESS PIPELINE LLC
370 VAN GORDON ST # 4000, LAKEWOOD, CO 802281519
Phone: 877 546-5877

HISTORICAL FINANCIALS
Company Type: Private

Income Statement				FYE: December 31
	REVENUE ($ mil.)	NET INCOME ($ mil.)	NET PROFIT MARGIN	EMPLOYEES
12/17	893	298	33.4%	41
12/16	730	178	24.5%	—
Annual Growth	22.3%	67.0%	—	—

2017 Year-End Financials
Return on assets: 1.9%
Return on equity: 33.4%
Current ratio: 0.10
Cash ($ mil.): 25

ROPER HOSPITAL, INC.

EXECUTIVES

Pres, David L Dunlap
Admin, Matthew Severance
Prin, Karen Fraser
Emergency Medicine Specialist, John F Walters
Director, Bobbie Maner
Information Technology Manager, Carolyn Brown
Director of Engineering, Peter Dinicola
Emergency Medicine Specialist, John Walters
Director of Infection Control, Cile Guerry
Coordinator, Judy Graham
Purchasing Coordinator, Lisa Thompson

LOCATIONS

HQ: ROPER HOSPITAL, INC.
  316 CALHOUN ST, CHARLESTON, SC 294011125
Phone: 843 724-2000
Web: WWW.RSFH.COM

HISTORICAL FINANCIALS

Company Type: Private

| Income Statement | | | FYE: December 31 | |
	REVENUE ($ mil.)	NET INCOME ($ mil.)	NET PROFIT MARGIN	EMPLOYEES
12/17	375	34	9.2%	2,100
12/16	386	47	12.2%	—
12/14	369	57	15.6%	—
12/13	392	54	14.0%	—
Annual Growth	(1.1%)	(10.9%)	—	—

2017 Year-End Financials

Return on assets: 0.2%   Cash ($ mil.): —
Return on equity: 9.2%
Current ratio: 1.00

ROSEMOUNT-APPLE VALLEY-EAGAN SCHOOL BOARD

EXECUTIVES

Chairperson, Rob Duchscher
Teacher, Tyler Pauly
Teacher, Amanda Konop
Teacher, Ann Hortsch
Education Specialist, Betsy Galles
Occupational Specia, Marcia Behm
Teacher, Michael Sullivan
Psychologist, Terri Cairns
Special Education Teacher, Corrine Simmons
School Counselor, Quincy Davis
Auditors: MALLOY MONTAGUE KARNOWSKI R

LOCATIONS

HQ: ROSEMOUNT-APPLE VALLEY-EAGAN SCHOOL
  BOARD
  3455 153RD ST W, ROSEMOUNT, MN 550684946
Phone: 651 423-7700
Web: WWW.DISTRICT196.ORG

HISTORICAL FINANCIALS

Company Type: Private

| Income Statement | | | FYE: June 30 | |
	REVENUE ($ mil.)	NET INCOME ($ mil.)	NET PROFIT MARGIN	EMPLOYEES
06/16	372	117	31.7%	3,600
06/14	339	(27)	—	—
06/13	337	10	3.2%	—
06/12	336	33	9.9%	—
Annual Growth	2.5%	37.2%	—	—

ROTARY INTERNATIONAL

The rotary phone may be a thing of the past but Rotary International (founded in 1905 and now with more than 1.2 million members) is still going strong. The service organization with a motto of Service Above Self comprises 34000-plus clubs in more than 200 countries and territories. Rotary service projects are intended to alleviate problems such as hunger illiteracy poverty and violence. Grants from the Rotary Foundation support its efforts. Along with its service projects Rotary aims to promote high ethical standards in the workplace. Membership in Rotary clubs is by invitation. Each club strives to include representatives from major businesses professions and institutions in its community.

Operations

Rotary (whose name arose from the early practice of rotating meetings among members' offices) boasts more than 34000 clubs globally with a membership of 1.2-plus million. In 2014 the organization had $24 million in its endowment fund.

Rotary began admitting women to its clubs in 1989. In 2014 women accounted for more than 16% of its global membership.

Geographic Reach

From its headquarters in Evanston Illinois Rotary operates in more than 200 countries.

Financial Performance

Rotary's revenues increased by 20% in 2014 due to a rise in contributions membership dues and net investment returns.

Net income increased by 29% that year as the result of higher revenues and a decline in grant expenses.

Strategy

As part of its Future Vision plan Rotary is working to partner with established organizations with expertise in any of Rotary's six areas of focus: peace and conflict prevention/resolution disease prevention and treatment water and sanitation maternal and child health basic education and literacy and economic and community development.

In its second century of operations Rotary has chosen the eradication of polio as one of its top priorities. Helping the organization meet these goals the Bill & Melinda Gates Foundation's initial grant of $100 million spurred a challenge grant with an additional $225 million. Rotary's working to raise an extra $200 million in grant funds. Other goals include expanding internationally and increasing the diversity of the organization's membership.

In 2014 the organization received a $70 million 2-to-1 match from the Bill & Melinda Gates Foundation by meeting its obligation to commit $35 million from the PolioPlus Fund toward the Global Polio Eradication Initiative.

In 2014 the Peace Corps and Rotary signed a letter of collaboration strengthening the organizations' cooperation to promote global development and volunteer service.

HISTORY

On February 23 1905 lawyer Paul Harris met with three friends in an office in Chicago's Unity Building. Inspired by the fellowship and tolerance of his boyhood home in Wallingford Vermont Harris proposed organizing a men's club to meet periodically for the purpose of camaraderie and making business contacts. The new endeavor was organized as the Rotary Club of Chicago and had 30 members by the end of the year.

As additional clubs followed the organization assumed its role as a civic and service organization (the installation of public comfort stations in Chicago's City Hall was one of its first projects). At the first convention of the National Association of Rotary Clubs in 1910 Harris was elected president. International clubs soon followed and by 1921 there were Rotary clubs on six continents.

In 1932 while struggling to revive a company with financial difficulties Rotarian Herbert Taylor devised a statement of business ethics that later became the Rotarian mantra. Taylor's "4-Way Test" consisted of the following questions: "Is it the truth? Is it fair to all concerned? Will it build goodwill and better friendships? Will it be beneficial to all concerned?"

During WWII Rotary clubs promoted war relief and peace fund efforts. Following WWII the clubs assisted in efforts to aid refugees and prisoners of war. The extent of Rotarian involvement in international issues became clear when 49 members assisted in drafting the United Nations Charter in 1945.

The first significant contributions to The Rotary Foundation followed Harris' death in 1947. These funds formed the bedrock for the foundation's programs and in 1965 the foundation created its Matching Grants and Group Study Exchange programs. Rotary International also welcomed younger members in the 1960s by creating its Interact and Rotaract clubs in 1962 and 1968 respectively.

The largest meeting of Rotarians occurred in 1978 when almost 40000 members attended the organization's Tokyo convention. But controversy was fast approaching the male-only organization. In 1978 a California Rotary club defied the male-only requirement and admitted two women. Claiming that the club had violated the organization's constitution Rotary International revoked the club's charter. A lengthy court battle ensued and a series of appeals landed the issue on the docket of the US Supreme Court. In 1987 the court ruled that the all-male requirement was discriminatory. Two years later Rotary International officially did away with its all-male status.

In the 1990s membership in Rotary clubs grew but at a slower pace than in the organization's past. Mary Wolfenberger was appointed the organization's first female CFO in 1993 (resigned 1997). In 1998 Rotary International joined with the United Nations to launch a series of humanitarian service projects in developing areas. In 1999 the organization spearheaded events to help flood victims in North Carolina and refugees in the Balkans. In 2000 the group created a program specializing in peace and conflict resolution. Rotary International established its first Internet-based Rotary club in early 2002. Also that year the group founded the Rotary Centers for International Studies which selects 70 scholars a year to participate in a master's-level peace studies program.

In addition to celebrating its 100th anniversary in 2005 the organization awarded grants in Sudan and Indonesia to stop polio and assist victims of the tsunami that struck Southeast Asia at the end of the year.

EXECUTIVES

Member Board Of Directors, Lori Carlson
Auditors: GRANT THORNTON LLP EVANSTON

LOCATIONS

HQ: ROTARY INTERNATIONAL
1 ROTARY CTR, EVANSTON, IL 602014422
Phone: 847 866-3000
Web: WWW.ROTARY.ORG

PRODUCTS/OPERATIONS

2014 Sales

	% of total
Contributions	54
Net investment return	26
Dues	14
Other activities	6
Total	**100**

HISTORICAL FINANCIALS

Company Type: Private

Income Statement — FYE: June 30

	REVENUE ($ mil.)	NET INCOME ($ mil.)	NET PROFIT MARGIN	EMPLOYEES
06/16	355	(17)	—	800
06/12	90	(1)	—	—
06/11	433	168	38.9%	—
06/10	0	0	15.3%	—
Annual Growth	251.1%	—	—	—

2016 Year-End Financials

Return on assets: 8.5%   Cash ($ mil.): 65
Return on equity: (-5.0%)
Current ratio: —

ROTH STAFFING COMPANIES, L.P.

Roth Staffing offers temporary and temp-to-hire staffing and permanent placement services through its specialized business lines. Ultimate Staffing Services specializes in administrative customer service clerical manufacturing & production positions. Ledgent Finance & Accounting focuses on accounting and finance professionals while Ledgent Technology & Engineering concentrates on professionals in those fields. Adams & Martin Group recruits legal professionals. The company serves clients in 21 US states and Washington DC through more than 100 branches and a number of on-premise locations.

Operations

Roth Staffing has six specialized business lines: Ultimate Staffing Service (the 11th largest administrative/clerical staffing company in the US) Ledgent Finance & Accounting Adams & Martin Group Ledgent Technology & Engineering and About Talent. The organization is also affiliated with Ultimate Locum Tenens.

In addition to staffing Roth Staffing Companies offers executive search services recruitment process outsourcing 1099 (independent contractor) management and payroll services.

Company Background

Roth Staffing was founded in 1994 by CEO Ben Roth. The company stands as the only firm in the industry ever ranked #1 on the Inc. 500 list of fastest-growing privately-owned companies.

EXECUTIVES

Founder And Ceo, Ben Roth
Executive Vice President, Pam Sexauer
President And Coo, Adam Roth
Vp Accounting And Finance, Pauline Francis
Sr. Vp Of Professional Services, Julie Hagan
Vp Ledgent Technology, Brett Roth
Senior Vice President Finance And Accounting, Mimi Taylor
Vice President Of Marketing, Staci Johnson

LOCATIONS

HQ: ROTH STAFFING COMPANIES, L.P.
450 N STATE COLLEGE BLVD, ORANGE, CA 928681708
Phone: 714 939-8600
Web: WWW.ROTHSTAFFING.COM

COMPETITORS

Adecco	On Assignment
Allegis Group	Randstad Holding
Kelly Services	Robert Half
Kforce	TrueBlue
ManpowerGroup	Volt Information

HISTORICAL FINANCIALS

Company Type: Private

Income Statement — FYE: December 31

	REVENUE ($ mil.)	NET INCOME ($ mil.)	NET PROFIT MARGIN	EMPLOYEES
12/16	344	7	2.1%	610
12/12	244	0	—	—
12/11	244	0	—	—
12/10	202	0	—	—
Annual Growth	9.3%	—	—	—

2016 Year-End Financials

Return on assets: 0.2%   Cash ($ mil.): —
Return on equity: 2.1%
Current ratio: 1.70

ROUND ROCK INDEPENDENT SCHOOL DISTRICT (INC)

EXECUTIVES

Supt, Dr Jess H Chvez
Prin, Georgia Mill
Supt, Dr Steven Flores
Executive Assistant, Lisa Ramirez
Education Specialist, Candy Squilla
Information Specialist, Debby Acevedo
Programmer Analyst, Mick Bull
Information Technology/Interne, Steve Burpee
Coordinator, Nicole Shannon
Human Resources, Frank Hernandez
Executive Assistant, Starla Taylor
Auditors: MAXWELL LOCKE & RITTER LLP AU

LOCATIONS

HQ: ROUND ROCK INDEPENDENT SCHOOL DISTRICT (INC)
1311 ROUND ROCK AVE, ROUND ROCK, TX 786814941
Phone: 512 464-5000
Web: WWW.ROUNDROCKISD.ORG

HISTORICAL FINANCIALS

Company Type: Private

Income Statement — FYE: June 30

	REVENUE ($ mil.)	NET INCOME ($ mil.)	NET PROFIT MARGIN	EMPLOYEES
06/18	546	(70)	—	4,500
06/17	533	(65)	—	—
06/16	523	64	12.3%	—
06/15	491	126	25.7%	—
Annual Growth	3.6%	—	—	—

2018 Year-End Financials

Return on assets: 2.0%   Cash ($ mil.): 364
Return on equity: (-12.9%)
Current ratio: 4.80

ROWAN UNIVERSITY

EXECUTIVES

Pres, Dr Ali Houshmand
Network Technician, Christine Gangloff
Procurement Staff, Christine M Brasteter
Facilities Manager, Gary Veacock
Accounting Staff, Hanmei Chen
Information, Hoi-Yi V Au
Assistant Professor, Jennifer Nicholson
Facilities, Mary Butts
Accounting Staff, MEI Zhang
Facilities, Paul Powell
Facilities, Zaruba Allen
Auditors: KPMG LLP SHORT HILLS NJ

LOCATIONS

HQ: ROWAN UNIVERSITY
201 MULLICA HILL RD, GLASSBORO, NJ 080281702
Phone: 856 256-4000
Web: WWW.ROWAN.EDU

HISTORICAL FINANCIALS

Company Type: Private

Income Statement — FYE: June 30

	REVENUE ($ mil.)	NET INCOME ($ mil.)	NET PROFIT MARGIN	EMPLOYEES
06/17	363	36	9.9%	1,932
06/16	329	(7)	—	—
06/13	196	25	13.0%	—
06/12	186	12	6.6%	—
Annual Growth	14.3%	24.0%	—	—

2017 Year-End Financials

Return on assets: 13.3%   Cash ($ mil.): 84
Return on equity: 9.9%
Current ratio: 1.00

RUBY PIPELINE, L.L.C.

EXECUTIVES

Pres-MBR, James J Cleary
MBR, William L Pease
Sr V Pres-MBR, Daniel B Martin
V Pres-MBR, Janice A Alperin
V Pres-MBR, Michael S Catt
Executive, Thomas Martin

LOCATIONS

HQ: RUBY PIPELINE, L.L.C.
1001 LOUISIANA ST, HOUSTON, TX 770025089
Phone: 713 420-2300
Web: WWW.KINDERMORGAN.COM

HISTORICAL FINANCIALS

Company Type: Private

Income Statement				FYE: December 31
	REVENUE ($ mil.)	NET INCOME ($ mil.)	NET PROFIT MARGIN	EMPLOYEES
12/17	344	61	17.9%	19
12/16	351	30	8.7%	—
Annual Growth	(2.0%)	101.6%	—	—

2017 Year-End Financials

Return on assets: 1.6%   Cash ($ mil.): 37
Return on equity: 17.9%
Current ratio: 0.60

RUDOLPH AND SLETTEN, INC.

Rudolph and Sletten ... the little-known tenth reindeer? More like the elves who built Santa's workshop. The firm is a mainstay of the California construction scene especially Silicon Valley. It has built corporate campuses for Apple Microsoft and Wells Fargo as well as Lucasfilm's Skywalker Ranch production facility. Rudolph and Sletten is one of the US' largest general building contractors with site selection design/build and construction management capabilities. Key projects also include biotech labs hospitals and schools. Onslow "Rudy" Rudolph founded the company in 1959 and was joined by partner Kenneth Sletten in 1962. Rudolph and Sletten is a subsidiary of Tutor Perini Corporation .

Geographic Reach

Redwood City California-based Rudolph and Sletten has regional offices in San Francisco Sacramento Irvine San Diego and Stockton California. The firm is licensed to build in California Arizona Nevada Washington Colorado Idaho Oregon Oklahoma and Texas.

Sales and Marketing

Big name clients have included a number of prestigious institutions such as Childrens Hospital Los Angeles The University of Southern California Genentech and the Monterey Bay Aquarium. The company reports that more than 95% of its business comes from repeat customers.

Financial Performance

California is Rudolph and Slatten's largest market representing an estimated $666 million in revenue in 2013.

Strategy

To capitalize on San Francisco's building boom the firm hired several San Francisco construction veterans in early 2014 to expand its operations there. Rudolph and Sletten is currently working on projects in Mission Bay and the Financial District.

The firm is renowned for its green building practices with nearly half the staff Leadership in Energy and Environmental Design (LEED)-accredited; it aims for 100% accreditation by 2013. Its own corporate headquarters was Gold LEED-certified based on its use of recycled materials energy and water efficiency and sustainable site. Other sustainable projects undertaken by Rudolph and Sletten include the Lawrence Berkeley National Laboratory and the NOAA Fisheries Services Southwest Science Center.

EXECUTIVES

Senior Vice President Preconstruction Services, Michael Mohrman

Auditors: DELOITTE & TOUCHE LLP LOS AN

LOCATIONS

HQ: RUDOLPH AND SLETTEN, INC.
2 CIRCLE STAR WAY FL 4, SAN CARLOS, CA 940706200
Phone: 650 216-3600
Web: WWW.RSCONST.COM

PRODUCTS/OPERATIONS

Major Markets

Biotechnology/pharmaceutical
Commercial office and corporate campuses
Education
Gaming and hospitality
Government
Health care
Industrial
Justice
Sports and entertainment
Technology

Selected Services

Estimating
Scheduling
Value engineering
Constructibility review
Building Information Modeling (BIM)
Construction
Construction management
Project management
Quality control
Disruption management
Commissioning
Self performed work
Sustainable cpnstruction
Safety

COMPETITORS

Charles Pankow Builders	Kitchell
Clark Construction Group	McCarthy Building
	PCL Constructors
DPR Construction	Summit Builders
Devcon Construction	Swinerton
Hathaway Dinwiddie Construction	Turner Construction
	Webcor Builders
Hensel Phelps Construction	Whiting-Turner

HISTORICAL FINANCIALS

Company Type: Private

Income Statement				FYE: December 31
	REVENUE ($ mil.)	NET INCOME ($ mil.)	NET PROFIT MARGIN	EMPLOYEES
12/16	1,307	14	1.1%	400
12/15	940	7	0.7%	—
12/14	637	3	0.5%	—
12/13	665	(0)	—	—
Annual Growth	25.2%	—	—	—

RUDOLPH LIBBE INC.

EXECUTIVES

Pres, Timothy Alter
Vice President, Philip J Rudolph
Chm, William Rudolph
Treasurer, Allan J Libbe
Manager, Brian Neal
Maintenance Manager, Brian Schwartz
Manager, Brian Seeger
Vice-President, James Philo
Safety Director, Mark Hoffman
Safety Director, Tim Clark
Vice-President, Bradley Deal

LOCATIONS

HQ: RUDOLPH LIBBE INC.
6494 LATCHA RD, WALBRIDGE, OH 434659788
Phone: 419 241-5000
Web: RLGBUILDS.COM/COMPANIES/RUDOLPH-LIBBE-INC/

HISTORICAL FINANCIALS

Company Type: Private

Income Statement				FYE: December 31
	REVENUE ($ mil.)	NET INCOME ($ mil.)	NET PROFIT MARGIN	EMPLOYEES
12/17	362	6	1.8%	500
12/16	300	7	2.5%	—
12/14	246	6	2.7%	—
12/06	199	2	1.4%	—
Annual Growth	5.6%	8.0%	—	—

2017 Year-End Financials

Return on assets: 13.7%   Cash ($ mil.): 15
Return on equity: 1.8%
Current ratio: 1.10

RUSH UNIVERSITY MEDICAL CENTER

EXECUTIVES

President, Larry J Goodman
Assistant To Doctor Henry Blac, Norma Sandoval
Program Director, Norman Wool
Oncologist, Philip Bonomi
Managing Director, Pincas Bitterman
Director, Tibor Glant
Gynecology/Obstetrics Speclst, Xavier Pombar
Orthopedist, Jonathan Rubenstein
Gastroenterologist, Keith Bruninga
Manager, Carolyn Whitney

LOCATIONS

HQ: RUSH UNIVERSITY MEDICAL CENTER
1653 W CONGRESS PKWY, CHICAGO, IL 606123833
Phone: 312 942-5000
Web: WWW.RUSH.EDU

HISTORICAL FINANCIALS

Company Type: Private

Income Statement				FYE: June 30
	REVENUE ($ mil.)	NET INCOME ($ mil.)	NET PROFIT MARGIN	EMPLOYEES
06/17	2,267	302	13.3%	8,000
06/16	1,502	83	5.6%	—
06/15	1,408	(22)	—	—
06/14	1,969	208	10.6%	—
Annual Growth	4.8%	13.2%	—	—

2017 Year-End Financials

Return on assets: 3.4%   Cash ($ mil.): 99
Return on equity: 13.3%
Current ratio: 0.70

RUSSELL & SMITH FORD, INC.

EXECUTIVES

Chm, Michael G Smith
President, Charles M Smith Jr
Vice President, Daniel L Chernault
Vice President, Mark D Rehkopf
Training and Manag, Rhonda Walker
Finance Manager, Amanda Jones
Fleet Staff, Bob Ford
Sales Associate, Connie Ford
Controller, John Lohse
Accounting Staff, Judy Walker
Sales Staff, Peter Lindberg
Auditors: SVADLENAK SEE & COMPANY PC

LOCATIONS

HQ: RUSSELL & SMITH FORD, INC.
3440 SOUTH LOOP W, HOUSTON, TX 770255296
Phone: 713 663-4111
Web: WWW.RSFORD.COM

HISTORICAL FINANCIALS

Company Type: Private

Income Statement				FYE: May 31
	REVENUE ($ mil.)	NET INCOME ($ mil.)	NET PROFIT MARGIN	EMPLOYEES
05/15	291	3	1.2%	310
05/14	304	4	1.5%	—
05/13	265	3	1.3%	—
05/12	222	2	0.9%	—
Annual Growth	9.4%	19.0%		

2015 Year-End Financials

Return on assets: 3.1%   Cash ($ mil.): 8
Return on equity: 1.2%
Current ratio: 0.30

RYMAN HOSPITALITY PROPERTIES, INC.

Ryman Hospitality Properties (formerly Gaylord Entertainment) may be hollerin' for attention in the hospitality game but it's no corporate hayseed. Its properties consist of resort hotels tethered closely to attractions that appeal to the meetings and conventions market. They include the Gaylord Opryland Resort & Convention Center in Nashville the Gaylord Palms Resort in Florida (close to Disney World) the Gaylord Texan Resort near Dallas and the Gaylord National Resort and Convention Center in the Washington DC area. Ryman's hotels are managed by hotel giant Marriott. In 2012 the company changed its name convered to a REIT and sold its hotel brand and management business to Marriott.

HISTORY

The origins of Gaylord Entertainment can be traced back to the Oklahoma Publishing Co. a newspaper publishing company founded by Edward K. Gaylord Ray Dickinson and Roy McClintock in 1903. The publisher of The Daily Oklahoman Oklahoma Publishing branched into radio in 1928 with the purchase of Oklahoma City radio station WKY. With its 1949 creation of Oklahoma City television station WKY-TV Oklahoma Publishing made the leap into television.

Edward K. Gaylord died in 1974 at the age of 101 and his son Edward L. Gaylord was appointed CEO. Under his leadership the company purchased Opryland USA in 1983 — an acquisition that netted it the Grand Ole Opry Opryland Themepark and the Opryland Hotel. Opryland USA also launched country music cable network The Nashville Network that year.

In 1991 the increasingly diverse Oklahoma Publishing spun off its entertainment and broadcast holdings in the form of public company Gaylord Entertainment which established its headquarters in Nashville Tennessee. Gaylord Entertainment acquired a majority interest in cable music network Country Music Television (CMT) the same year. It later expanded CMT into Latin America Asia and the Pacific Rim. CMT also made a brief foray into Europe but that initiative was ended in 1998.

Facing a consolidating entertainment and media landscape Gaylord sold The Nashville Network and the US operations of CMT to Westinghouse (now CBS) in 1997. It also sold television station KSTW that year. The company expanded its reach into Christian music with the purchase of Word Entertainment and its 1997 acquisition of Blanton Harrell Entertainment gave Gaylord a presence in artist management. Terry London was appointed CEO in 1997.

The company closed its Opryland theme park in 1998 in the face of declining attendance and broke ground at the same site for the Opry Mills entertainment shopping and restaurant complex (opened 2000). Gaylord also purchased a Nashville Ramada Inn in 1998 (later renaming it Radisson Hotel at Opryland). With its 1998 acquisition of Paris-based Pandora Investment Gaylord branched into film distribution.

In 1999 the company formed Opryland Hospitality Group to oversee expansion of the Opryland hotel concept across the US. It also sold its last television station KTVT in Dallas/Fort Worth to CBS. Edward K. Gaylord II succeeded his father as chairman in 1999. That year the company launched its Internet division GETdigitalmedia (later renamed Gaylord Digital) and moved online with the purchase of Christian Web sites Musicforce.com and Lightsource.com. Later the same year the company expanded its Internet presence with the purchase of Songs.com a music Web site focused on independent artists. But in late 2000 the company announced it would close its Internet unit. Also in 2000 the company bought Corporate Magic a firm focused on producing entertainment events for corporate audiences.

At the end of 2000 Gaylord sold Musicforce.com to Christian Book Distributors. Following that sale it sold Lightsource.com to LifeAudio.com in early 2001. That year the company sold its film and television production units and announced a restructuring in order to cut costs. It also renamed Opryland Hotels to Gaylord Opryland while expanding into Texas and Florida. Colin Reed was appointed CEO in 2001.

Between 2001 and 2003 Gaylord Entertainment sold Word Entertainment to Warner Music Group the Opry Mills shopping and restaurant complex to The Mills Corporation the Acuff-Rose Music Publishing business to Sony/ATV two of its Nashville radio stations to Cumulus Media and its majority interest in the Oklahoma City Redhawks minor league baseball team.

Edward L. Gaylord officially retired from the company in 2003 at age 83. Also that year the company significantly expanded its hospitality business with the purchase of ResortQuest a vacation and condominium property management firm. In 2004 the Gaylord family sold more than half its shares in the company making Gabelli Funds the majority owner.

In 2005 Gaylord acquired 50% of Corporate Magic a Dallas-based provider of production support for corporate meetings and events. It did so to support its meeting and convention facilities.

The company unloaded its minority interest in minor league hockey team the Nashville Predators in 2005. Two years later it sold ResortQuest to a subsidiary of Leucadia National Corp. for $35 million. Also in 2007 it sold its interest in sporting goods store operator Bass Pro Group. In 2008 the company opened the Gaylord National Resort and Convention Center in the Washington DC area. The property has some 2000 rooms and approximately 450000 square feet of meeting space.

Also in 2008 Gaylord terminated plans to acquire the Westin La Cantera Resort in San Antonio for about $253 million citing a tough economic environment. In addition the 2008 sale of its ResortQuest subsidiary an online booking service in vacation rentals property management and resort real estate sales fit the company's strategy of selling off assets that aren't related to its Grand Ole Opry or its operations in the meetings and convention market.

In 2009 the company responded to weak earnings by cutting approximately 500 jobs across all areas of the business. Gaylord reported steep dip in profits in 2010 primarily due to harsh flooding in Nashville when the Cumberland River rose to historic levels flowing over protective levees. The flood resulted in property damage and temporary closures at its properties in Nashville causing lost revenues and an increase in expenses. Also in 2010 Gaylord sold its 50% stake in Corporate Magic back to that company's CEO.

The company changed its name to Ryman Hospitality Properties in 2012. It also converted to an REIT and sold the Gaylord brand to Marriott which now manages Ryman's hotel properties and certain other entertainment holdings.

EXECUTIVES

Evp Ryman Hospitality Properties; President Opry Entertainment Group, Stephen G. (Steve) Buchanan
Chairman And Ceo, Colin V. Reed, age 70, $782,830 total compensation
Svp Investments Design And Construction, Bennett D. Westbrook, age 51, $318,447 total compensation
President And Cfo, Mark Fioravanti, age 56, $469,407 total compensation
Svp Asset Management, Patrick Chaffin, age 44, $274,975 total compensation
Svp General Counsel And Secretary, Scott J. Lynn, age 44, $364,876 total compensation
Senior Vice President And Corporate Controller, Jennifer Hutcheson
Auditors: ERNST & YOUNG LLP NASHVILLE

LOCATIONS

HQ: RYMAN HOSPITALITY PROPERTIES, INC.
1 GAYLORD DR, NASHVILLE, TN 372141207
Phone: 615 316-6000
Web: WWW.RYMANHP.COM

PRODUCTS/OPERATIONS

2015 Sales

	$ mil.	% of total
Hospitality	994	91
Entertainment (previously Opry and Attractions)	97	9
Total	**1,092**	**100**

2015 Sales

	$ mil.	% of total
Food and beverage	461	42
Rooms	404	37
Other hotel revenue	129	12
Entertainment (previously Opry and Attractions)	97	9
Total	**1,092**	**100**

Select Operations

Hospitality
Gaylord Opryland Resort & Convention Center (Tennessee)
Gaylord Palms Resort & Convention Center (Florida)
Gaylord Texan Resort & Convention Center
Radisson Hotel at Opryland (Tennessee)

Attractions
Gaylord Springs Golf Links (golf club Tennessee)
General Jackson Showboat
Grand Ole Opry
Ryman Auditorium
Wildhorse Saloon
WSM-AM

COMPETITORS

CKX
CKX
Caesars Entertainment
Caesars Entertainment
Disney Parks & Resorts
Disney Parks & Resorts
Elvis Presley Enterprises
Elvis Presley Enterprises
Herschend Entertainment
Herschend Entertainment
Hershey Entertainment
Hershey Entertainment
Hilton Worldwide
Hilton Worldwide
Kennywood
Kennywood
Las Vegas Sands
Las Vegas Sands
Live Nation Entertainment
Live Nation Entertainment
MGM Resorts
MGM Resorts
Marriott
Marriott
New York Convention Center Operating Corporation
New York Convention Center Operating Corporation
SeaWorld
SeaWorld
Welk Group
Welk Group

HISTORICAL FINANCIALS

Company Type: Private

Income Statement				FYE: December 31
	ASSETS ($ mil.)	NET INCOME ($ mil.)	INCOME AS % OF ASSETS	EMPLOYEES
12/16	2,405	159	6.6%	1,000
12/15	2,331	111	4.8%	—
12/14	2,413	126	5.2%	—
12/13	2,424	113	4.7%	—
Annual Growth	(0.3%)	12.0%	—	—

2016 Year-End Financials
Return on assets: 14.2%   Sales ($ mil): 1,149
Return on equity: 13.9%

S & B ENGINEERS AND CONSTRUCTORS, LTD.

S & B Engineers and Constructors makes it possible for others to burn the midnight oil. The employee-owned company specializes in engineering procurement and construction of process plants in the chemical petrochemical refining power generation infrastructure and pulp and paper industries. S&B also flexes its engineering muscle on transportation waste and wastewater and environmental and telecommunications proj-

ects for public sector clients. Founded in 1967 by James Slaughter and William Brookshire to serve refineries and other process plants along the Texas and Louisiana gulf coasts the company has expanded services globally with two offices in India.

Operations

The company has divisions that focus on specific geographic areas and services. S&B's Engineers and Constructors division provides engineering procurement and construction services for combustion turbine combined and simple cycle projects as well as environmental AQCS retrofit projects for existing coal plants.

Ford Bacon & Davis (acquired in 1996) does much of its business in the southern US where it takes on engineering and design projects for oil gas and chemical companies. It not only constructs new plants but is often hired to rebuild facilities that have been damaged by fires or explosions.

The firm's Plant Services division provides small capital construction supplemental maintenance turnaround professional services asset management and other plant services including productivity studies and specialty training. S&B Infrastructure caters to private and government clients — ranging from federal to state to local authorities — while its private sector services extend from land development to industrial to pipeline client needs.

S&B India services its parent company's US clients as well as clients in India and other countries.

Geographic Reach

Houston-based S & B Engineers and Constructors boasts about a dozen offices throughout Texas (including four in Houston) a handful of offices in Louisiana and a single office in Greenville South Carolina. S&B India (established in 2000) has engineering centers in Bangalore and New Delhi.

Sales and Marketing

The company primarily serves the refining and chemical/petrochemical industry which alone accounts for more than half of its projects. About 25% of its projects are in the Midstream industry while remaining business comes from the Cogen and industrial power alternative energy and other industries.

Financial Performance

Its projects generate roughly $5 billion a year.

Strategy

S & B continues to grow its reputation with each project completed which in turn should lead to more business opportunities.

As an example S&B inked a deal with Chevron Phillips Chemical Company back in 2012 to engineer and build a plant that leverages the energy company's 2nd-generation on-purpose 1-hexene technology — which would be the world's largest on-purpose 1-hexene plant capable of producing up to 250000 metric tons (551000000 lbs) per year at the energy firm's Cedar Bayou Chemical Complex in Baytown Texas. In late 2014 not long after the completion of the project the company was recognized for the 1-Hexene plant as it received the top Excellence in Construction award in the heavy industrial category and first runner up for the "Best of Houston" award by the Associated Builders and Contractors (ABC) of Greater Houston.

EXECUTIVES

President, James G. Slaughter
Svp Engineering, Charles R. Reid
Svp Construction, Tommy H. Collins
Vice President, James Harrod
Vice President Process Technology, Guy Suffridge
Legal Secretary, Raymond Harper
Vice President Business Development, Harvey Hensley
Vice President Procurement, K K Malone

Vice President Business Development, Greg Hafer
Vice President Construction Services, Kirk Morrow
Vice President Human Resources, Ralph J Morales
Vice President Field Operations Manager, David Taylor
Vice President Operations, Kathryn Hanneman
Vice President Business Development, Blane Vincent
Co-founder And Chairman, William A. Brookshire
Auditors: ERNST & YOUNG LLP HOUSTON T

LOCATIONS

HQ: S & B ENGINEERS AND CONSTRUCTORS, LTD.
7825 PARK PLACE BLVD, HOUSTON, TX 770874697
Phone: 713 645-4141
Web: WWW.SBEC.COM
Selected Locations
US
Austin TX
Baton Roug
El Paso TX
Fort Worth TX
Freeport TX
Greenville SC
Houston
Longview TX
McAllen TX
Monroe LA
New Orleans
San Antonio
India
Bangalore
New Delhi

PRODUCTS/OPERATIONS

Selected Projects
Sulfur Tailgas Treating Unit Blaine WA
Crude Upgrade Project El Segundo CA
Pipeline Terminal Project Los Angeles CA
Refinery Revamp Project Bakersfield CA
Fractionation Expansion Project Billings MT
Gas Plant Project Meeker CO
SMR Project Port Arthur TX
ABF Program BP Refinery Texas City
Low Sulfur Gasoline & Diesel Projects Houston TX
Fine Paper Machine Project Kingsport TN

Selected Services
Construction
Engineering
Modules and skids
Plant services
Procurement
Project management

Selected Divisions
Ford Bacon & Davis
S&B India
S&B Infrastructure
S&B Plant Services
S&B Power Division

COMPETITORS

Bechtel	KBR Building Group
CH2M HILL	Parsons Corporation
Fluor	Turner Industries
Jacobs Engineering	Zachry Inc.
KBR	

HISTORICAL FINANCIALS

Company Type: Private

Income Statement				FYE: December 31
	REVENUE ($ mil.)	NET INCOME ($ mil.)	NET PROFIT MARGIN	EMPLOYEES
12/17	679	0	—	2,400
12/16	950	0	—	—
12/13	0	0	—	—
12/12	0	0	—	—
Annual Growth	—	—	—	—

2017 Year-End Financials
Return on assets: 6.0%   Cash ($ mil.): 38
Return on equity: —
Current ratio: 0.70

SACHEM CENTRAL SCHOOL DISTRICT AT HOLBROOK

EXECUTIVES

Supt, James J Nolan
Asst Supt, Bruce H Singer
Asst Supt, Gail A Grenzig
Asst Supt, Paul E Manzo
Asst Supt, Jill Karp
SEC, Carol Truglio
Safety/Security Director, Wayne Wilson
Trustee, Bill Coggin
Teacher, Mary Bernhard
Auditors: TOSKI & CO PC CPAS WILLIAM

LOCATIONS

HQ: SACHEM CENTRAL SCHOOL DISTRICT AT
HOLBROOK
51 SCHOOL ST, LAKE RONKONKOMA, NY 117792231
Phone: 631 471-1336
Web: WWW.SACHEM.EDU

HISTORICAL FINANCIALS
Company Type: Private

Income Statement				FYE: June 30
	REVENUE ($ mil.)	NET INCOME ($ mil.)	NET PROFIT MARGIN	EMPLOYEES
06/18	328	12	3.9%	2,500
06/13	287	(13)	—	—
06/06	0	0	—	—
Annual Growth	—	—	—	—

2018 Year-End Financials

Return on assets: 1.3%   Cash ($ mil.): 27
Return on equity: 3.9%
Current ratio: —

SACRAMENTO CITY UNIFIED SCHOOL DISTRICT

EXECUTIVES

Supt, Jose Banda
Cfo, Tom Barrinson
C-Level Human Resources, Robert Garcia
Superintendent, Jorge Aguilar
Auditors: CROWE HORWATH LLP SACRAMENTO

LOCATIONS

HQ: SACRAMENTO CITY UNIFIED SCHOOL DISTRICT
5735 47TH AVE, SACRAMENTO, CA 958244528
Phone: 916 643-7400
Web: WWW.SCUSD.EDU

HISTORICAL FINANCIALS
Company Type: Private

Income Statement				FYE: June 30
	REVENUE ($ mil.)	NET INCOME ($ mil.)	NET PROFIT MARGIN	EMPLOYEES
06/17	625	71	11.5%	6,500
06/16	656	47	7.2%	—
06/11	509	(0)	—	—
06/06	434	0	—	—
Annual Growth	3.4%	—	—	—

SACRAMENTO MUNICIPAL UTILITY DISTRICT

The Sacramento Municipal Utility District (SMUD) doesn't want its name to be mud. One of the largest locally owned electric utilities in the US SMUD serves more than 624770 residential and commercial customer meters (a service area population of 1.4 million) in California's Sacramento and Placer counties. The utility generates about 70% of its electricity (its 1300-MW capacity is derived primarily from hydroelectric and cogeneration power plants) and buys the rest. SMUD also sells power to wholesale customers andhas one of the largest solar energy distribution systems in the US.

Operations

The utility operates more than 10470 miles of transmission and distribution lines across its 900-sq.-mi. service area. It gets power from varied sources including hydropower natural-gas-fired generators renewable energy (such as solar and wind power) and purchases power on the wholesale market.

The company has installed 600000 smart meters at customer locations across its entire service area.

Geographic Reach

SMUD generates transmits and distributes electricity to a territory that includes Sacramento Sacramento County and a small portion of Placer County.

Financial Performance

In fiscal 2015 SMUD's net revenue decreased by 4% due to lower wholesale revenues as the result of lower surplus gas sales driven by a decrease in gas prices and less gas sold and lower energy prices and sales.

The company's net income decreased by 23% due to lower net sales and an increase in administrative general and customer and maintenance expenses.

In fiscal 2015 SMUD's operating cash inflow decreased by 15%.

Strategy

In response to market deregulation and the nationwide push for carbon emission reduction SMUD has increased its generation capacity placing a priority on renewable energy sources. As part of this green energy push the company has a 15-year deal with Shell Energy (which expires in 2024) to buy landfill gas from sites in Texas. SMUD has installed more than 600000 smart meters to help customers to better control their power use.

In 2015 the company invested $3.3 billion in electric utility plant assets and construction work in progress.

The utility even works with local dairies to install anaerobic digesters to turn manure into renewable energy.

Company Background

In 2012 SMUD announced that it is the leading utility in the US in terms of new homes which had solar panels installed during construction. The utility commenced the SMUD Solar Smart Homes program in 2006 and had constructed more than 1000 homes with solar panels by 2012.

The company has been delivering power to customers in the region since 1946 but its history goes back to 1923 when citizens voted to create SMUD as a community-owned electric service. However years of engineering studies political battles and legal wrangling delayed SMUD's purchase of PG&E' s local electrical system.

In March 1946 the California Supreme Court denied PG&E's final petition to halt the sale and nine months later SMUD finally began operations.

EXECUTIVES

Cfo Finance And Enterprise Planning, James A. (Jim) Tracy
Ceo And General Manager, Arlen Orchard
Chief Grid Strategy And Operations Officer, Paul Lau
President Board Of Directors, Nancy Bui-Thompson
Assistant Treasurer, Tim Ryan
Assistant Treasurer, Larry Stark
Treasurer, Noreen Roche-Carter
Board Member, David Davis
Auditors: BAKER TILLY VIRCHOW KRAUSE L

LOCATIONS

HQ: SACRAMENTO MUNICIPAL UTILITY DISTRICT
6201 S ST, SACRAMENTO, CA 958171818
Phone: 916 452-3211
Web: WWW.SMUD.ORG

PRODUCTS/OPERATIONS

2015 Sales

	% of total
Commercial & industrial	47
Residential	42
Wholesale power	6
Street lighting & other	5
Total	**100**

Selected Products and Services

Conservation programs
Customer billing programs
Diagnostic services
Electric vehicle charging stations
Energy assistance programs
Energy-efficient appliances and equipment
Energy management
Green energy programs
Power quality and environmental services
Security lighting
Shade trees for customers
Solar water heating
Surge protection
Tree trimming

COMPETITORS

AES
Avista
Duke Energy
Edison International

Los Angeles Water and Power
PG&E Corporation
Sempra Energy

HISTORICAL FINANCIALS
Company Type: Private

Income Statement
FYE: December 31

	REVENUE ($ mil.)	NET INCOME ($ mil.)	NET PROFIT MARGIN	EMPLOYEES
12/17	1,559	181	11.6%	2,213
12/16	1,494	195	13.1%	—
12/15	1,474	128	8.7%	—
12/14	1,529	163	10.7%	—
Annual Growth	0.6%	3.6%	—	—

2017 Year-End Financials
Return on assets: 5.4%
Return on equity: 11.6%
Current ratio: 0.60
Cash ($ mil.): 227

SADDLEBACK MEMORIAL MEDICAL CENTER

Saddleback Memorial Medical Center part of Memorial Health Services (MHS) serves the residents of southern Orange County in California. With some 325 beds the not-for-profit medical center provides general medical and surgical services as well as specialty care in areas such as cancer heart disease and physical rehabilitation. It operates two campuses one in Laguna Hills and one in San Clemente. The medical center also features several facilities for women's health including the Saddleback Women's Hospital and the Memorial-Care Breast Center. In addition Saddleback Memorial provides home health care and hospice services.

Operations
Saddleback Memorial Center sees about 16000 inpatients each year. It also handles some 48000 emergency room visits and 6900 inpatient and outpatient surgeries.

The main hospital campus — Saddleback Memorial-Laguna Hills — is home to the Saddleback Women's Hospital and the MemorialCare Cancer Institute while both the Laguna Hills and San Clemente locations house MemorialCare Breast Center and Memorial Heart and Vascular Institute sites. The Saddleback Memorial-San Clemente campus offers additional specialty services such as weight-loss surgery and infusion therapy. Saddleback Memorial Medical Center is recognized in its industry for its care services in areas including endocrinology (diabetes) gastroenterology and orthopedics.

Strategy
As part of parent MHS' efforts to provide quality care and reduce medical expenses in the California health care market Saddleback Memorial has expanded and upgraded its facilities and partnered with area physicians' groups. In 2014 it opened the new MemorialCare Cancer Institute near its Laguna Hills location; the center features the True-Beam radiation system a more accurate and powerful machine than the ones Saddleback used previously.

EXECUTIVES

Nursing Director, Robert Montgomery
Managing Director, Maureen Nicart

LOCATIONS

HQ: SADDLEBACK MEMORIAL MEDICAL CENTER
24451 HEALTH CENTER DR # 1, LAGUNA HILLS, CA 926533689
Phone: 949 837-4500
Web: WWW.MEMORIALCARE.ORG

COMPETITORS

Children's Hospital of Orange County	Tenet Healthcare Western Medical Center - Santa Ana
Hoag Memorial Hospital	
Southwest Healthcare	
St. Joseph Hospital of Orange	

HISTORICAL FINANCIALS
Company Type: Private

Income Statement
FYE: June 30

	REVENUE ($ mil.)	NET INCOME ($ mil.)	NET PROFIT MARGIN	EMPLOYEES
06/16	349	50	14.4%	1,209
06/15	337	43	12.8%	—
Annual Growth	3.5%	16.9%	—	—

2016 Year-End Financials
Return on assets: 3.5%
Return on equity: 14.4%
Current ratio: 1.10
Cash ($ mil.): —

SAINT AGNES MEDICAL CENTER

Protecting and caring for the vulnerable Saint Agnes continues to ward off death for the patients at Saint Agnes Medical Center. The medical center provides health care to Valley residents of Fresno California through a 436-bed acute care hospital. Along with general surgery the hospital offers a variety of services including asthma management bariatric surgery (for which it has scored statewide accolades) cardiac rehabilitation hospice care and home care. The facility also runs an internal medicine physician residency and a nurses' residency program. Saint Agnes is part of Trinity Health one of the largest Catholic health care systems in the US.

Operations
Saint Agnes Medical Center is a 436-bed medical campus that has some 2600 staff members. The system typically logs more than 200 emergency department visits per day.

Geographic Reach
Saint Agnes Medical Center provides care to residents of California's Fresno Madera Kings and Tulare counties.

Financial Performance
In fiscal 2017 (ended June) Saint Agnes Medical Center had operating revenues of $483 million.

Strategy
In 2017 Saint Agnes Medical Center established a graduate medical education program which offers residency programs for internal medicine physicians and for nurses. As a teaching hospital the facility is better positioned to attract physicians to its growing community as well as training new ones who may stick around. Other programs in the works include family practice and emergency medicine physician residencies.

Company Background
The hospital system was established in 1929 by nine Holy Cross Sisters.

Saint Agnes Medical Center sponsors a number of community outreach programs throughout the Valley including adult day care senior activity programs health care clinics for the uninsured and services for poor and homeless women.

EXECUTIVES

Coo, Mark T. Bateman
Chief Medical Officer, Stephen Soldo
Cfo, Phil Robinson
Chief Nursing Officer, Debi Pasley
President And Ceo, Jim Leonard
Evp And, Rick OConnell
Pharm D, Tai Kosiyangkakul
Vice President Of Information Technology, Richard H Blanks
Medical Director, Hector Ramos
Medical Director, Lesley Hanes
Chairman, Michael Martinez
Treasurer, Andrea Lanier

LOCATIONS

HQ: SAINT AGNES MEDICAL CENTER
1303 E HERNDON AVE, FRESNO, CA 937203309
Phone: 559 450-3000
Web: WWW.SAMC.COM

PRODUCTS/OPERATIONS

Selected Programs and Services
Cancer Services
Emergency Services
Endoscopy
Heart & Vascular
Home Health Care
Hospice
Imaging Services
Laboratory Services
Neuroscience
Occupational Health Center
Orthopaedics
Surgery
Palliative Care
Pulmonary Rehabilitation
Women's Services
Wound Care Hyperbaric Medicine and Amputation Prevention

Selected Facilities
Breast Center
Cancer Center
The California Eye Institute at Saint Agnes
Child Development Center
Home Health and Hospice
Medical Library
Occupational Health Center
Outpatient Surgery North
Satellite Labs
Wound Care Hyperbaric Medicine and Amputation Prevention

COMPETITORS

Community Medical Centers	Memorial Hospitals Association
Dignity Health	Northern Inyo Hospital
HCA	Tenet Healthcare

HISTORICAL FINANCIALS
Company Type: Private

Income Statement
FYE: June 30

	REVENUE ($ mil.)	NET INCOME ($ mil.)	NET PROFIT MARGIN	EMPLOYEES
06/16	486	11	2.3%	2,400
06/15	478	24	5.1%	—
06/13	503	19	3.8%	—
06/10	438	8	1.8%	—
Annual Growth	1.7%	5.6%	—	—

2016 Year-End Financials
Return on assets: 11.7%
Return on equity: 2.3%
Current ratio: 1.50
Cash ($ mil.): 79

SAINT ALPHONSUS REGIONAL MEDICAL CENTER, INC.

Saint Alphonsus Regional Medical Center makes medical care its primary mission. The 384-bed hospital provides Boise Idaho and the surrounding region (including eastern Oregon and northern Nevada) with general acute and specialized health care services. Its facilities and operations include a level II trauma center an orthopedic spinal care unit an air transport service and a home health and hospice division. Saint Alphonsus Regional Medical Center is part of Trinity Health's four-hospital Saint Alphonsus Health System which serves Boise and Nampa in Idaho and Ontario and Baker City in Oregon. The Sisters of the Holy Cross founded the hospital in 1894.

Operations
Saint Alphonsus Regional Medical Center provides outpatient services through the 70 affiliated physician practices that make up the Saint Alphonsus Medical Group. It also operates the Saint Alphonsus Health Plaza which provides urgent care and outpatient surgery laboratory rehabilitation and primary care services.

The hospital also offers rural or homebound patients telemedicine services through which remote physician visits are conducted using audio or video.

Geographic Reach
Saint Alphonsus Regional Medical Center serves a territory that includes portions of southwestern Idaho northern Nevada and eastern Oregon.

Strategy
Saint Alphonsus Regional Medical Center expands its facilities to improve medical care in its service territory. In 2014 it opened its newly expanded and renovated emergency department which included a 30% increase in square footage. Also that year it became the first hospital in the region to utilize the EndoWrist Stapler technology on the da Vinci robotic system for minimally invasive surgeries.

EXECUTIVES

Vice President Human Resources And Mission, Susan Gibson
Director Of Pharmacy, Mark T Phillips
Nursing Director, Karen Hodge
Vice President Finance, Lannie Checketts

LOCATIONS

HQ: SAINT ALPHONSUS REGIONAL MEDICAL CENTER, INC.
1055 N CURTIS RD, BOISE, ID 837061309
Phone: 208 367-2121

COMPETITORS

Ascension Health	St. Luke's Health
HCA	System
Intermountain Health Care	

SAINT FRANCIS HOSPITAL AND MEDICAL CENTER FOUNDATION, INC.

Saint Francis takes care of the hearts of Hartford Connecticut. The Saint Francis Hospital and Medical Center is a not-for-profit regional medical center with some 620 beds and 65 bassinets. The hospital specializes in cardiology oncology neurology orthopedics and women's and children's health services. It also offers behavioral health weight management trauma care and injury rehabilitation programs. Saint Francis serves as a teaching hospital affiliated with the University of Connecticut Schools of Medicine and Dentistry. It also operates laboratories a home health and hospice agency and other entities. Saint Francis is part of Catholic health care system Trinity Health.

Operations
Saint Francis' on-campus specialty centers include the Hoffman Heart and Vascular Institute which specializes in open-heart surgeries and catheterization procedures.

Strategy
Saint Francis has initiated a number of internal cost-reduction efforts to keep its operations and finances healthy. It is also improving its internal information management systems to increase efficiencies at its facilities. Trinity Health which acquired Saint Francis in 2015 is investing at least $275 million through 2020 towards capital projects and programmatic investments in the hospital's region. Recently introduced programs include the Center for Diabetes and Metabolic Care's Inpatient Glycemic Initiative.

Company Background
Saint Francis joined the Trinity Health Network in 2015.

EXECUTIVES

President, John Rodis
Vp Finance, Jennifer S. Schneider
Vp Facilities Support Services And Construction, Robert J. (Bob) Falaguerra
Vp And Chief Development Officer Saint Francis Foundation, Lynn Rossini
Vp Operations, Thomas M. Burke
Vp Professional Nursing Practice And Quality; Chief Nursing Officer, Denise M. Peterson
Physical Therapy, Dan Henck

LOCATIONS

HQ: SAINT FRANCIS HOSPITAL AND MEDICAL CENTER FOUNDATION, INC.
114 WOODLAND ST, HARTFORD, CT 061051208
Phone: 860 714-4006
Web: WWW.STFRANCISCARE.ORG

COMPETITORS

Backus
Bristol Hospital
Connecticut Children's Medical Center
Griffin Health
Hartford Health Care
Hospital of Central Connecticut
Lawrence & Memorial Hospital
MidState Medical Center
Stamford Health
University of Connecticut Health Center
Yale New Haven Health System

HISTORICAL FINANCIALS
Company Type: Private

Income Statement   FYE: September 30

	REVENUE ($ mil.)	NET INCOME ($ mil.)	NET PROFIT MARGIN	EMPLOYEES
09/17	769	52	6.8%	3,270
09/14	670	17	2.6%	—
09/10	651	(10)	—	—
Annual Growth	2.4%	—	—	—

2017 Year-End Financials
Return on assets: 3.7%   Cash ($ mil.): 16
Return on equity: 6.8%
Current ratio: 0.90

SAINT FRANCIS HOSPITAL, INC.

EXECUTIVES

Ceo, Jake Henry
Human Resources, Brenda Garner
Director, Carl Bogler
Director, Karen Cochran
Vice-President, Marcus McKinney
Senior Vice-President, Pete Aran
Director, Philip Marcus
Director, Tiffani Fagan
V Chm, Peter C Boylan
Vice-President Engineering, Mike Wilson
Coordinator, Nancy Sanders

LOCATIONS

HQ: SAINT FRANCIS HOSPITAL, INC.
6161 S YALE AVE, TULSA, OK 741361992
Phone: 918 502-2050
Web: WWW.SAINTFRANCIS.COM

HISTORICAL FINANCIALS
Company Type: Private

Income Statement   FYE: June 30

	REVENUE ($ mil.)	NET INCOME ($ mil.)	NET PROFIT MARGIN	EMPLOYEES
06/16	913	128	14.0%	4,000
06/15	877	171	19.6%	—
06/13	910	190	21.0%	—
06/12	838	157	18.7%	—
Annual Growth	2.2%	(5.0%)	—	—

HISTORICAL FINANCIALS
Company Type: Private

Income Statement   FYE: June 30

	REVENUE ($ mil.)	NET INCOME ($ mil.)	NET PROFIT MARGIN	EMPLOYEES
06/15	556	40	7.3%	3,500
06/14	572	46	8.0%	—
06/13	545	43	7.9%	—
06/10	449	13	3.1%	—
Annual Growth	4.3%	24.1%	—	—

2015 Year-End Financials
Return on assets: 6.1%   Cash ($ mil.): 267
Return on equity: 7.3%
Current ratio: 3.70

Return on assets: 5.0%   Cash ($ mil.): 312
Return on equity: 14.0%
Current ratio: 3.80

SAINT JOSEPH REGIONAL MEDICAL CENTER-SOUTH BEND CAMPUS INC

EXECUTIVES

President, Nancy Helleyer
Treas, Charles Viater
SEC, Jason Schultz
Cfo, Janice Dunn
Cntrl, Mike Boardley
Coordinator, Karyn C Delgado
Ophthalmologist, Steve Gerber
Coordinator, Slavica Stoyanovich
Information Technology/Interne, John Whitaker
Internal Medicine Practitioner, Arthur Schroeder

LOCATIONS

HQ: SAINT JOSEPH REGIONAL MEDICAL CENTER-SOUTH BEND CAMPUS INC
5215 HOLY CROSS PKWY, MISHAWAKA, IN 465451469
Phone: 574 335-5000
Web: WWW.SJMED.COM

HISTORICAL FINANCIALS

Company Type: Private

| Income Statement | | | FYE: June 30 |
	REVENUE ($ mil.)	NET INCOME ($ mil.)	NET PROFIT MARGIN	EMPLOYEES
06/15	324	18	5.8%	680
06/12	77	(6)	—	—
06/06	81	(2)	—	—
06/05	80	0	0.7%	—
Annual Growth	15.0%	42.4%	—	—

2015 Year-End Financials

Return on assets: 6.9%   Cash ($ mil.): 1
Return on equity: 5.8%
Current ratio: 2.00

SAINT JOSEPH'S HOSPITAL OF MARSHFIELD, INC.

EXECUTIVES

Ceo, Michael Kryda
President, Michael A Schmidt
V Pres-Fin-Cfo, John Skadin
Executive Director, Judy Riedel

Vice President, Steve Pelton
Registered Nurse, Linda Weis-Smith
Administrator, Paul Nedd
Facilities Manager, Wayne Pattengill
Auditors: DELOITTE TAX LP MILWAUKEE WI

LOCATIONS

HQ: SAINT JOSEPH'S HOSPITAL OF MARSHFIELD, INC.
611 N SAINT JOSEPH AVE, MARSHFIELD, WI 544491832
Phone: 715 387-1713

HISTORICAL FINANCIALS

Company Type: Private

| Income Statement | | | FYE: June 30 |
	REVENUE ($ mil.)	NET INCOME ($ mil.)	NET PROFIT MARGIN	EMPLOYEES
06/15*	382	64	16.9%	2,200
09/10	348	31	9.2%	—
09/09	342	21	6.4%	—
09/08	1,063	0	—	—
Annual Growth	(13.6%)	770.7%	—	—

*Fiscal year change

2015 Year-End Financials

Return on assets: 8.1%   Cash ($ mil.): 93
Return on equity: 16.9%
Current ratio: 4.60

SAINT LUKE'S HEALTH SYSTEM, INC.

Caring for the residents of Missouri's largest city is no mean feat but Saint Luke's Health System manages it through 10 area hospitals and a host of clinics located throughout Kansas City. The not-for-profit system's flagship facility is Saint Luke's Hospital which offers a Level I trauma center and internationally recognized cardiac and stroke care. Its Crittenton Children's Center is a behavioral health center serving children and their families on an inpatient and outpatient basis. Saint Luke's Health System is a network of almost 320 doctors providing primary and specialty care through clinics and other locations. The system is affiliated with the University of Missouri- Kansas City School of Medicine.

Operations

The health system offers a heart transplant program treatment for complex brain and spinal cord diseases advanced surgical care liver and kidney transplantation programs and a Level III neonatal intensive care unit. Other specialized services include women's health cancer treatment rehabilitation and home care.

Saint Luke Health System also engages extensively in medical research; its more than 330 researchers conduct more than 430 studies each year. Its activities have drawn funding and sponsorship from the National Institutes of Health the American Heart Association and the Saint Luke's Hospital Foundation.

Saint Luke's Health System BJC HealthCare of St. Louis CoxHealth of Springfield (Missouri) and Memorial Health System of Springfield Illinois make up The BJC Collaborative. Through economies of scale and the sharing of resources the multi-system Collaborative seeks to achieve higher quality care for the patients served by these independent not-for-profit health care organizations.

While remaining independent Collaborative members have more than 4820 hospital beds in Missouri Illinois and Kansas and combined annual revenues of almost $7 billion allowing the members of the BJC Collaborative to focus on achieving savings; deploying clinical programs and services to improve access to quality of health care for patients; lowering health care costs; and creating additional efficiencies.

Geographic Reach

In addition to the Kansas City metropolitan area (some 2 million people) Saint Luke's Health System's service area spans 67 counties in Missouri and Kansas.

Strategy

To expand its market penetration the system will open two Convenient Care clinics — one in Kansas and another in Missouri — during 2016. Additionally Saint Luke's has broken ground on a specialty clinic in Mission Farms in Kansas. That project is expected to be complete in 2017. Also in 2017 a specialty clinic will be opened in Blue Springs Missouri.

Company Background

The predecessor to Saint Luke's Hospital was founded in 1882 by Episcopal priest Henry David Jardine.

EXECUTIVES

Svp Hospital Operations, Julie L. Quirin
Svp And Chief Nurse Executive, Katherine A. (Kathy) Howell
Ceo Saint Lukeâ's Hospital Of Kansas City, Jani L. Johnson
Svp Finance And Administration And Cfo, Chuck Robb
President And Ceo, Melinda L. Estes
Svp And Chief Physician Executive, Leonardo J. Lozada
Infection Control Director, CHERYL DAVIS
Medical Director, Tim Pluard

LOCATIONS

HQ: SAINT LUKE'S HEALTH SYSTEM, INC.
901 E 104TH ST, KANSAS CITY, MO 641314517
Phone: 816 932-2000
Web: WWW.SAINTLUKESKC.ORG

PRODUCTS/OPERATIONS

2015 Sales

	% of total
Hospital	61
Other university	39
Total	**100**

Selected facilities

Anderson County Hospital (Garnett Kansas)
Crittenton Children's Center (Kansas City Missouri)
Hedrick Medical Center (Chillicothe Missouri)
Saint Luke's Cushing Hospital (Leavenworth Kansas)
Saint Luke's East (Lee's Summit Missouri)
Saint Luke's Hospital (Kansas City Missouri)
Saint Luke's Northland Hospital (Kansas City Missouri)
Saint Luke's Northland Hospital (Smithville Missouri)
Saint Luke's South (Overland Park Kansas)
Wright Memorial Hospital (Trenton Missouri)

Selected Services

Cancer services
Heart and vascular
Home care and hospice
Neuroscience
Surgical services
Transplant services
Women's and maternity services

COMPETITORS

Ascension Health	Truman Medical Centers
Children's Mercy	University of Kansas

Hospital
CoxHealth
Heartland Regional
Medical
Shawnee Mission
Medical Center

Medical Center
Via Christi Health
System

HISTORICAL FINANCIALS
Company Type: Private

Income Statement   FYE: December 31

	REVENUE ($ mil.)	NET INCOME ($ mil.)	NET PROFIT MARGIN	EMPLOYEES
12/17	1,721	88	5.2%	5,111
12/15	155	(3)	—	—
12/14	140	(0)	—	—
Annual Growth	130.6%	—	—	—

2017 Year-End Financials
Return on assets: 4.5%   Cash ($ mil.): 225
Return on equity: 5.2%
Current ratio: 1.90

SAINT LUKE'S HOSPITAL OF BETHLEHEM, PENNSYLVANIA

EXECUTIVES

Pres, Richard A Anderson
Sr V-Pres Finance, Thomas P Lichtenwalner
Human Resources Director, Andrew Seidel
Gynecology/Obstetrics, Christopher B Gilbert
Security Staff, William Paslawsky
Senior Director, Jared King
Information Specialist, Laura Wetzel
Information Specialist, Matthew McDonnell
Coordinator, Lisa Johnson
Orthopedic Surgeon, William Delong Jr
Manager, Scott Siegfried
Auditors: WITHUMSMITHBROWN PC MORRISTOW

LOCATIONS

HQ: SAINT LUKE'S HOSPITAL OF BETHLEHEM, PENNSYLVANIA
   801 OSTRUM ST, BETHLEHEM, PA 180151000
Phone: 484 526-4000
Web: WWW.SLHN.ORG

HISTORICAL FINANCIALS
Company Type: Private

Income Statement   FYE: June 30

	REVENUE ($ mil.)	NET INCOME ($ mil.)	NET PROFIT MARGIN	EMPLOYEES
06/18	890	126	14.2%	9,599
06/15	660	31	4.8%	—
06/14	629	36	5.8%	—
Annual Growth	9.1%	36.3%	—	—

2018 Year-End Financials
Return on assets: 9.7%   Cash ($ mil.): 91
Return on equity: 14.2%
Current ratio: 0.80

SAINT LUKE'S HOSPITAL OF KANSAS CITY

EXECUTIVES

Ceo, Julie Quirin
Exec Dir, Debbie Wilson
Coo, Brad Simmons
Cfo, Amy Nachtigal
Chief of Medicine, George A Pagels
Optometrists, Terry D Anderson
Emergency Medicine Specialist, David J Scheffler
Executive of Information Techn, Denise Kintigh
Coordinator, Denise Mogg
Scientist, Larry Chapman
Chief of Medicine, Donald Campbell

LOCATIONS

HQ: SAINT LUKE'S HOSPITAL OF KANSAS CITY
   4401 WORNALL RD, KANSAS CITY, MO 641113241
Phone: 816 932-2000
Web: WWW.SONUSMETROMKE.COM

HISTORICAL FINANCIALS
Company Type: Private

Income Statement   FYE: December 31

	REVENUE ($ mil.)	NET INCOME ($ mil.)	NET PROFIT MARGIN	EMPLOYEES
12/17	699	63	9.1%	5,000
12/16	641	26	4.1%	—
12/15	561	0	0.0%	—
12/14	527	25	4.8%	—
Annual Growth	9.9%	36.6%	—	—

2017 Year-End Financials
Return on assets: 4.2%   Cash ($ mil.): 28
Return on equity: 9.1%
Current ratio: 1.70

SAINT MARYS HOSPITAL

EXECUTIVES

Pres, Robert R Waller
Director, Cindy Molko
Clinical Director, Joyce Dube

LOCATIONS

HQ: SAINT MARYS HOSPITAL
   1216 2ND ST SW, ROCHESTER, MN 559021970
Phone: 507 255-5123
Web: WWW.MAYOCLINIC.ORG

HISTORICAL FINANCIALS
Company Type: Private

Income Statement   FYE: December 31

	REVENUE ($ mil.)	NET INCOME ($ mil.)	NET PROFIT MARGIN	EMPLOYEES
12/16	2,091	556	26.6%	3,250
12/15	1,963	503	25.6%	—
Annual Growth	6.6%	10.6%	—	—

2016 Year-End Financials
Return on assets: 0.4%   Cash ($ mil.): —
Return on equity: 26.6%
Current ratio: 2.50

SAINT PAUL REGIONAL WATER SERVICES

EXECUTIVES

Gen Mgr, Steve Schneider
Project Engineer, Issac Afwerke

LOCATIONS

HQ: SAINT PAUL REGIONAL WATER SERVICES
   1900 RICE ST, SAINT PAUL, MN 551136810
Phone: 651 266-3530
Web: WWW.WASHINGTONBIOTECH.COM

HISTORICAL FINANCIALS
Company Type: Private

Income Statement   FYE: December 31

	REVENUE ($ mil.)	NET INCOME ($ mil.)	NET PROFIT MARGIN	EMPLOYEES
12/15	57,542	13,928	24.2%	247
12/93	24	2	10.0%	—
12/92	24	3	13.1%	—
Annual Growth	40.2%	44.0%	—	—

2015 Year-End Financials
Return on assets: 3.1%   Cash ($ mil.): 201
Return on equity: 24.2%
Current ratio: 0.40

SAINT PETER'S UNIVERSITY HOSPITAL, INC.

EXECUTIVES

Chairman, Bipin Patel
Chairman, John A. Carlson
Assistant Secretary Trustee, Kathleen Killion

LOCATIONS

HQ: SAINT PETER'S UNIVERSITY HOSPITAL, INC.
   254 EASTON AVE, NEW BRUNSWICK, NJ 089011766
Phone: 732 745-8600
Web: WWW.SAINTPETERSHCS.COM

PRODUCTS/OPERATIONS

Selected Services
Adult care
Cancer care
Community health
Diagnostic technology
Heart health
Maternity
Meet the staff
Movement sports rehabilitation
Nicu
Nursing at saint peters
Nutrition and weight
Outreach
Parent education
Pediatric and adolescent
Support groups
Surgery
Womens health
Adult and Family Health Services
Adult Intensive Care
Audiology

Emergency Medicine
Endocrinology
Hospice Program (Inpatient)
Intensive Care
Interstitial Cystitis Support Group
Lithotripsy
Ophthalmology
Osteoporosis/Bone Density
Pain Management
Primary Care
Pulmonary Medicine
Rheumatology
Sleep and Breathing Disorders
Thyroid
Urology
Wound Care and Hyperbaric Services
Adult Day Center
Allergy and Immunology
Dermatology
Dialysis
Emergency Medicine Physicians
Endoscopy/Same Day Services
Gastroenterology
Geriatric Medicine
Infectious Diseases
Internal Medicine
Interventional Radiology
Memory Assessment
Orthopedics
Otolaryngology (Ear Nose and Throat)
Pulmonary Function Laboratory Services
Respiratory Care Services
Skilled Nursing Care
Stroke
Urinary Incontinence and Pelvic Pain Program
Vascular Disease

COMPETITORS

CentraState Healthcare System
JFK Medical Center
Princeton HealthCare
Raritan Bay Medical Center
Robert Wood Johnson University Hospital
Robert Wood Johnson University Hospital at Rahway
Saint Barnabas Medical

HISTORICAL FINANCIALS

Company Type: Private

Income Statement				FYE: December 31
	REVENUE ($ mil.)	NET INCOME ($ mil.)	NET PROFIT MARGIN	EMPLOYEES
12/17	440	(7)	—	3,000
12/16	447	32	7.4%	—
12/15	405	3	0.8%	—
12/13	403	(2)	—	—
Annual Growth	2.3%	—	—	—

2017 Year-End Financials

Return on assets: 8.0% Cash ($ mil.): 13
Return on equity: (-1.6%)
Current ratio: 0.70

SAINT TAMMANY PARISH HOSPITAL SERVICE DISTRICT 1

St. Tammany Parish Hospital serves communities in St. Tammany Parish and Washington Parish along the northern shores of Lake Ponchartrain in eastern Louisiana. The not-for-profit hospital has about 240 beds and offers acute care diagnostic rehabilitation and community wellness services. It also includes centers and clinics specializing in surgery breast care cardiology and sleep disorders. In addition St. Tammany Parish Hospital operates a home health and hospice agency an outpatient services center and a primary care physicians' office. The company's facilities are served by doctors in St. Tammany Physicians Network.

Geographic Reach

The hospital serves patients in St. Tammany Parish and Washington Parish in southeastern Louisiana.

Financial Performance

More than half of St. Tammany Parish Hospital's billable revenues in 2012 came from insurance companies; Medicare makes up one third while Medicaid and self-pay patients account for about 10% of sales.

Strategy

In response to growing demand for primary care on the North Shore of Lake Ponchartrain in 2013 the hospital broke ground on a $21 million project that will expand the emergency department to treat more mental health-related emergencies.

Company Background

The hospital opened its doors in 1954.

EXECUTIVES

Pres- Ceo, Joan Coffman
Sr Vp-Cfo, David Mabe
Attorney, Lane Carson
Health Professional, Lawrence Spencer
Health Professional, Miki Mullins
Internal Medicine Practitioner, Gladys Izaguirre
Coordinator, Gina Martin
Staff, Jeffrey Loose
Coordinator, Marlise Eschete
Coordinator, Toby Tournillon
Cardiology, Arnisha Batts

LOCATIONS

HQ: SAINT TAMMANY PARISH HOSPITAL SERVICE DISTRICT 1
1202 S TYLER ST, COVINGTON, LA 704332330
Phone: 985 898-4000
Web: WWW.STPH.ORG

PRODUCTS/OPERATIONS

Selected Services and Facilities
Adult Rehabilitation
Adult Rehabilitation Outpatient
Adult Weight Management
Angiography
Breast Center
Bronchoscopy
Cardiac Care (Heart)
Cardiac Cath Lab
Cardiac Rehab Outpatient
Cardiac Rehabilitation
Cardiology
Cardiology Non-Invasive
Center for Wound Care and Hyperbaric Medicine
Colonoscopy
Community Wellness Center
Coumadin Clinic
Covington Surgery Center
Critical Care
CT Scan
Diabetes Education Program
Diagnostic X-ray
EGD (Esophagogastroduodenoscopy)
Embolizations Emergency Services
Endoscopic Retrograde Cholangioancreatography
Endoscopy
ERCP
Esophageal Motility Studies
Family Medical Clinic Franklinton
Fluoroscopy
Gynecologic Surgery
Hospital Medicine
Hospitalist
Hyperbaric Medicine
Intensive Care Unit (ICU)
Interventional Radiology
Kyphoplasty
Labor & Delivery Suite
Lymphedema Management
Mammography
Mary Bird Perkins Cancer Center
MaternalChild Services
Medical Nutrition Therapy
Medical Surgical Nursing Care
MRI
Neonatal Intensive Care Unit
Nephrostograms
New Family Center
Nuclear Medicine
Occupational Therapy
Oncology Nursing Care
Outpatient Pavilion
Pacemaker Clinic
Parenting Center
Pediatric Care
Pediatric Rehabilitation Outpatient
Pediatric Unit
Physical Therapy
Post-Operative Care
Pre-Operative Care
Primary Care Physicians
Prostate Cancer
Prostatectomy
Pulmonary Rehab
Radio Frequency Ablation
Radiology/Imaging
Respiratory Services
Rehabilitation Services
Robotic Surgery
Sigmodoscopy
Sleep Disorders Center
Speech Therapy
St. Tammany Physician's Network Covington
St. Tammany Physician's Network Mandeville
St. Tammany Physician's Network Masonville
Surgery Inpatient
Surgery Outpatient
Ultrasound
Urologic Surgery
Vertebroplasty
Wellness Works
Women's Health
Wound Care

COMPETITORS

Ascension Health	Our Lady of the Lake
Baton Rouge General	RMC
Dynacq Healthcare	Regency Hospital
General Health System	River Parishes
HCA	Hospital
Medical Properties Trust	Woman's Hospital

HISTORICAL FINANCIALS

Company Type: Private

Income Statement				FYE: December 31
	REVENUE ($ mil.)	NET INCOME ($ mil.)	NET PROFIT MARGIN	EMPLOYEES
12/17	306	23	7.5%	1,520
12/16	293	21	7.3%	—
12/14	246	20	8.1%	—
12/11	223	16	7.6%	—
Annual Growth	5.4%	5.3%	—	—

2017 Year-End Financials

Return on assets: 4.0% Cash ($ mil.): 52
Return on equity: 7.5%
Current ratio: 2.00

SAINT TAMMANY PARISH SCHOOL BOARD

EXECUTIVES

Pres, Stephen Loup
Supt, Gayle Sloan
Deputy-Supt, William Folse
Prin, Cheryl Arabie
President, Elizabeth B Heintz
Vice President, Robert R Womack
School Board President, Neal Hennegan
Teacher, Kayla Jones
General Manager, Kim Taylor
Teacher, Richard Thompson
Teacher, Robin Pratt
Auditors: LA PORTE APAC COVINGTON LA

LOCATIONS

HQ: SAINT TAMMANY PARISH SCHOOL BOARD
321 N THEARD ST, COVINGTON, LA 704332835
Phone: 985 892-2276
Web: WWW.STPSB.COM

HISTORICAL FINANCIALS
Company Type: Private

Income Statement				FYE: June 30
	REVENUE ($ mil.)	NET INCOME ($ mil.)	NET PROFIT MARGIN	EMPLOYEES
06/17	501	5	1.1%	4,400
06/16	505	(21)	—	—
06/15	475	49	10.4%	—
06/14	464	24	5.2%	—
Annual Growth	2.6%	(38.2%)	—	—

2017 Year-End Financials
Return on assets: 1.5%   Cash ($ mil.): 150
Return on equity: 1.1%
Current ratio: —

SALEM HEALTH

Salem Hospital serves the healthcare needs of residents in and around Oregon's Willamette Valley. The acute care hospital boasts about 455 beds and a medical staff of 440-plus physicians that represents some 45 specialty areas such as oncology joint replacement obstetrics diabetes weight loss and mental health among others. The not-for-profit hospital offers a range of services from emergency and critical care to rehabilitation and community wellness programs. Its Center for Outpatient Medicine provides cancer care outpatient surgery and imaging services and has a sleep disorders center. Salem Hospital is part of Salem Health which also includes West Valley Hospital and Willamette Health Partners.

Operations
The Oregon hospital also has a Family Birth Center that offers family-health education services and neonatal intensive-care services. Additionally it provides space to community support services to benefit families.

Salem Hospital operates under the guidance of a 15-member volunteer Board of Trustees.

Strategy
As with many healthcare institutions in this age of reform Salem Hospital is working hard to improve patient experience and the quality of healthcare it provides while reducing the cost of care

and eliminating waste within its systems. It has been improving clinical documentation to ensure payments are received standardizing care processes improving scheduling of surgeries leaving 30 open positions unfilled and cutting another 30 positions.

Inspired by Toyota's lean production processes the hospital entered into a five-year contract with John Black and Associates in 2010 to begin what it projects to be a transformation that will be accomplished incrementally over the next 20 years. Its goal is to improve care using a holistic patient-centered approach and reduce waste in terms of waits inventory and other day-to-day processes.

Salem Hospital set a goal of becoming a Magnet hospital in 2003 and accomplished the feat in 2010. (Only 6% of hospitals in the US have achieved Magnet status.) Magnet certification is awarded to hospitals that meet a set of criteria that measures the quality and strength of their nursing staffs as set by the American Nurses' Credentialing Center an affiliate of the American Nurses Association. Criteria includes patient outcomes job satisfaction and low turnover.

In 2009 the hospital opened a new patient tower. In 2010 it sold its money-losing home care department to LHC Group as a way of cutting operating costs.

EXECUTIVES

Vice President Of Strategy And Business Integration, Lori James-Nielsen
Medical Director, Lisa Lewis
Vice President Of Surgical Services, Denise Hoover
Vice President, Bahaa Wanly
Auditors: KPMG LLP PORTLAND OREGON

LOCATIONS

HQ: SALEM HEALTH
890 OAK ST SE, SALEM, OR 973013905
Phone: 503 561-5200
Web: WWW.SALEMHEALTH.ORG

PRODUCTS/OPERATIONS

Selected Services
Bariatrics
Cancer
Diabetes
Gynecology
Heart
Joint replacement
Neurosciences
Obstetrics
Orthopedics
Pain management
Psychiatric medicine
Psychology
Rehabilitation
Spine
Sleep
Stroke
Weight-loss surgery
Wound care

COMPETITORS

Adventist Health System West
Asante Health System
Kadlec Regional Medical Center
Kaiser Foundation Hospitals
Legacy Emanuel Hospital and Health Center
Legacy Health System
Oregon Health & Science University
PeaceHealth Southwest Medical Center
Providence St. Joseph Health

HISTORICAL FINANCIALS
Company Type: Private

Income Statement				FYE: June 30
	REVENUE ($ mil.)	NET INCOME ($ mil.)	NET PROFIT MARGIN	EMPLOYEES
06/18*	773	99	12.8%	3,400
09/14	584	58	10.0%	—
09/13	531	61	11.6%	—
Annual Growth	7.8%	10.1%	—	—

*Fiscal year change

2018 Year-End Financials
Return on assets: 6.4%   Cash ($ mil.): 15
Return on equity: 12.8%
Current ratio: 1.10

SALEM-KEIZER SCHOOL DISTRICT 24J

EXECUTIVES

Supt, Thirsty Perry
Supt, Kay Baker
Supt, Paula Radich
Safety/Security Director, John Van Dreal
Teacher Personnel Director, Mary Paulson
Bus Finance Purchasing Directo, Susan Dodd
Auditors: GROVE MUELLER & SWANK PC

LOCATIONS

HQ: SALEM-KEIZER SCHOOL DISTRICT 24J
2450 LANCASTER DR NE # 100, SALEM, OR
973051200
Phone: 503 399-3000
Web: WWW.SALKEIZ.K12.OR.US

HISTORICAL FINANCIALS
Company Type: Private

Income Statement				FYE: June 30
	REVENUE ($ mil.)	NET INCOME ($ mil.)	NET PROFIT MARGIN	EMPLOYEES
06/17	519	(13)	—	4,000
06/16	516	(15)	—	—
06/06	319	8	2.7%	—
06/04	319	8	2.7%	—
Annual Growth	3.8%	—	—	—

SALINAS VALLEY MEMORIAL HEALTHCARE SYSTEMS

The primary facility of the Salinas Valley Memorial Healthcare System (a public hospital district) is Salinas Valley Memorial Hospital which opened in 1953 and has some 270 acute-care beds. The medical center includes a comprehensive cancer center joint replacement clinic regional heart and spine centers a level III neonatal intensive care unit and a women's and children's unit. Salinas Valley Memorial Healthcare System also operates the Summerville Harden Ranch an 80-bed assisted-living facility and a network of outpatient care clinics. The system has collaborative relationships with other area care providers as well as a partnership with NASA that allows earthbound physicians to assist astronauts with medical emergencies in space.

Operations

The system has some 300 board-certified physicians across a range of specialties and partners with affiliates throughout the region. Its other programs include the Harden Memorial Heart Program a wound healing center diagnostics and sleep medicine. Its emergency department sees more than 44000 patients each year.

Financial Performance

In 2014 revenue increased 1% to $351 million as net patient service revenues rose. Net income fell 3% to $26 million though as operating expenses including salaries and benefits increased. Cash flow from operations slipped 16% that year to $38 million.

Strategy

Salinas Valley Memorial Healthcare System partnered with MedAssist in late 2013 to expand its regional care services. The partners provide personalized assistance to help consumers enroll in the state's Health Insurance Exchange.

EXECUTIVES

Senior Vice President And Patient Care And Cardiovascular Services, Irene Neumeister
Vice President Of Information Technology, James Brennan
Treasurer, Chris Orman
Assistant Treasurer, Carissa Purnell
Auditors: MOSS ADAMS LLP SAN FRANCISCO

LOCATIONS

HQ: SALINAS VALLEY MEMORIAL HEALTHCARE SYSTEMS
450 E ROMIE LN, SALINAS, CA 939014029
Phone: 831 757-4333
Web: WWW.SVMH.COM

PRODUCTS/OPERATIONS

2014 Sales

	% of total
Net patient revenue	98
Other revenue	2
Total	**100**

Selected Services

Anesthesiology
Angiography
Art & Music Therapy
Gynecology
Health Education
Health Promotion
Heart Health
Palliative Medicine
Pediatrics
Pharmacy
Physical Therapy
Plastic & Reconstructive Surgery
Positron Emission Tomography (PET)
Pre-Surgery Orientation
Tele-Care
Treadmill Stress Test
Vascular Care

COMPETITORS

Community Hospital of the Monterey Peninsula
Dignity Health
John Muir Health
Sequoia Healthcare District
Stanford Health Care
Sutter Health
UCSF Medical

HISTORICAL FINANCIALS

Company Type: Private

Income Statement   FYE: June 30

	REVENUE ($ mil.)	NET INCOME ($ mil.)	NET PROFIT MARGIN	EMPLOYEES
06/17	494	50	10.1%	1,800
06/16	366	44	12.0%	—
06/15	344	37	10.9%	—
06/05	284	14	5.0%	—
Annual Growth	**4.7%**	**11.1%**	**—**	**—**

2017 Year-End Financials

Return on assets: 2.7%   Cash ($ mil.): 103
Return on equity: 10.1%
Current ratio: 2.20

SALMON LEGACY CREEK HOSPITAL

EXECUTIVES

Pres, Lee Domanico
Sr Vice President, P Campbell Groner III
Chief of Pediatrics, Jacquelin Smith
Supervisor Respiratory Care, Curtis Morrison
Manager, Julie Bogh
Mso Supervisor, Michelle Tynan
Physician Obstetrics, Deborah Saner
Physician Obstetrics, Laura McGuire

LOCATIONS

HQ: SALMON LEGACY CREEK HOSPITAL
2211 NE 139TH ST, VANCOUVER, WA 986862742
Phone: 360 487-1000
Web: WWW.LHS.ORG

HISTORICAL FINANCIALS

Company Type: Private

Income Statement   FYE: March 31

	REVENUE ($ mil.)	NET INCOME ($ mil.)	NET PROFIT MARGIN	EMPLOYEES
03/17	324	38	11.9%	700
03/15	286	37	13.2%	—
03/13	199	10	5.4%	—
03/12	218	10	4.6%	—
Annual Growth	**8.3%**	**31.0%**	**—**	**—**

2017 Year-End Financials

Return on assets: 7.7%   Cash ($ mil.): —
Return on equity: 11.9%
Current ratio: 1.70

SALT LAKE CITY SCHOOL DISTRICT

EXECUTIVES

Dir, Alan Kearsley
Buss Admn, Janet Roberts
Bus Coord, Allison Sisam
Administrative Assistant, Frank Frampton
Auditors: SQUIRE & COMPANY PC OREM UT

LOCATIONS

HQ: SALT LAKE CITY SCHOOL DISTRICT
440 E 100 S, SALT LAKE CITY, UT 841111841
Phone: 801 578-8307
Web: WWW.SLCSCHOOLS.ORG

HISTORICAL FINANCIALS

Company Type: Private

Income Statement   FYE: June 30

	REVENUE ($ mil.)	NET INCOME ($ mil.)	NET PROFIT MARGIN	EMPLOYEES
06/17	285	1	0.6%	3,200
06/16	276	13	4.8%	—
06/15	266	7	2.9%	—
06/14	252	7	2.9%	—
Annual Growth	**4.2%**	**(37.2%)**	**—**	**—**

SALT RIVER PROJECT AGRICULTURAL IMPROVEMENT AND POWER DISTRICT

One of the US's largest government-owned utilities Salt River Project (SRP) provides Phoenix with two types of currents: electric and water. Electricity comes from the Salt River Project Agricultural Improvement and Power District a political subdivision of the State of Arizona that has a generating capacity of about 8300 MW and distributes power to more than 984000 homes and businesses. The district sells excess power to wholesale customers. Water comes from the Salt River Valley Water Users' Association a private firm that delivers 1 million acre-feet of water per year to residents and agricultural irrigators; the association also operates dams canals reservoirs and wells in its service area.

Operations

Staying true to its mission of providing water and electricity to SRP customers the company owns or has stakes in a dozen major power generating plants fueled by diverse sources including nuclear hydro coal biomass and natural gas.

Geographic Reach

It serves residential commercial industrial and agricultural power customers in a 2900-square-mile service territory spanning parts of Maricopa Gila and Pinal counties in Arizona. In addition the enterprise has mining loads in an adjacent 2400-square-mile area in Gila and Pinal counties. SRP is the region's top water supplier delivers about 800000 acre-feet of water annually with a service area of more than 375 square miles and with management responsibilities for a watershed covering 13000 square miles.

The Association provides the water supply for an area of 248200 acres within the major portions of the cities of Phoenix Avondale Glendale Mesa Tempe Chandler Peoria Scottsdale and Tolleson; the Town of Gilbert; and the Gila River Indian Community.

Financial Performance

The company's net revenues increased by 6% in 2014 primarily due to higher wholesale revenues.

The increase in wholesale revenues was primarily due to an increase in kWh sold and higher wholesale power prices as well as a $38.6 million higher gain realized from fair value adjustments on wholesale positions.

Strategy

SRPis aiming to get 20% of its power from renewable sources by 2020 in order to meet tightening environmental regulations. In fiscal 2012 renewables (primarily hydroelectric power and including some purchased green power from third parties) accounted for more than 9% of its total generating capacity. In addition to hydropower the company is investing in wind geothermal landfill gas and solar power generation technologies.Initiatives include the Dry Lake Wind Project (the first commercial wind farm in Arizona) and an incentive program that rewards customers for installing solar panels at their homes and businesses.

It is also pushing conservation measures and installed about 1 million smart meters (efficient automated systems that allow customers to monitor and reduce energy use) by the end 2013.

In order to upgrade its older coal plants and to build additional generation transmission distribution and irrigation assets&SRP has earmarked $5.6 billion in capital improvements by 2015.

Mergers and Acquisitions

In 2015 SRP acquired Los Angeles Department of Water and Power's share of the Navajo Generating Station. SRP is looking to significantly reduce emissions from the plant by 2020 to meet EPA requirements.

In 2013 it acquired a 625 MW gas-fired power plant from Sempra U.S. Gas & Power.

Company Background

SRP was founded in 1903 under the Natural Reclamation Act.

EXECUTIVES

Ceo And General Manager, Mark B. Bonsall
Associate General Manager And Ceo Power System, Mike Hummel
Associate General Manager And Chief Financial Executive, Aidan McSheffrey
President, David Rousseau
Vice President, John R. Hoopes
Auditors: PRICEWATERHOUSECOOPERS LLP PH

LOCATIONS

HQ: SALT RIVER PROJECT AGRICULTURAL IMPROVEMENT AND POWER DISTRICT
1521 N PROJECT DR, TEMPE, AZ 852811206
Phone: 602 236-5900
Web: WWW.SRPNET.COM

PRODUCTS/OPERATIONS

2016 Sales

	$ mil.	% of total
Retail electric	2,749	90
Water	15	1
Other	282	9
Total	**3,047**	**100**

Selected Subsidiaries

Salt River Project Agricultural Improvement and Power District (electric utility)
New West Energy Corporation (energy support services)
Papago Park Center Inc. (real estate facility management)
SRP Captive Risk Solutions Ltd. (domestic captive property boiler and machinery insurer)
Salt River Valley Water Users' Association

COMPETITORS

American States Water	PacifiCorp
American Water	Pinnacle West
Calpine	Sempra Energy
NV Energy	Southwest Gas
PG&E Corporation	UNS Energy
PNM Resources	Xcel Energy

HISTORICAL FINANCIALS
Company Type: Private

Income Statement
FYE: April 30

	REVENUE ($ mil.)	NET INCOME ($ mil.)	NET PROFIT MARGIN	EMPLOYEES
04/17*	3,084	247	8.0%	4,336
01/10	2,217	517	23.3%	—
Annual Growth	4.8%	(10.0%)	—	—

*Fiscal year change

2017 Year-End Financials

Return on assets: 6.0%
Return on equity: 8.0%
Current ratio: 0.70

Cash ($ mil.): 313

SAMARITAN HEALTH SERVICES, INC.

EXECUTIVES

Pres, Larry Mullins
Gynecology/Obstetrics, Jodell J Boyle
Administrative Assistant, Barbara Croney
Chief of Medicine, Darrell Prins
Chief of Cardiology, Bob Vanderford
Doctor, David Eason
Director of Laboratory, Harlan Akers
Doctor, Jodell Boyle
Coordinator, Lisa Ely
Human Resources, Christie Herber
Executive Officer, Pat Zeller

LOCATIONS

HQ: SAMARITAN HEALTH SERVICES, INC.
3600 NW SAMARITAN DR, CORVALLIS, OR 973303737
Phone: 541 757-5111
Web: WWW.SAMHEALTH.ORG

HISTORICAL FINANCIALS
Company Type: Private

Income Statement
FYE: December 31

	REVENUE ($ mil.)	NET INCOME ($ mil.)	NET PROFIT MARGIN	EMPLOYEES
12/17	1,101	26	2.4%	4,550
12/08	1	0	—	—
12/04	65	(1)	—	—
12/03	368	3	0.9%	—
Annual Growth	8.1%	16.1%	—	—

2017 Year-End Financials

Return on assets: 3.5%
Return on equity: 2.4%
Current ratio: 1.30

Cash ($ mil.): 156

SAMARITAN'S PURSE

EXECUTIVES

Chb-Ceo, Franklin Graham
Vice President, Phyllis Payne
South Sudan Country Direc, Phil Ewert
Counsel, Alexa Shelley

Information Technology Project, Lucas Bruch
Director, Nicole Sheldon
Information Technology Manager, Brad Harmon
Human Resources Coordinator, Holly Krider
Director, Enrique Carrasco
Programmer Analyst, Jim Bates
Human Resources, Amy L Greene
Auditors: DIXON HUGHES GOODMAN LLP CHAR

LOCATIONS

HQ: SAMARITAN'S PURSE
801 BAMBOO RD, BOONE, NC 286078721
Phone: 828 262-1980
Web: WWW.SAMARITANSPURSE.ORG

HISTORICAL FINANCIALS
Company Type: Private

Income Statement
FYE: December 31

	REVENUE ($ mil.)	NET INCOME ($ mil.)	NET PROFIT MARGIN	EMPLOYEES
12/17	800	189	23.7%	525
12/16	634	51	8.0%	—
12/15	599	82	13.7%	—
12/14	520	31	6.0%	—
Annual Growth	15.5%	82.8%	—	—

2017 Year-End Financials

Return on assets: 2.2%
Return on equity: 23.7%
Current ratio: 7.10

Cash ($ mil.): 230

SAN ANTONIO INDEPENDENT SCHOOL DISTRICT FAC

EXECUTIVES

Supt, Dr Sylvester Syl Perez
President, Ed Garza
Vice President, Olga M Hernandez
SEC, Arthur V Valdez
Information Specialist, Mark McRae
Superintendent, Pedro Martinez
Law Specialist, Andrea Tena
Federal Program Director, Barbara Rodriguez
Public Relations Director, Carmen Gonzalez
Information Director, Eddie Martinez
Educator, Esther Alvarado
Auditors: GARZA/GONZALEZ & ASSOCIATES S

LOCATIONS

HQ: SAN ANTONIO INDEPENDENT SCHOOL DISTRICT FAC
141 LAVACA ST, SAN ANTONIO, TX 782101039
Phone: 210 554-2200
Web: WWW.SAISD.NET

HISTORICAL FINANCIALS
Company Type: Private

Income Statement
FYE: June 30

	REVENUE ($ mil.)	NET INCOME ($ mil.)	NET PROFIT MARGIN	EMPLOYEES
06/16	659	43	6.5%	7,600
06/15	624	(14)	—	—
06/14*	600	(110)	—	—
08/09	549	6	1.2%	—
Annual Growth	2.6%	30.2%	—	—

2016 Year-End Financials

Return on assets: 2.7%   Cash ($ mil.): 189
Return on equity: 6.5%
Current ratio: —

SAN ANTONIO REGIONAL HOSPITAL

LOCATIONS

HQ: SAN ANTONIO REGIONAL HOSPITAL
255 E BONITA AVE BLDG 1, POMONA, CA 917671923
Phone: 909 962-6430

HISTORICAL FINANCIALS
Company Type: Private

Income Statement   FYE: December 31

	REVENUE ($ mil.)	NET INCOME ($ mil.)	NET PROFIT MARGIN	EMPLOYEES
12/16	348	8	2.5%	8
12/15	306	10	3.4%	—
Annual Growth	13.9%	(16.2%)	—	—

2016 Year-End Financials

Return on assets: 6.6%   Cash ($ mil.): 10
Return on equity: 2.5%
Current ratio: 1.00

SAN ANTONIO REGIONAL HOSPITAL

EXECUTIVES

Chm, Jim Milhiser
President, Harris F Koenig
Cfo, Roger Parsons
Diagnostic Radiologist, Arvind K Kumar
Radiology, Mark Girguis
Chief of Cardiology, Carlos Canizales
Director, Karen Stephenson
Emergency Medicine Specialist, Nancy Loomis
Chief of Radiology, Peter Yoo
Information Specialist, Fred Trimble
Health Care Director, Gail Lindsay

LOCATIONS

HQ: SAN ANTONIO REGIONAL HOSPITAL
999 SAN BERNARDINO RD, UPLAND, CA 917864920
Phone: 909 985-2811
Web: WWW.SARH.ORG

HISTORICAL FINANCIALS
Company Type: Private

Income Statement   FYE: December 31

	REVENUE ($ mil.)	NET INCOME ($ mil.)	NET PROFIT MARGIN	EMPLOYEES
12/16	316	25	8.0%	2,000
12/15	290	2	0.8%	—
12/13	266	(3)	—	—
12/11	282	9	3.4%	—
Annual Growth	2.3%	21.3%	—	—

2016 Year-End Financials

Return on assets: 8.5%   Cash ($ mil.): 6
Return on equity: 8.0%
Current ratio: 1.00

SAN FRANCISCO BAY AREA RAPID TRANSIT DISTRICT

If you're going to San Francisco — from Oakland Berkeley or another Bay Area community — San Francisco Bay Area Rapid Transit District (BART) can take you there. BART's trains carry about 365000 daily weekday riders from more than 45 stations over more than 100 miles of track including the 3.6 mile Transbay Tube under the San Francisco Bay that links the City by the Bay with Oakland and other East Bay communities. Directors elected from nine districts in Alameda Contra Costa and San Francisco counties oversee BART which operates with an annual budget of about $480 million. Construction on the rail system began in 1964 and BART carried its first passengers in 1972.

Operations

BART which has the oldest fleet in the US has awarded Bombardier about $896 million to design and make more than 400 train cars that may be ready for use by 2017. The contract represents the first phase of a $2.5 billion project to replace BART's fleet of some 670 cars with a larger fleet of more than 770 new cars. Three-fourths of the project's cost is being paid by the federal government with the remainder coming from BART.

Another major project is the $1.3 billion Earthquake Safety Program which is almost finished and scheduled for completion in 2016. The program includes bolting 2.5-inch steel plates on the concrete wall of the Transbay Tube — which carries about half of BART's daily weekday riders — and similar strengthening measures for more than 30 stations more than 20 miles of elevated track and other facilities.

Geographic Reach

BART serves the Bay Area through its 45 stations spanning the four counties of Alameda Contra Costa San Francisco and San Mateo.

Financial Performance

In 2014 the company's revenue increased by 4% to $463 million due to a spike in passenger fares along with higher parking rates implemented in 2014 at several stations. BART was also helped by an increase in advertising revenue and a rise in ground lease revenue resulting from the reassignment of its original ground lease at West Dublin Station to a new lessee. In addition its net income increased by 8% in 2014 due to the increase in revenues along with lower transportation expenses.

EXECUTIVES

Vice President Information Technology, William Longstaff
Auditors: MACIAS GINI & O'CONNELL LLP O

LOCATIONS

HQ: SAN FRANCISCO BAY AREA RAPID TRANSIT DISTRICT
300 LAKESIDE DR, OAKLAND, CA 94604
Phone: 510 464-6000
Web: WWW.BART.GOV

HISTORICAL FINANCIALS
Company Type: Private

Income Statement   FYE: June 30

	REVENUE ($ mil.)	NET INCOME ($ mil.)	NET PROFIT MARGIN	EMPLOYEES
06/16	545	331	60.8%	3,347
06/06	275	(2)	—	—
06/05	0	0	—	—
06/04	234	(101)	—	—
Annual Growth	7.3%	—	—	—

2016 Year-End Financials

Return on assets: 40.7%   Cash ($ mil.): 265
Return on equity: 60.8%
Current ratio: 0.80

SAN JOSE MEDICAL SYSTEMS, L.P

EXECUTIVES

Ptnr-Ceo, Mike Johnson
Information, Shirley Joyal
Director of Mis/Is, Darrel Odell
Director, Cheryl Mosses
Director of Nutrition, Kenneth Smith
Manager, John Macdonald
Manager, Lisa Hansford
Lab Manager, Lisa Vanwyk
Director, Todd Maxwell
Associate Chief Operating Offi, Veeral Shah
Director, Daniel Pratt

LOCATIONS

HQ: SAN JOSE MEDICAL SYSTEMS, L.P
225 N JACKSON AVE, SAN JOSE, CA 951161603
Phone: 408 259-5000
Web: WWW.REGIONALMEDICALSANJOSE.COM

HISTORICAL FINANCIALS
Company Type: Private

Income Statement   FYE: December 31

	REVENUE ($ mil.)	NET INCOME ($ mil.)	NET PROFIT MARGIN	EMPLOYEES
12/16	446	27	6.2%	1,200
12/15	395	12	3.1%	—
Annual Growth	13.2%	125.2%	—	—

2016 Year-End Financials

Return on assets: 2.4%   Cash ($ mil.): —
Return on equity: 6.2%
Current ratio: 1.90

SAN JOSE UNIFIED SCHOOL DISTRICT

EXECUTIVES

Supt, Vincent Matthews
President, Richard Garcia
Pres-Sup, Pamela Foley
MBR, Veronica Grijalva Lewis
Admin-MBR, Dianne Duane
President, Sandra Engel
Assistant, Thomas Rousseau
Teacher, Becky Allen
Teacher, Betty Estrada
Teacher, Carmen Lobach
Teacher, Cathie Katz

LOCATIONS

HQ: SAN JOSE UNIFIED SCHOOL DISTRICT
855 LENZEN AVE, SAN JOSE, CA 951262736
Phone: 408 535-6000
Web: WWW.SJUSD.ORG

HISTORICAL FINANCIALS
Company Type: Private

Income Statement   FYE: June 30

	REVENUE ($ mil.)	NET INCOME ($ mil.)	NET PROFIT MARGIN	EMPLOYEES
06/17	431	(63)		4,500
06/16	446	24	5.4%	—
06/05	2	0	3.1%	—
06/02	303	26	8.7%	—
Annual Growth	2.4%	—	—	—

SAN JOSE WATER COMPANY

EXECUTIVES

Ceo, W Richard Roth
Chb, Charles Toeniskoetter
V-President, Geaorge Belhumeur
V Pres-ADM, Richard Balocco
V-President, Scott Yoo
Cfo, Angela Yip
Director, Frederick R Ulrich Jr
Administrative Assistant, Steve Jones
Customer Staff, Dru Redwine
Security Staff, Jim Wollbrinck
Customer Representativ, Karin Gsoell

LOCATIONS

HQ: SAN JOSE WATER COMPANY
110 W TAYLOR ST, SAN JOSE, CA 951102131
Phone: 408 288-5314
Web: WWW.SJWATER.COM

COMPETITORS

American States Water	SouthWest Water
American Water	United Water Inc.
California Water Service	Veolia Water North America
Los Angeles Water and Power	

HISTORICAL FINANCIALS
Company Type: Private

Income Statement   FYE: December 31

	REVENUE ($ mil.)	NET INCOME ($ mil.)	NET PROFIT MARGIN	EMPLOYEES
12/17	366	45	12.4%	300
12/16	318	43	13.8%	—
12/00	0	12		—
12/99	115	16	14.4%	—
Annual Growth	6.6%	5.7%	—	—

2017 Year-End Financials

Return on assets: 6.1%   Cash ($ mil.): 5
Return on equity: 12.4%
Current ratio: 0.30

SAN JUAN REGIONAL MEDICAL CENTER, INC.

EXECUTIVES

Chb, Mike Jakino
Pres-Ceo, Rick Wallace
Vice President, J Michael Philips
Cfo, Michael Philips
Cso, John Buffington
MD Cmo, Robert Fabrey
Cno, Suzanne Smith
Manager, Cindy Baez
Information Specialist, Linda Jimerson
Human Resources, Melissa Lane
Director of Information Techno, Michael Richards
Auditors: ERNST & YOUNG US LLP PHOENIX

LOCATIONS

HQ: SAN JUAN REGIONAL MEDICAL CENTER, INC.
801 W MAPLE ST, FARMINGTON, NM 874015630
Phone: 505 609-2000
Web: WWW.SANJUANREGIONAL.COM

HISTORICAL FINANCIALS
Company Type: Private

Income Statement   FYE: June 30

	REVENUE ($ mil.)	NET INCOME ($ mil.)	NET PROFIT MARGIN	EMPLOYEES
06/18	316	17	5.5%	1,700
06/17	318	12	4.0%	—
06/16	280	16	5.8%	—
06/15	260	15	6.1%	—
Annual Growth	6.7%	3.2%	—	—

2018 Year-End Financials

Return on assets: 3.8%   Cash ($ mil.): 15
Return on equity: 5.5%
Current ratio: 1.40

SAN JUAN UNIFIED SCHOOL DISTRICT

EXECUTIVES

Supt, Pat Jaurequi
Supt, Glynn Thompson
Assistant Superintendent, Rick Messer
Information Technology/Interne, Bart Hubbard
Director, Peggy Purvis
Teacher, Juliann Wolney
Teacher, Michelle Lavery
Teacher, Brent Fanchar
Teacher, Carla Elkins
Teacher, Deb House
Teacher, Herbert Larsh
Auditors: CROWE HORWATH LLP SACRAMENTO

LOCATIONS

HQ: SAN JUAN UNIFIED SCHOOL DISTRICT
3738 WALNUT AVE, CARMICHAEL, CA 956083099
Phone: 916 971-7700
Web: WWW.SANJUAN.EDU

HISTORICAL FINANCIALS
Company Type: Private

Income Statement   FYE: June 30

	REVENUE ($ mil.)	NET INCOME ($ mil.)	NET PROFIT MARGIN	EMPLOYEES
06/17	577	104	18.2%	4,200
06/16	576	(6)	—	—
06/08	0	0	—	—
06/07	386	31	8.1%	—
Annual Growth	4.1%	12.8%	—	—

SAN RAMON VALLEY UNIFIED SCHOOL DISTRICT

EXECUTIVES

Spdt, Mary Shelton
Coordinator, Peter Campopiano
Teacher, Andy Bonner
Information Specialist, Carol Zuschneid
Payroll Staff, Bonnie Torre
Staff, Sharon Clore
Contact Lens Specialist, Kathryn Murphy
Maintenance Director, Craig Cesco
Research Director, Mao Vang
Information Specialist, Rita Szeto
Coordinator, Sandy Cattarusa

LOCATIONS

HQ: SAN RAMON VALLEY UNIFIED SCHOOL DISTRICT
699 OLD ORCHARD DR, DANVILLE, CA 945264331
Phone: 925 552-5500
Web: WWW.SRVUSD.NET

HISTORICAL FINANCIALS
Company Type: Private

Income Statement				FYE: June 30
	REVENUE ($ mil.)	NET INCOME ($ mil.)	NET PROFIT MARGIN	EMPLOYEES
06/17	375	(21)	—	3,000
06/16	368	(10)	—	—
06/09	0	(0)	—	—
06/06	0	0	—	—
Annual Growth	—	—	—	—

SANCTUS, LLC

EXECUTIVES

MBR-Ceo, Stephen St Andre
Controller, Melissa Hellman
Employee Rel Mgr, Patti Belanger
Manager, Alex Kelin
Consultant, Diana Echeverri
Assistant Controller, Meenu Mathew
Consultant, Nick Haddad
Consultant, Rechelle Gryparis

LOCATIONS

HQ: SANCTUS, LLC
348 E MAPLE RD, BIRMINGHAM, MI 480096313
Phone: 248 594-2396
Web: WWW.SHIFTDIGITAL.COM

HISTORICAL FINANCIALS
Company Type: Private

Income Statement				FYE: December 31
	REVENUE ($ mil.)	NET INCOME ($ mil.)	NET PROFIT MARGIN	EMPLOYEES
12/16	365	34	9.3%	250
12/15	287	27	9.5%	—
12/14	205	18	9.2%	—
12/12	107	17	16.5%	—
Annual Growth	35.8%	17.7%	—	—

2016 Year-End Financials
Return on assets: 14.1% Cash ($ mil.): 3
Return on equity: 9.3%
Current ratio: 1.40

SANFORD

Sanford is one of the largest not-for-profit integrated health care systems in the US. It primarily serves rural areas through its network of more than 40 regional and community hospitals in nine states including the Dakotas Iowa Minnesota and Nebraska. The organization operating as Sanford Health also operates local clinics and long-term care centers. In addition to primary care and general hospital services Sanford's medical centers and specialty outpatient practices provide care in fields including senior living cancer cardiology vascular health neurology orthopedics pediatrics virology and women's health. In early 2019 Sanford merged with Good Samaritan Society which specializes in senior care.

Operations
In addition to its 40-plus hospitals Sanford's network includes about 200 senior living facilities (long-term care assisted-living and independent living centers) and 140 clinics. Altogether the facilities in the Sanford Health network handle some 50000 inpatient admissions and about 1.35 million outpatient visits each year. The network's 1400 physicians provide care in more than 80 specialist fields.

Along with its health care facilities Sanford Health also operates Sanford Laboratories based in Sioux Falls and Rapid City South Dakota. The system maintains Sanford Research a not-for-profit research organization that draws upon the physicians of Sanford Health and researchers at the University of South Dakota. Sanford Research conducts some $100 million in research projects each year. Finally the Sanford Health Plan is a not-for-profit health plan that serves individuals and employers across the system's region.

Geographic Reach
Sanford Health has locations in more than 125 communities in nine states including California Iowa Minnesota Nebraska North Dakota Oklahoma Oregon and South Dakota. It also has clinical affiliates in locations including Ghana Africa; Karmiel Israel; and Baja Mexico.

Strategy
Growth plans for Sanford include the construction of hospital and clinic facilities in Minnesota and North Dakota and new health care and research facilities in South Dakota. A $700 million gift from local philanthropist T. Denny Sanford is enabling the establishment of several new facilities. That contribution is also supporting the organization's research programs in children's health and initiatives to find cures for conditions including breast cancer and type 1 diabetes.

In addition Sanford Health expands by acquiring small community medical centers. The system is also growing by striking partnerships with small regional health care providers.

In 2018 the system merged with long-time collaborator Neuropsychiatric Research Institute. That transaction expanded Sanford's research activities; Sanford ultimately hopes to establish a major research center in its hometown of Fargo North Dakota.

Mergers and Acquisitions
In early 2019 Sanford merged with senior health services provider The Evangelical Lutheran Good Samaritan Society. The transaction combined Sanford's hospital system with Good Samaritan's senior living facilities creating an integrated health care research and insurance entity.

In 2018 Sanford Research absorbed Neuropsychiatric Research Institute which focuses on eating disorders and obesity. With that acquisition Sanford intends to establish a major research program in Fargo North Dakota.

Company Background
Sanford was created from the 2009 merger of two Dakota health care legends: South Dakota's Sanford Health and North Dakota's MeritCare Health System. Both date back to the 1890s. Following the merger the two units briefly kept their separate identities but in 2010 organized under the Sanford Health-MeritCare name. The operating name was later shortened to Sanford Health.

EXECUTIVES

Director Of Pharmacy, Jesse Breidenbach
Medical Director, Julie Blehm
Clinic Manager, Colleen Hughes
Clinic Manager, Laura Potthoff
Vice President Of Research Sanford Health, David Pearce
Managing Director, Jorge Gilbert
Director Of Nursing, Kellee Johnk
Vice President Sales, James Schneider
Vice President Marketing Fargo Region, Jennifer Cresap
Secretary, Kayla Moen
Auditors: DELOITTE & TOUCHE LLP MINNEAP

LOCATIONS

HQ: SANFORD
801 BROADWAY N, FARGO, ND 581023641
Phone: 701 234-6000
Web: WWW.SANFORDHEALTH.ORG

PRODUCTS/OPERATIONS

Selected Major Regional Medical Centers
Sanford Bemidji Medical Center (Bemidji Minnesota)
Sanford Medical Center Bismarck (Bismarck North Dakota)
Sanford Medical Center Fargo (Fargo North Dakota)
Sanford USD Medical Center Sioux Falls (Sioux Falls South Dakota)

COMPETITORS

Altru Health	Rapid City Regional
Avera Health	Hospital
Catholic Health	St. Alexius Medical
Initiatives	Center
Mayo Clinic	St. Mary's Healthcare
North Memorial Health	Wellmark
Care	

HISTORICAL FINANCIALS
Company Type: Private

Income Statement				FYE: June 30
	REVENUE ($ mil.)	NET INCOME ($ mil.)	NET PROFIT MARGIN	EMPLOYEES
06/17	4,411	175	4.0%	17,400
06/15	1	(18)	—	—
06/14	3	(11)	—	—
Annual Growth	939.2%	—	—	—

2017 Year-End Financials
Return on assets: 2.6% Cash ($ mil.): 101
Return on equity: 4.0%
Current ratio: 1.10

SANFORD HEALTH

EXECUTIVES

Pres, Kelby K Krabbenhoft
Sr V Pres-Coo, Becky Nelson
Pres-Clinic, Dan Blue
Pres-Regional Health Services, Ed Weiland
Pres-Foundation, Brian Mortensen
Pres-Health Plan, Ruth Krystopolski
Ex V Pres, Dave Link
Cfo, Michelle Bruhn
Manager Staff, Donna Schneider
Point of Contact, Ronda Hinsch
Emergency Room Coordinator, Maria Botker
Auditors: DELOITTE & TOUCHE LLP MINNEA

LOCATIONS

HQ: SANFORD HEALTH
1305 W 18TH ST, SIOUX FALLS, SD 571050401
Phone: 605 333-1720
Web: WWW.SANFORDHEALTH.ORG

HISTORICAL FINANCIALS

Company Type: Private

Income Statement

FYE: June 30

	REVENUE ($ mil.)	NET INCOME ($ mil.)	NET PROFIT MARGIN	EMPLOYEES
06/17	4,411	175	4.0%	2,939
06/16	4,231	114	2.7%	—
06/12	2,516	72	2.9%	—
06/11	2,312	264	11.5%	—
Annual Growth	11.4%	(6.6%)	—	—

2017 Year-End Financials

Return on assets: 2.6%
Return on equity: 4.0%
Current ratio: 1.10
Cash ($ mil.): 101

SANSUM CLINIC

EXECUTIVES

M D, Pres-Ceo, Kurt Ransohoff
CIO, Tom Colbert
Cfo, Chad Hine
Cao, Paul Jaconette
Director, Donny Flores
Urology Specialist, Alex Koper
Administrator, Gary Cummings
Manager, Annikan Keesee
Human Resources, Claudio Alunan
Director, Julie Martin
Nursing Director, Ke Neary
Auditors: MOSS ADAMS LLP SAN FRANCISCO

LOCATIONS

HQ: SANSUM CLINIC
470 S PATTERSON AVE, SANTA BARBARA, CA 931112404
Phone: 805 681-7700
Web: WWW.SANSUMCLINIC.ORG

HISTORICAL FINANCIALS

Company Type: Private

Income Statement

FYE: December 31

	REVENUE ($ mil.)	NET INCOME ($ mil.)	NET PROFIT MARGIN	EMPLOYEES
12/16	287	3	1.1%	900
12/13	223	2	1.1%	—
12/01	95	0	0.9%	—
12/00	88	0	0.2%	—
Annual Growth	7.7%	20.2%	—	—

2016 Year-End Financials

Return on assets: 10.4%
Return on equity: 1.1%
Current ratio: 1.20
Cash ($ mil.): 19

SANTA BARBARA COTTAGE HOSPITAL

EXECUTIVES

Chm, Gretchen Milligan
Pres-Ceo, Ronald C Werft
Exec Vice President, Steven Fellows
Prin, Karen Jones Grandidier

Chief of Medicine, Robert S Wright
Coordinator, Ruben Orozco
Executive Assistant, Teresa Guzman-Petter
Safety Manager, Marsha Baselice
Neurosurgeon, Thomas H Jones
Director Neurovascular, Alois Zauner
Vice President Information TEC, Bill Worthington

LOCATIONS

HQ: SANTA BARBARA COTTAGE HOSPITAL
400 W PUEBLO ST, SANTA BARBARA, CA 931054353
Phone: 805 682-7111
Web: WWW.COTTAGEHEALTHSYSTEM.ORG

HISTORICAL FINANCIALS

Company Type: Private

Income Statement

FYE: December 31

	REVENUE ($ mil.)	NET INCOME ($ mil.)	NET PROFIT MARGIN	EMPLOYEES
12/17	646	178	27.6%	1,786
12/16	603	42	7.0%	—
12/15	610	(15)	—	—
12/14	38	32	83.3%	—
Annual Growth	156.0%	77.2%	—	—

2017 Year-End Financials

Return on assets: 9.1%
Return on equity: 27.6%
Current ratio: 0.60
Cash ($ mil.): 13

SANTA CLARA UNIFIED SCHOOL DISTRICT

EXECUTIVES

Supt, Stanley Rose III
Information Technology Manager, Min Chae
Psychologist, Nuzhath Quadri
Accountant, Patricia Eagels
Teacher, John Sugrue
Teacher, Laura Rubio
Teacher, Brenda Bricco
Teacher, Jenny Maehara
Teacher, Kristin Dentone
Teacher, Karen Kanani
Teacher, Kristen Moriarty

LOCATIONS

HQ: SANTA CLARA UNIFIED SCHOOL DISTRICT
1889 LAWRENCE RD, SANTA CLARA, CA 950512166
Phone: 408 423-2000
Web: WWW.SCUSD.NET

HISTORICAL FINANCIALS

Company Type: Private

Income Statement

FYE: June 30

	REVENUE ($ mil.)	NET INCOME ($ mil.)	NET PROFIT MARGIN	EMPLOYEES
06/17	330	(8)	—	2,000
06/16	279	9	3.4%	—
06/05	0	0	53.8%	—
06/04	99	(5)	—	—
Annual Growth	9.7%	—	—	—

SANTA CLARA VALLEY MEDICAL CENTER

EXECUTIVES

Ceo, Paul E Lorenz
Human Resources Director, Dave Manson
Internal Medicine Practitioner, Susan X Zhao
Pathologist, Wendy Wu
Coordinator, Cindy Stewart
Facilities Manager, Dave Gord
Pathologist, Sharmila Pramanik
Internist, Amina Martel
Director of Planning, Joy Alexiou
Nurse Practitioner Family, Leslyn Watson
Facility Manager, Alex Gallego

LOCATIONS

HQ: SANTA CLARA VALLEY MEDICAL CENTER
751 S BASCOM AVE, SAN JOSE, CA 951282699
Phone: 408 885-5000
Web: WWW.SCVMCREHAB.ORG

HISTORICAL FINANCIALS

Company Type: Private

Income Statement

FYE: June 30

	REVENUE ($ mil.)	NET INCOME ($ mil.)	NET PROFIT MARGIN	EMPLOYEES
06/16	490	61	12.4%	1,936
06/15	417	21	5.1%	—
Annual Growth	17.5%	187.4%	—	—

2016 Year-End Financials

Return on assets: 8.5%
Return on equity: 12.4%
Current ratio: 1.40
Cash ($ mil.): 439

SANTA ROSA MEMORIAL HOSPITAL INC

EXECUTIVES

Ceo, Todd Salnas
Vice President, Gary Greensweig
Cfo, Mich Riccioni
Chief Nursing Officer, Kathrine Hardin
Manager, Jennifer Triplitt
Operations Manager, Joanne Bell
Facilities Manager, Michael Fink
Director, Aynna Yee
Chief Engineer, Tony Stilman
Emergency Medicine Specialist, Edward M West Jr
Corporate Communications Staff, Vanessa Degier

LOCATIONS

HQ: SANTA ROSA MEMORIAL HOSPITAL INC
1165 MONTGOMERY DR, SANTA ROSA, CA 954054897
Phone: 707 546-3210
Web: WWW.STJOESONOMA.ORG

HISTORICAL FINANCIALS
Company Type: Private

Income Statement   FYE: June 30

	REVENUE ($ mil.)	NET INCOME ($ mil.)	NET PROFIT MARGIN	EMPLOYEES
06/17	518	55	10.7%	2,100
06/16	509	49	9.7%	—
06/15	489	64	13.1%	—
06/14	387	47	12.2%	—
Annual Growth	10.1%	5.4%	—	—

2017 Year-End Financials
Return on assets: 4.1%   Cash ($ mil.): —
Return on equity: 10.7%
Current ratio: 1.00

SAPP BROS., INC.

Need air in those 18 wheels? Sapp BrosA Travel Centers (formerly Sapp Bros Truck Stops) has the usual air gas food but also offers human conveniences such such as laundry rooms mailbox rentals private showers and TV lounges. The company operates a chain ofA some 15 truck stops — readily identifiable by the giant red-and-white coffeepot logo — along interstate highways from Utah to Pennsylvania; with a concentration in Nebraska. Half of the locations also operate service centers offering oil changes new tires and safety checks. Its sister company Sapp Bros Petroleum distributes fuels and lubricants to more than 200 retailers. TheA firm is run by CEO Bill Sapp one of the four founding Sapp brothers.

Geographic Reach
Omaha-based Sapp Bros. has travel centers in eight states: Nebraska Iowa Utah Colorado Wyoming Kansas Illinois and Pennsylvania.

Strategy
To raise its profile and rev up its business Sapp Bros. in 2013 joined the roster of VP Racing Fuels's retail brand partners. The benefits of the affiliation include association with an attractive retail image competitive credit card rates and the ability to source unbranded fuel for its travel centers.

EXECUTIVES

Chb, William Sapp
Ceo, Allen J Marsh
President, Andy Richard
President, Dan Adams
V Pres Finance, Kevin Musil
Director of Information Techno, John Miller
Store Manager, Jennifer Adams
Auditors: KPMG LLP OMAHA NEBRASKA

LOCATIONS

HQ: SAPP BROS., INC.
9915 S 148TH ST, OMAHA, NE 681383876
Phone: 402 895-7038
Web: WWW.SAPPBROS.NET

2012 Locations

	No.
Nebraska	8
Iowa	2
Colorado	1
Illinois	1
Kansas	1
Pennsylvania	1
Utah	1
Wyoming	1
Total	**16**

COMPETITORS

Exxon Mobil	Stuckey's
Love's Country Stores	TravelCenters of
Pilot Flying J	America

HISTORICAL FINANCIALS
Company Type: Private

Income Statement   FYE: September 30

	REVENUE ($ mil.)	NET INCOME ($ mil.)	NET PROFIT MARGIN	EMPLOYEES
09/17	990	11	1.2%	1,700
09/16	802	18	2.3%	—
09/15	1,128	20	1.8%	—
09/14	1,566	12	0.8%	—
Annual Growth	(14.2%)	(2.7%)	—	—

2017 Year-End Financials
Return on assets: 3.6%   Cash ($ mil.): 2
Return on equity: 1.2%
Current ratio: 0.70

SARASOTA COUNTY PUBLIC HOSPITAL DISTRICT

Sarasota County Public Hospital Board which does business as the Sarasota Memorial Health Care System is a publicly owned hospital system serving residents in and around Sarasota on Florida's western coast. It operates Sarasota Memorial Hospital a not-for-profit acute-care facility with more than 800 beds (and more than 900 doctors) that provides general medical and surgical care as well as specialized care in areas such as heart disease cancer and neuroscience. The system also features a skilled nursing facility walk-in medical centers an outpatient surgical center and home health care operations. Additionally the hospital conducts clinical trials and has an educational affiliation with Florida State University.

Operations
Sarasota Memorial has the only obstetrics program and neonatal intensive care unit in the county and its Bayside Center includes one of the county's only inpatient behavioral health facilities. The health care system's Charter Health Plan program offers group health insurance to local business owners.

Sarasota Memorial receives some 32000 inpatient visits and 950000 outpatient and physician visits each year.

Geographic Reach
Sarasota Memorial serves Florida's Sarasota County.

Sales and Marketing
Medicare and Medicaid combined account for some 60% of Sarasota Memorial's net patient service revenue. Self-pay and managed care make up the remainder.

Financial Performance
Sarasota's total revenues increased by 9% in fiscal 2016 (ended September) due to a 9% increase in net patient revenue due to higher volume. The company reported $107 million in excess revenues over expenses that year a 13% decline versus the prior year. Operating expenses including salaries fringe benefits and supplies costs all increased in 2016.

Cash flow from operations increased 38% to $85.8 million thanks to an increase in cash received from patient care services.

Strategy
Sarasota Memorial seeks to improve its financial performance by pursuing profitable inpatient and outpatient growth through an aggressive focus on physician alignment and integration and capturing new patients residing in high growth areas. The system has also been opening new facilities to boost patient service revenues. In 2016 it opened its sixth urgent care center. The following year it opened a 74000-sq.-ft. Rehabilitation Pavilion the only site of its kind in Sarasota County to offer comprehensive inpatient and outpatient rehabilitation services.

The system also introduced its nurse residency program and an internal medicine residency program in 2017.

Company Background
Sarasota Memorial was founded as a community hospital in 1925.

EXECUTIVES

Vp And Cio, Denis Baker
President And Ceo, David Verinder, age 51
Chief Nursing Officer, Jan Mauck
Cfo, William Woeltjen
Chief Of Medical Operations, R. Stephen Taylor
Medical Records Director, Diane Settle
Director Managed Care, Steve Rhodes
Director Of Nursing, Diane Mcmahon
Board Secretary, Donna Desisto
Chairman, Gregory Carter
Second Vice Chairwoman, Marguerite G. Malone
Second Vice Chairman, Alex Miller

LOCATIONS

HQ: SARASOTA COUNTY PUBLIC HOSPITAL DISTRICT
1700 S TAMIAMI TRL, SARASOTA, FL 342393509
Phone: 941 917-9000
Web: WWW.SMH.COM

PRODUCTS/OPERATIONS

2016 Sales

	% of total
County Public Hospital District	
Sarasota Memorial Hospital	59
Corporate Division	2
Nursing & Rehabilitation Center	1
Charter Plan	-
SMH Health Care Inc.	33
Physician Services Inc.	5
Total	**100**

COMPETITORS

All Children's Hospital	HCA
Bayfront Health	St. Joseph's-Baptist Health Care
Encompass Health	Tampa General Hospital
Florida Hospital Tampa Bay Division	

HISTORICAL FINANCIALS
Company Type: Private

Income Statement   FYE: September 30

	REVENUE ($ mil.)	NET INCOME ($ mil.)	NET PROFIT MARGIN	EMPLOYEES
09/17	793	99	12.6%	4,200
09/16	12	0	4.0%	—
09/15	590	131	22.3%	—
09/14	524	92	17.6%	—
Annual Growth	14.8%	2.6%	—	—

2017 Year-End Financials
Return on assets: 4.0%   Cash ($ mil.): 27
Return on equity: 12.6%
Current ratio: 0.80

SARATOGA HOSPITAL

EXECUTIVES

Ceo, Angelo G Calbone
V Chm, Theresa M Skaine
Chm, Michael H Iacolucci
Network Analyst, Josh Maines
Chief of Medicine, Roland Phillips
Manager, Sharman Lisieski
Director, Terri Bedard
Director, Timothy Brooks
Respiratory Therapy Director, Christopher Torino
Coordinator, Barbara Post
Director, Jason Bernad
Auditors: KPMG LLP ALBANY NEW YORK

LOCATIONS

HQ: SARATOGA HOSPITAL
211 CHURCH ST, SARATOGA SPRINGS, NY
128661090
Phone: 518 587-3222
Web: WWW.SARATOGAHOSPITAL.ORG

HISTORICAL FINANCIALS

Company Type: Private

Income Statement — FYE: December 31

	REVENUE ($ mil.)	NET INCOME ($ mil.)	NET PROFIT MARGIN	EMPLOYEES
12/17	328	258	78.9%	2,000
12/16	279	14	5.1%	—
12/15	259	12	4.9%	—
12/14	240	16	6.8%	—
Annual Growth	10.9%	151.0%	—	—

2017 Year-End Financials

Return on assets: 3.4%
Return on equity: 78.9%
Current ratio: 2.50

Cash ($ mil.): 69

SAVANNAH HEALTH SERVICES, LLC

Memorial Health University Medical Center wants to provide memorable health care to residents of Savannah Georgia and surrounding areas. An affiliate of Mercer University School of Medicine the tertiary care facility provides such services as cardiac and trauma care and rehabilitation. Also known as Memorial University Medical Center (MUMC) the hospital has some 620 beds and includes the MUMC Children's Hospital. It also operates specialty cancer care and women's health centers as well as research programs. Founded in 1955 MUMC is the flagship facility in a broader system of entities known as Memorial Health which includes affiliated primary and specialty care clinics in the region.

Operations

MUMC's cancer center the Curtis and Elizabeth Anderson Cancer Institute provides cancer treatment and surgical procedures; it also conducts research efforts to discover and develop new cancer therapies. The Women's Health Institute offers obstetrics gynecology and neonatology. MUMC also includes a level I trauma center and a Heart and Vascular Institute as well as programs in orthopedics neurology gastroenterology urology and pulmonary care. The affiliated Memorial Health Uni-

versity Physicians (MHUP) group operates primary and specialty care offices in the area.

Geographic Reach

MUMC serves a 35-county region in southeastern Georgia and southern South Carolina. The medical center serves as a regional referral center for several smaller community hospitals in the area. Affiliates include Bacon County Hospital Evans Memorial Hospital and Liberty Regional Medical Center.

Strategy

In 2012 Memorial Health formed an affiliation with Novant Health. The partnership will help the MUMC organization cut costs provide for future growth opportunities and improve its operational infracfructure. By joining the Novant Health Shared Services group MUMC will gain access to a larger base of supply chain clinical engineering information technology and best practices resources.

EXECUTIVES

Pres-Ceo, Magaret Gill
SEC, Helen Dean Downing
Treas, J Harry Haslam Jr
Coo, Mary Chatman
Senior Vice-President, David Byck

LOCATIONS

HQ: SAVANNAH HEALTH SERVICES, LLC
4700 WATERS AVE, SAVANNAH, GA 314046220
Phone: 912 350-8000
Web: WWW.MEMORIALHEALTH.COM

COMPETITORS

Appling
Beaufort Memorial Hospital
Doctors Hospital of Augusta
Liberty Regional Medical Center
Redmond Regional Medical Center
South Georgia Medical Center
St. Joseph's/Candler Health System
Tift Regional Medical Center
Universal Health Services
University Health Services
Walton Rehabilitation Hospital

HISTORICAL FINANCIALS

Company Type: Private

Income Statement — FYE: December 31

	REVENUE ($ mil.)	NET INCOME ($ mil.)	NET PROFIT MARGIN	EMPLOYEES
12/15	466	9	2.1%	4,700
12/14	469	32	6.9%	—
12/13	547	38	7.1%	—
12/08	453	(29)	—	—
Annual Growth	0.4%	—	—	—

2015 Year-End Financials

Return on assets: 10.3%
Return on equity: 2.1%
Current ratio: 1.20

Cash ($ mil.): 15

SAVANNAH-CHATHAM COUNTY BOARD OF EDUCATION

EXECUTIVES

Pres, Jolene Byrne
Executive of Information Techn, Cathy Mc Culloch
Director of Networking, Carl Eller
Marketing Staff, Lisa Campbell
Auditors: KRT CPAS PC SAVANNAH GEOR

LOCATIONS

HQ: SAVANNAH-CHATHAM COUNTY BOARD OF EDUCATION
208 BULL ST, SAVANNAH, GA 314013843
Phone: 912 395-5534
Web:
WWW.INTERNET.SAVANNAH.CHATHAM.K12.GA.US

HISTORICAL FINANCIALS

Company Type: Private

Income Statement — FYE: June 30

	REVENUE ($ mil.)	NET INCOME ($ mil.)	NET PROFIT MARGIN	EMPLOYEES
06/17	500	(30)	—	4,800
06/16	493	21	4.3%	—
06/07	373	20	5.4%	—
06/06	330	10	3.3%	—
Annual Growth	3.8%	—	—	—

SAVE THE CHILDREN FEDERATION, INC.

Save the Children helps poor and malnourished children in some 15 US states and nearly 120 countries focusing on such areas as health and nutrition economic development education child protection and HIV/AIDS. The humanitarian organization also participates in international disaster relief efforts focusing on children and their families. Save the Children spends about 90% of its budget on program services with the rest allocated to administration and fundraising. The group was founded in 1932 inspired by the international children's rights movement begun in the UK in 1919 by Eglantyne Jebb founder of the British Save the Children Fund. It is a member of the International Save the Children Alliance.

Operations

Some 43% of the humanitarian organization's work is centered in Asia with 34% in Africa. Save the Children spends the rest of its time in the US Latin America and the Middle East.

In 2012 alone Save the Children helped 125 million girls and boys worldwide.

Geographic Reach

Save the Children operates programs in some 120 countries including the US. It comprises 29 member organizations worldwide.

Financial Performance

The global aid organization's revenue declined by 3.5% in 2012 versus 2011 due largely to a 12% drop in private gifts grants and contributions which account for nearly half of its total revenue. Save the Children directed 89% of its expenses to programs which benefit children and allow the humanitarian organization to keep private costs (includes fundraising and management and general) at about 10% – one of the best ratios for nonprofit organizations.

Strategy

With about 28% of its program services devoted to emergencies and 20% to education Save the Children in 2014 partnered with The Malala Fund to help vulnerable Syrian and Jordanian children return to school. As part of the partnership Save the Children is launching a pair of education projects. Another large portion of Save the Children's program services are focused on Health and Nutrition (25%) and Hunger & Livelihoods (10%).

EXECUTIVES

Vice President Policy And Humanitarian Response, Michael Klosson
Vice President, Gary Shaye
Vice President, Robert Clay
Associate Vice President Humanitarian Response, Gerald Anderson
Auditors: KPMG LLP NEW YORK NY

LOCATIONS

HQ: SAVE THE CHILDREN FEDERATION, INC.
501 KINGS HWY E STE 400, FAIRFIELD, CT 068254861
Phone: 203 221-4000
Web: WWW.SAVETHECHILDREN.ORG

Selected Countries of Operation
Australia
Brazil
Canada
Denmark
Dominican Republic
Fiji
Finland
Germany
Guatemala
Honduras
Hong Kong
Iceland
India
Italy
Japan
Jordan
Korea
Lithuania
Mexico
Netherlands
New Zealand
Norway
Romania
South Africa
Spain
Swaziland
Sweden
Switzerland
United Kingdom
United States

HISTORICAL FINANCIALS

Company Type: Private

Income Statement				FYE: December 31
	REVENUE ($ mil.)	NET INCOME ($ mil.)	NET PROFIT MARGIN	EMPLOYEES
12/16	652	(7)	—	3,000
12/15	678	(10)	—	—
Annual Growth	(3.9%)	—	—	—

2016 Year-End Financials

Return on assets: 4.4%   Cash ($ mil.): 46
Return on equity: (-1.2%)
Current ratio: 0.60

SAWNEE ELECTRIC MEMBERSHIP CORPORATION

EXECUTIVES

Vice President Of Operations, Chet Blackstock
Auditors: MCNAIR MCLEMORE MIDDLEBROOKS &

LOCATIONS

HQ: SAWNEE ELECTRIC MEMBERSHIP CORPORATION
543 ATLANTA RD, CUMMING, GA 300402701
Phone: 770 887-2363
Web: WWW.SAWNEE.COM

COMPETITORS

Cobb EMC   Jackson Electric
Georgia Power   Membership

HISTORICAL FINANCIALS

Company Type: Private

Income Statement				FYE: December 31
	REVENUE ($ mil.)	NET INCOME ($ mil.)	NET PROFIT MARGIN	EMPLOYEES
12/16	346	0	—	300
12/15	337	0	—	—
12/14	346	0	—	—
12/13	335	0	—	—
Annual Growth	1.1%	—	—	—

2016 Year-End Financials

Return on assets: 10.8%   Cash ($ mil.): 24
Return on equity: —
Current ratio: 1.00

SCAI HOLDINGS, LLC

SCAI Holdings (dba SCA or Surgical Care Affiliates) can stitch 'em up and move 'em out. The company operates one of the largest networks of outpatient surgery centers in the US. (Also known as ambulatory surgical centers or ASCs these facilities charge less than hospitals to perform routine surgeries.) SCA operates more than 200 surgery centers and surgical hospitals in about 35 states. The centers offer non-emergency day surgeries in orthopedics ophthalmology gastroenterology pain management otolaryngology (ear nose and throat) urology and gynecology. The company went public in 2013 but was acquired by insurance giant UnitedHealth in 2017 for some $2.3 billion.

Change in Company Type

In early 2017 Surgical Care Affiliates agreed to be acquired by UnitedHealth for some $2.3 billion. The renamed SCAI joined UnitedHealth's OptumHealth division which itself operates hundreds of health care facilities.

Operations

SCA's outpatient surgery centers are operated in partnership with more than 40 health care systems such as Indiana University Health Sutter Health Texas Health Resources and MemorialCare. It has approximately 3000 physician partners.

Geographic Reach

SCA's facilities are located in 34 states across the US. Its largest markets are Texas California and North Carolina which respectively accounted for 14% 14% and 13% of net patient revenues in 2014. Other large markets include Alabama Connecticut Florida and Idaho.

Sales and Marketing

SCA's sales and marketing efforts are directed at physicians who are responsible for referring patients to its facilities. It also directly negotiates agreements with insurance companies and Medicare. Outpatient surgery centers which perform procedures that don't require an overnight stay are able to charge less than full service hospitals. This 'day surgery' model can be attractive to both patients and insurance companies looking to keep costs down.

As such SCA sees a lot of opportunity in building up its portfolio of outpatient surgery centers. The company estimates there are approximately 5400 Medicare-certified centers in the US and still plenty of opportunity to invest and partner in new facilities.

Payments from non-governmental third-party payors represented more than 60% of the firm's net patient revenues in 2014; Medicare payments accounted for 20%.

Financial Performance

SCA has seen solid revenue growth for the past four years. In 2014 revenue increased 9% to $897.3 million on higher net patient revenue a result of both higher admission numbers and the addition of more facilities. Management fee revenues also rose that year (again thanks to acquisitions).

After four years of reporting losses the company became profitable in 2014 with net income of $32 million. This was driven by the higher revenue as well as the absence of loss from extinguishment of debt and a decline in interest expenses. At the end of 2014 the company's accumulated deficit totaled $176 million.

Cash flow from operations has been on the rise as of late. In 2014 it increased 27% to $210.6 million.

Strategy

In order to expand its network of facilities SCA strives to buy existing surgical facilities and develop new facilities in partnership with area physicians and health care systems. During 2014 it acquired controlling stakes in 28 consolidated facilities. It also added three affiliated facilities with three new health system partners.

Mergers and Acquisitions

In 2014 Surgical Care Affiliates acquired a controlling interest in 15 ASCs for $138.1 million. Other purchases that year included a 51% stake in an ASC in California and a 59% stake in an ASC in Maryland.

Company Background

SCA is the former outpatient surgery unit of HealthSouth. HealthSouth sold the division to private equity firm TPG in 2007.

EXECUTIVES

Evp And Cfo, Peter Clemens
President And Ceo, Andrew P. Hayek
Evp And Chief Development Officer, Joseph T. (Joe) Clark
Evp And Coo, Michael Rucker
Svp Sales And Market Development, Winborne Macphail
Svp Perioperative Services, Gerry Biala
Svp Clinical Services And Training, Linda Lansing
Evp And General Counsel, Rich Sharff
Vice President, Ali Reza
Chairman, Todd B. Sisitsky
Auditors: PRICEWATERHOUSECOOPERS LLP BI

LOCATIONS

HQ: SCAI HOLDINGS, LLC
510 LAKE COOK RD STE 400, DEERFIELD, IL
600154971
Phone: 847 236-0921
Web: WWW.SCASURGERY.COM

PRODUCTS/OPERATIONS

2014 Sales by Payor

	% of total
Managed care & other discount plans	62
Medicare	20
Workers' compensation	10
Patients & other third-party payors	5
Medicaid	3
Total	**100**

2014 Sales

	$ mil
% of total	
Net patient revenues	91
Management fee revenue	7
Other revenues	2
Total	**100**

COMPETITORS

HCA	United Surgical
Novamed Inc.	Partners
Symbion	Universal Health
Tenet Healthcare	Services

HISTORICAL FINANCIALS
Company Type: Private

Income Statement — FYE: December 31

	REVENUE ($ mil.)	NET INCOME ($ mil.)	NET PROFIT MARGIN	EMPLOYEES
12/16	1,281	226	17.7%	5,248
12/15	1,051	273	26.0%	—
12/14	864	157	18.2%	—
12/13	802	52	6.6%	—
Annual Growth	**16.9%**	**62.5%**	**—**	**—**

2016 Year-End Financials

Return on assets: 4.1%
Return on equity: 17.7%
Current ratio: 0.90
Cash ($ mil.): 131

SCHOOL BOARD OF BROWARD COUNTY, THE (INC)

EXECUTIVES

Chair, Nora Rupert
V Chair, Heather Brinkworth
Asst Contrl, Lauris N Hazelwood
Accounting Staff, Darla Timmons
Staff, Carol Burton
Coordinator, Bernadette Lohrer
Accounting Staff, Chanda Peoples
Coordinator, Jennifer Austin
Acting Director, Lori Canning
Coordinator, Rachael Garafola
Board of Directors, Ann Murray
Auditors: MOORE STEPHENS LOVELACE PA

LOCATIONS

HQ: SCHOOL BOARD OF BROWARD COUNTY, THE (INC)
600 SE 3RD AVE, FORT LAUDERDALE, FL 333013125
Phone: 754 321-0000
Web: WWW.BROWARDSCHOOLS.COM

HISTORICAL FINANCIALS
Company Type: Private

Income Statement — FYE: June 30

	REVENUE ($ mil.)	NET INCOME ($ mil.)	NET PROFIT MARGIN	EMPLOYEES
06/17	2,738	5	0.2%	5,265
06/09	2,548	(274)	—	—
06/08	2,811	75	2.7%	—
Annual Growth	**(0.3%)**	**(25.3%)**	**—**	**—**

SCHOOL DISTRICT OF THE CITY OF ALLENTOWN

EXECUTIVES

Spdt, C Russell Mayo
Administrative Secretary, Barbara Fenstermaker
Director, Brian Cote
Coordinator, Patricia Welle
Assistant Director, Rosanne Minarovic
Director, Troy Price
Coordinator, Barbara Kautzman
Board of Directors, Janine Allen
Academic Advisor, Janine Kish
Executive Director, Christina Mazzella
Administrative Secretary, Danielle Trevorah

LOCATIONS

HQ: SCHOOL DISTRICT OF THE CITY OF ALLENTOWN
31 S PENN ST, ALLENTOWN, PA 181025409
Phone: 484 765-4001
Web: WWW.ALLENTOWNSD.ORG

HISTORICAL FINANCIALS
Company Type: Private

Income Statement — FYE: June 30

	REVENUE ($ mil.)	NET INCOME ($ mil.)	NET PROFIT MARGIN	EMPLOYEES
06/17	283	(12)	—	2,000
06/16	268	(3)	—	—
06/03	109	1	1.2%	—
06/01	117	(9)	—	—
Annual Growth	**5.7%**	**—**	**—**	**—**

2017 Year-End Financials

Return on assets: 2.8%
Return on equity: (-4.5%)
Current ratio: —
Cash ($ mil.): 31

SCHWAB CHARITABLE FUND

EXECUTIVES

Exec Dir, Susan Heldman
Pres, Kim Laughton
Chb, Carrie Schwab-Pomerantz
Dir, Brooks Walker
Mgr, Margae Diamond
Offc Mgr, Michael Smithwick
Auditors: DELOITTE & TOUCHE LLP SAN FRA

LOCATIONS

HQ: SCHWAB CHARITABLE FUND
211 MAIN ST, SAN FRANCISCO, CA 941051905
Phone: 415 667-9131
Web: WWW.SCHWABCHARITABLE.ORG

HISTORICAL FINANCIALS
Company Type: Private

Income Statement — FYE: June 30

	REVENUE ($ mil.)	NET INCOME ($ mil.)	NET PROFIT MARGIN	EMPLOYEES
06/17	3,147	1,551	49.3%	26
06/16	2,018	819	40.6%	—
06/12	722	172	23.9%	—
06/11	822	308	37.5%	—
Annual Growth	**25.1%**	**30.9%**	**—**	**—**

2017 Year-End Financials

Return on assets: 0.2%
Return on equity: 49.3%
Current ratio: 1.00
Cash ($ mil.): 11

SCOTT & WHITE MEMORIAL HOSPITAL

EXECUTIVES

Ceo, Robert Pryor
President, Shahin Motakef
Coo, Donny Sequin
Cfo, Ken Johnson
Accounting Staff, Bud Watson
Chief of Cardiology, Nancy Ellis
Doctor, Jim Airhart
Chief Information Security Off, Steve Sullivan
Senior Director, Stephen Bush
Doctor, Erin Bird
Doctor, David Havemann

LOCATIONS

HQ: SCOTT & WHITE MEMORIAL HOSPITAL
2401 S 31ST ST, TEMPLE, TX 765080001
Phone: 254 724-2111
Web: WWW.SW.ORG

COMPETITORS

Baylor Health	Shriners Hospitals For
Community Health	Children
Systems	St. David's Health
Cook Children's Health	Care
Care System	St. David's Round Rock
Dell Children's	Medical Center
Medical Center	Texas Children's
HCSC	Hospital
Hill Country	
Seton Healthcare	
Network	

HISTORICAL FINANCIALS
Company Type: Private

Income Statement   FYE: August 31

	REVENUE ($ mil.)	NET INCOME ($ mil.)	NET PROFIT MARGIN	EMPLOYEES
08/15*	1,166	(156)	—	8,000
06/14	832	87	10.5%	—
08/13	881	76	8.6%	—
08/10	902	41	4.6%	—
Annual Growth	5.3%	—	—	—

*Fiscal year change

2015 Year-End Financials
Return on assets: 4.9%
Return on equity: (-13.5%)
Current ratio: 0.10
Cash ($ mil.): 52

SCOTTSDALE HEALTHCARE CORP.

Scottsdale Healthcare a not-for-profit organization serves the health care needs of central Arizona residents. Its operations include three acute care hospitals that combined boast some 900 beds. Scottsdale Healthcare also operates other campuses that offer physician offices a cancer center home health and other health care services. It conducts clinical research through the Scottsdale Healthcare Research Institute. The group's Essential Touch Wellness Center and Boutique provides spa-like stress-reduction therapies. With nearly 2000 medical and surgical staff members the company offers some 35 medical specialties. Scottsdale Healthcare is an affiliate of Scottsdale Lincoln Health Network along with John C. Lincoln Health Network.

Operations
The group's hospitals are Scottsdale Healthcare Osborn Medical Center (trauma orthopedics neurosurgery cardiovascular and critical care) Scottsdale Healthcare Shea Medical Center (full-service hospital including emergency medical and surgical critical care cardiovascular and oncology services) and Scottsdale Healthcare Thompson Peak (patient-family centered medical/surgical hospital). Additionally Scottsdale Healthcare operates five Urgent Care Plus clinics the Piper Outpatient Surgery Center at the Shea Medical Center the Greenbaum Surgical Specialty Hospital at Osborn Medical center and the Scottsdale Healthcare Primary Care network of primary care physicians.

Geographic Reach
Scottsdale Healthcare serves central Arizona specifically in an around the entire Northeast Valley as well as the area north of Loop 101.

Strategy
Since 2012 the health care network has been expanding into Northeast Phoenix to deepen its relationships with community physicians and diversify beyond its three-hospital Scottsdale campuses. To this end it opened new Scottsdale Healthcare Primary Care physician offices in 2013 — one each in Phoenix and Tempe — to join existing locations in Arcadia Scottsdale and Grayhawk.

What makes Scottsdale Healthcare stand out is its military training program the only one of its kind in the country. Its Readiness Skill Sustainment Training Program gives National Guard Air Force Reserve and nearby Air Force base personnel 12 days of training in treating trauma burns and other wounds they might encounter when deployed in a war zone. Participants also work in intensive care ride along with EMS personnel and get orthopedics and operating room practice. It has since expanded the program to include a $1.6-million military trauma training center which serves military medical personnel with classroom and simulation training and trains civilian paramedics and firefighters.

The organization performs clinical research through the Scottsdale Healthcare Research Institute. Through the institute the organization conducts clinical trials in a range of disciplines including cancer and other complex diseases.

In 2014 Scottsdale Healthcare formed an affiliation with John C. Lincoln Health Network. The combined networks operating under the moniker Scottsdale Lincoln Health Network include five hospitals with some 3700 affiliated physicians and an extensive outpatient services network.

The group opened a new 28-bed unit at its Scottsdale Healthcare Thompson Peak Hospital in 2013. The unit provides care to orthopedic and spine surgery patients.

Company Background
Scottsdale Healthcare was established in 1962 as City Hospital of Scottsdale.

EXECUTIVES

Vp And Cio, James R. (Jim) Cramer
President And Ceo, Thomas J. (Tom) Sadvary
Svp Medical Affairs, James F. Burke
Svp And Chief Clinical Officer, Peggy J. Reiley
Evp Healthcare Operations, Gary E. Baker
President Scottsdale Healthcare Foundation, John N. Ferree
Svp And Cfo, Todd LaPorte
Vp And Administrator Thompson Peak Hospital, Kim Post
Chief Medical Officer; Vp Physician Alignment, Richard Silver
Evp, Laura R. Grafman
Chief Operating Officer, Bruce Pearson
Assistant Vice President Supply Chain Consolidated Services, Michael Hildebrandt
Vice President, Richard Silver
Associate Vice President Of Laboratory Services, Marybeth Hess
Vice President Human Resources, Carol Henderson
Senior Vice President And Chief Clinical Officer, Joanne Clavelle
Senior Vice President General Counsel, Alan Kelly
Vice President Research, Mark Slater
Radiology Director, Julie Hughes
Associate Vice President Nursing Practice, Kathy Zarubi
Vice President, Janice Miller
Vice President Major Gifts, Jan Miller
Vice President Finance, Brian Steines
Vice President Pharmacy Services At Thompson Peak Medical Center, Harry Alberti
Assistant Vice President Project Management Office, Amy Clay
Medical Records Director, Apollonia Seianna
Vice President Strategic Planning Business Development, Craig Jensen
Assistant Vice President Ciso, Jerry Walters
Senior Vice President Executive Hospitals Chief Clinical Officer, Kimberly Post
Vice President Government And Community Affairs, Michelle Pabis
Vice President Procurement And Supply Chain, Tim Miller
Chairman, Steven M. (Steve) Wheeler, age 70
Vice Chairman, Brad A. Gazaway
Auditors: ERNST & YOUNG US LLP PHOENIX

LOCATIONS
HQ: SCOTTSDALE HEALTHCARE CORP.
8125 N HAYDEN RD, SCOTTSDALE, AZ 852582463
Phone: 480 882-4000
Web: WWW.HONORHEALTH.COM

PRODUCTS/OPERATIONS

Selected Services
Bariatric Weight Loss Surgery
Cancer Care
Community Health
Corporate Health
Diabetes Management
Diagnostic Imaging Services
Digestive Health
Emergency Services
Heart & Vascular
Home Health Services
Infusion & Treatment Services
Minimally Invasive Surgery
Neurosciences
Nutrition Services
Orthopedic Services
Outpatient Therapy Services
Pediatrics
Sleep Disorders Center
Trauma Center
Wound Management
Urgent Care Plus
Urology Services

COMPETITORS

Banner Health	Sun Health
Community Health Systems	Universal Health Services
Dignity Health	University of Arizona Health Network
Flagstaff Medical Center	Yuma Regional Medical Center
Mayo Clinic	
Phoenix Children's Hospital	

HISTORICAL FINANCIALS
Company Type: Private

Income Statement   FYE: December 31

	REVENUE ($ mil.)	NET INCOME ($ mil.)	NET PROFIT MARGIN	EMPLOYEES
12/17	1,763	104	6.0%	17,000
12/16	1,716	92	5.4%	—
12/14*	88	9	11.2%	—
09/09	808	11	1.5%	—
Annual Growth	10.2%	31.2%	—	—

*Fiscal year change

2017 Year-End Financials
Return on assets: 4.9%
Return on equity: 6.0%
Current ratio: 1.90
Cash ($ mil.): 122

SCRIPPS HEALTH

Scripps Health houses many a script-writing physician in its hospitals. The not-for-profit health system serves the San Diego area through five acute-care hospitals. Altogether the health system is home to approximately 1700 inpatient beds and a network of outpatient clinics. The system also offers home health care and operates community outreach programs. Its hospitals along with several outpatient Scripps Clinic and Scripps Coastal Medical Center locations employ some 3000 affiliated general practice and specialty physicians.

Operations
Scripps Health's facilities include the 700-bed Scripps Mercy Hospital which has a main campus

in San Diego and a satellite campus in Chula Vista as well as Scripps Green Hospital (173 beds in La Jolla) Scripps Memorial Hospital Encinitas (138 beds) and Scripps Memorial Hospital La Jolla (444 beds). The system's network also includes the new Prebys Cardiovascular Institute (168 beds) about a dozen coastal medical centers two wellness centers and about 20 specialty centers.

In 2016 the system had more than 445000 hospital outpatient visits 21500 surgeries and 1.2 million medical office visits.

Scripps Health is the official health care provider for the San Diego Padres baseball team.

Financial Performance
Scripps Health had $2.9 billion in revenues in fiscal 2016 (ended September). Some $2.2 billion of that revenue came from net patient service income while $0.5 billion came from capitation premiums. After operating expenses the system had $292.3 million in excess of revenues over expenses attributable to controlling interests.

Strategy
Scripps Health's overall strategy is to remain on the cutting edge of technology in order to treat patients more effectively therefore reporting better patient outcomes (which in turns makes it eligible for certain government incentives). It also aims to make itself the destination of choice for patients — both locally and globally — for cardiac cancer and other types of specialty care. For example it partners with renowned oncology center MD Anderson to operate the Scripps MD Anderson Cancer Center slated to open in mid-2018.

As a major provider in the larger San Diego area Scripps Health is constantly evaluating its scope of services to meet the ever-increasing demand for health care. The company is building several outpatient clinics including cancer treatment and cardiac care centers. It is also expanding and upgrading its hospitals. In addition Scripps Health has launched an initiative to increase the number of clinical trials conducted at its facilities.

However after missing its budget for the first time in more than a dozen years Scripps Health announced plans to lower operating costs through restructuring efforts. It ultimately aims to rely more heavily on outpatient care and wellness services to reduce hospital visits. Layoffs are part of the restructuring plans: For example the system eliminated the CEO positions at its five hospitals. The hospitals are now led by chief operations executives reporting to regional (North and South) CEOs. Additionally Scripps Health shut down its loss-making hospice operations in 2017.

EXECUTIVES

Svp And Chief Executive Scripps Green Hospital, Robin B. Brown

Svp And Chief Executive Scripps Memorial Hospital La Jolla, Gary G. Fybel

Svp And Chief Executive Scripps Mercy Hospital, Tom Gammiere

Cfo And Treasurer, Richard K. Rothberger

Svp And Chief Executive Scripps Memorial Hospital Encinitas, Carl J. Etter

President And Ceo, Christopher D. Van Gorder

Corporate Svp And Chief Medical Officer, James LaBelle

Svp And Chief Executive Scripps Medical Foundation, Shiraz M. Fagan

Corporate Svp And Cio, Andy Crowder

Assistant Vice President Information Services, Clark Kegley

Vice President Finance, June Komar

Medical Director, Renee Smilde

Vice President Medical Services Regional Sites, Peter D Aldrich

Corporate Senior Vice President General Counsel And Corporate Secretary, Richard Sheridan

Medical Director, Martin Charlat

Vice President Managed Care, Karri Rodgers

Corporate Vice President Chief Experience Officer, Ghazala Sharieff

Medical Director Of Respiratory Care, Bao Q Luu

Vice Chairman, Mark Sherman

LOCATIONS

HQ: SCRIPPS HEALTH
10140 CAMPUS POINT DR AX415, SAN DIEGO, CA 921211520

Phone: 800 727-4777
Web: WWW.SCRIPPS.ORG

Selected Facilities
Scripps Clinic (outpatient centers)
Scripps Coastal Medical Center (outpatient centers)
Scripps Green Hospital (La Jolla)
Scripps Memorial Hospital Encinitas
Scripps Memorial Hospital La Jolla
Scripps Mercy Hospital (San Diego)
Scripps Mercy Hospital Chula Vista

COMPETITORS

Adventist Health System West	Palomar Health
Cedars-Sinai Medical Center	Paradise Valley Hospital
Community Health Systems	Prospect Medical
Dignity Health	Rady Children's Hospital
Grossmont Hospital	Sharp HealthCare
HCA	Tenet Healthcare

HISTORICAL FINANCIALS
Company Type: Private

Income Statement   FYE: September 30

	REVENUE ($ mil.)	NET INCOME ($ mil.)	NET PROFIT MARGIN	EMPLOYEES
09/15	2,943	371	12.6%	13,445
09/08	1,953	18	0.9%	—
09/07	1,781	223	12.6%	—
Annual Growth	6.5%	6.5%	—	—

2015 Year-End Financials
Return on assets: 12.9%   Cash ($ mil.): 464
Return on equity: 12.6%
Current ratio: 0.70

SCRIPPS NETWORKS INTERACTIVE, INC.

Lifestyle TV is a livelihood for this company. Scripps Networks Interactive operates six lifestyle cable networks including Home & Garden Television (home building and decoration) the Food Network (culinary programs) DIY - Do It Yourself Network (home repair and improvement) the Cooking Channel (culinary how-to programming) and the Travel Channel (travel and tourism). The company additionally owns music channel Great American Country and has minority interests in Asian Food Channel and regional sports network FOX Sports Net South. It also owns a 50% stake in UKTV. Trusts for the Scripps family own majority control of the company. In 2017 Discovery Communications agreed to buy Scripps Networks in a $14.6 billion deal.

Operations
Scripps Networks has two reportable segments: US networks and International Networks. Its US network segment accounts for almost 85% of total revenue.

Geographic Reach
Scripps Networks is based in Knoxville Tennessee. The company has additional offices located in Atlanta Chicago Dallas Detroit Los Angeles New York City San Francisco Miami Chevy Chase Maryland and Washington DC. Scripps Networks maintains international offices in London Milan SA?o Paulo Sydney the Philippines and Singapore.

The company's Cooking Channel is available in Canada. HGTV is available in the Asia-Pacific region the Middle East North Africa and New Zealand. Scripps Networks has also expanded Food Network across Latin America and Australia.

Sales and Marketing
Cable programmers such as Scripps Networks generate most of their revenue through advertising and carriage fees paid by cable system operators and satellite TV service providers. To help keep viewer loyalty and ratings high the company targets its channels toward specific interests rather than airing programming for a general audience.

The company advertises its products through broadcast television networks online and mobile outlets radio programming and print media. Scripps Networks spent $161.1 million on advertising and promotions in fiscal 2016.

Financial Performance
Scripps Networks reported about $3.4 billion in revenue for fiscal 2016. That was an increase of more than $400 million compared to the $3 billion the company reported for revenue the previous fiscal year. The increase was due to increased advertising sales and affiliate fee revenues.

Scripps Networks' net income was $673 million in fiscal 2016. That was an increase of about $67 million compared to the prior fiscal period when the company claimed a net income of $606 million primarily as a result of an increase in total revenue.

The company ended fiscal 2016 with $948 million in cash from operating activities which was an increase compared to fiscal 2015 when Scripps Networks ended the year with $814 million in cash from operations.

Strategy
Scripps Networks is focused on growing advertising revenues by increasing video plays and attracting more unique visitors to its websites through site enhancements and adding more video. Its strategy also includes trying to attract a broader audience through programming on national video streaming sites developing new sources of revenue that capitalize on traffic growth at the company's own websites and capitalizing on the movement of advertising dollars to mobile platforms.

The growth of the company's international business continues to be a strategic priority. Scripps Networks has expanded in Asia Europe and Latin America in recent years.

EXECUTIVES

Chairman President And Ceo, Kenneth W. (Ken) Lowe, age 68, $1,683,858 total compensation

Coo, Burton F. Jablin, age 59, $1,110,000 total compensation

Evp Operations, Mark S. Hale, age 59, $600,000 total compensation

Head Of International Lifestyle Channels, Derek Chang, age 50

President International And Interim President Tvn, Jim Samples

Cfo, Lori A. Hickok, age 54, $775,000 total compensation

Chief Revenue Officer, Steven J. (Steve) Gigliotti

President Diy - Do It Yourself Network, Bob Baskerville, age 54

President Content Distribution And Marketing, Henry Ahn

President Hgtv And Diy Network, Kathleen Finch
Evp Digital Sales, Beth Lawrence
Evp Digital, Tamara Franklin
Evp Corporate Giving And Community Relations,
James B. (Jim) Clayton
Evp And Chief Legal Officer, Cynthia L. Gibson, age
54, $680,000 total compensation
President National Ad Sales And Marketing, Jon
Steinlauf
Evp And Chief Communications Officer, Dylan P.
Jones
Svp Culinary, Katherine Alford
Evp And Chief Human Resources Officer, Nello-
John (NJ) Pesci, age 56
Senior Vice President Engineering And
Distribution Technologies, Mike Donovan
Vice President Programming And Production,
John Feld
Vice President Corporate Finance, Peter Feret
Senior Vice President Corprate Advertising Sales,
John Dailey
Vice President Engineering And Distribution
Technologies, Bart Palmer
Auditors: DELOITTE & TOUCHE LLP CINCIN

LOCATIONS

HQ: SCRIPPS NETWORKS INTERACTIVE, INC.
9721 SHERRILL BLVD, KNOXVILLE, TN 379323330
Phone: 865 694-2700
Web: WWW.DISCOVERY.COM

2016

	% of total
United States	85
Poland	13
Other International	2
Total	**100**

PRODUCTS/OPERATIONS

2016 sales

	% of total
operating revenue	
U.S Networks	84
International Networks	16
Total	**100**

2016 sales

	% of total
Advertising	71
Distribution	26
other	3
Total	**100**

Selected Operations

Lifestyle media
　Cooking Channel
　DIY Network
　Food Network (75%)
　Fox Sports Net South (7%)
　Great American Country
　HGTV (Home & Garden Television)
　Travel Channel (65%)
　UKTV (50%)
　Asian Food Channel (100%)
Interactive Services
　CookingChanneltv.com
　DIYNetwork.com
　FoodNetwork.com
　GACTV.com
　HGTV.com
　TravelChannel.com

COMPETITORS

A&E Networks	NBCUniversal
ABC Cable Networks	PBS
AMC Networks	Turner Broadcasting
MTV Networks	

HISTORICAL FINANCIALS

Company Type: Private

Income Statement　　　　　　　　　　　　　FYE: December 31

	REVENUE ($ mil.)	NET INCOME ($ mil.)	NET PROFIT MARGIN	EMPLOYEES
12/17	3,561	814	22.9%	3,500
12/16	3,401	847	24.9%	—
12/15	3,018	778	25.8%	—
12/14	2,665	726	27.3%	—
Annual Growth	**10.1%**	**3.9%**	**—**	**—**

2017 Year-End Financials

Return on assets: 1.4%　　　　　　　Cash ($ mil.): 130
Return on equity: 22.9%
Current ratio: 1.80

SEALASKA CORPORATION

Sealaska Corporation is a native-owned investment firm active in natural resources manufacturing services and gaming. The holding company owns land in southeastern Alaska home to the Tlingit Haida and Tsimshian peoples. Sealaska core holdings include Sealaska Timber Corporation Alaska Coastal Aggregates Sealaska Constructors Sealaska Environmental Services and Colorado-based information technology services provider Managed Business Solutions. Subsidiary End-to-End Enterprises manages the company's gaming business. Sealaska's subsidiaries operate throughout North America and around the world. Its companies often win government contracts for construction environmental and engineering projects.

Operations
More than 60% of Sealaska's revenues came from its services segment during 2015 which includes subsidiary Sealaksa Environmental Services Sealaksa Constructors Sealaska Government Services Sealaska Technical Services Synergy Systems and Managed Business Solutions.

Nearly 30% of Sealaska's revenues are earned by its natural resources business which oversees land management and stewardship functions for all Sealaska lands. Sealaska owns about 290000 acres of timberland as well as the minerals rights to construction-grade aggregates on more than 565000 acres. Sealaska Timber harvest timber and markets logs for the domestic and export markets.

The company's Investment Business Segment (5% of revenues) comprised the Majorie V. Young Shareholder Permanent Fund and the Investment and Growth Fund. Its Gaming segment is managed by its subsidiary End-to-End Enterprises.

Geographic Reach
Juneau-based Sealaska has offices through the US and several other countries including Canada and Mexico as well as Europe.

Financial Performance
Sealaska's annual revenues have fallen 65% since 2012 as its portfolio holdings (such as its civil construction business in Hawaii and its natural resources business) haven't all fared well. The firm has rebounded from losses in 2013 however as it's sold off its less successful businesses and reduced costs.

The firm's revenue fell 10% to $109.4 million during 2015 with volatile markets causing a nearly $7 million decline in investment gains.

Revenue declines in 2015 caused Sealaska's net income to plunge 20% to $12 million though operational improvements helped dampen the blow. The firm's services business in particular managed to grow its profits despite a small sales decline as it focused more on higher value added work. Sealaska's operating cash levels spiked nearly 80% to $18.62 million after adjusting its earnings for non-cash expenses such as investment losses.

Strategy
Sealaska continued in 2016 to target acquisitions in businesses operating in the natural foods and seafood maritime services environmental service niche construction and data analytics sectors. The company adopted a 2012-2017 plan designed to transform Sealaska into a financially sustainable and profitable company driven by its core cultural values. To that end in 2013 the company sold its interest in its Nypro KA?naak joint venture and the Sealaska Global Logistics business and exited the security guard services business (acquired in 2010) to support future acquisitions.

Company Background
Sealaska is the largest of 13 corporations formed under the Alaska Native Claims Settlement Act (ANCSA) of 1971 which promised some 44 million acres of land to Alaska natives. The company is owned by some 21600 tribal member shareholders.

Subsidiary Haa AanA (meaning "our land") was established in 2009 as a way to promote the culture social and economic viability of Southeast Alaska. Haa AanA has assisted tribal members with their efforts to establish businesses such as a new oyster farms in southeastern Alaska. Haa AanA also promotes renewable energy initiatives such as a biomass heating system for commercial buildings. In 2012 Haa AanA launched a nonprofit community development financial institution in order to provide financing and promote economic development.

EXECUTIVES

Evp, Richard P. (Rick) Harris, $240,000 total
compensation
President And Ceo, Chris E. McNeil, $350,000 total
compensation
Manager Information Systems, Robert (Rob)
Johnson
Vp And Cfo, Doug Morris
President & Ceo Haa Aan Llc, Russell A. Dick
President And Ceo, Anthony Mallott
Manager Natural Resources, Ron Wolfe
President And Ceo Sealaska Timber Corporation
(stc), Wade Zammit
President And Ceo Sealaska Environmental
Services, Derik Frederiksen
President And Ceo Managed Business Solutions
(mbs) And Mbs Systems, Jon Duncan
Coo, Terry Downes
Coo Sealaska Environmental Services, Lewis Ivers
Chairman, Albert M. Kookesh, age 69
Vice Chair, Rosita F. Worl, age 80
Auditors: KPMG LLP ANCHORAGE AK

LOCATIONS

HQ: SEALASKA CORPORATION
1 SEALASKA PLZ STE 400, JUNEAU, AK 998011276
Phone: 907 586-1512
Web: WWW.SEALASKA.COM

PRODUCTS/OPERATIONS

2014 Sales

	$ mil.	% of total
Services	81	67
Natural Resources	33	28
Investments	6	5
Gaming	0	—
Corporate & other	0	—
Total	**121**	**100**

Selected Subsidiaries
Alaska Coastal Aggregates
End-to-End Enterprises LLC (gaming)
Haa Aaní LLC
Managed Business Solutions (majority owned)
Sealaska Constructors LLC
Sealaska Environmental Services
Sealaska Timber Corporation

COMPETITORS

Tembec   chugach alaska
West Fraser Timber

HISTORICAL FINANCIALS
Company Type: Private

Income Statement   FYE: December 31

	REVENUE ($ mil.)	NET INCOME ($ mil.)	NET PROFIT MARGIN	EMPLOYEES
12/17	293	45	15.6%	1,400
12/16	145	15	11.0%	—
12/15	109	13	12.5%	—
12/14	121	15	12.6%	—
Annual Growth	34.1%	44.1%	—	—

2017 Year-End Financials

Return on assets: 7.8%   Cash ($ mil.): 36
Return on equity: 15.6%
Current ratio: 1.00

SECURITIES INVESTOR PROTECTION CORPORATION

EXECUTIVES

Vice President Operations, Karen Saperstein
Avp Operations, Timothy Timanus
Auditors: GRANT THORNTON MCLEAN VA

LOCATIONS

HQ: SECURITIES INVESTOR PROTECTION
CORPORATION
1667 K ST NW STE 1000, WASHINGTON, DC
200061620
Phone: 202 371-8300
Web: WWW.SIPC.ORG

HISTORICAL FINANCIALS
Company Type: Private

Income Statement   FYE: December 31

	ASSETS ($ mil.)	NET INCOME ($ mil.)	INCOME AS % OF ASSETS	EMPLOYEES
12/16	2,944	362	12.3%	39
12/15	2,652	169	6.4%	—
12/14	2,362	307	13.0%	—
12/11	1,606	131	8.2%	—
Annual Growth	12.9%	22.4%	—	—

2016 Year-End Financials

Return on assets: 0.2%   Sales ($ mil): 486
Return on equity: 74.4%

SECURITY FINANCE CORPORATION OF SPARTANBURG

Folks looking for a little financial security just might turn to Security Finance Corporation of Spartanburg. Founded in 1955 the consumer loan company provides personal loans typically ranging from $100 to $600 (some states however allow loan amounts as high as $3000). Customers can also turn to Security Finance for credit reports and tax preparation services. The company operates approximately 900 offices in more than 15 states that are marketed under the Security Finance Sunbelt Credit and PFS banner names. A subsidiary of Security Group the financial institution also has locations operating as Security Financial Services in North Carolina and Longhorn Finance in Texas.

Operations
Security Finance boasts some 900 offices nationwide that operate under the Security Finance Sunbelt Credit and PFS names. The company specializes in offering consumers loans to individuals. It also provides consumer credit reports and assistance as well as tax preparation services.

Geographic Reach
From its headquarters in South Carolina Security Finance boasts offices in more than 15 states nationwide.

Company Background
Security Finance exited Colorado in 2010 after the state's attorney general general office filed a compliant that the company had been refinancing some consumer loans more than three times a year (the limit under Colorado law). The company agreed to repay acquisition fees that it had charged the customers for refinancing the loans.

EXECUTIVES

Pres, Heidi Bolton
Chb, Susan A Bridges
V Chb, C H Edwards
Treas-Cfo, A Greg Williams
SEC, Marshall T Walsh
Asst Treas, Beadie H Townsel
Coo, Judy Perkins
Project Leader, Richard Roth
Cash Management, Brenda Seagle
Unix Administrator, Bob Saccamano
Database Administrator, Dick Dobbins
Auditors: ELLIOTT DAVIS DECOSIMO LLC G

LOCATIONS

HQ: SECURITY FINANCE CORPORATION OF
SPARTANBURG
181 SECURITY PL, SPARTANBURG, SC 293075450
Phone: 864 582-8193
Web: WWW.SECURITY-FINANCE.COM

Selected Locations
Alabama
Florida
Georgia
Idaho
Illinois
Louisiana
Missouri
Nevada
New Mexico
North Carolina
Oklahoma
South Carolina
Tennessee
Texas
Utah
Wisconsin

PRODUCTS/OPERATIONS

Selected Banners
Longhorn Finance (Texas)
PFS
Security Finance
Security Financial Services (North Carolina)
Sunbelt Credit

COMPETITORS

1st Franklin Financial	DFC Global
ACE Cash Express	EZCORP
Advance America	FirstCash
Bank of America	OneMain
Capital One	OneMain Financial
Cash Plus	Value Financial
Community Choice	Services
Financial	World Acceptance

HISTORICAL FINANCIALS
Company Type: Private

Income Statement   FYE: December 31

	ASSETS ($ mil.)	NET INCOME ($ mil.)	INCOME AS % OF ASSETS	EMPLOYEES
12/16	625	70	11.3%	2,500
12/15	651	78	12.1%	—
12/14	648	83	12.8%	—
12/13	616	62	10.2%	—
Annual Growth	0.5%	4.1%	—	—

2016 Year-End Financials

Return on assets: 6.5%   Sales ($ mil): 558
Return on equity: 12.7%

SECURITY GROUP, INC.

EXECUTIVES

Chb, Susan A Bridges
V Chb, Clarence Edwards
Pres, Ray Biggs
V Pres-Fin, A Greg Williams
Treas, Beadie H Townsel
Controller, Patricia Pendergrass
Information Technology Manager, Stacy Jordon
Administrator, Hughey Brandon
Auditors: ELLIOTT DAVIS DECOSIMO LLC G

LOCATIONS

HQ: SECURITY GROUP, INC.
181 SECURITY PL, SPARTANBURG, SC 293075450
Phone: 864 582-8193
Web: WWW.SECURITY-FINANCE.COM

HISTORICAL FINANCIALS
Company Type: Private

Income Statement   FYE: December 31

	ASSETS ($ mil.)	NET INCOME ($ mil.)	INCOME AS % OF ASSETS	EMPLOYEES
12/16	1,002	87	8.8%	2,500
12/15	1,020	97	9.6%	—
12/14	1,040	135	13.0%	—
12/13	1,263	107	8.5%	—
Annual Growth	(7.4%)	(6.4%)	—	—

2016 Year-End Financials

Return on assets: 7.4%   Sales ($ mil): 635
Return on equity: 13.8%

SEFCU SERVICES, LLC

EXECUTIVES

Mng MBR, Michelle Raymond
MBR, Robert Maclasco
Broker, Linda Deluke
Loan Officer, Bob Wilson
Sales Manager Origina, Steve Ferris

LOCATIONS

HQ: SEFCU SERVICES, LLC
 700 PATROON CREEK BLVD, ALBANY, NY 122061067
Phone: 518 783-1234
Web: WWW.SEFCUMORTGAGESERVICES.COM

HISTORICAL FINANCIALS

Company Type: Private

Income Statement				FYE: December 31
	ASSETS ($ mil.)	NET INCOME ($ mil.)	INCOME AS % OF ASSETS	EMPLOYEES
12/17	3,555	21	0.6%	102
12/16	3,328	18	0.6%	—
Annual Growth	6.8%	16.0%	—	—

2017 Year-End Financials

Return on assets: 48.5%   Sales ($ mil): 110
Return on equity: 19.8%

SELECTRANSPORTATION RESOURCES LLC

EXECUTIVES

Co-Mgr, Rick Stewart
V Pres, Robert Garwood
Information Technology Manager, Josh Howe
Sales Staff, Richard Worsham
Sales Staff, Mark Steck
Human Resources Director, Jered Bonasera
Sales and Marketing Staff, Kevin Horelica
Front Counter Sales, Greg Fuson
Parts Manager, Bill Simko
Shop Manager, David Noack
Sales Executive, Joseph Jasinski
Auditors: DOERENMAYHEW CPAS AND ADVISOR

LOCATIONS

HQ: SELECTRANSPORTATION RESOURCES LLC
 9550 NORTH LOOP E, HOUSTON, TX 770291230
Phone: 713 672-4115
Web: WWW.SELECTRANSPORTATION.COM

HISTORICAL FINANCIALS

Company Type: Private

Income Statement				FYE: December 31
	REVENUE ($ mil.)	NET INCOME ($ mil.)	NET PROFIT MARGIN	EMPLOYEES
12/17	302	0	—	366
12/16	355	0	—	—
12/15	0	0	—	—
12/14	371	0	—	—
Annual Growth	(6.7%)			

2017 Year-End Financials

Return on assets: 3.7%   Cash ($ mil.): 18
Return on equity: —
Current ratio: 0.70

SEMCO ENERGY, INC.

EXECUTIVES

Vice President Manager Director, Tracy Vincent
Auditors: ERNST & YOUNG LLP DETROIT MI

LOCATIONS

HQ: SEMCO ENERGY, INC.
 1411 3RD ST STE A, PORT HURON, MI 480605480
Phone: 810 987-2200
Web: WWW.SEMCOENERGYGAS.COM

COMPETITORS

AEP	Halliburton
ARB	Southwest Gas
Chugach Electric	Tengasco
Consumers Energy	WEC Energy
DTE Electric	

HISTORICAL FINANCIALS

Company Type: Private

Income Statement				FYE: December 31
	REVENUE ($ mil.)	NET INCOME ($ mil.)	NET PROFIT MARGIN	EMPLOYEES
12/16	575	51	9.0%	500
12/14	674	51	7.6%	—
12/13	608	48	8.0%	—
12/12	582	41	7.2%	—
Annual Growth	(0.3%)	5.5%	—	—

2016 Year-End Financials

Return on assets: 9.6%   Cash ($ mil.): 4
Return on equity: 9.0%
Current ratio: 0.20

SEMINOLE ELECTRIC COOPERATIVE, INC.

This Seminole is not only a native Floridian but it has also provided electricity in the state since 1948. Seminole Electric Cooperative generates and transmits electricity for 10 member distribution cooperatives that serve 1.4 million residential and business customers in 42 Florida counties. Seminole Electric has more than 3350 MW of primarily coal-fired generating capacity. The cooperative also buys electricity from other utilities and independent power producers and it owns 350 miles of transmission lines. Some 90% of its power load uses the transmission systems of other utilities through long-term contracts.

Operations

Seminole Electric's primary resources include the 1300 MW Seminole Generating Station and the 810 MW Richard J. Midulla Generating Station. The coop's renewable energy resources include waste-to-energy facilities landfill gas-to-energy facilities and a biomass facility. It also buys power as needed on the market.

Seminole Electric has more than 350 miles of transmission line.

Geographic Reach

The company serves customers in 45 counties in northeast south central and southeast Florida.

Financial Performance

In 2013 the coop's revenues declined by 1% due to lower rates and as well as a reduction in Member energy requirements and lower volumes sold to Non-Members.

Seminole Electric's net income increased by 48% in 2013 thanks to lower operating costs as a result of the absence of asset impairment costs and a drop in interest expenses.

The company's operating cash inflow increased to $86.05 million in 2013 (from $34.81 million in 2012) primarily due to improved net income and a change in working capital.

Strategy

The coop is seeking to respond to the State of Florida's push to get more power generation from renewable sources. In 2014 the company generating about 58% of its electricity from coal 35% from natural gas and 7% from green energy sources (up from 5.5% in 2011 making Seminole Electric one of the largest green energy providers in Florida).

Company Background

In 2012 it also made major environmental improvements to its main power plant the coal-fired Seminole Generating Station. In 2011 Seminole Electric boosted its portfolio of purchased green energy to more than 140 MW (including 113 MW from waste-to-energy facilities).

Seminole Electric was formed in 1948 to aggregate the power demands of its members and is governed by a board of trustees representing the 10 member utilities. The cooperative built its first power plant in the 1970s.

EXECUTIVES

Vp Administration, Al Garcia
Auditors: PRICEWATERHOUSECOOPERS LLP TA

LOCATIONS

HQ: SEMINOLE ELECTRIC COOPERATIVE, INC.
 16313 N DALE MABRY HWY, TAMPA, FL 336181427
Phone: 813 963-0994
Web: WWW.SEMINOLE-ELECTRIC.COM

PRODUCTS/OPERATIONS

Members

Central Florida Electric Cooperative
Clay Electric Cooperative
Glades Electric Cooperative
Lee County Electric Cooperative
Peace River Electric Cooperative
Sumter Electric Cooperative
Suwannee Valley Electric Cooperative
Talquin Electric Cooperative
Tri-County Electric Cooperative
Withlacoochee River Electric Cooperative

COMPETITORS

Duke Energy	NextEra Energy
Florida Power & Light	Progress Energy
Florida Public Utilities	Southern Company
JEA	TECO Energy

HISTORICAL FINANCIALS

Company Type: Private

Income Statement				FYE: December 31
	REVENUE ($ mil.)	NET INCOME ($ mil.)	NET PROFIT MARGIN	EMPLOYEES
12/17*	1,067	23	2.2%	528
03/17	1,052	33	3.2%	—
12/16	1,067	20	1.9%	—
09/16	1,091	21	2.0%	—
Annual Growth	(2.2%)	11.2%	—	—

*Fiscal year change

2017 Year-End Financials

Return on assets: 3.3%   Cash ($ mil.): 82
Return on equity: 2.2%
Current ratio: 0.60

SENTARA HEALTHCARE

Sentara Healthcare is not-for-profit organization that operates a network of hospitals and other health facilities primarily in the coastal Hampton Roads area of southeastern Virginia. The system includes a dozen acute care hospitals housing a total of more than 2000 beds. One of its hospitals Sentara Norfolk includes a dedicated cardiac hospital with more than 100 beds. In addition to its acute care facilities Sentara Healthcare operates several outpatient care facilities as well as nursing homes rehab centers medical practices imaging centers and home health agencies. Its Optima Health unit provides HMO PPO and other health insurance products to about 450000 Virginians.

Operations

Across the Sentara Healthcare system the organization boasts a medical staff of about 3800. The medical system's multi-specialty physicians group the Sentara Medical Group has more than 380 primary care and specialty physicians. Its Sentara Senior Services unit operates about 10 nursing and assisted living centers.

The health care group also runs the 160-bed Sentara Princess Anne Hospital an acute care facility located on the Princess Anne outpatient campus in Virginia Beach. Opened in mid-2011 it operates through a 70%-owned joint venture with Bon Secours Health System. The $145 million facility encompasses five stories and offers comprehensive surgical procedures intensive care advanced cardiac care and a maternity center.

Geographic Reach

Sentara Healthcare is the region's largest integrated health care provider serving more than 2 million residents. Its facilities serve customers throughout southeastern and northern Virginia as well as in northeastern North Carolina. It operates in the Virginia cities of Alleghany Charlottesville Hampton Roads Harrisonburg Richmond and Roanoke. In North Carolina Sentara has a presence in Currituck and Elizabeth City.

Financial Performance

The system's revenues increased 9% to $4.7 billion in 2014 due to an increase in net patient services revenues and other operating revenues. Net income fell 82% to $156 million though as salaries and wages increased medical claims and other operating expenses rose and investment gains declined. Cash flow from operations decreased 25% that year to $318 million as a result of the lower net income plus an increase in cash used in receivables and changes in employee compensation and benefits.

Strategy

While it is already one of the largest health care organizations in the state Sentara Healthcare continues to grow through acquisitions construction (both expansions and new buildings) and mergers. In 2014 it acquired the assets and operations of Albemarle Hospital Albemarle Physician Services and Regional Medical Services through a 30-year capital lease agreement with Pasquotank County and Albemarle Hospital Authority. The businesses were combined into newly formed subsidiary SAMC. In 2015 Sentara Leigh Hospital opened a new tower as part of a larger renovation project.

Also in 2015 the system launched a new retail website shopsentara.com which offers over-the-counter health care products including medications vitamins exercise equipment diabetic care supplies and educational books.

Company Background

Sentara Healthcare was founded in 1888 as Norfolk's 25-bed Retreat for the Sick.

EXECUTIVES

Senior Vice President Human Resources, Michael Taylor
Ceo, Howard P. Kern
Svp And Cio, Bertram S. (Bert) Reese
Svp And Cfo, Robert A. (Rob) Broerman
Svp; President Sentara Health Plans And Optima Health, Michael M. Dudley
President Sentara Leigh Hospital, Teresa L. (Terrie) Edwards
President Sentara Careplex Hospital, Debra A. Flores
Corporate Vp Sentara Norfolk General Hospital Sentara Careplex Hospital And Sentara Williamsburg Regional Medical Center, Mary L. Blunt
President Sentara Martha Jefferson Hospital, Jonathan S. Davis
President Sentara Virginia Beach General Hospital, Elwood B. (Bernie) Boone
Chief Nursing Officer, Genemarie McGee
Svp And Chief Medical Officer, Terry Gilliland
President Sentara Williamsburg Regional Medical Center, David J. (Dave) Masterson
President Sentara Norfolk General Hospital, Kurt Hofelich
President Sentara Life Care Corporation, Bruce Robertson
President Sentara Princess Anne Hospital, Thomas B. Thames
Corporate Vp; President Sentara Rmh Medical Center, Jim Krauss
Corporate Vp; President Sentara Medical Group, Robert (Doug) Culling
Corporate Vp, Michael Gentry
President Sentara Enterprises, Linda R. Huffer
President Sentara Obici Hospital, Steve Julian
President Sentara Halifax Regional Hospital, Chris A. Lumsden
Corporate Vp; President Sentara Northern Virgnia Medical Center, Stephen D. Porter
President Sentara Albemarle Medical Center, Coleen Santa Ana
Corporate Vice President, Terrie Edwards
Vice President Coporate Strategy, Grace Hines
Vice President And Executive Medical Director Clinical Effectiveness, Gene Burke
Vice President Network Management, Rachel Schneider
Vice President, Ken Krakaur
Vice President Finance, Lester Eljaiek
Director Of Him, Marsha Rooks
Vice President Operations, Valerie Keane
Vice President And Chief Information Security Officer, Daniel Bowden
Vice President Of Medical Affairs, David Schwartz
Vice President Government Relations And Health Policy, Paul Speidell
Vice President For Clinical Informatics And Transformation, David Mohr
Medical Director Hematopathology Division, Steve Fisher
Vice President Medical Affairs, Michael Ashby
Chairman, Bob Fort
Vice Chairman, Henry (Sandy) Harris
Auditors: KPMG LLP NORFOLK VIRGINIA

LOCATIONS

HQ: SENTARA HEALTHCARE
6015 POPLAR HALL DR, NORFOLK, VA 235023819
Phone: 800 736-8272
Web: WWW.SENTARA.COM

PRODUCTS/OPERATIONS

Selected Hospitals
Charlottesville
  Martha Jefferson Hospital
  MJH Outpatient Care Center
  Health Services at Proffit Road
  Health Services at Spring Creek
  Sentara Home Care Services
  Optima Health
Hampton Roads
  Sentara CarePlex Hospital
  Sentara Heart Hospital
  Sentara Leigh Hospital
  Sentara Norfolk General Hospital
  Sentara Obici Hospital
  Sentara Princess Anne Hospital
  Sentara Virginia Beach General Hospital
  Sentara Williamsburg Regional Medical Center
  Orthopaedic Hospital at Sentara CarePlex
  Sentara Northern Virginia Medical Center
  Martha Jefferson Hospital
  RMH Healthcare
Harrisonburg
  RMH Healthcare
  Optima Health
Northern Virginia
  Sentara Northern Virginia Medical Center
  Sentara Lake Ridge
  Sentara Medical Group physicians
  Sentara Home Care Services
  Sentara Heart and Vascular Center
  Optima Health

Selected Services
Cancer
Cardiac (Heart)
Digestive (Colorectal)
Home Care
Imaging
Maternity
Neurosciences
Rehabilitation
Seniors
Thoracic
Transplant
Trauma/Emergency Services
Urology
Vascular
Weight Loss Surgery
Women's

COMPETITORS

Aetna
Anthem Health Plans of Virginia
Bon Secours Health
CIGNA
Carilion Clinic
Centra Health Inc.
Children's Hospital of The King's Daughters
Franklin Hospital Corp.
HCA Capital Division
Humana
Inova
Kaiser Foundation Health Plan of the Mid-Atlantic
Norton Community Hospital
Novant Health
Riverside Health System (Virginia)
Twin County Regional Healthcare
UnitedHealth Group

HISTORICAL FINANCIALS

Company Type: Private

Income Statement   FYE: December 31

	REVENUE ($ mil.)	NET INCOME ($ mil.)	NET PROFIT MARGIN	EMPLOYEES
12/17	5,297	580	11.0%	28,000
12/16	5,083	329	6.5%	—
12/15	4,833	139	2.9%	—
12/14	4,694	359	7.7%	—
Annual Growth	4.1%	17.3%	—	—

2017 Year-End Financials

Return on assets: 2.6%   Cash ($ mil.): 704
Return on equity: 11.0%
Current ratio: 1.10

SENTARA HOSPITALS - NORFOLK

EXECUTIVES

Ceo, David L Bernd
Pres, Howard Kern
SEC, Jeffrey King
Cfo, Robert A Broermann
Pres-Cfo, Kern Howard P
Director, Cindy Parker
Vice-President, Peggy Evans
Neurology Specialist, Dana Adkins
Cardiac Physician, Gary Zeevi
Nurse, Brenda Smith
Manager, Don Barry
Auditors: KPMG LLP NORFOLK VIRGINIA

LOCATIONS

HQ: SENTARA HOSPITALS - NORFOLK
600 GRESHAM DR, NORFOLK, VA 235071904
Phone: 757 388-3000
Web: WWW.SENTARA.COM

HISTORICAL FINANCIALS

Company Type: Private

Income Statement   FYE: December 31

	REVENUE ($ mil.)	NET INCOME ($ mil.)	NET PROFIT MARGIN	EMPLOYEES
12/17	877	63	7.2%	167
12/16	831	100	12.1%	—
12/15	791	92	11.7%	—
12/14	748	76	10.2%	—
Annual Growth	5.5%	(6.2%)	—	—

SENTARA RMH MEDICAL CENTER

Sentara RMH Medical Center (RMH) formerly known as Rockingham Memorial Hospital serves residents in Virginia's Shenandoah Valley offering some 240 beds. In addition to emergency services and general surgeries and care procedures RMH offers specialized services including cardiovascular care cancer treatment sleep disorder diagnosis behavioral health care medical imaging orthopedic procedures obstetrics and rehabilitation as well as home health hospice and wellness services. Founded in 1912 RMH is part of the Sentara Healthcare system.

Operations

Sentara RMH Medical Center is part of Sentara Healthcare a 125-year old non-profit system which operates more than 100 care sites across Virginia and North Carolina including 12 acute care hospitals.

Geographic Reach

Sentara RMH Medical Center is located in Harrisonburg Virginia and serves residents in seven surrounding counties.

Strategy

Sentara RMH Medical Center continues to be recognized for its specialty care in recent years. In late 2014 the U.S. News and World Report awarded the Sentara RMH Medical Center "high performing" status in three specialty areas — gastroenterology and GI surgery pulmonology and geriatrics — and ranked it the 15th best hospital in Virginia out of nearly 130 hospitals.

EXECUTIVES

Vice President Human Resources Development And Support Services, Mark Zimmerman
Vice President, Gregory Montgomery
Director Of Pharmacy, Betsy Early
Medical Records Director, Karen Phipps
Infection Control Director, REBECCA BRUBAKER
Auditors: KPMG LLP NORFOLK VA

LOCATIONS

HQ: SENTARA RMH MEDICAL CENTER
2010 HEALTH CAMPUS DR, ROCKINGHAM, VA 228018679
Phone: 540 433-4100
Web: WWW.SENTARACAREERS.COM

PRODUCTS/OPERATIONS

Selected Services
Bariatric Surgery
Behavioral Health
Blood Donor Center
Business Office
Center for Sleep Medicine
Chaplain Services
Childcare Connection
Community Health
East Rockingham Health Center
Emergency Department
Family Birthplace
Gifts & Floral
Grief and Loss Services
Hahn Cancer Center
Healthsource
Heart and Vascular Center
Home Care Services
Hospice
Hospitalists
Image Recovery Center
Imaging Services
Joint Services
Laboratory Services
Lifeline
Luray Health Center
Mount Jackson Health Center
New Market Health Center
Occupational Health Center
Orthopedics and Sports Medicine
Palliative Care
Pharmacy
Physician Billing
Pulmonary Services
Rehab Services
Security
Senior Advantage
South Main Health Center
Surgical Services
Valley Behavioral Medicine
Virginia Funkhouser Health Sciences Library
Volunteer Services
Wellness Center
Women's Center

COMPETITORS

Carilion Clinic	University of Virginia
Centra Health Inc.	Health System
HCA Capital Division	Valley Health
Loudoun Healthcare	Virginia Hospital &
MedStar Health	Healthcare

HISTORICAL FINANCIALS

Company Type: Private

Income Statement   FYE: December 31

	REVENUE ($ mil.)	NET INCOME ($ mil.)	NET PROFIT MARGIN	EMPLOYEES
12/17	431	39	9.2%	1,892
12/15	408	46	11.4%	—
12/13	374	31	8.3%	—
12/08	264	10	3.8%	—
Annual Growth	5.6%	16.4%	—	—

2017 Year-End Financials

Return on assets: 1.3%   Cash ($ mil.): 6
Return on equity: 9.2%
Current ratio: 4.10

SERVCO PACIFIC INC.

Servco Pacific's business flows through an ocean's worth of enterprises. The company sells passenger vehicles (including Toyota Subaru Suzuki and Chevrolet models) and commercial trucks through dealerships in Hawaii and Australia. In addition Servco Home & Appliance wholesales kitchen and bath products to building professionals throughout the South Pacific; Servco Raynor Overhead Doors installs residential and commercial garage doors; Servco Insurance Services offers insurance coverage for businesses and individuals; and Servco School & Office Furniture outfits educational institutions and government agencies with desks seating and other furnishings. Servco Pacific was founded by Peter Fukunaga in 1919.

Operations

The diversified firm sells insurance through Servco Insurance Services (SIS) in Washington state. It clients are in the fishing shipping and cargo industries in several states including Alaska. SIS also operates in Hawaii where sister chains Servco Home & Appliance Servco Forklift & Industrial Equipment and Servco Automotive also operate. Servco Tire Company sells tires on Maui and in Honolulu.

Geographic Reach

Honolulu-based Servco Pacific has insurance offices in Seattle and Tacoma Washington. Its other businesses operate in Hawaii (Kauai Maui Oahu and the Big Island); and Australia (New South Wales Queensland).

Financial Performance

The private company reports revenue of approximately $800 million annually.

Strategy

Servco Pacific through its Australian subsidiary has been expanding its Toyota dealer operations in recent years. During 2010 the company acquired majority stakes in Sunshine Toyota of Queensland and Dubbo City Toyota of New South Wales. It also purchased Pacific Toyota in Cairns in 2009. The deals have significantly grown Servco Pacific's business in Australia part of a bid to strengthen its international presence; altogether Servco Pacific owns five dealerships in the country. The firm started operating in Australia in late 2007 with the acquisition of a Toyota dealership in Brisbane. Closer to home Servco is acquiring dealerships in Hawaii amid a influx of off-island businesses including Lithia Motors to Hawaii.

Mergers and Acquisitions

In February 2014 Servco acquired the assets of Maui's Island Subaru dealership in Kahului. The newly-acquired dealership will operate as Servco Subaru.

EXECUTIVES

Chb-Ceo, Mark H Fukunaga
Pres-Coo, Eric Fukunaga
Sr V Pres- Cfo, Jeffery A Bell
Vice President, Glenn K Inouye
Exec Vice President, Patrick D Ching
Sr Vice President, Brian K Horikami
Group Vice President, John Harris
Group Vice President, Sheryl Delsol
Vp, Alan Young
Executive Officer, Vicky Lowe
Sales Associate, Michael Menez

LOCATIONS

HQ: SERVCO PACIFIC INC.
2850 PUKOLOA ST STE 300, HONOLULU, HI
968194475
Phone: 808 564-1300
Web: WWW.SERVCO.COM

PRODUCTS/OPERATIONS

Selected Operations
Automotive
  Rex Tire and Supply
  Scion Dealers of Hawaii
  Subaru Dealers of Hawaii
  Suzuki Dealers of Hawaii
  Servco Australia
  Servco Chevy
  Servco Lexus
  Servco Truck & Commercial
  Toyota Dealers of Hawaii
Servco Home and Appliance Distribution
Servco Insurance Services
Servco Raynor Overhead Doors
Servco School and Office Furniture

COMPETITORS

AutoNation	HD Supply
Citigroup	Inchcape
Fletcher Jones	Lithia Motors

HISTORICAL FINANCIALS

Company Type: Private

Income Statement   FYE: December 31

	REVENUE ($ mil.)	NET INCOME ($ mil.)	NET PROFIT MARGIN	EMPLOYEES
12/17	1,629	26	1.6%	925
12/16	1,435	29	2.1%	—
12/12	923	15	1.7%	—
12/11	429	5	1.2%	—
Annual Growth	24.9%	30.7%	—	—

2017 Year-End Financials

Return on assets: 10.2%   Cash ($ mil.): 30
Return on equity: 1.6%
Current ratio: 0.20

SETON HALL UNIVERSITY

Seton Hall University is a Catholic institution with an enrollment of almost 10000 students (5500 undergraduates and 4300 graduates) who hail from 70 countries. The university offers more than 90 undergraduate and graduate degree programs as well as more than a dozen doctoral programs at eight colleges and schools including the Whitehead School of Diplomacy and International Relations Stillman School of Business and Immaculate Conception Seminary School of Theology. Seton Hall also offers degree and certificate programs online. Seton Hall is the US' oldest diocesan university and is under purview of the Archdiocese of Newark.

Operations
Some 80% of its undergraduate student live on campus.

Seton Hall has a student-to-faculty ratio of 14:1. About 97% of its students receive financial aid.

Geographic Reach
Seton Hall's campus is in a South Orange New Jersey suburban setting about 30 minutes from New York City.

Strategy
Expanding its academic profile in 2015 Seton Hall and Hackensack University Health Network agreed to form a new four-year school of medicine. This partnership will establish the first private school of medicine in New Jersey and provide a major economic boost to the region.

Company Background
Formed in 1856 Seton Hall University was named after Mother Elizabeth Ann Seton the first American-born saint (and an aunt of school founder Bishop James Roosevelt Bayley). Originally called Seton Hall College it became a university in 1950 and became coeducational in 1968.

EXECUTIVES

Evp Administration, Mary J. Meehan
Cfo, Stephen A. Graham
Evp And Provost, Larry A. Robinson
Dean School Of Theology, Joseph R. Reilly
Dean School Of Health And Medical Sciences,
  Brian B. Shulman
Cio, Stephen G. Landry
Dean School Of Diplomacy And International Relations, Andrea Bartoli
Dean College Of Education And Human Services,
  Grace M. May
Dean Of Students, Karen Van Norman
Dean Stillman School Of Business, Joyce Strawser
Dean University Libraries, John E. Buschman
Dean College Of Nursing, Marie Foley
Dean School Of Law, Kathleen M. Boozang
Dean Continuing Education And Professional Studies, Karen Passaro
Interim Dean College Of Arts And Sciences,
  Chrysanthy M. Grieco
Interim Dean College Of Communication And The Arts, Deirdre Yates
Chairman, John J. Myers
Vice Chairman, Bernard A. Hebda
Treasurer, August Pimentel
Auditors: GRANTTHORNTON LLP ISELIN NJ

LOCATIONS

HQ: SETON HALL UNIVERSITY
400 S ORANGE AVE, SOUTH ORANGE, NJ 070792697
Phone: 973 761-9000
Web: WWW.SHU.EDU

PRODUCTS/OPERATIONS

Selected Schools & Colleges
College of Arts and Sciences
College of Education and Human Services
College of Nursing
Immaculate Conception Seminary School of Theology
School of Health and Medical Sciences
School of Law
Stillman School of Business
Whitehead School of Diplomacy & International Relations

HISTORICAL FINANCIALS

Company Type: Private

Income Statement   FYE: June 30

	REVENUE ($ mil.)	NET INCOME ($ mil.)	NET PROFIT MARGIN	EMPLOYEES
06/17	287	32	11.2%	2,700
06/16	281	(12)	—	—
06/15	272	3	1.5%	—
06/14	270	52	19.4%	—
Annual Growth	2.0%	(15.2%)	—	—

2017 Year-End Financials

Return on assets: 16.1%   Cash ($ mil.): 22
Return on equity: 11.2%
Current ratio: —

SEVENTY SEVEN ENERGY LLC

Seventy Seven Energy (formerly Chesapeake Oilfield Services) is a company that was spun off from Chesapeake Energy one of the top onshore energy companies in the US. Chesapeake Energy reorganized six of its oilfield services subsidiaries into then Chesapeake Oilfield Services to create a new publicly traded entity that offers drilling hydraulic fracturing and trucking services as well as renting tools and manufacturing natural gas compressor equipment. It operates in onshore plays in the US. The company filed for Chapter 11 bankruptcy protection in 2016. In 2017 the company was bought by Patterson-UTI in a $1.76 billion stock deal including debt.

Operations
The company conducts business through three operating segments: Hydraulic Fracturing Drilling and Oilfield Rentals.

The hydraulic fracturing segment (51% of Seventy Seven Energy's total revenues in 2015) operates through Performance Technologies and provides high-pressure hydraulic fracturing services and other well stimulation services. This unit owns 11 hydraulic fracturing fleets with an aggregate of 440000 horsepower and six of these fleets are contracted in the Anadarko Basin and the Eagle Ford and Utica Shales. The fracturing process consists of pumping a fracturing fluid into a well at sufficient pressure to fracture the formation.

The drilling segment (38%) operates through Nomac Drilling and provides land drilling services for oil and natural gas E&P activities.

The oilfield rentals segment (11%) operates through Great Plains Oilfield Rental and provides premium rental tools and specialized services for land-based oil and natural gas drilling completion and workover activities. It offers an extensive line of rental tools including a full line of tubular products specifically designed for horizontal drilling and completion with high-torque premium-connection drill pipe drill collars and tubing.

Geographic Reach
Seventy Seven Energy operates in the Anadarko and Permian Basins and the Eagle Ford Haynesville Marcellus Niobrara and Utica Shales.

Sales and Marketing
The company got 70% of its revenues from Chesapeake Energy (CHK) and its affiliates in 2015.

Financial Performance
In 2015 Seventy Seven Energy's net revenues decreased by 46%.

Drilling revenues decreased due to lower revenue days driven by a drop in demand by non-CHK customers.

Hydraulic fracturing revenues declined due to a decrease in revenue per stage driven by market pricing pressure.

Oilfield rental revenues decreased due to a decline in utilization and pricing pressure.

In 2015 Seventy Seven Energy's net loss grew by 2675% due to lower revenues loss on sale of a business loss on sales of property and equipment net and impairment of goodwill.

Cash from operating activities increased by 7% due to the changes in the timing of collection of accounts receivable and the decline in overall operational activity.

Strategy
Chesapeake Energy decided to spin off its oilfield services in order to keep that activity separate from exploration and production. With exploration pro-

duction and oilfield services under one umbrella the company only had one customer - itself. By separating the oilfield services unit Chesapeake Energy reduces its risk should exploration and production slow down much as it did with natural gas drilling and the shift to natural gas liquids.

Nomac Drilling continued to upgrade its rig fleet in 2015 making 80% of its rig fleet capable of drilling on multi well pads. As one of the most active drillers in the United States Nomac also continues to diversify its customer base serving more than 20 different operators.

Seventy Seven Energy expects to spend $100 million in aggregate growth and maintenance capital expenditures in 2016. It also intends to explore opportunistic complementary acquisitions particularly within the hydraulic fracturing segment.

In 2015 the company completed the previously disclosed sale of Hodges Trucking Company L.L.C. to a wholly-owned subsidiary of Aveda Transportation and Energy Services Inc. for $42 million.

Company Background
The company was formed in October 2011 and filed to go public in April 2012 in an initial public offering seeking up to $862.5 million. It completed the spinoff in July 2014 and renamed the company Seventy Seven Energy.

EXECUTIVES

Svp Corporate Development Cfo And Treasurer, John E. Vollmer, age 62
President And Ceo, William A. (Andy) Hendricks, age 53
Auditors: PRICEWATERHOUSECOOPERS LLP OK

LOCATIONS

HQ: SEVENTY SEVEN ENERGY LLC
777 NW 63RD ST, OKLAHOMA CITY, OK 731167601
Phone: 405 608-7777
Web: WWW.77NRG.COM

PRODUCTS/OPERATIONS

SERVICES
Drilling
Pumping
Rentals

Selected Subsidiaries
Compass Manufacturing L.L.C. (maufatures natural gas compression equipment)
Great Plains Oilfield Rental L.L.C. (tool and equipment rental)
Hodges Trucking Company L.L.C. (trucking services)
Nomac Drilling L.L.C. (drilling services)
Oilfield Trucking Solutions L.L.C. (trucking services)
Performance Technologies L.L.C. (hydraulic fracturing)

2015 Sales

	in mil.	% of total
Drilling	436.4	38
Hydraulic fracturing	575.4	51
Oilfield rentals	76.5	7
Oilfield trucking	42.7	4
other operations	0.2	-
Total	**1131.2**	**100**

COMPETITORS

Baker Hughes	Parker Drilling
Basic Energy	Patterson-UTI Energy
FTS International	Precision Drilling
Halliburton	RPC
Helmerich & Payne	Superior Energy
Key Energy	Trinidad Drilling
Nabors Industries	Weatherford
Oil States	International
International	

HISTORICAL FINANCIALS
Company Type: Private

Income Statement
FYE: December 31

	REVENUE ($ mil.)	NET INCOME ($ mil.)	NET PROFIT MARGIN	EMPLOYEES
12/15	1,131	(221)	—	1,700
12/14	2,080	(7)	—	
Annual Growth	(45.6%)	—	—	—

2015 Year-End Financials
Return on assets: 4.8%
Return on equity: (-19.6%)
Current ratio: 1.90
Cash ($ mil.): 130

SFPP, L.P.

EXECUTIVES

Gen Ptnr, Park Shaper
Gen Ptnr, Richard D Kinder
Financial Analyst, Stephen Seibly

LOCATIONS

HQ: SFPP, L.P.
1100 W TOWN AND COUNTRY R, ORANGE, CA 928684647
Phone: 714 560-4400
Web: WWW.KINDERMORGAN.COM

HISTORICAL FINANCIALS
Company Type: Private

Income Statement
FYE: December 31

	REVENUE ($ mil.)	NET INCOME ($ mil.)	NET PROFIT MARGIN	EMPLOYEES
12/17	302	270	89.5%	375
12/16	298	188	63.1%	
12/99	204	113	55.4%	
Annual Growth	2.2%	4.9%	—	—

SGT, LLC

Like its acronym name suggests SGT (aka Stinger Ghaffarian Technologies) is used to taking military orders; in this case very specific technical ones. An engineering services firm SGT provides aerospace engineering project management IT systems development and related services to NASA the US Navy the US Air Force and other primarily military-related government entities through contracts. The company also offers science-related services such as earth climate and planetary modeling and analysis. SGT's facilities are located near airfields and other military facilities.

Geographic Reach
SGT operates a more than dozen offices including in Houston Cleveland and Los Angeles White Sands (New Mexico) and Wallops Island (Virginia).

Sales and Marketing
The company serves the aerospace and aeronautics sectors in addition to civilian agencies and national security entities.

Strategy
SGT grows by signing contracts and working with other partners. In early 2017 it won a $45 million contract to support the National Oceanic

and Atmospheric Administration (NOAA). Under the contract SGT will support the National Mesonet Program which brings non-federal meteorological data sources to NOAA for use in operations at weather forecast offices and numerical modeling information at the National Centers for Environmental Protection. To achieve this SGT is working in partnership with Earth Networks Weather Telematics WeatherFlow Synoptic Data Corp. Sonoma Technology Inc. Panasonic Avionics Corp. and the University of Oklahoma.

Company Background
SGT was founded in 1994 by Harold Stinger and Kam Ghaffarian.

EXECUTIVES

Evp Business Development, Charlie Goorevich
President And Ceo, Kam Ghaffarian
Cfo, Joe Morway
Coo, Dave Wolt
Svp Civil Defense Business, Wayne Friedman
Chairman, Harold Stinger
Auditors: GRANT THORNTON LLP MCLEAN VI

LOCATIONS

HQ: SGT, LLC
7701 GREENBELT RD STE 400, GREENBELT, MD 207706521
Phone: 301 614-8600
Web: WWW.SGT-INC.COM

COMPETITORS

Ball Aerospace	QSS Group
CACI International	Sierra Nevada Corp
CDI Government Services	Techshot
Digital Fusion	United Space Alliance
Lockheed Martin Space Systems	

HISTORICAL FINANCIALS
Company Type: Private

Income Statement
FYE: September 30

	REVENUE ($ mil.)	NET INCOME ($ mil.)	NET PROFIT MARGIN	EMPLOYEES
09/15	570	23	4.2%	2,300
09/13	416	15	3.7%	
09/12	374	9	2.4%	
09/08	292	8	2.8%	
Annual Growth	10.0%	16.3%	—	—

2015 Year-End Financials
Return on assets: 6.4%
Return on equity: 4.2%
Current ratio: 1.30
Cash ($ mil.): —

SHAKE-N-GO FASHION, INC.

EXECUTIVES

Chb, James K Kim
Vice President, Mike Kim
Treas, Betty Kim
Information Technology Manager, Yunsung Han
Manager, Young Ryoo
Merchandiser, Jenny Yang
Chief Operations Officer, Danny Khym
Controller, Jessica Cho
Auditors: FRIEDMAN LLP NEW YORK NY

LOCATIONS

HISTORICAL FINANCIALS

Company Type: Private

Income Statement				FYE: December 31
	REVENUE ($ mil.)	NET INCOME ($ mil.)	NET PROFIT MARGIN	EMPLOYEES
12/16	315	29	9.2%	200
12/15	301	25	8.6%	—
12/09	200	16	8.5%	—
12/08	170	7	4.2%	—
Annual Growth	8.0%	19.3%	—	—

2016 Year-End Financials

Return on assets: 3.1%   Cash ($ mil.): 3
Return on equity: 9.2%
Current ratio: 0.80

SHANDS JACKSONVILLE HEALTHCARE, INC.

EXECUTIVES

Pres, Susan Brownie
Secretary, Robin Hanlon
Information Specialist, Neville Chan
Program Director, Freenae Williams
Vice-President, Gregory Fache
Information Specialist, Phil Lambert
Internal Medicine Practitioner, Robert Kim
Cardiac Physician, Theodore Bass
Internal Medicine Practitioner, Hammad Bhatti
Internal Medicine Practitioner, Myint Thway
Internal Medicine Practitioner, Mohammad Shahid

LOCATIONS

HQ: SHANDS JACKSONVILLE HEALTHCARE, INC.
  655 W 8TH ST, JACKSONVILLE, FL 322096511
Phone: 904 244-0411
Web: WWW.MESOTHELIOMAATTORNEYFLORIDA.NET

HISTORICAL FINANCIALS

Company Type: Private

Income Statement				FYE: June 30
	REVENUE ($ mil.)	NET INCOME ($ mil.)	NET PROFIT MARGIN	EMPLOYEES
06/16	665	22	3.3%	3,000
06/13	522	(5)	—	—
06/12	515	(22)	—	—
Annual Growth	6.6%	—	—	—

2016 Year-End Financials

Return on assets: 6.6%   Cash ($ mil.): 73
Return on equity: 3.3%
Current ratio: 1.70

SHANDS JACKSONVILLE MEDICAL CENTER, INC.

Close to the shifting sands of the northern Florida coast Shands Jacksonville Medical Center (doing business as UF Health Jacksonville) offers a range of services to the 19 counties it serves in Florida and southern Georgia. The 695-bed hospital includes a cardiovascular center Level III neonatal intensive care unit and a Level I trauma center. It also operates primary and specialty clinics in the Jacksonville area. The medical center is affiliated with the University of Florida and is the largest of seven hospitals in the Shands HealthCare family.

Operations

UF Health Jacksonville operates about 40 outpatient care centers. Overall its facilities handle some 34000 inpatient visits and 600000 outpatient visits per year. The hospital's affiliation with the University of Florida (UF) includes collaborative treatment and research programs in areas including cancer cardiovascular neurology orthopedic and pediatric care.

Together with its UF colleagues and affiliates UF Health Jacksonville provides a wide range of health care services across the continuum of care on an inpatient and outpatient basis. Backed by a team of more than 400 faculty physicians it offers nearly 100 specialty services.

Geographic Reach

UF Health Jacksonville's facilities are located in Jacksonville Florida and surrounding areas of northeastern Florida and southeastern Georgia.

Financial Performance

The company's revenues increased by 3% in 2014 due to growth in net patient service revenues as a result of a growth in inpatient and outpatient volumes. Medicare accounted for 25% net patient revenues; Medicaid 31%.

UF Health Jacksonville reported net income of $3 million in 2014 over a net loss in 2013 due to higher interest and a loss on the disposal of capital assets.

Operating cash flow in 2014 decreased by 8% due to higher payments to suppliers and vendors.

Strategy

UF Health Jacksonville has plans to build a second campus on the north side of Jacksonville to meet the needs of a growing community. It's also exploring ways to increase clinical efficiencies such as implementing an electronic health record (EHR) system (with help from federal stimulus funding); it also is looking to maximize funding opportunities for its research programs.

The company is looking to develop a Health Science Center Medical Education on Jacksonville Regional Campus including undergraduate graduate and health-related professions.

It also plans to build a 92-bed hospital wing for the North Campus which will provide greater access to more health care services for the center's residents as well as those living in surrounding communities. Construction is scheduled to begin in 2015 with completion in 2017.

In 2015 UF Health North opened the six-story 210000-square-foot outpatient medical complex in North Jacksonville which includes a 28-bed emergency room advanced imaging a midwife-led birth center rehabilitation services and more than 20 specialty services.

Company Background

Founded in 1870 as the Duval Hospital and Asylum UF Health Jacksonville started the first cancer program in Florida in 1948.

EXECUTIVES

Director Of Nursing, Angel Mills
Auditors: PRICEWATERHOUSECOOPERS LLP T

LOCATIONS

HQ: SHANDS JACKSONVILLE MEDICAL CENTER, INC.
  655 W 8TH ST, JACKSONVILLE, FL 322096511
Phone: 904 244-5576
Web: WWW.JAX.UFL.EDU

PRODUCTS/OPERATIONS

Selected Services

Cancer services
Cardiovascular services
Neuroscience services
Orthopaedic services
Pediatrics
Poison Center
Trauma and critical care services
Women and families

COMPETITORS

Baptist Health System	Ocala Regional Medical
Bay Medical Center	Center
Brooks Rehabilitation	Orange Park Medical
Florida Hospital Tampa	Orlando Health
Bay Division	Palms West Hospital
Mayo Clinic	St. Vincent's Health
Jacksonville	System
Nemours Foundation	
North Florida Regional	
Medical Center	

HISTORICAL FINANCIALS

Company Type: Private

Income Statement				FYE: June 30
	REVENUE ($ mil.)	NET INCOME ($ mil.)	NET PROFIT MARGIN	EMPLOYEES
06/16	663	23	3.6%	3,000
06/15	480	10	2.2%	—
06/10	592	19	3.2%	—
06/09	591	7	1.2%	—
Annual Growth	1.6%	18.8%	—	—

2016 Year-End Financials

Return on assets: 8.2%   Cash ($ mil.): 68
Return on equity: 3.6%
Current ratio: 1.50

SHANDS TEACHING HOSPITAL AND CLINICS, INC.

While its full name is Shands Teaching Hospital and Clinics most people call it UF&Shands. The network affiliated with the University of Florida Health Science Center provides health care services to patients in north-central and northeast Florida. The company is made up of seven not-for-profit acute care community and specialty hospitals as well as more than 80 physician practices and outpatient rehabilitation centers. It also operates a home health care agency. The Shands network has some 1700 licensed beds and about 1000 affiliated University of Florida doctors. Specialty services include oncology pediatrics cardiovascular transplants and neurological care.

Operations

In 2013 the organization along with the University of Florida launched the UF Health brand for their combined operations.

UF&Shands consists of the main teaching hospital at the University of Florida; it includes UF Health Shands Cancer Hospital UF Health Shands Psychiatric Hospital UF Health Shands Rehab Hospital as well as outpatient rehabilitation centers and a home health care agency. UF Health Jacksonville has some 700 beds and 400 full-time faculty members.

The hospital has a 40% stake in Community Health Systems which operates three rural community hospitals in Lake City Starke and Live Oak Florida.

Geographic Reach
UF&Shands operates hospitals in Gainesville and Jacksonville Florida.

Financial Performance
Revenues increased 3% to $1.2 billion in 2014 as net patient revenues and other operating revenues rose. Net income fell by 7% though to $66 million that year as a result of rising non-operating costs such as interest expenses and net losses on disposal of assets.

Cash flow from operations declined 7% to $127 million in 2014 as a result of increased salary and benefit expenses as well as supplier and vendor payments.

Strategy
UF&Shands operates with the goal of improving the diversity of its academic health center and engagement within its communities. It focuses on patient care education and research. Its Gainesville campus is getting an expansion gaining a new building that will include 216 beds and 20 operating rooms. In 2015 it was announced that its neonatal intensive care unit on the same campus will get a $20.7 million renovation and expansion; that project is expected to be completed in 2017.

EXECUTIVES

Svp And Cfo, William J. (Bill) Robinson
Interim Ceo, Ed Jimenez
Vp Nursing And Patient Services, Irene Alexaitis
Svp And Cio, Kari Cassel
Evp Regional And Governmental Affairs, Timothy M. Goldfarb
President And Svp Health Affairs, David S. Guzick
Vice President, Marvin Dewar

LOCATIONS

HQ: SHANDS TEACHING HOSPITAL AND CLINICS, INC.
1600 SW ARCHER RD, GAINESVILLE, FL 326103003
Phone: 352 265-0111
Web: WWW.SHANDS.UFL.EDU

PRODUCTS/OPERATIONS

Selected Hospitals
UF Health Jacksonville (Jacksonville)
UF Health Physicians (Gainesville and Jacksonville)
UF Health Shands HomeCare and Shands Jacksonville Home Health (Gainesville and Jacksonville)
UF Health Shands Hospital (Gainesville)
UF Health Shands Psychiatric Hospital (Gainesville)
UF Health Shands Rehab Centers (Gainesville)
UF Health Shands Rehab Hospital (Gainesville

COMPETITORS

Baptist Health System	Mayo Clinic
Bay Medical Center	Jacksonville
Brooks Rehabilitation	North Florida Regional
Florida Hospital Tampa	Medical Center
Bay Division	Orlando Health
Florida Hospital	Palms West Hospital
Waterman	St. Vincent's Health
Lawnwood Medical	System
Center	

HISTORICAL FINANCIALS
Company Type: Private

Income Statement   FYE: June 30

	REVENUE ($ mil.)	NET INCOME ($ mil.)	NET PROFIT MARGIN	EMPLOYEES
06/15	1,242	81	6.6%	3,071
06/14	1,243	66	5.3%	—
06/10	1,040	(67)	—	—
06/09	1,735	(183)	—	—
Annual Growth	(5.4%)	—	—	—

2015 Year-End Financials
Return on assets: 4.3%   Cash ($ mil.): —
Return on equity: 6.6%
Current ratio: 1.00

SHANNON MEDICAL CENTER

EXECUTIVES

Chm, Len Mertz
Exec Dir-President, Bryan Horner
Vice President, Wilma Stuart
Cfo-Vice President, Shane Plymell
Dir, James Johnson
Dir-Sec-Treas, Robert Eckert
Dir, Joe Henderson
Dir, Michael Boyd
Dir, Oran Berry III
Dir, Michael Oliphant
Dir, Virginia Noelke

LOCATIONS

HQ: SHANNON MEDICAL CENTER
120 E HARRIS AVE, SAN ANGELO, TX 769035904
Phone: 325 653-6741
Web: WWW.SHANNONHEALTH.COM

HISTORICAL FINANCIALS
Company Type: Private

Income Statement   FYE: September 30

	REVENUE ($ mil.)	NET INCOME ($ mil.)	NET PROFIT MARGIN	EMPLOYEES
09/17	289	40	14.1%	1,568
09/16	274	43	15.7%	—
09/15	251	35	14.3%	—
09/14	269	38	14.2%	—
Annual Growth	2.5%	2.3%	—	—

2017 Year-End Financials
Return on assets: 8.0%   Cash ($ mil.): 345
Return on equity: 14.1%
Current ratio: 8.50

SHARP CHULA VISTA AUXILIARY INC

EXECUTIVES

Ceo, Chris Boyd
Manager, Patti Ennis
Manager, Elvira Nonog

LOCATIONS

HQ: SHARP CHULA VISTA AUXILIARY INC
751 MEDICAL CENTER CT, CHULA VISTA, CA
919116617
Phone: 619 421-6110
Web: WWW.SHARP.COM

HISTORICAL FINANCIALS
Company Type: Private

Income Statement   FYE: September 30

	REVENUE ($ mil.)	NET INCOME ($ mil.)	NET PROFIT MARGIN	EMPLOYEES
09/17	363	22	6.2%	34
09/16	366	28	7.9%	—
09/15	367	12	3.3%	—
09/12	298	25	8.6%	—
Annual Growth	4.0%	(2.8%)	—	—

2017 Year-End Financials
Return on assets: 5.5%   Cash ($ mil.): —
Return on equity: 6.2%
Current ratio: 0.90

SHARP CHULA VISTA MEDICAL CENTER

EXECUTIVES

Ceo, Chris Boyd
Physician Recruiter, Lori Moody
Director, Kimberly Castillo
Bloodless Center Manager, Jorge Martinez
Admin Assist, Dolly Delarosa
Ambulatory Director, Karen Simpson
Auditors: LB ERNST & YOUNG US LLP SAN D

LOCATIONS

HQ: SHARP CHULA VISTA MEDICAL CENTER
8695 SPECTRUM CENTER BLVD, SAN DIEGO, CA
921231489
Phone: 858 499-5150
Web: WWW.SHARP.COM

HISTORICAL FINANCIALS
Company Type: Private

Income Statement   FYE: September 30

	REVENUE ($ mil.)	NET INCOME ($ mil.)	NET PROFIT MARGIN	EMPLOYEES
09/17	407	30	7.5%	99
09/16	379	14	3.7%	—
09/15	383	22	5.9%	—
09/14	315	11	3.6%	—
Annual Growth	8.9%	39.6%	—	—

2017 Year-End Financials
Return on assets: 9.6%   Cash ($ mil.): 1
Return on equity: 7.5%
Current ratio: 1.20

SHARP CHULA VISTA MEDICAL CENTER

EXECUTIVES

Ceo, Chris Boyd
President, Michael Murphy
Cfo, Rick King
Administrative Assistant, Andrew Moyers
Director, Michael James
Sales and Marketing Staff, Daniel Dredla
Supervisor, Marie Parayno
Purchasing Agent, Fred Lees
Director, Lorna McGrory
General Manager, Vennie Henderson
Certified Pharmacy Technician, Anne Cara

LOCATIONS

HQ: SHARP CHULA VISTA MEDICAL CENTER
751 MEDICAL CENTER CT, CHULA VISTA, CA
919116617
Phone: 619 502-5800
Web: WWW.SHARP.COM

HISTORICAL FINANCIALS

Company Type: Private

Income Statement   FYE: September 30

	REVENUE ($ mil.)	NET INCOME ($ mil.)	NET PROFIT MARGIN	EMPLOYEES
09/15	367	12	3.3%	1,600
09/14	298	16	5.6%	—
09/13	304	19	6.5%	—
09/12	298	25	8.6%	—
Annual Growth	7.1%	(22.5%)	—	—

2015 Year-End Financials

Return on assets: 4.1%   Cash ($ mil.): 1
Return on equity: 3.3%
Current ratio: 1.10

SHARP HEALTHCARE

Sharp HealthCare stands on the cutting edge of health care delivery in Southern California. The system of not-for-profit hospitals and health care facilities is the largest in the San Diego area. The network includes four acute-care hospitals (Sharp Chula Vista Sharp Coronado Sharp Grossmont and Sharp Memorial) as well as three specialty hospitals for women's care psychiatry and chemical dependence. It also operates two physician medical groups and a number of urgent care and outpatient facilities and clinics. With some 2100 beds and about 2600 physicians Sharp HealthCare offers cancer and cardiac care fertility and maternity services surgical procedures and hospice care.

Operations

Altogether the Sharp HealthCare facilities handle 1600 surgeries each year. In addition to medical services the organization operates its own health plan; the Sharp Health Plan is a not-for-profit HMO serving tens of thousands of members in and around San Diego.

The Sharp Grossmont hospital which serves eastern San Diego County is run by Grossmont Hospital Corporation a subsidiary holding a 30-year lease to manage the facility. One of the system's specialty operations Sharp Mary Birch Hospital for Women & Newborns claims to deliver more babies than any other hospital in California.

Sharp's two medical groups are Sharp Community and Sharp Rees-Stealy which between them comprise more than 1100 doctors providing both primary and specialty care.

Geographic Reach

In addition to its operating bases in San Diego Sharp HealthCare has California facilities in Carmel Valley Chula Vista El Cajon La Mesa Mira Mesa Otay Ranch Point Loma Rancho Bernado San Diego Scripps Ranch Serra Mesa and Sorrento Mesa.

Financial Performance

Sharp's net revenues have trended upward in recent years. The company's revenues grew by $100 million in 2014 due to increase in net patient revenue and premiums. Revenues from the Medicare and Medi-Cal programs accounted for 30% and 24% respectively of Sharp's gross patient charges.

The company's net income decreased by 4% due to pension-related changes other than net periodic pension cost and increase in employee benefits and medical fees expenses.

Sharp's operating cash flow decreased by 48% in 2014.

Strategy

Sharp HealthCare improves its services to area residents through facility upgrades.

In 2015 the company launched Sharp Health News an online news site featuring engaging and original stories about medical breakthroughs new technology and health and wellness.

In 2014 Sharp HospiceCare opened its newest hospice residence BonitaView the first facility of its kind in the South Bay area of San Diego County for end-of-life care designed around the needs of patients and their families.

The organization installed new imaging equipment at the Sharp Memorial Outpatient Pavilion in 2013 and a opened the new Sharp Rees-Stealy center in Del Mar in 2014.

Company Background

In 2011 the system doubled the capacity of Sharp Chula Vista Medical Center's emergency department at a cost of $12 million and in 2012 the Chula Vista hospital opened a new cancer center.

The system began as a single hospital in 1955 named for a local pilot who died in WWII.

EXECUTIVES

Senior Vice President Human Resources, Ky Lewis
President And Ceo, Michael W. (Mike) Murphy
Evp Hospital Operations, Daniel L. (Dan) Gross
Svp And Ceo Sharp Healthcare Foundation, Bill Littlejohn
Svp And Cio, Ken Lawonn
President And Ceo Sharp Health Plan, Melissa Hayden-Cook
Svp And Ceo Sharp Memorial Hospital, Tim Smith
Svp And Ceo Sharp Chula Vista Medical Center, Pablo Velez
Svp And Ceo Sharp Coronado Hospital, Susan Stone
Ceo Sharp Rees-stealy Medical Group, Stacey Hrountas
Svp And Ceo Sharp Mary Birch Hospital For Women & Newborns, Trisha Khaleghi
Svp Marketing And Communications, Diane Gage Lofgren
Svp And Ceo Sharp Grossmont Hospital, Scott Evans
Svp And Cfo, Staci Dickerson
Ceo Sharp Community Medical Group, Paul Durr
Legal Secretary, Jenna Haynes
Director Of Nursing And Patient Care Services, Maryjo Webb
Vice President Business Development, Donna Thompson
Infection Control Director, Gina Newman

Senior Vice President Of Business Development, Alison Fleury
Vice President Materials Management, Linda Johnson
Vice President Of Compensation And Benefits, Anne Stephenson
Vice President Corporate Compliance, Paul Belton
Director Of Pharmacy, Kenneth Schell
Vice President Patient Care Continuum, Christiana Paul
Vice President Of Finance, Donna Serpico
Ambulatory Services Director, Rosanne Ketter-Hanna
Senior Vice President, Randi Larsson
Vice President Workforce Support Services, Anne Davis
Vice President, Mehra Li
Vice President Information Services, Kara Marx
Vice President, Harry Henderson
Vice President Oncology Service Line, Nancy Harris
Vice President Patient Care Information Systems, Sandra McCullough
Medical Librarian, Lise Bretton
Medical Director, Mark Jabro
Senior Vice President Clinical Effectiveness, Amy Adome
Vice President Quality, Patricia J Atkins
Chair, Richard Freeman
Vice Chair, Lori Moore
Treasurer, James Brown
Board Member, Shawna Fallon
Secretary, Linda Byrd
Board Member, Henry Garcia
Secretary, Nancy Earl
Auditors: ERNST & YOUNG LLP SAN DIEGO

LOCATIONS

HQ: SHARP HEALTHCARE
8695 SPECTRUM CENTER BLVD, SAN DIEGO, CA
921231489
Phone: 858 499-4000
Web: WWW.SHARP.COM

PRODUCTS/OPERATIONS

2014 Sales

	% of total
Net patient revenue	62
Premium	35
Other	3
Total	**100**

Selected Programs and Services

Alcohol and drug dependency
Bloodless medicine
Cancer treatment
Complimentary and alternative medicine
Diabetes
Ear nose and throat
Eating disorders
Emergency and trauma
Endoscopy
Executive health
Eye care
Flu care
Health and wellness
Heart and vascular care
   Heart valve surgery
Home care
Hospice
Integrative and complementary medicine
International patient services
Laboratory services
Men's health
Mental health
Neurology
Nutrition
Occupational health
Orthopedics
Pediatrics
Pregnancy and childbirth
Primary care and family health
Radiology and diagnostic imaging
Rehabilitation and physical therapy

Robotic surgery
Safety and injury prevention
Senior care and services
Skilled nursing
Sleep disorders
Stroke and neurology
Transplant
Travel medicine
Urgent care
Weight loss
    Weight management support
    Weight-loss surgery (bariatric)
Women's care
Worksite wellness
Wound care and hyperbaric medicine

Selected Facilities

Sharp Chula Vista Medical Center (340 beds)
Sharp Coronado Hospital (180 beds)
Sharp Grossmont Hospital (540 beds La Mesa)
Sharp Mary Birch Hospital for Women & Newborns (170 beds San Diego)
Sharp McDonald Center (20 beds San Diego)
Sharp Memorial Hospital (675 beds San Diego)
Sharp Mesa Vista Hospital (150 beds San Diego)

COMPETITORS

Adventist Health	Rady Children's
System West	Hospital
Dignity Health	Scripps Health
HCA	Sutter Health
Palomar Health	Tenet Healthcare
Paradise Valley	Tri-City Healthcare
Hospital	District

HISTORICAL FINANCIALS

Company Type: Private

Income Statement				FYE: September 30
	REVENUE ($ mil.)	NET INCOME ($ mil.)	NET PROFIT MARGIN	EMPLOYEES
09/15	3,396	355	10.5%	14,000
09/14	1,234	(12)	—	—
09/13	1,158	(11)	—	—
09/09	897	(0)	—	—
Annual Growth	24.8%	—	—	—

2015 Year-End Financials

Return on assets: 7.7%   Cash ($ mil.): 305
Return on equity: 10.5%
Current ratio: 1.50

SHARP MEMORIAL HOSPITAL

The docs and the scalpels are sharp at Sharp Memorial Hospital. The flagship facility of Sharp HealthCare the not-for-profit hospital has roughly 675 beds and is a designated trauma center for San Diego County. Specialties include cardiac care women's health multi-organ transplantation and cancer treatment. It also provides skilled nursing home health and hospice services. Sharp Memorial Hospital first opened in 1955. Sharp HealthCare completed reconstruction efforts on the Sharp Memorial facility in 2009; the new hospital has improved inpatient surgery emergency trauma and intensive care facilities.

Operations

Along with a full range of inpatient services Sharp Memorial's Outpatient Pavilion provides patients with cancer care women's imaging and endoscopy services. The center also conducts outpatient surgery procedures ranging from LASIK to orthopedic surgeries. More and more hospitals are

adding outpatient services to their roster because they tend to be reimbursed at higher rates. The facility also provides patient education services such as community health classes.

Sharp Memorial which provides some $199 million in community benefits (including charity care and outreach efforts) each year is affiliated with a number of other hospitals clinics and physician groups through its parent organization.

EXECUTIVES

Pharmacy Manager, Kim Allen

LOCATIONS

HQ: SHARP MEMORIAL HOSPITAL
    7901 FROST ST, SAN DIEGO, CA 921232701
Phone: 858 939-3636
Web: WWW.SHARP.COM

COMPETITORS

Adventist Health	Scripps Health
System West	Tenet Healthcare
Grossmont Hospital	Tri-City Healthcare
Palomar Health	District
Rady Children's	
Hospital	

HISTORICAL FINANCIALS

Company Type: Private

Income Statement				FYE: September 30
	REVENUE ($ mil.)	NET INCOME ($ mil.)	NET PROFIT MARGIN	EMPLOYEES
09/17	1,158	237	20.5%	3,500
09/16	1,200	290	24.2%	—
09/15	1,195	240	20.1%	—
09/14	1,042	227	21.9%	—
Annual Growth	3.6%	1.3%		—

2017 Year-End Financials

Return on assets: 2.7%   Cash ($ mil.): 1
Return on equity: 20.5%
Current ratio: 1.30

SHARYLAND UTILITIES, L.P.

EXECUTIVES

Chm, Hunter Hunt
Director, BJ Flowers

LOCATIONS

HQ: SHARYLAND UTILITIES, L.P.
    1900 N AKARD ST, DALLAS, TX 752012300
Phone: 214 978-8958
Web: WWW.SHARYLAND.COM

HISTORICAL FINANCIALS

Company Type: Private

Income Statement				FYE: December 31
	REVENUE ($ mil.)	NET INCOME ($ mil.)	NET PROFIT MARGIN	EMPLOYEES
12/17	324	21	6.6%	95
12/16	290	15	5.4%	—
Annual Growth	11.5%	38.1%	—	—

2017 Year-End Financials

Return on assets: 8.9%   Cash ($ mil.): 25
Return on equity: 6.6%
Current ratio: 0.70

SHAWNEE MISSION MEDICAL CENTER, INC.

Shawnee Mission Medical Center (SMMC) cares for Kansas City residents primarily on the Kansas-side. The health care facility located in the city's southwest suburbs has some 500 inpatient beds. It also offers outpatient surgery and other health services in areas such as pediatrics rehabilitation oncology and radiology. The medical center's emergency department receives some 50000 visits each year. SMMC also operates satellite facilities including the Shawnee Mission Outpatient Pavilion in nearby Lenexa which offers emergency and outpatient diagnostic general practice and surgical care. SMMC is part of Adventist Health System.

Operations

SMMC handles some 20000 inpatient admissions each year as well as some 200000 outpatient visits. Its staff includes about 700 physicians who specialize in about 50 fields of medicine. Specialist care centers include a Chest Pain Emergency Center and the Center for Women's Health. The hospital also provides primary and specialty care through the Shawnee Mission Physicians Group including after-hours clinical care and cardiology and reproductive medicine services. SMMC delivers more babies per year than any other hospital in the metropolitan area.

Geographic Reach

SMMC is located on a more than 50-acre campus in Shawnee Mission (near Kansas City) in Johnson County Kansas and serves the surrounding area. The main hospital campus includes a free-standing surgery center six physician practice buildings a child-care center for associates and a community health center.

Strategy

The SMMC organization looks at community needs to determine where it should grow. In 2013 the hospital opened a $44 million new birthing center to meet the growing need for obstetric services in the Kansas City area. The expansion effort tripled the size of the medical center's labor and delivery and postpartum rooms allowing it to accommodate up to 5000 births annually and added a level III neonatal intensive care unit.

The facility is also adding to its technological abilities to better serve the community. In late 2014 it deployed the eMediTrack platform to help document and analyze data for compliance and accreditation readiness.

Company Background

SMMC is part of a network of more than 500 health care facilities sponsored by the Seventh-day Adventist Church.

EXECUTIVES

Nursing Director, Sheri Hawkins
Medical Director, Lolitta Aznaurova
Director Of Radiology, Lyle Ackerman
Executive Vice President And Chief Finan, Karsten Randolph
Respiratory Therapy Director, Jane Burdolski
Vice President, Andrew Weston
Director Of Radiology, Janelle Paul

LOCATIONS

HQ: SHAWNEE MISSION MEDICAL CENTER, INC.
9100 W 74TH ST, SHAWNEE MISSION, KS 662044004
Phone: 913 676-2000
Web: WWW.SHAWNEEMISSION.ORG

PRODUCTS/OPERATIONS

Selected Centers and Services
Bariatric Surgery
Behavioral Health
Britain Center (Cancer)
Center for Pain Medicine
CorporateCare
Diabetes
Emergency Services
Express Care
GI Services
Hand Specialty Center
HEALTHaware
Heart and Vascular Center
Home Health Care
Maternity
Holistic Care
Men's Health Program
Neurology
Nutrition and Weight Loss
Orthopedics
Plastic Surgery
Radiology
Rehabilitation Services
Reproductive Medicine
Robotic Surgery
Sleep Disorders Center
SM Outpatient Pavilion
SportsCare
Support Groups
Surgical Services
TherapyPlus
Transfer Center Urgent Care
Weight Loss Surgery
Women's Health
Wound Care Center

COMPETITORS

Ascension Health
  Children's Mercy
    Hospital
CoxHealth
HCA
Heartland Health
Mercy Health
Saint Luke's Health
  System
Sisters of Charity of
  Leavenworth
Truman Medical Centers
University of Kansas
  Medical Center
Via Christi Health
  System

HISTORICAL FINANCIALS

Company Type: Private

Income Statement   FYE: December 31

	REVENUE ($ mil.)	NET INCOME ($ mil.)	NET PROFIT MARGIN	EMPLOYEES
12/17	480	66	13.8%	1,850
12/16	454	54	12.0%	—
12/15	435	38	8.7%	—
12/14	385	25	6.6%	—
Annual Growth	7.6%	37.2%	—	—

2017 Year-End Financials
Return on assets: 2.5%
Return on equity: 13.8%
Current ratio: 5.90
Cash ($ mil.): 330

SHAWNEE MISSION SCHOOL DISTRICT

EXECUTIVES

Superintendent, Michael Fulton
Administrator, Bonnie Welty
Payroll Supervisor, Cherie Locke
History Teacher, Curt White
Secretary, Kathy Crawford
Education, Lori Harmon
Food Director, Martha Berry
Social Worker, Melissa Gillette
Accounting Clerk, Pat Deveau
Teacher, Ryan Wagoner
Special Education, Susan Johnson

LOCATIONS

HQ: SHAWNEE MISSION SCHOOL DISTRICT
8200 W 71ST ST, SHAWNEE MISSION, KS 662041715
Phone: 913 993-6200
Web: WWW.SMSD.ORG

HISTORICAL FINANCIALS

Company Type: Private

Income Statement   FYE: June 30

	REVENUE ($ mil.)	NET INCOME ($ mil.)	NET PROFIT MARGIN	EMPLOYEES
06/16	316	(56)	—	4,132
06/15	319	106	33.4%	—
06/13	314	(11)	—	—
06/12	325	(8)	—	—
Annual Growth	(0.7%)	—	—	—

2016 Year-End Financials
Return on assets: 5.6%
Return on equity: (-17.9%)
Current ratio: 1.50
Cash ($ mil.): 98

SHELL MEDICAL PLAN

Auditors: PNCEWATERHOUSECOOPERS LLP PIT

LOCATIONS

HQ: SHELL MEDICAL PLAN
, PHOENIX, AZ 85072
Phone: 800 352-3705

HISTORICAL FINANCIALS

Company Type: Private

Income Statement   FYE: December 31

	REVENUE ($ mil.)	NET INCOME ($ mil.)	NET PROFIT MARGIN	EMPLOYEES
12/16	617	5	1.0%	2
12/15	571	(40)	—	—
12/13	536	6	1.2%	—
Annual Growth	4.8%	(1.6%)	—	—

2016 Year-End Financials
Return on assets: —
Return on equity: 1.0%
Current ratio: —
Cash ($ mil.): 58

SHERMAN ADVOCATE HOSPITAL

EXECUTIVES

Pres-Ceo, Richard B Floyd
Cfo, Eric Krueger
Staff Coordinator, Elizabeth Mc Guigan
Finance Director, Tim Stadelmann

LOCATIONS

HQ: SHERMAN ADVOCATE HOSPITAL
1425 N RANDALL RD, ELGIN, IL 601232300
Phone: 847 742-9800
Web: WWW.SHERMANHEALTH.COM

HISTORICAL FINANCIALS

Company Type: Private

Income Statement   FYE: December 31

	REVENUE ($ mil.)	NET INCOME ($ mil.)	NET PROFIT MARGIN	EMPLOYEES
12/17	308	21	7.1%	1,685
12/16	296	20	6.8%	—
12/14*	277	4	1.6%	—
04/09	213	(0)	—	—
Annual Growth	4.2%	—	—	—

*Fiscal year change

2017 Year-End Financials
Return on assets: 5.4%
Return on equity: 7.1%
Current ratio: 0.70
Cash ($ mil.): 14

SHI INTERNATIONAL CORP.

Businesses that need more than boxes of hardware and software can call SHI International. The company distributes scores of computer hardware and software products from suppliers such as Adobe Cisco Microsoft VMware Symantec and Lenovo. It resells PCs networking products data storage systems printers software and keyboards among other items. SHI offers a range of professional services including software licensing asset management managed desktop services systems integration and vocational training. The company serves corporate government and health care customers from more than 30 offices across the US Canada the UK Germany France and Hong Kong. SHI was founded in 1989 by Chairman Koguan Leo.

Operations

SHI serves several sectors and verticals. The company specializes in software and hardware procurement deployment planning configuration data center optimization IT asset management and cloud computing as well as custom IT solutions.

Geographic Reach

Based in Somerset New Jersey SHI has a global reach through its 30-plus offices located across the US Canada the UK Germany France and Hong Kong. In the US the company operates primarily in Texas and California but also in Arizona Colorado Florida Georgia Illinois Indiana Kansas Massachusetts Michigan Minnesota Missouri New Jersey New York Pennsylvania Virginia and Washington. Specifically its cloud briefing center is housed in New York City and its corporate call center runs from Austin Texas. The company's 420000-sq.-ft. headquarters operates beside its 305000-sq.-ft. Integration Center in Somerset New Jersey.

Financial Performance

SHI International rang up $6.8 billion in sales in 2015 a 14% increase versus the prior year. SHI's Strategic Enterprise Commercial Enterprise Corporate and Public Sector divisions contributed nearly equally to the revenue total for the year and growth outside the U.S. was steady with SHI's Canada U.K. and France divisions each posting double-digit growth. In addition SHI recognized over $1 billion in revenue from cloud products and solutions.

The seller of IT products and services boasts a 99% annual customer retention rate.

Strategy

The company has transformed itself from a $1 million regional reseller of software to a $5 billion global provider of information technology products and services.To this end SHI has invested some $20 million in a new data center that provides cloud services specifically what the company terms infrastructure-as-a-service (IaaS). The data center is one of six in the US that houses virtual machines for IT professionals to provide services such as application deployment disaster recovery software-as-a-service (SaaS). It also offers on-demand burst computing services where customers use the additional bandwidth to handle peaks in demand.

SHI's professional services unit already provides some cloud services and data center consulting. SHI sees IaaS as a logical extension of the software asset management (SAM) service it already provides. Under the SAM program SHI handles software deployment licensing compliance and inventories across a business.

SHI partners with Omaha Nebraska-based information security software specialist Solutionary to manage data security services using its Active-Guard software product to block computer network security breaches as data center security is one of the biggest concerns for businesses in a cloud computing environment.   Awards and Recognition

SHI is the largest minority and women-owned Business Enterprise (MWBE) in the US. The company's ranked 13th on CRN's 2015 Solution Provider 500 list of the largest IT solution providers in North America.

EXECUTIVES

President And Ceo, Thai Lee, age 61
Vp And General Manager, Hal Jagger
Vice President Internal Audit And Finance Operations, Kevin Boyles
Vice President, Melissa Graham
Chairman, Koguan Leo
Auditors: COHNREZNICK LLP NEW YORK NEW

LOCATIONS

HQ: SHI INTERNATIONAL CORP.
290 DAVIDSON AVE, SOMERSET, NJ 088734145
Phone: 732 764-8888
Web: WWW.SHI.COM

PRODUCTS/OPERATIONS

Selected Products
Accessories
Peripherals
Hardware
Memory
Software

Selected Services
Cloud services
Computer vocational training services
Data center services

Events
Hardware services
Networking
POLARIS Software asset management
Storage
Strategic consulting
Webinars

COMPETITORS

ASI Computer	Computacenter
Technologies	Ingram Micro
Agilysys	Insight Enterprises
Arrow Electronics	PC Mall
Avnet	Softchoice
CDW	Tech Data
CompuCom	

HISTORICAL FINANCIALS

Company Type: Private

Income Statement   FYE: December 31

	REVENUE ($ mil.)	NET INCOME ($ mil.)	NET PROFIT MARGIN	EMPLOYEES
12/17	8,243	197	2.4%	3,800
12/16	7,268	104	1.4%	—
12/15	6,540	69	1.1%	—
12/14	5,797	89	1.5%	—
Annual Growth	12.5%	30.3%	—	—

2017 Year-End Financials

Return on assets: 13.4%   Cash ($ mil.): 116
Return on equity: 2.4%
Current ratio: 1.20

SIGNAL ENERGY, LLC

EXECUTIVES

Pres, Greg Pawson
Procurement Manager, Denver Eshee
Safety Director, Ed Pontis
Project Engineer, Grace Jackson
Sales and Marketing Staff, John Kinard
Site Quality Manager, Bill Manuel
Solar Power Generation Project, Bob Elliott
Project Manager, Branen Hurst
Project Engineer, Tanner Knauth
Project Engineer, Taylor Craig
Scheduler, Audra Smith

LOCATIONS

HQ: SIGNAL ENERGY, LLC
2034 HAMILTON PLACE BLVD # 400,
CHATTANOOGA, TN 374216102
Phone: 423 443-4190
Web: WWW.SIGNALENERGY.COM

HISTORICAL FINANCIALS

Company Type: Private

Income Statement   FYE: December 31

	REVENUE ($ mil.)	NET INCOME ($ mil.)	NET PROFIT MARGIN	EMPLOYEES
12/15	339	2	0.7%	43
12/08	92	6	6.5%	—
Annual Growth	20.4%	(12.4%)	—	—

2015 Year-End Financials

Return on assets: 47.6%   Cash ($ mil.): 80
Return on equity: 0.7%
Current ratio: 1.00

SIGNATURE CONSULTANTS LLC

Signature Consultants wants your John Hancock when it comes to signing up for its staffing services. The company provides information technology staffing services to clients from a variety of industries. Signature places IT professionals with expertise in areas like project management Web application development database administration storage and network security. The firm has experience placing IT professionals across such industries as aerospace automotive banking and financial services education electronics government technology pharmaceutical and manufacturing.

Operations

Signature has more than 1100 IT consultants to support run and manage clients' technology needs.

Geographic Reach

Signature provides information technology staffing services from more than 15 locations throughout the US. The company has its National Service Center in Boston Massachusetts and Regional Service Centers in Charlotte North Carolina; Orlando Florida; Fort Lauderdale Florida; and Boston Massachusetts.

Company Background

The privately owned company was founded in 1996.

EXECUTIVES

President And Ceo, Jay Cohen
Coo, Mark Nussbaum
Cfo, Philip Monti
Cio, Chris Tyrell
President National Accounts, Geoff Gray
National Account Manager, Chad Kelly
Senior Vice President Of Business Development, Dan McLean
Senior Vice President Of Human Resources, Candace Whitaker
National Accounts Manager, Debbie Robertson
Vice President Strategy And Development, Alex Ruegg
National Account Manager, Shannon Haggerty
National Account Manager, Christopher Michaud
Senior Vice President Of Sales, Giffney Keith
Auditors: GRANT THORNTON LLP FORT LAUDE

LOCATIONS

HQ: SIGNATURE CONSULTANTS LLC
200 W CYPRESS CREEK RD # 400, FORT
LAUDERDALE, FL 333092175
Phone: 954 677-1020
Web: WWW.SIGCONSULT.COM

COMPETITORS

Adecco	Kelly Services
Allegis Group	Motion Recruitment
Butler America	Partners
CDI	RCM Technologies
COMFORCE	Technisource

HISTORICAL FINANCIALS

Company Type: Private

Income Statement

FYE: December 31

	REVENUE ($ mil.)	NET INCOME ($ mil.)	NET PROFIT MARGIN	EMPLOYEES
12/16	314	5	1.8%	1,450
12/15	253	1	0.5%	—
12/14	235	4	1.8%	—
12/13	202	3	1.9%	—
Annual Growth	15.8%	14.1%	—	—

2016 Year-End Financials

Return on assets: 5.2% Cash ($ mil.): 3
Return on equity: 1.8%
Current ratio: 1.30

SIGNATURE FINANCIAL LLC

EXECUTIVES

Ceo-MBR, Joseph J Depaolo
MBR, Eric Howell
Human Resources Manager, Mark Driggers
Executive Sales Officer, Stephen Port

LOCATIONS

HQ: SIGNATURE FINANCIAL LLC
565 5TH AVE AT46TH, NEW YORK, NY 100172413
Phone: 646 865-0767
Web: WWW.SIGNATURE-BANK.COM

HISTORICAL FINANCIALS

Company Type: Private

Income Statement

FYE: December 31

	ASSETS ($ mil.)	NET INCOME ($ mil.)	INCOME AS % OF ASSETS	EMPLOYEES
12/17	43,119	387	0.9%	11
12/16	39,047	396	1.0%	—
12/15	33,450	373	1.1%	—
Annual Growth	13.5%	1.9%	—	—

2017 Year-End Financials

Return on assets: — Sales ($ mil): 1,502
Return on equity: 25.8%

SILICON GRAPHICS INTERNATIONAL CORP.

Silicon Graphics International (SGI) handles computing on a large scale. The company provides high-performance computer servers that are based on the Linux operating system and designed for large-scale data center deployments. SGI also offers data storage servers as well as modular data center systems sold under the ICE brand. Its equipment is tailored to quickly access analyze process manage visualize and store large amounts of data. SGI targets the IT Internet financial services government and electronics sectors as well as scientific community. Clients have included Amazon.com (18% of sales in 2014) Microsoft Yahoo! and Deutsche Bank. In November 2016 SGI was acquired by Hewlett-Packard Enterprise.

Change in Company Type

HPE closed on the $275 million deal for SGI in November 2016. HPE plans to deploy SGI's supercomputing capabilities to beef up HPE's enterprise offerings to provide faster and higher capacity analytics to customers. The deal is expected to close in early 2017.

Operations

About 74% of SGI's sales come from of its product business and the other 26% was generated by the services unit.

The product segment contains products from both High Performance Computing (HPC) and High Performance Data Analytics (HPDA) operating segments as well as compute solutions which include scale-out computing scale-up computing software and cloud/web products.

The service segment focuses on technical services such as hardware and software maintenance system installation and configuration. The division also offers consulting systems design and support as well as on-site staffing for customers.

Geographic Reach

About 46% of SGI's revenue comes from customers outside the US. Overall North America and South America accounted for 54% of SGI's sales followed by Asia/Pacific at 24% of revenue and Europe at 20%.

SGI is based in Milpitas California and conducts assembly and testing at a plant in Chippewa Falls Wisconsin. SGI's offices in Japan France Germany and the UK are used for sales services research and development and administration.

Sales and Marketing

SGI has more than 6500 customers who it reaches through a direct sales force in nearly 20 countries and a network of resellers and distributors.

Government agencies generate about 45% of SGI's revenue. Government customers include education and research institutions. A portion of those sales are made through system integrators.

Financial Performance

SGI reported its 2016 (ended June) financial results before the HP Enterprise deal.

In 2016 SGI had a bit of a bounce in revenue with a 2% increase to about $524 million. A 5% rise in product sales came from large strategic project wins in Europe and Asia. Services sales notched down 2% for the year.

The sales rise helped reduce SGI's net loss to $11 million in 2016 from $48 million in 2015. A reduction in headcount helped reduce the loss.

Cash flow from operations popped into positive territory at $27 million on decreases in accounts receivable and inventory compared to a negative $97 million in 2015.

Strategy

SGI is moving away from it older cloud computing business and directing its attention and resources to areas that should bring higher margins. Those areas include High Performance Computing High Performance Data Analytics storage and services. The company will expand its business in several vertical markets including weather and climate; physical sciences; life sciences; energy aerospace and automotive; financial services; internet; and media and entertainment.

Those changes set the company in good stead for its acquisition by HP Enterprise particularly in the data analytics area.

Company Background

The company took its pre-HP form when Rackable Systems bought the assets of high-performance computer pioneer Silicon Graphics Inc. (SGI) for $42.5 million in cash in 2009. Rackable expanded its product line customer base and geographic reach with the acquisition and the company adopted the better-known SGI brand in an effort to tap a larger global market. Uniquely for a computer maker the company performs all of its manufacturing assembly and testing at a facility in the US.

EXECUTIVES

President And Ceo, Jorge L. Titinger, $585,000 total compensation
Svp And Cto, Eng Lim Goh
Evp And Coo, Cassio Conceicao, $376,250 total compensation
Svp And Cfo, Mack Asrat
Chairman, Ronald D. Verdoorn
Auditors: DELOITTE & TOUCHE LLP SAN JOS

LOCATIONS

HQ: SILICON GRAPHICS INTERNATIONAL CORP.
940 N MCCARTHY BLVD, MILPITAS, CA 950355128
Phone: 669 900-8000
Web: WWW.HPE.COM/US/EN/SOLUTIONS/HPC-HIGH-PERFORMANCE-COMPUTI

2016 Sales

	$ mil.	% of total
Americas	295	56
Asia Pacific	130	24
Europe Middle East & Africa	107	20
Total	532	100

PRODUCTS/OPERATIONS

2016 Sales

	$ mil.	% of total
Product	394	74
Service	138	26
Total	532	100

Selected Products

Modular data center infrastructure (ICE Cube)
Servers
  Blade (Scale Out)
  Half-depth rack-mount
  Standard depth rack-mount
Software
Storage
  Arrays (OmniStor)
  Massive array of idle disks (MAID platform)
  Servers and clusters (Altix)
  Storage (InfiniteStorage)
  Visualization systesm (Virtu)

COMPETITORS

Cirrascale	Microsoft
Cray	NEC
Dell	NetApp
EMC	Quantum Corporation
Egenera	Super Micro Computer
Fujitsu	Symantec
HP	Toshiba
Hitachi Data Systems	Unisys
IBM	

HISTORICAL FINANCIALS

Company Type: Private

Income Statement

FYE: June 24

	REVENUE ($ mil.)	NET INCOME ($ mil.)	NET PROFIT MARGIN	EMPLOYEES
06/16	532	(11)	—	1,100
06/15	521	(39)	—	—
06/14	529	(52)	—	—
06/13	767	(2)	—	—
Annual Growth	(11.4%)	—	—	—

2016 Year-End Financials

Return on assets: 10.5% Cash ($ mil.): 92
Return on equity: (-2.1%)
Current ratio: 1.10

SILVER BAY REALTY TRUST CORP.

EXECUTIVES

President Ceo And Director, Thomas W. Brock, age 70
Coo, Lawrence B. Shapiro, age 61, $250,000 total compensation
Evp Finance, Griffin P. Wetmore
Chairman, Irvin R. Kessler, age 62

LOCATIONS

HQ: SILVER BAY REALTY TRUST CORP.
3300 FERNBROOK LN N, PLYMOUTH, MN 554475338
Phone: 952 358-4400
Web: WWW.SILVERBAYREALTYTRUSTCORP.COM

PRODUCTS/OPERATIONS

2015 Sales

	$ mil.	% of total
Rental Income	111	98
Other Income	2	2
Total	**113**	**100**

COMPETITORS

American Homes 4 Rent	MAA
Beazer Homes	Waypoint Homes Realty
Colony American Homes	Trust Inc.

HISTORICAL FINANCIALS

Company Type: Private

Income Statement				FYE: December 31
	ASSETS ($ mil.)	NET INCOME ($ mil.)	INCOME AS % OF ASSETS	EMPLOYEES
12/16	1,218	(2)	—	5
12/15	1,224	(9)	—	
12/14	1,002	(56)	—	
12/13	846	(24)	—	
Annual Growth	**12.9%**	—	—	

2016 Year-End Financials

Return on assets: 14.1%   Sales ($ mil): 126
Return on equity: (-2.1%)

SILVER CROSS HEALTH SYSTEM

EXECUTIVES

Pres-Ceo, Paul Pawlak
Sr V Pres, John Krepps
Sr V Pres, Ruth Colby
V Pres, Wayne Aardsma
Exec V Pres, Mary Bakken
Manager, Karen Helman
Information Specialist, Steve Davis
Coordinator, Nika Nelson
Accounting Staff, Georgia Chiovatero
Coordinator, Juliana McWherter
Coordinator, Cindy Lanham
Auditors: KPMG LLP CHICAGO IL

LOCATIONS

HQ: SILVER CROSS HEALTH SYSTEM
1900 SILVER CROSS BLVD, NEW LENOX, IL
604519509
Phone: 815 300-1100
Web: WWW.SILVERCROSS.ORG

HISTORICAL FINANCIALS

Company Type: Private

Income Statement				FYE: September 30
	REVENUE ($ mil.)	NET INCOME ($ mil.)	NET PROFIT MARGIN	EMPLOYEES
09/17	385	32	8.3%	1,600
09/16	366	22	6.1%	—
09/15	348	(61)	—	—
09/14	347	7	2.1%	—
Annual Growth	**3.5%**	**63.8%**	—	—

2017 Year-End Financials

Return on assets: 6.7%   Cash ($ mil.): 34
Return on equity: 8.3%
Current ratio: 0.80

SILVER CROSS HOSPITAL AND MEDICAL CENTERS

Silver Cross Hospital and Medical Centers serve the Illinois counties of Will Grundy and Cook through its 290-bed main hospital campus and nine satellite facilities throughout the area. Services provided by the medical facility include cardiovascular care women's health rehabilitation and behavioral health care. Its outpatient facilities provide primary and specialty care services such as medical imaging and dialysis. The Silver Cross Hospital and Medical Centers name comes from the emblem (the Maltese Cross) of the Christian organization that founded the not-for-profit hospital the International Order of The King's Daughters and Sons.

Operations

Thomson Reuters' Truven a leading source of healthcare intelligence has named Silver Cross Hospital and Medical Centers one of the "100 Top Hospitals" in the nation for seven consecutive years.

The Illinois medical facility maintains a staff of more than 100 physicians. It specializes in offering diagnostic imaging rehabilitation therapy dialysis women's health services and emergency services.

Geographic Reach

Silver Cross Hospital and Medical Centers serves patients in the Illinois counties of Cook Grundy and Will.

Strategy

In 2012 the hospital opened a replacement facility in New Lenox to house its main hospital and to keep pace with population growth in its service territory. The $400-million Silver Cross Hospital facility has about 290 private patient rooms. The 70-acre New Lenox campus also includes two medical offices buildings and the University of Chicago Medicine Comprehensive Cancer Center.

Silver Cross Hospital and Medical Centers also collaborates with the Rehabilitation Institute of Chicago to provide outpatient rehabilitation services at four of the health system's locations.

It added a sleep disorders center in 2012 at its New Lenox (Route 6) location.

Company Background

Silver Cross Hospital admitted its first patient in Joliet Illinois in 1895.

EXECUTIVES

Pres-Ceo, Paul Pawlak
Exec Vice President, Mary Bakken
Vice President, Geoffrey Tryon
Vice President, Kevin Lane
Cfo, William Brownlow
Coordinator, Sue Garrison
Registered Nurse, Susan Ross
Education Specialist, William Kallal
Coordinator, Debbie Liebendorfer
Network Engineer, Robert Bobich
Instructor, Scott Pucel
Auditors: KPMG LLP CHICAGO IL

LOCATIONS

HQ: SILVER CROSS HOSPITAL AND MEDICAL CENTERS
1900 SILVER CROSS BLVD, NEW LENOX, IL
604519509
Phone: 815 300-1100
Web: WWW.SILVERCROSS.ORG

Selected Locations

Headquarters
New Lenox Illinois
Locations with Silver Cross Services
East Joliet
Homer Glen
New Lenox (Route 6)
New Lenox (Route 30)
West Joliet
Professional Office Buildings with Silver Cross Medical Staff
East Joliet
Frankfort
Home Glen
Lemont
New Lenox (Route 6)
New Lenox (Route 30)
West Joliet

PRODUCTS/OPERATIONS

Selected Departments/Facilities

Behavioral Health/Chemical Dependency
Birthing Center
Cancer Center
Cardiology
Center for Women's Health
Colon Cancer Screening
Diagnostic Imaging
Diabetes
Dialysis
Encore Shop
Emergency Department
Free-Standing Emergency Care Center
Home Health Care
Incontinence & Pelvic Floor Disorders
Interventional Radiology
Joint Replacement Education
Intensive Care
Outpatient Infusion Center
Pediatric Services
Pet Therapy
Prostate Health
Pulmonary Program
  Rehabilita
Surgery - Same Day
Surgery - Using the da Vinci Robot
Senior Advantage
Silver Cross Emergency Medical Services System
Sleep Disorders Center
Weight Loss Surgery
Wound Healing & Treatment Center
Selected Services
Behavioral health care
Birthing services
Cancer care
Cardiovascular care/Cath Lab
Cardiopulmonary Rehabilitation
Chemical Dependency Services
Chemo and Radiation
Colon cancer screening/Colonoscopies
Da Vinci Robotic Surgery
Diabetes management
Diagnostic testing and imaging (ultrasound x-ray MRI PET/CT scan etc.)
Dialysis
Dietary Counseling
Emergency care
Health educational programs and screenings

Home health care
Hospitalists
Infusion Therapy (chemotherapy etc.)
Incontinence Care
Intensive care
Laboratory testing
Lifeline Emergency Personal Response Service
Mammography
Medical/Surgical inpatient care
Neonatal care
Neurology/Neurosurgery
Obstetrical/gynecological care
Orthopedic care
Pain management
Pastoral care
Pediatric care
Pulmonary care
Rehabilitation (physical speech occupational)
Senior Advantage Program
Sleep Disorders Carre
Support Groups
Stroke care
Surgery (outpatient & inpatient)
Weight Loss Surgery
Women's Health
Wound care

COMPETITORS

Adventist Health System Sunbelt Healthcare
 Advocate Health Care
 Covenant Ministries
 Elmhurst Memorial Healthcare
 Mercy Hospital and Medical Center
 Northwestern Memorial HealthCare
 Sinai Health System
 St. Bernard Hospital and Health Care Center
 University of Chicago Medical Center

HISTORICAL FINANCIALS

Company Type: Private

Income Statement				FYE: September 30
	REVENUE ($ mil.)	NET INCOME ($ mil.)	NET PROFIT MARGIN	EMPLOYEES
09/15	335	(59)	—	1,600
09/14	320	10	3.2%	—
09/13	306	6	2.1%	—
09/08	244	21	8.6%	—
Annual Growth	4.6%	—	—	—

2015 Year-End Financials

Return on assets: 5.0%   Cash ($ mil.): 28
Return on equity: (-17.7%)
Current ratio: 0.90

SINAI HEALTH SYSTEM

You don't have to scale any mountains to reach this Sinai. Sinai Health System provides medical care for the residents of West Side of Chicago. The system is comprised of its flagship Mount Sinai Hospital Holy Cross Hospital Schwab Rehabilitation Hospital and the Sinai Children's Hospital. The health system's Sinai Medical Group provides primary and specialty care through a range of clinics in the area. The Sinai Community Institute offers health wellness and educational programs for all ages and the Sinai Urban Health Institute conducts research and disease outreach programs. Altogether the system has some 700 inpatient beds and 800 physicians.

Operations

Mount Sinai Hospital's service territory in western Chicago includes a number of African-American and Latino communities. Specialties at the 320-bed facility include cancer care cardiovascular care birthing urology orthopedics and mental

health. Its level I trauma center is one of four trauma centers in the city. The hospital's medical training programs serve 700 students per year and include eight residency programs.

Sinai Children's Hospital includes a level III neonatal intensive care unit (ICU) for newborn care as well as a general pediatric ICU. Specialty pediatric services offerings include trauma surgery and viral disease care. Schwab Rehabilitation hospital is a 100-bed inpatient facility for both adults and children. Its services include injury recovery and physical therapy. The Sinai Medical Group includes about 300 area physicians providing general and specialty care to adults and children. Sinai Community Institute focuses on services for children seniors young adults and minorities ranging from prenatal care and parenting education to employment services and job training.

Financial Performance

Revenues for Sinai Health System dropped 6% to $383 million in 2012 due to higher community benefit expenses. The network spends some $90 million annually on community benefits including health outreach programs and the provision of charity care for uninsured and under-insured patients (which make up a high percentage of its customer base). Net income also fell 720% to $2.5 million in 2012 as a result of the decline in revenues.

Strategy

Expansion of facilities is an important part of the Sinai Health System's growth efforts. It added the Holy Cross Hospital to its roster of facilities in 2013. Construction efforts include the building of a new Sinai Community Institute facility to increase clinical health programs.

Sinai Health System conducts a number of quality improvement disease prevention and social service initiatives to enhance the services its provides to Chicago residents. Its patient-centered disease management program provides preventative care assistance to heart disease and diabetes patients (and their physicians) with assistance from the Sinai electronic health record (EHR) system.

Research is also a priority especially in the area of controlling the spread of disease in urban areas. In 2012 the Sinai Urban Health Institute formed a partnership with insurance company BCBS of Illinois to collaborate on a program to reduce health disparities in the care of diabetes patients.

Mergers and Acquisitions

Holy Cross Hospital was acquired by Sinai Health System in January 2013 after the transaction was approved by the state regulatory agencies. The facilities have a shared mission to serve economically challenged communities in Chicago. Though Holy Cross Hospital is a member of the Sinai Health System it retains its Catholic identity through its sponsorship by the Sisters of St. Casimir.

EXECUTIVES

Interim Vice President, Claude Hall
Senior Vice President For Government Affairs, Roberta Rakove
Vice President And Cno, Lori Paccura
Executive Vice President And General Counsel, Rachel Dvorken
Vice President Of Human Resources, Aaron Austin

LOCATIONS

HQ: SINAI HEALTH SYSTEM
 1500 S FAIRFIELD AVE, CHICAGO, IL 606081782
Phone: 773 542-2000
Web: WWW.SINAI.ORG

PRODUCTS/OPERATIONS

Selected Operations
Holy Cross Hospital

Mount Sinai Hospital
Schwab Rehabilitation Hospital
Sinai Children's Hospital
Sinai Community Institute
Sinai Medical Group
Sinai Urban Health Institute

COMPETITORS

Advocate Health Care
 Children's Hopsital of Chicago
 Covenant Ministries
 Elmhurst Memorial Healthcare
 Gottleib Memorial Hospital
 Mercy Hospital and Medical Center
 Northwestern Memorial HealthCare
 Rush System for Health
 St. Bernard Hospital and Health Care Center
 University of Chicago Medical Center
 Weiss Memorial Hospital

HISTORICAL FINANCIALS

Company Type: Private

Income Statement				FYE: March 31
	ASSETS ($ mil.)	NET INCOME ($ mil.)	INCOME AS % OF ASSETS	EMPLOYEES
03/15*	1,297	(3)	—	6,000
06/08	9	0	—	—
06/06	9	0	—	—
06/05	4	0	0.4%	—
Annual Growth	77.1%	—	—	—

*Fiscal year change

2015 Year-End Financials

Return on assets: 15.4%   Sales ($ mil): 599
Return on equity: (-0.5%)

SINAI HOSPITAL OF BALTIMORE, INC.

Sinai Hospital of Baltimore part of the LifeBridge Health network provides medical care in northwestern Baltimore. The 470-bedA hospital isA a not-for-profit medical centerA that includesA such facilities as a heart center a children's hospital a cancer institute and a rehab center. Other specialties include orthopedics neurology and women's care. Medical students from Johns Hopkins University and the University of Maryland do some of their training at the hospital. Sinai Hospital of Baltimore was founded in 1866 as the Hebrew Hospital and Asylum and becameA a subsidiaryA of LifeBridge when it merged with other area providers in 1998.

Operations

The Sinai Hospital of Baltimore handles about 26000 inpatient admissions and some 75000 emergency room visits per year. It also conducts about 20000 inpatient and outpatient surgeries annually.

The medical center conducts a number of education and training programs including residencies and fellowships for about 400 medical students each year. It is a designated training site for the Johns Hopkins University's ambulatory and internal medicine clerkships.

Strategy

Sinai Hospital of Baltimore has completed several expansion efforts in recent years. In 2012 it opened a new dedicated inpatient hospice unit as well as a new center for geriatric surgery.A In addition the 20-bed Friedman Neurological Rehabilitation CenterA was completedA that year.

EXECUTIVES

Ceo, Neil Meltzer
Chief Medical Officer, Daniel C Silverman
Chm, Brian L Moffet
Treas, Barry F Levin
SEC, Nancy Hackerman
Staff, Roger Sheets
Coordinator, John Wall
Coordinator, Ndubuisi Mbah
Occupational Specia, Amy Herman
Practice Manager, Lisa Lipton
Manager, Sakinah Abdullah

LOCATIONS

HQ: SINAI HOSPITAL OF BALTIMORE, INC.
2401 W BELVEDERE AVE, BALTIMORE, MD
212155270
Phone: 410 601-5678
Web: WWW.SSCSI.COM

PRODUCTS/OPERATIONS

Selected Centers

Alvin & Lois Lapidus Cancer Institute at LifeBridge
Health
Center for Joint Preservation and Replacement
Children's Hospital at Sinai
ER-7 Emergency Center
Heart Center at Sinai
International Center for Limb Lengthening
Krieger Eye Institute
Louis and Phyllis Friedman Neurological Rehabilitation
Center
Rubin Institute for Advanced Orthopedics
Sandra and Malcolm Berman Brain & Spine Institute
Sinai Rehabilitation Center
The Spine Center at Sinai

Selected Services

Allergy and Immunology
Anesthesia
Cardiology
Cancer/Medical Oncology
Dermatology
Dialysis
Emergency Medicine
Endocrinology and Metabolism
Family Medicine
Gastroenterology
General Internal Medicine
Geriatric Medicine
Infectious Diseases
Nephrology (kidneys)
Pulmonary and Critical Care Medicine
Rheumatology (joints tendons)
Neurology
Neurosurgery
Obstetrics and Gynecology
Ophthalmology (eye care)
Oral and Maxillofacial Surgery and Dentistry
Orthopedic Surgery
Otolaryngology (ear nose & throat)
Pathology
Pediatrics
Pharmacy
Physical Medicine and Rehabilitation
Psychiatry
Radiation Oncology
Radiology
Surgery
Urology

COMPETITORS

Anne Arundel Medical Center	Johns Hopkins Health System
Ascension Health	MedStar Health
Bon Secours Health	Meritus Health
Franklin Square Hospital Center	University of Maryland Medical System
GBMC	

HISTORICAL FINANCIALS

Company Type: Private

Income Statement   FYE: June 30

	REVENUE ($ mil.)	NET INCOME ($ mil.)	NET PROFIT MARGIN	EMPLOYEES
06/17	769	63	8.2%	4,497
06/16	690	26	3.9%	—
06/15	677	45	6.7%	—
06/14	714	41	5.8%	—
Annual Growth	2.5%	14.9%	—	—

2017 Year-End Financials

Return on assets: 8.3%   Cash ($ mil.): 66
Return on equity: 8.2%
Current ratio: 1.10

SMART CIRCLE INTERNATIONAL LLC

EXECUTIVES

Ceo, Michael Meryash
President, George Graffy
Vice President, Chad Powers
Cfo, Michael Shimada
Compliance Officer, Andrew Rosenthal
Compliance Manager, Ivan Scherer

LOCATIONS

HQ: SMART CIRCLE INTERNATIONAL LLC
4490 VON KARMAN AVE, NEWPORT BEACH, CA
926602008
Phone: 949 587-9207
Web: WWW.SMARTCIRCLE.COM

HISTORICAL FINANCIALS

Company Type: Private

Income Statement   FYE: January 1

	REVENUE ($ mil.)	NET INCOME ($ mil.)	NET PROFIT MARGIN	EMPLOYEES
01/17*	370	28	7.7%	95
12/15	355	28	7.9%	—
12/14	349	24	7.0%	—
12/13	272	20	7.6%	—
Annual Growth	10.7%	11.3%	—	—

*Fiscal year change

2017 Year-End Financials

Return on assets: 2.9%   Cash ($ mil.): 14
Return on equity: 7.7%
Current ratio: 0.60

SMDC MEDICAL CENTER

EXECUTIVES

Ceo, Peter Person
Ceo, John Smylie
Gen Counsel, James N Abelsen
Director, Donna Van Kessel
Scientist, Stephen Waring

LOCATIONS

HQ: SMDC MEDICAL CENTER
502 E 2ND ST, DULUTH, MN 558051913
Phone: 218 726-4000
Web: WWW.SMDCMEDICALCENTER.ORG

HISTORICAL FINANCIALS

Company Type: Private

Income Statement   FYE: June 30

	REVENUE ($ mil.)	NET INCOME ($ mil.)	NET PROFIT MARGIN	EMPLOYEES
06/17	504	0	0.0%	750
06/16	500	16	3.4%	—
06/15	502	19	4.0%	—
06/14	475	11	2.4%	—
Annual Growth	2.0%	(79.3%)	—	—

2017 Year-End Financials

Return on assets: 6.9%   Cash ($ mil.): 63
Return on equity: —
Current ratio: 3.70

SMITHSONIAN INSTITUTION

The Smithsonian Institution has many hats from the one worn by Harrison Ford in the Indiana Jones movies to the one worn by Abraham Lincoln the night he was assassinated. One of the world's leading cultural institutions the Smithsonian houses some 155 million objects in 19 museums and galleries most of which are on the National Mall in Washington DC. Roughly 30 million people visit every year to view the Smithsonian's exhibits on art music TV and film science history and other subjects. Admission to all but one of the Smithsonian's facilities is free; only the Cooper-Hewitt National Design Museum in New York charges admission.

Operations

A board of regents that includes the vice president and the chief justice of the US six members of Congress and nine private citizens leads the institution. The Smithsonian's exhibits display items such as the Declaration of Independence the ruby slippers worn by Judy Garland in The Wizard of Oz and the Wright brothers' first airplane. Along with its museums and galleries the Smithsonian also operates the National Zoo and nine research facilities and publishes magazines and books.

Among its museums are the African American Museum Archives of American Art Natural History Museum and the Smithsonian Castle.

Geographic Reach

The Smithsonian Institution is located in Washington DC. The world's largest museum and research complex averages about 30 million visitors per year.

Financial Performance

With operating revenue in 2016 of $1.5 billion (up about 20% from the prior year) the Smithsonian receives nearly 55% of its funding from federal appropriations. Contributions and private grants account for nearly 20% and business activities brought in more than 10%.The Institution's net assets have grown steadily over the past five years from $3 billion in 2012 to $3.8 billion in 2016.

Strategy

Recent initiatives at the Institution include the grand opening of the National Museum of African

American History and Culture in late 2016 as well as plans for a $900 million overhaul of the Air and Space Museum (scheduled to start in 2018) and a $2 billion upgrade and expansion of its South Mall Campus (scheduled to start in 2022).

The institution aims to expand the Smithsonian's global relevance in the 21st century. As part of this strategy it released a strategic plan that focuses on four priorities or "grand challenges" as they are called. They include unlocking the mysteries on the universe understanding and sustaining a biodiverse planet valuing world cultures and understanding the American experience.

HISTORY

English chemist James Smithson wrote a proviso to his will in 1826 that would lead to the creation of the Smithsonian Institution. When he died in 1829 he left his estate to his nephew Henry James Hungerford with the stipulation that if Hungerford died without heirs the estate would go to the US to create "an Establishment for the increase and diffusion of knowledge among men." Hungerford died in 1835 without any heirs and the US government inherited more than $500000 in gold.

Congress squandered the money after it was received in 1838 but perhaps feeling pangs of guilt covered the loss. The Smithsonian was finally created in 1846 and Princeton physicist Joseph Henry was named its first secretary. That year it established the Museum of Natural History the Museum of History and Technology and the National Gallery of Art. The Smithsonian's National Museum was developed around the collection of the US Patent Office in 1858. The Smithsonian continued to expand adding the National Zoological Park in 1889 and the Smithsonian Astrophysical Observatory in 1890.

The Freer Gallery a gift of industrialist Charles Freer opened in 1923. The National Gallery was renamed the National Collection of Fine Arts in 1937 and a new National Gallery created with Andrew Mellon's gift of his art collection and a building opened in 1941. The Air and Space Museum was established in 1946.

More museums were added in the 1960s including the National Portrait Gallery in 1962 and the Anacostia Museum (exhibits and materials on African-American history) in 1967. The Kennedy Center for the Performing Arts was opened in 1971. The Collection of Fine Arts was renamed the National Museum of American Art and the Museum of History and Technology was renamed the National Museum of American History in 1980.

The Smithsonian placed its first-ever contribution boxes in four of its museums in 1993.

A planned exhibit featuring the Enola Gay — the plane that dropped the atomic bomb on Hiroshima — created a firestorm in 1994 with critics charging that the exhibit downplayed Japanese aggression and US casualties in WWII. The original exhibit was canceled in 1995 the director of the Air and Space Museum resigned and a scaled-down version of the exhibit premiered. In 2004 the exhibit attracted more protestors prompting Smithsonian officials to evacuate and temporarily close the museum.

Large contributions from private donors continued in the 1990s; the Mashantucket Pequot tribe gave $10 million from its casino operations in 1994 for the Smithsonian's planned American Indian museum and prolific electronics inventor Jerome Lemelson donated $10.4 million in 1995. The museum celebrated its sesquicentennial in 1996 amid news that $500 million in repairs were needed over the next 10 years.

California real estate developer Kenneth Behring gave the largest cash donation ever to the museum

in 1997 — $20 million for the National Museum of Natural History. Short of funds the Smithsonian had to cut back on its 150th-anniversary traveling exhibit that year. The Smithsonian announced a $26 million renovation for the National Museum of Natural History in 1998. Two years later Behring quadrupled his record-breaking 1997 donation of $20 million by giving $80 million to the National Museum of American History. Catherine Reynolds withdrew most of her $38 million gift in 2002 after the Smithsonian Institution refused to implement her ideas for an exhibit at the National Museum of American History.

The National Museum of the American Indian opened on the National Mall in 2004.

Secretary Lawrence Small resigned under pressure in March 2007 amid criticism of his spending practices. CristiA?n Samper director of the Smithsonian's National Museum of Natural History was named acting secretary. A report on the matter issued by the Smithsonian in June said its Board of Regents failed to provide the oversight that might have prevented Small's extravagant spending.

In July 2008 Wayne Clough became the 12th secretary of the Smithsonian.

EXECUTIVES

John And Adrienne Mars Director National Air And Space Museum, John R. (Jack) Dailey
Director Government Relations, Penelope (Nell) Payne, age 61
Director Advancement And Philanthropic Giving, Virginia B. (Ginny) Clark
Secretary, David J. Skorton
Director National Postal Museum, Allen R. Kane
Director National Museum Of African American History And Culture, Lonnie G. Bunch, age 63
Director Equal Employment And Minority Affairs, Era L. Marshall
Director Smithsonian Marine Station At Fort Pierce, Valerie J. Paul
Director Smithsonian Affiliations, Harold A. Closter
Director Smithsonian Institution Libraries, Nancy E. Gwinn
Ombudsman, Chandra P. Heilman
Director Smithsonian Center For Education And Museum Studies, Stephanie L. Norby
Chief Of Staff Office Of The Regents, John K. Lapiana
Director Smithsonian Environmental Research Center, Anson (Tuck) Hines
Director Smithsonian Institution Archives, Anne Van Camp
Acting Provost And Under Secretary For Museums And Research, Richard Kurin
Director National Museum Of African Art, Johnnetta B. Cole
Director Smithsonian Tropical Research Center, Matthew Larsen
Deputy Under Secretary For Collections And Interdisciplinary Support, Scott Miller
General Counsel, Judith E. Leonard
Director Harvard-smithsonian Center For Astrophysics, Charles R. Alcock
Director Smithsonian Latino Center, Eduardo D az
Director Smithsonian Museum Conservation Institute, Robert J. Koestler
Director Cooper-hewitt Smithsonian Design Museum, Caroline Baumann
Director National Zoological Park, Dennis Kelly
Director Consortia For The Humanities, Michelle Anne Delaney
Director Office Of Facilities Engineering And Operations, Nancy Bechtol
President Smithsonian Enterprises, Christopher Liedel
Inspector General, Cathy Helm
Director Smithsonian Exhibits, Susan Ades
Cio, Deron Burba

Editor-in-chief Smithsonian Magazine, Michael Caruso
Director Finance And Accounting, Jean Garvin
Director Office Of Planning Management And Budget, David Voyles
Acting Director Office Of Policy And Analysis, Whitney Watriss
Director Office Of Fellowships And Internships, Eric Woodard
Director The Smithsonian Associates, Fredie Adelman
Director Smithsonian American Art Museum And The Renwick Gallery, Elizabeth (Betsy) Broun
Director Hirshhorn Museum And Sculpture Garden, Melissa Chiu
Director National Museum Of American History Behring Center, John Gray
Director Archives Of American Art, Kate Haw
Director National Museum Of Natural History, Kirk Johnson
Director Smithsonianâ's Center For Folklife And Cultural Heritage, Michael Atwood Mason
Director Freer Gallery Of Art And Arthur M. Sackler Gallery, Julian Raby
Director National Portrait Gallery, Kim Sajet
Interim Director Smithsonian Institution Traveling Exhibition Service, Myriam Springuel
Director Consortia For Science, Pierre Comizzoli
Chancellor Board Of Regents, John G. Roberts, age 64
Auditors: KPMG LLP WASHINGTON DC

LOCATIONS

HQ: SMITHSONIAN INSTITUTION
1000 JEFFERSON DR SW, WASHINGTON, DC 205600009
Phone: 202 633-1000
Web: WWW.SI.EDU

PRODUCTS/OPERATIONS

2016 Operating Revenue

	% of total
Federal appropriations	53
Contributions & private grants	18
Business activities	11
Government grants & contracts	8
Endowment	5
Other	5
Total	**100**

Selected Museums and Research Centers

Anacostia Community Museum
Arthur M. Sackler Gallery
Arts and Industries Building
Center for Folklife and Cultural Heritage
Conservation and Research Center
Cooper-Hewitt National Design Museum (New York)
Freer Gallery of Art
Hirshhorn Museum and Sculpture Garden
National Air and Space Museum
National Museum of African Art
National Museum of American History
National Museum of Natural History
National Museum of the American Indian
National Museum of the American Indian - George Gustav Heye Center (New York)
National Science Research Center
National Portrait Gallery
National Postal Museum
National Zoological Park
Smithsonian American Art Museum
Smithsonian Astrophysical Observatory
Smithsonian Center for Latino Initiatives
Smithsonian Center for Materials Research and Education
Smithsonian Environmental Research Center (SERC)
Smithsonian Institution Building (The Castle)
Smithsonian Museum Conservation Institute
Smithsonian Tropical Research Institute

HISTORICAL FINANCIALS

Company Type: Private

Income Statement				FYE: September 30
	REVENUE ($ mil.)	NET INCOME ($ mil.)	NET PROFIT MARGIN	EMPLOYEES
09/17	1,514	153	10.1%	6,100
09/16	1,541	192	12.5%	—
09/15	1,412	50	3.6%	—
09/14	1,452	279	19.2%	—
Annual Growth	1.4%	(18.1%)	—	—

2017 Year-End Financials

Return on assets: 19.5%   Cash ($ mil.): 440
Return on equity: 10.1%
Current ratio: 0.50

SMMH PRACTICE PLAN, INC.

Auditors: KPMG LLP PITTSBURGH PA

LOCATIONS

HQ: SMMH PRACTICE PLAN, INC.
7175 SALTSBURG RD, PITTSBURGH, PA 152352252
Phone: 412 795-6069

HISTORICAL FINANCIALS

Company Type: Private

Income Statement				FYE: June 30
	REVENUE ($ mil.)	NET INCOME ($ mil.)	NET PROFIT MARGIN	EMPLOYEES
06/15	2,060	27	1.3%	26
06/14	2,005	570	28.4%	—
06/13	1,985	402	20.3%	—
06/12	1,976	(90)	—	—
Annual Growth	1.4%	—	—	—

2015 Year-End Financials

Return on assets: 4.8%   Cash ($ mil.): 49
Return on equity: 1.3%
Current ratio: 0.60

SNYDER'S-LANCE, INC.

If you're familiar with the munchies named Toastchee Nip Chee and Captain's Wafers Snyder's-Lance (formerly Lance) has undoubtedly helped you satisfy a snack attack. The company produces single-serve multi-pack and family-sized packages of bakery products and sweet and savory snack foods including cookies crackers nuts potato chips and pretzels. Its snacks are sold under the Lance Cape Cod Tom's Archway and Snyder's brands at food retailers mass merchants and convenience and club stores in the US. International brands include Kettle Chips and Metcalfe's popcorn. The company also makes private-label and branded snacks for food makers. Snyder's-Lance agreed to its acquisition by The Campbell Soup company in 2017 in a $4.9 billion deal.
Change in Company Type

In late 2017 Snyder's-Lance agreed to its acquisition by The Campbell Soup Company which is looking to boost its snack foods division. The deal is expected to close for around $4.9 billion.

Operations

Synder's-Lance manufactures pretzels sandwich crackers kettle cooked chips pretzel crackers cookies potato chips tortilla chips restaurant style crackers popcorn nuts and other salty snacks. It generates around 80% of its sales from its owned branded products with the remainder coming from third-party branded products and other branded products.

The company has R&D facilities in Hanover Pennsylvania and Salem Oregon.

Geographic Reach

Based in North Carolina Snyder's-Lance operates manufacturing facilities in the US in California North Carolina Oregon Pennsylvania Iowa Indiana Georgia Arizona Massachusetts Florida Ohio and Wisconsin as well as in the UK.

Sales and Marketing

The snack food giant sells its products to mass merchandisers club stores discount stores convenience stores foodservice operators and other retailers the likes of drug stores the military schools and government facilities. Wal-Mart its largest customer represents nearly 15% of the company's revenues.

The company distributes snack food products nationwide using a large direct-store-delivery (DSD) network consisting of some 3000 distribution routes served mostly by Independent Business Owners (IBOs) and others that are company-owned.

Financial Performance

After a few years of sluggish growth in fiscal 2016 Snyder's-Lance's sales jumped 27% to $2.1 billion thanks to the acquisitions of Diamond Foods in February and Metcalfe in September of that year. The company also grew its core business particularly its Lance sandwich crackers Snack Factory pretzel crisps Cape Cod chips and the Late July brand.

Net income fell $35.2 million to $14.9 million due to acquisition expenses higher advertising spend and impairment charges relating to changes in manufacturing operations.

Cash from operations increased 79% to $261.2 million due to lower income tax as the company used net operating losses acquired in the Diamond Foods transaction to offset taxes payable.

Strategy

Snyder's-Lance seeking revenue growth abroad through acquisitions. In 2016 it acquired Diamond Foods which does a roaring trade for its Kettle Chips brand in the UK as well as the US; and Metcalfe which makes the UK's best-selling upmarket ready-to-eat popcorn. The two acquisitions also play into Snyder's-Lance's strategy of growing its "better-for-you" product segment.

Mergers and Acquisitions

In early 2016 the company acquired Diamond Foods makers of Diamond and Emerald nuts for about $1.3 billion. The move added snack brands as well as UK and US distribution might to Snyder's-Lance. Later in 2016 to maintain focus on its core products the company sold its Diamond of California culinary nut business to private equity firm Blue Road Capital. Diamond of California had been one of four Diamond Foods brands at the time of Snyder's-Lance's acquisition.

Also in 2016 it acquired all of Metcalfe's Skinny Limited (it previously owned a 26% stake) the maker of the UK's leading upmarket popcorn brand as well as a range of corn and rice cake products.

EXECUTIVES

President Ceo And Director, Brian J. Driscoll, age 60
Svp And Chief Supply Chain Officer, Patrick S. McInerney, $379,950 total compensation
Svp And Chief Marketing And Innovation Officer, Rodrigo F. Troni Pena, age 51, $338,250 total compensation
Evp And Cfo, Alexander W. Pease, age 46, $90,538 total compensation
President Dsd Division, Francis B. (Frank) Schuster, age 51, $341,813 total compensation
President Direct Division, John T. Maples
President Clearview Division, Peter L. Michaud
Managing Director Kettle Foods Limited (uk), Ashley Hicks
Division Vp And General Manager Growth And Developing Markets, Matthew T. Insolia
Vice President Corporate Human Resources, Vanessa Higgins
Vice President Distribution, Greg Wolljung
Vice President Marketing, Eric Van De Wal
Vice President Finance, Ron Trull
Vice President, Rick Puckett
Vice President Of Financial Accounting And External Reporting, Joey Pruitt
Vice President Of Engineering, Rob Miller
Vice President Information Technology Global Thermal Equipment And Services, Robert F Foster
Vice President National Account Strategy, John McGinn
Vice President Of Strategic Innovation, Tim Old
Chairman, James W. Johnston, age 71
Auditors: PRICEWATERHOUSECOOPERS LLP CH

LOCATIONS

HQ: SNYDER'S-LANCE, INC.
13515 BALNTYN CORP PL, CHARLOTTE, NC 282772706
Phone: 704 554-1421
Web: WWW.SNYDERSLANCE.COM

PRODUCTS/OPERATIONS

2015 Revenue

	% of total
Branded products	70
Private brands	20
Other	10
Total	100

Selected Brands

Archway
Brent
Bugles
Cape Cod Potato Chips
Captain's Wafers
Choc-o-Lunch
Delicious
Diamond of California
Don Pablo's
EatSmart
Emerald
Grande
Jays
Kettle brand
KETTLE
Krunchers!
Lance
Nekot
Nipchee
Pop Secret
Pretzel Crisps
Sam's
Salerno
Snyder's of Hanover
Stella D'oro
Texas Pete
Thunder
Toastchee
Toasty
Tom's
Van-o-Lunch
Vista

COMPETITORS

American Pop Corn	Kettle Foods
Beer Nuts	King Nut Companies
Bridgford Foods	Legacy Bakehouse
Campbell Soup	McKee Foods
Chattanooga Bakery	Mondelez International
ConAgra	Old Dutch Foods
Evans Food Products	Otis Spunkmeyer
Flowers Foods	Pepperidge Farm
Frito-Lay	Poindexter Nut
General Mills	Pretzels Inc.
Golden Enterprises	Procter & Gamble
Inventure foods	Snappy Popcorn
John Sanfilippo & Son	Weaver Popcorn Company
Kellogg U.S. Snacks	

HISTORICAL FINANCIALS

Company Type: Private

Income Statement   FYE: December 30

	REVENUE ($ mil.)	NET INCOME ($ mil.)	NET PROFIT MARGIN	EMPLOYEES
12/17	2,226	149	6.7%	5,900
12/16*	2,109	14	0.7%	—
01/15	1,620	192	11.9%	—
12/13	1,761	79	4.5%	—
Annual Growth	6.0%	17.2%	—	—

*Fiscal year change

2017 Year-End Financials

Return on assets: 5.0%   Cash ($ mil.): 18
Return on equity: 6.7%
Current ratio: 0.80

SOCORRO INDEPENDENT SCHOOL DISTRICT

EXECUTIVES

Supt, Jose Espinoza
Supt, Charles Fighs
Cfo, Tony Reza
Staff, Philip A Acosta
Public Relations Director, Daniel Escobar
Coordinator, Rachel Tarango
Coordinator, Susie Godina
Chief Operating Officer, Thomas Eyeington
Project Coordinator, Zaide Cabezuela
Director of Information Techno, Jenifer Hansen
Human Resources District Recor, Margarita Hita
Auditors: GIBSON RUDDOCK PATTERSON LLC

LOCATIONS

HQ: SOCORRO INDEPENDENT SCHOOL DISTRICT
12440 ROJAS DR, EL PASO, TX 799285261
Phone: 915 937-0100
Web: WWW.SISD.NET

HISTORICAL FINANCIALS

Company Type: Private

Income Statement   FYE: June 30

	REVENUE ($ mil.)	NET INCOME ($ mil.)	NET PROFIT MARGIN	EMPLOYEES
06/17	453	200	44.1%	6,000
06/16	443	(4)	—	—
Annual Growth	2.4%	—	—	—

2017 Year-End Financials

Return on assets: 1.7%   Cash ($ mil.): 191
Return on equity: 44.1%
Current ratio: —

SOUTH BROWARD HOSPITAL DISTRICT

South Broward Hospital District (dba Memorial Healthcare System) is a community-owned health services network that provides health service to residents of Florida's Broward Dade and Palm Beach counties. The system's major hospitals include Memorial Regional Hospital Memorial Hospital Pembroke Memorial Hospital West and Memorial Hospital Miramar. The hospitals have a combined capacity of roughly 1900 licensed beds and provide services including diagnostic emergency surgical and rehabilitative care. Memorial also operates a pediatric hospital cardiac and vascular medicine institute a cancer treatment center and a center for women's health as well as nursing home facilities (120 beds) and community clinics.

Operations

The system's hospitals include Memorial Regional Memorial Regional South Joe DiMaggio Children's Memorial West Memorial Miramar Memorial Pembroke and the Memorial Manor nursing home.

Memorial Regional offers a cardiac and vascular institute a cancer institute and a neuroscience center.

Geographic Reach

Memorial Healthcare System operates health care facilities in Florida and Washington.

Financial Performance

In 2015 revenue increased 12% to $1.8 billion as net patient service earnings rose primarily due to an increase in surgical procedures given. Net income rose 89% to $191.4 million that year due to the higher revenue and a decrease in depreciation and amortization. Operating cash flow also increased rising 68% to $292.4 million.

Strategy

Memorial Healthcare System provides care in a number of ways including through home health services and health care plans. It is adding two additional health plans in 2016 to reach a goal of managing more than 100000 lives in the network.

During 2016 the company entered into a partnership with Holy Cross Physician Partners creating the Atlantic Coast Health Network. The new network represents some 1400 physicians.

EXECUTIVES

President And Ceo, Frank V. Sacco
Evp And Chief Administrative Officer, Matthew J. Muhart
Svp And Chief Medical Officer, Stanley W. Marks
Evp And Coo, Aurelio M. Fernandez
Vp Information Security, Robert Gutholc
Director Physician Recruitment, Ken Bolis
Ambulatory Services Director, Debby Nath
Vice President Of Property Management, David Schlemmer
Vice President Marketing Communications, S S Khan
Respiratory Therapy Director, Sandy Santoro
Respiratory Therapy Director, Darlene Moretti
Senior Vice President And Chief Development Officer, Kevin Janser
Ambulatory Services Director, Christine Manget

Vice President Finance North Mississippi Health Services, Lynn Holland
Chairman, Jose Basulto
Vice Chairman, Vic Narang
Secretary Department, Lorena Abreu
Secretary, Ruth Marcus
Auditors: ERNST & YOUNG LLP BOCA RATON

LOCATIONS

HQ: SOUTH BROWARD HOSPITAL DISTRICT
3501 JOHNSON ST, HOLLYWOOD, FL 330215421
Phone: 954 987-2000
Web: WWW.MHS.NET/SERVICES/NEUROLOGY

PRODUCTS/OPERATIONS

2015 Sales

	% of total
Net patient service	92
Disproportionate share distribution	5
Other operating revenue	3
Total	**100**

Selected Facilities

Esther L. Grossman Women's Health & Resource Center
Memorial Cancer Institute
Memorial Hospital Miramar
Memorial Hospital Pembroke
Memorial Hospital West
Memorial Manor
Memorial Outpatient Center
Memorial Primary Care Center - Dania Beach
Memorial Primary Care Center - Hollywood
Memorial Primary Care Center - Miramar
Memorial Primary Care Center - West Hollywood
Memorial Regional Hospital
  Joe DiMaggio Children's Hospital
Memorial Regional Hospital South
Memorial Regional Hospital Fitness & Rehabilitation Center
Memorial Same Day Surgery Center
Memorial Urgent Care Center
Same Day Surgery Center at Memorial Hospital West

COMPETITORS

Baptist Health South Florida	Florida Hospital Heartland
Boca Raton Regional Hospital	HCA
Broward Health	Jackson Health System
Continucare	MJHHA
	South Miami Hospital

HISTORICAL FINANCIALS

Company Type: Private

Income Statement   FYE: April 30

	REVENUE ($ mil.)	NET INCOME ($ mil.)	NET PROFIT MARGIN	EMPLOYEES
04/18	2,014	64	3.2%	9,200
04/17	1,937	134	6.9%	—
04/16	1,897	188	9.9%	—
04/15	854	(649)	—	—
Annual Growth	33.1%	—	—	—

2018 Year-End Financials

Return on assets: 5.1%   Cash ($ mil.): 526
Return on equity: 3.2%
Current ratio: 2.10

SOUTH CAROLINA PUBLIC SERVICE AUTHORITY (INC)

This company turns the lights on in South Carolina. South Carolina Public Service Authority known as Santee Cooper (after two interconnected river systems) provides wholesale electricity to 20 cooperatives and two municipalities that serve more than 2 million customers in South Carolina. It directly retails electricity to more than 174000 customers. One of the largest US state-owned utilities Santee Cooper operates in all 46 counties in South Carolina and has stakes in power plants (fossil-fueled nuclear hydro and renewable) that give it more than 5180 MW of generating capacity. Its Santee Cooper Regional Water System also distributes water to customers in its service area.

Operations
Santee Cooper operates 5029 miles of transmission lines and more than 2841 miles of distribution lines. It also operates 105 transmission stations and 54 distribution substations. The company is the leading renewable energy producer in South Carolina.

Geographic Reach
In addition to supplying power to 20 cooperatives in all 46 counties in South Carolina Santee Cooper also supplies power directly to 29 large industrial customers in 10 counties Charleston Air Force Base the town of Bamberg and the City of Georgetown.

Sales and Marketing
The company serves more than 2 million customers in South Carolina. It directly retails electricity to more than 174000 customers.

Financial Performance
In 2015 Santee Cooper's net revenues decreased by 6% to $1.9 billion compared due to lower kilowatt-hour sales (down 3%) and demand usage (down 2%).

The company's net income decreased by 73% to $34.4 million as the result of lower net revenues and higher electric maintenance expenses.

In 2015 Santee Cooper's operating cash inflow decreased by 77% to $237.6 million.

Strategy
With a eye toward getting 40% of its power from non-carbon emitting sources and conservation by 2020 the company has begun to invest heavily in nuclear solar wind and other renewable energy sources.

In 2015 the company agreed to changes in its agreement with Westinghouse Electric which acquired assets of a second partner in the V.C. Summer Nuclear Station plant construction consortium giving Westinghouse more control over the project.

In 2014 Santee Cooper in collaboration with Central Electric Power Cooperative and the state's electric cooperatives agreed to buy the total energy output of Colleton Solar Farm a utility-scale solar power farm being built by TIG Sun Energy a subsidiary of the North Charleston-based InterTech Group. The solar array consists of 10010 photovoltaic panels. Some panels are fixed while other panels follow the direction of the sun to maximize the production of solar energy.

South Carolina Resources Santee Cooper Central Electric Power Cooperative and the state's electric cooperatives agreed in 2013 to build Colleton Solar Farm the largest solar farm in the state (3000 kilowatts of electricity).

Mergers and Acquisitions
In 2014 South Carolina Electric & Gas Company (SCE&G) principal subsidiary of SCANA Corporation and Santee Cooper announced an agreement for SCE&G to acquire from Santee Cooper a 5% ownership interest in the two new nuclear units which are under construction at V.C. Summer Nuclear Station in Jenkinsville. Under the ownership agreement SCE&G owns 55%; Santee Cooper 45%. The 5% ownership interest would be acquired in three stages with 1% to be acquired at the commercial operation date of the first new nuclear unit (late 2017 or the first quarter of 2018); an additional 2% to be acquired no later than the first anniversary of such commercial operation date; and the final 2% to be acquired no later than the second anniversary date of such commercial operation date.

Company Background
Santee Cooper is a government-owned entity.

Historically the $48.2 million Santee Cooper project (55% federal loan and 45% federal grant) which connected the Santee and Cooper rivers and established hydroelectric dams and a transmission grid began to generate electricity for the first time in 1942. It was founded in 1934.

EXECUTIVES

Vice President Human Resource Management, W Brown
Svp Corporate Planning And Bulk Power, Lonnie N. Carter
Svp And Cfo, Jeff Armfield
Svp Nuclear Energy, Michael Crosby
Evp Competitive Markets And Generation, Marc R. Tye
Svp And Cio, Dom Maddalone
Svp Power Delivery, Arnold R. Singleton
2nd Vice Chairman, Barry Wynn
Chairman, W. Leighton Lord
1st Vice Chairman, William A. Finn
Auditors: CHERRY BEKAERT LLP RALEIGH N

LOCATIONS

HQ: SOUTH CAROLINA PUBLIC SERVICE AUTHORITY (INC)
1 RIVERWOOD DR, MONCKS CORNER, SC 294612998
Phone: 843 761-4121
Web: WWW.SANTEECOOPER.COM

PRODUCTS/OPERATIONS

2015 Sales

	$ mil.	% of total
Electricity	1,856	99
Water	8	-
Other	15	1
Total	**1,879**	**100**

COMPETITORS

Delmarva Power	PS Energy
Dominion Energy	Progress Energy
Duke Energy	SCANA
Florida Public Utilities	TVA
MLGW	Utilities Inc.
North Carolina Electric Membership	

HISTORICAL FINANCIALS
Company Type: Private

Income Statement   FYE: December 31

	REVENUE ($ mil.)	NET INCOME ($ mil.)	NET PROFIT MARGIN	EMPLOYEES
12/17	1,756	90	5.2%	1,748
12/15	1,879	34	1.8%	—
12/13	1,816	65	3.6%	—
12/12	1,887	84	4.5%	—
Annual Growth	(1.4%)	1.4%	—	—

2017 Year-End Financials
Return on assets: 17.3%   Cash ($ mil.): 731
Return on equity: 5.2%
Current ratio: 1.10

SOUTH CENTRAL POWER COMPANY INC

Although South Central Power Company may sound like a power plant in Watts Los Angeles it is in fact a member-owned cooperative that provides electricity to consumers and businesses in southern Ohio. An affiliate of the nationwide Touchstone Energy Cooperative network the electric cooperative provides power to more than 115570 customers over 11000 miles of power lines. In addition to distributing electricity South Central Power also provides outdoor lighting surge suppression products security systems water heater switches and other energy-related services.

Geographic Reach
South Central Power's operations cover 24 counties in Ohio.

Financial Performance
In 2012 the company's revenues grew by 7% thanks to a rise in revenues from residential customers (more than 1320 new customers were added that year). Net income grew by 67% as the result of higher net sales and lower operating costs.

Company Background
South Central Power was formed in 1936. It joined the Touchstone Energy Cooperatives network in 1998.

EXECUTIVES

Pres-Ceo, Rick Lemonds
Vice President, Tom Musick
Vice President, Cathy Bitler
Treas, Kenneth Davis
Cfo, Rebecca Witt
Prin, James Evans
Prin, Richard Poling
Prin, Mike Hummel
Administrator, Bret Rice
Auditors: GBQ PARTNERS LLC COLUMBUS OH

LOCATIONS

HQ: SOUTH CENTRAL POWER COMPANY INC
2780 COONPATH RD NE, LANCASTER, OH 431309343
Phone: 740 653-4422
Web: WWW.SOUTHCENTRALPOWER.COM

HISTORICAL FINANCIALS

Company Type: Private

Income Statement				FYE: December 31
	REVENUE ($ mil.)	NET INCOME ($ mil.)	NET PROFIT MARGIN	EMPLOYEES
12/16	282	14	5.1%	235
12/15	273	22	8.1%	—
12/14	266	21	8.0%	—
12/13	257	17	6.9%	—
Annual Growth	3.1%	(6.7%)	—	—

2016 Year-End Financials

Return on assets: 7.7% Cash ($ mil.): 5
Return on equity: 5.1%
Current ratio: 0.60

SOUTH COAST AIR QUALITY MANAGEMENT DISTRICT

EXECUTIVES

Ceo, Raymond E Robinson
Exec Dir, Barry R Wallerstein
Business Manager, Sylvia Oroz
Manager, Fred Lettice
Manager, Sarah West
and Programming Superv, David Yeh
and Programming Superv, Francis Goh
Human Resources Analyst, Jeanell Bradley
and Programming Superv, Saad Karam
and Programming Superv, Scott Johnson
Supervisor, David Coel
Auditors: EDUCATORS BENEFIT CONSULTANTS

LOCATIONS

HQ: SOUTH COAST AIR QUALITY MANAGEMENT DISTRICT
21865 COPLEY DR, DIAMOND BAR, CA 917654178
Phone: 909 396-2000
Web: WWW.AQMD.GOV

HISTORICAL FINANCIALS

Company Type: Private

Income Statement				FYE: June 30
	REVENUE ($ mil.)	NET INCOME ($ mil.)	NET PROFIT MARGIN	EMPLOYEES
06/17	361	119	33.1%	780
06/16	247	23	9.6%	—
06/15	276	(65)	—	—
06/14	0	0	—	—
Annual Growth	—	—	—	—

2017 Year-End Financials

Return on assets: 8.1% Cash ($ mil.): 627
Return on equity: 33.1%
Current ratio: —

SOUTH GEORGIA MEDICAL CENTER

EXECUTIVES

Principal, Johnny Ball

LOCATIONS

HQ: SOUTH GEORGIA MEDICAL CENTER
2501 N PATTERSON ST, VALDOSTA, GA 316021785
Phone: 229 333-1000
Web: WWW.SGMC.ORG

HISTORICAL FINANCIALS

Company Type: Private

Income Statement				FYE: September 30
	REVENUE ($ mil.)	NET INCOME ($ mil.)	NET PROFIT MARGIN	EMPLOYEES
09/15	310	(2)	—	9
09/14	296	15	5.4%	—
Annual Growth	4.8%	—	—	—

2015 Year-End Financials

Return on assets: 5.9% Cash ($ mil.): 26
Return on equity: (-0.7%)
Current ratio: 1.10

SOUTH MIAMI HOSPITAL, INC.

South Miami Hospital offers primary and tertiary health care services to the residents living near the University of Miami. The hospital has about 470 beds and is one of the largest members of Baptist Health South Florida a top regional health system. Specialty services include emergency care cardiovascular services oncology neurology women's health metabolic care and rehabilitation. It operates an addiction treatment residential facility provides home health care and provides child development diagnostic and early intervention services. South Miami Hospital was founded in 1960.

Operations

South Miami Hospital handles 15000 inpatient admissions each year as well as 30000 emergency room visits 5000 outpatient surgeries and 4000 births. It has about 1300 physicians on its medical staff.

As part of the broader Baptist Health South Florida system South Miami Hospital benefits from shared resources including procurement administration and technology the coordination of which helps the member facilities control costs during times of economic trouble and rising medical care expenses in the US.

Strategy

The Baptist Health system facilities including South Miami Hospital are installing electronic health record (EHR) systems to manage patient records across the system. Such EHR systems are designed to improve quality and lower expenses by facilitating communication between care providers and increasing patient involvement in condition management.

In addition South Miami Hospital has improved its services through expansion and renovation projects. It has added specialty units for robotic surgery birthing heart care and neonatal intensive care. In addition it completed an $80 million two-story construction in 2013 that enhanced the medical center's emergency surgery and imaging departments.

EXECUTIVES

Ceo, Lincoln S Mendez
President, Javier Hermandev-Lichto
SEC, Domingo C Rodriguez
Tres, George M Corrigan
Staff Coordinator, Christine Stiltner Angulo
Chief of Ob/Gyn, Rene A Paez
Chief of Emergency, Tracey C Patricoff
Chief of Medicine, Jorge Murillo
Staff Coordinator, Maria Cabrera
Radiology Director, Eileen Loring
Health Professional, Ghassan Haddad

LOCATIONS

HQ: SOUTH MIAMI HOSPITAL, INC.
6200 SW 73RD ST, SOUTH MIAMI, FL 331434679
Phone: 786 662-4000

COMPETITORS

Adventist Health System Sunbelt Healthcare
Broward Health
H. Lee Moffitt Cancer Center & Research Institute
HCA
Jackson Health System
Larkin Community Hospital
Miami Children's Hospital
Mount Sinai Medical Center of Florida
South Broward Hospital District
UF&Shands
University of Miami Hospital

HISTORICAL FINANCIALS

Company Type: Private

Income Statement				FYE: September 30
	REVENUE ($ mil.)	NET INCOME ($ mil.)	NET PROFIT MARGIN	EMPLOYEES
09/17	484	6	1.4%	2,205
09/16	492	3	0.7%	—
09/15	495	40	8.2%	—
09/14	505	53	10.6%	—
Annual Growth	(1.4%)	(50.0%)	—	—

2017 Year-End Financials

Return on assets: — Cash ($ mil.): —
Return on equity: 1.4%
Current ratio: 0.60

SOUTH NASSAU COMMUNITIES HOSPITAL INC

EXECUTIVES

Ceo, Richard J Murphy
Cfo, Gerard Haas
Chief Officer, Daniel McAluey
Health Professional, Carol Cannella
Vice-President Engineering, Lori Allocca
Information Specialist, Michael Tsymbalyuk
Director, Patrice Kelly
Manager, George Dunn
Technology Computer Coordinato, Robert Burns

LOCATIONS

HQ: SOUTH NASSAU COMMUNITIES HOSPITAL INC
1 HEALTHY WAY, OCEANSIDE, NY 115721551
Phone: 516 632-3000
Web: WWW.SOUTHNASSAU.ORG

HISTORICAL FINANCIALS

Company Type: Private

Income Statement				FYE: December 31
	REVENUE ($ mil.)	NET INCOME ($ mil.)	NET PROFIT MARGIN	EMPLOYEES
12/17	451	(47)	—	2,800
12/16	437	(33)	—	—
12/15	423	(3)	—	—
12/14	434	13	3.0%	—
Annual Growth	1.3%	—	—	—

2017 Year-End Financials

Return on assets: 4.7%　　Cash ($ mil.): 20
Return on equity: (-10.5%)
Current ratio: 0.50

SOUTH SHORE HOSPITAL, INC.

EXECUTIVES

Pres-Ceo, Gene E Green
Cfo-Sr Vice President, Michael Cullen
Sr Vice President, Margaret Holda
Sr Vice President, Christopher J Oconnor
Coo, Joseph Cahill
V Pres Clinical*, Edward Liao
Pres Acute Care Oprs, Timothy Quigley
Medical Staff, Joseph Jiang
Medical Staff, A K Elamine
Registered Nurse, Kim Noble
Vice-President Sales and Marke, Margaret M Holda

LOCATIONS

HQ: SOUTH SHORE HOSPITAL, INC.
55 FOGG RD, SOUTH WEYMOUTH, MA 021902455
Phone: 781 624-8000
Web: WWW.SOUTHSHOREHOSPITAL.ORG

HISTORICAL FINANCIALS

Company Type: Private

Income Statement				FYE: September 30
	REVENUE ($ mil.)	NET INCOME ($ mil.)	NET PROFIT MARGIN	EMPLOYEES
09/17	563	9	1.7%	2,375
09/16	558	17	3.1%	—
09/15	522	50	9.6%	—
09/14	495	30	6.1%	—
Annual Growth	4.4%	(31.5%)	—	—

2017 Year-End Financials

Return on assets: 6.0%　　Cash ($ mil.): 40
Return on equity: 1.7%
Current ratio: 0.40

SOUTH TEXAS ELECTRIC COOPERATIVE, INC.

EXECUTIVES

Pres, Gary Raybon
Vice President, Larry Huesser
SEC-Treas, Tommy Ermis
Asst SEC, Barbara Miller
Vice-President Information Ser, Darryl Klinitchek
Manager, John A Packard
Coordinator, Jessica Schwab
Compliance Staff, Travis Chrest
Fleet Manager Lead Mechanic, Hank Stall
Human Resources Manager, Melissa Tom
Executive Assistant, Michelle Gloor
Auditors: BUMGARDNER MORRISON AND COMPA

LOCATIONS

HQ: SOUTH TEXAS ELECTRIC COOPERATIVE, INC.
2849 FM 447, VICTORIA, TX 77905
Phone: 361 575-6491
Web: WWW.STEC.ORG

HISTORICAL FINANCIALS

Company Type: Private

Income Statement				FYE: December 31
	REVENUE ($ mil.)	NET INCOME ($ mil.)	NET PROFIT MARGIN	EMPLOYEES
12/17	495	26	5.4%	253
12/16	451	24	5.4%	—
12/15	416	31	7.5%	—
12/14	438	30	6.9%	—
Annual Growth	4.2%	(4.1%)	—	—

2017 Year-End Financials

Return on assets: 7.0%　　Cash ($ mil.): 67
Return on equity: 5.4%
Current ratio: 0.50

SOUTHCENTRAL FOUNDATION

EXECUTIVES

Ceo, Katherine Gottlieb
Board of Directors, Lee Olson
Vice President, Kevin Gottlieb
Vice President, Ileen Sylvester
Vice President, Chanda Aloysius
Vice President, Douglas EBY
Human Resources Director, April Kyle
Accounting Manager, Barbara Snell
Administrator, Grace Hamner
Director of Finance, Greg Encelewcki
Human Resources Director, Sandra Bolhing
Auditors: ALTMAN ROGERS & CO ANCHORAG

LOCATIONS

HQ: SOUTHCENTRAL FOUNDATION
4501 DIPLOMACY DR, ANCHORAGE, AK 995085919
Phone: 907 729-4955
Web: WWW.SOUTHCENTRALFOUNDATION.COM

HISTORICAL FINANCIALS

Company Type: Private

Income Statement				FYE: September 29
	REVENUE ($ mil.)	NET INCOME ($ mil.)	NET PROFIT MARGIN	EMPLOYEES
09/17	369	59	16.1%	1,600
09/16	345	45	13.0%	—
09/15	307	44	14.5%	—
09/14	369	133	36.1%	—
Annual Growth	0.1%	(23.5%)	—	—

2017 Year-End Financials

Return on assets: 3.7%　　Cash ($ mil.): 51
Return on equity: 16.1%
Current ratio: 1.20

SOUTHEAST MISSOURI HOSPITAL ASSOCIATION

EXECUTIVES

Ceo, Wayne Smith
President, James W Wente
Vice President, Karen Hendrickson
Cfo, David Storm
Cno, Judy Aslin
Director, April Henry
Accountant, Julie Arnzen
Coordinator, Carol Jordan
Vice-President, Dan Berry
Director of Pharmacy, Nicole Allcock
Management Vice-President, Brian Gilliland

LOCATIONS

HQ: SOUTHEAST MISSOURI HOSPITAL ASSOCIATION
1701 LACEY ST, CAPE GIRARDEAU, MO 637015230
Phone: 573 334-4822
Web: WWW.SEHEALTH.ORG

HISTORICAL FINANCIALS

Company Type: Private

Income Statement				FYE: December 31
	REVENUE ($ mil.)	NET INCOME ($ mil.)	NET PROFIT MARGIN	EMPLOYEES
12/17	299	1	0.6%	2,000
12/16	293	6	2.4%	—
12/15	289	5	1.9%	—
12/13	315	(31)	—	—
Annual Growth	(1.2%)	—	—	—

2017 Year-End Financials

Return on assets: 7.1%　　Cash ($ mil.): 33
Return on equity: 0.6%
Current ratio: 1.20

SOUTHEASTERN FREIGHT LINES, INC.

Less-than-truckload (LTL) carrier Southeastern Freight Lines hauls freight throughout the southern US with a fleet of about 2000 tractors and 6000 trailers. (LTL carriers consolidate freight from multiple shippers into a single truckload.)

Southeastern operates from a network of about 90 terminals in a dozen states (mainly in Texas) and Puerto Rico. Clients have included Lowe's and Home Depot. Through partnerships with carriers including Quik X Transportation A. Duie Pyle Dayton Freight and Oak Harbor Freight Lines Southeastern provides service throughout the US Mexico and Canada.

Operations

Southeastern provides assembly and distribution services and offers the transportation of carpet and carpet-related products and truckload shipments. The company's shipping services include partnerships with other regional carriers Internet connectivity for full shipment visibility and Excelerated Guaranteed Services. Southeastern serves all 48 states on the US mainland Canada and Mexico through the Southeastern Logistics Solutions (SLS) Supply chain services subsidiary.

The company daily picks up more than 20000 shipments and handles more than 1000 shipments of carpet. About 60% of its truct tractors are made by Volvo; 25% by International; and the rest are mainly made by Freightliner. Southeastern has in excess of 3500 48 ft. and 53 ft. vans and more than 2200 28 ft. trailers.

Geographic Reach

Southeastern operates across North America through service centers in Alabama (5) Arkansas (4) Florida (9) Georgia (11) Kentucky (4) Louisiana (5) Mississippi (2) North Carolina (11) Oklahoma (2) Puerto Rico South Carolina (5) Tennessee (5) Texas (20) and Virginia (5).

The company serves the remaining US states Canada the US Virgin Islands and Mexico through a network of service partners.

Sales and Marketing

Southeastern's customers have included such notable names as Home Depot Lowes Char-Broil 3M Logistics Noveon Quoizel and Martin Electronics.

Strategy

Although the company continues to concentrate on its core territory new facilities allow Southeastern to offer next-day and other services to additional markets. To attract and retain more business Southeastern has introduced a new subsidiary Southeastern Logistics Solutions. The logistics unit manages truckload and multimodal transportation services in the US through various transportation partnerships thereby providing a single-source solution for customers needing several types of carriers.

In 2016 Southeastern made a big move to extend its business in Canada launching a door-to-door LTL service linking the Southeastern US with Ontario and Quebec. The new cross-border service operates through a daily linehaul run between a gateway service center in Charlotte North Carolina and a Southeastern terminal in Toronto. Southeastern uses a Canadian agent to provide pickup and delivery services.

Company Background

The company was founded in 1950.

EXECUTIVES

Vice President Management Information Systems, Dave Robinson
Ceo, W. T. (Tobin) Cassels
Svp Finance, Russ Burleson
Vice President Finance, Tom Edge
Senior Vice President Of Operations, Keith Heaton
Vice President, Russell Garrett
Vice President National Accounts, Nelson Forrest
Vice President, Dean Baker
Regional Vice President, Keith Huggins
National Account Manager, Tommy Keeton
Vice President Of Benefits And Compensation, John Nolan

Senior Vice President, Richard Bogan
Vice President Of Operations, Dave Turner
Chairman, W. T. Cassels
Secretary, Richard Connor
Controller And Treasurer, Amy Rowe

LOCATIONS

HQ: SOUTHEASTERN FREIGHT LINES, INC.
420 DAVEGA DR, LEXINGTON, SC 290737485
Phone: 803 794-7300
Web: WWW.SEFL.COM

PRODUCTS/OPERATIONS

Selected Products and Services
Services
  Computer Support
  Downloads
  Drivers and Equipment
  Guaranteed Service
  International Service
  National Partnerships
  Special Services
Shipping
  Claims Inquiry
  Document Retrieval
  Forms
  Internet Invoicing
  Routing Guide
  Rules Tariff
  Tracing

COMPETITORS

AAA Cooper Transportation	R+L Carriers
	Saia
ArcBest	UPS Freight
Averitt Express	Vitran Express
Benton Express	Wilson Trucking
Estes Express	Xpress Global
FedEx Freight	YRC Worldwide
Old Dominion Freight	

HISTORICAL FINANCIALS
Company Type: Private

Income Statement				FYE: December 31
	REVENUE ($ mil.)	NET INCOME ($ mil.)	NET PROFIT MARGIN	EMPLOYEES
12/17*	1,126	109	9.8%	8,000
09/16	0	0	8.6%	—
/ 0	0			
Annual Growth	—	—	—	—

*Fiscal year change

2017 Year-End Financials
Return on assets: —
Return on equity: 9.8%
Current ratio: 2.20
Cash ($ mil.): 39

SOUTHERN BAPTIST HOSPITAL OF FLORIDA INC.

EXECUTIVES

Pres, Hugh Greene
Oo, Johm Wilbanks
Chmn, M C Harden
Vice President, Harvey Granger
Vice President, John Wilbanks
SEC-Treas, Richard L Sisisky
Health Professional, Christopher Carroll

Coordinator, John Polisknowski
Facilities Manager, Larry Peterson
Administrator of Oncology Serv, Lee Mengel
Director, Shannon Baum
Auditors: ERNST & YOUNG LLP JACKSONVIL

LOCATIONS

HQ: SOUTHERN BAPTIST HOSPITAL OF FLORIDA INC.
800 PRUDENTIAL DR, JACKSONVILLE, FL 322078202
Phone: 904 202-2000
Web: WWW.E-BAPTISTHEALTH.COM

HISTORICAL FINANCIALS
Company Type: Private

Income Statement				FYE: September 30
	REVENUE ($ mil.)	NET INCOME ($ mil.)	NET PROFIT MARGIN	EMPLOYEES
09/17	1,151	296	25.8%	4,000
09/16	1,129	205	18.2%	—
09/09	793	(21)	—	—
09/08	1,007	82	8.1%	—
Annual Growth	1.5%	15.4%	—	—

2017 Year-End Financials
Return on assets: 12.7%
Return on equity: 25.8%
Current ratio: 1.20
Cash ($ mil.): 2

SOUTHERN ILLINOIS HEALTHCARE E

Auditors: MCGLADREY LLP SPRINGFIELD IL

LOCATIONS

HQ: SOUTHERN ILLINOIS HEALTHCARE E
2370 N MCROY DR, CARBONDALE, IL 629015629
Phone: 618 457-5200
Web: WWW.SIH.NET

HISTORICAL FINANCIALS
Company Type: Private

Income Statement				FYE: March 31
	REVENUE ($ mil.)	NET INCOME ($ mil.)	NET PROFIT MARGIN	EMPLOYEES
03/15	528	36	6.8%	14
03/14	1	0	44.8%	—
Annual Growth	34279.8%	5154.4%	—	—

2015 Year-End Financials
Return on assets: 5.5%
Return on equity: 6.8%
Current ratio: 1.40
Cash ($ mil.): 12

SOUTHERN ILLINOIS HEALTHCARE ENTERPRISES, INC.

Southern Illinois Healthcare a nonprofit health care system operates the flagship 145-bed tertiary-care Memorial Hospital of Carbondale as well as Herrin Hospital (with 114 beds) and St. Joseph Memorial Hospital (with 25 beds). The hospitals serve residents of across southern Illinois. The nearly 280-bed system provides services such as birthing cardiac cancer and emergency care as well as surgery and rehabilitation. Its cardiac care is offered through an affiliation with the Prairie Heart Institute at St. John's Hospital in Springfield Illinois. The medical school at Southern Illinois University conducts its Family Practice Residency Program at Memorial Hospital of Carbondale.

Operations

Across its health system Southern Illinois Healthcare employs more than 3000 people. Physicians at its primary hospital Memorial Hospital of Carbondale represent nearly 40 medical specialties. It maintains the only dedicated pediatric unit in the region as well as the largest birthing center with Level II Plus Special Care Nursery.

St. Joseph Memorial Hospital is a full-service critical access hospital.

In addition to the patient hospitals the system includes two clinics two physician professional buildings an urgent care clinic and dedicated neurology cancer heart sleep and rehabilitation centers.

Geographic Reach

Most of Memorial Hospital of Carbondale's inpatient and outpatient visits come from residents of seven Illinois counties (Jackson Franklin Williamson Perry Johnson Union and Saline). St. Joseph Memorial Hospital serves the Murphysboro community.

Strategy

Teaming up to provide better care independent not-for-profit health care organizations BJC HealthCare of St. Louis CoxHealth of Springfield Missouri Memorial Health System of Springfield Illinois. and Saint Luke's Health System of Kansas City Missouri created The BJC Collaborative L.L.C. (in 2012). Blessing Health System of Quincy and Southern Illinois Healthcare joined the Collaborative in 2013.

Company Background

During 2012 Southern Illinois Healthcare collaborated with community partners to conduct a Community Health Needs Assessment to spotlight health and quality of life issues in the communities served by Southern Illinois Healthcare.

Southern Illinois Healthcare was first established by four doctors in 1946 as the Southern Illinois Hospital Corporation.

EXECUTIVES

Vice President And Chief Nursing Officer, Julie Firman
Auditors: RSM US LLP SPRINGFIELD ILLIN

LOCATIONS

HQ: SOUTHERN ILLINOIS HEALTHCARE ENTERPRISES, INC.
1239 E MAIN ST STE C, CARBONDALE, IL 629013176
Phone: 618 457-5200
Web: WWW.SIH.NET

PRODUCTS/OPERATIONS

Selected Facilities
Herrin Hospital
Memorial Hospital of Carbondale
St. Joseph Memorial Hospital

Selected Services
Birthing Center
Cancer
Senior Renewal
Heart
Infusion Therapy
Neurosciences
Occupational Health
Pediatrics
Rehabilitation
Robotic-assisted Surgery
Sleep Medicine
Stroke
Surgical Services
Weight Loss Surgery
Wound Healing

COMPETITORS

Community Health Systems
Heartland Health Memorial Hospital (Illinois)
Saint Francis Medical Center
St. John's Hospital (Illinois)

HISTORICAL FINANCIALS
Company Type: Private

Income Statement
FYE: March 31

	REVENUE ($ mil.)	NET INCOME ($ mil.)	NET PROFIT MARGIN	EMPLOYEES
03/18	624	30	4.9%	3,493
03/17	1	0	41.4%	—
03/16	1	0	29.6%	—
03/14	1	0	44.8%	—
Annual Growth	349.1%	157.9%	—	—

2018 Year-End Financials
Return on assets: 4.3%
Return on equity: 4.9%
Current ratio: 1.40
Cash ($ mil.): 18

SOUTHERN ILLINOIS UNIVERSITY INC

Southern Illinois University (SIU) helps to train future doctors dentists and other other professionals. The university enrolls some 32000 students at its two institutions — Southern Illinois University at Carbondale (SIUC which includes medical and law schools) and Southern Illinois University at Edwardsville (SIUE which houses education dental and nursing schools) — as well as smaller satellite centers. SIU offers associate baccalaureate master's doctoral and professional degrees. It also boasts a number of study abroad partnerships with international universities. Tracing its roots back to 1869 SIU is known for its extensive research programs.

Operations

Students across SIU's institutions hail from all 50 states and more than 100 countries. Combined the campuses have some 2600 faculty members and an annual budget of $870 million.

The Carbondale campus was chartered in 1869 as a teachers college while the Edwardsville campus was founded in 1957. Most of the university's doctoral programs are housed at the SIUC campus which conducts residencies through the School of Medicine. A majority of the institutions master's degrees are conferred at the SIUE campus.

Undergraduate and research programs are conducted at both primary SIU campuses. Students and faculty members participate in research programs in a number of fields including biology biodiversity and molecular science. The university receives $78.5 million in research grants annually.

Geographic Reach

From its flagship campus in Carbondale Illinois SIU reaches to Edwardsville and to other parts of Southern Illinois including Springfield through satellite campus locations. Its satellite schools include SIU School of Medicine SIU School of Dental Medicine and SIU School of Nursing.

Financial Performance

SIU logged increases of 2% in fiscal 2012 as compared to 2011 pointing to a rise in student tuition and fees private grants and contracts and sales and services for the gains. Net income for the same reporting period rose 17% due to a boost in non-operating revenues attributable to increases in gifts and contributions investment income and payments on behalf of the university.

Strategy

As part of its focus SIU is working to strengthen its undergraduate graduate and professional education. It's also concentrating on streamlining its administrative process while expanding its inter-campus and intra-campus collaboration through degree programs international education distributed learning fundraising and research opportunities for both students and faculty. SIU is also establishing partnerships with public and private sector groups.

EXECUTIVES

Senior Vice President Vice President For Financial And Administrative Affairs Siuu, Duane Stucky
Vice President, Andrew Podoll

LOCATIONS

HQ: SOUTHERN ILLINOIS UNIVERSITY INC
1400 DOUGLAS DR, CARBONDALE, IL 629014332
Phone: 618 536-3475
Web: WWW.SIUMED.EDU

HISTORICAL FINANCIALS
Company Type: Private

Income Statement
FYE: June 30

	REVENUE ($ mil.)	NET INCOME ($ mil.)	NET PROFIT MARGIN	EMPLOYEES
06/17	601	(59)	—	9,576
06/16	740	(104)	—	—
06/15	597	27	4.6%	—
06/14	694	47	6.8%	—
Annual Growth	(4.7%)	—	—	—

2017 Year-End Financials
Return on assets: 4.9%
Return on equity: (-9.9%)
Current ratio: 0.40
Cash ($ mil.): 4

SOUTHERN INDIANA GAS & ELECTRIC COMPANY

EXECUTIVES

Ceo, Carl L Chapman
Ceo, Niel C Ellerbrook
Exec V Pres-Cfo, Jerome A Benkert Jr
Sr Vice President, Ronald E Christian
V Pres-Treas, Robert Goocher
V Pres-Controller, M Susan Hardwick
President, William S Doty
Vice President, Daniel Bugher
Vice President, Ellis S Redd
Vice President, Eric J Schach
Board Member, Michael Smith

LOCATIONS

HQ: SOUTHERN INDIANA GAS & ELECTRIC COMPANY
1 VECTREN SQ, EVANSVILLE, IN 477081209
Phone: 812 424-6411
Web: WWW.VECTREN.COM

HISTORICAL FINANCIALS
Company Type: Private

Income Statement				FYE: December 31
	REVENUE ($ mil.)	NET INCOME ($ mil.)	NET PROFIT MARGIN	EMPLOYEES
12/17	661	86	13.1%	779
12/16	692	95	13.9%	—
12/03	438	48	11.1%	—
12/02	693	59	8.6%	—
Annual Growth	(0.3%)	2.6%	—	—

2017 Year-End Financials
Return on assets: 6.4%
Return on equity: 13.1%
Current ratio: 0.50
Cash ($ mil.): 2

SOUTHERN METHODIST UNIVERSITY INC

What do former first lady Laura Bush actress Kathy Bates and NFL Hall-of-Famer Doak Walker have in common? They're all graduates of Southern Methodist University (SMU). Founded in 1911 by what is now The United Methodist Church SMU is a nonsectarian private institution offering undergraduate graduate and professional degrees in arts business engineering humanities law science and theology through seven schools. It'sA one of a handful of schools nationwide to offer an academic major in human rights.A Some 11000 students attend the university which has a student-faculty ratio of 11:1. About 85% of the 700-member full-time faculty hold the doctorate or highest degree in their fields.

Operations
The university offers more than 120 undergraduate degrees and about 130 graduate degrees through seven schools.A SMU also offers more than two dozen doctorates. Most of theA its degrees are conferred in the humanities and sciences and business.

Geographic Reach

SMU is housed in more than 75 buildings. The Texas university operates through a main campus located in University Park within Dallas County. Also in Texas it maintains propertyA inA Dallas (19 acres) Highland Park (2 acres) and Plano (25 acres). In Taos New Mexico SMU holds 423 acres.

Sales and Marketing
SMU's enrollment includesA international students from 90 countries. The largest numbers of students in descending order are from India China Saudi Arabia Mexico Korea Taiwan (Province of China) Guatemala Thailand Iran and Canada.

Financial Performance
Endowment gifts from donors reached $14.9 million in 2012. The private university's revenue decreased by 9% in 2012 as compared to 2011 due to dips in tuition and fees net realized and unrealized gains grants and contracts. Net income also decreased by 44% during the same reporting period. Revenue declines and increases in program expenses contributed to the net income woes.

EXECUTIVES

Vice President Of Sales, Lori White
President, R. Gerald Turner, age 72
Dean Edwin L. Cox School Of Business, Albert W. Niemi, age 75
Dean Dedman School Of Law, John B. Attanasio
Dean And Director Central University Libraries, Gillian M. McCombs
Provost And Vp Academic Affairs, Paul W. Ludden
Vp Business And Finance, Christine (Chris) Regis
Dean Meadows School Of The Arts, José A. Bowen
Dean Annette Caldwell Simmons School Of Education And Human Development, David Chard
Dean Perkins School Of Theology, William B. Lawrence
Dean Research And Graduate Studies, James E. Quick
Cio, Joe Gargiulo
Chief Investment Officer And Treasurer, Michael A. Condon
Dean Dedman College Of Humanities And Sciences, William M. Tsutsui
Dean Lyle School Of Engineering, Marc P. Christensen
President Smu Student Body, Alexander Mace
President Smu Faculty Senate, Jose L. Lage
Vice President Executive Affairs, Thomas E Barry
Vice President Programming, Alex Munoz
Department Chair And O. Paul Corley Distinguished Chair In Organizational Behavior, Miguel Quinones
Provost Vice President Academic Affair, Ross Murfin
Department Chair Fire And Ems Technology, Mattie Eiland
Vice President For Development, Dominique Sims
Associate Vice President Information Technology Services, George Chrisman
Senior Vice President, James Gallegos
Vice President Academic Excellence, Olivia Waidmann
Vice President Technical Operations And Applied Research, Glenn Miller
Vice President And Treasurer, Andrew Hornung
Associate Vice President, Barry Ernie
Vice President Of Programming, William Hagens
Chair, Caren Prothro
Secretary, Suzanne Nelsen
Secretary, Scott Kingsley
Treasurer, Cole Bildstein
Auditors: KPMG LLP DALLAS TX

LOCATIONS

HQ: SOUTHERN METHODIST UNIVERSITY INC
6425 BOAZ LN, DALLAS, TX 75205
Phone: 214 768-2000
Web: WWW.SMU.EDU

PRODUCTS/OPERATIONS

Selected Schools and Divisions
Annette Caldwell Simmons School of Education and Human Development
Bobby B. Lyle School of Engineering
Cox School of Business
Dedman College of Humanities and Sciences
Dedman School of Law
Meadows School of the Arts
Perkins School of Theology

HISTORICAL FINANCIALS
Company Type: Private

Income Statement				FYE: May 31
	REVENUE ($ mil.)	NET INCOME ($ mil.)	NET PROFIT MARGIN	EMPLOYEES
05/18	652	96	14.7%	2,200
05/17	580	56	9.8%	—
05/13	563	115	20.5%	—
05/11	602	58	9.6%	—
Annual Growth	1.1%	7.4%	—	—

2018 Year-End Financials
Return on assets: 45.0%
Return on equity: 14.7%
Current ratio: —
Cash ($ mil.): 183

SOUTHERN MINNESOTA BEET SUGAR COOPERATIVE

Southern Minnesota Beet Sugar Cooperative (SMBSC) offers a sweet deal to its approximately 585 member/farmers. The co-op slices about 3 million tons of Minnesota-grown sugar beets annually. Converted products include baker's sugar and fruit sugar as well as molasses beet pulp pellets and shreds and raffinate (liquid from desugaring molasses). The co-op also provides member services such as seed agronomy research farm support products and workers' compensation insurance. SMBSC's refined and liquid sugars are marketed through Cargill Sweeteners; the by-products (dried beet pulp and beet molasses for use in cattle feed) are marketed by Midwest Agri-Commodities in North American and Europe.

Operations
The beet sugar processor's operations consist of a main factory with an annual processing capacity of about 3 million tons of harvested sugar beets. The factory campus comprises settling ponds water-holding lagoons receiving strips offsite receiving stations and 1100 acres of land some of which is planted with grass and irrigated with waste water from the ponds and treatment plant. In addition the co-op has several silos to hold bulk granulated sugar a warehouse to store industrial-size bags of sugar and more than a dozen thick-juice storage tanks. Campus expansions since the factory's start in 1975 have included a molasses desugarization facility increases to processing capacity and new equipment.

The co-op has grown both through investments in added capacity to attract new member/farmers and acquisitions. Acquired in 2005 subsidiary Spreckels Sugar Company operates a beet sugar factory in Brawley California. Sugar produced under the Spreckels Sugar brand is sold to markets in the western US. Based in Sheridan Wyoming SMBSC's Holly Seed a former subsidiary of Imperial Sugar also acquired in 2005 develops beet seed varieties to increase sucrose content and yields. Holly Seed partners with SESVanderHave to supply seeds adapted to growing sugar beets worldwide.

EXECUTIVES

Vice President Agriculture, Kelvin Thompsen
Vice President Of Agriculture, Todd Geselius
Vice President Of Finance And Chief Financial Officer, Ian O'connell
Auditors: PRICEWATERHOUSECOOPERS LLP M

LOCATIONS

HQ: SOUTHERN MINNESOTA BEET SUGAR COOPERATIVE
83550 COUNTY ROAD 21, RENVILLE, MN 562842319
Phone: 320 329-8305
Web: WWW.SMBSC.COM

PRODUCTS/OPERATIONS

Selected Products
Ag liming material
Baker's sugar
Beet pulp pellets
Beet pulp shreds
Fruit sugar
Granulated sugar
Liquid sucrose
Liquid sugar
Molasses
Raffinates
Refined sugar

COMPETITORS

Amalgamated Sugar
American Crystal Sugar
C&H Sugar
Connell Company
Florida Crystals
Imperial Sugar
King Ranch
M. A. Patout
Michigan Sugar Company
Minn-Dak Co-op
Sterling Sugars
Sugar Cane Growers Cooperative of Florida
Sugar Foods
U.S. Sugar
United Sugars
Western Sugar Cooperative

HISTORICAL FINANCIALS
Company Type: Private

Income Statement				FYE: August 31
	REVENUE ($ mil.)	NET INCOME ($ mil.)	NET PROFIT MARGIN	EMPLOYEES
08/17	418	99	23.7%	610
08/16	465	176	37.9%	—
08/15	350	101	28.9%	—
08/14	0	123	—	—
Annual Growth	—	(7.0%)	—	—

2017 Year-End Financials
Return on assets: 2.4%   Cash ($ mil.): 4
Return on equity: 23.7%
Current ratio: 0.90

SOUTHERN NATURAL GAS COMPANY, L.L.C.

EXECUTIVES

Pres-Ceo, Norman G Holmes
Exec V Pres-Cfo, John R Sult
V Pres-Controller-Cao, Rosa P Jackson
Senior Vp, Larry E Powell

LOCATIONS

HQ: SOUTHERN NATURAL GAS COMPANY, L.L.C.
1001 LOUISIANA ST, HOUSTON, TX 770025089
Phone: 713 420-2600
Web: WWW.ELPASO.COM

COMPETITORS

Alagasco
American Midstream Partners
Bridgeline
Crestwood Midstream Partners LP
Gulf South Pipeline
Panhandle Eastern Pipe Line
Piedmont Natural Gas
U.S. Transmission

HISTORICAL FINANCIALS
Company Type: Private

Income Statement				FYE: December 31
	REVENUE ($ mil.)	NET INCOME ($ mil.)	NET PROFIT MARGIN	EMPLOYEES
12/17	606	143	23.7%	3
12/16	609	169	27.8%	—
Annual Growth	(0.6%)	(15.2%)	—	—

2017 Year-End Financials
Return on assets: 3.4%   Cash ($ mil.): 3
Return on equity: 23.7%
Current ratio: 0.40

SOUTHERN NEW HAMPSHIRE HEALTH SYSTEM, INC.

EXECUTIVES

Pres, Michael S Rose
Information Specialist, Bob Kirby
Director, Amy Staly
Chief Information Officer, Andrew Watt
Coordinator, Sheryl Kall
Buyer, Pamela Silva
Supervisor, Peter Ong
Assistant, Arianna Tsoukalas
Records Director, Craig Warner
Assistant Director, Karen Flaherty
Microbiology Supervisor, Leann Hamilton
Auditors: BAKER NEWMAN & NOYES LLC MANC

LOCATIONS

HQ: SOUTHERN NEW HAMPSHIRE HEALTH SYSTEM, INC.
8 PROSPECT ST, NASHUA, NH 030603925
Phone: 603 577-2000
Web: WWW.SNHHS.ORG

HISTORICAL FINANCIALS
Company Type: Private

Income Statement				FYE: September 30
	REVENUE ($ mil.)	NET INCOME ($ mil.)	NET PROFIT MARGIN	EMPLOYEES
09/17	333	37	11.3%	1,201
09/16	313	13	4.3%	—
Annual Growth	6.5%	182.3%	—	—

2017 Year-End Financials
Return on assets: 5.8%   Cash ($ mil.): 40
Return on equity: 11.3%
Current ratio: 0.90

SOUTHERN NUCLEAR OPERATING COMPANY, INC.

EXECUTIVES

Site Vice President Joseph M. Farley Nuclear Plant Southern Nuclear, Dennis Madison
Vice President Of Fleet Operations Support, Bradley Adams

LOCATIONS

HQ: SOUTHERN NUCLEAR OPERATING COMPANY, INC.
42 INVERNESS CENTER PKWY, BIRMINGHAM, AL 352424809
Phone: 205 992-5000
Web: WWW.SOUTHERNCOMPANY.COM/OUR-COMPANIES/SOUTHERN-NUCLEAR.H

COMPETITORS

Duke Energy
NextEra Energy
Progress Energy

HISTORICAL FINANCIALS
Company Type: Private

Income Statement				FYE: December 31
	REVENUE ($ mil.)	NET INCOME ($ mil.)	NET PROFIT MARGIN	EMPLOYEES
12/16	922	0	0.0%	2,960
12/04	479	0	—	—
12/03	441	0	—	—
12/02	455	0	—	—
Annual Growth	5.2%	—	—	—

2016 Year-End Financials
Return on assets: 1.0%   Cash ($ mil.): 14
Return on equity: —
Current ratio: —

SOUTHERN OHIO MEDICAL CENTER

EXECUTIVES

Pres-Ceo, Randal M Arnett
Chb, Robert E Dever
Medical-Dir, Kendall Stewart
V Pres-Patient Srv, Claudia Burchett
Exec SEC, Cindy Brown
Nursing Director, Mary Dilts-Skaggs
Director, Richard Gilcher
Manager, Jeremy Janney
Telecommunications Executive, John Schaefer
Director, Wendi Waugh
Physician Recruiter, Diane Applegate

LOCATIONS

HQ: SOUTHERN OHIO MEDICAL CENTER
1805 27TH ST, PORTSMOUTH, OH 456622640
Phone: 740 354-5000
Web: WWW.SOMC.ORG

HISTORICAL FINANCIALS
Company Type: Private

Income Statement — FYE: June 30

	REVENUE ($ mil.)	NET INCOME ($ mil.)	NET PROFIT MARGIN	EMPLOYEES
06/18	394	19	4.8%	2,100
06/17	365	25	7.0%	—
06/15	351	54	15.4%	—
06/12	301	15	5.3%	—
Annual Growth	4.6%	3.1%	—	—

2018 Year-End Financials
Return on assets: 3.6%
Return on equity: 4.8%
Current ratio: 1.30
Cash ($ mil.): 22

SOUTHERN PIPE & SUPPLY COMPANY, INC.

EXECUTIVES

Vice President Of Sales, Mark Roebuck
Auditors: HORNE CPA LLP

LOCATIONS

HQ: SOUTHERN PIPE & SUPPLY COMPANY, INC.
4330 HIGHWAY 39 N, MERIDIAN, MS 393011082
Phone: 601 693-2911
Web: WWW.SOUTHERNPIPE.COM

Selected Locations

	No.
Mississippi	26
Alabama	17
Louisiana	16
Georgia	14
Arkansas	10
Florida	4
Tennessee	3
Total	**90**

PRODUCTS/OPERATIONS

Selected Products
Heating & cooling equipment
Kitchen & bath fixtures
Plumbing

Residential & commercial pipe valves & fittings
Tools & safety equipment
Water metering fire hydrants & fittings
Waterworks

COMPETITORS

Baker Distributing	Stuart C. Irby
Ferguson Enterprises	WinWholesale
HD Supply	Wolverine Tube
Lowe's	

HISTORICAL FINANCIALS
Company Type: Private

Income Statement — FYE: December 31

	REVENUE ($ mil.)	NET INCOME ($ mil.)	NET PROFIT MARGIN	EMPLOYEES
12/16	451	19	4.2%	767
12/15	436	19	4.6%	—
Annual Growth	3.6%	(4.5%)	—	—

SOUTHSIDE HOSPITAL

EXECUTIVES

Dir, Stephen Masiar
Exec Dir, Winifred Mack
Vice President, Robert Castano
Regional Manager, Michael Carter
Director, Lisa Burch
Human Resources Manager, Marge Miller
Senior Vice President, Margie Manzari
Director of Community Relation, Edward Fraser
Administrative Support Associa, Linda Sabatella
Director, Lori Ottaviano
Administrative Director of Lab, Mike Eller

LOCATIONS

HQ: SOUTHSIDE HOSPITAL
301 E MAIN ST, BAY SHORE, NY 117068458
Phone: 631 968-3000

PRODUCTS/OPERATIONS

Selected Services
Anesthesiology
Bloodless Medicine
Cancer Care
Cardiac Services
Center for Colorectal Health
Emergency Services
Neurosciences
Orthopaedics
Pain Management
Radiology
Rehabilitation
Surgery
Vascular Institute
Women's Health
Wound Healing Center

COMPETITORS

Brookhaven Memorial Hospital Medical Center
Catholic Health Services of Long Island
Good Samaritan Hospital Medical Center
Long Island College Hospital
Mercy Medical Center (NY)
NewYork-Presbyterian Healthcare
NuHealth

HISTORICAL FINANCIALS
Company Type: Private

Income Statement — FYE: December 31

	REVENUE ($ mil.)	NET INCOME ($ mil.)	NET PROFIT MARGIN	EMPLOYEES
12/17	447	(20)	—	1,900
12/16	419	(8)	—	—
12/15	381	(17)	—	—
12/14	357	(10)	—	—
Annual Growth	7.7%	—	—	—

2017 Year-End Financials
Return on assets: 11.0%
Return on equity: (-4.7%)
Current ratio: 0.70
Cash ($ mil.): —

SOUTHWEST GENERAL HEALTH CENTER

EXECUTIVES

Pres, L Jon Schurmeier
Prse, Thomas A Selden
Anesthesiologist, David Sfeir
Director, Jill Barber
Coordinator, Noreen Molek
Purchasing Agent, Dana Hardy
Manager, Gary Lenio
Doctor, Marilyn McNamara
Purchasing Manager, Karen Green
Health Care Director, Karen Miller
Coordinator, Mark Doris

LOCATIONS

HQ: SOUTHWEST GENERAL HEALTH CENTER
18697 BAGLEY RD, CLEVELAND, OH 441303417
Phone: 440 816-8000
Web: WWW.SWGENERAL.COM

HISTORICAL FINANCIALS
Company Type: Private

Income Statement — FYE: December 31

	REVENUE ($ mil.)	NET INCOME ($ mil.)	NET PROFIT MARGIN	EMPLOYEES
12/16	315	12	4.1%	2,500
12/15	303	13	4.3%	—
12/14	297	21	7.1%	—
12/13	311	23	7.5%	—
Annual Growth	0.4%	(18.0%)	—	—

2016 Year-End Financials
Return on assets: 5.1%
Return on equity: 4.1%
Current ratio: 1.10
Cash ($ mil.): 27

SOUTHWEST KEY PROGRAMS, INC.

EXECUTIVES

Pres, Juan J Sanchez
SEC, Rachel Luna

Treas, Melody Chung
Dir, Elizabeth Gonzales
Dir, Anselmo Villarreal
Dir, Victoria Garza
Dir, Rosa Santis
Dir, David Marshall
Dir, Orlando L Martinez
Mgr, Ting Sik Chor
Accounting Staff, Lee Siegismund

LOCATIONS

HQ: SOUTHWEST KEY PROGRAMS, INC.
6002 JAIN LN, AUSTIN, TX 787213104
Phone: 512 462-2181
Web: WWW.SWKEY.ORG

HISTORICAL FINANCIALS

Company Type: Private

Income Statement   FYE: August 31

	REVENUE ($ mil.)	NET INCOME ($ mil.)	NET PROFIT MARGIN	EMPLOYEES
08/17	318	11	3.6%	1,232
08/16	242	16	6.8%	—
08/15	159	8	5.4%	—
Annual Growth	41.4%	16.6%	—	—

2017 Year-End Financials

Return on assets: 1.0%   Cash ($ mil.): 61
Return on equity: 3.6%
Current ratio: 1.40

SOUTHWEST LOUISIANA HEALTH CARE SYSTEM, INC.

EXECUTIVES

President, Larry Graham
Supervisor, Julie Pruett
Buyer, Carla Robertson
Auditors: PRICEWATERHOUSECOOPERS LLP

LOCATIONS

HQ: SOUTHWEST LOUISIANA HEALTH CARE SYSTEM, INC.
1701 OAK PARK BLVD, LAKE CHARLES, LA 706018911
Phone: 337 494-3204
Web: WWW.LAKECHARLESHOSPITAL.COM

HISTORICAL FINANCIALS

Company Type: Private

Income Statement   FYE: December 31

	REVENUE ($ mil.)	NET INCOME ($ mil.)	NET PROFIT MARGIN	EMPLOYEES
12/17	356	6	1.9%	4
12/15	0	0	—	—
12/14	0	0	—	—
12/09	0	0	—	—
Annual Growth	575.8%	—	—	—

2017 Year-End Financials

Return on assets: 4.9%   Cash ($ mil.): 34
Return on equity: 1.9%
Current ratio: 0.90

SOUTHWEST RESEARCH INSTITUTE INC

If you're looking for research at an institute in the Southwest look no further. Founded in 1947 by oilman and rancher Thomas Slick Jr. Southwest Research Institute (SwRI) is an independent not-for-profit research and development institution that contracts to explore subjects in areas including automation and data systems applied physics space science and engineering and chemistry. SwRI has about 2700 scientists engineers and support staff at some 40 laboratories and offices in the US China and the UK. Customers include the private sector and government agencies. SwRI's Signature Science subsidiary researches national security environmental management and biotechnology.

Operations

SwRI provides contract research and development services to industrial and government clients. It keeps the scope of its work confidential and assigns patent rights arising from its sponsored research to the client. SwRI generally retains rights to Institute-funded advancements and holds more than 900 patents awarded to staff members.

The company operates through nearly a dozen technical divisions including Aerospace Electronics; Systems Engineering & Training; Applied Physics Chemistry & Chemical Engineering; Engine Emissions & Vehicl; Research; Geosciences & Engineering; Mechanical Engineering; and Space Science & Engineering.

Geographic Reach

The company is based in San Antonio Texas and the Institute has technical offices and laboratories in Ann Arbor Michigan.; Beijing China; Boulder Colorado; Hill Air Force Base (Ogden) Utah; Hanover and Rockville Maryland.; Minneapolis Minnesota; Oklahoma City Oklahoma.; Warner Robins Georgia; and Durham New Hampshire.

Strategy

SwRI's current projects include cooperative research focusing on safe reliable cost-effective energy storage systems for electric and hybrid-electric vehicle applications. In addition it has formed a consortium to conduct research and code development and apply advanced ROS (Robot Operating System)software to industrial applications.

EXECUTIVES

Vice President, David McComas
Associate Vice President Rd, Robin Mihran
Treasurer, Linda Boehme
Treasurer, Debra Streeter
Secretary, Melody Cherry
Secretary, Dorothea Martinez
Auditors: RSM US LLP AUSTIN TEXAS

LOCATIONS

HQ: SOUTHWEST RESEARCH INSTITUTE INC
6220 CULEBRA RD, SAN ANTONIO, TX 782385100
Phone: 210 684-5111
Web: WWW.SWRI.ORG

PRODUCTS/OPERATIONS

Selected Technical Divisions

Aerospace Electronics and Information Technology
Applied Physics
Applied Power
Automation and Data Systems
Chemistry and Chemical Engineering
Engine Emissions and Vehicle Research
Fuels and Lubricants Research
Geosciences and Engineering
Mechanical Engineering
Signal Exploitation and Geolocation

Space Science and Engineering
Training Simulation and Performance Improvement

COMPETITORS

Battelle Memorial	QinetiQ
Berkeley Lab	Southern Research
Brookhaven Lab	Institute
Lawrence Livermore Lab	

HISTORICAL FINANCIALS

Company Type: Private

Income Statement   FYE: September 28

	REVENUE ($ mil.)	NET INCOME ($ mil.)	NET PROFIT MARGIN	EMPLOYEES
09/18	583	38	6.6%	2,754
09/17	498	11	2.3%	—
09/16	559	6	1.2%	—
09/15	592	23	4.0%	—
Annual Growth	(0.5%)	17.3%	—	—

2018 Year-End Financials

Return on assets: 4.1%   Cash ($ mil.): 16
Return on equity: 6.6%
Current ratio: 0.70

SPARROW HEALTH SYSTEM

Ailing residents of central Michigan fly to Sparrow Health System for care. The not-for-profit network's hospitals include the flagship Sparrow Hospital Sparrow Clinton Memorial Hospital Sparrow Specialty Hospital and Carson City Hospital. The health system also operates dozens of satellite clinics a long-term-care center a hospice care provider medical equipment rental unit and athletic club. Through affiliate Physicians Health Plan Sparrow Health provides health plan coverage to some 70000 Michigan residents. Its Sparrow Physicians Health Network includes some 1000 physicians in the region.The system traces its roots back to 1896.

Operations

The Sparrow Health System is a not-for-profit community-governed organization. Its flagship facility Sparrow Hospital is a 700-bed regional referral hospital providing a range of general and specialty services. Community service is important to Sparrow Health as the organization provides millions of dollars worth of charity care underfunded services and community outreach services each year.

Geographic Reach

Sparrow Health's hospitals are located in Lansing St. John's Ionia and Carson City Michigan. It also has dozens of satellite care sites throughout central Michigan.

Strategy

Over the years Sparrow Health System has expanded its services and geographic reach through a series of affiliations. It is part the Mayo Clinic Care Network which allows it to improve the care it provides its patients. In 2016 Sparrow formalized its long-time affiliation with Hayes Green Beach Memorial Hospital which will become an official affiliate by 2019. That hospital is now undergoing a renovation and expansion.

To provide health care to a more sizable population the system regularly opens new health care facilities and expands its physicians care network; it has also been investing in modernizing itself through technological advances. Its Sparrow Care Network a physician-led clinically integrated organization has grown to include more than 650 physicians. In 2016 the system opened additional retail clinics (dubbed "Fast Care" sites) within area grocery stores. And in 2017 the system opened its Herbert-Herman Cancer Center and Plaza.

Sparrow has also been growing its mobile health clinics in partnership with local agencies and organizations.

One of Sparrow's hospitals Sparrow Carson Hospital has come under fire for infection-control issues. In 2018 it was dropped from its Medicare contract after an audit showed it wasn't in compliance with sterilization procedures. The accusations are serious as hospital-based infections are the third leading cause of deaths in the US.

Sparrow closed its St. Lawrence emergency department in mid-2018. It added about a dozen beds to its primary hospital to make up for the closure. It also opened a new urgent care center giving patients a choice of health care based on the severity of their ailments.

Company Background

Sparrow Health got its start in 1896 when a group of women set out with $400 a house on Ottawa Street (in Lansing Michigan) and a mission to care for the sick.

EXECUTIVES

President Ceo, Dennis Swan
President Php, Scott Wilkerson
Vp And Cio, Thomas A. (Tom) Bres
Cfo, Paula Reichle
Vp Sparrow Medical Group, Peter Graham
President Sparrow Clinton Hospital, Ed Bruun
President And Ceo Sparrow Ionia Hospital, William Roeser
Ceo Sparrow Specialty Hospital, Kira Carter-Robertson
Coo And Chief Nursing Officer, Barbara (Barb) McQuillan
Vp Strategic Planning And Marketing, Melissa Sears
Medical Director, Timur Raghib
Vice President Medical Education And Research, Ted Glynn
Director Of Pharmacy, Timothy Ekola
Medical Director, Kristin Bredin
Infection Control Director, KAREN SALOW
Vice President Sparrow Medical Group, Douglas Edema
Vice President Human Resources, Subhash Gupta
Chair, Barbara Given
Secretary, Teressia Green
Secretary, Leslie Sandin
Auditors: ERNST & YOUNG LLP

LOCATIONS

HQ: SPARROW HEALTH SYSTEM
1215 E MICHIGAN AVE, LANSING, MI 489121811
Phone: 517 364-1000
Web: WWW.GOODNEIGHBORPHARMACY.COM

PRODUCTS/OPERATIONS

Selected Services
Emergency room/Urgent Care
Laboratory
Medical Supply
Outpatient Rehabilitation
Pharmacy
Radiology

COMPETITORS

Bronson Battle Creek	Hurley Medical Center
Covenant HealthCare	McLaren Health Care
Crittenton Hospital	Munson Healthcare
Detroit Medical Center	Sheridan Community
Genesys Health System	Hospital
Genesys Regional	St. John Health

Medical Center
Henry Ford Health
System

Trinity Health (Novi)

HISTORICAL FINANCIALS
Company Type: Private

Income Statement   FYE: December 31

	REVENUE ($ mil.)	NET INCOME ($ mil.)	NET PROFIT MARGIN	EMPLOYEES
12/17	1,259	49	3.9%	3,400
12/16	1,286	63	5.0%	—
12/14*	1,156	(53)	—	—
03/11	251	19	7.9%	—
Annual Growth	25.8%	13.8%	—	—

*Fiscal year change

2017 Year-End Financials

Return on assets: 1.5%   Cash ($ mil.): 71
Return on equity: 3.9%
Current ratio: 1.10

SPECIAL SCHOOL DISTRICT OF ST. LOUIS COUNTY

EXECUTIVES

Supt, Donald Bohannon
Coordinator, David Detering
Director, John Koeper
Chief Information Officer, Nancy Ide
Occupational Specia, Carmen Bolt
Human Resources Manager, Darlene Deloach
Coordinator, Jeff Ferguson
Director of Information Techno, Daniel Burrus
Bus/Finance/Purchasing Directo, Kelly Alexander
Accounting Manager, Rhonda Wood
Manager of Management Informat, Rob Emerson
Auditors: SCHOWALTER & JABOURI PC ST

LOCATIONS

HQ: SPECIAL SCHOOL DISTRICT OF ST. LOUIS COUNTY
12110 CLAYTON RD, SAINT LOUIS, MO 631312599
Phone: 314 989-8100
Web: WWW.SSDMO.ORG

HISTORICAL FINANCIALS
Company Type: Private

Income Statement   FYE: June 30

	REVENUE ($ mil.)	NET INCOME ($ mil.)	NET PROFIT MARGIN	EMPLOYEES
06/18	452	25	5.7%	5,204
06/17	433	16	3.9%	—
06/16	425	23	5.5%	—
06/13	366	3	0.9%	—
Annual Growth	4.3%	50.3%	—	—

SPECTRA ENERGY CORP

Spectra Energy covers the spectrum of natural gas activities — gathering processing transmission storage and distribution. The company now part of Enbridge operates more than 15400 miles of transmission pipeline and has 305 billion cu. ft. of storage capacity in the US and Canada. Units include U.S. Gas Transmission Texas Eastern Transmission Natural Gas Liquids Division and Market Hub Partners. It also has stakes in DCP Midstream Maritimes & Northeast Pipeline Gulfstream Natural Gas System Spectra Energy Income Fund and 75% of Spectra Energy Partners. Its Union Gas unit distributes gas to 1.5 million Ontario customers. In 2017 Spectra merged with Enbridge creating the largest energy infrastructure company in North America.

Change in Company Type

In 2017 Enbridge acquired Spectra Energy for $28 billion. The combination of the two companies created the largest energy infrastructure company in North America with a pro-forma enterprise value of about $127 billion. Enbridge shareholders owned 57% of the combined company (Enbridge) and Spectra Energy shareholders 43%.

Operations

Spectra Energy has managed its businesses in four reportable segments: Spectra Energy Partners Distribution Western Canada Transmission & Processing and Field Services.

Spectra Energy Partners provides transmission storage and gathering of natural gas for customers in various regions of the Midwestern northeastern and southeastern US and operates a crude oil pipeline system that connects Canadian and U.S. producers to refineries in the U.S. Rocky Mountain and Midwest regions. Spectra Energy Partners has accounted for about 50% of the company's revenue.

Distribution about 30% of revenue provides retail natural gas distribution service (its Union Gas unit distributes gas to 1.5 million customers in 400 communities in Ontario). It also provides natural gas transportation and storage services to other utilities and energy market customers.

Western Canada Transmission & Processing about 20% of revenue provides its customers with transportation services to move natural gas natural gas gathering and processing services and NGL extraction fractionation transportation storage and marketing services.

Field Services gathers processes treats compresses transports and stores natural gas; it also fractionates transports gathers processes stores markets and trades NGLs. Its DCP Midstream joint venture is 50% owned by Phillips 66. DCP operates in 17 US states.

Transportation storage and processing of natural gas have accounted for about two-thirds of Spectra Energy's revenue.

Geographic Reach

Spectra Energy?s Spectra Energy Partners operates in northeastern and southeastern US and operates a crude oil pipeline system that connects Canadian and US producers to refineries in the Rocky Mountains and the Midwest. The Distribution segment serves natural gas customers in Ontario Canada. Western Canada Transmission & Processing serves customers in western Canada and the northern US. Field Services gathers natural gas from the Mid-Continent Rocky Mountain East Texas-North Louisiana Barnett Shale Gulf Coast South Texas Central Texas Antrim Shale and Permian Basin.

All told Spectra Energy has more than 100 facilities across North America.

Sales and Marketing

Spectra Energy's customers (end-users) purchase gas directly from suppliers or marketers as well as through retail and wholesale outlets.

Financial Performance

Spectra Energy reported a 6% decline in revenue in 2016 to $4.9 billion from 2015. Each segment posted lower revenue for 2016. Lower energy prices were passed on to customers and warmer weather meant they used less energy. Revenue also was hurt by a weaker Canadian dollar. The Distribution segment did see some growth with additional customers and the Dawn Parkway Expansion Project.

The company?s net income jump some 250% to $693 million in 2016 from 2015 mostly because of charges and costs the company had in 2015 but not 2016.

Spectra has cash flow from operations of about $2 billion in 2016 down from about $2.2 billion in 2015. The difference was driven by non-cash goodwill impairments in 2015 offset by higher earnings.

Company Background

In 2012 Spectra Energy acquired one-third of DCP Sand Hills Pipeline and DCP Southern Hills Pipeline (NGL pipelines) from DCP Midstream for $459 million.

In 2012 Spectra Energy opened a new natural gas processing plant in Dawson Creek British Columbia part of its $1.5 billion investment strategy in infrastructure. That year it also signed a deal with BG Group to develop a pipeline from northeast British Columbia to serve BG Group's potential LNG export facility in Prince Rupert on the northwest coast of the province.

To raise cash in 2012 it sold a 38.76% interest in Maritimes & Northeast Pipeline to Spectra Energy Partners for $375 million.

In a move to boost its Gulf Coast natural gas storage position in 2010 Spectra Energy acquired the Bobcat Gas Storage asset from Haddington Energy Partners and GE Energy Financial Service for about $540 million.

The company was founded in 2006.

EXECUTIVES

Cfo, J. Patrick (Pat) Reddy, $634,900 total compensation
Vice President Of It, Mark Wyatt
Vice President, John Bremner
Chief Administrative Officer, Dorothy M. Ables, $475,488 total compensation
Chairman President And Ceo, Gregory L. (Greg) Ebel, $1,133,000 total compensation
President Spectra Energy Transmission West And Canadian Lng, R. Mark Fiedorek
President Us Transmission And Storage, William T. (Bill) Yardley, $409,500 total compensation
President Union Gas, Stephen W. (Steve) Baker
General Counsel, Reginald D. (Reggie) Hedgebeth, $568,033 total compensation
Chief Development Officer, Guy G. Buckley, $438,333 total compensation
Vice President, Gregory Rizzo
Senior Vice President, Carlo V Dechiro
Board Member, Nora Brownell
Auditors: DELOITTE & TOUCHE LLP HOUSTON

LOCATIONS

HQ: SPECTRA ENERGY CORP
5400 WESTHEIMER CT, HOUSTON, TX 770565353
Phone: 713 627-5400
Web: WWW.ENBRIDGE.COM

2016 Sales

	% of total
U.S.	50
Canada	50
Total	**100**

PRODUCTS/OPERATIONS

2016 Sales

	$ mil.	% of total
Spectra Energy Partners	2,533	52
Distribution	1,370	28
Western Canada Transmission & Processing	1,005	20
Others	8	-
Total	**4,916**	**100**

2016 Sales

	$ mil.	% of total
Transportation storage and processing of natural gas	3,251	66
Distribution of natural gas	1,144	23
Transportation of crude oil	359	7
Sales of natural gas liquids	68	2
Other	94	2
Total	**4,916**	**100**

Selected Mergers and Acquisitions

COMPETITORS

Entergy	Piedmont Natural Gas
Enterprise Products	TransMontaigne
Kinder Morgan	Williams Companies
Koch Industries Inc.	

HISTORICAL FINANCIALS

Company Type: Private

Income Statement — FYE: December 31

	REVENUE ($ mil.)	NET INCOME ($ mil.)	NET PROFIT MARGIN	EMPLOYEES
12/16	4,916	1,020	20.7%	8,700
12/15	5,234	460	8.8%	—
Annual Growth	(6.1%)	121.7%	—	—

SPECTRUM HEALTH HOSPITALS

EXECUTIVES

Pres, Kevin R Splaine
Vice President, Joseph J Fifer
President, David M Krhovsky
V Pres, William L Bush
Support Manager, James Lapeer
Telecommunications Manager, Larry Walter
Operations Staff, Bonnie Tryon
Vice-President Finance, Ron Knaus
Coordinator, Jeanne Roode
Pediatrician, Bradd Hemker
Internist, Aparna Gadekar

LOCATIONS

HQ: SPECTRUM HEALTH HOSPITALS
100 MICHIGAN ST NE MC-498, GRAND RAPIDS, MI 495032560
Phone: 616 391-1774
Web: WWW.SPECTRUM-HEALTH.ORG

HISTORICAL FINANCIALS

Company Type: Private

Income Statement — FYE: June 30

	REVENUE ($ mil.)	NET INCOME ($ mil.)	NET PROFIT MARGIN	EMPLOYEES
06/16	1,905	196	10.3%	11,000
06/15	1,764	196	11.1%	—
06/08	2,595	(21)		—
06/06	1,013	77	7.6%	—
Annual Growth	6.5%	9.8%	—	—

2016 Year-End Financials

Return on assets: 4.7%   Cash ($ mil.): 206
Return on equity: 10.3%
Current ratio: 1.70

SPECTRUM HEALTH SYSTEM

EXECUTIVES

Pres, Richard C Breon
Svp-Cfo, Matthew Cox
Coordinator, Josh Miller
Administrative Director, Larry Genzink
Information Specialist, Bob Gillett
Director, Cynthia Pollock
Administrator, David S Mulka
Executive, Deborah Sorensen
Fleet Staff, Greg Elderkin
Administrator, Jodi Scully
Database Administrator, Michael Busche

LOCATIONS

HQ: SPECTRUM HEALTH SYSTEM
100 MICHIGAN ST NE, GRAND RAPIDS, MI 495032560
Phone: 616 391-1774
Web: WWW.SPECTRUMHEALTH.ORG

COMPETITORS

Ascension Health	HealthPlus of Michigan
Blue Cross Blue Shield of Michigan	McLaren Bay
Borgess Health	McLaren Health Care
Bronson Battle Creek	Mercy Health Hackley
Bronson Health Care	Munson Healthcare
CareSource	OmniCare Health Plan
Covenant HealthCare	Sheridan Community Hospital
Great Lakes Health Plan	Total Health Care
Hayes Green Beach Memorial Hospital	Zeeland Community Hospital
Health Alliance Plan of Michigan	

HISTORICAL FINANCIALS

Company Type: Private

Income Statement — FYE: June 30

	REVENUE ($ mil.)	NET INCOME ($ mil.)	NET PROFIT MARGIN	EMPLOYEES
06/18	6,004	332	5.5%	16,996
06/17	5,681	357	6.3%	—
06/10	1,446	142	9.9%	—
Annual Growth	19.5%	11.2%	—	—

2018 Year-End Financials

Return on assets: 10.1%   Cash ($ mil.): 707
Return on equity: 5.5%
Current ratio: 0.90

SPF ENERGY, INC.

Super-jobber SPF Energy is also a super-pumper of petroleum. The company's Super-pumper subsidiary runs a chain of about 15 convenience stores and gas stations in Minnesota Montana and North Dakota under the Cenex Conoco Exxon Sinclair Tesoro and Shell banners. Its Farstad Oil subsidiary offers bulk transportation of petroleum products including the annual distribution of about 250 million gallons of gas 20 million gallons of propane and 2.5 million gallons of lubricants. The Farstad fleet serves businesses and government agencies from Montana to eastern Minnesota and from northern Wyoming to the Canadian border. SPF Energy is owned by North American fuel wholesaler Parkland Fuel Corporation.

Change in Company Type

Parkland Fuel Corporation acquired SPF Energy in 2014 for CAD $113 million. It bought the Superpumper and Farstad Oil operator for its growth potential in the northwestern US and annual production of 1.1 million liters of refined petroleum product.

Operations

SPF Energy operates Superpumper which runs convenience stores and gas stations under a variety of big-name banners in Minnesota Montana and North Dakota.

The company also serves all of North Dakota and Montana as well as portions of Minnesota South Dakota and Wyoming through its Farstad Oil business. The unit maintains a fleet of more than 50 trucks.

Altogether SPF Energy services more than 200 independent gasoline stations 60 of which operate under a major brand name.

EXECUTIVES

Pres-Ceo, Jeffrey Farstad
Vice President, Dennis Krueger
Sec-Treas-Cfo, Bruce Hest

LOCATIONS

HQ: SPF ENERGY, INC.
100 27TH ST NE, MINOT, ND 587035164
Phone: 701 852-1194
Web: WWW.SPFENERGY.COM

PRODUCTS/OPERATIONS

Selected Brands
Cenex
Conoco
Exxon
Shell
Sinclair
Tesoro

COMPETITORS

BP
Redwood Coast
Petroleum
Wilson Oil

HISTORICAL FINANCIALS

Company Type: Private

Income Statement				FYE: December 31
	REVENUE ($ mil.)	NET INCOME ($ mil.)	NET PROFIT MARGIN	EMPLOYEES
12/16	442	7	1.6%	300
12/14	1,026	16	1.6%	—
12/13	1,012	8	0.9%	—
12/12	1,062	5	0.5%	—
Annual Growth	(19.7%)	7.7%	—	—

2016 Year-End Financials

Return on assets: 3.1%   Cash ($ mil.): —
Return on equity: 1.6%
Current ratio: 0.90

SPIRE ALABAMA INC.

With all the gas a customer could possibly need Alagasco is THE gas co. in Alabama. A unit of Spire (formerly The Laclede Group) in 2015 utility Alabama Gas Corporation (Alagasco) distributed natural gas to 425000 commercial and industrial customers in about half of the counties in the state. The utility also provides gas transportation services to large end users who purchase wholesale gas from suppliers. Alagasco has seven operating districts: Anniston Birmingham Gadsden Montgomery Opelika Selma and Tuscaloosa. The Alagasco distribution system includes 11230 miles of mains and more than 12000 miles of service lines.

Change in Company Type

Seeking to increase its customer base in 2014 The Laclede Group (now Spire) bought Alagasco from Energen for about $1.6 billion.

Operations

The company distributes natural gas to residential commercial and industrial customers in about half of the counties in Alabama. Alagasco purchases natural gas through interstate and intrastate suppliers and distributes the purchased gas to residential commercial and industrial customers and other natural gas end users. The company also provides transportation services to large industrial and commercial customers on its distribution system.

Alagasco's distribution system is connected to two major interstate natural gas pipeline systems Southern Natural Gas and Transcontinental Gas Pipe Line. It is also connected to two intrastate natural gas pipeline systems and to Alagasco's two liquefied natural gas (LNG) facilities.

In 2015 Alagasco purchased natural gas from 15 different suppliers to meet current gas sales storage injection and LNG liquefaction requirements of which six are under long-term supply agreements.

Alagasco also has 13 operation centers and two business centers.

Geographic Reach

Alagasco serves customers in more than 170 cities towns and other communities in 28 Alabama counties.

Financial Performance

The company is part of Spire's Gas Utility segment which contributed 96% to the parent company's total net sales in 2015. Alagasco's residential commercial and small industrial markets represented 79% of Spire's 2015 operating revenues.

Strategy

Recognizing the need for green energy options to reduce carbon emissions and dependence on foreign oil the company has a fleet of natural gas vehicles (NGVs) designed to run only on natural gas and bi-fuel NGVs which have two separate fueling systems natural gas and conventional fuel (gasoline or diesel).

Company Background

Alagasco dates back to 1852 when the Montgomery City Council passed an ordinance authorizing the Montgomery Gas Light Company to provide gas lighting for that city. Following a series of mergers and expansions the company became the Alabama Gas Corporation (Alagasco) a publicly traded entity in 1953. In 1979 it was acquired by Energen in a corporate reorganization.

EXECUTIVES

President And Coo, Dudley C. Reynolds, $310,000 total compensation
Vp System Integrity, Kenneth A. (Ken) Smith
Vp Rates And Regulations, Amy E. Watson

LOCATIONS

HQ: SPIRE ALABAMA INC.
2101 6TH AVE N STE 210, BIRMINGHAM, AL 352032761
Phone: 205 326-8100
Web: WWW.ALAGASCO.COM

COMPETITORS

Alabama Power
Duke Energy
Ferrellgas Partners
Sempra Energy

HISTORICAL FINANCIALS

Company Type: Private

Income Statement				FYE: September 30
	REVENUE ($ mil.)	NET INCOME ($ mil.)	NET PROFIT MARGIN	EMPLOYEES
09/18	500	1	0.3%	819
09/17	400	58	14.5%	—
09/16	368	53	14.4%	—
09/15	479	48	10.0%	—
Annual Growth	1.5%	(70.0%)	—	—

SPIRE MISSOURI INC.

EXECUTIVES

Pres-Ceo, Steven L Lindsey
Chb, Suzanne Sitherwood
Cfo, Steven P Rasche
Asst V Pres-Reg Admin, R Lawrence Sherwin

LOCATIONS

HQ: SPIRE MISSOURI INC.
700 MARKET ST, SAINT LOUIS, MO 631011829
Phone: 314 342-0500
Web: WWW.LACLEDEGAS.COM

HISTORICAL FINANCIALS

Company Type: Private

Income Statement				FYE: September 30
	REVENUE ($ mil.)	NET INCOME ($ mil.)	NET PROFIT MARGIN	EMPLOYEES
09/18	1,285	129	10.1%	2,271
09/17	1,171	113	9.6%	—
09/16	1,087	105	9.7%	—
09/15	1,416	105	7.4%	—
Annual Growth	(3.2%)	7.1%	—	—

2018 Year-End Financials

Return on assets: 6.4%   Cash ($ mil.): 2
Return on equity: 10.1%
Current ratio: 0.10

SPIRIT REALTY CAPITAL, INC.

EXECUTIVES

Pres-Ceo, Jackson Hsieh
Exec V Pres-Cfo, Phillip D Joseph Jr
Exec V Pres-Chief Acquisitions, Boyd Messmann
Exec V Pres Asset Management, Mark L Manheimer

Sr V Pres-Chief Hr Officer, Michelle M Greenstreet
Sr V Pres-Cao, Prakash J Parag
Chb, Richard I Gilchrist
Evp-Cfo, Michael Hughes
Senior Vice President and Head, Bill Totherow
Auditors: ERNST & YOUNG LLP DALLAS TX

LOCATIONS

HQ: SPIRIT REALTY CAPITAL, INC.
  2727 N HARWOOD ST STE 300, DALLAS, TX
  752012407
Phone: 480 606-0820

HISTORICAL FINANCIALS
Company Type: Private

Income Statement				FYE: December 31
	ASSETS ($ mil.)	NET INCOME ($ mil.)	INCOME AS % OF ASSETS	EMPLOYEES
12/17	7,263	77	1.1%	71
12/16	7,677	97	1.3%	—
12/14	8,017	(33)	—	—
12/13	7,231	1	0.0%	—
Annual Growth	0.1%	160.4%	—	—

2017 Year-End Financials
Return on assets: 22.3% Sales ($ mil): 668
Return on equity: 11.5%

SPOKANE PUBLIC SCHOOLS

EXECUTIVES

Spdt, Shelley Redinger
Board Member, Susan Chapin
Principal, Chase Middle School, John Andes
Before/After School Coordinato, Lorna Spear
Director, Doug Wordell
Information Technology/Interne, Lindsay Fry
Business Manager, Pam Austin
Staff, Michele Adams
Secretary, Nicole Stanley
Education Assistant, Rebecca Oestreich
Teacher, Barbara Bolich
Auditors: PAT MCCARTHY OLYMPIA WA

LOCATIONS

HQ: SPOKANE PUBLIC SCHOOLS
  200 N BERNARD ST, SPOKANE, WA 992010206
Phone: 509 354-5900
Web: WWW.SPOKANESCHOOLS.ORG

HISTORICAL FINANCIALS
Company Type: Private

Income Statement				FYE: August 31
	REVENUE ($ mil.)	NET INCOME ($ mil.)	NET PROFIT MARGIN	EMPLOYEES
08/17	437	(32)	—	3,226
08/16	414	31	7.6%	—
08/15	403	6	1.7%	—
08/14	374	(27)	—	—
Annual Growth	5.3%	—	—	—

2017 Year-End Financials
Return on assets: 6.7% Cash ($ mil.): 115
Return on equity: (-7.4%)
Current ratio: —

SPORTS, INC.

EXECUTIVES

Pres, Tony Cardinal
Pres-Dir, Barry Cory
Vice President, Chad Wyffels
V Pres & Asst SEC-Treas, Nancy Wilson
Dir, Mark Daniels
Dir, John Phillips
Executive Officer, Frances Hines
Accounting Staff, Shannon Peterschick
Marketing Manager, Andy Eames
Marketing Manager, Travis Elam
Marketing Staff, Corry Arntzen
Auditors: JUNKERMIER CLARK CAMPANELLA

LOCATIONS

HQ: SPORTS, INC.
  333 2ND AVE N, LEWISTOWN, MT 594572700
Phone: 406 538-3496
Web: WWW.SPORTSINC.COM

HISTORICAL FINANCIALS
Company Type: Private

Income Statement				FYE: December 31
	REVENUE ($ mil.)	NET INCOME ($ mil.)	NET PROFIT MARGIN	EMPLOYEES
12/17	913	0	0.0%	38
12/16	963	0	0.0%	—
12/15	841	0	0.0%	—
12/14	780	0	0.0%	—
Annual Growth	5.4%	(12.0%)	—	—

2017 Year-End Financials
Return on assets: 12.5% Cash ($ mil.): —
Return on equity: —
Current ratio: 1.00

SPRING BRANCH INDEPENDENT SCHOOL DISTRICT (INC)

EXECUTIVES

Supt, Scott R Muri
Director of Teacher Personnel, Lori Cummings
Purchasing Director, Barbara Robillard
Education Specialist, Alice Dunlap
Human Resources, Denise Putch
Teacher, Harrington Richard
Teacher, Merry Morgan
Sales and Marketing Staff, Robbi Raine
Teacher, Susan Walter
Manager, Trudy Murota
Special Education Director, Joni Warren
Auditors: WHITLEY PENN HOUSTON TEXAS

LOCATIONS

HQ: SPRING BRANCH INDEPENDENT SCHOOL
  DISTRICT (INC)
  955 CAMPBELL RD, HOUSTON, TX 770242803
Phone: 713 464-1511
Web: WWW.DISCOVERWESTHOUSTON.COM

HISTORICAL FINANCIALS
Company Type: Private

Income Statement				FYE: June 30
	REVENUE ($ mil.)	NET INCOME ($ mil.)	NET PROFIT MARGIN	EMPLOYEES
06/17	500	(4)	—	4,484
06/16	451	(38)	—	—
06/13	353	(67)	—	—
06/11	368	(26)	—	—
Annual Growth	5.2%	—	—	—

SPRING INDEPENDENT SCHOOL DISTRICT

EXECUTIVES

Secretary, Kim Parker
Director of Communications, Karen Garrison
Director, Gerardo Rochin
Director, Karla Sandoval
Safety Director, Darryl Simon
Assistant, Grace Nickerson
Administrator, Kelly Easton
Teacher, Ashley Sanders
Coordinator, Carol Briggs

LOCATIONS

HQ: SPRING INDEPENDENT SCHOOL DISTRICT
  16717 ELLA BLVD, HOUSTON, TX 770904213
Phone: 281 891-6000
Web: WWW.SPRINGISD.ORG

HISTORICAL FINANCIALS
Company Type: Private

Income Statement				FYE: June 30
	REVENUE ($ mil.)	NET INCOME ($ mil.)	NET PROFIT MARGIN	EMPLOYEES
06/17	401	220	54.8%	9
06/16	410	13	3.3%	—
06/15	0	0	36.3%	—
06/14	0	(0)	—	—
Annual Growth	1774.6%	—	—	—

2017 Year-End Financials
Return on assets: 1.7% Cash ($ mil.): 9
Return on equity: 54.8%
Current ratio: —

SPRING VALLEY HOSPITAL MEDICAL CENTER

EXECUTIVES

Ceo, Leonard Freehof
Director Risk Management, Fred Neujahr

LOCATIONS

HQ: SPRING VALLEY HOSPITAL MEDICAL CENTER
5400 S RAINBOW BLVD, LAS VEGAS, NV 891181825
Phone: 702 853-3000
Web: WWW.SPRINGVALLEYHOSPITAL.COM

HISTORICAL FINANCIALS

Company Type: Private

Income Statement				FYE: December 31
	REVENUE ($ mil.)	NET INCOME ($ mil.)	NET PROFIT MARGIN	EMPLOYEES
12/17	350	51	14.6%	8
12/16	314	43	13.7%	—
12/15	300	36	12.2%	—
Annual Growth	7.9%	18.0%	—	—

SPRINGFIELD SCHOOL DISTRICT R12

EXECUTIVES

Supt, Dr John Jungmann
Administrative Assistant, Amanda George
Administrative Coordinator, Pam Bodine
Application Support Manager, Roger Smith
Exec Ofc Liaison, Kathy Looten
Secretary, Carol Parker
Executive Assistant To Chief H, Deborah Rion
Director of It, Rick Green
Director of Professional Learn, Kathy Gross
Director of Finance, Kimberly Mulvaney

LOCATIONS

HQ: SPRINGFIELD SCHOOL DISTRICT R12
1359 E SAINT LOUIS ST, SPRINGFIELD, MO
658023409
Phone: 417 523-0000
Web: WWW.HILLCREST.SPSK12.ORG

HISTORICAL FINANCIALS

Company Type: Private

Income Statement				FYE: June 30
	REVENUE ($ mil.)	NET INCOME ($ mil.)	NET PROFIT MARGIN	EMPLOYEES
06/17	293	(0)	—	3,000
06/16	281	(106)	—	—
06/15	277	(20)	—	—
06/14	271	144	53.2%	—
Annual Growth	2.6%	—	—	—

2017 Year-End Financials

Return on assets: —
Return on equity: (-0.1%)
Current ratio: —

Cash ($ mil.): 59

SRC HOLDINGS CORPORATION

EXECUTIVES

Pres, John P Stack
V Pres, Dennis Sheppard
Treas, Laura Ruzicka
Mgr, William D Sheppard
Controller, Beth Marsh
Supply Chain Manager, Joe Hoffman
Inventory, Mary Blunt
Shipping Manager, Earl Light
Auditors: KPM CPAS PC SPRINGFIELD MIS

LOCATIONS

HQ: SRC HOLDINGS CORPORATION
531 S UNION AVE, SPRINGFIELD, MO 658022659
Phone: 417 862-2337
Web: WWW.SRCHOLDINGS.COM

HISTORICAL FINANCIALS

Company Type: Private

Income Statement				FYE: January 28
	REVENUE ($ mil.)	NET INCOME ($ mil.)	NET PROFIT MARGIN	EMPLOYEES
01/18	390	25	6.4%	1,500
01/17	381	19	5.2%	—
01/16	403	17	4.4%	—
01/15	383	24	6.3%	—
Annual Growth	0.6%	1.3%	—	—

2018 Year-End Financials

Return on assets: 7.6%
Return on equity: 6.4%
Current ratio: 0.90

Cash ($ mil.): 13

SRI INTERNATIONAL

SRI International sometimes called "Silicon Valley's soul" is a not-for-profit think tank pondering advances in biotechnology chemicals and energy computer science electronics and public policy — and ways to commercialize those advances. It focuses on technology research and development business strategies and analysis. The organization has patents and patent applications in IT communications robotics and pharmaceuticals. SRI's clients have included Samsung General Motors and AT&T. The artificial intelligence it designed for the Department of Defense became Apple's Siri. Originally founded in 1946 as Stanford Research Institute SRI became fully independent in 1970.

Operations

SRI has conceived such innovations as the computer mouse magnetic encoding for checks and high-definition television not to mention some of the foundations of personal computing the Internet and stealth technology. It also provides basic and applied research laboratory and advisory services tech development and venture opportunities.

Geographic Reach

SRI operates 17 offices across the US (California Connecticut Florida Maryland Michigan Montana New Jersey Pennsylvania Texas and Virginia) along with four international offices in Puerto Rico Dubai Japan and Greenland. The organization's 2500 employees (including about 1000 scientists and researchers) work at research centers worldwide.

Sales and Marketing

SRI brings its research and development innovations to the marketplace by licensing its intellectual property and creating new ventures. SRI has created and launched more than 50 ventures with a total market capitalization exceeding $20 billion. It has conducted more than $4 billion in R&D since the early 2000s for clients and partners and worked with government partners including the National Institutes of Health and the Defense Advanced Research Projects Agency for more than 50 years. In fact Department of Defense clients contributed about 63% of sales in 2013. Its venture partners include Draper Fisher Jurvetson Horizon Ventures Intel Capital Khosla Ventures Kleiner Perkins Caufield & Byers and Mayfield Fund.

Strategy

SRI continues to invest in R&D on behalf of its clients. It built a $2.8 million 40000-square-foot bio-science research and development facility in Virginia to facilitate ongoing R&D.

EXECUTIVES

President Information And Computing Sciences, William Mark
Director Business Development, Scott Seaton
Ceo, William Jeffrey
Vp; President Products And Solutions, Mark A. Clifton
Svp Shared Services, Michael Page
Vp Cfo And Treasurer, Luther Lau
Vp; President Sri Ventures, Manish Kothari
Vp; President Sri Education, Denise Glyn Borders
Vp Corporate And Marketing Communications, Katie Keating
President Sri Biosciences, Greg Kovacs
Chairman, Mariann Byerwalter, age 58
Auditors: PRICEWATERHOUSECOOPERS LLP SA

LOCATIONS

HQ: SRI INTERNATIONAL
333 RAVENSWOOD AVE, MENLO PARK, CA
940253493
Phone: 650 859-2000
Web: WWW.SRI.COM

PRODUCTS/OPERATIONS

Selected Research Areas

Biosciences Health and Medical Systems
Chemistry Materials and Energy
Computing and Information Technology
Defense and Security
Education and Learning
Ocean and Space
Robotics Sensors and Devices

COMPETITORS

Aerospace Corporation	MITRE
Battelle Memorial	PAREXEL
Bayer Corp.	RAND Corporation
CACI International	Research Triangle
Charles Stark Draper	Institute
Laboratory	SwRI
DaVinci Institute	University of
DuPont	California
IQVIA	Wellcome Trust
MIT	Westat

HISTORICAL FINANCIALS

Company Type: Private

Income Statement

FYE: December 30

	REVENUE ($ mil.)	NET INCOME ($ mil.)	NET PROFIT MARGIN	EMPLOYEES
12/17	456	3	0.7%	2,437
12/16	503	6	1.3%	—
12/15	513	2	0.5%	—
12/14	539	0	0.0%	—
Annual Growth	(5.4%)	228.2%	—	—

2017 Year-End Financials

Return on assets: 12.7% Cash ($ mil.): 13
Return on equity: 0.7%
Current ratio: 1.50

SSM HEALTH CARE CORPORATION

The mission of SSM Health began with five nuns who fled religious persecution in Germany in 1872 only to arrive in St. Louis in the midst of a smallpox epidemic. They formed their first hospital there in 1877. Today the Midwest-based not-for-profit system sponsored by the Franciscan Sisters of Mary owns some 25 acute care hospitals with about 4500 licensed beds; it also has management or affiliation agreements with a number of other area hospitals. Additionally the company offers more than 300 outpatient facilities including physicians' practices home care and hospice services post-acute facilities and an insurance company.

Operations

In southern Wisconsin SSM Health facilities include St. Clare Hospital in Baraboo St. Mary's Janesville Hospital in Janesville and St. Mary's Hospital in Madison. Southern Illinois locations include St. Mary's Good Samaritan Hospital in Mount Vernon and St. Mary's Hospital in Centralia. The company owns and operates about 10 hospitals in Missouri; these include Cardinal Glennon Children's Hospital and DePaul Hospital. Oklahoma hospitals include St. Anthony Hospital in Oklahoma City and St. Anthony Shawnee Hospital in Shawnee.

SSM Health has some 9500 physicians on its staff. The system has some 176000 inpatient admissions and some 1.6 million outpatient visits each year.

The system participates in a Medicare Accountable Care Organization (ACO). It also has a pharmacy benefit arm.

Geographic Reach

SSM Health's facilities are located in Illinois Missouri Oklahoma and Wisconsin.

Sales and Marketing

Managed care payments account for about half of SSM Health's net patient revenue before provision for uncollectible accounts; Medicare accounts for about 30% and Medicaid accounts for about 15%.

The system spent $20666 on advertising on 2016 up from $17956 in 2015.

Financial Performance

SSM Health's operating revenue increased 12% to $6.1 billion due largely to a rise in net patient service revenues and an increase in other revenue. Premiums earned and investment income also rose that year.

However operating expenses increased across most areas and the system reported a decrease in excess of revenues over expenses which fell 52% to $99.4 million. Similarly operating cash flow fell 51% to $220.4 million in 2016. Factors contributing to that drop included an increase in pension-related changes and in provisions for uncollectible accounts and bad debts.

Strategy

SSM Health often partners with other care providers which helps it expand without having to invest in new facilities from the ground up.

Like most health systems SSM has been challenged with lower government reimbursement rates. It is implementing a financial improvement initiative which includes some company layoffs.

Mergers and Acquisitions

SSM Health has been making a number of acquisitions to expand its network. For example in 2016 it doubled its stake in St. Clare Surgical Center to 60% and acquired the rest of Physicians Surgery Center at DePaul it didn't already own. SSM also took over the operations of about 25 health clinics located in Walgreens stores in Greater St. Louis.

In early 2018 the system acquired Agnesian HealthCare and Monroe Clinic (both based in Wisconsin) adding four hospitals eight post-acute facilities and several outpatient facilities.

EXECUTIVES

Svp Strategic Development, William P. Thompson
Svp Finance, Kris A. Zimmer
President Hospital Operations, Chris Howard
Evp; President Health Care Delivery Finance And Integration, Gaurov Dayal
Svp Strategy Communications And Marketing, Paula J. Friedman
President Ssm St. Joseph Health Center, Mike Bowers
Evp; President Physician And Ambulatory Operations, Shane Peng
Chief Nursing Officer, Maggie Fowler
Svp And Cio, Phillip Loftus
President St. Maryâ's Hospital, Jon Rozenfeld
President Ssm Health At Home, Alison Ruehl
Auditors: DELOITTE & TOUCHE LLP STLOUI

LOCATIONS

HQ: SSM HEALTH CARE CORPORATION
10101 WOODFIELD LN # 100, SAINT LOUIS, MO 631322944
Phone: 314 994-7800
Web: WWW.SSMHC.COM

PRODUCTS/OPERATIONS

Selected Facilities

Illinois
St. Mary's Good Samaritan (joint sponsorship with Felician Services two hospitals in Mt. Vernon and Centralia)
Missouri
St. Francis Hospital & Health Services (Maryville)
St. Mary's Health Center (Jefferson City)
SSM Cardinal Glennon Children's Medical Center (St. Louis)
SSM DePaul Health Center (Bridgeton)
SSM St. Clare Health Center (St. Louis)
SSM St. Joseph Health Center (St. Charles)
SSM St. Joseph Health Center (Wentzville)
SSM St. Joseph Hospital West (Lake St. Louis)
SSM St. Mary's Health Center (Richmond Heights)
Oklahoma
Bone & Joint Hospital (Oklahoma City)
Shawnee Medical Center Clinic (Shawnee)
St. Anthony Hospital (Oklahoma City)
Unity Health Center (Shawnee)
Wisconsin
Boscobel Area Health Care (managed hospital and clinics Boscobel)
Columbus Community Hospital (affiliate Columbus)
Edgerton Hospital and Health Services (Edgerton)
St. Clare Hospital (Baraboo)

St. Clare Meadows Care Center (nursing home Madison)
St. Mary's Care Center (nursing home Madison)
St. Mary's Hospital (Madison)
St. Mary's Janesville Hospital (Janesville)
Stoughton Hospital (affiliate Stoughton)
Uplands Hill Health (affiliate hospital and nursing care Dodgeville)

COMPETITORS

Adventist Health System Sunbelt Healthcare
Advocate Health Care
Allina Hospitals
Ascension Health
BJC HealthCare
Carle Physician Group
Community Health Systems
HCA
Hospital Sisters Health System
Mayo Clinic
Mercy Health
Meriter Health Services
MetroSouth Medical
Rush System for Health
Tenet Healthcare
University of Wisconsin Hospital and Clinics
VITAS Healthcare

HISTORICAL FINANCIALS

Company Type: Private

Income Statement

FYE: December 31

	REVENUE ($ mil.)	NET INCOME ($ mil.)	NET PROFIT MARGIN	EMPLOYEES
12/17	6,497	245	3.8%	24,230
12/16	6,109	(30)	—	—
12/13	1,177	32	2.8%	—
Annual Growth	53.3%	65.9%	—	—

2017 Year-End Financials

Return on assets: 18.7% Cash ($ mil.): 126
Return on equity: 3.8%
Current ratio: 0.30

SSM HEALTH CARE OF OKLAHOMA, INC.

EXECUTIVES

Ceo, Joe Hodges
V Pres of Fin, Shasta Manuel
Vice President, Cynthia Brundige
Vice President, Kersey Winfree
Regional Cfo, Garrick Muller
Admin Asst of Pres, Donna Retter
Physician, Blake Parsons
Chief of Psychiatric, Brent Bell

LOCATIONS

HQ: SSM HEALTH CARE OF OKLAHOMA, INC.
1000 N LEE AVE, OKLAHOMA CITY, OK 731021036
Phone: 405 272-7000
Web: WWW.SAINTSOK.COM

HISTORICAL FINANCIALS
Company Type: Private

Income Statement   FYE: December 31

	REVENUE ($ mil.)	NET INCOME ($ mil.)	NET PROFIT MARGIN	EMPLOYEES
12/17	507	15	3.0%	3,000
12/16	454	13	3.0%	—
12/14	444	9	2.1%	—
12/01	196	(11)	—	—
Annual Growth	6.1%	—	—	—

2017 Year-End Financials
Return on assets: 5.2% Cash ($ mil.): 44
Return on equity: 3.0%
Current ratio: 88.10

ST BARNABAS MEDICAL CENTER (INC)

Part of the Saint Barnabas Health Care System Saint Barnabas Medical Center is a 600-bed acute-care hospital that provides a full range of health services to residents of Livingston New Jersey and surrounding areas. The not-for-profit medical center provides general inpatient and outpatient care programs as well as burn and perinatal care. It also houses units specializing in organ transplant stroke care cardiac surgery and comprehensive cancer treatment. Its Institute for Reproductive Medicine and Science provides assisted reproductive technology services. Saint Barnabas Medical Center treats some 35000 inpatients and more than 85000 emergency-room patients each year.

Operations
In combination with its satellite Saint Barnabas Ambulatory Care Center the medical center serves about 300000 outpatients per year. Saint Barnabas Medical Center is also a teaching affiliate of several regional schools includingA the University of Medicine and Dentistry of New Jersey and Drexel University College of Medicine.

Company Background
New Jersey's first hospital Saint Barnabas Medical Center was founded in 1865 in a private home.

EXECUTIVES
Medical Director, Adrian L Connolly
Assistant Vice President Legal Affairs, Margaret H Campbell
Auditors: KPMG LLP NEW YORK NY

LOCATIONS
HQ: ST BARNABAS MEDICAL CENTER (INC)
94 OLD SHORT HILLS RD # 1, LIVINGSTON, NJ 070395668
Phone: 973 322-5000

COMPETITORS
Atlantic Health
Children's Specialized Hospital
Chilton Medical Center
East Orange General Hospital
Hackensack Meridian Health
Hackensack University Medical Center
JFK Medical Center
Newark Beth Israel Medical Center
Raritan Bay Medical Center
Robert Wood Johnson University Hospital
Robert Wood Johnson University Hospital at Rahway
Saint Peter's University Hospital
St. Joseph's Healthcare System

Trinitas Regional Medical Center
Virtua Health

HISTORICAL FINANCIALS
Company Type: Private

Income Statement   FYE: December 31

	REVENUE ($ mil.)	NET INCOME ($ mil.)	NET PROFIT MARGIN	EMPLOYEES
12/17	818	113	13.9%	4,000
12/16	760	84	11.1%	—
12/15	728	87	12.0%	—
12/14	730	86	11.8%	—
Annual Growth	3.8%	9.5%	—	—

2017 Year-End Financials
Return on assets: 4.4% Cash ($ mil.): —
Return on equity: 13.9%
Current ratio: 0.70

ST DAVID'S SOUTH AUSTIN MEDICAL CENTER

EXECUTIVES
Director Of Surgery, Susan Triggs

LOCATIONS
HQ: ST DAVID'S SOUTH AUSTIN MEDICAL CENTER
901 W BEN WHITE BLVD, AUSTIN, TX 787046903
Phone: 512 447-2211
Web: WWW.STDAVIDS.COM

COMPETITORS
Hill Country   University Health
Seton Healthcare   System
Network

HISTORICAL FINANCIALS
Company Type: Private

Income Statement   FYE: October 31

	REVENUE ($ mil.)	NET INCOME ($ mil.)	NET PROFIT MARGIN	EMPLOYEES
10/17	328	55	16.9%	1,400
10/16	289	50	17.4%	—
10/15*	260	53	20.7%	—
12/14	0	0	9.3%	—
Annual Growth	1392.8%	1717.1%	—	—

*Fiscal year change

2017 Year-End Financials
Return on assets: 2.6% Cash ($ mil.): —
Return on equity: 16.9%
Current ratio: 3.00

ST ELIFRANCISCAN & ELIZABETH HEALTH

EXECUTIVES
President /Ceo, Terry Wilson
Director, John Francis
Nurse, Cheryl Ransom
Chief Financial Officer, Keith Lauter

LOCATIONS
HQ: ST ELIFRANCISCAN & ELIZABETH HEALTH
1701 S CREASY LN, LAFAYETTE, IN 479054972
Phone: 765 502-4000

HISTORICAL FINANCIALS
Company Type: Private

Income Statement   FYE: December 31

	REVENUE ($ mil.)	NET INCOME ($ mil.)	NET PROFIT MARGIN	EMPLOYEES
12/16	347	20	6.0%	69
12/15	56	4	8.4%	—
Annual Growth	515.4%	334.8%	—	—

ST JOHN MACOMB-OAKLAND HOSPITAL

EXECUTIVES
Prin, Kam Parekh
Surgeon, Roger Bigelow
Auditors: DELOITTE TAX LLP CINCINNATI

LOCATIONS
HQ: ST JOHN MACOMB-OAKLAND HOSPITAL
28000 DEQUINDRE RD, WARREN, MI 480922468
Phone: 586 753-0094
Web: WWW.STJOHN.ORG

HISTORICAL FINANCIALS
Company Type: Private

Income Statement   FYE: June 30

	REVENUE ($ mil.)	NET INCOME ($ mil.)	NET PROFIT MARGIN	EMPLOYEES
06/16	415	20	4.8%	22
06/15	405	24	6.1%	—
06/14	398	24	6.2%	—
Annual Growth	2.1%	(10.1%)	—	—

2016 Year-End Financials
Return on assets: 7.7% Cash ($ mil.): 1
Return on equity: 4.8%
Current ratio: 1.50

ST LOUIS CHILDREN'S HOSPITAL

EXECUTIVES

Pres, Joan Magruder
Sr Vice President, Michael Dehaven
Vice President, David Aplington
Exec Asst, Diana Easton
Coordinator, Karen Rieker
Distribution/Shipping/Transpor, Lynne Andreski
Director of Laboratory, Susan Deuser
Manager Media, Bryan Camp
Pediatric Nurse Practitioner, Carole Branch
It Manager, Cindy Derby
Pedodontist, Daniel Stoeckel

LOCATIONS

HQ: ST LOUIS CHILDREN'S HOSPITAL
    1 CHILDRENS PL, SAINT LOUIS, MO 631101081
Phone: 314 454-6000
Web: WWW.STLOUISCHILDRENS.ORG

HISTORICAL FINANCIALS
Company Type: Private

Income Statement   FYE: December 31

	REVENUE ($ mil.)	NET INCOME ($ mil.)	NET PROFIT MARGIN	EMPLOYEES
12/17	609	62	10.2%	2,959
12/16	563	58	10.3%	—
12/15	527	50	9.5%	—
12/14	513	36	7.1%	—
Annual Growth	5.9%	19.6%	—	—

2017 Year-End Financials
Return on assets: 0.9%   Cash ($ mil.): —
Return on equity: 10.2%
Current ratio: 1.10

ST LUKE'S HOSPITAL & HEALTH NETWORK INC

EXECUTIVES

Pres, Richard A Anderson
Sr V Pres, Rthomas P Lichtenwalner
Information Technology Manager, James Derr
Program Director, Beverly Surovi
Accountant, Mike Vega
Media Specialist, Anne Kemp
Chief Information Officer, Chad Brisendine
Coordinator, Kathleen Hedges
Interim President, Lisa Giovanni
Biomedical Engineer, Beverly Hodgkins
Administrator, Brian Repetz

LOCATIONS

HQ: ST LUKE'S HOSPITAL & HEALTH NETWORK INC
    801 OSTRUM ST, BETHLEHEM, PA 180151000
Phone: 484 526-4000
Web: WWW.SLHN.ORG

ST LUKE'S METHODIST HOSPITAL INC

EXECUTIVES

Pres-Ceo, Theodore Townsend Jr
Chb, James Sealy
Dentist, Duane Voshell DDS
Scientist, Teresa Allie
Doctor, James Snipes
Customer Manager, Rhonada Weber

LOCATIONS

HQ: ST LUKE'S METHODIST HOSPITAL INC
    1026 A AVE NE, CEDAR RAPIDS, IA 524025074
Phone: 319 369-7211
Web: WWW.STLUKESCR.ORG

HISTORICAL FINANCIALS
Company Type: Private

Income Statement   FYE: December 31

	REVENUE ($ mil.)	NET INCOME ($ mil.)	NET PROFIT MARGIN	EMPLOYEES
12/16	378	2	0.6%	2,000
12/15	373	15	4.1%	—
12/14	319	90	28.4%	—
12/13	383	23	6.1%	—
Annual Growth	(0.5%)	(55.4%)	—	—

2016 Year-End Financials
Return on assets: 7.5%   Cash ($ mil.): 15
Return on equity: 0.6%
Current ratio: 2.40

ST LUKE'S-ROOSEVELT HOSPITAL CENTER

EXECUTIVES

Pres, Frank Cracolici
Sr Vice President, Robert Catalano
Manager, Anthony Grillo
Scientist, Emilia Sordillo
Doctor, Petros Levounis
Coordinator, Brian Aarons
Manager, Jeff Horvath
Infectious Disease Specialist, Luz Lugo

Radiologist, Rafael Ortiz
Administrator, Sheila Monroe
Director of Operations, Barbara Nusbaum
Auditors: ERNST & YOUNG US LLP INDIANAP

LOCATIONS

HQ: ST LUKE'S-ROOSEVELT HOSPITAL CENTER
    1111 AMSTERDAM AVE, NEW YORK, NY 100251716
Phone: 212 523-4000
Web: WWW.MOUNTSINAI.ORG/LOCATIONS/ST-LUKES

HISTORICAL FINANCIALS
Company Type: Private

Income Statement   FYE: December 31

	REVENUE ($ mil.)	NET INCOME ($ mil.)	NET PROFIT MARGIN	EMPLOYEES
12/16	901	53	5.9%	6,000
12/15	859	61	7.1%	—
12/14	1,160	(17)	—	—
Annual Growth	(11.9%)	—	—	—

2016 Year-End Financials
Return on assets: 10.8%   Cash ($ mil.): 39
Return on equity: 5.9%
Current ratio: 0.50

ST MARY'S MEDICAL CENTER

EXECUTIVES

Ceo, Davide Carbone
Chief Financial Officer, Thomas Schlemmer
Chief Operating Officer, Joey Bulfin
Controller, Howard Brown
Cno, Sharon Hayes
Occupational Specia, Laura J Gadberry
Training and Direc, Tamara Batteiger
Pharmacist, Tonya Graham
Physical Therapist Prn, Brittany Williams
Compliance Director, Donna Lewis
Chief of Pediatrics, Lawrence Adams

LOCATIONS

HQ: ST MARY'S MEDICAL CENTER
    901 45TH ST, MANGONIA PARK, FL 334072413
Phone: 561 844-6300
Web: WWW.STMARYSMC.COM

HISTORICAL FINANCIALS
Company Type: Private

Income Statement   FYE: May 31

	REVENUE ($ mil.)	NET INCOME ($ mil.)	NET PROFIT MARGIN	EMPLOYEES
05/16	319	45	14.1%	56,605
05/15	320	52	16.4%	—
Annual Growth	(0.2%)	(13.9%)	—	—

2016 Year-End Financials
Return on assets: 5.2%   Cash ($ mil.): —
Return on equity: 14.1%
Current ratio: 1.70

HISTORICAL FINANCIALS
Company Type: Private

Income Statement   FYE: June 30

	REVENUE ($ mil.)	NET INCOME ($ mil.)	NET PROFIT MARGIN	EMPLOYEES
06/16	648	47	7.4%	75
06/15	602	38	6.4%	—
Annual Growth	7.6%	24.9%		

2016 Year-End Financials
Return on assets: 9.2%   Cash ($ mil.): 43
Return on equity: 7.4%
Current ratio: 0.90

ST PATRICK HOSPITAL CORPORATION

Feeling a little green? St. Patrick Hospital and Health Sciences Center is there to help. The not-for-profit hospital boasts some 250 beds (acute-care and transitional) and serves nearly 20 counties in and around Missoula Montana. Its specialty services include cancer treatment surgery and occupational health. The center also provides Life Flight air transport to critically ill or injured patients. The hospital provides outpatient primary and specialty care through a host of affiliated physician practices and clinics throughout the area. St. Patrick Hospital and Health Sciences Center is part of Providence Health & Services which has two hospitals and more than 40 clinics across Montana.

Operations

The center's facility annual admits more than 7900 patients and logs more than 37900 days of patient care. Its physician offices and outpatient services are located adjacent to the hospital. They comprise the Western Montana Clinic the Montana Neuroscience Institute the Montana Cancer Center and the International Heart Institute. Outpatient services provided by St. Patrick Hospital and Health Sciences Center include physical occupational speech diabetic and cardiac rehabilitation.

In 2013 the hospital was awarded Magnet recognition by the American Nurses Credentialing Center's Magnet Recognition Program.

Geographic Reach

St. Patrick Hospital and Health Sciences Center serves those who reside in Missoula Montana and the surrounding counties which generate 95% of its patient volume.

Strategy

St. Patrick Hospital and Health Sciences Center is looking to expand its comprehensive women's and children's services. Its new services will include inpatient obstetrical and newborn care (with a Level 2 neonatal intensive care unit); an expanded inpatient and outpatient pediatric program; and outpatient obstetrical/gynecological and perinatology care.

Company Background

St. Patrick Hospital and Health Sciences Center was founded in 1873 by the Sisters of Providence.

EXECUTIVES

Physical Therapy Director Physical Rehab Services Director Occupational Therapy Director, Anita Nash

LOCATIONS

HQ: ST PATRICK HOSPITAL CORPORATION
500 W BROADWAY ST, MISSOULA, MT 598024008
Phone: 406 543-7271
Web: MONTANA.PROVIDENCE.ORG/LOCATIONS-DIRECTORY/S/ST-PATRICK-

PRODUCTS/OPERATIONS

Selected Services
Cardiology
Cancer Center
Diabetes Care Center
Diagnostic Imaging
Emergency Department
First STEP
Joint Replacement
Laboratory
Life Flight
Neurobehavioral Medicine
Neurology
Broadway Pharmacy
Rehabilitation
Sleep Center
Stroke Center
Surgery

COMPETITORS

Billings Clinic	St. James Healthcare
Glendive Medical Center	Wyoming Medical Center
St. Alexius Medical Center	

HISTORICAL FINANCIALS

Company Type: Private

Income Statement   FYE: December 31

	REVENUE ($ mil.)	NET INCOME ($ mil.)	NET PROFIT MARGIN	EMPLOYEES
12/17	338	29	8.8%	1,460
12/16	300	1	0.7%	—
12/15	289	15	5.3%	—
12/05	191	8	4.3%	—
Annual Growth	4.8%	11.4%		

2017 Year-End Financials

Return on assets: 2.9%   Cash ($ mil.): 1
Return on equity: 8.8%
Current ratio: 1.70

ST. AGNES HEALTHCARE, INC.

If you're in agony in Charm City St. Agnes HealthCare is here to help. The Catholic health system provides a spectrum of medical services to the residents of southwest Baltimore. Its flagship facility St. Agnes Hospital has 276 beds and offers a comprehensive range of medical and surgical services including treatment in areas such as oncology cardiovascular disease bariatric medicine women's health plastic surgery and orthopedics. The system also includes a multispecialty physicians group (Seton Medical Group) and a diagnostic imaging center. St. Agnes HealthCare is a member of Ascension Health. The health system traces its roots to 1862 when the Daughters of Charity set up a local infirmary in 1862.

Operations

St. Agnes Hospital handles about 25000 inpatient visits each year as well as 84000 emergency room visits 11000 surgeries and 2000 births. The medical center is also a teaching facility providing training programs including residencies in a number of medical and surgical specialties including advanced laparoscopic surgery internal medicine and surgical oncology.

Financial Performance

St. Agnes Hospital reported revenues of $423 million for fiscal 2012. It also reported total assets of more than $520 million and income from recurring operations of nearly $22 million.

Strategy

St. Agnes Hospital has completed a $200 million multi-year campus revitalization project. The project included a new patient tower which opened in 2011 as well as a parking garage and the Hackerman-Patz House for families of patients being treated for long-term ailments. The final phase completed in 2013 was the opening of a new 60000-square-foot medical office building providing specialties including cardiology respiratory care renal care and an expanded cancer center.

St. Agnes HealthCare plans to further expand its facilities in future years to meet the rising needs of its service territory. For instance in 2013 the organization announced plans to develop a mixed-use center that will provide community services including senior housing and recreation facilities. The organization also opened a new primary care facility in Baltimore during 2013.

In addition St. Agnes Hospital is part of a quality improvement collaboration with St. Joseph Medical Center called Mission Health Partners. The initiative is designed to expand access to health care in the region through the sharing of resources and best practices.

EXECUTIVES

Medical Director Of The Breast Center, Diana Griffiths
Avp Quality And Safety, Cheri Hahn
Director Of Nursing, Susan Hartman
Board Director, Irene Knott
Board Director, James Sellmger
Board Director, Margaret Hayes
Board Director, Mohannad Jishi

LOCATIONS

HQ: ST. AGNES HEALTHCARE, INC.
900 S CATON AVE, BALTIMORE, MD 212295201
Phone: 667 234-6000
Web: WWW.STAGNES.ORG

COMPETITORS

Anne Arundel Medical Center	Johns Hopkins Health System
Bon Secours Health	Levindale Hospital
Doctors Community Hospital	LifeBridge Health
Franklin Square Hospital Center	MedStar Health
GBMC	MedStar Union Memorial Hospital
Good Samaritan Hospital of Maryland	Sinai Hospital of Baltimore
Harbor Hospital	University of Maryland Medical System

HISTORICAL FINANCIALS

Company Type: Private

Income Statement   FYE: June 30

	REVENUE ($ mil.)	NET INCOME ($ mil.)	NET PROFIT MARGIN	EMPLOYEES
06/16	447	7	1.7%	2,506
06/15	438	23	5.3%	—
06/10	400	50	12.7%	—
06/09	336	(11)	—	—
Annual Growth	4.2%	—	—	—

2016 Year-End Financials

Return on assets: 10.4%   Cash ($ mil.): 9
Return on equity: 1.7%
Current ratio: 1.00

ST. ALEXIUS MEDICAL CENTER

EXECUTIVES

Ceo, Len Wilk
Cfo, Robin Chopp
Engineer, Alexander Darnall
Radiation Oncologist, Rajiv J Patel
Obstetrician Gynecologist, Anna Bobba
Director, Bruce Polier

Specialist, Connie Grzeszczak
Cardiology Director, Arthur Nazarian
Materials Coordinator, Barbara Kerr
Vice President, John Sullivan
Radiology Director, Scott Baker
Auditors: DELOITTE TAX LLP CHICAGO IL

LOCATIONS

HQ: ST. ALEXIUS MEDICAL CENTER
1555 BARRINGTON RD BLDG 1, HOFFMAN
ESTATES, IL 601691099
Phone: 847 884-9800
Web: WWW.ALEXIANBROTHERSHEALTH.ORG

HISTORICAL FINANCIALS

Company Type: Private

Income Statement   FYE: June 30

	REVENUE ($ mil.)	NET INCOME ($ mil.)	NET PROFIT MARGIN	EMPLOYEES
06/17	359	44	12.4%	1,500
06/16	353	55	15.8%	—
06/15	351	42	12.1%	—
06/14	344	30	8.9%	—
Annual Growth	1.5%	13.3%	—	—

2017 Year-End Financials

Return on assets: 5.7%   Cash ($ mil.): —
Return on equity: 12.4%
Current ratio: 3.00

ST. ALEXIUS MEDICAL CENTER

EXECUTIVES

Vice President Community Services, Julie Jeske

LOCATIONS

HQ: ST. ALEXIUS MEDICAL CENTER
900 E BROADWAY AVE, BISMARCK, ND 585014520
Phone: 701 530-7000
Web:
WWW.CHISTALEXIUSHEALTH.ORG/LOCATIONS/BIS
MARCK

PRODUCTS/OPERATIONS

Selected Services

Acceleration
Arthritis Clinic
Balance and Dizziness Center
Behavioral and Mental Health
Cardiac Rehabilitation
Clinical Research Services
Community Health
Community Pharmacy
Deep Brain Stimulation
Dialysis
EAP
Emergency & Trauma
Family Practice Clinic
Geriatrics (Older Adults)
Heart and Vascular Center
Home Care and Hospice
Human Performance Center
Kidney Dialysis
Mandan Clinic
Minot Medical Clinic
Neonatology Clinic
Nephrology Clinic
Neurology
Neuroscience
Neurosurgery
Occupational Health and Wellness
  Occupation

Orthopedics
Pediatric Cardiology Clinic
Pediatric Neurology Clinic
Physical Medicine & Rehabilitation
  Physical T
Radiology Services
  Rehabilita
Spine Center
Stroke Center
Surgical Services
Telemedicine and Videoconferencing Services
Therapy at HPC
Urology Clinic
Women's Health

COMPETITORS

Altru Health   Sanford
Avera Health   Health-MeritCare
Billings Clinic
Catholic Health
  Initiatives

HISTORICAL FINANCIALS

Company Type: Private

Income Statement   FYE: June 30

	REVENUE ($ mil.)	NET INCOME ($ mil.)	NET PROFIT MARGIN	EMPLOYEES
06/16	323	(10)	—	1,947
06/15	289	148	51.2%	—
06/14	308	14	4.6%	—
06/13	291	(1)	—	—
Annual Growth	3.5%	—	—	—

ST. ANTHONY'S HOSPITAL, INC.

EXECUTIVES

Medical Director, Andrea Woods

LOCATIONS

HQ: ST. ANTHONY'S HOSPITAL, INC.
1200 7TH AVE N, SAINT PETERSBURG, FL
337051388
Phone: 727 825-1100
Web: WWW.STANTHONYSFOUNDATION.ORG

Selected facilities

St. Anthon
St. Anthony's Outpatient Center - St. Petersburg
St. Anthony's Outpatient Imaging Centers
St. Anthony's Physician's Surgery Center
St. Anthony's Resource Center
Susan Sheppard McGillicuddy Breast Center
Carillon Surgery Center

PRODUCTS/OPERATIONS

Selected services

Behavioral Health
Bariatrics
Breast Center
BayCare HomeCare
Cancer Care
Center for Intestinal Continence
Center for Joint Replacement
Center for Robotic Surgery
Emergency Services
Faith Community Nursing
Heart - Cardiac Care
Laboratory Services
Imaging Services
Neuroscience
Orthopedics
Palliative Care

Minimally Invasive Skull Base Institute
Respiratory Services
Sleep Disorders Center
Stroke
Surgical Services
Vascular Services
Wound Healing Center

COMPETITORS

All Children's Hospital
Bayfront Health
Florida Hospital Tampa Bay Division
H. Lee Moffitt Cancer Center & Research Institute
Manatee Memorial Hospital
Northside Hospital and Heart Institute
Shriners Hospitals For Children
St. Joseph's-Baptist Health Care
Tampa General Hospital

HISTORICAL FINANCIALS

Company Type: Private

Income Statement   FYE: December 31

	REVENUE ($ mil.)	NET INCOME ($ mil.)	NET PROFIT MARGIN	EMPLOYEES
12/16	330	51	15.6%	1,076
12/14	252	34	13.7%	—
12/13	248	24	9.9%	—
12/12	203	28	13.9%	—
Annual Growth	13.0%	16.1%	—	—

ST. ANTHONY'S MEDICAL CENTER

St. Anthony's Medical Center applies its skills to medical cases in the Midwest. The hospital serves residents in the areas surrounding St. Louis Missouri as well as portions of southwestern Illinois. With about 770 beds and some 800 affiliated physicians the hospital provides a comprehensive offering including inpatient and outpatient medical surgical diagnostic and behavioral health care. The hospital operates a level II trauma center cancer and chest pain units and a pediatric emergency center as well as several urgent care facilities. It also offers home health hospice laboratory and pharmacy services. St. Anthony's Medical Center was founded in 1900 by the Franciscan Sisters of Germany.

Operations

St. Anthony's Medical Center's ER is staffed by an independently owned group of emergency physicians (Emergency Physicians of St. Louis) who provide services to the hospital on a contract bases. The physician-group model of employment aims to improve patient flow and reduce waiting times at the ER.

In fiscal 2015 (ended June) the hospital had some 27000 inpatient admissions and more than 77700 emergency department visits delivered more than 1100 babies and performed more than 13000 surgeries.

Geographic Reach

St. Anthony's Medical Center is one of the largest hospitals in the St. Louis metropolitan area. It serves a population base of more than 900000 people in 10 counties in Missouri and Illinois. It also operates four urgent care centers in surrounding communities of Arnold Big Bend Fenton and Lemay.

Strategy

In 2014 St. Anthony's Medical Center became one of the first hospitals in the nation to implant the newly approved Medtronic Reveal LINQ In-sertable Cardiac Monitor System a miniature cardiac monitor in a stroke patient.

EXECUTIVES

Executive Vice President Chief Financial Officer, John Skeans
Vice President, Robert Griesbaum
Medical Director, Homan Joseph
Auditors: BKD LLP ST LOUIS MISSOURI

LOCATIONS

HQ: ST. ANTHONY'S MEDICAL CENTER
  10010 KENNERLY RD, SAINT LOUIS, MO 631282106
Phone: 314 525-1000
Web: WWW.STANTHONYSMEDCENTER.COM

PRODUCTS/OPERATIONS

Selected Services
Acute Rehabilitation
Audiology/Hearing
Behavioral Health
Breast Center
Cancer Care Center
Diabetes Education
Emergency/Trauma
Heart Specialty Center
Home Care
Hospice Field Program
Hyland Behavioral Health
Long-term Acute Care
Neuroscience and Stroke
Occupational Medicine
Oncology
Orthopedics
Ostomy Clinic
Outpatient Imaging
Pediatric Services
Physical Therapy
Pregnancy and Birth
Pharmacy
Pulmonary
Radiology/Imaging Centers
Rehabilitation (cardiac and acute)
Senior Services
Sleep Disorder Center
Social Services (Care Management)
Speech Therapy
Sports & Therapy
Stroke
Surgery
Urgent Care Centers
Urological Gynecology
Vestibular Rehab
Weight Management
Women's Medical/Surgical Unit
Wound Treatment

COMPETITORS

Ascension Health	Mercy Hospital St.
BJC HealthCare	Louis
Barnes-Jewish Hospital	RehabCare
Christian Hospital	SSM Health Care
CoxHealth	Saint Francis Medical
HCA	Center
Memorial Hospital	St. Luke's Hospital
(Illinois)	(MO)
Mercy Health	Tenet Healthcare

HISTORICAL FINANCIALS

Company Type: Private

Income Statement   FYE: June 30

	REVENUE ($ mil.)	NET INCOME ($ mil.)	NET PROFIT MARGIN	EMPLOYEES
06/17	451	(43)	—	3,900
06/15	482	1	0.3%	—
06/14	424	13	3.1%	—
06/13	443	38	8.7%	—
Annual Growth	0.5%	—	—	—

2017 Year-End Financials

Return on assets: 16.2%   Cash ($ mil.): 17
Return on equity: (-9.6%)
Current ratio: 0.90

ST. BARNABAS HOSPITAL

EXECUTIVES

Chb, Victor Wright
President, Scott Cooper
Cfo, Todd Gorlewski
Deputy Director, Andino James
Administrative Assistant, Liza De La Cruz
Director of Engineering, Michael Chiappone
Senior Manager, Robert Karpinos
Administrative Assistant, Grace Facciabene
Director of Behavioral Health, Halana Finnie
Chief Operating Officer, Leonard Walsh
Program Director, Nelson Eng

LOCATIONS

HQ: ST. BARNABAS HOSPITAL
  4422 3RD AVE, BRONX, NY 104572594
Phone: 718 960-9000
Web: WWW.SBHNY.ORG

HISTORICAL FINANCIALS

Company Type: Private

Income Statement   FYE: December 31

	REVENUE ($ mil.)	NET INCOME ($ mil.)	NET PROFIT MARGIN	EMPLOYEES
12/17	310	(17)	—	2,119
12/16	334	(18)	—	—
12/15	333	(17)	—	—
12/14	313	(6)	—	—
Annual Growth	(0.3%)	—	—	—

2017 Year-End Financials

Return on assets: 13.3%   Cash ($ mil.): 4
Return on equity: (-5.7%)
Current ratio: 0.40

ST. BERNARD'S HOSPITAL, INC.

EXECUTIVES

Ceo, Chris B Barber
President, Ben E Owens
Chief of Medicine, Ben Cranfill
Director, Beverly Harralson
Director, Pat Hamilton
Manager, Krista Agee
Chief Technology Officer, Pam Wheaton
Manager, Lance Brown
Chief Information Officer, Charles Pigg
Assistant Manager of Nuclear M, Shawnda Krupicki
Director, Ann Graeber

LOCATIONS

HQ: ST. BERNARD'S HOSPITAL, INC.
  225 E JACKSON AVE, JONESBORO, AR 724013119
Phone: 870 207-7300
Web: WWW.STBERNARDS.INFO

HISTORICAL FINANCIALS

Company Type: Private

Income Statement   FYE: September 30

	REVENUE ($ mil.)	NET INCOME ($ mil.)	NET PROFIT MARGIN	EMPLOYEES
09/17	304	32	10.6%	2,000
09/16	344	22	6.6%	—
09/15	270	30	11.2%	—
09/14	248	20	8.3%	—
Annual Growth	7.1%	16.1%	—	—

2017 Year-End Financials

Return on assets: 4.0%   Cash ($ mil.): 45
Return on equity: 10.6%
Current ratio: 2.40

ST. CLAIR HEALTH CORPORATION

EXECUTIVES

Ceo, James Collins
Information Technology/Interne, Kaizad Kadwa
Human Resources, Mary Franzetta
Information Technology/Interne, Ted Hacker
Supervisor, Albert Harms
Doctor, Karl Bushman
Diagnostic Radiologist, Scott Patterson
Director Pediatric and, Dayle Griffin
Nurse, Karen Gasper
Public Relations Staff, Kathy Clark
Coordinator, Jonelle Tygielski

LOCATIONS

HQ: ST. CLAIR HEALTH CORPORATION
  1000 BOWER HILL RD, PITTSBURGH, PA 152431873
Phone: 412 561-4900
Web: WWW.STCLAIR.ORG

COMPETITORS

Allegheny General	UPMC
Hospital	UPMC Mercy
Excela Health	West Penn Allegheny
Heritage Valley Health	Health System

HISTORICAL FINANCIALS

Company Type: Private

Income Statement   FYE: June 30

	REVENUE ($ mil.)	NET INCOME ($ mil.)	NET PROFIT MARGIN	EMPLOYEES
06/18	344	58	16.9%	1,504
06/17	329	54	16.7%	—
06/16	0	0	54.9%	—
06/14	0	0	47.2%	—
Annual Growth	706.2%	523.4%	—	—

2018 Year-End Financials

Return on assets: 4.5%   Cash ($ mil.): 21
Return on equity: 16.9%
Current ratio: 1.40

ST. DOMINIC-JACKSON MEMORIAL HOSPITAL

EXECUTIVES

Pres, Claude W Harbarger
SEC-Treas, Sister Mary Trinita
President, Lester Diamond
Project Manager, Craig Church
Dietician, Alice Taylor
Director of Patient Access Ser, Aaron Watson
Surgeon, James Grady
Engineer, Justin Huff
Officer, Renee Beckum
Materials Management Director, Wayne McKee
Surgeon, William Harris
Auditors: I BKD LLP JACKSON MS

LOCATIONS

HQ: ST. DOMINIC-JACKSON MEMORIAL HOSPITAL
969 LAKELAND DR, JACKSON, MS 392164606
Phone: 601 200-6776
Web: WWW.STDOM.COM

HISTORICAL FINANCIALS
Company Type: Private

Income Statement   FYE: December 31

	REVENUE ($ mil.)	NET INCOME ($ mil.)	NET PROFIT MARGIN	EMPLOYEES
12/15	478	(0)		2,400
12/14	418	16	4.1%	—
12/13	0	0	—	—
12/08	337	(51)	—	—
Annual Growth	5.1%	—	—	—

2015 Year-End Financials

Return on assets: 6.4%   Cash ($ mil.): 51
Return on equity: (-0.1%)
Current ratio: 3.50

ST. FRANCIS HOSPITAL, ROSLYN, NEW YORK

Sure St. Francis Hospital can handle yourA gall bladderA and sinus difficulties butA it's really on top of your heart problems. The hospital's Heart CenterA — New York State's only specially designated cardiac center — providesA surgicalA diagnostic and treatment services.A The 365-bed St. Francis Hospital also has centers for ENT (ear nose and throat) orthopedic vascular prostate cancer gastrointestinal and general surgery services. As part of Catholic Health Services of Long Island St. Francis opened its doors in 1954 to children and adults. It was originally established as St. Francis Hospital and Sanatorium for Cardiac Children in 1936.

Operations

St. Francis Hospital's Heart Center performs about 8000 cardiac catheterizationsA 3000 coronary angioplasties andA about 1500 open-heart operations every year.A The center'sA DeMatteis Center for Cardiac Research and Education works to developA improved techniques for heart disease diagnosis including conducting clinical trials throughA partnerships with device and equipment makersA and provides patient education and fitness programs.

Geographic Reach

St. Francis Hospital is located in Roslyn New York. In addition it has satellite New YorkA locations in Greenvale (DeMatteis Center for Cardiac Research and Education) West Islip (South Bay Cardiovascular Center) and Hicksville (Bishop McHugh Health Center) as well as administrative offices in Port Washington.

Strategy

St. Francis HospitalA has expanded in recent years to keep up with growing patient demand. It opened the Bishop McHugh Health Center to provide outpatient primary care services for uninsured and underinsured patients in 2012.

The hospital completed its largest expansion project to date in 2009 with the construction of theA $190 million Nancy and Frederick DeMatteis Pavilion; the projectA increased the hospital's clinical space by about 40% and added 85 beds.

EXECUTIVES

Pres-Ceo, Alan Guerci
Sr V Pres-Cfo, William C Arms
Sr Vp-Coo, Martin A Bieber
Vp-Development & Public Relati, Linda Cavallo-Miller
R.N., Sr V Pres, Ann Cella Rn
Vp-Human Resources, Betty Anson
Exec V Pres, Ruth Hennessey
Sr V Pres, Jack Soterakis
PH 516 705-1925, Jenny Mitchell
Chief Anesthesiology, H Sinan Berkay
Director of Discharge Planning, Mary Anne Highland
Auditors: PRICEWATERHOUSECOOPERS LLP NE

LOCATIONS

HQ: ST. FRANCIS HOSPITAL, ROSLYN, NEW YORK
100 PORT WASHINGTON BLVD, ROSLYN, NY 115761347
Phone: 516 562-2000

PRODUCTS/OPERATIONS

Selected Services
Anesthesiology
Breast Surgery
Cardiology
Cardiothoracic Surgery
Diabetes Care Center
Emergency Medicine
Gastroenterology
General Surgery
Hematology/Oncology
Nephrology
Neurology
Orthopedic Surgery
Otolaryngology
Podiatry
Psychiatry
Pulmonary Medicine
Radiology
Rehabilitation
Urology
Vascular Services
Women's Center

COMPETITORS

Bronx-Lebanon Hospital
Brookhaven Memorial Hospital Medical Center
Calvary Hospital
Continuum Health Partners
Franklin Hospital
Huntington Hospital
Mather Memorial Hospital
MediSys Health Network
Memorial Sloan-Kettering
New York City Health and Hospitals
NewYork-Presbyterian Healthcare
Northwell Health
NuHealth

HISTORICAL FINANCIALS
Company Type: Private

Income Statement   FYE: December 31

	REVENUE ($ mil.)	NET INCOME ($ mil.)	NET PROFIT MARGIN	EMPLOYEES
12/15	614	37	6.2%	2,184
12/08	385	28	7.4%	—
12/04	366	47	12.9%	—
12/02	828	0	—	—
Annual Growth	—	152.0%	—	—

2015 Year-End Financials

Return on assets: 13.6%   Cash ($ mil.): 34
Return on equity: 6.2%
Current ratio: —

ST. FRANCIS MEDICAL CENTER

LOCATIONS

HQ: ST. FRANCIS MEDICAL CENTER
3630 E IMPERIAL HWY, LYNWOOD, CA 902622609
Phone: 310 900-8900
Web: WWW.STFRANCISMEDICALCENTER.ORG

HISTORICAL FINANCIALS
Company Type: Private

Income Statement   FYE: June 30

	REVENUE ($ mil.)	NET INCOME ($ mil.)	NET PROFIT MARGIN	EMPLOYEES
06/16	451	28	6.4%	212
06/15	500	70	14.1%	—
06/14	407	21	5.3%	—
Annual Growth	5.2%	15.7%	—	—

2016 Year-End Financials

Return on assets: 1.0%   Cash ($ mil.): 21
Return on equity: 6.4%
Current ratio: 1.20

ST. JOHN HOSPITAL AND MEDICAL CENTER

St. John Hospital & Medical Center is part of the larger Detroit area-based St. John Health regional health care system. Besides providing acute and trauma care the 770-bed teaching hospital operates specialized cancer and pediatric centers a hip and knee center an inpatient mental health unit and a Parkinson's Disease clinic. It also operates the only emergency trauma center on Detroit's East Side. The hospital was established in 1952 and has grown to include a 200-physician medical team that specializes in more than 50 medical and surgical fields. It boasts 34000 admissions; 14500 surgical visits; and more than 126500 emergency center visits each year.

Operations

Its emergency center is a Level II Trauma Center that boasts Chest Pain Center and Heart Failure

Center accreditations. St. John Hospital also operates a large inpatient pediatric unit PICU and Level III NICU or Level II Special Care Nursery. The hospital runs the Van Elslander Cancer Center.

Strategy

St. John Hospital expanded its operations by opening the Elaine E. Blatt Endoscopy Department and a new pediatric burn treatment room both in 2012. It also expanded its mammography service capabilities with the purchase of Lakeshore Mammograph giving it more than a dozen new mammography sites across southeastern Michigan. In addition St. John Hospital opened a new cardiac catheterization lab that brought new diagnostic options to patients in the Michigan Blue Water Area.

EXECUTIVES

Ceo, Mark Taylor
Obstetrician, Nathan V Wagstaff
Treasurer, David Stone
Internal Medicine Practitioner, Jason M Donaghue
Chief of Medicine, Michael C Wiemann
Senior Manager, Corey Kennard
Consultant, Laticia Clemons
Internal Medicine Practitioner, Victoria Dufour
Supervisor, Kenneth Tucker
Information Specialist, Meghan McGinn
Coordinator, Nancy Derita

LOCATIONS

HQ: ST. JOHN HOSPITAL AND MEDICAL CENTER
28000 DEQUINDRE RD, WARREN, MI 480922468
Phone: 313 343-4000

PRODUCTS/OPERATIONS

Selected Services and Operations
Alternative Health
Breast Care
Breast Feeding (Lactation) Consultation
Cracchiolo Inpatient Rehabilitation Center
Diabetes Education and Care
Diagnostic and Imaging Services
Echocardiogram
Emergency
Heart and Vascular Care
Hip and Knee Center
Minimally Invasive Surgery
Minor Emergency
Neonatal Intensive Care Unit (NICU)
Obstetrics
Oncology (cancer)
Parkinson's Movement Disorder Clinic
Pediatrics
Physical Therapy
Spine Center
TravelCare
Urgent Care
Wound Care

COMPETITORS

Beaumont Health System
Crittenton Hospital
Detroit Medical Center
Henry Ford Health System

Mount Clemens Regional Medical Center
Trinity Health (Novi)

HISTORICAL FINANCIALS
Company Type: Private

Income Statement				FYE: June 30
	REVENUE ($ mil.)	NET INCOME ($ mil.)	NET PROFIT MARGIN	EMPLOYEES
06/15	753	36	4.8%	5,000
06/09	638	1	0.3%	—
06/05	0	0		—
06/03	1,642	9	0.6%	—
Annual Growth	(6.3%)	12.0%	—	—

2015 Year-End Financials
Return on assets: 0.5%
Return on equity: 4.8%
Current ratio: 0.20

Cash ($ mil.): 1

ST. JOHN'S HOSPITAL OF THE HOSPITAL SISTERS OF THE THIRD ORDER OF ST. FRANCIS

Truck-struck Homer Simpson might use his last gasp trying to blurt out "St. John's Hospital of the Hospital Sisters of the Third Order of St. Francis-Springfield" to his ambulance driver but he might be better off using the hospital's more common name St. John's. D'oh! The 440-bed St. John's Hospital serves residents of central and southern Illinois with general and specialized health care services. The teaching hospital affiliated with Southern Illinois University's School of Medicine has centers devoted to women and children's health trauma cardiac care cancer orthopedics and neurology. It also operates area health clinics. Founded in 1875 St. John's is part of the Hospital Sisters Health System.

Operations

The facility is Hospital Sisters Health System's flagship hospital. It has grown to boast about 700 physicians podiatrists and dentists from more than 30 specialties. In addition to educating medical students through Southern Illinois University's School of Medicine St. Johns also supports those working on careers in nursing through its own nursing school St. John's College. It also offers courses in pharmacy pathology respiratory therapy and electroneurodiagnostics (brain disorder diagnostics) professions.

St. John's physicians perform more than 15000 surgical procedures each year. It also receives some 54000 emergency department visits and helps deliver about 2000 babies annually.

Financial Performance

In 2014 revenue fell 26% to $450 million; this was primarily due to an 89% decline in contributions investments and foundation assets.

Strategy

The hospital has been expanding its offerings to provide more specialized services to area residents. Recent additions include 3-D mammographies and expanded children's surgical services. St. John's is also focused on improving access to health care through technology such as telemedicine. In 2014 it partnered with Greenville Regional Hospital to provide advanced treatment to stroke patients at their home hospital through STAT Stroke TeleMedicine.

Other strategic initiatives at the hospital include increasing doctor and nurse retention rates growing nursing school enrollment rates and increasing patient satisfaction scores. Part of its efforts to reach more patients has led St. John's to open new outpatient health centers in areas near the main hospital facility. The hospital has also renovated its main buildings including the revamp of its day surgery and intermediate care departments.

EXECUTIVES

Ceo, Charles Lucore
Cfo, Larry Ragel

Coo, Dave Olejniczak
Doctor, Nestor A Ramirez Lopez
Telecommunications Staff, Bonnie Williams
Vice-President Legal, Amy Bulpitt
Emergency Management Facilitat, Brian Churchill
Pharmacist, Diane Martin
Chief Officer, Gurpreet Mander
Director, Harold Jones
Analyst, Jeff Thomas
Auditors: CROWE HORWATH LLP CHICAGO IL

LOCATIONS

HQ: ST. JOHN'S HOSPITAL OF THE HOSPITAL SISTERS OF THE THIRD ORDER OF ST. FRANCIS
800 E CARPENTER ST, SPRINGFIELD, IL 627690002
Phone: 217 544-6464
Web: WWW.ST-JOHNS.ORG

PRODUCTS/OPERATIONS

2014 Sales

	% of total
Amount generated for taking care patients excluding provision	95
Other contributions	5
Other	
Total	**100**

Selected Services
AthletiCare
Behavioral Health Services
Birth Center
Cancer Institute
Center for Living
Children's Hospital
Connect
Emergency/Trauma Care
Gastroenterology
Health Centers | Priority Care
Home Health
Hospice
Intensive Care Unit
Lab
Neurosciences Institute
Orthopedics
Pain Management Center
Prairie Heart Institute
Radiology
Regional Wound Care Center
Sleep Center
Stroke Treatment
Surgery | daVinci
TherapyCare | Rehab
Third Age Living
Women's Services

COMPETITORS

Advocate Health Care
Blessing Hospital
Community Health Systems
Decatur Memorial Hospital

Memorial Health System
Memorial Hospital (Illinois)
Southern Illinois Healthcare

HISTORICAL FINANCIALS
Company Type: Private

Income Statement				FYE: June 30
	REVENUE ($ mil.)	NET INCOME ($ mil.)	NET PROFIT MARGIN	EMPLOYEES
06/16	494	3	0.7%	3,000
06/15	501	3	0.8%	—
06/14	500	10	2.1%	—
06/08	393	(8)		—
Annual Growth	2.9%	—	—	—

2016 Year-End Financials
Return on assets: 8.1%
Return on equity: 0.7%
Current ratio: —

Cash ($ mil.): 3

ST. JOSEPH HOSPITAL OF ORANGE

If you're feeling green or blue in Orange County St. Joseph Hospital of Orange is there to help get back to feeling pink and rosy. The California hospital provides general medical and surgical services as well as specialty care such as women's health mental health services oncology cardiology and physical rehabilitation. Part of the St. Joseph Health System the hospital provides primary care and specialty outpatient services through a network of affiliated physician practices. It also operates low-income and mobile clinics. The hospital has about 468 beds and a medical staff of some 1000.

Operations

In addition to physician group affiliates St. Joseph Hospital Affiliated Physicians and St. Joseph Heritage Medical Group the hospital also partners with the Childrens Hospital of Orange County to help expand pediatric care throughout the region. The hospital has more than 20100 inpatient discharges and about 290400 outpatient visits a year.

Geographic Reach

St. Joseph Hospital serves Orange County California and the greater Los Angeles metropolitan area.

Strategy

St. Joseph Hospital has been working to expand its community outreach programs related to cancer through a number of projects including offering improved access to clinical trials; providing better overall access to cancer care; and implementing measures to garner support for the implementation of cancer electronic health records. St. Joseph Hospital is using stimulus money and about a $3 million award from the National Cancer Institute Community Cancer Centers Program to help fund its various projects.

Company Background

The company was founded in 1929 by the Sisters of St. Joseph of Orange.

EXECUTIVES

Vice President Operations, Tom Hill
Vice President, Linda Simon
Vice President Performance Improvement, Mary Ann Vincent
Ambulatory Services Director, James Pierog

LOCATIONS

HQ: ST. JOSEPH HOSPITAL OF ORANGE
1100 W STEWART DR, ORANGE, CA 928683891
Phone: 714 633-9111
Web: WWW.SJO.ORG

PRODUCTS/OPERATIONS

Selected Services

Bariatric Surgery
Behavioral Health
Cancer
Nasal & Sinus Center
Heart & Vascular Center
Kidney Dialysis Center
Maternity
Orthopedic Services
Sleep Disorders Center

COMPETITORS

Anaheim Regional Medical Center
Children's Hospital of Orange County
Citrus Valley Health
Providence St. Joseph Health
Southwest Healthcare
Sutter Health
Tenet Healthcare

Partners
Hoag Memorial Hospital
Memorial Health Services
Pasadena Hospital Association
Torrance Memorial Medical Center
Trinity Health (Novi)
Western Medical Center - Santa Ana

HISTORICAL FINANCIALS

Company Type: Private

Income Statement — FYE: June 30

	REVENUE ($ mil.)	NET INCOME ($ mil.)	NET PROFIT MARGIN	EMPLOYEES
06/17	655	29	4.5%	3,300
06/16	599	11	2.0%	—
06/15	567	2	0.5%	—
06/14	566	(5)	—	—
Annual Growth	4.9%	—	—	—

2017 Year-End Financials

Return on assets: 5.5%
Return on equity: 4.5%
Current ratio: 0.80
Cash ($ mil.): 14

ST. JOSEPH HOSPITAL, INC.

EXECUTIVES

Ceo, Bain J Farris
Prin, Barb Jahn
Internal Medicine Practitioner, Thomas Perille
Manager of Accounting, Edna Palmer
Executive Assistant, Judy Holbrook
Neurologist, Patricia G Soffer
Registration Manager, Tricia Fox
or Materials Manager, Clarke McDonald
Director, Kelli Lewis

LOCATIONS

HQ: ST. JOSEPH HOSPITAL, INC.
1375 E 19TH AVE, DENVER, CO 802181114
Phone: 303 837-7111
Web: WWW.SCLHEALTH.ORG/LOCATIONS/SAINT-JOSEPH-HOSPITAL/

HISTORICAL FINANCIALS

Company Type: Private

Income Statement — FYE: December 31

	REVENUE ($ mil.)	NET INCOME ($ mil.)	NET PROFIT MARGIN	EMPLOYEES
12/16	530	(49)	—	2,400
12/15	498	37	7.5%	—
Annual Growth	6.5%	—	—	—

2016 Year-End Financials

Return on assets: 2.5%
Return on equity: (-9.4%)
Current ratio: 0.90
Cash ($ mil.): —

ST. JOSEPH MERCY OAKLAND FOUNDATION

EXECUTIVES

Ceo, Jack Weiner
Contrl, Avinash Sidar
Neurology, Richard D Fessler
Information Technology Manager, Jeffrey Gillespie
Coordinator, Jeff Johnson
Operations Supervisor, Elizabeth Shaker
Manager, Amy Heeg
Director, Tanya Gurne
Trustee, Luann Hannasch
Svp Operations, Frank Sawyer
Manager of Annual, Donna Raphael

LOCATIONS

HQ: ST. JOSEPH MERCY OAKLAND FOUNDATION
44405 WOODWARD AVE, PONTIAC, MI 483415023
Phone: 248 858-3000
Web: WWW.STJOESOAKLAND.ORG

HISTORICAL FINANCIALS

Company Type: Private

Income Statement — FYE: June 30

	REVENUE ($ mil.)	NET INCOME ($ mil.)	NET PROFIT MARGIN	EMPLOYEES
06/15	379	20	5.3%	4,000
06/09	356	(11)	—	—
Annual Growth	1.1%	—	—	—

2015 Year-End Financials

Return on assets: 4.5%
Return on equity: 5.3%
Current ratio: 0.90
Cash ($ mil.): 2

ST. JOSEPH'S HOSPITAL AND MEDICAL CENTER

EXECUTIVES

Ceo-Pres, William A McDonald
Cfo, Jack Robinson
Chm, Rosemary Smith
E-Business Point of Contact, Cindy Johnson
Chief of Neonatology, Adel M Zauk
Administrative Assistant To Vp, Christine Strangeway
Director of Environmental Svs, John Di' Giovani
Chief of Pulmonary Medicine, M Aness Khan
Doctor, Aldo Khoury
Director of Quality Improvemen, Theresa Szucs
Vice President Human Resources, John P Bruno

LOCATIONS

HQ: ST. JOSEPH'S HOSPITAL AND MEDICAL CENTER
703 MAIN ST, PATERSON, NJ 075032691
Phone: 973 754-2000
Web: WWW.STJOSEPHSHEALTH.ORG

HISTORICAL FINANCIALS

Company Type: Private

Income Statement

FYE: December 31

	REVENUE ($ mil.)	NET INCOME ($ mil.)	NET PROFIT MARGIN	EMPLOYEES
12/16	763	(12)	—	4,000
12/15	752	60	8.0%	—
12/08	472	(41)	—	—
12/06	437	17	3.9%	—
Annual Growth	5.7%	—	—	—

2016 Year-End Financials

Return on assets: 5.7%   Cash ($ mil.): 132
Return on equity: (-1.6%)
Current ratio: 1.80

ST. JOSEPH'S HOSPITAL HEALTH CENTER

With about 430 inpatient beds St. Joseph's Hospital Health Center serves the residents of 16 central New York counties. The not-for-profit hospital system provides general emergency and surgical care as well as specialty services in areas such as obstetrics cardiology dialysis and wound care. In addition to its inpatient facilities the organization operates a home health agency a nursing school medical and dental residency programs and several outpatient care centers. Its Franciscan Companies affiliate offers some ancillary services including the provision of medical supplies home health equipment and senior services. St. Joseph's Hospital Health Center was founded in 1869.

Operations

With a total of some 800 physicians St. Joseph's Hospital Health Center admits some 28000 inpatients each year. It also handles some 957000 emergency room visits and about 640000 outpatient visits annually. The hospital provides about $22 million in charity and community care each year as well.

Geographic Reach

St. Joseph's Hospital Health Center's service territory includes the New York counties of Broome Cayuga Chenango Cortland Delaware Herkimer Jefferson Lewis Madison Oneida Onondaga Oswego Otsego St. Lawrence Tioga and Tompkins.

Financial Performance

In 2013 revenue rose 7% to $626 million as patient and other revenue grew. Net income also improved by 33% due to better investment returns.

Strategy

St. Joseph's Hospital Health Center is conducting a massive $220 million expansion program at its main campus. The first phase opened in 2011 and includes a larger emergency room facility with chest pain and psychiatric units. The hospital broke ground on the second phase of the project in 2012. The program will add a new patient tower surgery facilities a sterilization center and an intensive care unit. In 2013 it opened a sleep center and a new surgical suite at the hospital. The following year St. Joseph's expanded its primary care center in west Syracuse and launched it electronic health record system.

Mergers and Acquisitions

In 2013 the center purchased Upstate Surgical Group creating a general surgery group in St. Joseph's ambulatory surgery group.

In late 2010 St. Joseph's Hospital Health Center boosted its physician network significantly by acquiring North Medical a physician practice organization that operates five practices: Family Physicians Urgent Care Orthopedics & Rehabilitation The Women's Place and Living Proof Longevity Centre. Its practices are home to about 80 physicians and mid-level practitioners.

EXECUTIVES

Prin, Kathryn Howe Ruscitto
Esq., Chb, George Deptula
SEC, Sister Mary Obrist
Prin, Lucinda Drescher
Prin, Balasubramaniam Sivakumar
Vice President, Sallie Büttner
Sr Vice President, Mary W Brown
Vice President, Annemarie Czyz
Vice President, Charles J Fennell
Accounting Staff, Doreen Moltrup
Coordinator, Darlene Sorendo

LOCATIONS

HQ: ST. JOSEPH'S HOSPITAL HEALTH CENTER
   301 PROSPECT AVE, SYRACUSE, NY 132031899
Phone: 315 448-5113
Web: WWW.SJHSYR.ORG

PRODUCTS/OPERATIONS

Selected Services

Centers of Excellence
   Cardiac Services
   The Center for Orthopedic and Spine Care
   Vascular Services
   Women and Children's Services
   Wound Care
   Home Care
   Dialysis
   Bariatric (Weight Loss) Services
Other Services and Centers
   Aesthetic Services
   Behavioral Health
   da Vinci Robotic Surgery
   Emergency Services
   Imaging
   Infusion (CPEPCNY)
   Interventional Radiology
   Medical Equipment
   Obstetric Services
   Palliative Care
   Pharmacy
   Physical Medicine & Rehabilitation
   Pulmonary Services
   Sleep Laboratory
   Social Adult Day Care
   Surgical Services
   Urology Services
Outpatient Services
   Dental Services
   Family Medicine Center
   Obstetrics and Gynecology
   Pediatric Office
   Physician Health
   Primary Care
   Westside Family Health Center

COMPETITORS

Catholic Health System
Ellis Hospital
Kaleida Health
Lifetime Health
Oneida Healthcare Center
SUNY Upstate Medical University
United Health Services Hospitals
Upstate University Hospital at Community General

HISTORICAL FINANCIALS

Company Type: Private

Income Statement

FYE: December 31

	REVENUE ($ mil.)	NET INCOME ($ mil.)	NET PROFIT MARGIN	EMPLOYEES
12/15	542	(2)	—	3,300
12/14	523	0	0.1%	—
12/09	436	5	1.2%	—
12/08	399	6	1.6%	—
Annual Growth	4.5%	—	—	—

2015 Year-End Financials

Return on assets: 7.4%   Cash ($ mil.): 36
Return on equity: (-0.5%)
Current ratio: 1.10

ST. JOSEPHS MEDICAL CENTER INC

EXECUTIVES

Pres, Donald J Wiley
V Pres Bus Dev't & Strategy*, Kathy Tohrman
V Pres Hr, Nancy Vargas
V Pres Medical Affirs, Dr Susan McDonald
Vice President of Nursing Svs, Rae Charos
V Pres Support Srvces, Terry Spring
Customer Source Liaison, Esther Basilio
Director Physician Recruitment, Doug O' Ryan
Coordinator of Gift Shop, Linda Marino
Chief of Pediatric, Steven Billigmeier
Chief Staff, Prafad Dighe

LOCATIONS

HQ: ST. JOSEPHS MEDICAL CENTER INC
   1800 N CALIFORNIA ST, STOCKTON, CA 952046019
Phone: 209 943-2000

HISTORICAL FINANCIALS

Company Type: Private

Income Statement

FYE: June 30

	REVENUE ($ mil.)	NET INCOME ($ mil.)	NET PROFIT MARGIN	EMPLOYEES
06/16	478	23	5.0%	150
06/15*	482	48	10.1%	—
12/05	0	0	—	—
Annual Growth	—	—	—	—

*Fiscal year change

2016 Year-End Financials

Return on assets: 2.8%   Cash ($ mil.): 16
Return on equity: 5.0%
Current ratio: 1.00

ST. JUDE HOSPITAL

St. Jude Medical Center gets sickly Southern Californians on their feet again. The faith-based not-for-profit acute care facility with some 385 beds serves the residents of Orange County. The medical center provides an onsite cancer center (the Virginia K. Crosson Cancer Center) and a heart institute that offers cardiac surgeries and rehabilitation programs. It also provides inpatient and outpatient physical rehabilitation services and a variety of community outreach programs. Established by the Sisters of St. Joseph of Orange religious order in the 1950s St. Jude Medical Center is part of the St. Joseph Health System.

Operations
Beyond the medical center's campus St. Jude operates its Heritage Medical Group with outpatient locations throughout its region. The medical group includes specialists in plastic surgery rheumatology and gastroenterology. Altogether St. Jude employs some 700 physicians. It handles more than 17000 inpatient admissions each year as well as 13000 surgeries 2000 births and 54000 emergency room visits.

The organization spends some $47 million in community benefits including outreach and charity care. Its mobile and fixed-site community clinics offer medical dental and preventative care services for low-income residents.

Geographic Reach
St. Jude serves residents in communities in California's Orange County including Brea Buena Park Fullerton La Habra Placentia and Yorba Linda.

Strategy
St. Jude is expanding its facilities through the construction of a new $312 million patient tower schedule to open in late 2014. The Northwest Tower will feature private patient rooms as well as enhanced surgical and data management capabilities. Other improvement measures include technology upgrades such as a new neurovascular surgical system added in 2012.

In October 2011 St. Jude Medical Center closed its 12-bed pediatric unit and redirected patients younger than 16 to nearby Children's Hospital of Orange County. St. Jude's NICU (neonatal intensive care unit) remains open and the hospital continues to provide emergency and outpatient services to children.

EXECUTIVES

Medical Records Director, Pamela Frey
Vice President Healthy Communities, Barry Ross
Occupational Medicine, Robert Maurer
Vice President Human Resources, Lisa Schoening

LOCATIONS

HQ: ST. JUDE HOSPITAL
101 E VALENCIA MESA DR, FULLERTON, CA 928353875
Phone: 714 871-3280
Web: WWW.STJOE.ORG

COMPETITORS

Anaheim Regional Medical Center	Memorial Health Services
Children's Hospital of Orange County	Western Medical Center - Santa Ana
Hoag Memorial Hospital	

HISTORICAL FINANCIALS

Company Type: Private

Income Statement   FYE: June 30

	REVENUE ($ mil.)	NET INCOME ($ mil.)	NET PROFIT MARGIN	EMPLOYEES
06/17	544	45	8.3%	2,600
06/16	490	4	0.9%	—
06/15	458	8	2.0%	—
06/14	477	51	10.8%	—
Annual Growth	4.4%	(4.4%)	—	—

ST. LUKE'S EPISCOPAL-PRESBYTERIAN HOSPITALS

St. Luke's Episcopal-Presbyterian Hospital doing business as St. Luke's Hospital provides health care services to St. Louis residents and surrounding areas of eastern Missouri. The medical center houses more than 490 beds and offers general medical and surgical care as well as specialty services in areas such as heart disease cancer neuroscience orthopedics pediatrics and women's health. St. Luke's also operates half a dozen urgent care clinics in St. Louis and St. Charles counties providing treatment for minor emergencies such as cuts and animal bites as well as a skilled-nursing facility rehabilitation hospital and several diagnostic imaging centers. The not-for-profit hospital was founded in 1866.

Operations
In 2014 St. Luke's Hospital had more than 18000 inpatients and 315000 outpatients performed some 17500 surgeries facilitated 1800 births and had more than 30000 emergency department visits.

Financial Performance
In fiscal 2014 (ended June) operating revenue in excess of expense totaled $20.4 million. Total operating revenue grew 4% to $478 million that year.

Strategy
St. Luke's Hospital continues to grow via expansion projects. In 2013 the medical center renovated its neonatal special care nursery adding six private rooms and areas for twins and other multiples to stay together. The following year it opened a new urgent care center and a new facility with the state's only Open Upright MRI scanner. Other urgent care centers and physicians' offices are in the works. In 2015 the hospital broke ground on a $40 million outpatient building on its campus; it is expected to open in late 2016.

The company also grows by adding physicians to its network. During 2014 it added 34 new physicians to its staff with specializations in the areas of primary care neurology oncology cardiovascular orthopedics and others. In all the medical staff has more than 60 specialties.

EXECUTIVES

Pres-Ceo, Christine Candio
V Pres-Fin, Brian Spillers
Infection Control Coordi, Joan Jenne
Chief of Patho, Suzanne Dintzis
Chief of Radio, Gary H Omell
Oncology, Amit Bhatt
Pediatrician, Daniel Wachsstock
Information Technology Influen, Kelle Wymore
Financial Analyst, Stephanie Pieper
Manager, Vivian Smith
Information Technology Influen, Antoinette Hoeing
Auditors: KPMG LLP OKLAHOMA CITY OK

LOCATIONS

HQ: ST. LUKE'S EPISCOPAL-PRESBYTERIAN HOSPITALS
232 S WOODS MILL RD, CHESTERFIELD, MO 630173406
Phone: 314 434-1500
Web: WWW.STLUKES-STL.COM

PRODUCTS/OPERATIONS

Selected Services
Brain and spine
Cardiac
Orthopedic
Pulmonary
Sleep medicine
Women's services

COMPETITORS

Barnes-Jewish Hospital	St. Anthony's Medical
CHRISTUS Health	Center
Mercy Health	Tenet Healthcare
SSM Health Care	

HISTORICAL FINANCIALS

Company Type: Private

Income Statement   FYE: June 30

	REVENUE ($ mil.)	NET INCOME ($ mil.)	NET PROFIT MARGIN	EMPLOYEES
06/15	470	49	10.6%	3,000
06/04	274	11	4.1%	—
06/03	263	9	3.5%	—
06/02	1,170	0	—	—
Annual Growth	—	148.2%	—	—

2015 Year-End Financials

Return on assets: 9.3%   Cash ($ mil.): 68
Return on equity: 10.6%
Current ratio: 0.90

ST. LUKE'S HEALTH NETWORK, INC.

EXECUTIVES

Vice President Administration, Alice Wilson
Interim President Visiting Nurse Association Of St Lukes, Lisa Giovanni
Auditors: WITHUMSMITHBROWN PC MORRISTOW

LOCATIONS

HQ: ST. LUKE'S HEALTH NETWORK, INC.
801 OSTRUM ST, BETHLEHEM, PA 180151000
Phone: 610 954-4000
Web: WWW.STLUKESPAWILDMED.COM

PRODUCTS/OPERATIONS

Selected Services
Cancer Center
Children's health
Diagnostic and Treatment Centers
Emergency
Heart Center
Neuroscience
Orthopaedics
Radiology/Imaging
Regional Breast Center (Center Valley)
Urgent Care Centers
Women's Imaging & Health Centers

COMPETITORS

Ascension Health	Sacred Heart Hospital
Evangelical Community Hospital	of Allentown
LVHN	Wyoming Valley Health Care System
Moses Taylor Hospital	
Reading Hospital and Medical Center	

Company Type: Private

Income Statement — FYE: June 30

	REVENUE ($ mil.)	NET INCOME ($ mil.)	NET PROFIT MARGIN	EMPLOYEES
06/18	1,844	159	8.6%	2,958
06/17	1,521	121	8.0%	—
06/15	0	0	—	—
06/14	67	0	—	—
Annual Growth	128.7%	—	—	—

2018 Year-End Financials

Return on assets: 6.3%
Return on equity: 8.6%
Current ratio: 0.80

Cash ($ mil.): 106

ST. LUKE'S HEALTH SYSTEM, LTD.

To Catholics St. Luke is also known as the "beloved physician" and St. Luke's Health System strives to live up to its namesake. The regional not-for-profit health system provides a range of health services to residents of Idaho eastern Oregon and northern Nevada. St. Luke's is home to six general acute care hospitals with a total of about 860 beds. Its flagship facility is the 400-bed St. Luke's Boise Medical Center which also includes a full-service children's hospital. St. Luke's also runs a network of cancer care sites under the name Mountain States Tumor Institute as well as a number of urgent care family practice and specialty health centers.

Operations

St. Luke's hospitals handle about 50000 inpatient visits 35000 surgeries and 8000 births each year. The network also sees about 700000 outpatients annually through its urgent care family health and specialty care centers. The company's diagnostic care operations include about five imaging centers and eight breast cancer detection clinics. Overall St. Luke's employs about 1000 physicians.

The Boise campus is home to its tertiary care services - cancer heart and the Children's Hospital - meaning the most acute cases from the region are brought there for the most specialized care. St. Luke's Children's Hospital sees 85000 patient visits a year has Idaho's first and only Pediatric Intensive Care Unit and has the state's largest and most experienced Level III Newborn Intensive Care Unit. Its Boise campus is also the base of St. Luke's Mountain States Tumor Institute (MSTI which cares for about 820 cancer patients a day) and St. Luke's Heart services one of the top 50 cardiovascular programs in the US.

Geographic Reach

St. Luke's has Idaho operations in Boise Caldwell Eagle Fruitland Jerome Ketchum McCall Meridian Mountain Home Nampa and Twin Falls.

Strategy

The growing need for care from each of these leading service lines is a significant part of the Integrated Care Model that has guided the company's Master Plan. St. Luke's has been investing a significant amount of money to upgrade and expand its facilities in recent years.

In 2014 the federal courts ordered St. Luke's to divest Saltzer Medical Group (Idaho's state's largest independent multi-specialty physician practice) after concluding that St. Luke's 2012 acquisition of Saltzer violated Section 7 of the Clayton Act and the Idaho Competition Act.

Company Background

In 2011 St. Luke's completed a $130 million project to rebuild the St. Luke's Magic Valley Medical Center. The new hospital building had about 190 beds and expanded emergency cancer and cardiac centers. The health system was also working to expand its Boise Medical Center's heart and vascular and pediatric departments as well as its system-wide MSTI facilities.

The health system has also expanded its outpatient network to include new family practice emergency care and urgent care clinics in recent years. The network opened a St. Luke's Nampa emergency care clinic and medical complex in 2012. In addition to updating its facilities the St. Luke's Health System was working to upgrade its information technology assets.

St. Luke's added its fifth and sixth acute care hospitals in 2010 and 2011 when the 15-bed St. Luke's McCall (formerly McCall Memorial Hospital) and 25-bed St. Luke's Jerome (formerly St. Benedicts Medical Center) hospitals joined the health network through affiliation and merger agreements.

The health system was formed in 2006 when the three hospitals of the old St. Luke's Regional Medical Center network (Boise Meridian and Wood River) merged with Magic Valley Regional Medical Center a former county facility in Twin Falls Idaho.

EXECUTIVES

President Ceo And Director, David C. Pate
Nursing Director, Katie Schimmelpfennig
Medical Director, Rourke Yeakley
Chairman, Jon Miller
Auditors: DELOITTE & TOUCHE LLP BOISE

LOCATIONS

HQ: ST. LUKE'S HEALTH SYSTEM, LTD.
190 E BANNOCK ST, BOISE, ID 837126241
Phone: 208 381-2222
Web: WWW.SLHS.ORG

PRODUCTS/OPERATIONS

Selected Idaho Facilities

St. Luke's Boise Medical Center (Boise)
  St. Luke's Children's Hospital
St. Luke's Clinics (multiple locations)
St. Luke's Eagle Urgent Care (Eagle)
St. Luke's Jerome Medical Center (Jerome)
St. Luke's Magic Valley Medical Center (Twin Falls)
St. Luke's McCall Memorial Hospital (McCall)
St. Luke's Meridian Medical Center (Meridian)
St. Luke's Mountain States Tumor Institute (multiple locations)
St. Luke's Wood River Medical Center (Hailey/Ketchum)

COMPETITORS

Ascension Health
Benedictine Health System
HCA
Intermountain Health Care
Saint Alphonsus Regional Medical Center
Trinity Health (Novi)

HISTORICAL FINANCIALS

Company Type: Private

Income Statement — FYE: September 30

	REVENUE ($ mil.)	NET INCOME ($ mil.)	NET PROFIT MARGIN	EMPLOYEES
09/17	2,327	10	0.4%	7,891
09/16	1,937	48	2.5%	—
09/09	49	0	—	—
Annual Growth	62.0%	—	—	—

Return on assets: 6.5%
Return on equity: 0.4%
Current ratio: 1.00

Cash ($ mil.): 155

ST. LUKE'S HOSPITAL OF DULUTH

St. Luke's cares for colds cancers and other conditions in the chilly northern US. St. Luke's Hospital provides a variety of health care services to patients in northeastern Minnesota northwestern Wisconsin and parts of Michigan. The medical center has some 270 beds and a staff of about 370 physicians. Services include cardiology emergency medicine pediatrics oncology rehabilitation and vascular surgery. In addition to acute care services the organization offers primary and specialty health care services through a network of outpatient clinics.

Operations

The medical system consists of two hospitals (St. Luke's Hospital and Lake View Hospital) 14 primary care clinics 24 specialty clinics and two pharmacies.

St. Luke's handles about 11000 inpatient visits per year as well as 900 births 10300 surgeries and 73600 emergency room or urgent care visits. Its emergency room serves as a regional trauma center. St. Luke's also sees about 485000 patients annually at its primary and specialty care clinics. Its outpatient service divisions include Q Care (express medical clinic) St. Luke's Orthopedics and St. Luke's Infusion Therapy Clinic. The hospital conducts medical studies through a partnership with the Whiteside Institute for Clinical Research; it also has collaborative care relationships with the Pavilion Surgery Center and the Lake View Memorial Hospital.

Geographic Reach

St. Luke's serves a 17-county region in three states — encompassing northeastern Minnesota northwestern Wisconsin and the western Upper Peninsula of Michigan — through its acute care hospital in Duluth Minnesota and about 40 outpatient clinics providing primary and specialty care services.

Financial Performance

St. Luke's reported $823.5 million in patient services revenue in 2013. After contractual deductions and other obligations total revenues were reported at about $355 million.

Strategy

In 2013 St. Luke's Laurentian Medical Clinic completed a $2 million dollar expansion increasing its size by 60% allowing it to become an ambulatory care center. The clinic offers primary care visiting specialists urgent care and imaging services including low dose CT ultrasound MRI scans and mobile echocardiography.

To expand its services for area residents in 2012 St. Luke's completed construction of a new medical office building which is located adjacent to the main hospital facilities and will include centers for sports medicine pediatrics neurosurgery and plastic surgery. Also that year St. Luke's opened its da Vinci Si surgical system suite which allows surgeons to conduct minimally invasive surgical procedures using the robotic system.

St. Luke's launched its iPad Project in the Birthing Center allowing new mothers and families can check out an iPad for the duration of their stay. The $100000 project was funded by St.

Luke's Foundation's annual Circle of Light event and individual donors.

In 2012 the health system added two urgent care clinics: The Northland Obstetrics & Gynecology Lake View Pharmacy opened as part of the Lake View campus in Two Harbors; St. Luke's Campus Building A opened expanding patient access to specialty care.

Company Background

In 2011 St. Luke's formed a new maternal child health department to improve its birthing services; the new unit provides labor and delivery nursery and pediatric services.

St. Luke's Hospital was founded in 1881. What was established as a typhoid response clinic became the city of Duluth's first hospital.

EXECUTIVES

Pres-Ceo, John Strange
Cfo, James Wuellner
Internal Medicine Practitioner, Benjamin M Trok
Family Practitioner, Daniel Campbell
Neurology Specialist, James Macnutt
Internal Medicine Practitioner, Luke Midlo
Surgeon, Michael Stellmaker
Health Professional, Winna Taylor
Cardiovascular Specialist, Disha Mookherjee
Emergency Medicine Specialist, Brandon Hankey
Emergency Medicine Specialist, Daniel Freeman

LOCATIONS

HQ: ST. LUKE'S HOSPITAL OF DULUTH
915 E 1ST ST, DULUTH, MN 558052193
Phone: 218 726-5555
Web: WWW.SLHDULUTH.COM

Selected Services Centers and Affiliates
Birthing Center
Breast Center
Cardiac Care
Cancer Care
Diagnostic Imaging
Emergency Care
Family Medicine
Laboratory Services
Lake View Pharmacy
Lake View Memorial Hospital
Northland Pharmacy
Pavilion Outpatient Surgery Center
Physical Rehabilitation Services
Sleep Center
St. Luke's Center for Diagnostic Imaging
St. Luke's Foundation
Surgery
Urgent Care
Whiteside Institute for Clinical Research

COMPETITORS

Allina Hospitals	North Memorial Health
CentraCare Health	Care
First Care	Sanford Bemidji
Gillette Children's	Spectrum Health
Howard Young Health	
Care	

HISTORICAL FINANCIALS

Company Type: Private

Income Statement				FYE: December 31
	REVENUE ($ mil.)	NET INCOME ($ mil.)	NET PROFIT MARGIN	EMPLOYEES
12/17	471	22	4.7%	2,200
12/16	434	9	2.1%	—
12/13	377	2	0.8%	—
12/09	307	8	2.6%	—
Annual Growth	5.5%	13.5%	—	—

2017 Year-End Financials
Return on assets: 4.5%   Cash ($ mil.): 83
Return on equity: 4.7%
Current ratio: 2.60

ST. MARY MEDICAL CENTER

EXECUTIVES

Chb, Ron Gigliotti
President, Greg Wozniak
Cfd, Sharon Prosera
Clinical Coordinator, Jeanette M Bernacki
Coordinator, Christopher Martinez
Outpatient Pharmacy Manager, Jack O' Brien
Cardiology, George Heyrich
Coordinator, Nicole Lattanzio
Personnel Manager, Laura James
Coordinator, Sheilagh Volz
Human Resources Manager, Amy Slavick

LOCATIONS

HQ: ST. MARY MEDICAL CENTER
1201 LANGHORNE NEWTOWN RD, LANGHORNE, PA 190471295
Phone: 215 710-2000
Web: WWW.STMARYHEALTHCARE.ORG

HISTORICAL FINANCIALS

Company Type: Private

Income Statement				FYE: June 30
	REVENUE ($ mil.)	NET INCOME ($ mil.)	NET PROFIT MARGIN	EMPLOYEES
06/16	419	26	6.3%	2,400
06/15	443	64	14.5%	—
Annual Growth	(5.5%)	(59.1%)	—	—

2016 Year-End Financials
Return on assets: 4.4%   Cash ($ mil.): 219
Return on equity: 6.3%
Current ratio: 10.60

ST. MARY MEDICAL CENTER

EXECUTIVES

Ceo-Pres, Alan H Garrett
Chief Financial Officer, Marilyn Drone
Cfo, Tracey Fernandez
Coo, Kelly Linden
Vice President, Judy Wagner
Vice President, Paul Kaminski
Vice President, Dennis Haghighat
Board of Trustee, Diana Carloni - O'Malley
Infection Control, Susan Biewend
Cardiovascular Services*, Donna Nash
Anesthesiologist*, Jasvinder Singh

LOCATIONS

HQ: ST. MARY MEDICAL CENTER
18300 US HIGHWAY 18, APPLE VALLEY, CA 923072206
Phone: 760 242-2311
Web: WWW.STMARYAPPLEVALLEY.COM

HISTORICAL FINANCIALS

Company Type: Private

Income Statement				FYE: June 30
	REVENUE ($ mil.)	NET INCOME ($ mil.)	NET PROFIT MARGIN	EMPLOYEES
06/16	333	47	14.1%	1,350
06/15	325	38	11.7%	—
06/14	283	11	4.1%	—
06/13	288	19	6.8%	—
Annual Growth	5.0%	33.7%	—	—

2016 Year-End Financials
Return on assets: 0.4%   Cash ($ mil.): 22
Return on equity: 14.1%
Current ratio: 1.80

ST. MARY'S HEALTH, INC.

St. Mary's Medical Center of Evansville is a 433-bed hospital serving Indiana's River City. It is the primary facility in regional St. Mary's Health System which is in turn part of Ascension Health. The Evansville hospital provides emergency trauma diagnostic surgical and rehabilitative services as well as specialized cancer cardiac orthopedic and neurological services. With a total of some 750 physicians St. Mary's Health System also includes St. Mary's Hospital for Women & Children (100 beds adjacent to the main hospital) and St. Mary's Warrick (a 25-bed hospital in Boonville Indiana) as well as specialty outpatient surgical cancer and home health units in surrounding areas of southern Indiana.

Operations

St. Mary's Medical Center of Evansville admits some 17000 inpatients annually. It also handles around 64000 emergency room visits and performs approximately 4700 inpatient and 18000 outpatient surgeries each year.

Company Background

St. Mary's Medical Center of Evansville was originally a Marine Hospital built by the US government. When the government shuttered its doors city business leaders bought the building in 1872 and partnered with the Daughters of Charity to operate a community hospital.

EXECUTIVES

Managing Director, Roger Johnson
Board Member, Anthony Stephens
Auditors: DELOITTE TAX LLP INDIANAPOLIS

LOCATIONS

HQ: ST. MARY'S HEALTH, INC.
3700 WASHINGTON AVE, EVANSVILLE, IN 477140541
Phone: 812 485-4000
Web: WWW.STVINCENTEVANSVILLE.ORG

PRODUCTS/OPERATIONS

Selected Services
Breast Center
Cancer Care Services
Children's Health Care Services and Programs
Community Outreach Services
Convenient Care Centers
Diabetic Foot Clinic
Diabetes Services
Emergency Services Department
Endoscopy Suite
Foundation

Heart Services
Home Health Services
Hospitalists
Imaging/Radiology
Infusion Center
Laboratory Services
LifeFlight
Medical Equipment
Mental Health Services
Neurosciences & Stroke Care
Occupational Medicine Services
Orthopedic Healthcare
Palliative Care
Pastoral Care
Quality and Patient Safety
Rehabilitation Services
Respiratory Care
Senior Services
Sleep Disorders Center
Surgical Services
Trauma Services
Volunteers & Auxiliary
Weight Management Center
Women's Services and Programs
Women's Wellness Center

COMPETITORS

Ball Memorial Hospital
Community Health
 Network
Daviess Community
 Hospital
Deaconess Health
 System
Good Samaritan
 Hospital (IN)

Henry County Memorial
 Hospital
Kosciusko Community
 Hospital
Memorial Hospital
 (Logansport)

HISTORICAL FINANCIALS

Company Type: Private

Income Statement — FYE: June 30

	REVENUE ($ mil.)	NET INCOME ($ mil.)	NET PROFIT MARGIN	EMPLOYEES
06/16	495	66	13.3%	3,500
06/15	574	52	9.2%	—
06/13	468	48	10.4%	—
06/11	0	0	—	—
Annual Growth	—	—	—	—

2016 Year-End Financials

Return on assets: 2.5%   Cash ($ mil.): 11
Return on equity: 13.3%
Current ratio: 0.50

ST. MARY'S HEALTH, INC.

LOCATIONS

HQ: ST. MARY'S HEALTH, INC.
 3700 WASHINGTON AVE, EVANSVILLE, IN 477140541
Phone: 812 485-7623

HISTORICAL FINANCIALS

Company Type: Private

Income Statement — FYE: June 30

	REVENUE ($ mil.)	NET INCOME ($ mil.)	NET PROFIT MARGIN	EMPLOYEES
06/15	487	71	14.7%	5
06/11	20	4	22.9%	—
06/10	19	2	15.0%	—
Annual Growth	89.4%	88.8%	—	—

2015 Year-End Financials

Return on assets: 2.6%   Cash ($ mil.): 12
Return on equity: 14.7%
Current ratio: 0.40

ST. MARY'S HOSPITAL & MEDICAL CENTER, INC.

EXECUTIVES

Ceo, Brian Davidson
Exec Vice President, Reza Kaleel
Vice President, Sister Barbara Aldrich
Vice President, Dan Prinster
Cfo, Terri Chinn
Controller, Thad Ritter
Director, Roy Cromer
Oncologist, Vernon J King
Cardiac Physician, Kelly Arnold
Chief of Radiology, Michael E Holt
Officer, Ryan Stringfellow

LOCATIONS

HQ: ST. MARY'S HOSPITAL & MEDICAL CENTER, INC.
 2635 N 7TH ST, GRAND JUNCTION, CO 815018209
Phone: 970 298-2013
Web: WWW.SSMHEALTH.COM/LOCATIONS/ST-MARYS-
 HOSPITAL-MADISON

HISTORICAL FINANCIALS

Company Type: Private

Income Statement — FYE: December 31

	REVENUE ($ mil.)	NET INCOME ($ mil.)	NET PROFIT MARGIN	EMPLOYEES
12/16	450	37	8.2%	2,000
12/15	436	54	12.4%	—
12/14	410	45	11.1%	—
12/09	360	50	13.9%	—
Annual Growth	3.3%	(4.2%)	—	—

2016 Year-End Financials

Return on assets: 2.2%   Cash ($ mil.): 2
Return on equity: 8.2%
Current ratio: 1.70

ST. MARY'S MEDICAL CENTER

EXECUTIVES

Chb, SIS Kathleen Hofer
President, Kathleen Hofer
President, James Garvey
Vice President, Timothy Backous
Vice President, Hugh P Renier
Occupational Therapy Director, Heidi McLeod
Human Resources, Dave Warren
Administrator, Michael Laughlin
Emergency Medicine Specialist, Amanda J Carlson
Anesthesiologist, James P Gregory
Psychologist, Regina E Dixon

LOCATIONS

HQ: ST. MARY'S MEDICAL CENTER
 407 E 3RD ST, DULUTH, MN 558051984
Phone: 218 786-4000
Web: WWW.SCLHEALTH.ORG/LOCATIONS/ST-MARYS-
 MEDICAL-CENTER/

HISTORICAL FINANCIALS

Company Type: Private

Income Statement — FYE: June 30

	REVENUE ($ mil.)	NET INCOME ($ mil.)	NET PROFIT MARGIN	EMPLOYEES
06/16	402	12	3.1%	4,209
06/15	396	40	10.3%	—
06/14	439	66	15.1%	—
06/13	419	65	15.6%	—
Annual Growth	(1.4%)	(42.3%)	—	—

2016 Year-End Financials

Return on assets: 2.3%   Cash ($ mil.): 144
Return on equity: 3.1%
Current ratio: 5.90

ST. MARY'S MEDICAL CENTER

EXECUTIVES

Vice President Of Human Resources, Susan
 Robinson
Infection Control Director, JACKIE BATHLOW
Admissions Director, RUTH HARSHBARGER

LOCATIONS

HQ: ST. MARY'S MEDICAL CENTER
 2900 1ST AVE, HUNTINGTON, WV 257021241
Phone: 304 526-1234
Web: WWW.ST-MARYS.ORG

COMPETITORS

Adena Health System
 CAMC Health
 Clinch Valley Medical
 Center
 Fairfield Medical
 Center

Highlands Health
Pikeville Medical
 Center

HISTORICAL FINANCIALS

Company Type: Private

Income Statement — FYE: September 30

	REVENUE ($ mil.)	NET INCOME ($ mil.)	NET PROFIT MARGIN	EMPLOYEES
09/17	382	26	7.1%	2,000
09/16	372	5	1.4%	—
09/15	311	(42)	—	—
09/14	401	10	2.7%	—
Annual Growth	(1.6%)	35.2%	—	—

2017 Year-End Financials

Return on assets: 9.4%   Cash ($ mil.): 13
Return on equity: 7.1%
Current ratio: 1.90

ST. PETER'S HEALTH CARE SERVICES

Auditors: DELOITTE & TOUCHE LLP ROCHEST

LOCATIONS

HQ: ST. PETER'S HEALTH CARE SERVICES
315 S MANNING BLVD, ALBANY, NY 122081707
Phone: 518 525-1550
Web: WWW.SPHCS.ORG

HISTORICAL FINANCIALS

Company Type: Private

Income Statement				FYE: June 30
	REVENUE ($ mil.)	NET INCOME ($ mil.)	NET PROFIT MARGIN	EMPLOYEES
06/17	1,327	37	2.9%	6,000
06/16	552	39	7.1%	—
06/15	527	44	8.5%	—
06/14	509	21	4.1%	—
Annual Growth	37.6%	21.7%	—	—

2017 Year-End Financials

Return on assets: 6.8%   Cash ($ mil.): 124
Return on equity: 2.9%
Current ratio: 0.70

ST. VINCENT HEALTHCARE

EXECUTIVES

Pres-Ceo, Steve Loveless
Coo, Jack Bell
Executive Officer, Joan Thullbery
Director, Michael Schabacker
Administrative Assistant, Brett Close
Materials Director, Jeff Morganflash
Supervisor, Karen Broeder
Manager, Cathy Smith
Hematologist, David Christianson
Hematologist, Troy Fiddler
Internal Medicine Practitioner, Amy Fishburn

LOCATIONS

HQ: ST. VINCENT HEALTHCARE
1233 N 30TH ST, BILLINGS, MT 591010127
Phone: 406 657-7000
Web: WWW.SCLHEALTH.ORG/LOCATIONS/ST-VINCENT-HEALTHCARE/

HISTORICAL FINANCIALS

Company Type: Private

Income Statement				FYE: December 31
	REVENUE ($ mil.)	NET INCOME ($ mil.)	NET PROFIT MARGIN	EMPLOYEES
12/17	471	55	11.8%	1,800
12/16	428	15	3.7%	—
12/15	439	58	13.3%	—
12/14	440	40	9.2%	—
Annual Growth	2.3%	11.4%	—	—

2017 Year-End Financials

Return on assets: 3.6%   Cash ($ mil.): —
Return on equity: 11.8%
Current ratio: 1.70

ST. VINCENT HOSPITAL

EXECUTIVES

Ceo, Bruce Tassin
President, Alex Valdez
Vice President, Kathy Armijo Etre
Vice President, Lillian Montoya
Coo, Jason Adams
Cfo, Bob Moon
Coordinator, Cathy Montano
Director of Quality Improvemen, Kathleen Hessler
Scientist, Aida Thompson
Coordinator, Debbie Ronan
Program Director, Luis Rigales

LOCATIONS

HQ: ST. VINCENT HOSPITAL
1631 HOSPITAL DR STE 100, SANTA FE, NM 875057631
Phone: 505 983-3361
Web: WWW.STVIN.ORG

HISTORICAL FINANCIALS

Company Type: Private

Income Statement				FYE: June 30
	REVENUE ($ mil.)	NET INCOME ($ mil.)	NET PROFIT MARGIN	EMPLOYEES
06/16	382	18	4.8%	2,000
06/15	374	26	7.0%	—
06/14	365	6	1.7%	—
06/13	368	3	1.0%	—
Annual Growth	1.3%	73.4%	—	—

2016 Year-End Financials

Return on assets: 4.3%   Cash ($ mil.): 38
Return on equity: 4.8%
Current ratio: 1.70

ST. VINCENT HOSPITAL OF THE HOSPITAL SISTERS OF THE THIRD ORDER OF ST. FRANCIS

EXECUTIVES

Chb-Pres, Mary Beth Culnan
Ceo, Theresa Shuck
Vice President, Joseph J Neidenbach
Oncology, Sally M Schlise
Doctor, Jane Seidl
Information Specialist, Nikki Vieau
Director, Bobbi Giles
Divisional Director, Donna Boehm
Plant Manager, Rocky Compton
Program Manager, Doreen Kluth
Auditors: CROWE HORWATH LLP CHICAGO IL

LOCATIONS

HQ: ST. VINCENT HOSPITAL OF THE HOSPITAL SISTERS OF THE THIRD ORDER OF ST. FRANCIS
835 S VAN BUREN ST, GREEN BAY, WI 543013575
Phone: 920 433-0111
Web: WWW.STVINCENTHOSPITAL.ORG

HISTORICAL FINANCIALS

Company Type: Private

Income Statement				FYE: June 30
	REVENUE ($ mil.)	NET INCOME ($ mil.)	NET PROFIT MARGIN	EMPLOYEES
06/16	505	(35)	—	2,360
06/15	480	29	6.0%	—
06/11	424	26	6.3%	—
06/10	376	16	4.4%	—
Annual Growth	5.0%	—	—	—

2016 Year-End Financials

Return on assets: 3.9%   Cash ($ mil.): 13
Return on equity: (-7.0%)
Current ratio: 1.00

ST. VINCENT INFIRMARY MEDICAL CENTER

EXECUTIVES

Ceo, Peter Banko
Dir, Peggy Loyd
General, Randy Cason
Director, Erin Holloway
Coordinator, Sharmin Moody
Physical Therapy Director, Jennie Gregory
Information Technology/Interne, Jennifer Rice
Marketing Specialist, Ben Sheppard
Doctor, Brian Bean
Human Resources Specialist, Jennifer Ward
Director Respiratory Care, John Lindsey

LOCATIONS

HQ: ST. VINCENT INFIRMARY MEDICAL CENTER
2 SAINT VINCENT CIR, LITTLE ROCK, AR 722055423
Phone: 501 552-3000
Web: WWW.STVINCENTHEALTH.COM

HISTORICAL FINANCIALS

Company Type: Private

Income Statement				FYE: June 30
	REVENUE ($ mil.)	NET INCOME ($ mil.)	NET PROFIT MARGIN	EMPLOYEES
06/15	358	(14)	—	2,824
06/14	407	(45)	—	—
06/13	382	(46)	—	—
06/09	310	(19)	—	—
Annual Growth	2.4%	—	—	—

ST. VINCENT'S BIRMINGHAM

EXECUTIVES

Pres-Ceo, Curtis James
Optometrists, Madelyn Jones
Coordinator, Cheryl Rutledge
Scientist, Andrea Garrison
Vice-President, Suzannah Campbell

Coordinator, Carol Christian
Facilities Specialist, J Taylor
Director, Liz Moore
Coordinator, Terrie Reddrick-Maull
Specialist, Becky McKinney
Chief Nursing Officer, Kim Parrish
Auditors: DELOITTE TAX LLP CINCINNATI

LOCATIONS

HQ: ST. VINCENT'S BIRMINGHAM
    810 SAINT VINCENTS DR, BIRMINGHAM, AL
    352051601
Phone: 205 939-7000

HISTORICAL FINANCIALS

Company Type: Private

Income Statement — FYE: June 30

	REVENUE ($ mil.)	NET INCOME ($ mil.)	NET PROFIT MARGIN	EMPLOYEES
06/16	381	18	4.8%	1,478
06/15	382	42	11.1%	—
06/14	391	32	8.3%	—
06/13	386	38	10.0%	—
Annual Growth	(0.4%)	(22.2%)	—	—

2016 Year-End Financials

Return on assets: 3.9%   Cash ($ mil.): 1
Return on equity: 4.8%
Current ratio: 0.90

ST. VINCENT'S MEDICAL CENTER, INC

EXECUTIVES

Pres, Moody Chisolm
President, Blain Claypool
Vice President, Sean Fitzpatrick
Vice President, Ann Carey
Coo, Gene Miyamoto
Coo, Donnie Romine
Director of Quality Improvemen, Betsy Miller
Customer Representativ, Lynn Phifer
Customer Representativ, Trellis Hart
Engineering Executive, Spencer Hall
Coordinator, Rebecca Timberlake
Auditors: DELOITTE TAX LLP CINCINNATI

LOCATIONS

HQ: ST. VINCENT'S MEDICAL CENTER, INC
    4205 BELFORT RD STE 4030, JACKSONVILLE, FL
    322161475
Phone: 904 308-7300

HISTORICAL FINANCIALS

Company Type: Private

Income Statement — FYE: June 30

	REVENUE ($ mil.)	NET INCOME ($ mil.)	NET PROFIT MARGIN	EMPLOYEES
06/15	452	32	7.3%	3,535
06/14	445	33	7.4%	—
06/10	448	34	7.7%	—
06/09	377	(32)	—	—
Annual Growth	3.1%	—	—	—

2015 Year-End Financials

Return on assets: 5.8%   Cash ($ mil.): 2
Return on equity: 7.3%
Current ratio: 2.20

ST. VRAIN VALLEY SCHOOL DISTRICT RE-1J

EXECUTIVES

Prin, Don Hedad
Administrative Assistant, Darrin Tams
Food Director, Shelly Allen
Member, Joie Siegrist
Human Resources Administrator, Amy Keen
Secretary, Coleen Campbell
Director, Shari Parrs
Assistant Superintendent, Patty Quinones
Teacher, Diane Sherman
Program Manager, Gina Sanchez
Education Specialist, Gordon Nancy
Auditors: RUBINBROWN LLP DENVER CO

LOCATIONS

HQ: ST. VRAIN VALLEY SCHOOL DISTRICT RE-1J
    395 S PRATT PKWY, LONGMONT, CO 805016436
Phone: 303 776-6200
Web: WWW.SVVSD.ORG

HISTORICAL FINANCIALS

Company Type: Private

Income Statement — FYE: June 30

	REVENUE ($ mil.)	NET INCOME ($ mil.)	NET PROFIT MARGIN	EMPLOYEES
06/18	401	(84)	—	3,500
06/17	383	223	58.2%	—
Annual Growth	4.6%	—	—	—

STANFORD HEALTH CARE

Doctors patients medical students and researchers gather at Stanford Health Care (formerly Stanford Hospital and Clinics). As Stanford University's primary medical teaching facility the more than 600-bed Stanford Hospital specializes in such areas as cardiac care cancer treatment neurology surgery and organ transplant. The affiliated Stanford Clinics is a physician group practice organization that represents more than 100 specialized fields of medicine. Stanford Health Care is part of the Stanford Medicine organization which also includes the nearby Stanford University School of Medicine and the 310-bed Lucile Packard Children's Hospital (named for the wife of Hewlett-Packard co-founder David Packard).

Operations

Stanford Health Care handles some 25000 inpatient admissions each year more than 50000 emergency room visits and about 425000 outpatient encounters. The organization boasts such specialized clinics as the Byers Eye Institute the Stanford Comprehensive Cancer Center the Stanford Center for Marfan Syndrome and Aortic Disorders and the California VitreoRetinal Center. It also operates centers for orthopedic brain blood and marrow transplant and other specialist procedures.

Educational programs include medical and graduate student training as well as residency and fellowship programs. The organization also conducts research in medical and biological fields.

Additionally the system owns stakes in physician network University HealthCare Alliance radiation therapy facility Stanford Emanuel Radiation Oncology Center health care advocacy firm Care-Counsel and HMO plan University HealthCare Advantage.

Geographic Reach

Stanford Health Care operates in more than 15 locations in the San Francisco Bay Area.

Sales and Marketing

Stanford Health Care receives 70% of its revenues from managed care (commercial insurance) providers. Another 20% of patient service income is sourced to Medicare and Medicaid programs.

Financial Performance

Revenue increased 10% to $3 billion in fiscal 2014 (ended August) due to higher net patient service revenues primarily from managed care and Medicare fee increases. However net income dropped 22% to $432.2 million that year as operating costs rose and the system reported losses on investments.

Cash flow from operations grew 8% to $366.5 million in fiscal 2014 largely due to a change in working capital items.

Strategy

To remain at the forefront of medicine and technology the hospital is constructing a new $2 billion 600-bed facility next to its existing building. Local high-tech firms including Apple Hewlett-Packard and Intel are kicking in $15 million and technology partnerships to support the project. As corporate partners the firms will help to develop and integrate state-of-the-art information technology for the new facility.

Other growth projects include the construction of a new outpatient cancer clinic in San Jose. The center opened in 2014.

Also in 2014 the system changed its name from Stanford Hospitals and Clinics to Stanford Health Care. That change signified the broader scope of its operations which go beyond inpatient and outpatient facilities to include affiliated physician practices and health plans.

In fiscal 2015 Stanford Health Care engineers developed and launched a new MyHealth mobile application for the iPhone. The app connects with Epic electronic health records and Apple's HealthKit enabling patients to monitor their health data. MyHealth provides consumers with such capabilities as telehealth (video) physician visits appointment scheduling online payments and the ability to manage prescriptions and access test results.

EXECUTIVES

President And Ceo, David Entwistle
Vp And Chief Marketing Officer, Deborah Italiano
Chief Risk Officer, Jeff Driver
Vp Clinical Cancer Center And Cardiovascular Health, Sridhar Seshadri
Chief Medical Officer, Norman W. Rizk
Coo, Quinn L. McKenna
Cio, Pravene Nath
Coo, James Hereford
Interim Cfo, David Connor
Chief Quality Officer, Raj Behal
Chief Medical Information Officer, Christopher (Topher) Sharp
Clinic Manager, Diana Felix
Clinic Manager, Cindy Tse
Western Region Vice President, Todd Walter
Vice President Technology And Research, Daphne Chang
Advisory Board Member, Ramsey Cheung
Auditors: PRICEWATERHOUSECOOPERS LLP SA

LOCATIONS

HQ: STANFORD HEALTH CARE
300 PASTEUR DR, STANFORD, CA 943052200
Phone: 650 723-4000
Web: WWW.STANFORDHOSPITAL.COM

PRODUCTS/OPERATIONS

2014 Sales

	$ mil.	% of total
Net patient service revenue	2,839	95
Premium revenue	60	2
Other revenue	98	3
Total	**2,998**	**100**

Selected Services

Heart Center
Neurosciences
Orthopaedics
Sports Medicine
Stanford Cancer Center
Surgical Services
Transplant

COMPETITORS

Dignity Health	Sutter Health
Sequoia Capital	UCSF Medical

HISTORICAL FINANCIALS

Company Type: Private

Income Statement				FYE: August 31
	REVENUE ($ mil.)	NET INCOME ($ mil.)	NET PROFIT MARGIN	EMPLOYEES
08/17	4,454	450	10.1%	5,045
08/15	3,570	372	10.4%	—
08/10	2,141	186	8.7%	—
08/09	1,769	(56)	—	—
Annual Growth	12.2%	—	—	—

2017 Year-End Financials

Return on assets: 6.9%   Cash ($ mil.): 710
Return on equity: 10.1%
Current ratio: 1.20

STAR OF THE WEST MILLING COMPANY

All hands are on the mill floor at Star of the West Milling. The company operates five flour mills in four US states an about 10 storage elevators. The mills and elevators store and process wheat corn and soybeans. Its flour milling capacity is about 20000 lbs. per day. North Star Bean a division of Star of the West processes beans such as navy pinto kidney and black beans into dry commodity products. The company also owns Eastern Michigan Grain an elevator that offers grain handling and marketing services. Star of the West Milling sells its flour and beans worldwide to canning and packaging customers the likes of Kellogg General Mills Nabisco and Pepperidge Farm.

Geographic Reach

Michigan-based Star of the West Milling has operations in Indiana Michigan Ohio New York and North Dakota. It has five flour mills in four different states and nine country elevators.

Strategy

The company in mid-2013 announced it will spend about $3 million to expand its facility in Rapson Michigan. The project includes a new fertilizer plant dry bean receiving facility and more space for grain storage. Star of the West Milling

has grown steadily without any devastating blows to its bottom line during the economic slump. Also instead of setting aside cash for a rainy day or paying off debt Star of the West Milling in 2011 invested more than $8 million in new equipment and building additions in an effort to boost production and improve sales. The new machinery cleans and separates wheat and uses optical sorting to identify and remove imperfect kernels. Star of the West Milling in turn hopes to expand its capabilities further to include whole wheat production to cater to customer requests.

Company Background

Star of the West Milling was founded by the Hubinger family in 1870; its name was taken from a side-wheel merchant steamer of the same name that secretly transported soldiers and supplies to Fort Sumpter site of the first battle of the Civil War.

EXECUTIVES

Chb, Gary Rummel
President, Arthur A Loeffler
Vice Chb, William A Zehnder III
Vice President, Michael Fassezke
Vice President, James Howe
SEC, Drew Zehnder
Dir, Robert Krafft
Executive Officer, Gary Pickelmann
Receptionist, Gretchen Smith
Information Technology Manager, Alan McTaggart
Area Manager, Keith Weber
Auditors: YEO & YEO SAGINAW MI

LOCATIONS

HQ: STAR OF THE WEST MILLING COMPANY
121 E TUSCOLA ST, FRANKENMUTH, MI 487341731
Phone: 989 652-9971
Web: WWW.STAROFTHEWEST.COM

PRODUCTS/OPERATIONS

Selected Products

Beans
  Black beans
  Cranberry beans
  Dark red kidney beans
  Great northern beans
  Light red kidney beans
  Navy beans (pea beans)
  Pink beans
  Pinto beans
  Small reds
  Small white beans
  Yelloweye beans
Flour
  Cardinal flour
  Cracked wheat
  Crushed wheat
  Heavy bran flakes
  Heritage Brand All Purpose
  Light bran
  Patriot whole wheat flour
  Peerless flour
  Perfection pretzel flour
  Soft wheat flour and specialty products
  Special soft white wheat cake flour
Grain
  Corn
  Soybeans
  Wheat
Plant food

COMPETITORS

Bay State Milling	Italgrani
Bunge Milling	Kelley Bean
C.H. Guenther & Son	North Dakota Mill
CGC	Seaboard
Chippewa Valley Bean	US Soy
DeBruce Grain	Wilkins Rogers
Horizon Milling	

HISTORICAL FINANCIALS

Company Type: Private

Income Statement				FYE: December 31
	REVENUE ($ mil.)	NET INCOME ($ mil.)	NET PROFIT MARGIN	EMPLOYEES
12/16	380	5	1.6%	239
12/15	396	11	2.8%	—
12/14	0	12		—
12/13	416	15	3.7%	
Annual Growth	(3.0%)	(27.3%)	—	—

2016 Year-End Financials

Return on assets: 11.2%   Cash ($ mil.): 2
Return on equity: 1.6%
Current ratio: 0.50

STATE BOARD FOR COMMUNITY COLLEGES AND OCCUPATIONAL EDUCATIONAL SYSTEM

EXECUTIVES

Pres, Nancy McCallin
V Pres, Cliff Richardson
Administrative Assistant, Frank Vazquez
Coordinator, Marilyn Smith
Director, Jenyl Johnson
Information Technology Manager, Ken Campion
Technician, Vincent Smith
Sales Manager, Eileen Clymo
Administrative Assistant, Daniel Baniszewski
Director, Lauren Jones
Director, Linda Bigley
Auditors: KPMG LLP DENVER COLORADO

LOCATIONS

HQ: STATE BOARD FOR COMMUNITY COLLEGES AND OCCUPATIONAL EDUCATIONAL SYSTEM
9101 E LOWRY PL, DENVER, CO 802306011
Phone: 303 595-1552
Web: WWW.SANDRACLARKFINEART.COM

HISTORICAL FINANCIALS

Company Type: Private

Income Statement				FYE: June 30
	REVENUE ($ mil.)	NET INCOME ($ mil.)	NET PROFIT MARGIN	EMPLOYEES
06/16	460	(9)	—	2,658
06/15	0	(0)		—
06/13	0	0	3.0%	—
06/09	0	0	—	—
Annual Growth	140.5%	—	—	—

2016 Year-End Financials

Return on assets: 4.7%   Cash ($ mil.): 319
Return on equity: (-2.1%)
Current ratio: 4.20

STATE OF CALIFORNIA

EXECUTIVES

Governor, Gavin Newsom
Consultant, A Kirk McKenzie
Chief Licensing/Information Te, Brian Desmarais
Chief Information Security Off, Carol Kelly
Budgets and Fiscal STA, Caroline McNeil
Computer Support Staff Represe, Cheryl Drefs
Budgets and Fiscal STA, Diane Herteg
Chief Technology Support Servi, Jim Rengstorff
AG Technician II, Jose Antonio Diaz
Analyst, Karen Bianchi Walsh
California Attorney General, Xavier Becerra
Auditors: JOHN F COLLINS II CPA DEPUTY

LOCATIONS

HQ: STATE OF CALIFORNIA
STATE CAPITAL, SACRAMENTO, CA 95814
Phone: 916 445-2864
Web: WWW.CA.GOV

HISTORICAL FINANCIALS
Company Type: Private

Income Statement — FYE: June 30

	REVENUE ($ mil.)	NET INCOME ($ mil.)	NET PROFIT MARGIN	EMPLOYEES
06/16	255,725	4,798	1.9%	208,580
06/15	249,923	6,252	2.5%	—
06/14	219,871	8,082	3.7%	—
06/13	204	8	3.9%	—
Annual Growth	976.7%	742.3%	—	—

STATE OF NEW YORK MORTGAGE AGENCY

EXECUTIVES

Vice President, Daniel Murphy
Assistant Vice President, Robert Rosado
Vice President Special Projects, Mark Flescher
Vice President Internal Audit, Stephen Chopey
Senior Vice President, Michael Friedman
Senior Vice President Policy Initiatives, Arlo Chase
Vice President, Michael Esposito
Vice President Government Relations, Joseph Palozzola
Auditors: DELOITTE & TOUCHE LLP NEW YOR

LOCATIONS

HQ: STATE OF NEW YORK MORTGAGE AGENCY
641 LEXINGTON AVE FL 4, NEW YORK, NY 100224503
Phone: 212 688-4000
Web: WWW.NYHOMES.ORG

HISTORICAL FINANCIALS
Company Type: Private

Income Statement — FYE: October 31

	ASSETS ($ mil.)	NET INCOME ($ mil.)	INCOME AS % OF ASSETS	EMPLOYEES
10/17	5,228	34	0.7%	221
10/16	5,187	63	1.2%	—
10/09	5,225	162	3.1%	—
10/08	5,224	30	0.6%	—
Annual Growth	0.0%	1.3%	—	—

2017 Year-End Financials
Return on assets: —   Sales ($ mil): 156
Return on equity: 22.3%

STATE OF OKLAHOMA

EXECUTIVES

Governor, Kevin Stitt
Lt Gov, Todd Lamb
General Counsel-Sec, James Williamson
Vice-President, Patrick Brown
Staff, Chris Turner
Auditors: GARY A JONES CPA CFE OKLAH

LOCATIONS

HQ: STATE OF OKLAHOMA
421 NW 13TH ST STE 220, OKLAHOMA CITY, OK 731033784
Phone: 405 521-2342
Web: WWW.OK.GOV

HISTORICAL FINANCIALS
Company Type: Private

Income Statement — FYE: June 30

	REVENUE ($ mil.)	NET INCOME ($ mil.)	NET PROFIT MARGIN	EMPLOYEES
06/17	17,175	48	0.3%	37,613
06/16	16,789	(1,025)	—	—
06/15	17,331	314	1.8%	—
06/14	17,465	303	1.7%	—
Annual Growth	(0.6%)	(45.9%)	—	—

2017 Year-End Financials
Return on assets: 9.4%   Cash ($ mil.): 6,099
Return on equity: 0.3%
Current ratio: 1.80

STATE OF RHODE ISLAND AND PROVIDENCE PLANTATIONS

EXECUTIVES

Governor, Gina M Raimondo
Lt Gov, Daniel J McKee
State Controller, Lawrence C Franklin Jr
Policy Director, Kelly Mahoney
Auditors: DENNIS E HOYLE CPA-OFFICE OF

LOCATIONS

HQ: STATE OF RHODE ISLAND AND PROVIDENCE PLANTATIONS
82 SMITH ST STE 102, PROVIDENCE, RI 029031121
Phone: 401 222-2080
Web: WWW.GOPROVIDENCE.COM

HISTORICAL FINANCIALS
Company Type: Private

Income Statement — FYE: June 30

	REVENUE ($ mil.)	NET INCOME ($ mil.)	NET PROFIT MARGIN	EMPLOYEES
06/17	7,012	215	3.1%	13,535
06/16	6,860	(10)	—	—
06/15	6,787	160	2.4%	—
06/14	6,282	(46)	—	—
Annual Growth	3.7%	—	—	—

2017 Year-End Financials
Return on assets: 12.6%   Cash ($ mil.): 1,215
Return on equity: 3.1%
Current ratio: 1.10

STATE OF TEXAS

EXECUTIVES

Governor, Greg Abbott
Chief of Staff, Luis Saenz
Deputy Chief of Staff, David Whitley
Chief Operating Officer, Reed Clay
Deputy Chief of Staff, Jordan Hale
Director, Nichole Vance
Senior Adviser For State Opera, Steven Albright
Texas District Attorney, Andria Bender
Offc Manager, Connie Lucas
Executive Assistant, Daniel Womack
Executive Assistant, Debbie Maldonado
Auditors: JOHN KENT CPA AUSTIN TEXAS

LOCATIONS

HQ: STATE OF TEXAS
CAPI BLDG 1100 N CONG AVE, AUSTIN, TX 78701
Phone: 512 463-2000

HISTORICAL FINANCIALS
Company Type: Private

Income Statement — FYE: August 31

	REVENUE ($ mil.)	NET INCOME ($ mil.)	NET PROFIT MARGIN	EMPLOYEES
08/17	115,336	1,882	1.6%	144,175
08/15	107,350	1,993	1.9%	—
08/14	109,860	8,184	7.4%	—
08/13	0	0	—	—
Annual Growth	—	—	—	—

2017 Year-End Financials
Return on assets: 6.5%   Cash ($ mil.): 29,217
Return on equity: 1.6%
Current ratio: 1.10

STATEN ISLAND UNIVERSITY HOSPITAL

Staten Island University Hospital (SIUH) ferries health care services to residents of New York City's fastest growing borough and surrounding areas at its two medical campuses. Established in 1861

SIUH maintains about 715 beds and is a teaching affiliate of the State University of New York's Brooklyn Health Science Center. Its larger north campus includes units specializing in cardiology pathology cancer blood-related diseases burn treatment trauma and women's health. The south campus site offers specialty programs such as sleep medicine geriatric psychiatry and substance abuse services. A member of Northwell Health SIUH employs approximately 1200 physicians.

Operations

SIUH's Heart Institute of Staten Island located on the north campus is a joint venture between the hospital and Richmond University Medical Center. The Heart Institute specializes in cardiac diagnostics and "beating heart" surgeries.

The hospital operates several general physician practice and specialty health clinics on Staten Island. It also provides a home visit program and hospital-based hospice services.

SIUH is an affiliate of the SUNY Health Science Center at Brooklyn; its campuses serve as clinics for the Hofstra North Shore-LIJ School of Medicine which SIUH owns in partnership with Hofstra University.

In 2013 SIUH had nearly 3000 births nearly 45000 hospital discharges about 126000 emergency department visits and more than 16000 ambulatory surgeries.

EXECUTIVES

Pres, Anthony C Ferreri
Exec Vice President, Robin Wittenstein
V Pres-Fin-Controller, John Steiger
Cfo, Thomas Reca
Exec Vice President, Nicholas Caruselle
Sr Vice President, Margaret Dialto
Vice President, John P Demoleas
SEC, Arthur Fried
Exec Dir, Donna Proske
Staff, Vincent Logatto
Sr Hr Rep, Jenie Grodowski

LOCATIONS

HQ: STATEN ISLAND UNIVERSITY HOSPITAL
475 SEAVIEW AVE, STATEN ISLAND, NY 103053436
Phone: 718 226-9000
Web: WWW.NORTHWELL.EDU/FIND-CARE/LOCATIONS/STATEN-ISLAND-UNIV

PRODUCTS/OPERATIONS

Selected Services
Behavioral Health
Cancer Services
Cardiac Services
Cardiovascular and Thoracic Surgery
Medical Services including Endocrinology Gastroenterology Nephrology and Pulmonary
Neuroscience and Spine Services
Orthopedic Services
Pediatrics
Rehabilitation Medicine
Surgical Services including General Surgery Colorectal Head & Neck and Urology
Trauma and Burn Services
Women's Health

Selected Centers of Care
Center for Bariatric Surgery
Comprehensive Breast Center
Heart Institute
Institute of Sleep Medicine
Level III Perinatal Center
New York Head & Neck Institute at Staten Island University Hospital
Regional Burn Center
Stroke Center
The Elizabeth A. Connelly Emergency and Trauma Center
The Sanford R. Nalitt Institute for Cancer and Blood Related Diseases; Children's Cancer Center

COMPETITORS

Bronx-Lebanon Hospital
Catholic Healthcare System
CenterLight Health System Inc.
Continuum Health Partners
Eger Health Care
Kingsbrook Jewish Medical Center
Maimonides Medical Center
MediSys Health Network
New York City Health and Hospitals
NewYork-Presbyterian Healthcare

HISTORICAL FINANCIALS
Company Type: Private

Income Statement   FYE: December 31

	REVENUE ($ mil.)	NET INCOME ($ mil.)	NET PROFIT MARGIN	EMPLOYEES
12/17	891	69	7.8%	5,700
12/16	871	57	6.6%	—
12/15	850	41	4.9%	—
12/14	811	51	6.4%	—
Annual Growth	3.2%	10.2%	—	—

2017 Year-End Financials
Return on assets: 4.7%   Cash ($ mil.): 5
Return on equity: 7.8%
Current ratio: 0.80

STEEL OF WEST VIRGINIA, INC.

EXECUTIVES

Pres-Ceo, Timothy R Duke
Vice President, John O'Connor
Maintenance Manager, Chuck Jones
Engineer, Charles Abbott
Sales Staff, Jamie Powers
Plant and Facilities Manager, Scott Boggs
Assistant, Roger Hutchinson
Accounts Payable, Brandi Vickers
Distribution Shipping Transpor, James Kirby
Information Technology Staff, Rodney Wayne
Administrative Assistant, Trena Schneider

LOCATIONS

HQ: STEEL OF WEST VIRGINIA, INC.
17TH ST & 2ND AVE, HUNTINGTON, WV 25703
Phone: 304 696-8200
Web: WWW.STEELDYNAMICS.COM

PRODUCTS/OPERATIONS

Selected Products
C channels
Channels for auto lifts
Conductor rails
Forklift hanger bars
Guardrail posts
I-beams
Industrial truck masts
J-bars
Manufactured housing beams
Mine light rail
Off-highway frame components
Offset J-bars
Roller side bearings
S-beams
Solar panel supports
Truck trailer crossmembers
W-beams

COMPETITORS

Cascade Steel
Commercial Metals
Jersey Shore Steel
Morton Industrial Group
Nucor

HISTORICAL FINANCIALS
Company Type: Private

Income Statement   FYE: December 31

	REVENUE ($ mil.)	NET INCOME ($ mil.)	NET PROFIT MARGIN	EMPLOYEES
12/17	310	0	—	92
12/16	319	0	—	—
12/15	341	0	—	—
12/14	357	0	—	—
Annual Growth	(4.6%)	—	—	—

2017 Year-End Financials
Return on assets: —   Cash ($ mil.): —
Return on equity: —
Current ratio: 1.10

STEPHEN GOULD CORPORATION

Others can worry about what's inside — Stephen Gould Corporation concentrates on the package. The company provides a full range of packaging-related design and printing services for customers worldwide. Its products include gift packaging point-of-purchase displays product merchandising and retail and industrial packaging. Stephen Gould Corporation also provides graphic design and package-engineering services as well as assembly and fulfillment. The company was originally founded in 1939 by Stephen Gould David Golden and Leonard Beckerman.

Geographic Reach

Stephen Gould Corporation operates from about 40 facilities; branches are located primarily in the US (more than 20 states) but also in China Ireland Malaysia and Mexico.

EXECUTIVES

Executive Vice President Operations, John Golden

LOCATIONS

HQ: STEPHEN GOULD CORPORATION
35 S JEFFERSON RD, WHIPPANY, NJ 079811043
Phone: 973 428-1500
Web: WWW.STEPHENGOULD.COM

PRODUCTS/OPERATIONS

Selected Products and Services
Products
Aerospace reusable cases
Corrugated containers
Gift packaging
Industrial packaging
Point of sale packaging
Protective packaging
Services
Creative services
Logistics & facilities
Package design & engineering

COMPETITORS

Consolidated Carqueville
Focus Packaging & Display group
Fort Dearborn
Gibraltar Packaging
Metro Packaging and Imaging
R.R. Donnelley
WS Packaging Group

HISTORICAL FINANCIALS

Company Type: Private

Income Statement				FYE: December 31
	REVENUE ($ mil.)	NET INCOME ($ mil.)	NET PROFIT MARGIN	EMPLOYEES
12/17	678	7	1.1%	325
12/16	665	11	1.8%	—
12/13	526	3	0.7%	—
12/12	526	3	0.7%	—
Annual Growth	5.2%	14.7%	—	—

2017 Year-End Financials

Return on assets: 16.2%
Return on equity: 1.1%
Current ratio: 1.40

Cash ($ mil.): 7

STEPHENS PIPE & STEEL, LLC

EXECUTIVES

MBR-Pres, Terry L Stephens
Purchasing Manager, Donna Johnson
General Manager, Ted Eysenbach
Manager of Management Informat, Patrick Ford
Information Technology Manager, Treva Cowell
Human Resources, Courtney Powell
Executive Assistant, Melissa Wade
Sales and Marketing Assistant, Angie Pennington
Sales Manager, David Gaskin
Sales and Marketing Staff, Alex Gosser
Payroll Manager, Freda Mathis
Auditors: BKD LLP BOWLING GREEN KY

LOCATIONS

HQ: STEPHENS PIPE & STEEL, LLC
2224 E HIGHWAY 619, RUSSELL SPRINGS, KY
426427928
Phone: 270 866-3331
Web: WWW.SPSFENCE.COM

HISTORICAL FINANCIALS

Company Type: Private

Income Statement				FYE: October 1
	REVENUE ($ mil.)	NET INCOME ($ mil.)	NET PROFIT MARGIN	EMPLOYEES
10/16	342	46	13.5%	1,000
10/15*	305	27	8.8%	—
09/14	294	25	8.7%	—
09/13	273	24	9.1%	—
Annual Growth	7.8%	22.8%	—	—

*Fiscal year change

2016 Year-End Financials

Return on assets: 2.5%
Return on equity: 13.5%
Current ratio: 2.40

Cash ($ mil.): —

STEPHENSON WHOLESALE COMPANY, INC.

EXECUTIVES

Vice President Facilities, Frank Cross
Auditors: BDO USA LLP DALLAS TEXAS

LOCATIONS

HQ: STEPHENSON WHOLESALE COMPANY, INC.
230 S 22ND AVE, DURANT, OK 747015646
Phone: 580 920-0125
Web: WWW.INWSUPPLY.COM

COMPETITORS

Associated Wholesale Grocers	Eby-Brown
C&S Wholesale	GSC Enterprises
Core-Mark	H. T. Hackney
	McLane

HISTORICAL FINANCIALS

Company Type: Private

Income Statement				FYE: December 31
	REVENUE ($ mil.)	NET INCOME ($ mil.)	NET PROFIT MARGIN	EMPLOYEES
12/17	295	(5)	—	305
12/16	297	(0)	—	—
12/15	316	0	0.3%	—
12/14	325	1	0.4%	—
Annual Growth	(3.2%)	—	—	—

2017 Year-End Financials

Return on assets: 0.2%
Return on equity: (-1.8%)
Current ratio: 0.80

Cash ($ mil.): 2

STEVENS TRANSPORT, INC.

Staying cool is a must for Stevens Transport. An irregular-route refrigerated truckload carrier (or reefer) Stevens hauls temperature-controlled cargo throughout the US covering the 48 contiguous states. Through alliances Stevens also covers every province in Canada and every state in Mexico. The company operates a fleet of about 2000 Kenworth and Peterbuilt tractors and 3500 Thermo King refrigerated trailers from a network of more than a dozen service centers. Partnerships with railroads allow Stevens to arrange intermodal transport of temperature-controlled cargo. The company also provides third-party logistics services. Stevens Transport was founded in 1980.

Operations

The company owns 49% of B2B Transport which provides an array of transportation related services to large mid-sized and small companies throughout North America.

Geographic Reach

Stevens Transport maintains its operations across Canada Mexico and the US through its partnerships with BNSF Norfolk Southern CSX and Union Pacific. It has 13 logistics offices located in Canada and throughout the US.

Sales and Marketing

Stevens has provided refrigerated shipping services for such big names as General Mills Kraft Foods M&M Mars Procter & Gamble and Wal-Mart.

Strategy

Even in a US economy ripe with unpredictable fuel costs and a decline in consumer confidence one thing has always worked in Stevens' favor: people will always need their food. The company has managed to maintain a steady growth rate by keeping costs down updating the technology of its trucking equipment and maintaining an efficient operating structure. Along these lines in 2012 it implemented new mobile computing platforms across its fleet of tractors to enhance its customer services and optimize productivity.

EXECUTIVES

Vice President Risk Management, William Tallent
Upper Management Vice President, Millie Braucht
Executive Vice President, Mike Richey
Vice Chairman, Todd Aaron
Auditors: SADDOCK & CO PLLC DALLAS T

LOCATIONS

HQ: STEVENS TRANSPORT, INC.
9757 MILITARY PKWY, DALLAS, TX 752274805
Phone: 972 216-9000
Web: WWW.STEVENSTRANSPORT.COM

PRODUCTS/OPERATIONS

Selected Services
Intermodal
International
Logistics
Truckload

COMPETITORS

C.R. England	Marten Transport
Central Refrigerated Service	Navajo Shippers Prime Inc.
Comcar	Southern Refrigerated
Covenant Transportation	Transport
Frozen Food Express	TransAm Trucking
Henderson Trucking	Watkins Associated Industries
Jim Palmer Trucking	Willis Shaw Express
KLLM Transport Services	

HISTORICAL FINANCIALS

Company Type: Private

Income Statement				FYE: December 31
	REVENUE ($ mil.)	NET INCOME ($ mil.)	NET PROFIT MARGIN	EMPLOYEES
12/15	668	87	13.0%	2,100
12/12	607	85	14.0%	—
12/11	566	76	13.5%	—
12/08	550	0	0.0%	—
Annual Growth	2.8%	505.7%	—	—

2015 Year-End Financials

Return on assets: 0.6%
Return on equity: 13.0%
Current ratio: 3.20

Cash ($ mil.): 152

STEWART'S SHOPS CORP.

I scream you scream we all scream for Stewart's ice cream — especially if we live in upstate New York or Vermont home to some 330 Stewart's Shops. The chain of convenience stores sells more than 3000 products across 30-plus counties. They include dairy items groceries food to go (soup sandwiches hot entrees) beer coffee gasoline and of course ice cream. In addition to its retail business the company owns about 100 rental properties including banks hair salons and apartments near its stores. Stewart's Shops formerly known as Stewart's Ice Cream Company was established in 1945. The founding Dake family owns about two-thirds of the company; employee compensation plans own the rest.

Operations
The convenience store chain which spans New York and Vermont offers consumers milk ice creams coffee to-go foods beer gasoline and groceries. As part of its business Stewart's Shops also acquires and develops (preferably adjacent) properties the likes of shops banks hair salons and apartments that it then leases or sells.

Stewart's Shops makes its own dairy products including its own ice cream in more than 50 flavors that are hand-dipped and packaged. Recognized for its quality products the company relies on a group of about 45 farmers in New York to supply its milk.

The vertically-integrated company which makes about 75% of the items it sells also offers private-label goods and national brands in its stores. Its private-label brands extend far beyond dairy products to include soda chips bread and juices.

Geographic Reach
Based in New York Stewart's Shops operates a chain of convenience stores across upstate New York and in Vermont.

Sales and Marketing
Stewart's Shops serves consumers through its New York and Vermont shops; two-thirds of its stores sell gas.

Strategy
The convenience store operator regularly extends its reach. In 2014 it's focused on Syracuse New York following several store openings in 2013 in Keeseville Herkimer Rotterdam and Heuvelton New York. The latter shops boast an expanded cooler walk-in beer cave and seating.

The company is also investing in environmentally friendly facilities. In 2013 for instance it had 2400 solar panels installed at its manufacturing and distribution center. Stewart's Shops anticipates that the effort will save nearly $40000 a year in energy costs at the plant after about a 5-year period.

It enlisted the help of Paragon Software in 2014 to automate the planning of daily and seasonal deliveries. In turn Stewart's Shops aims to lower mileage reduce fuel usage and improve truckload efficiencies.

EXECUTIVES

Senior Vice President Of Information Technology Operations, Dave Caruso
Auditors: SAXBST LLP ALBANY NEW YORK

LOCATIONS

HQ: STEWART'S SHOPS CORP.
2907 STATE ROUTE 9, BALLSTON SPA, NY 120204201
Phone: 518 581-1201
Web: WWW.STEWARTSSHOPS.COM

PRODUCTS/OPERATIONS

Selected Products
Beverages
Coffee
Ice Cream
Food to go
Gasoline
Groceries
Milk

COMPETITORS

7-Eleven	Hannaford Bros.
Ben & Jerry's	Kroger
Carvel	McDonald's
Cumberland Farms	Sunoco
Exxon Mobil	TravelCenters of
Friendly's Ice Cream	America
Golub	

HISTORICAL FINANCIALS
Company Type: Private

Income Statement				FYE: December 31
	REVENUE ($ mil.)	NET INCOME ($ mil.)	NET PROFIT MARGIN	EMPLOYEES
12/17	1,542	92	6.0%	3,800
12/16	1,405	80	5.7%	—
12/14	1,610	59	3.7%	—
12/13	1,577	73	4.7%	—
Annual Growth	(0.6%)	5.9%	—	—

2017 Year-End Financials
Return on assets: 4.7%
Return on equity: 6.0%
Current ratio: 0.80
Cash ($ mil.): 50

STILLWATER MINING COMPANY

EXECUTIVES

Pres-Ceo, Michael J McMullen
Cfo, Christopher M Bateman
V Pres Safety Health & Hr, Kristen K Koss
V Pres Mine Oprs, Dee L Bray
Foreman/Supervisor, Dave Crabtree
Blitz Project Manager, David Sabourin
Nye Warehouse Supervisor, Kevin Prosenick
Accounting Team Member, Luttschwager Yvonne
Technical Manager, Stanford Foy
Auditors: KPMG LLP BILLINGS MONTANA

LOCATIONS

HQ: STILLWATER MINING COMPANY
26 W DRY CREEK CIR # 400, LITTLETON, CO 801204475
Phone: 406 373-8700
Web: WWW.STILLWATERMINING.COM

COMPETITORS

Anglo American Platinum	Impala Platinum
	Lonmin
Aquarius Platinum	North American
Diadem Resources	Palladium
Franco-Nevada	Vale Limited

HISTORICAL FINANCIALS
Company Type: Private

Income Statement				FYE: December 31
	REVENUE ($ mil.)	NET INCOME ($ mil.)	NET PROFIT MARGIN	EMPLOYEES
12/16	711	9	1.3%	1,432
12/15	726	(23)	—	—
12/14	943	68	7.3%	—
12/13	1,039	(302)	—	—
Annual Growth	(11.9%)	—	—	—

2016 Year-End Financials
Return on assets: 5.2%
Return on equity: 1.3%
Current ratio: 1.40
Cash ($ mil.): 123

STOCKTON UNIFIED SCHOOL DISTRICT

EXECUTIVES

Supt, Dr Steve Lowder
President, Sara L Cazares
Vice President, Gloria Allen
Consultant, Claudia Moreno
Executive Officer, John New
Psychologist, Scott Runion
Research/Development Director, Mong Thi Nguyen

LOCATIONS

HQ: STOCKTON UNIFIED SCHOOL DISTRICT
701 N MADISON ST, STOCKTON, CA 952021634
Phone: 209 933-7000
Web: WWW.STOCKTONUSD.NET

HISTORICAL FINANCIALS
Company Type: Private

Income Statement				FYE: June 30
	REVENUE ($ mil.)	NET INCOME ($ mil.)	NET PROFIT MARGIN	EMPLOYEES
06/17	557	36	6.6%	3,000
06/16	527	98	18.6%	—
06/11	354	(1)	—	—
06/02	277	1	0.4%	—
Annual Growth	4.7%	26.3%	—	—

STORMONT-VAIL HEALTHCARE, INC.

EXECUTIVES

Ceo, Randall Peterson
Ceo, Randy Peterson
Vice President, Tracy O'Rourke
Sr V Pres-Medi Dir, Kent Palmberg
V Pres-Medi Svc Div, Deb Yocum
V Pres-Chf Info Offc, Janet Stanek
V Pres-Patient Care Svcs, Carol Perry
V Pres-Fclty Mgmt, David Cuningham
V Pres-Hr, Bernard Becker

LOCATIONS

HQ: STORMONT-VAIL HEALTHCARE, INC.
  1500 SW 10TH AVE, TOPEKA, KS 666041301
Phone: 785 354-6000
Web: WWW.STORMONTVAIL.ORG

HISTORICAL FINANCIALS

Company Type: Private

Income Statement				FYE: September 30
	REVENUE ($ mil.)	NET INCOME ($ mil.)	NET PROFIT MARGIN	EMPLOYEES
09/17	654	70	10.8%	4,500
09/16	634	30	4.8%	—
09/15	582	(9)	—	—
09/14	582	24	4.3%	—
Annual Growth	4.0%	41.4%	—	—

2017 Year-End Financials

Return on assets: 2.2%   Cash ($ mil.): 60
Return on equity: 10.8%
Current ratio: 2.00

STRATA SOLAR, LLC

EXECUTIVES

Ceo, Markus Wilhelm
Cao, Cathy Wilhelm
Manager, Jay Cobb
Chief Financial Officer, Dave Scoglio
Chief Operating Officer, Michael Belikoff
Accountant, Sharese Turnage
Operations Staff, Alexander Lytton
Coordinator, Benjamin Vollmer
Senior Vice-President, Brian O'Hara
Coordinator, Davis Plunkett
Human Resources, Michael Carrington

LOCATIONS

HQ: STRATA SOLAR, LLC
  50101 GOVERNORS DR # 280, CHAPEL HILL, NC
  275179517
Phone: 919 960-6015
Web: WWW.STRATASOLAR.COM

HISTORICAL FINANCIALS

Company Type: Private

Income Statement				FYE: December 31
	REVENUE ($ mil.)	NET INCOME ($ mil.)	NET PROFIT MARGIN	EMPLOYEES
12/17	350	1	0.6%	106
12/16	415	19	4.6%	—
Annual Growth	(15.6%)	(89.8%)	—	—

2017 Year-End Financials

Return on assets: 5.6%   Cash ($ mil.): 4
Return on equity: 0.6%
Current ratio: 0.30

STV GROUP, INCORPORATED

STV Group helps create the systems through which SUVs LRVs and 747s can travel. Its subsidiaries and partnerships provide architectural engineering environmental construction management interior design and planning services for infrastructure projects that include airports light-rail systems ports and railroads. STV Group's security division conducts threat assessments and mitigates safety strategies for facilities. Its STV Canada Consulting joint venture is developing the Ottawa Light Rail Transit Project. The group serves public and private clients worldwide but primarily in the US. The employee-owned STV Group was founded in 1912 and taken private in 2001.

Operations

The engineering firm operates its business through four divisions: Transportation and Infrastructure Construction Management Buildings and Facilities and STV Energy Services. Transportation and Infrastructure caters to the public transportation industry offering transportation systems and facility planning design and construction management. The company's Construction Management unit oversees projects nationwide ranging from $100000 to hundreds of millions of dollars. Its Buildings and Facilities division specializes in contextual architectural and engineering design and documentation. STV Energy Services is an expert in pipeline projects for the oil and gas industry. Its work consists of new cross-country pipelines relocating existing pipelines drilled crossings and related facilities.

Established in 2011 the Ottawa-based STV Canada Consulting serves as STV Group's Canadian arm. Along with STV Group other joint venture partners include Morrison Hershfield Limited URS Canada Inc. and Jacobs Associates Canada Corp. The group is focused on the preliminary engineering and project management services for the Ottawa Light Rail Transit Project for the City of Ottawa.

Geographic Reach

STV Group operates predominantly in the US but serves clients worldwide.

Sales and Marketing

STV Group serves several markets such as the transportation design-build institutional building commercial building advanced technology and industrial and defense markets.

Mergers and Acquisitions

STV Group in 2013 acquired Oakland California's VBN an architectural firm. With VBN as a holding STV Group can better serve its Western region clients and extend its reach in the higher education market and specifically community colleges.

EXECUTIVES

Vice President Of Transportation And Infrastructure Divisions Systems Group, Dominic Sabatini
Vice President Of Construction Management Division, Gert Koerner
Auditors: GRASSI & CO CPAS PC JERI

LOCATIONS

HQ: STV GROUP, INCORPORATED
  205 W WELSH DR, DOUGLASSVILLE, PA 195188713
Phone: 610 385-8200
Web: WWW.STVINC.COM

PRODUCTS/OPERATIONS

Selected Markets
Aviation
Aviation/Transportation Architecture
Bridges
Bus Transportation
Data Centers and Mission-Critical Facilities
Defense Systems
Education - Colleges and Universities
Education - PreK through 12
Energy (Petroleum and Gas)
Environmental
Facilities - Capital Improvement Programs
Federal
Freight
Health and Science
Highways and Roadways
Hospitality and Commercial
Industrial
Justice and Institutional
Laboratory and High-Tech
Land Development
Military
Ports
Rail Transportation
Renewable and Alternative Energy
Security
Sustainable Design
Tunnels

COMPETITORS

AECOM	HNTB Companies
Black & Veatch	Jacobs Engineering
CH2M HILL	Louis Berger
Day & Zimmermann	Michael Baker
Einhorn Yaffee	Parsons Brinckerhoff
Epstein	Parsons Corporation
HDR	Skidmore Owings

HISTORICAL FINANCIALS

Company Type: Private

Income Statement				FYE: September 30
	REVENUE ($ mil.)	NET INCOME ($ mil.)	NET PROFIT MARGIN	EMPLOYEES
09/17	322	8	2.8%	1,700
09/16	301	6	2.3%	—
09/03	138	4	3.0%	—
09/02	213	6	3.2%	—
Annual Growth	2.8%	1.8%	—	—

2017 Year-End Financials

Return on assets: 6.8%   Cash ($ mil.): 44
Return on equity: 2.8%
Current ratio: 1.60

SUASIN CANCER CARE INC.

EXECUTIVES

Prin, Winlove B Suasin
Auditors: ERNST & YOUNG US LLP SAN DIEG

LOCATIONS

HQ: SUASIN CANCER CARE INC.
  1301 PUNCHBOWL ST, HONOLULU, HI 968132402
Phone: 512 583-0205
Web: WWW.QUEENS.ORG/THE-QUEENS-MEDICAL-CENTER/QUEENS-MEDICAL-

HISTORICAL FINANCIALS
Company Type: Private

Income Statement				FYE: June 30
	REVENUE ($ mil.)	NET INCOME ($ mil.)	NET PROFIT MARGIN	EMPLOYEES
06/15	1,003	50	5.0%	4
06/14	851	31	3.7%	—
06/13	856	109	12.8%	—
Annual Growth	8.2%	(32.4%)	—	—

2015 Year-End Financials
Return on assets: 30.8%
Return on equity: 5.0%
Current ratio: 0.30

Cash ($ mil.): 29

SUFFOLK CONSTRUCTION COMPANY, INC.

Suffolk Construction Company provides construction services from top to bottom. The company kicks off the building process with pre-construction services and follows through with design/build general contracting and construction management. Suffolk Construction builds for both the public and private organizations in the science and technology health care education government and commercial sectors operating in the Northeast Mid-Atlantic Southeast and West Coast regions of the US. Founded in 1982 the privately-held firm is owned by president and CEO John Fish whose family has been in construction for four generations.

Geographic Reach
The Boston-based construction firm operates nationwide across the Northeast Mid-Atlantic Southeast and West Coast regions. Its offices are located Boston; Miami; Los Angeles; San Diego; San Francisco; Tarrytown New York; and Estero Florida.

Sales and Marketing
Suffolk Construction offers its services for projects in the assisted living aviation and transportation commercial education entertainment government healthcare hospitality non-profit residential retail and science and technology sectors.

The company has also worked on projects for federal and local governments. In the past Suffolk has built for the Army Corps of Engineers the US Marine Corps and US Navy.

Strategy
Suffolk reemphasized its "Build Smart" approach in 2015 which is designed to boost productivity and cut costs in the construction management process on every project. Before the company breaks ground at a job site it uses technologies such as virtual models and Building Information Modeling (BIM) to build projects virtually. The practice minimizes risk lessens design conflicts and issues and lowers costs for Suffolk Construction clients.

Suffolk Construction serves several sectors to keep the company thriving even in challenging times. The firm extended its reach into the growing health care sector by launching National Healthcare Group which specializes in building health care projects nationwide.

Company Background

Already a successful builder in the New England area Suffolk Construction has expanded nationally in the past through acquisitions. In 2009 it bought Massachusetts-based William A. Berry & Son creating Suffolk's Berry Division which specializes in health care and biomedical projects.

Suffolk Construction also acquired The Dietze Construction Group based in Ashburn Virginia in 2010. The deal strengthened Suffolk's position in the Mid-Atlantic region and expanded its ability to serve the government health care education science/technology and commercial sectors. Giving the company a boost in the West Suffolk Construction acquired Southern California-based ROEL Construction in 2011.

EXECUTIVES

Chairman And Ceo, John F. Fish
President West Region, Andrew J. (Andy) Ball
Evp And Chief Accounting Officer, Michael (Mike) Azarela
President And General Manager Northeast Region, Mark L. DiNapoli
Svp Florida Operations, Rex B. Kirby
General Manager San Diego, Wayne Hickey
Chief Operating Officer San Francisco Office, Michael (Mike) DiNapoli
Executive Vice President Work Acquisition Northeast Region, Peter Welsh
President Healthcare/science And Technology & Chief Innovation Officer, Peter Campot
Vice President And Chief Information Officer, Corren Collura
Evp And General Manager Mid-atlantic Region, Stephen Skinner
Vice President & Chief Operating Officer Commercial Education And Government Northeast Region, Angus Leary
Executive Vice President Of National Business Development, Christopher Woods
Vice President Of Marketing And Communications, Dan Antonellis
Senior Vice President Chief Information Officer, Kevin McDonough
Executive Vice President And General Manager, Jeffrey Gouveia
Vice President Retail, Mike DiNapoli
Executive Vice President And Chief Innovation Officer, Chris Mayer
Vice President Of Operations, John Sykes
Vice President Preconstruction, David Slomsky
Vice President, Christopher Debruin
Treas, Mike Lindblom

LOCATIONS
HQ: SUFFOLK CONSTRUCTION COMPANY, INC.
65 ALLERTON ST, BOSTON, MA 021192923
Phone: 617 445-3500
Web: WWW.SUFFOLK.COM

PRODUCTS/OPERATIONS

Selected Services
Building information modeling
Construction management
Design/build
General contracting
Preconstruction
Sustainable building

COMPETITORS

Balfour Beatty Construction	Pepper Construction
Clark Enterprises	Swinerton
DooleyMack	Turner Corporation
Kraus-Anderson	Tutor Perini
McCarthy Building	Walsh Group
	Whiting-Turner

HISTORICAL FINANCIALS
Company Type: Private

Income Statement				FYE: August 31
	REVENUE ($ mil.)	NET INCOME ($ mil.)	NET PROFIT MARGIN	EMPLOYEES
08/15	2,500	0	—	1,150
08/14	1,761	0	—	—
08/13	1,825	0	—	—
Annual Growth	17.0%			

2015 Year-End Financials
Return on assets: 24.3%
Return on equity: —
Current ratio: 1.10

Cash ($ mil.): 126

SUFFOLK UNIVERSITY

Auditors: KPMG LLP BOSTON MA

LOCATIONS
HQ: SUFFOLK UNIVERSITY
8 ASHBURTON PL, BOSTON, MA 021082770
Phone: 617 573-8000
Web: WWW.SUFFOLK.EDU

HISTORICAL FINANCIALS
Company Type: Private

Income Statement				FYE: June 30
	REVENUE ($ mil.)	NET INCOME ($ mil.)	NET PROFIT MARGIN	EMPLOYEES
06/15	315	23	7.6%	6
06/14	322	26	8.1%	—
Annual Growth	(2.1%)	(8.2%)	—	—

2015 Year-End Financials
Return on assets: 11.8%
Return on equity: 7.6%
Current ratio: —

Cash ($ mil.): 1

SUMMERLIN HOSPITAL MEDICAL CENTER, LLC

EXECUTIVES

Ceo-Dir-Mbr, Robert Freymuller
Coo-MBR, Claude Wise
Cfo-MBR, Bonny Sorensen
Dentist, Maurice Gregory DDS
Chief Staff, George Tu
Information Specialist, Jorge Romero
Food Director, Scott Scribner
Physician, Cathy Aja

LOCATIONS
HQ: SUMMERLIN HOSPITAL MEDICAL CENTER, LLC
657 N TOWN CENTER DR, LAS VEGAS, NV 891446367
Phone: 702 233-7000
Web: WWW.SUMMERLINHOSPITAL.COM

COMPETITORS

Desert Springs Hospital
Dignity Health
Sunrise Hospital and Medical Center
University Medical Center of Southern Nevada
Valley Hospital

HISTORICAL FINANCIALS

Company Type: Private

Income Statement				FYE: December 31
	REVENUE ($ mil.)	NET INCOME ($ mil.)	NET PROFIT MARGIN	EMPLOYEES
12/17	424	80	18.9%	600
12/16	404	60	15.1%	—
12/15	375	47	12.7%	—
12/01	0	0	—	—
Annual Growth	—	—	—	—

SUMMIT HEALTH

EXECUTIVES

Pres-Ceo, Norman P Epstein
Prin, Patrick O'Donnell
Assistant Controller, Lori Leedy
Nurse Manager, Barbara Messner
Engineer, Roger Shadle
Administrative Assistant, Audra Price
Payroll Staff, Joann Cramer
Administrative Assistant, Julie Frey
Human Resources, Margie Gyurisin
Buyer, Sara Johnson
Physician Recruiter, Tammie Chute
Auditors: SMITH ELLIOTT KEARNS & COMPANY

LOCATIONS

HQ: SUMMIT HEALTH
112 N 7TH ST, CHAMBERSBURG, PA 172011720
Phone: 717 267-3000
Web: WWW.SUMMITHEALTH.ORG

HISTORICAL FINANCIALS

Company Type: Private

Income Statement				FYE: June 30
	REVENUE ($ mil.)	NET INCOME ($ mil.)	NET PROFIT MARGIN	EMPLOYEES
06/18	539	33	6.3%	2,968
06/17	520	85	16.4%	—
06/16	480	(37)	—	—
06/15	445	9	2.2%	—
Annual Growth	6.6%	50.5%	—	—

2018 Year-End Financials

Return on assets: 1.8%   Cash ($ mil.): 36
Return on equity: 6.3%
Current ratio: 1.20

SUN-MAID GROWERS OF CALIFORNIA

The Sun-Maid's basket runneth over. Sun-Maid Growers is the producer of Sun-Maid Raisins. Packaged in the familiar red boxes with the smiling red-sunbonneted maid Lorraine Collett Petersen offering her basket laden with grapes the brand is seen in just about every food store in the US. In addition to offering every toddler's (and moms of toddlers) favorite little-red-boxed snack the grower-owned cooperative manufactures industrial and food service products and exports to more than 50 countries. The company's other dried fruits include pitted prunes currants apricots cranberries figs dates apples fruit bits and tropical fruit mixtures. Founded in 1912 the coop is owned by 750 family farmers.

Operations

Sun-Maid whose growers harvest some 200 million pounds of grapes every year also licenses its brand for products including raisin bread raisin muffins and raisin cookie mix as well as chocolate- and vanilla yogurt-covered raisins. Retail products make up about half of the co-op's sales; ingredient products comprise the rest.

Geographic Reach

Headquartered in Kingsburg California Sun-Maid's facilities are located in California's Central Valley — the world's largest raisin producing area — where vineyards belonging to some 750 family farmers span approximately 50000 acres.

Sales and Marketing

Sun-Maid Growers hired Meredith Xcelerated Marketing as its agency of record in 2016. It developed advertising around a promotional tie-in to the November 2016 release "Trolls" a movied starring Anna Kendrick and Justin Timberlake. Agency MBMG will handle media duties.

EXECUTIVES

Vice President Sales, Tomo Naito
Vice President Customer Service, John Slinkard
Vice President General Manager, Peter Pete Penner
Vice President Sales Admin, Karen Schoelen
Auditors: KPMG LLP SACRAMENTO CA

LOCATIONS

HQ: SUN-MAID GROWERS OF CALIFORNIA
13525 S BETHEL AVE, KINGSBURG, CA 936319232
Phone: 559 897-6235
Web: WWW.SUNMAID.COM

PRODUCTS/OPERATIONS

Selected Products

Bakery
    Oatmeal raisin cookie mix
    Raisin bread
    Raisin muffins
Dried apples
Dried California apricots
Dried Calimyrna figs
Dried chopped dates
Dried cranberries
Dried fruit bits
Dried golden raisins and cherries
Dried Mediterranean apricots
Dried mission figs
Dried mixed fruit
Dried pitted dates
Dried pitted plums
Dried tropical trio
Raisins
    Baking raisins
    Chocolate yogurt-covered raisins
    Chocolate-covered raisins
    Golden raisins
    Jumbo raisins
    Vanilla yogurt-covered raisins
    Zante currants

COMPETITORS

Cherry Central
    Cooperative Inc.
Dole Food
Encore Fruit Marketing
Florida Food Products
    Inc
Fresh Del Monte

Meridian Nut Growers
Multiple Organics
National Raisin
Pinnacle Foods
Riviana Foods
Shoreline Fruit
SunOpta

Produce
General Mills
Gold Harbor
Golden West Nuts
Graceland Fruit
Kendall Frozen Fruits
Lion Raisins

Sunview Vineyards
Tree Top
Tropical Nut & Fruit
United Natural
Valley Fig Growers
Waymouth Farms
Welch's

HISTORICAL FINANCIALS

Company Type: Private

Income Statement				FYE: July 31
	REVENUE ($ mil.)	NET INCOME ($ mil.)	NET PROFIT MARGIN	EMPLOYEES
07/17	360	20	5.6%	800
07/16	382	15	3.9%	—
07/15	384	13	3.4%	—
07/14	389	11	3.0%	—
Annual Growth	(2.5%)	19.3%	—	—

2017 Year-End Financials

Return on assets: 8.0%   Cash ($ mil.): 1
Return on equity: 5.6%
Current ratio: 0.40

SUNDT CONSTRUCTION, INC.

EXECUTIVES

Ceo-Pres, G Michael Hoover
Evp-Coo, Thomas S Case
Svp-Gen Counsel, Ronald Stuff
Svp/Cfo/Treas, Kevin M Burnett
Vp, Todd Calder
Payroll Staff, Karolyn Comstock
Coordinator, Kevin Moore
Vice-President Business Develo, Cade Rowly
Coordinator, Lisa Maldonado
Manager, Robert Sanchez
Manager, Terri Babcock
Auditors: MAYER HOFFMAN & MCCANN

LOCATIONS

HQ: SUNDT CONSTRUCTION, INC.
2620 S 55TH ST, TEMPE, AZ 852821903
Phone: 480 293-3000
Web: WWW.SUNDT.COM

HISTORICAL FINANCIALS

Company Type: Private

Income Statement				FYE: September 30
	REVENUE ($ mil.)	NET INCOME ($ mil.)	NET PROFIT MARGIN	EMPLOYEES
09/17	1,134	0	—	1,000
09/16	813	0	—	—
09/13	895	0	—	—
09/12	0	0	—	—
Annual Growth	—	—	—	—

2017 Year-End Financials

Return on assets: 11.9%   Cash ($ mil.): 99
Return on equity: —
Current ratio: 1.30

SUNKIST GROWERS, INC.

Sunkist Growers is one business that is least susceptible to an outbreak of scurvy among its employees. America's oldest continually operating citrus cooperative the company is owned by California and Arizona citrus growers who farm some 300000 acres of citrus trees. Sunkist offers traditional and organic fresh oranges lemons limes grapefruit and tangerines worldwide. The co-op which operates some 20 packing facilities also makes juice and cut fruit packaged in jars. Fruit that doesn't meet fresh market standards is turned into oils and peels for use in food products made by other manufacturers. Sunkist's customers include food retailers and manufacturers and food-service providers worldwide.

Operations

The cooperative's seasonal citrus includes Meyer lemons mandarin oranges Clementine oranges blood oranges and tangelos. Sunkist is one of the most recognized brand names in the world.

Through some 40 licensing agreements the Sunkist name appears on more than 600 beverages and other products — from vitamins to candy to soda to pistachios. It offers Sunkist Fruit Gems (gummie candies) made for the company by the Jelly Belly Candy Company.

Some 45% of Sunkist's fresh fruit sales revenues come from markets outside the US as well as more than 20% of its processed products revenues. To maintain its reach abroad Sunkist works with the US government and the governments of foreign countries to open new markets that are off limits to Western citrus growers.

Geographic Reach

California-based Sunkist operates in the Americas Europe the Middle East and Asia Pacific.

Sales and Marketing

Sunkist regularly advertises worldwide to encourage use of its citrus products and build its brand. Additionally the company leverages television to get its name out such as its alliance with the NBC motivational weight loss competition The Biggest Loser .

Sunkist which has operated a centralized sales organization since 2009 sells its products primarily to food retailers and manufacturers as well as to foodservice providers worldwide. The company is the largest marketing cooperative in the global fruit and vegetable industry.

Financial Performance

Gross annual sales of Sunkist-brand products exceed $1.2 billion worldwide.

Strategy

The company has been focused on market and portfolio expansion and getting the most from its citrus juice and oils and for-profit businesses. It is working to extend its reach to new markets such as India the Middle East and Eastern Europe where its core product has not historically been traded. To reach beyond citrus and expand its products portfolio Sunkist is concentrating on table grapes. Through a pilot program with its existing citrus growers the company markets Sunkist-branded California table grapes grown by them.

It also worked in recent years to improve the productivity of its Tipton juice processing plant. To this end Sunkist in 2012 entered a 50:50 joint venture agreement with fellow juice processor Ventura Coastal. Under the name Ventura Coastal LLC the entity operates the Ventura Coastal plant in Visalia and the Sunkist plant in Tipton. Beginning in 2013 Sunkist also partnered with Greene River Marketing to sell its Florida citrus in promising domestic and export markets.

The 2011-2012 growing season got off to a late start thanks to slow maturing fruit. Its navel orange crop grew to a manageable 88 million cartons as compared to a challenging 93-million-carton crop the previous year. Lemons started slowly as well but both demand and price picked up. Protected groves fared well during the year while unprotected ones — those outside the traditional growing areas — did not. More susceptible to the cold mandarins crops have suffered.

EXECUTIVES

Executive Vice President Sales And Marketing, Kevin Fiori
Managing Director Sunkist Global, Michael Nomoto
Vice President Of Finance, Richard French

LOCATIONS

HQ: SUNKIST GROWERS, INC.
27770 ENTERTAINMENT DR # 120, VALENCIA, CA 913551092
Phone: 661 290-8900
Web: WWW.SUNKIST.COM

PRODUCTS/OPERATIONS

Selected Products
Fresh fruit
 Grapefruit
 Melo Golds
 Oro Blancos
 Pummelos
 Sweeties
 Texas Rio Star
 Western
 Lemons
 Eurkea/Lisbon
 Meyer
 Limes
 Key
 Persian
 Mandarins
 Clementine
 Honey
 Royal
 Satsuma
 Shasta Gold
 W. Murcott
 Oranges
 Cara Cara
 Moro
 Navel
 Valencia
 Tangelos
 Minneola
 Orlando
 Tangerines
 Dancy
 Fairchild
 Pixie
Packaged fruit
 Beverage concentrates
 Carbonated beverages (under license)
 Chilled fruit jellies (under license)
 Fruit juice
 Fruit juice drinks
 Fruit snacks (under license)
 Powdered fruit drinks
 Vitamins (under license)

COMPETITORS

Alico Inc.	Lionel Hitchen
Big Heart Pet Brands	Louis Dreyfus Group
Chiquita Brands	M&B Products
Citrus World	Old Orchard
Coca-Cola	Orchard House Foods
Dole Food	R & Z Ventures
Dundee Citrus Growers	Silver Springs
Edinburg Citrus	Southern Gardens
Fresh Del Monte	Citrus
Produce	Sunny Delight
Freshco	Tropicana
Great Western Juice	U.S. Sugar
King Ranch	Wonderful Company
Lake Placid Groves	

HISTORICAL FINANCIALS
Company Type: Private

Income Statement — FYE: October 31

	REVENUE ($ mil.)	NET INCOME ($ mil.)	NET PROFIT MARGIN	EMPLOYEES
10/17	1,299	9	0.7%	500
10/16	1,207	7	0.6%	—
10/15	1,150	5	0.5%	—
10/14	1,234	6	0.5%	—
Annual Growth	1.7%	10.0%	—	—

2017 Year-End Financials
Return on assets: 1.4% Cash ($ mil.): 36
Return on equity: 0.7%
Current ratio: 1.20

SUNLIGHT GIVING FOUNDATION

EXECUTIVES

Pres, Tegan Bradford

LOCATIONS

HQ: SUNLIGHT GIVING FOUNDATION
855 EL CMINO REAL STE 250, PALO ALTO, CA 94301
Phone: 650 321-3453

HISTORICAL FINANCIALS
Company Type: Private

Income Statement — FYE: December 31

	REVENUE ($ mil.)	NET INCOME ($ mil.)	NET PROFIT MARGIN	EMPLOYEES
12/15	389	378	97.1%	3
12/14	0	0	60.3%	—
Annual Growth	129624.0%	208966.0%	—	—

2015 Year-End Financials
Return on assets: — Cash ($ mil.): 131
Return on equity: 97.1%
Current ratio: —

SUNOCO PIPELINE L.P.

LOCATIONS

HQ: SUNOCO PIPELINE L.P.
4041 MARKET ST, UPPER CHICHESTER, PA 190143121
Phone: 610 859-5700

HISTORICAL FINANCIALS
Company Type: Private

Income Statement — FYE: December 31

	REVENUE ($ mil.)	NET INCOME ($ mil.)	NET PROFIT MARGIN	EMPLOYEES
12/17	804	1,419	176.6%	3
12/16	1,070	796	74.4%	—
Annual Growth	(24.9%)	78.2%	—	—

SUNSOUTH LLC

EXECUTIVES

Mng MBR, Marty Howard
MBR, Lester H Killebrew
MBR-Dir, Andy Wendland
MBR, David Parkman
MBR, Allen Wise
Administrator, Anita Brown
Manager, Dewayne Williams
Auditors: MCCLINTOCK NELSON & ASSOCIATE

LOCATIONS

HQ: SUNSOUTH LLC
 4100 HARTFORD HWY, DOTHAN, AL 363054900
Phone: 334 678-7861
Web: WWW.SUNSOUTH.COM

HISTORICAL FINANCIALS
Company Type: Private

Income Statement			FYE: December 31
	REVENUE ($ mil.)	NET INCOME ($ mil.)	NET PROFIT MARGIN	EMPLOYEES
12/17	290	8	2.8%	318
12/16	278	7	2.7%	—
12/15	264	6	2.5%	—
12/14	273	10	4.0%	—
Annual Growth	2.1%	(9.3%)	—	—

2017 Year-End Financials
Return on assets: 24.4%   Cash ($ mil.): —
Return on equity: 2.8%
Current ratio: 0.10

SURDNA FOUNDATION INC

EXECUTIVES

Administrator, Phillip Henderson
Iii-Ceb-Dir, John E Andrus
Dir, Christopher Davenport
Dir, Lawrence S C Griffith
Dir, Sandra T Kaupe
V-Chairman-Dir, Elizabeth Kelly
Dir, Edith D Thorpe
President, Ed Skaloot
Treasurer, Frederick Moon III
Program Director, Shawn Escoffery
Assistant, Helen Chin

LOCATIONS

HQ: SURDNA FOUNDATION INC
 200 MADISON AVE FL 25, NEW YORK, NY 100164001
Phone: 212 557-0010
Web: WWW.SURDNA.ORG

HISTORICAL FINANCIALS
Company Type: Private

Income Statement				FYE: June 30
	ASSETS ($ mil.)	NET INCOME ($ mil.)	INCOME AS % OF ASSETS	EMPLOYEES
06/15	1,009	115	11.4%	12
06/14	1,037	4	0.5%	—
06/13	929	52	5.7%	—
06/10	754	(22)	—	—
Annual Growth	6.0%	—	—	—

2015 Year-End Financials
Return on assets: 1.2%   Sales ($ mil): 162
Return on equity: 70.8%

SUTTER HEALTH

Whether you drink too much in Wine Country hit some rough waters off the Marin Headlands or trip during a hike through the redwood forest it's likely Sutter Health is just a stone's throw away. The Northern California not-for-profit health care system is one of the nation's largest with more than 4300 acute care beds. After being formed through the merger of Sutter Health and California Healthcare System Sutter Health now caters to residents of more than 100 communities from the California Bay Area to the beaches of Hawaii. Its services are provided through affiliated doctors from a host of health care facilities including acute care hospitals home health networks and skilled nursing facilities.

Operations

Sutter Health affiliates provide acute care services health education home health care hospice care adult day care prenatal clinics immunization services and other specialized health care services.

The system's health plan network includes 25 hospitals and campuses and dozens of other facilities with more than 5000 providers serving some 40000 members throughout Northern California.

In 2015 the system reported more than 11 million outpatient visits; 190054 discharges; and 797057 emergency room visits.

Geographic Reach

Sutter Health structures its governance into two geographic regions across Northern California: the Bay Area (which also includes Hawaii) and the Valley. Each area has its own board that oversees affiliates within the region.

Financial Performance

In 2015 Sutter Health reported $11 billion in total operating revenue up from $10.2 billion in 2014. Net income from operations totaled $287 million in 2015 a 10% decline from 2014; the drop in income was driven by higher operating expenses and a decline in investment income.

Strategy

In 2016 Sutter Health announced plans to open dialysis and chemotherapy infusion centers at its Sutter Coast Hospital facility in Crescent City.

However the system made waves that year when it said it would shutter its Alta Bates Summit Medical Center in Berkeley by 2030. Community members responded by calling for Sutter Health to keep the hospital open; Sutter plans to consolidate the facility's services with those of its sister campus Summit Medical Center which is three miles away. The move to close a hospital which has seen decreased patient stays is not unusual as many health systems are pushing to broaden their service offerings on an outpatient basis.

Like most other health care organizations across the country Sutter Health is using technology to keep its patients informed about their medical care. The company is part of a national group participating in a program called Care Everywhere a technology that enables medical teams from separate hospitals and clinics to share a patient's medical records at the time he or she receives care. Through this technology Sutter Health is linked with UC Davis Health System Stanford Health Care and Santa Cruz County Health Services to share vital patient information.

EXECUTIVES

President And Ceo, Sarah Krevans, age 59
Svp And Cfo, Robert D. (Bob) Reed, age 66
President Sutter Health Central Valley Region, David P. Benn
President Sutter Health East Bay Region, David Bradley
Svp And Cio, Jonathan (Jon) Manis
Svp; Executive Officer Sutter Medical Network, Jeffrey Burnich
President Sutter Health West Bay Region, Mike Cohill
President Sutter Health Sacramento Sierra Region, James E. Conforti
President Sutter Health Peninsula Coastal Region, Jeff Gerard
Ceo Sutter Solano Medical Center, Abhishek Dosi
Vice President Finance And Treasurer, Svend Ryge
Revenue Cycle Vice President, Suzy Cliff
Vice President, Theresa Frei
Director Managed Care, Jan Voge
Senior Vice President And General Counse, Florence Di Benedetto
Vice President Strategy And Business Development Sutter Health Medical And Markets Network, Todd Smith
Legal Secretary, May Vang
Medical Director, Jeff Jenkins
Medical Director Pediatric Gastroenterology, Fadi Haddad
Chair, Geraldine R. Brinton

LOCATIONS

HQ: SUTTER HEALTH
 2200 RIVER PLAZA DR, SACRAMENTO, CA 958334134
Phone: 916 733-8800
Web: WWW.SUTTERHEALTH.ORG

Selected Hospitals
Alta Bates Summit Medical Center (Berkeley Oakland)
California Pacific Medical Center (San Francisco)
Eden Medical Center (Castro Valley)
Kahi Mohala (Ewa HI)
Marin General Hospital (Greenbrae)
Memorial Hospital Los Banos (Los Banos)
Memorial Medical Center (Modesto)
Menlo Park Surgical Hospital
Mills-Peninsula Health Services (Burlingame)
Novato Community Hospital (Novato)
Sutter Amador Hospital (Jackson)
Sutter Auburn Faith Hospital (Auburn)
Sutter Coast Hospital (Crescent City)
Sutter Davis Hospital (Davis)
Sutter Delta Medical Center (Antioch)
Sutter Lakeside Hospital (Lakeport)
Sutter Maternity & Surgery Center of Santa Cruz
Sutter Medical Center (Sacramento)
Sutter Medical Center of Santa Rosa
Sutter Roseville Medical Center
Sutter Solano Medical Center (Vallejo)
Sutter Tracy Community Hospital (Tracy)

PRODUCTS/OPERATIONS

Selected Operations (Northern California Southern Oregon and Hawaii)
Acute Care Hospitals
Neonatal Intensive Care Units
Cancer Centers
Cardiac Centers

Acute Rehabilitation Centers
Medical Foundations
Trauma Centers
Behavioral Health Services
Education Centers and Physician Training Programs
Express Medical Clinics
Home Health and Hospice Services
Long-term Care Centers
Medical Research Centers
Occupational Health Services
Long-Term Care Centers
Irene Swindells Alzheimer's Residential Care Center San Francisco
Sutter Oaks Nursing Center Sacramento
Sutter Senior Care PACE Program Sacramento
Cancer Centers
Alta Bates Summit Comprehensive Cancer Center Berkeley and Oakland
California Pacific Medical Center San Francisco
Dorothy E. Schneider Cancer Center at Mills-Peninsula Health Services Burlingame
Eden Medical Center Castro Valley
Memorial Regional Cancer Center Modesto
Sutter Auburn Faith Hospital Auburn
Sutter Cancer Center Sutter Medical Center Sacramento
Sutter Cancer Center Sutter Roseville Medical Center Roseville
Sutter Solano Cancer Center Vallejo
Programs listed above are approved by the American College of Surgeons' Commission on Cancer.
Research Institutes
California Pacific Medical Center San Francisco
Palo Alto Medical Foundation Research Institute Palo Alto
Sutter Health Institute for Research and Education San Francisco
Sutter Institute for Medical Research Sacramento
Home Health and Hospice Services
Coming Home Hospice
Cohen Cormier Home Attendant & Care Management
Sutter Auburn Faith VNA & Hospice
Sutter Care at Home
Sutter Coast Home Care
Sutter Infusion & Pharmacy Services / Emeryville and Sacramento
Sutter Lakeside Home Medical Services
Sutter Lif
Sutter North Home Health Agency
VNA of the Central Valley
VNA of Santa Cruz County
Express Medical Clinics
Sutter Express Care (Three locations in Sacramento & Placer counties)

COMPETITORS

Adventist Health System West
Alta Bates Summit Medical Center
Ascension Health
California Pacific Medical Center
Children's Hospital & Research Center at Oakland
Dignity Health
HCA
Hawai'i Pacific Health
Kuakini Health System
Memorial Health Services
Providence St. Joseph Health
Rehabilitation Hospital of the Pacific
Stanford Health Care
Tenet Healthcare
UCSF Medical

HISTORICAL FINANCIALS

Company Type: Private

Income Statement				FYE: December 31
	REVENUE ($ mil.)	NET INCOME ($ mil.)	NET PROFIT MARGIN	EMPLOYEES
12/17	12,444	1,060	8.5%	48,000
12/16	11,873	422	3.6%	—
12/15	10,998	84	0.8%	—
12/14	9,715	(405)	—	—
Annual Growth	8.6%	—	—	—

2017 Year-End Financials

Return on assets: 6.9%   Cash ($ mil.): 395
Return on equity: 8.5%
Current ratio: 0.70

SUTTER ROSEVILLE MEDICAL CENTER

EXECUTIVES

Ceo, Patrick Brady
Pharmacist, Charles Elliot
Human Resources Manager, Julie Fralick
Case Manager, Mary Nourot
Director of Philanthropy, Suzanne Zolfo
Hematology Supervisor, Alex Alba
Hematologist, Sivakumar Reddy

LOCATIONS

HQ: SUTTER ROSEVILLE MEDICAL CENTER
1 MEDICAL PLAZA DR, ROSEVILLE, CA 956613037
Phone: 916 781-1000
Web: WWW.SUTTERROSEVILLE.ORG

HISTORICAL FINANCIALS

Company Type: Private

Income Statement				FYE: December 31
	REVENUE ($ mil.)	NET INCOME ($ mil.)	NET PROFIT MARGIN	EMPLOYEES
12/17	669	126	18.9%	1,700
12/16	628	121	19.3%	—
12/15	558	74	13.3%	—
12/12	484	95	19.6%	—
Annual Growth	6.7%	5.9%	—	—

2017 Year-End Financials

Return on assets: 1.6%   Cash ($ mil.): —
Return on equity: 18.9%
Current ratio: 2.30

SUTTER SANTA ROSA REGIONAL HOSPITAL

EXECUTIVES

President, Barbara Eichhorn
Vice President, Shirley Flournoy
Recording Secretary, Vonna Holz
Correspondingsecretary, Jan Tracy
Treasurer, Ann Marie Luffler
Coordinator, Vilona Sample
Engineer, Dan Harmeson
Supervisor, Dana Kettmann
Buyer, Mike Freitas
Coordinator, Patricia Holsworth

LOCATIONS

HQ: SUTTER SANTA ROSA REGIONAL HOSPITAL
30 MARK WEST SPRINGS RD, SANTA ROSA, CA 954031436
Phone: 707 576-4000
Web: WWW.SUTTERSANTAROSA.ORG

HISTORICAL FINANCIALS

Company Type: Private

Income Statement				FYE: December 31
	REVENUE ($ mil.)	NET INCOME ($ mil.)	NET PROFIT MARGIN	EMPLOYEES
12/17	308	52	17.0%	122
12/16	255	16	6.3%	—
12/15	213	(14)	—	—
12/14	175	(19)	—	—
Annual Growth	20.7%	—	—	—

2017 Year-End Financials

Return on assets: 1.3%   Cash ($ mil.): —
Return on equity: 17.0%
Current ratio: 0.40

SUZANO PULP AND PAPER AMERICA, INC

EXECUTIVES

Prin-Mng Dir, Fernando Silveira
Pres, David Feffer
V-Pres, Daniel Feffer
Contrl, Eduardo Melendez
Auditors: BARNES SMALL & MCGEE CPAS BO

LOCATIONS

HQ: SUZANO PULP AND PAPER AMERICA, INC
800 CORPORATE DR STE 320, FORT LAUDERDALE, FL 333343618
Phone: 954 772-7716
Web: WWW.SUZANO.COM.BR

HISTORICAL FINANCIALS

Company Type: Private

Income Statement				FYE: December 31
	REVENUE ($ mil.)	NET INCOME ($ mil.)	NET PROFIT MARGIN	EMPLOYEES
12/16	347	0	0.3%	19
12/15	369	1	0.3%	—
12/14	346	1	0.3%	—
12/13	270	0	0.3%	—
Annual Growth	8.7%	(0.8%)	—	—

2016 Year-End Financials

Return on assets: 25.0%   Cash ($ mil.): 14
Return on equity: 0.3%
Current ratio: 0.50

SWEDISH HEALTH SERVICES

Swedish Health Services doing business as Swedish Medical Center is the largest not-for-profit health provider in the greater Seattle area. Swedish Medical operates five acute care hospitals; it also runs two ambulatory care centers and the Swedish Medical Group physician practice organization which has more than 100 primary and specialty care offices in the greater Puget Sound region.

Swedish Medical is affiliated with Providence St. Joseph Health a Catholic not-for-profit organization with 50 hospitals in seven states.

Operations
Swedish Medical has more than 2800 physicians and its hospitals are home to more than 1500 beds. The network's facilities see over 57000 inpatients per year as well as 175000 emergency room visits more than 9000 births and about 39000 surgeries. Swedish Medical operates numerous institutes across its campuses including its Cancer Institute Heart and Vascular Institute Neuroscience Institute and Orthopedic Institute. Other medical specialties include transplants pediatrics and women's health.

Swedish Medical also conducts clinical research programs with as many as 700 trials being conducted at one time making it one of the largest clinical trial sites in the US. The network's research programs are supported by government and commercial partners.

Geographic Reach
Swedish Medical has three hospital locations in Seattle as well as hospitals in Edmonds and Issaquah Washington. Its ambulatory centers (with emergency and specialty facilities) are located in Redmond and Everett Washington.

Financial Performance
In 2013 the system reported $2 billion in revenue (96% of which came from patient care services) and $59 million in net operating income.

Strategy
The company grows both organically and through partnerships. Through its affiliation with Providence St. Joseph Health Swedish Medical combined with Providence's Washington facilities under a new not-for-profit holding company. The two health systems retain their independent identities but share clinical and IT resources to work towards reducing medical costs and increasing the quality of care in the region.

The company announced a $63.5 million expansion to its Swedish Edmonds hospital campus in 2014. The two-story expansion will include a new emergency department and an outpatient diagnostic imaging center.

Also in 2014 Swedish Medical launched a hematologic malignancies program to research and treat blood-based cancers such as leukemia multiple myeloma and lymphoma.

To balance the costs of growth Swedish Medical occasionally exits underperforming businesses. In 2012 for instance the company ceased operations of its Swedish Visiting Nurse Services program which provide home health care hospice and therapy services. The unit had incurred continuous losses since 2009.

Company Background
Not-for-profit Swedish Medical began in 1910 as a single hospital with 24 beds.

EXECUTIVES

Interim Chief Executive Swedish Medical Group, Jon Younger, age 64
Chief Operating And Administrative Officer, June Altaras
Ceo, R. Guy Hudson
Interim Chief Medical Officer, Charles Watts
President And Chief Development Officer Swedish Medical Center Foundation, Harold A. (Jay) Vogelsang
Vice President Of Patient Care Services Chief Nursing Officer, Nancy Wood
Medical Director Swedish Cardiac Surgery, Glenn Barnhart
Nursing Director, Margo Bykoned
Clinic Supervisor, Shermece Brown
Chairman, Teresa Bigelow

LOCATIONS
HQ: SWEDISH HEALTH SERVICES
747 BROADWAY, SEATTLE, WA 981224379
Phone: 206 386-6000
Web: WWW.SWEDISH.ORG

PRODUCTS/OPERATIONS

Selected Washington Facilities
Ballard Campus (Seattle)
Cherry Hill Campus (Seattle)
Edmonds Campus (Edmonds)
First Hill Campus (Seattle)
Issaquah Campus (Issaquah)
Mill Creek Campus (ambulatory center in Everett)
Redmond Campus (ambulatory center in Redmond)

Selected Institutes and Services
Cancer Institute
Emergency Services
Heart and Vascular Institute
Neuroscience Institute
Orthopedic Institute
Pediatric Specialty Care
Primary Care
Pregnancy and Childbirth
Surgical Services
Transplant Program
Women's Health

COMPETITORS

Franciscan Health System
Harrison Medical Center
MultiCare Health System
Overlake Hospital
PeaceHealth
Seattle Children's Hospital
University of Washington
Wenatchee Valley Medical Center
Yakima Valley Memorial

HISTORICAL FINANCIALS
Company Type: Private

Income Statement				FYE: December 31
	REVENUE ($ mil.)	NET INCOME ($ mil.)	NET PROFIT MARGIN	EMPLOYEES
12/16	1,278	(2)	—	9,700
12/15	1,240	56	4.6%	—
12/14	1,127	79	7.1%	—
Annual Growth	6.5%	—	—	—

2016 Year-End Financials
Return on assets: 2.1%
Return on equity: (-0.2%)
Current ratio: 1.60
Cash ($ mil.): 29

SWEDISHAMERICAN HOSPITAL

EXECUTIVES

Ceo, Bill Gorski
V Pres-Oprs, Michael F Richter
Cfo, Don Haring
Exec Vice President, John R Mecklenburg
SEC, David R Rydell
Information Specialist, Amira Christiansen
Coordinator, Dick Robinson
Information Specialist, Nathan Sweeney
Coordinator, Patricia R Yocum
Security Staff, Matthew Bartsch
Coordinator, Julie Gadow

LOCATIONS
HQ: SWEDISHAMERICAN HOSPITAL
1401 E STATE ST, ROCKFORD, IL 611042315
Phone: 815 968-4400
Web: WWW.SWEDISHAMERICAN.ORG

HISTORICAL FINANCIALS
Company Type: Private

Income Statement				FYE: June 30
	REVENUE ($ mil.)	NET INCOME ($ mil.)	NET PROFIT MARGIN	EMPLOYEES
06/18	527	31	6.0%	1,599
06/17	495	16	3.4%	—
Annual Growth	6.3%	87.0%	—	—

2018 Year-End Financials
Return on assets: 2.5%
Return on equity: 6.0%
Current ratio: 1.00
Cash ($ mil.): 62

SWEETWATER UNION HIGH SCHOOL DISTRICT

EXECUTIVES

Supt, Karen Janney
Manager, Armando Murillo
Administrative Assistant, Blanca Hernandez
Manager, Cesar Canizales
Administrative Assistant, Ligaya Quitilen
School Psychologist, Clarisa Gomez
Senior Administrative Assistan, Colleen Keeran
Senior Buyer, Don Prince
Senior Administrative Assistan, Erika Gonzales
School Psychologist, Karla Hermosillo-Alca
School Psychologist, Nitza Romero
Auditors: CHRISTYWHITE ACCOUNTANCY CORPO

LOCATIONS
HQ: SWEETWATER UNION HIGH SCHOOL DISTRICT
1130 FIFTH AVE, CHULA VISTA, CA 919112812
Phone: 619 691-5500
Web: WWW.SWEETWATERSCHOOLS.ORG

HISTORICAL FINANCIALS
Company Type: Private

Income Statement				FYE: June 30
	REVENUE ($ mil.)	NET INCOME ($ mil.)	NET PROFIT MARGIN	EMPLOYEES
06/17	546	(48)	—	3,521
06/16	525	77	14.8%	—
06/09*	0	0	—	—
12/05	0	0	—	—
Annual Growth	—	—	—	—

*Fiscal year change

SWINERTON BUILDERS

Swinerton Builders a subsidiary of Swinerton focuses on commercial and sustainable construction and renovation projects. Operating primarily in the western US its interiors group offers interior tenant finishes and remodeling working on such projects as high-tech and lab renovations hospitals retail facilities and seismic upgrades. The employee-owned company's building group focuses on new construction and retrofitting for such projects as the San Francisco Museum of Modern Art a Lockheed Martin launch vehicle assembly plant in Colorado and the Bay Bridge toll operations building in San Francisco. Swinerton Builders operates from offices in California Colorado Hawaii Texas New Mexico and Washington.

Operations

As part of its business Swinerton Builders is involved in high-tech and lab renovations hospitals retail facilities and seismic upgrades as well as new construction and retrofitting projects.

Swinerton Builders also constructs many buildings to meet environmental standards. Green projects have ranged from fire stations and retail outlets to college facilities and hotels. Swinertons' own corporate offices in California are solar powered.

Geographic Reach

The building arm of Swinerton serves the western US through offices in California Colorado Hawaii Texas Oregon and Washington. Its offices are located across California as well as in Austin Texas; Denver Colorado; Portland Oregon; Seattle Washington; and Honolulu Hawaii.

Sales and Marketing

Swinerton Builders serves a variety of sectors involving: critical facilities education government healthcare hospitality interiors multi-family residential native American and renewable energy projects. Its clients have included NASA the Federal Aviation Administration Bureau of Indian Affairs and several military and governmental entities including the US Air Force US Army US Department of Agriculture US Department of Homeland Security and the US National Park Service.

Strategy

Swinerton Builders continues to work on high-value projects around the country. In 2015 after being selected from a two-phase best value selection process the company secured a contract to lead the design-build construction project of a $46 million parking building (with some 1795 parking spaces) at the Denver International Airport (DIA) in Colorado.

The company's Swinerton Renewable Energy unit which builds and offers services to the solar utility industry expanded its capabilities in 2013 by adding comprehensive operations and maintenance (O&M) services for any solar facility across North America. The unit also launched a monitoring platform named SOLV to manage all the operational needs of customers with solar utility plants.

EXECUTIVES

Chb, Jeffrey C Hoopes
Pres-Coo, Gary J Rafferty
Exec V Pres, Frank Foellmer
Exec V Pres, Eric Foster
Sr V Pres-Cfo-Sec, Linda G Schowalter
Sr V Pres-Cao, John T Capener
Sr V Pres, Donald D Adair
V Pres, Kerry M Atkinson
V Pres, David C Callis
V Pres, Scott V Conrad
V Pres, George S Ehara
Auditors: CLIFTONLARSONALLEN WALNUT CRE

LOCATIONS

HQ: SWINERTON BUILDERS
  260 TOWNSEND ST, SAN FRANCISCO, CA 941071719
Phone: 415 421-2980
Web: WWW.SWINERTON.COM

PRODUCTS/OPERATIONS

Selected Services
BIM/VD&C
Corporate Services
Critical Facilities
General Contracting
Government Construction
Management & Consulting
Preconstruction
Renewable Energy
Sustainable Construction/LEED

COMPETITORS

Andersen Construction	Hensel Phelps
Charles Pankow	Construction
Builders	J.F. Shea
Clark Builders Group	Jaynes Companies
Cordoba	Kitchell
DPR Construction	Torix General
Devcon Construction	Contractors
Gilbane Building	Turner Corporation
Company	W. L. Butler
Hathaway Dinwiddie	Webcor Builders
Construction	Whiting-Turner

HISTORICAL FINANCIALS
Company Type: Private

Income Statement — FYE: December 31

	REVENUE ($ mil.)	NET INCOME ($ mil.)	NET PROFIT MARGIN	EMPLOYEES
12/17	3,306	39	1.2%	900
12/16	3,664	53	1.5%	—
12/15	2,826	28	1.0%	—
12/14	1,862	13	0.7%	—
Annual Growth	21.1%	43.5%	—	—

2017 Year-End Financials
Return on assets: 18.0% Cash ($ mil.): 122
Return on equity: 1.2%
Current ratio: 1.00

SWVA, INC.

EXECUTIVES

Ceo-Pres, Timothy R Duke
Cfo, Dexter Childers
Dir of Mis/Is, Cindy Kahl

LOCATIONS

HQ: SWVA, INC.
  17TH ST & SECOND AVE, HUNTINGTON, WV 25703
Phone: 304 696-8200
Web: WWW.STEELDYNAMICS.COM

HISTORICAL FINANCIALS
Company Type: Private

Income Statement — FYE: December 31

	REVENUE ($ mil.)	NET INCOME ($ mil.)	NET PROFIT MARGIN	EMPLOYEES
12/17	281	0	—	9
12/16	307	0	—	—
12/15	307	0	—	—
12/14	326	0	—	—
Annual Growth	(4.8%)	—	—	—

2017 Year-End Financials
Return on assets: — Cash ($ mil.): —
Return on equity: —
Current ratio: 1.00

SYRACUSE CITY SCHOOL DISTRICT

EXECUTIVES

Spdt, Jaime Alicea
Spdt, Sharon Contrerasn
Director, Patricia Clark
Teacher, Frederick Seeburger Jr
Teacher, Annie Delaney
Teacher, Lacey Dowd
Teacher, Laurie Alfieri
Teacher, Lynn Branagan
Teacher, Meghan Bishop
Teacher, Marlene Baxter
Superintendent, Sharon Contreras
Auditors: BONADIO & CO LLP SYRACUSE

LOCATIONS

HQ: SYRACUSE CITY SCHOOL DISTRICT
  725 HARRISON ST, SYRACUSE, NY 132102395
Phone: 315 435-4499
Web: WWW.SYRACUSECITYSCHOOLS.COM

HISTORICAL FINANCIALS
Company Type: Private

Income Statement — FYE: June 30

	REVENUE ($ mil.)	NET INCOME ($ mil.)	NET PROFIT MARGIN	EMPLOYEES
06/17	489	4	1.0%	4,361
06/16	464	(12)	—	—
Annual Growth	5.3%	—	—	—

2017 Year-End Financials
Return on assets: 4.6% Cash ($ mil.): 33
Return on equity: 1.0%
Current ratio: —

SYRACUSE UNIVERSITY

Syracuse University is a serious school with a silly mascot. While it wasn't until 1995 that Otto the Orange was officially adopted as the school's mascot Syracuse's tradition of quality higher educationA dates back to 1870. The school enrolls more than 21000 undergraduate and graduate students and hasA some 1000A full-time faculty members on its campus inA central New York State. It offers about 500 degree programs in areas such as communications computer science engineering psychology art mathematics music and information. Notable alumni include Dick Clark Ted Koppel Joyce Carol Oats Joe Biden and Aaron Sorkin.

Operations

Syracuse's degree programs are organized under 13 schools in the fields of architecture arts and sciences education engineering and computer science graduate studies sports information law management public affairs communication visual and performing arts and continuing education.

Several of the colleges have research centers in areas such asA accounting pop culture investment biomaterials health engineering energy technology business management and public affairs. Overall the university has sponsored programs in research teaching and other areas with a total of about $80 million in funding much of which comes from the federal and state governments.

Geographic Reach

Syracuse's studentA population includes residents of all 50 US states and international students from about 125 countries. In addition to its main campus in central New York State the university also has satelliteA campuses in New York City Los Angeles and Washington DC.A It also has an extensive study abroad program with some 40% of its student body enrolling in curriculum programs inA countries including Chile China France Italy SpainA Turkey and the UK.

Financial Performance

Syracuse reported a 3% decrease in revenues to $819 million in 2012 due to lower gains on investment transactions (slightly offset by higher tuition and fees).A However net income in 2012A dipped into the redA due to investment losses increased expenses and interest rate swapA and currency forward agreements.

Student tuition and fees are the largest component of university revenues accounting for about 55% of earnings.A Syracuse chargesA full-time undergraduate tuition of some $38000 per year. Auxiliary enterprises includingA room board bookstore sales and parking fees account for about a quarter of annual revenues.

Syracuse has a total endowment worthA some $940 million as of mid-2012.

Company Background

Syracuse is an education corporation that operates under the direction of an independent board of trustees under the New York Not-for-Profit Corporation Law. The university was granted a charter by the state of New York in 1870.

EXECUTIVES

Senior Vice President, Janet E Lord
Senior Vice President And Chief Advancem, Matt Molen
Vice President And Chief Development Officer, Elizabeth O'Rourke
Vice President Of Internal Affairs, Emanuel Mirabal
Senior Vice President, Lisa Dolak
Associate Vice President International Advancement Aea International, Alexandra Epsilanty
Vice President Alumni Engagement, Sue Ballard
Board Member, Andrew Erickson
Auditors: KPMG LLP SYRACUSE NY

LOCATIONS

HQ: SYRACUSE UNIVERSITY
900 S CROUSE AVE STE 620, SYRACUSE, NY 132444407
Phone: 315 443-1870
Web: WWW.SYRACUSE.EDU

PRODUCTS/OPERATIONS

Selected Academic Units
College of Arts and Sciences
College of Law
College of Visual and Performing Arts
University College
David B. Falk College of Sports and Human Dynamics
Graduate School
L.C. Smith College of Engineering and Computer Science
Martin J. Whitman School of Management
Maxwell School of Citizenship and Public Affairs
School of Architecture
School of Education
School of Information Studies
S.I. Newhouse School of Public Communications

HISTORICAL FINANCIALS
Company Type: Private

Income Statement FYE: June 30

	REVENUE ($ mil.)	NET INCOME ($ mil.)	NET PROFIT MARGIN	EMPLOYEES
06/17	994	197	19.9%	4,350
06/12	818	(73)	—	—
06/11	839	145	17.3%	—
06/10	978	(0)	—	—
Annual Growth	0.2%	—	—	—

2017 Year-End Financials
Return on assets: 14.4%   Cash ($ mil.): 224
Return on equity: 19.9%
Current ratio: —

T. D. WILLIAMSON, INC.

Keeping onshore and offshore pipelines operating safely flowing freely is what T. D. Williamson is all about. A leading global pipeline equipment and services provider the company designs manufactures and maintains oil field machinery and systems including pipeline pigging (scraping) gas leak detection pipeline inspection plugging tapping valve and clamp and cathodic protection equipment. The company also offers general pipeline training turnkey and repair services. T. D. Williamson operates a global network of sales offices and representatives.

Operations

T.D. Williamson provides pipeline equipment and services for onshore and offshore applications including geometry and magnetic flux leakage inspection hot tapping and plugging pig technology services pigging and non-tethered plugging and pipeline cleaning. Its major operating subsidiary is TDW Offshore Services.

Geographic Reach

Serving oil and gas companies in every major oil patch the company has strategically located international service centers and/or manufacturing plants worldwide including in Belgium India Mexico Singapore South Africa the UAE the UK the US and Venezuela.

Strategy

T.D. Williamson leverages its leading market position by offering a broad spectrum of technical experience and a continuously refined portfolio of customized services and state-of-the-art equipment. Its support personnel includes engineers project managers and technicians who are accessible to clients on a 24/7 basis.

Growing its operations in the Middle East in 2014 the company opened a new maintenance center in Abu Dhabi to complement its existing hot tap and STOPPLE plugging service center. The expansion is in keeping with T.D. Williamson's plans to strengthen its inspection business in the Gulf region and to provide turnkey facilities and back-up for the preparation maintenance and mobilization of inline inspection equipment.

Expanding its geographic network in 2013 T.D. Williamson opened a service center in Abu Dhabi and in 2012 an office in Kazakhstan.

The company puts a strong emphasis on innovation and product development.

In 2013 TDW Offshore Services signed a deal with Centrica Storage Limited to provide pipeline isolation services using its SmartPlug Technology. The tool makes allows operators to gain significant benefits in the form of reduced downtime and associated costs by safely isolating pressure in an active pipeline and maintaining production while maintenance is carried out.

Company Background

It conducted a successful pipeline intervention in 2012 using the SmartPlug pressure isolation tool. Carried out for Talisman Malaysia Limited the operation allowed the safe replacement of a shutdown valve on a key section of a gas export pipeline without having to bleed down the line.

In 2012 the company developed and deployed a new proprietary inline inspection reporting software — Interactive Report 2013 — a data visualization tool that makes it easy for users to filter and view their pipeline inspection data.

That year the company unveiled its Subsea 1200RC Tapping Machine a compact remote-controlled subsea machine that allows hot tapping (tying in to a pressurized system while under full operating conditions) to be carried out with increased safety from a diving support vessel.

Growing its project contract portfolio in 2012 T.D. Williamson signed a three-year global pipeline intervention and isolation services contract with BP (one of only four such contracts awarded worldwide by BP).

T.D. Williamson has expanded internationally in the last two decades. With opening of service centers in Dubai Jamnagar (India) Moscow Rayong (Thailand) and Warsaw in 2007 it had locations in every continent except Antarctica. It opened a facility in India in 2010 in order to respond to the growing pipeline business in that country (which is expected to double from 25000 km. by 2015).

In 2011 it created the Global Pipeline Integrity Center in Salt Lake City Utah to combine the TDW inline inspection engineering manufacturing operations service center and data analysis functions in one location.

The company was founded by T.D. Williamson Sr. in 1920 as The Petroleum Electric Company an electrical contracting firm to supply electric motors for gas booster stations oil well drilling equipment and electric generator stations used by the local oil and gas industry in the US. It adopted the T.D. Williamson name in 1933.

EXECUTIVES

Chb, Stephen Williamson
Pres-Ceo, Robert D McGrew
Sr V Pres, Bruce A Thames
V Pres, Mike Benjamin
V Pres-Human Resources, David R Miller
Sr V Pres-Gen Mgr Western Reg, D Bruce Binkley
SEC, Barbara K Bucholtz
Auditors: PRICEWATERHOUSECOOPERS LLP TU

LOCATIONS

HQ: T. D. WILLIAMSON, INC.
6120 S YALE AVE STE 1700, TULSA, OK 741364235
Phone: 918 493-9494

PRODUCTS/OPERATIONS

TDW Products
Cathodic Protection Equipment
Gas Leak Detection
Pipeline Drilling and Hot Tapping Machines
Pipeline Fittings
Pigging Products and Accessories
Pipeline Plugging Equipment
Pipeline Rehabilitation Products
Pipeline Valves
Services
Gas Leak DetectionHot

COMPETITORS

Cameron International	Oil States
Cypress Energy	International
Partners	T3 Energy Services
Halliburton	Weatherford
J-W Operating	International
National Oilwell Varco	

HISTORICAL FINANCIALS
Company Type: Private

Income Statement				FYE: December 31
	REVENUE ($ mil.)	NET INCOME ($ mil.)	NET PROFIT MARGIN	EMPLOYEES
12/15	539	0	—	1,425
12/02	116	1	1.5%	—
12/01	106	2	2.4%	—
12/00	91	2	2.5%	—
Annual Growth	12.6%	—	—	—

2015 Year-End Financials
Return on assets: —
Return on equity: —
Current ratio: 0.40
Cash ($ mil.): 30

TA CHEN INTERNATIONAL, INC.

EXECUTIVES

Ceo, Johnny Hsieh
V Pres, James Chang
V Pres, John Hellighausen
Cfo, Andrew Chang

LOCATIONS

HQ: TA CHEN INTERNATIONAL, INC.
5855 OBISPO AVE, LONG BEACH, CA 908053715
Phone: 562 808-8000
Web: WWW.TACHEN.COM

HISTORICAL FINANCIALS
Company Type: Private

Income Statement				FYE: December 31
	REVENUE ($ mil.)	NET INCOME ($ mil.)	NET PROFIT MARGIN	EMPLOYEES
12/17	1,257	32	2.6%	500
12/14	1,178	27	2.3%	—
12/13	904	8	1.0%	—
Annual Growth	8.6%	38.0%	—	—

2017 Year-End Financials
Return on assets: 1.2%
Return on equity: 2.6%
Current ratio: 0.90
Cash ($ mil.): 3

TACOMA PUBLIC SCHOOLS

EXECUTIVES

Supt, Carla Fantorno
President, Debbie Winskill
Vice President, Kurt Miller
Coo, Christopher Williams
Coordinator, David Syth
Coordinator, Deana Siegel
Teacher, Karen Vialle
Superintendent, Carla J Santorno
Executive Director, Stephen Murakami

Accounting Staff, Dee Kirkevold
Athletic Director, Jennifer Kubista

LOCATIONS

HQ: TACOMA PUBLIC SCHOOLS
601 S 8TH ST, TACOMA, WA 984054614
Phone: 253 571-1000
Web: WWW.TACOMA.K12.WA.US

HISTORICAL FINANCIALS
Company Type: Private

Income Statement				FYE: August 31
	REVENUE ($ mil.)	NET INCOME ($ mil.)	NET PROFIT MARGIN	EMPLOYEES
08/17	469	3	0.8%	3,700
08/06	41	(2)	—	—
08/05	41	(2)	—	—
08/04	330	58	17.7%	—
Annual Growth	2.7%	(19.3%)	—	—

2017 Year-End Financials
Return on assets: 5.4%
Return on equity: 0.8%
Current ratio: —
Cash ($ mil.): 11

TACOMA PUBLIC UTILITIES

City of Tacoma Department of Public Utilities (Tacoma Public Utilities) is fated to fulfill the electric and water desires of the City of Destiny's dwellers. The municipal utility's Tacoma Power unit generates transmits and distributes electricity to 160000 homes and businesses in Tacoma Washington. Tacoma Water serves more than 300000 customers; the division's water supply comes from wells and the Green River Watershed. Tacoma Public Utilities also oversees Tacoma Rail a freight-switching railroad with 75 customers and more than 200 miles of track and the Click! Network a high-speed data network that serves 23790 cable TV customers via more than 1460 miles of fiber-optic and coaxial cable.

Operations
Tacoma Power has more than 2330 miles of transmission and distribution lines; Tacoma Water stores 68 million gallons of water in the McMillin Reservoir and 73 million gallons in 18 other reservoirs and standpipes; Tacoma Rail operates 14 diesel locomotives.

Tacoma Power also owns which provides telecommunications services such as cable television broadband and wholesale internet services.

About 64% of Tacoma Water's customers are inside the city limits of Tacoma; some 55% of Tacoma Power's customers are located inside the city limits of Tacoma.

Tacoma Rail handles more than 165000 freight shipments per year.

Geographic Reach
Tacoma Power provides electric service to the city of Tacoma Fircrest University Place Fife parts of Steilacoom Lakewood Joint Base Lewis-McChord and unincorporated Pierce County as far south as Roy. Tacoma Water provides direct service to customers in Pierce and King counties. Tacoma Rail provides freight connections for customers in greater Tacoma and Olympia Washington.

Financial Performance
The company's revenues grew by 6% to $387.9 million in 2012 primarily due to an average rate

increase of 6% which lifted revenues by $14 million. Wheeling revenues grew by $2.9 million primarily due to the assignment of a portion of Tacoma Power's 3rd Intertie capacity and a rate increase for the Open Access Transmission Tariff. Telecommunications revenues grew by $0.8 million. Wholesale revenues increased $5.4 million after the transfer of $12 million to the rate stabilization fund in 2012.

Average daily prices decreased 19% but this was more than offset by a 17% increase in volume.

However net income decreased by 23% to 159.1 million in 2012 due to higher operating costs as a result of 6.6% increase in purchased power expenses. Bonneville Power Administration purchases increased by $11 million due to contract changes. Administrative and general expenses increased 11.3% in 2012 (costs included an increase of $1.4 million in contributions to the self-insurance fund).

Strategy
Tacoma Public Utilities operates entirely from revenues generated from the sale of its utility and rail services not from taxes. To adjust to declining revenues the divisions cut operating and maintenance costs postpone some capital projects and cut jobs through attrition and adjusted rates.

Company Background
In 2011 Tacoma Rail with the help of a $2.5 million grant from the EPA and Puget Sound Clean Air Agency purchased three eco-friendly locomotives for $4.3 million.

Established in 1892 Tacoma Public Utilities is the largest department of the City of Tacoma and is governed by the five-member Public Utilities Board. Tacoma Rail has provided rail transportation as a public entity since 1914.

EXECUTIVES

Board Member, Sam Benscoter
Auditors: MOSS ADAMS LLP TACOMA WASHIN

LOCATIONS

HQ: TACOMA PUBLIC UTILITIES
3628 S 35TH ST, TACOMA, WA 984093192
Phone: 253 502-8600
Web: WWW.MYTPU.ORG

PRODUCTS/OPERATIONS

2012 Sales

	% of total
Power	89
Telecom services	6
Other	5
Total	**100**

COMPETITORS

Avista	Puget Energy
CSX	Seattle City Light
Edison International	Union Pacific
PG&E Corporation	

HISTORICAL FINANCIALS
Company Type: Private

Income Statement				FYE: December 31
	REVENUE ($ mil.)	NET INCOME ($ mil.)	NET PROFIT MARGIN	EMPLOYEES
12/15	410	(1)	—	1,407
12/13	414	19	4.8%	—
12/11	364	20	5.7%	—
12/10	62	5	8.1%	—
Annual Growth	45.5%	—	—	—

TAKEUCHI MFG. (U.S.), LTD.

EXECUTIVES

Pres-SEC, Clay Eubanks
Cfo, Renee Paulk
SEC, George Stewart
Training and Manag, David Steger
Regional Manager, Chad Rackley
Advertising Sales Manager, David Pearson
National Warranty Manager, Gary Bryan
Staff Accountant, Jocelyn Cardona
Regional Business Manager, Steve Depriest
National Marketing Manager, Tammie Snodgrass
Manager Director, Angy Lamb

LOCATIONS

HQ: TAKEUCHI MFG. (U.S.), LTD.
519 BONNIE VALENTINE WAY, PENDERGRASS, GA
305674233
Phone: 706 693-3602
Web: WWW.TAKEUCHI-US.COM

HISTORICAL FINANCIALS
Company Type: Private

Income Statement				FYE: December 31
	REVENUE ($ mil.)	NET INCOME ($ mil.)	NET PROFIT MARGIN	EMPLOYEES
12/17	408	5	1.4%	104
12/16	367	13	3.7%	—
12/15	339	11	3.5%	—
12/09	48	0	2.0%	—
Annual Growth	30.6%	25.4%	—	—

2017 Year-End Financials

Return on assets: 0.8%   Cash ($ mil.): 64
Return on equity: 1.4%
Current ratio: 0.50

TALEN ENERGY SUPPLY, LLC

EXECUTIVES

Svp And Chief Administrative Officer, James E. (Jim) Schinski
Svp And Chief Commercial Officer, Clarence J. (Joe) Hopf
President And Ceo, Paul A Farr
Svp Cfo And Chief Accounting Officer, Jeremy R. McGuire
Svp And Chief Nuclear Officer, Timothy S. Rausch
Auditors: ERNST & YOUNG LLP PHILADELPHI

LOCATIONS

HQ: TALEN ENERGY SUPPLY, LLC
600 HAMILTON ST STE 600 # 600, ALLENTOWN, PA
181012105
Phone: 888 211-6011
Web: WWW.TALENENERGY.COM

HISTORICAL FINANCIALS
Company Type: Private

Income Statement				FYE: December 31
	REVENUE ($ mil.)	NET INCOME ($ mil.)	NET PROFIT MARGIN	EMPLOYEES
12/16	3,913	(352)	—	4,981
12/15	4,481	(341)	—	—
12/14	3,736	410	11.0%	—
12/13	4,653	(229)	—	—
Annual Growth	(5.6%)	—	—	—

2016 Year-End Financials

Return on assets: 14.1%   Cash ($ mil.): 135
Return on equity: (-9.0%)
Current ratio: 0.60

TALLAHASSEE MEMORIAL HEALTHCARE, INC.

Tallahassee Memorial HealthCare (TMH) aims to take the hassle out of health care. The community health system serves residents of Florida's state capital and its surrounding communities. The system is anchored by Tallahassee Memorial Hospital a not-for-profit facility with more than 770 beds and about 560 physicians on staff who represent some 50 different specialties. TMH provides general medical and surgical care as well as specialty care in areas such as oncology rehabilitation women's and children's health obesity and diabetes. TMH also has a trauma center offers a family practice residency program and provides primary medical care through a handful of regional clinics.

Operations

TMH is Florida's eighth-largest hospital boasting more than 24000 inpatient admissions per year. As part of its operations TMH has a 60-bed psychiatric hospital and offers adult day care and home health care services. It operates the only Level II trauma center in the region which benefits from newly added telemedicine equipment that includes videoconferencing. Trauma centers are specially trained and equipped to handle severe injuries and all such patients in the area are routed to trauma certified facilities.

The system partners with the H. Lee Moffitt Cancer Center & Research Institute in Tampa to allow cancer patients to participate in clinical trials and other experimental and research opportunities.

The system offers a range of cardiovascular services from diagnostic procedures to open-heart surgery a designated acute brain and spinal cord injury center and a 110000-sq.-ft. childbirth facility — the region's only Level Three Neonatal Intensive Care Unit.

In 2014 the hospital had 122100 emergency and urgent care visits and 29586 general admissions.

Geographic Reach

TMH serves 17 counties across North Florida and South Georgia.

Financial Performance

In 2014 TMH's net revenues increased by 7% due to higher net patient service revenues (net of contractual allowances and discounts).

The company's net income rose by 15% due to higher net revenues and a decrease in interest.

TMH's operating cash inflow in 2014 increased by 16%.

Strategy

The medical facility operates the Tallahassee Memorial Transition Center created in partnership with Capital Health Plan and Florida State University College of Medicine. The center was designed to improve wellness through new approaches and collaborative research. Looking to position itself as a regional center for healthcare Tallahassee Memorial has plans to roll out more new services and add physicians.

In 2015 the hospital and Apalachee Center expanded their agreement to include administrative management of Tallahassee Memorial behavioral health services by Apalachee Center to improve behavioral health services in the community. As part of an earlier agreement the company will continue to provide some psychiatric medical coverage for Apalachee Center's inpatient services as well as providing all psychiatric medical services at the Tallahassee Memorial Behavioral Health Center.

In 2014 TMH and Doctors' Memorial Hospital signed an agreement to create an equal governance partnership between the two institutions that will ultimately enhance services to Doctors' Memorial Hospital and expand its role in Taylor County's health care system.

To expand its capabilities TMH opened the Tallahassee Memorial Emergency Center - Northeast in mid-2013 and broke ground in 2013 on a new surgery and adult intensive care facility that's anticipated to cost as much as $175 million.

Company Background

TMH was founded in 1948.

EXECUTIVES

Vp And Cfo, William (Bill) Giudice
Vp And Coo, Jason Moore
Vp And Cio, Don Lindsey
President Tmh Foundation, Paula Fortunas
Chief Medical Officer, Dean Watson
Administrator Behavioral Health Center, Carl Mahler
Director Premier Health And Fitness Center, Len Harvey
Administrator Orthopedic And Neurological Services, Judy Greenwald
Administrator Surgery Services, David Thompson
President And Ceo, G. Mark OÅ'Bryant
Vp And Chief Nursing Officer, Barbara Alford
Administrator Cancer Center, Matt Sherer
Interim Administrator Emergency Medicine Services, Eric Hartigan
Administrator Heart And Vascular Center, Terri McDonald
Administrator Regional Development Population Health And Telemedicine, Lauren Faison
Administrator Womenâ's Pavilion And Childrenâ's Center, Connie Styons
Chairman, Glenda Thornton

LOCATIONS

HQ: TALLAHASSEE MEMORIAL HEALTHCARE, INC.
1300 MICCOSUKEE RD, TALLAHASSEE, FL
323085054
Phone: 850 431-1155
Web: WWW.TMH.ORG

PRODUCTS/OPERATIONS

2014 sales

	% of total
Hospitals	97
TMHV	1
Medicus	2
Total	**100**

Selected Services

Behavioral Health Center
Rehabilitation Center

Cancer Center
Bixler Emergency Center
Heart & Vascular Center
Diabetes Center
Orthopedic Center
NeuroScience Center
Surgical Services
Women's Pavilion
Home Health Care
Clinical Genetics Center
Bariatric Center
Chronic Pain Management
Lipid Center

COMPETITORS

Adventist Health System Sunbelt Healthcare
Baptist Health System
Bay Medical Center
H. Lee Moffitt Cancer Center & Research Institute
HCA
Jackson County Hospital of Florida
Munroe Regional Health System
Sacred Heart Health System
UF&Shands

HISTORICAL FINANCIALS

Company Type: Private

Income Statement				FYE: September 30
	REVENUE ($ mil.)	NET INCOME ($ mil.)	NET PROFIT MARGIN	EMPLOYEES
09/15	589	38	6.5%	6,430
09/14	532	33	6.2%	—
09/13	566	31	5.6%	—
09/12	479	40	8.4%	—
Annual Growth	7.1%	(1.4%)	—	—

2015 Year-End Financials

Return on assets: 9.1%
Return on equity: 6.5%
Current ratio: 3.30

Cash ($ mil.): 227

TALLGRASS PONY EXPRESS PIPELINE LLC

EXECUTIVES

Ceo- Pres, David Dehaemers Jr

LOCATIONS

HQ: TALLGRASS PONY EXPRESS PIPELINE LLC
4200 W 115TH ST, LEAWOOD, KS 662112609
Phone: 913 928-6060
Web: WWW.TALLGRASSENERGYLP.COM

HISTORICAL FINANCIALS

Company Type: Private

Income Statement				FYE: December 31
	REVENUE ($ mil.)	NET INCOME ($ mil.)	NET PROFIT MARGIN	EMPLOYEES
12/17	354	191	54.2%	1
12/16	375	214	57.0%	—
Annual Growth	(5.8%)	(10.4%)	—	—

TARRANT COUNTY HOSPITAL DISTRICT

If Fort Worth residents are searching for health care they need look no further than Tarrant County Hospital District (dba JPS Health Network). Founded in 1906 in Fort Worth Texas the network's flagship facility John Peter Smith Hospital has approximately 540 beds and provides specialty services including orthopedics cardiology and women's health. JPS Health Network also includes behavioral health treatment center Trinity Springs Pavilion and the JPS Diagnostic & Surgery Hospital of Arlington. The company provides family medical dental and specialty care through dozens of health care centers in northern Texas.

Operations
JPS Hospital is a member of the Council of Teaching Hospitals and Health Systems (COTH).

Sales and Marketing
The health system carries a Level 1 Trauma designation across the spectrum of health care specialties meaning it is the referral hospital of choice for patients who are terribly injured.

Strategy
The health system works to improve the health of Tarrant County as a whole by training health care workers and physicians about working outside the hospital walls and within the community. The institution sponsors programs that are accredited through the Accreditation Council for Graduate Medical Education (ACGME) American Osteopathic Association (AOA) and the Council on Podiatric Medical Education (CPME).

JPS Health Network opened JPS Medical Home Southeast Tarrant a primary and specialty care facility in 2014. The following year the system relocated its Pain Management Clinic to a renovated site in Fort Worth.

EXECUTIVES

Cfo, David Salsberry
Manager, Gary Floyd
Coo, Bill Whitman
Senior Vice President Of Human Resources And Learning, Nikki Sumpter
Vice President Chief Strategy Officer, Merianne Roth
Department Chairman, Kellie Flood-Shaffer
Chair, Scott W. Fisher
Vice-chair, Trent Petty

LOCATIONS

HQ: TARRANT COUNTY HOSPITAL DISTRICT
1500 S MAIN ST, FORT WORTH, TX 761044917
Phone: 817 921-3431
Web: WWW.JPSHEALTHNET.ORG

Primary Locations – Texas
Ambulatory Surgery Center (Fort Worth)
Cardiology Center (Fort Worth)
Enrollment & Eligibility Center (Fort Worth)
Family Medicine & Surgical Specialty Center (Fort Worth)
Healing Wings AIDS Center (Fort Worth)
John Peter for Cancer Care (Fort Worth)
JPS Urgent Care Center (Fort Worth)
Lifespan Family Medicine & Pediatrics (Fort Worth)
Patient Care Pavilion (Fort Worth)
Professional Building-Medicine Clinic (Fort Worth)
Trinity Springs Pavilion for Psychiatric Services (Fort Worth)

PRODUCTS/OPERATIONS

Selected Services
Behavioral Services
Cancer

Cardiology
Dental
Geriatrics
Healing Wings HIV/AIDS Center
Orthopedics and Sports Medicine
Robotic Surgery
School-Based Health Centers
Sexual Assault Nurse Examiner Program
Stroke / N
Surgical Services
Trauma Services
Women's Services

COMPETITORS

Baylor University Medical Center	Presbyterian Hospital of Dallas
CHRISTUS Health	Southwestern Medical
Community Health Systems	Center
Cook Children's Health Care System	Tenet Healthcare Texas Health Resources
HCA	The Methodist Health System
Harris Methodist Fort Worth Hospital	Universal Health Services
Parkland Health & Hospital System	

HISTORICAL FINANCIALS

Company Type: Private

Income Statement				FYE: September 30
	REVENUE ($ mil.)	NET INCOME ($ mil.)	NET PROFIT MARGIN	EMPLOYEES
09/16	576	18	3.2%	3,000
09/15	557	48	8.7%	—
09/14	285	48	16.9%	—
Annual Growth	42.1%	(37.9%)	—	—

2016 Year-End Financials

Return on assets: 6.4%
Return on equity: 3.2%
Current ratio: 2.60

Cash ($ mil.): 181

TATA AMERICA INTERNATIONAL CORPORATION

EXECUTIVES

President, Surya Kant
Vp Marketing And Communications, John Lenzen
Cfo, S. Mahalingam
Auditors: DELOITTE HASKINS & SELLS LLP

LOCATIONS

HQ: TATA AMERICA INTERNATIONAL CORPORATION
101 PARK AVE RM 2603, NEW YORK, NY 101782604
Phone: 212 557-8038
Web: WWW.TCS.COM

PRODUCTS/OPERATIONS

Selected Subsidiaries
IT Services
Tata Business Support Services
Tata Communications
Tata Consultancy Services
Tata Elxsi
Tata Interactive Systems
Tata Technologies
Engineering
Tata AutoComp Systems
Services

Campton Place
Taj Boston
The Pierre
Consumer Products
Eight O'Clock Coffee
Good Earth
Tanishq
Tata Tea Inc.
Tetley
Chemicals
General Chemical

COMPETITORS

Accenture	HCL Technologies
Atos North America	HP Enterprise Services
CIBER	IBM Global Services
Capgemini North	ICP Inc.
America	Infosys
Cognizant Tech	NTT Data
Solutions	Syntel
Computer Sciences	Unisys
Corp.	Wipro Technologies
Fujitsu America	Zensar Technologies

HISTORICAL FINANCIALS
Company Type: Private

Income Statement
FYE: March 31

	REVENUE ($ mil.)	NET INCOME ($ mil.)	NET PROFIT MARGIN	EMPLOYEES
03/18	8,197	121	1.5%	1,700
03/17	845	168	19.9%	—
03/16	755	118	15.7%	—
03/15	6,800	111	1.6%	—
Annual Growth	6.4%	3.0%	—	—

2018 Year-End Financials
Return on assets: 12.7%
Return on equity: 1.5%
Current ratio: 0.90
Cash ($ mil.): 15

TATA COMMUNICATIONS (AMERICA) INC.

EXECUTIVES

Ceo, Vinod Kumar
Pres, Julie Woods-Moss
Cfo, Pratibha K Advani
Executive Administrator, Allison Ponturo
Assistant Manager Information, Arjendra Rangdale
Client Director, Bejan Rafii
Senior Manager, Daniel Ferreira
Senior Regional Bid Manager US, Deborah Brooks
Program Manager, Deepak Bhatt
Sales Engineer, Dinesh Sawant
Head of Mobile Money Enablemen, Dingemans Frederic

LOCATIONS

HQ: TATA COMMUNICATIONS (AMERICA) INC.
2355 DULLES CORNER BLVD # 700, HERNDON, VA 201716154
Phone: 703 657-8400
Web: WWW.TATACOMMUNICATIONS.COM

HISTORICAL FINANCIALS
Company Type: Private

Income Statement
FYE: March 31

	REVENUE ($ mil.)	NET INCOME ($ mil.)	NET PROFIT MARGIN	EMPLOYEES
03/18	444	6	1.4%	100
03/17	482	(1)		—
03/16	485	21	4.5%	—
03/15	546	2	0.5%	—
Annual Growth	(6.7%)	27.7%	—	—

2018 Year-End Financials
Return on assets: 9.9%
Return on equity: 1.4%
Current ratio: 0.30
Cash ($ mil.): —

TEAM INDUSTRIES HOLDING CORPORATION

It takes a team TEAM Industries to make the drivetrains that and other vehicles parts. The Ricke family owned company designs tests manufacturers and assembles powertrain transmissions drivetrains gear sets and chassis components for snowmobile all-terrain vehicle lawn mowers and other vehicles through partnerships with CNH Ford Honda Ingersoll-Rand Kawasaki Textron Yamaha and other OEMs. TEAM maintains half a dozen facilities throughout Minnesota and North Carolina; its manufacturing capabilities run from ductile iron and shaft machining to aluminum diecasting and gear/spline making. The company also offers engineering R&D and testing services.

Operations

The company sells its products through six locations: TEAM Andrews acts as its precision machining gear manufacturing and metallurgical lab; TEAM Audubon specializes in gear cutting and heat treating; TEAM Bagley is its corporate headquarters; TEAM Detroit Lakes has expertise in aluminum die casting; TEAM Park Rapids works with CNC (computer numerical control) machining and loctite (a brand of adhesives) impregnation casting; and Motek-TEAM Industries is another metallurgical lab with a focus on induction hardening.

Geographic Reach

TEAM operates six manufacturing facilities five in Minnesota (Audubon Bagley Cambridge Detroit Lakes and Park Rapids) and one in North Carolina (Andrews) with more than 850000 sq. ft. of total manufacturing space.

Company Background

The company was established in 1967 as Motek Engineering and Manufacturing by Don and Bea Ricke.

EXECUTIVES

Pres-Ceo, David Ricke
Exec Vice President, Michael Matthews
Cfo, Steve Kast
Manager, Duwayne Cookman
Distribution/Shipping/Transpor, John Rooney
Health Professional, Mark Unger
Auditors: MYSLAJEK KEMP & SPENCER LTD

LOCATIONS

HQ: TEAM INDUSTRIES HOLDING CORPORATION
105 PARK AVE NW, BAGLEY, MN 566219558
Phone: 218 694-3550

PRODUCTS/OPERATIONS

Selected Products
Axle assemblies and housings (spiral straight bevel or hypoid gearing)
Continuously variable transmissions (10-200 horsepower & up to 10000 rpm)
Differentials (with a variety of traction control mechanisms)
Gear sets
Transaxles (for a variety of electric or gas powered vehicles)
Transmissions and gear boxes (using parallel axis gears crossed axis gears worm sets planetary)
Wet brake assemblies

Selected Market Applications
Agricultural
All-terrain vehicles
Alternative on-road vehicles
Automotive
Golf carts
Lawn & garden
Marine
Motorcycles
Off-highway construction & others
Personal watercraft
Snowmobiles
Turf care
Utility vehicles

COMPETITORS

American Axle & Manufacturing	GKN
BorgWarner	Lippert Components
Dana	Magna International
Federal-Mogul	Meritor
	Visteon

HISTORICAL FINANCIALS
Company Type: Private

Income Statement
FYE: September 30

	REVENUE ($ mil.)	NET INCOME ($ mil.)	NET PROFIT MARGIN	EMPLOYEES
09/17	286	22	7.8%	1,100
09/16	279	19	6.9%	—
09/12	288	25	8.8%	—
09/11	251	22	9.1%	—
Annual Growth	2.2%	(0.3%)	—	—

2017 Year-End Financials
Return on assets: 7.5%
Return on equity: 7.8%
Current ratio: 1.50
Cash ($ mil.): 31

TEAM MARKETING ALLIANCE, LLC

EXECUTIVES

Principal, Ted Schultz
Marketing Staff, Justin Jenkins
Marketing Staff, Dusty Campbell
Grain Marketing Specialist, Quentin Yoho
Controller, Tricia Jantz
Auditors: LINDBURG VOGEL PIERCE FARIS CE

LOCATIONS

HQ: TEAM MARKETING ALLIANCE, LLC
307 W COLE ST, MOUNDRIDGE, KS 671077533
Phone: 620 345-3560
Web: WWW.TMAGRAIN.COM

HISTORICAL FINANCIALS

Company Type: Private

Income Statement				FYE: February 28
	REVENUE ($ mil.)	NET INCOME ($ mil.)	NET PROFIT MARGIN	EMPLOYEES
02/17	314	23	7.5%	17
02/16	334	13	4.0%	—
Annual Growth	(6.0%)	77.2%	—	—

TEKSYSTEMS, INC.

TEKsystems a subsidiary of staffing giant Allegis provides IT consulting and staffing services from locations in North America and Europe. Considered one of the nation's largest IT staffing firms the company places more than 80000 technical professionals each year who work in a variety of fields including biotechnology telecommunications and construction and engineering. TEKsystems has 100 offices serving about 6000 clients. In addition the company runs the thingamajob.com website which is an online job board for technical staff. Spinning off of fellow Allegis unit Aerotek TEKsystems was formed in 1994 to focus on the IT needs of clients.

Geographic Reach

The company has more than 100 locations throughout North America Europe and Asia.

Sales and Marketing

TEKsystems works to help its clients control cost mitigate risk and deliver quality product outcomes.

Strategy

The company has used strategic partnerships to grow its business.

EXECUTIVES

President, Keith Bozeman
Auditors: PRICEWATERHOUSECOOPERS LLP BA

LOCATIONS

HQ: TEKSYSTEMS, INC.
7437 RACE RD, HANOVER, MD 210761112
Phone: 410 540-7700
Web: WWW.TEKSYSTEMS.COM

PRODUCTS/OPERATIONS

SELECTED SERVICES
IT STAFFING SOLUTIONS
Communications Staffing Services
Digital Services
End User Services
IT Applications Staffing Services
IT Direct Placement Services
Network Infrastructure Staffing Services
TEKsystems Staffing Quality Process
Time and Expense
IT SERVICES
Applications Services
Education Services
Global Delivery Network
Infrastructure Services
Project Governance
IT TALENT MANAGEMENT EXPERTISE
Local Market

Selected Markets Served
Communications
Financial services
Government
Information technology
Expertise

COMPETITORS

Acro Service	Info Technologies
Adecco	Kelly Services
CDI	ManpowerGroup
CorSource Technology Group	Prosum
	Robert Half

HISTORICAL FINANCIALS

Company Type: Private

Income Statement				FYE: December 31
	REVENUE ($ mil.)	NET INCOME ($ mil.)	NET PROFIT MARGIN	EMPLOYEES
12/17	4,350	0	—	2,900
12/16	4,132	0	—	—
12/14	3,618	0	—	—
12/13	3,551	0	—	—
Annual Growth	5.2%	—	—	—

2017 Year-End Financials

Return on assets: 2.8%   Cash ($ mil.): 41
Return on equity: —
Current ratio: 2.90

TELCO INTERCONTINENTAL CORP

EXECUTIVES

Pres-Ceo, Frank C Liang
V Pres-Sec-Treas, MEI-Yun Liang
Operations Manager, Sue Yu
Customer Service, Ester Xiang
Manager, Jane Liang
Manager, Albert Robinson
Information Technology Special, Benjamin Yao

LOCATIONS

HQ: TELCO INTERCONTINENTAL CORP
9812 WHITHORN DR, HOUSTON, TX 770955001
Phone: 281 500-8270
Web: WWW.TELCOINTERCON.COM

HISTORICAL FINANCIALS

Company Type: Private

Income Statement				FYE: December 31
	REVENUE ($ mil.)	NET INCOME ($ mil.)	NET PROFIT MARGIN	EMPLOYEES
12/16	15,167	226	1.5%	24
12/15	19,067	1,371	7.2%	—
Annual Growth	(20.5%)	(83.5%)	—	—

2016 Year-End Financials

Return on assets: 3.4%   Cash ($ mil.): 3,055
Return on equity: 1.5%
Current ratio: 22.50

TEMECULA VALLEY UNIFIED SCHOOL DISTRICT SCHOOL FACILITIES CORPORATION

EXECUTIVES

Supt, Tim Ritter
Asst Supt Bus Scvs, Lori Ordway-Teck
Transportation Director, Jason Osborn
Manager, Mark Rogers
Supervisor, Robert Gates
Supervisor, Don Fails
Coordinator, Jim Miller
Assistant Director, Breck Smith
Clerk, Rosanne Lilienfeld
Buyer, Michelle Kurtz
Accountant, Cindy Estrada
Auditors: VAVRINEK TRINE DAY & CO LL

LOCATIONS

HQ: TEMECULA VALLEY UNIFIED SCHOOL DISTRICT SCHOOL FACILITIES CORPORATION
31350 RANCHO VISTA RD, TEMECULA, CA 925926200
Phone: 951 676-2661
Web: WWW.TVUSD.K12.CA.US

HISTORICAL FINANCIALS

Company Type: Private

Income Statement				FYE: June 30
	REVENUE ($ mil.)	NET INCOME ($ mil.)	NET PROFIT MARGIN	EMPLOYEES
06/17	305	(10)	—	2,866
06/05	207	0	—	—
Annual Growth	3.3%	—	—	—

TENNESSEE STATE SCHOOL BOND AUTHORITY

EXECUTIVES

Prin, Jerald Nicely
Chief Engineer, Paul Degges

LOCATIONS

HQ: TENNESSEE STATE SCHOOL BOND AUTHORITY
SUITE 1600 JAMES K. POLK, NASHVILLE, TN 372430001
Phone: 615 401-7872

Income Statement   FYE: June 30

	ASSETS ($ mil.)	NET INCOME ($ mil.)	INCOME AS % OF ASSETS	EMPLOYEES
06/17	2,258	(6)	—	3
06/16	2,200	9	0.4%	—
Annual Growth	2.6%	—	—	—

2017 Year-End Financials

Return on assets: 55.3%   Sales ($ mil): 67
Return on equity: (-10.2%)

TERRA NITROGEN COMPANY, L.P.

Making the earth's soil produce more crops is the long term mission of Terra Nitrogen which manufactures nitrogen fertilizer products. The company operates a plant in Oklahoma that produces ammonia and urea ammonium nitrate (UAN) solutions. Farmers use the company's products to improve both the quantity and the quality of crops. It sells its products to parent company agrochemical giant CF Industries which in turn sells nitrogen products wholesale to dealers distributors and national farm retail chain outlets primarily in the central and Southern Plains and Corn Belt regions of the US. CF Industries has indirect ownership of Terra Nitrogen's general partner and controls the company.

Operations

Terra Nitrogen's primary asset is a nitrogen manufacturing facility in Verdigris Oklahoma. The Verdigris site has two ammonia plants two nitric acid plants and two UAN plants. The Oklahoma facility has access to an abundant supply of natural gas through the ONEOK (Panhandle) intrastate gas pipeline.

In 2013 the company produced about 1.1 million tons of ammonia and 2 million tons of UAN and sold about 2.3 million tons of nitrogen fertilizers.

It conducts its operations through an operating partnership Terra Nitrogen Limited Partnership (TNLP). Terra Nitrogen GP Inc. (TNGP) a wholly-owned subsidiary of CF Industries is the general partner of both TNCLP and TNLP. Terra Nitrogen GP Inc. has full control of TNCLP's business affairs.

Financial Performance

Terra Nitrogen's revenues decreased by 6% in 2013 due to lower production as a result of a planned plant turnaround that was completed during the third quarter of 2013.

Net income decreased by 10% 2013 due to lower revenues and higher costs. The average cost of goods sold per ton increased to $96 per ton in 2013 from $85 per ton in fiscal 2012. The increase was due to higher natural gas prices a rise in maintenance costs resulting from increased maintenance activities a jump in payroll costs (associated with a plant turnaround) and higher depreciation costs.

Strategy

In 2012 the company broke ground on two additional on-site storage tanks with capacities of 30000 tons of ammonia and 50000 tons of UAN. These projects are expected to be completed in 2014.

Company Background

CF Industries acquired former owner Terra Industries in 2010. As a result CF Industries became the sole customer of Terra Nitrogen's products in 2011.

EXECUTIVES

Pres-Ceo, W Anthony Will
Sr V Pres-Cfo, Dennis P Kelleher
Board of Directors, Michael Jackson
Auditors: KPMG LLP CHICAGO ILLINOIS

LOCATIONS

HQ: TERRA NITROGEN COMPANY, L.P.
4 PARKWAY NORTH BLVD # 400, DEERFIELD, IL 600152502
Phone: 847 405-2400

COMPETITORS

CVR   Mosaic Company
Koch Industries Inc.   PCS Nitrogen
LSB Industries

HISTORICAL FINANCIALS
Company Type: Private

Income Statement   FYE: December 31

	REVENUE ($ mil.)	NET INCOME ($ mil.)	NET PROFIT MARGIN	EMPLOYEES
12/17	397	153	38.7%	8
12/16	418	209	50.0%	—
12/15	581	306	52.8%	—
12/14	648	370	57.1%	—
Annual Growth	(15.1%)	(25.4%)	—	—

2017 Year-End Financials

Return on assets: 6.9%   Cash ($ mil.): 81
Return on equity: 38.7%
Current ratio: 2.40

TESLA ENERGY OPERATIONS, INC.

Ready to get off the grid? SolarCity can help. The company sells installs finances and monitors turnkey solar energy systems that convert sunlight into electricity. Its systems either mounted on a building's roof or the ground are used by residential commercial and government customers such as eBay Intel Wal-Mart and Homeland Security. SolarCity doesn't manufacture its systems but uses solar panels from Trina Solar Yingli Green Energy and Kyocera Solar and inverters from Power-One SMA Solar Technology and Schneider Electric. In late 2016 SolarCity was acquired by Tesla Motors in a deal worth $2.6 billion.

Change in Company Type

SolarCity was acquired by Tesla Motors for $2.6 billion in late 2016. Both companies will be led by Elon Musk and expect to achieve cost synergies of $150 million in the first full year after closing. By combining Tesla's new electric vehicles with SolarCity's newest solar products the companies expect to lower hardware costs reduce installation costs and improve their manufacturing efficiency.

Operations

SolarCity's main selling point is that it offers renewable energy for less than traditional utility companies. While customers feel good about choosing an alternative energy source they're also usually saving money. Much of the costs associated with

new installation and monthly fees are offset by SolarCity's investment funds. To date the company has formed more than 20 investment funds and raised more than $1.5 billion from banks and other companies such as Credit Suisse Google PG&E Corporation and U.S. Bancorp. (Two funds however are being audited by the IRS.) SolarCity also depends on federal and state tax rebates and credits to lower costs and create incentives for fund investors. For example the federal government offers a tax credit of 30% to install solar power through 2016. (After 2016 the tax credit will fall to 10%.)

Electricity is sold under long-term contracts; generally customers agree to a 20-year term. Customers are either signed up as leases or power purchase agreements. Lease customers pay a fixed monthly rate while the rate for power purchase agreement customers depends on the amount of electricity the solar energy system produces. The vast majority of its customers (some 90%) "rent" the solar installations instead of buying them outright in order to keep SolarCity in charge of the product warranty.

Geographic Reach

California-based SolarCity serves customers in 16 states and the District of Columbia. Its offices and warehouses reside in Arizona California Colorado Connecticut Hawaii Maryland Massachusetts Nevada New Jersey New York Oregon Texas Canada and China. The company earned over 75% of its revenue collectively from California Arizona Colorado Hawaii and New York.

Sales and Marketing

The company's client list includes residential customers commercial entities such as Wal-Mart eBay Intel and Safeway and government entities such as the U.S. Military. SolarCity sells its products and services through a direct outside sales force from 64 sales offices in 16 states and Washington DC. (Most states have one sales office but its home state of California has 12.) It also has a call center.

Financial Performance

Fast-growing SolarCity is posting impressive revenue gains but no profits yet. Indeed the solar services company reported $255 million in sales in 2014 an increase of 56% versus 2013. The company credited the double-digit gain for 2014 to a major increase in the installation and operation of solar energy systems under lease and power purchase agreements in new and existing markets along with an increase in sales of solar energy systems and components. SolarCity's net loss for 2014 was fueled by an increase in sales and marketing costs and interest expenses.

Strategy

SolarCity installs about one of every four solar energy systems in the US but is still hungry for more. The company's products and services are available through home-improvement-retail-giant The Home Depot. Also in 2014 the company partnered with electronics retailer Best Buy to offer its products and services through some 60 Best Buy stores in California Arizona Hawaii New York and Oregon. SolarCity also partners with more than 100 homebuilders including Pulte and Del Webb. Other channel partners include Tesla Motors Viridian Energy Honda Acura and BMW.

While residential customers are important to the company going forward SolarCity is seeking to install larger solar energy systems for businesses and government customers. The company is also growing its business through acquisitions.

Mergers and Acquisitions

In mid-2014 SolarCity acquired Silevo a solar panel technology and manufacturing company. The acquisition helped to manage the company's supply chain and control the design and manufacturing of solar cells and photovoltaic panels that are a key component of its solar energy systems.

The deal also enabled SolarCity to utilize and combine Silevo's technology with economies of scale to achieve significant cost reductions.

Company Background

SolarCity was founded in 2006 by CEO Lyndon Rive and his brother COO and CTO Peter Rive. The Rives are cousins of non-executive chairman Elon Musk a notable entrepreneur who co-founded PayPal and also heads Tesla Motors and SpaceX.

EXECUTIVES

Ceo, Lyndon R. Rive, $275,000 total compensation
Cto, Peter J. Rive, $275,000 total compensation
Evp General Counsel And Secretary, Seth R. Weissman, $270,000 total compensation
Evp Strategy And Global Markets, Marco Krapels
Evp Customer Operations, Brendon Merkley
Cfo, J. Radford Small
President Global Sales And Customer Experience, Toby Corey
Vice President Customer Account Management Group, Paul Brandt
Vice President Regional Sales, Courtney Reynolds
Vice President Of Information Technology, John Germain
Vice President Talent Acquisition And Analytics, Raj Dev
Svp Information Systems, Ming Wu
Vice President Inside Sales, Paul Bajus
Chairman, Elon Musk
Auditors: ERNST & YOUNG LLP LOS ANGELES

LOCATIONS

HQ: TESLA ENERGY OPERATIONS, INC.
3055 CLEARVIEW WAY, SAN MATEO, CA 944023709
Phone: 650 638-1028
Web: WWW.SOLARCITY.COM

PRODUCTS/OPERATIONS

2013 Sales

	$ mil.	% of total
Operating leases	82	51
Solar energy system	81	49
Total	**163**	**100**

Selected Products and Services

Products
Solar energy systems (panels inverters and mounting racks)

Services

Energy efficiency upgrades
Home energy evaluations

COMPETITORS

AEE Solar	Real Goods Solar
Ameresco	SolarCraft Services
Chevron	SunEdison
Conergy Inc.	SunPower
First Solar	Sunvalley Solar
REC Solar	

HISTORICAL FINANCIALS

Company Type: Private

Income Statement				FYE: December 31
	REVENUE ($ mil.)	NET INCOME ($ mil.)	NET PROFIT MARGIN	EMPLOYEES
12/16	730	(820)	—	12,000
12/15	399	(768)	—	—
12/14	255	(375)	—	—
12/13	163	(151)	—	—
Annual Growth	64.6%	—	—	—

2016 Year-End Financials

Return on assets: 28.4% Cash ($ mil.): 290
Return on equity: (-112.3%)
Current ratio: 0.20

TEXAS A&M FOUNDATION

EXECUTIVES

Pres, Tyson Voelkel
President, Dr Eddie J Davis
Senior Vice President, John R Stropp
Senior Vice President, James J Palincsar
V Pres-Cfo, Doyle Thompson
Vice President, Liska Lusk
Support Manager, Dennis Allen
Support Manager, Steve Herring
Manager, John Adamson
Administrative Assistant, Shelly Daughters
Director, Don Birkelbach
Auditors: BKD LLP HOUSTON TX

LOCATIONS

HQ: TEXAS A&M FOUNDATION
401 GEORGE BUSH DR, COLLEGE STATION, TX 778402811
Phone: 979 845-8161
Web: WWW.TXAMFOUNDATION.COM

HISTORICAL FINANCIALS

Company Type: Private

Income Statement				FYE: June 30
	ASSETS ($ mil.)	NET INCOME ($ mil.)	INCOME AS % OF ASSETS	EMPLOYEES
06/16	1,783	105	5.9%	95
06/13	1,505	97	6.5%	—
06/12	1,313	66	5.0%	—
06/11	0	43	—	—
Annual Growth	—	19.6%	—	—

2016 Year-End Financials

Return on assets: 1.0% Sales ($ mil): 205
Return on equity: 51.3%

TEXAS AROMATICS, LP

EXECUTIVES

Pres, Melbern G Glasscock
V Pres, Trenton L Kelley
Operations Staff, Natalie Pappas
Sales Executive, Staci Voll
Accounting Team Member, Vivian Mursuli
Auditors: WEAVER AND TIDWELL LLP HOU

LOCATIONS

HQ: TEXAS AROMATICS, LP
3555 TIMMONS LN STE 700, HOUSTON, TX 770276450
Phone: 713 520-2900
Web: WWW.TEXASAROMATICS.COM

HISTORICAL FINANCIALS

Company Type: Private

Income Statement				FYE: December 31
	REVENUE ($ mil.)	NET INCOME ($ mil.)	NET PROFIT MARGIN	EMPLOYEES
12/17	470	9	2.0%	20
12/16	449	11	2.6%	—
12/15	531	10	2.0%	—
12/14	961	10	1.1%	—
Annual Growth	(21.2%)	(2.7%)	—	—

2017 Year-End Financials

Return on assets: 4.6% Cash ($ mil.): 36
Return on equity: 2.0%
Current ratio: 1.80

TEXAS CHILDREN'S HOSPITAL

Texas Children's Hospital (TCH) is the flagship facility of Texas Children's Hospital Integrated Delivery System. Founded in 1954 the not-for-profit hospital provides full-service medical care for children conducts extensive research and trains pediatric medical professionals. Part of the Texas Medical Center complex it has clinical facilities for every ailment ranging from psychological troubles to surgery and physical rehabilitation as well as specialized heart cancer and neurological care. TCH is the primary pediatric training facility for Baylor College of Medicine.

Operations

TCH comprises a 491-bed tertiary care pediatric facility a 115-bed obstetrics and gynecological care facility focusing on high-risk births (both located on the Texas Medical Center campus) and a 44-bed full-service pediatric facility in west Houston. The hospital includes the Jan and Dan Duncan Neurological Research Institute and the Feigin Center for pediatric research.

The hospital's staff includes more than 1500 primary physicians and other medical specialists as well as some 6000 nurses. The hospital has satellite facilities in and around Houston and it operates the Texas Children's Pediatric Associates primary care network of more than 170 physicians. The company also runs the Texas Children's Health Plan which offers Medicaid and Texas CHIP (Children's Health Insurance Plan) programs.

TCH's International coordinates care for sick children who come to Texas Children's Hospital from abroad. The international segment also sends out medical teams to care for critically ill children throughout Latin America the Middle East Europe Africa and Asia. For instance it has established a number of AIDS clinics in African countries.

The hospital performs more than 25000 surgeries annually. It has some 1.9 million patient encounters some 31000 admissions and about 117000 emergency department visits each year.

Geographic Reach

TCH includes four main facilities — its main hospital and Texas Children's Pavilion for Women at the Medical Center Texas Children's West Campus in the Houston suburb of Katy and Texas Children's The Woodlands in that suburb (opening in 2017).

Financial Performance

Though most of its revenue comes from patient care fees TCH relies heavily on donations and federal funding to supplement its operations. For instance the hospital and Baylor College of Medicine represent one of the most active and well-funded pediatric research programs in the US with more than 800 basic research and clinical studies backed by more than $100 million in annual grants.

Increased patient revenue and premiums led to a 9% rise in revenue for 2014 from $2.3 billion to $2.5 billion. Net income fell 29% to $257 million due to a decline in investment returns and increased operating expenses including salaries and benefits supplies and pharmaceuticals. Cash flow from operations rose 63% to $257 million as a result of higher accounts payable.

Strategy

TCH has been opening new facilities some in suburban locations and expanding others to reach additional patients. In 2013 it introduced the da Vinci robotic system and expanded its children's hematology center to include a dozen exam rooms and four acute care rooms. It also opened its oculoplastic clinic for pediatric patients.

In 2014 the hospital opened its in vitro fertilization lab the first in Houston to utilize the EmbryoScope embryo monitoring system. It is also building an eight-bed isolation unit at its west campus.

EXECUTIVES

President And Ceo, Mark A. Wallace, age 66
Physician-in-chief, Mark W. Kline
Evp And Cfo, Benjamin (Ben) Melson
Obstetrician/gynecologist-in-chief, Michael A. Belfort
President Texas Children's Hospital The Woodlands, Michelle Riley-Brown
President Texas Children's Hospital West Campus, Chanda Cashen Chac n
Cio, Myra Davis
Medical Director Center For Telehealth, Larry Jefferson
Senior Vice President For Development, John Scales
Assistant Vice President Facilities Operations, Bert Gumeringer
Senior Executive Assistant To H. Mallory Caldwell Senior Vice President, Leticia Ybarra
Nursing Director, Tangula Taylor
Vice President And General Counsel, Lance Lightfoot
Assistant Vice President, Diane M Scardino
Nursing Director, Gail M Parazynski
Medical Director, Edward Mason
Vice President, Douglas Spade
Vice President, Rachel Shupe
Vice President, Maria Javallana
Vice President For Public Affairs, Shawn Davis
Assistant Vice President For Finance, Kimberly Cotner
Senior Vice President, David Holcomb
Senior Vice President, Linda Waldred
Director Of Nursing, Tanjula Taylor
Medical Director Blue Bird Circle Multiple Sclerosis Clinic, Timothy Lotze
Vice President, Debra Ward
Medical Director, Sanghamitra Misra
Vice President Of Purchasing, Sabrina Cowans
Assistant Vice President, Sara Montenegro
Treasurer Hospital, Doreen Mascari
Treasurer, Dorine Mascari

LOCATIONS

HQ: TEXAS CHILDREN'S HOSPITAL
6621 FANNIN ST, HOUSTON, TX 770302399
Phone: 832 824-1000
Web: WWW.TEXASCHILDRENS.ORG

PRODUCTS/OPERATIONS

2014 Sales

	% of total
Net patient revenue	60
Premium revenue	34
Medicaid & other supplemental reimbursement	2
Net assets released from restrictions for operations	1
Grants	1
Other income	2
Total	**100**

2014 Net Patient Revenue

	% of total
Managed care	61
Medicaid managed care	15
Medicaid	13
Self-pay	6
Commercial	5
Total	**100**

Selected Serives

Bariatric/weight control services
Certified trauma center
Chemotherapy
Dental services
Heart catheterization—diagnostic (child)
Genetic testing/counseling
HIV-AIDS services
Heart catheterization—treatment (child)
Kidney dialysis
Chemotherapy
Physical rehabilitation
Psychiatric services (Child/adolescent services Consultation and Outpatient care)
Sleep center
Sports medicine
Urgent-care center
Women's health center
Wound management services

COMPETITORS

CHRISTUS Health
Children's Hospital of Philadelphia
Children's Medical Center of Dallas
Cook Children's Health Care System
Dell Children's Medical Center
Mayo Clinic
Memorial Hermann Healthcare

Methodist Hospital System
Shriners Hospitals For Children
St. Jude Children's Research Hospital
St. Luke's Episcopal Hospital
Tenet Healthcare

HISTORICAL FINANCIALS

Company Type: Private

Income Statement

FYE: September 30

	REVENUE ($ mil.)	NET INCOME ($ mil.)	NET PROFIT MARGIN	EMPLOYEES
09/15	1,546	96	6.3%	6,000
09/14	1,383	70	5.1%	—
09/13	1,229	78	6.4%	—
09/12	2,043	289	14.2%	—
Annual Growth	(8.9%)	(30.6%)	—	—

2015 Year-End Financials

Return on assets: 4.6%
Return on equity: 6.3%
Current ratio: 0.80
Cash ($ mil.): 93

TEXAS CHRISTIAN UNIVERSITY INC

Home of the Horned Frogs (the school mascot) Texas Christian University (TCU) offers bachelor's master's and doctorate degrees in more than 200 fields of study. Almost 10400 undergraduate and graduate students attend the university's nine colleges and schools the cover fields of study ranging from liberal arts to engineering to business. TCU has 630 full-time faculty members and a student-to-faculty ratio of 13:1. It also has one of the NCAA's top football programs. TCU is affiliated with the Disciples of Christ a Protestant denomination.

Operations

The TCU academic programs are organized under nine schools in fields including liberal arts communication education fine arts science and engineering nursing and health and business. It offers 119 bachelors 53 masters and 28 doctoral degrees.

Tuition fees room and board and books cost about $55630 per year.

Geographic Reach

TCU's campus takes up about 280 acres about five miles from downtown Fort Worth.

Financial Performance

The university reported a 2015-2016 annual budget of $646 million. It had total investments (as at June 30 2016) of $1.5 billion.

Strategy

TCU is investing in facility upgrades and enhancement efforts as part of its strategic plan entitled Academy of Tomorrow. Over the past few years the school has upgraded academic administrative recreational and residence facilities including the construction of a new commons building on the eastern end of its campus. In 2015 it completed a $32.8 million upgrade of its main library.

Company Background

Brothers Addison and Randolph Clark established the school in 1873 as Addran Male and Female College (the school changed its name to Texas Christian University in 1902).

EXECUTIVES

Chancellor, Victor J. Boschini
Vice Chancellor Academic Affairs And Provost, R. Nowell Donovan
Vice Chancellor Finance And Administration, Brian G. Gutierrez
Chief Investment Officer, James R. Hille
Cto, Bryan Lucas
Dean Addran College Of Liberal Arts, F. Andrew Schoolmaster
Dean Neeley School Of Business, O. Homer Erekson
Vice Chancellor Marketing And Communication, Tracy Syler-Jones
Dean College Of Science And Engineering, Philip S. (Phil) Hartman
Vice Chancellor For Human Resources, Yohna Chambers
Dean Harris College Of Nursing & Health Sciences Professor And Executive Director Of The Health Innovation Institute, Susan Weeks
Dean Of The Bob Schieffer College Of Communication, Kris Bunton
Dean College Of Fine Arts, Anne Helmreich
Board Vice President, Kellie Sebastian
Vice President Of Membership Development, Gillian Hogan
Panhellenic Vice President Of Community Involvement, Katie Hamilton

Vice President Of External Affairs, Jake Neal
Financial Vice President Of Delta Sigma Pi, Julie
  Brandenburg
Panhellenic Vice President Recruitment, Simone
  Elices
Sigma Phi Epsilon Vice President Of
  Communications, Dillon Smith
Vice President Finance, Carol Campbell
Student Body Vice President For External Affairs,
  Hillary Shepheard
Executive Vice President And Dean, Nancy Ramsay
Student Body Vice President, Ryker Thompson
Vice President Of Regions, Clor Proell
Ama Vice President Of Licensing, Jacky Meacham
Vice President Of Communication, Alexandra
  Peters
Vice President Of Membership, Blake Brumley
Vice President, John Hillman
Chairman, Clarence Scharbauer
Vice Chairman, Mark L. Johnson
Vice Chair, Kit Tennison Moncrief
Auditors: PRICEWATERHOUSECOOPERS LLC FO

LOCATIONS

HQ: TEXAS CHRISTIAN UNIVERSITY INC
  2800 S UNIVERSITY DR, FORT WORTH, TX
  761290001
Phone: 817 257-7000
Web: WWW.TCU.EDU

PRODUCTS/OPERATIONS

Selected Colleges and Schools
AddRan College of Liberal Arts
College of Communication
College of Education
College of Fine Arts
College of Science and Engineering
Harris College of Nursing and Health Sciences
John V. Roach Honors College
Neeley School of Business
Relationship with Brite Divinity School

HISTORICAL FINANCIALS

Company Type: Private

Income Statement				FYE: May 31
	REVENUE ($ mil.)	NET INCOME ($ mil.)	NET PROFIT MARGIN	EMPLOYEES
05/18	521	185	35.6%	3,400
05/17	499	123	24.7%	—
05/14	637	154	24.2%	—
05/12	441	(4)	—	—
Annual Growth	2.8%	—	—	—

2018 Year-End Financials

Return on assets: 15.9%   Cash ($ mil.): 11
Return on equity: 35.6%
Current ratio: —

TEXAS COUNTY AND DISTRICT RETIREMENT SYSTEM

EXECUTIVES

Exec Dir, Gene Glass
Cao, Ray Smith
Deputy Dir, Amy Bishop
Staff, Brad Eddins
Network Analyst, Brad Watkins
CIO, Stephen Kell
Auditors: KPMG LLP AUSTIN TX

LOCATIONS

HQ: TEXAS COUNTY AND DISTRICT RETIREMENT
  SYSTEM
  901 S MO PAC EXPY IV500, AUSTIN, TX 787465776
Phone: 512 328-8889
Web: WWW.TCDRS.ORG

HISTORICAL FINANCIALS

Company Type: Private

Income Statement				FYE: December 31
	ASSETS ($ mil.)	NET INCOME ($ mil.)	INCOME AS % OF ASSETS	EMPLOYEES
12/16	26,387	1,761	6.7%	108
12/15	24,654	(182)	—	—
12/14	24,832	0	—	—
12/10	18,116	2,178	12.0%	—
Annual Growth	6.5%	(3.5%)	—	—

2016 Year-End Financials

Return on assets: 0.9%   Sales ($ mil): 3,030
Return on equity: 58.1%

TEXAS EASTERN TRANSMISSION, LP

EXECUTIVES

Pres-Ceo-Ptnr, Martha B Wyrsch
Manager, Wayne Thibodeaux
Director, Joe Carvelli
Auditors: DELOITTE & TOUCHE LLP HOUSTO

LOCATIONS

HQ: TEXAS EASTERN TRANSMISSION, LP
  5400 WESTHEIMER CT, HOUSTON, TX 770565353
Phone: 713 627-5400
Web: WWW.DUKE-ENERGY.COM

HISTORICAL FINANCIALS

Company Type: Private

Income Statement				FYE: December 31
	REVENUE ($ mil.)	NET INCOME ($ mil.)	NET PROFIT MARGIN	EMPLOYEES
12/17	1,389	347	25.0%	700
12/16	1,350	329	24.4%	—
12/12	956	406	42.5%	—
Annual Growth	7.8%	(3.1%)	—	—

TEXAS HEALTH RESOURCES

Texas Health Resources (THR) is takin' care of the Dallas/Fort Worth and North Texas region. The not-for-profit system includes about 30 acute care and short-stay hospitals including owned managed and joint venture facilities. THR also operates outpatient and surgical centers and physicians' offices and it maintains affiliations with imaging diagnostic rehabilitation facilities and home health agencies. THR's network includes more than 5500 doctors and more than 3800 licensed beds. Its Research and Education Institute for Texas Health Resources provides clinical studies management medical device testing and medical training services.

Operations

THR's hospitals operate under names including Texas Health Presbyterian Texas Health Arlington Memorial Texas Health Harris Methodist and Texas Health Huguley. The company operates 20 outpatient facilities and it coordinates general practice care through its physician practice groups. Its Texas Health MedSynergies unit provides office management services for doctors' offices.

Geographic Reach

THR's primary service territory includes about 25 counties in north-central Texas. It has locations in towns including Allen Alliance Arlington Azle Burleson Cleburne Craig Ranch Dallas Denton Flower Mound Fort Worth Huguley Kaufman Plano Richardson Rockwall Southlake Stephenville and Sherman.

Sales and Marketing

The organization promotes its medical services through print television outdoor online and radio advertising.

Strategy

In order to keep up with the growing population of North Texas in 2007 THR launched a $1.5 billion initiative to expand its facilities over a 10-year period. Project efforts thus far have included establishing a joint venture hospital in Flower Mound and the expansion of existing facilities. For instance in 2015 it opened a 70000 sq. ft. cancer center at Presbyterian Hospital Dallas. In 2017 it completed an expansion at its Texas Health Alliance facility which included adding 24 private beds; the same facility will also expand its emergency department. THR has also opened a number of outpatient surgery imaging wellness and specialist centers and it is now building a new 74-bed hospital campus in Frisco Texas.

In 2016 the system established a joint venture with emergency room operator Adeptus Health through which Adeptus? 27 North Texas First Choice Emergency Rooms as well as its First Texas Hospital in Carrollton became part of THR. The move helped THR as it works to expand its access points to emergency health care (an area it has struggled with).

Other expansion moves include the 2016 purchase of Forest Park Medical Center Fort Worth for $141 million and the creation of a jointly owned health plan with health insurer Aetna.

THR has also built up its information technology networks including the implementation of electronic health record (EHR) systems. In addition the organization is adding new medical professional training programs.

Company Background

THR was formed in 1997 by the merger of Harris Methodist Health System Presbyterian Healthcare System and Arlington Memorial Hospital Foundation. In 2008 the organization rebranded its hospitals unifying them all under the Texas Health Resources name.

THR had originally been the minority shareholder in a venture with Triad Hospitals to own Presbyterian Hospital of Denton. However THR grew dissatisfied when Triad was acquired by Community Health Systems in 2007. After a long legal tussle THR paid $100 million to acquire the hospital outright in 2009 and changed its name to Texas Health Presbyterian Hospital Denton. Texas Health Presbyterian found itself the focus of international media attention in 2014 when it treated the first case of Ebola on US soil.

EXECUTIVES

Evp People And Culture, Bonnie Bell

Evp Southeast Zone Operations Leader, Oscar L. Amparan

Sevp And Chief Clinical Officer, Daniel W. Varga

Evp And Cfo, Ronald R. (Ron) Long

Evp North Zone Operations Leader, Brett S. McClung

Sevp And Coo, Barclay E. Berdan

Svp And Chief Nurse Executive, Joan S. Clark

Executive Vice President And Southwest Zone Operations Leader, Kirk King

Sevp And Coo, Jeffrey L. Canose

Evp Southwest Zone Clinical Leader, Harold Berenzweig

Evp Southeast Zone Clinical Leader, Mark C. Lester

Evp North Zone Clinical Leader, Elizabeth Ransom

Evp Population Health; President Texas Health Population Health Education And Innovation Center, Tricia Nguyen

President Texas Health Physicians Group, Shawn D. Parsley

Director Of Pharmacy Pharmacy Director Service Director, Rebecca Wilson

Senior Vice President And Chief People Officer, Michelle Kirby

Vice President Operations Thpg, Lori Clay

Senior Vice President Of Communications, Paul Szablowski

Vice President Chief Nursing Officer, Rosemarie Aznavorian

Services Cmrp Senior Vice President Supply Chain Management, Shaun Clinton

Vice President, Laura McWhorter

Vice President, John Wilson

Vice President Applications And Ehr, Susan Soch

Vice President Of Planning And Placement, Mark Morales

Senior Vice President Chief Operating Officer, James Berg

Vice President Assistant, Susan Garrett

Vice President Governance, Luanne Stout

Vice President Revenue Planning, Scott Auzenne

Vice President Treasury Services, Sandy Reeves

Director Managed Care, Larry Olive

Radiology Medical Director, David Robinson

Medical Director Of Adolescent Services, Robert Harden

Vice President Corporate Controller, David Jackson

Vice President Applications And Ehr, Cynda Grimes

Director Of Pharmacy, Mikyoung Kim

Vice President, Douglas White

Director Of Him, Que Le

Vice President Supply Chain Management, Becky Daniel

Vice President Health Information Services, Diann Brown

Vice President Of Operations, Jennifer Stephenson

Pharmacy Manager, Jerry James

Director Of Radiology, Dung Pham

Vice President Stakeholder Engagement, Mark Riordan

Vice President Operations, Jennifer Mha

Ache Member Vice President Strategy And Business, Virginia Rose

Chairman, John R. Ferguson

Vice Chairman, Wesley R. Turner

Secretary, Stacey Mcjunkin

Secretary, Bernadina Richey

Secretary, Chandra Rhodes

Auditors: KMPG LLP DALLAS TEXAS

LOCATIONS

HQ: TEXAS HEALTH RESOURCES
612 E LAMAR BLVD STE 400, ARLINGTON, TX 760114125
Phone: 682 236-7900
Web: WWW.TEXASHEALTH.ORG

PRODUCTS/OPERATIONS

Selected Facilities and Affiliates

Acute Care and Specialty Hospitals
Texas Health Arlington Memorial
Texas Health Harris Methodist Hospital Fort Worth
Texas Health Huguley Hospital Fort Worth South
Texas Health Presbyterian Hospital Dallas
Texas Health Presbyterian Hospital Flower Mound
Texas Health Presbyterian Hospital Rockwall
Texas Health Center for Diagnostics & Surgery Plano
Texas Heath Heart & Vascular Hospital Arlington
USMD Hospital at Arlington
USMD Hospital at Fort Worth

Affiliates
Envision Imaging of North Fort Worth
Texas Rehabilitation Partners
Two Forest Imaging Dallas
Southwest Diagnostic Imaging Center

COMPETITORS

Community Health Systems
Cook Children's Health Care System
HCA
JPS Health Network
Parkland Health & Hospital System
Southwestern Medical Center
Tenet Healthcare
The Methodist Health System

HISTORICAL FINANCIALS

Company Type: Private

Income Statement				FYE: December 31
	REVENUE ($ mil.)	NET INCOME ($ mil.)	NET PROFIT MARGIN	EMPLOYEES
12/17	4,688	869	18.6%	21,277
12/13	718	285	39.8%	—
12/09	334	2	0.9%	—
12/06	2,287	2,299	100.5%	—
Annual Growth	6.7%	(8.5%)	—	—

2017 Year-End Financials

Return on assets: 5.1%   Cash ($ mil.): 435
Return on equity: 18.6%
Current ratio: 0.90

TEXAS HEART HOSPITAL OF THE SOUTHWEST, L.L.P.

EXECUTIVES

Ptnr-Ceo, Mark Valentine
Ptnr-Coo, Gary Brock
Vpres- Dir, Morgan Brad
Coordinator, Alaina Cyr

LOCATIONS

HQ: TEXAS HEART HOSPITAL OF THE SOUTHWEST, L.L.P.
1100 ALLIED DR, PLANO, TX 750935348
Phone: 469 241-8900
Web: WWW.THEHEARTHOSPITALBAYLOR.COM

HISTORICAL FINANCIALS

Company Type: Private

Income Statement				FYE: December 31
	REVENUE ($ mil.)	NET INCOME ($ mil.)	NET PROFIT MARGIN	EMPLOYEES
12/16	297	73	24.6%	139
12/15	261	62	24.1%	—
12/14	253	62	24.8%	—
Annual Growth	8.4%	8.1%	—	—

2016 Year-End Financials

Return on assets: 3.0%   Cash ($ mil.): 80
Return on equity: 24.6%
Current ratio: 3.10

TEXAS PERMANENT SCHOOL FUND MANAGEMENT COMPANY, INC.

EXECUTIVES

Prin, Elizabeth Jones
Manager, Nick Tramontana
Auditors: LISA R COLLIER CPA CFE CID

LOCATIONS

HQ: TEXAS PERMANENT SCHOOL FUND MANAGEMENT COMPANY, INC.
1701 CONGRESS AVE, AUSTIN, TX 787011402
Phone: 512 463-1814
Web: WWW.TEA.STATE.TX.US

HISTORICAL FINANCIALS

Company Type: Private

Income Statement				FYE: August 31
	ASSETS ($ mil.)	NET INCOME ($ mil.)	INCOME AS % OF ASSETS	EMPLOYEES
08/17	44,517	4,154	9.3%	4
08/16	38,820	1,519	3.9%	—
Annual Growth	14.7%	173.4%	—	—

2017 Year-End Financials

Return on assets: 0.2%   Sales ($ mil): 5,375
Return on equity: 77.3%

TEXAS STATE UNIVERSITY

Texas State University-San Marcos has about 38800 students pursuing degrees in about 100 undergraduate programs 90 graduate programs and a dozen doctoral programs. Comprising eight colleges as well as a graduate school Texas State University-San Marcos is the largest school in the Texas State University system which includes Angelo State University Lamar University Sam Houston State University and Sul Ross State University.

It also offers bachelor's and graduate-level courses at a campus in Round Rock.The school has 209 buildings on its San Marcos cmapus.

Geographic Reach

Texas State's main campus in the Central Texas community of San Marcos consists of some 490 acres. The university also operates some 5000 acres of recreational and instruction properties in the area.

Strategy

As Texas State is ranked among the top US colleges for awarding degrees to bachelor's degrees to Hispanic students the university targets a portion of its marketing efforts towards minority students. About 50% of its student body is composed of ethnic minorities. Texas State also enrolls students through international efforts.

To accommodate its growing student base Texas State has been expanding its campus facilities. It opened the Angelina and San Gabriel residence halls in 2016 and the Performing Arts Center in 2014.

Also in 2014 the school became a member of the American Academic Research Institute in Iraq (TAARII) which promotes scholarly research on Iraq and ancient Mesopotamia by providing graduate and post-graduate fellowships for Americans and Iraqis. Other TAARII members include Columbia University Georgetown University and Harvard.

Company Background

The former Southwest Texas State University (the name was changed in 2003) was originally a teacher's college founded by the state legislature in 1903.

EXECUTIVES

Assistant Vice President Budgeting Financial Planning And Analysis, Gordon Thyberg
President, Denise M. Trauth
Vp Student Affairs, Joanne Smith
Provost And Vp Academic Affairs, Eugene J. (Gene) Bourgeois
Vp University Advancement, Barbara Breier
Vp Finance And Support Services, Eric Algoe
Vp Information Technology, Ken Pierce
Presidential Fellow, Lisa Kay Lloyd
Dean College Of Applied Arts, Jaime Chahin
Dean Mccoy College Of Business Administration, Denise T. Smart
Dean College Of Education, Stan Carpenter
Dean College Of Fine Arts And Communication, John Fleming
Dean College Of Health Professions, Ruth B. Welborn
Dean Honors College, Heather C. Galloway
Dean College Of Liberal Arts, Michael J. Hennessy
Interim Dean College Of Science And Engineering, Robert Habingreither
Dean University College, Daniel A. Brown
Dean The Graduate College, Andrea Golato
Vice President Financial Services, Debra Jones
Associate Vice President Instructional Technologies Support T, Milt Nielsen
Associate Vice President And Dean Of Students, Margarita Arellano
Vice President For Finance Support Services, William A Nance
Vice President Information Technology, Kenneth Pierce
External Vice President Alex Cooper, Ryan Goodrum
Board Secretary, John Blair
Board Member, Jane Saunders
Y.o.u Treasurer, Keeasha Shaw

LOCATIONS

HQ: TEXAS STATE UNIVERSITY
601 UNIVERSITY DR, SAN MARCOS, TX 786664684
Phone: 512 245-2111
Web: WWW.TXSTATE.EDU

PRODUCTS/OPERATIONS

Schools and Colleges
College of Applied Arts
College of Education
College of Fine Arts and Communication
College of Health Professions
College of Liberal Arts
College of Science
The Graduate College
McCoy College of Business Administration
University College (general studies)

HISTORICAL FINANCIALS
Company Type: Private

Income Statement — FYE: August 31

	REVENUE ($ mil.)	NET INCOME ($ mil.)	NET PROFIT MARGIN	EMPLOYEES
08/16	436	34	7.9%	3,156
08/15	404	25	6.2%	—
08/14	377	73	19.4%	—
08/13	329	61	18.6%	—
Annual Growth	9.8%	(17.5%)	—	—

2016 Year-End Financials
Return on assets: 7.8%   Cash ($ mil.): 268
Return on equity: 7.9%
Current ratio: 1.20

TEXAS STATE UNIVERSITY SYSTEM

EXECUTIVES

Chancellor, Brian McCall
Vice Chancellor For Finance, Claire Jackson
Director of Public Relations, Mike Wintemute
Manager, Lamar Urbanovsky
Teacher, Michael Hennessy
Manager, Terrie Purser
Administrative Assistant, Donna Givens
Officer, Linda Camarillo
Assistant General Counsel, Rhonda Beassie
Associate, Rob Parnell
Administration Director, Carol Treadway

LOCATIONS

HQ: TEXAS STATE UNIVERSITY SYSTEM
601 COLORADO ST, AUSTIN, TX 787012904
Phone: 512 463-1808
Web: WWW.TSUS.EDU

HISTORICAL FINANCIALS
Company Type: Private

Income Statement — FYE: August 31

	REVENUE ($ mil.)	NET INCOME ($ mil.)	NET PROFIT MARGIN	EMPLOYEES
08/17	854	145	17.1%	3,196
08/16	846	126	14.9%	—
08/15	6	71	1147.5%	—
08/14	6	71	1147.5%	—
Annual Growth	416.5%	27.0%	—	—

2017 Year-End Financials
Return on assets: 9.3%   Cash ($ mil.): 487
Return on equity: 17.1%
Current ratio: 1.00

TEXLA ENERGY MANAGEMENT, INC.

EXECUTIVES

Pres, Lacy H Williams II
Cfo-V Pres, Randy Miller
Vice-President, Scott Beasley
Auditors: MOHLE ADAMS LLP HOUSTON TEXA

LOCATIONS

HQ: TEXLA ENERGY MANAGEMENT, INC.
1100 LA ST STE 4700, HOUSTON, TX 77002
Phone: 713 655-9900
Web: WWW.TEXLAENERGY.COM

HISTORICAL FINANCIALS
Company Type: Private

Income Statement — FYE: December 31

	REVENUE ($ mil.)	NET INCOME ($ mil.)	NET PROFIT MARGIN	EMPLOYEES
12/17	1,291	3	0.3%	19
12/04	949	2	0.3%	—
12/03	596	1	0.2%	—
12/02	271	2	0.9%	—
Annual Growth	11.0%	1.8%	—	—

2017 Year-End Financials
Return on assets: 6.4%   Cash ($ mil.): 7
Return on equity: 0.3%
Current ratio: 1.10

THE ADMINISTRATORS OF THE TULANE EDUCATIONAL FUND

EXECUTIVES

Vice President For Development, Luann Dozier
Assistant Vice President Of University Financial Aid, Georgia Whiddon
Auditors: DELOITTE & TOUCHE LLP NEW ORL

LOCATIONS

HQ: THE ADMINISTRATORS OF THE TULANE EDUCATIONAL FUND
6823 SAINT CHARLES AVE, NEW ORLEANS, LA 701185665
Phone: 504 865-5000
Web: WWW.TULANEGREENWAVE.COM

Selected Campuses
Tulane University main uptown campus
The F. Edward Hebert Research Center (Louisiana)
The School of Continuing Studies (Louisiana and Mississippi)
The Health Sciences downtown campus
School of Medicine

School of Public Health and Tropical Medicine
Tulane Medical Center and Technology Services
The North Shore campus
Tulane National Primate Research Center (Louisiana)
The A.B. Freeman School of Business (Texas)

PRODUCTS/OPERATIONS

Selected Schools and Colleges
A.B. Freeman School of Business
Faculty of Liberal Arts and Sciences
Graduate School
Law School
Newcomb College
School of Architecture
School of Engineering
School of Medicine
School of Public Health and Tropical Medicine
School of Social Work
Tulane College
University College

HISTORICAL FINANCIALS
Company Type: Private

Income Statement				FYE: June 30
	REVENUE ($ mil.)	NET INCOME ($ mil.)	NET PROFIT MARGIN	EMPLOYEES
06/16	924	(63)	—	5,500
06/15	1,054	40	3.9%	—
06/10	738	48	6.5%	—
06/09	737	0	—	—
Annual Growth	3.3%	—	—	—

2016 Year-End Financials
Return on assets: 11.4%   Cash ($ mil.): 22
Return on equity: (-6.9%)
Current ratio: —

THE ADVANCED CENTER FOR REHABILITATION MEDICINE INC

EXECUTIVES

Pres, David W Osborne
Technical Staff, David Rysz
Officer, Keith Shuster
Business Manager, Eddy Jean-Felix
Director, Joanne Svogun
Psychiatrist, Harold Ginsberg
Manager, Jacqueline Gomez
Director of Radiology, Alan Levine
Executive Assistant, Barbara Dicarlo
Director, Ismael Velez
Payroll Manager, James Zimmerman

LOCATIONS

HQ: THE ADVANCED CENTER FOR REHABILITATION MEDICINE INC
24 STEVENS ST, NORWALK, CT 068503852
Phone: 203 852-2000

HISTORICAL FINANCIALS
Company Type: Private

Income Statement				FYE: September 30
	REVENUE ($ mil.)	NET INCOME ($ mil.)	NET PROFIT MARGIN	EMPLOYEES
09/16	390	11	3.0%	2
09/15	377	23	6.2%	—
09/14	340	33	9.7%	—
09/13	352	16	4.8%	—
Annual Growth	3.5%	(11.4%)	—	—

2016 Year-End Financials
Return on assets: 12.2%   Cash ($ mil.): 30
Return on equity: 3.0%
Current ratio: 0.50

THE AEROSPACE CORPORATION

A not-for-profit company The Aerospace Corporation provides space-related research development and advisory services primarily for US government programs. Its chief sponsor is the US Air Force and its main customers have included the Space and Missile Systems Center of Air Force Space Command and the National Reconnaissance Office. Other clients have included NASA and the National Oceanic and Atmospheric Administration as well as commercial enterprises universities and international organizations. Areas of expertise include launch certification process implementation systems engineering and technology application. The Aerospace Corporation was established in 1960 and operates through about 20 offices.

Operations
Officially The Aerospace Corporation operates a federally funded research and development center or FFRDC for the Air Force. The Aerospace FFRDC is one of more than 40 established to help government agencies with tasks related to aviation defense energy health and human services space and tax administration.

Geographic Reach
The US relies on space systems for intelligence communications navigation and weather making Aerospace's mission assurance and systems engineering services vital to national security.

Strategy
Among the company's projects are work on the next generation of satellites including the Global Positioning System IIF Space Based Space Surveillance Advanced Extremely High Frequency Wideband Global Satcom and Space Based Infrared System programs. These new satellites will provide new capabilities and replace systems from the 1970s and 1980s.

Scientists at The Aerospace Corporation also have been developing a nanosatellite to test high-efficiency solar cells under space conditions. Solar cells made by Spectrolab (a subsidiary of Boeing Space and Intelligence Systems) and EMCORE convert sunlight into electricity. The nanosatellite only 14 pounds is one of many such small satellites pioneered by Aerospace. Compared to larger satellites nanosatellites are less expensive to launch and operate.

EXECUTIVES

Senior Vice President General Counsel Secretary, Gordon Louttit
Evp, David J. Gorney

General Manager Computers And Software, William C. (Willie) Krenz
Vp Vaeros, Edward M. (Ed) Swallow
Svp National Systems Group, Catherine J. Steele
Vp Cfo And Treasurer, Ellen M. Beatty
Svp Operations And Support Group, Wayne H. Goodman
President And Ceo, Steven J. (Steve) Isakowitz
Vp Space Launch Operations, Randolph L. (Randy) Kendall
Vp Space Program Operations, Malina M Hills
Vice President Space Launch Operations, Ray F Johnson
Executive Vice President, Glenn E Peterson
Vice President, Rita Lollock
Vice President Technology, Sherrie Zacharius
Vice President Space Program Operations, Stephen E Burrin
Senior Vice President Technology, John Parsons
Vice President, Shirley Dohzen
Vice President Technology, Lawrence Greenberg
Vice President And Associate General C, Malissia Clinton
Vice President, Ed Swallow
Vice President Chief Human Resources Officer, Heather Laychak
Vice President, Jamie Morin
Chairman, Barbara M. Barrett, age 66
Vice Chairman, Michael B. Donley
Auditors: DELOITTE & TOUCHE LLP LOS ANG

LOCATIONS

HQ: THE AEROSPACE CORPORATION
2310 E EL SEGUNDO BLVD, EL SEGUNDO, CA 902454609
Phone: 310 336-5000
Web: WWW.AEROSPACE.ORG

PRODUCTS/OPERATIONS

Selected Services
Civil and Commercial
CORDS
Cyber Security
Labs
Launch Support
Mission Assurance
Systems Engineering
Technical Resources

COMPETITORS

AKKA Technologies   QinetiQ
Orbital Research

HISTORICAL FINANCIALS
Company Type: Private

Income Statement				FYE: September 30
	REVENUE ($ mil.)	NET INCOME ($ mil.)	NET PROFIT MARGIN	EMPLOYEES
09/15	916	(15)	—	3,920
09/14	881	5	0.6%	—
09/13	868	0	0.0%	—
09/12	903	4	0.5%	—
Annual Growth	0.5%	—	—	—

2015 Year-End Financials
Return on assets: 4.2%   Cash ($ mil.): 23
Return on equity: (-1.7%)
Current ratio: 0.40

THE AMERICAN ENDOWMENT FOUNDATION

EXECUTIVES

Pres, Philip T Tobin
Vice Pres, Thomas J Tobin
Director, Laura Malone
Grants Administrator, Angela Barak
Grant Administrator, Cheryl Gerbracht
Administrator, Dawn Davis
Vice President Investments, Jeff Scherer
Executive Vice President, John Farren
Administrator, Kristin Wilcoxson
Vice President, Shannon Baker
Associate, Adrienne Rouan
Auditors: MALONEY & NOVOTNY LLC CANTON

LOCATIONS

HQ: THE AMERICAN ENDOWMENT FOUNDATION
5700 DARROW RD STE 118, HUDSON, OH 442365026
Phone: 330 655-7552
Web: WWW.AEFONLINE.ORG

HISTORICAL FINANCIALS
Company Type: Private

Income Statement				FYE: December 31
	REVENUE ($ mil.)	NET INCOME ($ mil.)	NET PROFIT MARGIN	EMPLOYEES
12/16	848	349	41.2%	5
12/15	640	335	52.3%	—
12/12	133	86	64.7%	—
12/11	68	42	61.6%	—
Annual Growth	65.4%	52.6%	—	—

2016 Year-End Financials

Return on assets: 0.4%
Return on equity: 41.2%
Current ratio: 18.60
Cash ($ mil.): 70

THE AMERICAN JEWISH JOINT DISTRIBUTION COMMITTEE INC

EXECUTIVES

Ceo, Alan H Gill
Chm-Chb, Dr Irving A Smokler
President, Penny Blumenstein
Board MBR, Ellen Heller
Assistant, Linda Levi
Manager, Eliot Goldstein
Manager, Jeffrey P Edelstein
Public Relations Director, Michael Geller
Assistant General Counsel, Rachel Lubert
Coordinator, Stephanie Brown
Associate, Angelina Efraimov
Auditors: I GRANT THORNTON LLP NEW YOR

LOCATIONS

HQ: THE AMERICAN JEWISH JOINT DISTRIBUTION COMMITTEE INC
220 E 42ND ST RM 400, NEW YORK, NY 100175833
Phone: 212 687-6200
Web: WWW.JDC.ORG

HISTORICAL FINANCIALS
Company Type: Private

Income Statement				FYE: December 31
	REVENUE ($ mil.)	NET INCOME ($ mil.)	NET PROFIT MARGIN	EMPLOYEES
12/15	294	25	8.5%	840
12/13	352	22	6.4%	—
12/09	221	(25)	—	—
Annual Growth	4.9%	—	—	—

2015 Year-End Financials

Return on assets: 19.0%
Return on equity: 8.5%
Current ratio: 1.00
Cash ($ mil.): 53

THE ANDREW W MELLON FOUNDATION

EXECUTIVES

Vice President, Marit Westermann

LOCATIONS

HQ: THE ANDREW W MELLON FOUNDATION
140 E 62ND ST, NEW YORK, NY 100658124
Phone: 212 838-8400
Web: WWW.MELLON.ORG

HISTORICAL FINANCIALS
Company Type: Private

Income Statement				FYE: December 31
	REVENUE ($ mil.)	NET INCOME ($ mil.)	NET PROFIT MARGIN	EMPLOYEES
12/17	980	655	66.9%	70
12/16	487	151	31.1%	—
12/09	0	0	—	—
12/06	876	655	74.7%	—
Annual Growth	1.0%	0.0%	—	—

2017 Year-End Financials

Return on assets: —
Return on equity: 66.9%
Current ratio: —
Cash ($ mil.): 2

THE ASSOCIATED PRESS

This just in: The Associated Press (AP) is reporting tonight and every night wherever news is breaking. AP is one of the world's largest news gathering organizations with news bureaus in about 100 countries. It provides news photos graphics and audiovisual services that reach people daily through print radio TV and the Web. It also offers advertising management and distribution services. The not-for-profit cooperative is owned by 1500 US daily newspaper members. A group of New York newspapers founded the AP in 1846 in order to chronicle the US-Mexican War more efficiently. Founding papers include The New York Sun The Journal of Commerce The Courier and Enquirer The New York Herald and The Express .

Operations

The AP has about 3200 employees globally working around 280 locations worldwide.

Geographic Reach

The Associated Press is headquartered in New York City. The AP serves 1700 newspapers and 5000 radio and television outlets in the US many of which are members.

Financial Performance

In fiscal 2014 the AP's total annual revenue increased by 1% to $604 million compared to $595 million in fiscal 2013. The company's net income increased dramatically to $140 million in fiscal 2014 compared to $3.26 million in fiscal 2013 mainly due to increased gross revenue and interest income.

Strategy

In recent years the AP has shifted its focus away from providing content to newspapers and towards serving online media sources; some of the company's biggest customers now include media outlets such as Google MSN and Yahoo!. It has also focused on developing AP Direct its live video news agency service. It sells its back catalog of video through AP Video Archives.

To cope with the decline in print readership the news co-op is continuing to invest in digital initiatives. It is currently undergoing a multimillion-dollar upgrade of its newsgathering infrastructure to increase its video coverage of global events. It is also pushing to increase its high definition footage to broadcast and digital markets and ensure that its video and images integrate seamlessly with new digital workflows to drive value for customers.

HISTORY

The Associated Press traces its roots to 1846 when New York Sun publisher Moses Yale Beach agreed to share news arriving by telegraph about the Mexican-American War with four other New York newspapers. The cooperative news gathering effort was later established as the AP which began selling wire reports to other papers and started creating regional associations. Adapting to changing technologies and public interests AP began covering sports financial and public interest stories in the 1920s and was selling news reports to radio stations in the 1940s. Advancements during WWII included using transatlantic cable and radio-teletype circuits to deliver news and photos.

In the late 1960s AP and Dow Jones introduced services to improve business and financial reporting. AP improved photo delivery reception and storage in the 1970s with the advent of Laserphoto and the Electronic Darkroom. It began transmitting news by satellite and offering color photographs to newspapers in the 1980s. In 1985 Louis Boccardi took over the job as president and CEO of AP.

AP adjusted to the media-heavy culture of the 1990s by launching the APTV international news video service and the All News Radio network in 1994. It then moved onto the Internet with The WIRE in 1996 and began offering online access to its Photo Archive in 1997. It bought Worldwide Television News in 1998 combining it with APTV to form AP Television News Limited (APTN). The following year it purchased the radio news contracts of UPI after the rival organization announced it was getting out of broadcast news.

In 2000 AP created an Internet division AP Digital to focus on marketing news to online providers. The cooperative continued its Internet focus the following year launching AP Online en EspaA±ol (news for Spanish-language websites) and AP Entertainment Online (multimedia entertainment news for websites). Also that year AP bought the Newspaper Industry Communication Center from the Newspaper Association of America.

In 2002 the company launched an expanded editorial partnership with Dow Jones Newswires increasing the amount of financial news distributed on AP wires. Later that year it acquired Capitolwire a provider of state government news. Boccardi stepped down as CEO in 2003 handing the reins to former USA TODAY publisher Tom Curley.

AP relocated in 2004 from Rockefeller Plaza (its home for 65 years) to a new headquarters on the west side of Manhattan that features a 105000-sq.-ft. newsroom and serves as a central hub of digital news streams.

The organization moved to strengthen its sports information coverage in 2005 merging its AP MegaSports operation with News Corporation's STATS Inc. to form STATS LLC a 50-50 joint venture that provides sports-related information content and statistical analysis.

The following year AP launched The Online Video Network (OVN) service to provide news video to AP member and customer websites. The co-op responded to the harsh economy by cutting costs in 2008 with consolidation of its print broadcast and digital sales and marketing units. It continued its cost-cutting efforts in 2009 when it cut some 90 jobs instituted a hiring freeze and bought out about 100 employees.

EXECUTIVES

President & Ceo, Gary B. Pruitt, age 60
Svp And Executive Editor, Kathleen Carroll
Svp And Cio, Lorraine Cichowski
Svp And Cfo, Ken Dale
Svp And Cto, Gianluca D'Aniello
Chairman, Mary E. Junck, age 71
Auditors: ERNST & YOUNG LLP NEW YORK N

LOCATIONS

HQ: THE ASSOCIATED PRESS
200 LIBERTY ST FL 19, NEW YORK, NY 102812102
Phone: 212 621-1500
Web: WWW.AP.ORG

PRODUCTS/OPERATIONS

Selected Products and Services
AP Digital News (Internet and wireless news delivery)
AP Images (photo services)
AP Mobile (mobile applications)
APTN (AP Television News international television news service)
ENPS (electronic news production system)
Online Video Network (video content distribution)

COMPETITORS

Agence France-Presse	GlobeNewswire
Bloomberg L.P.	Marketwire
Business Wire	New York Times
Comtex News	PR Newswire
Corbis	Reuters
Dow Jones	TEGNA
E. W. Scripps	Tribune Media
Getty Images	UPI

HISTORICAL FINANCIALS

Company Type: Private

Income Statement   FYE: December 31

	REVENUE ($ mil.)	NET INCOME ($ mil.)	NET PROFIT MARGIN	EMPLOYEES
12/17	510	(73)	—	3,533
12/16	556	1	0.3%	—
12/15	568	183	32.3%	—
12/14	604	140	23.3%	—
Annual Growth	(5.5%)	—	—	—

2017 Year-End Financials

Return on assets: 1.8%   Cash ($ mil.): 7
Return on equity: (-14.5%)
Current ratio: 0.40

THE AULTMAN HOSPITAL

EXECUTIVES

Ceo, Christopher E Remark
Pres, Edward J Roth III
Cfo, Mark Wright
Cntrl, George Film
Assistant Vice-President, Chris Parrish
Secretary, Monica Tomlinson
Health Professional, Chris Schlachter
Internal Medicine Practitioner, Gilbert R Rowley
Auditor, Logan Miller
Internal Medicine Practitioner, Muhannad Samaan
Coordinator, Shelley Lanning

LOCATIONS

HQ: THE AULTMAN HOSPITAL
2600 6TH ST SW, CANTON, OH 447101799
Phone: 330 452-9911
Web: WWW.AULTMAN.ORG

HISTORICAL FINANCIALS

Company Type: Private

Income Statement   FYE: December 31

	REVENUE ($ mil.)	NET INCOME ($ mil.)	NET PROFIT MARGIN	EMPLOYEES
12/16	315	5	1.9%	3,027
12/15	307	0	0.2%	—
12/13	470	2	0.5%	—
12/12	471	(1)	—	—
Annual Growth	(9.6%)	—	—	—

THE BIG TEN CONFERENCE INC

EXECUTIVES

Comm, Jim Delany
SEC, Chad Hawley
Treas, Brad Traviolia
Production, Wt Robinson
Administrative Assistant, Mary Jo O'Donoghue

Coordinator, Bill Carollo
Director of Information Techno, Brandon Winbush
Associate Director, Brett McWethy
Chief Communications Officer, Diane Dietz
Assistant Commissioner Communi, Jason Yellin
Controller, Julie Suderman
Auditors: RSM US LLP CHICAGO IL

LOCATIONS

HQ: THE BIG TEN CONFERENCE INC
5440 PARK PL, ROSEMONT, IL 600183732
Phone: 847 696-1010
Web: WWW.BIGTEN.ORG

HISTORICAL FINANCIALS

Company Type: Private

Income Statement   FYE: June 30

	REVENUE ($ mil.)	NET INCOME ($ mil.)	NET PROFIT MARGIN	EMPLOYEES
06/16	483	(10)	—	25
06/15	448	12	2.8%	—
06/14	338	2	0.6%	—
06/13	318	5	1.9%	—
Annual Growth	14.9%	—	—	—

2016 Year-End Financials

Return on assets: 0.6%   Cash ($ mil.): 28
Return on equity: (-2.2%)
Current ratio: 3.30

THE BLOOMBERG FAMILY FOUNDATION INC

EXECUTIVES

Prin, Steve Fadem
Associate, Matt Lipsky
Auditors: GELLER & COMPANY LLC NEW YORK

LOCATIONS

HQ: THE BLOOMBERG FAMILY FOUNDATION INC
909 3RD AVE, NEW YORK, NY 100224731
Phone: 212 205-0100
Web: WWW.BLOOMBERG.ORG

HISTORICAL FINANCIALS

Company Type: Private

Income Statement   FYE: December 31

	REVENUE ($ mil.)	NET INCOME ($ mil.)	NET PROFIT MARGIN	EMPLOYEES
12/15	1,194	736	61.7%	2
12/14	1,328	1,048	79.0%	—
12/13	809	538	66.5%	—
12/09	452	279	61.8%	—
Annual Growth	17.6%	17.5%	—	—

2015 Year-End Financials

Return on assets: —   Cash ($ mil.): 73
Return on equity: 61.7%
Current ratio: —

THE BOLDT GROUP INC

EXECUTIVES

Pres, Oscar C Boldt
Vice President, Thomas J Boldt
SEC, Michelle M Gawinski
Project Financial Coordinator, Maria Drezek
Project Manager, Adam Dvorak
Administrative Office Manager, Ann Backus
Vice President Central Operati, Gus Schultz
Administrator, Jennifer Weaver
Senior Project Manager, Pete Selmo
Senior Buyer, Robin Rusch
Project Executive, Ryan Yoho
Auditors: SCHENCK SC APPLETON WISCONSI

LOCATIONS

HQ: THE BOLDT GROUP INC
2525 N ROEMER RD, APPLETON, WI 549118623
Phone: 920 739-7800

HISTORICAL FINANCIALS

Company Type: Private

Income Statement				FYE: December 31
	REVENUE ($ mil.)	NET INCOME ($ mil.)	NET PROFIT MARGIN	EMPLOYEES
12/17	989	0	—	1,500
12/16	1,022	17	1.7%	—
12/15	978	0	—	—
12/14	874	0	—	—
Annual Growth	4.2%	—	—	—

2017 Year-End Financials
Return on assets: 14.4%   Cash ($ mil.): 31
Return on equity: —
Current ratio: 1.00

THE BRANCH GROUP INC

EXECUTIVES

Ceo, J William Karbach
V Pres-SEC, Terry Keffer
Cfo, Melanie Wheeler
Exec Vice President, Tony Brown
Exec Vice President, Larry Dickenson
Coo, Steve Aud
Contractor, W M Jordan
Auditors: KPMG LLP ROANOKE VIRGINIA

LOCATIONS

HQ: THE BRANCH GROUP INC
442 RUTHERFORD AVE NE, ROANOKE, VA
240162116
Phone: 540 982-1678
Web: WWW.BRANCHGROUP.COM

PRODUCTS/OPERATIONS

Selected Subsidiaries
Branch & Associates Inc. (builder construction services)
Branch Highways Inc. (highway bridge airport infrastructure and site development)
E.V. Williams Inc. (highway site development and concrete paving construction servises)
G.J. Hopkins Inc. (mechanical and electrical construction services)
R. E. Daffan (construction and architectural services)

COMPETITORS

Bechtel
English Construction
Company
Fluor
K3 Construction
KBS
S. W. Rodgers
Tetra Tech Tesoro
Turner Corporation
Whiting-Turner

HISTORICAL FINANCIALS

Company Type: Private

Income Statement				FYE: December 31
	REVENUE ($ mil.)	NET INCOME ($ mil.)	NET PROFIT MARGIN	EMPLOYEES
12/17	363	0	—	800
12/16	393	0	—	—
12/15	392	0	—	—
12/14	384	0	—	—
Annual Growth	(1.9%)	—	—	—

2017 Year-End Financials
Return on assets: 11.8%   Cash ($ mil.): 21
Return on equity: —
Current ratio: 0.90

THE BRANDT COMPANIES LLC

EXECUTIVES

MBR, Barry Moore
MBR, Mark Zilbermann
MBR, Mike Arthurs
Controller, Jeff Welsh
Vice-President, Christian Beasley
Vice-President, John Dunn
Manager, Wes Miller
Senior Project Manager, Brad Veraska
Project Manager, Demarcus Warren
Supervisor, Jennifer Groves
Administrative Assistant, Leslie Padon
Auditors: PAYNE & SMITH LLC DALLAS TX

LOCATIONS

HQ: THE BRANDT COMPANIES LLC
1728 BRIERCROFT CT, CARROLLTON, TX 750066400
Phone: 972 241-9411
Web: WWW.BRANDT.US

HISTORICAL FINANCIALS

Company Type: Private

Income Statement				FYE: December 31
	REVENUE ($ mil.)	NET INCOME ($ mil.)	NET PROFIT MARGIN	EMPLOYEES
12/17	497	14	3.0%	1,500
12/16	418	11	2.8%	—
12/15	398	12	3.2%	—
12/14	384	10	2.7%	—
Annual Growth	8.9%	11.7%	—	—

2017 Year-End Financials
Return on assets: 6.9%   Cash ($ mil.): 4
Return on equity: 3.0%
Current ratio: 1.10

THE BRIGHAM AND WOMEN'S HOSPITAL INC

EXECUTIVES

Pres, Elizabeth G Nabel
Immunologist, Annemieke De Jong
Director of Mis/Is, Charles Riley
Director of Risk Management, David Seaver
Chief Officer, Stanley W Ashley
Scientist, Ali Tavakkolizadeh
Vice-Chairman, David Faxon
Staff, Deborah Dillon
Clinical Director, Harvey Mamon
Pathologist, Jeffrey Krane
Doctor, John Ready

LOCATIONS

HQ: THE BRIGHAM AND WOMEN'S HOSPITAL INC
75 FRANCIS ST, BOSTON, MA 021156106
Phone: 617 732-5500
Web: WWW.BRIGHAMANDWOMENS.ORG

HISTORICAL FINANCIALS

Company Type: Private

Income Statement				FYE: September 30
	REVENUE ($ mil.)	NET INCOME ($ mil.)	NET PROFIT MARGIN	EMPLOYEES
09/17	2,128	55	2.6%	8,376
09/16	1,938	94	4.9%	—
09/15	1,811	60	3.4%	—
09/14	1,797	151	8.4%	—
Annual Growth	5.8%	(28.3%)	—	—

2017 Year-End Financials
Return on assets: 2.4%   Cash ($ mil.): 60
Return on equity: 2.6%
Current ratio: 0.70

THE BROAD INSTITUTE INC

EXECUTIVES

Pres-Ceo-Dir, Eric Lander
Principal, Derek Martyn
Exec V Pres-Vice President, Alan Fein
Dir, David Baltimore
Coo, Samantha Singer
Cso, Todd Golub
Cdo, Justine Levin
Cco, Clare Midgley
Cpo, Andy Porter
Scientist, Ashlee M Earl
Scientist, Heng LI
Auditors: PRICEWATERHOUSECOOPERS LLP BO

LOCATIONS

HQ: THE BROAD INSTITUTE INC
415 MAIN ST, CAMBRIDGE, MA 021421027
Phone: 617 714-7000
Web: WWW.BROADINSTITUTE.ORG

HISTORICAL FINANCIALS
Company Type: Private

Income Statement   FYE: June 30

	REVENUE ($ mil.)	NET INCOME ($ mil.)	NET PROFIT MARGIN	EMPLOYEES
06/17	451	23	5.2%	800
06/16	377	(45)	—	—
06/15	355	37	10.6%	—
06/14	411	108	26.4%	—
Annual Growth	3.1%	(40.1%)	—	—

2017 Year-End Financials
Return on assets: 1.8%   Cash ($ mil.): 169
Return on equity: 5.2%
Current ratio: 1.10

THE BROOKDALE HOSPITAL MEDICAL CENTER

EXECUTIVES

Director, Kusum Viswanathan
Internal Medicine Practitioner, Ali Shahzad
Internal Medicine Practitioner, Bair Cadet
Internal Medicine Practitioner, Hamza Minhas
Internal Medicine Practitioner, Mark Dukshtein
Vice-President, Omar Ishmael
Internal Medicine Practitioner, Punit Sachdev
Internal Medicine Practitioner, Robert Adrah
Internal Medicine Practitioner, Swathi Kondapalli
Internal Medicine Practitioner, Vinod Namana
Manager, Raymond Fredericks

LOCATIONS

HQ: THE BROOKDALE HOSPITAL MEDICAL CENTER
  1 BROOKDALE PLZ, BROOKLYN, NY 112123198
Phone: 718 240-5000
Web: WWW.BROOKDALE.EDU

HISTORICAL FINANCIALS
Company Type: Private

Income Statement   FYE: December 31

	REVENUE ($ mil.)	NET INCOME ($ mil.)	NET PROFIT MARGIN	EMPLOYEES
12/15	483	(24)	—	5
12/14	476	(18)	—	—
Annual Growth	1.5%	—	—	—

2015 Year-End Financials
Return on assets: 15.0%   Cash ($ mil.): 13
Return on equity: (-5.0%)
Current ratio: 0.70

THE CARLE FOUNDATION

EXECUTIVES

Ceo, James C Leonard
Dir, Scott Hendrie
Vice President, John Snyder
Treas, Robert Tonkinson
Exec V Pres, Matthew Gibb
Human Resources, Dallas Knauer
Doctor, Mark E Faith
Registered Nurse, Amanda Dodd
Graphic Designer, Amanda Johnston
Registered Nurse, Laura Christman
Business Analyst, Sandy Gayer
Auditors: ERNST & YOUNG US LLP INDIANAP

LOCATIONS

HQ: THE CARLE FOUNDATION
  611 W PARK ST, URBANA, IL 618012529
Phone: 217 383-3311
Web: WWW.CARLE.COM

HISTORICAL FINANCIALS
Company Type: Private

Income Statement   FYE: December 31

	REVENUE ($ mil.)	NET INCOME ($ mil.)	NET PROFIT MARGIN	EMPLOYEES
12/15	2,493	51	2.0%	5,284
12/13	249	52	20.9%	—
12/11*	1,608	0	0.0%	—
06/10	135	72	53.3%	—
Annual Growth	62.4%	(5.6%)	—	—

*Fiscal year change

2015 Year-End Financials
Return on assets: 0.9%   Cash ($ mil.): 192
Return on equity: 2.0%
Current ratio: 0.50

THE CHARLES STARK DRAPER LABORATORY INC

The Charles Stark Draper Laboratory guides research into space under water and across continents. The not-for-profit corporation develops guidance navigation and control technologies for aircraft submarines missiles and spacecraft. It works with NASA the US Department of Defense and commercial businesses to develop technologies and fabricate prototypes. The organization also solves healthcare problems with its work in biomedical engineering. The lab boasts more than 850 engineers and scientists. Originally known as the Instrument Lab the laboratory was renamed in 1970 and became an independent institution three years later.

Operations
Draper Lab's innovations include a personal navigation system that allows soldiers to find their way in GPS-denied areas. It has also developed a micro-avionics system for a 20-gram nano air vehicle that's capable of flying in realistic wind conditions and equipped with a digital video recorder the size of a postage stamp.

The corporation boasts expertise in guidance navigation and control sytems; advanced algorithms and software; fault-tolerant computing; modeling and simulation; and microelectromechanical system (MEMS) and multichip module technology.

Geographic Reach
Draper Lab maintains operations in Cambridge Massachusetts; Houston; Huntsville Alabama; Tampa and St. Petersburg Florida; and Washington D.C.

Financial Performance
In fiscal 2013 Draper Lab made up for traction lost the previous year. Its revenue rose by 3% to $528 million in 2013 from 2012's $514 million. The company's revenues had decreased in 2012 by 3% due in part to a drop in subcontracts.

Primary funding sources include the US Navy the US Army other national security sponsors NASA and select non- Department of Defense sponsors.

Strategy
Fueled by the brain power and expertise of its hundreds of engineers Draper Lab aims to solve problems by designing developing and deploying solutions built using advanced technologies. Its primary areas of focus include space exploration security healthcare and energy.

Draper Lab completed the first missile flight of the MK6 MOD 1 boost guidance system for the Trident II D5 submarine-launched ballistic missile in 2012 with completely successful results. This flight was the culmination of 10 years of work by the laboratory in collaboration with the Navy Strategic Systems Program and a team of independent support contractors.

Another significant milestone was the deployment of the first close-in collection systems using its patented integrated ultra-high density (iUHD) packaging technology — the next generation of Draper Lab's vanishingly small systems (VSS) design techniques.

The lab's investments in biomedical and energy systems are paying dividends with a growing list of sponsors in each area. To this end Draper Lab is working with Shell Oil to design a backup system that will assist operators in getting an oil well under control in the event of a drilling accident. It's also partnering with the State of Rhode Island to prototype a clean energy research center in collaboration with Brown University and the University of Rhode Island.

Draper Lab continues to work alongside Progress Energy to improve the effectiveness of coal plant operation by improving combustion efficiency and monitoring critical equipment status to anticipate failures. Through a partnership with the Defense Advanced Research Projects Agency it's creating a versatile microfluidic platform that can incorporate up to 10 individually engineered microphysiological organ system modules in an interacting circuit.

Company Background
The organization was founded in 1932 by MIT professor Charles Stark Draper as a teaching lab.

EXECUTIVES

Vice President For Programs, Darryl Sargent
Vp Finance And Administration And Treasurer, Elizabeth Mora
President And Ceo, Kaigham (Ken) Gabriel
Vice President, Len Polizzotto
Vice President Of Information Technology, Diane Chilante
Vice President For Commercial, Tara Clark
Chairman, Franklin C. (Frank) Miller
Auditors: MOODY FAMIGLIETTI & ANDRONICO

LOCATIONS

HQ: THE CHARLES STARK DRAPER LABORATORY INC
555 TECHNOLOGY SQ, CAMBRIDGE, MA 021393539
Phone: 617 258-1000
Web: WWW.DRAPER.COM

PRODUCTS/OPERATIONS

Selected Research Areas
Biomedical engineering
  Tissue engineering
  Sensor development
Space systems
  Military space systems
  Planetary exploration
  Scientific spacecraft
  Space transportation
Special operations
  Robotics
  Small low-power electronics
  Surveillance systems
Strategic systems
  Inertial guidance systems
Tactical systems
  Precision engagement systems
  Manned/unmanned systems
  Missile defense

COMPETITORS

Applied Research Associates Institute for Defense Analyses	QinetiQ Quantum Research

HISTORICAL FINANCIALS

Company Type: Private

Income Statement   FYE: July 31

	REVENUE ($ mil.)	NET INCOME ($ mil.)	NET PROFIT MARGIN	EMPLOYEES
07/16*	676	36	5.5%	1,134
06/14	522	28	5.4%	—
06/13	542	17	3.2%	—
06/12	514	(20)	—	—
Annual Growth	7.1%	—	—	—

*Fiscal year change

2016 Year-End Financials
Return on assets: 13.7%   Cash ($ mil.): 51
Return on equity: 5.5%
Current ratio: 1.20

THE CHARLOTTE-MECKLENBURG HOSPITAL AUTHORITY

TheA medical facilities under the watchful eye of theA Charlotte-Mecklenburg Hospital AuthorityA care for the injured and infirmed.A As the largest health care system in the Carolinas the organizationA operating asA Carolinas HealthCare System (CHS)A ownsA or managesA more thanA 30A affiliated hospitals.A It also operates long-term care facilities research centers rehabilitation facilitiesA surgery centersA home health agencies radiation therapy facilities and other health care operations.A Collectively CHSA facilities have more than 6400 beds and affiliated physician practices employ more than 1700 doctors. The network's flagship facility is the 875-bedA Carolinas Medical Center in Charlotte North Carolina.

EXECUTIVES

Ceo, Eugene A Woods
Exec Vp Pres-Cfo, Greg A Gombar
Exe Vice President, Paul S Franz
Director*, Kara King
V Pres-Fin, Mary Ann Rouse
Staff, Sarah Laborde
Svp and Chief Compliance, Eugene A Deladdy Jr
Human Resources Information MA, Suzanne Greenway
Accounting Staff, Gladys Stanley
Management Associate II, Nina McDowell
Superintendent II, Ryan Prince
Auditors: KPMG LLP CHARLOTTE NC

LOCATIONS

HQ: THE CHARLOTTE-MECKLENBURG HOSPITAL AUTHORITY
1000 BLYTHE BLVD, CHARLOTTE, NC 282035812
Phone: 704 355-2000
Web: WWW.CAROLINASHEALTHCARE.ORG

PRODUCTS/OPERATIONS

2010 Revenue

	% of total
Tertiary & acute care services	72
Physicians' services	16
Post-acute care services	3
Specialty services	2
Other services & non-operating activities	7
Total	**100**

Selected Hospitals and Health Care Pavilions
AnMed Health Medical Center
AnMed Health Rehabilitation Hospital
AnMed Health Women's and Children's Hospital
Anson Community Hospital
Bon Secours/St. Francis Hospital
Cannon Memorial Hospital
Carolinas Medical Center
Carolinas Medical Center - Kannapolis (health care pavilion)
Carolinas Medical Center - Lincoln
Carolinas Medical Center - Mercy
Carolinas Medical Center - NorthEast
Carolinas Medical Center - Pineville
Carolinas Medical Center - Steele Creek (health care pavilion)
Carolinas Medical Center - Union
Carolinas Medical Center - University
Carolinas Medical Center - Waxhaw (health care pavilion)
Carolinas Rehabilitation
Carolinas Rehabilitation - Mount Holly
Cleveland Regional Medical Center
CMC - Randolph
Columbus Regional Healthcare System
Crawley Memorial Hospital
Grace Hospital
Kings Mountain Hospital
Levine Children's Hospital
MedWest - Harris
MedWest - Haywood
MedWest - Swain
Roper Hospital
Roper St. Francis - Mount Pleasant Hospital
Scotland Memorial Hospital
Stanly Regional Medical Center
St. Luke's Hospital
Valdese Hospital
Wallace Thomson Hospital
Wilkes Regional Medical Center

COMPETITORS

Alamance Regional Medical Center	Haywood Regional High Point Regional Health System
CaroMont	McLeod Health
Community Health Systems	Mission Hospitals
Cone Health	Morehead Memorial Hospital
Conway Medical Center	New Hanover Regional Medical Center
Cumberland County Hospital System	Novant Health
Davis Regional Medical Center	Palmetto Health

Duke University Health System	Presbyterian Healthcare
FirstHealth of the Carolinas	Rex Healthcare
Georgetown Hospital System	Soliant Health
Grand Strand Regional Medical Center	Tenet Healthcare
HCA	UNC Hospitals
	Upstate Affiliate
	Vidant Health
	WakeMed

HISTORICAL FINANCIALS

Company Type: Private

Income Statement   FYE: December 31

	REVENUE ($ mil.)	NET INCOME ($ mil.)	NET PROFIT MARGIN	EMPLOYEES
12/17	5,991	829	13.9%	62,000
12/16	5,676	493	8.7%	—
12/15	5,478	(247)	—	—
12/12	4,501	249	5.5%	—
Annual Growth	5.9%	27.2%	—	—

2017 Year-End Financials
Return on assets: 4.4%   Cash ($ mil.): 136
Return on equity: 13.9%
Current ratio: 0.80

THE CHEROKEE NATION

EXECUTIVES

Chief, Chad Smith
Human Resources, Loretta McNac
Director, Kim Carroll
Director, Kip Martin
Controller, Sharon Swepston
Accounting Manager, Larry T Smith
Manager, Tina Gonzalez
Information Specialist, Jeff Carroll
Human Resources Analyst, Ramona Mays
Law Specialist, Kristen T Mankiller
Project Coordinator, Ruth Hummingbird

LOCATIONS

HQ: THE CHEROKEE NATION
17675 S MUSKOGEE AVE, TAHLEQUAH, OK 744645492
Phone: 918 453-5000

HISTORICAL FINANCIALS

Company Type: Private

Income Statement   FYE: September 30

	REVENUE ($ mil.)	NET INCOME ($ mil.)	NET PROFIT MARGIN	EMPLOYEES
09/16	541	1	0.4%	5,500
09/15	511	(15)	—	—
09/05	226	15	6.7%	—
09/04	203	14	6.9%	—
Annual Growth	8.5%	(15.3%)	—	—

2016 Year-End Financials
Return on assets: 28.0%   Cash ($ mil.): 313
Return on equity: 0.4%
Current ratio: —

THE CHESTER COUNTY HOSPITAL

EXECUTIVES

Ceo-Pres, Michael Duncan
Pres-Ex Dir, H L Perry Pepper
V Pres-Coo, Patricia Rayburn
V Pres-Fin, Kenneth E Flickinger
V Pres-Fin, Paul Vanore
V Pres-Hr, Michael Barber
Prin, William E Luginbuhl
Optometrists, Michelle Dorian
Pharmacist, Mary Lucas
Family and General Dentistry, Jeffrey N Melini
Director of Infection Control, Charleen Faucette
Auditors: PNCEWATERHOUSECOOPERS LLP PHI

LOCATIONS

HQ: THE CHESTER COUNTY HOSPITAL
701 E MARSHALL ST, WEST CHESTER, PA
193804421
Phone: 610 431-5000
Web: WWW.CHESTERCOUNTYHOSPITAL.ORG

HISTORICAL FINANCIALS
Company Type: Private

Income Statement   FYE: June 30

	REVENUE ($ mil.)	NET INCOME ($ mil.)	NET PROFIT MARGIN	EMPLOYEES
06/16	311	9	3.0%	2,000
06/15	298	10	3.5%	—
06/14	265	14	5.3%	—
06/13	271	11	4.2%	—
Annual Growth	4.7%	(6.8%)	—	—

2016 Year-End Financials

Return on assets: 3.2%   Cash ($ mil.): 18
Return on equity: 3.0%
Current ratio: —

THE CHILDREN'S HOSPITAL CORPORATION

The Children's Hospital Corporation dba Boston Children's Hospital is a 400-bed hospital that offers acute health care and specialty services for children from birth through age 21. The medical center is Harvard Medical School's main teaching hospital for children's health care and it is the world's largest pediatric research center. Its John F. Enders Pediatric Research facility provides research for the treatment of childhood diseases. Specialty services are offered in the fields of cardiovascular surgery digestive care neurology oncology ophthalmology orthopedics autism spectrum disorder blood diseases and fetal care. The not-for-profit hospital was founded in 1869.

Operations
Boston Children's Hospital handles about 25000 inpatient visits per year as well as 27000 surgeries and more than 200000 radiological exams. Its 200+ specialized clinical programs handle about 560000 appointments annually. The hospital is considered a safety-net hospital and as such is one of the largest providers of medical care to low-income children in the state. About 30% of the hospital's patients are either uninsured or have health care coverage through public assistance.

In addition to its educational and research partnerships with Harvard the medical center collaborates with other universities as well as drug makers medical equipment firms and research institutes. Altogether it has some 1100 scientists at its research centers including the Enders Pediatric Research Laboratories and the Karp Family Research Laboratories. Children's Hospital Boston receives up to some $225 million in research funding per year.

Along with the main hospital the system operates a handful of primary and specialty care centers throughout the Boston area. It also operates a cancer clinic within the main campus through a partnership with the Dana Farber Cancer Institute.

In 2017 Boston Children's Hospital was named the country's best pediatric hospital by U.S. News & World Report for the fifth year in a row.

Geographic Reach
Boston Children's Hospital has satellite locations and affiliates throughout Massachusetts. In addition to its main campus in Boston it has satellites in Lexington North Dartmouth Peabody and Waltham; doctors' offices in Brockton Milford Norwood and Weymouth; and affiliates in Beverly Fall River Milford New Bedford South Weymouth Wareham and Winchester.

Strategy
Due to increasing economic troubles and health reform measures in the US Boston Children's Hospital has been working to cut costs. Despite the cost-control efforts the main campus is undergoing expansion renovation and modernization efforts as part of a 10-year expansion plan.

EXECUTIVES

Senior Vice President, Wendy Warring
Ceo, James Mandell
Coo, Sandra L. Fenwick, age 67
Cfo, Doug Vanderslice
Svp And Cio, Daniel Nigrin
Svp Patient Care Operations Chief Nursing Officer And Trustee, Eileen Sporing
Surgeon-in-chief And Trustee, James Kasser
Trustee, Paul R. Hickey
Executive Director Satellite Clinical Operations, Julee Bolg
President Children's Hospital Trust, Lynn Susman
Svp And Chief Marketing And Communications Officer, Margaret Coughlin
Chief Investment Officer, Phil Rotner
Executive Director Satellite Administrative Operations, Jane Venti
Executive Vice President Of, Kevin Churchwell
Medical Director, Michael Rivkin
Vice President For Research Chief Scientific Off, Bruce Zetter
Vice President Patient Safety Quality And Clinical Regulatory, Nina Rauscher
Director Of Pharmacy, Crystal Tom
Director Of Pharmacy, Al Patterson
Executive Vice President, Stavroula Osganian
Clinic Director, Hans C Oettgen
Director Of Medical Records, Mary Radley
Vice President, Inez Stewart
Vice President Of Marketing And Business Development, Lynne Hancock
Senior Vice President Network Development And Strategic Partnerships, Warring Wendy
Clinical Director, Leslie Lehmann
Vice President Clinical Services, Michael Gillespie
Senior Vice President And General Counse, Michele Garvin
Vice President Enterprise Contracting And Pricing, Randy Cook
Senior Vice President Real Estate Planning And Development, Lisa Hogarty
Medical Records Director, Mark Quinter
Chair, Stephen R. Karp

LOCATIONS

HQ: THE CHILDREN'S HOSPITAL CORPORATION
300 LONGWOOD AVE, BOSTON, MA 021155737
Phone: 617 355-6000
Web: WWW.CHILDRENSHOSPITAL.ORG

PRODUCTS/OPERATIONS

Selected Services
Major centers
  Brain Center
  Cancer and Blood Diseases Center
  Heart Center
  Orthopedic Center
  Transplant Center
Other Services
  Airway breathing and lungs
  Allergies and asthma
  Anatomy and function
  Bone joint and muscle
  Brain and nervous system
  Cancer and blood disorders
  Common childhood health topics and conditions
  Craniofacial anomalies
  Diet and nutrition
  Digestive metabolic and renal disorders
  Ears nose and throat
  Emergency medicine and trauma
  Eyes and vision
  Genetic disorders and birth defects
  Heart blood and circulation
  International patient care
  Medical tests
  Newborns
  Psychiatric (mental) conditions
  Reproductive and urinary conditions
  Skin and vascular
  Viruses and infections

COMPETITORS

Baystate Medical Center	Nemours Foundation
Beth Israel Deaconess Medical Center	Newton-Wellesley Hospital
Boston Medical Center	Northeast Health System
Cambridge Health Alliance	Partners HealthCare
Cape Cod Hospital	Shriners Hospitals For Children
Children's Hospital of Philadelphia	Steward Health Care
	Sturdy Memorial

HISTORICAL FINANCIALS
Company Type: Private

Income Statement   FYE: September 30

	REVENUE ($ mil.)	NET INCOME ($ mil.)	NET PROFIT MARGIN	EMPLOYEES
09/15	1,061	(5)	—	8,000
09/14	1,514	111	7.3%	—
09/09*	1,348	94	7.0%	—
06/05	4	0	13.0%	—
Annual Growth	71.3%	—	—	—

*Fiscal year change

2015 Year-End Financials

Return on assets: 12.9%   Cash ($ mil.): —
Return on equity: (-0.5%)
Current ratio: 0.60

THE CHILDREN'S HOSPITAL OF ALABAMA

EXECUTIVES

Ceo, William Michael Warren Jr
Exec V Pres-Coo, Thomas G Shufflebarger
Exec V Pres, Mike McDevitt
Financial Analyst, Catherine Davidson
Facilities Manager, David Cantrell
Interim Radiology Director, Jim Adkins
Quality Utilization Management, Junaye Wharton
Chargemaster Coordinator, Lessette Bourque
Staff Nurse, Lisa Lorino
Nurse Educator, Lynn Zinkan
Director Employee Relations Hu, Michelle Galipeau
Auditors: WARREN AVERETT LLC BIRMINGHA

LOCATIONS

HQ: THE CHILDREN'S HOSPITAL OF ALABAMA
1600 7TH AVE S, BIRMINGHAM, AL 352331711
Phone: 205 939-9100
Web: WWW.CHILDOFCHILDRENS.ORG

HISTORICAL FINANCIALS

Company Type: Private

Income Statement   FYE: December 31

	REVENUE ($ mil.)	NET INCOME ($ mil.)	NET PROFIT MARGIN	EMPLOYEES
12/17	736	113	15.4%	3,329
12/16	713	86	12.1%	—
12/15	670	(8)	—	—
12/14	698	32	4.6%	—
Annual Growth	1.8%	52.0%	—	—

2017 Year-End Financials

Return on assets: 5.9%
Return on equity: 15.4%
Current ratio: 2.10

Cash ($ mil.): 150

THE CHILDRENS HOSPITAL LOS ANGELES

Childrens Hospital Los Angeles (CHLA) is dedicated to treating the youngest critical care patients in the region. The about 570-bed hospital specializes in treating seriously ill and injured children from its neonatal intensive care unit to its pediatric organ transplant center. CHLA's pediatric specialists also provide care at its ambulatory care center in Arcadia and through about 40 off-site practice sites. The hospital's pediatric specialties include cancer kidney failure and cystic fibrosis care. CHLA serves more than 107000 children every year. It is one of only 12 children's hospitals in the nation (and the only one in California) ranked in all 10 pediatric specialties by U.S. News & World Report .

Operations

The CHLA medical staff includes about 600 physicians most of which are members of the CHLA Medical Group. Its emergency department treats some 71000 patients and the hospital sees more than 343000 outpatients annually. Nearly 50% of its patients are under the age of four. CHLA is also the only freestanding level I Pediatric Trauma Center in LA County approved by the Committee on Trauma of the American College of

Surgeons and among only 5% of US hospitals to be designated as a Magnet Hospital by the American Nurses Credentialing Center.

It is also a teaching hospital through its affiliation with the Keck School of Medicine of the University of Southern California and is home to the Saban Research Institute which conducts biomedical research into pediatric diseases. CHLA's training programs include 575 medical students 85 full-time residents three chief residents and 98 fellows.

Financial Performance

Revenue decreased 7% to $803 million in 2014 due to a decline in net patient service revenue. Also that year the company reported a net loss of $30 million due to the decline in revenue and higher operating expenses.

Strategy

CHLA is expanding its facilities to keep up with demand. In 2015 it opened the doors of a new outpatient center in Encino.

Company Background

Although it sometimes operates as Children's Hospital Los Angeles the absent apostrophe in the legal Childrens Hospital of Los Angeles name is no accident. The intentional spelling honors the original incorporation documents filed in 1901 when the institution was founded as Childrens Hospital Society of Los Angeles.

EXECUTIVES

Associate Vice President, Anna Weiser
Vice President Health System Development, Lara Khouri

LOCATIONS

HQ: THE CHILDRENS HOSPITAL LOS ANGELES
4650 W SUNSET BLVD, LOS ANGELES, CA 900276062
Phone: 323 660-2450
Web: WWW.CHLA.ORG

COMPETITORS

Cedars-Sinai Medical Center
Children's Hopsital of Chicago
Children's Hospital & Research Center at Oakland
Children's Hospital Boston
Children's Hospital of Orange County
Children's Hospital of Philadelphia
Children's National Medical Center
Cincinnati Children's Hospital
Cook Children's Health Care System
Dignity Health
Good Samaritan Hospital (Los Angeles)
Hollywood Presbyterian Medical Center
Nationwide Children's Hospital
Shriners Hospitals For Children

HISTORICAL FINANCIALS

Company Type: Private

Income Statement   FYE: June 30

	REVENUE ($ mil.)	NET INCOME ($ mil.)	NET PROFIT MARGIN	EMPLOYEES
06/18	1,393	247	17.8%	3,000
06/17	1,035	(14)	—	—
06/15	891	27	3.0%	—
06/14	823	(46)	—	—
Annual Growth	14.1%	—	—	—

2018 Year-End Financials

Return on assets: 5.7%
Return on equity: 17.8%
Current ratio: 1.00

Cash ($ mil.): 105

THE CHRIST HOSPITAL

Perched on the hilltop of Mt. Auburn The Christ Hospital oversees the health of ailing residents throughout Greater Cincinnati. Along with the flagship 528-bed hospital the organization operates about 100 outpatient and physician practice locations throughout the area. The Christ Hospital offers specialized care in a variety of fields including cardiac care cancer treatment kidney transplantation spine treatment and orthopedics. The not-for-profit hospital also provides an internal medicine residency program a family medicine residency program and a school of nursing. The Christ Hospital conducts research through its Lindner Clinical Trial Center.

Operations

The Christ Hospital is a general medical and surgical facility with 24977 admissions a year. It performed 7320 annual inpatient and 17373 outpatient surgeries and its emergency room had 52066 visits.

Physicians at the center have participated in more than 1000 clinical research trials in obesity diabetes adult stem cell protocols and congestive heart failure among a range of other therapeutic specialties.

The hospital works with the Ohio Heart & Vascular Center to provide comprehensive heart care to Cincinnati and the surrounding region. As part of the affiliation The Christ Hospital owns some assets related to the Ohio Heart & Vascular Center and employs its physicians and other staff. The agreement allows the two to make use of each others resources and to better serve heart patients in rural areas.

Strategy

In 2015 The Christ Hospital completed the expansion of its main campus at Mt. Auburn in a major $265 million initiative that included a new orthopedic and spine center with connectors to its existing buildings a parking garage and a materials management building.

That year the hospital opened its Montgomery Outpatient Center in Ohio and a new primary care office in Kenwood. It also announced plans to build a comprehensive medical center in the fast growing Butler County community of Liberty Township.

Company Background

The hospital expanded its outpatient capabilities in 2012 by opening its newly constructed The Christ Hospital Outpatient Center in Green Township and by adding a new center in Fort Wright Kentucky. The Green Township center is home to physician practices in cardiology OB-GYN internal and family medicine. It also offers physical and occupational therapy laboratory services and diagnostic testing services including digital X-ray ultrasound echocardiogram and vascular screening. The Fort Wright center offers cardiovascular care and screening services family medicine diagnostic imaging (X-ray screening mammography and general ultrasound) and wound healing obstetrics and gynecology and lab services.

Along with expanding via new construction The Christ Hospital grows its outpatient locations by acquiring local physician practices in a range of specialties. The system was particularly focused on increasing its orthopedic and urogynecological holdings during 2010 while acquisitions in 2011 and 2012 include a breast surgery practice a family medicine center a hematology-oncology group and an internal medicine practice.

The Christ Hospital was founded in 1889. At one time it was a part of UC Health a health care organization based in Ohio until the two ended their affiliation following a years-long court battle. It began operating independently again in 2008.

EXECUTIVES

President Ceo, Susan Croushore
Vp And Chief Nursing Officer, Deborah (Debbie) Hayes
Vp And Chief Medical Officer, Berc Gawne
Vp And Cfo, Chris Bergman
Cio, Alex Vaillancourt
President Of The Christ College Of Nursing, Nathan Long
President Of The Christ Hospital Foundation, Richard F. Kammerer

LOCATIONS

HQ: THE CHRIST HOSPITAL
2139 AUBURN AVE, CINCINNATI, OH 452192989
Phone: 513 585-2000
Web: WWW.THECHRISTHOSPITAL.COM

PRODUCTS/OPERATIONS

Selected Services
Cancer Services
Comprehensive Medicine
Heart & Vascular
Orthopaedics & Sports Medicine
Primary Care
Spine
Women's Health

COMPETITORS

Bethesda North	Premier Health
Cincinnati Children's	Partners
Hospital	St. Elizabeth
Deaconess Associations	Healthcare
Kettering Health	TriHealth
Network	UC Health

HISTORICAL FINANCIALS

Company Type: Private

Income Statement				FYE: June 30
	REVENUE ($ mil.)	NET INCOME ($ mil.)	NET PROFIT MARGIN	EMPLOYEES
06/17	929	14	1.5%	4,000
06/16	681	90	13.2%	—
06/15	647	89	13.9%	—
06/14	0	0	—	—
Annual Growth	—	—	—	—

2017 Year-End Financials
Return on assets: 5.8%
Return on equity: 1.5%
Current ratio: 1.40
Cash ($ mil.): 46

THE CHRISTIAN BROADCASTING NETWORK INC

Standards & Practices probably won't find much wrong with these TV programs. The Christian Broadcasting Network (CBN) is one of the leading producers of religious television programming in the country offering news and entertainment shows with a spiritual message. Its centerpiece is The 700 Club a daily show featuring a mix of news and commentary interviews feature stories and Christian ministry co-hosted by CBN founder Pat Robertson. The company's programs are syndicated to broadcast and cable TV outlets that reach audiences around the world. CBN generates most of its revenue through ministry donations.

Operations

CBN has a broad portfolio of ministries and services.

This portfolio includes The 700 Club & Prayer Center. CBN's The 700 Club program brings a magazine-style mix of news interviews testimonies and insights from Christian leaders. CBN's Prayer Center provides prayer as well as biblical guidance and resources to callers.

The 700 Club Interactive is a show designed for viewer interaction and uses a chat community Skype live phone calls and social networking.

CBN is launching a massive media campaign to promote the Bible under the brand Superbook .

Orphan's Promise ministers to the physical spiritual and educational needs of orphaned and vulnerable children.

CBN's Operation Blessing International's core programs include disaster relief medical aid hunger relief orphan care water wells and community development.

CBN.com offers streaming video teaching; indepth discipleship courses; Online Bible; CBN Radio; Bible teachings; my.CBN.com a social network; and free downloads of videos widgets and articles.

Geographic Reach

CBN programs have aired in 108 languages (from Mandarin to Spanish and from Turkish to Welsh) in 218 different countries and territories. It currently broadcasts in 139 countries with programs and content translated into 62 languages. The company has offices in Africa Asia Europe the Middle East North America (Canada and US) and Russia and the Commonwealth of Independent States.

Financial Performance

The company's revenue increased to $542 million during fiscal 2013 a 11% increased from previous year's $487 million. The spike was largely due to increases in revenue from Gifts in kind by 24% to $245 million in fiscal 2013 compared to $197 million in fiscal 2012 and additional investment gain and other revenues.

EXECUTIVES

Chm, Pat Robertson
Ceo, Gordon Robertson
Operations Manager, Mark Nowak
Administrative Assistant, Lora Moore
Engineer, Alex Monroe
Manager, Ryan Vanloon
Associate, Alegra Hassan
Public Relations Staff, Estella Torres
Software Engineer, Gandhi Basnet
Director, John Samples
Supervisor, Jonathan McCormick
Auditors: KPMG LLP MC LEAN VA

LOCATIONS

HQ: THE CHRISTIAN BROADCASTING NETWORK INC
977 CENTERVILLE TPKE, VIRGINIA BEACH, VA 234631001
Phone: 757 226-3030
Web: WWW.CBN.COM

COMPETITORS

Eden Communications	Thomas Nelson
Guideposts	Trinity Broadcasting
Integrity Media	Zondervan
Salem Media	

HISTORICAL FINANCIALS

Company Type: Private

Income Statement				FYE: March 31
	REVENUE ($ mil.)	NET INCOME ($ mil.)	NET PROFIT MARGIN	EMPLOYEES
03/16	307	(7)	—	941
03/15	293	(8)	—	—
03/14	301	5	1.8%	—
03/11	285	6	2.4%	—
Annual Growth	1.5%	—	—	—

2016 Year-End Financials
Return on assets: 6.5%
Return on equity: (-2.3%)
Current ratio: 1.50
Cash ($ mil.): 29

THE CITY OF SEATTLE-CITY LIGHT DEPARTMENT

City of Seattle - City Light Department (Seattle City Light) keeps guitars humming and coffee grinders running in the Seattle metropolitan area. The US's 10th largest municipally owned power company Seattle City Light transmits and distributes electricity to almost 1 million residential commercial industrial and government customers and owns hydroelectric power plants with more than 1800 MW of generation capacity. The utility also purchases power from the Bonneville Power Administration and other generators and it sells power to wholesale customers.

Operations

The company owns and operates generating transmission and distribution facilities and supplies electricity to 408000 customer meters in Seattle and certain surrounding communities. It also supplies electrical energy to other City agencies at rates prescribed by City ordinances.

Geographic Reach

The Seattle City Light service area includes all of the City of Seattle portions of the cities of Burien Tukwila SeaTac Shoreline Lake Forest Park and Renton as well as parts of unincorporated King County.

Financial Performance

Seattle City Light reported a revenue increase of 5% (to $842.2) in 2013 primarily due to increased retail power revenues stemming from a 4% rate increase and a 1.2% Bonneville Power Administration pass-through rate adjustment.

It net income increased that year due to higher retail power sales rate stabilization account unearned revenue transferred-in power related revenues and capital contributions. These were partially offset by higher expenses for generation customer service administrative and general taxes depreciation interest and lower investment earnings.

In 2013 Seattle City Light's operating cash inflow decreased to $229.7 (from $243.5 million in 2012) was due to higher tax paid and increased cash paid to a supplier.

Strategy

The company's long term objective is to continue to secure reliable low-cost and environmentally-sensitive power for its customers. To lower costs the utility is pushing its customers to conserve by taking green energy options such as installing more energy-efficient appliances and by buying renewable energy credits (allowing customers to pay for slightly higher costs of integrating renewable energy into the region's power grid).

Seattle City Light's six-year strategic plan adopted in 2012 calls for an annual rate increase of 4.7% to pay for expanding Seattle City Light's infrastructure and services including building its first electric substation for 30 years.

In 2013 the company added two new service request types to the 'Find It Fix It' smartphone app enabling Smartphone to report illegal dumping and streetlight outages in addition to its existing features for reporting abandoned vehicles graffiti potholes and parking enforcement issues.

That year Seattle City Light and the Seattle Aquarium announced the start of construction for the largest solar array at any aquarium on the West Coast as part of the utility's Community Solar and Green Up programs. The $330000 system will cover a large portion of the south side of the Seattle Aquarium's roof. Most of its 247 solar panels will produce electricity on behalf of City Light customers who want to buy solar power through the utility's Community Solar program. The rest of the panels are being installed as a demonstration project through the utility's voluntary Green Up renewable energy program with the electricity produced helping to power the Aquarium's operations.

Company Background

Evolving from several neighborhood electric companies that began serving Seattle in 1886 Seattle City Light was created in 1910 to power the city's streetlights. In 2005 the electric utility became the first in the US to become greenhouse gas neutral in its power generation.

EXECUTIVES

Superintendent, Jorge Carrasco
President City University Of Seattle, Richard Carter
Chief Technical Officer, Michael Mattmiller
Auditors: BAKER TILLY VIRCHOW KRAUZE LLP

LOCATIONS

HQ: THE CITY OF SEATTLE-CITY LIGHT DEPARTMENT
700 5TH AVE STE 3200, SEATTLE, WA 981045065
Phone: 206 684-3200
Web: WWW.SEATTLE.GOV

PRODUCTS/OPERATIONS

2013 Sales

	% of total
Non-residential	63
Residential	37
Total	**100**

COMPETITORS

Avista	PacifiCorp
Cascade Natural Gas	Portland General
IDACORP	Electric
NV Energy	Puget Energy
NW Natural	Xcel Energy

HISTORICAL FINANCIALS

Company Type: Private

Income Statement				FYE: December 31
	REVENUE ($ mil.)	NET INCOME ($ mil.)	NET PROFIT MARGIN	EMPLOYEES
12/17	989	120	12.2%	1,600
12/16	903	85	9.4%	—
12/09	723	34	4.7%	—
12/08	877	131	15.0%	—
Annual Growth	1.3%	(1.0%)	—	—

2017 Year-End Financials
Return on assets: 10.3%   Cash ($ mil.): 129
Return on equity: 12.2%
Current ratio: 0.80

THE CLEAR CREEK INDEPENDENT SCHOOL DISTRICT

EXECUTIVES

Supt, Greg Smith
Payroll Staff, Lynn Sonora
Accounting Staff, Amanda Anderson
Accounting Staff, Brandi Sonora
Vice-President Engineering, Lauren M Tragni
Board of Directors, Dee Scott
Assistant, Ann Thornton
Coordinator, Felicia Andrews
Assistant, Sharon McHenry
Teacher, Robert Phillips
Accounting Staff, Teresa Ritter
Auditors: NULL-LAIRSON PC TEXAS CITY

LOCATIONS

HQ: THE CLEAR CREEK INDEPENDENT SCHOOL DISTRICT
2425 E MAIN ST, LEAGUE CITY, TX 775732743
Phone: 281 284-0000
Web: WWW.CCISD.NET

HISTORICAL FINANCIALS

Company Type: Private

Income Statement				FYE: August 31
	REVENUE ($ mil.)	NET INCOME ($ mil.)	NET PROFIT MARGIN	EMPLOYEES
08/16	411	(103)	—	3,250
08/09	354	(41)	—	—
08/06	0	0	—	—
08/05	444	0	0.0%	—
Annual Growth	(0.7%)	—	—	—

2016 Year-End Financials
Return on assets: 6.5%   Cash ($ mil.): 119
Return on equity: (-25.1%)
Current ratio: —

THE CLEVELAND CLINIC FOUNDATION

Cleveland Clinic Foundation operates the not-for-profit Cleveland Clinic an academic medical center with more than 1400 beds at its main campus. The clinic specializes in cardiac care digestive disease treatment and urological and kidney care along with education and research opportunities. It has an international care center children's hospital and an outpatient center. It also contains research and educational institutes covering clinical drug research ophthalmic studies and cancer research as well as physician and scientist training programs. The Foundation — also known as the Cleveland Clinic Health System — operates 11 regional hospitals in Ohio Florida Abu Dhabi and London.

Operations

The Cleveland Clinic Foundation operates more than 150 outpatient facilities in northern Ohio. These include outpatient family health centers ambulatory surgery centers physician offices specialized cancer centers and wellness centers. The system represents 140 medical specialties and subspecialties.

The foundation operates the Lerner College of Medicine and the Lerner Research Institute through a partnership with Case Western Reserve University and it has continuing education nursing and residency programs. The Cleveland Clinic Foundation also operates Cleveland Clinic Innovations a unit that oversees collaborative research and technology commercialization programs with partners including MedStar Health and the University of Notre Dame. Cleveland Clinic educates some 1800 residents and fellows and receives some $270 million in research funding (from grants contracts and federal support) each year.

Altogether the medical centers known as the Cleveland Clinic Health System include some 4500 beds and employ about 3000 full-time physicians. The facilities handle 157000 hospital admissions and more than 5 million outpatient visits each year. In 2014 it had more than 202000 surgical cases.

Geographic Reach

In addition to its Cleveland center the foundation operates regional hospitals and numerous family and specialty health centers in northeastern Ohio. The Cleveland Clinic Foundation operates a handful of hospitals and clinics in Florida and it has several brain clinics for neurological treatment in Nevada. It also provides management services for a hospital in Ashtabula Ohio.

National and global expansion efforts are a big part of the organization's growth strategy. Internationally Cleveland Clinic Foundation operates a health and wellness center in Canada and manages health centers in the United Arab Emirates. Its facilities treat patients from more than 130 countries.

Sales and Marketing

Cleveland Clinic Foundation receives about 60% of its net patient service revenue from managed care and commercial insurance reimbursements. Medicare reimbursements account for 30% with the remainder of patient revenue coming from self-pay and Medicaid customers.

Strategy

Cleveland Clinic Foundation got some national media attention when President Barack Obama visited as part of the debate around health care reform and many publications around the country held it up as a model for delivering high quality care at lower costs. Cleveland Clinic's cost-cutting innovations include paying doctors a salary rather than by procedure (the group practice model) and interactive supply closets that perform their own inventory and summon robotic refill carts from the warehouse.

The foundation also improves its service offerings through facility and program expansion efforts as well as partnerships with other regional providers.

Mergers and Acquisitions

In early 2019 Cleveland Clinic expanded its operations in the Sunshine State when it acquired Martin Health System and its three hospitals in Southeast Florida. It also acquired Indian River Medical Center located on Florida's Treasure Coast.

Company Background

The foundation began in 1921 when a group of Cleveland doctors teamed up to improve medical care and education. The Cleveland Clinic hospital has conducted breakthrough medical innovations through its history such as the first face transplant in 2008 and it is regularly named to the US News & World Report's list of America's Best Hospitals.

EXECUTIVES

Cio, C. Martin Harris
President And Ceo, Delos M. (Toby) Cosgrove
Ceo Cleveland Clinic Regional Hospitals, David L. Bronson
Controller And Chief Accounting Officer, Steven C. Glass
Ceo Cleveland Clinic Abu Dhabi, A. Marc Harrison
Chief Medical Operations Officer, Robert Wyllie
Chief Of Operations, William (Bill) Peacock
Interim Ceo Sheikh Khalifa Medical City, Ben Frank
Interim Executive Chief Nursing Officer, K. Kelly Hancock
Chair Department Of Palm Ccm, Herbert Wiedemann
Medical Director, Kevin Hopkins
Medical Director, Vladimir Burdjalov
Medical Director Molecular Oncology, Roger D Klein
Director Of Pharmacy, William P Kernan
Vice President Of Medical Operations, William Riebel
Director Of Health Information Management, Gale McNeill
Medical Director, William Zafirau
Vice President Marketing, Janet Day
Nursing Director, Julie Fetto
Assistant Vice President Operations, Janet Gulley
Vice President Of Operations, Vicky Snyder
Medical Director, Purva Grover
Chairman, Robert E. (Bob) Rich
Vice Chairman, Joseph M. (Joe) Scaminace
Secretary, Lynn Meyers
Secretary, Tina Grobe
Secretary, Jennifer Gaizutis
Secretary, Marcie Chonko
Secretary, Pam Staub
Board Member, Donna Munic-Miller
Secretary, Christine Hughes
Secretary, Jan Kodish
Board Member, Alfred Melillo
Secretary, Patricia Gaines
Secretary, Marianne Simon
Auditors: ERNST & YOUNG LLP CLEVELAND

LOCATIONS

HQ: THE CLEVELAND CLINIC FOUNDATION
9500 EUCLID AVE, CLEVELAND, OH 441950002
Phone: 216 636-8335
Web: WWW.MY.CLEVELANDCLINIC.ORG

Selected Facilities
Ashtabula County Medical Center (Ashtabula Ohio; management contract)
The Cleveland Clinic (Cleveland Ohio)
  Cleveland Clinic Children's Hospital
  Cleveland Clinic International Center
Cleveland Clinic Canada (Toronto)
Cleveland Clinic Children's Hospital for Rehabilitation (Shaker Campus in Cleveland Ohio)
Cleveland Clinic Family Health Centers (multiple locations in northeast Ohio)
Cleveland Clinic Florida (Weston Florida)
Cleveland Clinic Florida (West Palm Beach Florida)
Cleveland Clinic Lou Ruvo Center for Brain Health (Elko Nevada)
Cleveland Clinic Lou Ruvo Center for Brain Health (Las Vegas Nevada)
Cleveland Clinic Lou Ruvo Center for Brain Health (Reno Nevada)
Euclid Hospital (Euclid Ohio)
Fairview Hospital (Cleveland Ohio)
Hillcrest Hospital (Mayfield Heights Ohio)
Lakewood Hospital (Lakewood Ohio)
Lutheran Hospital (Cleveland Ohio)
Marymount Hospital (Garfield Heights Ohio)
Medina Hospital (Medina Ohio)

Richard E. Jacobs Health Center (Avon Ohio)
South Pointe Hospital (Warrensville Heights Ohio)

Selected Institutes
Children's and Pediatric Institute
College of Medicine
Digestive Disease Institute
Education Institute
Glickman Urological and Kidney Institute
Lerner Research Institute
Neurological Institute
Orthopedic and Rheumatologic Institute
Stanley Shalom Zielony Institute for Nursing Excellence
Sydell and Arnold Miller Family Heart and Vascular Institute
Taussig Cancer Institute

PRODUCTS/OPERATIONS

2014 Net Patient Service Revenue

	% of total
Managed care & commercial	61
Medicare	29
Self-pay	7
Medicaid	3
Total	**100**

COMPETITORS

Akron Children's Hospital	Parma Community General Hospital
Catholic Health Initiatives	Premier Health Partners
Deaconess Associations	Robinson Memorial Hospital
Kettering Health Network	Shriners Hospitals For Children
Lake Health	Summa Health System
Mayo Clinic	University Hospitals Health System
Memorial Sloan-Kettering	Washington Hospital Center
MetroHealth System	
OhioHealth	

HISTORICAL FINANCIALS
Company Type: Private

Income Statement
FYE: December 31

	REVENUE ($ mil.)	NET INCOME ($ mil.)	NET PROFIT MARGIN	EMPLOYEES
12/17	8,407	1,150	13.7%	44,000
12/16	8,037	513	6.4%	—
12/14	4,290	405	9.4%	—
12/13	6,450	900	14.0%	—
Annual Growth	**6.8%**	**6.3%**	**—**	**—**

2017 Year-End Financials
Return on assets: 6.0%   Cash ($ mil.): 241
Return on equity: 13.7%
Current ratio: 0.50

THE CLEVELAND ELECTRIC ILLUMINATING COMPANY

EXECUTIVES

Pres, John E Skory
Exec V Pres-Cfo, Mark T Clark
V Pres-Contrl, Harvey L Wagner
Exec V Pres-Gen Cnsl, L L Vespoli
V Pres-Treas, J F Pearson
Executive Vice President Gene, Leila Vespoli
Member Board of Directors, Richard Grigg
Auditors: PRICEWATERHOUSECOOPERS LLP CL

LOCATIONS

HQ: THE CLEVELAND ELECTRIC ILLUMINATING COMPANY
76 S MAIN ST, AKRON, OH 443081812
Phone: 800 589-3101
Web: WWW.FIRSTENERGYCORP.COM

COMPETITORS

Columbia Gas of Ohio	Ohio Power
DPL	Vectren Energy
Dominion East Ohio	Delivery of Ohio
Duke Energy Ohio	

HISTORICAL FINANCIALS
Company Type: Private

Income Statement
FYE: December 31

	REVENUE ($ mil.)	NET INCOME ($ mil.)	NET PROFIT MARGIN	EMPLOYEES
12/16	928	37	4.0%	897
12/10	1,221	73	6.0%	—
12/09	1,676	(10)	—	—
12/08	1,815	284	15.7%	—
Annual Growth	**(8.0%)**	**(22.4%)**	**—**	**—**

THE COLLEGE OF WILLIAM & MARY

Not every Tom Dick and Harry gets into The College of William & Mary. The median SAT score for incoming freshmen is about 1345 (out of 1600). The second-oldest college in the US (Harvard is the oldest) William & Mary (W&M) is a "public ivy" university with an enrollment of 8300 undergraduate and graduate students. W&M offers more than 30 undergraduate and 10 graduate programs at schools of arts and sciences business education law and marine sciences. It also conducts research programs. Among its notable alumni are The Daily Show 's Jon Stewart and three US presidents: Thomas Jefferson James Monroe and John Tyler.

Operations
With a student-faculty ratio of 12:1 W&M offers about 60 majors for undergraduate students. The school with its more than 20 research centers also offers undergraduate research opportunities that blend with graduate and faculty research projects.

The college employs some 600 full-time faculty members to lead its undergraduate professional and graduate study programs.

Geographic Reach
W&M is located on a 1200-acre campus in Williamsburg Virginia; it also has a satellite learning center in Washington DC and a 40-acre campus in Gloucester Point (the Virginia Institute of Marine Science campus). About 65% of the undergraduate students who attend W&M are from within the Commonwealth of Virginia; others come from all US states and more than 50 foreign countries.

Financial Performance
W&M increased revenues 12% to $270 million during 2012 due to increased income from student tuition and fees grants and contracts and auxiliary enterprises. However net income fell 57% to $21 million due increased operating expenses in areas including student aid academic support instruction and student services.

W&M has an endowment of almost $625 million.

Strategy

The college has increased spending on its aid and support programs in order to maintain quality in its academic offerings as well as to support growing enrollment levels. The university limits growth to about 200 new undergraduates each year however to reflect its commitment to remain small. Financial aid funds have increased as family situations and higher tuition and fees have caused students to demonstrate an increased need for assistance.

The university which relies on state support of its operations for about 13% of its budget is also committed to supporting its faculty and staff by making annual salary raises a top priority.

In fiscal 2011 W&M expanded its facilities by adding new buildings to house the School of Education and the Cohen Career Center.

Company Background

The university was chartered as The College of William & Mary in 1693 by King William III and Queen Mary II. It is the birthplace of several collegiate traditions including the formation of the first academic Greek society in the US - the Phi Beta Kappa honor society.

EXECUTIVES

Executive Vice President Alumni Association, Karen Cottrell

LOCATIONS

HQ: THE COLLEGE OF WILLIAM & MARY
261 RICHMOND RD, WILLIAMSBURG, VA 23185
Phone: 757 221-3966
Web: WWW.WM.EDU

PRODUCTS/OPERATIONS

Selected Programs of Study

Accounting
American Studies
American Legal Studies
Anthropology
Applied Science
Biochemistry
Biology
Black Studies
Business Administration
Chemistry
Classical Studies (Latin Greek Hebrew)
Computer Science
Dance
Economics
Education
English
Environmental Science/Studies
Film Studies
Fine Arts
Geology
Government
History
International Relations
International Studies
Kinesiology
Law
Linguistics
Literary and Cultural Studies
Marine Science
Mathematics
Medieval and Renaissance Studies
Military Science
Modern Languages (Arabic Chinese French German Italian Japanese Portuguese Russian and Spanish)
Music
Philosophy
Physics
Psychology
Public Policy
Religion
Sociology
Theatre and Speech
Women's Studies

HISTORICAL FINANCIALS

Company Type: Private

Income Statement — FYE: June 30

	REVENUE ($ mil.)	NET INCOME ($ mil.)	NET PROFIT MARGIN	EMPLOYEES
06/17	329	38	11.6%	3,500
06/16	350	40	11.6%	—
06/11	94	63	67.5%	—
06/06	178	(96)	—	—
Annual Growth	5.7%	—	—	—

2017 Year-End Financials

Return on assets: 13.3%
Return on equity: 11.6%
Current ratio: 0.40
Cash ($ mil.): 25

THE COMMUNITY HOSPITAL GROUP INC

JFK Medical Center plays a central role in health care in central New Jersey. The medical center is an acute care facility with some 500 beds and 950 physicians providing emergency surgical trauma and other inpatient services. The hospital includes the JFK New Jersey Neuroscience Institute which treats stroke and other neurological conditions and the JFK Johnson Rehabilitation Institute which treats traumatic injuries. JFK Medical Center also offers diagnostic imaging cancer care senior and hospice care and family practice services. It is also a teaching hospital affiliated with several area universities. The hospital is part of the JFK Health System.

Strategy

To expand its capacity for emergency services JFK Medical Center launched construction of a new ER pavilion in 2013. The project includes the addition of a three-story structure above the existing ER facilities. To keep pace with cutting-edge medical technologies the hospital has also made recent investments in upgrades to its diagnostic imaging cardiac catheterization and wound healing equipment.

EXECUTIVES

Pres-Ceo, John P McGee
Exec Vice President, Louis P Amato
SEC, Peter Cappareli
Treas, Robert J Mc Kenna
Training and Direc, Robert Phillips
Information Technology Busines, Catherine Hofmann
Human Resources, Annamarie McPherson
Network Administrator, Dan Mleczko
Family Practitioner, John Metz
Records Director, Nawal Haque
Human Resources Director, Patricia Cooke
Auditors: BAKER TILLY

LOCATIONS

HQ: THE COMMUNITY HOSPITAL GROUP INC
98 JAMES ST STE 400, EDISON, NJ 088203902
Phone: 732 321-7000
Web: WWW.CARDIOMEDICALGROUP.COM

PRODUCTS/OPERATIONS

Selected Centers and Affiliates

Adult Medical Day Program
Haven Hospice
JFK at Home
JFK Dental Clinic
JFK Family Medicine Center
JFK Hartwyck Nursing Convalescent and Rehabilitation Centers
JFK Johnson Rehabilitation Institute (JRI)
JFK Mediplex Surgery Center
JFK New Jersey Neuroscience Institute
JFK Medical Center Muhlenberg Campus/JFK-Muhlenberg Snyder Schools
Whispering Knoll Assisted Living

COMPETITORS

Ball Memorial Hospital	Newton Medical Center
Bergen Regional Medical	Princeton HealthCare
Capital Health System	Robert Wood Johnson University Hospital
CentraState Healthcare System	Saint Peter's University Hospital
Henry County Memorial Hospital	St. Joseph's Healthcare System
Monmouth Medical Center	

HISTORICAL FINANCIALS

Company Type: Private

Income Statement — FYE: December 31

	REVENUE ($ mil.)	NET INCOME ($ mil.)	NET PROFIT MARGIN	EMPLOYEES
12/17	551	(13)	—	3,000
12/16	532	28	5.3%	—
12/14	467	(3)	—	—
12/10	427	(17)	—	—
Annual Growth	3.7%	—	—	—

2017 Year-End Financials

Return on assets: 7.6%
Return on equity: (-2.4%)
Current ratio: 1.00
Cash ($ mil.): 39

THE CONLAN COMPANY

EXECUTIVES

Ceo, Gary D Condron
President, Kevin Turpin
Vice President, Tom Lutz
Vice President, Ryan Triesenberg
Cfo, Bill Hayne
Exec Vice President, David Staley
Exec Vice President, Stuart Price
Sr Vice President, Scott Austin
Vice President, Charles King
Vice President, Ronnie Cupp
Administrator, Janeen Sheard
Auditors: SMITH ADCOCK AND COMPANY LLP

LOCATIONS

HQ: THE CONLAN COMPANY
1800 PARKWAY PL SE # 1010, MARIETTA, GA 300678293
Phone: 770 423-8000
Web: WWW.CONLANCOMPANY.COM

HISTORICAL FINANCIALS

Company Type: Private

Income Statement — FYE: December 31

	REVENUE ($ mil.)	NET INCOME ($ mil.)	NET PROFIT MARGIN	EMPLOYEES
12/17	930	40	4.3%	391
12/16	772	41	5.3%	—
12/15	589	13	2.3%	—
12/14	0	11	—	—
Annual Growth	—	50.6%	—	—

2017 Year-End Financials
Return on assets: 13.6%   Cash ($ mil.): 69
Return on equity: 4.3%
Current ratio: 0.30

THE COOPER HEALTH SYSTEM

The Cooper Health System keeps folks along the Delaware River shoreline feeling fine. The not-for-profit organization includes clinics and hospitals located throughout southern New Jersey and the Delaware Valley including the 600-bed Cooper University Hospital and The Children's Regional Hospital. Cooper University Hospital is a teaching campus for the University of Medicine and Dentistry of New Jersey providing training for medical students nurses residents fellows and health professionals. Its more than 700 physicians operate in about 80 specialties. Founded in 1887 the health care system provides trauma cancer cardiology neuroscience psychiatric and orthopedic specialty centers.

Operations

Cooper Health System is home to the area's Level I Southern New Jersey Regional Trauma Center; the Cooper Cancer Institute the Cooper Heart Institute the Cooper Bone & Joint Institute the Cooper Neurosciences Institute and critical care medicine. Carrying the Level 1 moniker means that Cooper Health System will be the referral of hospital of choice for patients' with massive injuries in the service area.

In 2013 Cooper Health System had 26600 hospital admissions and 81000 emergency department visits.

Geographic Reach

The Cooper Health System operates clinics hospitals and home health services in New Jersey Pennsylvania and Delaware. Cooper University Hospital serves as Southern New Jersey's major tertiary-care referral hospital for specialized services.

Sales and Marketing

HMO payments accounted for 34% of Cooper's net patient revenue in 2013 while commercial payments accounted for 27%.

Financial Performance

The system's revenue increased 6% to $874 million in 2013 as net patient service earnings rose. Net income rose 57% to $90 million on increased investment returns and contributions for capital acquisitions.

Cash flow from operations declined 26% to $47 million that year due to changes in prepaid expenses and a decline in accrued payable and accrued expenses.

Strategy

As demand for health care services has grown in the areas in which Cooper Health System serves Cooper University Hospital itself has also been forced to expand. Additions include all private rooms more operating suites intensive care and laboratory units and a new larger lobby area. Cooper Health System also built a new emergency department.

In 2014 the system's university health care division established a partnership with Kennedy Health System to expand cardiac services in Gloucester County. The partners opened a Cardiac Catheterization Laboratory at Kennedy University Hospital that year.

Mergers and Acquisitions

Cooper University Health Care acquired a 20% interest in AmeriHealth New Jersey in 2014. Cooper and AmeriHealth plan to work together to develop co-branded health products.

EXECUTIVES

President And Ceo Cooper University Health Care, Adrienne Kirby
Evp Government Relations And Public Policy, Gary S. Young
President Ceo And Director, John P. Sheridan
Svp Operations, Maureen P. Barnes
Sevp And General Counsel, Gary J. Lesneski
Sevp And Cfo, Douglas E. Shirley
Chief Of Staff To The President; Ceo Cooper University Hospital, Louis S. Bezich
Svp Patient Care Services And Chief Nursing Officer, Dianne Charsha
Interim Chief Medical Officer; Chair Of The Radiology Department, Raymond L. Baraldi
Director Of Pharmacy, Jaqueline Sutton
Vice President Quality, Adrienne Elberfeld
Vice President, Dorothy Duffy
Clinical Director, Jeanne Greer
Clinical Director, Karen N Gruber
Vice President, Beth Green
Medical Director, Magdy Takla
Medical Director, Helen Haupt
Associate Vice President Applications, Dustin Hufford
Clinical Director, Deborah Schoy
Chairman, George E. Norcross, age 62
Vice Chairman, Joan S. Davis
Auditors: ERNST & YOUNG LLP ISELIN NJ

LOCATIONS

HQ: THE COOPER HEALTH SYSTEM
   1 COOPER PLZ, CAMDEN, NJ 081031461
Phone: 856 342-2000
Web: WWW.COOPERHEALTH.ORG

PRODUCTS/OPERATIONS

2013 Net Patient Revenue

	%of total
HMO	34
Commercial	27
Medicare	19
Blue cross	13
Self-pay	3
Medicaid	4
Total	**100**

Selected Services

Adult Health Institute
Bariatric and Metabolic Surgery Center
Joint Replacement and Reconstruction Program
Manual Physical Therapy Program
Musculoskeletal Ultrasound
Neuromuscular Program
Orthopaedic Trauma Program
Otology/Neurotology
Pituitary Tumor and Neuroendocrine Program
Podiatry
Pulmonary Medicine
Rhinology / ENT Allergy / Skull-Base Surgery
Spine Center
Sports Medicine
Urogynecology
Urology
Women's Heart Program

COMPETITORS

Abington Memorial Hospital
Albert Einstein Healthcare Network
Aria Health
AtlantiCare
Capital Health System
Children's Hospital of Philadelphia
Crozer-Keystone Health System
Inspira Health Network
Lourdes Health
Mercy Health System

North Philadelphia Health System
Princeton HealthCare
Shore Memorial Hospital
Universal Health Services
University of Pennsylvania Health System
Virtua Health

HISTORICAL FINANCIALS

Company Type: Private

Income Statement

FYE: December 31

	REVENUE ($ mil.)	NET INCOME ($ mil.)	NET PROFIT MARGIN	EMPLOYEES
12/17	1,197	33	2.8%	4,900
12/16	1,168	82	7.1%	—
12/15	1,055	64	6.1%	—
12/14	944	60	6.4%	—
Annual Growth	**8.2%**	**(17.8%)**	—	—

2017 Year-End Financials

Return on assets: 2.5%   Cash ($ mil.): 229
Return on equity: 2.8%
Current ratio: 2.20

THE DAVID AND LUCILE PACKARD FOUNDATION

EXECUTIVES

Dir, Julie Packard
Chief Investment Officer, John Moehling

LOCATIONS

HQ: THE DAVID AND LUCILE PACKARD FOUNDATION
   343 2ND ST, LOS ALTOS, CA 940223696
Phone: 650 948-7658
Web: WWW.PACKARD.ORG

HISTORICAL FINANCIALS

Company Type: Private

Income Statement

FYE: December 31

	REVENUE ($ mil.)	NET INCOME ($ mil.)	NET PROFIT MARGIN	EMPLOYEES
12/16	355	(116)	—	6
12/15	265	(106)	—	—
12/14	333	(21)	—	—
Annual Growth	**3.2%**	—	—	—

2016 Year-End Financials

Return on assets: 5.6%   Cash ($ mil.): 78
Return on equity: (-32.7%)
Current ratio: 0.90

THE DCH HEALTH CARE AUTHORITY

The DCH Healthcare Authority is concerned with the Druid City's health. The company which does business as DCH Health System provides health services to residents of Tuscaloosa and several other communities in Western Alabama. Its flagship facility is the 580-bed DCH Regional Medical Center a full-service teaching hospital located near the University of Alabama campus. DCH Health System also includes the Northport Pickens County and Fayette medical centers which together house 320 acute-care beds. The hospitals offer a full range of inpatient and outpatient services including primary diagnostic emergency surgical rehabilitative and home health care.

Operations

Several of the system's hospitals operate specialty centers. For instance DCH Regional has cancer and cardiology clinics while the Northport Medical Center has specialty rehabilitation and mental health departments. In addition Fayette Medical Center houses a 120-bed nursing home.

The DCH Health System which serves more than a quarter of a million people is community-owned and is governed by a board appointed by various city and county authorities as well as the hospitals' medical staff.

Strategy

As part of the system's plan to grow the next generation of health care providers it partners with the University of Alabama's College of Community Health Sciences and with Capstone College of Nursing. DCH Health System also expands as needed to keep up with the community. In 2014 it announced the construction of a $12 million 75-bed nursing and rehab hospital near Northport Medical Center.

Company Background

The "DCH" in the organization's name stands for Druid City Hospital the name of the system's first hospital which opened in 1923. Druid City is a nickname for Tuscaloosa.

EXECUTIVES

President And Ceo, Bryan N. Kindred
Cfo, John Winfrey
Administrator Dch Regional Medical Center, Bill Cassels
Administrator Pickens County Medical Center, Wayne McElroy
Administrator Northport Medical Center, Luke Standeffer
Administrator Fayette Medical Center, Barry S. Cochran
Executive Vice President Of Information Technology, Robin Holmes
Occupational Medicine, Peter G Casten
Director Of Radiology, John Files
Chairman, Samuel F. Clabaugh
Auditors: MORRISON & SMITH LLP TUSCALO

LOCATIONS

HQ: THE DCH HEALTH CARE AUTHORITY
809 UNIVERSITY BLVD E, TUSCALOOSA, AL 354012029
Phone: 205 759-7111
Web: WWW.DCHSYSTEM.COM

PRODUCTS/OPERATIONS

Selected Alabama Facilities
DCH Regional Medical Center (Tuscaloosa)
Fayette Medical Center (Fayette)
Northport Medical Center (Northport)
Pickens County Medical Center (Carrollton)

COMPETITORS

Baptist Health (AL)
Children's Health System
East Alabama Medical Center
Gadsden Regional Medical Center
Health Care Authority of the City of Huntsville
Jackson Hospital & Clinic of Alabama
University of South Alabama Health System

HISTORICAL FINANCIALS
Company Type: Private

Income Statement — FYE: September 30

	REVENUE ($ mil.)	NET INCOME ($ mil.)	NET PROFIT MARGIN	EMPLOYEES
09/17	516	8	1.7%	4,683
09/16	531	23	4.5%	—
09/13	463	16	3.6%	—
09/12	454	23	5.2%	—
Annual Growth	2.6%	(18.3%)	—	—

2017 Year-End Financials

Return on assets: 2.4% Cash ($ mil.): 74
Return on equity: 1.7%
Current ratio: 1.90

THE DELONG CO INC

EXECUTIVES

Pres-Ceo, David Delong
Treas, William C Delong
SEC, Charles R Delong
Chief Technology Officer, Brandon Bickham
Manager, Pat Mullooly
Executive Officer, Cherie Schutt
Project Coordinator, John Elvekrog
Executive Officer, Cathy Chrislaw
Executive Officer, Erin Hamburg
Executive Officer, Rick Keller
Supervisor, Jessica Denison
Auditors: CLIFTONLARSONALLEN LLP DIXON

LOCATIONS

HQ: THE DELONG CO INC
214 ALLEN ST, CLINTON, WI 535259496
Phone: 800 356-0784
Web: WWW.DELONGCOMPANY.COM

HISTORICAL FINANCIALS
Company Type: Private

Income Statement — FYE: September 30

	REVENUE ($ mil.)	NET INCOME ($ mil.)	NET PROFIT MARGIN	EMPLOYEES
09/16*	1,029	4	0.4%	350
12/15	1,029	4	0.4%	—
09/14	1,306	19	1.5%	—
09/13	1,326	25	1.9%	—
Annual Growth	(8.1%)	(45.9%)	—	—
*Fiscal year change

2016 Year-End Financials

Return on assets: 1.2% Cash ($ mil.): 1
Return on equity: 0.4%
Current ratio: 1.10

THE DETROIT INSTITUTE OF ARTS

EXECUTIVES

Dir-Pres-Ceo, Graham W J Beal
Chm, Eugene A Gargaro Jr

Coo, Nettie Seabrooks
Internal Medicine Practitioner, Lisa Lorenzo
Vice-President, H W Burdett
Manager, Jennifer Gustafson

LOCATIONS

HQ: THE DETROIT INSTITUTE OF ARTS
5200 WOODWARD AVE, DETROIT, MI 482024094
Phone: 313 833-7900
Web: WWW.DIA.ORG

HISTORICAL FINANCIALS
Company Type: Private

Income Statement — FYE: June 30

	REVENUE ($ mil.)	NET INCOME ($ mil.)	NET PROFIT MARGIN	EMPLOYEES
06/15	606	28	4.7%	350
06/14	52	13	26.0%	—
06/09	47	0	—	—
06/08	58	(8)	—	—
Annual Growth	39.7%	—	—	—

2015 Year-End Financials

Return on assets: 0.4% Cash ($ mil.): 49
Return on equity: 4.7%
Current ratio: —

THE DREES COMPANY

The Drees Company is a big homebuilder in Cincinnati and one of the nation's top private builders. Drees targets first-time and move-up buyers with homes that are priced from about $100000 to more than $1 million. Drees also builds condominiums townhomes and patio homes. Its homes portfolio ranges from its former Zaring Premier Homes luxury division to the company's more financially accessible and modest Marquis Homes division. Drees is active in Florida Indiana Kentucky Maryland North Carolina Ohio Tennessee Texas Virginia and Washington DC. The family-owned firm was founded in 1928.

Operations

In addition to home building architecture energy efficiency upgrades and design services Drees also provides new construction financing solutions through its subsidiary and mortgage lending business First Equity Mortgage which has closed more than $1 billion in loans.

Geographic Reach

Headquartered in Fort Mitchell Kentucky Drees operates across nearly 10 states in cities including Cincinnati and Cleveland Ohio; Indianapolis; Nashville; Raleigh North Carolina; Jacksonville Florida; Austin Houston and Dallas Texas; and the Greater Washington DC area.

Sales and Marketing

In recent years Drees has concentrated on the fast-growing "move up" segment market targeting home buyers looking to upgrade into larger houses.

In 2012 Drees converted its longtime Zaring Premier Homes luxury brand name to its flagship Drees Homes brand. While the move required rebranding in the greater Cincinnati area Drees is banking on its brand reputation and recognition. It also allowed the residential homebuilder to consolidate its advertising sales and marketing efforts.

Financial Performance

While full details of the private company could not be found Drees' CEO David Drees announced in July 2013 that he expected the company to reach $629 million in revenue by April 1 2014.

Looking further back Drees had revenues as high as $1.2 billion in 2006 which slid dramatically following the financial crisis to $490 million in revenue in 2010. To its benefit Texas markets — specifically Austin and Dallas — remained active throughout the recession. Drees was also helped by entering the recession with a relatively low debt load of $364 million. By March 2013 Drees had sold land to generate cash flow and reduced its debt to $125 million.

Strategy

Ranked among the top 25 largest national homebuilders by BUILDER Magazine Drees has been steadily expanding over the past few years to capitalize on an improving housing market.

In recent years Drees has concentrated on the fast-growing and lucrative "move up" segment of the homebuyer's market targeting home owners that are looking to upgrade to larger houses with higher-end amenities. In late 2014 the company landed a $100 million contract to build 237 homes in three Cincinnati-based residential communities with the average house priced between $307000 and $360000. In September 2014 the company entered its first ever foray into the Houston Texas market with plans to price its houses there for more than $300000 — prime pricing to lure these "move up" buyers.

Company Background

A family-operated enterprise since its founding by immigrant Theodore Drees in 1928 the company is run by the third generation of the Drees family.

EXECUTIVES

Chb-Ceo, Ralph Drees
Pres-Coo, David Drees
V Pres-Sec-Treas, Lawrence Herbst
Market Executive, Dana Scrivner
Vice President, Daniel Jones
Vice President Human Resources, Effie McKeehan
Administrator, James Roberts
Art Director, John Bough
Sales and Marketing Executive, Mark Gripshover
Market Executive, Sara McGettrick
Manager, Adam Ballash
Auditors: DELOITTE & TOUCHE LLP CINCINN

LOCATIONS

HQ: THE DREES COMPANY
515 S CAPITAL OF TEXAS HWY, WEST LAKE HILLS, TX 787464314
Phone: 859 578-4200
Web: WWW.DREESHOMES.COM

Selected Locations
Florida
  Jacksonville
Indiana
  Indianapolis
Kentucky
  Fort Mitchell
Maryland
  Frederick
North Carolina
  Raleigh
Ohio
  Cincinnati
  Cleveland
  Dayton
Tennessee
  Nashville
Texas
  Austin
  Dallas
Washington DC

COMPETITORS

D.R. Horton	Lennar
Fischer Homes	M/I Homes
KB Home	PulteGroup

HISTORICAL FINANCIALS

Company Type: Private

Income Statement				FYE: March 31
	REVENUE ($ mil.)	NET INCOME ($ mil.)	NET PROFIT MARGIN	EMPLOYEES
03/16	722	31	4.3%	549
03/15	669	36	5.4%	—
03/14	683	35	5.3%	—
03/13	584	19	3.3%	—
Annual Growth	7.3%	17.6%	—	—

2016 Year-End Financials

Return on assets: 4.8%
Return on equity: 4.3%
Current ratio: —
Cash ($ mil.): 10

THE EMPIRE DISTRICT ELECTRIC COMPANY

Empire District Electric (EDE) light ups the middle of the US. The utility transmits and distributes electricity to a population base of more than 450000 (about 217000 customers in southwestern Missouri and adjacent areas of Arkansas Kansas and Oklahoma. It also supplies water to three Missouri towns and natural gas throughout most of the state. EDE's interests in fossil-fueled and hydroelectric power plants give it a generating capacity of 1377 MW; it also wholesales power. The company also provides fiber-optic services. In early 2017 the company was bought by an Algonquin Power & Utilities unit in a C$3.2 billion (US$2.3 billion) deal.

Operations

EDE operates its businesses in three segments: electric gas and other. The electric segment serves an area of 10000 sq. ml. located principally in southwestern Missouri and also includes smaller areas in southeastern Kansas northeastern Oklahoma and northwestern Arkansas. It also provides water service to three towns in Missouri.

Coal-fired generating units 1 and 2 at the Iatan Plant are jointly-owned by KCP&L (a subsidiary of Great Plains Energy) Missouri Joint Municipal Electric Utility Commission Kansas Electric Power Cooperative and EDE with EDE's share of ownership being 12% in each plant. The Plum Point Energy Station is a 670-MW coal-fired generating facility near Osceola Arkansas of which EDE owns 50 MW of capacity.

EDE's natural gas operations distribute natural gas through The Empire District Gas Company. Its principal gas utility properties consist of about 87 miles of transmission mains and approximately 1160 miles of distribution mains.

EDE's other segment consists of its fiber optics business (which it also uses in its own utility operations).

In 2013 the company generated about 90% of its revenue from its electric segment.

Geographic Reach

The company serves customers in Arkansas Kansas Missouri and Oklahoma.

Sales and Marketing

EDE supplies retail electric service to 119 incorporated communities (and to various unincorporated areas) and wholesale service to four municipally owned distribution systems. The largest urban area it serves is the city of Joplin Missouri and its immediate vicinity with a population of 160000. Its three largest classes of customers are residential commercial and industrial which provided 43% 30% and 15% respectively of its electric operating revenues in 2013. The company derived about 90% of its retail electric revenues from Missouri.

Its gas operations serve 44000 customers in northwest north central and west central Missouri. It provides natural gas distribution to 48 communities and 377 transportation customers. The largest urban area it serves is the city of Sedalia with a population of more than 20000. Residential and commercial provided 63% and 27% respectively of its gas operating revenues in 2013.

EDE also has 118 fiber customers.

Financial Performance

The company's revenues increased by 7% in 2013 due to improved revenues across all of its segments. Electric sales increased due to higher electric rates a growth in customers and colder weather (which increased demand). However commercial sales decreased due to a net unbilled sales adjustment recorded in 2012; Industrial sales decreased due to operating reductions by several large industrial customers; and it wholesale sales decreased due to the closure of a large dairy facility in Monett Missouri.

EDE's gas retail sales and revenues increased due to the colder weather; and other revenues also increased due to a growth in Southwest Power Pool transmission revenues in 2013.

The company's net income increased by 14% in 2013 primarily due to higher revenues and as well as an increased allowance for equity funds used during construction.

EDE has seen growth in revenues since 2009 however it decreased in 2012 due to lower demand as a result of milder winter temperatures that year. The company has seen a healthy growth in cash flow from operations since 2009.

Strategy

The company has been boosting its generating capacity including through its partial ownership in the Plum Point Energy Station in Arkansas and through several wind farm contracts. Total property additions for the three years ending in 2013 totaled $398 million and retirements during the same period totaled $39 million.

Seeking to boost its revenues to cover maintenance and expansion costs in 2013 EDE filed for rate increases for its Arkansas and Missouri electric customers.

In 2013 the company filed an Integrated Resource Plan with the Missouri Public Service Commission to introduce additional demand-side management programs to help its customers use energy more efficiently.

Company Background

In May 2011 EDE's power system suffered extensive damage as as a result of the major tornado that tore through Joplin Missouri. Initial damage reports from the Joplin tornado included the loss of 130 transmission poles.

Mild weather and the global recession suppressed demand and revenues in 2009 but lower gas and power costs helped EDE post an increase in operating income for that year. Cooler-than-normal winter weather and warmer-than-usual summer weather and a rate increase helped to boost power usage and lifted the company's revenues in 2010. A shrinking gas customer base due to depressed economic conditions led to lower gas revenues that year. Lower expenses allowed EDE to report an overall improved net income position in 2010.

EXECUTIVES

President Ceo And Director, Bradley P. Beecher,
  $532,500 total compensation

Vp And Coo Gas, Ronald F. Gatz, $262,500 total compensation
Vp And Coo Electric, Kelly S. Walters, $312,500 total compensation
Vp Finance And Cfo, Laurie A. Delano, $295,000 total compensation
Vp Energy Supply And Delivery Operations, Blake A. Mertens, $240,000 total compensation
Chairman, D. Randy Laney

LOCATIONS

HQ: THE EMPIRE DISTRICT ELECTRIC COMPANY
602 S JOPLIN AVE, JOPLIN, MO 648012337
Phone: 417 625-5100
Web: WWW.EMPIREDISTRICT.COM

PRODUCTS/OPERATIONS

Selected Subsidiaries
EDE Holdings Inc. (nonregulated operations)
Empire District Industries Inc. (fiber-optic services)
The Empire District Gas Company

COMPETITORS

AEP	Great Plains Energy
Ameren	OGE Energy
Associated Electric	Southern Union
Berkshire Hathaway	Spire
Energy	Westar Energy
Charter Communications	Western Farmers
Entergy	Electric
Grand River Dam	Xcel Energy
Authority	

HISTORICAL FINANCIALS

Company Type: Private

Income Statement				FYE: December 31
	REVENUE ($ mil.)	NET INCOME ($ mil.)	NET PROFIT MARGIN	EMPLOYEES
12/17	584	36	6.3%	749
12/16	568	64	11.3%	—
12/15	605	56	9.3%	—
12/14	652	67	10.3%	—
Annual Growth	(3.6%)	(18.2%)	—	—

2017 Year-End Financials

Return on assets: 7.4%   Cash ($ mil.): 5
Return on equity: 6.3%
Current ratio: 0.40

THE EVANGELICAL LUTHERAN GOOD SAMARITAN SOCIETY

EXECUTIVES

Vice President Mission Effectiveness And Senior Pastor, Greg Wilcox
Vice President Of Finance, Joe Herdina
Vice President Mergers And Acquisitions, Mark Scharnberg
Director Of Nursing Services, Dena McFaddin
Director Of Nursing Services, Mari Stelter
Executive Manager, John Mcelderry
Auditors: CLIFTON LARSON ALLEN LLP MINN

LOCATIONS

HQ: THE EVANGELICAL LUTHERAN GOOD SAMARITAN SOCIETY
4800 W 57TH ST, SIOUX FALLS, SD 571082239
Phone: 866 928-1635
Web: WWW.CAREERLATTICE.COM

COMPETITORS

BPM Senior Living	Genesis Healthcare
Brookdale Senior	Golden Horizons
Living	Kindred Healthcare
Enlivant	RehabCare
Extendicare	Select Medical
Five Star Senior	Sunrise Senior Living
Living	

HISTORICAL FINANCIALS

Company Type: Private

Income Statement				FYE: December 31
	REVENUE ($ mil.)	NET INCOME ($ mil.)	NET PROFIT MARGIN	EMPLOYEES
12/15	1,011	(33)	—	24,000
12/13	979	0	0.0%	—
12/07	841	17	2.1%	—
12/06	836	44	5.3%	—
Annual Growth	2.1%	—	—	—

2015 Year-End Financials

Return on assets: 4.5%   Cash ($ mil.): 17
Return on equity: (-3.3%)
Current ratio: 0.50

THE FINISH LINE INC

The Finish Line sells performance and casual footwear and apparel through about 590 Finish Line stores in more than 45 states about 70 JackRabbit stores and 300-plus branded shops inside department stores (Macy's). Its core Finish Line stores are bigger than competitors' and offer a wider array of clothing accessories and other merchandise including jackets backpacks sunglasses and watches. Finish Line offers big brand names (such as adidas NIKE and Timberland) and also markets its own private-label line of T-shirts socks and other basics. The company also sells athletic shoes and apparel online.It became a subsidiary of European sports retailer JD Sports in mid-2018.

Operations

The retailer's namesake stores average some 5400 sq. ft.; its JackRabbit stores average 3650 sq. ft. Footwear accounts for 88% of Finish Line's net sales. While Finish Line purchases products from some 120 suppliers NIKE products (some sold exclusively at Finish Line) generate about 70% of total sales. About 89% of the retailer's merchandise is purchased from its five largest suppliers. Apparel and accessories (also referred to as softgoods) account for about 12%.

Geographic Reach

The Indianapolis-based company has Finish Line stores in 47 states and the District of Columbia. Its largest markets are Texas Florida California Illinois Pennsylvania and Ohio home to about a quarter of Finish Line stores. Its 72 JackRabbit stores are located in 17 states and the District of Columbia with Texas Michigan New York and New Jersey accounting about half of all locations. The shoe retailer also has branded Finish Line shops inside department stores (including Macy's) in more than a dozen states.

Sales and Marketing

Nearly all of the company's merchandise is shipped directly from suppliers to its distribution center in Indianapolis Indiana where the it processes and ships the merchandise by contract and common carriers to its stores/shops or directly to customers.

Finish Line reported $44.2 million in advertising expenses in fiscal 2016 (ended February) up from $39.2 million and $41.8 million in 2015 and 2014 respectively.

Financial Performance

The company has achieved record-setting growth over the years with revenues peaking at $1.89 billion in 2016 a company milestone. Profits however nosedived by 73% from $82 million in 2015 to $22 million in 2016.

Footwear sales increased 5% in 2016 primarily driven by percentage increases in the low-single digits in men's low teens in women's and mid-single digits in kids' footwear sales. Softgoods sales were negatively impacted by the replacement of the company's warehouse and order management system in the third quarter of 2016.

The massive drop in profits for 2016 was driven by a large spike in selling general and administrative expenses related to the company's supply chain issues as a result of the replacement of its warehouse and order management system.

Strategy

As its brick-and-mortar operation is streamlined Finish Line is focusing more on its e-commerce and mobile businesses. The company is investing in its online channel with design and content upgrades mobile and tablet applications and an expanded presence on social media and platform enhancements. Indeed the company considers its online sites (finishline.com and run.com) to be its most visible stores attracting about 496000 visitors daily.

Company Background

In 1976 boyhood friends Alan Cohen (a lawyer) and David Klapper (a retailer) founded Athletic Enterprises the Indiana franchisee for The Athlete's Foot. By 1981 they had all The Athlete's Foot stores that the state's big malls could hold — about a dozen. To expand beyond those confines the pair teamed up with Dave Fagin and Larry Sablosky and formed The Finish Line.

EXECUTIVES

Vice President And Corporate Controller, Beau J Swenson
Evp And Cfo, Edward W. (Ed) Wilhelm, age 60, $530,000 total compensation
Evp And President Running Specialty Group, Bill Kirkendall, age 64, $355,385 total compensation
Evp And Coo, Melissa Greenwell, age 51
Ceo, Samuel M. (Sam) Sato, age 54, $635,000 total compensation
Evp And Chief Omnichannel Officer, Imran Jooma, age 46, $31,673 total compensation
Vice President Of Human Resources And Payroll, Cindy Cook
Vice President Store Operations And Trai, Greg Davis
Senior Vice President Supply Chain, Debbie Fortnum
Senior Vice President Planning And Allocation, Brad Eckhart
Vice President Of Information Systems, Sue Perry
Executive Vice President And Chief Financial Officer, Ed Wilhelm
Senior Vice President Legal And Human Resources And General Counsel And Corporate Secretary, Chris Eck
Executive Vice President Chief Information And Technology Officer, AJ Sutera
Vice President Digital Operations, Arianne Parisi
Chairman, Glenn S. Lyon, age 68

Board Member, Richard Crystal
Board Member, Torrence Boone
Board Member, Catherine Langham

LOCATIONS

HQ: THE FINISH LINE INC
3308 N MITTHOEFER RD, INDIANAPOLIS, IN
462352332
Phone: 317 899-1022
Web: WWW.FINISHLINE.COM

2016 Stores

	No.
Finish Line	589
Jack Rabbit	72
Branded shops within department store	392
Total	**1,053**

PRODUCTS/OPERATIONS

2016 Sales

	$ mil.	% of total
Footwear	1,681	89
Softgoods	207	11
Total	**1,888**	**100**

2016 Sales

	$ in mil
% of total	
Brick and Mortar store	67
Digital	15
Shops within department store	13
Jack Rabbit sales	5
Total	**100**

Selected Brands

adidas
Asics
Brooks
Lacoste
Mizuno
New Balance
NIKE
Pastry
Puma
Reebok
Saucony
The North Face
Timberland
Under Armour

Selected Products

Accessories
  Athletic equipment
  Athletic socks
  Backpacks
  Gym bags
  Headbands and sweatbands
  Shoe care
  Shoe insoles and liners
  Shoe laces
  Sunglasses
  Watches
Fan
  High school
  MLB
  NBA
  NCAA
  NFL
  Kids
  Shoes
  Clothing
Men's
  Caps
  Hats
  Jackets
  Jerseys
  Pants
  Shoes
  Shorts
  Socks
  Sweatshirts/fleece
  Tanks
  T-shirts
  Workout clothing
Women's
  Caps
  Hats

Jackets
Jerseys
Pants
Shoes
Shorts
Socks
Sweatshirts/fleece
Tanks
T-shirts
Team clothing
Workout clothing

COMPETITORS

Academy Sports	Patagonia Inc.
DSW	REI
Dick's Sporting Goods	Rack Room Shoes
Foot Locker	Sears
Genesco	Sports Authority
Hat World	Target Corporation
Hibbett Sports	Wal-Mart
J. C. Penney	Zappos.com
Kmart	shoebuy.com
Modell's	

HISTORICAL FINANCIALS

Company Type: Private

Income Statement · FYE: March 3

	REVENUE ($ mil.)	NET INCOME ($ mil.)	NET PROFIT MARGIN	EMPLOYEES
03/18*	1,838	14	0.8%	12,700
02/17	1,844	(18)	—	—
02/16	1,888	21	1.2%	—
02/15	1,820	79	4.4%	—
Annual Growth	**0.3%**	**(43.5%)**	**—**	**—**

*Fiscal year change

2018 Year-End Financials

Return on assets: 6.7%
Return on equity: 0.8%   Cash ($ mil.): 93
Current ratio: 0.60

THE FIRST DISTRICT ASSOCIATION

EXECUTIVES

Ceo, Clinton Fall
SEC, Kevin Schueler
Controller, Tom Middendorf

LOCATIONS

HQ: THE FIRST DISTRICT ASSOCIATION
101 S SWIFT AVE, LITCHFIELD, MN 553552800
Phone: 320 693-3236
Web: WWW.FIRSTDISTRICT.COM

HISTORICAL FINANCIALS

Company Type: Private

Income Statement · FYE: September 30

	REVENUE ($ mil.)	NET INCOME ($ mil.)	NET PROFIT MARGIN	EMPLOYEES
09/17	609	19	3.2%	150
09/16	553	19	3.5%	—
09/15	615	13	2.2%	—
09/14	745	27	3.7%	—
Annual Growth	**(6.5%)**	**(10.8%)**	**—**	**—**

THE FISHEL COMPANY

The Fishel Company reels in revenues by laying out lines. The company (also known as Team Fishel) provides engineering construction management and maintenance services for electric and gas utility and communications infrastructure projects. The aerial and underground utility contractor designs and builds distribution networks for telecommunications cable and broadband television gas transmission and distribution and electric utilities throughout the US. It also counts municipalities state and federal agencies universities commercial building owners financial services companies health care providers manufacturers and residential real estate developers among its clients.

Operations

The company's products and services include Structured Cabling Systems Data Center build-outs Wireless Networks and Building Security and Automation. It has installed more than 16000 communications networks for the healthcare financial education manufacturing logistics and government sectors.

Geographic Reach

The Fishel Company is licensed to do business in some two dozen states. It operates from 32 offices located in about 15 states including Arkansas Arizona California Florida Georgia Kentucky Nevada New Mexico Ohio Oklahoma Pennsylvania Tennessee Texas and Virginia.

Sales and Marketing

The company's power customers include American Electric Power Arizona Public Service Arkansas Valley Electric Dayton Power & Light Dominion Virginia Power Duke Energy Entergy and First Electric Cooperative among others.

In addition to utilities and power coops the company serves other markets including Repair and Planning Broadband Broadband Network Services Enterprise Solutions and Advanced Technology Services.

Strategy

Fishel Company is tracking its business to a Vision 2020 initiative which has a three-pronged goal of customer development operational excellence and teammate development. Its customer development focus involves natural gas distribution power transmission and distribution (T&D) construction and fiber network installation. Operational excellence goals are centered on bidding and pricing project management and being accident-free. Its teammate management focus comprises leadership development performance management workforce planning and continuous improvement.

The company has strategic business relationships with TE Connectivity Andrews Wireless Belden Commscope Corning Cable Systems Legrand Ortronics Leviton Nexans Berktek OASIS and Panduit.

Company Background

Kenneth Fishel founded the firm in 1936 as an underground contractor for telephone companies.

EXECUTIVES

Vice President, Vance Mauldin
Vice President Central Region, Scott Keeler
Vice Chairman, Eric Smith

LOCATIONS

HQ: THE FISHEL COMPANY
1366 DUBLIN RD, COLUMBUS, OH 432151093
Phone: 614 274-8100
Web: WWW.FISHELCO.COM

Selected Locations

Arizona

Arkansas
California
Florida
Georgia
Kentucky
Nevada
New Mexico
Ohio
Oklahoma
Pennsylvania
Tennessee
Texas
Virginia

PRODUCTS/OPERATIONS

Selected Services

Emergency restoration repair & maintenance
Fiber overbuilds
GPS survey
Network installation
Permitting
Project management
Right of way
Site Design
Utility construction

Selected Markets

Commercial industrial advanced logistics
Electric Distribution & Transmission
Financial & health care
Gas distribution & transmission pipeline
Telecom & broadband cable
Wireless backhaul

COMPETITORS

Dycom	MYR Group
EMCOR	MasTec
IES Holdings	Pike Corporation
MDU Construction Services	Quanta Services

HISTORICAL FINANCIALS

Company Type: Private

Income Statement   FYE: December 31

	REVENUE ($ mil.)	NET INCOME ($ mil.)	NET PROFIT MARGIN	EMPLOYEES
12/16	341	8	2.6%	1,400
12/15	301	10	3.3%	—
12/14	311	8	2.8%	—
12/13	306	10	3.4%	—
Annual Growth	3.7%	(5.2%)	—	—

2016 Year-End Financials

Return on assets: 4.8%   Cash ($ mil.): —
Return on equity: 2.6%
Current ratio: 0.70

THE FORD FOUNDATION

As one of the nation's largest philanthropic organizations the Ford Foundation can afford to be generous. The foundation offers grants to individuals and institutions worldwide that work to meet its goals of strengthening democratic values reducing poverty and injustice promoting international cooperation and advancing human achievement. The Ford Foundation's charitable giving has run the gamut from A (Association for Asian Studies) to Z (Zanzibar International Film Festival). The foundation has an endowment of about $10 billion. Established in 1936 by Edsel Ford whose father founded the Ford Motor Company the foundation no longer owns stock in the automaker or has ties to the founding family.

Operations

The foundation which is governed by an international board of trustees makes grants in all 50 US states and supports programs in more than 50 countries.

It boasts about 10 regional offices in Latin America Africa the Middle East and Asia.

Geographic Reach

Based in New York the Ford Foundation is a grantmaking foundation that primarily serves the US but also global programs.

Strategy

The Ford Foundation's programs address several social justice issues including democratic and accountable government freedom of expression access to education economic fairness and opportunity sexuality and reproductive rights sustainable development social justice metropolitan opportunity and human rights.

A small portion of its endowment is set aside for social investing. The foundation's funds typically finance critical projects set new business models and develop sustainable organizations. By investing $1 million or more in initiatives the Ford Foundation's investment strategy aims to make a noteworthy impact and encourage other investors to also fund projects.

EXECUTIVES

Vice President Secretary, Ken Monteiro
Program Vice President, Martin Abregu
Vice President Talent Human Resources,
  Samantha Gilbert
Secretary, Karen Mcburnie

LOCATIONS

HQ: THE FORD FOUNDATION
  320 E 43RD ST FL 4, NEW YORK, NY 100174890
Phone: 212 573-5370
Web: WWW.FORDFOUNDATION.ORG

PRODUCTS/OPERATIONS

Selected Core Issues

Democratic and accountable government
Economic fairness
Education opportunity and scholarship
Freedom of expression
Human rights
Metropolitan opportunity
Sexuality and reproductive health rights
Social justice philanthropy
Sustainable development

HISTORICAL FINANCIALS

Company Type: Private

Income Statement   FYE: December 31

	ASSETS ($ mil.)	NET INCOME ($ mil.)	INCOME AS % OF ASSETS	EMPLOYEES
12/15	12,114	(270)	—	556
12/14*	12,400	(7)	—	—
09/11	10,344	(5)	—	—
09/09	10,234	0	—	—
Annual Growth	2.8%	—	—	—

*Fiscal year change

2015 Year-End Financials

Return on assets: 14.6%   Sales ($ mil): 486
Return on equity: (-55.5%)

THE FRESH MARKET INC

When it comes to food fresh is best. The Fresh Market operates about 160 full-service upscale specialty grocery stores in some 25 US states from Florida to Wisconsin. As the name suggests the chain specializes in perishable goods (two-thirds of sales) including fruits and vegetables meat and seafood. The stores average 21000 sq. ft. about a third to half the size of a conventional supermarket. However customers won't find the nonfood items sold in most grocery stores these days such as cleaning and cooking supplies. Founded by husband-and-wife team Ray and Beverly Berry who opened their first store in 1982 The Fresh Market which went public in 2010 was acquired by Apollo Global Management in mid-2016.

Geographic Reach

The fast-growing chain operates grocery stores in 26 states primarily located in the Southeast Midwest Northeast and Mid-Atlantic region. New markets include California and Texas. However established markets Florida North Carolina and Georgia are home to more than half of The Fresh Market's stores.

Sales and Marketing

The Fresh Market spends far less on advertising than its conventional competitors relying primarily on word-of-mouth publicity to attract customers. Indeed the grocery chain reported advertising costs of only $3862 in fiscal 2013 (ended January) or just 0.3% of annual sales up from $2652 in the previous year. In-store marketing activities include cooking classes and demonstrations tours and product demonstrations. It also distributes a weekly online newsletter named "Fresh Idea" to promote new products seasonal produce recipes and weekly specials.

Financial Performance

Fueled by the addition of new stores The Fresh Market's fiscal 2013 (ended January) sales increased 20% versus the prior year to more than $1.3 billion. Net income rose 25% over the same period to about $64 million due to higher sales and decreased interest expanse. Same-store sales at Fresh Market stores increased 6% year over year. Indeed fiscal 2013 marked the fifth consecutive year of rising sales and the second consecutive year of rising profits (since the 2010 IPO).

Strategy

The Fresh Market's recipe for growth is to continue to open stores at a rapid pace in new and existing markets and to increase sales at older stores. Indeed the grocery chain has announced plans to double its store count in the Southeast to more than 200 locations. Currently 104 of its 160 stores are located in the region. In fiscal 2014 it plans to open a record 22 locations. Ultimately management believes the US can support at least 500 of its upscale grocery stores. The Fresh Market is forecasting same-store sales to increase 4% to 6% in the coming year. The chain caters to its affluent customers by offering high-margin specialty foods such as hand-trimmed aged steaks fresh seafood hand-stacked fresh produce and a high level of customer service. Its smaller store footprint gives the retailer more flexibility in picking locations.

EXECUTIVES

President And Ceo, Richard A. (Rick) Anicetti, age 61
Svp Merchandising And Marketing, Marc Jones, age 46, $285,697 total compensation
Svp And General Counsel, Scott Duggan, age 52, $254,510 total compensation
Evp And Cfo, Jeffrey (Jeff) Ackerman, age 54, $407,231 total compensation
Svp Real Estate And Development, Randy Young, age 60, $279,971 total compensation
Vice President Finance, Jeffrey B Short
President, Ray Berry, age 77
Auditors: ERNST & YOUNG LLP CHARLOTTE

LOCATIONS

HQ: THE FRESH MARKET INC
628 GREEN VALLEY RD # 500, GREENSBORO, NC 274087791
Phone: 336 272-1338
Web: WWW.THEFRESHMARKET.COM

2016 Stores

	No.
Florida	45
North Carolina	22
Virginia	16
Georgia	15
Illinois	9
Tennessee	9
South Carolina	9
Alabama	6
Indiana	5
Louisiana	5
New York	5
Ohio	5
Pennsylvania	5
Maryland	4
Connecticut	3
Kentucky	3
New Jersey	3
Arkansas	2
Wisconsin	2
Delaware	1
Massachusetts	1
Mississippi	1
New Hampshire	1
Oklahoma	1
Total	**178**

COMPETITORS

Earth Fare	Trader Joe's
Food Lion	Wal-Mart
Kroger	Wegmans
Publix	Weis Markets
Safeway	Whole Foods
Sprouts	Winn-Dixie
Target Corporation	

HISTORICAL FINANCIALS

Company Type: Private

Income Statement				FYE: January 31
	REVENUE ($ mil.)	NET INCOME ($ mil.)	NET PROFIT MARGIN	EMPLOYEES
01/16	1,857	65	3.5%	12,600
01/15	1,753	63	3.6%	—
01/14	1,511	50	3.4%	—
01/13	1,329	64	4.8%	—
Annual Growth	11.8%	0.7%	—	—

2016 Year-End Financials

Return on assets: 2.7%
Return on equity: 3.5%
Current ratio: 0.50
Cash ($ mil.): 60

THE GEISINGER CLINIC

EXECUTIVES

Ceo, Glenn D Steele Jr
Sr V Pres-Treas, Frank J Trembulak
Vice-President Information Ser, David Macko
Senior Information Technology, Erica Schaeffer
Chief Clinical Informatics Off, Alistair Erskine
Associate Vice President, Kelly Moore
Director, Mark Mossel
Director, Stephen Dunkle
Distribution Center Manager, Walter Karl

LOCATIONS

HQ: THE GEISINGER CLINIC
100 N ACADEMY AVE, DANVILLE, PA 178229800
Phone: 570 271-6211
Web: WWW.GEISINGER.ORG

HISTORICAL FINANCIALS

Company Type: Private

Income Statement				FYE: June 30
	REVENUE ($ mil.)	NET INCOME ($ mil.)	NET PROFIT MARGIN	EMPLOYEES
06/15	991	(12)	—	12,000
06/14	849	(3)	—	—
06/10	572	(3)	—	—
06/09	504	(22)	—	—
Annual Growth	11.9%	—	—	—

2015 Year-End Financials

Return on assets: 7.6%
Return on equity: (-1.3%)
Current ratio: —
Cash ($ mil.): 23

THE GEORGE WASHINGTON UNIVERSITY HOSPITAL

EXECUTIVES

Ceo, Kimberly D Russo
Coo, Nicole Dollison
Cfo, George Sprinkel
Cmo, Bruno Petinaux

LOCATIONS

HQ: THE GEORGE WASHINGTON UNIVERSITY HOSPITAL
900 23RD ST NW, WASHINGTON, DC 200372342
Phone: 202 715-4000
Web: WWW.GWHOSPITAL.COM

HISTORICAL FINANCIALS

Company Type: Private

Income Statement				FYE: December 31
	REVENUE ($ mil.)	NET INCOME ($ mil.)	NET PROFIT MARGIN	EMPLOYEES
12/15	505	48	9.6%	2,300
12/14	450	33	7.4%	—
Annual Growth	12.0%	46.4%	—	—

THE GEORGETOWN UNIVERSITY

Georgetown University is the oldest Catholic university in the US. The institution's 17400 undergraduate and graduate students are instructed by more than 2340 faculty members (representing both full- and part-time) in nine schools ranging from the university's renowned Law Center to the Edmund A. Walsh School of Foreign Service and the Georgetown School of Medicine. The system has a student-teacher ratio of about 10:1. The university is also home to the Georgetown University Medical Center and has forged numerous ties with its neighboring institutions in the Washington DC community.

Operations

The Georgetown University Medical Center provides a variety of medical services to area residents in addition to serving as a teaching and research facility for the university. The medical center has several specialty medicine and research programs through a partnership with MedStar's Georgetown University Hospital including Huntington disease care and brain development studies. Georgetown's research institutes are working to discover new medical treatments including potential breast cancer therapies. The university receives some $179 million in research funding each year.

Geographic Reach

Georgetown University's main campus (54 buildings including the medical center) is located on about 100 acres on the banks of the Potomac in Washington DC. It also has locations in downtown Washington DC and in Arlington Virginia.

Internationally Georgetown University operates a School of Foreign Service campus in Qatar. The university also has study abroad programs in Argentina Turkey China Chile Italy and England and a nursing study program with the Australian Catholic University.

Financial Performance

Georgetown University reported about $1.12 billion in revenues in fiscal 2014 virtually flat with the previous year. Its earnings come from student tuition and fees grants and contracts auxiliary activities and other sources. In fiscal 2015 undergraduate tuition was $46200 per student (up from $44280 in fiscal 2014 and $42360 in fiscal 2013).

Strategy

Georgetown University expands and upgrades its facilities periodically to keep pace with modern technologies and appeal to a variety of students.

To expand its outreach programs Georgetown University built a new location for its School of Continuing Studies in downtown Washington DC. The new campus located near the Law Center opened in late 2013 and extends the reach of the university's presence downtown as it works to expand beyond its historical campus. It also officially launched its McCourt School of Public Policy in 2013.

It also launches new degree programs such as the MIDP (master's of international development policy) and the Master of Science in Global Health.

Company Background

In 2010 Georgetown University received its largest philanthropic gift ever when it was granted a nearly $90 million endowment to support medical research at the university's medical center from a charitable trust established by the will of the late Harry Toulmin in 1965.

Georgetown University was founded in 1789 by John Carroll the nation's first Catholic bishop. At the time of its founding Georgetown University's historic campus was located in Georgetown Maryland; the location is now part of the Washington DC metropolitan area. Among Georgetown University's alumni are President Bill Clinton basketball great Patrick Ewing and former US Surgeon General Antonia Novello.

EXECUTIVES

Associate Vice President For Federal Relations, Scott Fleming
Vice President Institutional Diversity And Equity, Rosemary Kilkenny
Associate Vice President Alumni Relations, William Reynolds

Managing Director Mission And Ministry, Aaron Johnson
Vice President Of Financial Institutions, Andres Rengifo
Executive Vice President Of Learning, Byron Price
Assistant Vice President, Regina Bleck
Special Assistant For Global Engagement Office Of The Vice President For Global Engagement, Meredith Bircher
Vice President For Global Engagement, Tom Banchoff
Associate Vice President Advancement Services, Jo Grainger
Assistant Vice President For Student Health, Vince WinklerPrins
Associate Vice President And University Registrar, Annamarie Bianco
Assistant Vice President For Emergency Management, Tonya Coultas
Vice President Of Marketing And Communications Student Government Association Mba Class Of 2018, Mercedes Castro
Associate Vice President For Strategic Communications, Meghan Dubyak
Associate Vice President Communications Office Of Advancement, Amy Levin
Vice President For Strategy, Eugenie Dieck
Director Of Admissions, Brittany Odoms
Secretary Of The University, Edward Quinn
Secretary, Chip Smith
Auditors: PRICEWATERHOUSE COPES LLP MCL

LOCATIONS

HQ: THE GEORGETOWN UNIVERSITY
37TH & O ST NW, WASHINGTON, DC 200570001
Phone: 202 687-0100
Web: WWW.GEORGETOWN.EDU

PRODUCTS/OPERATIONS

Selected Schools
Edmund A. Walsh School of Foreign Service
Georgetown College
Graduate School of Arts and Sciences
Law Center
McCourt School of Public Policy
Robert E. McDonough School of Business
School of Medicine
School of Nursing and Health Studies
School for Summer and Continuing Education

HISTORICAL FINANCIALS

Company Type: Private

Income Statement				FYE: June 30
	REVENUE ($ mil.)	NET INCOME ($ mil.)	NET PROFIT MARGIN	EMPLOYEES
06/18	1,249	130	10.4%	9,700
06/17	1,203	185	15.4%	—
06/13	1,120	188	16.8%	—
06/12	1,038	(88)	—	—
Annual Growth	3.1%	—	—	—

2018 Year-End Financials
Return on assets: 12.0%   Cash ($ mil.): 122
Return on equity: 10.4%
Current ratio: —

THE GOOD SAMARITAN HOSPITAL OF MD INC

EXECUTIVES

Pres-Ceo, Jeffrey A Matton
Cfo, Deana Stout
Chm, Anthony Read
SEC, Walter Jura
Administrative Coordinator, Tammy M Phillips
Auditors: KPMG LLP BALTIMORE MARYLAND

LOCATIONS

HQ: THE GOOD SAMARITAN HOSPITAL OF MD INC
5809 NICHOLSON LN PH 1503, ROCKVILLE, MD 208525707
Phone: 443 444-3780
Web: WWW.GOODSAM-MD.ORG

PRODUCTS/OPERATIONS

Selected Services and Divisions
Belvedere Green (senior living)
Burn Reconstruction Center
Cancer Care/Oncology
Cardiology/Heart Care
Diabetes/Endocrinology
Diagnostic Imaging
Ear Nose and Throat
Emergency Services
Gastroenterology
Good Health Center
Kidney Care/Nephrology
MedStar Good Samaritan Nursing Center (senior living)
MedStar Pharmacy
Orthopedics
Pain Management
Pediatrics
Physical Therapy
Plastic Surgery
Primary Care Center
Pulmonary Services
Rehabilitation Services
Renal Dialysis
Rheumatology [Rheumatoid Arthritis/Sjgren's Syndrome]
Senior Living
Sleep Center
Sports Medicine
Stroke Rehabilitation
Surgical Services
Transitional Care
Urology
Vascular Services
Weight Management - Good Weighs
Women's Health
Woodbourne Woods (senior living)
Wound Healing Center

COMPETITORS

Adventist HealthCare
Anne Arundel Medical Center
Ascension Health
Bon Secours Health
Children's National Medical Center
Christiana Care
Civista Health
GBMC
Inova
Johns Hopkins Health System
Levindale Hospital
Novant Health
Sentara Healthcare
University of Maryland Medical System
Valley Health
Virginia Hospital Center

HISTORICAL FINANCIALS

Company Type: Private

Income Statement				FYE: June 30
	REVENUE ($ mil.)	NET INCOME ($ mil.)	NET PROFIT MARGIN	EMPLOYEES
06/16	315	7	2.5%	2,146
06/15	325	16	5.2%	—
06/14	318	9	3.0%	—
06/11	331	14	4.2%	—
Annual Growth	(1.0%)	(11.0%)	—	—

2016 Year-End Financials
Return on assets: 7.0%   Cash ($ mil.): —
Return on equity: 2.5%
Current ratio: 1.60

THE GREATER FAIRBANKS COMMUNITY HOSPITAL FOUNDATION INCORPORATED

EXECUTIVES

Exec Dir, Shelley D Ebenal
Pres, Jeffry Cook
Prin, James H Little
Prin, Krissy Floyd
Prin, Missey Kohler
Board Certified Family Physici, Mary Klingner
Auditors: KOHLER SCHMITT & HUTCHISON P

LOCATIONS

HQ: THE GREATER FAIRBANKS COMMUNITY HOSPITAL FOUNDATION INCORPORATED
1650 COWLES ST, FAIRBANKS, AK 997015907
Phone: 907 452-2955
Web: WWW.FAIRBANKSHOSPITALFOUNDATION.COM

HISTORICAL FINANCIALS

Company Type: Private

Income Statement				FYE: December 31
	REVENUE ($ mil.)	NET INCOME ($ mil.)	NET PROFIT MARGIN	EMPLOYEES
12/17	292	19	6.8%	1,331
12/16	59	30	51.9%	—
12/09	35	5	15.8%	—
12/08	0	0	—	—
Annual Growth	137.4%	—	—	—

2017 Year-End Financials
Return on assets: 1.6%   Cash ($ mil.): 33
Return on equity: 6.8%
Current ratio: 3.30

THE HARDIN MEMORIAL HOSPITAL FOUNDATION INC

EXECUTIVES

Vice President Chief Medical Officer, Stephen Toadvine
Director Of Pharmacy And Cardiopulmonary Services, Kevin Sullivan
Admissions Director, Karen Muzzillo
Admissions Director, Belinda Carter
Respiratory Therapy Director, Melanie Whitlock
Vice President And Chief Medical Officer, Jody Prather
Vice President, Jenny Sickles
Assistant Vice President Emergency Services, Deanna Parker
Director Icu Coronary Care Unit, Mona Bryan
Assistant Vice President Revenue Cycle, Michelle Brown
Secretary, Vicki Grimes
Secretary, Emily Gray

LOCATIONS

HQ: THE HARDIN MEMORIAL HOSPITAL FOUNDATION INC
913 N DIXIE AVE, ELIZABETHTOWN, KY 427012503
Phone: 270 737-1212
Web: WWW.HMH.NET

Selected facilities
Hardin Memorial Hospital (Elizabethtown)
CareFirst Urgent Care Center (Radcliff)
Family Care Center - North Hardin (Radcliff)
Family Care Center - South Hardin (Sonora)
Family Care Center Magnolia (Magnolia)
Bardstown Diagnostic Center

PRODUCTS/OPERATIONS

Selected services
Birthplace
Cancer Care Services
Comprehensive Cardiac Services
Critical Care
Emergency Department
HomeCare Home Health Agency
Laboratory Services
Les Langley Pediatric Unit
LifeSpring Psychiatric Unit
Nursing Facility
Outpatient Surgery and Endoscopy Center
Pulmonary Services
Radiology Services
Rehabilitation Services
Wellness on Wheels®; Mobile Health Unit
Women's Care Center
WorkWell Occupational Health Services

COMPETITORS

Appalachian Regional Healthcare
Catholic Health Initiatives
Jewish Hospital & St. Mary's HealthCare
Kindred Healthcare
Norton Healthcare
University of Kentucky Chandler Hospital

HISTORICAL FINANCIALS
Company Type: Private

Income Statement
FYE: June 30

	REVENUE ($ mil.)	NET INCOME ($ mil.)	NET PROFIT MARGIN	EMPLOYEES
06/17	318	(1)	—	1,480
06/16	290	15	5.2%	—
06/15*	215	18	8.5%	—
12/10	0	0	23.9%	—
Annual Growth	516.9%	—	—	—

*Fiscal year change

2017 Year-End Financials
Return on assets: 3.8%
Return on equity: (-0.4%)
Current ratio: 2.40
Cash ($ mil.): 47

THE HEALTH CARE AUTHORITY OF THE CITY OF HUNTSVILLE

EXECUTIVES

Eo, David Spillers
Cfo, Kelly Towers
V Pres, Michael W Brown
Chief of Medicine, Richard Spera
Chief Staff, John C Harrison
Chief of Psychology/Psychiatry, Anupama Yedla
Director of Neonatal Care, Lynn Lee
Offc Manager, Nancy Bishop
Chief of Radiology, Timothy Baker
Auditors: WARREN AVERETT LLC HUNTSVILL

LOCATIONS

HQ: THE HEALTH CARE AUTHORITY OF THE CITY OF HUNTSVILLE
101 SIVLEY RD SW, HUNTSVILLE, AL 358014421
Phone: 256 265-1000
Web: WWW.HUNTSVILLEHOSPITAL.ORG

HISTORICAL FINANCIALS
Company Type: Private

Income Statement
FYE: June 30

	REVENUE ($ mil.)	NET INCOME ($ mil.)	NET PROFIT MARGIN	EMPLOYEES
06/18	1,524	53	3.5%	8,000
06/17	1,407	46	3.3%	—
06/07	591	49	8.3%	—
06/06	548	25	4.6%	—
Annual Growth	8.9%	6.5%	—	—

2018 Year-End Financials
Return on assets: 4.1%
Return on equity: 3.5%
Current ratio: 0.80
Cash ($ mil.): 125

THE HEALTHCARE AUTHORITY FOR BAPTIST HEALTH AND AFFILIATE OF UAB HEALTH SYSTEM

EXECUTIVES

Ceo, Russell Tyner
Vice President, Ben F Kelley Jr
Cfo, Katrina Belt
Coo, Robin Barca
Health Professional, Sumana Kakivayi
Executive Officer, Kathy Fain
Physician Recruiter, Bonita Lancaster
Nurse Manager, Bridget Wilson
Benefits Manager, Lynda Thacker
Manager, Donna Pabalate
Operations Manager, Emily Coaker

LOCATIONS

HQ: THE HEALTHCARE AUTHORITY FOR BAPTIST HEALTH AND AFFILIATE OF UAB HEALTH SYSTEM
2105 E SOUTH BLVD, MONTGOMERY, AL 361162409
Phone: 334 286-2987
Web: WWW.BAPTISTFIRST.ORG

HISTORICAL FINANCIALS
Company Type: Private

Income Statement
FYE: June 30

	REVENUE ($ mil.)	NET INCOME ($ mil.)	NET PROFIT MARGIN	EMPLOYEES
06/16	385	16	4.3%	1,500
06/05	360	21	6.0%	—
Annual Growth	0.6%	(2.3%)	—	—

2016 Year-End Financials
Return on assets: 1.1%
Return on equity: 4.3%
Current ratio: 0.80
Cash ($ mil.): 14

THE HERTZ CORPORATION

EXECUTIVES

Pres-Ceo, Kathryn V Marinello
Non Exec Chb, Henry R Keizer
Cfo, Jamere Jackson
Exec V Pres-Cmo, Jodi J Allen
Exec V Pres-Gen Counsel-Sec, Richard J Frecker
Sr V Pres-Cao, Robin C Kramer
Group Pres Rent A Car Int'l, Michel Taride
Evp-Chief Hr Officer, Murali Kuppuswamy
Manager, Jillian Hader
Manager, Jim Rafferty

HQ: THE HERTZ CORPORATION
8501 WILLIAMS RD, ESTERO, FL 339283325
Phone: 239 301-7000
Web: WWW.HERTZ.COM

HISTORICAL FINANCIALS
Company Type: Private

Income Statement
FYE: December 31

	REVENUE ($ mil.)	NET INCOME ($ mil.)	NET PROFIT MARGIN	EMPLOYEES
12/17	8,803	332	3.8%	37,000
12/16	8,803	(488)	—	—
12/15	10,535	276	2.6%	—
Annual Growth	(8.6%)	9.7%	—	—

2017 Year-End Financials
Return on assets: 10.7%
Return on equity: 3.8%
Current ratio: —
Cash ($ mil.): 1,072

THE INGALLS MEMORIAL HOSPITAL

Ingalls Memorial Hospital serves Chicago's south suburbs. With more than 560 beds the main hospital offers a variety of acute and tertiary health care services including cancer treatment cardiovascular care orthopedic surgery rehabilitation services neurosurgery women's health and other clinical services. It also includes specialty centers in areas such as sleep therapy and addiction treatment. Ingalls Memorial Hospital also acts as a health system operating outpatient offices and clinics and providing home health and hospice services in the area.

Operations
Ingalls Memorial Hospital employs 450 physicians who specialize in 30 fields. The medical center sees about 18000 inpatient admissions per year. It also handles about 1100 births and more than 50000 emergency department visits annually.

In addition to the hospital the health system includes a handful of family care centers and several urgent care and surgery clinics as well as outpatient rehabilitation wellness and cancer support centers. Ingalls Health System also operates home health and hospice agencies and it provides community health screenings and other outreach programs.

Each year Ingalls hosts more than 200 free health screenings educational programs and health fairs that reach nearly 50000 individuals. These include free or discounted mammograms; free prostate screenings; and free or deeply discounted children's physicals and immunizations for hundreds of area children preparing for school.

Ingalls Health System also includes a Wellness Center in Homewood; Cancer Care Center and Same Day Surgery in Tinley Park; Ingalls Center for Outpatient Rehabilitation in Calumet City; and Ingalls Home Care & Hospice which provides skilled nursing support and therapy services throughout the Southland.

Geographic Reach
Ingalls Memorial Hospital's main campus encompasses some 22 acres in the south suburbs of Chicago. Its family and urgent care centers are located in Calumet City Flossmoor Matteson and Tinley Park. The system also includes rehabilitation centers in Calumet City and South Holland; a wellness center in Homewood; and a cancer and surgery center in Tinley Park.

Strategy
To improve primary care services Ingalls Memorial Hospital has conducted expansion and renovation efforts at several of its family clinic locations in recent years. It is also growing its range of advanced cancer treatment offerings.

In 2015 Ingalls opened its intensive outpatient program at the Ingalls Family Care Center in Tinley Park. A short-term behavioral health treatment program for adults ages 18 and above the program treats individuals struggling with depression stress and anxiety. It expanded its services to Tinley Park to serve more patients in need of outpatient therapy west of the hospital's main campus in Harvey. The program helps participants take charge of their own well-being through skill development in areas like positive lifestyle changes self-image stress management problem solving communication and relationships.

In 2015 Ingalls also launched an online risk assessment to screen for depression.

Company Background
The company's infusion center was the first Chicago-area cancer center to administer a new prostate cancer drug Provinge in 2012. Ingalls first introduced intensive outpatient therapy at its Flossmoor Family Care Center in 2012.

Ingalls Health System was founded by Chicago-area industrialist Frederick Ingalls in 1923.

EXECUTIVES

Director Of Nursing, Shirley Corbett

LOCATIONS

HQ: THE INGALLS MEMORIAL HOSPITAL
1 INGALLS DR, HARVEY, IL 604263558
Phone: 708 333-2300
Web: WWW.INGALLS.ORG

PRODUCTS/OPERATIONS

Selected Services
Advanced Orthopedic Institute
  Joint Center
  Spine Center
  Sports Medicine
  Rehabilitative Services
Behavioral Health
  Inpatient Adult Care
  Addictions
  Adolescent
  Depression Risk
Cancer Care
  Newly Diagnosed
  Research
  Technology and Treatments
Heart and Vascular
  Diabetes
  Heart Care Center
  Leg Veins
  Stroke
Home Care and Hospice
  Palliative Care
Interventional Radiology
  Interventional Oncology
  Uterine Fibroids
  Vein Clinic
Irwin Retina Center
  Clinical Research
  Diabetic Retinopathy
  Macular Degeneration
Neurosciences
  Stroke
  Concussion Program
  Sleep Centers
Occupational Health
  Employer Resource Center
  Worksite Wellness and Prevention
Outpatient Services
  Advanced Imaging
  Pharmacy
  Same Day Surgery
  Urgent Aid
Rehabilitation Services
  Acute Care
  Day Rehabilitation
  Home Care
  Inpatient Rehabilitation
  Outpatient Rehabilitation
Wellness
  Complementary Medicine
  Nutrition and Weight Management
Women's Services
  Breast Center
  Maternity Unit
  Osteoporosis
  Uterine Fibroids
Additional Services
  Complementary Medicine
  Dermatology
  Diabetes
  Dialysis
  Ear/Nose/Throat
  Gastroenterology
  Occupational Health
  Ophthalmology
  Pain Management
  Pediatrics
  Rheumatology
  Therapies
  Urinary Incontinence
  Weight Management
  Wound Care

COMPETITORS

Advocate Health Care
Alexian Brothers Health System
Loyola University Health System
MetroSouth Medical
Mount Sinai Hospital
NorthShore University HealthSystem
Rush System for Health
Saint Margaret Mercy Healthcare
St. Bernard Hospital and Health Care Center
Vanguard MacNeal Hospital
WellGroup HealthPartners

HISTORICAL FINANCIALS
Company Type: Private

Income Statement
FYE: September 30

	REVENUE ($ mil.)	NET INCOME ($ mil.)	NET PROFIT MARGIN	EMPLOYEES
09/15	285	7	2.6%	2,296
09/14	292	26	9.2%	—
09/13	290	34	11.8%	—
09/12	293	36	12.6%	—
Annual Growth	(0.9%)	(41.7%)	—	—

2015 Year-End Financials
Return on assets: 7.7%
Return on equity: 2.6%
Current ratio: 0.70
Cash ($ mil.): 16

THE INSTITUTE OF ELECTRICAL AND ELECTRONICS ENGINEERS INCORPORATED

A leading technology-related professional group The Institute of Electrical and Electronics Engineers (IEEE) has almost 430000 members including 100000-plus students in 160 countries. The IEEE provides technical and professional information to members on topics such as aerospace systems biomedical engineering computers consumer electronics electric power and telecommunications. It sponsors more than 1300 annual conferences and publishes a variety of technical literature including journals magazines and conference proceedings. The IEEE was formed in 1964 in a combination of the American Institute of Electrical Engineers (founded in 1884) and the Institute of Radio Engineers (founded in 1912).

Operations
Conferences and periodicals together contribute about three-fourths of IEEE's total revenue. The remaining revenue comes from memberships and public imperatives.

Geographic Reach
Nearly 50% of IEEE members live and practice their craft in the US. China India and the Pacific Rim countries account for nearly a fifth of its membership.

Financial Performance
IEEE's revenue rose some 2% in fiscal 2013 to $412.7 million from 2012's $405.3 million. Standard revenue — with an 8% increase — together with Periodicals' 4% boost in revenue contributed to the gains offset in part by other income. IEEE reported $55.1 million in profits in 2013 a $27 million increase thanks to higher sales offset by rising operating expenses across its business. The organization's cash flow in 2013 logged a $32 million bump from gains on the sale of investments.

Strategy
The institute caters to engineers who hail from a wide range of specialties — from aerospace and electronic systems to ultrasonics and frequency control — with nearly 40 different types of society memberships. The organization's membership grew despite the recent downturn in the global economy and continues to increase during the recovery. Among the IEEE more than one-fifth of its members are under the age of 30 and men outnumber women 9:1.

EXECUTIVES

Director, E. James (Jim) Prendergast
Managing Director Ieee-usa, Chris Brantley
Managing Director Educational Activities, Doug Gorham
Managing Director Member And Geographic Activities, Cecelia Jankowski
Cfo, Thomas Siegert
Managing Director Technical Activities, Mary Ward-Callan
President And Ceo, Howard E. Michel
Cio, Cherif Amirat
Managing Director Ieee-standards Association, Konstantinos Karachalios
Vice President, Forrest Sass
Vice President Executive Officer, Fjellstad Chris

LOCATIONS

HQ: THE INSTITUTE OF ELECTRICAL AND ELECTRONICS ENGINEERS INCORPORATED
445 HOES LN, PISCATAWAY, NJ 088544141
Phone: 212 419-7900
Web: WWW.IEEE.ORG

2013 Members

	% of total
US	47
India China & Pacific Rim	18
Canada	3
Other regions	32
Total	**100**

PRODUCTS/OPERATIONS

2013 Sales

	$ mil.	% of total
Periodicals	157	38
Conferences	153	37
Memberships & public imperatives	67	17
Standards	32	8
Other income	1	-
Total	**412**	**100**

Selected IEEE Societies
Aerospace and Electronic Systems
Antennas and Propagation
Broadcast Technology
Circuits and Systems
Communications
Computational Intelligence
Electromagnetic Compatibility
Geoscience and Remote Sensing

HISTORICAL FINANCIALS
Company Type: Private

Income Statement				FYE: December 31
	REVENUE ($ mil.)	NET INCOME ($ mil.)	NET PROFIT MARGIN	EMPLOYEES
12/17	496	49	9.9%	1,068
12/16	480	22	4.7%	—
12/09	338	18	5.5%	—
12/08	0	0	—	—
Annual Growth	—	—	—	—

2017 Year-End Financials
Return on assets: 10.9%   Cash ($ mil.): 16
Return on equity: 9.9%
Current ratio: 0.20

THE IRVINE JAMES FOUNDATION

EXECUTIVES

Pres-Ceo, Donald Howard
Director of Finance, Casey Budesilich
Dir Technology, Ekta Chopra
Program Director, Elizabeth Gonzalez
Digital Communications Officer, Joyce Sood
Director of Impact Assessment, Kim Howard
Senior Communications Officer, Leslie Payne
Senior Accountant, Michael Quach
Senior Program Officer, Rafael Morales
Leadership Awards Officer, Jessica Kaczmarek
Director of Program Operations, Josephine Ramirez

LOCATIONS

HQ: THE IRVINE JAMES FOUNDATION
1 BUSH ST FL 8, SAN FRANCISCO, CA 941044414
Phone: 415 777-2244
Web: WWW.222SECOND.COM

HISTORICAL FINANCIALS
Company Type: Private

Income Statement				FYE: December 31
	ASSETS ($ mil.)	NET INCOME ($ mil.)	INCOME AS % OF ASSETS	EMPLOYEES
12/15	2,185	38	1.8%	36
12/14	1,611	44	2.7%	—
12/09	1,507	(57)	—	—
12/08	1,379	0	—	—
Annual Growth	6.8%	—	—	—

2015 Year-End Financials
Return on assets: 4.3%   Sales ($ mil): 137
Return on equity: 28.2%

THE J G WENTWORTH COMPANY

EXECUTIVES

Vice President Information Technology, George Schwartz
Auditors: ERNST & YOUNG LLP BOSTON MAS

LOCATIONS

HQ: THE J G WENTWORTH COMPANY
1200 MORRIS DR STE 300, CHESTERBROOK, PA 190875507
Phone: 484 434-2300
Web: WWW.JGWENTWORTH.COM

PRODUCTS/OPERATIONS

2015
$ mil % contribu

	$ mil	% contribu
Structured Settlements and Annuity Purchasing	269	91
Home Lending	26	9
Total	**296**	**100**

Selected Brands
J.G. Wentworth
Peachtree

Selected Products and services
Home Lending
Lending Marketplace
Prepaid Cards
Structured Settlement Payment Purchasing

HISTORICAL FINANCIALS
Company Type: Private

Income Statement				FYE: December 31
	REVENUE ($ mil.)	NET INCOME ($ mil.)	NET PROFIT MARGIN	EMPLOYEES
12/17	428	(210)	—	751
12/16	324	(98)	—	—
12/15	296	(197)	—	—
12/14	494	96	19.5%	—
Annual Growth	(4.6%)	—	—	—

2017 Year-End Financials
Return on assets: 6.1%   Cash ($ mil.): 35
Return on equity: (-49.1%)
Current ratio: —

THE JACKSON LABORATORY

The Jackson Laboratory (JAX) was into genetics before genetics was cool. Founded in 1929 the not-for-profit organization is a leading researcher of human diseases their causes and their potential cures. Much of its research into mammalian genetics is focused on mice which share a similar genetic makeup to humans. In addition to its own research in areas such as cancer immunology and metabolic disease the organization maintains colonies of mice and supplies them under the brand name JAX to other laboratories around the globe. Additionally JAX offers educational programs — including internships workshops and predoctoral programs — for both current and future scientists.

Geographic Reach
The organization has one location in Sacramento California and two each in Farmington Connecticut and Bar Harbor Maine.

Financial Performance
JAX receives operating revenue from public sector support in the form of federal grants private sector support in the form of private foundation grants philanthropic contributions and resource revenue in the form of cost and fees collected for JAX Mice & Services its service for supplying mice models used for research. The organization's operating revenue increased by 5% from $230 million to $240 million in 2013 over 2012; about 75% of it from National Institutes of Health grants.

Strategy
JAX has spent a couple of years and at least $227 million acquiring and upgrading facilities at its California and Maine locations. Part of the organization's mandate is educating scientists. To that end in 2013 it purchased a website content and assets from the National Coalition of Health Professional Education in Genetics and hired three of its employees.

The following year JAX and Chinese company Wuhan Frasergen Bioinformatics created a cancer research facility in Wuhan China that will let Chinese researchers use the Laboratory's cancer tools.

EXECUTIVES

Evp And Coo, Charles E. Hewett
President And Ceo, Edison T. Liu
Scientific Director The Jackson Laboratory For Genomic Medicine, Charles Lee
Preisdent Jax Mice Clinical And Research Services, Auro Nair
Vp And Cfo, S. Catherine (Katy) Longley
Scientific Director And Professor The Jackson Laboratory For Mammalian Genetics, Nadia Rosenthal
Senior Vice President Of Human Resources, Raymond Robledo
Vice President Development And Communications, Kristen Rozansky
Vice President For Research, Ken Fasman
Chairman, David J. Roux, age 61

LOCATIONS
HQ: THE JACKSON LABORATORY
600 MAIN ST, BAR HARBOR, ME 046091500
Phone: 207 288-6000
Web: WWW.JAX.ORG

PRODUCTS/OPERATIONS

2015 Sources of Revenue

	% of total
Program Revenues	70
Government Support	26
Foundation Grants	2
Philanthropic Gifts	1
Other Revenue	1
Total	**100**

Selected Services
Breeding and rederivation services
Cryopreservation & recovery services
Genome science services
In Vivo pharmacology services
Surgical and preconditioning services

COMPETITORS
Charles River Laboratories
Deltagen
Harlan Laboratories
Howard Hughes Medical Institute
Taconic
Whitehead Institute for Biomedical Research

HISTORICAL FINANCIALS
Company Type: Private

Income Statement				FYE: December 31
	REVENUE ($ mil.)	NET INCOME ($ mil.)	NET PROFIT MARGIN	EMPLOYEES
12/16	327	46	14.2%	1,950
12/15	304	22	7.5%	—
12/14	274	76	27.8%	—
12/13	257	41	15.9%	—
Annual Growth	8.3%	4.2%	—	—

2016 Year-End Financials
Return on assets: 11.7%   Cash ($ mil.): 9
Return on equity: 14.2%
Current ratio: —

THE JAMAICA HOSPITAL

Jamaica Hospital Medical Center has been operating in the Queens Borough of New York since before the nation of Jamaica even was born. The hospital serves Queens and eastern Brooklyn with general medical pediatric psychiatric and ambulatory care services. The facility has about 430 beds. Its specialty services include a coma recovery unit a dialysis center a psychiatric emergency department a rehabilitation center as well as a traumatic brain injury recovery unit. The hospital also operates a nursing home with more than 220 beds as well as family practice ambulance and home health services. Jamaica Hospital Medical Center is a subsidiary of MediSys Health Network.

Operations
Jamaica Hospital Medical Center treats some 130000 patients annually through its emergency department which contains a level I regional trauma center. The hospital also handles about 2000 births each year in its labor and delivery wing.

In addition to acute care services the hospital is a teaching facility associated with several educational organizations including Cornell University's Weill Medical College the Mount Sinai School of Medicine and St. George's University School of Medicine. It provides residency and training programs in areas including dentistry podiatry physician assistant and osteopathic medicine. Some of its residency programs are conducted in partner-

---

ship with other regional health centers including the New York Hospital and the Montefiore Medical Center.

The Ambulatory Care Centers include a Sleep Clinic where sleep disorders in adults and children are evaluated and treated.

In 2014 the hospital had nearly 120000 patients were treated in the Emergency Department; 300000 patients were seen in the Ambulatory Care Centers (with locations at the main campus and also at the offsite centers in the community); and some 2904 deliveries were performed.

Geographic Reach
Jamaica Hospital Medical Center serves a population greater than 1.2 million in Queens and eastern Brooklyn.

Strategy
To improve care for area residents Jamaica Hospital Medical Center has expanded its sleep medicine division to include a new sleep disorder diagnosis center for adults and children. The hospital has also expanded its community care provisions through partnerships with area businesses and organizations.

Upgrading its technology in 2015 the company introduced da Vinci Robot Now at its Flushing location.

Company Background
Jamaica Hospital Medical Center was founded in 1892.

EXECUTIVES
Ceo, Neil Foster Phillips
Finance Vice President, Manzar Sassani
Director of Planning*, Ann Corrigan
Financial Officer, Joylene Porter
Human Resources, Matilda Miceli
Director, Robert Mendelson
Chief Marketing Officer, Michael Hinck
Project Director, Nallibe Luna
Emergency Medicine Specialist, Ravinder Nagpaul
Supervisor, Rebecca Roberts
Coordinator, Thomas Pawelzik

LOCATIONS
HQ: THE JAMAICA HOSPITAL
8900 VAN WYCK EXPY FL 4N, JAMAICA, NY
114182897
Phone: 718 206-6290
Web: WWW.JAMAICAHOSPITAL.ORG

PRODUCTS/OPERATIONS

Selected Centers and Services
Advanced Center for Psychotherapy
Allergy and Immunology
Ambulatory Care
Anesthesia
Cardiology
Clinical Services
Corporate Health
Critical Care Medicine
Dental
Dermatology
Dialysis-Island Rehabilitation
Emergency Medicine
Family Medicine
Gastroenterology
Home Health
Infectious Disease
Lupus Center
MediSys Family Care Centers
Nephrology
Neurology
Nursing
OB-GYN
Oncology
Orthopedic Surgery
Palliative Care
Pathology
Pediatrics
Podiatry
Prehospital Care

Psychiatry
Pulmonary Medicine
Radiology
Rehabilitation
Rheumatology
Surgery
TCU
The Brady Institute
Trump Pavilion~Jamaica Hospital Nursing Home
Women's Health
Women's Health Center

COMPETITORS

Catholic Healthcare
  System
Continuum Health
  Partners
Maimonides Medical
  Center

Montefiore Medical
New York City Health
  and Hospitals
NewYork-Presbyterian
  Healthcare
Northwell Health

HISTORICAL FINANCIALS

Company Type: Private

Income Statement   FYE: December 31

	REVENUE ($ mil.)	NET INCOME ($ mil.)	NET PROFIT MARGIN	EMPLOYEES
12/17	436	(45)	—	3,251
12/16	439	(7)	—	
12/15	422	(32)	—	
12/09	447	(2)	—	
Annual Growth	(0.3%)	—	—	—

2017 Year-End Financials

Return on assets: 9.7%   Cash ($ mil.): 2
Return on equity: (-10.4%)
Current ratio: 0.30

THE JUDGE GROUP INC

If your business requires staffing technology consulting or training services The Judge Group will be predisposed to render a verdict in your favor. The company offers temporary and permanent employee placement services in a wide variety of service and manufacturing sectors but specializes in technology staffing. The company's technology consulting services address such areas as enterprise content management and strategy. It also offers training for IT-related and other professional functions through its Berkeley division. Martin Judge founded the company in 1970.

Geographic Reach

The Judge Group operates from a network of more than 30 offices throughout the US and has locations in Asia and Canada.

Strategy

The company's growth strategy revolves around the opening of offices in select markets and by entering alliances with other human resources services firms. Over the last few years it has launched offices in Baltimore Houston Milwaukee and Phoenix. In 2013 it opened its newest office in Ottawa Ontario. Throughout 2015 it opened new US offices in Oregon Connecticut and Maryland.

The Judge Group has also expanded its international reach by launching Judge China a firm which provides clients with consulting expertise for accessing markets in the most populous country in the world through offices in Beijing and Shanghai.

EXECUTIVES

Coo, Katy A. Wiercinski
Cfo, Robert G. Alessandrini, $137,308 total
  compensation
President Direct Placement, Stephen D. Green

President International, Gary R. Morris
President North America, Brian T. Anderson
Evp Talent Acquisition, Dennis F. Judge
President Berkeley Training, Peter Pedone
**President Technology Solutions/unified
  Communications,** James D. Miner
Evp Sales, Michael Tedesco
President Judge Healthcare, Mick J. Angelichio
Ceo, Martin E. Judge
Evp And Chief Marketing Officer, Peter L. Fong
Vp Training And Development And Cio, Kenneth F.
  (Ken) Krieger
Managing Vice President, Frank Santoro
Vice President Recruiting, Brian Blasko
Vice President, Linda Wertman
Legal Secretary, Nadine Kowal
Associate Vice President, Larry Burt

LOCATIONS

HQ: THE JUDGE GROUP INC
  151 S WARNER RD STE 100, WAYNE, PA 190872125
Phone: 610 667-7700
Web: WWW.JUDGE.COM

PRODUCTS/OPERATIONS

Selected Services
Corporate training
  Custom content development
  Information technology training
  Professional development
  Project staffing and logistics
Enterprise-wide staffing
  Financial services
  Food/beverage
  Government
  Health care
  Insurance
  Manufacturing
  Pharmaceutical
  Retail/supermarkets
  Technology
  Utilities/telecom
  Wholesale distribution
Technology consulting
  Application design and development
  Audio visual design and implementation
  E-discovery and compliance
  Enterprise content management
  Research validation and compliance
  SAP implementation services
  Technology strategy and architecture

COMPETITORS

Accenture
Adecco
Aquent
Butler America
CDI
IBM Global Services
Kelly Services

Kenexa
Kforce
ManpowerGroup
NTT Data
RCM Technologies
Unisys

HISTORICAL FINANCIALS

Company Type: Private

Income Statement   FYE: September 30

	REVENUE ($ mil.)	NET INCOME ($ mil.)	NET PROFIT MARGIN	EMPLOYEES
09/17	380	2	0.7%	7,000
09/16	342	1	0.4%	
09/15	323	3	1.2%	
09/13	273	1	0.4%	
Annual Growth	8.5%	22.9%	—	—

2017 Year-End Financials

Return on assets: 6.9%   Cash ($ mil.): —
Return on equity: 0.7%
Current ratio: 1.90

THE LANCASTER GENERAL HOSPITAL

Lancaster General Health (LG Health) is a 690-bed integrated health care delivery system serving residents of Lancaster County Pennsylvania and surrounding areas. Its flagship Lancaster General Hospital (LGH) - opened in 1893 - is known for its cardiology orthopedic and intensive care specialties. A separate Women & Babies hospital cares for those just making it into the world. The not-for-profit system also includes multiple outpatient clinics a rehab hospital home care services and a nursing center and health care college as well as a medical group of more than 300 physicians operating at more than 40 practices throughout the region.

Operations

Facilities in the LG Health system include the 533-bed flagship LGH the 98-bed Women & Babies Hospital the 59-bed Lancaster Rehabilitation Hospital and 14 outpatient centers. Specialty services include open-heart surgery obstetrics neurosurgery trauma care and behavioral health. The system also operates a number of outpatient programs such as a diabetes and nutritional Center and a sleep medicine center.

Every year LG Health sees some 972000 outpatients delivers some 4000 babies and performs around 38000 surgeries.

Geographic Reach

The system serves Pennsylvania's Lebanon Berks Dauphin York Chester and Lancaster counties.

Sales and Marketing

Commercial and HMO payments together account for about 40% of net patient revenues; Medicare accounts for another 35% while Medicaid accounts for some 10%.

Financial Performance

LG Health's revenue rose 5% to $969 million in fiscal 2014 (ended June) on higher net patient revenue and medical services revenue. However net income fell 51% to $117 million as income from contributions and gifts declined; a change in pension liability also hurt the system's bottom line.

Cash flow from operations declined 43% to $43 million in fiscal 2014 as more cash was used in patient accounts receivable and changes were made in prepaid expenses assets and benefits.

Strategy

LG Health continues to make strategic investments to better serve its patients and the community. In 2013 the health system completed construction on the Ann B. Barshinger Cancer Center which opened its doors that year. Two years later it announced plans to expand LGH in a $60 million project that will add a new eight-story patient tower. With the addition of 60 new private rooms and the space for 80 more rooms as demand requires the hospital will have the room to convert its existing semi-private rooms to private rooms.

The system also partners with others in the community to improve patient care. In 2014 it formed an alliance with the University of Pennsylvania Health System to develop innovative care research and education programs.

EXECUTIVES

Senior Vice President Business Development,
  Susan Wynne
Svp And Cio, Gary Davidson
**Evp Chief Population Health Officer; President
  Lg Health Innovation Solutions Inc.,** Marion A.
  McGowan

President And Ceo, Thomas E. (Tom) Beeman
Evp Chief Administrative And Legal Officer And Corporate Secretary, Robert P. Macina
Svp Post-acute Care, Geoffrey W. Eddowes
Evp And Cfo, Dennis R. Roemer
Svp Chief Physician Executive And Chief Medical Officer, Lee M. Duke
Svp Hospital Operations And Nurse Executive; President Lancaster General Hospital, Karen Flaherty-Oxler
Medical Director, Jeffrey Kirchner
Senior Vice President, Joseph Puskar
Vice President Of Operations, Christopher Maley
Vice President General Manager, Norma Ferndinand
Vice President Legal Services, Margaret F Costella
Vice President Of Operations, Rich Paoletti
Vice President Of Customer Service, Carolyn Carlson
Vice President, Stacey Youcis
Vice President And Controller, Doug Rinehart
Medical Director Oncology Program, Randall Oyer
Vice President Hospital Operations, Tammy Ober
Senior Vice President Hospital Operations, William Mccune
Chairman, C. Clair McCormick
Vice Chairman, Philip R. Wenger
Board Member, Christine Vlassis
Secretary, Pamela Miller
Secretary, Sheila Loreto

LOCATIONS

HQ: THE LANCASTER GENERAL HOSPITAL
555 N DUKE ST, LANCASTER, PA 176022207
Phone: 717 544-5511
Web: WWW.LANCASTERGENERALHEALTH.ORG

PRODUCTS/OPERATIONS

2014 Sales

	% of total
Net patient services revenue less provision for bad debts	95
Medical services	4
Other revenue	1
Other	.
Total	**100**

Selected Specialties

Cardiology
Emergency medical
Intensive care
Neurology
Oncology
Radiology
Rehabilitation
Urology

COMPETITORS

Altoona Regional
Ascension Health
Catholic Health Initiatives
Evangelical Community Hospital
Hanover Healthcare
Holy Spirit
Lewistown Hospital
Main Line Health System
Memorial Hospital (PA)
PinnacleHealth System
Saint Vincent Health System
St. Luke's University Health Network
University of Pennsylvania Health System
WellSpan Health

HISTORICAL FINANCIALS

Company Type: Private

Income Statement   FYE: June 30

	REVENUE ($ mil.)	NET INCOME ($ mil.)	NET PROFIT MARGIN	EMPLOYEES
06/16	958	122	12.8%	7,000
06/15	920	110	12.1%	—
06/14	867	(13)	—	—
06/13	823	(15)	—	—
Annual Growth	**5.2%**	—	—	—

2016 Year-End Financials

Return on assets: 2.9%   Cash ($ mil.): 23
Return on equity: 12.8%
Current ratio: 1.40

THE LANE CONSTRUCTION CORPORATION

Lane likes people to be in the fast lane. For more than a century the heavy civil contractor and its affiliates have been widening paving and constructing lanes for highways bridges runways railroads dams and mass transit systems in the eastern and southern US. The group also produces bituminous and precast concrete and mines aggregates at plants and quarries in the northeastern mid-Atlantic and southern US. Additionally it sells and leases construction equipment. Founded in 1902 Lane Construction has offices in more than 20 states and is owned by descendants of Lane and employees.

Operations

Lane Construction specializes in heavy civil construction services and products in the transportation infrastructure and energy industries. During the past decade Lane Construction has participated in more than 70 design-building projects with a combined value of more than $4 billion.

Beyond its construction projects Lane operates divisions that manufacture bituminous and precast concrete with mine aggregates at 70 plants and 12 quarries throughout the U.S.

Lane's business divisions are spread across the US and include: Civil Wall Solutions Cold River Materials Prestress of the Carolinas Senate Asphalt Virginia Paving Company and Virginia Sign & Lighting Company.

Lane affiliates include New Hampshire-based Cold River Materials Senate Asphalt of Washington D.C. and Virginia Paving and Virginia Sign & Lighting Co. among about a half a dozen others. In 2013 its Rea Contracting division in the Carolinas changed its name to Lane Construction Corp.

Geographic Reach

Lane Construction has offices in more than 20 US states including Florida Illinois Maine North Carolina Pennsylvania Texas and Virginia. While most of Lane's projects take place along the East Coast it also operates in the South/Southwest and has international operations — under the Lane Worldwide Infrastructure Inc. name — in the Middle East.

Financial Performance

While full financials of the privately-held company were not available Lane Construction has posted annual revenues of more than $1 billion since 2010.

Strategy

The company continues to work for both public and private entities on a variety of high-value projects. In early 2015 the contractor was working on a joint-venture project with Skanska and Granite Construction Company on the $2.3 billion "I-4 Ultimate project" which involves design build finance operating and maintenance work on 21 miles of Interstate 4 from Orange County to Seminole County in Florida.

Also as of early 2015 Lane reported that it recently completed its $1.5-billion construction project on the I-495 Express Lanes in Virginia in one of the largest public-private joint ventures in the US. The same team also completed a $722 million expansion and improvement project on 29 miles of the I-95 Express (high occupancy toll road) lanes in Virginia. Both of these Virgina-based projects were completed ahead of schedule.

EXECUTIVES

Ceo, Robert E Alger
Ex Vice President, Kirk D Junco
Ex Vice President, Donald P Dobbs
SEC, Ann M Falsey
Assistant Vice President Engin, Thomas R Larson
Payroll Staff, Jennifer Shum
Regional Vice-President, James Hughes
Accounting Staff, Joanne Ptak
Os Job Cost Coordinator, Ana Garofalo
Associate Engineer, Andrea Roccasalvo
Chief Estimator, Andy Kaiyala
Auditors: KPMG LLP HARTFORD CT

LOCATIONS

HQ: THE LANE CONSTRUCTION CORPORATION
90 FIELDSTONE CT, CHESHIRE, CT 064101212
Phone: 203 235-3351
Web: WWW.LANECONSTRUCT.COM

PRODUCTS/OPERATIONS

Selected Projects

Airports
Bridges
Design-Build
Federal
Heavy Civil
Highways
Public Private Partnerships
Plants & Paving
Rail
Specialty Paving

Selected Divisions

Civil Wall Solutions
Cold River Materials Prestress of the Carolinas
Senate Asphalt
Sunquip
Sunrise Materials
Virginia Paving Company
Virginia Sun & Lighting Company
Wardwell
White Bros.

COMPETITORS

Angelo Iafrate
Austin Industries
Balfour Beatty Inc
Bechtel
Clark Enterprises
Granite Construction
J.F. White Contracting
MBC Holding
Peter Kiewit Sons'
Sargent Corp
Skanska USA Civil
The Middlesex Corporation
Turner Corporation
Tutor-Saliba
Vecellio & Grogan
Walsh Group

HISTORICAL FINANCIALS
Company Type: Private

Income Statement   FYE: December 31

	REVENUE ($ mil.)	NET INCOME ($ mil.)	NET PROFIT MARGIN	EMPLOYEES
12/17	1,476	18	1.3%	3,500
12/16	1,196	39	3.3%	—
12/15	1,115	(16)	—	—
12/14	1,093	8	0.8%	—
Annual Growth	10.5%	32.0%	—	—

2017 Year-End Financials
Return on assets: 9.1%   Cash ($ mil.): 94
Return on equity: 1.3%
Current ratio: 0.90

THE MARY IMOGENE BASSETT HOSPITAL

EXECUTIVES

Pres-Ceo, Vance M Brown
Exec V Pres-Coo, Bertine McKenna
V Pres-Cfo, Sue Andrews
Cco, Steven Heneghan
Evp-Chief Operating Officer, Ronette Wiley
Administrative Director, Scott Bonderoff
Vice-President, Scott Groom
Director, William Richtsmeier
Vascular Surgery, Shelby S Cooper
Rheumatology Specialist, David T Griger
Program Manager, Kelly Stone

LOCATIONS

HQ: THE MARY IMOGENE BASSETT HOSPITAL
  1 ATWELL RD, COOPERSTOWN, NY 133261394
Phone: 607 547-3456
Web: WWW.BASSETT.ORG

HISTORICAL FINANCIALS
Company Type: Private

Income Statement   FYE: December 31

	REVENUE ($ mil.)	NET INCOME ($ mil.)	NET PROFIT MARGIN	EMPLOYEES
12/16	443	5	1.3%	3,200
12/15	412	(2)	—	—
12/14	486	18	3.7%	—
12/13	451	7	1.6%	—
Annual Growth	(0.6%)	(6.8%)	—	—

2016 Year-End Financials
Return on assets: 5.1%   Cash ($ mil.): 4
Return on equity: 1.3%
Current ratio: 1.00

THE MASSACHUSETTS GENERAL HOSPITAL

The General Hospital Corporation is no soapy daytime drama. Doing business as Massachusetts General Hospital (or Mass General) the 200-year-old acute care facility is Harvard Medical School's original and largest teaching hospital. With some 1000 beds Mass General has its main campus in Boston and operates several health centers in surrounding communities. Its specialized medical departments include cancer cardiology and heart surgery; neurology and neurosurgery; and diabetes and endocrinology. As a leading research facility Mass General hosts a number of clinical drug and device trials and has an annual research budget of more than $850 million. The hospital is a founding member of the Partners HealthCare System (along with Brigham and Women's).

Operations
Founded in 1811 Mass General is the oldest and largest general hospital in New England as well as one of the oldest hospitals in the nation. It holds Level I certifications for adult and pediatric trauma and burn care making it a regional referral center for other area hospitals. The hospital also provides outpatient care through doctors' offices of the Mass General Physicians Organization.

Mass General Hospital for Children administers pediatric care services including primary care and rare disease treatment.

Additionally Mass General operates one of the largest hospital-based research networks in the nation consisting of more than 30 clinical departments and centers and conducting some 1200 clinical trials at any given time. With Harvard Mass General offers about 30 residency programs 145 fellowships and continuing medical education programs.

Each year the hospital has some 48000 inpatients more than 100000 emergency department visits and performs more than 42000 operations.

Geographic Reach Mass General's main hospital is located in downtown Boston. The medical center also operates clinics and community locations in Boston Charleston Chelsea Danvers Everett Foxborough Revere and Waltham.

EXECUTIVES

President And Trustee, Peter L. Slavin
Chief Radiation Oncology, Jay S. Loeffler
Chief Neurosurgery, Robert L. Martuza
Chief Orthopaedic Surgery, Harry E. Rubash
Director Cancer Center, Daniel A. Haber
Chief Of Pathology, David N. Louis
Chief Dermatology, David E. Fisher
Chief Molecular Biology, Robert E. Kingston
Chief Of Radiology, James Brink
Surgeon-in-chief And Chair Department Of Surgery, Keith D. Lillemoe
Chief Urology Service, Michael L. Blute
Physician-in-chief Department Of Medicine, Katrina A. Armstrong
Chief Department Of Emergency Medicine, David FM Brown
Chief Neurology Service, Merit Ester Cudkowicz
Chief Department Of Obstetrics And Gynecology, Jeffrey Lawrence (Jeff) Ecker
Chief Pediatric Surgery And Surgeon-in-chief Massgeneral Hospital For Children, Allan Moises Goldstein
Physician-in-chief Of Massgeneral Hospital For Children And Chief Of Partners Pediatrics, Ronald Ellis Kleinman
Chief Of Psychiatry, Jerrold Frank Rosenbaum
Chief Oral And Maxillofacial Surgery, Maria J. Troulis
Chief Of Anesthesia Critical Care And Pain Medicine, Jeanine P. Wiener-Kronish
Chief Physical Medicine And Rehabilitation, Ross D. Zafonte
Medical Director, Leonard Kaban
Clinical Director, Donald Lawrence
Medical Director, Mary Sabatini
Vp Graduate Medical Education, Debra Weinstein
Medical Director, Ido Weinberg
Senior Vice President Of Technology, Ronald S Newbower
Senior Vice President For Finance, Sally Boemer
Senior Vice President Surgical And Anesthesia Services And Clinical Business Development, Ann Prestipino
Nursing Director, Maureen Schnider
Senior Vice President Human Resources, Jeff Davis
Senior Vice President For Research, Harry Orf
Nursing Director, Hiyam Nadel
Nursing Director, Christina Stone
Medical Director Non Acute Care Services, Terrence O'Malley
Senior Vice President For Finance, Sally Mason
Medical Director, Darshan Mehta
Director Of Health, Goldberg Ross
Board Member, Daniel Rosenthal
Trustee, Cathy E. Minehan, age 70
Board Member, Antonia Stephen
Board Member, Frank Pedlow
Deputy Treasurer, Michael Manning

LOCATIONS

HQ: THE MASSACHUSETTS GENERAL HOSPITAL
  55 FRUIT ST, BOSTON, MA 021142696
Phone: 617 726-2000
Web: WWW.MGHBIOMED.COM

Selected Research Centers
AIDS
Cancer
Cardiovascular research
Computational and integrative biology
Cutaneous biology
Human genetics
Medical imaging
Neurodegenerative disorders
Photomedicine
Regenerative medicine
Reproductive biology
Systems biology
Transplantation biology

COMPETITORS

Beth Israel Deaconess Medical Center	Elliot Health System
Boston Medical Center	Emerson Hospital
Cambridge Health Alliance	Milford Regional Medical Center
Cape Cod Hospital	New England Alliance for Health
Care New England	Northeast Health System
CareGroup	Southcoast Hospitals Group
Catholic Medical Center	Steward Health Care
Children's Hospital Boston	Sturdy Memorial
Dana-Farber	Winchester Healthcare

HISTORICAL FINANCIALS
Company Type: Private

Income Statement   FYE: September 30

	REVENUE ($ mil.)	NET INCOME ($ mil.)	NET PROFIT MARGIN	EMPLOYEES
09/15	2,452	211	8.6%	10,156
09/14	2,201	186	8.5%	—
09/13	2,274	148	6.5%	—
09/12	2,281	267	11.7%	—
Annual Growth	2.4%	(7.6%)	—	—

2015 Year-End Financials
Return on assets: 1.3%   Cash ($ mil.): 99
Return on equity: 8.6%
Current ratio: 1.10

THE MEDICAL CENTER

EXECUTIVES

V Pres-Coo-Ownr, James R Wheeler
V Pres-Oper, Kevin Sass
Vice President, Wayne Joyner
Chief Staff, David Flowers
Scientist, Dan Cullison
Manager, Jerri Freeman
Health Care Director, Dionne Rowan
Coordinator, Michael Zimmermann
Chief of Radiology, Nishant De Quadros
Urology Specialist, Thomas Stewart
Director of Network, Bobby Childs
Auditors: DIXON HUGHES GOODMAN LLP CHAR

LOCATIONS

HQ: THE MEDICAL CENTER
   710 CENTER ST, COLUMBUS, GA 319011547
Phone: 706 660-6255
Web: WWW.CRHS.NET

HISTORICAL FINANCIALS

Company Type: Private

Income Statement				FYE: June 30
	REVENUE ($ mil.)	NET INCOME ($ mil.)	NET PROFIT MARGIN	EMPLOYEES
06/15	390	(28)	—	1,500
06/14	366	(4)	—	—
06/10	316	15	4.9%	—
06/08	283	12	4.5%	—
Annual Growth	4.6%	—	—	—

2015 Year-End Financials
Return on assets: 13.1%   Cash ($ mil.): 1
Return on equity: (-7.2%)
Current ratio: 0.30

THE MEDICAL CENTER OF CENTRAL GEORGIA INC

EXECUTIVES

Ceo, Ninfa M Saunders
Coo, Mike Gilstrap
Sr V Pres-Cfo, Virgil E Cooper Jr
Cfo, Rhonda S Perry
SEC, Kenneth B Banks
Chief of Medicine, Charles Buafo
Prin, David King

LOCATIONS

HQ: THE MEDICAL CENTER OF CENTRAL GEORGIA INC
   777 HEMLOCK ST, MACON, GA 312012155
Phone: 478 633-1000
Web: WWW.MCCG.ORG

HISTORICAL FINANCIALS

Company Type: Private

Income Statement				FYE: September 30
	REVENUE ($ mil.)	NET INCOME ($ mil.)	NET PROFIT MARGIN	EMPLOYEES
09/16	660	2	0.4%	3,750
09/15	717	93	13.0%	—
09/14	683	80	11.8%	—
09/09	656	10	1.7%	—
Annual Growth	0.1%	(18.3%)	—	—

2016 Year-End Financials
Return on assets: 2.9%   Cash ($ mil.): 29
Return on equity: 0.4%
Current ratio: 3.90

THE MEDICAL COLLEGE OF WISCONSIN INC

EXECUTIVES

Ceo-Pres, John R Raymond Sr
Prin, T Michael Bolger
Exec Vice President, Joseph E Kerschner
Cfo, Marjorie Spencer
Acct Mgr, Angela M Summers
Hematology, Sara Klemm
Pediatrics, Steven Leuthner
Scientist, Candice Klug
Pediatrics, Carey Ehlert
Program Director, Cheryl Maurana
Research and Staff, Colin J Humphries
Auditors: PRICEWATERHOUSECOOPERS LLP BO

LOCATIONS

HQ: THE MEDICAL COLLEGE OF WISCONSIN INC
   8701 W WATERTOWN PLANK RD, MILWAUKEE, WI 532263548
Phone: 414 456-8296
Web: WWW.MCW.EDU

HISTORICAL FINANCIALS

Company Type: Private

Income Statement				FYE: June 30
	REVENUE ($ mil.)	NET INCOME ($ mil.)	NET PROFIT MARGIN	EMPLOYEES
06/15	1,036	107	10.4%	4,700
06/13	926	123	13.4%	—
06/11	936	63	6.8%	—
06/10	839	20	2.5%	—
Annual Growth	4.3%	39.0%	—	—

2015 Year-End Financials
Return on assets: 18.4%   Cash ($ mil.): 101
Return on equity: 10.4%
Current ratio: 0.40

THE MEDICAL UNIVERSITY OF SOUTH CAROLINA

Established in 1824 the Medical University of South Carolina (MUSC) provides Charleston with a wide range of health-related services including medical care training and research. The 50-acre medical school has 1300 faculty members and trains about 2750 full- and part-time students and residents each year through its six schools which cover medical pharmacy nursing dental health professional and graduate training. The MUSC Health organization includes the MUSC Medical Center in Charleston which has some 700 beds and includes a children's hospital and a psychiatric institute as well as the University Medical Associates physician practice organization.

Operations

MUSC has extensive research facilities and programs in areas including bioengineering and translational sciences. The university also participates in drug discovery clinical trial research programs. Its technology transfer program allows small start-up companies to license or purchase research programs that are nearing commercial development stages.

Financial Performance

MUSC is primarily funded by grants and contracts (27% of revenue) and sales and services (also 27% in revenue). State and capital appropriations account for 15% of revenue while student tuition and fees account for 13%. In fiscal 2014 (ended June) the university reported a less-than 1% rise in total revenue to $642.4 million versus $640.7 million in 2013. The modest rise was attributed to an increase in tuition earnings but slightly offset by reductions in both grants/contracts and sales/services revenues.

Strategy

The MUSC strategic plan is focused around four major expansion initiatives: innovation and technology entrepreneurial activity cross-departmental collaboration and globalization. The innovation technology and entrepreneurial goals are centered around the MUSC medical and clinical research organizations which aim to increase external funding resources through grants collaborations and technology transfer agreements. Its collaboration initiative aims to increase inter-professional relationships across its patient care education and research divisions. The university has also been expanding its educational and research facilities.

The university has a total operating budget of some $1.1 billion.

Mergers and Acquisitions

In 2018 MUSC agreed to buy four hospitals in South Carolina from Community Health Systems for an undisclosed price. The purchase will more than double the beds in the university's portfolio. The hospitals including Springs Memorial in Lancaster will be the first ever acquired by MUSC.

Company Background

MUSC was created by an act of South Carolina's General Assembly in 1824. It is historically recognized as the first medical school in the South.

EXECUTIVES

Evp Finance And Operations, Lisa P. Montgomery
Dean College Of Medicine, Raymond N. DuBois
President, David Cole
Interim Vp Medical Affairs, Bruce Elliott

Vp Clinical Operations; Ceo And Executive Director Medical Center, Patrick J. Cawley
Cio, Michael J. Caputo
Business Services Univ Press N Chas, Gordon D Jr Knight
Vice President Academic Affairs, Laura M Walters
Business Services Univ Press, Earl Reginald Harney
Director Of Respiratory Therapy, Seo Na Ji
Auditors: KPMG LLP GREENSBORO NC

LOCATIONS

HQ: THE MEDICAL UNIVERSITY OF SOUTH CAROLINA
171 ASHLEY AVE, CHARLESTON, SC 294258908
Phone: 843 792-2123
Web: WWW.MUSC.EDU

COMPETITORS

Beaufort Memorial Hospital	Grand Strand Regional Medical Center
Carolinas Hospital System	North Carolina State University
Conway Medical Center	Roper St. Francis Healthcare
Duke University	

HISTORICAL FINANCIALS

Company Type: Private

Income Statement   FYE: June 30

	REVENUE ($ mil.)	NET INCOME ($ mil.)	NET PROFIT MARGIN	EMPLOYEES
06/18	992	4	0.4%	5,500
06/17	914	9	1.0%	—
06/13	780	26	3.3%	—
06/09	836	3	0.4%	—
Annual Growth	1.9%	1.8%	—	—

2018 Year-End Financials

Return on assets: —
Return on equity: 0.4%
Current ratio: 2.50
Cash ($ mil.): 322

THE METHODIST HOSPITALS INC

The Methodist Hospitals Inc. is a not-for-profit community-based health care system that provides medical care to Indiana residents. More than 580 physicians representing some 60 specialties serve its two campus hospitals which have a combined total of about 640 beds. The system provides care for a range of specialized areas from neurology and neurosurgery oncology and home health and hospice to rehabilitation and orthopedics. The emergency department treats more than 59000 patients a year. The system also provides screenings charitable care and community education programs. The Methodist Hospitals established in 1923 reinvests all of its profits to improve patient care.

Operations

The system operates two main hospitals - Northlake in Gary and Southlake in Merrillville. The two campuses which are 14 miles apart are both full-service facilities. It also runs the Midlake Campus an outpatient facility with physician offices and other services in Gary a gastro-intestinal specialty center in Southlake and addiction treatment and inpatient Geriatric Behavioral Health Services units at its Northlake campus.

In 2012 The Methodist Hospitals invested more than $60 million in equipment technology and patient programs.

Geographic Reach

Methodist's main service areas include Lake and Porter counties extending west to the border east to LaPorte and south to Lowell.

Financial Performance

In 2012 the hospitals reported their fourth consecutive year of increasing profitability with $303 million in net revenue.

Strategy

The system keeps its not-for-profit operations profitable by investing in technology and facilities. After major upgrades at both hospitals and the installation of a state-of-the-art computer-assisted operating suite The Methodist Hospitals in 2013 opened an addiction treatment facility in Northlake and a GERD (gastroesophageal reflux disease) center in Southlake.

EXECUTIVES

Vice President Physician Integration, James Kirchner
Infection Control Director, Michelle Devries
Medical Director, Venkatrama R Galapati
Vice President And Chief Quality Officer, Vincent Sevier
Secretary, Diane Lewis
Auditors: PLANTE & MORAN PLLC SCHAUMBUR

LOCATIONS

HQ: THE METHODIST HOSPITALS INC
600 GRANT ST, GARY, IN 464026001
Phone: 219 886-4000
Web: WWW.METHODISTHOSPITALS.ORG

PRODUCTS/OPERATIONS

Selected Services

Behavioral health sciences
Bloodless medicine (surgery without blood transfusions)
Cardiovascular
　Cardiopulmonary rehabilitation
Diabetes Center
Emergency/trauma services
Home health
Maternity
NeuroScience Institute
　Gamma Knife (non-invasive brain surgery)
　Multiple Sclerosis Center
　Spine Care Center
　Stroke Center
Oncology Institute
Orthopedic services
Outpatient
Rehabilitation
Surgical weight loss/ bariatric services
Women's services
　Advanced obstetrical services
Wound Center

Selected Affiliations

American Cancer Society
American Heart Association
American Lung Association
Anthem Coronary Service Network
Edgewater Systems for Balanced Living
Gary Career Center
Gary Southshore Railcats
Indiana State Medical Association
Indiana University Northwest Campus
　Medical School
　Radiological Tech Program
　Respiratory Program
　School of Nursing
International Association for Healthcare Security and Safety
Ivy Technical Vocational School
Lakeshore Kids Immunization Fair
March of Dimes
Multiple Sclerosis Society
National Alliance for Mentally Ill (NAMI)
Purdue University Calumet Campus
　School of Nursing

Purdue University North Central Campus
　School of Nursing
Valparaiso University
　School of Nursing
Rosalind Franklin University

HISTORICAL FINANCIALS

Company Type: Private

Income Statement   FYE: December 31

	REVENUE ($ mil.)	NET INCOME ($ mil.)	NET PROFIT MARGIN	EMPLOYEES
12/17	366	8	2.2%	3,260
12/16	360	4	1.2%	—
12/15	279	1	0.6%	—
12/14	324	6	1.9%	—
Annual Growth	4.1%	9.5%	—	—

2017 Year-End Financials

Return on assets: 3.1%
Return on equity: 2.2%
Current ratio: 1.30
Cash ($ mil.): —

THE METROHEALTH SYSTEM

Helping Cleveland's metropolitan citizens stay healthy (and healing them when they aren't) is what MetroHealth System is all about. At the center of the system is MetroHealth Medical Center a level I trauma center and acute care hospital that serves as a teaching affiliate for Case Western Reserve University. Services include oncology behavioral health vascular care orthopedics burn care and pediatrics. The system also operates outpatient clinics long-term care facilities a regional rehabilitation clinic a heart and vascular center two skilled nursing centers an outpatient center and a medical helicopter program. MetroHealth is owned by Ohio's Cuyahoga County.

Operations

More than 550 primary care and specialty care physicians and more than 1700 registered nurses practice within MetroHealth. On an annual basis MetroHealth Medical Center provides care to more than 28000 inpatients and delivers 2900 newborns. More than 950000 visits are recorded in the medical center's outpatient centers along with 17500 surgical cases and 100000 emergency room visits.

The system affiliates with Akron Children's Hospital to expand access to pediatric care throughout the region. Through the partnership Akron Children's provides specialty care at MetroHealth's main campus in the areas of pediatric cardiology gastroenterology cancer and blood disorders and critical care. The MetroHealth affiliation is Akron Children's fourth location in Cuyahoga County.

Geographic Reach

MetroHealth is one of the largest most comprehensive health care providers in Northeast Ohio serving the medical needs of the Greater Cleveland area through more than 15 locations.

Strategy

As emergency rooms continue to burst at the seams more hospitals are finding ways to divert non-emergency patients to more appropriate care settings. MetroHealth has done that with its MetroExpressCare unit for residents who need to see a doctor and would probably otherwise end up at the emergency room. The family medicine physicians who see patients at MetroExpressCare

are also available to establish longer-term relationships with patients coming to MetroHealth for the first time. If the physician determines that it's a more serious problem the patient can be referred to MetroHealth's emergency department.

Having options such as MetroExpressCare available is especially important to MetroHealth because it is its region's safety net hospital. As such it receives the lion's share of uninsured patients many of whom end up in the ER because ERs are required to see all patients regardless of their ability to pay under the Emergency Medical Treatment and Active Labor Act. Being able to provide a less expensive option to those patients decreases MetroHealth's bad debt (or unpaid patient bills) and helps reduce crowding at its ER.

To serve non-ER patients Metrohealth opens a new clinic each year on average.

Mergers and Acquisitions

In 2018 MetroHealth agreed to buy Recovery Resources a not-for-profit organization that provides behavioral health and addiction services. MetroHealth will work with Recovery Resources to offer mental illness and addiction care the latter of which is very much in the nation's consciousness. In fact opioid addiction is one of MetroHealth's key areas of focus for the future. The deal will also expand MetroHealth's operations into Cuyahoga County. The purchase price was not disclosed.

Company Background

MetroHealth has been serving the medical needs of the Greater Cleveland community since 1837. It has been a major affiliate of Case Western Reserve University since 1914.

EXECUTIVES

Coo, Daniel K. Lewis
President And Ceo, Akram Boutros
Vp Marketing And Communications, Elizabeth Heller Allen, age 64
Assistant Operations Director, Sara Laskey
Chief Nursing Officer, Mavis Bechtle
Chief Medical Officer And Chief Quality Officer, Alfred F. Connors
Cfo, Craig Richmond
Vp And Associate Cio, Donald Reichert
President Medical Staff, Sherrie Dixon-Williams
Medical Director, Carolyn Dziwis
Vice President Marketing And Communications, Elizabeth Allen
Medical Director, William Cappaert
Medical Director, Michael Infeld
Medical Director, Gary Clark
Senior Vice President And Chief Of Staff, Michael Stern
Vice Chairman, J. B. Silvers
Chairman, Thomas M. McDonald
Secretary, Georgette Malcolm
Secretary, Fran Foster
Secretary Organizational Development, Tina Erickson
Auditors: RSM US LLP CLEVELAND OHIO

LOCATIONS

HQ: THE METROHEALTH SYSTEM
2500 METROHEALTH DR, CLEVELAND, OH 441091900
Phone: 216 398-6000
Web: WWW.METROHEALTH.ORG

Selected Locations
J. Glen Smith Health Center (In partnership with the City of Cleveland Cleveland)
MetroHealth Asia Town Health Center (Cleveland)
MetroHealth Beachwood Health Center (Beachwood Ohio)
MetroHealth Broadway Health Center (Cleveland)
MetroHealth Brooklyn Health Center (Cleveland)
MetroHealth Buckeye Health Center (Cleveland)

MetroHealth Center for Sleep Medicine South Campus (Independence Ohio)
MetroHealth Center for Sleep Medicine West Campus (Westlake Ohio)
MetroHealth Lakewood Health Center (Lakewood)
MetroHealth Lee-Harvard Health Center (Cleveland)
MetroHealth Medical Center Main Campus (Cleveland)
MetroHealth Old Brooklyn Campus (Cleveland)
MetroHealth Pepper Pike Health Center (Pepper Pike Ohio)
MetroHealth Premier Health Center (Westlake Ohio)
MetroHealth Rehabilitation Institute of Ohio (Cleveland)
MetroHealth Strongsville Health Center (Strongsville Ohio)
MetroHealth West 150th Health and Surgery Center (Cleveland)
MetroHealth Westlake Health Center (Westlake)
MetroHealth West Park Health Center (Cleveland)
The Elisabeth Severance Prentiss Center for Skilled Nursing Care at MetroHealth (Cleveland)
Thomas F. McCafferty Health Center (In partnership with the City of Cleveland Cleveland)

PRODUCTS/OPERATIONS

MetroHealth System Departments and Services

Aamoth Family Pediatric Wellness Center
Adolescent Clinic (Teen Health)
Advanced Gynecology (Center for Advanced Gynecology)
Advantage (MetroHealth Advantage)
Allergy & Immunology Clinic
Allergy Services (Department of Ear Nose & Throat)
Amigas Unidas Program
Anesthesiology
Art Therapy
Arthritis Center (Rheumatology)
Audiology
Bariatric Surgery (Weight Loss Surgery Program)
Behavioral Health (Child and Teen Mental Health Services)
Birth Control Procedures
Birthing Services
Bone Health and Surgery (Orthopaedics)
BREAST Program (Community Breast Cancer Outreach)
Burn Care Center
Cancer Care Center
Cardiology Cardiovascular (Heart & Vascular Center)
Center for Advanced Gynecology
Center for Behavioral Health (Child and Teen Mental Health Services)
Centers for Community Health
Center for Sleep Medicine
Cerebrovascular
Childbirth Education
Child Life and Education
Children's Health (Pediatrics)
Children's Health Specialties
Closing the Gap (MetroHealth Buckeye Health Center)
Comprehensive Care Program (Services for Children with Special Needs)
Concussion Clinic
Cosmetic Dermatology
Dentistry and Oral Health
Dermatology
Diabetes Self-Management Program
Digital Mammogram
Ear Nose and Throat (ENT/Otolaryngology)
Emergency Medicine/Emergency Department
Endocrinology
Endoscopy Suite (Gastroenterology)
ExpressCare (MetroExpressCare)
Family Medicine Clinic at MetroHealth Medical Center
Fertility Services
Freedom From Smoking
Gastroenterology and Endoscopy Suite
Genetics Clinic
Geriatrics (Senior Health & Wellness Center)
Gynecology
Gynecology Advanced (Center for Advanced Gynecology)
Gynecologic Oncology
Hand Center
Heart & Vascular Center
Hematology and Oncology (Cancer Care Center)
High-Risk Pregnancy Services
Hospital Medicine
Immunology (Allergy & Immunology Clinic)
Infectious Disease
Infertility Clinic
Infusion Therapy (Allergy & Immunology Clinic)
Internal Medicine Clinic at MetroHealth Medical Center

Internal Medicine and Pediatrics (Med-PEDS)
Kids' Health (Pediatrics
Kids' Korner Free Daycare Service at MetroHealth Medical Center
Latina Clinic: English | En espa?ol
LGBT Pride Clinic (At Thomas F. McCafferty Health Center Health Center)
Life Flight (Metro Life Flight)
Long-Term/Skilled Nursing Care
Maternal-Fetal Medicine (High-Risk Pregnancy Services)
Medicine (Department of Medicine)
Mental Health (Psychiatry)
Metro Life Flight
MetroHealth Advantage
MetroExpressCare
MetroHealth Rehabilitation Institute of Ohio
MetroHealth Select Health Plan
MetroHealth Simulation Center
Mi MetroHealth Mi Comunidad
MyChart
Neonatology Neonatal Intensive Care Unit (NICU)
Nephrology
Neurology
Neurosciences
Northeast Ohio Chapter of the National Spinal Cord Injury Association (NSCIA)
Northeast Ohio Regional Spinal Cord Injury System (NORSCIS)
Nose Ear and Throat (ENT Otolaryngology)
Nursing
Nutrition
Obstetrics
Obstetrics and Gynecology
Occupational Medicine
Oncology (Cancer Care Center)
Opthalmologic (Eye) Surgery
Oral Health (Dentistry)
Oral and Maxillofacial Surgery
Orthopaedics
Osteopathic Medicine
Otolaryngology (Ear Nose and Throat)
Pain Management
Palliative Care
Pastoral Care
Pathology
Pediatrics
Permanent Birth Control Procedures
Pharmacy
Pregnancy Resources
Pride Clinic (At Thomas F. McCafferty Health Center Health Center)
Psychiatry (Behavioral/Mental Health)
Pulmonary and Critical Care
Quality Indicators
Radiology
Rehab Rehabilitation Services (MetroHealth Rehabilitation Institute of Ohio)
Reiki
Reproductive Endocrinology and Infertility Clinic
Rheumatology (Arthritis Center)

Select Health Plan

Senior Health and Wellness Center
Simulation Center
Skeletal (Orthopaedics)
Skilled Nursing/Long-Term Care
Sleep Medicine Sleep Studies
Spanish-language Information
Special Needs Services for Children (Comprehensive Care)
Spine Center
Stroke Stroke & Cerebrovascular Center
Surgery
Throat (Otolaryngology ENT)
Teen Health
Trauma Burns and Critical Care
Travel Clinic
Urgent Care (MetroExpressCare)
Urology
Vascular Health and Surgery (Heart & Vascular Center)
Weight Loss Surgery Program (Bariatric Surgery)
X-ray (Radiology)

COMPETITORS

AdCare	Lake Health
Catholic Health Initiatives	OhioHealth
	Premier Health
Cincinnati Children's Hospital	Partners
	Robinson Memorial
Community Health	Hospital

Systems
Kettering Health
Network

The Cleveland Clinic
University Hospitals
Health System

HISTORICAL FINANCIALS
Company Type: Private

Income Statement
FYE: December 31

	REVENUE ($ mil.)	NET INCOME ($ mil.)	NET PROFIT MARGIN	EMPLOYEES
12/17	1,090	(86)	—	6,000
12/15	888	37	4.2%	—
12/13	813	41	5.1%	—
12/09	673	58	8.7%	—
Annual Growth	6.2%	—	—	—

2017 Year-End Financials
Return on assets: 5.5%
Return on equity: (-7.9%)
Current ratio: 0.90

Cash ($ mil.): 23

THE METROPOLITAN MUSEUM OF ART

You won't find too much about a certain New York baseball team at this Met. One of the world's premier cultural institutions The Metropolitan Museum of Art (also known as "the Met") acquires and exhibits artwork from around the world. Its collection of more than 2 million pieces ranges from the prehistoric era to the present day. In addition to hosting exhibits the Met loans artwork to other museums publishes books and catalogs and develops educational programs. It also displays art online. The City of New York owns the museum's 2 million-sq.-ft. complex which is located on the east side of Central Park; the museum itself owns its art collection. The Met was founded in 1870.

Operations
Highlights from the collection at the Met's Main Building on Fifth Avenue include American and European paintings and Egyptian and Islamic art. The institution's holdings also include The Cloisters museum and gardens located in Fort Tryon Park in Upper Manhattan. The Cloisters is devoted to the art and architecture of medieval Europe.

Strategy
The Met redesigned its website to optimize its marketing of the collection. New features include gallery overviews an interactive floor plan and suggested itineraries for planning museum visits.

EXECUTIVES

Chb, James R Houghton
Sr Vice President, Emily Kernan Rafferty
V Pres-Sec-Gen Couns, Sharon H Cott
Vice President, Philip T Venturino
Vice President, J Nicholas Cameron
V Pres-Com, Harold Holzer
Dir, Thomas P Campbell
Dir, Philippe De Montebello
Asst Contrl, Ryan Puzycki
Information Specialist, Archer Huntington
Information Specialist, David Aronow
Auditors: PRICEWATERHOUSECOOPERS LLP N

LOCATIONS

HQ: THE METROPOLITAN MUSEUM OF ART
1000 5TH AVE, NEW YORK, NY 100280198
Phone: 212 535-7710
Web: WWW.METMUSEUM.ORG

PRODUCTS/OPERATIONS

Selected Curatorial Departments
American Decorative Arts
Ancient Near Eastern Art
Arts of Africa Oceania and the Americas
Asian Art
Costume Institute
Drawings and Prints
Egyptian Art
European Paintings
Greek and Roman Art
Islamic Art
Medieval Art
Modern Art
Musical Instruments
Photographs

COMPETITORS

American Museum of Natural History
Brooklyn Museum
Museum of the City of New York
Smithsonian

HISTORICAL FINANCIALS
Company Type: Private

Income Statement
FYE: June 30

	REVENUE ($ mil.)	NET INCOME ($ mil.)	NET PROFIT MARGIN	EMPLOYEES
06/18	369	237	64.4%	2,372
06/16	379	(247)	—	—
06/15	361	(7)	—	—
Annual Growth	0.7%	—	—	—

2018 Year-End Financials
Return on assets: 8.6%
Return on equity: 64.4%
Current ratio: 0.10

Cash ($ mil.): 34

THE MIDDLE TENNESSEE ELECTRIC MEMBERSHIP CORPORATION

Middle Tennessee Electric Membership Corporation's service territory is smack dab in the middle of Tennessee. The utility cooperative distributes electricity to 190750 residential and business customers (member/owners) in four counties (Cannon Rutherford Williamson and Wilson) via more than 10470 miles of power lines connected to 34 electric distribution substations. Middle Tennessee Electric purchases its power supply from the Tennessee Valley Authority. The corporation is Tennessee's largest electric cooperative and the sixth largest in the US.

Geographic Reach
The cooperative serves customers in Cannon Rutherford Williamson and Wilson counties. According to a US Census report three of Tennessee's five fastest growing counties (Rutherford Williamson and Wilson) are in Middle Tennessee Electric's service area which also includes three of Tennessee's top five fastest-growing cities — LaVergne Smyrna and Franklin.

Strategy
To harness green energy as a way to limit fossil fuel power sources and reduce carbon emissions the utility cooperative is installing solar panels for customers. In 2012 the company completed a 850-panel solar field next to the City of Franklin's water plant. That year Middle Tennessee Electric had 70 solar projects operating across its service area and 30 more in the planning stages.

Company Background
Middle Tennessee Electric was formed in 1936 as part of a national rural electrification push.

EXECUTIVES

Vice President Of Information Systems, John Florida
Vice President Of Operations, Keith Thomason
Vice President Of Information Systems, Gray Bateman
Secretary Treasurer And Director, Will Jordan
Auditors: WINNETT ASSOCIATES PLLC SHELB

LOCATIONS

HQ: THE MIDDLE TENNESSEE ELECTRIC MEMBERSHIP CORPORATION
555 NEW SALEM HWY, MURFREESBORO, TN 371293390
Phone: 615 890-9762
Web: WWW.MTEMC.COM

HISTORICAL FINANCIALS
Company Type: Private

Income Statement
FYE: June 30

	REVENUE ($ mil.)	NET INCOME ($ mil.)	NET PROFIT MARGIN	EMPLOYEES
06/16	542	10	1.9%	410
06/13	524	27	5.3%	—
06/12	510	19	3.8%	—
06/11	1,841	0	—	—
Annual Growth	—	781.4%	—	—

2016 Year-End Financials
Return on assets: 10.7%
Return on equity: 1.9%
Current ratio: 1.90

Cash ($ mil.): 74

THE MOSES H CONE MEMORIAL HOSPITAL

EXECUTIVES

Ceo, Terry Akin
Exec V Pres-Cfo, Jeff Jones
Coo, Judy Schanel
Trustee, William V Nutt
Chief of Medicine, Vanessa Haygood
Director, Edee Merritt
Director, Sheryl Booth
Manager, Christine Brannock
Information Specialist, Dana Dark
Manager of Pharmacy, Deanne Brooks
Director of Facilities, Ed Gillespie
Auditors: DELOITTE & TOUCHE LLP RALEIG

LOCATIONS

HQ: THE MOSES H CONE MEMORIAL HOSPITAL
1200 N ELM ST, GREENSBORO, NC 274011020
Phone: 336 832-7000
Web: WWW.CONEHEALTH.COM

HISTORICAL FINANCIALS
Company Type: Private

Income Statement
FYE: September 30

	REVENUE ($ mil.)	NET INCOME ($ mil.)	NET PROFIT MARGIN	EMPLOYEES
09/17	1,836	142	7.7%	12,000
09/16	1,678	49	3.0%	—
09/15	1,545	(27)	—	—
09/14	1,403	78	5.6%	—
Annual Growth	9.4%	22.1%	—	—

2017 Year-End Financials
Return on assets: 4.3%   Cash ($ mil.): 57
Return on equity: 7.7%
Current ratio: 0.50

THE MOSES H CONE MEMORIAL HOSPITAL OPERATING CORPORATION

Cone Health (formerly Moses Cone Health System) serves patients in central North Carolina through five acute and specialty careA hospitals with a total of more than 1000 beds. Its facilities include Moses H. Cone Memorial Hospital Wesley LongA Community Hospital Annie Penn Hospital Moses Cone Behavioral Health Center and the Women's Hospital of Greensboro.A Specialty services include rehabilitation cancer treatment neurology and heart and vascular care. The health care provider also operatesA outpatientA clinics andA nursing homes. Founded in 1911; its flagship hospitalA was named after textile giant Cone Denim's founder Moses Cone (it was started in Cone's honor by his wife Bertha Cone).

Strategy

Cone Health is expanding through strategic partnerships and organic growth. In October 2012 the five-hospital system entered into a 10-year management services agreement with Carolinas HealthCare SystemA the largest health-care system in the Carolinas and the second-largest public system in the US. Hospital officials expect the moveA willA improve its purchasing and negotiating power while providing management expertise to Cone Health's hospitals. (Under the terms of the agreement the ownership and direct management of Cone Health remains local but the hospital's CEO CFO and COO all became employees of Carolinas HealthCare System.) The management agreement with Carolinas HealthCare System is not expected to affect Cone Health's pending merger with North Carolina-based Alamance Regional Medical Center. The intent of the merger announced in late 2011 isA to broadenA the health system'sA service area and create efficiencies for the network. The merger of Cone Health and 210-bed Alamance is subject to antitrust review by the Federal Trade Commission.

Also in 2012 Cone Health embarked on a $7.7 million renovation of its Annie Penn Hospital (slated for completion in fall 2014). It also opened a new emergency department at Wesley Long Hospital that year.

EXECUTIVES

Executive Vice President Of Health Services, Tim Clontz
Vice President Fund Development, William Porter
Senior Executive Assistant To Mickey W. Foster Mha President Moses Cone Hospital; Senior Vice President, Michelle King
Vice President Service Line Administrator, Anne Macner
Executive Vice President Strategic Development, Jim Roskelly
Vice President Nursing Services, Susan Pedaline
Director Of Nursing, Mona Easter
Director Of Nursing Services, Marjorie Jenkins
Vice President Of Marketing, Tom Dorle
Vice President Heart And Vascular Services Imaging Services, Rich Lundy
Assistant Treasurer, Sally Hammond

LOCATIONS

HQ: THE MOSES H CONE MEMORIAL HOSPITAL OPERATING CORPORATION
1200 N ELM ST, GREENSBORO, NC 274011020
Phone: 336 832-7000
Web: WWW.CONEHEALTH.COM

PRODUCTS/OPERATIONS

Selected Operations
Annie Penn Hospital
Cone Health Behavioral Health Hospital
Cone Health Cancer Center
Cone Health Cancer Center at Annie Penn Hospital
Cone Health Cancer Center at Randolph Hospital
Cone Health Center for Pain and Rehabilitative Medicine
Cone Health Developmental and Psychological Center
Cone Health Heart and Vascular Center
Cone Health MedCenter High Point
Cone Health MedCenter Kernersville
Cone Health Nutrition and Diabetes Management Center
Cone Health Occupational Health Services
Cone Health Outpatient Rehabilitation
Cone Health Sleep Disorders Center
Cone Health Sports Medicine Centers
Cone Health Urgent Care Center
Cone Health Wound Care and Hyperbaric Center
HealthServe Community Health Clinic
LeBauer HealthCare
LeBauer HeartCare
Moses Cone Surgery Center
North Elam Medical Plaza
Pediatric Sub-Specialists of Greensboro
Penn Nursing Center
Radiology/Imaging Services
Reidsville Community Physicians
Smith-McMichael Cancer Center at Morehead Hospital
The Clinic at Walmart-Burlington
The Moses H. Cone Memorial Hospital
Triad Cardiac and Thoracic Surgery
Vascular and Vein Specialists of Greensboro
Wesley Long Hospital
Wesley Long Surgery Center
Women's Hospital

COMPETITORS

Alamance Regional Medical Center	High Point Regional Health System
Carolinas HealthCare System	Morehead Memorial Hospital
Cumberland County Hospital System	Novant Health
	Rex Healthcare
Danville Regional Medical Center	Tenet Healthcare
	UNC Hospitals
Duke University Health System	WakeMed
FirstHealth of the Carolinas	

HISTORICAL FINANCIALS

Company Type: Private

Income Statement   FYE: September 30

	REVENUE ($ mil.)	NET INCOME ($ mil.)	NET PROFIT MARGIN	EMPLOYEES
09/18*	2,001	102	5.1%	536
12/17	481	37	7.7%	—
09/16	1,678	62	3.8%	—
09/13	893	(14)	—	—
Annual Growth	17.5%	—	—	—

*Fiscal year change

2018 Year-End Financials
Return on assets: 3.6%   Cash ($ mil.): 62
Return on equity: 5.1%
Current ratio: 0.50

THE NATURE CONSERVANCY

The Nature Conservancy is a nonprofit dedicated to preserving the diversity of Earth's wildlife by saving some 120 million acres of land 5000 miles of rivers and 100 marine areas in every US state and more than 35 countries worldwide. The organization boasts more than 1 million members. The Nature Conservancy originally carried out its mission by simply buying land but it has evolved to incorporate other methods to further its goals. In addition to land acquisition the organization partners with government corporate and private entities to reduce harmful use of natural areas to create conservation-friendly public policy and to increase conservation funding. The Nature Conservancy was founded in 1951.

Geographic Reach

Based in Arlington Virginia The Nature Conservancy operates in more than 35 countries worldwide and in all 50 US states. The organization works in Africa the Asia-Pacific region the Caribbean Europe and the Americas.

Financial Performance

The Nature Conservancy has posted two years of increased support and revenue after a dropoff in 2012. In 2014 it marshaled revenue of $1.1 billion up 17% from 2013. Dues and contributions were 28% higher in 2014 rising to $560 million. Investmetn income more than doubled to $235 million in 2014. The nonprofit had 24% less in land sales and gifts in 2014. Program efficiency remained strong at 73%.

Dues and Contributions from individuals represent about 50% The Nature Conservancy's total support and revenue. Land sales and gifts contribute nearly 12%.

Strategy

In 2014 The Nature Conservancy completed a five-year plan that put it on financially stable and sustainable ground. To expand its impact it launched NatureVest to source low-cost 'impact capital.' Such a project in Kenya its Livestock to Markets program helps communities get a better price for their cattle while managing grazing lands that also support wildlife.

The nonprofit uses about 75% of its funds on projects. Most of its donations come from individual contributors. The Nature Conservancy also makes money from the sale and lease of lands. The group is unapologetic about its pragmatic science-based approach to conservation. It has angered fellow environmentalists in the past because of its willingness to partner with governments and businesses as well as to just pay people to leave land alone. However the Nature Conservancy says its non-confrontational approach that is rooted in science has actually enabled its success.

In early 2014 The Nature Conservancy purchased nearly 120000 acres of forest rivers and wildlife habitat in the Lower Blackfoot River watershed of Montana for $85 million.

EXECUTIVES

Coo, Lois E. Quam, age 57
President And Ceo, Mark R. Tercek
Evp, Peter Wheeler
Cfo And Chief Administrative Officer, Stephen (Steve) Howell
Chief External Affairs Officer, Glenn T. Prickett
Evp Latin America, Joseph (Joe) Keenan
Regional Managing Director Africa, David Banks
Regional Managing Director Asia Pacific, Charles E. Bedford

Director California, Mark Burget
Evp Global Conservation Initiatives, William (Bill) Ginn
Senior Science Advisor, Peter Kareiva
Chief Conservation Officer, Brian McPeek
Chief External Affairs Officer, Glenn Pricket
Global Managing Director Lands, Justin Adams
Chief Development Officer, Jim Asp
Global Managing Director Water, Giulio Boccaletti
Global Managing Director Oceans, Maria Damanaki
Global Managing Director Cities, Pascal Mittermaier
Regional Managing Director Latin American Region, Aurelio Ramos
Managing Director Public Policy, Lynn Scarlett
Acting Chief Scientist, Heather Tallis
Chief Of Staff And Acting Chief Marketing Officer, Janine M. Wilkin
Vice President, Laurel Mayer
Marketing And Government Relations, Shannon Crownover
Director Of Government Relations, Susan Donovan
Vice Chairman, James E. (Jim) Rogers
Chairman, Thomas J. Tierney
Board Director, Teresa Beck
Auditors: PRICEWATERHOUSECOOPERS LLP MC

LOCATIONS

HQ: THE NATURE CONSERVANCY
4245 FAIRFAX DR STE 100, ARLINGTON, VA 222031650
Phone: 703 841-5300
Web: WWW.NATURE.ORG

Selected Areas of Operation
Africa
Australia
Asia & the Pacific Islands
Caribbean
Central America
Europe
North America
South America

PRODUCTS/OPERATIONS

2014 Dues & Contributions

	%
Individuals	37
Foundations	28
Bequests	23
Other organizations	6
Corporations	6
Total	**100**

HISTORICAL FINANCIALS
Company Type: Private

Income Statement				FYE: June 30
	REVENUE ($ mil.)	NET INCOME ($ mil.)	NET PROFIT MARGIN	EMPLOYEES
06/17	1,143	306	26.8%	3,400
06/16	803	(8)	—	—
06/14	949	201	21.2%	—
06/13	859	106	12.4%	—
Annual Growth	**7.4%**	**30.1%**	**—**	**—**

2017 Year-End Financials
Return on assets: 10.2%   Cash ($ mil.): 55
Return on equity: 26.8%
Current ratio: —

THE NEBRASKA MEDICAL CENTER

Cornhuskers take note: If health care is what you seek The Nebraska Medical Center aims to please. The not-for-profit health system provides tertiary care at two campuses in Omaha University Hospital and Clarkson Hospital that collectively house about 680 licensed beds. The medical center the largest health care facility in Nebraska is the primary teaching facility of the University of Nebraska Medical Center (UNMC). It also serves as a designated trauma facility for eastern Nebraska and western Iowa and provides highly specialized care including organ transplantation. Its Clarkson West Medical Center campus houses outpatient surgery facilities an emergency room and doctors' offices.

Operations
The system has more than 1000 physicians. In 2013 it had some 51000 emergency department visits more than 24500 inpatient admissions and about 428000 outpatient visits.

In addition to University Hospital and Clarkson Hospital Nebraska Medical Center operates a network of 40 specialty and primary care clinics in and around Omaha. The health system's Centers of Excellence include its Cancer Center Heart Center Neurological Sciences Transplant Center and Women's Health.

Geographic Reach
In addition to serving the residents of Omaha the Nebraska Medical Center serves as a designated trauma facility for patients in eastern Nebraska and western Iowa.

Strategy
Like most other health care providers the Nebraska Medical Center is looking for ways to cut costs in the face of decreasing reimbursements from federal payers (such as Medicare and Medicaid) and as pressure from health care reform mounts and hospitals are required to implement expensive digital record-keeping and physician order entry systems. One way that Nebraska Medical Center has sought to reduce its expenses it by signing up with companies such as Medassets to receive sourcing and group purchasing (GPO) medical device and clinical consulting services for items used most by its physicians and for its pharmacy services.

The medical center and its sponsoring university are looking to expand its medical facilities to keep pace with a growing and aging population. UNMC is developing a new cancer center at the medical center's Omaha campus. Plans include three facilities - a multidisciplinary outpatient clinic a 98-lab research tower and a hospital tower with 108 beds dedicated to oncology patients. The project (estimated to cost $370 million) is expected to create 1200 new jobs by 2020 and pump $100 million annually into Nebraska's economy.

The system is also working with UNMC to add a new outpatient center to the university's midtown campus. The Lauritzen Outpatient Center will feature 10 operating rooms including four dedicated to opthalmic surgical procedures.

EXECUTIVES

Respiratory Therapy Director, Marlon Mcgough
Auditors: KPMG LLP OMAHA NE

LOCATIONS

HQ: THE NEBRASKA MEDICAL CENTER
987400 NEBRASKA MED CTR, OMAHA, NE 681980001
Phone: 402 552-2000
Web: WWW.NEBRASKAMEDICALCENTER.COM

PRODUCTS/OPERATIONS

Selected Services
Cancer Center
General Health Services
Heart and Vascular Services
Neurological Sciences
Transplantation

COMPETITORS

BryanLGH Medical Center
CHI Health
Children's Hospital & Medical Center
Fremont Area Medical Center
Madonna Rehabilitation Hospital
Methodist Health System
Saint Elizabeth Regional Medical Center

HISTORICAL FINANCIALS
Company Type: Private

Income Statement				FYE: June 30
	REVENUE ($ mil.)	NET INCOME ($ mil.)	NET PROFIT MARGIN	EMPLOYEES
06/17	1,389	74	5.4%	4,100
06/16	1,119	60	5.4%	—
Annual Growth	**24.1%**	**22.1%**	**—**	**—**

2017 Year-End Financials
Return on assets: 6.3%   Cash ($ mil.): 67
Return on equity: 5.4%
Current ratio: 1.10

THE NEW SCHOOL

When James Lipton asks you what your favorite swear word is you know you've made it. The New School's drama department (formerly called The Actor's Studio) was made famous by the cable show Inside the Actors Studio which features Lipton interviewing movie and television stars. TheA school offers degrees in theater for playwriting directing and acting and has taught "Method" acting to grads such as Marlon Brando and Robert De Niro. It is also home to Parsons The New School for Design and has schools devoted to general studies liberal arts social research management and urban policy and music. More than 10500A traditional students andA 5600 continuing education students are enrolled at The New School.

Operations
The New School offers more than 90 degree and diploma programs and majors to a population of undergraduate and graduate students who come from all 50 states and more than 100 foreign countries (about one-quarter of its students hail from international locations). It boasts small class sizes and a student-teacher ratio of about 10:1.

The New School for Public Engagement is the university's founding division and is composed of five schools: Milano School of International Affairs Management and Urban Policy; School of Language Learning and Teaching; School of Media Studies; School of Undergraduate Studies; and School of Writing. It has since added six divisions: Drama Jazz Lang Mannes Parsons and Social Research.

Financial Performance

The New School's 2011 revenue grew by more than 5% vs. 2010. Net income increased 13% over the same period.

Strategy

Parsons' new academic center in Paris is slated to open in fall 2013. The Paris site will offer students a program that addresses the global nature of contemporary art and design practice and reflects Europe's culture and philosophy.

The New School was founded in 1919 by a group ofA university professors and intellectualsA in New York City as place for students wanting to explore their creativity and engage in deep thought while studying liberal arts. Dozens of years later The New School has gained a reputation for its unconventional teaching methods as well as for being the home of many world-renowned institutes including the think tank The World Policy Institute. It also hosts the annual National Book Awards which has helped establish the careers of some ofA the country'sA most recognized authors including Richard Powers and Jonathan Franzen.

EXECUTIVES

Vice President For Finance And Business And Treasurer, Steve Stabile
Deputy Provost And Senior Vice President For Academic Affairs, Bryna Sanger
Assistant Vice President, Irwin Kroot
Vice President Humran Resource, Jaber Farida
Vice President And General Manager Canadian Operations, Miriam Aronoff
Associate Vice President, Monique Rinere
Auditors: KPMG LLP NEW YORK NY

LOCATIONS

HQ: THE NEW SCHOOL
66 W 12TH ST, NEW YORK, NY 100118871
Phone: 212 229-5600
Web: WWW.NEWSCHOOL.EDU

PRODUCTS/OPERATIONS

Selected Schools
Eugene Lang College The New School for Liberal Arts
Mannes College The New School for Music
Milano The New School for Management and Urban Policy
The New School for Drama
The New School for General Studies
The New School for Jazz and Contemporary Music
The New School for Public Engagement
The New School for Social Research
Parsons The New School for Design

HISTORICAL FINANCIALS

Company Type: Private

Income Statement				FYE: June 30
	REVENUE ($ mil.)	NET INCOME ($ mil.)	NET PROFIT MARGIN	EMPLOYEES
06/18	411	28	7.0%	855
06/16	370	(15)	—	—
06/15	354	34	9.6%	—
06/14	332	82	24.8%	—
Annual Growth	5.5%	(23.0%)	—	—

2018 Year-End Financials

Return on assets: 17.3% Cash ($ mil.): 6
Return on equity: 7.0%
Current ratio: —

THE NEW YORK AND PRESBYTERIAN HOSPITAL

The New York and Presbyterian Hospital is a learned institution: The not-for-profit hospital is affiliated with both the Columbia University College of Physicians & Surgeons and the Weill Cornell Medical College of Cornell University. Known as NewYork-Presbyterian Hospital the organization includes two major medical centers Columbia University Medical Center and Weill Cornell Medical Center which conduct educational and research programs in partnership with the universities. The two facilities combined have about 2600 beds and offer specialized programs for burns digestive diseases pediatrics women's health and other conditions. NewYork-Presbyterian Hospital is part of the NewYork-Presbyterian Healthcare System.

Operations

Altogether the NewYork-Presbyterian Hospital campuses handle some 2 million patient visits each year (both on an inpatient and outpatient basis) including inpatient admissions and more than 310000 emergency room visits and about 15000 births. The facilities employ a total of more than 6500 physicians including residents and fellows. NewYork-Presbyterian Hospital provides more than $108 million in charity and community care services each year.

Geographic Reach

In addition to its flagship campuses NewYork-Presbyterian/Columbia and NewYork-Presbyterian/Weill Cornell NewYork-Presbyterian Hospital operates two small community hospitals in Manhattan — the Allen Hospital and the Lower Manhattan Hospital — and an inpatient mental health facility (the Westchester Division). The broader NewYork-Presbyterian Healthcare System operates facilities in other areas of New York as well as in New Jersey and Connecticut. The NewYork-Presbyterian Hospital/Columbia campus houses the Morgan Stanley Children's Hospital as well as other specialist units.

Sales and Marketing

Medicare and Medicaid recipients account for more than 60% of NewYork-Presbyterian Hospital's patients. Commercial managed care organizations and insurance firms as well as self-pay customers account for the rest.

Financial Performance

NewYork-Presbyterian Hospital's revenue in fiscal 2015 totaled $4.8 billion.

Strategy

As the health care landscape has become increasingly complex and competitive especially with changing regulations and the push to provide more integrated patient care NewYork-Presbyterian Hospital has made some major organizational changes. Chief among its goals is to provide a patient-centered model of care creating a system that can easily be accessed by its patient consumers. It recently established its Community and Population Health division which includes community programs and initiatives ambulatory care network sites and the management of its new Accountable Care Organization.

It has also expanded beyond its former base of Manhattan in order to provide a regional system of care. For example the system took ownership of former affiliate Brooklyn Methodist in early 2017 with the intention of investing in the hospital's development; the move falls in line with its strategy of providing integrated care for communities particularly in light of a number of recent hospital failures in the borough.

Mergers and Acquisitions

New York Methodist Hospital (now NewYork-Presbyterian Brooklyn Methodist Hospital) was added to the organization in early 2017. Brooklyn Methodist will gain funds for a new $400 million ambulatory care building as part of the new relationship.

Company Background

NewYork-Presbyterian Hospital was formed through the 1998 merger of the New York Hospital (founded in 1771) and the Presbyterian Hospital (founded in 1868). New York Hospital was known for advancing care in areas including women's health and surgery while the Presbyterian Hospital was known for its pediatric division and its cancer center.

EXECUTIVES

Vice President Risk Management And Associate General Counsel, John Campano
Vice President Capital Planning And Development, Ellie Dalton
Evp Cfo And Treasurer, Phyllis R. Lantos
President And Ceo, Steven J. (Steve) Corwin
Chief Nursing Officer; Vp Patient Services Newyork-presbyterian/columbia, Wilhelmina Manzano
Vp Medical Affairs, Laura L. Forese
Svp And Chief Medical Officer, Richard S. Liebowitz
Cio, William Lee
Evp Chief Legal Officer And General Counsel, Maxine Frank
Director Of Nursing, Laurie Walsh
Finance Vice President, Ana Arroyo
Director Of Health Information, Deborah Forde
Information Security Vice President, Howard Goldman
Vice President Compensation Benefits And Hris, Mary Falkowitz
Senior Vice President And Chief, Karen S Westervelt
Vice President And Chief Learning, Andrea Procaccino
Operations Vice President, Elizabeth Vega
Vice President Finance, William Farrell
Finance Vice President, Noemi Lopez
Senior Vice President And Chief Quality, Henry Ting
Director Of Pharmacy, Ralph Lizo
Vice President Of Business Planning, Craig Evans
Vice President Finance, Lugeion Y Carter
Chairman, Frank A. Bennack, age 85
President Ceo And Trustee, Herbert Pardes, age 84
Assistant Treasurer, Sedare Coradine

LOCATIONS

HQ: THE NEW YORK AND PRESBYTERIAN HOSPITAL
525 E 68TH ST, NEW YORK, NY 100654870
Phone: 212 746-5454
Web: WWW.NEWYORK-PRESBYTERIANHOSPITAL.ORG

PRODUCTS/OPERATIONS

2016 Patient Mix

	% of total
Medicare Managed	9
Medicare FFS	22
Medicaid Managed	23
Medicaid FFS	7
Managed Care and Other	37
Self-Pay	1
Workers Comp	1
Total	**100**

Selected Services
Cancer
Children's Health
Digestive

Geriatrics
Heart
Mens Health
Neuroscience
Orthopedic
Psychiatry
Rehabilitation Medicine
Transplant
Vascular
Womens Health

COMPETITORS

Ascension Health
 Beth Israel Medical
  Center
Bronx-Lebanon Hospital
Catholic Healthcare
 System
Continuum Health
 Partners
Lenox Hill Hospital
Lutheran HealthCare
Maimonides Medical
 Center

MediSys Health Network
Memorial
 Sloan-Kettering
Montefiore Medical
New York City Health
 and Hospitals
Northwell Health
Winthrop-University
 Hospital
Yale New Haven Health
 System

HISTORICAL FINANCIALS

Company Type: Private

Income Statement				FYE: December 31
	REVENUE ($ mil.)	NET INCOME ($ mil.)	NET PROFIT MARGIN	EMPLOYEES
12/17	5,616	762	13.6%	23,709
12/16	4,935	496	10.1%	—
12/14	4,206	197	4.7%	—
12/13	4,264	595	14.0%	—
Annual Growth	7.1%	6.4%	—	—

2017 Year-End Financials

Return on assets: 9.0%   Cash ($ mil.): 1,725
Return on equity: 13.6%
Current ratio: 2.10

THE NEW YORK PUBLIC LIBRARY

EXECUTIVES

Ceo, Anthony Marx
Prin, Davi Offensent
Prin, Kathleen Riegelhaupt
Manager, Karen Van Westering
Manager, Denise Medina
Director, Craig Senecal
Teacher, Laverne Clark
Librarian, Ling Rice
Coordinator, Richard Foster

LOCATIONS

HQ: THE NEW YORK PUBLIC LIBRARY
 5TH AVE & 42ND ST, NEW YORK, NY 10018
Phone: 212 592-7400
Web: WWW.NYPL.ORG

PRODUCTS/OPERATIONS

Research Centers
Humanities and Social Sciences Library
The New York Public Library for the Performing Arts
Schomburg Center for Research in Black Culture
Science Industry and Business Library

HISTORICAL FINANCIALS

Company Type: Private

Income Statement				FYE: June 30
	REVENUE ($ mil.)	NET INCOME ($ mil.)	NET PROFIT MARGIN	EMPLOYEES
06/17	341	25	7.3%	3,645
06/16	300	(93)	—	—
06/09	362	(166)	—	—
Annual Growth	(0.8%)	—	—	—

2017 Year-End Financials

Return on assets: 26.4%   Cash ($ mil.): 150
Return on equity: 7.3%
Current ratio: 0.30

THE NEWTRON GROUP L L C

Some contractors bomb but The Newtron Group keeps on ticking. Through subsidiaries The Newtron Group offers a variety of industrial electrical and other specialty construction and contracting services nationwide. Services include instrumentation and control systems installation and maintenance; fiber optic installation and testing; industrial pipe and panel fabrication; aviation services; and electrical heat tracing. Newtron serves clients in such industries as refining power generation mining petrochemical and gas transmission. Subsidiaries include electrical contractor Triad Electric & Controls fiber optics firm Com-Net Services and NGI National Constructors. Founded in 1973 The Newtron Group serves the US from offices in California Louisiana Mississippi and Texas.

Operations
The Newtron Group held around a dozen subsidiary companies as of early 2016 with five under the Newtron brand including Newtron Beaumont which constructs and maintains electrical and instrumentation systems; Newtron Mechanical which deals with mechanical systems; Newtron Electrical Services which works with electrical meters breaker box replacement parking lot light and other electrical systems.

Other subsidiaries include: NGI National Constructors which constructs union projects; Triad Electric & Controls an open-shop contractor for electrical and instrumentation projects; and Executive Aviation Inc. a full-service Fixed Base Operator (FBO).

Geographic Reach
The Baton Rouge-based Newtron Group works on projects across the contiguous US from offices in California and on the coasts of Louisiana Mississippi and Texas.

Sales and Marketing
The group serves primarily the refining petrochemical power generation pulp and paper mining and metals and gas transmission industries (as of early 2016).

Strategy
Focusing on six core industries The Newtron Group and its subsidiaries continued in 2016 to work on projects ranging from small-capital projects and maintenance contracts up to multi-million dollar grassroots projects.

EXECUTIVES

Vp Marketing, Duff Schempf
President, Glen Redd
Auditors: HANNIS T BOURGEOIS LLP BATON

LOCATIONS

HQ: THE NEWTRON GROUP L L C
 8183 W EL CAJON DR, BATON ROUGE, LA 708158093
Phone: 225 927-8921
Web: WWW.THENEWTRONGROUP.COM

PRODUCTS/OPERATIONS

Selected Subsidiaries
Com-Net Services Inc. (fiber optics)
Executive Aviation Inc. (hangar space fuel supplies)
Newtron Inc. (electrical and instrumentation)
Newtron Heat Trace (industrial heat tracing)
Newtron Mechanical (industrial mechanics)
Triad Electric and Controls Inc. (electrical and instrumentation)
Triad Control Systems Inc. (control panel fabrication)

Selected Industries
Cement
Electronics
Food processing
Gas transmission
Metals and mining
Petrochemical
Pharmaceuticals
Power generation
Pulp and paper
Refining
Semiconductors
Waste treatment

COMPETITORS

EMCOR
 Fisk Electric
 Industrial Specialty
  Contractors

Jelec
MMR Group
Motor City Electric
Pike Corporation

HISTORICAL FINANCIALS

Company Type: Private

Income Statement				FYE: June 30
	REVENUE ($ mil.)	NET INCOME ($ mil.)	NET PROFIT MARGIN	EMPLOYEES
06/18	489	0	—	3,500
06/17	450	0	—	—
06/16	436	0	—	—
06/15	430	0	—	—
Annual Growth	4.4%	—	—	—

2018 Year-End Financials

Return on assets: 1.4%   Cash ($ mil.): 20
Return on equity: —
Current ratio: 1.80

THE NORWALK HOSPITAL ASSOCIATION

EXECUTIVES

Ceo, Daniel Debarba Jr
Ceo-President, Jeffrey Cole
Chb, Diane M Allison
Treas, Andrew J Whittingham
SEC, Barbara Butler
Chief of The Med Staff, Dr Steve Michaelson
It Mgr, Eric Jostrand
Internal Med, Denise K Lautenbach
Internal Med, Elizabeth J Goman
Neurology, James L Thompson
Internal Med, Rahim Rahimyar

LOCATIONS

HQ: THE NORWALK HOSPITAL ASSOCIATION
34 MAPLE ST, NORWALK, CT 068503894
Phone: 203 852-2000
Web: WWW.NORWALKHOSPITAL.ORG

HISTORICAL FINANCIALS
Company Type: Private

Income Statement				FYE: September 30
	REVENUE ($ mil.)	NET INCOME ($ mil.)	NET PROFIT MARGIN	EMPLOYEES
09/15	355	39	11.2%	1,660
09/14	323	37	11.6%	—
09/13	351	(4)	—	—
09/12	388	28	7.4%	—
Annual Growth	(2.9%)	11.2%	—	—

2015 Year-End Financials
Return on assets: 7.3%   Cash ($ mil.): 43
Return on equity: 11.2%
Current ratio: 1.00

THE ORANGE COUNTY PUBLIC SCHOOL DISTRICT

EXECUTIVES

Superintendent, Barbara Jenkins
Maintenance Staff, Damaris Vazquez
Teacher, Danielle Green
Coordinator, David Garver
Purchasing Agent, David M Shames
Coordinator, Debbie Pappas
Executive of Information Techn, Giovanna Bravo
Academic Advisor, Jill Kilsgaard
Coordinator, Jody Bernier
Administrative Secretary, Lashonda Moore
Administrative Secretary, Lashonda West

LOCATIONS

HQ: THE ORANGE COUNTY PUBLIC SCHOOL DISTRICT
445 W AMELIA ST, ORLANDO, FL 328011128
Phone: 407 317-3200
Web: WWW.OCPS.NET

HISTORICAL FINANCIALS
Company Type: Private

Income Statement				FYE: June 30
	REVENUE ($ mil.)	NET INCOME ($ mil.)	NET PROFIT MARGIN	EMPLOYEES
06/18	2,506	107	4.3%	19,858
06/17	2,341	(25)	—	—
06/16	2,263	145	6.4%	—
Annual Growth	5.2%	(14.1%)	—	—

2018 Year-End Financials
Return on assets: 3.7%   Cash ($ mil.): 624
Return on equity: 4.3%
Current ratio: —

THE PENNSYLVANIA HOSPITAL OF THE UNIVERSITY OF PENNSYLVANIA HEALTH SYSTEM

Early to bed early to rise may have made Ben Franklin healthy wealthy and wise. But for those not so healthy he (along with Dr. Thomas Bond) found it wise to establish Pennsylvania Hospital the nation's first such medical institution. The hospital is now a part of the University of Pennsylvania Health System (UPHS) and offers a comprehensive range of medical surgical and diagnostic services to the Philadelphia County area. Housing some 520 beds Pennsylvania Hospital offers specialized care in areas such as orthopedics vascular surgery neurosurgery and obstetrics; it is also a leading teaching hospital and a center for clinical research.

Operations
Pennsylvania Hospital has an average of about 29000 inpatient admissions per year including 5200 births as well as 115000 outpatient and emergency care visits. The medical center has more than 800 physicians on its medical staff. In addition to its extensive medical care services the company conducts medical training programs through its relationship with the University of Pennsylvania School of Medicine. Medical and clinical research programs are conducted with the school and with other research entities including government agencies. The hospital also collaborates with other UPHS entities including the Penn Presbyterian Medical Center and the Hospital of the University of Pennsylvania. The medical center also provides educational services across academic programs inlcuding Clinical Psychology Internship Program Medicine OB/GYN Pathology Radiology Sports Medicine Fellowship Surgery and Vascular Surgery Fellowship.

Financial Performance
For the fiscal year 2014 (ended June 30) Pennsylvania Hospital's revenues increased by 8.4% with a 9% increase in net patient service revenues 94% of total revenues); offset by a 1% decline in other revenues.

The company's net loss for the year decreased by 38% due to higher revenues and a decline in employee benefits paid.

Strategy
To improve the quality of care in the region UPHS is expanding specialist programs at its facilities.

In 2014 Pennsylvania Hospital opened its new Well Mother & Baby Unit which will represent Philadelphia's first all-private maternity suite unit. The new unit is part of Pennsylvania Hospital's $61 million long-range facility master plan and expands the company's offerings by providing private rooms to all of their maternity patients along with an array of obstetrical services from conception to discharge from the hospital following childbirth.

In 2013 UPHS expanded the orthopedic surgery program at Pennsylvania Hospital. The medical center is also enhancing services in fields including stroke care and women's health.

Company Background

The hospital was founded in 1751 by Benjamin Franklin and Dr. Thomas Bond to care for the sick-poor and insane of Philadelphia.

EXECUTIVES

Vice President, Kevin Guynn
Managing Director, Mitchell Schnall
Clinical Director, Dan Wilson
Medical Director, Charles Orellana
Medical Records Director, Scott Gilyard
Clinical Performance Vice President, John M Bruza
Vice Chair Department Of Neurology; Chief Of Neur, Howard I Hurtig
Auditors: LB PRICEWATERHOUSECOOPERS LLP

LOCATIONS

HQ: THE PENNSYLVANIA HOSPITAL OF THE UNIVERSITY OF PENNSYLVANIA HEALTH SYSTEM
800 SPRUCE ST, PHILADELPHIA, PA 191076130
Phone: 215 829-3000
Web: WWW.PENNMEDICINE.ORG

PRODUCTS/OPERATIONS

Selected Centers
ALS Center
Birthing Suite
Center for Bloodless Medicine and Surgery
Crisis Response Center
CyberKnife
Diabetes Education Center
Joan Karnell Cancer Center
Pain Management Center
Parkinson's Disease and Movement Disorders Center
Penn Comprehensive Neurosciences Center
Penn Orthopaedic Institute
Penn Center for Voice
Sports Medicine and Rehabilitation Center
Sleep Disorders Center
Vascular Center
Women's Imaging Center

Selected Services
Behavioral health
Heart and vascular
Neonatology
Neurosurgery
Obstetrics (including high-risk maternal and fetal services)
Orthopedics
Otorhinolaryngology (ENT)
Urology
Vascular medicine/surgery

COMPETITORS

Abington Memorial Hospital
Albert Einstein Healthcare Network
Aria Health
Bryn Mawr Hospital
Children's Hospital of Philadelphia
Crozer-Keystone Health System
Fox Chase Cancer Center
Jefferson Health
North Philadelphia Health System
TUHS
The Magee Memorial Hospital for Convalescents

HISTORICAL FINANCIALS
Company Type: Private

Income Statement				FYE: June 30
	REVENUE ($ mil.)	NET INCOME ($ mil.)	NET PROFIT MARGIN	EMPLOYEES
06/15	579	21	3.7%	2,200
06/14	534	(2)	—	—
06/10	485	27	5.7%	—
06/09	453	0	—	—
Annual Growth	4.2%	—	—	—

2015 Year-End Financials
Return on assets: 4.2%   Cash ($ mil.): —
Return on equity: 3.7%
Current ratio: 0.30

THE PENNSYLVANIA STATE UNIVERSITY

The Pennsylvania State University system is one of the largest state university systems in the US. Penn State has an enrollment of almost 96000 students; 13600 of them are graduate students. It offers 160 undergraduate and 150 graduate programs at about 20 campuses. The school's oldest and largest campus with about half of the system's undergraduate students is at University Park in central Pennsylvania. Other sites include the College of Medicine in Hershey Pennsylvania and the Dickinson School of Law in Carlisle Pennsylvania. It generates about $8.5 billion in annual direct and indirect economic impacts within Pennsylvania.

Operations

The university is known for its academic medical center and biomedical research. Its health-related programs include the Schools of Nursing Medicine Dental Medicine and Veterinary Medicine. The school's biomedical research ranks in the top 5 of National Institutes of Health funding.

The school offers a broad range of disciplines including medicine humanities engineering cyberscience and social science.

Financial Performance

Penn State had an annual operating budget in 2014-15 of $4.6 billion and an annual endowment of more than $2 billion. Its annual research funding is roughly $813 million of which $492 million comes from federal sources.

Strategy

In 2015 the university announced a new $30 million investment in economic development and student career success. This investment includes a one-time start-up and capital investment as well as annual funding of more than $5 million.

In 2014 the fundraising campaign For the Future: The Campaign for Penn State Students surpassed its goal raising about $2.2 billion in private support.

Company Background

Chartered in 1855 to apply scientific principles to farming Penn State has conferred almost 800000 degrees since its founding.

The university's storied football program was hit in 2012 with a four year postseason ban the significant reduction of scholarships the vacating of 112 wins and a $60 million fine all stemming from the school's handling of the child molestation scandal involving former coach Jerry Sandusky. However in 2015 the NCAA reversed its decision on the vacationing of wins restoring the late head coach Joe Paterno as the winningest coach in major college football history.

EXECUTIVES

Vice President Student Affairs, Damon Sims
Svp Finance And Business And Treasurer, David J. Gray
Dean University Libraries And Scholarly Communications, Barbara I. Dewey
Dean Undergraduate Education, Robert N. Pangborn
Dean College Of Medicine, A. Craig Hillemeier
Dean College Of Arts And Architecture, Barbara O. Korner
Dean College Of Earth And Mineral Sciences, William E. Easterling
Dean College Of Education, David H. Monk
Dean College Of Health And Human Development, Ann C. (Nan) Crouter
Dean College Of The Liberal Arts, Susan Welch
Dean College Of Nursing, Paula Milone-Nuzzo

Dean Schreyer Honors College, Christian M. M. Brady
President, Eric J. Barron, age 67
Dean Smeal College Of Business, Charles H. Whiteman
Evp And Provost, Nicholas P. Jones
Chief Investment Officer, John Pomeroy
Dean Graduate School, Regina Vasilatos-Younken
Dean College Of Agricultural Sciences, Richard Roush
Dean College Of Communications, Marie Hardin
Dean College Of Engineering, Amr S. Elnashai
Senior Vice President For Finance And Business Treasurer, Cynthia Hall
Vice President, Victor Sparrow
Department Head, Scott Wing
Vice President, Emily Sandall
Vice President For Strategic Communications, Lawrence Lokman
Operating Room Director, Jennifer Butch
Vice Chairman, Ira M. Lubert, age 68
Chairman, Keith E. Masser
Board Member, Eric Smith
Board Member, Malcolm Taylor
Auditors: DELOITTE & TOUCHE LLP PHILADE

LOCATIONS

HQ: THE PENNSYLVANIA STATE UNIVERSITY
201 OLD MAIN, UNIVERSITY PARK, PA 168021503
Phone: 814 865-4700
Web: WWW.PSU.EDU

PRODUCTS/OPERATIONS

Selected Colleges

College of Agricultural Sciences
College of Arts and Architecture
Smeal College of Business
College of Communications
College of Earth and Mineral Sciences
College of Education
College of Engineering
College of Health and Human Development
College of Information Sciences and Technology
School of International Affairs
School of Law
College of the Liberal Arts
College of Medicine
School of Nursing
Eberly College of Science
Graduate School
Schreyer Honors College

Selected Campuses

Penn State Abington Penn State Altoona
Penn State Beaver
Penn State Berks
Penn State Brandywine
Penn State DuBois
Penn State Erie The Behrend College
Penn State Fayette The Eberly Campus
Penn State Greater Allegheny
Penn State Harrisburg
Penn State Hazleton
Penn State Lehigh Valley
Penn State Mont Alto
Penn State New Kensington
Penn State Schuylkill
Penn State Shenango
Penn State Wilkes-Barre
Penn State Worthington Scranton
Penn State York

HISTORICAL FINANCIALS

Company Type: Private

Income Statement — FYE: June 30

	REVENUE ($ mil.)	NET INCOME ($ mil.)	NET PROFIT MARGIN	EMPLOYEES
06/17	6,059	635	10.5%	44,000
06/16	5,764	233	4.0%	—
06/15	5,293	289	5.5%	—
06/14	5,148	974	18.9%	—
Annual Growth	5.6%	(13.3%)	—	—

2017 Year-End Financials

Return on assets: 11.4%
Return on equity: 10.5%
Current ratio: 2.00
Cash ($ mil.): 1,761

THE PEPPER COMPANIES INC

EXECUTIVES

Pres-Ceo, J Stanley Pepper
SEC, Richard S Pepper
Exec V Pres-Gen Counsel, Thomas M O'Leary
Exec V Pres, Christopher R Averill
Auditors: DELOITTE & TOUCHE LLP CHICAGO

LOCATIONS

HQ: THE PEPPER COMPANIES INC
643 N ORLEANS ST, CHICAGO, IL 606543608
Phone: 312 266-4703
Web: WWW.THOMASDHAYWARD.COM

HISTORICAL FINANCIALS

Company Type: Private

Income Statement — FYE: September 30

	REVENUE ($ mil.)	NET INCOME ($ mil.)	NET PROFIT MARGIN	EMPLOYEES
09/17	1,119	22	2.0%	1,100
09/16	1,179	21	1.8%	—
09/11	1,177	10	0.9%	—
09/10	911	7	0.9%	—
Annual Growth	3.0%	15.8%	—	—

2017 Year-End Financials

Return on assets: 18.3%
Return on equity: 2.0%
Current ratio: 1.10
Cash ($ mil.): 41

THE PEW CHARITABLE TRUSTS

Green is the grease The Pew Charitable Trusts uses to help not-for-profits run smoothly. Among the nation's largest private foundations it was established in 1948 in memory of Sun Oil founder Joseph Pew and his wife Mary by four of their children. Seven trusts were created between 1948 and 1979 to promote public health and welfare and to strengthen communities. With more than $5 billion in assets it distributes more than $100 million in grants annually to charitable organizations in culture education environment health and human services public policy and religion. The Pew Trusts has strong ties to Philadelphia and allocates a portion of its grants to programs in that area.

Operations
The non-profit organization also operates through the Pew Center on the States; the Pew Environment Group; the Pew Health Group; and the Pew Research Center. The organization became an independent public charity in 2004.

Geographic Reach
Pew has primary offices in Philadelphia and Washington DC.

Strategy
The Pew Charitable Trusts focuses its efforts on improving public policy informing the public of the latest topics and stimulating civic life mostly in the Philadelphia area. To that end in 2013 Pew announced it will provide almost $8.5 million over the next three years to 46 Philadelphia-area organizations serving some of the area's most disadvantaged children and their families. The aim is to improve the lives of poor children by offering support to instill social and learning skills thereby overcoming obstacles to academic success.

The non-profit organization has a broad reach beyond Philadelphia. Indeed its activities range from evaluating children's dental health policies across the 50 US states to investigating the impact of industrial-scale chicken farming on the nation's land and waterways. The Pew Environment Group is active in protecting boreal forest in Canada and the oceans' shark population through the establishment of shark sanctuaries.

EXECUTIVES

Executive Vice President, Joshua S Reichert
Managing Director Communications, Melissa MskolfieldpewtrustsOrg
Senior Vice President General Counsel And Corporate Secretary, James McMillan
Vice President Human Resources, Elaine Bowman
Vice President, Tom Dillon
Vice President Information Technology And Chief Information Officer, Chris Contakes
Auditors: GRANT THORNTON LLP PHILADELPH

LOCATIONS

HQ: THE PEW CHARITABLE TRUSTS
2005 MARKET ST FL 28, PHILADELPHIA, PA 191037019
Phone: 215 575-9050
Web: WWW.PEWTRUSTS.ORG

PRODUCTS/OPERATIONS

Selected Program Areas
Arts and Culture
Children and Youth
Computers and the Internet
Sentencing and Corrections
Education
Elections
Environment
Family Financial Security
Government Performance
Health
Hispanics in America
Media and Journalism
National Civic Initiatives
Philadelphia Area
Public Opinion
Religion and Public Life
Science
State Policy and Performance

HISTORICAL FINANCIALS
Company Type: Private

Income Statement — FYE: June 30

	REVENUE ($ mil.)	NET INCOME ($ mil.)	NET PROFIT MARGIN	EMPLOYEES
06/17	708	407	57.6%	500
06/13	588	299	50.9%	—
06/12	85	(286)		—
06/11	991	711	71.8%	—
Annual Growth	(5.4%)	(8.9%)		

2017 Year-End Financials
Return on assets: 1.9% Cash ($ mil.): 10
Return on equity: 57.6%
Current ratio: —

THE PITTSBURGH FOUNDATION

EXECUTIVES

President, Grant Oliphant
Controller, Mary Wilson
Director, Freida Shapira
Director Allegheny County Depa, Claudette Lewis
Assistant Controller, Bryan Tait
Vice-President, John Ellis
Director, Lindsay Aroesty
Vice-President, McCrae Martino
Marketing Manager, Christopher Whitlatch
Auditors: SCHNEIDER DOWNS & CO INC PITT

LOCATIONS

HQ: THE PITTSBURGH FOUNDATION
5 PPG PL STE 250, PITTSBURGH, PA 152225414
Phone: 412 391-5122
Web: WWW.PITTSBURGHFOUNDATION.ORG

HISTORICAL FINANCIALS
Company Type: Private

Income Statement — FYE: December 31

	ASSETS ($ mil.)	NET INCOME ($ mil.)	INCOME AS % OF ASSETS	EMPLOYEES
12/16	1,037	6	0.6%	40
12/14	1,031	83	8.1%	—
12/13	942	64	6.8%	—
12/09	635	(15)		—
Annual Growth	7.3%	—	—	—

2016 Year-End Financials
Return on assets: 26.2% Sales ($ mil): 63
Return on equity: 10.3%

THE QUEEN'S HEALTH SYSTEMS

EXECUTIVES

Ceo, Arthur A Ushijima
Pres, Gary A Okamoto
Exec V Pres, Tracy Woo
Asst Treas, Kanoe Margol
Pres, William G Obana
V Pres, Mark Yamakawa
V Pres, Eric K Martinson
V Pres, Janice Kalanihuia
Senior Corporate Communication, Makana McClellan
Vice President, Kathy Morimoto
Vice President Human Resources, Nona Tamanaha
Auditors: ERNST & YOUNG US LLP SAN DIEG

LOCATIONS

HQ: THE QUEEN'S HEALTH SYSTEMS
1301 PUNCHBOWL ST, HONOLULU, HI 968132402
Phone: 808 691-5900
Web: WWW.QUEENSHEALTHSYSTEMS.COM

HISTORICAL FINANCIALS
Company Type: Private

Income Statement — FYE: June 30

	REVENUE ($ mil.)	NET INCOME ($ mil.)	NET PROFIT MARGIN	EMPLOYEES
06/17	1,279	173	13.6%	4,500
06/15	118	7	6.0%	—
06/11	24	3	14.2%	—
06/10	25	5	22.4%	—
Annual Growth	75.2%	63.1%	—	—

2017 Year-End Financials
Return on assets: 8.0% Cash ($ mil.): 80
Return on equity: 13.6%
Current ratio: 1.00

THE REGENTS OF THE UNIVERSITY OF COLORADO

EXECUTIVES

Exec Dir, Bruce Benson
Researcher, Blake Redabaugh
Poc, Melissa Englund
Project Coordinator, Gabriele Cheatham
Information Specialist, Nik Levinsky
Coordinator, Heidi Eckhoff
Internal Medicine Practitioner, Samantha Miles
Coordinator, Angela Annan
Assistant Professor, Jung-In Kim
Assistant Professor, Lindsay Thurman
Assistant Professor, Scott De La Cruz
Auditors: CLIFTONLARSONALLEN LLP GREENW

LOCATIONS

HQ: THE REGENTS OF THE UNIVERSITY OF COLORADO
3100 MARINE ST STE 48157, BOULDER, CO 803031058
Phone: 303 735-6624
Web: WWW.UCDENVER.EDU

PRODUCTS/OPERATIONS

Selected Campuses
University
University of Colorado - Colorado Springs
University
University of Colorado Anschutz Medical Campus

Income Statement				FYE: June 30
	REVENUE ($ mil.)	NET INCOME ($ mil.)	NET PROFIT MARGIN	EMPLOYEES
06/17	3,728	77	2.1%	12,980
06/16	3,451	72	2.1%	—
06/10	2,261	337	14.9%	—
Annual Growth	7.4%	(19.0%)		

2017 Year-End Financials

Return on assets: 3.9% Cash ($ mil.): 115
Return on equity: 2.1%
Current ratio: 0.70

THE ROBERT PACKER HOSPITAL

EXECUTIVES

Prin, Joseph A Scopelliti
Cfo, Minh Dang
Director of Laboratory, Ceil Miller
Scientist, Bob Warzyniak
Coordinator, Robin Cooper
Director, Susan Hall
Internal Medicine Practitioner, Richard Evans
Coordinator, Sheree Vail
Oncology Director, Staci Thompson
Auditors: LB PRICEWATERHOUSECOOPERS LLP

LOCATIONS

HQ: THE ROBERT PACKER HOSPITAL
1 GUTHRIE SQ STE B, SAYRE, PA 188401698
Phone: 570 888-6666
Web: WWW.GUTHRIE.ORG

HISTORICAL FINANCIALS
Company Type: Private

Income Statement				FYE: June 30
	REVENUE ($ mil.)	NET INCOME ($ mil.)	NET PROFIT MARGIN	EMPLOYEES
06/16	335	48	14.6%	1,400
06/15	324	61	18.9%	—
06/14	292	47	16.4%	—
06/10	254	46	18.1%	—
Annual Growth	4.7%	1.0%		

2016 Year-End Financials

Return on assets: 10.8% Cash ($ mil.): 6
Return on equity: 14.6%
Current ratio: 0.50

THE RUDOLPH/LIBBE COMPANIES INC

EXECUTIVES

Chm, Bill Rudolph
President, Allan J Libbe
SEC, John A Libbe

Treas-Cfo, Robert Pruger
President, Frederick W Rudolph
President, Philip J Rudolph
Project Engineer, Alex Simon
Project Engineer, Kyle Stang
Business Manager, Brad Delventhal
Project Manager, Mike Rokicki
Safety Manager, Neil Smith
Auditors: REHMANN ROBSON TOLEDO OH

LOCATIONS

HQ: THE RUDOLPH/LIBBE COMPANIES INC
6494 LATCHA RD, WALBRIDGE, OH 434659788
Phone: 419 241-5000
Web: RLGBUILDS.COM/COMPANIES/RUDOLPH-LIBBE-INC/

COMPETITORS

Albert M. Higley
Atlas Industrial Holdings
Danis
Messer Construction
Ruhlin
Skanska USA Building

HISTORICAL FINANCIALS
Company Type: Private

Income Statement				FYE: December 31
	REVENUE ($ mil.)	NET INCOME ($ mil.)	NET PROFIT MARGIN	EMPLOYEES
12/17	567	20	3.5%	600
12/16	502	23	4.8%	—
12/15	425	16	3.8%	—
12/14	17	14	83.2%	—
Annual Growth	218.1%	11.1%	—	—

2017 Year-End Financials

Return on assets: 9.9% Cash ($ mil.): 22
Return on equity: 3.5%
Current ratio: 1.20

THE SAINT CLOUD HOSPITAL

EXECUTIVES

Pres, Craig Broman
Cfo, Greg Klugherz
Coordinator, Kevin Mentzer
Purchasing Coordinator, Mary Janski
Administrative Assistant, Patty Decknatel
Emergency Medicine Specialist, Mathias J Christianson
Chief of Medicine, Richard Jolkovsky
Nurse, Ann Zierden
Human Resources Executive, Donna Gabler
Coordinator, Jason Foos
Chief of Medicine, Peter Charvat
Auditors: MCGLADREY LLP MINNEAPOLIS MN

LOCATIONS

HQ: THE SAINT CLOUD HOSPITAL
1406 6TH AVE N, SAINT CLOUD, MN 563031901
Phone: 320 251-2700
Web: WWW.CENTRACARE.COM

Income Statement				FYE: June 30
	REVENUE ($ mil.)	NET INCOME ($ mil.)	NET PROFIT MARGIN	EMPLOYEES
06/18	864	39	4.5%	4,957
06/16	756	3	0.5%	—
06/15	767	170	22.2%	—
06/14	754	72	9.6%	—
Annual Growth	3.5%	(14.3%)	—	—

2018 Year-End Financials

Return on assets: 4.7% Cash ($ mil.): 33
Return on equity: 4.5%
Current ratio: 1.50

THE SALVATION ARMY

EXECUTIVES

Pres-Trus, William A Bamford III
President-Trustee, William A Bamfordiii
V Pre-Trustee, Kenneth O Johnson Jr
Chb-Trustee, David E Jeffrey
Treasurer-Trustee, Donald W Lance
Secretary, Michael J Southwick
Fist Asst Treas-Trustee, D Sue Foley
2nd Assistant Treasurer, Thomas O Henson
Asst SEC-Legal, Richard D Allen
Asst Sec-Property*, Jorge E Diaz
Second Asst Sec-Property*, Adolph M Orlando
Auditors: GRANT THORNTON LLP NEW YORK

LOCATIONS

HQ: THE SALVATION ARMY
440 W NYACK RD OFC, WEST NYACK, NY 109941739
Phone: 845 620-7200
Web: WWW.SALVATIONARMY.ORG

HISTORICAL FINANCIALS
Company Type: Private

Income Statement				FYE: September 30
	REVENUE ($ mil.)	NET INCOME ($ mil.)	NET PROFIT MARGIN	EMPLOYEES
09/16	859	(224)	—	10,447
09/12	1,034	207	20.0%	—
09/09	782	(96)	—	—
09/08	288	(463)	—	—
Annual Growth	14.6%	—	—	—

2016 Year-End Financials

Return on assets: 4.8% Cash ($ mil.): 122
Return on equity: (-26.2%)
Current ratio: 0.20

THE SCHOOL BOARD OF MIAMI-DADE COUNTY

EXECUTIVES

Chb, Perla Tabares Hantman
Staff, Martin A Berkowitz
Administrative Assistant, Ana Herrera

Manager, Administrativ I Mendez-Cartaya
Senior Programmer Analyst, Fred Young
Secretary, Gehane Sterling
Information Technology Liaison, Liliam Weglarz
Administrative Director, Tabitha Fazzino
Auditors: MCGLADREY LLP MIAMI FLORIDA

LOCATIONS

HQ: THE SCHOOL BOARD OF MIAMI-DADE COUNTY
1450 NE 2ND AVE, MIAMI, FL 331321308
Phone: 305 995-1000
Web: WWW.DADESCHOOLS.NET

HISTORICAL FINANCIALS

Company Type: Private

Income Statement				FYE: June 30
	REVENUE ($ mil.)	NET INCOME ($ mil.)	NET PROFIT MARGIN	EMPLOYEES
06/17	3,728	448	12.0%	9
06/16	3,631	136	3.8%	—
06/13	3,302	(127)	—	—
06/12	3,220	(237)	—	—
Annual Growth	3.0%	—	—	—

2017 Year-End Financials

Return on assets: 1.2%   Cash ($ mil.): 314
Return on equity: 12.0%
Current ratio: 1.10

THE SCHOOL DISTRICT OF OSCEOLA COUNTY FL

EXECUTIVES

Supt, Melba Luciano
Cbfo, Bill Collins
Principal, George Sullivan
Coordinator, Jean Riggs
Public Information Director, Dana Lee Schafer
Food Director, Nancy Perry
Accounting Staff, Pam Fordham
Management Info Dir, Robert Curran Sr
Coordinator, Sonia Esposito
Project Manager, Mark Scheuer
Senior Buyer, Megan Pearison
Auditors: MOORE STEPHENS LOVELACE PA

LOCATIONS

HQ: THE SCHOOL DISTRICT OF OSCEOLA COUNTY FL
817 BILL BECK BLVD, KISSIMMEE, FL 347444492
Phone: 407 870-4600

HISTORICAL FINANCIALS

Company Type: Private

Income Statement				FYE: June 30
	REVENUE ($ mil.)	NET INCOME ($ mil.)	NET PROFIT MARGIN	EMPLOYEES
06/17	638	117	18.4%	6,250
06/16	601	37	6.2%	—
06/15	545	6	1.3%	—
06/14	527	(21)	—	—
Annual Growth	6.6%	—	—	—

2017 Year-End Financials

Return on assets: 0.6%   Cash ($ mil.): 107
Return on equity: 18.4%
Current ratio: —

THE SCHOOL DISTRICT OF PHILADELPHIA

EXECUTIVES

Spdt, William Hite Jr
Cfo, Matthew E Stanski
Food Director, Wayne T Grasela
Coordinator, Judy Anderson
Teacher, Abram Taber
Coordinator, Ana Ramirez
Computer Specialist, Danielle Schultz
Teacher, Eileen Kulikowski
Webmaster, Ezra Miller
Teacher, Julia Smith
Director, Ladeva Davis
Auditors: CHRISTY BRADY CPA PHILADELPH

LOCATIONS

HQ: THE SCHOOL DISTRICT OF PHILADELPHIA
440 N BROAD ST, PHILADELPHIA, PA 191304090
Phone: 215 400-4000
Web: WWW.PHILASD.ORG

HISTORICAL FINANCIALS

Company Type: Private

Income Statement				FYE: June 30
	REVENUE ($ mil.)	NET INCOME ($ mil.)	NET PROFIT MARGIN	EMPLOYEES
06/17	3,250	220	6.8%	21,065
06/16	3,064	23	0.8%	—
06/11	2,930	(259)	—	—
06/10	2,872	101	3.5%	—
Annual Growth	1.8%	11.8%	—	—

2017 Year-End Financials

Return on assets: 3.8%   Cash ($ mil.): —
Return on equity: 6.8%
Current ratio: —

THE SCHOOL DISTRICT OF WEST PALM BEACH COUNTY

EXECUTIVES

Coordinator, Elizabeth Parsley
Coordinator, Michelle Lindo
Network Technician, John Martin
Secretary, Brenda Jiampetti
Teacher, Deborah Stewart
Human Resources, Dionne Jelks
Teacher, Gail Sherman
Administrative Secretary, Michelle Martin
Manager, Nancy Reese
Electrical Engineer, Shams Moghadam
Secretary, Carole Cyr
Auditors: RSM US LLP WEST PALM BEACH F

LOCATIONS

HQ: THE SCHOOL DISTRICT OF WEST PALM BEACH COUNTY
3300 FOREST HILL BLVD, WEST PALM BEACH, FL 334065813
Phone: 561 434-8747
Web: WWW.PALMBEACHSCHOOLS.ORG

HISTORICAL FINANCIALS

Company Type: Private

Income Statement				FYE: June 30
	REVENUE ($ mil.)	NET INCOME ($ mil.)	NET PROFIT MARGIN	EMPLOYEES
06/17	2,146	78	3.7%	29,653
06/16	1,986	64	3.2%	—
06/15	1,903	(61)	—	—
Annual Growth	6.2%	—	—	—

THE SCOULAR COMPANY

The Scoular Company doesn't move food from farm to table but it does handle a good portion of the trip. The company buys sells stores handles and transports agricultural products (mainly grains) worldwide. It gets the mainstays of farming — corn hay millet rice sorghum soybeans and wheat — where they need to go. The company transports these products via rail truck barge and seagoing container vessels. Scoular's other divisions offer fishmeal products for farm-animal pet and aquaculture feeds; ingredients for food manufacturers; renewable fuels; and truck freight brokering. It has customers in Asia Africa the Americas and Europe. George Scoular founded the business in Nebraska in 1892.

Operations

The company operates 130 independent units that together make up a grain marketing network that handles 420 million bushels of grain annually and includes facilities in 18 states Canada and Mexico. In addition to buying selling handling and transporting grain Scoular offers risk management services.

Geographic Reach

Omaha-based Scoular and it affiliates have operations in 18 US states as well as in Calgary and Montreal Canada Mexico Argentina Brazil Uruguay China and Singapore. The company has nearly 30 merchandising offices and some 93 grain-handling facilities in North America with a storage capacity topping 130 million bushels.

Sales and Marketing

Scoular serves customers in the aquaculture flour milling food processing and manufacturing grain production industrial ag processing livestock feeding and manufacturing pet food manufacturing and renewable fuels sectors. Its services include bagging blending cleaning containerizing organic certifying packaging sorting sourcing and storage.

Financial Performance

Scoular's sales totaled $5.9 billion in 2015 compared with about $6 billion in 2014.

Strategy

The company has built itself out piece by piece scouring the landscape for businesses that fit into its portfolio through acquisition or partnership. In 2015 Scoular formed a joint venture with Nova del Mar in Mexico in which Scoular will market fishmeal that Nova makes from fish from the Sea of Cortez.

Mergers and Acquisitions

Scoular capped off two years of smaller acquisitions with the purchase of the Specialty Crops Division of Legumex Walker Inc. a global merchandiser and processor of special crops for some (Canadian) $94 million. The business processes special crops at 14 facilities in Canada the US and China. Some of the special crops are lentils whole and split peas edible beans chickpeas canaryseed flaxseed and sunflower seed.

In August 2013 Scouler acquired the assets of Kansas-based Tribune Grain which include a grain elevator in Tribune Kansas that's located on the Kansas and Oklahoma Railroad as well as two seasonally-operated rural truck facilities. (In addition to the Tribune area facilities Scoular operates 10 other grain elevators in Kansas and eastern Colorado.)

EXECUTIVES

Vice President, Randall Foster
Vice President, John Heck
Chairman And President, David M. Faith
Svp And Division General Manager, Todd McQueen
Svp And Division General Manager, John Messerich
Cfo, Richard A. (Rick) Cogdill
Ceo, Paul T. Maass
Cio, Jeff Schreiner
Svp And Division General Manager, Bob Ludington
Vice President Finance And Tre, Roger L Barber
Vice President Finance, Omer Sagheer
Auditors: KPMG LLP OMAHA NEBRASKA

LOCATIONS

HQ: THE SCOULAR COMPANY
2027 DODGE ST STE 200, OMAHA, NE 681021229
Phone: 402 342-3500
Web: WWW.SCOULARBALLROOM.COM

PRODUCTS/OPERATIONS

Selected Customer Industries Products and Services
Aquaculture (feed ingredients)
  Animal fats
  Animal proteins
  Fish oil
  Fishmeal
  Grain byproducts
  Vegetable fats
  Vegetable proteins
Flour milling (buying selling storing and shipping)
  Durum
  Hard red spring
  Hard red winter
  Soft red winter
Food manufacturing and processing (conventional organic and functional ingredients blending packaging co-packing)
  Ingredients
  Proteins
  Dairy
  Pea
  Potato
  Rice
  Soy
  Specialty flours
  Soy
  Starches
  Pea
  Potato
  Rice
  Tapioca
  Textured proteins
  Soy
Grain production (marketing buying storing handling and shipping programs)
  Corn
  Hay
  Millet
  Rice
  Sorghum
  Soybeans
  Wheat
Industrial ag processing (feedstock supply byproduct marketing and crush risk management)
  Products
  Citrus pulp
  Distillers grains
  Hominy feed
  Wheat mill feeds
  Whole cottonseed
Identity-preserved grain

Corn
Soybeans
Wheat
White corn
Livestock feeding and feed manufacturing (grain and feed ingredient sourcing risk management)
  Grains and oilseeds
  Barley
  Canola
  Corn
  Field peas
  Flax
  Lentils
  Rye
  Soybeans
  Wheat
  Other
  Canola meal
  Citrus pulp
  Distillers grains
  Hominy feed
  Wheat mill feed
  Whole cottonseed
Pet food manufacturing (ingredients)
  Products
  Fats
  Flours
  Gravy dust mix
  Proteins
  Starches
  Yellow corn
  Sourcing and solutions
  Animal oils
  Animal proteins
  Fish oil
  Fishmeal
  Frozen fish
  Fruits
  Grain products
  Pea protein fiber flour and starch
  Pomaces
  Specialty starches flours
  Variety meats
  Vegetable oils
  Vegetable proteins
  Vegetables
Transportation
  Container and vessel (freight forwarding logistics and documentation in more than 50 countries)
  Rail truck and barge (logistics for shipping agricultural products in North America)

COMPETITORS

ADM	Excel Maritime
Andersons	Carriers
Bartlett and Company	Louis Dreyfus Group
Bunge Limited	Syntroleum
CHS	TBS International
Cargill	TORM
DeBruce Grain	

HISTORICAL FINANCIALS

Company Type: Private

Income Statement — FYE: May 31

	REVENUE ($ mil.)	NET INCOME ($ mil.)	NET PROFIT MARGIN	EMPLOYEES
05/17	4,366	25	0.6%	801
05/16	4,667	(10)	—	—
05/15	234	14	6.0%	—
05/14	228	29	13.0%	—
Annual Growth	167.4%	(5.4%)	—	—

2017 Year-End Financials

Return on assets: 4.5%   Cash ($ mil.): 37
Return on equity: 0.6%
Current ratio: 0.50

THE SCRIPPS RESEARCH INSTITUTE

The Scripps Research Institute (TSRI) is a not-for profit organization that performs basic biomedical research in molecular and cellular biology chemistry immunology neuroscience disease and vaccine development. TSRI receives the majority of its funding from federal agencies such as the National Institutes of Health. TRSI opened a second facility in Florida in 2009. Its staff includes more than 2900 scientists and lab technicians and the organization traces its history back to 1924 when philanthropist Ellen Browning Scripps founded Scripps Metabolic Clinic.

Geographic Reach
TRSI is located on campuses in La Jolla California and Jupiter Florida.

Financial Performance
TSRI reported revenue of $393.3 million in 2011. That figure was down slightly from the $406.3 million the organization claimed in revenue for 2010.

TSRI receives the majority of its funding from the National Institutes of Health. Other contributors include the American Cancer Society the American Heart Association the Cystic Fibrosis Foundation the Leukemia & Lymphoma Society and the Juvenile Diabetes Association.

EXECUTIVES

Executive Vice President, Douglas Bingham
Vice President Office Of Sponsored Programs, Kaye Wynne
Auditors: DELOITTE TAX LLP SAN DIEGO C

LOCATIONS

HQ: THE SCRIPPS RESEARCH INSTITUTE
10550 N TORREY PINES RD, LA JOLLA, CA
920371000
Phone: 858 784-1000
Web: WWW.SCRIPPS.EDU

COMPETITORS

Battelle Memorial	Life Technologies
Berkeley Lab	Corporation
Brookhaven Lab	MITRE
IQVIA	SRI International
Lawrence Livermore Lab	SwRI

HISTORICAL FINANCIALS

Company Type: Private

Income Statement — FYE: September 30

	REVENUE ($ mil.)	NET INCOME ($ mil.)	NET PROFIT MARGIN	EMPLOYEES
09/16	348	(16)	—	99
09/09	375	(18)	—	—
09/08	464	137	29.7%	—
09/05	387	63	16.3%	—
Annual Growth	(1.0%)	—	—	—

2016 Year-End Financials

Return on assets: 9.9%   Cash ($ mil.): 14
Return on equity: (-4.6%)
Current ratio: 0.20

THE SOMMERS COMPANY

EXECUTIVES

Pres, Jimmy F Sommers
SEC-Treas, Sarah W Sommers
Vice President, Wynelle Sommers
Coo, Randy Sommers
Cntrl, Michael Dionne
Vice-President, Nicholas Pastorelli
Auditors: TJS DEEMER DANA LLP SAVANNAH

LOCATIONS

HQ: THE SOMMERS COMPANY
  1000 SOMMERS BLVD, RICHMOND HILL, GA
  313248817
Phone: 800 654-6466
Web: WWW.SOMMERSOIL.COM

HISTORICAL FINANCIALS

Company Type: Private

Income Statement				FYE: June 30
	REVENUE ($ mil.)	NET INCOME ($ mil.)	NET PROFIT MARGIN	EMPLOYEES
06/18	454	1	0.3%	30
06/16	296	1	0.4%	—
06/15	426	1	0.3%	—
06/14	587	1	0.2%	—
Annual Growth	(6.2%)	(0.7%)	—	—

2018 Year-End Financials

Return on assets: 3.0%
Return on equity: 0.3%
Current ratio: 1.20

Cash ($ mil.): 5

THE SOUTHEASTERN CONFERENCE

EXECUTIVES

Commissioner, Greg Sankey
Commissioner, Michael Flive
Commissioner, Mark Womack
Director Video Creative Servic, B Romano
Assistant Commissioner, Will Lawler
Auditors: BARFIELD MURPHY SHANK & SMITH

LOCATIONS

HQ: THE SOUTHEASTERN CONFERENCE
  2201 RICHARD ARRINGTN JR, BIRMINGHAM, AL
  352031103
Phone: 205 949-8960
Web: WWW.SECSPORTS.COM

HISTORICAL FINANCIALS

Company Type: Private

Income Statement				FYE: August 31
	REVENUE ($ mil.)	NET INCOME ($ mil.)	NET PROFIT MARGIN	EMPLOYEES
08/16	639	17	2.7%	30
08/15	527	17	3.3%	—
08/14	325	2	0.7%	—
08/13	314	(3)	—	—
Annual Growth	26.7%	—	—	—

2016 Year-End Financials

Return on assets: —
Return on equity: 2.7%
Current ratio: —

Cash ($ mil.): 26

THE STELLAR COMPANIES INC

EXECUTIVES

Ceo, Ronald H Foster Jr
Pres-Coo, Michael S Santarone
V Pres Fin, Clint Pyle
Cfo, Scott V Witt
Project Coordinator, Daniel Weibelt
Auditors: RSM US LLP JACKSONVILLE FLOR

LOCATIONS

HQ: THE STELLAR COMPANIES INC
  2900 HARTLEY RD, JACKSONVILLE, FL 322578221
Phone: 904 899-9393

HISTORICAL FINANCIALS

Company Type: Private

Income Statement				FYE: September 30
	REVENUE ($ mil.)	NET INCOME ($ mil.)	NET PROFIT MARGIN	EMPLOYEES
09/17	508	7	1.6%	600
09/16	285	6	2.3%	—
09/15	336	2	0.9%	—
09/14	341	0	0.1%	—
Annual Growth	14.3%	212.5%	—	—

2017 Year-End Financials

Return on assets: 15.3%
Return on equity: 1.6%
Current ratio: 0.80

Cash ($ mil.): 16

THE SUNDT COMPANIES INC

Sundt has put its stamp on the Southwest. Through Sundt Construction and other subsidiaries The Sundt Companies offers preconstruction construction management general contracting and design/build services for commercial government and industrial clients. Projects include commercial buildings military bases light rails airports and schools. It builds mostly in Arizona Nevada California New Mexico and Texas. Sundt has overseen some notable projects including the development of the top-secret town of Los Alamos New Mexico (where the first atomic bomb was built) and the relocation of the London Bridge to Arizona. Sundt Companies was formed in 1998 as a holding company for various company interests.

Operations

The Sundt Companies performs its work through various divisions: Industrial; concrete; building; heavy civil; and federal. The building division is divided into geographic regions: California; Southwest; and Texas; as well as a Federal Division.

Strategy

Like its peers Sundt is dealing with the lingering effects of the construction downturn that greatly impacted the Southwest. (The company lost more than $750 million in government projects due to state budget constraints.) Indeed Sundt anticipates that it may be 2015 before it sees a strong economy for construction. In the meantime the firm has relied on a healthy backlog of projects and diversification efforts to sustain its business. To that end it entered new geographic markets in 2012 including New Mexico where it is building new dorms at New Mexico State University. It also recently began construction of new schools in El Paso Texas its first in the city. The firm formed a new Criminal Justice Specialization group in 2012 to win courthouse and detention facility work.

Sundt also has focused on making investments in improving technology used in the preconstruction and construction process. It also grew its self-perform work capabilities when it acquired Foley Masonry and Tile Inc. in 2010. Also that year Sundt opened a new office in San Antonio as part of the company's growth plan. The company expanded once again in 2011. It opened new offices to support projects in New Mexico North Carolina and Texas.

EXECUTIVES

Pres-Ceo, Mike Hoover
Svp/Cfo, Kevin M Burnett
Coo, Thomas S Case
Sr V Pres-Gen Counsel, Ronald Stuff
Manager, Raquel Collett
Executive Vice President Chief, Raymond C Bargull
Auditors: MAYER HOFFMAN & MCCANN

LOCATIONS

HQ: THE SUNDT COMPANIES INC
  2015 W RIVER RD STE 101, TUCSON, AZ 857041676
Phone: 520 750-4600
Web: WWW.SUNDT.COM

PRODUCTS/OPERATIONS

Selected Projects

Aviation
Commercial buildings
Concrete construction
Courthouses
Federal government
Hospitality
Hospitals & health care
Infrastructure & site development
Juvenile detention facilities
K-12 schools
Mining
Mission critical/Data center
Municipal buildings
Parking structures
Power plants & alternative energy
Prisons
Research & development facilities
Residential
Retail
Roads & bridges
Student housing & dormitories
Universities & community colleges
Water & wastewater treatment

Selected Services

Build-to-suit
Construction manager at risk (CMAR)
Construction/program manager
Design-bid-build/general contractor (DBB)
Preconstruction
Self-perform contracting

COMPETITORS

Austin Industries	McCarthy Building
CORE Construction	Meadow Valley
Charles Pankow Builders	O'Neil Industries
DPR Construction	Peter Kiewit Sons'
	Swinerton

Granite Construction Tutor Perini
Hunt Construction Weitz
Kitchell

HISTORICAL FINANCIALS
Company Type: Private

Income Statement
FYE: September 30

	REVENUE ($ mil.)	NET INCOME ($ mil.)	NET PROFIT MARGIN	EMPLOYEES
09/17	1,134	0	—	2,200
09/16*	813	0	—	—
06/16	0	0	—	—
09/15	934	0	—	—
Annual Growth	10.2%	—	—	—

*Fiscal year change

2017 Year-End Financials
Return on assets: 11.9% Cash ($ mil.): 53
Return on equity: —
Current ratio: 0.90

THE SUSAN THOMPSON BUFFETT FOUNDATION

EXECUTIVES

Pres, Allen Greenberg

LOCATIONS

HQ: THE SUSAN THOMPSON BUFFETT FOUNDATION
808 CONAGRA DR BLDG 5, OMAHA, NE 681025002
Phone: 402 943-1300
Web: WWW.BUFFETTSCHOLARSHIPS.ORG

HISTORICAL FINANCIALS
Company Type: Private

Income Statement
FYE: December 31

	REVENUE ($ mil.)	NET INCOME ($ mil.)	NET PROFIT MARGIN	EMPLOYEES
12/17	304	(241)	—	3
12/15	250	(111)	—	—
12/14	246	(296)	—	—
12/09	128	123	95.9%	—
Annual Growth	11.4%	—	—	—

2017 Year-End Financials
Return on assets: 0.4% Cash ($ mil.): 5
Return on equity: (-79.4%)
Current ratio: —

THE TRUSTEES OF PRINCETON UNIVERSITY

This prince's kingdom is covered with ivy. As one of the eight elite Ivy League schools in the Northeastern US Princeton is a research university that offers students degrees across 34 departments and 47 interdisciplinary certificate programs. It boasts more than 8000 students (5300 undergraduate and 2700 graduate students). The highly selective school which enjoys an undergraduate student-faculty ratio of 6:1 admits about 8% of its total applicants. Nobel Prize winners associated with Princeton include Woodrow Wilson writer Toni Morrison and physicist Richard Feynman. One of the nation's wealthiest universities Princeton has an endowment of more than $16 billion.

Operations
The Princeton campus comprises six residential colleges that are organized by grade level (freshmen sophomores juniors and seniors).

The university which is supported by 1140 faculty members that include visitors and part-time appointments operates three schools: the School of Architecture School of Engineering and Applied Science and the Woodrow Wilson School of Public and International Affairs. Princeton also has a large research base with some $200 million in funding per year primarily from federal grants. Its plasma physics research laboratory has a sizable research contract with the federal government.

Geographic Reach
Located in Princeton New Jersey Princeton's campus includes some 180 buildings that cover about 500 acres.

Sales and Marketing
Princeton sources its students from more than 98 countries. International graduate students hail primarily from Canada China India Germany and Korea. Some 60% of the university's undergraduate students receive financial aid. The average undergraduate financial aid reward for the Class of 2016 is $39700.

Financial Performance
For an Ivy League university with a top reputation in the US and internationally Princeton has not suffered as a result of turbulent economic conditions as much as some of its lower-ranked peers.

Company Background
Founded in 1746 as the College of New Jersey Princeton is the fourth-oldest college in the nation. In 1756 the college was moved to Nassau Hall which served as the temporary capitol of the US in 1783 and is still part of the Princeton campus.

EXECUTIVES

Vp Finance And Treasurer, Carolyn N. Ainslie
President, Christopher L. Eisgruber
Dean Admission, Janet L. Rapelye
Dean Undergraduate Students, Kathleen Deignan
President Princeton University Investment Co., Andrew K. Golden
Dean Religious Life And The Chapel, Alison L. Boden
Dean Wilson School Of Public And International Affairs, Cecilia E. Rouse
Vp Information Technology And Cio, Jay Dominick
Dean School Of Engineering And Applied Science, H. Vincent Poor
Provost, David S. Lee
Dean Of The Faculty, Deborah A. Prentice
Dean Graduate School, Sanjeev R. Kulkarni
Dean Of The College, Jill S. Dolan
Dean Research, Pablo G. Debenedetti
Dean School Of Architecture, Monica Ponce de Leon
Evp, Treby Williams
Program Assistant Vice President For Pppl, Janice Huang
Payroll Manager Payroll Office Of The Vice President For Finance And Treasurer, Lora J Benson
Communications Specialist Office Of The Vice President For Facilities, Cynthia L Suter
Executive Assistant Office Of The Vice President For Development, Deborah A Small
Vice President For Campus Life, Rochelle Calhoun
Assistant Vice President For Strategic Donor Engagement, Tim McGowan
Trustee, Kathryn A. Hall
Vice Chairman, Brent L. Henry

Senior Financial Data Analyst And Treasurer, Elizabeth Totten
Secretary, Hassan Ejaz
Secretary, Elizabeth Haile
Treasurer, Liam Collins
Auditors: PRICEWATERHOUSECOOPERS LLP N

LOCATIONS

HQ: THE TRUSTEES OF PRINCETON UNIVERSITY
1 NASSAU HALL, PRINCETON, NJ 085442001
Phone: 609 258-3000
Web: WWW.ETCWEB.PRINCETON.EDU

PRODUCTS/OPERATIONS

Select Councils Institutes and Centers
Bendheim Center for Finance
Center for Migration and Development
Center for the Study of Religion
Council of the Humanities
Council on Science and Technology
Davis Center for Historical Studies
James Madison Program in American Ideals and Institutions
Lewis-Sigler Institute for Integrative Genomics
Liechtenstein Institute on Self-Determination
Princeton Environmental Institute (PEI)
Princeton Institute for International and Regional Studies (PIIRS)
Princeton Institute for the Science and Technology of Materials (PRISM)
Princeton Writing Program
Program of Freshman Seminars in the Residential Colleges
Program in Law and Public Affairs
Program in Neuroscience
University Center for Human Values

COMPETITORS

Brown University	Harvard University
Columbia University	Penn
Cornell University	Rutgers University
Dartmouth	Yale University

HISTORICAL FINANCIALS
Company Type: Private

Income Statement
FYE: June 30

	REVENUE ($ mil.)	NET INCOME ($ mil.)	NET PROFIT MARGIN	EMPLOYEES
06/18	2,012	2,582	128.3%	6,000
06/17	1,813	2,096	115.6%	—
06/16	1,687	(628)	—	—
06/15	1,621	1,827	112.8%	—
Annual Growth	7.5%	12.2%	—	—

2018 Year-End Financials
Return on assets: 2.1% Cash ($ mil.): 23
Return on equity: 128.3%
Current ratio: —

THE TRUSTEES OF THE UNIVERSITY OF PENNSYLVANIA

The University of Pennsylvania (commonly called Penn) was founded by Benjamin Franklin when he had a little down time between establishing a country and experimenting with lightning. Since opening its doors to students in 1751 the Ivy League university has accumulated a notable list of accomplishments including the creation of one of the first medical schools in the US. The university currently has a total of almost 25000 students who pursue their studies in four undergraduate schools and a dozen graduate and professional schools including the renowned Wharton School and the Annenberg School for Communications. Its student-teacher ratio is a very low 6:1.

Operations
The University of Pennsylvania's research staff includes more than 4300 faculty and 1100 postdoctoral fellows plus some 5400 academic support staff and graduate student trainees.

The university is also responsible for inventing the Electronic Numerical Integrator and Computer (ENIAC) the first general-purpose electronic computer. The ENIAC was constructed and operated at The Moore School of Electrical Engineering now part of the School of Engineering and Applied Science. The school still has on display four of the original 40 panels of ENIAC which represents one-tenth of its original size.

Geographic Reach
The University of Pennsylvania is located in the heart of downtown Philadelphia.

Financial Performance
The University of Pennsylvania has an annual budget of about $7.3 billion. Its endowment is about $9.6 billion. The school is heavily involved with research operating more than 165 research centers and institutes.

Company Background
Former University of Pennsylvania president Judith Rodin was the first female to head an Ivy League university.

EXECUTIVES

Vp It And Cio, Thomas H. (Tom) Murphy
Evp, Craig R. Carnaroli
President And Trustee, Amy Gutmann
Ceo University Of Pennsylvania Health System, Ralph W. Muller
Dean School Of Arts And Sciences, Rebecca W. Bushnell
Dean Annenberg School For Communication, Michael X. Delli Carpini
Dean School Of Law, Michael A. Fitts
Dean School Of Social Policy And Practice, Richard Gelles
Dean School Of Engineering And Applied Science, Eduardo D. Glandt
Dean School Of Nursing, Afaf I. Meleis
Dean School Of Veterinary Medicine, Joan C. Hendricks
Dean Wharton School, Thomas S. Robertson
Dean School Of Dental Medicine, Denis F. Kinane
Provost, Vincent Price
Dean Graduate School Of Education, Andrew C. (Andy) Porter
Dean Penndesign, Marilyn Jordan Taylor
Vp Finance And Treasurer, Stephen D. Golding
Evp Health System; Dean Raymond And Ruth Perelman School Of Medicine, J. Larry Jameson
Medical Director, Helene L Glassberg
Medical Director, Kevin Steinberg
Medical Director, Daniel Wolf
Vice President, Gilbert Saunders
Chair, David L. Cohen
Vice Chair, David M. Silfen
Auditors: PRICEWATERHOUSECOOPERS LLC PH

LOCATIONS

HQ: THE TRUSTEES OF THE UNIVERSITY OF PENNSYLVANIA
3451 WALNUT ST RM 440A, PHILADELPHIA, PA 191046205
Phone: 215 898-5000
Web: WWW.HILTON.COM

PRODUCTS/OPERATIONS

Selected Schools
Annenberg School for Communication
The College at Penn (School of Arts and Sciences)
Graduate School of Education
Graduate School of Fine Arts
Law School
School of Arts and Sciences
School of Dental Medicine
School of Engineering and Applied Science
School of Medicine
School of Nursing
School of Social Work
School of Veterinary Medicine
The Wharton School

HISTORICAL FINANCIALS

Company Type: Private

Income Statement   FYE: June 30

	REVENUE ($ mil.)	NET INCOME ($ mil.)	NET PROFIT MARGIN	EMPLOYEES
06/17	9,194	1,734	18.9%	20,433
06/10	4	0	5.1%	—
06/09	5,221	(1,285)	—	—
06/08	5,092	133	2.6%	—
Annual Growth	6.8%	33.0%	—	—

2017 Year-End Financials
Return on assets: 2.6%   Cash ($ mil.): 972
Return on equity: 18.9%
Current ratio: —

THE TURNER CORPORATION

The Turner Corporation a subsidiary of German construction giant HOCHTIEF is the leading general building and construction management firm in the US (as ranked by Engineering News-Record) ahead of rivals Bechtel and Fluor. The firm operates primarily through subsidiary Turner Construction and has worked on notable projects such as Madison Square Garden the UN headquarters Yankee Stadium the Taipei 101 Tower and the 68000-seat open-air stadium for the San Francisco 49ers. Known for its large projects also offers services for midsized and smaller projects and provides interior construction and renovation services.

Operations
Turner works on more than 1500 projects in a year totaling $8 billion in volume. The group has divisions dedicated to serving the aviation health care biotechnology public assembly sports education justice and industrial sectors. Its homeland security group was established in order handle a growing demand for security systems and protection. The unit installed detection equipment in some 450 airports throughout the US. Turner Corporation also has an arm specializing in green building with a focus on Leadership in Energy and Environmental Design (LEED) -certified projects. Turner Green Building has more than 400 LEED projects and green projects either completed or in progress.

Turner Corporation has subsidiaries providing auxiliary operations. Turner's risk management department offers contract review project safety and claims handling. Turner Logistics handles procurement and supply chain management for projects and Turner Facilities Management Solutions offers ongoing operations services. Also the Turner School of Construction Management provides training for local subcontractors.

Geographic Reach
Dallas-based Turner Corporation boasts a network of offices across the US (with most in California and Ohio) and Canada (Vancouver and Toronto) with an global presence in 20 countries in Europe Africa East Asia India Latin America and the Caribbean.

Sales and Marketing
Turner works on variety of projects from several sectors. It's known for its work in the categories of healthcare education offices commercial properties cultural facilities sports facilities and hotels. The company is also a leader in the green building category.

Strategy
With the construction market rebounding from the economic downturn Turner is looking to high-growth markets in the US and overseas. As of early 2015 it was working on more than 1900 projects 80% of which were Education Commercial or Interior project-related. Some of these projects included the 17000 sq. ft- interior remodel for Salesforce's Vancouver office; the 325000 sq. ft-construction of the LEED-Certified RAND Corporation Headquarters in Santa Monica California; and the 25000-seat Charlotte Coliseum event arena for the City of Charlotte North Carolina.

The company has also been making moves to expand its business abroad in recent years. In 2012 for example Turner partnered with one of India's largest real estate developers Sahara Prime City Ltd. to form Sahara Turner which would lead the development and construction of multiple townships across the country with an approximate value of $2.5 billion by 2017. It also purchased a majority stake in Clark Builders Canada to capitalize on the country's growing construction market.

Turner often partners with fellow US-based HOCHTIEF subsidiary Flatiron which specializes in civil engineering. Examples of the teamwork are the expansions of airports in San Diego and Sacramento.

HISTORY

At the turn of the century an engineer and devout Quaker named Henry Chandlee Turner was convinced that a new type of steel-reinforced concrete (called the Ransome system) would change the construction industry. With this conviction and with the help of his partner D. H. Dixon Turner bought the rights to the technology for $25000 and in 1902 founded Turner Construction Company.

One of the company's early projects was building the stairways for New York's first subway stations. As the Ransome method proved to be successful Turner's reputation grew. Defense contracts during WWI raised Turner's take to $35 million in 1918.

Before the Depression Turner was building high-rises hotels and stadiums. During the economic crash that started in 1929 the company survived by building retail stores churches and public buildings a strategy it would employ successfully in later recessions.

Henry Turner retired in 1941. His brother Archer Turner managed the company during most of the war effort. As WWII raged more than 80% of the company's work was defense-related. Projects included building and managing a submarine base in Oak Ridge Tennessee during the development of the atomic bomb.

In 1947 Henry C. Turner Jr. the founder's son became president and within four years he had led the company to more than $100 million in sales. By the time he stepped down as chairman in 1970 the firm had built skyscrapers futuristic airports and such landmarks as Madison Square Garden and the United Nations Secretariat and Plaza in New York City. Turner went public in 1969.

Howard S. Turner (the final family member to head the business) led the company during the 1970s. The company extended its global presence opening offices in more countries including Iran Pakistan and the United Arab Emirates. Turner also developed construction management services.

In 1984 The Turner Corporation was formed as a holding company for the construction company and the subsidiaries created or acquired as a result of diversification. Property development was one of these activities but by 1987 Turner had begun to dispose of its real estate holdings. It did not move quickly enough however and when the real estate market crashed Turner was caught with a large portfolio.

As commercial projects slowed Turner sought work in more sectors including public works and amusement projects (aquariums arenas hospitals and universities). By 1994 these areas accounted for 70% of business. In 1993 as the building slump continued Turner began a cost-cutting plan which included laying off workers and closing offices. That year the company set up an $8.5 million re-structuring reserve and as the real estate market eased into recovery Turner sold more of its real estate holdings.

In 1996 Turner won a contract to build a 10000-seat arena in Salt Lake City to be used for the 2002 Winter Olympics. In 1997 Turner contracted to renovate 811 schools and build two campuses in California's San Fernando Valley and in 1998 it was chosen to manage the construction of the Kansas City Motor Speedway.

Profits were recovering quickly. Nonetheless in 1999 the company agreed to be acquired by German construction giant HOCHTIEF in a $370 million deal that ended Turner's joint venture with Switzerland's Karl Steiner. The company also relocated its corporate headquarters to Dallas that year to take advantage of the construction boom in the US Southwest.

In 2000 Turner created three new business groups to serve the aviation pharmaceutical and sports sectors. By the next year Turner's sports group was working on 17 projects. In 2001 the company was a member of the construction team that responded to the September 11 devastation at Ground Zero in New York City. The next year the company celebrated its 100th anniversary with an exhibit at the National Building Museum in Washington DC; the exhibit featured drawings and photos of some of Turner's notable projects during the past century. In 2003 Turner Construction acquired the assets of Tompkins Builders the third-largest construction company in the Washington DC area from former rival J.A. Jones Construction Co.

Turner Construction which celebrated its 100th anniversary in 2002 has ranked among the leading general builders in the US since WWI. For 80 of the 100 years the group had a Turner among its senior executives. Howard S. Turner was the last member of the family to serve in the company's senior ranks. The company's appointment of Peter Davoren in 2003 as president of Turner Construction reflected the rise of a new generation of leaders for the unit. Davoren was additionally appointed chairman and CEO in 2007.

Turner Construction announced in 2008 that it had signed the contract on its 15000th major project.

EXECUTIVES

Pres-Chb-Ceo, Peter J Davoren
Sr V Pres-Cfo & Treas, Karen Gould
V Pres-Finance & Asst Treas, Don Oshiro
Attrny, Richard L Smith Jr

Svp, Turner, Thomas B Gerlach Jr
Safety Manager, Wayne Baruch
Senior Project Manager, Gary McAssey
Manager, Reed McMains
Superintendent, Roy Burnham
Engineer, Anthony Baxley
Project Engineer, Bernardo Lomeli
Auditors: DELOITTE & TOUCHE LLP DALLAS

LOCATIONS

HQ: THE TURNER CORPORATION
  375 HUDSON ST RM 700, NEW YORK, NY 100143667
Phone: 212 229-6000
Web: WWW.TURNERCONSTRUCTION.COM

PRODUCTS/OPERATIONS

Selected Related Companies

E. E. Cruz (infrastructure)
Flatiron Construction Corp. (transportation construction civil engineering)
Clark Builders (51% Canada)

Selected Markets Served

Aviation
Commercial
Cultural and entertainment
Data center
Education
Government
Green building
Health care
Infrastructure
Industrial
Interiors
Pharmaceutical
Public Assembly
Religious
Research and development
Residential/hotel
Sports

Selected Services

Building information modeling
Building maintenance
Construction management
Design-build
Design-build/finance
Facilities management
General construction
Lean construction
Logistics
Medical planning and procurement
Preconstruction consulting
Program management
Project management

COMPETITORS

Balfour Beatty Construction	Hunt Construction
Bechtel	Imperial Construction Group
Clark Construction Group	Jacobs Engineering
Fluor	Parsons Corporation
Gilbane Building Company	Peter Kiewit Sons'
	Skanska
	Structure Tone

HISTORICAL FINANCIALS

Company Type: Private

Income Statement   FYE: December 31

	REVENUE ($ mil.)	NET INCOME ($ mil.)	NET PROFIT MARGIN	EMPLOYEES
12/15	10,523	107	1.0%	5,000
12/14	10,560	95	0.9%	—
12/13	9,522	80	0.8%	—
12/12	8,575	74	0.9%	—
Annual Growth	7.1%	12.9%	—	—

2015 Year-End Financials

Return on assets: 25.8%   Cash ($ mil.): 880
Return on equity: 1.0%
Current ratio: 1.00

THE UNION MEMORIAL HOSPITAL

Not quite for time immemorial but MedStar Union Memorial Hospital (formerly Union Memorial Hospital) has been caring for patients for more than 160 years. The Baltimore-area facility is a specialty acute-care hospital with about 250 beds and more than 620 physicians. Areas of clinical research and expertise include cardiac care orthopedics and sports medicine. In addition it offers a range of inpatient and outpatient services including diabetes and endocrine center eye surgery center general surgery oncology and thoracic and vascular surgery. MedStar Union Memorial offers postgraduate programs orthopedic surgery residencies and hand surgery fellowships. The company is a part of MedStar Health.

Operations

MedStar Union Memorial offers a full array of diagnostic medical surgical and rehabilitative services. The hospital provides graduate medical education through residency programs and fellowship programs. MedStar Union Memorial offers 19 postgraduate first year positions in medicine; a surgical training program; and an orthopedic surgical program. MedStar's Online Clinical Library provides access both onsite and offsite to electronic resources for drug information evidence-based medicine point of care full-test textbooks and more the 400 full-text journals.

The hospital offers 231 acute care beds and 18 rehab beds.

Strategy

Pushing innovation in 2013 MedStar Union Memorial became the first hospital in the US to offer the Rotation Medical Rotator Cuff System a new minimally invasive technology for patients suffering from rotator cuff disease.

To emphasize it parent's brand as part of its future growth strategy Union Memorial Hospital changed its name to MedStar Union Memorial Hospital in 2012.

Company Background

As Union Memorial the company celebrated its sesquicentennial anniversary in 2004. The hospital has been repeatedly recognized as among "America's Best Hospitals" by U.S. News & World Report. It's also considered one of the top 100 hospitals for intensive care and cardiovascular services.

The hospital was founded in 1839.

EXECUTIVES

Vice President Of Human Resources, Holly Adams

LOCATIONS

HQ: THE UNION MEMORIAL HOSPITAL
  201 E UNIVERSITY PKWY, BALTIMORE, MD
  212182891
Phone: 410 554-2865
Web: WWW.MEDSTARUNIONMEMORIAL.ORG

PRODUCTS/OPERATIONS

Selected Facilities

Arnold Palmer SportsHealth Center
The Curtis National Hand Center
The Harry and Jeanette Weinberg Heart Institute
Union Memorial Orthopaedics and Sports Medicine
Vascular Institute

COMPETITORS

Anne Arundel Medical Center	LifeBridge Health
Johns Hopkins Health System	St. Agnes HealthCare
	University of Maryland Medical System

HISTORICAL FINANCIALS

Company Type: Private

Income Statement

FYE: June 30

	REVENUE ($ mil.)	NET INCOME ($ mil.)	NET PROFIT MARGIN	EMPLOYEES
06/16	416	4	1.0%	2,400
06/15	413	10	2.4%	—
06/14	427	20	4.8%	—
06/13	408	(1)	—	—
Annual Growth	0.6%	—	—	—

2016 Year-End Financials

Return on assets: 2.9%
Return on equity: 1.0%
Current ratio: 1.20

Cash ($ mil.): —

THE UNITED ILLUMINATING COMPANY

EXECUTIVES

Pres-Ceo, James P Torgerson
Chb, Nathaniel D Woodson
Pres-Coo, Anthony J Vallillo
V Pres-Finance-Cfo, Richard Nicholas
Vp-Info Tech/CIO, W Marie Zanavich
Vp-Controller, Steven P Favuzza
Technical Specialist, Premjith L Singh
Treasurer, Kurt Mohlman
Coordinator, Tammie Jones
Supervisor, Frankie Nieves
Engineer, Rich Pinto

LOCATIONS

HQ: THE UNITED ILLUMINATING COMPANY
157 CHURCH ST FL 16, NEW HAVEN, CT 065102103
Phone: 203 499-2000
Web: WWW.UINET.COM

HISTORICAL FINANCIALS

Company Type: Private

Income Statement

FYE: December 31

	REVENUE ($ mil.)	NET INCOME ($ mil.)	NET PROFIT MARGIN	EMPLOYEES
12/17	921	105	11.4%	920
12/16*	866	84	9.7%	—
06/00	344	34	10.0%	—
Annual Growth	5.6%	6.4%	—	—

*Fiscal year change

THE UNITY HOSPITAL OF ROCHESTER

EXECUTIVES

President, Timothy McCormick
Health Care Director, Kathy Bello

LOCATIONS

HQ: THE UNITY HOSPITAL OF ROCHESTER
89 GENESEE ST, ROCHESTER, NY 146113201
Phone: 585 723-7000

HISTORICAL FINANCIALS

Company Type: Private

Income Statement

FYE: December 31

	REVENUE ($ mil.)	NET INCOME ($ mil.)	NET PROFIT MARGIN	EMPLOYEES
12/15	433	(24)	—	3,000
12/14	435	0	0.1%	—
12/12	398	8	2.1%	—
Annual Growth	2.8%	—	—	—

2015 Year-End Financials

Return on assets: 2.6%
Return on equity: (-5.6%)
Current ratio: 0.90

Cash ($ mil.): 25

THE UNIVERSITY OF CHICAGO

The University of Chicago ranks among the world's most esteemed major universities. It has an enrollment of more than 15000 students about two-thirds of which are graduate and professional students. It has a student-to-faculty ratio of about 7:1. The school's undergraduate branch offers a core curriculum based on the Great Books; students can choose from majors in about 50 areas. Among its graduate programs are the University of Chicago Law School and Booth School of Business both of which consistently rank in the top 10 according to U.S. News & World Report. The school also operates the University of Chicago Medical Center and has extensive research operations.

Operations

Founded in 1890 by John D. Rockefeller the University of Chicago has steadfastly stood its ground against trends in education curriculum requiring all students take courses that expose them to the social biological and physical sciences as well as humanities mathematics and language. It has also built up an extensive array of medical research and auxiliary enterprises. Among its many affiliated institutions are the Argonne National Laboratory the Yerkes Observatory and the University of Chicago Press.

Altogether the university's 14 divisions and schools employ some 2200 full-time faculty members.

Geographic Reach

Students attending the university primarily study at its 200-acre main campus on the South Side of Chicago but the university's Graduate School of Business also maintains campuses in downtown Chicago Hong Kong London Paris and Singapore. The University of Chicago is establishing a major academic center in Delhi India as well.

Financial Performance

The University of Chicago's top revenue producer is its medical center as patient care income accounts for about 45% of annual earnings. Student tuition and fees endowment payouts and government funding (grants and contracts) each account for more than 10% of sales. Other sources of income include auxiliary activities investment and asset payouts and private gifts grants and contracts. The university has an endowment of more than $6 billion.

Strategy

Recent expansion efforts on the University of Chicago campus include the establishment of an Institute of Politics for public and social service majors the construction of a new 10-story hospital pavilion on the medical center campus and the opening of on-campus child care facilities.

The university has also been renovating some of its buildings including its research facilities. In addition the University of Chicago is working to extend its research programs through partnerships with other like-minded organizations.

The University of Chicago has expanded its laboratory model to include new urban labs which are designed to use academic research to address problems in Chicago and other cities.

HISTORY

The University of Chicago took its name from the first U of C a small Baptist school that operated from 1858 to 1886. The school incorporated in 1890 was born when William Rainey Harper the man who was to become the University's first president convinced Standard Oil's John D. Rockefeller to provide a founding gift of $600000. Members of the American Baptist Education Society chipped in another $400000 and department store owner Marshall Field donated the land for the campus.

The university opened in 1892 with a faculty of 103 and 594 students. As it grew the university took over property that had been used in the Columbian Exposition of 1892-93 eventually surrounding the fair's former midway. (The school's football team later earned the nickname "Monsters of the Midway" while being coached by the legendary Amos Alonzo Stagg; this was before withdrawing from intercollegiate play in 1939. Legend has it that the university retains the right to rejoin the Big Ten.)

Only four years after its founding the university's enrollment of 1815 exceeded Harvard's. By 1907 43% of its 5000 students were women. Robert Maynard Hutchins president from 1929 to 1951 revolutionized the university and American higher education by insisting on the study of original sources (the Great Books) and competency testing through comprehensive exams. He organized the college and graduate divisions into their present structure reaffirming the role of the university as a place for intellectual exploration rather than vocational training. In 1942 the U of C ushered in the nuclear age when Enrico Fermi created the first controlled nuclear chain reaction in the school's abandoned football stadium.

From the 1950s through the 1970s the university purchased and restored Frank Lloyd Wright's famed Robie House and built the Joseph Regenstein Library (1970). In 1978 Hanna Holborn Gray became the first woman to be named president of a major university. Gray abolished the decade-old Lascivious Costume Ball a major social event (some would say the only social event) at the university.

EXECUTIVES

Vice President For Strategic Initiatives, David Greene
Vice President Communications, Julie Peterson
President, Robert J. (Bob) Zimmer
Vp And Chief Investment Officer, Mark A. Schmid, age 58
Dean Of Students, Michele Rasmussen
Evp Research Innovation And National Laboratories, Eric D. Isaacs
Evp Medical Affairs And Dean Biological Sciences Division And Pritzker School Of Medicine, Kenneth S. Polonsky

Dean The College, John W. Boyer
Dean Divinity School, Richard Rosengarten
Evp, David B. Fithian
Dean School Of Social Service Administration,
Neil B. Guterman
Dean Physical Sciences Division, Edward (Rocky)
Kolb
Dean Faculty Of Molecular Engineering, Matthew
Tirrell
Vp And Cfo, Ivan Samstein
Provost, Daniel Diermeier
Executive Vice Provost, Sian Beilock
Interim Dean Harris School Of Public Policy,
Kerwin Charles
Dean Law School, Thomas J. Miles
Dean Graham School Of Continuing Liberal And
Professional Studies, Mark R. Nemec
Dean Division Of The Social Sciences, David
Nirenberg
Dean Humanities Division, Anne Walters Robertson
Interim Dean Booth School Of Business, Douglas
J. Skinner
Vice President, Rob Vivoda
Vice President, Kyle Shen
Associate Vice President Research And National
Laboratories, Laurence Hill
Civic Engagement Vice President For College
Common Year, Sarah Geinosky
Development Vice President For, Margaret Kucera
Civic Engagement Vice President For College
Common Year, Deniz Inal
Civic Engagement Vice President For Urban
Teaching Program, Ikeisha Daniels
Civic Engagement Vice President For College
Common Year, Janel Beem
Civic Engagement Vice President For College
International Studies, Bruno Betat
Civic Engagement Vice President For College
Common Year, Serena May
Civic Engagement Vice President For College
Political Science, Rebecca Radding
Civic Engagement Vice President For College
Common Year, Cynthia Rosa
Enrollment Vice President For College Common
Year, Anna Akers-Pecht
Vice President, Kevin Chen
Vice President, Dick Rubin
Vice President Engineering, Robin Deneau
Vice President Finance Planning And Analysis,
James Fair
Vice President Of Finance, Marianna Zhang
Civic Engagement Vice President For
Anthropology, Zada Johnson
Vice President, Jason Zhou
Medical Director Peds Liver Transplant, Ruba
Azzam
Senior Vice President National Sales Manager,
Jose Gomez-urquiza
Vice President, Joshua Klopfenstein
Vice President Of Finance, Samir Khan
Vice President Civic Engagement, Derek Douglas
Assistant Vice President For Student Life, Michael
Hayes
Vice President Marketing, Michael Kristofka
Associate Vice President Shared Services, Ronald
Kolbash
Assistant Vice President Campus Planning
Sustainability, Alicia Berg
Vice Chairman, Dennis J. Keller, age 76
Chairman, Joseph Neubauer, age 77
Vice Chairman, Mary Louise Gorno
Secretary, Anna Girlich
Secretary, Nicolas Chua
Secretary, Ailsa Lipscombe
Auditors: KPMG LLP CHICAGO IL

LOCATIONS
HQ: THE UNIVERSITY OF CHICAGO
5801 S ELLIS AVE STE 1, CHICAGO, IL 606375418
Phone: 773 702-1234
Web: WWW.UCHICAGO.EDU

PRODUCTS/OPERATIONS

Selected Schools and Divisions
Biological Sciences Division
Chicago Booth School of Business
Divinity School
Graham School of Continuing Liberal and Professional
Studies
Harris School of Public Policy Studies
Humanities Division
Institute for Molecular Engineering
Law School
Oriental Institute
Physical Sciences Division
Pritzker School of Medicine
School of Social Service Administration
Social Sciences Division
The College (undergraduate studies)

Selected Undergraduate Majors
African and African American Studies
Ancient Studies
Art History
Biological Chemistry
Cinema and Media Studies
Classical Studies
Early Christian Literature
East Asian Languages and Civilization
English Language and Literature
Geographical Studies
Geophysical Sciences
Germanic Studies
History
History Philosophy and Social Studies of Science and
Medicine
International Studies
Jewish Studies
Latin American Studies
Medieval Studies
Music
Near Eastern Languages and Civilizations
Physics
Political Science
Psychology
Public Policy Studies
Religion and the Humanities
Romance Languages and Literatures
Russian Civilization
Sociology
South Asian Languages and Civilizations
Visual Arts

HISTORICAL FINANCIALS
Company Type: Private

Income Statement — FYE: June 30

	REVENUE ($ mil.)	NET INCOME ($ mil.)	NET PROFIT MARGIN	EMPLOYEES
06/17	4,355	980	22.5%	12,120
06/13	3,238	371	11.5%	—
06/12	2,207	(93)	—	—
06/11	2,271	218	9.6%	—
Annual Growth	11.5%	28.4%	—	—

2017 Year-End Financials
Return on assets: 23.1%   Cash ($ mil.): 50
Return on equity: 22.5%
Current ratio: —

THE UNIVERSITY OF CHICAGO MEDICAL CENTER

It may have received its official dedication on Halloween but The University of Chicago Medical Center (UCMC) works hard to make visiting the hospital a little less spooky. UCMC is a complex of facilities located on The University of Chicago campus that include the acute care Bernard A. Mitchell Hospital the Comer Children's Hospital a women's health and maternity facility and an outpatient care center. Established in 1927 (and dedicated on Halloween of that year) the complex includes the affiliated University of Chicago Pritzker School of Medicine and forms the clinical arm of The University of Chicago Division of Biological Sciences. UCMC houses about 550 beds.

Operations
Its Bernard A. Mitchell Hospital includes helicopter transportation operations emergency level-one pediatric trauma services and regional burn and peri-natal units. The roughly 155-bed Comer Children's Hospital offers disease care education and research as well as expanded newborn intensive care services.

UCMC sees some 23000 inpatients and 75000 emergency room visits per year. The hospital is one of the largest providers of uncompensated care in Illinois providing millions of dollars in charity care every year.

As part of the university's Biological Sciences division UCMC operates medical research centers focused on cancer immunology diabetes cardiology and neurology. The cancer center is especially intent on discovering improved treatment and prevention measures using gene and protein-based treatments. The Gwen and Jules Knapp Center for Biomedical Discovery works on discovery programs for a variety of medical conditions including diabetes cancer and pediatrics.

Geographic Reach
UCMC is located in Hyde Park on the south side of Chicago. Its main medical campus includes the Center for Care and Discovery Comer Children's Hospital Bernard A. Mitchell Hospital Chicago Lying-in Hospital and Duchossois Center for Advanced Medicine. UCMC also manages a network of area physicians and specialty clinics located in Chicago and its suburbs as well as in northwestern Indiana.

Strategy
UCMC is widening its service offerings through facility construction efforts. It completed a 1.2 million sq. ft. medical research and patient-centered care hospital pavilion on its main campus (named the Center for Care and Discovery) in 2012; the new facility opened its doors to 145 patients the following year.

Mergers and Acquisitions
In 2016 UCMC merged with community hospital system Ingalls Health which is now part of the UChicago Medicine brand. The combination of the health care partners allows the group to provide care across a full spectrum from routine visits to complicated treatments for life-threatening issues.

Company Background
First Lady Michelle Obama served as VP for community and external affairs at UCMC; she resigned from her post in early 2009 when she made the move to the White House.

EXECUTIVES

President, Sharon O'Keefe
Evp Medical Affairs; Dean Division Of The Biological Sciences And Pritzker School Of Medicine, Kenneth S. Polonsky
Vp Legal And Government Affairs And General Counsel, Susan S. Sher
Coo And Associate Dean, Carolyn S. Wilson
Cfo, James M. Watson
Vice President Finance, Gary Gasbarra
Vice President Revenue Cycle, Charlie Brown
Associate Vice President Individual Giving, Karen Paciero
Vice President Chief Pharmacy Officer, Kevin Colgan
Vice Chairman, Craig J. Duchossois
Vice Chairman, James S. (Jim) Frank
Chairman, Emily Nicklin
Auditors: PRICEWATERHOUSECOOPERS LLP WA

LOCATIONS

HQ: THE UNIVERSITY OF CHICAGO MEDICAL CENTER
  5841 S MARYLAND AVE, CHICAGO, IL 606371443
Phone: 773 702-1000
Web: WWW.UCHOSPITALS.EDU

PRODUCTS/OPERATIONS

Selected Services
Cancer
Endocrinology
Gastroenterology
Geriatrics
Heart
Kidney disease
Neurosciences
Orthopaedics
Respiratory disease
Surgery
Transplantation
Women's services

Selected Facilities
Bernard A. Mitchell Hospital
Center for Care and Discovery
Chicago Lying-in Hospital (Maternity and Women's Hospital)
Comer Children's Hospital
Duchossois Center for Advanced Medicine (outpatient care and diagnostics)
Gwen and Jules Knapp Center for Biomedical Discovery
LaRabida Children's Hospital (affiliated facility)
Mercy Hospital (affiliated facility)
University of Chicago Pritzker School of Medicine
Weiss Memorial Hospital (affiliated facility)

COMPETITORS

Advocate Health Care
Alexian Brothers Health System
Covenant Ministries
Elmhurst Memorial Healthcare
Loyola University Health System
Mercy Hospital and Medical Center
NorthShore University HealthSystem
Northwest Community Healthcare
Northwestern Memorial HealthCare
Rush System for Health
Silver Cross Hospital
Sinai Health System
St. Bernard Hospital and Health Care Center

HISTORICAL FINANCIALS
Company Type: Private

Income Statement
FYE: June 30

	REVENUE ($ mil.)	NET INCOME ($ mil.)	NET PROFIT MARGIN	EMPLOYEES
06/18	2,212	49	2.2%	5,000
06/15	1,610	148	9.2%	—
06/14	1,495	114	7.7%	—
06/09	1,294	(190)	—	—
Annual Growth	6.1%	—	—	—

2018 Year-End Financials
Return on assets: 11.4%   Cash ($ mil.): 211
Return on equity: 2.2%
Current ratio: 1.00

THE UNIVERSITY OF DAYTON

More than 10000 students make the University of Dayton one of the nation's largest Catholic universities and the largest private university in Ohio. The institution offers some 80 majors. Students are recruited on a national basis and from foreign countries. The student population approximates 7500 undergraduate and 2400 graduate students. It has a student-to-faculty ratio of 16:1. Well-known alumni include the late author and columnist Erma Bombeck and Super Bowl-winning NFL coaches Jon Gruden and Chuck Noll.

Geographic Reach
The university's students are primarily from Ohio and nine other Midwestern and Eastern US states.

Financial Performance
In fiscal 2016 the University of Dayton had $117.6 million in research sponsorship making it the 9th leading school for sponsored research among private comprehensive research universities without medical schools. It is the top US Catholic university for sponsored engineering research and development #2 nationally for federally sponsored materials research and development.

Company Background
The University of Dayton was founded in 1850 by the Society of Mary (the Marianists).

EXECUTIVES

Vice President Finance And Administrative Services, Thomas E Burkhardt
Associate Provost And Cio, Thomas D. (Tom) Skill
Dean University Libraries, Kathleen M. Webb
President, Eric F. Spina
Dean College Of Arts And Science, Paul H. Benson
Dean School Of Business Administration, Paul M. Bobrowski
Dean School Of Education And Health Sciences, Kevin R. Kelly
Dean College Of Arts And Sciences, Jason Pierce
Dean School Of Law, Andrew L. Strauss
Dean School Of Engineering, Eddy Rojas
Vp Finance And Administrative Services, Andy Horner
Vice President Of Facilities Management, Beth Keyes
Vice President Advancement, James Brothers
Vice President Student Development, William Fischer
Assistant Vice President And Director Of Leadership Development, Christine M Schramm

Co Chair Department Of Religious Studies, Joseph Kozar
Assistant Vice President For Student Development, Cari Wallace
Assistant Vice President And Treasurer, Phillip Chick
Vice President For Student Development, Bill Fischer
Vice President For Finance And Administrative Services, Andrew Horner
Vice President Of Communication: Vice President Of Finance, Erin Clark
Associate Vice President For Financial Support Services, Thomas Madden
Vice President For Facilities Management And Planning, Rick Assoc
Chairman, Steven D. Cobb
Vice Chairman, Martin A. Solma
Auditors: MCGLADREY LLP DAYTON OHIO

LOCATIONS

HQ: THE UNIVERSITY OF DAYTON
  300 COLLEGE PARK AVE, DAYTON, OH 454690002
Phone: 937 229-2919
Web: WWW.UDAYTON.EDU

HISTORICAL FINANCIALS
Company Type: Private

Income Statement
FYE: June 30

	REVENUE ($ mil.)	NET INCOME ($ mil.)	NET PROFIT MARGIN	EMPLOYEES
06/16	521	(11)	—	4,500
06/14	460	126	27.4%	—
06/13	444	96	21.7%	—
06/12	418	(21)	—	—
Annual Growth	5.6%	—	—	—

2016 Year-End Financials
Return on assets: 3.3%   Cash ($ mil.): 74
Return on equity: (-2.1%)
Current ratio: —

THE UNIVERSITY OF IOWA

EXECUTIVES

President, J. Bruce Harreld, age 68
Svp And University Treasurer, Douglas K. True
Dean College Of Law, Gail B. Agrawal
Cio, Steve R. Fleagle
Dean Graduate College, John C. Keller
Dean College Of Dentistry, David C. Johnsen
Dean College Of Engineering, P. Barry Butler
Dean College Of Public Health, Susan J. Curry
Dean College Of Liberal Arts And Sciences, Chaden Djalali
Dean Tippie College Of Business, Sarah Fisher Gardial
Dean College Of Engineering, Alec B. Scranton
Dean Carver College Of Medicine, Debra Schwinn
Dean College Of Nursing, Rita A. Frantz
Dean College Of Pharmacy, Donald E. Letendre
Dean University College, Beth F. Ingram
Assistant Vice President Of Medical Affairs, Jennifer Vermeer
Associate Vice President Donor Relations, Erin Lewis
Assistant Vice President And Executive Director, Marie Kerbeshian

President Board Of Regents, Bruce L. Rastetter, age 61
President Pro Tem Board Of Regents, Katie S. Mulholland
Secretary, Kathy Bell
Secretary Transplant, Catherine A Chapman
Auditors: MARY MOSIMAN CPA DES MOINES

LOCATIONS

HQ: THE UNIVERSITY OF IOWA
5W JEFFERSON ST # 101, IOWA CITY, IA 52242
Phone: 319 335-3500
Web: WWW.UIHEALTHCARE.ORG

PRODUCTS/OPERATIONS

Selected Colleges
College of Dentistry
College of Education
College of Engineering
College of Law
College of Liberal Arts and Sciences
College of Nursing
College of Pharmacy
College of Public Health
Graduate College
Henry B. Tippie College of Business
Roy J. and Lucille A. Carver College of Medicine

HISTORICAL FINANCIALS

Company Type: Private

Income Statement — FYE: June 30

	REVENUE ($ mil.)	NET INCOME ($ mil.)	NET PROFIT MARGIN	EMPLOYEES
06/16	2,859	253	8.9%	17,000
06/11	2,067	253	12.3%	—
06/08	1,684	150	8.9%	—
06/06	1,556	(237)	—	—
Annual Growth	6.3%	—	—	—

2016 Year-End Financials
Return on assets: 3.6%
Return on equity: 8.9%
Current ratio: 0.70
Cash ($ mil.): 144

THE UNIVERSITY OF KANSAS HOSPITAL

EXECUTIVES

Ceo, Bob Page
Pediatric Urologist, J Pat Murphy
Chief of Medicine, Bart McCann
Principal, Linsey Gregory
Internal Medicine Practitioner, Ahmad Tarakji
Neurology Specialist, Bhavana Patel
Internal Medicine Practitioner, Calvin Madrigal
Internal Medicine Practitioner, Donald Campbell Jr
Anesthesiologist, Nicholas Kaup
Anesthesiologist, Nicolas Patonai
Associate Professor, Shannon Criss

LOCATIONS

HQ: THE UNIVERSITY OF KANSAS HOSPITAL
4000 CAMBRIDGE ST, KANSAS CITY, KS 661608501
Phone: 913 588-5000
Web: WWW.KUMED.COM

HISTORICAL FINANCIALS

Company Type: Private

Income Statement — FYE: June 30

	REVENUE ($ mil.)	NET INCOME ($ mil.)	NET PROFIT MARGIN	EMPLOYEES
06/15	1,362	156	11.5%	10,000
06/02	321	6	2.0%	—
Annual Growth	11.8%	28.1%	—	—

2015 Year-End Financials
Return on assets: 4.1%
Return on equity: 11.5%
Current ratio: 1.70
Cash ($ mil.): 140

THE UNIVERSITY OF NORTH CAROLINA AT CHARLOTTE

The University of North Carolina at Charlotte is the second-largest of 17 institution members of the University of North Carolina system. Known as UNC Charlotte the university offers about 170 undergraduate and graduate programs including education architecture business and engineering. The university spans 1000 acres across four Charlotte campuses including a research campus with programs in manufacturing opto-electronics and information technology. More than 1000 full-time faculty members serve more than 27000 students — representing 22000 undergraduates and 5000 post-graduates. UNC Charlotte founded in 1946 to serve returning WWII veterans became a member of the UNC System in 1965.

Operations
UNC Charlotte which comprises four campuses in Charlotte North Carolina is supported by a $153 million endowment. Average annual in-state tuition and fees run $6107; out-of-state tuition and fees average $18636. The school is among the fastest-growing in the UNC System.

Sales and Marketing
The university which maintains an operating budget of about $543 million attracts slightly more women than men with 50.5% vs. 49.5% respectively. Of its 22000 undergraduate enrollment entering freshmen account for more than 3000.

Strategy
With the backing of the larger University of North Carolina system UNC Charlotte in fall 2012 began offering a bachelor's degree in neurodiagnostics and sleep science (NDSS). The degree offered in collaboration with UNC Chapel Hill's Department of Allied Health Sciences is the first of its kind in the world.

The university is also working to expand and improve its campuses. As part of its campus master plan UNC Charlotte completed seven major construction projects in recent years for buildings and infrastructure. These include the Center City Building Energy Production and Infrastructure Center (EPIC) Miltimore Residence Hall Motorsports Research Building Prospector Building north parking deck and a regional utility plant to support the EPIC building. The City Center Building costs $50.4 million to complete. At 11 stories the building serves as UNC Charlotte's academic and community engagement programming space.

In 2014 the UNC Charlotte opened an early college high school on its campus. The school's curriculum focuses on science technology engineering and math (STEM) courses with a special emphasis on energy and engineering. The high school welcomed its first class of 100 freshmen that fall.

Company Background
Initially offering evening classes the Charlotte Center opened in September 1946 to serve 278 freshmen and sophomore students on the Central High School grounds.

EXECUTIVES

Gpsg Vice President And Research Fair Committee Chairperson, Elizabeth G Shockey
Admissions Director, Amy Barsanti
Vice President, Christopher Dong
Board Member, Jane Neese
Secretary, Tracy Worthey
Auditors: BETH A WOOD CPA RALEIGH NO

LOCATIONS

HQ: THE UNIVERSITY OF NORTH CAROLINA AT CHARLOTTE
9201 UNIVERSITY CITY BLVD, CHARLOTTE, NC 282230001
Phone: 704 687-5727
Web: WWW.PUBLICHEALTH.UNCC.EDU

PRODUCTS/OPERATIONS

Selected Colleges
Colleges o
Business
Computing and Informatics
Education
Engineering
Health and Human Services
Liberal Arts & Sciences

HISTORICAL FINANCIALS

Company Type: Private

Income Statement — FYE: June 30

	REVENUE ($ mil.)	NET INCOME ($ mil.)	NET PROFIT MARGIN	EMPLOYEES
06/17	331	58	17.8%	3,030
06/16	319	67	21.0%	—
06/15	292	39	13.4%	—
06/14	269	27	10.2%	—
Annual Growth	7.1%	29.0%	—	—

2017 Year-End Financials
Return on assets: 4.2%
Return on equity: 17.8%
Current ratio: 5.00
Cash ($ mil.): 236

THE UNIVERSITY OF TOLEDO

One of Ohio's 14 state universities The University of Toledo (UT) is the third-largest by operating budget. It enrolls about 23000 students and offers more than 350 programs of study including master's degree and doctoral programs in more than 60 instructional departments. The university has a student-to-faculty ratio of 19:1. Its 14 colleges focus on subjects ranging from visual and performing arts to business and innovation as well as education engineering law medicine nursing pharmacy languages and human services. The school also operates the University of Toledo Medical Center.

Operations

The University of Toledo Medical Center affiliated with UT is a teaching hospital has three hospitals located on the UT Health Science Campus with a total of 320 beds in all three hospitals combined (the UT Medical Center a Rehabilitation Hospital and the Kobacker Center).

The UT Medical Center features a Level I trauma center and extensive medical training programs on UT's Health Science Campus. It provides treatments for strokes and cancer that are unique within the state. Other specialties include kidney transplants and cardiology.

Geographic Reach

UT students come from 45 US states and about 80 international countries. The school has an extensive distance learning program. In addition to the main campus in Toledo UT operates several satellite centers in Toledo (including the Health Science Campus the Scott Park Campus and the Center for the Visual Arts facility) and the Lake Erie Research and Education Center in Oregon Ohio.

Strategy

UT is working to enhance resources to better serve students as well as patients of its medical center. In addition to infrastructure and building projects UT is focused on recruiting and retaining quality faculty members and enhancing the quality and ranking of its academic programs. The university is also enhancing research and technology resources including collaborations with other schools and organizations.

Company Background

UT and the Medical University of Ohio merged in 2006. UT is accredited by the Higher Learning Commission of the North Central Association of Colleges and Schools.

UT was established in 1872 and became a member of the state university system in 1967.

EXECUTIVES

Interim Svp Finance And Administration, Lawrence (Larry) Kelley
Interim Dean Scott Honors College, Kelly Moore
Dean College Of Pharmacy And Pharmaceutical Sciences, Johnnie L. Early
President, Sharon L. Gaber
Dean College Of Engineering, Nagi Naganathan
Evp; Ceo Ut Medical Center, David R. Morlock
Interim Provost And Evp Academic Affairs, John A. Barrett
Evp; Dean College Of Medicine And Life Sciences, Christopher J. Cooper
Vice Provost; Executive Dean College Of Applied Science And Technology, Todd A. Rickel
Dean College Of Health Sciences, Christopher D. Ingersoll
Dean College Of Languages Literature And Social Sciences, Jamie Barlowe
Dean College Of Natural Sciences And Mathematics, Karen S. Bjorkman
Dean College Of Communication And The Arts, Debra A. Davis
Interim Dean College Of Social Justice And Human Service, Thomas G. (Tom) Gutteridge
Dean College Of Business And Innovation, Gary S. Insch
Dean College Of Graduate Studies, Patricia R. Komuniecki
Dean College Of Adult And Lifelong Learning, Dennis S. Lettman
Vp Cio And Cto, William McCreary
Interim Dean Herb College Of Education, Virginia Keil
Dean College Of Law, D. Benjamin Barros
Interim Dean College Of Nursing, Kelly Phillips
Interim Dean Youcollege, Julie Fischer-Kinney

Vice President Information Technology And Chief Officer, Godfrey Ovwigho
Associate Vice President For Finance, Bryan Dadey
Vice President, Kevin Kucera
Nursing Director, Andrew Fox
Associate Vice President For Academic Finance, Brenda Grant
Associate Vice President, Jovita Williams
Office Of The Vice President For Stude, Tracy Jahns
Vice President Of Information Technology, Dana Xiao
Vice President Student Affairs, David Meabon
Interim Vice President For Student Affairs, Phillip Cockrell
Interim Vice President For Enrollment Management, Stephanie Sanders
Assistant Vice President Enrollment Services And Financial Aid, Steve Schissler
Chairman, Sharon S. Speyer
Vice Chairman, Steven M. Cavanaugh
Secretary 1 Ali Adminstration, Sarah Moomey
Secretary 1 Neurology, Mildred Wegener
Secretary 2 Medicine, Lisa Johnston
Secretary 1 College Of Nursing, Roni Hoskins
Secretary Communication, Patricia Damschroder
Secretary 1 Nursing Advertising, Nora Longsworth
Treasurer, Anne Riley
Secretary, Debra Middleton
Secretary, Traci Mcdaniel
Secretary 2 Psychiatry, Jacquelyn Mcbee
Secretary, Jane Lawrence
Secretary, Sandra Dunbar
Secretary, Tamara Golkiewicz
Secretary, Tana Felkey
Secretary 1, Lilla Horton
Secretary General Inquiries, Jessica Bergman
Auditors: PLANTE & MORAN PLLC TOLEDO

LOCATIONS

HQ: THE UNIVERSITY OF TOLEDO
2801 W BANCROFT ST, TOLEDO, OH 436063390
Phone: 419 530-4636
Web: WWW.UTOLEDO.EDU

HISTORICAL FINANCIALS

Company Type: Private

Income Statement				FYE: June 30
	REVENUE ($ mil.)	NET INCOME ($ mil.)	NET PROFIT MARGIN	EMPLOYEES
06/17	728	(62)	—	7,000
06/16	753	(34)	—	—
06/12	724	2	0.3%	—
06/10	0	0	3.9%	—
Annual Growth	179.9%	—	—	—

2017 Year-End Financials

Return on assets: 3.5%
Return on equity: (-8.6%)
Current ratio: 1.00

Cash ($ mil.): 48

THE UNIVERSITY OF VERMONT HEALTH NETWORK INC

EXECUTIVES

Ceo, John Brumsted
General Manager, Steve Warren

Administrative Assistant, Dale Devino
Coordinator, Linnea Oosterman
Staff, Lynz Parker
Coordinator, Mercy Gingras
Customer Representativ, Ann Young
Registered Nurse, Catherine Falduto
Lead Recruiter and Talent Acqu, Megan Brunovsky
Senior Epic Cache Database ADM, Ross Mohn
Bachelor of Science In Nurse, Sarah Thomas
Auditors: PRICEWATERHOUSECOOPERS LLP BO

LOCATIONS

HQ: THE UNIVERSITY OF VERMONT HEALTH NETWORK INC
462 SHELBURNE RD, BURLINGTON, VT 054016947
Phone: 844 886-4325
Web: WWW.UVMHEALTH.ORG

HISTORICAL FINANCIALS

Company Type: Private

Income Statement				FYE: September 30
	REVENUE ($ mil.)	NET INCOME ($ mil.)	NET PROFIT MARGIN	EMPLOYEES
09/17	1,933	161	8.4%	1,300
09/16	1,748	92	5.3%	—
Annual Growth	10.6%	74.2%	—	—

2017 Year-End Financials

Return on assets: 2.9%
Return on equity: 8.4%
Current ratio: 1.70

Cash ($ mil.): 264

THE UNIVERSITY OF VERMONT MEDICAL CENTER INC

The University Of Vermont Medical Center (formerly Fletcher Allen Health Care) provides medical care in the Green Mountain State. The company operates an academic medical center in alliance with the University of Vermont. The not-for-profit health system serves residents of Vermont and northern New York through three primary hospital campuses and more than 130 outpatient clinics patient care sites and outreach programs. Its acute care medical centers have a combined 560-bed capacity and a medical staff of some 800 health care providers representing medical specializations including emergency/trauma care pediatrics and women's health. The health care system is a subsidiary of Fletcher Allen Partners.

Operations

The health system receives some 60000 emergency visits each year and its hospitals handle more than 50000 inpatient and outpatient visits per year as well as 2000 births.

Working with the University of Vermont's College of Medicine and College of Nursing and Health Sciences The University Of Vermont Medical Center helps connect bedside experience with medical research to improve overall quality of care. It also provides hands-on educational services for medical and nursing students as well as professionals undergoing specialty training.

Geographic Reach

The University Of Vermont Medical Center serves 160000 people who live in Vermont's Chittenden and Grand Isle counties.

Financial Performance

The company's revenues accounted for 68% of Fletcher Allen Partners' total revenues in 2014.

Strategy
In order to provide a cohesive health network in the region the health system is working to create an integrated care network in its service territory. It is also working to build out its IT and data management capabilities

The University of Vermont Medical Center also has affiliations with other area providers to increase referrals and cooperative care including Alice Hyde Medical Center Canton-Potsdam Hospital Moses Ludington Hospital Central Vermont Medical Center Champlain Valley Physicians Hospital and the Elizabethtown Community Hospital. It seeks to form new partnerships with additional facilities.

In 2015 the company changed its name from Fletcher Allen Health Care to The University of Vermont Medical Center as part of a branding strategy approved by the Fletcher Allen Partners and University of Vermont boards.

Company Background
The hospital system was created through the 1995 merger of the Fanny Allen Hospital (which opened in 1894) the Medical Center Hospital of Vermont (or Mary Fletcher Hospital founded in 1876) and the University Health Center (formed in 1971). The hospitals are now known as Fanny Allen Campus Medical Center Campus and UHC Campus.

Fletcher Allen Health Care completed the implementation of an electronic health records (EHR) system that connects patient records at all of its facilities in 2010.

EXECUTIVES

Medical Director, Terry Rabinowitz
Svp And Cio, Charles (Chuck) Podesta
President And Ceo, John R. Brumsted
Svp And Cfo, Roger Deshaies
President And Ceo University Of Vermont Medical Group, Paul Taheri
Vp Marketing And Communications, Teresa Murphy
Svp Coo And Chief Nursing Officer, Sandra L. Felis
Chief Medical Officer, Stephen Leffler
Interim President Uvm Medical Group Fletcher Allen, Howard Schapiro
Chief Medical Information Officer, Adam P. Buckley
Ceo Inter-lakes Health, Chip Holmes
Director Of Government Relations, Meg O'donnell
Vice President Hospital Services, Dawn Lebaron
Vice President Human Resources, Laurie Gunn
Vice President Information Systems And Supply Chain Services, Charles Miceli
Director Of Radiology, Paula Gonyea
Chairman, John Powell
Auditors: PRICEWATERHOUSECOOPERS LLP BO

LOCATIONS
HQ: THE UNIVERSITY OF VERMONT MEDICAL CENTER INC
111 COLCHESTER AVE, BURLINGTON, VT 054011473
Phone: 802 847-0000
Web: WWW.UVMHEALTH.ORG

PRODUCTS/OPERATIONS

Selected Services
Cancer Care
Heart & Vascular
Orthopedics
Primary Care
Urgent Care
Women's Health

COMPETITORS

Albany Medical Center   Rutland Regional
Ellis Hospital   Medical Center

New England Alliance for Health
NewYork-Presbyterian Healthcare
Northwell Health
Southwestern Vermont Health Care
Springfield Hospital
St. Peter's Health Partners

HISTORICAL FINANCIALS
Company Type: Private

Income Statement   FYE: September 30

	REVENUE ($ mil.)	NET INCOME ($ mil.)	NET PROFIT MARGIN	EMPLOYEES
09/17	1,246	129	10.4%	7,000
09/16	1,181	85	7.2%	
Annual Growth	5.5%	52.0%	—	—

2017 Year-End Financials
Return on assets: 3.1%   Cash ($ mil.): 150
Return on equity: 10.4%
Current ratio: 1.60

THE VALLEY HOSPITAL INC

The Valley Hospital is second to none when it comes to its Same-Day Service program. More than one-third of the company's annual patients experience its longstanding continuum of one-day service; fully half the surgeries performed are same-day. The not-for-profit hospital is a 450-bed facility providing general and emergency services to residents of New Jersey's Bergen County. The hospital belongs to the Valley Health System which also includes subsidiaries Valley Home Care and Valley Health Medical Group and is an affiliate member of NewYork-Presbyterian Healthcare. The Valley Hospital New Jersey's second busiest has more than 800 physicians on its medical staff.

Operations
The Valley Hospital is well known for its cardiology cancer maternity and neonatal care programs (including its neonatal ICU). Its key services also include emergency care orthopedics and neurosciences. The hospital's emergency department treated more than 75000 patients in 2013. That year the hospital also admitted more than 49240 patients and the delivered almost 3200 babies.

The Valley Hospital's cardiac service includes a full range of diagnostic and interventional cardiac treatment services including cardiac surgery coronary angioplasty and electrophysiology studies. The hospital is also known for its work in lung cancer diagnosis and treatment radiation oncology (including tomotherapy) chemotherapy and infusion GYN oncology prostate cancer care and other clinical and support services.

Geographic Reach
The hospital serves more than 440000 people in 32 towns in Bergen County and surrounding communities.

Strategy
The medical system is looking to improve its facilities and technology in order to keep up with demand. The Valley Hospital is the first and only hospital in northern New Jersey to offer brain and spinal surgery with a state-of-the-art O-armA® surgical imaging system purchased through a $1 million grant from The Bolger Foundation.

In 2012 The Valley Hospital Valley became the first hospital in northern New Jersey to offer the latest breast imaging technology — 3D breast tomosynthesis.

That year it also enhanced its capacity to perform minimally invasive surgery with the acquisition of the robotic da VinciA® Surgical System funded by a $1.6 million donation from The Bolger Foundation.

In 2012 the hospital opened a new Women's and Children's Resource Center to coordinate wide range of services for women and their families.

EXECUTIVES

Director Of Pharmacy, Ron Krych

LOCATIONS
HQ: THE VALLEY HOSPITAL INC
223 N VAN DIEN AVE, RIDGEWOOD, NJ 074502736
Phone: 201 447-8000
Web: WWW.VALLEYHEALTHCAREERS.COM

PRODUCTS/OPERATIONS

Selected Services
Adoption Screening and Evaluation Program
Ambulatory Infusion Center
Anticoagulation Management Service
Autism Services
Auxiliary
Barrett's Esophagus Center
Bariatric Surgery
Bereavement Services
Biplane
Bladder Cancer Care
Breast Center
Cancer Care
Capsule Endoscopy
Cardiac MRI
Cardiac Rehabilitation
Cardiac Surgery
Cardiology
Center for Childbirth
Kireker Center for Child Development
Center for Metabolic and Weight Loss Surgery
Center for Family Education
Center for Women's Heart Health
Center for Youth Fitness
Clinical Trials Oncology
Clinical Trials Cardiology
Colonoscopy
Community Resources
Complementary Medicine
Concussion Management Program
Continence Services
Cosmetic Laser Treatment
Critical Care
Diabetes Support Services
Diagnostic Imaging
Doula Program
Emergency Services
Emergency Services Pediatric
Employee Recognition
Endoscopic Ultrasound
Epilepsy Monitoring Program Adult
Epilepsy Center Pediatric
ERCP
Esophagogastroduodenoscopy (EGD)
Extended Care

COMPETITORS

Bergen Regional Medical
Englewood Hospital and Medical Center
Hackensack Meridian Health
Hackensack University Medical Center
Jersey City Medical Center
Newton Medical Center
Raritan Bay Medical Center
Robert Wood Johnson University Hospital at Rahway

HISTORICAL FINANCIALS

Company Type: Private

Income Statement | | | | FYE: December 31

	REVENUE ($ mil.)	NET INCOME ($ mil.)	NET PROFIT MARGIN	EMPLOYEES
12/17	657	80	12.2%	2,900
12/16	638	73	11.6%	—
12/15	621	83	13.4%	—
12/14	605	56	9.3%	—
Annual Growth	2.8%	12.6%	—	—

2017 Year-End Financials

Return on assets: 3.7%   Cash ($ mil.): 4
Return on equity: 12.2%
Current ratio: 0.90

THE VANDERBILT UNIVERSITY

The house that Cornelius built Vanderbilt University was founded in 1873 with a $1 million grant from industrialist Cornelius Vanderbilt. Since then the university's endowment has grown to $4.1 billion making the Nashville school a haven for its roughly 12600 students and more than 4200 full-time faculty members. Boasting a 7:1 student-faculty ratio Vanderbilt offers undergraduate and graduate programs in areas such as education and human development divinity engineering and the arts and sciences. The university operates 10 schools and colleges. Vanderbilt's Owen Graduate School of Management and its medical school regularly rank near the top in national surveys.

Operations

A major research university Vanderbilt receives millions of dollars each year in research funding from a variety of sources.

Vanderbilt is closely affiliated with the comprehensive Vanderbilt University Medical Center (VUMC) which conducts clinical trials and trains medical students. It's home to an acute care hospital a children's hospital and several clinics as well as the university's medical school research facilities and nursing programs. In 2016 Vanderbilt and VUMC officially split severing financial and legal ties (but not their ongoing affiliations).

Financial Performance

Vanderbilt University's revenue increased 3% to $1.3 billion in fiscal 2017 (ended June). Tuition and education fees less student financial aid contributed 21% of that revenue while grants and contracts contributed 18%. The Department of Health and Human Services (primarily the National Institutes of Health) was the largest source of government grants and contracts.

The school's expenses totaled $1.2 billion that year. Salaries wages and benefits as well as supplies and services made up the bulk of those expenses.

Strategy

Vanderbilt works to retain and recruit world-class faculty expand its hospitals and clinics and enhance its athletic facilities. For example it opened a new engineering and science building in 2016.

In 2016 Vanderbilt separated from its medical center (which restructured as the not-for-profit Vanderbilt University Medical Center or VUMC). The move allowed VUMC to be financially independent while still collaborating with the university for research and education.

Company Background

During its first 40 years of existence Vanderbilt was under the auspices of the Methodist Episcopal Church South. The Vanderbilt Board of Trust severed its ties with the church in 1914 after a dispute with the bishops over who would appoint university trustees.

EXECUTIVES

Chancellor, Nicholas S. Zeppos
Vice Chancellor Health Affairs And Dean School Of Medicine, Jeffrey R. Balser
Dean Of The Blair School Of Music, Mark Wait
Dean Peabody College, Camilla Benbow
Associate Provost And Dean Of Students, Mark Bandas
Dean Of The School Of Divinity, Emilie M. Townes
Vice Chancellor Finance And Cfo, Brett Sweet
Dean Of The Law School, Chris Guthrie
Vice Chancellor For Information Technology, John M. Lutz
Dean Of The School Of Engineering, Philippe Fauchet
Vice Chancellor General Counsel And Secretary, Audrey J. Anderson
Provost And Vice Chancellor For Academic Affairs, Susan Wente
Vice Chancellor For Administration, Eric Kopstain
Vice Provost For Enrollment And Dean Of Admissions, Douglas L. Christiansen
Interim Dean Of Libraries, Joseph D. Combs
Dean Of The Owen Graduate School Of Management, M. Eric Johnson
Dean Of The School Of Nursing, Linda Norman
Vice Chairman, Jackson W. Moore, age 69
Chairman, Mark F. Dalton, age 67
Vice Chairman, John Winkelried
Auditors: PRICEWATERHOUSECOOPERS LLP NE

LOCATIONS

HQ: THE VANDERBILT UNIVERSITY
2301 VANDERBILT PL, NASHVILLE, TN 372350002
Phone: 615 322-7311
Web: WWW.VANDERBILT.EDU

PRODUCTS/OPERATIONS

Selected Schools and Colleges
Blair School of Music
College of Arts and Science
Divinity School
Graduate School
Law School
Owen Graduate School of Management
Peabody College of Education and Human Development
School of Engineering
School of Medicine
School of Nursing

HISTORICAL FINANCIALS

Company Type: Private

Income Statement | | | | FYE: June 30

	REVENUE ($ mil.)	NET INCOME ($ mil.)	NET PROFIT MARGIN	EMPLOYEES
06/18	1,366	511	37.4%	21,000
06/17	1,311	374	28.6%	—
06/16	1,270	(569)	—	—
06/15	4,121	131	3.2%	—
Annual Growth	(30.8%)	57.3%	—	—

2018 Year-End Financials

Return on assets: 7.0%   Cash ($ mil.): 602
Return on equity: 37.4%
Current ratio: —

THE WASHINGTON UNIVERSITY

Washington University also known as Washington University in St. Louis (WUSTL) is the gateway to higher education for more than 13000 students. Founded in 1853 the independent university offers 90 bachelor's master's and doctoral degrees and has about 3400 faculty members. It offers approximately 1500 courses in fields such as arts and sciences business design and visual arts engineering law medicine and social work. WUSTL which has multiple campuses in and near the city of St. Louis also offers associate degree and continuing education programs. The affiliated Washington University Medical Center is an acute-care hospital that also provides educational training and research services.

Operations

The Medical Campus conducts extensive collaborative studies between students faculty and hospital staff as well as external institutions. Areas of research include genome sequencing of cancer patients and children's developmental studies. The 2000-acre Tyson Research Center outside the city is a biological field station that conducts environmental studies and research activities including renewable energy and sustainability programs some of which is coordinated with outside groups.

The university has an 8:1 student-to-faculty ratio. Its libraries contain more than 3.6 million books journals and other print materials and have access to more than 65000 electronic journals and a half million e-books.

In the academic year ending spring 2015 annual undergraduate educational costs totaled $45700.

Geographic Reach

In addition to the main 170-acre Danforth Campus in St. Louis WUSTL's facilities include the nearby 165-acre Medical Campus (housing the School of Medicine and the hospital facilities). Other operations include three smaller satellite academic campuses and music research and art centers in the greater St. Louis area.

Financial Performance

In fiscal 2015 revenue increased 9% to $2.7 billion on higher tuition and fees endowment spending distribution gifts and patient services. However a decline in non-operating revenue such as investment returns led to a 71% drop in net income which fell to $270 million.

Cash flow from operations spiked 522% to $104 million as less cash was used in net gains on investments.

Strategy

WUSTL has made efforts to extend its collaborations with third parties which can help bring in academic and research funds. In addition the university has worked to attract more government research grants in recent years. It is also upgrading some classroom and student facilities as well as hiring more experienced teachers and medical staff members to maintain its tuition auxiliary enterprise (lodging and vending) health services and research income expectations.

EXECUTIVES

Executive Vice Chancellor Administration, Henry S. Webber
Executive Vice Chancellor Alumni And Development Programs, David T. Blasingame
Executive Vice Chancellor And General Counsel, Michael R. Cannon
Chancellor, Mark S. Wrighton, age 69
Vice Chancellor Finance And Cfo, Barbara A. Feiner

Executive Vice Chancellor Medical Affairs And Dean School Of Medicine, Larry J. Shapiro
Dean Olin Business School, Mahendra R. Gupta
Dean Sam Fox School Of Design And Visual Arts, Carmon Colangelo
Dean George Warren Brown School Of Social Work, Edward F. Lawlor
Dean School Of Law, Kent D. Syverud
Provost And Executive Vice Chancellor Academic Affairs, H. Holden Thorp, age 54
Dean School Of Engineering And Applied Science, Ralph S. Quatrano
Dean Faculty Of Arts And Sciences, Barbara A. Schaal
Dean College Of Arts And Sciences, Jennifer R. Smith
Dean Graduate School Of Arts And Sciences, Richard J. Smith
Cio, Michael P. (Mike) Caputo
Vice Chairman, John F. McDonnell, age 79
Vice Chairman, David W. Kemper, age 67
Vice Chairman, Craig D. Schnuck, age 69
Vice Chairman, Stephen F. Brauer, age 73
Auditors: PRICEWATERHOUSECOOPERS LLP L

LOCATIONS

HQ: THE WASHINGTON UNIVERSITY
1 BROOKINGS DR, SAINT LOUIS, MO 631304899
Phone: 314 935-8566
Web: WWW.WUSTL.EDU

PRODUCTS/OPERATIONS

2015 Sales

	% of total
Patient service	36
Grants	14
Tuition & fees	13
Endowment spending distribution	10
Gifts	7
Educational	6
Others	14
Total	**100**

Selected Schools and Colleges

College of Arts & Sciences
  Graduate School of Arts & Sciences
  University College and Summer School (Arts & Sciences)
George Warren Brown School of Social Work
Sam Fox School of Design & Visual Arts
School of Engineering & Applied Science
School of Law
School of Medicine
Olin Business School

COMPETITORS

Bucknell University	Southeast Missouri
Missouri State	State University
University	University of Missouri
Saint Louis University	

HISTORICAL FINANCIALS

Company Type: Private

Income Statement				FYE: June 30
	REVENUE ($ mil.)	**NET INCOME ($ mil.)**	**NET PROFIT MARGIN**	**EMPLOYEES**
06/18	3,543	1,011	28.6%	9,600
06/17	3,068	737	24.0%	—
06/16	2,876	(303)	—	—
06/15	2,707	270	10.0%	—
Annual Growth	9.4%	55.3%	—	—

2018 Year-End Financials

Return on assets: 13.7%   Cash ($ mil.): 366
Return on equity: 28.6%
Current ratio: —

THE WHITING-TURNER CONTRACTING COMPANY

Whiting-Turner Contracting provides construction management general contracting and design/build services primarily for large commercial institutional and infrastructure projects conducted across the US. A key player in retail construction the employee-owned company also undertakes such projects as biotech cleanrooms theme parks historical restorations senior living residences educational facilities stadiums and corporate headquarters. Clients past and present include the US military AT&T General Motors and Texas A&M University. Whiting-Turner Contracting operates from more than 30 offices across the US.

Geographic Reach

The Baltimore-based company has offices in Arizona California Colorado Connecticut Delaware Florida Georgia Maryland Massachusetts Missouri Nevada New Jersey New York North Carolina Ohio Pennsylvania Texas Virginia and Washington DC.

Sales and Marketing

The contractor works on projects across a wide range of industries related to arts and entertainment education federal and military healthcare industrial office retail multi-family residential sports and fitness transportation and utilities among other fields.

Strategy

Whiting-Turner prefers to grow organically instead of making acquisitions. It has been steadily expanding by opening new offices in places such as California Texas and Virginia. The company in 2016 continued to rank among the Engineering News Record (ENR) top domestic general building contractors in the nation.

Some of the firm's recently awarded projects (as of mid-2016) include the Tropicana Pedestrian Bridge the Jacksonville Lung Bio Facility the Westowne Elementary School the Lexington Market the Costco Meat Production Plant the Sentara Norfolk General Hospital and the CoolSprings Galleria among others.

Whiting-Turner Contracting's past projects include the Joseph B. Whitehead Building at Emory University Vanderbilt Hall at Yale University projects at Universal Studios theme park and a vaccine facility at Chesapeake Biological Laboratories. Projects in the firm's hometown of Baltimore have included the city's convention center and the football stadium for the Baltimore Ravens. More recent projects include the Horseshoe Casino Cleveland University of Maryland Baltimore County (UMBC) Performing Arts & Humanities Naval Facilities Engineering Command (NAVFAC) Jacksonville Sentara Princess Anne Hospital Norwalk Community College Texas A&M University at Galveston Mary Moody Northen Student Center renovation Opry Mills the College of Business & Economics Vinson Hall Parking Garage a Coastal Studies Institute facility a Blue Diamond Growers building and a USPS Call Center.

Company Background

G.W.C. Whiting and LeBaron Turner classmates at MIT founded the company in 1909 to build sewer lines.

EXECUTIVES

Vp Richmond, Dani Niccolucci
Svp Allentown, Jack DaSilva
Division Vp Fort Lauderdale, Robert (Rob) Mitchell

Division Vp Delaware And Maryland, James (Jim) Martini
Svp District Of Columbia, Richard L. Vogel
Division Vp Pleasanton, Troy Caldwell
Svp Irvine, Len Cannatelli
Svp Baltimore, Gino J. Gemignani
Division Vp Dallas, Espen S. Brooks
Vp Bridgewater, Chris Martinson
Svp Atlanta, Keith Douglas
Vp, Daniel (Dan) Bauer
Vp Boston, Kevin Shields
Division Vp Las Vegas, Paul Schmitt
Division Vp Chantilly, Kempton C. Haile
Vp Tampa, Brent A. Voyles
Vp Denver, Mark Faul
Vp San Diego, Steven Likins
Vp Orlando, Robert Minutoli
Division Vp Raleigh, Chris Carlson
Vp White Plains, David Brickley
Vp San Antonio, Daryl Steinbeck
Vp Norfolk, John Berotti
Senior Project Manager Sacramento, Jack Stackalis
Vp Cleveland, Jeff Maeder
Regional Manager Kansas City, Adam Eshelbrenner
Regional Manager Charlotte, Chris Woods
Regional Manager Houston, Michael Browning
President And Ceo, Timothy J. Regan, age 62
Sr V Pres, Frank Palmer
Vice President, Scott McMahon
Vice President, Nancy Beavers
Vice President, Samuel Wells
Vice President, Kirk Hemphill
Senior Vice President, Kevin Higgins
Ashe Chc Vice President, Bob Moore
Vice President, Jesse Beam
Leed Ap Banking Division C Vice President, Patricia Carper
Division Vice President, Ed Schlotterback
Vice President, Karen Evans
Vice President, Jim Groff
Vice President, Irene Knott
Vice President, David McGinnis
Vice President Field Operations, Phil Knight
Vice President, Jeff Jenkins
Vice President, Bruce Delawder
Vice President, J Scott Breig
Vice President, Sam Abutaleb
Vice President, Chris Hoyson
Vice President San Diego, Miguel Huerta
Vice President, Edward Mackowiak
Vice President, Tony Moag
Vice President San Diego, Steve Likins
Executive Vice President And Chief Executive Officer, Tim Regan
Vice President, Jeffrey Baxter
Vice President, Craig Rayner
Division Vice President, Jeffrey Dodds
Vice President, Bernard LaHatte
Vice President, Andrew Linden
Division Vice President, Maynard Grizzard
Vice President, Terry Powell
Senior Vice President, Stephen Lambertson
Vice President, Kit Fawthrop
Vice President, Ray MacKeen
Secretary, Willie Mcfarlin
Vice Chairman, Nelson Griffin

LOCATIONS

HQ: THE WHITING-TURNER CONTRACTING COMPANY
300 E JOPPA RD STE 800, BALTIMORE, MD 212863047
Phone: 410 821-1100
Web: WWW.WHITING-TURNER.COM

Selected Locations

Maryland - Baltimore (Headquarters)
California - Los Angeles
California - San Diego
Connecticut - New Haven
Delaware -
District of Columbia

Florida - Ft. Lauderdale
Georgia -
Maryland -
Massachuse
Missouri - Kansas City
Nevada - Las Vegas
New Jersey
New York - White Plains
Ohio - Cleveland
Pennsylvan
Texas - San Antonio
Virginia -

PRODUCTS/OPERATIONS

Selected Services
Construction management
  Agency
  At-risk
Design/build
General contracting
Preconstruction

Selected Markets
Biotechnology and pharmaceutical
Cleanroom and high-technology
Education
Entertainment
Federal/military
Food/beverage distribution
Health care
Historical restoration
Industrial and manufacturing
Interiors
Life sciences
Lodging and hospitality
Mission critical facilities
Mixed use
Offices and headquarters
Parking garages
Restaurants
Retail
Senior living
Sports
Sustainable
Technology
  Microelectronics
  Nano
Theme parks
Utilities
Warehouse and distribution

COMPETITORS

Barton Malow	J.E. Dunn Construction
Bechtel	Group
Choate Construction	Jacobs Engineering
Clark Construction	Kitchell
Group	McCarthy Building
DPR Construction	Peter Kiewit Sons'
Fisher Development	Skanska
Fluor	Suffolk Construction
Gilbane	Swinerton
Hensel Phelps	Turner Corporation
Construction	Tutor Perini
Hoffman Corporation	Weitz

HISTORICAL FINANCIALS
Company Type: Private

Income Statement   FYE: December 31

	REVENUE ($ mil.)	NET INCOME ($ mil.)	NET PROFIT MARGIN	EMPLOYEES
12/17	6,172	68	1.1%	3,193
12/16	5,522	90	1.6%	—
12/15	5,729	80	1.4%	—
12/14	6,347	75	1.2%	—
Annual Growth	(0.9%)	(3.1%)	—	—

2017 Year-End Financials
Return on assets: 22.4%   Cash ($ mil.): 243
Return on equity: 1.1%
Current ratio: 0.70

THE WILLIAM W BACKUS HOSPITAL

EXECUTIVES

Pres, David Whitehead
Administrative Assistant, William Jorsz
Manager, Kim Brown
Manager, Mary Johnson
Coordinator, Paula Provost
Coordinator, Amy Dunion
Regional President, Dave Whitehead
Administrative Assistant, Donna Carter
Psychologist, James F Odea
Surgeon, Larry Coletti
Physician Assistant, Lauren Palmer

LOCATIONS

HQ: THE WILLIAM W BACKUS HOSPITAL
  326 WASHINGTON ST, NORWICH, CT 063602740
Phone: 860 889-8331
Web: WWW.BACKUSHOSPITAL.ORG

HISTORICAL FINANCIALS
Company Type: Private

Income Statement   FYE: September 30

	REVENUE ($ mil.)	NET INCOME ($ mil.)	NET PROFIT MARGIN	EMPLOYEES
09/17	339	104	30.7%	1,300
09/16	319	43	13.7%	—
09/15	285	40	14.3%	—
09/14	293	48	16.6%	—
Annual Growth	5.0%	29.0%	—	—

2017 Year-End Financials
Return on assets: 1.2%   Cash ($ mil.): 32
Return on equity: 30.7%
Current ratio: 3.10

THE WILLIAMSPORT HOSPITAL

EXECUTIVES

Ceo, Steven Johnson
President, Mary Chaya
Vice President, George Mancheste
Cfo, Charles Santangelo
SEC, Sally Holly
Internal Medicine Practitioner, Robert M Lennie
Internal Medicine Practitioner, Lalita Mittal
Doctor, James Redka
Auditors: BKD LLP SPRINGFIELD MO

LOCATIONS

HQ: THE WILLIAMSPORT HOSPITAL
  700 HIGH ST, WILLIAMSPORT, PA 177013198
Phone: 570 321-1000
Web: WWW.SUSQUEHANNAHEALTH.ORG

HISTORICAL FINANCIALS
Company Type: Private

Income Statement   FYE: June 30

	REVENUE ($ mil.)	NET INCOME ($ mil.)	NET PROFIT MARGIN	EMPLOYEES
06/16	332	23	7.0%	1,300
06/15	322	19	5.9%	—
06/14	297	5	2.0%	—
06/09	172	9	5.7%	—
Annual Growth	9.9%	13.2%	—	—

2016 Year-End Financials
Return on assets: 12.8%   Cash ($ mil.): 38
Return on equity: 7.0%
Current ratio: 0.30

THE WILLS GROUP INC

The Wills Group willingly delivers petroleum products and related products and services to its customer base in southern Maryland and adjacent areas. The family-owned company operates four business subsidiaries: Dash-In Convenience Stores (with 35 locations including 18 franchises); DMO (provider of propane heating oil and HVAC equipment); and Southern Maryland Oil (SMO) and SMO Motor Fuels (distribution of diesel gasoline and kerosene products). More than 90% of SMO's gasoline products are Shell-branded fuels. The Wills Group supplies more than 300 dealer-operated gas stations in Delaware southern Maryland and Washington DC.

Operations
The Wills Group divides its business into four operations: Dash-In Convenience Stores (serving the Maryland; Delaware; and Tidewater Virgina regions); DMO (propane heating oil and HVAC equipment maker); and Southern Maryland Oil (SMO) and SMO Motor Fuels (distribution of diesel gasoline and kerosene products).

Company Background
The company was founded in 1926 by Jim Wills and Harold Swann. In 1942 The Wills Group was the first principal fuel supplier to the newly built Patuxent Naval Air Station. In 1972 the company developed the first branded self-service station in Maryland. In 2012 Lock Wills was serving as the president of The Wills Group.

EXECUTIVES

Ceo-Chb, J Blacklock Wills Jr
Evp-Finance-Administration-sec, Kenneth J Halperin
Pres, Retail Marketing Unit, Julian B Wills III
Pres. Smo Energy, Joseph M Wills
Asst SEC, Kim Purdy
Evp-Human Resources-Asst Treas, Melon Yeshoalul
Bkpr, Brooke Rieman
Manager, Jeff Harris
Manager, Sean Smith
Auditors: RSM US LLP

LOCATIONS

HQ: THE WILLS GROUP INC
  6355 CRAIN HWY, LA PLATA, MD 206464267
Phone: 301 932-3600
Web: WWW.WILLSGROUP.COM

COMPETITORS

Dixie Gas & Oil	Weis Markets
Petroleum Marketers	Woodfin Oil
Quarles Petroleum	

HISTORICAL FINANCIALS

Company Type: Private

Income Statement

FYE: September 30

	REVENUE ($ mil.)	NET INCOME ($ mil.)	NET PROFIT MARGIN	EMPLOYEES
09/17	654	27	4.3%	280
09/12	1,039	15	1.5%	—
09/11	1,052	17	1.7%	—
Annual Growth	(7.6%)	8.0%	—	—

2017 Year-End Financials

Return on assets: 7.4%
Return on equity: 4.3%
Current ratio: 1.10
Cash ($ mil.): 48

THEDACARE, INC.

ThedaCare is a community health system that provides a wide range of health services to residents of nine central Wisconsin counties. It consists of five hospitals including Appleton Medical Center Theda Clark Medical Center New London Family Medical Center Shawano Medical Center and Riverside Medical Center in Waupaca; more than 20 physician locations; and community health and wellness programs. The hospitals provide primary and acute care and offer many specialized diagnostic and medical services including behavioral health care and women's and children's services. ThedaCare also operates long-term care and assisted living facilities and provides occupational health and emergency transport services.

Operations

The health system operates five hospitals and 22 physician locations and manages 150000 patients per year.

Geographic Reach

ThedaCare serves patients in more than nine counties in Eastern Wisconsin.

Strategy

ThedaCare is expanding its facilities to keep pace with demand.

In 2013 it began construction on the ThedaCare Medical Center-Shawano which is being built to replace the 82-year-old Shawano Medical Center. The less-than-$50 million project is expected to open in 2015.

In 2012 the company opened a new outpatient unit (featuring five private rooms) at the New London Family Medical Center (renamed ThedaCare Medical Center-New London as part of a rebranding push in 2013).

Expanding its insurance options in 2013 ThedaCare joined Anthem Blue Cross and Blue Shield's Blue Priority Network. Blue Priority is Anthem Blue Cross and Blue Shield's Accountable Care Organization network offering in eastern Wisconsin and was launched in 2012.

EXECUTIVES

Cio, Keith Livingston
President And Trustee, Dean Gruner, age 63
Chief Medical Officer, Greg Long
Vp Spine And Orthopedic Business, Mary Downs
Cfo, Tim Olson
Coo, Maryjeanne Schaffmeyer
Chief Nursing Executive, Laura Reed
Chair, John Davis
Auditors: WIPFLI LLP MILWAUKEE WISCONS

LOCATIONS

HQ: THEDACARE, INC.
122 E COLLEGE AVE STE 2A, APPLETON, WI 549115741
Phone: 920 735-5560
Web: WWW.THEDACARE.ORG

PRODUCTS/OPERATIONS

Selected Facilities and Programs

Appleton Medical Center
The Heritage Community (senior living)
ThedaCare Medical Center-New London
Peabody Manor (senior living)
Riverside Medical Center
Shawano Medical Center
Theda Clark Medical Center
ThedaCare at Home
ThedaCare at Work (occupational health services)
ThedaCare Behavioral Health
ThedaCare Physicians

COMPETITORS

Aspirus
Beaver Dam Community Hospitals
Beloit Health System
Benedictine Health System
Children's Hospital and Health System
Columbia St. Mary's
Dean Health Systems Inc.
Howard Young Health Care
Luther Midelfort
Marian Health System
Marshfield Clinic Health System
Sacred Heart Hospital
Tomah Memorial Hospital
UW Medical Foundation
University of Wisconsin Hospital and Clinics

HISTORICAL FINANCIALS

Company Type: Private

Income Statement

FYE: December 31

	REVENUE ($ mil.)	NET INCOME ($ mil.)	NET PROFIT MARGIN	EMPLOYEES
12/17	909	88	9.7%	7,000
12/14	809	76	9.4%	—
12/13	720	129	18.0%	—
12/12	276	(3)	—	—
Annual Growth	26.9%	—	—	—

2017 Year-End Financials

Return on assets: 2.0%
Return on equity: 9.7%
Current ratio: 1.60
Cash ($ mil.): 29

THOMAS JEFFERSON UNIVERSITY

Thomas Jefferson University named after a founding father of diverse interests is itself diversifying the world of medical training. Its Sidney Kimmel Medical College (formerly Jefferson Medical College) boasts departments in surgery and specialized areas including obstetrics neurology and psychiatry. The Graduate Studies department offers programs in public health and biomedical studies. The College of Health Professions has programs in nursing pharmacy bioscience technologies and counseling. Founded as Jefferson Medical College in 1824 it has granted more than 30000 medical degrees. In mid-2017 the school merged with Philadelphia University a design-focused liberal arts school.

Operations

Thomas Jefferson University has six schools: Jefferson College of Biomedical Sciences; Sidney Kimmel Medical College; Jefferson College of Health Professions; Jefferson College of Nursing; Jefferson College of Pharmacy; and Jefferson College of Population Health. It also operates six academic centers: the Clinical Skills & Simulation Center; the Interprofessional Education Center; the Career Development Center; the Center for Teaching & Learning; the Sidney Kimmel Cancer Center; and the Institute of Emerging Health Professions. Plans are in place to establish the Philadelphia University Honors Institute and the Philadelphia University Design Institute. It also offers several continuing education programs.

The combined university serves some 7500 students.

The university's medical school tests or treats 46000 inpatients and more than 1 million outpatients each year.

Geographic Reach

Thomas Jefferson University has campuses in the Center City and East Falls areas of Philadelphia.

Strategy

In 2015 Thomas Jefferson University merged with Abington Health a Philadelphia health care organization with two hospitals and several clinics. The merger gave Abington access to the university's educational and training facilities and expands the university's reach to the Philadelphia suburbs. In 2016 the organization's medical operations combined forces with Aria Health which now operates as Aria — Jefferson Health.

When the school completed its merger with Philadelphia University in 2017 the enlarged university retained the Thomas Jefferson University moniker.

Seeking to increase its brand recognition Thomas Jefferson University has paid almost $4 million to put its name on the transit station at its campus. The station previously the Market East Station will be the Jefferson Station for five years. The university has an option to renew for a total of nine years.

EXECUTIVES

Medical Director Jefferson Sleep Disorders Center, Karl Doghramji
Vp Finance And Cfo, Richard J. Schmid
President, Stephen K. Klasko
Cio, Doug Herrick
Dean Jefferson Medical College, Richard J. Tykocinski
Dean Graduate School Of Biomedical Sciences, Gerald B. Grunwald
Dean School Of Health Professions, Janice Burke
Dean School Of Nursing, Beth A. Swan
Dean School Of Pharmacy, Rebecca S. Finley
Dean School Of Population Health, David Nash
Dean Students And Admissions, Clara A. Callahan
Evp Chief Operating Officer, Larry Merlis
Senior Vice President And Chief Medical Information Officer, John Kairys
Vice President Of Career Development, Natalie Chernets
Co Vice President, Thomas Neill
Medical Director, Anthony Prestipino
Vice President Supply Chain, Robert Burkholder
Vice President Finance, Kathleen Stinsman
Nursing Director, Edward Tawyea
Vice President, Michael White
Associate Medical Director, Maria Aini
Pharmacy Manager, Michael Roshko
Pharmacy Manager, Robert Mcnutt
Vice President And Chief Pharmacy Officer, Brian G Swift

Vice President For Musculoskeletal Services, Rick Webster
Radiology Director, Vijay M Rao
Vice President, Chris Smith
Vice President Informaticsand Clinical Integration, Charleeda Redman
Vice President, Timothy Knowlton
Vice President, Daisy Zhang
Vice President, Rebecca McIntosh
Senior Vice President Strategy And Business Development, Monica Doyle
Operating Room Director, James Rowe
Vice President, Kate Votta
Associate Vice President Of Development For The Sidney Kimmel Cancer Center And Clinical Programs, Jonathan Agree
Vice President, Joseph Anton
Chairman, Richard C. Gozon, age 80
Secretary, Gerri Anderson
Treasurer, Mai Nguyen
Treasurer, Stephanie Henry
Treasurer, Clairissa Cruz
Secretary, Sara Munie
Secretary, Amanda Lacue
Secretary, Katelyn Scharf
Treasurer, David Merkow
Secretary, Hirsh Sharma
Secretary A, Cindy Lawrence
Secretary I, Elizabeth Roznowski
Treasurer, Ludwig Koeneke-hernandez

LOCATIONS

HQ: THOMAS JEFFERSON UNIVERSITY
1020 WALNUT ST STE 1, PHILADELPHIA, PA 191075567
Phone: 215 955-6000
Web: WWW.JEFFERSON.EDU

PRODUCTS/OPERATIONS

Selected Research Centers and Institutes
Center for Translational Medicine
Daniel Baugh Institute
Delaware Health Science Alliance
Farber Institute for Neuroscience
Jefferson Coordinating Center for Clinical Research
Jefferson Vaccine Center
Kimmel Cancer Center

Selected Colleges and Schools
Sidney Kimmel Medical College
Jefferson Graduate School of Biomedical Sciences
Jefferson School of Health Professions
Jefferson School of Nursing
Jefferson School of Pharmacy
Jefferson School of Population Health

HISTORICAL FINANCIALS
Company Type: Private

Income Statement				FYE: June 30
	REVENUE ($ mil.)	NET INCOME ($ mil.)	NET PROFIT MARGIN	EMPLOYEES
06/17	3,951	700	17.7%	10,625
06/16	136	8	6.5%	—
Annual Growth	2788.6%	7723.4%	—	—

2017 Year-End Financials
Return on assets: 7.4%   Cash ($ mil.): 259
Return on equity: 17.7%
Current ratio: 1.20

THOMAS JEFFERSON UNIVERSITY HOSPITALS, INC.

Named after the "Man of the People" Thomas Jefferson University Hospitals (dba Jefferson Health) serves the people of the Keystone State with a medical staff of more than 1200 and some 1550 beds. The system provides acute tertiary and specialty medical care from a dozen hospitals nearly 20 outpatient centers and about 10 urgent care centers. The hospital also administers cardiac care at the Jefferson Heart Institute which provides everything from minimally invasive surgical procedures to heart transplants. Additionally Jefferson Health operates as the teaching hospital for Thomas Jefferson University.

Operations
As part of its operations Jefferson Health offers several premier programs to its patients as well as 35 different specialties. The system performed Delaware Valley's first liver transplant and designated a kidney transplant center for live and deceased donor transplants. In addition to transplantation it provides surgical services heart and vascular digestive diseases and bones and joints in addition to its Kimmel Cancer Canter and Jefferson Hospital for Neuroscience. In 2014 the health system logged more than 470000 outpatient visits 45000 admissions and about 115000 emergency room visits.

Geographic Reach
Through a handful of locations Jefferson Health provides health care services to the residents of Philadelphia and the Delaware Valley. It shares a 13-acre campus with Thomas Jefferson University.

Strategy
In October 2017 Jefferson Health merged with New Jersey-based Kennedy Health which operated three hospitals. The transaction followed closely on the heels of Jefferson's mergers with Aria Health and Abington Health.

In 2015 Jefferson Health added a new feature to its telemedicine program JeffConnect called On-Demand Virtual Care which allows patients to connect with an emergency medicine physician via computers and mobile devices.

That year the Philadelphia 76ers partnered with the Rothman Institute and Jefferson Health. The Rothman Institute will provide the Official Orthopedics & Urgent Care of the Philadelphia 76ers as well as the Official Team Physicians; Jefferson Health became an official hospital of the Philadelphia 76ers.

In 2014 the system opened the Jefferson Angioplasty Center the outpatient practice for Jefferson's interventional cardiologists. It is co-located with the Vascular Center allowing for streamlined consultations and convenience as the two specialties often see the same patients.

That year it also introduced genomic analyses of breast cancer in-house using the Prosigna Breast Cancer Prognostic Gene Signature Assay significantly reducing turn-around time for test results and allowing patients to begin effective treatment sooner.

Company Background
Thomas Jefferson University Hospital was founded in 1825.

EXECUTIVES

Blood Bank Director, Jay Herman

Vice President Clinical Resource Management, Patrice Miller
Vice President Finance, Elizabeth Smith
Managing Director Infectious Disease, Janna Williams

LOCATIONS

HQ: THOMAS JEFFERSON UNIVERSITY HOSPITALS, INC.
111 S 11TH ST, PHILADELPHIA, PA 191074824
Phone: 215 955-5806
Web: WWW.JEFFERSON.EDU

PRODUCTS/OPERATIONS

Selected Services
Cancer
Diabetes & Endocrinology
Ear Nose & Throat
Gastroenterology
Geriatrics
Gynecology
Nephrology
Orthopedics
Pulmonology
Rehabilitation
Urology

Selected University Locations
Jefferson at the Navy Yard
Jefferson Medical College
Jefferson College of Graduate Studies
Jefferson Radiology
Jefferson School of Health Professions
Jefferson School of Nursing
Jefferson School of Pharmacy
Jefferson School of Population Health
Jefferson Voorhees

COMPETITORS

Albert Einstein Healthcare Network
Bryn Mawr Hospital
Community Health Systems
Doylestown Hospital
Mercy Health System
North Philadelphia Health System
Our Lady of Lourdes Medical Center
Pennsylvania Hospital
TUHS
Universal Health Services
University of Pennsylvania Health System

HISTORICAL FINANCIALS
Company Type: Private

Income Statement				FYE: June 30
	REVENUE ($ mil.)	NET INCOME ($ mil.)	NET PROFIT MARGIN	EMPLOYEES
06/16	1,495	76	5.1%	4,701
06/15	1,456	42	2.9%	—
06/14	1,510	51	3.4%	—
06/10	1,250	49	4.0%	—
Annual Growth	3.0%	7.7%	—	—

2016 Year-End Financials
Return on assets: 6.2%   Cash ($ mil.): 57
Return on equity: 5.1%
Current ratio: 1.30

THOMAS SAINT MIDTOWN HOSPITAL

EXECUTIVES

Ceo, Bernie Sherry
President, Tom Beeman

Vice President, Richard Glenn
Cfo, Ken Venuto
Cfo, Renee Kessler
Coo, Joseph R Pino
Cfo, Pam Hess
Coordinator, Cheryl Stevens
Procurement Staff, Gena James
Chief of Medicine, Tracey E Doering
Board of Directors, Brian Wilcox

LOCATIONS

HQ: THOMAS SAINT MIDTOWN HOSPITAL
 2000 CHURCH ST, NASHVILLE, TN 372360002
Phone: 615 284-5555
Web: WWW.STHEALTH.COM/LOCATIONS/SAINT-
 THOMAS-MIDTOWN-HOSPITAL

PRODUCTS/OPERATIONS

Selected Services
Bariatrics & Weight Loss
Cancer care
Cardiac care
Center for Breast Health
Center for Sleep
Chest Pain Network
Childbirth
Diabetes
Emergency Services
Joint Replacement
Neurosciences
Orthopedics
Physical Therapy
Rehabilitation Services
Sleep Center
Seton Support Center
Specialty Clinics
Spine Services
Sports Medicine
Surgery
Women's Health
Wound Care

COMPETITORS

HCA	Southern Hills
Kindred Healthcare	Vanderbilt University
Select Medical	Medical Center

HISTORICAL FINANCIALS
Company Type: Private

Income Statement   FYE: June 30

	REVENUE ($ mil.)	NET INCOME ($ mil.)	NET PROFIT MARGIN	EMPLOYEES
06/16	434	54	12.6%	4,500
06/15	414	51	12.4%	—
06/14	407	39	9.7%	—
06/05	0	0	—	—
Annual Growth	—	—	—	—

2016 Year-End Financials
Return on assets: 2.8%   Cash ($ mil.): —
Return on equity: 12.6%
Current ratio: 0.90

THOMPSON CONSTRUCTION GROUP, INC.

EXECUTIVES

Pres-Ceo, Greg A Thompson
Vice President, Marco G Lardi
Vice President, Lewis E Thompson
Vice President, Harold Turner

Cfo SEC-Treas, Curtis Hutto
Human Resources Director, Janice Poplin
Chief Financial Officer, Diane Schultz
Manager, Mark Martin
Programmer Analyst, Robert Anglin
Project Manager, Roger Dial
Vice-President, Bill Bryant

LOCATIONS

HQ: THOMPSON CONSTRUCTION GROUP, INC.
 100 N MAIN ST, SUMTER, SC 291504948
Phone: 803 773-8005
Web: WWW.THOMPSONTURNER.COM

HISTORICAL FINANCIALS
Company Type: Private

Income Statement   FYE: December 31

	REVENUE ($ mil.)	NET INCOME ($ mil.)	NET PROFIT MARGIN	EMPLOYEES
12/17	351	16	4.8%	120
12/16	335	13	3.9%	—
12/15	282	7	2.6%	—
12/14	187	4	2.6%	—
Annual Growth	23.4%	51.4%	—	—

TMH PHYSICIAN ORGANIZATION

EXECUTIVES

V Pres-Ceo, John Lyle
Dir-Treas, Mike Giblin
Treas, Edward L Tyrrell
SEC, Marc L Boom
Manager, Ganesh Kalambur
Coordinator, Jennifer Hamilton
Information Specialist, Thomas Daubner
Vice-President, Liisa Ortegon
Vice-President, Hackett Carole
Manager, Jill Roach
Consultant, Jose Solis

LOCATIONS

HQ: TMH PHYSICIAN ORGANIZATION
 6565 FANNIN ST STE D200, HOUSTON, TX
 770302703
Phone: 713 441-4182
Web: WWW.TMHS.ORG

HISTORICAL FINANCIALS
Company Type: Private

Income Statement   FYE: December 31

	REVENUE ($ mil.)	NET INCOME ($ mil.)	NET PROFIT MARGIN	EMPLOYEES
12/15	413	0	0.2%	12
12/14	360	1	0.5%	—
Annual Growth	14.7%	(60.3%)	—	—

2015 Year-End Financials
Return on assets: 11.1%   Cash ($ mil.): 1
Return on equity: 0.2%
Current ratio: 0.50

TOLEDO PUBLIC SCHOOLS

EXECUTIVES

Pres, Bob Vasquez
Vice President, Chris Varwig
Chb, Cecelia Adams
Supt, Romules Durant
Board of Directors, Lisa Sobecki
Prin, Polly Taylor-Gerken
Accounting Staff, Bodi S Sharon
Accounting Staff, Gloria Eckhart
Accounting Staff, Joan Jockett
Coordinator, Paula Martin
Acting Director, Teresa Quinn
Auditors: MARY TAYLOR CPA TOLEDO OH

LOCATIONS

HQ: TOLEDO PUBLIC SCHOOLS
 1609 N SUMMIT ST, TOLEDO, OH 436041806
Phone: 419 729-8200
Web: WWW.TPS.ORG

HISTORICAL FINANCIALS
Company Type: Private

Income Statement   FYE: June 30

	REVENUE ($ mil.)	NET INCOME ($ mil.)	NET PROFIT MARGIN	EMPLOYEES
06/17	454	7	1.7%	3,600
06/16	441	13	3.2%	—
06/09	0	0	50.8%	—
06/07	529	48	9.1%	—
Annual Growth	(1.5%)	(16.6%)	—	—

2017 Year-End Financials
Return on assets: 5.5%   Cash ($ mil.): 160
Return on equity: 1.7%
Current ratio: —

TOM LANGE COMPANY, INC.

EXECUTIVES

Ceo, Phil Gumpert
Pres, Greg Reinauer
Vice President, Michael Smith
Sr V Pres, Jimmy Griswold
Sr V Pres, Bruce Rubin
SEC Treas, Hugh Seelbach
Director, Denise Jones
Account Coordinator, Mason Laughridge
Account Manager Atlanta, Amanda Johnson
Account Manager, Mark Babuscio
Account Manager Atlanta, Preston McBrayer
Auditors: KERBER ECK & BRAECKEL LLP S

LOCATIONS

HQ: TOM LANGE COMPANY, INC.
 755 APPLE ORCHARD RD, SPRINGFIELD, IL
 627035914
Phone: 217 786-3300
Web: WWW.TOMLANGE.COM

COMPETITORS

A. Duda & Sons	FreshPoint
Caito Foods Service	Get Fresh Produce

Coast Citrus Distributors
Cristina Foods
The Oppenheimer Group
Wilson Farms

HISTORICAL FINANCIALS

Company Type: Private

Income Statement

FYE: August 31

	REVENUE ($ mil.)	NET INCOME ($ mil.)	NET PROFIT MARGIN	EMPLOYEES
08/17	471	7	1.6%	110
08/16	466	2	0.6%	—
08/15	441	1	0.2%	—
08/14	447	(19)	—	—
Annual Growth	1.7%	—	—	—

2017 Year-End Financials

Return on assets: 5.9%
Return on equity: 1.6%
Current ratio: 1.50
Cash ($ mil.): 15

TOMPKINS TRUST COMPANY

EXECUTIVES

Chb, James Byrnes
Prin, Steven Garner
Assistant Vice President and C, Kathy Manley
Assistant Vice President, Ronald Davenport
Assistant Vice President, Stacie Maybee
Human Resources Officer, Diane Aramini
Vice President, Karen Parks

LOCATIONS

HQ: TOMPKINS TRUST COMPANY
110 N TIOGA ST, ITHACA, NY 148504320
Phone: 607 257-1909
Web: WWW.TOMPKINSTRUST.COM

HISTORICAL FINANCIALS

Company Type: Private

Income Statement

FYE: December 31

	ASSETS ($ mil.)	NET INCOME ($ mil.)	INCOME AS % OF ASSETS	EMPLOYEES
12/17	2,118	21	1.0%	1
12/16	1,962	23	1.2%	—
12/15	1,805	24	1.3%	—
12/14	1,682	22	1.3%	—
Annual Growth	8.0%	(0.7%)	—	—

2017 Year-End Financials

Return on assets: —
Return on equity: 17.3%
Sales ($ mil): 126

TORRANCE UNIFIED SCHOOL DISTRICT

EXECUTIVES

Ceo, Michael Wermers
Supdt, George Mannon

Teacher, Bradley Cheney
Manager, Karen Sopp
Dean, Laura Romero
Teacher, Lawrence Brady
Reading Specialist, Ann Kiely
Facilities Specialist, Dave Domski
Secretary, Lynn Spellman
Member, Mark Steffen
Vice-President, Mary Puccio

LOCATIONS

HQ: TORRANCE UNIFIED SCHOOL DISTRICT
2335 PLAZA DEL AMO, TORRANCE, CA 905013420
Phone: 310 972-6500
Web: WWW.TUSD.ORG

HISTORICAL FINANCIALS

Company Type: Private

Income Statement

FYE: June 30

	REVENUE ($ mil.)	NET INCOME ($ mil.)	NET PROFIT MARGIN	EMPLOYEES
06/17	286	(16)	—	1,806
06/16*	282	24	8.8%	—
02/09	0	0	21.9%	—
06/06	212	0		—
Annual Growth	2.7%	—	—	—

*Fiscal year change

2017 Year-End Financials

Return on assets: 16.5%
Return on equity: (-5.7%)
Current ratio: —
Cash ($ mil.): 318

TOTAL HEALTH CARE, INC.

Total Health Care provides health care coverage and related services to members in southeast Michigan (the greater Detroit area) and surrounding counties. Groups and individuals can choose Total Health Care for their health insurance. The HMO serves more than 80000 members through individual and group health plan policies. Total Health Care also has a contract with the State of Michigan to serve patients with coverage through Medicaid and the State's MI Child program. Pharmacy services are provided through a contracted network of pharmacy providers.

Operations

Total Health Care's network consists of more than 700 health care centers and more than 1200 primary care physicians.

Geographic Reach

The company operates in Wayne Oakland Macomb and Genesee counties.

Company Background

Total Health Care traces it roots to 1973. Its current from came from a reincorporation in 1982.

EXECUTIVES

Accounting Staff, Peggy Fritz
Customer Representativ, Mary Schmidt
Account Executive, Stefanie Sims
Member, Tiffany Woods
Chief Operating Officer, Randy Narowitz
Auditors: PLANTE & MORAN PLLC AUBURN HI

LOCATIONS

HQ: TOTAL HEALTH CARE, INC.
3011 W GRAND BLVD # 1600, DETROIT, MI 482023000
Phone: 313 871-2000
Web: WWW.THCMI.COM

PRODUCTS/OPERATIONS

Selected Services
Adult Primary Care
Alcohol and Substance Abuse Treatment Services
Behavioral and Mental Health Services
Dental Services
Health and Nutrition Education
HIV/AIDS Medical Care and Support Services
Immediate Care
On-Site Retail Pharmacy
Patient-Centered Medical Home
Pediatric and Adolescent Care
Women's Health

COMPETITORS

Aetna
Anthem
Blue Cross Blue Shield of Michigan
CIGNA
Florida Blue
Health Alliance Plan of Michigan
Health Net
Humana
Kaiser Foundation Health Plan
Molina Healthcare
Priority Health
UnitedHealth Group
Vista South Florida

HISTORICAL FINANCIALS

Company Type: Private

Income Statement

FYE: December 31

	REVENUE ($ mil.)	NET INCOME ($ mil.)	NET PROFIT MARGIN	EMPLOYEES
12/15	322	5	1.8%	100
12/14	272	5	1.8%	—
12/13	224	(6)	—	—
12/01	0	0	—	—
Annual Growth	—	—	—	—

2015 Year-End Financials

Return on assets: 13.2%
Return on equity: 1.8%
Current ratio: 1.20
Cash ($ mil.): 46

TOURO INFIRMARY

EXECUTIVES

Pres, James Montgomery
Scientist, Alexandra Windle
Coordinator, Ronnie Landry
Director of Admissions, Denise Eshleman
Chief Officer, Jeffrey Coco
Director, Sandy McCall

LOCATIONS

HQ: TOURO INFIRMARY
1401 FOUCHER ST, NEW ORLEANS, LA 701153593
Phone: 504 897-7011
Web: WWW.TOURO.COM

HISTORICAL FINANCIALS
Company Type: Private

Income Statement				FYE: December 31
	REVENUE ($ mil.)	NET INCOME ($ mil.)	NET PROFIT MARGIN	EMPLOYEES
12/16	289	24	8.6%	1,000
12/15	273	35	12.8%	—
12/14	271	9	3.4%	—
12/13	348	82	23.7%	—
Annual Growth	(6.1%)	(33.2%)	—	—

2016 Year-End Financials
Return on assets: 6.7%
Return on equity: 8.6%
Current ratio: 1.90

Cash ($ mil.): 29

TOWER FEDERAL CREDIT UNION

EXECUTIVES

Chb, George Cumberledge
President, Martin Breland
Treas, Charles Nossick
Chief Technology Officer, Allen W Bach
Chief Financial Officer, Allen Bach
Manager, Peggy Stavely
Technician, Terrell Moore
Network Analyst, Mike Aguilar
Accountant, Samantha Adams
Project Coordinator, Susan Moury
Information Specialist, Cindy Spurlin

LOCATIONS

HQ: TOWER FEDERAL CREDIT UNION
7901 SANDY SPRING RD # 102, LAUREL, MD
207073589
Phone: 301 497-7000
Web: WWW.TOWERFCU.ORG

HISTORICAL FINANCIALS
Company Type: Private

Income Statement				FYE: December 31
	ASSETS ($ mil.)	NET INCOME ($ mil.)	INCOME AS % OF ASSETS	EMPLOYEES
12/17	2,964	22	0.8%	490
12/16	2,925	18	0.6%	—
Annual Growth	1.3%	23.7%	—	—

2017 Year-End Financials
Return on assets: 37.4%
Return on equity: 26.3%

Sales ($ mil): 86

TOWN OF BROOKHAVEN

EXECUTIVES

Supervisor, Mark Lesko
Deputy Supervisor, Kathleen Walsh
Assistant Chief, Paul Degen
Coordinator, Donna Hall
Secretary, Anthony Vega
Senior Manager, Lisa Keys

Coordinator, Sarah Anker
Personnel Executive, Catherine Diamante
Purchasing Coordinator, Kathleen Koppenhoefer
Planning Staff, Tullio Bertoli
Director of Information Techno, W S Bradley
Auditors: TOSKI & CO PC WILLIAMSVIL

LOCATIONS

HQ: TOWN OF BROOKHAVEN
1 INDEPENDENCE HL FRNT, FARMINGVILLE, NY
117382150
Phone: 631 451-6680
Web: WWW.BROOKHAVEN.ORG

HISTORICAL FINANCIALS
Company Type: Private

Income Statement				FYE: December 31
	REVENUE ($ mil.)	NET INCOME ($ mil.)	NET PROFIT MARGIN	EMPLOYEES
12/17	321	27	8.7%	1,311
12/16	309	10	3.3%	—
12/12	306	53	17.5%	—
12/11	285	(56)	—	—
Annual Growth	2.0%	—	—	—

2017 Year-End Financials
Return on assets: 8.6%
Return on equity: 8.7%
Current ratio: 1.80

Cash ($ mil.): 184

TOWNSHIP HIGH SCHOOL DISTRICT 211 FOUNDATION

Township High School District 211 is the largest high school district in Illinois with some 12500 students attending its five high schools (grades 9 to 12) — James B. Conant William Fremd Hoffman Estates Palatine and Schaumburg — and two special education academies. The district's student-teacher ratio is nearly 14-to-1 and serves several suburban communities 25 miles northwest of Chicago. The school district started as one school (Palatine High School) in the Palatine-Schaumburg Township area in 1875 with the first graduating class in 1877.

Geographic Reach
Township High School District 211 serves the northwest suburbs of Chicago including the the communities of Hoffman Estates Inverness Palatine and Schaumburg as well as parts of Arlington Heights Elk Grove Village Hanover Park Rolling Meadows Roselle Streamwood and South Barrington.

Financial Performance
The school district reported revenue of nearly $240 million in 2012 nearly 85% of it coming from local property taxes.

EXECUTIVES

Department Chair Teacher, Kristy Loughin-Vance
Secretary To The Director Of Administrative Services, Pamela DE Groves
Board Member, Will Hinshaw
Auditors: BAKER TILLY VIRCHOW KRAUSE LL

LOCATIONS

HQ: TOWNSHIP HIGH SCHOOL DISTRICT 211
FOUNDATION
1750 S ROSELLE RD STE 100, PALATINE, IL
600677302
Phone: 708 359-3300
Web: WWW.D211.ORG

PRODUCTS/OPERATIONS

Schools
High Schools
James B. Conant High School
William Fremd High School
Hoffman Estates High School
Palatine High School
Schaumburg High School
Special Education Schools
District 211 Academy North
District 211 Academy South

HISTORICAL FINANCIALS
Company Type: Private

Income Statement				FYE: June 30
	REVENUE ($ mil.)	NET INCOME ($ mil.)	NET PROFIT MARGIN	EMPLOYEES
06/17	331	(15)	—	1,909
06/16	304	(10)	—	—
06/15	296	(17)	—	—
06/14	280	(8)	—	—
Annual Growth	5.7%	—	—	—

TOWNSHIP HIGH SCHOOL DISTRICT 214

EXECUTIVES

Pres, Alva Kreutcer
Prin, William J Dussling
Supt, David R Schuler
Vice President, Dan Petro
Facilities Manager, Brian Lichtenberger
Payroll Staff, Cathy Antos
Coordinator, Donna Archibald
Accounting Staff, Eileen Gattas
Coordinator, Karen Schwartzwald
Vice-President, Mark Hineman
Supervisor, Rose Collins
Auditors: BAKER TILLY VIRCHOW KRAUSE LL

LOCATIONS

HQ: TOWNSHIP HIGH SCHOOL DISTRICT 214
2121 S GOEBBERT RD, ARLINGTON HEIGHTS, IL
600054205
Phone: 847 718-7600
Web: WWW.D214.ORG

HISTORICAL FINANCIALS
Company Type: Private

Income Statement				FYE: June 30
	REVENUE ($ mil.)	NET INCOME ($ mil.)	NET PROFIT MARGIN	EMPLOYEES
06/17	337	8	2.5%	1,550
06/16	306	(14)	—	—
06/13	282	11	4.1%	—
06/12	259	15	6.0%	—
Annual Growth	5.4%	(11.5%)	—	—

2017 Year-End Financials
Return on assets: 0.3%   Cash ($ mil.): —
Return on equity: 2.5%
Current ratio: —

TRAMMO, INC.

Stockpiles of fertilizers liquefied petroleum gas (LPG) and petrochemicals are the "ammo" which international trader Trammo (formerly Transammonia) uses in its battle with competitors. The company trades distributes and transports these commodities around the world. Trammo's fertilizer business includes ammonia phosphates and urea. Its Sea-3 subsidiary imports and distributes propane to residential commercial and industrial customers in the northeastern US and Florida. The Trammochem unit trades in petrochemicals specializing in aromatics and olefins. Its Trammo Gas trades LPG and propane as well as ethane butane and natural gas in the US.

Operations

The company operates three divisions: Chemicals Commodities and Gas. The Chemicals Division's annual sales volumes is about 5.6 million metric tons. It key products include aromatics olefins and oxygenates. The Commodities Division accounts for two thirds of the Trammo's sales volumes and more than half of its revenues; it's worldwide traded volume is 29.2 million metric tons a year. The Gas Division's business areas include LPG business Trammo Gas and Petrochemicals Ltd and Sea-3 Inc. Trammo's international traded ammonia volume is 3 million metric tons annually.

Sea-3 is the largest importer and distributor of liquefied propane in the Northeastern US. It also supplies propane to the western and central portions of Florida. It moves 200000 metric tons of product per year.

Trammochem merchandises and trades in petrochemicals around the world.

Trammo Gas markets and trades LPG (primarily propane) in the US. Trammo Gas International Inc. operates two gas carriers which transport LPG worldwide for third parties.

Geographic Reach

Trammo has expanded its reach into the global market establishing merchandising and trading offices in Singapore China and the United Arab Emirates. Those offices complement its other global operations in Africa Asia Europe the Middle East and North and South America (Argentina Brazil and Chile). It has major representative offices in Beijing Cairo Dubai and Shanghai.

Its Fertilizers and Commodities Division's regional hubs are in Zurich Tampa Dubai Shanghai and Singapore; the Ammonia Division has hubs in Tampa and Dubai. The Chemicals Division maintains regional hubs in Zurich Dubai Shanghai and Singapore; while the Gas Division maintains hubs in Houston Tampa and Newington (New Hampshire).

Trammo has about 30 offices worldwide.

Sales and Marketing

To bridge the gap between the production locations and consumers sites Trammo owns and operates a fleet of railcars dedicated to transporting of molten sulfur in across the US. The Commodities Division about 650 railcars to ship dry and liquid fertilizers sulfur sulfuric acid and ammonia.

Strategy

In late 2016 it was reported that Trammo would exit the petrochemicals trading market following a reorganization.

In 2015 the company's Ammonia Division and Fertilizers and Commodities Division merged into a new division — Commodities. The merger allows Trammo to increase operational synergies use its global infrastructure to provide a larger portfolio of products and to more clearly present itself as a single company with different products.

Trammo opened offices in Ivory Coast and Dar Es Salaam in 2014 to strengthens its presence in the emerging African market.

Company Background

In 2013 Transammonia changed its name to Trammo to more accurately represent the broad spectrum of products and services it provides.

In 2010 the company's bulk carriers division entered the commodity shipping business. TA Bulk Carriers operates a fleet of 15 to 20 vessels which trade worldwide but focus on the handysize market (25000-35000 metric tons deadweight) in the Atlantic basin. In 2010 it transported about 2.9 million metric tons of cargo primarily fertilizers and grains.

Ronald Stanton founded the company in 1965 as an international ammonia trader. It branched into fertilizer merchandising and trading in 1967 LPG trading in 1978 and petrochemicals trading in 1987.

EXECUTIVES

Evp Coo And Cfo, Edward G. Weiner
Ceo Chemicals Division, Ashok Kishore
President Ceo Director And Ceo Commodities Division, Brent Hart
Svp Global Risk Management, Oliver K. Stanton
Executive Vice President General Counsel Sec, Fred Lowenfels
Senior Vice President Chief Accounting Officer, Robert Lovett
Vice President Of Human Resources, Pat Berry
Senior Vice President Ammonia Division, Bernard Rock
Vice President, Dudley Gray
Assistant Vice President, Donald Madden
Auditors: RSM US LLP

LOCATIONS

HQ: TRAMMO, INC.
1 ROCKEFELLER PLZ FL 9, NEW YORK, NY 100202078
Phone: 212 223-3200
Web: WWW.TRAMMO.COM

PRODUCTS/OPERATIONS

Major Subsidiaries
Sea-3 (liquefied propane)
Trammo Gas (LPG)
Trammo Gas International Inc. (LPG transportation for third parties)
Trammo Petroleum (crude oil and oil products)
Trammochem (petrochemicals)
Fertilizers and Commodities
Nitrogen BasedAnhydrous Ammo

COMPETITORS

BASF SE	HELM
CF Industries	Koch Industries Inc.
Cargill	Magellan Midstream
ConAgra	Yara

HISTORICAL FINANCIALS

Company Type: Private

Income Statement   FYE: December 31

	REVENUE ($ mil.)	NET INCOME ($ mil.)	NET PROFIT MARGIN	EMPLOYEES
12/17	3,006	31	1.0%	250
12/16	6,453	(229)	—	—
12/14	11,266	31	0.3%	—
12/13	11,315	(11)	—	—
Annual Growth	(28.2%)	—	—	—

2017 Year-End Financials

Return on assets: 7.1%   Cash ($ mil.): 71
Return on equity: 1.0%
Current ratio: 0.80

TRI-COUNTIES ASSOCIATION FOR THE DEVELOPMENTALLY DISABLED, INC.

EXECUTIVES

Pres, Bob Cobbs
Exec Dir, Omar Noorzad
Occupational Specia, Santa Barbara
Coordinator, Katy Kelly
Coordinator, Mildred Figueroa
Staff, Bob Nopar
Coordinator, Carlos Rodriguez
Coordinator, Michael Marvin
Coordinator, Colleen Duncan
Coordinator, Cynthia Marshall
Coordinator, Esequiel Vargas
Auditors: WINDES INC LONG BEACH CA

LOCATIONS

HQ: TRI-COUNTIES ASSOCIATION FOR THE DEVELOPMENTALLY DISABLED, INC.
520 E MONTECITO ST, SANTA BARBARA, CA 931033278
Phone: 805 962-7881
Web: WWW.TRI-COUNTIES.ORG

HISTORICAL FINANCIALS

Company Type: Private

Income Statement   FYE: June 30

	REVENUE ($ mil.)	NET INCOME ($ mil.)	NET PROFIT MARGIN	EMPLOYEES
06/17	293	0	0.0%	240
06/14	229	(0)	—	—
06/13	218	(0)	—	—
06/12	209	0	0.0%	—
Annual Growth	6.9%	12.2%	—	—

2017 Year-End Financials

Return on assets: 10.6%   Cash ($ mil.): 11
Return on equity: —
Current ratio: —

TRIAD E&C HOLDINGS, L.L.C.

EXECUTIVES

Manager, Brian Bordelon
SEC, Tami H Misuraca
Auditors: HANNIS T BOURGEOIS LLP BATON

LOCATIONS

HQ: TRIAD E&C HOLDINGS, L.L.C.
  8183 W EL CAJON DR, BATON ROUGE, LA 708158035
Phone: 225 927-8921

HISTORICAL FINANCIALS

Company Type: Private

Income Statement — FYE: June 30

	REVENUE ($ mil.)	NET INCOME ($ mil.)	NET PROFIT MARGIN	EMPLOYEES
06/18	317	0	—	2,000
06/17	293	0	—	—
06/16	306	0	—	—
06/15	291	0	—	—
Annual Growth	2.9%	—	—	—

2018 Year-End Financials

Return on assets: 1.5%
Return on equity: —
Current ratio: 1.70

Cash ($ mil.): 6

TRIAD ELECTRIC & CONTROLS INC

EXECUTIVES

Pres, Brian Bordelon
Secretary, Tami H Misuraca
V Pres-Gen Mgr, Eric Coco
V Pres-Gen Mgr, Wes Mincin
V Pres-Gen Mgr, Danny Campbell
Vp-Gen Mgr, Vincent Thibodaux
Project Coordinator, Clayton Mounger
Purchasing, Robert Evans
Auditors: HANNIS T BOURGEOIS LLP BATON

LOCATIONS

HQ: TRIAD ELECTRIC & CONTROLS INC
  2288 N AIRWAY DR, BATON ROUGE, LA 708158132
Phone: 225 923-0604
Web: WWW.TRIADELECTRICANDCONTROLS.COM

HISTORICAL FINANCIALS

Company Type: Private

Income Statement — FYE: June 30

	REVENUE ($ mil.)	NET INCOME ($ mil.)	NET PROFIT MARGIN	EMPLOYEES
06/18	297	0	—	2,000
06/17	281	0	—	—
06/16	286	0	—	—
06/15	269	0	—	—
Annual Growth	3.4%	—	—	—

2018 Year-End Financials

Return on assets: 1.3%
Return on equity: —
Current ratio: 1.80

Cash ($ mil.): 3

TRIBOROUGH BRIDGE & TUNNEL AUTHORITY

EXECUTIVES

V Pres-Pres, Michael C Ascher
Offc Mgr, Choling Blakey
Contrl, Jim Elkin
Engineer, Teresa Ceragioli

LOCATIONS

HQ: TRIBOROUGH BRIDGE & TUNNEL AUTHORITY
  ROBERT MOSES BLDG RANDAL, NEW YORK, NY 10035
Phone: 212 360-3000

HISTORICAL FINANCIALS

Company Type: Private

Income Statement — FYE: December 31

	REVENUE ($ mil.)	NET INCOME ($ mil.)	NET PROFIT MARGIN	EMPLOYEES
12/17	1,931	282	14.6%	1,500
12/16	1,895	202	10.7%	—
12/15	1,843	165	9.0%	—
12/07	1,263	79	6.3%	—
Annual Growth	4.3%	13.5%	—	—

2017 Year-End Financials

Return on assets: 11.5%
Return on equity: 14.6%
Current ratio: 0.10

Cash ($ mil.): 8

TRINITAS REGIONAL MEDICAL CENTER

EXECUTIVES

Pres, Gary Huran
Anesthesiology, Teimouraz V Vassilidze
Purchasing Agent, Myriam Canuto

LOCATIONS

HQ: TRINITAS REGIONAL MEDICAL CENTER
  225 WILLIAMSON ST, ELIZABETH, NJ 072023625
Phone: 908 351-0714
Web: WWW.TRINITASHOSPITAL.ORG

PRODUCTS/OPERATIONS

Selected ServicesAccess/ReferralAcute Partial HospitalAdolescent Substance Abuse ServicesAdult Psychiatric ServicesAdult Substance Abuse ServicesAfter School ProgramC.A.R.E Employee AssistanceChild Crisis InterventionChild/Adolescent Psychiatric Services

COMPETITORS

Atlantic Health
  CentraState Healthcare System
  East Orange General Hospital
Newton Medical Center
  Robert Wood Johnson University Hospital at Rahway
St. Joseph's Healthcare System

HISTORICAL FINANCIALS

Company Type: Private

Income Statement — FYE: December 31

	REVENUE ($ mil.)	NET INCOME ($ mil.)	NET PROFIT MARGIN	EMPLOYEES
12/17	296	9	3.2%	2,700
12/16	297	17	5.9%	—
Annual Growth	(0.3%)	(45.2%)	—	—

2017 Year-End Financials

Return on assets: 8.3%
Return on equity: 3.2%
Current ratio: 2.80

Cash ($ mil.): 132

TRINITY HEALTH

EXECUTIVES

Ceo, John M Kutch
Chm, Patrick Holien
Cfo, Dennis Empey
SEC-Treas, Karen Krebsbach
Personnel Executive, Renae Lenertz
Executive Assistant, Candy Cline
Director, Douglas A Becker
Accounting Staff, April Dandy
Vice-President Legal, Karen Haroutunian
Vice-President Finance, Lannie Checketts
Senior Financial Analyst, Laura Dolph
Auditors: CLIFTONLARSONALLEN LLP MINNEA

LOCATIONS

HQ: TRINITY HEALTH
  1 BURDICK EXPY W, MINOT, ND 587014406
Phone: 701 857-5260
Web: WWW.TRINITYHEALTH.ORG

HISTORICAL FINANCIALS

Company Type: Private

Income Statement — FYE: June 30

	REVENUE ($ mil.)	NET INCOME ($ mil.)	NET PROFIT MARGIN	EMPLOYEES
06/18	463	27	6.0%	2,600
06/17	445	15	3.5%	—
06/16	455	17	3.8%	—
06/15	430	16	3.9%	—
Annual Growth	2.4%	18.5%	—	—

2018 Year-End Financials

Return on assets: 4.6%
Return on equity: 6.0%
Current ratio: 1.60

Cash ($ mil.): 44

TRUMAN ARNOLD COMPANIES

It is not just jibber jabber — this jobber gets the job done by distributing wholesale petroleum across the US. Truman Arnold Companies (TAC) has more than 400 associates with fuel volume of more than 2 billion gallons a year and markets and distributes petroleum products to customers through its TAC Energy subsidiary. Through a partnership it operates two major petroleum terminals one in Arkansas and one in Texas which collectively have more than 1.3 million barrels of capacity. Through its TAC Air unit the company offers fixed-based operations (FBO) including aircraft fueling hangar and ground transportation services through 14 general aviation facilities located across the US.

Operations

TAC's Aviation Services Wholesale Petroleum Marketing Branded Petroleum Marketing and Petroleum Terminal Services operations function independently but take advantage of shared management and technical resources. The company's major subsidiaries include TAC Air TAC Energy Cowhorn Creek Fuel Base and Keystone Aviation.

The company's Aviation Services maintains a fleet of aircraft and is engaged in aircraft maintenance sales and brokerage and aircraft management.

Strategy

In 2015 TAC Energy launched ENERGIZE Online a new product that provides an improved user interface for managing fuel purchase transactions

Aviation Services is a growth market. In 2013 Keystone Aviation expanded its line of aviation products and services by making its Aurora Oregon shop a Cirrus Authorized Service Center to serve Cirrus owners in and around Oregon. In addition to Cirrus the Aurora location is an authorized service center for Daher-Socata. That year Keystone Aviation also became a Quest Aircraft (turboprops) distributor in California Colorado Nevada and Utah.

Mergers and Acquisitions

In 2015 TAC Air purchased the facilities of Central Flying Service at the Bill and Hillary Clinton National Airport in Little Rock and will operate its fueling ground handling hangar operations and other related services as part of the TAC Air network. Also included is the purchase of Airport Services Inc. which provides airline fueling services.

Company Background

The company opened its 13th FBO in 2009 in the Spirit of St. Louis Airport in Chesterfield Missouri. It opened an executive terminal (its first at any FBO location) at Blue Grass Airport in Kentucky in July 2010. To raise cash in October 2010 TAC Air sold its Greenville South Carolina FBO operation to Greenville Jet Center for undisclosed terms.

TAC has also grown its wholesale energy segment. In 2009 TAC Energy acquired Fuel Managers (which has operations in 18 states) for an undisclosed price. The acquisition of the fuel wholesaler helped to boost TAC Energy's position in the supply market in the Central and Western US.

To keep up with the growth of the company in 2011 TAC expanded its Dallas sales office. The company anticipates doubling in size by 2016 and sees Dallas as a key operational/sales hub for managing its growth.

In 2012 to gain operational and financial support from another private energy company TAC Energy also combined its Caddo Mills Texas and North Little Rock Arkansas terminal operations into a master limited partnership with JP Energy Partners LP.

Expanding its fuel supply businesses in 2013 TAC Energy completed construction of a new diesel exhaust fluid distribution hub. The expansion at the terminal enabled TAC Energy to become a Tier 1 distributor of TerraCair Ultrapure Diesel Exhaust Fluid.

The family-owned and -operated company was founded in 1964 by Texarkana businessman Truman Arnold. It once operated a chain of 125 Road Runner convenience stores in eight states before selling this network to Total Petroleum in 1989. TAC revived the brand in 2003.

EXECUTIVES

General Counsel And Senior Vice President, James H Day
President And Ceo, Gregory A. (Greg) Arnold
Svp And Cfo, Steve McMillen
Vp And Cio, Michael Davis
Chairman And Ceo, Truman Arnold
Auditors: THOMAS & THOMAS LLP TEXARKANA

LOCATIONS

HQ: TRUMAN ARNOLD COMPANIES
701 S ROBISON RD, TEXARKANA, TX 755016747
Phone: 903 794-3835
Web: WWW.TRUMANARNOLDCOMPANIES.COM

COMPETITORS

Atlantic Aviation	Signature Flight
Gulf Oil	Sun Coast Resources
Million Air	Warren Equities

HISTORICAL FINANCIALS

Company Type: Private

Income Statement   FYE: September 30

	REVENUE ($ mil.)	NET INCOME ($ mil.)	NET PROFIT MARGIN	EMPLOYEES
09/17	2,119	18	0.9%	550
09/16	1,525	18	1.2%	—
09/15	1,595	17	1.1%	—
09/14	2,259	11	0.5%	—
Annual Growth	(2.1%)	16.1%	—	—

2017 Year-End Financials

Return on assets: 4.5%   Cash ($ mil.): 3
Return on equity: 0.9%
Current ratio: 0.70

TRUSTEES OF BOSTON COLLEGE

Students at Boston College (BC) get both academic excellence and the Red Sox. Located six miles from downtown Boston the university enrolls 14100 full- and part-time students (about a third of whom are graduate students) from every state in the US and 80 other countries. It has a student-teacher ratio of 13:1. BC offers degrees in more than 50 fields of study through its schools and colleges on four campuses. The university also has more than 20 research centers including the Institute for Scientific Research and the Center for International Higher Education. BC is one of the oldest Jesuit Catholic universities in the nation and has the largest Jesuit community in the world.

Operations

About 70% of its undergraduate student body are self-identified as Roman Catholic.

The university is home to more than 20 centers and institutes designated for research and teaching. Research opportunities including participation in faculty research projects exist for both undergraduate and graduate students. It also houses 8 libraries with 2.9 million volumes.

The cost of tuition stood a $46670 for 2014-15.

Geographic Reach

The university has campuses in Brighton Chestnut Hill Dover and Newton Massachusetts. It also operates a campus in Dublin Ireland.

Financial Performance

BC has enjoyed steady growth from voluntary giving by its alumni. Its endowment has grown to $2.2 billion placing it among the top 40 in the US. In 2014 it reported an operating budget of $917 million. Its revenues of $702.7 million were 5% up on the previous year due to growth in tuition and fees as well as auxiliary enterprises.

Strategy

BC's strategic plan includes adding 100 new faculty positions expanding research by faculty and graduate students increasing student financial aid to more than $128 million annually and extending undergraduate opportunities in international study internships and student formation. In 2013 it announced plans to build a $90 million residence hall near its Chestnut Hill campus.

Company Background

The university was founded by Jesuits in 1863. During its first seven decades BC was an exclusively undergraduate institution that served sons of the Irish working class. Its liberal arts emphasis was on the Greek and Latin classics English and modern languages and philosophy and religion. Development into the college it is today did not begin until the 1920s when the Graduate School of Arts and Sciences the Law School and the Evening College (known today as the James A. Woods S.J. College of Advancing Studies) were inaugurated. All classes became co-educational in the 1970s and today BC has a fairly equal split among male and female students.

EXECUTIVES

Vice President Human Resources, Leo Sullivan
President, William P. Leahy
Chancellor, J. Donald Monan
Dean Carroll School Of Management, Andrew C. Boynton
Dean School Of Social Work, Alberto Godenzi
Evp, Patrick J. Keating
Associate Vp Applications And Systems Services, Michael Bourque
Financial Vp And Treasurer, John D. Burke
Provost And Dean Of Faculties, David Quigley
Dean Of Students, Tom Mogan
Dean School Of Theology And Ministry, Mark Massa
Dean Connell School Of Nursing, Susan Gennaro
Dean Lynch School Of Education, Maureen E. Kenny
Dean Law School, Vincent Rougeau
Interim Dean Morrissey College Of Arts And Sciences, Gregory Kalscheur
Dean Woods College Of Advancing Studies, James Burns
Assistant Vice President Inst Rsrch Plng Assess, Kelli Armstrong
Vice President Information Technology, Mark Ben
Vice President For Student Affairs, Barbara Jones
Vice President University Mission And, Joseph Appleyard
Assistant Vice President Planning And Budget, Steven Sass
Associate Vice President Alumni Relations, Joy Moore
Vice President, Madeleine G Moore
Office Of The Executive Vice President, Jeanne Marquardt
Vice President Assistant To President, Mary Lou Delong
Vice President For Research, Thomas Chiles
Department Chair, Richard Tresch
Director Administrative Services University Advancement Vice Presidents Office, Anne Campbell
Associate Vice President For Facilities Services, Martin Dugal
Vice President, Pat Ryan

LOCATIONS

HQ: TRUSTEES OF BOSTON COLLEGE
 140 COMMONWEALTH AVE, CHESTNUT HILL, MA
 024673800
Phone: 617 552-8000
Web: WWW.BC.EDU

PRODUCTS/OPERATIONS

Selected Colleges and Schools
Carolyn A. and Peter S. Lynch School of Education
College of Arts and Sciences
Graduate School of Arts and Sciences
Graduate School of Social Work
James A. Woods S.J. College of Advancing Studies
School of Law
School of Theology and Ministry
Wallace E. Carroll School of Management
William F. Connell School of Nursing

HISTORICAL FINANCIALS
Company Type: Private

Income Statement				FYE: May 31
	REVENUE ($ mil.)	NET INCOME ($ mil.)	NET PROFIT MARGIN	EMPLOYEES
05/18	835	169	20.2%	2,493
05/17	798	279	34.9%	—
05/14	702	221	31.5%	—
05/13	671	270	40.3%	—
Annual Growth	4.5%	(9.0%)	—	—

2018 Year-End Financials

Return on assets: 0.7%   Cash ($ mil.): 9
Return on equity: 20.2%
Current ratio: —

TRUSTEES OF DARTMOUTH COLLEGE

Part of the esteemed Ivy League Dartmouth CollegeA is a private four-year liberal arts college with an enrollment ofA more thanA 6000 students.A TheA universityA has an undergraduate college (offering about 40 programs)A and graduate schools of business engineering and medicine plus graduate programs in the arts and sciences. Its student-teacher ratio is about 6:1. It is also home to a number of centers and institutes including Children's Hospital at Dartmouth; Dartmouth Center on Addiction Recovery andA Education; and Center for Digital Strategies. Notable alumni include Daniel Webster Robert Frost Theodore "Dr. Seuss" Geisel and Nelson Rockefeller.

Operations
Dartmouth is located on a 270-acre campus located in Hanover New Hampshire.A It also conducts study-abroad programs in about 20 coun-

tries. Through its collective institutes and graduate schools the college conducts a number of research programs in areas including security capitalism energy and infectious disease. Altogether it has about 50 research-focused groups centers and institutes and attracts more than $200 million in sponsored research funding per year.

Financial Performance
For fiscal year 2011 Dartmouth reported revenues of some $763 million. Operating expenses for fiscal 2011 were some $738 million. Dartmouth has an endowment of some $3.5 billion.

Company Background
Dartmouth is the nation's ninth oldest college founded in 1769 by Reverend Eleazar Wheelock a Congregational minister from Connecticut. Land forA its campus in Hanover New Hampshire was conveyed by a charter from King George III; it was the last institution of higher education established in the US under colonial rule.

EXECUTIVES

LOCATIONS

HQ: TRUSTEES OF DARTMOUTH COLLEGE
 20 LEBANON ST, HANOVER, NH 037553564
Phone: 603 646-1110
Web: WWW.DARTMOUTH.EDU

PRODUCTS/OPERATIONS

Selected Divisions
Admissions and Financial Aid
Advancement Office
Campus Planning and Facilities
Dean of the College
Faculty of the Arts & Sciences
Finance and Administration
Geisel School of Medicine
President's Office
Provost's Office
Thayer School of Engineering
The Trustees of Dartmouth College
Tuck School of Business

HISTORICAL FINANCIALS
Company Type: Private

Income Statement				FYE: June 30
	REVENUE ($ mil.)	NET INCOME ($ mil.)	NET PROFIT MARGIN	EMPLOYEES
06/17	1,369	691	50.5%	5,000
06/16	859	(301)	—	—
06/15	876	236	27.0%	—
06/14	866	680	78.5%	—
Annual Growth	16.5%	0.5%		—

2017 Year-End Financials

Return on assets: 6.9%   Cash ($ mil.): 176
Return on equity: 50.5%
Current ratio: —

TRUSTEES OF INDIANA UNIVERSITY

Indiana University has been schooling Hoosiers (and others) since 1820. With a population of some 115000 students from all 50 states and more than 130 countries the university offers more than 1000 associate baccalaureate master's professional and doctoral degree programs at eight campuses: flagship institution IU-Bloomington; regional campuses in Fort Wayne Gary Kokomo New Albany Richmond and South Bend; and an urban campus in Indianapolis that is operated with Purdue University. The university has about 20000 faculty and professional and support staff. It has 200 research centers and institutes and offers courses in more than 70 languages.

Operations
The university offers more than 200 undergraduate majors and more than 300 graduate programs; it also boasts more than 300 study-abroad programs. It has a student-teacher ratio of about 17:1.

Indiana University has more than 306000 total living alumni including nearly 248000 Indiana residents. For the academic year 2014-15 the university charged undergraduate tuition and fees of $10388 for residents and $33240 for non-residents. It awarded $1.1 billion in financial aid that year.

Indiana University-Purdue University Indianapolis (IUPUI) is considered an "up and coming" university by U.S. News and World Report . With nearly 20 schools and degrees granted in more than 200 programs IUPUI enrolls more than 30000 students from both the Indiana University and Purdue University systems.

The IPFW Office of Research Engagement and Sponsored Programs supports research business efforts and establishes partnerships with area public and private organizations.

Geographic Reach
The university has major campuses in Bloomington and Indianapolis and regional campuses in Gary Kokomo New Albany Richmond and South Bend. It enrolls more than 50% of the students from the St. Joseph County area.

Financial Performance
Indiana University's revenues grew 1% in fiscal year 2015 to $2.2 billion. The largest single source of operating revenues for the university is student tuition and fees (accounting for 55% of total revenues). That year a 4% increase in student fees helped to offset a 40% decline in sales and services of educational units.

Net income fell 31% to $138 million in 2015 as interest earnings declined. Operating cash outflow remained flat at $534 million largely due to higher payments to employees.

Strategy
Indiana University is dedicated to keeping tuition increases as low as possible and providing extensive financial aid for qualified students. It also aims to educate its students on managing and reducing their student loan debt.

The university plans to expand and renovate its School of Public and Environmental Affairs building; the project will cost some $12 million and is expected to be complete in early 2017. In mid-2015 a new hall housing the Lilly Family School of Philanthropy was opened on the IUPUI campus. Also that year Indiana University completed the construction of a $53 million building for the new School of Global and International Studies.

The university will also continue to expand its Global Gateway Network. It officially opened offices in China and India in 2014; other target markets include the Middle East Europe Latin America and Africa.

Company Background

An 1820 statute created the Indiana Seminary the predecessor to Indiana University. In 1828 the legislature changed the name of the institution to Indiana College and in 1838 it established Indiana University.

EXECUTIVES

President, Michael A. McRobbie
Chancellor Iu Southeast, Sandra R. Patterson-Randles
Chancellor Iu South Bend, Una Mae Reck
Evp And Chancellor Iu-purdue University Indianapolis, Charles R. Bantz
Dean School Of Law, Lauren Robel
Interim Vp Cfo And Treasurer, MaryFrances McCourt
Evp University Regional Affairs Planning And Policy, John S. Applegate
Vp Information Technology And Cio, Bradley C. (Brad) Wheeler
Chancellor Iu Northwest, William J. Lowe
Interim Chancellor Iu East, Larry Richards
Interim Chancellor Iu Kokomo, Susan Sciame-Giesecke
Chancellor Iu-purdue University Fort Wayne, Vicky L. Carwein
President Of Indiana University On, Alfred Ryors
President To Assume Office, David Jordan
President And Professor Of Botany At Indiana University, John Coulter
President On, John Ryan
Vice President Corporate Communications Executive, William B Stephan
Assistant Vice President Finance, Linda Hunt
Associate Vice President Of Finance, Stew Cobine
Associate Vice President And University Budget Office Direct, Stephen Keucher
Associate Vice President Development, Jeff Lindauer
Executive Vice President, Peter Bogdanovich
Vice President Information Technology, Barbara Patrick
Associate Vice President For University Human Resources, John Whelan
Vice President, Julie Head
Vice President Of Engagement, Garrett Lance
Assoc Vice President Information Technology, Brad Wheeler
Vice President Information Technology Advancement Web Communications, Duane Schau
Vice President, Mike Sample
Vice President, Cory Cochran
Associate Vice President For International Services, Christopher Viers
Associate Vice President Marketing, Rob Zinkan
Senior Vice President Marketing, Mike Fowler
Assoc Vice President Student Dev Diversity, Edwardo Rhodes
Office Of The Vice President For Public Affairs And Government Relations (pagr), Martin McCrory
Executive Vice President, Mitch Ennis
Vice President And President Elect, Ballard C Campbell
Vice President Of Finance And Administra, Lauren Pruitt
Vice President Of Communications, Andrew J Harder
Net Impact Vice President Marketing, Jayna J Pedruczny
Vice President Of Lending And Hoosier Social Impact Fund, Molly Hallahan
Vice President, Tom Morrison
Associate Vice President University Academic Affairs, Steve Keucher

Associate Vice President Emeritus For Student Affairs, John Daum
Vice President Membership Meet John, John Isaacson
Vice President Of Project Management, Ethan Singer
Vice Chair, Patrick A. Shoulders
Chair, William R. Cast
Secretary, Deb Hankins
Treasurer, Teresa Andrews
Board Member, Melanie Castillo-Cullather
Secretary, Joyce Regester
Deputy Treasurer, Gentry Patrick Lee

LOCATIONS

HQ: TRUSTEES OF INDIANA UNIVERSITY
BRYAN HALL 107 S IND AVE ST BRYAN HA, BLOOMINGTON, IN 47405
Phone: 812 855-4848
Web: WWW.INDIANA.EDU

PRODUCTS/OPERATIONS

2015 Sales

	% of total
Student fees	51
Auxiliary enterprises	14
Federal grants & contracts	13
Non-governement grants & contracts	6
Sales and services of educational units	2
State & local grants & contracts	1
Other revenue	13
Total	**100**

HISTORICAL FINANCIALS
Company Type: Private

Income Statement				FYE: June 30
	REVENUE ($ mil.)	NET INCOME ($ mil.)	NET PROFIT MARGIN	EMPLOYEES
06/16	2,256	105	4.7%	16,000
06/15	2,207	138	6.3%	—
06/14	2,195	201	9.2%	—
06/13	2,146	189	8.8%	—
Annual Growth	1.7%	(17.7%)	—	—

2016 Year-End Financials
Return on assets: 11.4%
Return on equity: 4.7%
Current ratio: 1.10
Cash ($ mil.): 345

TRUSTEES OF MEASE HOSPITAL, INC.

EXECUTIVES

Ceo, Philip K Beauchamp
President, James Pfieffer
Fo, Carl Tremone
Pharmacist, Maikel Bolos
Pharmacist, Rodney Cavalier
Internal Medicine, Beverly Encarnacion
Auditors: ERNST & YOUNG US LLP ATLANTA

LOCATIONS

HQ: TRUSTEES OF MEASE HOSPITAL, INC.
601 MAIN ST, DUNEDIN, FL 346985848
Phone: 727 733-1111
Web: WWW.BAYCARE.ORG

HISTORICAL FINANCIALS
Company Type: Private

Income Statement				FYE: December 31
	REVENUE ($ mil.)	NET INCOME ($ mil.)	NET PROFIT MARGIN	EMPLOYEES
12/15	436	84	19.4%	2,000
12/14	430	101	23.6%	—
12/13	351	49	14.1%	—
12/09	336	31	9.4%	—
Annual Growth	4.5%	17.9%	—	—

2015 Year-End Financials
Return on assets: 4.2%
Return on equity: 19.4%
Current ratio: 2.50
Cash ($ mil.): —

TRUSTEES OF THE ESTATE OF BERNICE PAUAHI BISHOP

EXECUTIVES

Vice President, Colleen Wong
Vice President Human Resources, Winona White
Auditors: PRICEWATERHOUSECOOPERS LLP WA

LOCATIONS

HQ: TRUSTEES OF THE ESTATE OF BERNICE PAUAHI BISHOP
567 S KING ST STE 200, HONOLULU, HI 968133079
Phone: 808 523-6200
Web: WWW.KSBE.EDU

COMPETITORS

Edison Learning   Learning Care Group

HISTORICAL FINANCIALS
Company Type: Private

Income Statement				FYE: June 30
	REVENUE ($ mil.)	NET INCOME ($ mil.)	NET PROFIT MARGIN	EMPLOYEES
06/15	767	333	43.5%	1,500
06/14	915	482	52.7%	—
06/13	519	109	21.1%	—
06/10	333	(21)	—	—
Annual Growth	18.1%	—	—	—

2015 Year-End Financials
Return on assets: 7.3%
Return on equity: 43.5%
Current ratio: 0.10
Cash ($ mil.): 18

TRUSTEES OF TUFTS COLLEGE

Tufts University wants to light up the minds of New England scholars. The schoolA offers undergraduate and graduate degrees in areas such as education engineering psychology art English music and medicine. The university enrollsA some 11000 studentsA and has 1300 faculty members and itA offersA classesA in 70 fields atA three campuses in Massachusetts (Boston Medford/Somerville and Grafton). It also has an international campus in Talloires France.A Tufts University'sA Fletcher School of Law and Diplomacy is the oldest continuous international relations graduate program in the country. The school is also home to New England's only Veterinary School.

Operations

Tufts University has a number of research programs at all three campuses including clinical studies in medical dental veterinaryA and nutritional fields. It also has research programs in areas such as biology engineering and technology many of which are funded through grants and fellowship funds.

Financial Performance

Tufts University has an endowment of about $1.1 billion.

Strategy

Tufts University is working to expand the resourcesA its School of Medicine. In 2012 it moved to add a new medical research lab to study serious infectious diseases (such as tuberculosis)A within the Biomedical Research and Public Health Building. It also expanded the Cummings School of Veterinary Medicine by adding a new clinic for the care and study ofA pets withA obesity problems. The university also expands by adding new degree programs such as a doctorate in mamalian genetics in 2011.

Company Background

Tufts was founded in 1852 through a land donation from Boston-area businessman Charles Tufts to the Universalist Church. The school adopted its motto Pax et Lux (Peace and Light) in 1857.

EXECUTIVES

Interim Assistant To David Kahle Vice President For Information Technology And Cio, Lucy Nunn
Vice President For Operations, Linda Snyder
Vice President For Human Resources, Julien Carter
Auditors: PRICEWATERHOUSECOOPERS LLP BO

LOCATIONS

HQ: TRUSTEES OF TUFTS COLLEGE
169 HOLLAND ST STE 318, SOMERVILLE, MA 021442401
Phone: 617 628-5000
Web: WWW.TUFTS.EDU

PRODUCTS/OPERATIONS

Schools & Colleges
Cummings School of Veterinary Science
Graduate School of Arts & Sciences
The Fletcher School
Friedman School of Nutrition Science and Policy
Sackler School of Graduate Biomedical Sciences
School of Arts & Sciences
School of Dental Medicine
School of Engineering
School of Medicine
Tisch College of Citizenship and Public Service

HISTORICAL FINANCIALS

Company Type: Private

Income Statement				FYE: June 30
	REVENUE ($ mil.)	NET INCOME ($ mil.)	NET PROFIT MARGIN	EMPLOYEES
06/15	914	(25)	—	4,100
06/14	965	68	7.1%	—
06/13	768	127	16.6%	—
06/12	769	(100)	—	—
Annual Growth	5.9%	—	—	—

TRUVEN HOLDING CORP.

EXECUTIVES

Pres- Ceo, Mike Boswood
Exec V Pres, Phil Buckingham
Exec V Pres, Jon Newpol
Coo, Roy Martin
Gen Counsel, Andra Heller
Manager, Chris Schneider
Recruiting Manager, Richard Marciniak
Auditors: PRICEWATERHOUSECOOPERS LLP NE

LOCATIONS

HQ: TRUVEN HOLDING CORP.
100 PHOENIX DR STE 100 # 100, ANN ARBOR, MI 481082600
Phone: 734 913-3000
Web: WWW.TRUVENHEALTH.COM

HISTORICAL FINANCIALS

Company Type: Private

Income Statement				FYE: December 31
	REVENUE ($ mil.)	NET INCOME ($ mil.)	NET PROFIT MARGIN	EMPLOYEES
12/15	610	(75)	—	2,110
12/14	544	(37)	—	—
12/13	492	(344)	—	—
12/12	241	(54)	—	—
Annual Growth	36.2%	—	—	—

2015 Year-End Financials

Return on assets: 13.4%   Cash ($ mil.): 14
Return on equity: (-12.4%)
Current ratio: 0.60

TUCSON UNIFIED SCHOOL DISTRICT

EXECUTIVES

Supt, Elizabeth C Fagen
Supt, Ht Sanchez
Lead Lan Spec, Keith Mooney
Human Resources, Lisa Mc Corkel
Director, David Scott
Programmer, Shannon Toms
Coordinator, Kimberly Comey
Social Worker, Brenda Reeves
Teacher, Mercedes Leon
Teacher, Micaela Campos
Health Director, Nikki Stefan
Auditors: HEINFELD MEECH & CO PC TUC

LOCATIONS

HQ: TUCSON UNIFIED SCHOOL DISTRICT
1010 E 10TH ST, TUCSON, AZ 857195813
Phone: 520 225-6000
Web: WWW.TUSD1.ORG/HOME/404-MESSAGE

HISTORICAL FINANCIALS

Company Type: Private

Income Statement				FYE: June 30
	REVENUE ($ mil.)	NET INCOME ($ mil.)	NET PROFIT MARGIN	EMPLOYEES
06/16	446	1	0.3%	9,000
06/11	496	58	11.7%	—
06/06	426	29	7.0%	—
Annual Growth	0.5%	(27.6%)	—	—

2015 Year-End Financials

Return on assets: 15.6%   Cash ($ mil.): 37
Return on equity: (-2.8%)
Current ratio: 0.10

TUDOR INVESTMENT CORPORATION

EXECUTIVES

Vice President Software Development, Amit Wadhwa
Managing Director, Bjorn Nielsen
Auditors: ERNST & YOUNG LLP NEW YORK N

LOCATIONS

HQ: TUDOR INVESTMENT CORPORATION
200 ELM ST STE 200 # 200, STAMFORD, CT 069023826
Phone: 203 863-6700
Web: WWW.TUDORFUNDS.COM

COMPETITORS

Actua
Draper Fisher Jurvetson
EnTrust Capital
Hummer Winblad
Kleiner Perkins
Menlo Ventures
NEA
US Venture Partners
Wexford Capital
vCap Investments

HISTORICAL FINANCIALS

Company Type: Private

Income Statement				FYE: December 31
	ASSETS ($ mil.)	NET INCOME ($ mil.)	INCOME AS % OF ASSETS	EMPLOYEES
12/15	831	222	26.7%	291
12/14	819	(80)	—	—
12/13	905	486	53.7%	—
12/11	624	187	30.0%	—
Annual Growth	7.4%	4.4%	—	—

2015 Year-End Financials

Return on assets: —   Sales ($ mil): 784
Return on equity: 28.3%

TUFTS MEDICAL CENTER, INC.

EXECUTIVES

Int Pres-Ceo, Michael Wagner
Chb, Malcolm L Sherman
President, Deeb Salem
Cmo, Saul N Weingart
Nurse Manager Emergency, Simcha Weller

Neuroradiologist, Singh Bedi
Pathologist In Chief, Stephen Naber
Managing Director, Sunita Pereira
Non Employee Manager, Timothy McAlindon
Anesthesiologist, Virgil Manica
Child Neurology, David A Griesemer

LOCATIONS

HQ: TUFTS MEDICAL CENTER, INC.
  800 WASHINGTON ST, BOSTON, MA 021111552
Phone: 617 636-2254
Web: WWW.TUFTSMEDICALCENTER.ORG

HISTORICAL FINANCIALS

Company Type: Private

Income Statement — FYE: September 30

	REVENUE ($ mil.)	NET INCOME ($ mil.)	NET PROFIT MARGIN	EMPLOYEES
09/17	681	12	1.8%	3,800
09/16	646	14	2.3%	—
09/15	595	(18)	—	—
09/14	602	19	3.3%	—
Annual Growth	4.2%	(14.6%)	—	—

2017 Year-End Financials

Return on assets: 7.4%   Cash ($ mil.): 21
Return on equity: 1.8%
Current ratio: 0.90

TURLOCK IRRIGATION DISTRICT

LOCATIONS

HQ: TURLOCK IRRIGATION DISTRICT
  333 E CANAL DR, TURLOCK, CA 953803946
Phone: 209 883-8222
Web: WWW.TID.ORG

HISTORICAL FINANCIALS

Company Type: Private

Income Statement — FYE: December 31

	REVENUE ($ mil.)	NET INCOME ($ mil.)	NET PROFIT MARGIN	EMPLOYEES
12/17	378	59	15.8%	4
12/16	318	14	4.6%	—
Annual Growth	18.8%	305.9%	—	—

TURTLE & HUGHES, INC.

Turtle & Hughes' longevity has demonstrated that slow and steady really does win the race when it comes to distributing electrical and industrial equipment. The company's exhaustive lineup is sold through three subsidiaries: Turtle & Hughes Integrated Supply Turtle Data (wire cable and power protection devices) and Turtle Ebay Store. Its customers include industrial and construction companies electrical contractors telecommunications servers utilities and various government agencies. Family-owned the company is led by its fourth generation Jayne Millard its third female

CEO. One-third of Turtle & Hughes is employee-owned.

Operations

Turtle & Hughes provides electrical products such as alarms signals and annunciators; anchors and plugs; automation products; ballasts; batteries and flashlights; boxes and covers; breakers bus ducts panels and switchgears; programmable controls; time clocks; transformers; wires cables and cords; wiring accessories and devices; and others.

The company also offers industrial products such as adhesives/tapes and compounds brushes/brooms carbide tools cutting tools fasteners lubricating devices material handling products power transmissions precision tools soldering equipment solenoid valves struts/channels tooling accessories and other products.

Geographic Reach

Turtle & Hughes operates through 17 branches across the US.

Sales and Marketing

Turtle & Hughes' customers include industrial firms construction companies electrical contractors telecommunications servers utilities and various government agencies and municipalities.

Company Background

Turtle & Hughes was founded in 1923 as an electrical supply house.

EXECUTIVES

President, Jack Sinagra
Vice President Of Finance, Kevin Doyle
Ceo, Jayne Millard
Manager Corporate Operations, Chuck Noll
Evp; Branch Manager Bridgewater Distribution Center And Plainfield Branch, Rick Reffler
Executive Vice President Build A Brain Trust, Randy Roessle
President, Michael DeVoney
Chief Financial Officer, Chris Rausch
Vice President, Peter Landers
Vice President Export Sales, Abdul Hooda
National Accounts Manager, BLAKE VARBERO
Vice President, Norman Norman Blumenthal Blumenthal
National Sales Manager, Melissa Hartpence
Vice President And General Manager Of The Integrated Supply Division, Joseph Drummond
Vice President Sales, Tony Ventola
Vice President Sales, John Bernhardt
Vice President Sales, Anthony Ventola
Vice President, Cory Szatkiewicz
Senior Vice President, Al Fernandes
Chairman President And Ceo, Suzanne Turtle Millard
Auditors: EISNERAMPER LLP ISELIN NJ

LOCATIONS

HQ: TURTLE & HUGHES, INC.
  1900 LOWER RD, LINDEN, NJ 070366586
Phone: 732 574-3600
Web: WWW.TURTLE.COM

PRODUCTS/OPERATIONS

Selected Products
Datacom categories
  Anchors and fasteners
  Burial products/innerduct
  Cabinets and enclosures
  Cable management
  Cable tray/ladder rack
  Category rated and coax cable
  Connectivity
  Fiber-optic cable
  Hand tools
  Outside plant
  Power protection
  Raceway and duct systems
  Safety
  Security fencing
  Splices connectors and lugs

  Tools testers and safety
Electrical categories
  Alarms annunciators and signals
  Anchors and plugs
  Automation products
  Ballasts and transformers
  Batteries and flashlights
  Box enclosures
  Breakers panels and switchgears
  Cable trays and struts
  Conduit fittings
  Cord connectors
  Dimming controls
  Electrical tools
  Emergency lighting
  Enclosures
  Fans
  Fluorescent lighting
  Fuse holders and terminal blocks
  Generators
  Groundings
  Heat shrink
  Heating
  High-bay lighting
  Incandescent lighting
  Lamps
  Limit temp. and proximity switch
  Lugs and terminals
  Metering equipment
  Motor control
  Motors AC and DC drivers
  Outdoor lighting
  Pole line products
  Programmable controls
  Relays
  Strut/channel
  Test equipment
  Time clocks
  Transformers
  Wire cable and cord
  Wiring accessories
  Wiring devices
Industrial categories
  Adhesives and tapes
  Brushes and brooms
  Carbide tools
  Cutting fluid/lubricant
  Cutting tools
  Fasteners
  Hand tools
  Hoist chain and accessories
  Industrial abrasives
  Janitorial paper supplies
  Ladders
  Locks
  Lubricating devices
  Material handling
  MRO supplies
  Paint/markets
  Pipe hangers
  Pipe valves and fittings
  Pneumatics
  Pneumatic tools
  Power tools
  Safety equipment
  Saw blades
  Shim/shim stock
  Solenoid valves
  Strut/channel
  Tooling accessories

COMPETITORS

C. R. Laurence
Consolidated Electrical
Dillon Supply
Graybar Electric
Indoff
Interline Brands
Kennametal

MSC Industrial Direct
Prime Advantage
Rexel Inc.
Sonepar USA
Steiner Electric
W.W. Grainger
WESCO International

TUSTIN UNIFIED SCHOOL DISTRICT

EXECUTIVES

Supt, Gregory A Franklin Ed D
Cfo, Anthony Soria
Superintendent, Gregory A Franklin
Director of Information Techno, Jeremy Powell
Teacher, Lisa Herman
Teacher, Nancy Stuck
Teacher, Raquel Rasmussen
Manager, Shirley Robinson
Teacher, Janine Addison
Teacher, Katie Sanjurjo
Teacher, Marina Barrios
Auditors: NIGRO NIGRO & WHITE MURRIETA

LOCATIONS

HQ: TUSTIN UNIFIED SCHOOL DISTRICT
300 S C ST, TUSTIN, CA 927803633
Phone: 714 730-7515
Web: WWW.TUSTIN.K12.CA.US

HISTORICAL FINANCIALS
Company Type: Private

Income Statement				FYE: June 30
	REVENUE ($ mil.)	NET INCOME ($ mil.)	NET PROFIT MARGIN	EMPLOYEES
06/17	296	(4)	—	1,465
06/16	284	14	5.1%	—
06/09	0	(0)	—	—
06/08	0	(0)	—	—
Annual Growth	97.5%	—	—	—

2017 Year-End Financials
Return on assets: 9.5% Cash ($ mil.): 218
Return on equity: (-1.6%)
Current ratio: —

TUTOR PERINI BUILDING CORP.

EXECUTIVES

Pres/Ceo, Craig W Shaw
Evp, Robert Band
Treas/SEC, William B Sparks
Vp-Controller, Robert P Marano II
Vp, Shelton Grantham
Vp-Business Development, Richard J Rizzo
Employee Benefits Manager, Susan Muenzenberger
Quality Control Manager, Darrin Depratter
Administrative Assistant, Diana Rivero
Project Manager, Joe Schranz
Senior Vice President, Sam Sabin
Auditors: DELOITTE & TOUCHE LLP LOS AN

LOCATIONS

HQ: TUTOR PERINI BUILDING CORP.
5055 E WASHINGTON ST # 210, PHOENIX, AZ
850342036
Phone: 602 256-6777
Web: WWW.TUTORPERINIBUILDING.COM

HISTORICAL FINANCIALS
Company Type: Private

Income Statement				FYE: December 31
	REVENUE ($ mil.)	NET INCOME ($ mil.)	NET PROFIT MARGIN	EMPLOYEES
12/15	352	(16)	—	250
12/14	246	5	2.1%	—
12/13	321	15	4.7%	—
12/06	1,535	21	1.4%	—
Annual Growth	(15.1%)	—	—	—

TWIN RIVERS UNIFIED SCHOOL DISTRICT

EXECUTIVES

Spdt, Steve Martinez
Assoc Supt Bus Srvcs, Rob Ball
Principal, Kirk Williams
Food Director, Jill Van Dyke
Bus/Finance/Purchasing Directo, Ruth Hall
Secretary, Tammy Renfroe
Coordinator, David Yeroshek
Administrative Assistant, Bob Wilkerson
Human Resources Analyst, Jennifer Valencia
Executive, Ziggy Robeson
Elementary Summer School Princ, Jennifer Kramer
Auditors: GILBERT ASSOCIATES INC SACR

LOCATIONS

HQ: TWIN RIVERS UNIFIED SCHOOL DISTRICT
3222 WINONA WAY, NORTH HIGHLANDS, CA
956605508
Phone: 916 566-1600
Web: WWW.TWINRIVERSUSD.ORG

U. S. TOOL GRINDING, INC.

EXECUTIVES

Ceo-Pres, Bruce Williams
Vice President, Jim Galati
Vice President, Mike Baugh
Vice President, Brent Williams
Controller, Beth Allen
Site Manager, Darla Hebert
C-Level Human Resources, Stephanie Mitchell
Purchasing Coordinator, Sirena Couture
Operations Manager, Scott Stimac
Assistant, Laurie Melton
Buyer, Curtis Holt
Auditors: UHY LLP ST LOUIS MISSOURI

LOCATIONS

HQ: U. S. TOOL GRINDING, INC.
2000 PROGRESS DR, FARMINGTON, MO 636409158
Phone: 573 431-3856
Web: WWW.USTG.NET

HISTORICAL FINANCIALS
Company Type: Private

Income Statement				FYE: December 31
	REVENUE ($ mil.)	NET INCOME ($ mil.)	NET PROFIT MARGIN	EMPLOYEES
12/17	431	9	2.1%	900
12/16	414	11	2.7%	—
12/15	368	10	2.8%	—
Annual Growth	8.3%	(6.7%)	—	—

2017 Year-End Financials
Return on assets: 9.4% Cash ($ mil.): 3
Return on equity: 2.1%
Current ratio: 0.70

U.S. PIPELINE, INC.

EXECUTIVES

Prin, Kelly Osborn
Chb, Greg Curran
Treas, Imran Dossani
Cfo, Bret Roper

Accounting Staff, Fernando Gonzalez
Vice President Chief Technolog, Robert Dittmer
Auditors: LAPORTE APAC HOUSTON TEXAS

LOCATIONS

HQ: U.S. PIPELINE, INC.
8100 WASHINGTON AVE # 200, HOUSTON, TX
770071085
Phone: 281 531-6100
Web: WWW.USPIPELINE.COM

HISTORICAL FINANCIALS

Company Type: Private

Income Statement | | | | FYE: December 31

	REVENUE ($ mil.)	NET INCOME ($ mil.)	NET PROFIT MARGIN	EMPLOYEES
12/17	501	11	2.3%	1,500
12/16	72	0	0.6%	—
12/15	367	52	14.3%	—
12/14	557	0	—	—
Annual Growth	(3.5%)	—	—	—

2017 Year-End Financials

Return on assets: 4.3%   Cash ($ mil.): 15
Return on equity: 2.3%
Current ratio: 2.10

UC HEALTH, LLC.

UC Health is Cincinnati's scholarly health care provider. The medical provider is a partnership between the University of Cincinnati the 480-bed University of Cincinnati Medical Center and the University of Cincinnati Physicians organization. AdditionallyA UC HealthA is home to the 160-bed West Chester Hospital (a full-service community hospital) the Drake Center long-term acute care (rehabilitation) hospital theA UC HealthA Surgical Hospital and the Lindner Center of HOPE (mental health services). Specialized services include cancer cardiovascular neuroscience and metabolic disease treatment. The not-for-profit UC Health was formed in 1994.

Operations

After a major reorganization in 2010 the surviving UC Health organizationA core operations areA comprisedA of UniversityA Medical CenterA West Chester Medical Center and itsA primary and specialty careA centers.A Through its affiliation with the University of Cincinnati the medical organization conducts educational and research programs.

Strategy

UC Health is working to expand its network through acquisitions. For instance it added a new women's health practice to its provider network in 2012 to widen its specialty service offerings.

UC Health acquired full control of the Drake Center from former partner (and former network member) Jewish Hospital in 2011. It also added the Lindner Center of HOPE to its network that year.

Company Background

Formerly known as The Health Alliance of Greater CincinnatiA the company changed its name to UC HealthA in 2010 after a number of its hospital members left the system and the University of Cincinnati took control of the remaining operations. Rumors of dissolution had swirled around theA organization since its members began jumping ship starting in 2007.

Four of the organization's foundingA hospitals ultimatelyA left the system: The 175-bed Fort Hamilton Hospital (now part of Kettering Health Network) and the 210-bedA Jewish Hospital (now part of Catholic Healthcare Partners) departedA in 2010. Two otherA hospitals (St. Luke's and Christ Hospital)A broke off from the alliance after a long legal struggleA in 2007.

EXECUTIVES

Senior Vice President And Chief Human Resources Officer, Bob Griffith
Evp And Cfo, Rick Hinds
President And Ceo, Richard P. Lofgren
Chief Physicians Services, Myles Pensak
Coo, Peter N. Gilbert
President Uc Health Foundation, Chris Smith
Vice President Of Operations, Ron Rohlfing
Vice President Chief Marketing Officer, Anthony Condia
Senior Vice President And Cio, Jay Brown
Vice President Audit And Compliance, Alton Knight
Senior Vice President Strategic Planning And Business Development, Gayla Harvey
Vice President Information Systems And Technology, Mark Carey
Vice President Of Finance, John Renner
Health Director, Shirley Kendall
Vice President Care Coordination, Andrew Cusher
Senior Vice President, Kyle Taylor
Vice President Supply Chain, Robert Wiehe
Chair Department Of Radiation Oncology, William Barrett
Medical Records Director, Frances Matre
Auditors: DELOITTE TAX LLP CINCINNATI

LOCATIONS

HQ: UC HEALTH, LLC.
3200 BURNET AVE, CINCINNATI, OH 452293019
Phone: 513 585-6000
Web: WWW.UCHEALTH.COM

PRODUCTS/OPERATIONS

Selected Ohio Facilities
Drake Center (Cincinnati)
Linder Center of HOPE (Mason)
UC Health Surgical Hospital (West Chester)
University of Cincinnati Physicians (Cincinnati)
University of Cincinnati Medical Center (Cincinnati)
West Chester Hospital (West Chester)

COMPETITORS

Catholic Health Initiatives	Premier Health Partners
Cincinnati Children's Hospital	St. Elizabeth Healthcare
Kettering Health Network	The Christ Hospital Corporation
Mercy Hospital Springfield	TriHealth

HISTORICAL FINANCIALS

Company Type: Private

Income Statement | | | | FYE: June 30

	REVENUE ($ mil.)	NET INCOME ($ mil.)	NET PROFIT MARGIN	EMPLOYEES
06/18	1,661	40	2.5%	10,000
06/17	1,586	73	4.7%	—
06/10	138	(81)	—	—
06/09	102	0	—	—
Annual Growth	36.3%	—	—	—

2018 Year-End Financials

Return on assets: 4.0%   Cash ($ mil.): 76
Return on equity: 2.5%
Current ratio: 1.40

UCLA MEDICAL CENTER

EXECUTIVES

Pres, David Feinberg
Exec V Pres, Patricia Kapur
Internal Medicine Practitioner, Vicki Tran
Internist, Forster Chhean
Internist, Omar Kattan
Director, Karen Schnell

LOCATIONS

HQ: UCLA MEDICAL CENTER
1250 16TH ST, SANTA MONICA, CA 904041249
Phone: 310 319-3816
Web: WWW.UCHEALTH.COM

HISTORICAL FINANCIALS

Company Type: Private

Income Statement | | | | FYE: June 30

	REVENUE ($ mil.)	NET INCOME ($ mil.)	NET PROFIT MARGIN	EMPLOYEES
06/16	513	18	3.6%	1
06/15	479	44	9.3%	—
Annual Growth	7.3%	(58.1%)	—	—

2016 Year-End Financials

Return on assets: 10.0%   Cash ($ mil.): 15
Return on equity: 3.6%
Current ratio: 1.30

UGI UTILITIES, INC.

EXECUTIVES

Chairman And Ceo, Lon R Greenberg

LOCATIONS

HQ: UGI UTILITIES, INC.
2525 N 12TH ST STE 360, READING, PA 196052771
Phone: 610 796-3400
Web: WWW.UGI.COM

HISTORICAL FINANCIALS

Company Type: Private

Income Statement | | | | FYE: September 30

	REVENUE ($ mil.)	NET INCOME ($ mil.)	NET PROFIT MARGIN	EMPLOYEES
09/18	1,092	148	13.6%	1,520
09/17	887	116	13.1%	—
Annual Growth	23.1%	28.3%	—	—

2018 Year-End Financials

Return on assets: 8.0%   Cash ($ mil.): 10
Return on equity: 13.6%
Current ratio: 0.20

ULSTER COUNTY

EXECUTIVES

Prin, Mike Hein
Chm, Terry Bernardo
V Chm, James F Maloney
Comm of Fin, Paul J Hewitt
Min Leader, David Donaldson
Maj Leader, Kenneth J Ronk Jr

Prin, Burton Gulnic Jr
Analst, Larry Craig
Coordinator, Alanna Henneberry
Sergeant, Eddie Torres
Commissioner, Victor Work

LOCATIONS

HQ: ULSTER COUNTY
244 FAIR ST, KINGSTON, NY 124013806
Phone: 845 340-3000
Web: WWW.ULSTERCOUNTYNY.GOV

HISTORICAL FINANCIALS

Company Type: Private

Income Statement				FYE: December 31
	REVENUE ($ mil.)	NET INCOME ($ mil.)	NET PROFIT MARGIN	EMPLOYEES
12/17	306	(5)	—	1,800
12/16	322	8	2.7%	—
12/15	326	(11)	—	—
12/14	302	(5)	—	—
Annual Growth	0.4%	—	—	—

2017 Year-End Financials

Return on assets: 5.6%   Cash ($ mil.): 71
Return on equity: (-1.9%)
Current ratio: —

UMASS MEMORIAL COMMUNITY HOSPITALS, INC.

EXECUTIVES

Ceo, Eric Dickson
President, Michael J Greene
Treas, Todd Keating
General Counsel, Joseph Fournier
MD, Muhammad Ramzan
Physician Referral Marketing M, Sarah Latorre
Family Practitioner, Rama Takillapati
Auditors: PRICEWATERHOUSECOOPERS LLP B

LOCATIONS

HQ: UMASS MEMORIAL COMMUNITY HOSPITALS, INC.
119 BELMONT ST, WORCESTER, MA 016052903
Phone: 508 334-1000
Web: WWW.UMASSMEMORIALHEALTHCARE.ORG

HISTORICAL FINANCIALS

Company Type: Private

Income Statement				FYE: September 30
	REVENUE ($ mil.)	NET INCOME ($ mil.)	NET PROFIT MARGIN	EMPLOYEES
09/17	308	10	3.5%	10,000
09/16	305	12	4.2%	—
09/15	286	8	2.8%	—
09/08	332	9	2.9%	—
Annual Growth	(0.9%)	1.4%	—	—

2017 Year-End Financials

Return on assets: 5.2%   Cash ($ mil.): 32
Return on equity: 3.5%
Current ratio: 0.80

UMASS MEMORIAL COMMUNITY MEDICAL GROUP, INC.

EXECUTIVES

Prin, Thomas Pokoly
Director, Vasilios Chrisostomidis
Obstetrician, Stanley P Surette
Auditors: PRICEWATERHOUSECOOPERS LLP B

LOCATIONS

HQ: UMASS MEMORIAL COMMUNITY MEDICAL
GROUP, INC.
121 LINCOLN ST, WORCESTER, MA 016052429
Phone: 508 757-7745
Web: WWW.COSMETICSURGICENTER.COM

HISTORICAL FINANCIALS

Company Type: Private

Income Statement				FYE: September 30
	REVENUE ($ mil.)	NET INCOME ($ mil.)	NET PROFIT MARGIN	EMPLOYEES
09/15	468	7	1.6%	3
09/11	451	8	1.9%	—
09/09	400	7	1.8%	—
09/08	360	1	0.4%	—
Annual Growth	3.8%	25.5%	—	—

2015 Year-End Financials

Return on assets: 1.5%   Cash ($ mil.): 18
Return on equity: 1.6%
Current ratio: 0.70

UMASS MEMORIAL MEDICAL CENTER, INC.

EXECUTIVES

Ceo, John Obrien
Exec V Pres, Wendy Waring
Sr V Pres, Gary Lapidas
Treas, Todd Keating
Pres, Eric Dickson M D
Dermatology, Dori Goldberg
Dermatology, Mark J Scharf
Chief of Medicine, Robert Finberg
Vice-President Operations, Victoria Diamond
Vice-President Business Develo, Willis Chandler
Executive of Information Techn, Denise Skrocki
Auditors: PRICEWATERHOUSECOOPERS LLP BO

LOCATIONS

HQ: UMASS MEMORIAL MEDICAL CENTER, INC.
1 BIOTECH 365 PLNTN ST 365 PLANTATION,
WORCESTER, MA 01605
Phone: 508 334-1000
Web: WWW.UMASSMEMORIAL.ORG

HISTORICAL FINANCIALS

Company Type: Private

Income Statement				FYE: September 30
	REVENUE ($ mil.)	NET INCOME ($ mil.)	NET PROFIT MARGIN	EMPLOYEES
09/17	1,668	(62)	—	58
09/16	1,621	(130)	—	—
09/15	1,508	(10)	—	—
Annual Growth	5.2%	—	—	—

2017 Year-End Financials

Return on assets: 6.8%   Cash ($ mil.): 57
Return on equity: (-3.8%)
Current ratio: 0.50

UMASS MEMORIAL MEDICAL CENTER, INC.

EXECUTIVES

Manager, David Klein
Doctor, Kirk Johnson
Internal Medicine Practitioner, Timothy P Fitzgibbons
Vice President Operations, Alice Shakman
Patient Experience Project Coo, Ana Mechlin
Registered Nurse, April O'Brien
Vice President, Bryan Cheshire
Administrative Assistant, Carolyn Granger
MD, Catherine A Phillips
Clinical Supervisor Respirator, Cathy Biros
Senior Administrative Secretar, Charlene E Belsito
Auditors: PRICEWATERHOUSECOOPERS LLP BO

LOCATIONS

HQ: UMASS MEMORIAL MEDICAL CENTER, INC.
55 LAKE AVE N, WORCESTER, MA 016550002
Phone: 508 334-1000

HISTORICAL FINANCIALS

Company Type: Private

Income Statement				FYE: September 30
	REVENUE ($ mil.)	NET INCOME ($ mil.)	NET PROFIT MARGIN	EMPLOYEES
09/16	1,621	(130)	—	29
09/15	1,332	60	4.5%	—
09/14	1,258	19	1.6%	—
09/13	1,183	68	5.8%	—
Annual Growth	11.1%	—	—	—

2016 Year-End Financials

Return on assets: 6.3%   Cash ($ mil.): 124
Return on equity: (-8.0%)
Current ratio: 0.70

UNIFIED SCHOOL DISTRICT 259

EXECUTIVES

Supt, John Allison
Treas-Dir, Linda Jones
Cfo, Jim Freeman
Facilities, Debbie Kandt
Auditors: ALLEN GIBBS & HOULIK LC W

LOCATIONS

HQ: UNIFIED SCHOOL DISTRICT 259
903 S EDGEMOOR ST, WICHITA, KS 672183337
Phone: 316 973-4000
Web: WWW.USD259.ORG

HISTORICAL FINANCIALS

Company Type: Private

Income Statement				FYE: June 30
	REVENUE ($ mil.)	NET INCOME ($ mil.)	NET PROFIT MARGIN	EMPLOYEES
06/17	632	15	2.4%	5,406
06/16	622	(31)	—	—
06/15	626	(55)	—	—
06/14	613	21	3.4%	—
Annual Growth	1.0%	(10.3%)	—	—

2017 Year-End Financials
Return on assets: 1.9%   Cash ($ mil.): 166
Return on equity: 2.4%
Current ratio: —

UNION BANK AND TRUST COMPANY

Union Bank & Trust a subsidiary of financial services holding company Farmers & Merchants Investment operates more than 35 branches throughout Nebraska and in Kansas. As Nebraska's third-largest privately-owned bank it offers traditional deposit and trust services as well as insurance equipment finance and investment management services. Consumer loans account for the largest portion of the bank's portfolio followed by commercial real estate and farmland loans. Union Bank also originates business loans and residential mortgages. Affiliate company Union Investment Advisors manages the Stratus family of mutual funds. Another Farmers & Merchants unit Nelnet Capital offers brokerage services.

Operations
Union Bank has grown to become one of Nebraska's largest privately-owned banks. As of mid-2013 it boasted bank assets of $2.6 billion and trust assets of $11.8 billion.

Aside from its branches in Nebraska and Kansas Union Bank offers banking products and services through its online mobile and electronic banking services.

Geographic Reach
Union Bank operates mostly in Nebraska but also in Kansas.

Sales and Marketing
The bank primarily serves customers in Lincoln and Omaha as well as the Kansas City metropolitan area.

Strategy

Union Bank continues to expand its footprint in existing markets. The financial institution will have added three new Nebraska branches to its portfolio by 2014.

Company Background
The bank was originally founded in 1917 as Farmer's State Bank. It took on the Union Bank name in 1935 and became Union Bank & Trust in 1959.

EXECUTIVES

Vice President, Tom Marchael
Vice President Small Business Banking, Stephanie Dinger
Vice President, Kwassi Amevor
Vice President, Jon Hawthorne
Vice President Financial Reporting And Controller, Kimberly Keller

LOCATIONS

HQ: UNION BANK AND TRUST COMPANY
3643 S 48TH ST, LINCOLN, NE 685064390
Phone: 402 488-0941
Web: WWW.UBT.COM

PRODUCTS/OPERATIONS

Selected Services
Business banking
Investment & retirement
Personal banking
Wealth management

Selected Affiliates
InfoVisa
Nelnet Capital LLC
Nelnet Inc.
Union Agency Inc.
Union Equipment Finance LLC
Union Investment Advisors
Union Title Company LLC
Zelle

COMPETITORS

Bank of America	Great Western Bancorp
Bank of the West	JPMorgan Chase
Citigroup	Pinnacle Bancorp
First National of Nebraska	U.S. Bancorp
	Wells Fargo

HISTORICAL FINANCIALS

Company Type: Private

Income Statement				FYE: December 31
	ASSETS ($ mil.)	NET INCOME ($ mil.)	INCOME AS % OF ASSETS	EMPLOYEES
12/17	3,836	45	1.2%	800
12/16	3,595	40	1.1%	—
12/15	3,351	32	1.0%	—
12/14	3,040	29	1.0%	—
Annual Growth	8.1%	15.8%	—	—

2017 Year-End Financials
Return on assets: —   Sales ($ mil): 214
Return on equity: 21.4%

UNION COUNTY BOARD OF EDUCATION

EXECUTIVES

Supt, Mary Ellis
Facilities Director, Maurice Brown
Auditors: ANDERSON SMITH & WIKE PLLC WE

LOCATIONS

HQ: UNION COUNTY BOARD OF EDUCATION
400 N CHURCH ST, MONROE, NC 281124804
Phone: 704 296-9898
Web: WWW.UCPS.K12.NC.US

HISTORICAL FINANCIALS

Company Type: Private

Income Statement				FYE: June 30
	REVENUE ($ mil.)	NET INCOME ($ mil.)	NET PROFIT MARGIN	EMPLOYEES
06/17	369	1	0.4%	5,427
06/13	316	(8)	—	—
06/12*	318	2	0.7%	—
12/05	0	0	—	—
Annual Growth	—	—	—	—
*Fiscal year change				

2017 Year-End Financials
Return on assets: 1.1%   Cash ($ mil.): 33
Return on equity: 0.4%
Current ratio: —

UNION HOSPITAL, INC.

Union Hospital is the flagship facility of the Union Hospital Health Group a health care system that serves communities in western Indiana and eastern Illinois. The not-for-profit hospital has about 320 beds boasts an equal number of physicians and provides general medical and surgical care as well as specialty services in areas such as women's health newborn intensive care unit (Level II) cancer cardiovascular disease and sports medicine. It also offers occupational health and physical rehabilitation as well as medical training programs. Other facilities that comprise the Union system include Union Hospital Clinton physician practices specialty clinics and a home health agency.

Operations
Besides the main Union Hospital which averages some 17000 patient admissions each year the hospital operates Union Hospital Clinton specialty clinics a home health agency and physician practices.

Geographic Reach
The teaching hospital serves patients in west-central Indiana and eastern Illinois.

Strategy
Union Hospital's main campus underwent a nearly $180 million expansion project in recent years. The patient tower provides for private rooms instead of six- to eight-bed wards.

As part of a strategic focus to extend the reach of its operations Union Hospital partners with AP&S Clinic a multi-specialty physician group practice to expand the two entities' services. Operating as Union Health System the collaboration looks to increase coordination of care between physician specialists.

In 2015 Union Hospital partnered with the Ob Hospitalist Group to provide around-the-clock physician care for expectant mothers.

Company Background
Union Hospital's roots go back to 1892.

EXECUTIVES

Medical Director, Grace Walker
Director Of Medical Records, Pamala Alexander

LOCATIONS

HQ: UNION HOSPITAL, INC.
  1606 N 7TH ST, TERRE HAUTE, IN 478042780
Phone: 812 238-7000
Web: WWW.MYUNIONHOSPITAL.ORG

PRODUCTS/OPERATIONS

Selected Services
Acupuncture
Advanced Medical Technology
Asthma
Behavioral Healthcare
Breast Care
Cancer Care Services
Cardiovascular Testing
Clara Fairbanks Center for Women
Clay City Center for Family Medicine
Cork Medical Center
Family Medicine Center
  Infections
Joint Replacement Center
Landsbaum Center
Lugar Center for Rural Health
Medical Rehabilitation Center
Neonatal Intensive Care Unit (NICU)
Pediatrics
Pulmonary and Lung Health
Wound Healing Center
Union Hospital Terre Haute
Union Hospital Clinton
Union Hospital Foundation

COMPETITORS

Ascension Health	IU Health Bloomington
Carle Hospital	Hospital
Franciscan Alliance	Kosciusko Community
HCA	Hospital
IU Health	

HISTORICAL FINANCIALS
Company Type: Private

Income Statement				FYE: December 31
	REVENUE ($ mil.)	NET INCOME ($ mil.)	NET PROFIT MARGIN	EMPLOYEES
12/16	416	(11)	—	2,700
12/15	384	6	1.8%	—
12/14*	127	3	2.7%	—
08/10	400	(3)	—	—
Annual Growth	0.7%	—	—	—

*Fiscal year change

2016 Year-End Financials
Return on assets: 8.3%   Cash ($ mil.): 65
Return on equity: (-2.8%)
Current ratio: 1.60

UNITED CONCORDIA LIFE AND HEALTH INSURANCE COMPANY

EXECUTIVES

Ceo, Frederick Merkel
Fo, Daniel Wright
EC, Edward Bittner
Supervisor, Brenda Godusky

LOCATIONS

HQ: UNITED CONCORDIA LIFE AND HEALTH
  INSURANCE COMPANY
  4401 DEER PATH RD, HARRISBURG, PA 171103983
Phone: 717 260-7081
Web: WWW.UNITEDCONCORDIA.COM

HISTORICAL FINANCIALS
Company Type: Private

Income Statement				FYE: December 31
	REVENUE ($ mil.)	NET INCOME ($ mil.)	NET PROFIT MARGIN	EMPLOYEES
12/15	680	34	5.1%	1
12/14	731	57	7.9%	—
Annual Growth	(6.9%)	(39.8%)	—	—

2015 Year-End Financials
Return on assets: —   Cash ($ mil.): 54
Return on equity: 5.1%
Current ratio: 0.70

UNITED COOPERATIVE

EXECUTIVES

Ceo, David Cramer
Cfo, Damian Girten
Chm, Howard Bohl
SEC, Robin Craker
Manager, Greg Thomson
Director Juneau, David Bischoff
Manager, Greg Adkins
Vice-President, Alan Jentz

LOCATIONS

HQ: UNITED COOPERATIVE
  N7160 RACEWAY RD, BEAVER DAM, WI 539169315
Phone: 920 887-1756
Web: WWW.UNITEDCOOPERATIVE.COM

HISTORICAL FINANCIALS
Company Type: Private

Income Statement				FYE: December 31
	REVENUE ($ mil.)	NET INCOME ($ mil.)	NET PROFIT MARGIN	EMPLOYEES
12/17	644	49	7.7%	358
12/16	630	41	6.6%	—
12/15	579	41	7.1%	—
12/14	577	57	10.0%	—
Annual Growth	3.7%	(4.7%)	—	—

2017 Year-End Financials
Return on assets: 3.4%   Cash ($ mil.): 22
Return on equity: 7.7%
Current ratio: 0.40

UNITED FOOD AND COMMERCIAL WORKERS UNIONS AND FOOD EMPLOYERS BEN FUND

EXECUTIVES

Prin, Richard Klontz
Auditors: HEMMING MORSE CPA'S AND CONSUL

LOCATIONS

HQ: UNITED FOOD AND COMMERCIAL WORKERS
  UNIONS AND FOOD EMPLOYERS BEN FUND
  6425 KATELLA AVE, CYPRESS, CA 906305246
Phone: 714 220-2297
Web: WWW.SCUFCWFUNDS.COM

HISTORICAL FINANCIALS
Company Type: Private

Income Statement				FYE: March 31
	REVENUE ($ mil.)	NET INCOME ($ mil.)	NET PROFIT MARGIN	EMPLOYEES
03/17	593	3	0.5%	23
03/12	512	(34)	—	—
03/11	460	(74)	—	—
03/10	333	(165)	—	—
Annual Growth	8.6%	—	—	—

2017 Year-End Financials
Return on assets: 0.1%   Cash ($ mil.): 51
Return on equity: 0.5%
Current ratio: 237.50

UNITED HEALTH SERVICES HOSPITAL, INC.

United Health Services Hospitals (UHS Hospitals) can service injuries from a slip in the snow or a slipped discA to health that's just plain slipping.A The organizationA operates Binghamton General Hospital (about 200 beds) Wilson Medical Center (someA 280 beds) and a group of primary and specialty careA clinics inA upstate New York. Specialty services includeA cardiology dialysis neurology rehabilitation pediatricsA and psychiatry. The Wilson Medical Center serves as a teaching hospital offering residency and fellowship programs.A UHS Hospitals is a subsidiary of United Health Services which operates a network of affiliated hospitalsA clinicsA long-term care centers and home health agencies in the region.

Geographic Reach
Binghamton General is located in Binghamton New York while Wilson Medical Center is located in Johnson City New York both within the boundaries of Broome County.A UHSA HospitalsA also operates primary and specialty careA clinicsA in Broome Chenango Delaware and Tioga counties in upstate New York.

Strategy

United Health Services Hospitals is investing in equipment upgrades and facility improvementsA at Binghamton General to help the facility remain at the forefront of medical technology and services. Wilson Medical CenterA whichA acts as a regional referral centerA in areasA including emergency medicine newborn care neurology and heart surgery has also been the subject of enhancement measures. The hospital recently completed construction of the new Decker Center for Advanced Medical Treatment which offers high-tech diagnostic and acute care services.

EXECUTIVES

Vice President General Counsel, Jeffery Alexander
Nursing Director, Kay Boland
Vice President Of Quality, Amy Miller
Vice President Finance, Jennifer Morgan
Auditors: FUST CHARLES CHAMBERS LLP SYR

LOCATIONS

HQ: UNITED HEALTH SERVICES HOSPITAL, INC.
10-42 MITCHELL AVE, BINGHAMTON, NY 139031617
Phone: 607 762-2200

COMPETITORS

Albany Medical Center
Guthrie Healthcare
Kaleida Health
Lifetime Health
Oneida Healthcare Center
SUNY Upstate Medical University
St. Joseph's Hospital Health Center
Upstate University Hospital at Community General

HISTORICAL FINANCIALS
Company Type: Private

Income Statement				FYE: December 31
	REVENUE ($ mil.)	NET INCOME ($ mil.)	NET PROFIT MARGIN	EMPLOYEES
12/16	611	21	3.4%	5,000
12/15	575	13	2.3%	—
12/14	523	(23)	—	—
12/13	516	27	5.4%	—
Annual Growth	5.8%	(9.0%)	—	—

2016 Year-End Financials

Return on assets: 3.8%   Cash ($ mil.): 12
Return on equity: 3.4%
Current ratio: 0.80

UNITED HOSPITAL CENTER, INC.

EXECUTIVES

Pres, Michael C Tillman
V Pres-Fin-Cfo, Doug Coffman
Vice President, James C Rutkowski
Coordinator, John Backus
Physical Therapist, Ashley McClain
Emergency Medicine Specialist, Gary Oates
Nurse, Tammy Hicks
Public Relations Director, Matt Chisler
Nurse, Tabatha Hayhurst
Anesthesiologist, Eli Fleece
Gastroenterologist, Kimberly Fairley

LOCATIONS

HQ: UNITED HOSPITAL CENTER, INC.
327 MEDICAL PARK DR, BRIDGEPORT, WV
263309006
Phone: 681 342-1000
Web: WWW.UHCWV.ORG

HISTORICAL FINANCIALS
Company Type: Private

Income Statement				FYE: December 31
	REVENUE ($ mil.)	NET INCOME ($ mil.)	NET PROFIT MARGIN	EMPLOYEES
12/17	331	45	13.6%	2,000
12/16	319	19	6.1%	—
12/15	293	12	4.4%	—
12/14	280	17	6.4%	—
Annual Growth	5.8%	36.3%	—	—

2017 Year-End Financials

Return on assets: 4.3%   Cash ($ mil.): 41
Return on equity: 13.6%
Current ratio: 1.70

UNITED INDEPENDENT SCHOOL DISTRICT

EXECUTIVES

Supt, Roberto J Santos
Vice President, Juan Roberto Ramirez
EC, Ricardo Rodriguez
Network Manager, Cesar Tamez
Tech Prep Coordinator, Alicia Carrillo
Computer Technician, Gabriel Ramirez
Coordinator, Maria Dominguez
Coordinator, Mary Lopez
Coordinator, Veronica Slaughter
Librarian, Ana Gloria
Teacher, Ana Guerrero
Auditors: PATTILLO BROWN & HILL LLP BR

LOCATIONS

HQ: UNITED INDEPENDENT SCHOOL DISTRICT
201 LINDENWOOD DR, LAREDO, TX 780452429
Phone: 956 473-6201
Web: WWW.UISD.NET

HISTORICAL FINANCIALS
Company Type: Private

Income Statement				FYE: August 31
	REVENUE ($ mil.)	NET INCOME ($ mil.)	NET PROFIT MARGIN	EMPLOYEES
08/17	429	16	3.9%	6,900
08/16	464	(66)	—	—
08/15	444	64	14.5%	—
08/14	387	89	23.1%	—
Annual Growth	3.5%	(42.9%)	—	—

2017 Year-End Financials

Return on assets: 4.7%   Cash ($ mil.): 126
Return on equity: 3.9%
Current ratio: —

UNITED REGIONAL HEALTH CARE SYSTEM, INC.

If you take a fall in Wichita Falls United Regional Health Care System (URHCS) will be there. The health care provider serves the residents of northern Texas through two hospitals that combined have some 500 beds. Specialized services include emergency medicine cardiac care diagnostic imaging surgery obstetrics and pediatrics. The health care system also offers cancer treatment childbirth wound care and sleep diagnostic centers. It is the only comprehensive cardiac care facility and only Level II trauma center in the region. URHCS operates a Care Flight Helicopter to get those traumas to care quicker.

Operations

URHCS provides medical care including inpatient and outpatient services advanced diagnostics surgical specialties and life-saving emergency care and the area's only Level II Trauma Center. It also serves as the Primary Stroke Center for the region. Its centers of excellence include wound care center joint replacement program and stroke program; bariatric surgery program; breast imaging center of excellence; cardiovascular patient care. It has some 200 physicians on staff.

In 2012 the medical system reported 14163 admissions; 74778 emergency department visits; 48890 outpatient visits/observations; 9211 surgeries and 2144 births.

Geographic Reach

The hospital serves Wichita Falls and a surrounding nine-county area.

Financial Performance

In 2012 URHCS provided $27 million in charity care.

Strategy

Along with building and technological expansions URHCS has been focused on increasing the number of specialists in its employ. To that end the system created a recruitment program that targets medical students residents and fellows who have ties to Wichita Falls and the surrounding areas. Hospital administration and members of the physician staff offer support and guidance to potential recruits as they progress in their medical education or as they consider making a move from another hospital.

In recent years URHCS has recruited physicians in the areas of cardiovascular surgery neurosurgery orthopedic surgery and minimally invasive general and bariatric surgery to meet the community's increased need for those medical specialties.

In 2013 it expanded the Barnett Road Medical Building to have office space for physicians. The system also added laboratory and radiology services to the building.

In 2012 URHCS deployed Allscripts MDRX+1.09% Care Management's fully-integrated web-based solutions to help transform its administrative processes by streamlining and improving the quality of patient care enhancing operational efficiency and cutting costs. In addition new mobile access technology help physicians to securely access patient information and make care decisions for their patients via their iPhones and iPads.

Company Background

In 2011 URCHS initiated renovation of its Bethania Building and Administration Building and it relocated its Cardio-Pulmonary Rehab Facility. It also remodeled its United Regional Diagnostic building and extended the hospital's outpatient therapy space to accommodate more patients.

EXECUTIVES

Vice President Of Information Technology, Donnie Boydstun
Vice President Of Facilities Management, Rick Carpenter
Vice President Of Marketing, Stevie-Joe Brown
Vice President Of Finance, Bob Pert
Nursing Director, Jane Ritter

LOCATIONS

HQ: UNITED REGIONAL HEALTH CARE SYSTEM, INC.
  1600 11TH ST, WICHITA FALLS, TX 763014300
Phone: 940 764-3211
Web: WWW.UNITEDREGIONAL.ORG

PRODUCTS/OPERATIONS

Selected Medical Services
Advanced Technology
Bariatric Services
Cancer Care
Cardiac Services
Diabetes Education
Emergency and Trauma Services
ENT
Infusion Therapy
Neurology
Neurosurgery
Obstetrics
Orthopedics
Pediatrics
Pulmonary Rehabilitation
Radiology
Reference Laboratory
Respiratory
Stroke Program & Center of Distinction
Supportive Care
Surgical Services
Women's Services
Wound Care

COMPETITORS

HCA	Tenet Healthcare
Jackson County	Texas Health Denton
Memorial Hospital	Texas Health Resources
Mercy Health	

HISTORICAL FINANCIALS
Company Type: Private

Income Statement				FYE: December 31
	REVENUE ($ mil.)	NET INCOME ($ mil.)	NET PROFIT MARGIN	EMPLOYEES
12/16	333	53	16.0%	1,950
12/15	299	32	10.9%	—
12/14	310	46	15.0%	—
12/13	292	53	18.3%	—
Annual Growth	4.4%	(0.3%)	—	—

UNITED STATES BEEF CORPORATION

EXECUTIVES

Vice President Human Resources, Kim Thompson
Vice President Operations, Bo Davis
Senior Vice President Operations, Rick Morris
Vice President Finance, Lori Pumphrey

LOCATIONS

HQ: UNITED STATES BEEF CORPORATION
  4923 E 49TH ST, TULSA, OK 741357002
Phone: 918 665-0740
Web: WWW.USBEEFCORP.COM

COMPETITORS

American Dairy Queen	Mazzio's
Biglari Holdings	McDonald's
Boddie-Noell	NPC Restaurant
Burger King	Holdings
Captain D's	Panera Bread
Checkers Drive-In	Popeyes
Chick-fil-A	Quiznos
Chipotle	Sonic Corp.
Church's Chicken	Subway
Hardee's	Whataburger
Jack in the Box	YUM!
K-MAC	

HISTORICAL FINANCIALS
Company Type: Private

Income Statement				FYE: December 31
	REVENUE ($ mil.)	NET INCOME ($ mil.)	NET PROFIT MARGIN	EMPLOYEES
12/17	374	17	4.8%	7,000
12/15	351	14	4.2%	—
12/13	256	7	3.1%	—
12/12	246	7	3.0%	—
Annual Growth	8.7%	19.8%	—	—

2017 Year-End Financials
Return on assets: 1.3%
Return on equity: 4.8%
Current ratio: 0.10
Cash ($ mil.): 2

UNITED STATES FUND FOR UNICEF

The US Fund for UNICEF is one of about 40 committees in America that raises money for The United Nations Children's Fund (better known as UNICEF a not-for-profit organization that works for the human rights protection and development of children worldwide through education advocacy and fundraising. Among its dedicated programs are the five-year $100 million fundraising campaign for HIV/AIDS prevention and a campaign to protect mothers and newborns from tetanus. The US Fund for UNICEF derives revenue from public support — through its signature Trick-or-Treat for UNICEF program gifts corporate grants and the sale of greeting cards and educational materials. The organization was founded in 1947.

Geographic Reach
The US Fund for UNICEF operates a handful of regional offices in Atlanta Boston Chicago Houston Los Angeles and San Francisco.

Financial Performance
The organization's revenue increased by 1% in 2012 versus 2011 to more than $500 million. The US Fund attributed the gain to an increase in public support including major gifts Internet donations and gifts in kind. The increase in giving was partially offset by a decline in investment returns. Net income rose 7% over the same period despite an increase in expenses tied to program and support services.

Strategy
The US Fund for UNICEF is rallying around its "Believe in Zero" campaign which aims to reduce the number of preventable deaths of children under five years of age to zero. The number of under-five child deaths has dropped more than 40 percent since 1990 to 19000.

EXECUTIVES

Pres-Ceo, Caryl M Stern
V Chm, Anthony Pantaleoni
Hon Co-Chm, Jimmy Carter
Hon Co-Chm, Gerald R Ford
Chair Emeritus*, Hugh Downs
V Pres-Public Policy-Advocacy*, Martin S Rendon
Chb, Vince Hemmer
V Chb, Gary Cohen
Consultant, Anna Burlyaeva
Information Specialist, Christian Larsson
Director, Elizabeth De Velasco
Auditors: KPMG LLP NEW YORK NY

LOCATIONS

HQ: UNITED STATES FUND FOR UNICEF
  125 MAIDEN LN FL 11, NEW YORK, NY 100384999
Phone: 800 367-5437
Web: WWW.UNICEFUSA.ORG

HISTORICAL FINANCIALS
Company Type: Private

Income Statement				FYE: June 30
	REVENUE ($ mil.)	NET INCOME ($ mil.)	NET PROFIT MARGIN	EMPLOYEES
06/16	568	7	1.2%	230
06/15	500	(29)	—	—
06/14	606	67	11.2%	—
06/13	310	12	4.2%	—
Annual Growth	22.3%	(18.2%)	—	—

2016 Year-End Financials
Return on assets: —
Return on equity: 1.2%
Current ratio: 0.70
Cash ($ mil.): 65

UNITED STATES OLYMPIC COMMITTEE INC

EXECUTIVES

Ceo, Scott Blackmun, age 61
Chief Financial Officer, Walter Glover
Managing Director Information Technology, Trevor Miller
Vice President Principal Gifts And Board Relations, Christine Walshe
Auditors: DELOITTE TAX LLP CHICAGO IL

LOCATIONS

HQ: UNITED STATES OLYMPIC COMMITTEE INC
  1 OLYMPIC PLZ, COLORADO SPRINGS, CO 80903
Phone: 719 632-5551
Web: WWW.TEAMUSA.ORG

HISTORICAL FINANCIALS
Company Type: Private

Income Statement				FYE: December 31
	REVENUE ($ mil.)	NET INCOME ($ mil.)	NET PROFIT MARGIN	EMPLOYEES
12/16	336	78	23.4%	400
12/15	141	(57)	—	—
12/14	270	47	17.7%	—
12/13	168	(27)	—	—
Annual Growth	25.9%	—	—	—

2016 Year-End Financials
Return on assets: 9.2%
Return on equity: 23.4%
Current ratio: —

Cash ($ mil.): 158

UNIVERSITIES OF LOUISIANA SYSTEM

EXECUTIVES
President, Randy Moffett
Exec Dir, Caprice Leyoub
Coordinator, Renee Lorio
Controller, Rhonda Webber

LOCATIONS
HQ: UNIVERSITIES OF LOUISIANA SYSTEM
1201 N 3RD ST STE 7300, BATON ROUGE, LA 708025243
Phone: 225 342-6950
Web: WWW.ULSYSTEM.NET

HISTORICAL FINANCIALS
Company Type: Private

Income Statement				FYE: June 30
	REVENUE ($ mil.)	NET INCOME ($ mil.)	NET PROFIT MARGIN	EMPLOYEES
06/17	906	23	2.6%	4,500
06/16	845	25	3.0%	—
Annual Growth	7.2%	(4.5%)	—	—

2017 Year-End Financials
Return on assets: 6.7%
Return on equity: 2.6%
Current ratio: 2.10

Cash ($ mil.): 253

UNIVERSITY COMMUNITY HOSPITAL, INC.

University Community Health (doing business as Florida Hospital Tampa Bay Division) is a 1000-bed regional health care system with four locations spanning the Hillsborough Pinellas and Pasco counties of Florida. It oversees a network of eight hospitals in Florida's Tampa Bay area. Its four general hospitals — three located in Tampa and one in nearby Tarpon Springs — collectively house some 860 beds and provide emergency surgical and acute medical care as well as provide outpatient services. The system also includes a specialty heart hospital a women's hospital and a long-term acute care hospital. Florida Hospital Tampa Bay Division is part of the Adventist Health System.

Strategy
As part of the Adventist Health System's network the system has access to a broader statewide network of physicians and specialists as well as enhanced administrative and technological services organization.

In 2012 Florida Hospital Tampa Bay Division opened Florida Hospital Wesley Chapel and began work on three major construction projects including a new full-service Emergency Department (ED) expanding The Women's Center and exterior and interior upgrades to the main hospital which should add a total of 54000 sq. ft. to the scope of Florida Hospital Tampa.

Company Background
Its original name of University Community Health (UCH) reflected its proximity to the University of South Florida. UCH teamed up with Adventist Health in 2007 to build Wesley Chapel Medical Center. Buoyed by the success of the venture in 2010 UCH and Adventist Health reached an accord and UCH became a member of Adventist Health.

EXECUTIVES
V Pres, Michael Schultz
Acct, Lynn Addiscott
Acct, Ariel De Prada
Coo, Jack Chubb
Cno, Theresa Trivette
Chief of Medicine, Mitchell Ohara
Project Manager, Dorothy Hudson
Internal Medicine Practitioner, Ashley Robaina
Administrator, Julie Dunaway
Nurse, Amy Thatavakorn
Supervisor Cardiac Cath Lab, Frank Vansickle

LOCATIONS
HQ: UNIVERSITY COMMUNITY HOSPITAL, INC.
3100 E FLETCHER AVE, TAMPA, FL 336134613
Phone: 813 971-6000
Web: WWW.FLORIDAHOSPITAL.COM

PRODUCTS/OPERATIONS

Selected Centers
Diabetes and Endocrinology Institute
Don Lau Family Center for Cancer Care
Florida Hospital Pepin Heart Institute
Occupational Health Service
Orthopedic Care Center
Pediatric Care Center
Sleep Center
The Women's Center
Wound Healing Institute

Selected Hospitals
Florida Hospital at Connerton
Florida Hospital Carrollwood
Florida Hospital North Pinellas
Florida Hospital Pepin Heart Institute
Florida Hospital Tampa
Florida Hospital Wesley Chapel
Florida Hospital Zephyrhills
Long Term Acute Care

COMPETITORS
All Children's Hospital	Lakeland Regional Medical Center
BayCare Health System	Northside Hospital and Heart Institute
Bayfront Health	
HCA	Tampa General Hospital

HISTORICAL FINANCIALS
Company Type: Private

Income Statement				FYE: December 31
	REVENUE ($ mil.)	NET INCOME ($ mil.)	NET PROFIT MARGIN	EMPLOYEES
12/16	483	39	8.2%	8,000
12/15	460	38	8.4%	—
12/14	381	24	6.5%	—
12/13	510	33	6.6%	—
Annual Growth	(1.8%)	5.7%	—	—

2016 Year-End Financials
Return on assets: 2.8%
Return on equity: 8.2%
Current ratio: 3.50

Cash ($ mil.): 197

UNIVERSITY HEALTH SYSTEM

EXECUTIVES
Ceo, George B Hernandez Jr
Obstetrician, Courtney M Failor
Obstetrician, Lauren M Schaub
Pulmonary Disease Specialist, Patrick R Aguilar
Nephrology Specialist, Seema S Ahuja
Obstetrician, Tiffany Remsing
Director, Felix Alvarez
Surgeon, Abdulqader Alarhayem
Internal Medicine Practitioner, Aftab Haq
Surgeon, Agustin Cornejo
Internal Medicine Practitioner, AMI Patel-Yadav

LOCATIONS
HQ: UNIVERSITY HEALTH SYSTEM
4502 MEDICAL DR, SAN ANTONIO, TX 782294402
Phone: 210 358-4000
Web: WWW.UNIVERSITYHEALTHSYSTEM.COM

HISTORICAL FINANCIALS
Company Type: Private

Income Statement				FYE: December 31
	REVENUE ($ mil.)	NET INCOME ($ mil.)	NET PROFIT MARGIN	EMPLOYEES
12/16	533	82	15.4%	5,000
12/15	476	73	15.4%	—
12/14	407	23	5.7%	—
Annual Growth	14.4%	88.5%	—	—

2016 Year-End Financials
Return on assets: 25.3%
Return on equity: 15.4%
Current ratio: 0.30

Cash ($ mil.): 19

UNIVERSITY HEALTH SYSTEMS OF EASTERN CAROLINA, INC.

University Health Systems of Eastern Carolina is an integrated not-for-profit health system that serves residents of eastern North Carolina. Doing business as Vidant Health it operates nine hospitals including eight community hospitals and its tertiary care center Vidant Medical Center with 1400 beds and academic affiliation with the Brody School of Medicine at East Carolina University. Vidant Health also operates centers for surgery home health hospiceand wellness and engages in community health programs. Its physician group has more than 350 primary and specialty care providers who operate frommore than 50 locations.

Operations
In addition to its nine hospitals the organization includes the Vidant Home Health and Hospice organization the Vidant Wellness Centers and the growing line of Vidant Medical Group physician practice locations. Vidant Health's facilities handle some 64000 inpatient and 595000 emergency care and outpatient visits each year. The organization also provides some $135.5 million in annual community benefits including outreach programs and charity care.

Geographic Reach
The organization serves more than 1.4 million residents in 29 counties in eastern North Carolina.

Financial Performance
In 2014 Vidant Health reported a 0.2% decrease in revenues and a 37% drop in net income.

Strategy
Because the system operates as a not-for-profit enterprise it reinvests its earnings in capital improvements equipment and new services. Vidant Health reinvests all of its income back into capital projects equipment and access to services for the patients and communities it serves. In 2014 the system invested $38 million in capital assets which included investments in information systems medical equipment and infrastructure across the health system as well as architectural and design fees related to the construction of the new cancer tower on the Vidant Medical Center campus.

Across the region Vidant is focusing on cancer care and is creating a strong network of strategically located cancer services. In Washington the Marion L. Shepard Cancer Center a department of Vidant Beaufort Hospital underwent a major expansion including new high-technology radiation treatment equipment. This $4.8 million project helps patients receive cancer care in their home community.

Company Background
University Health Systems rebranded itself as Vidant Health in 2012 in its effort to reflect its "vibrant and vital" position within the region as it advances its transformation to patient- and family-centered care.

In 2012 the hospital invested in upgrades to several outpatient care centers adding a new medical office building in the community of Wallace and adding specialist rehabilitation and behavioral health care units to its Vidant Chowan Hospital facility. It also discontinued skilled nursing services at the Chowan location to focus more on outpatient care. In addition a new children's hospital and pediatric emergency room was opened at the Vidant Medical Center location.

Vidant Health is also working to upgrade its health information technology systems. During 2012 it successfully connected three of its community hospitals through its electronic health record (EHR) system.

EXECUTIVES
Ceo, Michael Waldrum
Chief ADM Officer, Janet Mullaney
Vp Corporate Planning and Stra, Mary Sue Collier
Emergency Medicine Specialist, Catherine V Myers
Human Resources, Brenda Dixon
Auditors: RSM US LLP CHICAGO IL

LOCATIONS
HQ: UNIVERSITY HEALTH SYSTEMS OF EASTERN CAROLINA, INC.
800 W H SMITH BLVD, GREENVILLE, NC 278343763
Phone: 252 847-6690
Web: WWW.ECU.EDU

PRODUCTS/OPERATIONS
Selected Hospitals
Vidant Beaufort Hospital (Washington)
Vidant Bertie Hospital (Windsor)
Vidant Chowan Hospital (Edenton)
Vidant Duplin Hospital (Kenansville)
Vidant Edgecombe Hospital (Tarboro)
Vidant Medical Center (affiliated with the Brody School of Medicine at East Carolina University Greenville)
Vidant Pungo Hospital (Belhaven)
Vidant Roanoke-Chowan Hospital (Ahoskie)
The Outer Banks Hospital (jointly owned with Chesapeake Regional Medical Center Nags Head)

Selected Services
Asthma Program (Pediatric)
Audiology
Behavioral & Mental Health
Cancer Care
Child Life
Children's Care
Children's Emergency Department
Children's Hospital
Community Health Programs
Diagnostic Imaging
Diabetes
Emergency Services
Endoscopy Services
Gamma Knife
Heart and Vascular Care
Heartburn Treatment Clinic
Home Health
Hospice Care
Hyperbaric Oxygen Therapy
Injury Prevention
Mammography
Medical Weight Loss (OPTIFAST)
Mental Health
MRI (Magnetic Resonance Imaging)
Neurosciences
Neurosurgery
Open MRI
Orthopedics
Pain Management
Pediatric Cardiology
Pediatric Rehabilitation
Pediatric Services
Pink Power Speaking Tour
Psychiatry
Radiology
Rehabilitation Center
Rehabilitation
Senior Services
Sleep Services
Specialty Services
Speech Pathology
Spine Surgery
Sports Medicine
Stroke Care
Surgical Services
Transplant Services
Trauma Services
Vascular Surgery
Weight Loss
Wellness & Prevention
Women's Care
Wound Healing

COMPETITORS
Alamance Regional Medical Center
Carolinas HealthCare System
Cumberland County Hospital System
Duke University Health System
Grace Hospital
Novant Health
Rex Healthcare
Rowan Regional Medical Center
UNC Hospitals
WakeMed

HISTORICAL FINANCIALS
Company Type: Private

Income Statement				FYE: September 30
	REVENUE ($ mil.)	NET INCOME ($ mil.)	NET PROFIT MARGIN	EMPLOYEES
09/15	1,581	(6)	—	15,000
09/14*	1,597	66	4.1%	—
12/13	400	31	7.9%	—
09/13	1,601	109	6.8%	—
Annual Growth	(0.6%)	—	—	—

*Fiscal year change

2015 Year-End Financials
Return on assets: 12.7%   Cash ($ mil.): 192
Return on equity: (-0.4%)
Current ratio: 1.80

UNIVERSITY MEDICAL CENTER INC

EXECUTIVES
Ceo, James Taylor
President, Ken Marshall
Sr Vice President, Mark Pfeifer
Cfo-Sr Vice President, Robert P Barbier
SEC, Amber Denham
Vice-President, Mary Jane Adams
Assistant Professor of Radiolo, Peter Hentzen
Assistant Professor of Radiolo, Richard Goldwin
Assistant Professor of Radiolo, Brian Aronson
Assistant Professor of Radiolo, Barbara Pawley
Director of Oncology, Den Ellen Coldiron

LOCATIONS
HQ: UNIVERSITY MEDICAL CENTER INC
530 S JACKSON ST, LOUISVILLE, KY 402021675
Phone: 502 562-3000
Web: WWW.UNIVERSITY-HOSPITAL.ORG

HISTORICAL FINANCIALS
Company Type: Private

Income Statement				FYE: June 30
	REVENUE ($ mil.)	NET INCOME ($ mil.)	NET PROFIT MARGIN	EMPLOYEES
06/16	501	35	7.1%	2,000
06/15	484	53	11.1%	—
/*	0	—	—	—
Annual Growth	—	—	—	—

*Fiscal year change

2016 Year-End Financials
Return on assets: 5.2%   Cash ($ mil.): 133
Return on equity: 7.1%
Current ratio: 1.90

UNIVERSITY MEDICAL CENTER OF SOUTHERN NEVADA

For those who want to learn while they heal the ill University Medical Center of Southern Nevada (UMC)— an affiliate of the University of Nevada School of Medicine might just be the place. The medical center includes a teaching hospital and a network of community and urgent care health centers. Among its specialized services are cancer treatment heart care pediatrics and rehabilitation. It also offers birthing wound and burn care neurological disorder Level II Pediatric Trauma Lions Burn Care Center and Level 1 trauma centers. UMC serves southern Nevada along with parts of Arizona California and Utah.

Operations

UMC is also home to Children's Hospital of Nevada. Services at University Medical Center of Southern Nevada are comprehensive and include everything from ambulatory surgery to a birthing center cancer care infection prevention and organ donation.

The hospital operates 10 Quick Care urgent care locations around Las Vegas. Quick Cares provide primary and urgent care which means they accept minor injuries such as fractures and flus and primary care for patients who don't necessarily need to be seen right away and can make an appointment.

UMC offers residency programs in a whole slew of specialties including dental (pediatric and adult) emergency medicine family medicine internal medicine OB-GYN psychiatry surgery and trauma surgery and ophthalmology.

For doctors who have put medical school behind them UMC provides a range of Continuing Education Courses to keep them up to date on the latest procedures and technology.

More than 6500 patients are treated at UMC's emergency room per month and more than 600 children are treated per week. UMC's lab processes 4 million test results annually using the latest in technology and automation for the greatest accuracy and increased patient outcomes.

Sales and Marketing

Medicare accounted for 20% of the Center's 2014 revenues; Medicaid and self pay 50%; and commercial HMO and PPO 20%.

Financial Performance

UMC's revenues decreased by 20% in 2014 due to a decline in net patient revenues and other operating revenues.

It reported a net loss of $56 million in 2014 due to a decline in revenues and an increase in purchase services expenses as the result of consulting services received for operational improvements.

UMC reported cash outflow of $42 million in 2014 over cash inflow of 2013.

Company Background

The medical center opened its doors in 1931 with 20 beds.

EXECUTIVES

Ceo, Anson Van Houweling
Coo, Tony Marinello
Chief Anesthesiology, Andres F Costas- Centiva
Chief Technology Officer, Ernie McKinley
Accounting Staff, Ruth Pio
Administrative Assistant, Holly T
Coordinator, April Reynolds
Director, Doug Spring

Web Developer, James Pham
Scientist, Cheryl Shutt
Chief of Radiology, Dianne Mazzu

LOCATIONS

HQ: UNIVERSITY MEDICAL CENTER OF SOUTHERN NEVADA
1800 W CHARLESTON BLVD, LAS VEGAS, NV 891022329
Phone: 702 383-2000
Web: WWW.UMCSN.COM

PRODUCTS/OPERATIONS

Selected Services
Bariatric Medicine
Birthing Center
Center for Transplantation
Emergency Services
Family Resource Center
Heart Center
HIV Wellness Center
Imaging Se
Infection Prevention
Interpretive Services
Lab Services
Lions Wound and Burn Care Center
Oncology Care Center
Outpatient Physical Therapy
Robotics
Surgical Services
Trauma Center

COMPETITORS

Desert Springs Hospital
Dignity Health
Summerlin Hospital
Sunrise Hospital and Medical Center
Valley Hospital

HISTORICAL FINANCIALS
Company Type: Private

Income Statement				FYE: June 30
	REVENUE ($ mil.)	NET INCOME ($ mil.)	NET PROFIT MARGIN	EMPLOYEES
06/15	530	49	9.3%	3,700
06/03	412	20	5.0%	—
06/02	0	0	—	—
Annual Growth	—	—	—	—

2015 Year-End Financials
Return on assets: 5.9%   Cash ($ mil.): 83
Return on equity: 9.3%
Current ratio: 2.00

UNIVERSITY OF ALABAMA

EXECUTIVES

Exec Dir, Kevin Stevens
Accounting Staff, Lisa H McKinney
Accounting Staff, Tina Dorroh
Assistant Professor, Jane Rasco
Assistant To President, Charles Hilburn
Staff, Jennings Bryant
Staff, June Vance
Staff, Paul A Leblanc
Staff, Raymond E White
Staff, Sunee Lavender
Staff, Michael Steinberg
Auditors: PRICEWATERHOUSECOOPERS LLP BI

LOCATIONS

HQ: UNIVERSITY OF ALABAMA
301 ROSE ADMIN BLDG, TUSCALOOSA, AL 354870001
Phone: 205 348-7840
Web: WWW.UA.EDU

HISTORICAL FINANCIALS
Company Type: Private

Income Statement				FYE: September 30
	REVENUE ($ mil.)	NET INCOME ($ mil.)	NET PROFIT MARGIN	EMPLOYEES
09/17	833	224	26.9%	3,950
09/11	544	80	14.7%	—
09/10	509	167	32.9%	—
Annual Growth	7.3%	4.2%	—	—

2017 Year-End Financials
Return on assets: 17.3%   Cash ($ mil.): 51
Return on equity: 26.9%
Current ratio: 0.30

UNIVERSITY OF ALABAMA HEALTH SERVICES FOUNDATION, P.C.

EXECUTIVES

Ceo, Will Ferniany
President, Anton Bueschen
Vice President, Reed F Jones
Cfo, Michael Heckman
President, Dr Jim Bonner
Exec Vice President, Patricia Pritchett
Exec Admin, Melanie Brewer
Corporate Counsel/Legal, Patricia J Pritchett
Project Coordinator, Niki Woodall
Facilities Manager, William Bryars
Controller, Stephanie McClinton
Auditors: PRICEWATERHOUSECOOPERS LLP BI

LOCATIONS

HQ: UNIVERSITY OF ALABAMA HEALTH SERVICES FOUNDATION, P.C.
500 22ND ST S STE 100, BIRMINGHAM, AL 352333110
Phone: 205 731-9600
Web: WWW.ALABAMAORGANCENTER.ORG

HISTORICAL FINANCIALS
Company Type: Private

Income Statement				FYE: September 30
	REVENUE ($ mil.)	NET INCOME ($ mil.)	NET PROFIT MARGIN	EMPLOYEES
09/15	561	1	0.2%	3,205
09/14	26	0	1.6%	—
09/13	520	10	1.9%	—
09/08	466	(21)	—	—
Annual Growth	2.7%	—	—	—

2015 Year-End Financials
Return on assets: 21.3%   Cash ($ mil.): 39
Return on equity: 0.2%
Current ratio: —

UNIVERSITY OF ALASKA SYSTEM

The University of Alaska System (UA) has this education thing down cold. UA governsA three major campuses: the University of Alaska Anchorage the University of Alaska Fairbanks and the University ofA Alaska Southeast whichA each anchor part of a regional system of 17 community colleges.A UA enrolls about 35000 students offering someA 500 degrees certificates and endorsements.A Programs include science engineering education business journalism and communications aviation health occupations history English arts and humanities and others.A An 11-member Board of Regents governs the system.A Founded in 1917 as Alaska Agricultural College and School of Mines it was named University of Alaska in 1935.

Operations
UA'sA system consists of the University of Alaska Anchorage University of Alaska Fairbanks and the University of Alaska Southeast. Across its three major campuses and regional community colleges UA boastsA some 7000 employees more than 4550 of which comprise its faculty and staff members.

Geographic Reach
The university system's footprint extends throughout several regions of Alaska.A UAA operates a campusA in Anchorage and another in Fairbanks. ItsA third campus which covers the southeastern region has facilities in the cities of Juneau Ketchikan and Sitka.

Financial Performance
The system logged a 1% decline in revenue in 2012 as compared to 2011 due to a drop in federal grants and contracts partially offset by an increase in student tuition and fees as well as a boost from state and local grants and contracts and private grants and contracts. Net income for the same reporting period rose by 16% thanks to an increase in state appropriations and state on-behalf contributions-pension revenue. Capital appropriations grants and contracts alsoA helped toA push UA's net income upward as well as additions to its permanent endowments.

Strategy
In addition to offeringA about 500 programs for associate bachelor's master's and doctorate degrees UA provides students with short-course workforce training to help local workers stay on top of the latest technologies and skills.

EXECUTIVES

Principal, Patrick Gamble
Scientist, Todd Sformo
Purchasing Coordinator, Renee Johnson
Assistant, Caty Oehring
Office Administrator, Janet Ballek
Executive Officer, Greg Krier
Security Staff, David Akin
Assistant Professor, Andrea Bersamin
Assistant Professor, Matt Reimer
Assistant Professor, Mouhcine Guettabi
Project Manager, Linda Baschky
Auditors: KPMG LLP ANCHORAGE AK

LOCATIONS

HQ: UNIVERSITY OF ALASKA SYSTEM
910 YUKON DR, FAIRBANKS, AK 997750001
Phone: 907 450-8079
Web: WWW.ALASKA.EDU

PRODUCTS/OPERATIONS

Selected Campuses
University of Alaska Anchorage
  Chugiak-Eagle River Campus
  Kachemak Bay Campus KPC
  Kenai Peninsula College
  Kodiak College
  Matanuska Susitna Campus
  Military Programs
  Prince William Sound Community College
University of Alaska Fairbanks
  Bristol Bay Campus
  Chukchi Campus
  College of Rural and Community Development
  Community and Technical College
  Interior-Aleutians Campus
  Kuskokwim Campus
  Northwest Campus
University of Alaska Southeast
  Juneau Campus
  Ketchikan Campus
  Sitka Campus

HISTORICAL FINANCIALS
Company Type: Private

Income Statement
FYE: June 30

	REVENUE ($ mil.)	NET INCOME ($ mil.)	NET PROFIT MARGIN	EMPLOYEES
06/17	387	(8)	—	6,629
06/07	352	40	11.5%	—
06/06	371	27	7.4%	—
Annual Growth	0.4%	—	—	—

2017 Year-End Financials
Return on assets: 6.2%   Cash ($ mil.): 86
Return on equity: (-2.2%)
Current ratio: 1.30

UNIVERSITY OF ARKANSAS SYSTEM

EXECUTIVES

Vice President For University Relations, Melissa Rust
Associate Vice President For Finance, Rita Fleming
Assoc Vice President For Benefits And Risk Management Services, Steve Wood
Vice President Community Service, Robyn Jilg
Secretary, Morril Harriman
Vice Chairman, Mark Waldrip
Auditors: ROGER A NORMAN JD CPA CFE

LOCATIONS

HQ: UNIVERSITY OF ARKANSAS SYSTEM
2404 N UNIVERSITY AVE, LITTLE ROCK, AR 722073608
Phone: 501 686-2500
Web: WWW.UASYS.EDU

PRODUCTS/OPERATIONS

Selected Campuses
Arkansas Archeological Survey
Arkansas School for Mathematics Sciences and the Arts (high school)
Clinton School of Public Service
Cossatot Community College of the University of Arkansas
Criminal Justice Institute
Division of Agriculture
Phillips Community College of the University of Arkansas
University of Arkansas Community College at Morrilton
University of Arkansas Fayetteville
University of Arkansas at Fort Smith
University of Arkansas at Little Rock
University of Arkansas for Medical Sciences
University of Arkansas at Monticello
University of Arkansas at Pine Bluff
Winthrop Rockefeller Institute

HISTORICAL FINANCIALS
Company Type: Private

Income Statement
FYE: June 30

	REVENUE ($ mil.)	NET INCOME ($ mil.)	NET PROFIT MARGIN	EMPLOYEES
06/17	2,297	88	3.9%	14,025
06/16	2,172	64	3.0%	—
06/15	1,970	30	1.6%	—
06/14	1,841	54	3.0%	—
Annual Growth	7.7%	17.4%	—	—

2017 Year-End Financials
Return on assets: 7.5%   Cash ($ mil.): 408
Return on equity: 3.9%
Current ratio: 1.50

UNIVERSITY OF CINCINNATI MEDICAL CENTER, LLC

EXECUTIVES

Ceo-Pres, Bryan Gibler
Chm, George L Strike
Trustee, Peter D Gosmak
Chief of Ob/Gyn, Arthur T Evans II
Director Records, Charlesetta Mc Cray
Chief Staff, Keith Wilson
Psychiatrist, Michael Wilson
Pathologist, Roger Smith
Anesthesiologist, Adil Qarni
Emergency Medicine Specialist, Andrew Golden
Emergency Medicine Specialist, Anita Goel
Auditors: DELOITTE TAX LLP CINCINNATI

LOCATIONS

HQ: UNIVERSITY OF CINCINNATI MEDICAL CENTER, LLC
234 GOODMAN ST, CINCINNATI, OH 452192364
Phone: 513 584-1000
Web: WWW.UCHEALTH.COM

HISTORICAL FINANCIALS
Company Type: Private

Income Statement
FYE: June 30

	REVENUE ($ mil.)	NET INCOME ($ mil.)	NET PROFIT MARGIN	EMPLOYEES
06/16	913	57	6.3%	5,000
06/15	873	64	7.4%	—
06/10	633	28	4.6%	—
06/09	562	20	3.6%	—
Annual Growth	7.2%	16.0%	—	—

2016 Year-End Financials
Return on assets: 1.0%   Cash ($ mil.): 2
Return on equity: 6.3%
Current ratio: 6.10

UNIVERSITY OF COLORADO HEALTH

EXECUTIVES

General Counsel, Emily Weber
Internal Medicine Practitioner, Darlene B Tad-Y
Coordinator, Carrie Macdonald
Coordinator, Jessica Berry
Coordinator, Meredith Snyder

LOCATIONS

HQ: UNIVERSITY OF COLORADO HEALTH
12401 E 17TH AVE STE F485, AURORA, CO
800452603
Phone: 720 848-1031
Web: WWW.UCHEALTH.ORG

HISTORICAL FINANCIALS

Company Type: Private

Income Statement			FYE: June 30	
	REVENUE ($ mil.)	NET INCOME ($ mil.)	NET PROFIT MARGIN	EMPLOYEES
06/18	4,341	747	17.2%	7,593
06/17	3,668	750	20.5%	—
Annual Growth	18.4%	(0.5%)	—	—

2018 Year-End Financials
Return on assets: 9.8%   Cash ($ mil.): 330
Return on equity: 17.2%
Current ratio: 0.90

UNIVERSITY OF DELAWARE

Delaware brings up images of many things our first president that famous river and now the private University of Delaware (UD). The school's flagship campus in Newark has an enrollment of roughly 17000 undergraduate and close to 4000 graduate students. The school also has four auxiliary campuses around the state. UD offers almost 150 undergraduate degrees about 120 master's programs and more than 50 doctoral programs as well as associate's and dual graduate programs through seven academic schools. Among its instructors are well-known authors scientists artists and Nobel Laureates.

Operations

UD is a Land Grant Sea Grant and Space Grant institution meaning the school is eligible for government grants in each of these areas. The Carnegie Foundation for the Advancement of Teaching also classifies UD as a research university with very high research activity — a designation given to less than 3% of US colleges and universities. UD ranks among the nation's top 100 universities in federal research and development support for science and engineering. The university even has its own 146-foot research vessel (named the Hugh R. Sharp) for undersea exploration.

The school has a student-teacher ratio of about 15:1. It has roughly 1130 faculty members nearly 80% of which are tenured. Almost 90% have doctorate or terminal professional degrees in their field. (A terminal degree is also referred to as a Ph.D and refers to the fact that no higher degree can be obtained on that track.)

UD's 2012-13 tuition and fees were $11682 (in-state) and $28772 (out-of-state).

Geographic Reach

The university has campuses in Dover Georgetown Lewes Newark and Wilmington.

Financial Performance

The school reported a 5% increase in revenues in 2012 as the result of an increase in tuition and fees contributions and sales and services of auxiliary enterprises.

However UD's net income dropped by 118% in 2012 over 2011 due to higher expenses and a larger net realized and unrealized loss and an increase in a post-retirement benefit obligation.

In 2012 the university was supported by $1.21 billion endowment.

Company Background

UD got its start in 1743 as a private academy and was chartered by the state of Delaware in 1833. In athletics the school began NCAA Division I competition for men in 1973 and for women in 1982. US Vice President Joe Biden and his wife Jill are both UD graduates.

EXECUTIVES

Pres, Patrick T Harker
Exec V Pres-Treas, Scott R Douglass
V Pres-SEC, Pierre Hayward
V Pres-Fin-Admn, Jennifer Davis
Vice Provost Academic Affairs, Havid N Rodr Guez
Information Technology Manager, Dave Heckman
Coordinator, Karen Peterson
Coordinator, Linda Robinson
Coordinator, Deborah Fields
Assistant Professor, Dan Freeman
Associate Professor, Owen C White
Auditors: KPMG LLP PHILADELPHIA PENNSY

LOCATIONS

HQ: UNIVERSITY OF DELAWARE
220 HULLIHEN HALL, NEWARK, DE 197160099
Phone: 302 831-2107
Web: WWW.UDEL.EDU

PRODUCTS/OPERATIONS

Selected Schools and Colleges
Agriculture and Natural Resources
Arts and Sciences
Business and Economics
Earth Ocean and Environment
Education and Human Development
Engineering
Health Sciences
25 Most Popular Majors (2011)
Biological Sciences
Nursing
Finance
Psychology
Elementary Teacher Education
Exercise Science
Mechanical Engineering
Accounting
English
Chemical Engineering
Criminal Justice
Political Science
Civil Engineering
Marketing
Hotel Restaurant & Institutional Management
History
Human Services
Communication Interest
International Relations
Fashion Merchandising
Business Administration
Dietetics
Communication
Management
Pre-Veterinary Medicine & Animal Biosciences

HISTORICAL FINANCIALS

Company Type: Private

Income Statement			FYE: June 30	
	REVENUE ($ mil.)	NET INCOME ($ mil.)	NET PROFIT MARGIN	EMPLOYEES
06/17	992	159	16.1%	3,600
06/14	908	225	24.9%	—
06/13	884	228	25.9%	—
06/12	0	(0)	—	—
Annual Growth	310.5%	—	—	—

2017 Year-End Financials
Return on assets: 9.0%   Cash ($ mil.): 51
Return on equity: 16.1%
Current ratio: —

UNIVERSITY OF FLORIDA

Founded in 1853 the University of Florida (UF) is the state's oldest university and one of the largest in the country with nearly 50000 students and some 5100 faculty and library staff members. UF is a major land-grant research university encompassing 2000 acres in Gainesville Florida. The university's 16 colleges offer more than 100 undergraduate majors and about 200 graduate programs including education law medicine psychology and philosophy. It is also a member of the Association of American Universities a confederation of the top research universities in North America. A founding member of the Southeastern Conference UF's athletic teams (the Florida Gators) are typically ranked nationally.

Operations

UF is active in research and operates more than 200 research institutes and centers including the Nanoscale Research Facility the Pathogens Research Facility and the Biomedical Sciences Building. It has research collaborations with the likes of Scripps Florida Moffitt Cancer Center and Burnham Institute for Medical Research. Altogether UF receives about $650 million in research grants annually.

UF also has extensive health education programs including nursing and pharmacy colleges. Its medical school conducts teaching and residency programs at several Shands hospitals.

Strategy

Like many public universities in the US UF is facing decreased funding from government agencies due to economic conditions. UF has also seen enrollment decreases in recent years but has keep tuition rates and fees low to attract and retain students.

To meet the needs of its large and diverse student population UF is conducting a number of expansion and renovation projects on its more than 900 buildings.

To combat budget shortfalls due to funding and economic conditions UF is also pursuing new research partnerships that will provide funding from commercial and institutional sources. The university is pursuing other revenue generation initiatives to become more financially independent.

Company Background

UF's alumni include Robert Cade the inventor of Gatorade; best-selling mystery novelist Michael Connelly; actress Faye Dunaway; and former US Senator and Florida Governor Bob Graham. Other UF alumni include two Nobel Prize winners and three NASA astronauts.

EXECUTIVES

Vp And Cfo, Michael V. (Mike) McKee
Svp Academic Affairs And Provost, Joseph (Joe) Glover
Dean Of Students, Jen Day Shaw
Dean Warrington College Of Business Administration, John Kraft
Vp And Cio, Elias G. Eldayrie
Svp Health Affairs; President Uf Health, David S. Guzick
Dean College Of Journalism And Communications, Diane H. McFarlin
Dean College Of Public Health And Health Professions, Michael G. Perri
Dean College Of Medicine, Michael Good
Dean College Of Education, Glenn E. Good
Dean College Of Arts, Lucinda Lavelli
Dean University Libraries, Judith C. Russell
Dean College Of Design Construction And Planning, Christopher Silver
Svp And Coo, Charles E. Lane
President, W. Kent Fuchs
Dean College Of Engineering, Cammy Abernathy
Dean College Of Health And Human Performance, Michael Reid
Interim Dean College Of Liberal Arts And Sciences, David E. Richardson
Interim Dean College Of Dentistry, Boyd Robinson
Dean College Of Nursing, Anna McDaniel
Dean College Of Pharmacy, Julie A. Johnson
Dean College Of Veterinary Medicine, James Lloyd
Dean College Of Agricultural And Life Sciences, Elaine Turner
Dean Ifas Extension, Nick Place
Dean Ifas Research, Jacqueline Burns
Dean Graduate School, Henry T. Frierson
Vice President Technology, Lin Ai
Vice President Research And Development, Suleyman Tufekci
Vice President Information Technology, Marjorie Chow
Medical Director, Sherri Flax
Vice President Parsons Brinckerhoff, Edward Racila
Chairman, Steven M. Scott
Board Member, Matthew Friedland
Auditors: SHERRILL F NORMAN CPA TALLA

LOCATIONS

HQ: UNIVERSITY OF FLORIDA
300 SW 13TH ST, GAINESVILLE, FL 326110001
Phone: 352 392-3261
Web: WWW.UFL.EDU

PRODUCTS/OPERATIONS

Selected Colleges
College of Agricultural and Life Sciences
College of Dentistry
College of Design Construction and Planning
College of Education
College of Engineering
College of Health and Human Performance
College of Journalism and Communications
College of Liberal Arts and Sciences
College of Medicine
College of Nursing
College of Pharmacy
College of Public Health and Health Professions
College of the Arts
College of Veterinary Medicine
Levin College of Law
Warrington College of Business Administration

HISTORICAL FINANCIALS
Company Type: Private

Income Statement FYE: June 30

	REVENUE ($ mil.)	NET INCOME ($ mil.)	NET PROFIT MARGIN	EMPLOYEES
06/17	1,897	62	3.3%	5,106
06/15	1,735	261	15.1%	—
06/12	3,939	64	1.6%	—
06/09	3,846	(343)	—	—
Annual Growth	(8.5%)	—	—	—

2017 Year-End Financials

Return on assets: 4.6%   Cash ($ mil.): 6
Return on equity: 3.3%
Current ratio: 0.20

UNIVERSITY OF FLORIDA JACKSONVILLE PHYSICIANS INC

EXECUTIVES

Chb, Robert Nuss
President, Guy Benrubi
Vice-President, Alan Berger
Secretary, Theodore Bass
Treasurer, Arshag Mooradian
Technology Specialist, Daniel Torres
Auditors: PERSHING YOAKLEY & ASSOCIATESP

LOCATIONS

HQ: UNIVERSITY OF FLORIDA JACKSONVILLE PHYSICIANS INC
653 W 8TH ST, JACKSONVILLE, FL 322096511
Phone: 904 244-9500
Web: WWW.UFHEALTHJAX.ORG

HISTORICAL FINANCIALS
Company Type: Private

Income Statement FYE: June 30

	REVENUE ($ mil.)	NET INCOME ($ mil.)	NET PROFIT MARGIN	EMPLOYEES
06/16	298	2	1.0%	375
06/15	291	8	2.8%	—
06/14	265	0	0.1%	—
06/11	229	12	5.4%	—
Annual Growth	5.4%	(25.4%)	—	—

2016 Year-End Financials

Return on assets: 6.0%   Cash ($ mil.): 43
Return on equity: 1.0%
Current ratio: 2.50

UNIVERSITY OF GEORGIA

Located in the quintessential college town of Athens The University of Georgia (UGA) offers a wide range of degree programs to nearly 35000 students. Forest resources veterinary medicine and law are a few of the school's academic programs.A UGA which also runsA 170-plus study-abroad and exchange programsA administers the prestigious Peabody Awards which honors media achievementsA and boasts one of the nation's largest map collections. Famous alumni include former US Senator Phil Gramm TV journalist Deborah Norville and former PBS president Pat Mitchell. The University of Georgia was chartered by the State of Georgia in 1785 and graduated its first class in 1804.

Operations

As part of its business UGA offers nearly two dozen bachelor's degrees in about 140 fields and roughly 35 master's degrees inA nearly 140 fields. Its doctorate or professional degrees cover a broad spectrum of disciplines such as law pharmacyA veterinary medicine and 90 other areas. The university has a student-teacher ratio of about 12:1.

Sales and Marketing

The university sources 80% of its students from the Peach State. Since 1851 25 Georgia governors have graduated from UGA. The institution also boasts nine Pulitzer Prize recipients 17 presidents or provosts of US colleges and universities and four members of the National Academy of Sciences.

Strategy

Despite its annual endowment of more than $50 million UGA has loggedA decreases in state appropriations in recent years due to overall declines in Georgia's budget. The result spurred UGA to cut its budget increaseA undergraduate tuition fees institute a "Special Institutional" mandatory fee of $200 per semester reduce employer health insurance contributions and increase energy conservation measures. Going forward UGA has also not ruled out the possibility of hiking tuition further citing that an increase ofA up toA 30% would help to replace all of the state fundingA the universityA has lost due toA the recession.

EXECUTIVES

Pres, Jere Morehead
Assistant, Taylor Burge
Assistant Professor, Alfie Vick
Assistant Professor, Amy Ross
Administrator, Audrey Greeson
Assistant Professor, Betina Kaplan
Director, Cathy Clutter
Associate Director, Chris Hocking
Information Technology Manager, Chris Peters
Associate Professor, David Berle
Graphic Designer, Dianne Johnson
Auditors: GREG S GRIFFIN ATLANTA GEOR

LOCATIONS

HQ: UNIVERSITY OF GEORGIA
424 E BROAD ST, ATHENS, GA 306021535
Phone: 706 542-2786
Web: WWW.UGA.EDU

PRODUCTS/OPERATIONS

Selected Schools and Colleges
Agricultural and Environmental Sciences
Arts and Sciences Business
Ecology
Education
Environment and Design
Family and Consumer Sciences
Forest Resources
Graduate School
Journalism and Mass Communication
Law
Pharmacy
Public Health
Public and International Affairs
Social Work
Veterinary Medicine
The GHSU/UGA Medical Partnership
Engineering

HISTORICAL FINANCIALS
Company Type: Private

Income Statement
FYE: June 30

	REVENUE ($ mil.)	NET INCOME ($ mil.)	NET PROFIT MARGIN	EMPLOYEES
06/17	975	142	14.6%	17,800
06/12	776	72	9.3%	—
06/11	691	(12)	—	—
Annual Growth	5.9%	—	—	—

2017 Year-End Financials
Return on assets: 3.5%
Return on equity: 14.6%
Current ratio: 1.90

Cash ($ mil.): 282

UNIVERSITY OF HAWAII

EXECUTIVES

Vice President, Bryan Tanaka
It Specialist Office Of The Vice President For Community Colleges, Gordon Furuto
Secretary To The Chancellor, Cynthia Vinluan
Auditors: ACCUITY LLP HONOLULU HAWAII

LOCATIONS

HQ: UNIVERSITY OF HAWAII
2444 DOLE ST, HONOLULU, HI 968222399
Phone: 808 956-8111
Web: WWW.HAWAII.EDU

Selected Campuses
Manoa
Hilo
West O'ahu
Hawai'i
Honolulu
Kapi'olani
Kaua'i
Leeward
Maui
Windward

HISTORICAL FINANCIALS
Company Type: Private

Income Statement
FYE: June 30

	REVENUE ($ mil.)	NET INCOME ($ mil.)	NET PROFIT MARGIN	EMPLOYEES
06/17	771	33	4.3%	12,000
06/16	799	(116)	—	—
06/06	0	0	—	—
06/02	406	0	—	—
Annual Growth	4.4%	—	—	—

2017 Year-End Financials
Return on assets: 7.9%
Return on equity: 4.3%
Current ratio: 0.50

Cash ($ mil.): 69

UNIVERSITY OF HOUSTON SYSTEM

EXECUTIVES

President University Houston - Clear Lake, William A. Staples
Associate Vice Chancellor For Central Computing And Telecommunication Services, Dennis Fouty
President University Of Houston - Downtown, William V. (Bill) Flores
Executive Vice Chancellor For Administration And Finance, Carl P. Carlucci, age 69
Chancellor; President University Of Houston, Renu Khator
President University Houston - Victoria, Philip Castille
Chairman, Jarvis V. Hollingsworth

LOCATIONS

HQ: UNIVERSITY OF HOUSTON SYSTEM
4302 UNIVERSITY DR, HOUSTON, TX 772042011
Phone: 713 743-0945
Web: WWW.UHSYSTEM.EDU

PRODUCTS/OPERATIONS

Selected Colleges and Schools
University of Houston
C.T. Bauer College of Business
College of Education
College of Liberal Arts and Social Sciences
College of Natural Sciences and Mathematics
College of Optometry
College of Pharmacy
College of Technology
Conrad N. Hilton College of Hotel and Restaurant Management
Cullen College of Engineering
Gerald D. Hines College of Architecture
Graduate College of Social Work
Honors College
Law Center
University of Houston-Clear Lake
School of Business
School of Education
School of Human Sciences and Humanities
School of Science and Computer Engineering
University of Houston-Downtown
College of Business
College of Humanities and Social Sciences
College of Public Service
College of Sciences and Technology
University of Houston-Victoria
School of Arts and Sciences
School of Business Administration
School of Education and Human Development
School of Nursing

HISTORICAL FINANCIALS
Company Type: Private

Income Statement
FYE: August 31

	REVENUE ($ mil.)	NET INCOME ($ mil.)	NET PROFIT MARGIN	EMPLOYEES
08/15	605	41	6.9%	12,608
08/14	742	46	6.2%	—
08/13	1	81	6095.0%	—
08/12	688	132	19.3%	—
Annual Growth	(4.2%)	(31.9%)	—	—

UNIVERSITY OF IOWA HOSPITALS AND CLINICS

EXECUTIVES

Ceo, Kenneth P Kates
Ceo, Gordon Williams
President, Sally Mason
Vice President, Jean Robillard
Prin, Ann Williamson
Coo, Sabi Singh
Family Practitioner, Shalina Shaik
Coordinator, Kathy Moser
Pediatrician, Catherina Pinnaro
Diagnostic Radiologist, John D Newell
Pediatrician, Ashley Sandeen

LOCATIONS

HQ: UNIVERSITY OF IOWA HOSPITALS AND CLINICS
200 HAWKINS DR, IOWA CITY, IA 522421009
Phone: 319 356-1616
Web: WWW.UIOWA.EDU

HISTORICAL FINANCIALS
Company Type: Private

Income Statement
FYE: June 30

	REVENUE ($ mil.)	NET INCOME ($ mil.)	NET PROFIT MARGIN	EMPLOYFFS
06/17	1,502	47	3.2%	7,638
06/16	1,395	117	8.4%	—
06/15	1,248	90	7.2%	—
06/10	943	52	5.6%	—
Annual Growth	6.9%	(1.4%)	—	—

2017 Year-End Financials
Return on assets: 9.5%
Return on equity: 3.2%
Current ratio: 1.00

Cash ($ mil.): 24

UNIVERSITY OF MAINE SYSTEM

University of Maine System is composed of seven public universities throughout Maine serving some 40000 students. It also operates eight regional outreach centers as well as distance education programs. The University of Maine System offers nearly 600 majors minors and concentrations; its flagship campus in Orono (UMaine) offers nearly 90 bachelor's degree programs more than 60 master's degree programs and about two dozen doctoral programs. UMaine was established in 1862 as the Maine College of Agriculture and Mechanic Arts; it adopted its current name in 1897. The University of Maine System was created in 1968 by the state legislature.

Financial Performance

In 2014 (ended June) the University of Maine System saw a $2 million increase in revenue vs. 2013. Net student fees remained at 36% of total revenue. Although money from tuition and fees dropped by $1 million residence and dining fees increased by $2 million. State appropriations the second biggest source of revenue remained at 29% of the total.

Strategy

The system acted to expand in Portland Maine and to maintain the number of campuses at the University of Southern Maine. It moved forward to on an opportunity to develop a professional and graduate center in Portland. The closing of campuses at USM had been proposed to save money but the system defended their value and kept them open.

EXECUTIVES

Rsvp Program Coordinator, Cindy Whitney
Auditors: BERRY DUNN MCNEIL & PARKER LL

LOCATIONS

HQ: UNIVERSITY OF MAINE SYSTEM
  5703 ALUMNI HALL STE 101, ORONO, ME 044695703
Phone: 207 973-3300
Web: WWW.UMIT.MAINE.EDU

PRODUCTS/OPERATIONS

System Universities
University of Maine
University of Maine at Augusta
University of Maine at Farmington
University of Maine at Fort Kent
University of Maine at Machias
University of Maine at Presque Isle
University of Southern Maine Maine Law School

HISTORICAL FINANCIALS

Company Type: Private

Income Statement   FYE: June 30

	REVENUE ($ mil.)	NET INCOME ($ mil.)	NET PROFIT MARGIN	EMPLOYEES
06/18	458	15	3.5%	3,000
06/17	448	20	4.6%	—
06/13	460	27	6.1%	—
06/12	476	37	8.0%	—
Annual Growth	(0.7%)	(13.6%)	—	—

2018 Year-End Financials

Return on assets: 3.7%   Cash ($ mil.): 1
Return on equity: 3.5%
Current ratio: 0.70

UNIVERSITY OF MARYLAND BALTIMORE WASHINGTON MEDICAL SYSTEM, INC.

EXECUTIVES

Pres, Karen Olscamp
Pres-Ceo, James R Walker
Chb, Melvin L Kelly
V Pres-Treas, Ronald C McGuirk
Sr Vice President, Ronald Andro
Cfo, Alfred Pietsch
Chief of Cardiology, J M J Ramirez
Director of Information Techno, John Norfolk
Doctor, Zeleke K Desse
Executive Secretary, Cheryl Nickoles
Director of Radiology, James Cary

LOCATIONS

HQ: UNIVERSITY OF MARYLAND BALTIMORE
  WASHINGTON MEDICAL SYSTEM, INC.
  301 HOSPITAL DR, GLEN BURNIE, MD 210615803
Phone: 410 787-4000
Web: WWW.MYBWMC.ORG

HISTORICAL FINANCIALS

Company Type: Private

Income Statement   FYE: June 30

	REVENUE ($ mil.)	NET INCOME ($ mil.)	NET PROFIT MARGIN	EMPLOYEES
06/18	398	18	4.6%	2,676
06/16	357	24	7.0%	—
06/15	355	26	7.5%	—
06/14	366	19	5.3%	—
Annual Growth	2.1%	(1.4%)	—	—

2018 Year-End Financials

Return on assets: 3.9%   Cash ($ mil.): 10
Return on equity: 4.6%
Current ratio: 0.60

UNIVERSITY OF MARYLAND MEDICAL SYSTEM CORPORATION

The 12 academic specialty and community hospitals of the University of Maryland Medical System (UMMS) dot the map of the state's eastern half on both sides of Chesapeake Bay. UMMS one of the largest employers in the Baltimore area has more than 2300 acute care beds and attends to such specialties as trauma care coma emergence kidney transplants orthopedic rehabilitation stroke intervention and pediatric care. University of Maryland Medical Center the system's teaching hub is one of the oldest academic hospitals in the US. In addition to its hospitals UMMS also includes community clinics to address mental health rehabilitation and primary care. The system was established in 1984.

Operations

UMMC's members hospitals include the University of Maryland Medical Center Baltimore Washington Medical Center Chester River Health System Civista Health System Kernan Orthopaedics and Rehabilitation Maryland General Hospital Mt. Washington Pediatric Hospital Shore Health System University of Maryland St. Joseph Medical Center and Upper Chesapeake Health.

University of Maryland Medical Center which houses about 800 beds is staffed entirely by physicians who double as faculty members at the University of Maryland School of Medicine (SOM) the system's longtime partner. The hospital contains additional specialty facilities dedicated to such areas as pediatrics cancer treatment cardiac disease diabetes organ transplants Parkinson's disease and shock trauma. The shock trauma center was the first of its kind in the world when it was founded in 1968.

Aside from its integral partnership with SOM UMMS has in recent years been bolstering its network of member hospitals to reach new markets in Maryland. Having been affilated with Upper Chesapeake Health (UCH) UMMS merged the systems in 2013. UCH owns a pair of hospitals in

northeastern Maryland an underserved corner of the state that UMMS hadn't yet entered.

Financial Performance

UMMS's revenue in fiscal 2012 was $2.8 billion.

Company Background

The system's flagship hospital began on its present site in 1823 as Baltimore Infirmary. It later was known for many years as University Hospital until Maryland's legislature changed it from a state-run single-building facility to a private not-for-profit medical system in 1984. In short order UMMS began expanding mainly by adding existing hospitals.

EXECUTIVES

President And Ceo University Of Maryland Medical Center, Jeffrey A. Rivest
Ceo Chester River Health System, James E. Ross
Senior Vice President Chief Information Officer, Jon P. Burns
President And Ceo Maryland General Health Systems And Hospita, Sylvia Smith Johnson
President And Ceo, Karen E. Olscamp, age 58
Evp And Cfo, Henry J. Franey
Medical Director, Melissa Frisch
Vice President Information Technology Services, Brian Cassel
Senior Vice President Finance, Hank Franey
Medical Director, Michael Schultz
Director Of Nursing, Margaret Burns
Chairman, Stephen A. Burch, age 68

LOCATIONS

HQ: UNIVERSITY OF MARYLAND MEDICAL SYSTEM
  CORPORATION
  250 W PRATT ST, BALTIMORE, MD 212012423
Phone: 410 328-8667
Web: WWW.UMMS.ORG

PRODUCTS/OPERATIONS

Selected Facilities and Affiliates
Baltimore Washington Medical Center
Chester River Health System
Civista Medical Center
Kernan Orthopaedics and Rehabilitation
Maryland General Hospital
Mt. Washington Pediatric Hospital
Shore Health System
  Dorchester General Hospital
  The Memorial Hospital at Easton
University of Maryland Medical Center
  Marlene and Stewart Greenebaum Cancer Center
  R Adams Cowley Shock Trauma Center
  University of Maryland Medical Center for Children
University of Maryland St. Joseph Medical Center
University Specialty Hospital
Upper Chesapeake Health
  Harford Memorial Hospital
  Upper Chesapeake Medical Center

COMPETITORS

Adventist HealthCare	Franklin Square
Anne Arundel Medical	Hospital Center
Center	GBMC
Ascension Health	Johns Hopkins Health
Bon Secours Health	System
Catholic Health	LifeBridge Health
Initiatives	MedStar Health
Dimensions Healthcare	

HISTORICAL FINANCIALS
Company Type: Private

Income Statement
FYE: June 30

	REVENUE ($ mil.)	NET INCOME ($ mil.)	NET PROFIT MARGIN	EMPLOYEES
06/16	1,358	(29)	—	12,000
06/15	1,413	13	0.9%	—
06/14	1,824	17	1.0%	—
06/12	2,504	(17)	—	—
Annual Growth	(14.2%)	—	—	—

2016 Year-End Financials
Return on assets: 9.3%
Return on equity: (-2.2%)
Current ratio: 0.70
Cash ($ mil.): 383

UNIVERSITY OF MARYLAND SHORE REGIONAL HEALTH, INC.

EXECUTIVES
Pres-Ceo, Kenneth Kozel
Svp-Chief Experience Ofcr, Susan Coe
Svp-Cfo, Joanne Hahey
Chief Medical Ofcr-Svp, William Huffner
Sr Nursing Vp-Chief Nursing of, Ruth Ann Jones
Manager, Joanne Thomson
Nurse Manager, Debbie Burke

LOCATIONS
HQ: UNIVERSITY OF MARYLAND SHORE REGIONAL HEALTH, INC.
219 S WASHINGTON ST, EASTON, MD 216012913
Phone: 410 822-1000

HISTORICAL FINANCIALS
Company Type: Private

Income Statement
FYE: June 30

	REVENUE ($ mil.)	NET INCOME ($ mil.)	NET PROFIT MARGIN	EMPLOYEES
06/18	319	25	8.1%	1,800
06/10	2	0	5.6%	—
Annual Growth	82.8%	91.1%	—	—

2018 Year-End Financials
Return on assets: 4.6%
Return on equity: 8.1%
Current ratio: 0.70
Cash ($ mil.): 12

UNIVERSITY OF MARYLAND UPPER CHESAPEAK HOUSE INC.

EXECUTIVES
Pres-Ceo, Lyle E Sheldon
Cfo, Jorsof Hoofman
Vice-President, Toni Shivery
Orthopedic Spine Surgeon, Spiro B Antoniades
Auditors: GRANT THORNTON LLP PHILADELPH

LOCATIONS
HQ: UNIVERSITY OF MARYLAND UPPER CHESAPEAK HOUSE INC.
520 UPPER CHESAPEAKE DR, BEL AIR, MD 210144339
Phone: 443 643-3460
Web: WWW.UCHS.ORG

HISTORICAL FINANCIALS
Company Type: Private

Income Statement
FYE: June 30

	REVENUE ($ mil.)	NET INCOME ($ mil.)	NET PROFIT MARGIN	EMPLOYEES
06/18	442	39	9.0%	46
06/16	15	0	0.0%	—
Annual Growth	426.0%	20823.9%	—	—

2018 Year-End Financials
Return on assets: 4.9%
Return on equity: 9.0%
Current ratio: 0.80
Cash ($ mil.): 41

UNIVERSITY OF MASSACHUSETTS

The University of Massachusetts (UMass) has been expanding across the commonwealth since its founding in 1863. About 72000 students are enrolled in UMass programs that range from art to journalism to engineering. The university's flagship campus in Amherst (with a student-teacher ratio of 18:1) offers its 22000 undergrad students degrees in more than 90 areas and its 6400 graduate students master's degrees in nearly 70 areas and doctorates in 50 areas. Its University of Massachusetts Medical School in Worcester has an affiliated teaching hospital and students studying medicine nursing and biomedical sciences. Other UMass campuses can be found in Boston Dartmouth and Lowell.

Operations
UMass Amherst is part of the Five Colleges consortium a partnership with other area universities including Amherst Hampshire Mount Holyoke and Smith colleges through which students at member institutions attend classes and benefit from being able to share resources at all of the schools.

The system's Boston and Dartmouth campuses are renowned for their academic programs. Boston is known as a research university with more than 90% of its faculty holding the highest degree available in their field. Dartmouth is credited with giving its students a "personalized' education that includes internships undergraduate research opportunities and service learning experiences.

Geographic Reach
While UMass serves students from all 50 US states and 100 other countries 80% of incoming freshmen are from the Commonwealth.

Financial Performance
Operating revenue increased at UMass 3% to $2.2 billion in fiscal 2014 due to increases in tuition and fees. Along with grants and contracts auxiliary services and services provided at the Worcester Medical School tuition and fees are the most significant sources of operating revenues.

UMass' endowment reached $758 million in 2014 when the fund grew by 14%. The endowment is being used for projects such as the Charles J. Hoff Scholarship. Created by former UMass trustee and alumnus Charles J. Hoff and his wife Josephine Hoff the scholarship is expected to provide financial support to more than 2500 students by 2017.

Strategy
UMass uses its funds to upgrade and expand it facilities. In 2014 it announced plans to build an academic center and home for administrative offices in downtown Boston. It also opened its first satellite center in Springfield which offers 40 courses in manufacturing cybersecurity IT and casino management based on area business needs. The center works with local community colleges to develop programs that allow students to transition from associate to bachelor degrees.

The university's Boston campus also received a new Integrated Sciences Complex completed in late 2014 and the General Academic Building slated for 2015.

Company Background
Notable UMass alumni include entertainer Bill Cosby singer Natalie Cole and former General Electric CEO Jack Welch.

EXECUTIVES
President, Robert L. Caret, age 70
Evp And Coo, James R. Julian
Svp Administration And Finance, Christine Wilda
Chancellor University Of Massachusetts Boston, J. Keith Motley
Chancellor University Of Massachusetts Amherst, Kumble R. (Swamy) Subbaswamy
Chancellor University Of Massachusetts Worcester, Michael F. Collins
Chancellor University Of Massachusetts Dartmouth, Divina Grossman
Vp And Cio, Robert Solis
Ceo Umass Online, John Cunningham
Chancellor Umass Lowell, Jacquie Moloney
Vice Chairman, Ruben J. King-Shaw, age 57
Vice Chairman, Maria D. Furman
Chairman, Victor Woolridge
Auditors: GRANT THORNTON LLP BOSTON MA

LOCATIONS
HQ: UNIVERSITY OF MASSACHUSETTS
1 BEACON ST, BOSTON, MA 021083107
Phone: 617 287-7000
Web: WWW.UMASS.EDU

PRODUCTS/OPERATIONS

Selected Colleges and Schools
College of Engineering
College of Humanities and Fine Arts
College of Natural Sciences and Mathematics
College of Social and Behavioral Sciences
Commonwealth College
Graduate School
School of Education
School of Management
School of Nursing
School of Public Health and Health Sciences

HISTORICAL FINANCIALS
Company Type: Private

Income Statement
FYE: June 30

	REVENUE ($ mil.)	NET INCOME ($ mil.)	NET PROFIT MARGIN	EMPLOYEES
06/17	2,442	325	13.3%	13,196
06/16	2,403	129	5.4%	—
06/12	2,055	255	12.4%	—
06/08	1,652	100	6.1%	—
Annual Growth	4.4%	14.0%	—	—

2017 Year-End Financials
Return on assets: 4.8%
Return on equity: 13.3%
Current ratio: 0.20
Cash ($ mil.): 108

UNIVERSITY OF MINNESOTA PHYSICIANS

EXECUTIVES
Ceo, Bobbi Daniels
Coo, Mary Johnson
Vice President, Barbara Gold
Senior Project Manager, Brent Krzmarzick
Assistant Professor, Ila Harris
Health Professional, Alison Williams
Director of Laboratory, Carol Johannes
Director, Sarah Byard
Coordinator, Anne Jedlicki
Executive Assistant, Kathy McNeil
Senior Director Business Intel, Jacob Wiatrowski
Auditors: KPMG LLP MINNEAPOLIS MN

LOCATIONS
HQ: UNIVERSITY OF MINNESOTA PHYSICIANS
720 WASHINGTON AVE SE # 200, MINNEAPOLIS, MN 554142924
Phone: 612 884-0600
Web: WWW.UMPHYSICIANS.COM

HISTORICAL FINANCIALS
Company Type: Private

Income Statement
FYE: June 30

	REVENUE ($ mil.)	NET INCOME ($ mil.)	NET PROFIT MARGIN	EMPLOYEES
06/15	482	10	2.2%	200
06/14	490	23	4.8%	—
06/13	452	12	2.8%	—
06/12	415	5	1.3%	—
Annual Growth	5.1%	24.7%	—	—

2015 Year-End Financials
Return on assets: 12.9%
Return on equity: 2.2%
Current ratio: 2.00
Cash ($ mil.): 95

UNIVERSITY OF MISSISSIPPI

They call her "Ole Miss" and she really is old: The University of Mississippi was chartered in 1844 as the first public university in the state and opened in 1848. Starting with 80 students the school's enrollment has grown to more than 23000 with most students attending the main Oxford campus. Ole Miss has additional campuses in Southaven (Desoto County) and Tupelo and it operates the University of Mississippi Medical Center in Jackson. The school is home to more than 30 research centers that specialize in business engineering law and other disciplines. Its academic institutes include the Croft Institute for International Studies and the William Winter Institute for Racial Reconciliation.

Operations
The Medical Center campus includes Mississippi's only children's hospital a women and infants' hospital and a critical care hospital. It is also home to the state's only Level 1 trauma center Level 4 neonatal intensive care nursery and organ transplant programs. Enrollment has grown at the university by some 59% since 2004 (when the school enrolled 14497 students).

Ole Miss has an endowment of approximately $462 million.

Geographic Reach
Minorities make up almost a fourth of Ole Miss students and more than 60% of all students at the university come from within the state. The student-faculty ratio is 19:1.

EXECUTIVES
Secretary, Frances E Clarkson

LOCATIONS
HQ: UNIVERSITY OF MISSISSIPPI
113 FALKNER, UNIVERSITY, MS 386779704
Phone: 662 915-6538
Web: WWW.OLEMISS.EDU

PRODUCTS/OPERATIONS

Selected Colleges and Schools
Colleges
The College of Liberal Arts
The Residential College
The Sally McDonnell Barksdale Honors College
The University of Mississippi
Booneville (branch)
Grenada (branch)
Southaven Campus
Tupelo Campus
The University of Mississippi Graduate School
The University of Mississippi Medical Center
Schools
Meek School of Journalism and News Media
Patterson School of Accountancy
School of Applied Science
School of Business Administration
School of Education
School of Engineering
School of Law
School of Nursing (at The University of Mississippi Medical Center)
School of Pharmacy

Selected Research Centers
Center for Advanced Infrastructure Technology
Center for Applied Electromagnetic Systems Research
Center for Archaeological Research
Center for Community Earthquake Preparedness
Center for Educational Research and Evaluation
Center for Excellence in Literacy Instruction
Center for Excellence in Teaching and Learning
Center for Health Behavior Research

Center for Intelligence and Security Studies
Center for Manufacturing Excellence
Center for Marine Resources and Environmental Technology
Center for Mathematics and Science Education
Center for Pharmaceutical Marketing and Management
Center for Population Studies
Center for Speech and Hearing Research
Center for the Study of Southern Culture
Center for Water and Wetland Resources
Center for Wireless Communications
INDO-US Joint Center for Research in Indian Systems of Medicine
Jamie Whitten National Center for Physical Acoustics
Magazine Innovation Center
National Center for Computational Hydroscience and Engineering
National Center for Justice and the Rule of Law
National Center for Natural Products Research
National Center for Remote Sensing Air and Space Law
National Sea Grant Law Center
Overby Center for Southern Journalism and Politics
Public Policy Research Center
Sarah Isom Center for Women's Studies
Sino-U.S. Traditional Chinese Medicines Research Center
University of Mississippi Geoinformatics Center

HISTORICAL FINANCIALS
Company Type: Private

Income Statement
FYE: December 31

	REVENUE ($ mil.)	NET INCOME ($ mil.)	NET PROFIT MARGIN	EMPLOYEES
12/17*	455	84	18.6%	8,700
06/17	681	15	2.3%	—
06/16	436	90	20.7%	—
06/15	401	101	25.4%	—
Annual Growth	4.4%	(5.9%)	—	—

*Fiscal year change

2017 Year-End Financials
Return on assets: 6.2%
Return on equity: 18.6%
Current ratio: 1.20
Cash ($ mil.): 80

UNIVERSITY OF MISSOURI HEALTH CARE

EXECUTIVES
Ceo-Pres, Mitch Wasden
Dir of Treas, Ann Toellner
Cfo, Kevin Necas
Clinic Coordinator, Andrea Beneke
Otolaryngologist, Jeffrey B Jorgensen
Purchasing Director, Carol Clark
Programmer Analyst, Cathy Schafer
Rheumatology Specialist, Chokkalingam Siva
Staff, Connie Dorflinger
Doctor, Debra Howenstine
Associate Professor, Joi Moore
Auditors: KPMG LLP

LOCATIONS
HQ: UNIVERSITY OF MISSOURI HEALTH CARE
1 HOSPITAL DR, COLUMBIA, MO 652015276
Phone: 573 882-4141
Web: WWW.HEALTH.MISSOURI.EDU

HISTORICAL FINANCIALS

Company Type: Private

Income Statement   FYE: June 30

	REVENUE ($ mil.)	NET INCOME ($ mil.)	NET PROFIT MARGIN	EMPLOYEES
06/16	749	62	8.4%	5,000
06/15	696	64	9.3%	—
06/08	0	0	1.0%	—
Annual Growth	140.0%	212.1%	—	—

2016 Year-End Financials

Return on assets: 2.3%
Return on equity: 8.4%
Current ratio: 0.90
Cash ($ mil.): 27

UNIVERSITY OF MISSOURI SYSTEM

Education isn't just for show in the Show Me State. The University of Missouri (UM) founded in 1839 educates about 76000 students at four campuses and through a statewide extension program; about a quarter of students are in graduate or professional programs. The university's campuses include flagship UM-Columbia (home to roughly 33000 students some 20 schools and colleges and the University of Missouri Health Sciences Center) UM-Kansas City UM-St. Louis and the Missouri University of Science and Technology. Nicknamed "Mizzou" the University of Missouri System has close to 6000 faculty members and a student-teacher enrollment of about 11:1.

Operations

In addition to its university campuses the University of Missouri System operates the University of Missouri Health System which encompasses University Hospital and Clinics Women's and Children's Hospital Ellis Fischel Cancer Center Rusk Rehabilitation Center Missouri Psychiatric Institute Missouri Orthopaedic Institute and University Physicians. Its hospitals and clinics provide high-risk obstetrics orthopedic surgery neurosciences and cardiovascular care among other services. It also has the region's only Level I Trauma Center.

Geographic Reach

The University of Missouri's four campuses are located in Columbia Kansas City Rolla and St. Louis. The system has an exchange program with South Africa through which UM students study at the University of the Western Cape in Bellville (Cape Town) South Africa and vice versa.

Financial Performance

The University of Missouri System had revenue of $3.1 billion in fiscal 2016. About one-third of that revenue came from net patient medical services; another 20% came from net tuition and fees. Its total operating expenses for that year totaled $2.8 billion. The system's endowment topped $1 billion for the first time in late 2017.

Strategy

The University of Missouri System has been strategically focused on five key priorities: attracting and retaining the best faculty and staff with competitive salaries benefits and workplace programs; expanding its online education offerings to improve students' success and bring in additional revenue; operating with efficiency and effectiveness; expanding research and economic development in the region; and improving communications with the community. However in early 2018 the system warned that growing state budget cuts

could hamper its ability to improve student services and that layoffs program cuts and tuition hikes may be necessary.

EXECUTIVES

Chancellor University Of Missouri-kansas City, Leo E. Morton, age 73
Chancellor University Of Missouri-st. Louis, Thomas F. (Tom) George
Chancellor Missouri University Of Science And Technology, Cheryl B. Schrader
Vp Information Technology, Gary K. Allen
Evp Academic Affairs And Interim Chancellor University Of Missouri-columbia, Henry C. (Hank) Foley
Vp Finance And Cfo, Brian D. Burnett
Chief Investment Officer, Thomas Richards
Interim President, Mike Middleton
Senior Vice President Sales Marketing An, Debbie Saunders
Medical Librarian, Venkataraman Ramachandran
Chairman, Donald L. Cupps
Vice Chairman, Pamela Q. Henrickson
Secretary, Lynda Larocque
Secretary, Annette Valentine
Secretary, Diane Temmen
Secretary Henry County, Verlinda Talley
Board Member, Thomas Voss
Auditors: BKD LLP KANSAS CITY MISSOUR

LOCATIONS

HQ: UNIVERSITY OF MISSOURI SYSTEM
321 UNIVERSITY HALL, COLUMBIA, MO 652113020
Phone: 573 882-2712
Web: WWW.MURR.MISSOURI.EDU

PRODUCTS/OPERATIONS

Selected Campuses

University of Missouri-Columbia
University of Missouri Health System (Columbia)
UM-Kansas City
UM-St. Louis
Missouri University of Science and Technology (Rolla)

Selected Colleges and Schools

College of Agriculture Food and Natural Resources
  School of Natural Resources
College of Arts and Sciences
  School of Music
College of Education
  School of Information Science and Learning Technologies
College of Engineering
College of Human Environmental Sciences
  School of Social Work
College of Veterinary Medicine
Graduate School
  Harry S Truman School of Public Affairs
School of Health Professions
School of Journalism
School of Law
School of Medicine
Sinclair College of Nursing
Trulaske College of Business
  School of Accountancy

HISTORICAL FINANCIALS

Company Type: Private

Income Statement   FYE: June 30

	REVENUE ($ mil.)	NET INCOME ($ mil.)	NET PROFIT MARGIN	EMPLOYEES
06/17	2,799	401	14.3%	30,282
06/16	2,702	108	4.0%	—
06/13	2,404	221	9.2%	—
06/12	2,273	76	3.3%	—
Annual Growth	4.2%	39.5%	—	—

2017 Year-End Financials

Return on assets: 5.5%
Return on equity: 14.3%
Current ratio: 0.70
Cash ($ mil.): 397

UNIVERSITY OF MONTANA

Sometimes referred to as the Harvard of the West The University of Montana's motto is Lux et Veritas (Light and Truth). The Big Sky Country certainly provides plenty of light for the university which is a leading producer of Rhodes Scholars. The University of Montana (UM) is a member of the Montana University System and offers associate's bachelor's master's first-professional and doctoral degrees as well as technical certificates. About 21000 undergraduate and graduate students enroll at UM's four campuses. Founded in 1893 UM also gets high marks for the physical beauty of its campus and nearby wilderness areas.

Operations

UM has about 900 faculty members and a student-to-faculty ratio of 19:1. Of its student population of about 21000 some 15000 students attend class at the main campus in Missoula.

The university's colleges include arts and sciences technology education and human sciences health professions and biomedical sciences visual and performing arts forestry and conservation and an honors college. Its schools include journalism law business administration education pharmacy social work fine arts and more. UM also offers undergraduate research opportunities and study abroad programs as well as student organizations intramural sports and work-study opportunities.

Geographic Reach

UM is located on a 200-acre campus containing about 65 buildings in Missoula Montana. It also has satellite campuses in Dillon (UM Western) Butte (Montana Tech) and Helena (Helena College of Technology). About two-thirds of students come from within the state.

Strategy

To increase enrollment of motivated students UM partners with area high schools to provide early college and recruitment programs. Other growth efforts include faculty and staff recruitment and development programs as well as curriculum enhancement efforts and procurement and technology improvements. Facility expansions also continue: In 2013 it selected a site for its new Missoula College satellite center.

EXECUTIVES

Vice President, Dawn Ressel
Vice President Marketing, Mario Schulzke
Board Member, Ken Thompson
Auditors: CINDY JORGENSON CPA HELENA

LOCATIONS

HQ: UNIVERSITY OF MONTANA
32 CAMPUS DR MAIN HALL, MISSOULA, MT 598120001
Phone: 406 243-6670
Web: WWW.UMT.EDU

PRODUCTS/OPERATIONS

2012 Revenue

	% of total
Student tuition & fees	47
Health care services	20
Auxiliary enterprises	6
Grants & contracts	4
Appropriated investment income	3
Contributions	3
Released net assets	2
Other	15
Total	**100**

Selected Colleges and Schools
College of Arts and Sciences
College of Education and Human Sciences
College of Forestry and Conservation
College of Health Professions and Biomedical Sciences
College of Technology
College of Visual and Performing Arts
Davidson Honors College
Graduate School
School for Extended and Lifelong Learning
School of Business Administration
School of Journalism
School of Law

HISTORICAL FINANCIALS
Company Type: Private

Income Statement				FYE: June 30
	REVENUE ($ mil.)	NET INCOME ($ mil.)	NET PROFIT MARGIN	EMPLOYEES
06/17	284	(156)		2,450
06/16	272	28	10.4%	—
06/13	259	(8)		—
06/12	264	7	2.8%	—
Annual Growth	1.5%	—	—	—

2017 Year-End Financials
Return on assets: 5.8%   Cash ($ mil.): 57
Return on equity: (-55.0%)
Current ratio: 1.20

UNIVERSITY OF NEBRASKA FOUNDATION

EXECUTIVES

Ceo, Brian Hastings
SEC-Gen Counel, Keith Miles
Dir, Dorothy Endacott
SEC, Susan Crotteau
Dean, Steven Willborn
Assistant, Gina Guernsey
Professor, Phillip Miller
Staff, Janelle L Gerry
Professor, William Lyons
Professor of Finance, Richard Defusco
Auditors: KPMG LLP OMAHA NE

LOCATIONS

HQ: UNIVERSITY OF NEBRASKA FOUNDATION
1010 LINCOLN MALL STE 300, LINCOLN, NE
685082882
Phone: 402 458-1100
Web: WWW.NUFOUNDATION.ORG

HISTORICAL FINANCIALS
Company Type: Private

Income Statement				FYE: June 30
	REVENUE ($ mil.)	NET INCOME ($ mil.)	NET PROFIT MARGIN	EMPLOYEES
06/15	294	28	9.6%	80
06/14	342	137	40.3%	—
06/13	307	102	33.3%	—
06/09	119	(8)		—
Annual Growth	16.2%	—	—	—

2015 Year-End Financials
Return on assets: 0.3%   Cash ($ mil.): 397
Return on equity: 9.6%
Current ratio: 28.00

UNIVERSITY OF NEW MEXICO

With more than 36630 students The University of New Mexico (UNM) based in Albuquerque is most renowned for its schools of medicine law and education. Students also attend one of the school's four branches located around the northern part of the state at Gallup Los Alamos Rio Rancho Taos and Valencia. Through its schools and colleges the university offers 96 bachelor's degrees 71 master's degrees 37 doctorate degrees as well as professional practice programs in law medicine and pharmacy. Its annual budget tops $2 billion. UNM employs more than 22000 people across the state.

Operations
The university also serves non-traditional students through its Evening and Weekend Degree Program which offers some 1000 classes each semester that contribute to about 40 different degree programs. About 12000 working students attend UNM at night each semester.

Most of its students come from in-state and continue to live in New Mexico after graduation.

In conjunction with the university's health sciences medical nursing and pharmacy school programs the university operates the UNM Health Sciences Center. It's the state's largest integrated health care treatment research and education facility. The teaching hospital operates a trauma center and specialized care units for oncology and pediatrics.

Geographic Reach
UNM's main campus is located in Albuquerque. Satellite campuses are in Gallup Los Alamos Rio Rancho Taos and Valencia. Only Los Alamos and Santa Fe offer graduate and upper division programs. The university hosts some 1500 international students and scholars.

Financial Performance
The majority of UNM's revenues (more than 60%) come from clinical operations and patient services from the UNM hospitals. Grants and contracts make up 18% while tuition and fees only account for 9% of the university's revenues.

In 2016 the university's revenues declined by $30 million to $1.56 billion due to lower other patient-related serivces and lower sales and serivces.

Operating expenses grew by about $112 million to $2.2 billion due to higher instruction research and public service costs and a rise in clinical operation expenses.

Company Background
UNM was founded in 1889.

EXECUTIVES

Dean School Of Engineering, Joseph L. Cecchi
Dean School Of Medicine, Paul B. Roth
Dean College Of University Libraries And Learning Sciences, Richard W. Clement
President, Robert G. Frank
Provost And Evp Academic Affairs, Chaouki T. Abdallah
Interim Dean Anderson School Of Management, Craig G. White
Dean College Of Arts And Sciences, Mark Peceny
Dean College Of Fine Arts, Kymberly Pinder
Dean Graduate Studies, Julie Coonrod
Dean Honors College, Catherine Krause
Dean College Of Nursing, Nancy Ridenour
Dean College Of Pharmacy, Lynda S. Welage
Dean School Of Architecture And Planning, Geraldine Forbes Isais
Dean School Of Law, David J. Herring
Dean School Of Public Administration, Mario Rivera
Dean College Of Education, S. Hector Ochoa
Financial Officer, Nicole Dopson
Cio, Gil Gonzales
President Board Of Regents, Jack L. Fortner
Auditors: KPMG LLP ALBUQUERQUE NEW MEX

LOCATIONS

HQ: UNIVERSITY OF NEW MEXICO
1800 ROMA BLVD NE, ALBUQUERQUE, NM
871310001
Phone: 505 277-0732
Web: WWW.UNM.EDU

PRODUCTS/OPERATIONS

2013 Sales

	% of sales
Clinical operations	42
Grants & contracts	21
Sales & services	16
Tuition & fees	10
Patients services	8
Other	3
Total	**100**

Schools and Colleges
Schools and Colleges
Anderson School of Management
College of Arts & Sciences
College of Education
College of Fine Arts
College of University Libraries & Learning Sciences
Honors College
School of Architecture & Planning
School of Engineering
School of Law
School of Public Administration
University College

HISTORICAL FINANCIALS
Company Type: Private

Income Statement				FYE: June 30
	REVENUE ($ mil.)	NET INCOME ($ mil.)	NET PROFIT MARGIN	EMPLOYEES
06/17	1,807	11	0.6%	18,362
06/16	1,893	6	0.3%	—
06/14	1,325	55	4.2%	—
06/13	1,516	19	1.3%	—
Annual Growth	4.5%	(13.1%)	—	—

2017 Year-End Financials
Return on assets: 10.8%   Cash ($ mil.): 341
Return on equity: 0.6%
Current ratio: 1.10

UNIVERSITY OF NORTH CAROLINA AT CHAPEL HILL

The University of North Carolina at Chapel Hill (UNC-Chapel Hill) has the education market cornered. One of the three original points making up North Carolina's Research Triangle (along with

Duke University and North Carolina State University) Carolina is the flagship campus of the University of North Carolina (UNC) system. The institution is consistently among the top-ranked research schools in the US. It enrolls some 29000 students and offers more than 250 undergraduate graduate and professional programs including law and medicine. It has 3200 full-time faculty members.

Operations

The university includes 15 schools and colleges as well as an adult learning center for continuing education programs. Its degree offerings include more than 100 master's degrees and about 70 doctorate programs.

UNC-Chapel Hill conducts extensive research programs in a variety of fields at its five health science schools (medicine dentistry pharmacy nursing and public health) its patient care facilities (operated through the University of North Carolina Hospitals affiliate) and its scientific teaching divisions (at the College of Arts and Sciences). The university attracted some $770 million in research grants and contracts during 2012. Funding sources include the National Institutes of Health. Research funding at UNC-Chapel Hill makes up more than half of awards for the entire UNC system.

Geographic Reach

UNC-Chapel Hill is located on a 730-acre campus that holds about 300 buildings. The university attracts students from all 50 US states and more than 145 international countries. It also has study abroad opportunities.

Financial Performance

UNC-Chapel Hill reported $2.5 billion in total revenues in 2012. Operating revenues make up the majority of earnings ($1.7 billion) from activities including student tuition fees federal grants and contracts and patient services. Non-operating revenues include state appropriations non-capital grants and gifts and investment income. Operating expenses ran at about $2.4 billion for 2012 and the university had a budget for fiscal 2013 of some $2.5 billion.

Strategy

To expand its international education opportunities in 2013 UNC-Chapel Hill formed a dual-degree partnership with Tsinghua University in China. The partnership offers business administration executive master's degrees.

Company Background

Chartered in 1789 Carolina is the oldest public university in the US. Notable alumni include author Thomas Wolfe and President James K. Polk as well as athlete Michael Jordan and journalist Charles Kuralt.

EXECUTIVES

Vice President Of Finance And Administration, Betty M Whichard

Vice President Of Special Events, Brandon Stephenson

Auditors: BETH A WOOD CPA

LOCATIONS

HQ: UNIVERSITY OF NORTH CAROLINA AT CHAPEL HILL
104 AIRPORT DR, CHAPEL HILL, NC 275995023
Phone: 919 962-1370
Web: WWW.UNC.EDU

PRODUCTS/OPERATIONS

Selected Schools Colleges and Centers
College of Arts and Sciences
Eshelman School of Pharmacy
Friday Center for Continuing Education
General College
Gillings School of Global Public Health
Graduate School
Kenan-Flagler Business School
School of Dentistry

School of Education
School of Government
School of Information and Library Science
School of Journalism and Mass Communication
School of Law
School of Medicine
School of Nursing
School of Social Work

Selected Academic Departments
African and AfroAmerican Studies
Air Force ROTC
Anthropology
Army ROTC
Art
Biology
Chemistry
Classics
Communication Studies
Dramatic Art
Economics
English and Comparative Literature
Exercise and Sport Science
Geography
History
Marine Sciences
Music
Nutrition
Pharmacology
Philosophy
Political Science
Psychology
Religious Studies
Sociology
Surgery

HISTORICAL FINANCIALS

Company Type: Private

Income Statement FYE: June 30

	REVENUE ($ mil.)	NET INCOME ($ mil.)	NET PROFIT MARGIN	EMPLOYEES
06/17	1,773	95	5.4%	12,204
06/11	1,704	391	23.0%	—
06/08	281	149	53.1%	—
06/05	3	2	57.7%	—
Annual Growth	66.3%	36.4%	—	—

2017 Year-End Financials

Return on assets: 5.0%   Cash ($ mil.): 155
Return on equity: 5.4%
Current ratio: 1.20

UNIVERSITY OF NORTH CAROLINA HOSPITALS

University of North Carolina Hospitals (UNCH) is at the heart of the UNC Health Care System (UNC HCS). The medical center provides acute care to the Tar Heel State through North Carolina Memorial Hospital North Carolina Children's Hospital North Carolina Neurosciences Hospital and North Carolina Women's Hospital. Combined the facilities have more than 800 beds. Specialties include cancer treatment at the North Carolina Cancer Hospital organ transplantation cardiac care orthopedics wound management and rehabilitation. Not-for-profit UNC HCS is owned by the state of North Carolina and is affiliated with the UNC-Chapel Hill School of Medicine.

Operations

UNCH operates under the umbrella of UNC HCS.

UNC HCS already extends beyond Chapel Hill and into the greater Triangle area through its network of primary care and specialty physician practices located in Orange Wake Durham Chatham and Lee counties. The system treats some 800000 people at UNC HCS practices and clinics annually.

UNCH handles more than 37000 patients each year and delivers 3500 babies annually.

North Carolina Children's offers 150 inpatient beds and a comprehensive children's outpatient center. Every year provides specialty care to more than 70000 children from all 100 North Carolina counties. The North Carolina Cancer Hospital is the clinical home of the UNC Lineberger Comprehensive Cancer Center. The state's only public cancer hospital the North Carolina Cancer Hospital treats patients from every county in North Carolina with more than 135000 patient visits a year.

Geographic Reach

UNCH not only serves patients from all North Carolina counties with about a third coming from the Research Triangle area it also serves patients from neighboring states.

Strategy

Being one of the primary health care providers in the area UNC HCS is nearly always expanding its services and service areas either through acquisitions or new construction.

In 2015 UNCH filed a petition with state regulators seeking the ability to add 42 acute-care beds at its Chapel Hill campus. If approved UNC estimates it will cost the hospital $17 million and would be completed by mid-2018.

UNC HCS planned to open a new 86-bed acute-care hospital in Hillsborough in 2015 as part of an effort to reduce pressure on its Chapel Hill campus. The construction of the hospital will cost about $200 million. The new facility will offer an emergency department outpatient surgery and a range of inpatient services to our patients in Alamance and Western Orange counties.

Dedicated cancer care and cancer research is another area in which UNC HCS is expanding. It opened a North Carolina Cancer Hospital at Rex Hospital in 2014.

The system is also building an Imaging Research Building expected to open in 2013 to house the Biomedical Research Imaging Center and serve as a state resource for handling the acquisition processing analysis storage and retrieval of scientific images.

In 2013 UNC HCS established the first stage of its Hillsborough campus with the opening of a 60000-square-foot medical office building. The building includes hospital services such as imaging laboratory pharmacy and medical and surgical oncology.

Company Background

In 2011 the hospital opened a new wing of the Newborn Critical Care Unit in the North Carolina Children's Hospital that houses 10 new patient beds bringing the number of beds in the unit to 58.

UNCH was founded in 1952 under the name North Carolina Memorial Hospital. In 1989 the North Carolina General Assembly created UNCH.

EXECUTIVES

Pres, Gary Park
Exec V Pres, Brian P Goldstein
Svp and Cfo, Chris Ellington
Sr V Pres, Mary Beck
V Pres, Amy Bragg
Otolaryngology, Jill A Alexander Ritch
Accounting Staff, Mike Sumner
Coordinator, Samara Robinson
Staff, David Reed
Staff, Douglas Robinson
Coordinator, Margaret Brooks

LOCATIONS

HQ: UNIVERSITY OF NORTH CAROLINA HOSPITALS
101 MANNING DR BLDG 2, CHAPEL HILL, NC
275144423
Phone: 919 966-5111
Web: WWW.UNCHEALTHCARE.ORG

PRODUCTS/OPERATIONS

Selected Facilities

North Carolina Cancer Hospital (Chapel Hill)
  UNC Lineberger Comprehensive Cancer Center
North Carolina Children's Hospital (Chapel Hill)
North Carolina Memorial Hospital (Chapel Hill)
North Carolina Neurosciences Hospital (Chapel Hill)
North Carolina Women's Hospital (Chapel Hill)

COMPETITORS

Alamance Regional Medical Center	Grady Health System
Carolinas HealthCare System	High Point Regional Health System
Cone Health	Morehead Memorial Hospital
Cumberland County Hospital System	New Hanover Regional Medical Center
Danville Regional Medical Center	Rowan Regional Medical Center
Duke University Health System	Vidant Health
Emory Healthcare	WakeMed

HISTORICAL FINANCIALS

Company Type: Private

Income Statement — FYE: June 30

	REVENUE ($ mil.)	NET INCOME ($ mil.)	NET PROFIT MARGIN	EMPLOYEES
06/18	1,892	88	4.7%	6,000
06/16	1,551	87	5.6%	—
06/15	1,385	110	8.0%	—
06/07	787	182	23.2%	—
Annual Growth	8.3%	(6.4%)	—	—

2018 Year-End Financials

Return on assets: 3.7%   Cash ($ mil.): 49
Return on equity: 4.7%
Current ratio: 0.80

UNIVERSITY OF NORTH DAKOTA

Way up in the Upper Midwest is the University of North Dakota (UND) the largest and oldest institution of higher learning in the state with an enrollment of approximately 15000 students. It offers undergraduate and graduate programs in close to 225 fields through nine colleges and schools (aerospace sciences arts and sciences business and public administration education and human development engineering and mines law medical and health sciences nursing and a graduate school). The university also has nearly 20 doctoral programs as well as certificate degree programs distance degree programs and a continuing education division. UND was founded in 1883 six years before North Dakota achieved statehood.

Operations

UND has an international reputation for research most notably in the health sciences nutrition energy and environmental protection aerospace and engineering. The university receives funding from various sources to perform research projects in areas that include neuroscience un-

manned aerial systems vaccines advanced electronics nanotechnology high-tech coatings and alternative fuels.

EXECUTIVES

Exec Dir, Robert Kelly
Payroll Staff, Joanne Barstad
Assistant Professor, Thad Rosenberger
Assistant Professor, Elizabeth Scharf
Assistant Professor, Saobo Lei
Assistant Professor, James Haskins
Coordinator, Whitney Duden
Auditors: ROBERT R PETERSON FARGO NORT

LOCATIONS

HQ: UNIVERSITY OF NORTH DAKOTA
264 CENTENNIAL DR, GRAND FORKS, ND
582026059
Phone: 701 777-4321
Web: WWW.UND.EDU

PRODUCTS/OPERATIONS

Selected Schools and Colleges

John D. Odegard School of Aerospace Sciences
College of Arts and Sciences
College of Business and Public Administration
College of Education and Human Development
School of Engineering and Mines
The Graduate School
School of Law
School of Medicine and Health Sciences
College of Nursing

HISTORICAL FINANCIALS

Company Type: Private

Income Statement — FYE: June 30

	REVENUE ($ mil.)	NET INCOME ($ mil.)	NET PROFIT MARGIN	EMPLOYEES
06/17	316	19	6.3%	2,756
06/16	311	57	18.4%	—
06/11	278	27	9.8%	—
06/09	637	(40)	—	—
Annual Growth	(8.4%)	—	—	—

2017 Year-End Financials

Return on assets: 2.9%   Cash ($ mil.): 36
Return on equity: 6.3%
Current ratio: 1.00

UNIVERSITY OF NORTH TEXAS SYSTEM

EXECUTIVES

Mgr, Cynthia Doll
Administrator, Carlos Fernandez
Auditors: GRANT THORNTON LLP DALLAS TX

LOCATIONS

HQ: UNIVERSITY OF NORTH TEXAS SYSTEM
1302 TEASLEY LN, DENTON, TX 762057946
Phone: 940 565-2281
Web: WWW.UNTHSC.EDU

HISTORICAL FINANCIALS

Company Type: Private

Income Statement — FYE: August 31

	REVENUE ($ mil.)	NET INCOME ($ mil.)	NET PROFIT MARGIN	EMPLOYEES
08/17	619	82	13.4%	6,561
08/16	631	47	7.5%	—
08/09	463	47	10.2%	—
08/08	428	61	14.4%	—
Annual Growth	4.2%	3.3%	—	—

2017 Year-End Financials

Return on assets: 10.7%   Cash ($ mil.): 210
Return on equity: 13.4%
Current ratio: 0.70

UNIVERSITY OF OREGON

This school's got all its ducks in a row. As one of the largest schools in the state the University of Oregon (UO) has an enrollment of more than 23600 students and some 1500 faculty members. It offers its students eight different schools and colleges plus a graduate college with fields of study range from the arts and journalism to business and law. Part of the Oregon University System UO also offers development services an honors program research institutes and continuing education courses. The school's athletic department organizes more than 15 sports activities including lacrosse and football; the teams are called The Ducks.

Operations

UO has a student-to-teacher ratio of 17:1 and an average class size of 20. Course offerings range across lecture discussion seminar activity laboratory independent study and independent research formats and UO has a total of about 300 academic programs and 25 research centers and institutes. The university's most popular majors for undergraduates include accounting architecture art biology business administration chemistry education economics English environmental science human physiology journalism political science public relations and sociology. Its freshman retention success rate is more than 85%.

Geographic Reach

UO is located on a 295-acre campus in Eugene Oregon that includes about 80 buildings. It also has a satellite campus in Portland. Students come to UO from all 50 US states (plus Washington DC and two US territories) as well as 95 foreign countries. More than half of students are Oregon residents. A number of students also participate in more than 200 study abroad and internship programs in 90 international locations.

Financial Performance

UO reported an 3% increase in revenues in 2016 to $692.7 million due to increased earnings from net student tuition and fees state and local grants and contracts net auxiliary enterprise sales and other operating revenue sources. However the university also reported a decline in its net position from $888.6 million in 2015 to $840.4 million in 2016 due to higher operating expenses and interest expenses as well as a decline in restricted and unrestricted assets.

Company Background

The Oregon State Legislature created the university in 1872 and students first enrolled in 1876.

EXECUTIVES

Dean School Of Music And Dance, Brad Foley
Interim President, Scott Coltrane
Svp And Provost, Frances Bronet
Vp Finance And Administration, Jamie Moffitt
Vice Provost Information Services And Cio, Melissa Woo
Dean College Of Arts And Sciences, W. Andrew Marcus
Dean Lundquist College Of Business, Cornelis A. (Kees) de Kluyver
Dean College Of Education, Randy Kamphaus
Dean School Of Law, Michael Moffitt
Dean Clark Honors College, Terry Hunt
Interim Dean School Of Journalism And Communication, Julianne Newton
Acting Dean School Of Architecture And Allied Arts, Brook Muller
Dean Graduate School, Scott Pratt
Vice President University Communications, Kyle Henley
Vice President And General Counsel, Kevin Reed
Vice President Communications, Justin Asarch
Assistant Vice President For Strategic Initiatives, Chris Edwards
Chairman, Charles M. (Chuck) Lillis
Vice Chairman, Ginevra Ralph
Board Member, Carl Hosticka
Auditors: MOSS ADAMS LLP PORTLAND OREG

LOCATIONS

HQ: UNIVERSITY OF OREGON
1585 E 13TH AVE, EUGENE, OR 974031657
Phone: 541 346-1000
Web: WWW.UOREGON.EDU

PRODUCTS/OPERATIONS

Colleges and Schools
Charles H. Lundquist College of Business
College of Arts and Sciences
College of Education
Graduate School
Robert D. Clark Honors College
School of Architecture and Allied Arts
School of Journalism and Communication
School of Law
School of Music and Dance

HISTORICAL FINANCIALS

Company Type: Private

Income Statement				FYE: June 30
	REVENUE ($ mil.)	NET INCOME ($ mil.)	NET PROFIT MARGIN	EMPLOYEES
06/18	740	(8)	—	7,971
06/17	713	31	4.5%	—
06/16	692	(48)	—	—
Annual Growth	3.4%	—	—	—

2018 Year-End Financials
Return on assets: 6.7%   Cash ($ mil.): 192
Return on equity: (-1.1%)
Current ratio: 1.30

UNIVERSITY OF PITTSBURGH

The University of Pittsburgh (Pitt for short) operates its flagship campus in the Oakland neighborhood of Pittsburgh. More than 35000 graduate and undergraduate students attend the main campus as well as four regional campuses. Pitt Panthers pursue degrees in about 400 disciplines including arts and sciences business law medicine and engineering. The school has a student-teacher ratio of 14:1. Pitt is also affiliated with the UPMC health system which operates about 20 hospitals numerous clinics and an insurance company. Pitt was founded in 1787 making it one of the oldest universities in the US.

Operations

Pitt is considered a leading US public research university and as such spends more than $700 million annually on research projects. Pitt is recognized for its work in about a dozen disciplines including computer modeling philosophy the humanities international studies aging neuroscience bioengineering commercial innovation education national preparedness drug discovery translational medicine and nanoscience. It was at Pitt that Jonas Salk developed the polio vaccine at what is now known as Salk Hall.

Notable Pitt alumni include Academy Award winner Gene Kelly Nobel Peace Prize winner Wangari Maathai Pulitzer Prize winner Michael Chabon and US Senator Orrin Hatch.

Geographic Reach

In addition to the main campus in Pittsburgh which houses 17 schools colleges and a center for social and urban research Pitt has regional campus locations in Bradford Greensburg Johnstown and Titusville.

Financial Performance

Pitt reported revenues of some $2 billion in 2014. Most of the university's revenues come from grants and contracts followed by student tuition and feescommonwealth appropriation endowment distributions and other sources of income.

Strategy

In addition to providing high quality education programs for its students Pitt works to engage in research scholarly and artistic projects that advance global learning. It also works to collaborate with government agencies and businesses to advance science medicine and technology seeking active partners as well as funding provider to further its programs.

EXECUTIVES

Chancellor, William Dietrich
Ceo, Mark Nordenberg
Fo, Arthur Ramicone
SEC, Gene B Ferketish
Treas, Amy K Marsh
Asst Treas, Susan Gilbert
Asst Treas, Paul Lawrence
Executive Assistant, Mary Jo Race
Coordinator, Gina Pomponio
Executive Asst, Stacy Czerniejewski
Staff, Robert Snyder
Auditors: KPMG LLP PITTSBURGH PENNSYLV

LOCATIONS

HQ: UNIVERSITY OF PITTSBURGH
4200 5TH AVE, PITTSBURGH, PA 152600001
Phone: 412 624-4141
Web: WWW.MEDSCHOOL.PITT.EDU

PRODUCTS/OPERATIONS

Selected Schools and Colleges
The John A. Swanson School of Engineering
The Joseph M. Katz Graduate School of Business
  College of Business Administration
Kenneth P. Dietrich School of Arts and Sciences
  College of General Studies
School of Dental Medicine
School of Education
School of Health and Rehabilitation Sciences
School of Information Sciences
School of Law
School of Medicine
School of Nursing
School of Pharmacy
School of Public and International Affairs
School of Public Health
School of Social Work
University Center for International Studies
University Honors College

HISTORICAL FINANCIALS

Company Type: Private

Income Statement				FYE: June 30
	REVENUE ($ mil.)	NET INCOME ($ mil.)	NET PROFIT MARGIN	EMPLOYEES
06/18	2,276	381	16.8%	9,607
06/17	2,169	487	22.5%	—
06/16	2,106	(212)	—	—
06/15	2,060	27	1.3%	—
Annual Growth	3.4%	141.5%	—	—

2018 Year-End Financials
Return on assets: 4.3%   Cash ($ mil.): 45
Return on equity: 16.8%
Current ratio: —

UNIVERSITY OF PITTSBURGH MEDICAL CENTER

For University of Pittsburgh students and area residents medical care is spelled UPMC. UPMC Jameson is a leading not-for-profit health care delivery system in western Pennsylvania. The organization operates about 20 hospitals including campuses in the Pittsburgh area regional and community hospitals and specialty facilities such as Children's Hospital of Pittsburgh and the Magee-Womens Hospital. Combined UPMC Jameson has more than 5100 inpatient beds. In addition the system provides care through hundreds of physician practices outpatient clinics cancer treatment facilities and rehab centers; it also offers health insurance home health care and long-term care through more than 15 senior living facilities.

Operations

UPMC Jameson is organized into four primary operating divisions. Provider Services includes tertiary community and regional hospitals; specialty services such as women's health and behavioral health; in-home care and senior living; contract services including pharmacy and laboratories; and the system's 3400 physicians and their practices. Insurance Services offers health insurance to employers and employees workers' compensation and disability services and behavioral health coverage to Medical Assistance beneficiaries. UPMC International Services exports the system's expertise abroad while UPMC Enterprises seeks commercialization opportunities and partnerships.

As an academic medical center affiliated with the University of Pittsburgh's Schools of Health Sciences UPMC Jameson also focuses on medical research in a wide range of areas including the fields of regenerative medicine and biosecurity some of which is funded by the National Institutes of Health. The system is also renowned for its organ transplantation programs as well as for its cancer care psychiatric pediatric and women's health services. In addition UPMC Jameson is a forerunner in the health care information technology field.

The system has some 5500 affiliated physicians. In a typical year it has some 287000 inpatient admissions more than 3.9 million outpatient visits and some 690000 emergency department visits. It performs some 189000 surgeries and more than 690000 home care visits.

Geographic Reach

The company's primary operating territory for its health and insurance segments is western Pennsylvania. Outside the US UPMC Jameson operates health care facilities in Ireland Italy Quatar Cyprus and the UK. It also provides management and consulting services in other international countries to improve global health care partly through partnerships with health equipment and technology firms.

Sales and Marketing

The majority of the company's hospital services are rendered to patients under Medicare Highmark Blue Cross Blue Shield (a major area insurer) and medical assistance programs. Its patient service revenue comes from Medicare accounts (which accounts for more than 30% of all patient revenue each year) Highmark (31%) other medical assistance programs (about 10%) and self-pay and commercial insurance.

Financial Performance

UPMC's revenues increased 12% to some $11.4 billion in 2014 due to increased patient service revenues which accounted for half of all earnings. Higher enrollment levels in the UPMC Health Plan (40% of sales) also contributed to growth that year. Net income rose 58% to $698 million on higher investment income and other factors. Meanwhile cash flow from operations increased 82% to $568.9 million.

Strategy

The UPMC network of facilities has grown over the years through acquisitions and new facility construction. On the flip side the company has occasionally sold or shut down less-profitable facilities in its network such as UPMC Braddock an underused suburban community hospital.

UPMC Jameson is advancing its technology systems to control costs and increase efficiencies. The health system has established electronic health record (EHR) systems at all of its hospitals and is working to share data with other area providers. In addition UPMC has partnerships with Alcatel-Lucent GE and IBM to help reduce medical expenses and increase the quality of care through IT initiatives.

In 2015 UMPC and The University of Pittsburgh School of Medicine launched the Center for Women's Health Research and Innovation which is devoted to research education and clinical practice while promoting community partnership and advocacy related to health care for women.

The following year UMPC acquired rural hospital Jameson Healthcare to become UMPC Jameson. Jameson had been operating in the red — a common problem for rural systems. UMPC Jameson plans to invest between $70 and $80 million to provide continuing services in Lawrence County (including maintaining facilities and recruiting new doctors) as well as to pay down debt.

Mergers and Acquisitions

In 2017 UMPC agreed to buy Pinnacle Health System. The purchase will add two hospitals to UPMC's network and will allow the system to sell health insurance beyond its core market in western Pennsylvania.

EXECUTIVES

President And Ceo, Jeffrey A. Romoff
Evp And Chief Administrative Officer, Gregory Peaslee
Evp And Cfo, Robert A. DeMichiei

Evp President Insurance Services Division And President And Ceo Upmc Health Plan, Diane P. Holder
Evp; President Hospital And Community Services Division, Elizabeth B. Concordia
Svp And Evp And Chief Operating Officer Health Services Division, Leslie C. Davis
Evp And Chief Legal Officer, W. Thomas (Tom) McGough
Evp And President International Commercial Services Division And President Upmc Cancercenter, Charles E. (Chuck) Bogosta
Svp And Chief Of Staff Office Of The President, David M. Farner
Evp Treasurer And President Upmc Enterprises, C. Talbot Heppenstall
Evp And Chief Medical Officer; President Physician Services Division, Marshall W. Webster
Svp And Chief Medical Officer, Steven D. Shapiro
Auditors: ERNST & YOUNG LLP

LOCATIONS

HQ: UNIVERSITY OF PITTSBURGH MEDICAL CENTER
200 LOTHROP ST, PITTSBURGH, PA 152132536
Phone: 412 647-8762
Web: WWW.UPMC.COM

Selected Pennsylvania Facilities

Children's Hospital of Pittsburgh of UPMC
Magee-Womens Hospital of UPMC (Pittsburgh)
UPMC Bedford Memorial (Everett)
UPMC East (Pittsburgh)
UPMC Hamlot (Erie)
UPMC Horizon (Greenville and Shenango Valley)
UPMC McKeesport (McKeesport)
UPMC Mercy (Pittsburgh)
UPMC Montefiore (Pittsburgh)
UPMC Northwest (Seneca and Oil City)
UPMC Passavant (McCandless and Cranberry)
UPMC Presbyterian (Pittsburgh)
UPMC Shadyside (Pittsburgh)
UPMC St. Margaret (Pittsburgh)
UPMC Western Psychiatric Institute and Clinic (Pittsburgh)

PRODUCTS/OPERATIONS

2014 Sales

	$ mil.	% of total
Patient services	5,776	51
Insurance services	4,813	42
Other	826	7
Total	**11,415**	**100**

Selected Services

Behavioral and Mental Health Services
Cancer
COPD and Emphysema Center
Dermatology
Diabetes and Endocrinology
Ear Nose and Throat
Emergency Medicine
Family/Primary Care Medicine
Gastroenterology
Geriatrics
Heart and Vascular
Imaging Services
Kidney Disease
Liver
Neurology
Ophthalmology
Pain Medicine
Pathology
Pediatrics
Pulmonology and Respiratory
Rehabilitation
Rheumatology
Sports Medicine
Stroke Care
Thyroid
Urology
Women's Health
Wound Healing Services

COMPETITORS

Allegheny General Hospital
AmeriHealth Mercy Health Plan
Blue Cross of Northeastern Pennsylvania
Butler Health System
Capital BlueCross
Conemaugh Health System
Excela Health
Geisinger Health System
HealthAmerica
Heritage Valley Health
Highmark
Independence Blue Cross
Jefferson Regional Medical Center of Pennsylvania
Ohio Valley General
PinnacleHealth System
St. Clair Health
Universal Health Services
West Penn Allegheny Health System

HISTORICAL FINANCIALS

Company Type: Private

Income Statement				FYE: June 30
	REVENUE ($ mil.)	NET INCOME ($ mil.)	NET PROFIT MARGIN	EMPLOYEES
06/16	12,848	(16)	—	80,000
06/15	614	326	53.1%	—
06/13*	10,188	441	4.3%	—
12/11	4,758	(2)	—	—
Annual Growth	28.2%	—	—	—

*Fiscal year change

2016 Year-End Financials

Return on assets: 3.7%   Cash ($ mil.): 431
Return on equity: (-0.1%)
Current ratio: 0.50

UNIVERSITY OF RHODE ISLAND

EXECUTIVES

Pres, David M Dooley
Vice President, Christina Valentino
Vice President, Gerald Sonnenfeld
Asst Contrl, Cindy Mayes
Assistant Professor, Aisling Caffrey
Assistant Professor, Blaire O Gagnon
Staff, Judith Mack
Assistant Professor, Lynn Clifford
Coordinator, Noemi Ramos-Desimone
Assistant Professor, Peter J Dadalt
Coordinator, Brian Gallagher
Auditors: O'CONNOR & DREW PC BRAINTRE

LOCATIONS

HQ: UNIVERSITY OF RHODE ISLAND
75 LOWER COLLEGE RD STE 0, KINGSTON, RI 028811974
Phone: 401 874-1000
Web: WWW.URI.EDU

PRODUCTS/OPERATIONS

Selected Schools and Colleges

College of Arts and Sciences
College of Business Administration
College of Continuing Education
College of Engineering
College of Environment and Life Sciences
College of Human Science and Services
College of Nursing
College of Pharmacy
Graduate School of Oceanography
University College

HISTORICAL FINANCIALS

Company Type: Private

Income Statement   FYE: June 30

	REVENUE ($ mil.)	NET INCOME ($ mil.)	NET PROFIT MARGIN	EMPLOYEES
06/18	440	45	10.3%	2,600
06/17	423	33	7.8%	—
06/16	413	15	3.9%	—
06/15	403	6	1.5%	—
Annual Growth	3.0%	94.3%	—	—

2018 Year-End Financials

Return on assets: 8.1%   Cash ($ mil.): 129
Return on equity: 10.3%
Current ratio: 2.50

UNIVERSITY OF RICHMOND

Suffering from arachnophobia? You may want to steer clear of the more than 4300 Spiders who are enrolled at the University of Richmond (UR).A URA consists ofA five schools: Jepson School of Leadership Studies Richmond School of Law Robins School of BusinessA School of Arts and Sciences and School of Continuing Studies.A The university offers some 60 undergraduate majors as well as graduate and master's programs in business accounting and law. UR also offers some 75 study-abroad programs in which more than half of its students participate. Founded in 1830 by Virginia Baptists as a seminary for men the school became Richmond College in 1840.

Operations

UR with about 320 full-time undergraduate faculty members boasts a student-faculty ratio of 9:1. Through its Richmond Quadrangle LLC (a wholly controlled affiliate of UR) the university owns and operates a building and land located in Richmond. UR's Spider Management Company LLC is another wholly controlled affiliate that provides investment research advice counsel and management related to the university's endowment assets.

Geographic Reach

From its campus in Richmond Virginia UR serves students from nearly all 50 US states including Puerto Rico and Washington D.C. Its student population consists of more than 3000 undergraduates that come more than 70 countries.

Financial Performance

Revenue for UR rose 8% in fiscal 2012 as compared to 2011 due to an increase in tuition and fees grants and contracts contributions endowment spending distribution and auxiliary enterprises. Net income for the same reporting period decreased by 112% thanks to rising operating expenses and declining contribution and net unrealized losses.

EXECUTIVES

Associate Vice President Human Resources, Carl K Sorensen
Vice President Advancement, Thomas Gutenberger
Assoc Vice President Controller, Laurie Melville
Vice President For Public Relations, Stefanie Mathew
Vice President For Public Relations, Mary Gardiner
Vice President Operations, Jason Hoogakker
Vice President For Administration, Ethan Mcwilliams

Chief Associate Vice President Of Public Safety, David Mccoy
Vice President And Chief Information Officer, Keith McIntosh
Vice President Enrollment Management, Stephanie Dupaul
Vice President For Communications, John Barry
Managing Director Barclays Capital, Stephen Aronson
Secretary, Jessica Myers
Treasurer, Michael Forsyth
Board Member, Nina Naruszewicz
Auditors: KPMG LLP RICHMOND VIRGINIA

LOCATIONS

HQ: UNIVERSITY OF RICHMOND
28 WESTHAMPTON WAY, RICHMOND, VA 231730002
Phone: 804 289-8133
Web: WWW.RICHMOND.EDU

PRODUCTS/OPERATIONS

Selected Schools

Arts and Sciences
Business
Leadership Studies
Law
Professional and Continuing Studies

HISTORICAL FINANCIALS

Company Type: Private

Income Statement   FYE: June 30

	REVENUE ($ mil.)	NET INCOME ($ mil.)	NET PROFIT MARGIN	EMPLOYEES
06/18	308	157	50.9%	1,400
06/16	283	(190)	—	—
06/13	253	185	73.0%	—
Annual Growth	4.0%	(3.2%)	—	—

2018 Year-End Financials

Return on assets: 27.7%   Cash ($ mil.): 56
Return on equity: 50.9%
Current ratio: —

UNIVERSITY OF SAN DIEGO

The University of San Diego (USD) is private college located close to southern California's beaches and the Mexican border. The coeducational Roman Catholic university has an enrollment of more than 7800 students USD offers more than 70 bachelor's master's and doctoral degrees in areas such as arts and sciences business administration education engineering law and nursing. It has a faculty of 440 full time staff members. The university also home to the Joan B. Kroc School of Peace Studies established in 2003 by the wife of McDonald's founder Ray Kroc.

Operations

Adjacent to the USD campus is the St. Francis Seminary; young men studying for the priesthood attend the university for the academic portion of their course work. USD is a very residential college; 94% of its freshman class live on the school's grounds in 10 separate living areas with styles that range from shared rooms to apartments. About 9% of its students hail from outside of the US.

USD offers more than 40 bachelor's degrees about 30 master's degrees in eight academic divisions as well as three doctoral degrees - two in nursing and one in leadership studies.

As a Carnegie-certified Doctoral/Research school the school is committed to graduate education through the doctorate awarding 50 or more doctoral degrees annually (USD regularly awards more than 360 doctoral degrees) and it gives high priority to research receiving more than $40 million annually in federal research support.

Financial Performance

Higher tuition and fees helped to lift USD's revenues from $328 million in 2015 to $343.8 million in 2016..

Strategy

The university undergoes a cycle of strategic initiatives every few years that shape the way it intends to move into the future.

In 2014 USD broke ground on a new health sciences building and opened a Madrid (Spain) location.

Company Background

USD was formed in 1972 by the merger of San Diego University and San Diego College for Women.

In 2003 school president Dr. Mary Lyons implemented a round of strategic initiatives focusing on Catholic-based social studies inclusion and diversity integrated learning internationalization and sustainability. It subsequently emphasized enrollment management building out the school's technology infrastructure expanding undergraduate research developing USD's endowment and raising the university's branding and marketing standards. Goals include international expansion engaging alumni and assessing programs aimed at expressing the university's Catholic character.

EXECUTIVES

Evp, Julie H. Sullivan, age 60
Vp Finance And Cfo, Terry Kalfayan
Vice Provost And Cio, Chris Wessells
Vp And Provost, Andrew T. Allen
President, James T. Harris
Assistant Vice President For Enrollment, Stephen Pultz
Vice President Student Affairs, Carmen M Vazquez
Vice President Of Administration, Kevin Ganley
Assistant Vice President Public Relations, Pamela Gray
Assistant Vice President For Student Affairs, Donald Godwin
Vice President Of Membership, Owen Buckley
Department Chair, Ann Garland
Department Chair, Angelo Orona
Director Of Admissions, Minh-Ha Hoang
Vice President Of Communications, Weston Preising
Vice President Of Administration, Peter Nelson
Vice President Of New Business Development For An International Manufacturing Company, Leslie Hennessy
Treasurer, Andrew Quintana
Auditors: MOSS ADAMS LLP SAN DIEGO CAL

LOCATIONS

HQ: UNIVERSITY OF SAN DIEGO
5998 ALCALA PARK FRNT, SAN DIEGO, CA 921102492
Phone: 619 260-4600
Web: WWW.SANDIEGO.EDU

PRODUCTS/OPERATIONS

Selected Schools and Colleges

College of Arts and Sciences
School of Business Administration
Engineering
Hahn School of Nursing and Health Science
Joan B. Kroc School of Peace Studies
School of Law
School of Leadership and Education Sciences

HISTORICAL FINANCIALS
Company Type: Private

Income Statement				FYE: June 30
	REVENUE ($ mil.)	NET INCOME ($ mil.)	NET PROFIT MARGIN	EMPLOYEES
06/18	365	103	28.3%	1,600
06/17	350	92	26.5%	—
06/15	453	56	12.5%	—
06/13	303	90	29.8%	—
Annual Growth	3.8%	2.7%	—	—

2018 Year-End Financials
Return on assets: 13.6%
Return on equity: 28.3%
Current ratio: —
Cash ($ mil.): 11

UNIVERSITY OF SAN FRANCISCO INC

Known for their devotion to education as well as their investment portfolio the Jesuits are evident to all who visit the University of San Francisco (USF). One of 28 Jesuit Catholic colleges and universities in the US the main USF campus sits on 55 acres near Golden Gate Park in San Francisco. The school which was formed in 1855 as St. Ignatius Academy enrolls more than 10000 students. It operates five schools and colleges including the schools of business and management education law and nursing and the colleges of arts and sciences. In addition to its main campus the university operates five satellite sites in Northern and Southern California.

Operations
USF operates a handful of schools and colleges including schools of management education law nursing and the colleges of arts and sciences. More than 400 full-time faculty members offer 100-plus undergraduate and degree programs. With an undergraduate student-faculty ratio of 15:1 USF's 10000-plus student enrollment includes 6250 undergraduates 2950 graduates 670 law students and 150 non-degree students.

The independent private not-for-profit university is one of the nation's most ethnically diverse schools. Some 43% of its students are Asian African-American Latino Native Hawaiian/Pacific Islander or multi-ethnic.

Financial Performance
USF logged a slight decrease in revenue in 2014 (ended May) as compared to 203. Meanwhile expenses rose 6.6% during the same reporting period. The university ended 2014 with net assets of $625 million compared to the $577 million of net assets reported in 2013.

Strategy
To keep up with growth USF opened a campus in downtown San Francisco at 101 Howard Street. The university also changed the name of its school of nursing to the School of Nursing and Health Professions to reflect the institution's commitment and expansion of its master of public health degree.

EXECUTIVES
Vp Business And Finance, Charles E. (Charlie) Cross
Chancellor, John Lo Schiavo
Provost And Academic Vp, Jennifer E. Turpin
Dean School Of Education, Walter H. Gmelch
Dean School Of Law, Jeffrey S. Brand

Dean University Library, Tyrone H. Cannon
Vice Provost And Dean Academic And Enrollment Services, Elizabeth J. Johnson
Dean School Of Nursing And Health Professions, Judith F. Karshmer
President, Paul J. Fitzgerald
Vp Information Technology, Stephen J. Gallagher
Dean College Of Arts And Sciences, Marcelo F. Camperi
Dean School Of Management, Michael J. Webber
Vice President For Development, Peter Wilch
Assistant Vice President Donor Engagement And Communications, Michelle Sklar
Assistant Vice President Marketing, Anneliese Mauch
Vice President Of Public Relations, Laureano Figueroa
Analyst Office Of The Vice President, Hien Pham
Vice President Of Academic Affairs, Donald E Heller
Vice President Of Internal Affairs, Francesca Bitton
Associate Vice President Alumni And Donor Engagement Director Women In Leadership And Philanthropy, Leslie Wetzel
Vice President Of Marketing Communications, Ellen Ryder
Vice Chair, Charles H. Smith
Chairman, Thomas E. Malloy
Secretary, Annmarie Belda
Auditors: MOSS ADAMS LLP SAN FRANCISCO

LOCATIONS
HQ: UNIVERSITY OF SAN FRANCISCO INC
  2130 FULTON ST, SAN FRANCISCO, CA 941171050
Phone: 415 422-5555
Web: WWW.USFCA.EDU

PRODUCTS/OPERATIONS

Selected Schools and Colleges
College of Arts
College of Sciences
School of Education
School of Law
School of Management
School of Nursing

HISTORICAL FINANCIALS
Company Type: Private

Income Statement				FYE: May 31
	REVENUE ($ mil.)	NET INCOME ($ mil.)	NET PROFIT MARGIN	EMPLOYEES
05/17	417	50	12.1%	1,200
05/13	375	71	19.0%	—
05/12	390	36	9.3%	—
05/11	380	55	14.5%	—
Annual Growth	1.6%	(1.5%)	—	—

2017 Year-End Financials
Return on assets: 11.8%
Return on equity: 12.1%
Current ratio: —
Cash ($ mil.): 89

UNIVERSITY OF SOUTH ALABAMA

When you go by the moniker USA and the campus beauty queen wins the Miss USA title year after year (the Pi Kappa Phi Miss USA pageant that is) you're standing on hallowed ground. In this case it's the ground of the University of South Alabama situated on the upper Gulf Coast. The school's crown jewel is its College of Medicine and other facilities including USA Medical Center USA Knollwood Hospital and USA Children's and Women's Hospital. USA also offers degrees in Health Arts and Sciences Business Education Engineering Nursing Computer and Information Sciences Continuing Education and Special Programs and the Graduate School. More than 14880 students call the USA home.

Operations
USA offers 41 different bachelor programs 31 masters programs and 10 doctoral programs.

Financial Performance
The school reported an 8% increase in revenues in 2012 thanks to higher tuition and fee rates and an increase in student enrollment and credit hours taken and a rise in net patient service revenues (29% of total 2012 revenues). Other operating revenues also increased in 2012 thanks to higher revenues from the Electronic Health Records Incentive Program.

USA reported net income in 2012 of $38 million (versus a net loss in 2011) due to decline in operating loss and an increase in non-operating revenues (primarily from higher investment returns and state appropriations).

The university saw an increase in revenues between 2010 and 2012 largely due to organic growth.

Strategy
USA is pushing to expand and strengthen its development program and increase student enrollment. In 2013 the school received a gift of $250000 from alumni Dr. and Mrs. Steven H. Stokes to start a new Center for Environmental Resiliency.

Company Background
Founded in 1963 USA has graduated more than 75000 students including 18200 teachers and school administrators (including 85% of Mobile's public school teachers).

EXECUTIVES
Assoc Vice President University Comp Services, Chris Cannon
Interim Associate Vice President For Academic Affairs, Julio Turrens
Vice President, John Smith
Secretary, Marcina Lang
Secretary, Gayle Moore
Secretary, Anita Perrette
Secretary, Karen Mandrella
Secretary Iv, Sharon Leibert
Auditors: KPMG LLP JACKSON MS

LOCATIONS
HQ: UNIVERSITY OF SOUTH ALABAMA
  307 N UNIVERSITY BLVD # 380, MOBILE, AL 366083074
Phone: 251 460-6101
Web: WWW.SOUTHALABAMA.EDU

PRODUCTS/OPERATIONS

USA Colleges and Schools
Arts and Sciences
Auburn University School of Pharmacy at USA
Computing
Continuing Education and Special Programs
Education
Engineering
Mitchell College of Business
Medicine
Nursing
Pat Capps Covey College of Allied Health Professions

HISTORICAL FINANCIALS

Company Type: Private

Income Statement

FYE: September 30

	REVENUE ($ mil.)	NET INCOME ($ mil.)	NET PROFIT MARGIN	EMPLOYEES
09/17	662	47	7.2%	5,403
09/16	624	25	4.1%	—
09/15	556	9	1.7%	—
09/14	503	6	1.3%	—
Annual Growth	9.6%	93.9%	—	—

2017 Year-End Financials

Return on assets: 9.5%
Return on equity: 7.2%
Current ratio: 1.00
Cash ($ mil.): 102

UNIVERSITY OF SOUTH CAROLINA

The Fighting Gamecocks lead the way at the University of South Carolina (USC). The university which comprises 14 colleges and schools offers more than 350 courses of study. Areas of study concentrate on medicine law business education science and math liberal arts and other fields. Nearly 2200 full-time faculty members teach a student body of some 46250 across eight campuses from South Carolina's Aiken to Union. USC's main campus is located on the site of its 1801 founding in the state's capital city of Columbia. Tuition runs about $10500 a year for residents and $27500 for out-of-state students. USC has an endowment of some $514 million.

Operations

USC offers more than 320 degree programs throughout its colleges and schools.

Geographic Reach

Outside Columbia University of South Carolina is supported by four-year campuses in Aiken Beaufort Spartanburg and Greenville as well as two-year campuses in Lancaster Sumter Allendale Walterboro and Union.

Financial Performance

USC's proposed budget for FY2012-13 includes unrestricted funds of $934.5 million and restricted funds of $428.4 million.

Strategy

In fiscal year 2012 the university's faculty generated $238 million in funding earmarked for research outreach and training programs. To this end USC is extending its reach toward the Congaree River in an effort to support research initiatives in nanotechnology health sciences the environment and information technologies.

EXECUTIVES

Pres, Harris Pastides
Vice President, Edward Walton
MBR, Allison Sweeney
Trustee, Eugene P Warr Jr
Trustee, Mack I Whittle Jr
Trustee, Mark W Buyck Jr
Trustee, Othniel H Wienges Jr
Dean, School of Law, Walter F Pratt Jr
Evp Academic Affairs, Interim, William T Moore
Trustee, William W Jones Jr
Assistant Professor, Alvaro C Cazurra
Auditors: ELLIOT DAVIS LLC COLUMBIA S

LOCATIONS

HQ: UNIVERSITY OF SOUTH CAROLINA
1600 HAMPTON ST 414, COLUMBIA, SC 292083403
Phone: 803 777-2001
Web: WWW.MAILBOX.SC.EDU

PRODUCTS/OPERATIONS

Selected Colleges

Arnold School of Public Health
College of Arts and Sciences
College of Education
College of Engineering & Computing
College of Hospitality Retail & Sport Management
College of Mass Communications & Information Studies
College of Nursing
College of Pharmacy
College of Social Work
Moore School of Business
School of Law
School of Medicine
School of Music
South Carolina Honors College
The Graduate School

HISTORICAL FINANCIALS

Company Type: Private

Income Statement

FYE: June 30

	REVENUE ($ mil.)	NET INCOME ($ mil.)	NET PROFIT MARGIN	EMPLOYEES
06/17	1,008	23	2.3%	5,100
06/13	801	10	1.3%	—
06/07	672	(221)	—	—
06/06	0	0	—	—
Annual Growth	—	—	—	—

2017 Year-End Financials

Return on assets: 1.7%
Return on equity: 2.3%
Current ratio: 3.40
Cash ($ mil.): 472

UNIVERSITY OF SOUTHERN CALIFORNIA

A Trojan horse filled with students is more than welcome at the University of Southern California (USC). Founded in 1880 the private university (with a Trojan mascot) grew up with the city of Los Angeles and is now one of the largest private employers in the city. California's oldest research university USC is recognized for distinguished programs in fields including business engineering film law medicine public administration science and theater. The university has two campuses in Los Angeles and additional centers and programs elsewhere in California Washington DC and overseas. USC has a total of some 41000 undergraduate and graduate students and almost 3790 full-time faculty members.

Operations

USC's programs are divided into about 20 undergraduate academic schools and colleges plus the USC Graduate School. More than half of its students are enrolled in graduate programs.

The Health Science Center includes a number of academic and medical care institutions including the USC School of Pharmacy the Herman Ostrow School of Dentistry and the USC University Hospital. Its Keck School of Medicine trains physicians at the University Hospital as well as through partnerships with area hospital operators including the Childrens Hospital Los Angeles and the Los An-

geles County Department of Health Services. In addition the medical school's faculty and students conduct medical disease research.

As a leading US private research university USC conducts $600 million in research each year at its various institutions in areas including national security cultural affairs technology and scientific innovation. The medical school receives more than $150 million in research grants from the federal government each year.

Geographic Reach

USC's primary 230-acre University Park campus in Los Angeles is home to most of the university's undergraduate programs and professional schools as well as its graduate program. It also includes the university's main admissions and administration offices. The university's 80-acre Health Sciences Campus is also located in Los Angeles.

USC has one of the largest international student populations among US universities. In addition to educating students from China India and other countries at its US campuses USC pursues international educational medical and research collaborations (including study abroad programs) with institutions in developing nations such as Ethiopia Kenya Rwanda and Uganda.

Financial Performance

USC has an endowment of $4.6 billion. Tuition and fees run at around $48400 per student per year.

USC's revenues increased from $3.9 billion in fiscal 2013 to $4.8 billion in fiscal 2014 thanks to a growth in investments higher gifts and pledges and the expansion of its healthcare services. Net income followed suit growing from $66.3 million in fiscal 2013 to $66.7 million in fiscal 2014 on higher revenues.

Strategy

In its educational programs USC strives to combine liberal arts and professional learning programs as well as athletics and extracurricular activities to provide a well-rounded student experience. It is also expanding its online learning programs to enhance continuing education programs. The university places great focus on keeping its research programs among the top-ranked programs in the US.

The university also invests in campus improvement and expansion projects. Broadening its health services in 2013 USC acquired the 158-bed Verdigo Hills Hospital for $9 million. Boosting its assets that year it also acquired the Pacific Asia Museum. Both purchases boosted the university's net assets by a total of $100 million.

HISTORY

Los Angeles was still a frontier town when a diverse group of local citizens led by Judge Robert Maclay Widney established the University of Southern California (USC) in 1880 (early rules for students included a prohibition against carrying guns to class). But Los Angeles grew quickly and USC grew with it. By 1910 the university had most of its major programs in place including law and medical schools. During the 1920s USC established the nation's first school of international relations (1924) and offered the first degree in cinema (1929).

The end of WWII and the GI Bill brought a major increase in enrollment forcing the university to expand. Some 50 new buildings were added in the 1950s and 1960s and another 37 were begun or completed in the 1970s. The university started increasing its fund-raising efforts in the 1980s. Steven Sample became president in 1991 and secured hundreds of millions in donations over the course of the decade including a $110 million grant in 1999 from the W.M. Keck Foundation for

USC's School of Medicine which was renamed Keck School of Medicine.

USC was named 1999 college of the year by Time magazine and the Princeton Review. In 2001 USC opened the Robert Zemeckis Center for Digital Arts the first US digital filmmaking school and in 2005 the university established a federal relations office in Washington DC.

In 2007 USC opened its Levan Institute for Humanities and Ethics and the Edward R. Roybal Institute for Applied Gerontology.

The university has also been conducting campus improvement projects. In 2010 USC completed construction of a new welcome center called the Ronald Tudor Campus Center and in 2011 it started construction of the new John McKay Athletics Center. In 2012 USC began work on a new journalism and communication building and a new student health center.

Notable alumni of USC include Marion Morrison (also known as John Wayne) who played tackle on the school's football team and the first man on the moon Neil Armstrong. Directors George Lucas and Robert Zemeckis are both USC film school graduates.

EXECUTIVES

Dean Annenberg School For Communication And Journalism, Ernest J. Wilson
Cfo, James M. Staten
President, Chrysostomos L. (Max) Nikias, age 65
Dean Thornton School Of Music, Robert A. Cutietta
Dean School Of Cinematic Arts, Elizabeth M. Daley
Dean School Of Social Work, Marilyn L. Flynn
Dean Rossier School Of Education, Karen Symms Gallagher
Dean Sol Price School Of Public Policy, Jack H. Knott
Dean Viterbi School Of Engineering, Yannis C. Yortsos
Chief Investment Officer, Lisa Mazzocco
Dean School Of Architecture, Qingyun Ma
Dean Marshall School Of Business, James G. Ellis, age 71
Dean Keck School Of Medicine, Carmen A. Puliafito
Dean University Libraries, Catherine Quinlan
Dean Dornsife College Of Letters Arts And Sciences, Steve A. Kay
Svp And Ceo Keck Medicine Of Usc, Thomas E. Jackiewicz
Dean Davis School Of Gerontology, Pinchas Cohen
Dean Leventhal School Of Accounting, William W. Holder
Dean Roski School Of Fine Arts, Erica Muhl
Dean Ostrow School Of Dentistry, Avishai Sadan
Provost And Svp Academic Affairs, Michael Quick
Interim Vice Provost Information Technology Services And Cio, Douglas Shook
Dean Usc Gould School Of Law, Andrew T. Guzman
Interim Dean Usc School Of Dramatic Arts, David Bridel
Interim Dean Usc School Of Pharmacy, Glen L. Stimmel
Senior Advisor To The Vice President For Student Affairs, Roopali Malhotra
Assistant Vice President Business Services Procure, Lila Mauro
Executive Vice President Human Resources And Administration, George Rose
Chairman, John Mork
Vice Chairman, Jeffrey Miller
Auditors: PRICEWATERHOUSECOOPERS LLP L

LOCATIONS

HQ: UNIVERSITY OF SOUTHERN CALIFORNIA
3720 S FLOWER ST FL 3, LOS ANGELES, CA 900894304
Phone: 213 740-7762
Web: WWW.USC.EDU

PRODUCTS/OPERATIONS

2012 Revenues

	$ mil.	% of total
Net student tuition & fees	977	29
Health care services	882	27
Gifts & pledges	527	16
Government contracts & grants	323	10
Auxiliary enterprises	254	8
Recovery of indirect costs	132	4
Sales & service	28	1
Endowment investment & other income	68	2
Other revenues	101	3
Adjustments	(62.8)	-
Total	**3,233**	**100**

Selected Schools

Annenberg School for Communication and Journalism
Dana and David Dornsife College of Letters Arts and Sciences
Davis School of Gerontology
Division of Biokinesiology and Physical Therapy
Division of Occupational Science and Occupational Therapy
Glorya Kaufman School of Dance
Gould School of Law
Graduate School
Herman Ostrow School of Dentistry
Keck School of Medicine
Leventhal School of Accounting
Marshall School of Business
Roski School of Fine Arts
Rossier School of Education
School of Architecture
School of Cinematic Arts
School of Dramatic Arts
School of Pharmacy
School of Social Work
Sol Price School of Public Policy
Thornton School of Music
Viterbi School of Engineering

HISTORICAL FINANCIALS

Company Type: Private

Income Statement				FYE: June 30
	REVENUE ($ mil.)	NET INCOME ($ mil.)	NET PROFIT MARGIN	EMPLOYEES
06/18	4,936	489	9.9%	22,700
06/13	3,861	587	15.2%	—
06/12	3,233	68	2.1%	—
Annual Growth	7.3%	38.8%	—	—

2018 Year-End Financials

Return on assets: 5.5%
Return on equity: 9.9%
Current ratio: —
Cash ($ mil.): 818

UNIVERSITY OF TEXAS AT AUSTIN

They say everything's bigger in Texas and The University of Texas at Austin (UT Austin) takes them at their word. With about 51000 students it is the flagship institution of the UT System's nine universities and six health institutions. UT Austin consistently ranks on the list of the country's largest student bodies and offers more than 100 undergraduate and 170 graduate degree programs. In addition to its 350-acre downtown Austin academic campus UT Austin maintains extensive research locations including the J.J. Pickle Research campus (also in Austin) the McDonald Observatory in West Texas and the Marine Science Institute on the Texas coast. The university was founded in 1883.

EXECUTIVES

President, William C. (Bill) Powers, age 72
Cio, Brad Englert
Evp And Provost, Gregory L. Fenves
Assoc. Vice President For Research, Jtinsley Oden
Assistant Vice President For Procurement Business Contracts Payment Services, Felix Alvarez
Vice President Executive Assistant Office Of The, Jeff Becker

LOCATIONS

HQ: UNIVERSITY OF TEXAS AT AUSTIN
110 INNER CAMPUS DR G3400, AUSTIN, TX 787123400
Phone: 512 471-3434
Web: WWW.UTEXAS.EDU

HISTORICAL FINANCIALS

Company Type: Private

Income Statement				FYE: August 31
	REVENUE ($ mil.)	NET INCOME ($ mil.)	NET PROFIT MARGIN	EMPLOYEES
08/17	1,669	751	45.0%	21,513
08/12	1,491	132	8.9%	—
08/08	5	2	38.1%	—
08/05	0	0	—	—
Annual Growth	—	—	—	—

2017 Year-End Financials

Return on assets: 7.3%
Return on equity: 45.0%
Current ratio: 0.50
Cash ($ mil.): 303

UNIVERSITY OF TEXAS SYSTEM

EXECUTIVES

Executive Vice Chancellor Business Affairs, Scott C. Kelley
Executive Vice Chancellor Academic Affairs, Pedro Reyes
President Ut Health Science Center At San Antonio, Francisco G. Cigarroa
Executive Vice Chancellor Health Affairs, Raymond S. Greenberg
Vice Chancellor Strategic Initiatives, Stephanie Bond Huie
Vice Chairman, R. Steven (Steve) Hicks, age 68
Chairman, Paul L. Foster, age 60
Vice Chairman, Wm. Eugene (Gene) Powell
Auditors: DELOITTE & TOUCHE LLP AUSTIN

LOCATIONS

HQ: UNIVERSITY OF TEXAS SYSTEM
210 W 7TH ST, AUSTIN, TX 787013099
Phone: 512 499-4587
Web: WWW.UTSYSTEM.EDU

PRODUCTS/OPERATIONS

Selected Institutions

Academic Institutions
The University of Texas at Arlington (established 1895)
The University of Texas-Pan American (Edinburg; 1927)
The University of Texas of the Permian Basin (Odessa; 1969)
Health Institutions
The University of Texas Health Science Center at Houston (established 1972)

The University of Texas M.D. Anderson Cancer Center (Houston 1941)

HISTORICAL FINANCIALS
Company Type: Private

Income Statement				FYE: August 31
	REVENUE ($ mil.)	NET INCOME ($ mil.)	NET PROFIT MARGIN	EMPLOYEES
08/16	13,282	1,589	12.0%	81,260
08/09	8,564	(3,592)	—	—
08/08	46	1	2.3%	—
Annual Growth	102.7%	148.6%	—	—

2016 Year-End Financials
Return on assets: 7.9% Cash ($ mil.): 2,545
Return on equity: 12.0%
Current ratio: 0.70

UNIVERSITY OF THE PACIFIC

Situated next to the largest body of water on earth the University of the Pacific holds a sizable body of knowledge. The school offers more than 80 undergraduate majors and about 20 graduate programs in such fields as art language biology business computer science engineering history and pharmacy. It offers undergraduate graduate and professional degree programs in nine colleges and enrolls about 7000 students at its main campus in Stockton California the McGeorge School of Law in Sacramento and the Arthur A. Dugoni School of Dentistry in San Francisco. California's first chartered institution of higher education University of the Pacific was founded in 1851.

Operations
University of the Pacific has about 500 full-time faculty members and a student-to-teacher ratio of 13:1. Tuition at the university runs at about $38000 per year.

Geographic Reach
More than 85% of University of the Pacific's students are California residents. The remainder of the university's student base comes from 35 other US states as well as 25 international countries.

Financial Performance
University of the Pacific reported a 5% revenue rise to $331 million in 2012 due to increased tuition as well as from private grants gifts and bequests. Net income decreased by 53% to $21 million however due to increased expenses and lower investment returns.

Endowment funds contributed about $8 million of University of the Pacific's operating budget in fiscal 2012. The school has a total endowment of some $200 million.

Strategy
University of the Pacific is expanding its academic programs in targeted fields such as health-related education and training programs. It also is working to increase technology resources and implement related learning models as new high-tech generations join its ranks.

Other initiatives include recruiting teachers with scholarly experience attracting diverse and ambitious students and increasing job preparedness programs for students. University of the Pacific is also working to increase enrollment and fundraising efforts to generate new resources that will support its growth plans.

EXECUTIVES
Apha Asp Vice President Of Professional Affairs, Barrett Smith
Auditors: ERNST & YOUNG US LLP SAN DIEG

LOCATIONS
HQ: UNIVERSITY OF THE PACIFIC
  3601 PACIFIC AVE, STOCKTON, CA 952110197
Phone: 209 946-2401
Web: WWW.PACIFIC.EDU

PRODUCTS/OPERATIONS

2015 Sales
	% of total
Net tuition and fees	68
Private grants gifts and bequests	10
Sales and services of auxiliary enterprises	9
Clinic fees	4
Government grants and contracts	3
Investment return distributed	3
Other	3
Total	100

Selected Programs
Chemistry
Chemistry-Biology
Communication
Computer Science
Dental Hygiene
Economics
English
Environmental Studies
Film Studies
French
Geological and Enviromental Sciences
Graphic Design
Pre-Pharmacy
Pre-Physical Therapy
Psychology
Religious Studies

Selected Schools and Colleges
Arthur A. Dugoni School of Dentistry
College of the Pacific (Arts and Sciences)
Conservatory of Music
Eberhardt School of Business
Gladys L. Benerd School of Education
McGeorge School of Law
School of Engineering and Computer Science
School of International Studies
Thomas J. Long School of Pharmacy and Health Sciences

HISTORICAL FINANCIALS
Company Type: Private

Income Statement				FYE: June 30
	REVENUE ($ mil.)	NET INCOME ($ mil.)	NET PROFIT MARGIN	EMPLOYEES
06/15	418	41	10.0%	1,500
06/13	447	147	32.9%	—
06/12	330	20	6.3%	—
06/11	317	43	13.8%	—
Annual Growth	7.2%	(1.2%)	—	—

2015 Year-End Financials
Return on assets: 5.7% Cash ($ mil.): 6
Return on equity: 10.0%
Current ratio: 0.10

UNIVERSITY OF VERMONT & STATE AGRICULTURAL COLLEGE

The University of Vermont (UVM) boasts scenic views and comprehensive secondary education. the university offers more than 100 majors through its seven undergraduate colleges as well 46 master's programs and 21 doctoral programs at its Graduate College and College of Medicine. UVM has an enrollment of more than 12820 students including undergraduate graduate medical and continuing education program participants. The university also conducts research programs in areas including translational science cancer care and transportation. UVM a public land grant university has more than 1360 faculty members.

Operations
UVM comes from Universitas Veridis Montis which is Latin for "University of the Green Mountains." Its campus consists of more than a dozen dining facilities — including a pair of convenience stores and Cyber Cafe — and nearly 40 residence halls for on-campus students. Off-campus UVM offers a research park four research farms nine natural areas (including the summit of Mount Mansfield) and the Rubenstein Ecosystem Science Laboratory in the Leahy ECHO Center for Lake Champlain.

Geographic Reach
The UVM campus which spans 460 acres in Burlington Vermont enrolls students from nearly all US states. The university also provides education to some 350 international students from more than 50 countries.

Financial Performance
As a public land grant university UVM draws a portion of its budget from the state of Vermont. Other sources of income include student tuition and fees charitable gifts and returns on investment funds. The university's office of technology commercialization brings in some income by licensing out research discoveries to spinoff entities.

Strategy
To attract and retain a quality student population UVM regularly conducts construction and renovation efforts on its campus facilities in areas ranging from academics and recreation to research and athletics.

Furthermore UVM seeks to provide more flexible education options for students including expanding its onlinep rograms.

Company Background
UVM is the fifth oldest university in the New England area after Harvard Yale Dartmouth and Brown. It's the first institution of higher education to declare public support for the freedom of religion and the first university to admit women and African-Americans into Phi Beta Kappa honor society.

Notable alumni include education philosopher John Dewey and film producer Jon Kilik.

Ira Allen founded the university in 1791 the same year that Vermont became the 14th state. Located in between the Adirondack and Green mountain ranges UVM's motto is the Latin phrase Universitas Viridis Montis or University of the Green Mountains.

EXECUTIVES
Vice President, Lee Stewart
Senior Vice President, David Rosowsky

Interim Vice President Of Development And
  Director Of Principal Gifts, Kathleen Kelleher
Vice President Of Operations, Gary Derr
Vice President For Executive Operations, Bethany
  Wolfe
Provost And Senior Vice President, John Hughes
Vice President, Willi Coleman
Vice President Enrollment Management,
  Christopher Lucier
Medical Director, Donald Weaver
Vice President Alumni Relations, Alan Ryea
Sga Vice President, Tyler Davis
Vice President Preconstruction Services, John
  Stetson
Department Chair (interim), Kyle Ikeda
Board Member, Jeanne Goldhaber
Board Member, Joshua Farley
Secretary, Richard Wolfson
Secretary Cardiovascular Group, Pam Burton
Auditors: KPMG LLP COLCHESTER VERMONT

LOCATIONS

HQ: UNIVERSITY OF VERMONT & STATE
  AGRICULTURAL COLLEGE
  85 S PROSPECT ST WTRMN, BURLINGTON, VT
  054050001
Phone: 802 656-3131
Web: WWW.UVM.EDU

PRODUCTS/OPERATIONS

Selected Colleges and Schools
College of Agriculture and Life Sciences
College of Arts and Sciences
College of Education and Social Services
College of Engineering and Mathematical Sciences
College of Medicine
College of Nursing and Health Sciences
Continuing Education
Graduate College
Honors College
Rubenstein School of Environment and Natural
  Resources
School of Business Administration

HISTORICAL FINANCIALS
Company Type: Private

Income Statement				FYE: June 30
	REVENUE ($ mil.)	NET INCOME ($ mil.)	NET PROFIT MARGIN	EMPLOYEES
06/17	613	34	5.6%	3,710
06/14	545	27	5.1%	—
06/13	557	19	3.4%	—
06/12	525	(30)	—	—
Annual Growth	3.1%	—	—	—

2017 Year-End Financials
Return on assets: 12.0%   Cash ($ mil.): 151
Return on equity: 5.6%
Current ratio: 1.20

UNIVERSITY OF VIRGINIA INVESTMENT

EXECUTIVES

Ceo, Lawrence E Kochard
Vice-President, Kristina Alimard
Auditors: KPMG LLP MCLEAN VA

LOCATIONS

HQ: UNIVERSITY OF VIRGINIA INVESTMENT
  560 RAY C HUNT DR, CHARLOTTESVILLE, VA
  229032981
Phone: 434 924-4245
Web: WWW.VIRGINIA.EDU

HISTORICAL FINANCIALS
Company Type: Private

Income Statement				FYE: June 30
	REVENUE ($ mil.)	NET INCOME ($ mil.)	NET PROFIT MARGIN	EMPLOYEES
06/17	389	370	95.0%	6
06/10	173	(422)	—	—
Annual Growth	12.3%	—	—	—

2017 Year-End Financials
Return on assets: 2.7%   Cash ($ mil.): 38
Return on equity: 95.0%
Current ratio: 4.00

UNIVERSITY OF WASHINGTON INC

The University of Washington (UW) is Husky
indeed with an annual enrollment of more than
54000 students. Founded in 1861 as the Territorial University of Washington UW (pronounced
"U-dub" by those on campus) has smaller branches
in Tacoma and Bothell in addition to its main campus in downtown Seattle. The university whose
mascot is a Husky offers more than 600 undergraduate graduate and professional degree programs through 16 colleges and schools. It also operates four hospitals: University of Washington
Medical Center Harborview Medical Center Northwest Hospital and Valley Medical Center.

Operations
With more than 300 programs University of
Washington confers some 12000 bachelor's mas-
ter's doctoral and professional degrees each year.
Its graduates include about 135 Fulbright and 35
Rhodes scholars. The school's top five bachelor
degree fields include biology psychology political
science economics and communications.

Research is a cornerstone of the university
which has nearly 300 specialized research centers.
The school's annual sponsored grant and contract
research funding exceeds $1.6 billion. Some 300
new companies have emerged based on UW research advances.

Financial Performance
In fiscal 2017 (ended June) operating revenue
for University of Washington totaled $5.8 billion.
Patient service revenues account for the largest
amount of funds received (38%) followed by federal grants and contracts (about 21%).

Operating expenses totaled $5.7 billion that year.
Salaries accounted for nearly half of those expenses.

EXECUTIVES

Dean School Of Medicine, Paul G. Ramsey
Svp Finance And Facilities, V'Ella Warren
Chancellor Bothell Campus, Bjong Wolf Yeigh
Dean School Of Law, Kellye Testy
Dean Libraries, Lizabeth A. (Betsy) Wilson
Interim Chancellor Tacoma Campus, Kenyon S.
  Chan
Dean School Of Public Health, Howard Frumkin

President, Ana Mari Cauce
Dean Undergraduate Academic Affairs, Ed Taylor
Vp Information Technology And Cio, Kelli Trosvig
Dean College Of Arts And Sciences, Robert Stacey
Interim Dean College Of Built Environments,
  John Schaufelberger
Dean School Of Dentistry, Joel H. Berg
Dean College Of Education, Tom Stritikus
Dean College Of Engineering, Michael B. Bragg
Dean College Of The Environment, Lisa Graumlich
Dean Evans School Of Public Affairs, Sandra
  Archibald
Dean Foster School Of Business, James Jiambalvo
Dean Graduate School, Dave Eaton
Dean Information School, Harry Bruce
Dean School Of Nursing, Azita Emami
Dean School Of Pharmacy, Thomas Baillie
Dean School Of Social Work, Edwina (Eddie)
  Uehara
Associate Vice President Financial Management,
  Susan Camber
Associate Vice President For Alumni Relations
  Uni, Paul Rucker
Medical Director, Jean Haulman
Senior Vice President Ecommerce Mobile D, Brian
  Jones
Associate Vice President, Lincoln Johnson
Vice President Of Marketing, Kristin Elko
Assistant Vice President For Student Life And,
  Pam Schreiber
Director Of Government Relations, Ian Goodhew
Medical Director, Rob Sweet
Associate Vice President College Access, Patricia
  Loera
Vice President External Affairs, Brian Taubeneck
Vice Chairman, William S. (Bill) Ayer
Chairman, Orin C. Smith
Board Of Directors Quarterly Editor: Vacant
  Librarian, Mary Schroeder
Auditors: KPMG LLP SEATTLE WASHINGTON

LOCATIONS

HQ: UNIVERSITY OF WASHINGTON INC
  4311 11TH AVE NE STE 600, SEATTLE, WA
  981056369
Phone: 206 543-2100
Web: WWW.WASHINGTON.EDU

PRODUCTS/OPERATIONS

Selected Colleges and Schools
College of Arts and Sciences
College of Built Environments
College of Education
College of Engineering
College of the Environment
Evans School of Public Affairs
The Graduate School
Information School
Michael G. Foster School of Business
School of Dentistry
School of Law
School of Medicine
School of Nursing
School of Pharmacy
School of Public Health
School of Social Work

HISTORICAL FINANCIALS
Company Type: Private

Income Statement				FYE: June 30
	REVENUE ($ mil.)	NET INCOME ($ mil.)	NET PROFIT MARGIN	EMPLOYEES
06/17	4,893	363	7.4%	27,228
06/16	5	(0)	—	—
06/15	4	0	5.6%	—
06/12	4,258	5	0.1%	—
Annual Growth	2.8%	127.9%	—	—

2017 Year-End Financials

Return on assets: 17.0%   Cash ($ mil.): 64
Return on equity: 7.4%
Current ratio: 0.60

UNIVERSITY OF WISCONSIN MEDICAL FOUNDATION, INC.

UW Medical Foundation provides administrative services to faculty physicians at the University of Wisconsin School of Medicine and Public Health. The foundation a not-for-profit entity is a physician practice organization that works in cooperation with the UW Hospital and Clinics and other medical offices and clinics throughout the Badger State. The foundation coordinates clinical sites and provides technical and professional staffing services as well as administrative support for legal marketing information technology and logistics functions.

Operations

UW Medical Foundation provides support services for more than 1200 member doctors located at about 45 physician practices and 60 clinical outreach locations. It also helps clinical practices with quality initiatives. The foundation provides some $200 million in charity care each year. Its community activities include sponsoring health outreach events and donating safety products to low-income families.

Physicians in the organization provide services across a number of medical specialties including oncology gastroenterology women's health kidney care orthopedics respiratory therapy and urology.

Company Background

The organization has expanded over time: UW Medical Foundation merged with Physicians Plus Medical Group in 1998 and with the University Community Clinics in 2003.

EXECUTIVES

Ceo, Alan Kaplan
Chb, Robert Golden
Coo, Robert Flannery
Sam Poc, Sarah Meyer
Information Specialist, Debra Hopke
Information Specialist, Jamie Buchanan
Hipaa Privacy Officer, Amanda Reese
Manager, Kari Pulfer
Auditors: MCGLADREY LLP PALOS HILLS IL

LOCATIONS

HQ: UNIVERSITY OF WISCONSIN MEDICAL
FOUNDATION, INC.
7974 UW HEALTH CT, MIDDLETON, WI 535625531
Phone: 608 821-4223
Web: WWW.UWMF.WISC.EDU

COMPETITORS

Ascension Health	Marian Health System
Beaver Dam Community	Meriter Health
Hospitals	Services
Beloit Health System	ProHealth Care
Catholic Health	SSM Health Care
Initiatives	Stoughton Hospital
Dean Health Systems	ThedaCare Inc.
Inc.	Tomah Memorial
Hospital Sisters	Hospital
Health System	

UNIVERSITY SYSTEM OF NEW HAMPSHIRE

The University of New Hampshire (UNH) is a liberal arts college that serves about 12600 undergraduate and more than 2200 graduate students. The institution offers more than 100 majors and academic programs of study at nine colleges and schools. The student-faculty ratio is 20:1. UNH is the flagship institution of the University System of New Hampshire. In 2007 the university graduated its first international class in Seoul under a program run by its Whittemore School of Business and Economics. Founded in 1866 as the New Hampshire College of Agriculture and the Mechanic Arts UNH is a designated land-grant sea-grant and space-grant chartered school.

Operations

UNH's most popular bachelor's programs include business administration undeclared liberal arts psychology English and communication followed by mechanical engineering biology biomedical science civil engineering and political science.

The University System of New Hampshire includes Keene State College Plymouth State University and Granite State College in addition to UNH.

Geographic Reach

In addition to its main campus in Durham UNH has a campus in Manchester and its School of Law is in Concord. Almost 60% of the school's student body comes from within state with a concentration of others coming from the northeastern region of the US. UNH is developing new academic programs expanding its online courses and opportunities and creating new international initiatives for faculty and students in Costa Rica Chile Ghana India South Korea and China.

Strategy

UNH is engaged in a strategic plan to support its growth through 2020. Its plan for creating a learning-centered environment includes such initiatives as establishing a New Venture Fund to promote collaborative research and teaching opportunities; developing new programs to support independent research and scholarship; commercializing UNH's intellectual capital; and promoting diversity and inclusiveness as well as international opportunities. It also includes making major capital investments in technology to build a high-capacity cyber-infrastructure and a learning portal to promote interdisciplinary collaboration; renovating restoring and adding on to facilities; and constructing a new center for the arts.

HISTORICAL FINANCIALS

Company Type: Private

Income Statement

FYE: June 30

	REVENUE ($ mil.)	NET INCOME ($ mil.)	NET PROFIT MARGIN	EMPLOYEES
06/18	784	40	5.2%	3,200
06/15	766	26	3.4%	—
06/14	724	33	4.6%	—
06/13	0	22	—	—
Annual Growth	—	12.8%	—	—

2018 Year-End Financials

Return on assets: 1.3%   Cash ($ mil.): 124
Return on equity: 5.2%
Current ratio: 1.10

EXECUTIVES

Chancellor, Todd Leach
President, Melinda Treadwell
Vice Chancellor, Catherine Provelcher
General Counsel, Ron Rodgers
President, James W Dean Jr
Assistant Professor, Lin Guo
Coordinator, Steve Wright
Assistant Professor, Weiwei MO
Assistant To President, Cheri O'Neil
Coordinator, Cynthia Nizzari-Mcclain
Manager, Scott Kimball
Auditors: KPMG LLP BOSTON MA

LOCATIONS

HQ: UNIVERSITY SYSTEM OF NEW HAMPSHIRE
5 CHENELL DR STE 301, CONCORD, NH 033018522
Phone: 603 862-1800
Web: WWW.KEENE.EDU

PRODUCTS/OPERATIONS

Selected Colleges and Schools

College of Engineering and Physical Sciences
College of Health and Human Services
College of Liberal Arts
College of Life Sciences and Agriculture
The Graduate School
Thompson School of Applied Science
University of New Hampshire at Manchester
University of New Hampshire School of Law
Whittemore School of Business and Economics
Special Academic Opportunities
Graduate Research Conference
Hamel Center for Undergraduate Reasearch
Honors program
International research opportunities program
Student internships
Study abroad
Undergraduate research opportunities program

HISTORICAL FINANCIALS

Company Type: Private

Income Statement

FYE: June 30

	REVENUE ($ mil.)	NET INCOME ($ mil.)	NET PROFIT MARGIN	EMPLOYEES
06/16	692	(9)	—	16,000
06/15	680	32	4.7%	—
06/14	0	128	—	—
06/13	800	111	14.0%	—
Annual Growth	(4.7%)	—	—	—

2016 Year-End Financials

Return on assets: 7.7%   Cash ($ mil.): 69
Return on equity: (-1.3%)
Current ratio: 0.60

UPMC ALTOONA

UPMC Altoona (formerly Altoona Regional Health System) moves patients upstream towards better health. Operating in Altoona and surrounding areas in central Pennsylvania the health system's facilities include Altoona Hospital an acute care center with 380 licensed beds that provides specialized care in areas including cardiovascular ailments cancer behavioral health and neurology as well as general emergency trauma birthing and surgery services. UPMC Altoona also offers a variety of outpatient care facilities and programs including home health care a primary care physicians' group and laboratory services. The not-for-profit system merged with Pennsylvania hospital operator University of Pittsburgh Medical Center (UPMC) in 2013.

Change in Company Type

In mid-2013 Altoona Regional Health System merged with UMPC to become UPMC Altoona. A new board was assigned to govern the system comprising two-thirds former Altoona Regional board members and one-third UPMC-appointed members. UPMC plans to invest some $250 million over 10 years to improve facilities and services so that UPMC Altoona can provide more specialized and advanced treatments.

Operations

The system maintains a level II adult trauma center to serve the most severely injured.

Each year UPMC Altoona has some 65000 emergency department visits and 18000 hospital admissions and performs some 5000 inpatient and 15000 outpatient surgeries.

Geographic Reach

The system provides services to residents of about 20 counties in central Pennsylvania.

Strategy

The company is working on expansions and additions to its existing facilities in order to provide its service area with more specialized treatments. In 2014 UPMC Altoona opened its eighth Center for Liver Diseases clinic at the outpatient Station Medical Center location. The following year it established the UPMC Altoona Breast Health Center in the same location; the center offers comprehensive breast health services.

Company Background

In 2004 Altoona Hospital's parent Central Pennsylvania Health Services Corporation and Bon Secours-Holy Family Hospital's parent Bon Secours Health System merged the two campuses and affiliated companies to form Altoona Regional Health System. The system merged with UPMC in 2013.

EXECUTIVES

Pres-Ceo, Jerry Murray
Sr Vice President, David L Cowger
Sr Vice President, Chris Ricken
Cfo, Charles R Zorger
Sr Vice President, Gary R Naugle
Lsw, Lori Craine

LOCATIONS

HQ: UPMC ALTOONA
620 HOWARD AVE, ALTOONA, PA 166014804
Phone: 814 889-2011
Web: WWW.ALTOONAREGIONAL.ORG

PRODUCTS/OPERATIONS

Selected Services
Behavioral Health
Birth & Growth
Cancer Care
Cardiac Care
Center for Weight Loss and Bariatric Surgery
Central Pennsylvania Cardiovascular Associates
Emergency Medicine and Trauma
HealthForce (Occupational Medicine)
Imaging Services
Institute for Sleep Medicine
Neurosurgery
Orthopedics
Physical Medicine and Rehabilitation
Primary Stroke Center
Surgical Services
Wound Care and Ostomy Program

COMPETITORS

Clearfield Area Health Services	J. C. Blair Memorial Hospital
Conemaugh Health System	Lancaster General PinnacleHealth System
Hanover Healthcare	WellSpan Health
Hershey Medical Center	

HISTORICAL FINANCIALS
Company Type: Private

Income Statement   FYE: June 30

	REVENUE ($ mil.)	NET INCOME ($ mil.)	NET PROFIT MARGIN	EMPLOYEES
06/15	394	25	6.5%	2,494
06/14	393	15	3.8%	—
Annual Growth	0.2%	70.1%		

2015 Year-End Financials
Return on assets: 5.4%   Cash ($ mil.): —
Return on equity: 6.5%
Current ratio: 2.30

UPMC HAMOT

EXECUTIVES

Pres-Ceo, John T Malone
Sr V Pres-Cfo, Stephen M Danch
Exec V Pres-Coo, V James Fiorenzo
Physician Asst, William Van Duzer
Pres Medical Staff, T Michael Simonian
Sr V Pres Outpatient, Debbie A Burbules
Sr V Pres Corp Svcs-Chief Comp, Donald K Inderlied
Pharmacy Svcs, Thomas J Thompson
Surgical Svcs, Emmett Verdecchia
Clinical Pharmacist, Mary Lourdes Brundige
Senior Project Coordinator, James Lazan

LOCATIONS

HQ: UPMC HAMOT
201 STATE ST, ERIE, PA 165500001
Phone: 814 877-6000
Web:
WWW.UPMC.COM/LOCATIONS/HOSPITALS/HAMOT

HISTORICAL FINANCIALS
Company Type: Private

Income Statement   FYE: June 30

	REVENUE ($ mil.)	NET INCOME ($ mil.)	NET PROFIT MARGIN	EMPLOYEES
06/15*	360	39	10.9%	3,159
12/14	0	(0)	—	—
06/09	302	0	—	—
Annual Growth	2.9%	—	—	—

*Fiscal year change

2015 Year-End Financials
Return on assets: 1.6%   Cash ($ mil.): —
Return on equity: 10.9%
Current ratio: 3.90

UPMC PASSAVANT

EXECUTIVES

Pres, Teresa G Petrick
Vice-President, Paul Eberhart
Vice-President Human Resources, Gary Mignagna
Director, Lou A Brindle
Maintenance Manager, Mark Salamacha
Vice-President, Paul Wheeler
Treasurer, Franklin Kelley

Manager, Corey D Conklin
Radiology, Lance R Williams
Chief Operating Officer, Donna Jasko
Information Technology Manager, Keith Biehl

LOCATIONS

HQ: UPMC PASSAVANT
9100 BABCOCK BLVD, PITTSBURGH, PA 152375815
Phone: 412 367-6700
Web: WWW.UPMCCANCERCENTER.COM

HISTORICAL FINANCIALS
Company Type: Private

Income Statement   FYE: June 30

	REVENUE ($ mil.)	NET INCOME ($ mil.)	NET PROFIT MARGIN	EMPLOYEES
06/16	339	5	1.6%	1,357
06/15	353	10	3.0%	—
06/09	298	32	10.8%	—
06/06	0	0	—	—
Annual Growth	—	—	—	—

2016 Year-End Financials
Return on assets: 1.1%   Cash ($ mil.): —
Return on equity: 1.6%
Current ratio: 5.60

UPPER CHESAPEAKE MEDICAL CENTER, INC.

EXECUTIVES

Pres, Lyle E Sheldon
Chairman of The Board, Roger E Schneider
Vice Chairman of The Board, Randall T Worthington
Secretary, James Lambdin
Treasurer, H William Acker
Safety Director, Amy Myers
Senior Analyst, Jeanne Scheeler
Director of Pastoral Care, Allen Siegel
Information Specialist, Curt Ohler
Director, James Ingram
Emergency Medicine Specialist, Joseph Cassilly

LOCATIONS

HQ: UPPER CHESAPEAKE MEDICAL CENTER, INC.
500 UPPER CHESAPEAKE DR, BEL AIR, MD 210144324
Phone: 443 643-1000
Web: WWW.UCHS.ORG

HISTORICAL FINANCIALS
Company Type: Private

Income Statement   FYE: June 30

	REVENUE ($ mil.)	NET INCOME ($ mil.)	NET PROFIT MARGIN	EMPLOYEES
06/15*	284	21	7.4%	850
12/14	263	15	5.9%	—
12/13	264	12	4.7%	—
12/12	237	15	6.5%	—
Annual Growth	9.5%	16.6%	—	—

*Fiscal year change

2015 Year-End Financials
Return on assets: 9.4%   Cash ($ mil.): 53
Return on equity: 7.4%
Current ratio: 2.80

UPPER MISSOURI G & T ELECTRIC CO-OPERATIVE INC

EXECUTIVES

President, Roger Sorenson
Ice Pres, Allen Thiessen
Controller, Della Pewonka
General Manager, Claire Vigesaa
Auditors: BRENNER AVERETT & CO PC SIDNE

LOCATIONS

HQ: UPPER MISSOURI G & T ELECTRIC CO-OPERATIVE INC
111 2ND AVE SW, SIDNEY, MT 592704017
Phone: 406 433-4100
Web: WWW.UPPERMO.COM

HISTORICAL FINANCIALS

Company Type: Private

Income Statement   FYE: December 31

	REVENUE ($ mil.)	NET INCOME ($ mil.)	NET PROFIT MARGIN	EMPLOYEES
12/17	531	0	—	2
12/16	486	0	—	—
12/14	319	0	—	—
12/13	253	11	4.7%	—
Annual Growth	20.4%	—	—	—

2017 Year-End Financials
Return on assets: 9.0%   Cash ($ mil.): 1
Return on equity: —
Current ratio: 1.00

USS-POSCO INDUSTRIES, A CALIFORNIA JOINT VENTURE

US and Korean steel manufacturing interests come together in the form of USS-POSCO Industries (UPI) a 50/50 joint venture between United States Steel (US Steel) and POSCO. The company operates a steel plant (formerly owned by US Steel) in Pittsburg Northern California. It manufactures flat-rolled steel sheets in various forms: cold-rolled steel galvanized steel and tinplate. In addition USS-POSCO churns out iron oxide which is used to make hard and soft ferrites. UPI sells its products to more than 150 customers in more than dozen states throughout the western US. End products include office furniture computer cabinets metal studs cans culverts and metal building materials.

Operations

UPI's main product lines include cold rolled sheet galvanized sheet hot rolled pickled and oiled sheet and tin plate. It has the capacity to produce about 1.5 million tons of product per year.

Geographic Reach

The company markets its products primarily in the western US.

Sales and Marketing

UPI ships steel products to more than 150 customers across North America. The company sells its products to a wide range of manufacturers whose end products include automotive parts computer cabinets culverts food packaging metal buildings metal studs and office furniture. About 1/3 of UPI's product line is tinplate for the canning industry.

Strategy

Its Korean co-owner supplied high quality raw materials for use at the plant. In order to stay competitive in the face of cheaper steel imports UPI jettisoned non-core product lines to focus on steel sheet and tin. However strong competition and poor market prices forced the company in 2011 to introduce furloughs at the plant and enforce temporary shutdowns of the facility.

Company Background

The company rebounded from a major fire in 2001. In 2010 UPI invested heavily in remediation measures to clean up soil and groundwater impacted by its plant activities.

US Steel teamed up with POSCO (then Pohang Iron & Steel Company) in 1986 as part of a major reorganization of the aging Pittsburg plant which first opened in 1910.

EXECUTIVES

Vice President Finance And Administration, Alan Gardner
Vice Chair, Chris Beltran
Auditors: KPMG LLP SACRAMENTO CALIFOR

LOCATIONS

HQ: USS-POSCO INDUSTRIES, A CALIFORNIA JOINT VENTURE
900 LOVERIDGE RD, PITTSBURG, CA 945652808
Phone: 800 877-7672
Web: WWW.USSPOSCO.COM

PRODUCTS/OPERATIONS

Selected Steel Products
Cold Rolled Annealed
Hot Dipped Galvanized
Hot Rolled Pickled and Oiled
Tinplate

COMPETITORS

AK Steel Holding Corporation	Gerdau Ameristeel
ArcelorMittal USA	Nucor
BlueScope Steel	Steel Dynamics

HISTORICAL FINANCIALS

Company Type: Private

Income Statement   FYE: December 31

	REVENUE ($ mil.)	NET INCOME ($ mil.)	NET PROFIT MARGIN	EMPLOYEES
12/15	648	(4)	—	759
12/08	1,198	11	1.0%	—
12/07	998	(40)	—	—
12/06	1,034	14	1.4%	—
Annual Growth	(5.1%)	—	—	—

2015 Year-End Financials
Return on assets: 1.1%   Cash ($ mil.): —
Return on equity: (-0.7%)
Current ratio: 0.30

UTAH ASSOCIATION OF REALTORS

EXECUTIVES

Ceo, Chrisopsher Kyler
Manager, Christopher Kyler
Auditors: II ECREDIT FINANCIAL SE ES IN

LOCATIONS

HQ: UTAH ASSOCIATION OF REALTORS
230 W TOWNE RIDGE PKWY # 500, SANDY, UT 840702002
Phone: 801 676-5200
Web: WWW.UTAHREALTORS.COM

HISTORICAL FINANCIALS

Company Type: Private

Income Statement   FYE: December 31

	REVENUE ($ mil.)	NET INCOME ($ mil.)	NET PROFIT MARGIN	EMPLOYEES
12/15	333	91	27.4%	8
12/10	3	1	37.7%	—
12/09	3	1	38.4%	—
Annual Growth	116.6%	104.8%	—	—

2015 Year-End Financials
Return on assets: 0.1%   Cash ($ mil.): 10
Return on equity: 27.4%
Current ratio: 4.40

UTAH HOUSING CORPORATION

EXECUTIVES

Ceo, Grant Whitaker
Cfo, Cleon Butterfield
Sr Vice President, Jonathan Hanks
Loan Officer, Scott Harmon
Loan Officer, Suzette Acord
Loan Officer, Kelly Peterson
Sales Manager, Adam Heap
Controller, Chad Moore
Conventional Loan Administrato, Howard Tolley
Servicing Vice Presid, Amy White
Loan Officer, Cathy McCarter
Auditors: DELOITTE & TOUCHE LLP SALT L

LOCATIONS

HQ: UTAH HOUSING CORPORATION
2479 S LAKE PARK BLVD, WEST VALLEY CITY, UT 841208217
Phone: 801 902-8200
Web: WWW.UTAHHOUSINGCORP.ORG

HISTORICAL FINANCIALS

Company Type: Private

Income Statement   FYE: June 30

	ASSETS ($ mil.)	NET INCOME ($ mil.)	INCOME AS % OF ASSETS	EMPLOYEES
06/18	1,934	36	1.9%	90
06/17	2,002	40	2.0%	—
06/16	1,830	23	1.3%	—
Annual Growth	2.8%	24.6%	—	—

2018 Year-End Financials
Return on assets: —
Return on equity: 32.6%
Sales ($ mil.): 113

UTAH STATE UNIVERSITY

Utah State University (USU) has more than 40 academic departments at colleges of agriculture arts business education and human services engineering science natural resources and humanities and social sciences. It offers about 170 bachelor's degree programs and more than 140 graduate degree programs. Biology elementary education mechanical and aerospace engineering and business administration are among the university's most popular majors. About 29000 students attend its main campus in northern Utah its three branch campuses or extension facilities located across the state. USU was established in 1888 as an agricultural college.

Operations

USU has a student-to-faculty ratio of 18:1. Alumni of the university include Greg Carr founder of the Greg C. Carr Foundation and Charlie Denson former president of NIKE.

Geographic Reach

USU students hail from all 50 US states and some 80 international countries. The university's students have the opportunity to study abroad through partnerships with 140 other institutions located around the world. USU's main campuses or branch offices in Utah are located in Brigham City Logan San Juan Tooele and Uintah Basin.

Financial Performance

Revenues increased at USU by 4% to some $340 million due to increased income from tuition and fees higher enrollment and increased state appropriations. The gain was offset by decreases in gifts grants and contracts. Net income fell 41% to $68 million due to higher operating expenses from salary benefit and other costs.

Strategy

To expand its facilities and meet growing student needs USU is adding a new school of business building and a new athletics center to its main campus. The university recently completed construction of a new $47 million agricultural building on the main campus as well as a new administration building on the USU Eastern campus. In addition USU is building a new distance education building on its Logan campus.

To further expand resources for students USU began offering a Master of Business Administration (MBA) program at the Brigham Young University's Idaho campus in 2013.

EXECUTIVES

Vice President University Advancement, Fross Peterson
Auditors: OFFICE OF THE STATE AUDITOR S

LOCATIONS

HQ: UTAH STATE UNIVERSITY
   1000 OLD MAIN HL, LOGAN, UT 843221000
Phone: 435 797-1057
Web: WWW.UTAHSTATEAGGIES.COM

HISTORICAL FINANCIALS
Company Type: Private

Income Statement   FYE: June 30

	REVENUE ($ mil.)	NET INCOME ($ mil.)	NET PROFIT MARGIN	EMPLOYEES
06/17	435	59	13.7%	6,000
06/16	401	88	22.2%	—
06/15	382	55	14.4%	—
06/14	362	68	19.0%	—
Annual Growth	6.4%	(4.7%)	—	—

2017 Year-End Financials
Return on assets: 1.9%
Return on equity: 13.7%
Current ratio: 0.50
Cash ($ mil.): 42

UTILITY DEBT SECURITIZATION AUTHORITY

LOCATIONS

HQ: UTILITY DEBT SECURITIZATION AUTHORITY
   333 EARLE OVINGTON BLVD, UNIONDALE, NY
   115533610
Phone: 516 222-7700
Web: WWW.LIPOWER.ORG

HISTORICAL FINANCIALS
Company Type: Private

Income Statement   FYE: December 31

	REVENUE ($ mil.)	NET INCOME ($ mil.)	NET PROFIT MARGIN	EMPLOYEES
12/17	297	30	10.2%	3
12/16	278	35	12.8%	—
Annual Growth	6.7%	(14.9%)	—	—

VAL VERDE UNIFIED SCH DIS

EXECUTIVES

Pres, Shelly Yarbrough
Vice President, Wraymond Sawyerr
Prin, Michael M Vargas
J.D., Prin, Fredy De Leon
Safety/Security Director, Mark Clark

LOCATIONS

HQ: VAL VERDE UNIFIED SCH DIS
   975 MORGAN ST, PERRIS, CA 925713103
Phone: 951 940-6100
Web: WWW.VALVERDE.EDU

HISTORICAL FINANCIALS
Company Type: Private

Income Statement   FYE: June 30

	REVENUE ($ mil.)	NET INCOME ($ mil.)	NET PROFIT MARGIN	EMPLOYEES
06/17	479	38	8.1%	1,500
06/16	458	(12)	—	—
06/11	362	(0)	—	—
06/01	88	(2)	—	—
Annual Growth	11.1%	—	—	—

VALLEY CHILDREN'S HEALTHCARE

EXECUTIVES

Ceo, Todd Suntrapak
Vice President, William Chaltraw
Network Engineer, David Irwin
Director, Denise Zeitler
Analyst, Joseph Hernandez
Vice-President, Kevin Shimamoto
Director, Lynn Horton
Network Engineer, Robert Schellenger
Engineer, Roger Deforest
Supervisor, Suzie Burt
Director, David McLean

LOCATIONS

HQ: VALLEY CHILDREN'S HEALTHCARE
   9300 VALLEY CHILDRENS PL, MADERA, CA
   936368761
Phone: 559 353-3000
Web: WWW.VALLEYCHILDRENS.ORG

HISTORICAL FINANCIALS
Company Type: Private

Income Statement   FYE: September 30

	REVENUE ($ mil.)	NET INCOME ($ mil.)	NET PROFIT MARGIN	EMPLOYEES
09/17	604	121	20.1%	2,800
09/16	601	83	13.9%	—
09/15	11	3	26.6%	—
Annual Growth	625.9%	531.3%	—	—

2017 Year-End Financials
Return on assets: 4.5%
Return on equity: 20.1%
Current ratio: 1.30
Cash ($ mil.): 13

VALLEY CHILDREN'S HOSPITAL

EXECUTIVES

Pres- Ceo, Todd Sunterapak
Cfo, Michele Waldrin
Coo, Jessie Hudgins
Executive, Stephanie Scott
Prin, Gordon Alexander

Human Resources, Heather San Julian
Manager, Anthony Caudill
Vice-President, Beverly Hayden-Pugh
Manager, Cynthia Hascall
Board of Directors, David Krause
General Practitioner, Lisa Gilliam

LOCATIONS

HQ: VALLEY CHILDREN'S HOSPITAL
   9300 VALLEY CHILDRENS PL, MADERA, CA
   936368762
Phone: 559 353-3000
Web: WWW.VALLEYCHILDRENS.ORG

HISTORICAL FINANCIALS

Company Type: Private

Income Statement   FYE: September 30

	REVENUE ($ mil.)	NET INCOME ($ mil.)	NET PROFIT MARGIN	EMPLOYEES
09/15	575	24	4.3%	1,800
09/13*	542	103	19.0%	—
06/05	457	(24)	—	—
09/02	219	0	0.3%	—
Annual Growth	7.7%	33.9%	—	—

*Fiscal year change

2015 Year-End Financials

Return on assets: 5.4%   Cash ($ mil.): 8
Return on equity: 4.3%
Current ratio: 1.00

VALLEY HEALTH SYSTEM LLC

EXECUTIVES

Ceo, Sam Kaufman
MBR, Greg Boyer
Registered Nurse, Jodi Cunningham
Doctor, Tina Sprague
Hematology Supervisor, Cade Gullickson
Staff Pharmacist, Dan Delnero

LOCATIONS

HQ: VALLEY HEALTH SYSTEM LLC
   620 SHADOW LN, LAS VEGAS, NV 891064119
Phone: 702 388-4000
Web: WWW.VALLEYHOSPITAL.NET

PRODUCTS/OPERATIONS

Selected Services
Cardiology
Care Management
Maternity Services
Medical Detox
Occupational Therapy
Physical Therapy
Radiology
Stroke Center
Surgery
Wound Healing & Hyperbaric Center

COMPETITORS

Desert Springs Hospital
Summerlin Hospital
Sunrise Hospital and Medical Center
University Medical Center of Southern Nevada

HISTORICAL FINANCIALS

Company Type: Private

Income Statement   FYE: December 31

	REVENUE ($ mil.)	NET INCOME ($ mil.)	NET PROFIT MARGIN	EMPLOYEES
12/16	283	14	5.3%	1,350
12/15	269	15	5.7%	—
12/14	244	5	2.3%	—
12/08	305	26	8.5%	—
Annual Growth	(0.9%)	(6.8%)	—	—

VALLEY MEDICAL FACILITIES, INC.

EXECUTIVES

Ceo, Donald W Spalding
President, Norman F Mitry
Cfo, Bryan Randall
Director, Cliff Glovier
Manager, Linda Schaefer
Director, Bruce Ferrero
Human Resources Director, Laurie Clemens
Software Developer, Cathy Kerr
Physician, Gaetano Licata
Secretary, Kathy Shipley
Customer Supervisor, Lynne Gallaher
Auditors: ARNETT CARBIS TOOTHMAN LLP PI

LOCATIONS

HQ: VALLEY MEDICAL FACILITIES, INC.
   720 BLACKBURN RD, SEWICKLEY, PA 151431459
Phone: 724 728-7000
Web: WWW.HERITAGEVALLEY.ORG

HISTORICAL FINANCIALS

Company Type: Private

Income Statement   FYE: June 30

	REVENUE ($ mil.)	NET INCOME ($ mil.)	NET PROFIT MARGIN	EMPLOYEES
06/15	368	18	5.0%	4,300
06/14	369	7	2.0%	—
06/13	359	(1)	—	—
06/10	362	4	1.1%	—
Annual Growth	0.3%	35.0%	—	—

2015 Year-End Financials

Return on assets: 11.0%   Cash ($ mil.): 14
Return on equity: 5.0%
Current ratio: 0.60

VALLEY PRESBYTERIAN HOSPITAL

EXECUTIVES

Ceo, Gustavo Valdespino
CIO, Ray Moss
Vpres-Chief Nursing Officer, Michelle Quigley
Sr V Pres, Jean Rico

Sr V Pres, Norma Resneder
Sr V Pres, Pegi Matsuda
Sr V Pres, Gayathri S Jith
Vp-Chief Information Officer, Jeffrey Allport
Svp Finance-Cfo, Janice Klostermeier
Chief Medical Officer, Clyde Wesp
Director, Bertha Rayas
Auditors: MOSS ADAMS LLP LOS ANGELES

LOCATIONS

HQ: VALLEY PRESBYTERIAN HOSPITAL
   15107 VANOWEN ST, VAN NUYS, CA 914054597
Phone: 818 782-6600
Web: WWW.VALLEYPRES.ORG

HISTORICAL FINANCIALS

Company Type: Private

Income Statement   FYE: October 31

	REVENUE ($ mil.)	NET INCOME ($ mil.)	NET PROFIT MARGIN	EMPLOYEES
10/17	319	25	7.8%	1,600
10/16	345	24	7.0%	—
10/15	389	51	13.3%	—
10/14	261	0	0.0%	—
Annual Growth	6.9%	878.7%	—	—

2017 Year-End Financials

Return on assets: 8.8%   Cash ($ mil.): 12
Return on equity: 7.8%
Current ratio: 0.40

VALLEY VIEW COMMUNITY UNIT SCHOOL DISTRICT 365U

Located about 35 miles southwest of downtown Chicago Valley View School District 365U provides education to 18000 elementary middle and high school students — the district also includes one alternative school and one preschool. The 20 schools included in the district (serving Romeoville and Bolingbrook communities) total approximately 2.4 million square feet. With more than 2000 full time employees Valley View School District 365U is one of Will County's largest employers. The seven-member school board (elected for a four-year term) hires and supervises the superintendent of schools and sets district policies.

Financial Performance

Valley View School District 365U reported a 3% decrease in revenues in 2012 due to a drop in operating grants and contributions payments in lieu of taxes general state aid and investment earnings.

However its net income decreased by 292% in 2012 over 2011 due to lower revenues and higher expenses. The hike in expenses was because of an increase in instruction support services and state on-behalf payments to teacher retirement and insurance funds.

The District reported that its budget for 2012-2013 was 8.9% higher than for 2011-2012.

Company Background

Valley View School District 365U was founded in 1952.

EXECUTIVES

Secretary Administrative A, Ann Harris

Auditors: EVANS MARSHALL & PEASE PC

LOCATIONS

HQ: VALLEY VIEW COMMUNITY UNIT SCHOOL
DISTRICT 365U
801 W NORMANTOWN RD, ROMEOVILLE, IL
604464330
Phone: 815 886-2700
Web: WWW.VVSD.ORG

PRODUCTS/OPERATIONS

Schools
High Schools (grades 9-12)
  Bolingbroke
  Romeoville
Middle Schools (grades 6-8)
  A. Vito Martinez
  Brooks Middle School
  Hubert H. Humphrey
  Jane Addams
  John J. Lukancic
Elementary Schools (grades K-5)
  Bernard J. Ward
  Beverly Skoff
  Independence
  Irene King
  Jamie McGee
  John R. Tibbott
  Jonas E. Salk
  Kenneth L. Hermansen
  Oak View
  Pioneer
  Robert C. Hill
  Wood View
Other
  Phoenix Experience (alternative school)

HISTORICAL FINANCIALS

Company Type: Private

Income Statement				FYE: June 30
	REVENUE ($ mil.)	NET INCOME ($ mil.)	NET PROFIT MARGIN	EMPLOYEES
06/17	332	11	3.6%	3,000
06/16	295	(8)	—	—
06/07*	190	220	116.0%	—
08/06	225	0	—	—
Annual Growth	3.6%	—	—	—

*Fiscal year change

VALUE DRUG COMPANY

Value Drug Company sees a great deal of value in keeping independent pharmacies competitive. The company is a purchasing cooperative of hundreds of independent drugstores that provides wholesale pharmaceutical distribution services to its members primarily in the central Pennsylvania area. Its products include pharmaceuticals and non-prescription medications hospital and convalescent equipment health and beauty aids nutritional supplies and other health care-related products. The company works with some of the world's largest pharmaceutical makers. Value Drug was founded in 1934 and incorporated in 1936. The company is led by president Greg Drew a former Rite-Aid executive.

Operations
The company's private-label line includes nearly 1000 over-the-counter products. Value Drug participates in such retail initiatives as the federal 340B Drug Discount Program an adult immunization tracking program and competitive generic sourcing program OptiSource.

Geographic Reach
Value Drug is located in Pennsylvania and serves a market area covering 15 states.

EXECUTIVES

National Account Manager, Ellen Breitenbach
Vice President Finance And Chief Financial Officer, David Zang
Vice President Of Operations, J Bover
Auditors: HILL BARTH & KING LLC WEXFOR

LOCATIONS

HQ: VALUE DRUG COMPANY
  195 THEATER DR, DUNCANSVILLE, PA 166357144
Phone: 814 944-9316
Web: WWW.VALUEDRUGCO.COM

COMPETITORS

AmerisourceBergen   Kinray
Cardinal Health   McKesson
H. D. Smith Wholesale   Quality King
  Drug

HISTORICAL FINANCIALS

Company Type: Private

Income Statement				FYE: December 31
	REVENUE ($ mil.)	NET INCOME ($ mil.)	NET PROFIT MARGIN	EMPLOYEES
12/17	842	0	0.1%	200
12/16	816	0	0.0%	—
12/15	779	3	0.4%	—
12/14	754	(0)	—	—
Annual Growth	3.8%	—	—	—

2017 Year-End Financials

Return on assets: 9.0%   Cash ($ mil.): 7
Return on equity: 0.1%
Current ratio: 0.90

VANCOUVER PUBLIC SCHOOLS

EXECUTIVES

Supt, Steven T Webb
Cfo, Steve Olsen
Asst Cfo, Mariane Cool
Executive of Information Techn, Linda Turner
Teacher, David Douglas
Staff, Sabrina Milam
Staff, Tamera Burleson
Teacher, Glenn Humphreys
Teacher, Patrick Godsil
Teacher, Alberto Alcantar
Security Staff, Brenda Legette
Auditors: PAT MCCARTHY STATE AUDITOR O

LOCATIONS

HQ: VANCOUVER PUBLIC SCHOOLS
  2901 FALK RD, VANCOUVER, WA 986616392
Phone: 360 313-1000
Web: WWW.VANSD.ORG

HISTORICAL FINANCIALS

Company Type: Private

Income Statement				FYE: August 31
	REVENUE ($ mil.)	NET INCOME ($ mil.)	NET PROFIT MARGIN	EMPLOYEES
08/17	301	71	23.7%	2,700
08/16	292	15	5.4%	—
08/15*	269	(1)	—	—
06/14	1	0	22.6%	—
Annual Growth	491.4%	500.8%	—	—

*Fiscal year change

2017 Year-End Financials

Return on assets: 3.1%   Cash ($ mil.): 2
Return on equity: 23.7%
Current ratio: —

VANGUARD NATIONAL TRAILER CORPORATION

EXECUTIVES

Ceo, Charles Mudd
SEC, Shen Jianwen
Regional Manager, Mary Blanchette
Human Resources Manager, Jake Pinkerton
Manager, Don Walton
Safety Manager, Candy Siegle
Sales Manager, Clif Cobb
Plant Manager, Kevin Black
Design Engineer, Loren Goodrich
Manager, Mark Hamilton
Buyer, Megan McWilliams

LOCATIONS

HQ: VANGUARD NATIONAL TRAILER CORPORATION
  289 WATER TOWER DR, MONON, IN 479598160
Phone: 219 253-2000
Web: WWW.VANGUARDTRAILER.COM

HISTORICAL FINANCIALS

Company Type: Private

Income Statement				FYE: December 31
	REVENUE ($ mil.)	NET INCOME ($ mil.)	NET PROFIT MARGIN	EMPLOYEES
12/16	333	22	6.6%	500
12/14	318	12	3.9%	—
Annual Growth	2.4%	33.1%	—	—

2016 Year-End Financials

Return on assets: 6.1%   Cash ($ mil.): 19
Return on equity: 6.6%
Current ratio: 1.00

VARIETY CHILDREN'S HOSPITAL

Miami Children's Hospital (MCH) a not-for-profit medical center boasts some 290 beds and offers more than 40 different health care specialties and sub-specialties represented by more than 650 physicians and more than 130 pediatric sub-specialists. Some specialties include pediatric emergency care cancer treatment orthopedics and rehabilitation services. The hospital's neonatal unit treats newborns referred from other hospitals. Miami Children's Hospital operates the region's only free-standing pediatric trauma center. The MCH Research Institute conducts more than 210 clinical research studies in 26 sub-specialties.

Operations

The health system also operates mobile health units that provide preventive care to uninsured children throughout its service area. The units provide immunizations tuberculosis tests and hearing and vision screenings among other services.

In 2012 the hospital had 11550 inpatient admissions 91901 emergency room visits and 14360 surgical cases. Its neonatology division admits more than 600 newborns each year virtually all of them referred from general acute-care hospitals because they are in need of an advanced level of tertiary care.

In 2012 Radiology performed a total of 129794 Diagnostic x-rays MRI's CT Scans and ultrasounds at the main campus. The LifeFlight Critical Care Transport Team transported 2480 patients by air and ground to Miami Children's Hospital in 2012.

Geographic Reach

MCH caters to young Florida residents and their families as well as those in South America and Europe through its Dan Marino Outpatient Center which assists children with special needs and provides neurological and development services for special needs children. Its six outpatient centers are based in Doral Miami Lakes Palmetto Bay Weston West Kendall and West Palm Beach.

Sales and Marketing

MCH markets its products and services through radio and television advertising

Financial Performance

Net patient revenues accounted for about 90% MCH's revenues in 2012.

Strategy

The hospital is at the tail end of a multiyear nearly $70 million project to install an electronic medical record system at the medical center. The first phase of the project which wrapped up in 2012 included new prescribing methods and lab test protocols. It will also engender better communication between hospital staff. The entire system should be installed by 2015.

In 2013 it also launched a smartphone app for Apple iOS devices that uses Wi-Fi triangulation technology to offer patients the convenience of an on-campus indoor GPS-like way-finding system along with other service enhancements.

Expanding its physical infrastructure in 2014 FIU Health broke ground on a 36000-sq.-ft. ambulatory care center on FIU's Modesto A. Maidique Campus in west Miami-Dade County. In partnership with MCH the campus will house the first dedicated pediatric ambulatory surgical center in South Florida.

As part of an expansion project aimed at meeting the growing needs of the community that year MCH also opened 20 new exam rooms in the Emergency Department.

In 2013 the Florida legislature approved HB 1159 a bill that amends a law to make it possible for MCH to build a 10-bed unit to provide obstetrical services for healthy mothers expecting babies pre-diagnosed with congenital conditions requiring clinical intervention immediately after birth.

In 2012 MCH completed a six-story Advanced Pediatric Care Pavilion and the 21000-sq.-ft. Miami Children's Hospital Midtown Outpatient Center. It also opened Miami Children's Hospital Nicklaus Outpatient Center.

On the media front in 2014 MCH launched the MCH Television Network an in-house television network providing patients and families a customized resource for news research and entertainment that specifically caters to MCH patients and their families. It also revamped its in-house radio station that year.

Company Background

Variety Children's Hospital opened in 1950 and became Miami Children's Hospital in 1986.

The hospital first opened its doors in the 1940s as Miami Tent #33 of Variety Clubs International.

EXECUTIVES

Ceo, Narendra M Kini
V Pres, Mario Murgado
SEC, Keith Ward
Treas, Tim M Birkenstock
Sr V Pres, Timothy Birkenstock
Sr V Pres, Jacqueline L Gonzalez
Sr V Pres, Edward Martinez
SEC, Jefry M Biehler
Mgr, Alfredo Guevara
Immunologist, Susan V Benenati
Chief of Icu/Ccu, Andre Rasznski

LOCATIONS

HQ: VARIETY CHILDREN'S HOSPITAL
3100 SW 62ND AVE, MIAMI, FL 331553009
Phone: 305 666-6511
Web: WWW.NICKLAUSCHILDRENS.ORG

PRODUCTS/OPERATIONS

Selected Services
Cardiology and Cardiovascular Surgery
Children's Medical Services Primary Care Program
Clinical Research
Dermatology Early Steps Southernmost Coast
Endocrinology & Diabetes
Gastroenterology
Hematology & Oncology
MCH Pediatric Care Center
Neuroscience Center
Neurosurgery
Ophthalmology
Orthopaedics
Otolaryngology Outpatient Centers
Pediatric Advanced Comprehensive Care Team
Pediatric Critical Care Medicine
Pediatric Hospital Medicine Team Pediatric Medicine
Pediatric Surgery & Anesthesiology
Psychiatry & Psychology
Pulmonology
Radiology
Rehabilitation Services
Rheumatology
Urology
Selected Locations
Miami Children's Hospital Dan Marino Center
Miami Children's Hospital Doral Center
Miami Children's Hospital Miami Lakes Rehabilitation Center
Miami Children's Hospital Nicklaus Care Center
Miami Children's Hospital Palmetto Bay Center
Miami Children's Hospital West Kendall Center

COMPETITORS

Adventist Health System Sunbelt Healthcare
All Children's Hospital
Baptist Health South Florida
Children's Hospital of Philadelphia
HCA
Jackson Health System
Mount Sinai Medical Center of Florida
NCH Healthcare
Shriners Hospitals For Children
South Broward Hospital District
South Miami Hospital
UF&Shands
University of Miami
University of Miami Hospital

HISTORICAL FINANCIALS
Company Type: Private

Income Statement   FYE: December 31

	REVENUE ($ mil.)	NET INCOME ($ mil.)	NET PROFIT MARGIN	EMPLOYEES
12/16	625	71	11.5%	3,700
12/14	618	77	12.5%	—
12/12	34	0	—	—
12/08	381	269	70.5%	—
Annual Growth	6.4%	(15.2%)	—	—

2016 Year-End Financials

Return on assets: 10.4%   Cash ($ mil.): 66
Return on equity: 11.5%
Current ratio: 1.00

VCU HEALTH SYSTEM AUTHORITY

EXECUTIVES

Ceo, John Duval
Pres, Michael RAO
Cfo-Evp, Dominic J Puleo
Coo, Deborah Davis
Project Coordinator, Adrienne Hayes
Associate Director, Alexa Warner
Human Resources, Angela Kendall
Coordinator, Arika Taylor
Human Resources, Dana Bock
Program Director, David Leszczyszyn
Programmer Analyst, Debbie Walton

LOCATIONS

HQ: VCU HEALTH SYSTEM AUTHORITY
1250 E MARSHALL ST, RICHMOND, VA 232985051
Phone: 804 828-9000
Web: WWW.VCUHEALTH.ORG/WOMENS-HEALTH/OUR-SERVICES/PREGNANCY-A

HISTORICAL FINANCIALS
Company Type: Private

Income Statement   FYE: June 30

	REVENUE ($ mil.)	NET INCOME ($ mil.)	NET PROFIT MARGIN	EMPLOYEES
06/18	3,399	162	4.8%	7,399
06/17	3,014	309	10.3%	—
06/05	899	47	5.3%	—
06/04	899	47	5.3%	—
Annual Growth	10.0%	9.1%	—	—

2018 Year-End Financials

Return on assets: 2.5%   Cash ($ mil.): 395
Return on equity: 4.8%
Current ratio: 1.60

VENTURE CONSTRUCTION COMPANY INC

EXECUTIVES

Assistant Vice President, Hilton Glynn
Assistant Vice President, Keith Smith
Assistant Vice President, Tony Hill

LOCATIONS

HQ: VENTURE CONSTRUCTION COMPANY INC
5660 PEACHTREE INDUS BLVD, NORCROSS, GA
300711496
Phone: 770 441-6555
Web: WWW.VENTURECONSTRUCTION.COM

COMPETITORS

Beck Group	Hardin Construction
Choate Construction	Pepper Construction
Embree Construction	Rodgers Builders
Falkenberg	Skanska USA Building
Construction	Tishman Construction
H.J. Russell	Turner Construction

HISTORICAL FINANCIALS

Company Type: Private

Income Statement   FYE: December 31

	REVENUE ($ mil.)	NET INCOME ($ mil.)	NET PROFIT MARGIN	EMPLOYEES
12/17	284	10	3.6%	177
12/16	292	7	2.7%	—
12/08	198	1	1.0%	—
12/07	0	0	—	—
Annual Growth	—	—	—	—

2017 Year-End Financials

Return on assets: 11.4%   Cash ($ mil.): 10
Return on equity: 3.6%
Current ratio: 1.10

VERMONT STUDENT ASSISTANCE CORPORATION

EXECUTIVES

Pres, Scott Giles
V Pres, Thomas A Little
SEC, David Larsen
Cfo, Michael Stuart
Compliance Staff, Jaye Oconnell
Coordinator, Cathy Hunter
Coordinator, Linda Thatcher
Information Specialist, Andrea Gould
Information Specialist, Deborah Lessor
Customer Staff, Elizabeth Metivier
Information Specialist, Erika Borthwick
Auditors: BERRY DUNN MCNEIL & PARKER LL

LOCATIONS

HQ: VERMONT STUDENT ASSISTANCE CORPORATION
10 E ALLEN ST, WINOOSKI, VT 054042209
Phone: 802 655-9602
Web: WWW.VSAC.ORG

HISTORICAL FINANCIALS

Company Type: Private

Income Statement   FYE: June 30

	ASSETS ($ mil.)	NET INCOME ($ mil.)	INCOME AS % OF ASSETS	EMPLOYEES
06/15	1,206	(2)	—	250
06/07	2,201	15	0.7%	—
06/06	1,858	15	0.8%	—
06/05	0	6	—	—
Annual Growth	—	—	—	—

2015 Year-End Financials

Return on assets: 3.7%   Sales ($ mil): 82
Return on equity: (-2.6%)

VIA CHRISTI HOSPITALS WICHITA, INC.

EXECUTIVES

Ceo, Michael Mullis
Vice President, Michael McCullough
Vice-President, Ed Hett
Information Technology Project, Mary Davenport
Director, Gregory Schuessler
Director, Fletcher Miller
Aprn, Jamie K Gilstrap
Aprn, Leighann M Persondek

LOCATIONS

HQ: VIA CHRISTI HOSPITALS WICHITA, INC.
929 N SAINT FRANCIS ST, WICHITA, KS 672143882
Phone: 316 268-5000
Web: WWW.VIA-CHRISTI.ORG

HISTORICAL FINANCIALS

Company Type: Private

Income Statement   FYE: September 30

	REVENUE ($ mil.)	NET INCOME ($ mil.)	NET PROFIT MARGIN	EMPLOYEES
09/15	538	36	6.7%	4,100
09/14	534	68	12.9%	—
09/13	534	24	4.5%	—
09/12	529	108	20.4%	—
Annual Growth	0.6%	(30.7%)	—	—

2015 Year-End Financials

Return on assets: 3.4%   Cash ($ mil.): 22
Return on equity: 6.7%
Current ratio: 2.10

VICTORY INTERNATIONAL GROUP, LLC

EXECUTIVES

Pres, Jiansheng Fan
Vice President, Amanda Meng

LOCATIONS

HQ: VICTORY INTERNATIONAL GROUP, LLC
14748 PIPELINE AVE STE B, CHINO HILLS, CA
917096024
Phone: 949 407-5888
Web: WWW.VICTORYINTLGROUP.COM

HISTORICAL FINANCIALS

Company Type: Private

Income Statement   FYE: December 31

	REVENUE ($ mil.)	NET INCOME ($ mil.)	NET PROFIT MARGIN	EMPLOYEES
12/15	873	42	4.8%	25
12/07	87	1	1.4%	—
Annual Growth	33.2%	55.5%	—	—

2015 Year-End Financials

Return on assets: 11.0%   Cash ($ mil.): 40
Return on equity: 4.8%
Current ratio: 1.00

VIKING YACHT COMPANY

Leif Eriksson's oceangoing Viking explorers could only dream of vessels like those made by the Viking Yacht Company. Viking Yacht can build more than 100 semi-custom fiberglass pleasure boats primarily used for sport fishing. About 90% of each yacht is made in-house. Its line of yachts vary in length from approximately 42 to 92 feet and include convertible and enclosed-bridge convertible vessels open sportfish models and a 52-foot sport yacht. The luxury boats are sold through a network of more than 40 dealers six of which are based outside the US. Founders and brothers Bob and Bill Healey own Viking Yacht Company.

Operations

Viking operates through several businesses and divisions. Atlantic Marine Electronics provides sales installation and service support for yacht electronics including navigation communication and entertainment systems equipment. Its Viking Yachting Center acts as a weather-protected storage area for boats up to 50 feet and provides full services to all brands of yachts including 250 deepwater slips a pool and pool house barbeque and picnic areas bathhouse fuel dock and nighttime security.

Palm Beach Towers designs and engineers aluminum tuna towers used aboard Viking yachts and other boats. In addition Palm Beach Towers produces fiberglass hardtops rod lockers and electronic boxes and other custom aluminum and fiberglass accessories. Palm Beach Towers has locations in New Jersey and Florida.

Sales and Marketing

The company has a sales network of waterfront locations across the US as well as in the Caribbean Central and South America Africa Asia Middle East and Australia.

Strategy

To attract additional customers Viking is focused on launching new models of yachts. It launched seven new models during 2011 and 2012 and in 2013 it launched sleek and sporty new generation 55 and 62 Convertibles ass had a 92 Convertible on the docket.

To help cut greenhouse gas emissions and control costs in 2012 Viking built a tri-generation power plant with six natural gas-fueled turbines at its New Jersey manufacturing facility enabling the company to produce its own electricity.

Company Background

Viking was founded in 1964 and has produced more than 4000 vessels.

EXECUTIVES

Vice President Of Sales, Joe Schwab
Auditors: EISNERAMPER LLP ISELIN NJ

LOCATIONS

HQ: VIKING YACHT COMPANY
ON THE BASS RIV RR 9, NEW GRETNA, NJ 08224
Phone: 609 296-6000
Web: WWW.VIKINGYACHTS.COM

PRODUCTS/OPERATIONS

Selected Models of Yachts
Enclosed Bridge Convertible
Motor Yachts
Open
Open Bridge Convertible
Sport Yacht

COMPETITORS

Brunswick Boat	Sea Fox Boats
Fountain Powerboat	Sea Ray Boats
Hatteras Yachts	Sunseeker
Marine Products Corp.	

HISTORICAL FINANCIALS

Company Type: Private

Income Statement				FYE: July 31
	REVENUE ($ mil.)	NET INCOME ($ mil.)	NET PROFIT MARGIN	EMPLOYEES
07/16	280	18	6.7%	775
07/15	245	17	7.2%	—
07/14	194	16	8.4%	—
07/13	154	10	6.7%	—
Annual Growth	22.0%	22.3%	—	—

2016 Year-End Financials

Return on assets: 4.1%
Return on equity: 6.7%
Current ratio: 0.40
Cash ($ mil.): 12

VILLANOVA UNIVERSITY IN THE STATE OF PENNSYLVANIA

The oldest and largest Roman Catholic institution of higher learning in Pennsylvania Villanova University offers more than 50 academic undergraduate programs at its six main colleges: Business Engineering Liberal Arts and Sciences Professional Studies and Nursing. The university also has a School of Law and it offers graduate programs in most of its disciplines. Villanova has an enrollment of more than 10730 full and part-time undergraduate and graduate students. It also reports a student-to-faculty ratio of 12:1. Average tuition is $45376 million per year.

Operations

While it is focused on providing a well-rounded Catholic-based liberal arts education to its students Villanova also strives to participate in the community of Philadelphia through outreach and service efforts. The school has 44 clubs and about 270 extracurricular activities and groups. In addition Villanova has some two dozen varsity sports offerings and prides itself on having produced about 60 Olympic athletes.

Student tuition and fees account for about two-thirds of sales. Other sources of income include auxiliary enterprises private gifts and grants endowment resources and government grants.

Geographic Reach

Villanova is located on a 270-acre campus with 76 buildings located in Radnor Township in Delaware County Pennsylvania. It also operates a 30-acre conference center location in close proximity to the main campus. The university's enrollment includes students from most US states and 50 international countries.

Financial Performance

Operating revenues in fiscal 2014 increased by 6% to $424.7 million on higher income from student tuition and fees private gifts and grants and other.

Strategy

The university has launched a long-term plan to upgrade the university's campus facilities. As part of the campus master plan in 2011 Villanova launched a $22.5 million project to enhance its landscape including adding aesthetic mobility and pedestrian solutions with the ultimate goal of making the campus vehicle-free. By 2013 the first two phases were completed with phase three efforts in progress including the redesign of the Alumni Quad. The university also plans to add more residence halls a performing arts center and retail and parking facilities.

In 2013 Villanova expanded its academic programs by adding new graduate programs in biochemical engineering and cybersecurity at the College of Engineering. In addition the School of Law opened a new center for law entrepreneurship and innovation as well as a clinic for interdisciplinary mental and physical health law.

Other strategic efforts include increasing the university endowment better defining its values and identity establishing national stature for scholarship and graduate offerings attracting high-quality students and revamping the undergraduate curriculum to enhance critical thinking and leadership skills among students.

In 2013 it launched a $600 million fundraising campaign aimed at cultivating academic innovation across its schools and colleges investing in recruiting and retaining quality teacher-scholars growing financial aid and student opportunities and continuing to improve the living-learning environment on Villanova's campus.

Company Background

Villanova was founded in 1842 by the friars of the Order of St. Augustine and named for St. Thomas of Villanova.

EXECUTIVES

Evp, Kenneth G. (Ken) Valosky
Vp Technology And Cio, Stephen W. Fugale
President And Trustee, Peter M. Donohue, age 66
Svp University Advancement, Michael J. (Mike) O'Neill
Dean College Of Nursing, M. Louise Fitzpatrick
Dean College Of Engineering, Gary A. Gabriele
Provost, Patrick G. Maggitti
Dean College Of Liberal Arts And Sciences, Adele Lindenmeyr
Dean Villanova School Of Business, Daniel Wright
Dean Villanova School Of Law, John Y. Gotanda
Dean College Of Professional Studies, Deborah J. Tyksinski
Director Athletics, Vincent P. Nicastro
Vp Finance, Neil J. Horgan
Vp Facilities Management, Robert H. Morro
Vice Chair, Joseph V. (Joe) Topper, age 62
Trustee, Paul A. Tufano
Auditors: PRICEWATERHOUSECOOPERS LLP PH

LOCATIONS

HQ: VILLANOVA UNIVERSITY IN THE STATE OF PENNSYLVANIA
800 E LANCASTER AVE, VILLANOVA, PA 190851603
Phone: 610 519-4500
Web: WWW1.VILLANOVA.EDU

PRODUCTS/OPERATIONS

Selected Schools and Programs
Undergraduate
    College of Arts & Sciences
    College of Engineering
    College of Nursing
    College of Professional Studies
    Villanova School of Business
Graduate Studies
    Engineering
    Liberal Arts and Sciences
    Nursing
    School of Law
    Villanova School of Business
Other Offerings
    Continuing Studies
    Part-Time Studies

HISTORICAL FINANCIALS

Company Type: Private

Income Statement				FYE: May 31
	REVENUE ($ mil.)	NET INCOME ($ mil.)	NET PROFIT MARGIN	EMPLOYEES
05/18	502	150	29.9%	2,022
05/13	401	101	25.4%	—
05/12	385	(4)	—	—
Annual Growth	4.5%	—	—	—

2018 Year-End Financials

Return on assets: 7.2%
Return on equity: 29.9%
Current ratio: —
Cash ($ mil.): 153

VIRGINIA COLLEGE BUILDING AUTHORITY

EXECUTIVES

Prin, Robert F McDonnell

LOCATIONS

HQ: VIRGINIA COLLEGE BUILDING AUTHORITY
101 N 14TH ST FL 3, RICHMOND, VA 232193665
Phone: 804 225-2142

HISTORICAL FINANCIALS

Company Type: Private

Income Statement

FYE: June 30

	ASSETS ($ mil.)	NET INCOME ($ mil.)	INCOME AS % OF ASSETS	EMPLOYEES
06/17	1,754	(98)	—	2
06/16	2,199	(327)	—	—
Annual Growth	(20.2%)	—	—	—

2017 Year-End Financials

Return on assets: —
Return on equity: (-20.7%)

Sales ($ mil): 476

VIRGINIA COMMONWEALTH UNIVERSITY

Virginia Commonwealth University (VCU) serves the common interests of its more than 30000 enrolled students. The university offers more than 200 certificate undergraduate graduate and doctoral programs through its 15 schools. Spread across two campuses in Richmond: Monroe Park and Medical College of Virginia (MCV) which includes the Schools of Allied Health Dentistry Medicine Nursing Pharmacy and Public Health. Specialty facilities include the VCU Medical Center and a branch campus of the School of the Arts in Qatar. Founded in 1917 as the Richmond School of Social Work and Public Health in 1968 the school merged with the Medical College of Virginia to form VCU.

EXECUTIVES

Associate Vice President Facilities Management, Brian Ohlinger
Director Manager Supervisor, Charles Daniel
Senior Vice President Finance And Administration, John Bennett
Associate Vice President, David Sarrett
Vice President, Allison Arden
Operating Room Director, Deborah Bolling
Cello Teacher The Music Tree School Concert Hall Assistant Vice President Assistant Technician, Celista Money
First National Vice President The U. S. Complete, Art Mourino

LOCATIONS

HQ: VIRGINIA COMMONWEALTH UNIVERSITY
912 W FRANKLIN ST, RICHMOND, VA 232849040
Phone: 804 828-0100
Web: WWW.VCU.EDU

HISTORICAL FINANCIALS

Company Type: Private

Income Statement

FYE: June 30

	REVENUE ($ mil.)	NET INCOME ($ mil.)	NET PROFIT MARGIN	EMPLOYEES
06/17	760	84	11.1%	11,000
06/16	737	37	5.1%	—
06/11	2,319	328	14.2%	—
06/06	448	40	9.0%	—
Annual Growth	4.9%	6.9%	—	—

2017 Year-End Financials

Return on assets: 12.0%
Return on equity: 11.1%
Current ratio: 0.50

Cash ($ mil.): 82

VIRGINIA HOUSING DEVELOPMENT AUTHORITY

Though Virginia is famous for its Civil War-era plantations these historic estates represent a lifestyle out of reach for most. For Virginians seeking a more modest homestead there's the Virginia Housing Development Authority (VHDA). The not-for-profit quasi-government agency founded by the Virginia General Assembly in 1972 provides developers of rentalA propertiesA and low- to moderate-income borrowers with low interest rate loans to renovate or purchase houses and apartments across the state. Its loan products are offered by more than 140 authorized lenders throughout Virginia. The VHDA is self-supporting issuing bonds to raise capital.

EXECUTIVES

Executive Director, Susan F. Dewey
Managing Director Rental Housing, Arthur N. (Art) Bowen
Managing Director Community Outreach, J. Michael Hawkins
Managing Director Executive Services, Llewellyn C. Anderson
Managing Director Homeownership, Janet Wiglesworth
Managing Director Internal Audit And Risk Management, Julie Camus
Managing Director Finance, Pat Carey
Acting Managing Director Information Technology Services, J. Kyle Howard
Chairman, Timothy M. Chapman
Vice Chairman, Sarah B. Stedfast
Auditors: KPMG LLP RICHMOND VA

LOCATIONS

HQ: VIRGINIA HOUSING DEVELOPMENT AUTHORITY
601 S BELVIDERE ST, RICHMOND, VA 232206504
Phone: 804 780-0789
Web: WWW.VHDA.COM

HISTORICAL FINANCIALS

Company Type: Private

Income Statement

FYE: June 30

	ASSETS ($ mil.)	NET INCOME ($ mil.)	INCOME AS % OF ASSETS	EMPLOYEES
06/18	7,292	132	1.8%	300
06/16	8,024	171	2.1%	—
06/15	8,070	176	2.2%	—
06/14	8,014	132	1.7%	—
Annual Growth	(2.3%)	(0.1%)	—	—

2018 Year-End Financials

Return on assets: 3.7%
Return on equity: 26.2%

Sales ($ mil): 505

VIRGINIA INTERNATIONAL TERMINALS, LLC

EXECUTIVES

Ceo, Joseph P Ruddy
Pres, Joseph Dorto
Dir, Regina P Brayboy
V Pres, Wilson S Goode
Dir, Franklin P Earley
SEC-Treas, William M Grace
Coo, Shawn Tiddettes
Corporate Counsel, John M Ryan
Customer Representativ, Becky Coore
Customer Representativ, Patty Marlow
Coordinator, Shirby Dunton
Auditors: PBMARES LLP HARRISONBURG VI

LOCATIONS

HQ: VIRGINIA INTERNATIONAL TERMINALS, LLC
601 WORLD TRADE CTR, NORFOLK, VA 23510
Phone: 757 440-7120
Web: WWW.PORTOFVIRGINIA.COM

COMPETITORS

Georgia Ports Authority	Port Authority of New York and New Jersey
North Carolina State Ports Authority	South Carolina Ports

HISTORICAL FINANCIALS

Company Type: Private

Income Statement

FYE: June 30

	REVENUE ($ mil.)	NET INCOME ($ mil.)	NET PROFIT MARGIN	EMPLOYEES
06/18	521	16	3.1%	400
06/17	478	(7)	—	—
06/10	203	2	1.1%	—
06/08	254	(6)	—	—
Annual Growth	7.4%	—	—	—

2018 Year-End Financials

Return on assets: 5.0%
Return on equity: 3.1%
Current ratio: 2.90

Cash ($ mil.): 19

VIRGINIA POLYTECHNIC INSTITUTE & STATE UNIVERSITY

Virginia Polytechnic Institute and State University more commonly known as Virginia Tech is the state's largest university enrolling more than 32000 students. The university offers more than 200 undergraduate graduate and professional degree programs through eight academic colleges. It has a student-teacher ratio of 16 to 1. The school's most popular majors include agriculture business biology animal sciences and engineering. Virginia Tech which was formed in 1872 serves the surrounding community through outreach and education programs.

Operations
Virginia charges $13230 tuition and fees for in-state undergraduates and $31014 tuition and fees for out-of-state undergraduates.

Virginia Tech manages a research portfolio of nearly $500 million. Research is focused on new developments in agriculture biotechnology energy management (including fuel-cell technology and power electronics) information and communication technology transportation and other fields.

Geographic Reach
Virginia Tech has more than 210 campus buildings a 2600-acre main campus in Blacksburg off-campus educational facilities in Alexandria Arlington Falls Church Leesburg Manassas and Middleburg and a study-abroad site in Switzerland. It has about 10 research institutes.

Financial Performance
Virginia Tech's operating revenue increased 1% to $1.03 billion in fiscal 2017 (ended June). The increase was primarily due to a 3% increase in student tuition and fees revenue – thanks to a growing student body as well an increase in tuition and fee rates – but was partially offset by a 4% decrease in grants and contracts.

Operating expenses totaled $1.4 billion in 2017 a 4% increase from 2016. The university ended the year with $151.4 million in cash and cash equivalents some $112.7 million less than it had at the end of the prior year.

The Virginia Tech Foundation manages the school's endowment which topped $1 billion for the first time in 2018.

Strategy
Virginia Tech's strategic plan focuses on four broad areas: experiential learning diversity and inclusion cross-sector partnerships and philanthropy. Its initiatives in these areas are part of its goal of becoming one of the top 100 universities in the world. Towards those ends the university has introduced new multidisciplinary undergraduate courses and has increased the percentage of incoming students from underrepresented or underserved groups.

It also continues to improve and expand its campuses with renovations to academic buildings sports facilities and residence halls.

The university will acquire the Virginia Tech Carilion School of Medicine (VTCSOM) in mid-2018. VTCSOM was established from a 10-year private-public partnership with Carilion Clinic.

Company Background
Virginia Tech was founded as a land-grant college in 1872.

EXECUTIVES

Svp And Provost, Mark G. McNamee
Vp Finance And Cfo, M. Dwight Shelton
Vp And Dean Graduate Education, Karen P. DePauw
Ceo Virginia Tech Foundation, John E. Dooley
Dean Pamplin College Of Business, Robert T. Sumichrast
Dean Virginia-maryland College Of Veterinary Medicine, Cyril Clarke
President, Timothy D. (Tim) Sands
Vp Information Technology And Cio, Scott F. Midkiff
Dean College Of Agriculture And Life Sciences, Alan Grant
Dean College Of Architecture And Urban Studies, A. Jack Davis
Dean College Of Engineering, Richard Benson
Dean College Of Liberal Arts And Human Sciences, Elizabeth Spiller
Dean College Of Natural Resources And Environment, Paul M. Winistorfer

Dean College Of Science, Lay Nam Chang
Dean University Libraries, Tyler O. Walters
Assistant Vice President For Finance, Charles Swaha
Department Chair, Dave Gerrard
Auditors: COMMONWEALTH OF VIRGINIA AUDIT

LOCATIONS

HQ: VIRGINIA POLYTECHNIC INSTITUTE & STATE UNIVERSITY
300 TURNER ST NW STE 4200, BLACKSBURG, VA 240616100
Phone: 540 231-6000
Web: WWW.VT.EDU

PRODUCTS/OPERATIONS

Selected Colleges
College of Agriculture and Life Sciences
College Architecture and Urban Studies
College of Engineering
College of Liberal Arts and Human Sciences
College of Natural Resources and Environment
College of Science
Pamplin College of Business
Virginia-Maryland Regional College of Veterinary Medicine

HISTORICAL FINANCIALS
Company Type: Private

Income Statement				FYE: June 30
	REVENUE ($ mil.)	NET INCOME ($ mil.)	NET PROFIT MARGIN	EMPLOYEES
06/17	1,031	64	6.2%	6,866
06/16	1,020	121	11.9%	—
06/15	1,129	114	10.2%	—
Annual Growth	(4.5%)	(25.3%)	—	—

2017 Year-End Financials
Return on assets: 13.6% Cash ($ mil.): 101
Return on equity: 6.2%
Current ratio: 0.70

VIRGINIA PREMIER HEALTH PLAN, INC.

EXECUTIVES

Ceo, Linda Hines
Transportation Coordinatr, Bernard Christmas
Compliance Manager, Audrey Thompson
Engineer, Jim Camp
It Assistant, Terry Nicholas
Director, Jill Cousins
Controller, Angel Moyer
Manager, Joel Blosser
Transportation Director, Randy Ledien
Registered Nurse, Renea Morgan
Manager, Suzanne Shelton
Auditors: KPMG LLP MC LEAN VA

LOCATIONS

HQ: VIRGINIA PREMIER HEALTH PLAN, INC.
600 E BROAD ST STE 400, RICHMOND, VA 232191800
Phone: 804 819-5164
Web: WWW.VAPREMIER.COM

HISTORICAL FINANCIALS
Company Type: Private

Income Statement				FYE: June 30
	REVENUE ($ mil.)	NET INCOME ($ mil.)	NET PROFIT MARGIN	EMPLOYEES
06/18	1,372	(14)	—	165
06/15	969	(0)	—	—
06/14*	749	14	1.9%	—
12/03	207	3	1.9%	—
Annual Growth	14.5%	—	—	—

*Fiscal year change

2018 Year-End Financials
Return on assets: 1.3% Cash ($ mil.): 31
Return on equity: (-1.1%)
Current ratio: 0.20

VIRGINIA WEST UNIVERSITY FOUNDATION INCORPORATED

EXECUTIVES

Vp Technology And Facilities, Mark Cottrill
Vp Investments And Chief Investment Officer, Rick Kraich
Coo Cfo And Treasurer, Michael Augustine
President And Ceo, Cindi Roth
Chairman, Robert L. Reynolds
Vice Chairman, Gary Pell
Auditors: DIXON HUGHES GOODMAN LLP MORG

LOCATIONS

HQ: VIRGINIA WEST UNIVERSITY FOUNDATION INCORPORATED
1 WATERFRONT PL FL 7, MORGANTOWN, WV 265015978
Phone: 304 282-4000
Web: WWW.WVUF.ORG

HISTORICAL FINANCIALS
Company Type: Private

Income Statement				FYE: June 30
	ASSETS ($ mil.)	NET INCOME ($ mil.)	INCOME AS % OF ASSETS	EMPLOYEES
06/17	1,690	42	2.5%	115
06/13	1,245	75	6.1%	—
06/12	1,110	37	3.4%	—
Annual Growth	8.8%	2.7%	—	—

2017 Year-End Financials
Return on assets: 7.2% Sales ($ mil): 145
Return on equity: 29.4%

VISALIA UNIFIED SCHOOL DISTRICT

EXECUTIVES

Supt, Craig Wheaton
Supt, Robert Groeber
Manager, Adam Brown
Director, Mat Brletic
Teacher, Larry Jarocki
Manager, Leeann Errotabere
Teacher, Ana Romo
Teacher, Bertha Ketchie
Teacher, Dena Gonzalez
Teacher, Elisa Bardonnex
Teacher, Jacob Fernandez
Auditors: CROWE HORWATH LLP SACRAMENTO

LOCATIONS

HQ: VISALIA UNIFIED SCHOOL DISTRICT
5000 W CYPRESS AVE, VISALIA, CA 932778300
Phone: 559 730-7529
Web: WWW.VISALIAEDFOUNDATION.ORG

HISTORICAL FINANCIALS
Company Type: Private

Income Statement   FYE: June 30

	REVENUE ($ mil.)	NET INCOME ($ mil.)	NET PROFIT MARGIN	EMPLOYEES
06/17	338	(4)	—	4,000
06/16	333	(14)	—	—
06/15	275	35	12.7%	—
06/14	242	(11)	—	—
Annual Growth	11.7%	—	—	—

VISTA UNIFIED SCHOOL DISTRICT INC

EXECUTIVES

Superintendent, Devin Vodicka
Supt, Joyce Bales
Asst Supt-Hr, Myrna Vallely
Asst Supt-Bus Svcs, Donna Caperton
Asst Supt-Curriculum & Instr, Jeane Luckey
Admn, Lorie Guva
Prin, David Lacey
Prin, Hector Menchaca
Prin, Mike Barnes
Prin, Rodney Goldenberg
Coordinator, John Weldy
Auditors: WILKINSON HADLEY KING & CO L

LOCATIONS

HQ: VISTA UNIFIED SCHOOL DISTRICT INC
1234 ARCADIA AVE, VISTA, CA 920843404
Phone: 760 726-2170
Web: WWW.VISTAUSD.ORG

HISTORICAL FINANCIALS
Company Type: Private

Income Statement   FYE: June 30

	REVENUE ($ mil.)	NET INCOME ($ mil.)	NET PROFIT MARGIN	EMPLOYEES
06/17	282	(7)	—	1,600
06/16	276	(2)	—	—
06/06	0	0	—	—
06/05	206	(28)	—	—
Annual Growth	2.6%	—	—	—

VITALANT

As its name suggests Blood Systems collects and provides blood to hospitals. The not-for-profit Blood Systems collects blood and provides blood products and services to more than 500 hospitals in about 20 states. Its network of blood bank facilities are operated through its United Blood Services and Blood Centers of the Pacific subsidiaries. Blood Systems also provides blood donor testing services through its Creative Testing Solutions (CTS) facilities. Its BioCARE division distributes plasma derivative products used in medical procedures.

Operations

Blood Systems gets more than half of revenues from blood component service fees made by the blood centers. Laboratory testing services (CTS) and sales of pharmaceutical products (BioCARE) make up most of the rest of sales.

The Blood Systems Research Institute conducts transfusion medicine research including investigational work on transfusion-transmitted diseases (such as HIV and HCV) and infectious diseases such as the West Nile Virus. It also prepares stem cells for research and therapeutic purposes.

The organization's community blood centers include LifeStream (active in Southern California) Blood Centers of the Pacific (Northern California) Bonfils Blood Center (Colorado) and Inland Northwest Blood Center (the Spokane Washington region). The CTS division tests more than 2.6 million blood donations annually from its facilities in Phoenix Dallas and Tampa. Another division Blood Systems Laboratories specializes in identifying antibodies in blood and stem cell processing.

Geographic Reach

Blood Systems has about 50 donor centers in Arizona California Colorado Idaho Louisiana Mississippi Montana Nevada New Mexico North Dakota South Dakota Texas Washington and Wyoming (through the United Blood Services and Blood Centers of the Pacific units). The company also has about 20 BioCARE locations and a handful of CTS and research labs scattered across the US.

Financial Performance

Blood Systems reported revenues of $743 million in 2013 a 1% increase over the previous year due to higher sales of laboratory testing services and pharmaceutical products. The company reported a net loss of $11 million that year (versus net income of $22.7 million in 2012) due to higher expenses related to the costs of blood collection pharmaceutical supplies and testing products.

Strategy

Blood Systems primarily operates in the western and midwestern US and tends to grow by entering new hospital service contracts in strategic markets. In addition the company is working to improve its IT systems to give customers better access to its blood supplies. It also invests in facility and equipment upgrades as well as product research and development efforts to improve quality.

In 2013 BioCARE opened CanyonCARE Rx a full-service pharmacy that specializes in hemophilia von Willebrand disease and other blood disorders. The division also established four new group purchasing organization (GPO) contracts a key focus area for BioCARE as it looks to expand its customer base.

Company Background

The company which was founded in 1943 as the Salt River Valley Blood Bank is governed by a voluntary board of directors consisting of community and medical industry leaders.

EXECUTIVES

Evp And General Counsel, Scott M. Nelson
Executive Vice President Chief Financial Officer, Susan L. Barnes
Evp And Chief Quality Officer, Mary Beth Bassett
Evp Business Services, Patrick Holt
President Chief Executive Officer, Daniel Connor
Executive Vice President Chief Medical & Scientific Officer, Ralph R. Vassallo
Auditors: GRANT THORNTON LLP PHOENIX A

LOCATIONS

HQ: VITALANT
6210 E OAK ST, SCOTTSDALE, AZ 852571101
Phone: 480 675-5600
Web: WWW.BLOODSYSTEMS.ORG

PRODUCTS/OPERATIONS

2013 Sales

	$ mil.	% of total
Blood component service fees	323	44
Laboratory testing services	208	28
Sales of pharmaceutical products	174	23
Other services & income	37	5
Total	**743**	**100**

Selected Services

Blood Centers
  Blood Components
  Component Therapy
  Commonly Ordered Derivatives
  Modified Blood Components
Laboratory Services
  Donor Counseling
  Histocompatibility Laboratory (HLA)
  Immunohematology Reference Laboratory (IRL)
Special Collections
  Directed Donation
  Perioperative Blood Salvage
  Pre-operative Autologous Donation (PAD)
  Stem Cell Processing
  Therapeutic (Clinical) Apheresis
Transfusion Medicine
  Blood Management Services
  Compatibility Services

COMPETITORS

CSL
Daxor
FFF Enterprises
Grifols Inc.
HemaCare
New York Blood Center
Puget Sound Blood Center
Red Cross
SeraCare Life Sciences

HISTORICAL FINANCIALS
Company Type: Private

Income Statement   FYE: December 31

	REVENUE ($ mil.)	NET INCOME ($ mil.)	NET PROFIT MARGIN	EMPLOYEES
12/16	1,129	1	0.1%	5,000
12/15	966	2	0.3%	—
12/14	0	(62)	—	—
12/13	743	65	8.8%	—
Annual Growth	15.0%	(71.6%)	—	—

2016 Year-End Financials
Return on assets: 6.5%   Cash ($ mil.): 49
Return on equity: 0.1%
Current ratio: 1.30

VOLUNTEERS OF AMERICA, INC.

There's a volunteer everywhere you look at Volunteers of America a national faith-based organization that provides community-level human services to more than 2 million people a year. It works to help abused and neglected children at-risk youth disabled people the homeless people with substance abuse problems the elderly and prisoners and former prisoners. The group operates from about 33 offices across the US and Puerto Rico and counts some 55000 volunteers in its ranks. It receives government grants as well as support from the public. Volunteers of America was organized in 1896 by Ballington and Maud Booth. Ballington's father William Booth founded the Salvation Army.

Operations

Volunteers of America is a nonprofit organization. It is a ministry of service that includes nearly 16000 paid professional employees dedicated to helping those in need rebuild their lives and reach their full potential. Its focus areas are Assistance with Basic Needs Community Outreach and Investment Correctional Re-Entry Services Housing Mental Health Senior Living and Care; and Substance Abuse.

The company is committed to encouraging positive development for children youth and families. Its programs include prevention early intervention crisis intervention and long-term services.

Geographic Reach

As its name suggests Volunteers of America helps more than 2 million people in more than 400 communities in 46 US states the District of Columbia and Puerto Rico.

Financial Performance

Volunteers of America's revenues increased by 13% in 2014 due to a growth in government grants and contracts and public support. Awards from the US government increased by $26 million.

Net income increased by 32% in 2014 thanks to the higher revenues.

In 2014 net cash provided by the operating activities increased by $7.7 million over 2013.

Strategy

In 2015 Volunteers of America partnered with CBS EcoMedia as an inaugural member of the Viewers to Volunteers (V2V) community. The new digital platform which launched at www.ViewerstoVolunteers.com channels advertising dollars into tangible quality of life improvements in communities across America.

It also teamed with Niagara Bottling the largest private-label bottled water supplier in the US to establish a new national collaboration that promises many exciting opportunities to enhance the lives of disadvantaged children and youth. Niagara provided $300000 in grants to three Volunteers of America programs near its bottling facilities.

In 2014 senior housing development firm Essential Decision created a strategic partnership with Volunteers of America working on several projects including The Homestead at Rochester The Homestead at Anoka and Tiffin Rehabilitation Center.

Volunteers of America expanded its charitable reach in 2013 with the opening of the Anoka Rehabilitation and Living Center a 120-bed skilled care center in Anoka Minnesota.

EXECUTIVES

Executive Vice President General Counsel, David T. Bowman
Executive Vice President Of External Affairs, Jatrice Martel Gaiter
President And Ceo, Michael (Mike) King
Executive Vice President Of Affiliate Relations, Margaret Ratcliff
Executive Vice President For Military Communities And Chief Medical Officer, Jonathan Sherin
Coo, Thomas Turnbull
Executive Vice President Chief Financial Officer, Joseph A. Budzynski
Executive Vice President Housing, Patrick Sheridan
Senior Vice President Legal Affairs, Sharon Geno
Senior Vice President Housing Development, Priya Jayachandran
Auditors: MADDOX & ASSOCIATES APC BATON

LOCATIONS

HQ: VOLUNTEERS OF AMERICA, INC.
 1660 DUKE ST STE 100, ALEXANDRIA, VA 223143427
Phone: 703 341-5000

PRODUCTS/OPERATIONS

2014 Revenue

	$ mil.	% of total
Public support	63	25
Government grants and contracts	18	7
Other	174	68
Total	**256**	**100**

Programs and Services
Children and Youth
Community Enhancement
Community
Elderly
Emergency Services
Employment and Training
Health Care
Homelessness
Housing
Intellectual and Developmental Disabilities
Mental Health
Substance Abuse
Veterans

HISTORICAL FINANCIALS

Company Type: Private

Income Statement				FYE: June 30
	REVENUE ($ mil.)	NET INCOME ($ mil.)	NET PROFIT MARGIN	EMPLOYEES
06/17	315	31	10.0%	3,000
06/14	0	(0)	—	—
06/13	238	13	5.6%	—
06/08	6	5	88.7%	—
Annual Growth	**54.1%**	**20.9%**	**—**	**—**

2017 Year-End Financials

Return on assets: 3.3%   Cash ($ mil.): 54
Return on equity: 10.0%
Current ratio: 1.60

W M KECK FOUNDATION INC

EXECUTIVES

Vice President, Howard Day
Vice President And Chief Administrative Officer, Jonathan D Jaffrey

LOCATIONS

HQ: W M KECK FOUNDATION INC
 550 S HOPE ST STE 2500, LOS ANGELES, CA 900712617
Phone: 213 680-3833
Web: WWW.WMKECK.ORG

HISTORICAL FINANCIALS

Company Type: Private

Income Statement				FYE: December 31
	ASSETS ($ mil.)	NET INCOME ($ mil.)	INCOME AS % OF ASSETS	EMPLOYEES
12/15	1,122	29	2.6%	23
12/14	1,234	8	0.7%	—
12/13	1,254	(21)	—	—
12/09	1,069	0	—	—
Annual Growth	**0.8%**			

2015 Year-End Financials

Return on assets: 1.2%   Sales ($ mil): 94
Return on equity: 31.1%

W. A. FOOTE MEMORIAL HOSPITAL

EXECUTIVES

Pres-Ceo, Georgia Fojtasek
Sr Vice President, Ondrea Bates
V Pres-Cno, Wendy Boersma
Chief of Medicine, Reddivalen Nagesh
Coordinator, Deborah Strohaver
Chief Financial Officer, Hendrik Schuur
Executive, Ahmad Zubairi
Manager, Andrew Caughey
Manager, Janet Martin
Coordinator, Kristine Kubish
Customer Billing Repre, Brandan Flaws

LOCATIONS

HQ: W. A. FOOTE MEMORIAL HOSPITAL
 205 N EAST AVE, JACKSON, MI 492011753
Phone: 517 205-4800
Web: WWW.ALLEGIANCEHEALTH.ORG

HISTORICAL FINANCIALS

Company Type: Private

Income Statement				FYE: June 30
	REVENUE ($ mil.)	NET INCOME ($ mil.)	NET PROFIT MARGIN	EMPLOYEES
06/16	477	(11)	—	3,500
06/15	462	(2)	—	—
06/09	371	(63)	—	—
06/08	338	(53)	—	—
Annual Growth	**4.4%**			

2016 Year-End Financials

Return on assets: 9.4%
Return on equity: (-2.5%)
Current ratio: 0.90

Cash ($ mil.): 26

W. DOUGLASS DISTRIBUTING, LTD.

EXECUTIVES

Gen Ptnr, William P Douglass
Ptnr, Brad Douglass
Ptnr, Joan Douglass
Ptnr, Diane McCarty
Cfo, Kim McKinney
Manager, Bob Appolito
Sales Staff, Marcia Hayes

LOCATIONS

HQ: W. DOUGLASS DISTRIBUTING, LTD.
325 E FOREST AVE, SHERMAN, TX 750908832
Phone: 903 893-1181
Web: WWW.DOUGLASSDIST.COM

HISTORICAL FINANCIALS

Company Type: Private

Income Statement				FYE: December 31
	REVENUE ($ mil.)	NET INCOME ($ mil.)	NET PROFIT MARGIN	EMPLOYEES
12/17	292	3	1.3%	130
12/16	248	0	0.2%	—
12/15	259	1	0.6%	—
12/14	403	0	0.2%	—
Annual Growth	(10.2%)	62.9%	—	—

2017 Year-End Financials

Return on assets: 3.8%
Return on equity: 1.3%
Current ratio: 0.60

Cash ($ mil.): —

W. K. KELLOGG FOUNDATION

EXECUTIVES

Ceo, Sterling K Speirn
Exec Vice President, Gregory A Lyman
Vice President, Paul J Lawler
Sr Vice President, La June Montgomery-Talley
Vice President, Gail D Mc Clure
Vice President, Richard M Foster
Vice President, Gregory B Taylor
Sr Vice President, James E McHale
Vice President, Gail C Christopher
Coo, Linh Nguyen
Chief Policy & Communications, Aranthan Jones II
Auditors: MITCHELL & TITUS LLP CHICAGO

LOCATIONS

HQ: W. K. KELLOGG FOUNDATION
1 MICHIGAN AVE E, BATTLE CREEK, MI 490174012
Phone: 269 968-1611
Web: WWW.WKKF.ORG

HISTORICAL FINANCIALS

Company Type: Private

Income Statement				FYE: August 31
	REVENUE ($ mil.)	NET INCOME ($ mil.)	NET PROFIT MARGIN	EMPLOYEES
08/16	404	(75)	—	200
08/15	350	(5)	—	—
08/13	329	92	28.0%	—
08/12	359	(106)	—	—
Annual Growth	3.0%	—	—	—

2016 Year-End Financials

Return on assets: 1.7%
Return on equity: (-18.7%)
Current ratio: —

Cash ($ mil.): 37

W.S. BADCOCK CORPORATION

W.S. Badcock furnishes homes down in Dixie and beyond. As one of the largest privately-owned furniture retailers in the US the company sells furnitureA for every room in the house. It sells its furniture and accessoriesA through more than 300 stores that operate under the banner namesA Badcock Home Furnishing Centers and Badcock &more.A Aside from its e-commerce site Badcock's stores networkA extends to nearly 10 southeastern states. Stores also carry appliances lawn equipment electronics mattresses rugs bedding lighting wall art and other decorative accessories. The company was founded by Henry S. Badcock in 1904 as a general mercantile store. Today it is in its fourth generation of family management.

Geographic Reach

Headquartered in Mulberry Florida with more than 1200 corporate employees W.S. Badcock operates primarily in the southeastern US. Its operations span the states of Georgia Alabama Mississippi Tennessee and the Carolinas expanding into Virginia West Virginia and Kentucky.

Strategy

Through the company's dealer business model more than 80% of Badcock's stores are individually owned. As part of the model the company does not require a franchise fee but instead consigns merchandise to the dealers. As opposed to the typical franchise systemA startup this consignment method aims to allow for a quicker startup along with the benefits of business ownership.

Already established in half a dozen states BadcockA has beenA expanding its store network in Virginia Kentucky and West Virginia. Despite a slowdown in its expansion plans amid the recession and downturn in furniture retailing the company aims to grow its stores network againA throughout the Southeast.

EXECUTIVES

Vice President Legal, Phil Bayt
Vice President And Controller, Greg Reeves
Senior Vice President Credit Services And Ar Management, Dave Gonyea
Executive Vice President, Bill Pou
Auditors: KPMG LLP TAMPA FL

LOCATIONS

HQ: W.S. BADCOCK CORPORATION
205 NW 2ND ST, MULBERRY, FL 338602405
Phone: 863 425-4921
Web: WWW.BADCOCK.COM

PRODUCTS/OPERATIONS

Selected Products
Accessories
Appliances
Electronics
Furniture
Mattresses

COMPETITORS

Aaron's Inc.	Ethan Allen
Ashley Furniture	Havertys
Baer's Furniture	Klaussner Furniture
Bassett Furniture	La-Z-Boy
City Furniture	Rooms To Go
El Dorado Furniture	Sealy

HISTORICAL FINANCIALS

Company Type: Private

Income Statement				FYE: June 30
	REVENUE ($ mil.)	NET INCOME ($ mil.)	NET PROFIT MARGIN	EMPLOYEES
06/18	802	33	4.2%	1,500
06/17	692	27	3.9%	—
06/16	681	25	3.8%	—
06/15	600	19	3.3%	—
Annual Growth	10.1%	19.5%	—	—

2018 Year-End Financials

Return on assets: 8.6%
Return on equity: 4.2%
Current ratio: 3.90

Cash ($ mil.): 3

WABASH VALLEY POWER ASSOCIATION INC

EXECUTIVES

Exec Dir-Ceo, Rick Coons
Cfo, Jeffrey A Conrad
Vice President, Katherine A Joyce
Vice President, Curtis E Taylor
Vice President, M Keith Thompson
Vice-President Business Develo, Greg Wagoner
Regional Economic, Diane Reinhart
Financial Analyst, Jeanette Surratt
Administrative Assistant, Stephanie Sohn
Controller, Theresay Young
Accounting, Denise Sewell
Auditors: DELOITTE & TOUCHE LLP INDIANA

LOCATIONS

HQ: WABASH VALLEY POWER ASSOCIATION INC
722 N HIGH SCHOOL RD, INDIANAPOLIS, IN 462143756
Phone: 317 481-2800
Web: WWW.WVPA.COM

Company Type: Private

Income Statement   FYE: December 31

	REVENUE ($ mil.)	NET INCOME ($ mil.)	NET PROFIT MARGIN	EMPLOYEES
12/17	702	19	2.7%	65
12/16	707	21	3.0%	—
12/15	740	18	2.4%	—
12/14	821	17	2.2%	—
Annual Growth	(5.1%)	2.1%	—	—

2017 Year-End Financials

Return on assets: 9.0%   Cash ($ mil.): 51
Return on equity: 2.7%
Current ratio: 0.40

WAKE FOREST UNIVERSITY

Demon Deacons may sound like a weary clergyman's nightmare but at Wake Forest they're something to cheer about. Wake Forest University (WFU) home of the Demon Deacon mascot is a private liberal arts institution that operates through about half a dozen colleges and schools: law medicine arts and sciences business and accountancy management and divinity. WFU provides more than 35 majors and offers a low student-faculty ratio of 11:1. Its 7700 students can also study abroad in France Spain Japan and Cuba among other countries. WFU was established in 1834 in Wake Forest North Carolina. It moved to its present location in Winston-Salem in 1956.

Operations

With more than 480 teaching faculty members WFU is ranked among the top 30 universities in the nation. It offers nearly 30 graduate-level programs and about a dozen areas of PhD study. Its graduate schools include those in arts and sciences law medicine management and divinity. It conducts its executive education programs including its evening and Saturday MBA degree programs at the Wake Forest University Charlotte Center the former International Trade Center building located at 200 North College St. that WFU has leased through Bank of America since 2011.

Geographic Reach

The school has several primary and affiliate campuses — Wake Forest main campus Wake Forest University Baptist Medical Center Piedmont Triad Research Park BB&T Field and The Reynolda Campus — all located in Winston-Salem North Carolina. WFU also operates university-owned properties for students studying abroad in Venice Vienna and London. The university extends its reach to France Spain Cuba and Japan through alliances with other universities. WFU students come from 48 US states and Washington DC and 46 other countries.

Sales and Marketing

Since 1986 the university has produced nearly a dozen Rhodes Scholars and several Marshall and Fulbright recipients. More than half of WFU's student body spends at least one semester studying abroad. They stay in houses owned by the university in London Venice or Vienna or they study at partner universities in Cuba Spain Japan or France.

Financial Performance

The not-for-profit university posted revenue of $1.4 billion in fiscal 2016 (ended June) compared to $1.2 billion a year earlier thanks to higher tuition and fees grants contributions and patient revenue among others. Operating excess declined from $48.1 million to $32.5 million as higher revenue topped a stronger increase costs in wages services and clinical and laboratory supplies.

Strategy

WFU's capital campaign are targeted toward scholarships faculty research strengthening the university's libraries and the construction of new facilities.

EXECUTIVES

President, Nathan O. Hatch
Associate Vp Information Technology And Cio, Mur Muchane
Ceo Wake Forest Baptist Medical Center, John D. McConnell, age 64
Provost, Rogan Kersh
Evp Finance And Administration And Cfo, Hof Milam
Dean Of The Divinity School, Gail R. O'Day
Dean School Of Medicine, Edward Abraham
Dean Z. Smith Reynolds Library, Lynn Sutton
Dean School Of Business, Charles L. Iacovou
Interim Dean School Of Law, Suzanne Reynolds
Dean Graduate Programs In Arts And Sciences, Brad Jones
Dean Graduate Programs In Biomedical Sciences, Dwayne Godwin
Co-interim Dean Of The College, Randall G. (Randy) Rogan
Co-interim Dean Of The College, Rebecca S. Thomas
Assistant Vice President Hospitality S, John Wise
Vice President, Mark Petersen
Vice President And General Counsel, James Morgan
Assistant Vice President Director Of Advancement Services, Snyder Tim
Vice President, Peter Marsh
Vice President For Student Life And Instructional Resources, Kenneth Zick
Associate Vice President And Editor At, Glenda Henson
Assistant Vice President Gift Planning And Marketing, Shaida Horner
Vice President Assistant, Shayla Herndon
Associate Vice President For Information Technology And Chief Officer Information Systems Department, Mary Muchane
Senior Vice President, Ed Wilson
Chair Board Of Trustees, Donald E. Flow
Vice Chair Board Of Trustees, Bobby R. Burchfield
Vice Chair Board Of Trustees, Donna A. Boswell
Auditors: KPMG LLP GREENSBORO NC

LOCATIONS

HQ: WAKE FOREST UNIVERSITY
1834 WAKE FOREST RD # 7326, WINSTON SALEM, NC 271096054
Phone: 336 758-5000
Web: WWW.WFU.EDU

PRODUCTS/OPERATIONS

Selected Schools
Graduate School
School of Business
School of Divinity
School of Law
School of Medicine
Undergraduate College

Company Type: Private

Income Statement   FYE: June 30

	REVENUE ($ mil.)	NET INCOME ($ mil.)	NET PROFIT MARGIN	EMPLOYEES
06/16	1,339	5	0.4%	4,860
06/13	496	82	16.6%	—
06/11	459	77	16.9%	—
06/10	1,155	97	8.5%	—
Annual Growth	2.5%	(38.3%)	—	—

2016 Year-End Financials

Return on assets: 18.9%   Cash ($ mil.): 95
Return on equity: 0.4%
Current ratio: —

WAKEMED

If you wake up in a hospital in Wake County North Carolina you may be at one of WakeMed health system's facilities. WakeMed is a network of medical centers including two hospitals outpatient and emergency clinics rehabilitation facilities skilled nursing centers laboratories physicians' offices and home care service agencies. Its hospitals the WakeMed Raleigh Campus and the WakeMed Cary Hospital include specialty divisions such as heart care stroke trauma critical care diabetes asthma and children's and women's centers. Combined its facilities offer more than 900 beds. WakeMed also conducts research and medical training programs.

Operations

WakeMed's a network of health care facilities include a 575-bed regional referral center with an adjoining 84-bed rehabilitation hospital in Raleigh; a 156-bed full-service community hospital in Cary; a freestanding emergency department outpatient surgery and diagnostic center with physicians' offices in North Raleigh; freestanding emergency departments and diagnostic centers in Apex Brier Creek and Garner; Raleigh Medical Park a pre-admission testing site adjacent to the Raleigh campus hospital; a medical office building with diagnostic and outpatient rehabilitation services in Clayton and Holly Springs; a medical office building with diagnostic outpatient rehabilitation and physician offices in West Raleigh; a mobile critical care transport service including an air ambulance service; and home health and outpatient rehabilitation services in Raleigh Cary Apex Zebulon and Fuquay-Varina.

These facilities handle about 46000 inpatient visits 7500 births and 249000 emergency room visits each year. The system's pediatric emergency room (located in the Raleigh Campus' children's hospital wing) sees about 40000 children per year. Other units provide mobile critical care and emergency transportation by ground and air. The organization also provides some $244 million in community benefits each year as well including charity care unpaid Medicare bills health profession education and improvement and outreach programs.

WakeMed's medical staff includes more than 1000 affiliated physicians and 1000 volunteers. The WakeMed Physician Practices organization includes about 260 doctors who operate primary care and specialist offices in the region.

Geographic Reach

The company facilities throughout Wake and Johnston counties include Raleigh Campus Cary

Hospital North Healthplex Apex Healthplex Brier Creek Healthplex Garner Healthplexa and Clayton Medical Park.

Strategy

In 2014 the company completed the construction on an expansion at WakeMed North Health-plex in Raleigh North Carolina. The $66.3 million project transformed the facility into a full-service facility called WakeMed North Hospital. The five-story 131000-square-foot 61-bed acute care hospital focuses on inpatient women's specialty services and offer a range of obstetric and gynecological services including comprehensive preventive diagnostic and therapeutic care. In addition WakeMed North Hospital will continue to serve men and children through the facility's existing emergency department and outpatient surgery rehabilitation imaging lab and physician services.

Company Background

The company has expanded its Raleigh Campus to include a new patient tower with intensive care cardiac care and pediatric facilities. Construction of the patient tower — featuring two new heart and vascular inpatient floors a mother's milk bank and Wake County's only dedicated Children's Hospital — was completed in 2010. The organization expanded its pediatric services further in 2012 when it formed a partnership with Duke Medicine to provide collaborative specialist care to children in the region. In addition WakeMed expanded the Raleigh Campus' rehabilitation unit in 2012 and 2013 by adding additional patient beds.

To expand its outpatient facilities WakeMed opened a sixth emergency department in 2011 at the Brier Creek Healthplex adding a dozen private rooms diagnostic imaging units lab services and doctors' offices. In 2012 the system added a new diagnostic clinic and an outpatient surgery center near the Raleigh Campus.

WakeMed was founded in 1961.

EXECUTIVES

President And Ceo, Donald R. Gintzig
Svp Finance Chief Compliance Officer And Cfo, Michael D. DeVaughn
Senior Vp Physician Services, John S. Piatkowski
Evp Operations And Ambulatory Development, Kathleen K. Gormley
Vp; Svp President And Ceo Harnett Health System, Kenneth Bryan
Evp And Coo, Tom Gettinger
Vice President Human Resources, Jeanene R Martin
Secretary Supplemental Staffing, Keri Raper
Auditors: ERNST & YOUNG US LLP CHARLOTT

LOCATIONS

HQ: WAKEMED
3000 NEW BERN AVE G100, RALEIGH, NC 276101231
Phone: 919 350-8000
Web: WWW.WAKEMED.ORG

PRODUCTS/OPERATIONS

Selected North Carolina Facilities
Blue Ridge Surgery Center (Raleigh)
Brier Creek Healthplex (Raleigh)
Knightdale Medical Building (Knightdale)
WakeMed Apex Healthplex (Apex)
WakeMed Brier Creek Medical Park (Raleigh)
WakeMed Cary Hospital (Cary)
WakeMed Clayton Medical Park (Clayton)
WakeMed Fuquay-Varina Outpatient and Skilled Nursing Facility (Fuquay-Varina)
WakeMed Garner HealthPlex (Garner)
WakeMed Home Health (Raleigh)
WakeMed North Healthplex (Raleigh)
WakeMed Raleigh Campus (Raleigh)
 WakeMed Rehab Hospital (Raleigh)
WakeMed Wake Forest Road Outpatient Rehab Center (Raleigh)

WakeMed Zebulon/Wendell Outpatient and Skilled Nursing Facility (Zebulon)

COMPETITORS

Carolinas HealthCare System	Morehead Memorial Hospital
Cone Health	Novant Health
Cumberland County Hospital System	Rex Healthcare
Duke University Health System	Rowan Regional Medical Center
FirstHealth of the Carolinas	Vidant Health

HISTORICAL FINANCIALS

Company Type: Private

Income Statement — FYE: September 30

	REVENUE ($ mil.)	NET INCOME ($ mil.)	NET PROFIT MARGIN	EMPLOYEES
09/15	1,065	(32)	—	16,933
09/09	883	0	—	—
09/08	837	12	1.5%	—
Annual Growth	3.5%	—	—	—

2015 Year-End Financials

Return on assets: 13.0%
Return on equity: (-3.1%)
Current ratio: 1.10

Cash ($ mil.): 467

WASHINGTON COUNTY BOARD OF EDUCATION

EXECUTIVES

Pres, Donna Brightman
Vice President, Justin Hartings
Information Technology/Interne, Donna French
Auditors: SMITH ELLIOTT KEARNS & COMPANY

LOCATIONS

HQ: WASHINGTON COUNTY BOARD OF EDUCATION
10435 DOWNSVILLE PIKE, HAGERSTOWN, MD 217401732
Phone: 301 766-2800
Web: WWW.WCPSHR.COM

HISTORICAL FINANCIALS

Company Type: Private

Income Statement — FYE: June 30

	REVENUE ($ mil.)	NET INCOME ($ mil.)	NET PROFIT MARGIN	EMPLOYEES
06/18	308	(1)	—	137
06/17	299	(2)	—	—
06/15	310	6	2.1%	—
06/14	306	(1)	—	—
Annual Growth	0.2%	—	—	—

2018 Year-End Financials

Return on assets: 2.3%
Return on equity: (-0.5%)
Current ratio: 0.80

Cash ($ mil.): 22

WASHINGTON HEALTHCARE PHYSICIANS, MARY

EXECUTIVES

Ceo, Fred M Ryan III
Chief Financial Officer, Sean T Barden
Chief Operating Officer, Walter J Kiwall
Health Professional, April Dillow
Director, Amy Lamb
Supervisor, Cathy Green
Manager, Karen Ennis
Manager, Linda Wallace
Marketing Director, Lisa Henry
Auditors: ARNETT CARBIS TOOTHMAN NEW CA

LOCATIONS

HQ: WASHINGTON HEALTHCARE PHYSICIANS, MARY
2300 FALL HILL AVE # 314, FREDERICKSBURG, VA 224013343
Phone: 540 741-1100
Web: WWW.MWMD-ACO.COM

HISTORICAL FINANCIALS

Company Type: Private

Income Statement — FYE: June 30

	REVENUE ($ mil.)	NET INCOME ($ mil.)	NET PROFIT MARGIN	EMPLOYEES
06/18*	328	1	0.4%	163
12/16	610	30	5.0%	—
12/15	584	17	3.1%	—
Annual Growth	(25.0%)	(73.8%)	—	—

*Fiscal year change

WASHINGTON HOSPITAL CENTER CORPORATION

Washington Hospital Center (doing business as MedStar Washington Hospital Center) may be the official hospital of the Washington Redskins but you don't have to be a professional football player to make use of the facility's services. The hospital at the heart of the MedStar Health system serves some 500000 patients living in and around the nation's capital each year. Washington Hospital Center has 912 beds and includes specialized care centers for cancer cardiovascular conditions and stroke. Other offerings include organ transplantation a regional burn treatment center and emergency air transportation. MedStar Washington also conducts clinical research and offers educational residency and fellowship programs.

Operations

MedStar Washington has about 1350 doctors and dentists on staff; many of whom are involved in Washington Hospital Center's 520 clinical research studies. The hospital is affiliated with the medical schools of The George Washington University Georgetown University Johns Hopkins and several other regional educational institutions. Its Cardiac Ventricular Assist Device program is accredited by The Joint Commission.

The hospital is also home to MedSTAR one of the country's top shock-trauma and medevac programs and also operates the region's only adult burn center.

MedStar Washington has some 390000 outpatient and 37000 inpatient visits each year. It also provides care for some 3500 births and some 87000 emergency department visits.

Company Background

Washington Hospital Center was created through the merger of three regional hospitals: Emergency Garfield and Episcopal Eye Ear and Throat. The actual idea of the Hospital Center was conceived in 1943 but it took nearly 15 years for funding planning and construction to be completed.

EXECUTIVES

Svp Medstar Washington Hospital Center; Chief Administrative Officer Medstar Heart And Vascular Institute, Cathie Monge
President, John Sullivan
Coo, Robert S. Ross
Cfo, William Gayne
Senior Vice President Administrative Services, James Hill
Vice President Performance Improvement And Safety, Frederick Finelli
Vice President Medical Staff Development, Anthony Watkins
Assistant Secretary And Assistant Treasu, Rafael Convit

LOCATIONS

HQ: WASHINGTON HOSPITAL CENTER CORPORATION
110 IRVING ST NW, WASHINGTON, DC 200103017
Phone: 855 546-1686
Web: WWW.WHCENTER.ORG

COMPETITORS

Adventist HealthCare	HSC Pediatric Center
Bon Secours Health	Inova
Children's National	Mary Washington
Medical Center	Healthcare
Dimensions Healthcare	Sibley Memorial
Doctors Community	Hospital
Hospital	Suburban Hospital

HISTORICAL FINANCIALS

Company Type: Private

Income Statement — FYE: June 30

	REVENUE ($ mil.)	NET INCOME ($ mil.)	NET PROFIT MARGIN	EMPLOYEES
06/16	1,166	36	3.1%	5,637
06/15	1,121	23	2.1%	—
06/14	1,107	22	2.1%	—
06/08	1,028	14	1.4%	—
Annual Growth	1.6%	12.3%	—	—

2016 Year-End Financials

Return on assets: 3.0%   Cash ($ mil.): —
Return on equity: 3.1%
Current ratio: 1.00

WASHINGTON REGIONAL MEDICAL CENTER

Washington Regional Medical System (formerly Washington Regional Medical Center) provides acute care services to the people of northwestern Arkansas. The system's main hospital has about 370 beds in Fayetteville and also includes assisted living facilities home health and hospice services and general practice and specialty clinics. Specialty services at the medical center include cardiac and vascular care (Walker Family Heart and Vascular Institute) emergency medicine kidney dialysis women's health services (Johnelle Hunt Women's Center) cancer treatment and rehabilitation.

Geographic Reach

Washington Regional Medical System's is the only not-for-profit community-owned and locally governed healthcare system in Northwest Arkansas.

Strategy

Upgrading its health record technology in 2013 the system contracted InteliChart Patient Portal and InteliChart Health Information Exchange (HIE). InteliChart's platform which includes interactive patient and HIE portals allows all of Washington Regional Medical System's providers to overcome interoperability challenges helping its care delivery teams to better manage patients as they transition between the health system's providers and care settings.

Company Background

Striving to expand its reach and attract additional patients Washington Regional Medical System in 2011 added Washington Regional Rheumatology Clinic Washington Regional Sleep Medicine and Harrison Family Practice Clinic to its network of clinics.

Washington Regional Medical System started out in 1950 as Washington County Hospital and moved into its modern facility in 2002. The system completed a $64 million expansion effort in 2008 that added over 100 beds and enhanced emergency senior support and pharmacy units.

EXECUTIVES

Pres-Ceo, William L Bradley
President, Mark Bever
Cfo, Dan Eckels
Vice President, Thomas J Olmstead
Vice President, Larry Shackelford
Director of Respiratory Therap, Bill Brown
Infection Control Coordinator, Nancy Malone
Chief of Dentistry, Annette K Sharma
Chief of Pediatric, Brent J Silvey
Chief Officer, David G Ratcliff
Chief Staff, Ted Fish

LOCATIONS

HQ: WASHINGTON REGIONAL MEDICAL CENTER
3215 N NORTHHILLS BLVD, FAYETTEVILLE, AR 727034424
Phone: 479 463-6000
Web: WWW.WREGIONAL.COM

PRODUCTS/OPERATIONS

Selected Medical Services
Assisted Living
Asthma
Bariatric
Bone Density
Cancer Services
Center for Exercise
Clinical Research
Diabetes Education
Dialysis
Emergency Services
Faith In Action
Gynecologic Oncology
Gynecology
Heart Health
Home Health
Hospice
Hyperbaric Oxygen Therapy
Imaging
IV Infusion
LIFELINE Personal Emergency Response System
Mammography
Neurology
Neurosurgery
Obstetrics
Pain Management
Pelvic Therapy
Senior Health
Senior Specialty Unit
Sleep Disorders
Urology
Women's Health
Wound Care
Hospitals Facilities and Clinics
Cancer Support Home
  Cancer Sup
  Cancer Sup
Centers for Health
  Pat Walker Center for Seniors
  Springdale Center for Health
Dialysis
  Benton County Dialysis Center
  Dialysis Center of Siloam Springs
  North Hills Dialysis Center
Exercise Center
  Washington Regional Center for Exercise
Hospital
  Washington Regional Medical Center
Medical Clinics
  Crossroads Medical Clinic
  East Springdale Family Clinic
  Eureka Springs Family Clinic
  Farmington Family Clinic
  Fayetteville Family Clinic
  Har-Ber Family Clinic
  Harrison Family Practice Clinic
  HerHealth - Johnelle Hunt Women's Center - Washington Regional Medical Center
  HerHealth
  Internal Medicine Associates
  Northwest Arkansas Neuroscience Institute
  Ozark Urology
  Rheumatology Clinic
  Shiloh Clinic
  Sleep Medicine Clinic
  Walker Heart Institute Cardiovascular Clinic
  Walker Heart Institute Harrison Cardiology Clinic
  Senior Health Clinic
  Washington Regional Diagnostic Clinic
  Washington Regional Memory Clinic
  Washington Regional Wound Care Clinic
Surgery Center
  North Hills Surgery Center

COMPETITORS

Baptist Health	Community Health
(Arkansas)	Systems
Baxter Regional	Mercy Health
Medical Center	Sparks Health System

HISTORICAL FINANCIALS

Company Type: Private

Income Statement — FYE: December 31

	REVENUE ($ mil.)	NET INCOME ($ mil.)	NET PROFIT MARGIN	EMPLOYEES
12/16	300	58	19.5%	2,000
12/15	245	45	18.5%	—
12/14	213	34	16.3%	—
12/12	205	33	16.4%	—
Annual Growth	10.0%	14.8%	—	—

2016 Year-End Financials

Return on assets: 7.5%   Cash ($ mil.): 36
Return on equity: 19.5%
Current ratio: 1.50

WASHINGTON REGIONAL MEDICAL SYSTEM

EXECUTIVES

Pres, Lary Shackelford
Sr V Pres-Cfo, Dan Eckels
Exe Vp, Mark Bevers
Sr Vp, Tom Olmstead
Coordinator, Darwin G Shope
Coordinator, Christina Hill
Hospitalist, Connie Drapcho
Hospitalist, Jon McCowan
Team Leader Ep, Lance House
Family Practitioner, Richard D Tutt
Director, Sabrina Lawrence

LOCATIONS

HQ: WASHINGTON REGIONAL MEDICAL SYSTEM
3215 N NORTHHILLS BLVD, FAYETTEVILLE, AR
727034424
Phone: 479 463-1000
Web: WWW.WREGIONAL.COM

HISTORICAL FINANCIALS
Company Type: Private

Income Statement				FYE: December 31
	REVENUE ($ mil.)	NET INCOME ($ mil.)	NET PROFIT MARGIN	EMPLOYEES
12/17	389	33	8.7%	2,100
12/12	239	33	13.8%	—
12/09	14	(3)	—	—
12/01	148	7	5.0%	—
Annual Growth	6.2%	10.0%	—	—

2017 Year-End Financials
Return on assets: 3.3% Cash ($ mil.): 31
Return on equity: 8.7%
Current ratio: 1.60

WASHINGTON SUBURBAN SANITARY COMMISSION (INC)

Used water in clean water out is the job description of the Washington Suburban Sanitary Commission (WSSC). The utility provides water and wastewater services in Maryland's Montgomery and Prince George's counties just outside the nation's capital. WSSC serves 460000 customers representing 1.8 million residents in an area of about 1000 square miles. The agency draws water from the Potomac and Patuxent rivers and maintains three reservoirs. The commission also operates two water filtration plants six wastewater treatment plants and some 11000 miles of sewer and water main lines including a network of nearly 5600 miles of fresh water pipeline and over 5400 miles of sewer pipeline.

Operations
WSSC's three reservoirs (Triadelphia Rocky Gorge and Little Seneca) along with Jennings Randolph Reservoir which it shares with Fairfax Water and the Washington Aqueduct have a total holding capacity of 27 billion gallons. Its two water filtration plants (Patuxent and Potomac) produce nearly 170 million gallons of drinking water daily. The commission handles some 72 million gallons of wastewater daily through its six treatment plants (Damascus Hyattstown Parkway Piscataway Seneca and Western Branch).

Financial Performance
The company reported operating revenue of about $698 million in fiscal 2014 (ended June) up about 2% from the prior year. The growth was powered by an increase in water and sewer billing rates.

WSSC's proposed budgets for 2014 and 2015 were $1.5 billion and $1.3 billion respectively.

Company Background
WSSC was established in 1918.

EXECUTIVES

Chief Engineer, Gary Gumm
General Manager, Jerry N. Johnson
Cfo, Yvette Downs
Cio, Mujib Lodhi
Chairman, Omar M. Boulware
Vice Chairman, Adrienne A. Mandel
Auditors: BCA WATSON RICE LLP WASHINGTO

LOCATIONS

HQ: WASHINGTON SUBURBAN SANITARY
COMMISSION (INC)
14501 SWEITZER LN, LAUREL, MD 207075901
Phone: 301 206-8000
Web: WWW.WSSCWATER.COM

HISTORICAL FINANCIALS
Company Type: Private

Income Statement				FYE: June 30
	REVENUE ($ mil.)	NET INCOME ($ mil.)	NET PROFIT MARGIN	EMPLOYEES
06/18	725	119	16.5%	2,000
06/17	725	179	24.7%	—
06/16	649	214	33.0%	—
06/15	645	192	29.9%	—
Annual Growth	4.0%	(14.7%)	—	—

2018 Year-End Financials
Return on assets: 28.7% Cash ($ mil.): 120
Return on equity: 16.5%
Current ratio: 0.40

WASHINGTON TEAMSTERS WELFARE TRUST

EXECUTIVES

Prin, Dean McInnes
Auditors: MILLER KAPLAN ARASE LLP SEATT

LOCATIONS

HQ: WASHINGTON TEAMSTERS WELFARE TRUST
2323 EASTLAKE AVE E, SEATTLE, WA 981023963
Phone: 206 329-4900
Web: WWW.WCTPENSION.ORG

HISTORICAL FINANCIALS
Company Type: Private

Income Statement				FYE: June 30
	REVENUE ($ mil.)	NET INCOME ($ mil.)	NET PROFIT MARGIN	EMPLOYEES
06/17	301	29	9.8%	3
06/12	228	(11)	—	—
06/10	196	(24)	—	—
06/09	192	0	—	—
Annual Growth	5.8%	—	—	—

2017 Year-End Financials
Return on assets: 0.1% Cash ($ mil.): 6
Return on equity: 9.8%
Current ratio: 76.90

WASHINGTON TOWNSHIP HEALTHCARE DISTRICT

EXECUTIVES

Ceo, Nancy Farber
Treas, Cathy Messman
Orthopedist, James M Hartford
Facilities Director, Robert Alfieri
Director, Bruce Nixon
Purchasing Director, Paulo Cruz
Director, Audrey Daly
Senior Director, David Divoky
Engineer, Greg Worth
Information Specialist, David Garcia
Pathologist, Elizabeth Treynor
Auditors: PRICEWATERHOUSECOOPERS LLP SA

LOCATIONS

HQ: WASHINGTON TOWNSHIP HEALTHCARE
DISTRICT
2000 MOWRY AVE, FREMONT, CA 945381716
Phone: 510 797-3342
Web: WWW.WHHS.COM

HISTORICAL FINANCIALS
Company Type: Private

Income Statement				FYE: June 30
	REVENUE ($ mil.)	NET INCOME ($ mil.)	NET PROFIT MARGIN	EMPLOYEES
06/18	526	27	5.3%	1,600
06/17	507	18	3.6%	—
Annual Growth	3.8%	50.6%	—	—

2018 Year-End Financials
Return on assets: 9.1% Cash ($ mil.): 34
Return on equity: 5.3%
Current ratio: 0.80

WASHOE COUNTY SCHOOL DISTRICT

EXECUTIVES

Spdt, Traci Davis
Payroll Staff, Barbara Hawkins
Coordinator, Diana Cox
Coordinator, Josephine J Johnson
Coordinator, Lynette Larson
Coordinator, Marianne Campbell
Coordinator, Mary Green
Information Specialist, Kelli Pennington
Staff, Mariah Evans
Coordinator, Trudy Nunn
Board of Director, Barbara Price

LOCATIONS

HQ: WASHOE COUNTY SCHOOL DISTRICT
425 E 9TH ST, RENO, NV 895122800
Phone: 775 348-0200
Web: WWW.WASHOESCHOOLS.NET

HISTORICAL FINANCIALS
Company Type: Private

Income Statement   FYE: June 30

	REVENUE ($ mil.)	NET INCOME ($ mil.)	NET PROFIT MARGIN	EMPLOYEES
06/17	640	57	8.9%	7,000
06/08	578	38	6.7%	—
06/06	479	67	14.1%	—
Annual Growth	2.7%	(1.5%)	—	—

WATONWAN FARM SERVICE, INC

EXECUTIVES

Ceo, Ed Bosanko
President, Todd Ludwig
Vice President, Mike Minnehan
Vice President, Craig Kilian
Dir, Harold Wolle
Treasurer, Dennis Hunwardsen
Manager, Energy Division, Randy Cole
Information Technology/Interne, Steve Gellert
Marketing Staff, Kevin Schweer
Financial Executive, Bill Day
Auditors: GARDINER THOMPSEN DES MOINES

LOCATIONS

HQ: WATONWAN FARM SERVICE, INC
233 W CIRO ST, TRUMAN, MN 560882018
Phone: 507 776-1244
Web: WWW.WFSAG.COM

COMPETITORS

ADM
Ag Processing Inc.
CHS
Cargill
Farm Service
  Cooperative
Farmers Cooperative
  Society
Gold-Eagle Cooperative
Heartland Co-op
Minn-Dak Co-op
NEW Cooperative
United Farmers
  Cooperative

HISTORICAL FINANCIALS
Company Type: Private

Income Statement   FYE: July 31

	REVENUE ($ mil.)	NET INCOME ($ mil.)	NET PROFIT MARGIN	EMPLOYEES
07/15	358	5	1.5%	255
07/14	468	7	1.7%	—
07/13	701	7	1.1%	—
07/12	592	6	1.1%	—
Annual Growth	(15.4%)	(7.9%)	—	—

2015 Year-End Financials

Return on assets: 1.9%   Cash ($ mil.): —
Return on equity: 1.5%
Current ratio: 0.30

WAUKESHA MEMORIAL HOSPITAL, INC.

Waukesha Memorial Hospital is a 300-bed teaching hospital that provides health care services for Wisconsin's Milwaukee Waukesha and DaneA counties. With aboutA 670 physicians representing several specialties and 2700 employees the hospitalA operates centers for excellence focused on cardiology oncology neurology women's health and orthopedics as well as emergency neonatal and family practice services.A Additionally Waukesha Memorial HospitalA conducts a physician residency program.A Established in 1914A theA medical facilityA is a subsidiary of not-for-profit ProHealth Care aA medical networkA that servesA southeastern Wisconsin with acute care and specialty health services.

Operations
ProHealth Care runs Waukesha Memorial Hospital alongside its other critical-care hospital Oconomowoc Memorial Hospital. As part of its operations the hospitalA boasts aA neuroscience center orthopedic center regional cancer center regional heartA and vascular center and a women's center. Its newborn intensive care unitA and its emergency department which averages more than 39000 visitsA are bothA Level III.

Geographic Reach
Despite its name Waukesha Memorial Hospital serves the residents of Milwaukee and Dane counties along with Waukesha County.

EXECUTIVES

Vpma, James Gardner
Vice President Of Revenue Cycle, Curtis Glaunert
Auditors: PLANTE & MORAN PLLC GRAND RA

LOCATIONS

HQ: WAUKESHA MEMORIAL HOSPITAL, INC.
725 AMERICAN AVE, WAUKESHA, WI 531885099
Phone: 262 928-1000

PRODUCTS/OPERATIONS

Selected Services
Birthing
  Blood / Ly
Bones Joints & Muscles
Brain & Nerves
Cancer
Cancer Second Opinion
Children's Health
CyberKnife
Diabetes

Diagnostic Services
Digestive
Ear Nose & Throat
Emergency Services/Urgent Care
Eyes & Vision
General Surgery
Genetics
Heart & Vascular
Infections
Integrative Medicine
Kidneys & Urinary System
  Lungs / Br
Men's Health
Mental Health
Nutrition
Orthopedic
Pain
Rehabilitation Services
Senior's Health
Sleep
Stroke
Wellness & Lifestyle
Women's Health

COMPETITORS

Children's Hospital and Health System
  Columbia St. Mary's
  Froedtert Hospital
  Hospital Sisters Health System
  Ministry Health Care
  SwedishAmerican Health System
  University of Wisconsin Hospital and Clinics

HISTORICAL FINANCIALS
Company Type: Private

Income Statement   FYE: September 30

	REVENUE ($ mil.)	NET INCOME ($ mil.)	NET PROFIT MARGIN	EMPLOYEES
09/17	470	59	12.6%	2,071
09/16	457	37	8.3%	—
09/15	460	29	6.3%	—
09/14	420	76	18.3%	—
Annual Growth	3.8%	(8.3%)	—	—

2017 Year-End Financials

Return on assets: 10.3%   Cash ($ mil.): 4
Return on equity: 12.6%
Current ratio: 1.00

WAUKESHA-PEARCE INDUSTRIES, INC.

Waukesha-Pearce Industries (WPI) wants its customers to start their engines. Through its Engine Division the company designs and packages engine-driven equipment such as power generators pumps blowers control panels and switchgear. WPI also offers a slate of heavy construction and mining products including earth movers and demolition equipment made by such OEMs as Komatsu and Gradall Industries through its Construction Machinery Division. As part of its business the company sells used equipment and leases heavy earth-moving equipment. Founded as Portable Rotary Rig Co. in 1924 by Louis M. Pearce Sr. the company is owned and run by the Pearce family.

Operations
WPI's Engine Equipment lineup includes its own Enginator used in field gas compression and power generation. Its Engine Division further supports WPI's performance by offering less economy-driven services such as certified remanufactured engines and revamping.

WPI's Construction Machinery arm benefits from a broad products portfolio paired with distributor affiliations. Such alliances include Bomag (compaction equipment) Allied/Rammer (demolition equipment) Esco Crushing (wearparts) Sennebogen (material handling) and Valmet (cranes). Like the Engine Equipment Division this segment is able to mitigate a recession's impact on capital equipment sales by providing repair and onsite maintenance services along with a multi-million-dollar inventory of used and rental equipment and parts.

The company also offers construction and mining products from equipment brands such as Komatsu Gradall Takeuchi Doppstadt NPK LaBounty and Vacall.

Geographic Reach
From its headquarters in Houston WPI serves customers through more than a dozen locations in Texas and another 15 across Louisiana Oklahoma New Mexico Arkansas Alabama Kansas California Rhode Island Pennsylvania and West Virginia. The company's training facility is located in Sugar Land Texas outside Houston.

Sales and Marketing
Core markets for WPI include land clearing highway and heavy construction site development mining scrap petrochemical energy exploration and utility construction as well as a number of government agencies.

EXECUTIVES

President, Louis M. Pearce
Vice President, Jim Adian

LOCATIONS

HQ: WAUKESHA-PEARCE INDUSTRIES, INC.
12320 MAIN ST, HOUSTON, TX 770356206
Phone: 713 723-1050
Web: WWW.WPI.COM

PRODUCTS/OPERATIONS

Selected Services
Earth moving
Gas compression
Mining
Power generation
Recycling
Service and replacement parts
Small engine and lawn

Selected Products
Engines
  Arrow VR engines
  BOB-CAT mowers
  Dresser Waukesha
  Generac Industrial
  Generac Residential
  HIPOWER generating sets
  Kohler engines
  Little Wonder products
  Mantis yard & garden products
  Powerhouse catalytic converters
  Remanufactured engines
  Revamp services
  Ryan turf renovation products
  WPI brand
Construction Machinery
  Allied/Rammer
  Bomag
  Bucyrus Blades
  Cummins Engines
  Dressta
  Esco
  Fleetguard Filters
  Gradall
  Hensley
  JRB
  Komatsu
  LaBounty
  Sennebogen
  Valmet

COMPETITORS

AGCO	Deere
Berry Companies	Dewey Electronics
Caterpillar	Emerson Electric
Connell Company	Kubota
Cummins Power Generation	

HISTORICAL FINANCIALS
Company Type: Private

Income Statement   FYE: March 31

	REVENUE ($ mil.)	NET INCOME ($ mil.)	NET PROFIT MARGIN	EMPLOYEES
03/16	423	2	0.5%	600
03/15	461	8	1.9%	—
03/11	248	4	1.9%	—
03/10	197	1	0.8%	—
Annual Growth	13.5%	3.2%	—	—

2016 Year-End Financials
Return on assets: 9.7%   Cash ($ mil.): —
Return on equity: 0.5%
Current ratio: 0.60

WAYNE COUNTY AIRPORT AUTHORITY

EXECUTIVES

Ceo, Joseph R Nardone
Prin, Lester Robinson
Customer Staff, John Orner
Real Estate Conultant, Wendy Sutton
Supervisor, Danielle Perkins
Auditors: PLANTE & MORAN PLLC SOUTHFIEL

LOCATIONS

HQ: WAYNE COUNTY AIRPORT AUTHORITY
11050 ROGELL DR BLDG 602, DETROIT, MI
482421144
Phone: 734 247-7678
Web: WWW.WCAA.US

HISTORICAL FINANCIALS
Company Type: Private

Income Statement   FYE: September 30

	REVENUE ($ mil.)	NET INCOME ($ mil.)	NET PROFIT MARGIN	EMPLOYEES
09/17	368	(24)	—	675
09/16	363	(30)	—	—
09/15	349	(60)	—	—
09/14	339	(22)	—	—
Annual Growth	2.7%	—	—	—

WAYNE J. GRIFFIN ELECTRIC, INC.

Wayne J. Griffin Electric brings a certain spark to New England and the Southeast. With offices in Massachusetts Georgia North Carolina and Alabama the electrical contractor offers construction and installation services on hospitals hotels industrial and high-tech buildings offices prisons research laboratories retirement communities and schools. The company's service division provides small project management and facility maintenance while its telecom division designs and installs fiber optics fire alarm and security systems as well as systems that control energy use from lighting to heating ventilation and air conditioning (HVAC). Founded in 1978 Wayne J. Griffin Electric is privately held.

Sales and Marketing
Since serving its first major customer the Coca-Cola Bottling Company at its Massachusetts plant Wayne J. Griffin Electric has been expanding into different commercial industrial and institutional sectors. It has worked for such clients as Boeing and EMC Corporation. It has also worked on electrical expansion projects for the Valley Creek Wastewater Treatment Facility in Alabama and the Raleigh-Durham International Airport in North Carolina.

Additional clients have included EMC Corporation TJX Companies Verizon and Liberty Mutual.

Strategy
Wayne J. Griffin Electric utilizes such tools as Building Information Modeling (BIM) technology to provide its customers with the best plans possible. The firm has continued to broaden its areas of expertise so that it can serve clients of many sectors from educational and institutional to industrial and corporate.

EXECUTIVES

President And Ceo, Wayne J. Griffin
Auditors: CITRIN COOPERMAN & COMPANY LL

LOCATIONS

HQ: WAYNE J. GRIFFIN ELECTRIC, INC.
116 HOPPING BROOK RD, HOLLISTON, MA
017461455
Phone: 508 429-8830
Web: WWW.WAYNEJGRIFFINELECTRIC.COM

COMPETITORS

ADCO Electrical	IES Holdings
Bergelectric	J.F. White Contracting
E-J Electric Installation Co.	Mass Electric
EMCOR	Quanta Services

HISTORICAL FINANCIALS
Company Type: Private

Income Statement   FYE: December 31

	REVENUE ($ mil.)	NET INCOME ($ mil.)	NET PROFIT MARGIN	EMPLOYEES
12/17	355	29	8.3%	1,100
12/16	333	27	8.2%	—
12/15	303	22	7.4%	—
12/14	293	27	9.4%	—
Annual Growth	6.6%	2.6%	—	—

2017 Year-End Financials
Return on assets: 6.8%   Cash ($ mil.): 38
Return on equity: 8.3%
Current ratio: 1.10

WAYNE STATE UNIVERSITY

Wayne State University is a public university with an annual enrollment of more than 27000 students and a student-to-teacher ratio of 16:1. It offers more than 350 bachelor's master's and doctoral degree programs as well as certificate specialist and professional programs through about a dozen colleges and schools. Located in midtown Detroit WSU traces its heritage back to 1868 with the founding of the Detroit Medical College now part of its School of Medicine. Prominent alumni include US Congressman John Conyers radio DJ Casey Kasem and actor Tom Sizemore.

Geographic Reach

WSU's 200-acre campus includes about 100 academic research and residential buildings. The university also has six satellite campuses around Detroit and five extension centers offering educational programs across southeastern Michigan.

It has affiliations with more than 100 institutions globally and offers study abroad programs in 20 countries.

The school hosts students from every US state and 70 countries.

Financial Performance

Operating revenue grew from $863 million in 2015 to $876 million in 2016 thanks to higher net student tuition and fees (31% of overall revenue) and higher non-operating revenue (including $39 million in capital gifts for the construction of a new business school).

Expenses dropped from $857 million in 2015 to $846 million in 2016 primarily due a reduction in academic staffing headcount.

Strategy

WSU is a partner in the University Research Corridor with the University of Michigan and Michigan State University. This program generates 95% of research in the state of Michigan.

It is also engaged in new construction. It is building a $50 million business school (the Mike Ilitch School of Business due to open in 2018) and WSU also plans to expand and improve its student housing facilities.

EXECUTIVES

Cio And Associate Vp Computing And
 Information Technology, Joseph F. Sawasky
President, M. Roy Wilson
Svp Academic Affairs And Provost, Margaret E.
 Winters
Cfo, Rick Nork
Assistant Vice President For Research
 Compliance, Phil Cunningham
Assistant Vice President, Mark Byrd
Clinical Director, BE Skip Mcclatchey
Chair, Gary S. Pollard
Vice Chair, Paul E. Massaron
Auditors: PLANTE & MORAN PLLC CLINTON

LOCATIONS

HQ: WAYNE STATE UNIVERSITY
 656 W KIRBY ST, DETROIT, MI 482023622
Phone: 313 577-2230
Web: WWW.WAYNE.EDU

PRODUCTS/OPERATIONS

Selected Colleges and Schools
College of Education
College of Engineering
College of Fine Performing and Communication Arts
College of Liberal Arts and Sciences
College of Nursing

Eugene Applebaum College of Pharmacy and Health
 Sciences
Irvin D. Reid Honors College
Law School
School of Business Administration
School of Library and Information Science
School of Medicine
School of Social Work
The Graduate School

HISTORICAL FINANCIALS

Company Type: Private

Income Statement   FYE: September 30

	REVENUE ($ mil.)	NET INCOME ($ mil.)	NET PROFIT MARGIN	EMPLOYEES
09/17	640	46	7.2%	8,500
09/11	520	(15)	—	—
09/05	445	37	8.4%	—
09/04	418	(3)	—	—
Annual Growth	3.3%			

2017 Year-End Financials
Return on assets: 15.6%   Cash ($ mil.): 355
Return on equity: 7.2%
Current ratio: 1.80

WELCH FOODS INC., A COOPERATIVE

Welch Foods has a taste for the grape. An operating subsidiary of the 1000-plus-farmer owner National Grape Cooperative Welch produces the Welch's brand grape and white grape juices and jellies. Its beverage line includes refrigerated and sparkling juices and cocktails frozen and shelf-stable concentrates and single-serve drinks. Welch supplies fresh grapes as well as preserved offerings (jams and spreads) which are also sold under the BAMA label. The co-op licenses the Welch's name to other manufactures of frozen fruit confections dried fruit and carbonated beverages among many. Its 400-plus products are purchased by grocery retailers and food service operators in the US and 40 other countries.

Geographic Reach

Massachusetts-based Welch Foods has vineyards in Pennsylvania Michigan New York Ohio Washington and Ontario Canada. It sells its products in the US and some 40 other countries.

Financial Performance

National Grape Cooperative and Welch Foods's sales grew to $608.5 million in 2014. Volume grew 4% during the year with its Bottled 100% Juice product leading the way with 11% growth though all core product categories showed market share and volume growth. Spread sales grew by 7% during the year while refrigerated juices grew by 8%.

The cooperative's net proceeds jumped significantly to $84 million in FY2014 the second highest level in its history according to the company.

Strategy

Welch Foods and National Grape Cooperative regularly introduce new juices and grape-based products and in 2015 stated it was "committed to research and development that will meet the growing demand for products that address consumers' health and nutrition needs." During 2014 it increased investment in its successful Bottled 100% Juice line and launched Farmer's Pick a new 100% Juice line featuring unfiltered juice. In mid-2012 the coop launched four new flavors (lemonade strawberry lemonade raspberry limeade and mango) of its sparkling juice cocktails resulting in a 29% increase in volume during the summer months and market share gain during the holiday season. Welch Foods low-growth spreads business got a boost in 2012 with the launch of Welch's Nautrals an all natural no high fructose corn syrup formation that resonated with consumers.

The co-op has also been making investments in efficiency to cut its overhead costs and boost proceeds for future growth. Its 2014 upgrade of its Sparkling line capacity and capabilities reduced material costs shortened lead teams eliminated waste and reduced overall costs by some $2 million per year. The new production line also doubled its processing speeds to up to 270 bottles per minute and introduced a new more efficient case configuration that allowed for more and better displays in retail stores.

EXECUTIVES

President And Ceo, Bradley C. Irwin, age 59
Chairman Of The Board, Joseph C. Falcone

LOCATIONS

HQ: WELCH FOODS INC., A COOPERATIVE
 300 BAKER AVE STE 101, CONCORD, MA 017422131
Phone: 978 371-1000
Web: WWW.WELCHS.COM

PRODUCTS/OPERATIONS

Selected Brands and Products
BAMA
 Jams jellies and preserves
 Peanut butter
Welch
 Bottled and canned juices
 Dried fruit
 Fresh table grapes
 Frozen juices
 Fruit juice bars
 Jams jellies and preserves
 Pourable concentrated juices
 Refrigerated juices
 Single-serve juices

COMPETITORS

Chiquita Brands	Old Orchard
Citrus World	Silver Springs
Coca-Cola	Smucker
Coloma Frozen Foods	Snapple
Dole Food	South Beach Beverage
Fresh Del Monte	Stapleton-Spence
Produce	Packing
Great Western Juice	Sun-Maid
Lion Raisins	Sunny Delight
Monster Beverage	Sunview Vineyards
Mott's	Tree Top
Naked Juice	Tropicana
National Raisin	Unilever NV
Ocean Spray	Wet Planet Beverages
Odwalla	

HISTORICAL FINANCIALS

Company Type: Private

Income Statement   FYE: August 31

	REVENUE ($ mil.)	NET INCOME ($ mil.)	NET PROFIT MARGIN	EMPLOYEES
08/16	600	83	14.0%	1,000
08/15	609	81	13.3%	—
08/14	609	76	12.6%	—
08/13	608	65	10.7%	—
Annual Growth	(0.5%)	8.8%	—	—

2016 Year-End Financials
Return on assets: 5.2%   Cash ($ mil.): 7
Return on equity: 14.0%
Current ratio: 0.50

WELLINGTON TRUST CO, NA

EXECUTIVES

Prin, Barry Mason
Information Specialist, Andrew Allen
Manager, Beth Evitts
Senior Vice President, Williams Gregory

LOCATIONS

HQ: WELLINGTON TRUST CO, NA
  280 CONGRESS ST, BOSTON, MA 022101023
Phone: 617 951-5500
Web: WWW.WELLINGTON.COM

HISTORICAL FINANCIALS

Company Type: Private

Income Statement   FYE: December 31

	ASSETS ($ mil.)	NET INCOME ($ mil.)	INCOME AS % OF ASSETS	EMPLOYEES
12/16	88	2	3.4%	2
12/15	94	1	1.2%	—
12/04	32	(0)	—	—
Annual Growth	8.9%	—	—	—

2016 Year-End Financials

Return on assets: —
Return on equity: 1.0%
Sales ($ mil.): 289

WELLSPAN MEDICAL GROUP (INC)

EXECUTIVES

Ceo, Tom McGann
Controller, Steffney Calp
Administrator, Laurie Brown

LOCATIONS

HQ: WELLSPAN MEDICAL GROUP (INC)
  140 N DUKE ST, YORK, PA 174011170
Phone: 717 851-6515

HISTORICAL FINANCIALS

Company Type: Private

Income Statement   FYE: June 30

	REVENUE ($ mil.)	NET INCOME ($ mil.)	NET PROFIT MARGIN	EMPLOYEES
06/16	375	(43)	—	709
06/15	336	(36)	—	—
06/14	251	(25)	—	—
06/13	228	(24)	—	—
Annual Growth	17.9%	—	—	—

2016 Year-End Financials

Return on assets: —
Return on equity: (-11.7%)
Current ratio: 0.60
Cash ($ mil.): 1

WELLSTAR HEALTH SYSTEM, INC.

With WellStar in your corner you won't need to wish upon a star for good health and wellness. The not-for-profit WellStar Health System is Georgia's largest health system with about a dozen hospitals two health parks a pediatric center and more than 200 medical office locations. The network's hospitals specialize in cardiac and cancer care diabetes treatments and women's health. WellStar's physician group includes more than 1100 providers. The network is also home to hospice and home care programs; Atherton Place an independent living center for senior citizens; and about 10 urgent care facilities.

Operations

WellStar's hospitals include Wellstar Cobb Hospital 382-beds; Wellstar Douglas Hospital 108-beds; WellStar Kennestone Hospital 633-beds; Wellstar Paulding Hospital 83-beds; and Wellstar Windy Hill Hospital 115-beds. The hospitals are connected to eight urgent care centers and 16 satellite diagnostic imaging centers.

Other network facilities offer outpatient medical imaging wound care and women's health and prenatal care. WellStar operates an outpatient cardiac group called Cardiovascular Medicine (CVM) one of Atlanta's largest cardiology groups joined the health system. WellStar CVM has 30 doctors practicing out of eight locations scattered throughout the region.

The health system also manages the WellStar Medical Group which is installing electronic medical records (EMR) at certain practices to connect patients with their records no matter which care site they visit. The project calls for EMRs to be put in place throughout the entire medical group as a way to improve quality of care and increase provider access to patient information. WellStar has more than 100 locations and 500 medical providers in 30 specialties.

The organization's WellStar Institute for Better Health provides patients and their families with programs resources and educational materials designed to promote healthy lifestyles. The institute also contributes to medical and scientific learning by supporting community-wide programs and keeping health care providers in the know about the latest treatments and procedures.

WellStar serves more than 1.4 million area residents; delivers more than 9000 babies each year; offers the only life-saving Level II trauma care in Cobb County; and serves more emergency room patients than any other health system in Georgia.

Financial Performance

The company's revenue increased by 6% to $1.6 billion in fiscal 2014 and revenues in excess of operating expenses grew by 22%.

It provides more than $200 million in unreimbursed care to the community WellStar incurred costs of more than $110 million to provide charity care to patients in Bartow Cherokee Cobb Douglas and Paulding counties in fiscal 2014. Its physicians and facilities made up a significant shortfall in reimbursements for patients on Medicaid ($25 million) and on Medicare ($98 million).

Strategy

To meet the growing demand in the market in 2015 WellStar Health System opened an Outpatient Surgery Center at the WellStar East Cobb Health Park.

WellStar Health System built a new hospital to replace the WellStar Paulding Hospital in Paulding County. In 2014 the company opened the Hiram-based hospital a 56-bed hospital with the capacity to expand to 112. There are four surgical suites and 40 emergency exam rooms plus a dedicated Pediatric Emergency Department. The hospital and adjacent medical office building were built next to WellStar's existing medical office building in Hiram. The campus includes an emergency department comprehensive surgical services a cancer center women's imaging and a range of other healthcare services.

Mergers and Acquisitions

In 2016 WellStar Health System acquired the Atlanta-based operations of Tenet Healthcare including five hospitals and 26 physician clinics. The purchase included Atlanta Medical Center (downtown) and Roswell's North Fulton Hospital.

Company Background

The hospital system was formed in 1993.

EXECUTIVES

Senior Vice President Supply Chain, Anthony Trupiano
President And Ceo, Reynold J. Jennings
Evp Human Resources Organizational Learning And Chief Compliance Officer, David Anderson
Svp; President Wellstar Cobb Hospital, Kem M. Mullins
Svp Real Estate And Construction And President Wellstar Paulding Hospital, Mark Haney
President And Ceo, Candice Saunders
Chief Medicine Division Officer, Jeffrey Tharp
Svp And Chief Nursing Executive, Mary Lou Wesley
Chief Cancer Network Officer, Michael Andrews
Chief Pediatrics Officer, Avril Beckford
Evp And Cfo, Jim Budzinski
Chief Obstetrics And Gynecology Officer, Perry (Chip) Busbee
Evp; President And Chief Administrative Medical Officer Wellstar Medical Group, Robert Jansen
Svp Post Acute Services; President Wellstar Windy Hill Hospital, Lou Little
Chief Cardiology Officer, Barry Mangel
Chief Surgical Officer, Bill Mayfield
Svp And Cio, Jon Morris
Chief Pulmonary Officer, Alan Muster
Svp; President Wellstar Douglas Hospital, Craig Owens
Evp And General Counsel, Leo Reichert
Svp; President Wellstar Kennestone Hospital, Dan Woods
Vp; Coo Wellstar Kennestone Hospital, Monte Wilson
Svp And President Wellstar Spalding Regional Hospital And Wellstar Sylvan Grove Hospital, Tamara Ison
Assistant Vice President, Cameron Crow
Senior Vice President Supply Chain, Tony Trupiano
Vice President Accounting, Jimmy Swartz
Director Of Pharmacy, Susan Jackson
Senior Vice President Managed Care, Barbara Corey
Vice President, Beth Loudermilk
Vice President Programming Information Technology, Sue-ellen Brogden
Executive Vice President Operations, Paul Johnson
Vice President Of Support Services, Jeralynn Scott
Senior Vice President Chief Nurse Executive, Jill Case-Wirth
Senior Vice President, Kim Ryan
Vice President Information Technology, Andrew Alberry
Assistant Vice President Human Resources, Detra Bickerstaff
Vice President Talent Acquisition, Sonya Aldy
Vice President And Assistant General Counsel, Keith Mauriello
Vice President, Guillermo Pierluisi

Assistant Vice President Chief Nursing Officer,
Ivy Spencer
Vice Chairman, Dan Smith
Auditors: PRICEWATERHOUSECOOPERS LLP PH

LOCATIONS

HQ: WELLSTAR HEALTH SYSTEM, INC.
805 SANDY PLAINS RD, MARIETTA, GA 300666340
Phone: 770 956-7827
Web: WWW.WELLSTAR.ORG

PRODUCTS/OPERATIONS

Selected Facilities
Atherton Place (Marietta Georgia)
The Jean and Mack Henderson Women's Center at
Kennestone (Marietta Georgia)
WellStar Cobb Hospital (Austell Georgia)
WellStar Community Hospice (Austell Georgia)
WellStar Douglas Hospital (Douglasville Georgia)
WellStar Kennestone Hospital (Marietta Georgia)
WellStar Paulding Hospital (Dallas Georgia)
WellStar Paulding Nursing Center (Dallas Georgia)
WellStar Windy Hill Hospital (Marietta Georgia)
Urgent Care Centers
Cooper Lake Urgent Care Center
Delk Road Urgent Care Center
Kennesaw Urgent Care Center
Shallowford Urgent Care Center
Towne Lake Urgent Care Center

COMPETITORS

Central Georgia Health Systems	Northeast Georgia Health System
Children's Healthcare of Atlanta	Phoebe Putney Memorial Hospital
DeKalb Medical	Piedmont Athens Regional
Doctors Hospital of Augusta	St. Mary's Health Care
Emory Healthcare	Tenet Healthcare
Floyd Medical Center	West Georgia Health System
Grady Health System	
HCA	

HISTORICAL FINANCIALS
Company Type: Private

Income Statement   FYE: June 30

	REVENUE ($ mil.)	NET INCOME ($ mil.)	NET PROFIT MARGIN	EMPLOYEES
06/15	823	49	6.0%	11,985
06/09	397	0	—	—
06/08	5	1	33.1%	—
Annual Growth	105.2%	60.9%	—	—

2015 Year-End Financials
Return on assets: 23.0%   Cash ($ mil.): 52
Return on equity: 6.0%
Current ratio: 0.40

WENATCHEE VALLEY HOSPITAL

EXECUTIVES

Chb, Thomas Carlson
Vice Chb, Mitchell Garrison
Dir, Jeffrey Monson

LOCATIONS

HQ: WENATCHEE VALLEY HOSPITAL
820 N CHELAN AVE, WENATCHEE, WA 988012028
Phone: 509 663-8711

HISTORICAL FINANCIALS
Company Type: Private

Income Statement   FYE: December 31

	REVENUE ($ mil.)	NET INCOME ($ mil.)	NET PROFIT MARGIN	EMPLOYEES
12/15	317	2	0.8%	500
12/14	295	7	2.7%	—
12/13	119	2	1.7%	—
Annual Growth	62.8%	8.2%	—	—

2015 Year-End Financials
Return on assets: 6.6%   Cash ($ mil.): 11
Return on equity: 0.8%
Current ratio: 0.50

WESLEY MEDICAL CENTER, LLC

EXECUTIVES

Ceo, Hugh Tappan
Prin, Carl Fitch
Chief Operating Officer, Bill Voloch
Cfo, Matt Leary
Office Manager, Dale Graham
Coordinator, Diana Lippoldt
Anesthesiologist, Jason Williams
Coordinator, Jeremy Pauly
Director, Nell Thompson
Information Technology/Interne, Larry Mitchell
Office Administrator, Rhonda Franssen

LOCATIONS

HQ: WESLEY MEDICAL CENTER, LLC
550 N HILLSIDE ST, WICHITA, KS 672144976
Phone: 316 962-2000
Web: WWW.WESLEYMC.COM

HISTORICAL FINANCIALS
Company Type: Private

Income Statement   FYE: December 31

	REVENUE ($ mil.)	NET INCOME ($ mil.)	NET PROFIT MARGIN	EMPLOYEES
12/17	608	80	13.3%	40
12/16	555	56	10.3%	—
12/15	545	60	11.1%	—
12/14	520	88	17.0%	—
Annual Growth	5.3%	(3.0%)	—	—

WEST CONTRA COSTA UNIFIED SCHOOL DISTRICT

EXECUTIVES

Pres, Charles T Ramsey
Ceo, Raul Ramirez
Supt, Matthew Duffy

Assistant Superintendent, Alan Del Simone
Education Assistant, Alia Khan
Occupational Specia, Kasey Dutra
Occupational Specia, Kendall Becker
Secretary, Perla Garcia
Information Technology Manager, Mark Terrill
Education Specialist, Saul Sanchez
Teacher, Alan Shearer
Auditors: CROWE HORWATH LLP SACRAMENTO

LOCATIONS

HQ: WEST CONTRA COSTA UNIFIED SCHOOL DISTRICT
1108 BISSELL AVE, RICHMOND, CA 948013135
Phone: 510 231-1100
Web: WWW.WCCUSD.NET

HISTORICAL FINANCIALS
Company Type: Private

Income Statement   FYE: June 30

	REVENUE ($ mil.)	NET INCOME ($ mil.)	NET PROFIT MARGIN	EMPLOYEES
06/17	451	(55)	—	3,800
06/16	457	83	18.2%	—
06/02	291	46	15.9%	—
06/01	279	8	3.1%	—
Annual Growth	3.1%	—	—	—

WEST PENN POWER COMPANY

LOCATIONS

HQ: WEST PENN POWER COMPANY
76 S MAIN ST BSMT, AKRON, OH 443081817
Phone: 800 686-0021

HISTORICAL FINANCIALS
Company Type: Private

Income Statement   FYE: December 31

	REVENUE ($ mil.)	NET INCOME ($ mil.)	NET PROFIT MARGIN	EMPLOYEES
12/17	1,009	110	11.0%	11
12/16	1,020	116	11.4%	—
Annual Growth	(1.1%)	(5.0%)	—	—

WEST VIRGINIA UNITED HEALTH SYSTEM, INC.

EXECUTIVES

Ceo, Christopher Colenda
Dir, David C Hardesty Jr
Pres, J Thomas Jones
Treas, Robert D'Alessandri
V Pres, Jeff Gibson
Staff, Amy Rogers
Auditors: BAKER TILLY VIECHON KROUSE L

LOCATIONS

HQ: WEST VIRGINIA UNITED HEALTH SYSTEM, INC.
1 MEDICAL CENTER DR, MORGANTOWN, WV
265061200
Phone: 304 598-4000
Web: WWW.WVUMEDICINE.ORG

PRODUCTS/OPERATIONS

Selected facilities
Barbour Country Family Medicine
Bridgeport Physicians Care
Chestnut Ridge Center
City Hospital
Doddridge Family Medicine
Elk Memorial Clinic
Harrisville Medical Center
Jefferson Memorial Hospital
Lumberport Family Medicine
Oakland Family Medicine Center
Pennsboro Medical Center
Pinewood Medical Center
Shinnston Healthcare Clinic
United Hospital Center
United Summit Center
WVU Hospitals

COMPETITORS

CAMC Health	West Penn Allegheny
HCA	Health System

HISTORICAL FINANCIALS

Company Type: Private

Income Statement				FYE: December 31
	REVENUE ($ mil.)	NET INCOME ($ mil.)	NET PROFIT MARGIN	EMPLOYEES
12/17	2,172	132	6.1%	7,000
12/16	1,877	103	5.5%	—
12/15	1,651	23	1.5%	—
12/14	9	(0)	—	—
Annual Growth	507.8%	—	—	—

2017 Year-End Financials
Return on assets: 6.3%   Cash ($ mil.): 121
Return on equity: 6.1%
Current ratio: 1.40

WEST VIRGINIA UNIVERSITY

West Virginia University (WVU) is the intellectual home of more than 29000 Mountaineers (the school's mascot) and the state's preeminent institution of higher learning. WVU offers more than 180 bachelor's master's doctoral and professional degree programs through some 15 colleges and schools. The university's clinical psychology and forestry programs have been recognized nationally and it boasts 100% post-graduate job placement for its nursing pharmacy and mining engineering majors. WVU also runs a two-year residential school Potomac State College in Keyser West Virginia.

Operations

Its 1099 acres campus university offers a joint petroleum and natural gas engineering major. It also operates eight experimental farms and four forests throughout the state in addition to WVU Jackson's Mill State 4-H Camp and Lifelong Learning Center near Weston. Some 93% of its full-time faculty have earned doctorates or first-professional degrees in their disciplines. More than 800 students traveled to another country for study abroad

courses in the 2011-12 academic year. Undergraduate tuition and fees for the 2012-13 year was reported as $9808.

WVU is an independent operating unit of the West Virginia Higher Education Fund.

Geographic Reach

The university's main campus is in Morgantown. It also has divisional campuses in Charleston Keyser Martinsburg and Montgomery.

Financial Performance

The university reported a 4% increase in revenues in 2012 due to a growth in capital grants and gifts revenue tuition and fees as well as revenues from auxiliary enterprise gifts and other sources. Capital grants and gifts increased by $55.9 million thanks to a donation of a master license agreement from Siemens PLM for educational software. Tuition and fees increased by $19.9 million in 2012 thanks to a fee rate hike and an increase in non-resident student enrollment. Auxiliary revenues grew by $12.2 million due to an increase in revenues from room and dining services auxiliary fees and athletics revenues. Organic growth has lifted the company's revenues since 2009.

Net income increased by 51% in 2012 due to a growth in other net non-operating revenues of $3.2 million as a result of a settlement agreement in the amount of $7.2 million partially offset by operating revenues.

Strategy

In addition to WVU's campus-based activities the university is focusing on expanding its online and distance learning options to increase educational access and research activities.

Company Background

WVU was founded in 1867 as a public land-grant institution. It one of only 11 schools in the US that are land-grant doctoral research universities with a comprehensive medical school.

EXECUTIVES

Pres, E Gordon Gee
Prin, Nigel Clark
Chief of Staff, Jay Cole
Exec Offcr For Policy Dev't, Jennifer Fisher
Interim Parent Rel'ns Dir, Lisa Hanselman
Chief Grievance Admin, Sue Keller
Executive Officer, Duke Perry
Manager, Becky De Witt
Assistant Professor, John Christian
Assistant Professor, Lori Sherlock
Coordinator, Tom Moran
Auditors: CLIFTONLARSONALLEN LLP PLYMOU

LOCATIONS

HQ: WEST VIRGINIA UNIVERSITY
103 STEWART HL, MORGANTOWN, WV 26506
Phone: 304 293-2545
Web: WWW.STAT.WVU.EDU

PRODUCTS/OPERATIONS

Selected Colleges and Schools
Benjamin M. Statler College of Engineering and Mineral Resources
College of Business and Economics
College of Creative Arts
College of Education and Human Services
College of Law
College of Physical Activity and Sport Sciences
Davis College of Agriculture Natural Resources and Design
Eberly College of Arts and Sciences
Perley Isaac Reed School of Journalism
Potomac State College of WVU
School of Dentistry
School of Medicine
School of Nursing
School of Pharmacy
School of Public Health
WVU Institute of Technology

HISTORICAL FINANCIALS

Company Type: Private

Income Statement				FYE: June 30
	REVENUE ($ mil.)	NET INCOME ($ mil.)	NET PROFIT MARGIN	EMPLOYEES
06/17	783	8	1.1%	6,245
06/06	476	43	9.1%	—
06/05	440	39	8.9%	—
Annual Growth	4.9%	(12.1%)	—	—

2017 Year-End Financials
Return on assets: 4.3%   Cash ($ mil.): 92
Return on equity: 1.1%
Current ratio: 0.80

WESTAT, INC.

Survey the market research business and you'll find Westat among the leaders of the pack. A statistical survey organization the company provides research and consulting services including study design and analysis data collection program evaluation and communications campaign development. It has technical expertise in survey and analytical methods computer systems technology biomedical science and clinical trials. Westat serves US state and local government clients in addition to businesses and foundations. It has offices in five US states as well as international locations around the world. The company was founded in 1963 and is employee-owned.

Geographic Reach

Westat has nine regional offices in the US along with offices in five countries overseas.

Strategy

In 2014 Westat and the Pew Research Center partnered with SurveyMonkey to explore methods and tools that can be used with new technologies to provide useful data in an era when contacting survey respondents and gaining cooperation is more difficult that ever.

Mergers and Acquisitions

In 2015 the company acquired Edvance Reseach an education research and technical assistance organization. That same year Westat also acquired Fenestra an information technology solutions company. The acquisitions enhanced Westat's research capabilities.

EXECUTIVES

Cto, James E. Smith
Vp Planning And Finance, Patricia Espey-English
Vice President, Boni Fash
Vice President, Laurie May
Vice President Of Information Systems, Greg Binzer
Vice President, Marsha Hasson
Senior Vice President Administration, Martha Palan
Vice President, Jane Shepherd
Vice President, Kerry Levin
Vice President, Sue Connor
Vice President, Roger Tourangeau
Vice President, David Morganstein
Senior Vice President Human Resources, Joseph Hunt
Vice President, Jim Greenlees
Vice President, Pat Ward
Vice President, Andrea Sedlak
Vice President, David Maklan
Vice President, Sherman Edwards
Vice President Human Resources, Louis Intili

Vice President Marketing And Business Development, Patti Espey-English
Board Member Senior Vice President Executive Advisor, Tom McKenna
Auditors: RUBINO & COMPANY BETHESDA MD

LOCATIONS

HQ: WESTAT, INC.
1600 RESEARCH BLVD, ROCKVILLE, MD 208503129
Phone: 301 251-1500
Web: WWW.WESTATCAREERS.JOBS

PRODUCTS/OPERATIONS

Selected Operations and Services
Program areas
  Alcohol tobacco and other drug studies
  Consulting services and marketing research
  Customer satisfaction
  Education
  Employment and training
  Energy
  Environmental protection
  Health and medical studies
  Housing
  Military human resources
  Organizational and personnel studies
  Science and technology
  Social services and community development
  Transportation
Research services
  Clinical trials management
  Conference planning and support
  Data analysis and reporting
  Data preparation and processing
  Focus groups
  Program evaluation
  Qualitative studies
  Statistical sample design
  Study design
Survey Services
  Data collection from institutions and businesses
  Data preparation and processing
  Design
  In-field measurement and biospecimen collection
  Interviewing
  Mail surveys
  On-site data collection coordination
  Telephone surveys
  Web-based surveys

COMPETITORS

Gallup	Nielsen
GfK	ORC International
Harris Interactive	QinetiQ
IMS Health	SDI Health
Ipsos	Social & Scientific
J.D. Power	Systems
Kantar Group	Walker Information
Maritz Research	

HISTORICAL FINANCIALS

Company Type: Private

Income Statement				FYE: December 31
	REVENUE ($ mil.)	NET INCOME ($ mil.)	NET PROFIT MARGIN	EMPLOYEES
12/16	510	23	4.7%	2,000
12/15	509	20	4.0%	—
12/14	517	22	4.3%	—
12/13	582	23	4.1%	—
Annual Growth	(4.3%)	0.2%	—	—

2016 Year-End Financials
Return on assets: 1.8%   Cash ($ mil.): 22
Return on equity: 4.7%
Current ratio: 1.50

WESTCHESTER COUNTY HEALTH CARE CORPORATION

EXECUTIVES

Ceo-Pres, Michael D Israel
Sr V Pres, Anthony Mahler
Cfo, Gary Brudnicki
Gen Counsel, Julie Switzer
Sr V Pres, John Morgan
Public Relations Director, David Billig
Director of Telecommunications, Carl Pugni
Director, Mary Delaney
Senior Vice-President, John Moustakakis
Senior Vice-President, Kara Bennorth
Information Specialist, Michelle Weinraub
Auditors: GRANT THORNTON NEW YORK NY

LOCATIONS

HQ: WESTCHESTER COUNTY HEALTH CARE
CORPORATION
100 WOODS RD, VALHALLA, NY 105951530
Phone: 914 493-7000
Web: WWW.WORKPLACEGROUP.COM

HISTORICAL FINANCIALS

Company Type: Private

Income Statement				FYE: December 31
	REVENUE ($ mil.)	NET INCOME ($ mil.)	NET PROFIT MARGIN	EMPLOYEES
12/16	2,008	45	2.3%	3,000
12/15	1,069	33	3.1%	—
12/13	918	6	0.7%	—
12/12	821	15	1.9%	—
Annual Growth	25.1%	30.7%	—	—

2016 Year-End Financials
Return on assets: 9.5%   Cash ($ mil.): 194
Return on equity: 2.3%
Current ratio: 1.10

WESTERN & SOUTHERN FINANCIAL GROUP, INC.

While its heritage may be Western and Southern Western & Southern Financial Group covers the northern and eastern US as well. The company offers a variety of life insurance products and annuities accident and supplemental health coverage mutual funds and other investment management products and services. Western & Southern's financial services include mutual fund administration trust services financial advisory and real estate development; it owns or manages some $68 billion in assets. The company is licensed in most states and in Washington DC.

Operations
Western & Southern Financial operates more than a dozen subsidiaries that offer everything from critical illness insurance to funds and annuities. Some of the company's subsidiaries include Western & Southern Life Insurance (life and health insurance products fixed annuities) and Western-Southern Life Assurance (universal life term life and annuities). Other insurance divisions include Columbus Life Insurance Integrity Life Insurance Lafayette Life Insurance and National Integrity Life Insurance Company.

Western & Southern also operates Fort Washington Investment Advisors to manage private equity assets for corporate and government institutions and wealthy individuals; that unit has some $49 billion under management. Other financial services offerings include mutual fund management through Touchstone Investments.

The company's Eagle Realty Group participates in commercial real estate investment. Eagle Realty's current projects include upscale hotels in Cincinnati's historic Lytle Park District.

Other member companies include IFS Financial Services Peppertree Partners Touchstone Advisors Touchstone Securities W&S Financial Group Distributors and W&S Brokerage Services.

Geographic Reach
Western & Southern Financial's Western & Southern Life Insurance subsidiary operates about 140 field offices around the US.

Sales and Marketing
Western & Southern Financial markets its products and services through a sales force of direct representatives; it also sells through a network of independent agents and financial planners. Altogether its sales network comprises some 52000 licensed entities.

Western & Southern's customer base is wide and varied consisting of individuals and families of all income levels large corporations small to mid-sized businesses financial institutions real estate investors and not-for-profit entities. The group conducts advertising through television commercials.

Financial Performance
Like many conservative mutual insurers Western & Southern Financial holds a long-term investment strategy that has served it well financially. In 2015 its revenue totaled $3.3 billion a record high for the group. The following year revenue remained relatively flat falling $2.3 million to stay at $3.3 billion. Although the company's insurance premiums and product charges rose 4% that year investment income and commissions and fees saw a decline.

An increase in policyholder benefits payouts and income tax expenses led net income to decline 3% to $387.7 million in 2016.

Strategy
Over the past few decades Western & Southern Financial has transformed into a diversified financial services juggernaut buying and launching money management firms and insurance and annuity businesses. Its strategy centers around four pillars: people technology product and multi-channel access.

In terms of people Western & Southern works to create a work culture to attract the best employees at all levels.

The group is also investing in technology to enhance its services and increase data and analytics capabilities. It has recently formed internal teams to work on improving clients' digital experiences. In 2016 the primary investment arm Fort Washington expanded its data governance capabilities as well as installing a new technology platform serving its private client group.

Another way the group grows is by launching new products aimed at filling gaps in its operations. For example in 2015 W&S Financial Group Distributors launched a new variable annuity living benefit rider Guaranteed Lifetime Income Advantage Plus. It also introduced Indextra a single premium deferred fixed indexed annuity issued by Integrity Life Insurance. The following year Touchstone Investments launched two new funds.

Finally to expand multi-channel access the company seeks to reach otherwise underserved middle-market customers by extending weekend and evening sales expanding its online sales presence and providing more bilingual sales information online.

Other initiatives as of late have included streamlining its organizational structure for higher operating efficiency.

Mergers and Acquisitions

In 2017 Western & Southern Financial subsidiary Touchstone Advisors agreed to buy certain assets of Sentinel Asset Management a National Life Holding Company subsidiary. Through that deal Touchstone's assets under management will increase to $20 billion.

Western & Southern Financial completed 20 new equity investments in 2016. Its total acquisition and related development costs totaled nearly $1 billion.

Company Background

Western & Southern was founded in 1888.

EXECUTIVES

President And Ceo Fort Washington Investment Advisors Inc., Maribeth S. Rahe
Chairman President And Ceo, John F. Barrett
President Eagle Realty Group Llc, Mario J. San Marco
Vp And Chief Accounting Officer, Bradley J. Hunkler
President And Ceo National Integrity Life Insurance Company; Ceo W&s Financial Group Distributors And Touchstone Investors, Jill T. McGruder
President W&s Financial Group Distributors Inc., Mark E. Caner
President Columbus Life Insurance Company, J. J. Miller
Svp And Chief Risk Officer, David T. Henderson
President The Lafayette Life Insurance Company, Bryan C. Dunn
President Touchstone Investments, Steven M. Graziano
President Insurance Profillment Solutions Llc, Robert J. DalSanto
Svp And Cio, Karen A. Chamberlain
Svp And Chief Actuary, Daniel W. Harris
President W&s Agency Group And W&s Brokerage Services Inc., Troy D. Brodie
Svp And Co-chief Investment Officer, Roger M. Lanham
Svp And Co-chief Investment Officer, Brendan M. White
Executive Vice President, James Clark
Vice President Procurement, James Essex
Avp Human Resources, Linda Lake
Assistant Vice President And Director Internal Audit, Rod Snyder
Vice President Finance, John McElhenny
Vice President Product Management, Katie Bezold
Assistant Vice President Of Investment Operations, Eric Walzer
Vice President Tax, Dan Larsen
Avp And Director Sales Support, Anthony Gigliotti
Avp And Assistant Treasurer, Cheryl Stotts
Senior Vice President, Connie Maccarone
Vice President Human Resources, Luc Sicotte
Assistant Vice President Marketing Operations, Valerie Holmes
Senior Vice President Human Resources, Kim Chiodi
Vp And Chief Compliance Officer, Bruce Maisel
Vice President, Mike Davis
Assistant Vice President And Director Of Planning, Fsa Hussey
Assistant Vice President Information Technology Business Operations, Matt Godsted
Senior Vice President Financial Institutions Distribution Wands Financial Group Distributors, Andrew Reiss

Senior Vice President Relationship Management Wands Financial Group Distributors, Charles White
Assistant Treasurer, Doug Perry

LOCATIONS

HQ: WESTERN & SOUTHERN FINANCIAL GROUP, INC.
400 BROADWAY ST, CINCINNATI, OH 452023312
Phone: 866 832-7719
Web: WWW.WESTERNSOUTHERN.COM

PRODUCTS/OPERATIONS

2016 Revenues

	$ mil.	% of total
Net investment income	1,633	49
Insurance premiums & product charges	1,414	43
Commissions fees & other income	253	8
Total	**3,302**	**100**

Selected Subsidiaries and Affiliates

Eagle Realty Group LLC
Fort Washington Investment Advisors Inc.
IFS Financial Services Inc.
  Touchstone Advisors Inc.
  Touchstone Securities Inc.
  W&S Financial Group Distributors Inc.
Integrity Life Insurance Company
  National Integrity Life Insurance Company
The Lafayette Life Insurance Company
The Western and Southern Life Insurance Company
  Insurance Profillment Solutions LLC
  Western-Southern Life Assurance Company
  W&S Agency Group
  W&S Brokerage Services Inc.

COMPETITORS

AEGON USA	MetLife
AIG	Nationwide Financial
American General	New York Life
Great American Financial Resources	Northwestern Mutual
	Penn Mutual
Guardian Life	Phoenix Companies
Jackson National Life	Principal Financial
John Hancock Financial Services	Protective Life
	Prudential
Lincoln Financial Group	Securian Financial

HISTORICAL FINANCIALS

Company Type: Private

Income Statement				FYE: December 31
	ASSETS ($ mil.)	NET INCOME ($ mil.)	INCOME AS % OF ASSETS	EMPLOYEES
12/16	44,749	387	0.9%	4,000
12/15	42	0	0.9%	—
12/08	13	(3)	—	—
12/06	32	0	1.0%	—
Annual Growth	106.2%	104.3%	—	—

WESTERN FARMERS ELECTRIC COOPERATIVE

Power also comes sweeping down the plain in Oklahoma thanks to the Western Farmers Electric Cooperative. Led by its coal- and natural gas-fueled generating plants — three in Anadarko one in Mooreland and one in Hugo (all in Oklahoma) — the generation and transmission co-op produces more than 1845 MW of capacity. It pipes power over 3700 miles of transmission lines to two-thirds of rural Oklahoma and parts of New Mexico. It also operates 264 substations and 59 switch stations. Western Farmers Electric Cooperative which is owned by its member distribution cooperatives supplies 22 distribution co-ops and Altus Air Force base which serve a total of a half million members.

Operations

The company maintains a well-balanced and diversified portfolio of generation resources reflecting a mix of technologies and fuel types. In 2013 coal represented 33% of Western Farmers Electric Cooperative's energy production with natural gas at 12 percent. Power generated from wind resources represents about 14% of the coop's energy mix hydro 7%. Economy purchases energy imbalance purchases and contract power (primarily natural gas) made up the balance.

Geographic Reach

Western Farmers Electric Cooperative's members consist of 22 distribution cooperatives (serving customers in Kansas Oklahoma New Mexico and Texas) and the Altus Air Force Base in Oklahoma.

Financial Performance

In 2013 the company's revenues increased by 15% to $525.3 million due to a 7.7% energy sales increase. (Its average MWh sales growth rate of 5.5% over the past three year is above the national average). Western Farmers Electric Cooperative also gets a small amount of off-system sales from three of its four New Mexico members. Power sales increased $64 million in 2013 due to higher MWh sales a slight increase in wholesale power rates and a 40% rise in natural gas prices.

Western Farmers Electric Cooperative's net income increased by 61% in 2013 due to higher sales and an increase in noninterest income.

That year the company's operating cash inflow increased to $53.3 million (compared to $21.2 million in 2012) primarily due to higher net income and increased coal and oil inventory.

Strategy

Western Farmers Electric Cooperative has diversified its fuel mix to meet green energy regulations and boasts one of the state's largest renewable energy portfolios. The diversity in generation mix helps reduce exposure to changing market conditions helping to keep rates competitive.

In 2013 the company signed a purchase with Apex Clean Energy through its subsidiary Balko Wind LLC for 100 MW of wind energy from the Balko Wind Project. With this agreement Apex has sold all the capacity of 300 MW project which will produce enough electricity to power over 110000 U.S. homes. This new site represents the fifth Oklahoma wind farm development that is a part of an ongoing commitment to diversify Western Farmers Electric Cooperative's portfolio of generation sources.

That year it also entered into a purchase and sale agreement with community-wind developer National Renewable Solutions to acquire the development assets for the Broadview Wind Projects in New Mexico. The two projects with a combined 19.8 MW capacity will each sell power over the next 20 years to Western Farmers Electric Cooperative. This wind farm site is in the service territory of Western Farmers Electric Cooperative member Farmers' Electric Cooperative.

In 2012 the company teamed up with Enel Green Power which that year began operating the 150-MW Rocky Ridge Wind Project in Kiowa and Washita counties Oklahoma. The energy generated by the wind farm will be bought by Western Farmers Electric Cooperative.

In 2012 Calpine Corporation agreed to supply Western Farmers Electric Cooperative with electric generation capacity and power (up to 280 MW) from Calpine's gas-fired Oneta Energy Center from June 2014 through 2035.

Company Background

Growing its geographic coverage in late 2010 Western Farmers Electric Cooperative added four New Mexico-based cooperatives (Farmers' Central Valley Lea County and Roosevelt County with a total of 400 MW of load) to its membership.

Responding to a growing demand for power in 2009 the power co-op completed an expansion project at its gas-fueled Anadarko plant adding some 145 MW of power generating capacity.

Western Farmers Electric Cooperative was organized in 1941 by western Oklahoma rural electric distribution cooperatives in order to secure power generation and distribution at an affordable rate. The co-op began generating power in 1950.

EXECUTIVES

Secretary Transmission Services, Kelli Keeling
Secretary, Shelly Trammell
Secretary T And D Engineering, Shelli Pearson
Auditors: KPMG LLP OKLAHOMA CITY OK

LOCATIONS

HQ: WESTERN FARMERS ELECTRIC COOPERATIVE
701 NE 7TH ST, ANADARKO, OK 730052297
Phone: 405 247-3351
Web: WWW.WFEC.US

COMPETITORS

Empire District Electric	OGE Energy
Entergy	ONEOK
Grand River Dam Authority	PG&E Corporation

HISTORICAL FINANCIALS
Company Type: Private

Income Statement   FYE: December 31

	REVENUE ($ mil.)	NET INCOME ($ mil.)	NET PROFIT MARGIN	EMPLOYEES
12/17	686	13	2.0%	378
12/16	655	24	3.7%	—
12/15	671	31	4.6%	—
12/14	702	40	5.8%	—
Annual Growth	(0.8%)	(30.9%)	—	—

2017 Year-End Financials
Return on assets: 12.1%   Cash ($ mil.): 11
Return on equity: 2.0%
Current ratio: 0.50

WESTERN GOVERNORS UNIVERSITY

EXECUTIVES

Ceo, Robert W Mendenhall
Chief Information Officer-Svp, David Morales
Mgr, David R Grow
Pres-Academic Advancement, Sally Johnstone
Information Specialist, Lavender Boyles
Senior Director, Jodi Neely
Coordinator, Juan Maestas
Manager, Mike Manning
Information Technology/Interne, Travis Hitz
Marketing Manager, Lori Bawden
Manager, David Larsen
Auditors: TANNER LLC SALT LAKE CITY UT

LOCATIONS

HQ: WESTERN GOVERNORS UNIVERSITY
4001 S 700 E STE 700, SALT LAKE CITY, UT
841072533
Phone: 801 274-3280
Web: WWW.WGU.EDU

HISTORICAL FINANCIALS
Company Type: Private

Income Statement   FYE: June 30

	REVENUE ($ mil.)	NET INCOME ($ mil.)	NET PROFIT MARGIN	EMPLOYEES
06/15	381	25	6.8%	208
06/12	200	4	2.5%	—
Annual Growth	23.9%	73.7%	—	—

2015 Year-End Financials
Return on assets: 7.9%   Cash ($ mil.): 24
Return on equity: 6.8%
Current ratio: 0.30

WESTERN MARYLAND HEALTH SYSTEM

EXECUTIVES

Sr V Pres-Cfo, Kimberly S Repac
Coo, Nancy D Adams
Cmo, Gerald Goldstien
Administrative Assistant, Jamie Perrin
Purchasing Coordinator, Mark Morgan
Registered Nurse, Samantha Jones
Pharmacist, Lanette Sipple
Human Resources, Robin Norris
Microbiology Supervisor, Albert Rosato
Internist, Kshitiz Alekh
Nurse Clinician III, Perry Monette
Auditors: KPMG LLP BALTIMORE MD

LOCATIONS

HQ: WESTERN MARYLAND HEALTH SYSTEM
12500 WILLOWBROOK RD, CUMBERLAND, MD
215026393
Phone: 240 964-7000
Web: WWW.WMHS.COM

HISTORICAL FINANCIALS
Company Type: Private

Income Statement   FYE: June 30

	REVENUE ($ mil.)	NET INCOME ($ mil.)	NET PROFIT MARGIN	EMPLOYEES
06/17	329	23	7.0%	1,879
06/16	319	9	3.0%	—
06/14	295	28	9.6%	—
06/13	301	17	5.9%	—
Annual Growth	2.3%	6.9%	—	—

2017 Year-End Financials
Return on assets: 3.8%   Cash ($ mil.): 47
Return on equity: 7.0%
Current ratio: 1.70

WESTERN MARYLAND HEALTH SYSTEM REHAB

EXECUTIVES

President, Barry Ronan
System Director, Joyce Emerick
Auditors: KPMG LLP BALTIMORE MD

LOCATIONS

HQ: WESTERN MARYLAND HEALTH SYSTEM REHAB
600 MEMORIAL AVE, CUMBERLAND, MD 215023765
Phone: 301 723-4200
Web: WWW.WMHS.COM

HISTORICAL FINANCIALS
Company Type: Private

Income Statement   FYE: June 30

	REVENUE ($ mil.)	NET INCOME ($ mil.)	NET PROFIT MARGIN	EMPLOYEES
06/17	329	23	7.0%	2,200
06/13	301	17	5.9%	—
06/11	296	15	5.2%	—
06/10	277	(2)	—	—
Annual Growth	2.5%	—	—	—

2017 Year-End Financials
Return on assets: 3.8%   Cash ($ mil.): 47
Return on equity: 7.0%
Current ratio: 1.70

WESTERN PENNSYLVANIA HOSPITAL

EXECUTIVES

Ceo, Dtephen M Patz
Treas, Laarry Fitzgerald
SEC, Jerry J Fedele
Internal Medicine Practitioner, Jeffrey Gordon
Internal Medicine Practitioner, Jenna McLendon
Chief of Medicine, Ladonna Feuge
Scientist, Leslie Dupal
Obstetrician Gynecologist, Erica B Smith
Obstetrician Gynecologist, Rebecca Schnatz
Internist, Swapna Goday
Anesthesiologist, Tracey Vogel

LOCATIONS

HQ: WESTERN PENNSYLVANIA HOSPITAL
4800 FRIENDSHIP AVE, PITTSBURGH, PA 152241722
Phone: 412 578-5000
Web: WWW.WPAHS.ORG

COMPETITORS

Allegheny General Hospital
Children's Hospital of Pittsburgh
Conemaugh Health System
Excela Health
Heritage Valley Health
Jefferson Regional Medical Center of Pennsylvania
Kettering Health Network
Ohio Valley General
St. Clair Health

UPMC
UPMC Mercy

HISTORICAL FINANCIALS
Company Type: Private

Income Statement   FYE: June 30

	REVENUE ($ mil.)	NET INCOME ($ mil.)	NET PROFIT MARGIN	EMPLOYEES
06/16	398	66	16.7%	37
06/15	335	32	9.5%	—
Annual Growth	18.5%	107.3%	—	—

2016 Year-End Financials
Return on assets: 5.0%   Cash ($ mil.): 1
Return on equity: 16.7%
Current ratio: 1.20

WESTERN STATE BANK

EXECUTIVES

Ceo, Brian L Houkom
Chb, Lee Anderson
President, Gary Lochow
Executive Vice-President Marke, Danette Frounfelter
Administrative Assistant, Jackie Anderson
Market President, Mike Bannach

LOCATIONS

HQ: WESTERN STATE BANK
  110 4TH ST SE, DEVILS LAKE, ND 583013634
Phone: 701 662-4936
Web: WWW.WESTERNBANKS.COM

HISTORICAL FINANCIALS
Company Type: Private

Income Statement   FYE: December 31

	ASSETS ($ mil.)	NET INCOME ($ mil.)	INCOME AS % OF ASSETS	EMPLOYEES
12/17	1,044	11	1.1%	75
12/16	960	13	1.4%	—
12/15	832	11	1.4%	—
12/14	755	10	1.4%	—
Annual Growth	11.4%	1.4%	—	—

2017 Year-End Financials
Return on assets: —   Sales ($ mil): 63
Return on equity: 18.0%

WESTERN STATES FIRE PROTECTION COMPANY INC

EXECUTIVES

Pres-Ceo, Gene Postma
Chb, Lee R Anderson Sr
SEC, William M Beadie
Residential Sales and Project, Greg Canjar
Corporate Alarm, Deanna Smith

Area Manager, Jeff Murphy
Sprinkler Fitter Foreman, Jon Dowdle
Auditors: KPMG

LOCATIONS

HQ: WESTERN STATES FIRE PROTECTION COMPANY INC
  7026 S TUCSON WAY, CENTENNIAL, CO 801123921
Phone: 303 792-0022
Web: WWW.WSFP.COM

COMPETITORS

COSCO Fire Protection	Tyco Fire & Security
China Fire	UTC Climate Controls &
Sharpfibre	Security
SimplexGrinnell	

HISTORICAL FINANCIALS
Company Type: Private

Income Statement   FYE: December 31

	REVENUE ($ mil.)	NET INCOME ($ mil.)	NET PROFIT MARGIN	EMPLOYEES
12/17	307	44	14.3%	1,429
12/16	292	40	13.9%	—
12/15	274	31	11.6%	—
12/14	260	26	10.0%	—
Annual Growth	5.7%	19.2%	—	—

2017 Year-End Financials
Return on assets: 1.5%   Cash ($ mil.): —
Return on equity: 14.3%
Current ratio: 0.80

WESTMORELAND REGIONAL HOSPITAL

EXECUTIVES

Ceo, David Gallatin
Sr V Pres-Cfo, Jeffrey T Curry
Vice President, Sharon P Smith
SEC, Dirk Kalp
Treas, Thomas L Sochacki
Ceo, Robert J Rogalski
Coordinator, Theresa Sarver
Purchasing Coordinator, Brenda Shumar
Manager, Carol Siko
Occupational Specia, Joni Beckman
Coordinator, Karen Edmunds

LOCATIONS

HQ: WESTMORELAND REGIONAL HOSPITAL
  532 W PITTSBURGH ST, GREENSBURG, PA 156012282
Phone: 724 832-4000
Web: WWW.EXCELAHEALTH.ORG

HISTORICAL FINANCIALS
Company Type: Private

Income Statement   FYE: June 30

	REVENUE ($ mil.)	NET INCOME ($ mil.)	NET PROFIT MARGIN	EMPLOYEES
06/18	571	36	6.4%	2,000
06/16	248	15	6.3%	—
06/15	245	24	9.8%	—
06/14	12	8	64.1%	—
Annual Growth	159.4%	45.7%	—	—

2018 Year-End Financials
Return on assets: 4.4%   Cash ($ mil.): 39
Return on equity: 6.4%
Current ratio: 1.40

WGL HOLDINGS, INC.

WGL Holdings owners of the regulated Washington Gas Light Company sells natural gas to more than 1 million customers in the District of Columbia Maryland and Virginia. It has about 600 miles of transmission mains more than 13000 miles of distribution mains and some 12500 miles of distribution lines. The company?s unregulated segment also provides energy marketing clean-energy products and services and midstream asset management. In July 2018 WGL Holdings was bought by Canada-based AltaGas for $6.4 billion deal.

Operations
WGL Holdings has four segments: Regulated Utility Retail Energy-Marketing Commercial Energy Systems and Midstream Energy Services.

Regulated Utility (more than 50% of revenue) consists of Washington Gas (regulated gas distribution/transportation services) and Hampshire Gas (regulated interstate natural gas storage services).

The Retail Energy-Marketing (some 40%) competes with regulated utilities and unregulated third-party marketers to sell natural gas and electricity to some 210000 customers in Maryland Virginia Delaware Pennsylvania and DC.

Commercial Energy Systems sells products like solar PV systems combined heat and power plants and natural gas fuel cells; it also provides installation services for technological upgrades. It generates 340000 megawatt hours of clean energy a year.

Midstream Energy Services manages natural gas storage and transportation assets.

Geographic Reach
WGL Holdings primarily operates in Washington DC Maryland and Virginia. It also serves customers across the US through its non-utility segments. Washington Gas has peak shaving facilities in Springfield Virginia (Ravensworth Plant) and Rockville Maryland (Rockville Plant).

Sales and Marketing
WGL sells and delivers natural gas and/or electricity directly to residential commercial and industrial customers. Washington Gas has some 1.2 million customers in the District of Columbia Maryland and Virginia while its Energy Services business count some 210000 retail customers in the same area.

Financial Performance
WGL has not been a growing company lately. In the last five years company revenue fell from $2.7 billion in 2014 to $2.3 billion in 2018. In 2018 (ended September 30) revenue fell less than a percentage point to $2.34 billion (compared to $2.35 billion in 2017). The fall came due to lower sales volumes in the retail energy (non-utility) business.

Net income slashed from $192 million in 2017 to $49 million in 2018 mostly due to a YOY $364 million increase in operation and maintenance costs related to the merger with AltaGas as well as a YOY $114 million increase in the utility cost of gas. Lower realized margins in the regulated utility segment further reduced its coffers.

Cash holdings at the company shot up from only $8 billion at the end of 2017 to $122 million at 2018 end. Operations provided $322 million and a further $715 million came in from financial activities which was offset by $923 million going into investments.

Company Background

WGL was established in the year 2000 as a Virginia corporation. On January 25 2017 WGL entered into an Agreement and Plan of Merger (Merger Agreement) to combine with AltaGas Ltd. a Canadian Corporation (AltaGas). On July 6 2018 the merger was consummated between AltaGas WGL and Wrangler Inc. (Merger Sub) a newly formed indirect wholly owned subsidiary of AltaGas.

EXECUTIVES

President And Coo Wgl Holdings Inc. And Washington Gas Light Company, Adrian P. Chapman, $551,000 total compensation

Svp And Cfo Wgl Holdings And Washington Gas Light Company, Vincent L. Ammann, $460,000 total compensation

Chairman And Ceo Wgl Holdings And Washington Gas Light Company, Terry D. McCallister, $824,000 total compensation

Vp Strategy Business Development And Non-utility Operations, Gautam Chandra, $420,000 total compensation

Svp General Counsel And Corporate Secretary, Leslie Thornton, $380,000 total compensation

Executive Vice President Business Development Of The Bank, Nigeria Poole

LOCATIONS

HQ: WGL HOLDINGS, INC.
1000 MAINE AVE SW, WASHINGTON, DC 200243494
Phone: 703 750-2000
Web: WWW.WGLHOLDINGS.COM

PRODUCTS/OPERATIONS

2018 Sales

	$ mil.	% of total
Retail energy marketing	1,009	42
Utility	1,248	53
Commercial energy services	79	3
Midstream energy services	40	2
Eliminations	(36.4)	-
Total	**2,341**	**100**

2018 Sales

	$ mil.	% of total
Non-utility	1,112	47
Utility	1,229	53
Total	**2,341**	**100**

Selected Subsidiaries

Hampshire Gas Company (underground natural gas storage)
Wrangler SPE LLC
Washington Gas Light Company (natural gas utility)
Washington Gas Resources Corp. (nonregulated business holding company)
Washington Gas Energy Services Inc. (retail energy services)
Washington Gas Energy Systems Inc. (commercial energy systems and HVAC services)

COMPETITORS

Appalachian Power	Northern Virginia
Comfort Systems USA	Electric Cooperative
Commerce Energy Group	Pepco Holdings
Constellation Energy	RGC Resources
Group	Rappahannock Electric
Dominion Energy	Cooperative
FirstEnergy	

HISTORICAL FINANCIALS

Company Type: Private

Income Statement — FYE: September 30

	REVENUE ($ mil.)	NET INCOME ($ mil.)	NET PROFIT MARGIN	EMPLOYEES
09/18	2,341	21	0.9%	1,586
09/17	2,354	177	7.6%	—
09/16	2,349	168	7.2%	—
09/15	2,659	132	5.0%	—
Annual Growth	(4.2%)	(45.8%)	—	—

2018 Year-End Financials

Return on assets: 22.2%   Cash ($ mil.): 57
Return on equity: 0.9%
Current ratio: 0.40

WHEATLAND UNION HIGH SCHOOL DISTRICT

EXECUTIVES

Supt, Glenn Sewll
Administrator, Lynne Tafoya
Teacher, Melissa Taylor
Superintendent, Vic Ramos
Auditors: RT DENNIS ACCOUNTANCY RANCHO

LOCATIONS

HQ: WHEATLAND UNION HIGH SCHOOL DISTRICT
1010 WHEATLAND RD, WHEATLAND, CA 956929798
Phone: 530 633-3100
Web: WWW.WHEATLANDHIGH.ORG

HISTORICAL FINANCIALS

Company Type: Private

Income Statement — FYE: June 30

	REVENUE ($ mil.)	NET INCOME ($ mil.)	NET PROFIT MARGIN	EMPLOYEES
06/17	9,186	(1,399)	—	76
06/16	8,941	94	1.1%	—
Annual Growth	2.7%	—	—	—

WHEATON FRANCISCAN

EXECUTIVES

Prin, James Gresham
Director of Emergency Room, Kathy Lord
Senior Manager, Susan Rusch
Internal Medicine Practitioner, Vipindas Chengat
Anesthesiologist, Brett J Longlais
Manager, Debbie Schlieder
Physical Therapist, Lora Sankey
Critical Care Clinical Nurse S, Maureen Greene
Director of Compliance, Richard Andersen

LOCATIONS

HQ: WHEATON FRANCISCAN
3070 N 51ST ST STE 601, MILWAUKEE, WI 532101663
Phone: 414 447-2000

HISTORICAL FINANCIALS

Company Type: Private

Income Statement — FYE: June 30

	REVENUE ($ mil.)	NET INCOME ($ mil.)	NET PROFIT MARGIN	EMPLOYEES
06/16	407	(10)	—	6
06/14	428	(13)	—	—
06/11	347	12	3.7%	—
06/10	0	0	39.1%	—
Annual Growth	175.8%	—	—	—

2016 Year-End Financials

Return on assets: 6.3%   Cash ($ mil.): —
Return on equity: (-2.5%)
Current ratio: 2.30

WHEATON FRANCISCAN SERVICES, INC.

Wheaton Franciscan Services Inc. (WFSI) is the not-for-profit parent company for more than 100 health care housing and social service organizations in Colorado Illinois Iowa and Wisconsin. Also known as Wheaton Franciscan Healthcare WFSI operates about 15 hospitals including Affinity Health System Rush Oak Park Hospital and United Hospital System with more than 1600 beds total. WFSI also includes long-term care centers home health agencies and physician offices. Its Franciscan Ministries division provides affordable housing units including assisted-living facilities and low-income dwellings. The health system is sponsored by The Franciscan Sisters Daughters of the Sacred Hearts of Jesus and Mary.

Operations

Many of WFSI's hospitals are operated in partnership with other area providers. For instance the Affinity Health System in Wisconsin is jointly sponsored by Wheaton Franciscan Sisters and Ministry Health Care while the Rush Oak Park Hospital in Illinois is operated through a partnership between WFSI and the Rush System for Health.

The health system partners with the YMCA of Milwaukee to try to address chronic health concerns of area residents. The two organizations converted a local YMCA campus into the YMCA Healthy Lifestyle Village. The center offers health screenings health education outpatient therapy and fitness services. WFSI and the YMCA have more Healthy Lifestyle Village campuses planned for other locations within their service areas.

The organization had a total of 1656 beds and 2620 housing units at the end of 2014.

In fiscal 2013 WSFI delivered more than 8000 babies and had more than 330000 emergency department visits. It reported more than 1580000 outpatient visits and some 64000 hospital admissions. It employs more than 500 physicians and has some 2000 affiliated physicians.

Geographic Reach

WFSI operates in Wisconsin Iowa Colorado and Illinois.

Financial Performance

The not-for-profit system's revenues were flat in fiscal 2014 at $1.8 billion. Net income totaled $184 million.

Strategy

To increase the scope of specialty health care services it can provide to the community WFSI recruits new physicians and specialists to the

Wheaton Franciscan Medical Group. The system also works to improve communication among its physicians and facilities by adding electronic health record (EHR) systems.

In 2013 the system opened a new 80000-sq.-ft. outpatient center specializing in neurology services.

Company Background
The Franciscan Sisters Daughters of the Sacred Hearts of Jesus and Mary (also known as the Wheaton Franciscan Sisters) founded WSFI in 1983 as a holding company for their ministry operations. The health system traces its roots back to the founding of the St. Mary's Hospital in Racine Wisconsin in 1882.

EXECUTIVES

Vice President And Associate General Counsel, Stacie Andritsch
Auditors: KPMG LLP CHICAGO IL

LOCATIONS

HQ: WHEATON FRANCISCAN SERVICES, INC.
400 W RIVER WOODS PKWY, GLENDALE, WI 532121060
Phone: 414 465-3000

PRODUCTS/OPERATIONS

Selected Operations
Franciscan Ministries Inc. (housing in Colorado Illinois Iowa and Wisconsin)
Illinois
  Marianjoy Rehabilitation Hospital (Wheaton)
  Rush Oak Park Hospital (affiliate Oak Park)
Iowa (Wheaton Franciscan Healthcare of Iowa)
  Covenant Medical Center (Waterloo)
  Mercy Hospital (Oelwein)
  Sartori Memorial Hospital (Cedar Falls)
Wisconsin
  Affinity Health System (partnership with Minstry Health Care)
  Calumet Medical Center (Chilton)
  Mercy Medical Center (Oshkosh)
  St. Elizabeth Hospital (Appleton)
  Wheaton Franciscan Healthcare of Southeast Wisconsin
  All Saints Hospital (two campuses in Racine)
  Elmbrook Memorial Hospital (Brookfield)
  Franklin Hospital (Franklin)
  St. Francis Hospital (Milwaukee)
  St. Joseph Hospital (Milwaukee)
  Wisconsin Heart Hospital (Wauwatosa)
  United Hospital System Inc. (affiliated system)
  Kenosha Medical Center (Kenosha)
  St. Catherine's Medical Center (Pleasant Prairie)

COMPETITORS

Advocate Health Care	KishHealth
Alden Management Services	Loyola University Health System
Children's Hospital and Health System	Ministry Health Care
Columbia St. Mary's	Morris Hospital
Elmhurst Memorial Healthcare	NorthShore University HealthSystem
FHN	OSF Healthcare System
Froedtert Hospital	ProHealth Care
Hospital Sisters Health System	Rockford Health System
	SwedishAmerican Health System

HISTORICAL FINANCIALS

Company Type: Private

Income Statement   FYE: June 30

	REVENUE ($ mil.)	NET INCOME ($ mil.)	NET PROFIT MARGIN	EMPLOYEES
06/15	1,809	18	1.0%	18,000
06/14	1,754	128	7.3%	—
06/13	1,763	177	10.1%	—
06/12	1,723	(112)	—	—
Annual Growth	1.6%	—	—	—

2015 Year-End Financials
Return on assets: 14.5%   Cash ($ mil.): 81
Return on equity: 1.0%
Current ratio: 1.00

WHEELING HOSPITAL, INC.

EXECUTIVES

Ceo, Ronald Viola
Asst Admin-V Pres, John Pastorius
Cfo, James Murdy
Pres, Kevin M Quirk
Analyst, Robert Hassler
Director of Patient Accounts, Maryann Kozusnik
Data Processing Staff, Mark Knox
Cardiac Physician, Edward Chiu
Chief of Medicine, Angelo Georges
Pediatrician, Brian Vaske
Registered Nurse, Casey McFarland
Auditors: DELOITTE & TOUCHE LLP PITTSBU

LOCATIONS

HQ: WHEELING HOSPITAL, INC.
1 MEDICAL PARK, WHEELING, WV 260036300
Phone: 304 243-3000
Web: WWW.WHEELINGHOSPITAL.ORG

HISTORICAL FINANCIALS

Company Type: Private

Income Statement   FYE: September 30

	REVENUE ($ mil.)	NET INCOME ($ mil.)	NET PROFIT MARGIN	EMPLOYEES
09/17	375	31	8.4%	1,228
09/16	340	37	10.9%	—
Annual Growth	10.2%	(15.2%)	—	—

2017 Year-End Financials
Return on assets: 4.8%   Cash ($ mil.): 134
Return on equity: 8.4%
Current ratio: 3.10

WHEELING POWER COMPANY

EXECUTIVES

Pres, E Linn Draper Jr
Treas, Peter J De Maria
V Pres, A Joseph Dowd
V Pres-Operations, William J Lhota
Vice President, G P Maloney
Vice President, David H Willaims Jr
SEC, John F Di Lorenzo Jr
District Manager, David Denham
Vice President, Joseph Vipperman
Vice President, G Maloney
Fleet Manager, Ken Paynter

LOCATIONS

HQ: WHEELING POWER COMPANY
4201 JACOB ST, WHEELING, WV 260034427
Phone: 740 699-7842
Web: WWW.AEP.COM

HISTORICAL FINANCIALS

Company Type: Private

Income Statement   FYE: December 31

	REVENUE ($ mil.)	NET INCOME ($ mil.)	NET PROFIT MARGIN	EMPLOYEES
12/16	310	27	8.9%	133
12/00	87	3	4.3%	—
Annual Growth	8.3%	13.3%	—	—

2016 Year-End Financials
Return on assets: 1.4%   Cash ($ mil.): —
Return on equity: 8.9%
Current ratio: 0.40

WHITE PLAINS HOSPITAL MEDICAL CENTER

EXECUTIVES

Pres-Ceo, Jon B Schandler
Chb, Paul Weissman
Pres, Susan Fox
Exec V Pres-Coo, Edward F Leonard
V Pres-Fin-Cfo, John Schiurba
Director, Edward Tangredi
Chief Operating Officer, Jeffrey Tiesi
Director, Kerri Elsabrout
Information Specialist, Gary Soso
Doctor, Vitaly Adler
Office Manager, Linda Gonzalez

LOCATIONS

HQ: WHITE PLAINS HOSPITAL MEDICAL CENTER
41 E POST RD, WHITE PLAINS, NY 106014607
Phone: 914 681-0600
Web: WWW.WPHOSPITAL.ORG

HISTORICAL FINANCIALS

Company Type: Private

Income Statement   FYE: December 31

	REVENUE ($ mil.)	NET INCOME ($ mil.)	NET PROFIT MARGIN	EMPLOYEES
12/16	460	23	5.1%	2,000
12/15	389	23	6.1%	—
12/14	353	8	2.3%	—
12/13	373	7	2.1%	—
Annual Growth	7.2%	44.8%	—	—

2016 Year-End Financials
Return on assets: 6.7%   Cash ($ mil.): 58
Return on equity: 5.1%
Current ratio: 1.10

WHITEWAVE FOODS COMPANY

WhiteWave Foods rides a wave of dietary changes as consumers seek alternatives to conventional foods. The company is best known for its refrigerated Silk soymilk in the US and Alpro brand soy products in Europe. WhiteWave also produces organic dairy products under the Horizon Organic label and dairy related foods including International Delight coffee creamers and LAND O'LAKES-branded creamers and dairy dessert toppings (licensed from dairy co-op Land O'Lakes). WhiteWave products are sold through natural food and grocery stores as well as mass merchandisers and restaurants and food service businesses in the US and Canada and parts of Europe. In 2017 French dairy giant Danone acquired the company for $12.5 billion.

Operations

WhiteWave's coffee creamers and beverages unit has been its biggest revenue producer accounting for 30% of revenue. The unit that sells foods and beverages made from plants brought in more than 25% of revenue with premium dairy goods generating almost 20% of revenue. The fresh foods and European units split the remaining 25% of revenue.

WhiteWave operates 15 production facilities around the world and sends some production to third-party co-packers.

Geographic Reach

WhiteWave?s North American business accounts for more than 85% of sales with the rest supplied by Europe which includes Belgium Germany the Netherlands the UK France Italy Portugal Spain and Sweden.

WhiteWave is a joint venture partner with China Mengniu Dairy Company Limited a Chinese dairy company. Through the JV the companies make market and sell premium plant-based beverages in China. The joint venture a 49/51 split between WhiteWave and Mengniu sells under the Silk ZhiPuMoFang brand in several major Chinese markets. Products include almond milk and walnut milk beverages in single-serve and multi-pack formats.

Sales and Marketing

WhiteWave Foods' largest customer is Wal-Mart Stores which accounts for about 15% of sales. The company?s 10 biggest customers account for about 50% of sales.

Financial Performance

WhiteWave has maintained healthy if not entirely organic revenue gains for the past eight years.

In 2016 it was more of the same with a 9% increase in revenue to $4.2 billion from 2015 driven by the acquisitions of Vega Wallaby and EIEIO in 2015 and IPP in 2016. Organic growth came from the American and European segments boosted by pricing and a favorable product mix in the Americas. Fresh Foods was the only part of the Americas segment to post lower 2016 sales which the company blamed on disruptions caused by a major software installation during the year. The strong US dollar in relation to the British pound and Euro shaved off some revenue from the Europe segment.

WhiteWave posted a 27% profit increase to $214 million in 2016 from 2015. Although it had higher costs due to acquisitions and increased marketing expenses were lower as a percentage of revenue in 2016 producing a healthy bottom line.

The higher net income helped nudge cash flow from operations to $316 million in 2016 from $315 million the year before. WhiteWave had a cash decrease from operating assets and liabilities due to lower accounts payable and accruals driven by the timing of cash disbursements bigger employee bonuses and increased headcount.

Strategy

In becoming part of Danone WhiteWave gets access to the bigger company?s resources and to the European market which has produced about 15% of revenue. Danone plans to use WhiteWave?s plant-based products to supplement its dairy-based offerings as consumers in the Americas and Europe turn to healthier foods. WhiteWave conducts research on new products and packing at facilities in Colorado California and Belgium.

Mergers and Acquisitions

In 2016 WhiteWave acquired Mexico based Innovation Packaging and Process (IPP) for about $18 million. IPP manufactures products for WhiteWave and third parties and the addition on in-house manufacturing could propel growth in Latin American markets.

In 2015 WhiteWave acquired Sequel Naturals which owns the Vega brand and has been a pioneer in developing plant-based nutrition products for some $550 million. This acquisition extended the company's plant-based foods and beverages platform into nutritional powders and bars.

In another 2015 deal WhiteWave bought EIEIO Inc. which owned the Magicow brand and other brands for $40 million. The acquisition expanded WhiteWave's portfolio of bulk coffee creamer and flavor dispensing products and provided new product capabilities to support growth in away-from-home channel.

EXECUTIVES

Chairman And Ceo, Gregg L. Engles, $1,120,000 total compensation
Us Group President Americas Foods And Beverages, Kevin C. Yost, $550,000 total compensation
President Americas Foods & Beverages, Blaine E. McPeak, $650,000 total compensation
Evp And General Counsel, Roger E. Theodoredis
Evp Human Resources, Thomas N. Zanetich, $445,000 total compensation
Evp Strategy And Corporate Development, Edward F. Fugger, $362,000 total compensation
President Europe Foods And Beverages, Bernard P. J. Deryckere, $504,076 total compensation
Evp And Cfo, Greg S. Christenson
Auditors: DELOITTE & TOUCHE LLP DENVER

LOCATIONS

HQ: WHITEWAVE FOODS COMPANY
12002 AIRPORT WAY, BROOMFIELD, CO 800212546
Phone: 303 635-4500
Web: WWW.WHITEWAVE.COM

2016 Sales

	% of total
North America	86
Europe	14
Total	**100**

PRODUCTS/OPERATIONS

2016 Sales

	$ mil.	% of total
Americas Foods & Beverages		
Plant-based food and beverages	1,065	25
Coffee creamers and beverages	1,199	29
Premium dairy	812	19
Fresh foods	542	13
Europe Foods & Beverages	578	14
Total	**4,198**	**100**

Selected Products and Brands

Europe
  Plant-based foods and beverages (Alpro Provamel)
  Almond
  Hazelnut
  Oat
  Rice
  Soy
North America
  Coffee creamers and beverages (Land O Lakes International Delight)
  Flavored coffee creamers
  Half & Half
  Iced coffee
  Unflavored coffee creamers
  Plant-based foods and beverages (Silk)
  Almond
  Coconut
  Soy
  Premium dairy (Horizon Organic)
  Organic milk
  Other organic dairy
  Other premium milk

COMPETITORS

Aurora Organic Dairy	Lifeway Foods
Eden Foods	Nestlé
Galaxy Nutritional Foods	Odwalla
	Old Home Foods
HP Hood	Organic Valley
Hain Celestial	Rockview Dairies
Kraft Heinz	Springfield Creamery

HISTORICAL FINANCIALS

Company Type: Private

Income Statement

FYE: December 31

	REVENUE ($ mil.)	NET INCOME ($ mil.)	NET PROFIT MARGIN	EMPLOYEES
12/15	3,866	168	4.4%	5,800
12/14	3,436	140	4.1%	—
12/13	2,542	99	3.9%	—
Annual Growth	**23.3%**	**30.4%**	**—**	**—**

2015 Year-End Financials

Return on assets: 14.2%   Cash ($ mil.): 38
Return on equity: 4.4%
Current ratio: 0.50

WHOLE FOODS MARKET, INC.

Whole Foods Market is the world's largest natural foods grocery chain. Founded in 1980 it pioneered the supermarket concept in natural and organic foods retailing. The company operates more than 470 stores throughout the US Canada and the UK and focuses on organic perishable and prepared products. It sells private-label items through its 365 Organic Everyday Value and Allegro Coffee lines and offers a variety of non-GMO vegan and gluten-free foods. In 2017 Amazon.com acquired Whole Foods which generates sales mostly in the US for about $13.7 billion.

HISTORY

With a $10000 loan from his father John Mackey started SaferWay Natural Foods in Austin Texas in 1978. Despite struggling Mackey dreamed of opening a larger supermarket-sized natural foods store. Two years later SaferWay merged with Clarksville Natural Grocery and Whole Foods Market was born. Led by Mackey that year it opened an 11000-sq.-ft. supermarket in the counterculture hotbed of Austin. The store was an instant success and a second store was added 18 months later in suburban Austin.

The company slowly expanded in Texas opening or buying stores in Houston in 1984 and Dallas in 1986. Whole Foods expanded into Louisiana in 1988 with the purchase of like-named Whole Food Co. a single New Orleans store owned by Peter Roy (who served as the company's president from 1993 to 1998). Sticking to university towns Whole Foods added another store in California the next year and acquired Wellspring Grocery (two stores North Carolina) in 1991. In 1992 it debuted its first private-label products under the Whole Foods name. Seeking capital to expand even more the company raised $23 million by going public in early 1992 with 12 stores.

Every competitor in the fragmented health foods industry became a potential acquisition and the chain began growing rapidly. In 1992 Whole Foods bought the six-store Bread & Circus chain in New England. The next year it added Mrs. Gooch's Natural Foods Markets (seven stores in the Los Angeles area). Its biggest acquisition came in 1996 when it bought Fresh Fields the second-largest US natural foods chain (22 stores on the East Coast and in Chicago). Although the purchase hurt profits in 1996 sales surpassed $1 billion for the first time in fiscal 1997 as Whole Foods neared 70 stores. In 1997 it introduced the less-expensive 365 private label and acquired the Granary Market (Monterey California) and Bread of Life (two stores South Florida) natural foods supermarkets.

Capitalizing on the growing popularity of nutraceuticals (natural supplements with benefits similar to pharmaceuticals) the company paid $146 million in 1997 for Amrion a maker of nutraceuticals and other nutritional supplements (merged with subsidiary WholePeople.com in 2000). It capped the year by buying coffee roaster Allegro Coffee. (Both companies are based in Boulder Colorado home of its former main rival the smaller Wild Oats.) Also in 1997 Whole Foods acquired the six-store Merchant of Vino natural foods and wine shop chain to foster the development of its wine departments.

In 1998 Whole Foods opened its first store in Boulder — a 39000-sq.-ft. superstore with amenities such as a juice bar and a prepared foods section. At year's end Roy resigned as president and was replaced by Chris Hitt. In 1999 Whole Foods bought four-store Boston-area chain Nature's Heartland.

In 2000 Whole Foods merged its online operations (wholefoods.com) with its direct marketing and nutritional supplement unit (Amrion) to form Wholepeople.com. Later that year the company merged Wholepeople.com with lifestyle marketing firm Gaiam; Whole Foods received a minority stake in Gaiam and started selling food online through Gaiam.com.

Hitt resigned in mid-2001 and Mackey took over his duties. Later that year Whole Foods acquired the three upscale Harry's Farmers Market stores in Atlanta; the sale did not include the Harry's In A Hurry stores which later shut down.

In 2002 Whole Foods crossed the border into Canada. Its first foreign store opened in downtown Toronto that May.

Mackey was named Entrepreneur of the Year in 2003 by consulting firm Ernst & Young. That year Whole Foods acquired Select Fish a Seattle-based seafood processor and distributor and opened a seafood distribution facility in Atlanta.

In 2004 Whole Foods opened a 59000-sq.-ft. store in the new Time Warner Center in Manhattan. The new store which includes a 248-seat cafe sushi bar wine shop and gourmet bakery is the largest supermarket in New York City. That year

the company acquired the UK organic-food retailer Fresh & Wild for $38 million.

To support its rapid growth in 2004 Whole Foods Market expanded its number of operating regions from eight to 10 by separating the Southwest region into the Southwest and Rocky Mountain regions and the Northern Pacific region into the Northern California and Pacific Northwest region. The company announced the opening of its first Gluten-Free Bakehouse a dedicated gluten-free baking facility located outside Raleigh North Carolina. Overall the company opened 12 new stores in 2004.

In January 2005 Whole Foods launched the Animal Compassion Foundation an independent non-profit organization dedicated to the compassionate treatment of livestock. The company moved that month to its new corporate headquarters across the street from its old location in downtown Austin. Its new flagship store opened its doors in March at the same location. In October Whole Foods increased its number of operating regions from 10 to 11 by separating the North Atlantic region into the North Atlantic and Tri-State regions. Overall in fiscal 2005 the company opened a dozen new stores including its first in Nebraska and Ohio. In 2006 the company acquired a store in Portland Maine and converted it to the Whole Foods Market banner.

In August 2007 Whole Foods acquired its main competitor — Boulder Colorado-based Wild Oats Markets — in a deal valued at about $565 million (plus $106 million in debt). In early October the company sold 35 Henry's Farmers Market and Sun Harvest stores to a subsidiary of Los Angeles-based Smart & Final for about $166 million. The stores in California and Texas were acquired with Wild Oats.

The company launched a bi-monthly magazine called Whole Foods Market Magazine at its midwestern stores in 2008. On the heels of its disappointing third-quarter results in August 2008 shares of the company's stock fell to a six-year low and Whole Foods suspended its dividend. Blaming the poor economy the company announced the layoffs of some 50 employees at its Austin headquarters in August 2008. Overall in fiscal 2008 the company introduced about 300 new private-label items.

For the first time in its 29-year history Whole Foods reported negative same-store sales in the quarter ended December 2008 as traffic in its stores fell.

In March 2009 the company reached a settlement in its long-running dispute with the FTC over its acquisition of Wild Oats in 2007. Whole Foods agreed to sell 32 stores including 19 Wild Oats locations that had already been closed. In exchange the FTC dropped its crusade to undo the merger. In December 2009 John Elstrott was named chairman of Whole Foods Market after Mackey voluntarily relinquished the chairmanship which he had held since 1980. In May 2010 Walter Robb formerly co-president of the company was promoted to co-CEO of Whole Foods a title he now shares with Mackey.

EXECUTIVES

Ceo, John P. Mackey, $1 total compensation
President And Coo, A. C. Gallo, $501,110 total compensation
President Florida Region, Juan Nu ±ez
Chairman Whole Kids Foundation And Whole Cities Foundation, Walter E. Robb, $501,110 total compensation
Evp Operations U.s. And Whole Foods 365, David Lannon, $501,110 total compensation
President Whole Foods Market 365â™, Jeff Turnas
Evp Operations, Christina Minardi

President Southern Pacific Region, Patrick Bradley
President Mid-atlantic Region, Scott Allshouse
President Rocky Mountain Region, Bill Jordan
President Midwest Region, Michael Bashaw
President North Atlantic Region, Laura Derba
Evp And Cio, Jason Buechel, $501,110 total compensation
President South Region, Omar Gaye
President Northern California Region, Rob Twyman
Evp Operations U.s. And The U.k., Kenneth (Ken) Meyer, $486,510 total compensation
Evp Growth And Business Development, James (Jim) Sud, $486,510 total compensation
Evp And Cfo, Keith Manbeck
President Pacific Northwest Region, Angela Lorenzen
Global Vp Marketing, Sonya Gafsi Oblisk
President Northeast Region, Nicole Wescoe
Executive Vice President Operations, Kenny Meyer
Vice President And Marketing Manager, Desa Abbamondi
Vice President Vendor Manager, Ray Hudson
Vice President Information Technology Manager, Tommy Gaskins
Vice President Administration, John Agnew
Senior Vice President Technology Manager, Pedro Adame
Regional Vice President Operations, Michael Howard
Vice President And Loan Officer And Branch Manager, Francisco Ibarra
Global Vice President Culinary And Hospitality, Tien Ho
Global Vice President Procurement Non Perishables, Don Clark
Assistant Vice President And Mortgage Market Manager, Craig Moore
Vice President Of Human Resources Learning And Development Od Oe And Facilities, Francis Lo
Chairman, John B. Elstrott
Auditors: ERNST & YOUNG LLP AUSTIN TEX

LOCATIONS

HQ: WHOLE FOODS MARKET, INC.
550 BOWIE ST, AUSTIN, TX 787034644
Phone: 512 477-4455
Web: WWW.WHOLEFOODSMARKET.COM

2017 Sales

	% of total
US	97
Canada & UK	3
Total	**100**

2017 Stores

	No.
US	
California	84
Massachusetts	31
Texas	32
Illinois	26
Florida	26
Colorado	19
New York	20
New Jersey	17
North Carolina	13
Arizona	10
Virginia	13
Other States	157
Canada	13
UK	9
Total	**470**

PRODUCTS/OPERATIONS

2017 sales

	% of total
Non-perishables	33
Prepared foods & bakery	19
Other perishables	48
Total	**100**

Selected Product Categories

Bakery
Body care
Educational products
Floral
Grocery
Household products
Meat and poultry
Nutritional supplements
Pet products
Prepared foods
Produce
Seafood
Specialty (beer wine cheese)
Textiles

COMPETITORS

ALDI	Publix
Albertsons	SUPERVALU
Costco Wholesale	Safeway
Fiesta Mart	Shaw's
GNC	Sobeys
H-E-B	Sprouts
J Sainsbury	Tesco
Kroger	Trader Joe's
Lidl	Wal-Mart
Loblaw	Winn-Dixie
Natural Grocers by	Wm Morrison
Vitamin Cottage	Supermarkets

HISTORICAL FINANCIALS

Company Type: Private

Income Statement				FYE: September 24
	REVENUE ($ mil.)	NET INCOME ($ mil.)	NET PROFIT MARGIN	EMPLOYEES
09/17	16,030	245	1.5%	89,000
09/16	15,724	507	3.2%	—
09/15	15,389	536	3.5%	—
09/14	14,194	579	4.1%	—
Annual Growth	4.1%	(24.9%)	—	—

2017 Year-End Financials

Return on assets: 2.3%
Return on equity: 1.5%
Current ratio: 0.40
Cash ($ mil.): 322

WICHITA, CITY OF (INC)

EXECUTIVES

Treasurer, Michelle Law
Auditors: ALLEN GIBBS & HOULIK LC CPA

LOCATIONS

HQ: WICHITA, CITY OF (INC)
455 N MAIN ST FL 5, WICHITA, KS 672021601
Phone: 316 268-4351
Web: WWW.WICHITA.GOV

HISTORICAL FINANCIALS

Company Type: Private

Income Statement				FYE: December 31
	REVENUE ($ mil.)	NET INCOME ($ mil.)	NET PROFIT MARGIN	EMPLOYEES
12/17	419	(9)	—	2,200
12/16	408	(3)	—	—
12/15	392	(8)	—	—
12/09	387	37	9.6%	—
Annual Growth	1.0%	—	—	—

2017 Year-End Financials

Return on assets: 10.2%
Return on equity: (-2.3%)
Current ratio: —
Cash ($ mil.): 252

WILDLIFE CONSERVATION SOCIETY

From Congo gorillas to humpback whales off the coast of Gabon all life is worth conserving to the Wildlife Conservation Society (WCS). The group founded in 1895 works to protect wildlife and lands throughout the world and to instill in humans a concern about nature. The not-for-profit organization operates New York City's Bronx Zoo New York Aquarium Central Park Zoo Prospect Park Zoo and the Queens Zoo. WCS's environmental education programs are used in US schools as well as those in other nations. The society has ongoing efforts in more than 60 countries to protect endangered species and ecosystems. About a quarter of the funding for its work comes from visitors at its handful of parks.

Operations
WCS manages about 500 conservation projects nationwide and works to educate millions of visitors at its handful of living institutions: the Bronx Zoo New York Aquarium Central Park Zoo Prospect Park Zoo and Queens Zoo. As part of its operations WCS manages more than 200 million acres of protected lands globally and retains a staff of 200-plus scientists.

Geographic Reach
The society operates country programs across four continents including Africa Asia Latin America and North America. It boasts ongoing efforts in 60-plus countries.

Sales and Marketing
WCS is working to ramp up its construction. The group's revised Master Plan includes enhancements at the Bronx Zoo's C.V. Starr Science Campus with the Special Care Unit and LaMattina Wildlife Ambassador Center the Queens Zoo's jaguar exhibit and the Ocean Wonders exhibit.

During the past decade WCS has spent $243 million to fund physical plant improvements on its five campuses. They were financed through grants from New York City and the federal government private gifts and the proceeds from WCS's Series 2004 tax-exempt bond issue.

Financial Performance
Despite the anemic economy in recent years WCS has logged healthy attendance of about 4 million visitors across its five New York City parks. As Americans chose to vacation at home WCS has benefited. With those visitors came a noteworthy boost in income from gate admissions exhibits and contributions from visitor services such as food merchandising and parking. Attendance-driven revenues reach more than $50 million.

The conservation group points to its operational diversity for being able to keep its head above water when funding from the state and other entities it had relied on had slimmed.

EXECUTIVES

Vice President Human Resources, Herman Smith
Vice President And Director Bronx Zoo, James Breheny
Sr. V Pres, Mary A Dixon
Auditors: KPMG LLP NEW YORK NY

LOCATIONS

HQ: WILDLIFE CONSERVATION SOCIETY
2300 SOUTHERN BLVD, BRONX, NY 104601090
Phone: 718 220-5100
Web: WWW.WCS.ORG

PRODUCTS/OPERATIONS

2014 Sales

	% of total
Contributed	26
Gate-and-exhibit admissions	15
Federal agencies	14
Visitor services	11
City of New York	10
Investment income	8
Membership dues	6
Non-governmental-organization grants	6
New York State	1
Education programs	1
Sponsorship licensing & royalties	0
Insurance proceeds	0
Other	1
Total	**100**

Selected Areas of Focus

Climate change
Natural resource exploitation
Sustainable development of human livelihoods

HISTORICAL FINANCIALS

Company Type: Private

Income Statement				FYE: June 30
	REVENUE ($ mil.)	NET INCOME ($ mil.)	NET PROFIT MARGIN	EMPLOYEES
06/18	336	31	9.3%	4,000
06/16	260	(23)	—	—
06/15	327	61	18.9%	—
06/14	253	24	9.7%	—
Annual Growth	7.3%	6.3%	—	—

2018 Year-End Financials

Return on assets: 17.6%
Return on equity: 9.3%
Current ratio: —
Cash ($ mil.): 53

WILL COUNTY

EXECUTIVES

Treasurer, Stephen Weber
Vice Chair, Ragan Freitag
Auditors: BAKER TILLY VIRCHOW KRAUSE LL

LOCATIONS

HQ: WILL COUNTY
302 N CHICAGO ST, JOLIET, IL 604324078
Phone: 815 740-4602

PRODUCTS/OPERATIONS

Departments

Animal Control (impoundment lost and found stray pickup)
Board of Review (for property assessment appeals)
Emergency Management Agency (emergency and disaster preparedness planning response and recovery)
Health Department (public health programs; health and dental care)
Highways (planning design and maintenance of county highways and bridges)
Human Resources (for county employees)
Information Communication and Technology Department (for county offices)
Land Use (stewardship of built and natural environments)
Purchasing (for county offices)

Sunny Hill Nursing Home
Supervisor of Assessments (property tax assessment)
Veterans Assistance Commission (provides financial assistance to veterans)
Workforce Investment Board (coordinates training education and employee recruitment programs)

HISTORICAL FINANCIALS
Company Type: Private

Income Statement				FYE: November 30
	REVENUE ($ mil.)	NET INCOME ($ mil.)	NET PROFIT MARGIN	EMPLOYEES
11/17	314	(45)	—	2,000
11/15	303	4	1.6%	—
11/14	0	0	—	—
11/13	297	(1)	—	—
Annual Growth	1.4%	—	—	—

2017 Year-End Financials
Return on assets: 5.7%
Return on equity: (-14.5%)
Current ratio: —
Cash ($ mil.): 120

WILLIAM BEAUMONT HOSPITAL

EXECUTIVES

Ceo-Pres, Gene Michalski
Pres, Brian Connolly
SEC, Gale R Colwell
Treas, Barbara Mahone
Chief Med, Ananias Diokno
Chm, Stephen R Howard
V Chm, Mark Shaevsky
Sr V Pres, Margaret Casey
Fo/Exe V Pres, John Keuten
Director, Hadley Mack French
Director, Martha James Quay

LOCATIONS

HQ: WILLIAM BEAUMONT HOSPITAL
  3601 W 13 MILE RD, ROYAL OAK, MI 480736712
Phone: 248 898-5000
Web: WWW.BEAUMONTHOSPITALS.COM

HISTORICAL FINANCIALS
Company Type: Private

Income Statement				FYE: December 31
	REVENUE ($ mil.)	NET INCOME ($ mil.)	NET PROFIT MARGIN	EMPLOYEES
12/17	1,473	71	4.9%	18,050
12/16	1,396	118	8.5%	—
12/15	1,300	142	10.9%	—
12/14	1,235	127	10.3%	—
Annual Growth	6.0%	(17.5%)	—	—

2017 Year-End Financials
Return on assets: 1.5%
Return on equity: 4.9%
Current ratio: 9.10
Cash ($ mil.): 175

WILLIS-KNIGHTON MEDICAL CENTER

EXECUTIVES

Pres, James K Elrod
Exec Vice President, Robert Huie
Vice President, Nila Willhoite
Chief Staff, James Burke
Doctor, Alan J Sorkey
Compliance Director, Ada Lowe
Facilities Manager, Jerry Ivey
Director, Trish Koopman
Supervisor, Patty Bouillon
Network Administrator, Glenn Ouellette
Op Case Manager, Jenna Strecker
Auditors: COLE EVANS & PETERSON SHREVEP

LOCATIONS

HQ: WILLIS-KNIGHTON MEDICAL CENTER
  2600 GREENWOOD RD, SHREVEPORT, LA 711033908
Phone: 318 212-4000
Web: WWW.WKHS.COM

HISTORICAL FINANCIALS
Company Type: Private

Income Statement				FYE: September 30
	REVENUE ($ mil.)	NET INCOME ($ mil.)	NET PROFIT MARGIN	EMPLOYEES
09/15	1,019	97	9.6%	3,089
09/11	807	76	9.4%	—
09/10	818	47	5.8%	—
Annual Growth	4.5%	15.4%	—	—

2015 Year-End Financials
Return on assets: 11.5%
Return on equity: 9.6%
Current ratio: 1.50
Cash ($ mil.): 273

WILMINGTON TRUST COMPANY

EXECUTIVES

Executive Vice President, Mark A Graham
Chief Executive Officer, Robert Harra
Group Vice President, Christine Neri
Vice President, Joe Baker
Vice President, Mary Pupillo
Assistant Vice President, Donald Haverstick
Vice President Business Application Support Manager, Gary Powers
Vice President, Jared Grunig
Vice President Software Development And Support, Glenn Force
Vice President, Murray Pinkus
Vice President, Jeanne Oller
Vice President, Margaret Pulgini
Vice President, Charles Hicks
Assistant Vice President, Steve Barone
Vice President, Wendy White
Vice President, Sandra Plowinske
Vice President Accounting Services Division, Janice Cirillo
Assistant Vice President Corporate Communications, Megen Morris
Vice President Of Marketing And Communications, Jim Klabe
Vice President Marketing, Sherry Costanzo
Senior Vice President Administration, John N Beeson
Vice President Corporate Client Services, Christie Longo
Vice President Client Development, Rob Barnett
Assistant Vice President, Laura Barone
Vice President Wilmington Funds Product Manager, Richard Murad
Vice President Mergers And Acquisitions Operations Manager, John Mark Mulvena
Assistant Vice President, William Morris
Vice President Director Of Wisd Vendor Management, Bill Cunnion
Assistant Vice President, Holly Hammer
Assistant Vice President, Liz Hudgens
Vice President, Virginia Machamer
Vice President And Chief Economist, Luke Tilley
Vice President Network And Desktop Computing, Rob Averbach
Vice President Director Client Services Institutional Custody, Amy Roe
Vice President, Jane Snyder
Vice President And Portfolio Manager, Luke Betterly
Vice President, Dan Gardner
Senior Vice President, James Riley
Vice President Wealth Advisory Senior Private Client Fiduciary Advisor, Latonya Hubbard
Vice President, Michelle Wojciechowicz
Vice President, Thomas Herring
Vice President Senior Fiduciary Advisor, Gina Cronin
Vice President, Jason Johnson
Vice President, Chris Slaybaugh
Vice President Senior Investment Advisor, Mark Stevenson
Assistant Vice President Of Lending, Mary Fisher
Group Vice President, Tom Pierce
Vice President, Rebecca Rogers
Vice President, Steve O'Neal
Private Banking Client Service Specialist Ii Assistant Vice President, Kimberly Hottes
Vice President Corporate Capital Markets, Aaron Soper
Assistant Vice President, Bonnie Metcalfe
Vice President, Carl Robinson
Vice President, Cheryl Fairbanks
Ccts Assistant Vice President, Clarice Wright
Assistant Vice President, Melissa Jalace-vasold
Vice President Senior Private Client Advisor, Sandra Besso Plowinske
Vice President, Ann Harris-johnson
Vice President, Greg Hasty
Vice President Regional Marketing Director, Laura Cleveland
Vice President Private Banking, Julie O'Donnell
Avp, Lisa Lewis
Assistant Vice President, Carleen Terranova
Vice President Private Banking Team Leader Private Banking, Anne St Clair
Vice President, Salvatore Corso
Assistant Vice President, Melissa Marion
Vice President, Larry Long
Assistant Vice President, Brenda Parker
Vice President, Al Miller
Vice President, Brenda Hough
Vice President, Barbara Obrien
Vice President, Charlie Buehler
Vice President And Senior Investment Advisor, Andrew Cloud
Assistant Vice President, Andrea Rybczynski
Vice President, Joseph Odonnell
Vice President, Renee Buchner
Assistant Vice President, Nancy Hagner
Assistant Vice President, Catherine Chandler
Vice President, Kyle Barry
Vice President, Denise Sbraccia

Assistant Vice President, Sophie Pendolino
Assistant Vice President, Donna Torres
Assistant Vice President, Christopher Hickok
Assistant Vice President, Ruth Ann Mcmillen
Vice President, Lynne Marshall
Vice President, Linda Squier
Assistant Vice President, Jose Paredes
Vice President, Howard Gordon
Vice President, David Bagley
Vice President Private Client Advisor, Ed Barone
Vice President, Kaye Crouch
Vice President, Nickole Garrison
Vice President Senior Private Banker, Nicholas
 Macechko
Assistant Vice President, Russell Whitley
Assistant Vice President, Matthew Lyndaker
Vice President And Investment Advisor, Darren
 Jordan
Vice President, Erin Miller
Vice President, William Gering
Vice President, James Deitrick
Vice President Senior Investment Advisor, Jeffrey
 Taylor
Vice President, Joseph Baker
Vice President, Stephen Seivold
Vice President, Theresa Drew
Assistant Vice President, Tammy Krawczyk
Vice President, Todd Bemiller
Vice President And Team Leader, Donald Hargadon
Vice President, Patrick Wood
Assistant Vice President, Susan Laratonda
Group Vice President Family Wealth, Anna Smith
Vice President Mortgage Backed Securities Trader
 And Analyst, Eric Smookler
Assistant Vice President, David Mcguire
Vice President Administrative, Meghan Ashue

LOCATIONS

HQ: WILMINGTON TRUST COMPANY
 1100 N MARKET ST, WILMINGTON, DE 198900001
Phone: 302 651-1000
Web: WWW.WILMINGTONTRUST.COM

HISTORICAL FINANCIALS

Company Type: Private

Income Statement				FYE: December 31
	ASSETS ($ mil.)	NET INCOME ($ mil.)	INCOME AS % OF ASSETS	EMPLOYEES
12/17	4,960	30	0.6%	518
12/16	3,685	17	0.5%	—
12/15	1,928	36	1.9%	—
Annual Growth	60.4%	(9.0%)	—	—

2017 Year-End Financials

Return on assets: —   Sales ($ mil.): 234
Return on equity: 12.9%

WINTER HAVEN HOSPITAL, INC.

Winter Haven Hospital serves eastern Polk County in central Florida with general medical surgical and emergency care. The health care facility also offers specialty care in areas such as cancer heart disease stroke and a memory clinic for patients suffering from dementia and other memory disorders. The hospital's Regency Medical Center provides maternity and other health care services for women and newborns. Outpatient care is provided through an ambulatory surgery and diagnostic center and several community clinics. Win-

ter Haven Hospital is owned by Tampa-based BayCare Health System; it was founded in 1926 as a charter hospital.

Change in Company Type

After determining that it needs to be part of a larger health care organization to compete in the changing marketplace the hospital agreed to be acquired by BayCare Health System in 2012. The following year BayCare acquired Winter Haven from local not-for-profit Mid-Florida Medical Services.

Operations

With nearly 530 licensed beds Winter Haven Hospital's main campus is the largest of the two inpatient facilities in its health care system; the other is its Regency Center for Women and Infants. Other facilities include a community blood center the ambulatory surgery center and half a dozen family health centers. Together the medical provider's facilities handle some 17000 inpatient visits per year as well as 60000 outpatients and 1600 births.

Winter Haven Hospital has more than 300 physicians on its staff providing a range of specialty services. It is affiliated with the University of Florida College of Medicine and Shands Healthcare in areas including oncology and urology. It also partnered with USF Polytechnic to expand its mental health services in 2012.

Geographic Reach

Winter Haven Hospital serves the roughly 660000 people in Polk County and Highlands County.

EXECUTIVES

Director Of Pharmacy, Tiffany Jones
Medical Records Director, Carolyn Murphy
Vice President, Carol Koeppel

LOCATIONS

HQ: WINTER HAVEN HOSPITAL, INC.
 200 AVENUE F NE, WINTER HAVEN, FL 338814193
Phone: 863 293-1121
Web: WWW.WINTERHAVENHOSPITAL.ORG

PRODUCTS/OPERATIONS

Selected Services and Centers
Ambulatory Surgery & Diagnostic Center
Bostick Heart Center
Cassidy Cancer Center
Clinical Laboratory
Community Blood Center
Community Calendar
Community Education
Diabetes Center
Emergency Department
Family Health Centers
Health Connection
Mental Health Services
Patient Services/Nursing
Professional Education
Radiation Oncology
Regency Center for Women and Infants
Rehabilitation Services
Respiratory Care Services
Stroke Center
Urology Care
Winter Haven Hospital Foundation

COMPETITORS

Adventist Health System Sunbelt Healthcare
 Bayfront Health
 DeSoto Memorial
 Florida Hospital Tampa Bay Division
 HCA
 Heart & Family Health Institute
 Lakeland Regional Medical Center
 Lee Memorial
 Manatee Memorial Hospital
 Northside Hospital and Heart Institute
 Oak Hill Hospital
 Orlando Health

Sarasota Memorial Health Care
St. Joseph's-Baptist Health Care
Tampa General Hospital
Tenet Healthcare

HISTORICAL FINANCIALS

Company Type: Private

Income Statement				FYE: December 31
	REVENUE ($ mil.)	NET INCOME ($ mil.)	NET PROFIT MARGIN	EMPLOYEES
12/16	293	30	10.3%	1,480
12/15	257	2	0.8%	—
12/14	262	4	1.6%	—
Annual Growth	5.7%	167.3%	—	—

2016 Year-End Financials

Return on assets: 3.4%   Cash ($ mil.): —
Return on equity: 10.3%
Current ratio: 1.90

WIPRO, LLC

EXECUTIVES

Ceo, Abidali Neemuchwala
President, Mallathur Balasubramanian
SEC, Mitchell Mackler
Cfo-Treas, Ashish Chawla
Auditors: FOR DELOITTE HASKINS & SELLS L

LOCATIONS

HQ: WIPRO, LLC
 2 TOWER CENTER BLVD # 2200, EAST BRUNSWICK,
 NJ 088161100
Phone: 732 509-1664
Web: WWW.WIPRO.COM

HISTORICAL FINANCIALS

Company Type: Private

Income Statement				FYE: March 31
	REVENUE ($ mil.)	NET INCOME ($ mil.)	NET PROFIT MARGIN	EMPLOYEES
03/18	585	(45)	—	800
03/13	120	(17)	—	—
Annual Growth	37.1%	—	—	—

2018 Year-End Financials

Return on assets: 36.4%   Cash ($ mil.): 22
Return on equity: (-7.8%)
Current ratio: 0.20

WISCONSIN ALUMNI RESEARCH FOUNDATION

EXECUTIVES

Dir, Carl Gulbrandsen
Managing Director, Erik Iverson
Director, Jeanan Moe
Controller, Lysa Thoeny
Manager, Ryan Abrams
Communications Marketing Manag, Jacqui Fuller
Licensing Manager, John Nagel
Auditors: LB MCGLADREY LLP MADISON WI

LOCATIONS

HQ: WISCONSIN ALUMNI RESEARCH FOUNDATION
614 WALNUT ST FL 13, MADISON, WI 537262336
Phone: 608 263-2500
Web: WWW.WARF.ORG

HISTORICAL FINANCIALS

Company Type: Private

Income Statement				FYE: June 30
	ASSETS ($ mil.)	NET INCOME ($ mil.)	INCOME AS % OF ASSETS	EMPLOYEES
06/18	3,065	(277)	—	27
06/17	2,931	45	1.6%	—
06/15	3,204	0	—	—
06/14	3,224	0	—	—
Annual Growth	(1.3%)	—	—	—

2018 Year-End Financials

Return on assets: 18.8%   Sales ($ mil): 69
Return on equity: (-399.8%)

WISCONSIN HOUSING AND ECONOMIC DEVELOPMENT AUTHORITY

EXECUTIVES

Exec Dir, Wyman B Winston
Chairman*, Ivan Gamboa
Chairman of The Board, Brad Guse
Director, Wyman Winston
Real Estate Consultant, David Sheperd
Financial Officer, Dan Besteman
Information Security Analyst, Erik Larson
Business Analyst, James Bennett
Officer, Tom Schrader

LOCATIONS

HQ: WISCONSIN HOUSING AND ECONOMIC
DEVELOPMENT AUTHORITY
201 W WASHINGTON AVE # 700, MADISON, WI
537032760
Phone: 608 266-7884
Web: WWW.WHEDA.COM

HISTORICAL FINANCIALS

Company Type: Private

Income Statement				FYE: June 30
	ASSETS ($ mil.)	NET INCOME ($ mil.)	INCOME AS % OF ASSETS	EMPLOYEES
06/18	2,475	33	1.4%	171
06/17	2,201	23	1.1%	—
06/16	2,082	38	1.9%	—
Annual Growth	9.0%	(6.2%)	—	—

2018 Year-End Financials

Return on assets: —   Sales ($ mil): 255
Return on equity: 13.3%

WITHAM MEMORIAL HOSPITAL

EXECUTIVES

Pres-Ceo, Raymond Ingham
Assistant of Nursing, Carla Terrell
Chief Staff, Robert M Watt
Chief of Radiology, Steven Fritsch
Executive Assistant, Amy Mitchell
Human Resources Coordinator, Brenda Strohl
Chief of Medicine, John Horvath
Purchasing Agent, Johnna Galvan
Director, Katy Bowman
Manager, Tonya Hart
Analyst, Glenn Davis
Auditors: BLUE & CO LLC INDIANAPOLIS

LOCATIONS

HQ: WITHAM MEMORIAL HOSPITAL
2605 N LEBANON ST, LEBANON, IN 460521476
Phone: 765 485-8000
Web: WWW.WITHAM.ORG

HISTORICAL FINANCIALS

Company Type: Private

Income Statement				FYE: December 31
	REVENUE ($ mil.)	NET INCOME ($ mil.)	NET PROFIT MARGIN	EMPLOYEES
12/17	436	29	6.7%	725
12/16	426	21	4.9%	—
12/15	380	18	4.8%	—
12/14	276	20	7.6%	—
Annual Growth	16.4%	12.0%	—	—

2017 Year-End Financials

Return on assets: 9.1%   Cash ($ mil.): 61
Return on equity: 6.7%
Current ratio: 1.50

WITHLACOOCHEE RIVER ELECTRIC COOPERATIVE INC

EXECUTIVES

Exec Vp, Billy E Brown
SEC-Treas, Alan Hingesbach
Treas, Charles V Smith
Human Resources, Connie Hobbs
Coordinator, Carol Molnar
Programmer Analyst, Pam Farmer
Director of Information Techno, Larry Darsey
General Manager, Billy Brown
Purchasing Agent, Katina Williams
Purchasing Coordinator, Dana Pitts
Information Technology/Interne, Roger Thomas
Auditors: PURVIS GRAY & COMPANY LLP DAD

LOCATIONS

HQ: WITHLACOOCHEE RIVER ELECTRIC
COOPERATIVE INC
14651 21ST ST, DADE CITY, FL 335232920
Phone: 352 567-5133
Web: WWW.WREC.NET

HISTORICAL FINANCIALS

Company Type: Private

Income Statement				FYE: December 31
	REVENUE ($ mil.)	NET INCOME ($ mil.)	NET PROFIT MARGIN	EMPLOYEES
12/16	458	26	5.8%	458
12/15	474	24	5.1%	—
12/14	459	28	6.2%	—
12/13	433	16	3.8%	—
Annual Growth	1.9%	16.6%	—	—

2016 Year-End Financials

Return on assets: 4.6%   Cash ($ mil.): 154
Return on equity: 5.8%
Current ratio: 0.40

WOLF CREEK FEDERAL SERVICES, INC.

EXECUTIVES

Pres, Kukuk Steven
SEC, David Totemoff Sr
Exec V Pres, Angela Astle
SEC-Tres, McDaniel Matthew
Information Technology Manager, Danita Vroman
Shareholder Specia, Jayme Johnson
Vice President of Finance, Angie Astle
Transportation Maintenance Sup, Chris Finnegan
Member, Mel Lynch
Idiq Manager, Nena La France
Benefits Manager, Niki Little

LOCATIONS

HQ: WOLF CREEK FEDERAL SERVICES, INC.
3800 CNTRPINT DR STE 1200, ANCHORAGE, AK
99503
Phone: 907 563-8866
Web: WWW.CHUGACH-AK.COM

HISTORICAL FINANCIALS

Company Type: Private

Income Statement				FYE: December 31
	REVENUE ($ mil.)	NET INCOME ($ mil.)	NET PROFIT MARGIN	EMPLOYEES
12/17	306	22	7.2%	1,600
12/16	293	20	7.1%	—
12/15	155	9	6.4%	—
12/14	60	4	7.4%	—
Annual Growth	71.3%	70.3%	—	—

WOLVERINE POWER SUPPLY COOPERATIVE, INC.

EXECUTIVES

Vice President Generation, Dan Decoeur
Vice President, Daniel DeCoeur
Vice President General Counsel, Joseph Baumann
Auditors: PLANTE & MORAN PLLC CHICAGO

LOCATIONS

HQ: WOLVERINE POWER SUPPLY COOPERATIVE, INC.
10125 W WATERGATE RD, CADILLAC, MI 496018458
Phone: 231 775-5700
Web: WWW.WPSCI.COM

COMPETITORS

ITC Holdings Corp.
Lansing Board of Water
  and Light
Midland Cogeneration
Venture

HISTORICAL FINANCIALS
Company Type: Private

Income Statement				FYE: December 31
	REVENUE ($ mil.)	NET INCOME ($ mil.)	NET PROFIT MARGIN	EMPLOYEES
12/17	433	18	4.3%	110
12/16	431	27	6.3%	—
12/15	389	23	6.0%	—
12/10	294	(16)	—	—
Annual Growth	5.7%	—	—	—

2017 Year-End Financials
Return on assets: 7.4%   Cash ($ mil.): 7
Return on equity: 4.3%
Current ratio: 0.90

WOMAN'S HOSPITAL FOUNDATION INC

EXECUTIVES

President And Ceo, Teri G. Fontenot
Evp And Coo, Stephanie Anderson
Vp And Cio, Paul Kirk
Svp Patient Care Nicu And Respiratory Therapy; Chief Nursing Officer, Patricia Johnson
Chief Medical Officer, Susan Puyau
Vp And Cfo, Greg Smith
President Foundation For Woman's, Beverly Brooks Thompson
Director Of Infection Control, Jennifer Freeny

LOCATIONS

HQ: WOMAN'S HOSPITAL FOUNDATION INC
100 WOMANS WAY, BATON ROUGE, LA 708175100
Phone: 225 927-1300
Web: WWW.WOMANS.ORG

PRODUCTS/OPERATIONS

Selected Services
Audiology
Breast Care
Breastfeeding
Cancer Care
Childbirth
Day Spa
Diabetes Care
Fertility
Fitness Club
Genetics
Health Screenings
Heart Health
Mammography
Metabolic Health
Nutrition
Philanthropy
Pregnancy
Social Services
Weight Loss

COMPETITORS

Amedisys
Baton Rouge General
General Health System
Lane Regional Medical
  Center
Our Lady of the Lake
RMC
River Parishes
  Hospital
Tenet Healthcare

HISTORICAL FINANCIALS
Company Type: Private

Income Statement				FYE: September 30
	REVENUE ($ mil.)	NET INCOME ($ mil.)	NET PROFIT MARGIN	EMPLOYEES
09/16	288	47	16.3%	1,850
09/15	503	36	7.2%	—
09/12	217	22	10.3%	—
09/11	219	46	21.0%	—
Annual Growth	5.7%	0.4%	—	—

2016 Year-End Financials
Return on assets: 1.2%   Cash ($ mil.): 172
Return on equity: 16.3%
Current ratio: 4.50

WOMEN & INFANTS HOSPITAL OF RHODE ISLAND

EXECUTIVES

Ceo, Dennis D Keefe
Exec Vice President, Patricia R Recupero
Compliance Staff, Ralph Handlesman
Chief of Medicine, Carol Mnning
Coordinator, Bernice Dimauro
General Practice, Brian G Kwetkowski
Obstetrician, Vivian Sung
Chief Officer, Robert Insoft
Auditors: PRICEWATERHOUSECOOPERS LLP BO

LOCATIONS

HQ: WOMEN & INFANTS HOSPITAL OF RHODE
ISLAND
101 DUDLEY ST, PROVIDENCE, RI 029052499
Phone: 401 274-1100
Web: WWW.WOMENANDINFANTS.ORG

HISTORICAL FINANCIALS
Company Type: Private

Income Statement				FYE: September 30
	REVENUE ($ mil.)	NET INCOME ($ mil.)	NET PROFIT MARGIN	EMPLOYEES
09/16	504	35	7.0%	2,800
09/15	428	3	0.8%	—
09/14	438	19	4.5%	—
09/13	411	14	3.6%	—
Annual Growth	7.0%	33.5%	—	—

2016 Year-End Financials
Return on assets: 7.3%   Cash ($ mil.): 66
Return on equity: 7.0%
Current ratio: 2.40

WORCESTER POLYTECHNIC INSTITUTE

EXECUTIVES

Pres-Ceo, Dennis D Berkey
Exec V Pres-Cfo, Jeffrey Soloman
Contlr, Chary Dellows
Sr ADM, Randy Robinson
Assistant Professor, Carolann Koleci
Scientist, David Paydarfar
Scientist, Peder C Sen
Scientist, George D Pins
Network Engineer, Hossein Hakim
Scientist, Lawrence Lifshitz
Scientist, Satya S Hivkumar
Auditors: PRICEWATERHOUSECOOPERS LLP HA

LOCATIONS

HQ: WORCESTER POLYTECHNIC INSTITUTE
100 INSTITUTE RD, WORCESTER, MA 016092280
Phone: 508 831-5000
Web: WWW.WPI.EDU

HISTORICAL FINANCIALS
Company Type: Private

Income Statement				FYE: June 30
	REVENUE ($ mil.)	NET INCOME ($ mil.)	NET PROFIT MARGIN	EMPLOYEES
06/15	312	4	1.4%	873
06/13	199	38	19.4%	—
06/12	182	(5)	—	—
06/11	174	76	44.0%	—
Annual Growth	15.6%	(50.8%)	—	—

2015 Year-End Financials
Return on assets: 8.0%   Cash ($ mil.): 23
Return on equity: 1.4%
Current ratio: 0.10

WORLD WIDE TECHNOLOGY, LLC

World Wide Technology (WWT) has a broad view of its business. The company primarily provides such IT services as network design and installation systems and application integration and procurement. It also offers a range of Web-based products and services including e-commerce systems development order tracking and catalog management. WWT serves businesses in the automotive retail and telecommunications industries as well as government agencies. Top clients have included Dell the State of Missouri and the State of Alaska. WWT was founded in 1990.

Geographic Reach

WWT has more than 25 facilities throughout the world and about 2 million-sq.-ft of warehouse and distribution space in the US. It also has three distribution outlets in Brazil Mexico and Singapore as well as facilities in London; Amsterdam; Hong Kong; and Chengdu China.

Mergers and Acquisitions

In 2015 WWT purchased St. Louis-based software development firm Asynchrony. The strategic acquisition will allow WWT to deliver complete custom user-facing software and the systems and infrastructure that support it.

EXECUTIVES

Ceo, James P. (Jim) Kavanaugh
Vp Enterprise Commercial & Service Provider Sales, Mark J. Catalano
Cfo, Thomas W. (Tom) Strunk
Vp Corporate Properties, Dan B. Svoboda
President, Joseph G. (Joe) Koenig
Vp And General Manager U.s. East And Europe Sales & Operations, Matt Horner
Vp Supply Chain Operations, Kurt Grimminger
Vp Global Supply Chain, Mark Franke
Vice President Of Information Technology, Mike P. Taylor
Vice President Sales Operations, Tim Loughman
Vice President Business Development, Tariq Hafeez
Vice President Professional Services, Tom Gain
Vice President Of Information Technology, Michael Taylor
Vice President Head Of Asia Pacific, Nilesh Mistry
Vice President Security Solutions, Michael McGlynn
Area Vice President Global Service Provider, Kraig Ecker
Chairman, David L. Steward

LOCATIONS

HQ: WORLD WIDE TECHNOLOGY, LLC
1 WORLD WIDE WAY, SAINT LOUIS, MO 631463002
Phone: 314 569-7000
Web: WWW.WWT.COM

PRODUCTS/OPERATIONS

Selected Services
IT Products and Solutions
  Facilities Infrastructure
  Integration and Staging
  Leasing
  Managed Services
  Order Management and Reporting
  Pre-Sales Support
  Value Added Reseller
Professional Services
  Configuration
  Implementation
  Planning and Design
  Training
Supply Chain Services
  Business Process Outsourcing
  Logistics/Warehousing
  Material Planning and Scheduling
  Outsourced Procurement
  Supplier Management

COMPETITORS

Accenture	HP Enterprise Services
Black Box	IBM Global Services
Computer Sciences Corp.	PC Mall
	Rose International
DataSpan	Unisys
Dynamics Research	WebLinc
En Pointe	

HISTORICAL FINANCIALS
Company Type: Private

Income Statement				FYE: December 31
	REVENUE ($ mil.)	NET INCOME ($ mil.)	NET PROFIT MARGIN	EMPLOYEES
12/15	5,927	95	1.6%	1,052
12/14	5,057	95	1.9%	—
12/13	4,545	77	1.7%	—
12/12	3,396	57	1.7%	—
Annual Growth	20.4%	18.3%	—	—

2015 Year-End Financials
Return on assets: 17.7%   Cash ($ mil.): 46
Return on equity: 1.6%
Current ratio: 1.00

WORLD WILDLIFE FUND, INC.

A fuzzy-wuzzy with kung fu strength the panda embodies mission of the World Wildlife Fund (WWF). The conservation organization has worked on more than 13000 projects in about 100 countries to save endangered species and natural areas as well as to address threats such as global warming and the exploitation of forests. By 2020 WWF aims to conserve 15 of the world's more ecologically important regions. Its work crosses Africa Asia Latin America North America and Eurasia through national affiliates in about 100 countries. The group publishes data on wildlife wild places and global environmental challenges. Founded in 1961 WWF is joined by 1.1 million members in the US and some 5 million overseas.

Geographic Reach
While the Anchorage Alaska-based WWF is active in some 100 countries the organization targets the world's most ecologically important regions for conservation including the Arctic Amazon Congo Basin the Galapagos eastern Himalayas and the Northern Great Plains in the US.

Financial Performance
The conservation organization's total revenue including pledges for future years remained flat from 2013 to 2014 hovering around the $266 million mark. The consistent revenue was due to the success of the Arctic Home campaign with The Coca-Cola Company. Support from individual donors remained the single largest source of WWF's unrestricted revenue.

Strategy
In 2014 WWF opened its new Myanmar office in an effort to develop a green economy and help conserve the country's diverse species such as tigers elephants and Irrawaddy dolphins.

EXECUTIVES

Managing Director, Kerry Cesareo
Vice President Program Operations, Kristine Vega
Vice President, Todd Shelton
Senior Vice President And Chief Scientist, Rebecca Shaw
Vice President Of International Finance, Raj Kundra
Vice President Membership And Partner Marketing, Terence Macko
Senior Vice President Of Private Sector Engagement, Sheila Bonini
Auditors: BDO USA LLP MCLEAN VIRGINIA

LOCATIONS

HQ: WORLD WILDLIFE FUND, INC.
1250 24TH ST NW FL 2, WASHINGTON, DC 200371193
Phone: 202 293-4800
Web: WWW.WORLDWILDLIFE.ORG

PRODUCTS/OPERATIONS

2015 Expenses

	% of total
Program	84
Fundraising	11
Finance & administration	5
Total	**100**

2015 Revenue

	% of total
Individual contributions	32
In-Kind & other revenues	19
Government grants & contracts	19
Foundation contributions	9
Network revenues	7
Corporations	4
Other/non-operating contributions	10
Total	**100**

Selected Goals
Ensure that the value of nature is reflected in the decisions made by individuals communities governments and businesses
Mobilize hundreds of millions of people to support conservation
Protect and restore species and their habitats
Strengthen local communities' ability to conserve the natural resources they depend upon
Transform markets and policies to reduce the impact of the production and consumption of commodities

HISTORICAL FINANCIALS
Company Type: Private

Income Statement				FYE: June 30
	REVENUE ($ mil.)	NET INCOME ($ mil.)	NET PROFIT MARGIN	EMPLOYEES
06/16	323	(0)		400
06/14	227	6	3.0%	—
06/13	229	25	11.1%	—
06/12	208	16	8.1%	—
Annual Growth	11.6%	—	—	—

2016 Year-End Financials
Return on assets: 5.2%   Cash ($ mil.): 41
Return on equity: (-0.1%)
Current ratio: 1.20

WORLEY & OBETZ, INC.

Auditors: HOROVITZ RUDOY & ROTEMAN LLC

LOCATIONS

HQ: WORLEY & OBETZ, INC.
85 WHITE OAK RD, MANHEIM, PA 175458550
Phone: 717 665-6891
Web: WWW.WORLEYOBETZ.COM

HISTORICAL FINANCIALS
Company Type: Private

Income Statement				FYE: August 31
	REVENUE ($ mil.)	NET INCOME ($ mil.)	NET PROFIT MARGIN	EMPLOYEES
08/17	677	2	0.4%	68
08/16	584	1	0.3%	—
08/15	520	2	0.4%	—
08/14	466	1	0.4%	—
Annual Growth	13.2%	14.0%	—	—

2017 Year-End Financials
Return on assets: 1.5%   Cash ($ mil.): —
Return on equity: 0.4%
Current ratio: 1.40

WOUNDED WARRIOR PROJECT, INC.

EXECUTIVES

Ceo, Steven Nardizzi
Chb, Jonathan Woodson
Vice Chm, Kathleen Widmer
Vice Chb, Guy McMichael III
Coordinator, Erica Neu
Controller, Cindy McDonald
Coordinator, Brandy Jaworski
Coordinator, Kate Brett
Coordinator, Lisa Villont
Auditors: GRANT THORNTON LLP JACKSONVIL

LOCATIONS

HQ: WOUNDED WARRIOR PROJECT, INC.
4899 BELFORT RD STE 300, JACKSONVILLE, FL
322566033
Phone: 904 296-7350
Web: WWW.WOUNDEDWARRIORPROJECT.ORG

HISTORICAL FINANCIALS

Company Type: Private

Income Statement			FYE: September 30
	REVENUE ($ mil.)	NET INCOME ($ mil.)	NET PROFIT MARGIN	EMPLOYEES
09/15	398	47	11.8%	3
09/13	234	76	32.6%	—
09/12	154	59	38.4%	—
09/11	74	16	22.0%	—
Annual Growth	52.3%	30.3%	—	—

2015 Year-End Financials

Return on assets: 7.2%   Cash ($ mil.): 75
Return on equity: 11.8%
Current ratio: 2.60

XANTERRA HOLDING CORPORATION

EXECUTIVES

Pres-Ceo, Andrew Todd
V Pres, Michael F Welch

LOCATIONS

HQ: XANTERRA HOLDING CORPORATION
6312 S FIDDLERS GREEN CIR # 600, GREENWOOD
VILLAGE, CO 801114943
Phone: 303 600-3400
Web: WWW.XANTERRA.COM

HISTORICAL FINANCIALS

Company Type: Private

Income Statement			FYE: December 27
	REVENUE ($ mil.)	NET INCOME ($ mil.)	NET PROFIT MARGIN	EMPLOYEES
12/17	395	48	12.1%	3,500
12/16	414	9	2.4%	—
12/15	385	47	12.4%	—
12/14	390	72	18.6%	—
Annual Growth	0.4%	(12.9%)	—	—

2017 Year-End Financials

Return on assets: 14.0%   Cash ($ mil.): 22
Return on equity: 12.1%
Current ratio: 0.20

XANTERRA, INC.

EXECUTIVES

Pres, Andrew N Todd
Vice President, Michael F Welch
Sales Manager, Phyllis Nefsky

LOCATIONS

HQ: XANTERRA, INC.
6312 S FIDDLERS GREEN CIR 600N, GREENWOOD
VILLAGE, CO 801114920
Phone: 303 600-3400
Web: WWW.XANTERRA.COM

HISTORICAL FINANCIALS

Company Type: Private

Income Statement			FYE: December 27
	REVENUE ($ mil.)	NET INCOME ($ mil.)	NET PROFIT MARGIN	EMPLOYEES
12/17	384	50	13.0%	3,500
12/16	376	29	7.9%	—
12/15	350	53	15.2%	—
12/14	358	79	22.2%	—
Annual Growth	2.4%	(14.3%)	—	—

2017 Year-End Financials

Return on assets: 14.3%   Cash ($ mil.): 20
Return on equity: 13.0%
Current ratio: 0.20

YAKIMA VALLEY MEMORIAL HOSPITAL ASSOCIATION INC

Whether you're a major yakker or quiet as a mouse Yakima Valley Memorial Hospital serves the health care needs of patients of all types. The health provider's acute-care hospital skilled-nursing facilities and outpatient specialty treatment facilities serve patients in and around Yakima in Washington State. The hospital has about 225 beds and provides a variety of services such as heart care orthopedics pediatrics cancer treatment women's health and mental health care. It also offers sleep and wound care and provides home health and hospice services. The organization is a not-for-profit group governed by a board of directors.

Operations

Yakima Valley Memorial Hospital sees about 15000 inpatients each year as well as 77000 emergency room visits and 3100 births. It serves a total of more than 130000 patient per year.

The organization provides a full range of inpatient and outpatient services that include critical care surgery diagnostics cancer care heart care orthopedics a family birthplace a neonatal intensive care unit pediatrics physical therapy and psychiatric care. Its Children's Village provides care for kids with special health or development needs. Other specialty units include the Garden Village skilled nursing center and the Cottage in the Meadow hospice facility. The organization also runs a community education program and a maternal health preventative care program.

Among its staff are 330 physicians representing 35 medical specialties.

Geographic Reach

In addition to its main 26-acre campus in Yakima Washington the organization has 15 locations throughout Yakima County.

Financial Performance

During 2012 the hospital provided $73.7 million in Community Benefits (22% more than in 2011). Included in this number was more than $33 million to cover a shortfall from Medicare funding. Net patient revenue in 2012 was $286 million.

Strategy

Yakima Valley Memorial Hospital is upgrading its infrastructure and its technologies to better serve area residents. In 2013 for instance it added digital breast screening systems to its mammography center and in 2012 the facility invested $1.3 million to replace aging beds.

In 2013 the hospital announced that it was looking for a partner to help it with several challenges including Medicare reimbursement cuts state Medicaid funding woes and the high costs of health information technology. The three prospective groups (which submitted proposals) included Virginia Mason Medical Center in Seattle; Seattle-based Swedish Health Services and Renton-based Providence Health & Services; and Vancouver (Washington)-based PeaceHealth and the University of Washington Medicine Medicine in Seattle.

Company Background

Yakima Valley Memorial Hospital was founded in 1950.

EXECUTIVES

Vice President, Jim Aberle
Ceo, Russ Myers
Pharmacist Manager, Kelly Groth
Senior Vice President, Mely Davenport
Medical Records Director, Jamie Beaman
Vice President, Gail Weaver
Chairman, James Berg
Vice Chairman, Scott Wagner
Auditors: MOSS-ADAMS LLP YAKIMA WASHIN

LOCATIONS

HQ: YAKIMA VALLEY MEMORIAL HOSPITAL
ASSOCIATION INC
2811 TIETON DR, YAKIMA, WA 989023761
Phone: 509 249-5129
Web: WWW.YAKIMAMEMORIAL.ORG

PRODUCTS/OPERATIONS

Selected Services and Locations

16th Avenue Pavilion
Apple Valley Family Medicine
Cardiac Rehabilitation and Wellness Center
Cascade Surgical Partners
Children's Village
Family Medicine of Yakima
Garden Village
Home Health and Hospice
Memorial Cornerstone Medicine
Memorial Hospitalist Program
Memorial's Valley Imaging
North Star Lodge Cancer Center
'Ohana Mammography Center
Pacific Crest Family Medicine
Selah Family Medicine
Sleep Center at Memorial
Surgi-Center at Memorial
The Springs Rehabilitation and Occupational Medicine
Water's Edge Pain Relief Institute
Yakima Gastroenterology Associates
Yakima Internal Medicine
Yakima Neurosurgery Associates
Yakima Plastic Surgery Associates
Yakima Vascular Associates

COMPETITORS

Adventist Health   Overlake Hospital
System West   PeaceHealth
Catholic Health   Providence Health &

Initiatives
Franciscan Health
  System
HCA
Harrison Medical
  Center
MultiCare Health
  System

Services-Washington
Providence St. Joseph
  Health
Swedish Health
  Services
Watson Institute

HISTORICAL FINANCIALS
Company Type: Private

Income Statement   FYE: December 31

	REVENUE ($ mil.)	NET INCOME ($ mil.)	NET PROFIT MARGIN	EMPLOYEES
12/17	457	0	0.1%	1,150
12/16*	424	83	19.6%	—
10/12	309	(6)	—	—
10/09	276	(18)	—	—
Annual Growth	6.5%	—	—	—

*Fiscal year change

2017 Year-End Financials
Return on assets: 5.9%   Cash ($ mil.): 23
Return on equity: 0.1%
Current ratio: 1.00

YALE NEW HAVEN HEALTH SERVICES CORPORATION

Yale New Haven Health System is a health care haven for residents of Southern Connecticut Southwestern Rhode Island and parts of New York's Westchester County. The company operates Yale-New Haven Hospital Greenwich Hospital Bridgeport Hospital and Lawrence & Memorial Hospital and has a contract relationship with The Westerly Hospital in Rhode Island (Northeast Medical Group) as well as children's cancer psychiatric care hospitals. In addition Yale New Haven Health Services operates outpatient facilities and provides such managed care services as network contracting as well as disease management programs. The system is affiliated with Yale University's medical school and has a grand total of about 2560 beds.

Operations
Through its Yale-New Haven Bridgeport Greenwich Lawrence & Memorial and Northeast Medical Group delivery networks the company provides comprehensive cost effective advanced patient care. The system's clinical services include primary and preventive care specialty acute and sub-acute care rehabilitation skilled nursing and coordination of home care. In 2016 the health system which has about 6300 doctors treated more than 114000 inpatients and about 1.9 million outpatients.

Yale New Haven Health System in affiliation with the Yale School of Medicine and other universities and colleges educates health professionals and advances clinical care. Its provides more than $300 million in community benefits and community-building activities.

The 1541-bed Yale-New Haven Hospital is an acute and tertiary care hospital; it includes Yale-New Haven Children's Hospital Yale-New Haven Psychiatric Hospital and the Smilow Cancer Hospital.

The 393-bed Bridgeport Hospital serves almost 19000 inpatients and more than 230000 outpatients a year.

The 206-bed Greenwich Hospital is a community teaching hospital.

Lawrence & Memorial Hospital is a 280-bed general and acute care hospital serving parts of Connecticut New York and Rhode Island.

Northeast Medical Group is a not-for-profit multispecialty medical foundation. Its Westerly Hospital (served by the Yale New Haven Health System) is a 125-bed not-for-profit acute care community hospital serving southern Rhode Island and southeastern Connecticut.

Geographic Reach
Yale New Haven Health System serves patients in Southern Connecticut Southwestern Rhode Island and parts of New York's Westchester County.

Financial Performance
Yale New Haven Health System's revenues totaled $3.8 billion in fiscal 2016 (ended September).

Mergers and Acquisitions
Growing its network in 2016 Yale New Haven Health System acquired Lawrence & Memorial Hospital with 280 beds.

Company Background
Yale New Haven Health System was formed in 1996.

EXECUTIVES

Evp, Marna P. Borgstrom
Evp Corporate And Financial Services; Cfo And Svp Finance Yale-new Haven Hospital, James M. Staten
Evp; President And Ceo Greenwich Hospital And Greenwich Health Care System, Frank A. Corvino
Svp Medical Affairs; Chief Of Staff And Svp Medical Affairs Yale-new Haven Hospital, Peter N. Herbert
Evp And Coo Yale-new Haven Hospital, Richard D'Aquila
Evp; President And Ceo Bridgeport Hospital, William M. (Bill) Jennings, age 51
Chief Information Officer, Daniel Barchi
Evp And Coo, Christopher OConnor
Ceo Northeast Medical Group, Robert Nordgren
Executive Vice President Ynhhs, Richard DAquila
Chairman, Julia M. McNamara, age 76
Auditors: ERNST & YOUNG US LLP INDIANAP

LOCATIONS

HQ: YALE NEW HAVEN HEALTH SERVICES CORPORATION
789 HOWARD AVE, NEW HAVEN, CT 065191300
Phone: 888 461-0106
Web: WWW.YALENEWHAVENHEALTH.ORG

PRODUCTS/OPERATIONS

Selected Facilities
Bridgeport Hospital (Bridgeport Connecticut)
Greenwich Hospital (Greenwich Connecticut)
Yale-New Haven Hospital (New Haven Connecticut)
  Yale-New Haven Children's Hospital
  Yale-New Haven Psychiatric Hospital
  Smilow Cancer Hospital at Yale-New Haven

COMPETITORS

Bristol Hospital
Griffin Hospital
Hartford Health Care
Hospital of Central Connecticut
Kent Hospital
Memorial Sloan-Kettering
MidState Medical Center
New Milford Hospital
NewYork-Presbyterian Hospital
Saint Francis Hospital and Medical Center
Stamford Health
University of Connecticut Health Center

Waterbury Hospital
Westchester Medical Center
Western Connecticut Health Network
Yale-New Haven Hospital Saint Raphael Campus

HISTORICAL FINANCIALS
Company Type: Private

Income Statement   FYE: September 30

	REVENUE ($ mil.)	NET INCOME ($ mil.)	NET PROFIT MARGIN	EMPLOYEES
09/15	449	19	4.4%	22,490
09/13	427	35	8.2%	—
09/09	149	5	3.6%	—
09/08	141	2	1.5%	—
Annual Growth	17.9%	37.1%	—	—

2015 Year-End Financials
Return on assets: 17.3%   Cash ($ mil.): 25
Return on equity: 4.4%
Current ratio: 0.90

YALE UNIVERSITY

What do former President George W. Bush and actress Meryl Streep have in common? They are Yalies. Yale University is one of the nation's most prestigious private liberal arts institutions as well as one of its oldest (founded in 1701). Yale comprises an undergraduate college a graduate school and more than a dozen professional schools. Programs of study include architecture law medicine and drama. Its 12 residential colleges (a system borrowed from Oxford) serve as dormitory dining hall and social center. The school has around 12000 students and nearly 4000 faculty members.

Operations
Yale's graduate students of which there are more than 6500 outnumber its more than 5300 undergrads. Undergraduate tuition runs at around $42000 per year plus $13000 in room and board. Graduate tuition is about $35000 per year. The university has some 4000 faculty members.

The university has extensive research programs affiliated with its graduate school and its graduate-level professional schools which cover architecture art divinity drama engineering and applied science forestry and environmental studies law management medicine music nursing and public health.

Yale also operates the Yale University Press which publishes works of academics and professionals including e-books and traditional books. It published 475 titles during 2012 and has produced about 9000 titles in total.

Geographic Reach
Yale's facilities cover a total of 1100 acres including a 340-acre central campus with 260 buildings in New Haven Connecticut; a 140-acre West Campus on the edge of New Haven; and 600 acres of athletic fields and natural preserve areas outside of town. Yale's students come from all 50 US states and about 110 foreign countries.

Financial Performance
Sales for Yale have grown over the last five years and the university showed a 1% increase in revenues to more than $2.8 billion in 2012 due to higher student income grants and contracts (for research and training programs) medical service revenues and other income sources. Endowment income and grants and contracts are the largest source of revenue.

Yale's annual operating budget is about $2.7 billion.

Yale's roughly $19 billion endowment ranks as one of the largest in the US. Yale's Endowment grew about 9% in 2010 producing a gain of $1.4 billion.

Company Background

Yale was founded in 1701 through the vision of a group of colonial clergymen who began planning for a university in the 1640s. It was named Yale College in 1718 after a Welsh merchant Elihu Yale who made a sizable donation to the institution.

EXECUTIVES

Associate Vice President Federal Relations, Richard Jacob

Clinical Director, Thomas Carpenter

Vice Chairman, John Geibel

Board Member, Larry NG

Board Member, Elizabeth Sullivan

Board Member, Kim Beckett

Auditors: PRICEWATERHOUSECOOPERS LLP HA

LOCATIONS

HQ: YALE UNIVERSITY
105 WALL ST, NEW HAVEN, CT 065118917
Phone: 203 432-2550
Web: WWW.YALE.EDU

PRODUCTS/OPERATIONS

Colleges and Schools
Graduate School of Arts and Sciences
Professional schools
  School of Architecture
  School of Art
  Divinity School
  School of Drama
  School of Engineering & Applied Science
  School of Forestry & Environmental Studies
  Law School
  School of Management
  School of Medicine
  School of Music
  School of Nursing
  School of Public Health
  Institute of Sacred Music
Yale College (undergraduate studies)
Residential Colleges
Berkeley College
Branford College
Calhoun College
Davenport College
Ezra Stiles College
Jonathan Edwards College
Morse College
Pierson College
Saybrook College
Silliman College
Timothy Dwight College
Trumbull College

HISTORICAL FINANCIALS

Company Type: Private

Income Statement   FYE: June 30

	REVENUE ($ mil.)	NET INCOME ($ mil.)	NET PROFIT MARGIN	EMPLOYEES
06/18	3,848	3,270	85.0%	11,000
06/17	3,647	2,447	67.1%	—
06/16	3,449	(846)	—	—
06/13	2,936	1,965	66.9%	—
Annual Growth	5.6%	10.7%	—	—

2018 Year-End Financials

Return on assets: 11.2%   Cash ($ mil.): 587
Return on equity: 85.0%
Current ratio: —

YALE-NEW HAVEN HOSPITAL, INC.

Yale-New Haven supports its community and the brainiacs at Yale. Yale-New Haven Hospital (YNHH) is the flagship member of the Yale New Haven Health System. It provides tertiary care in more than 100 medical specialties to residents of southwestern Connecticut. The not-for-profit hospital has more than 1500 beds on two campuses. Its main location includes the Yale-New Haven Children's Hospital and the Yale-New Haven Psychiatric Hospital. Smilow Cancer Hospital with 170 beds is also part of the hospital complex. YNHH provides cardiac and cancer care performs organ transplants and offers a variety of outpatient clinics. The medical center serves as the primary teaching hospital for Yale University's medical school.

Operations

YNHH handles some 80000 inpatient admissions each year including more than 5000 births. It also has more than 150000 emergency room and urgent care encounters. The hospital's campuses employ some 4250 medical staffers.

A key component of the main hospital facility is the Smilow Cancer Hospital which conducts cancer care and research in partnership with Yale University's Cancer Center.

Financial Performance

YNHH's patient services contribute the bulk of the hospital's total operating revenue. In fiscal 2016 (ended September) operating revenue increased 5% to $2.7 billion as patient volume rose. However operating expenses also increased that year; supplies and other expenses rose to $1.3 billion (versus $1.2 billion in fiscal 2015). Total operating expenses in 2016 reached $2.6 billion. All told the hospital's excess of revenue over expenses increased 50% to $158.5 million.

Strategy

Despite facing challenges including state budget cuts YNHH has been working on the integration of its second campus Saint Raphael. The hospital has also invested some $100 million towards capital improvements at the campus. The combined organization allows YNHH to increase coordination of care and reduce redundancies for area communities.

EXECUTIVES

Evp Coo And Trustee, Marna P. Borgstrom

Svp Patient Services And Chief Nursing Officer, Patricia Sue Fitzsimons

Svp Operations; Executive Director Women's And Children's Services, Cynthia N. Sparer

President And Trustee, Richard D'Aquila

Svp Patient Safety And Quality And Chief Medical Officer, Thomas J. Balcezak

Svp Operations; Executive Director Smilow Cancer Hospital, Abe Lopman

Evp And Cfo Yale New Haven Health System And Cfo Yale New Haven Hospital (ynhh), Vincent Tammaro

Management Vice President Director, Margot Manacchio

Vice Chairman, Julia M. McNamara, age 76

Chair, Mary C. Farrell, age 68

Secretary, Mariela Shukis

Secretary, Michelle Apuzzo

Secretary, Sheryl Raffile

LOCATIONS

HQ: YALE-NEW HAVEN HOSPITAL, INC.
20 YORK ST, NEW HAVEN, CT 065103220
Phone: 203 688-4242
Web: WWW.YNHH.ORG

PRODUCTS/OPERATIONS

Selected Services
Ambulatory (outpatient) services
Bariatric surgery
Blood draw stations
Dental center
Diabetes and endocrinology
Diagnostic radiology
Ear nose and throat
Emergency services
Endocrine surgery
Gastroenterology
Geriatrics
Kidney disease
Maternity
Psychiatry
Pulmonology
Urology

COMPETITORS

Bristol Hospital	St. Vincent's Health
Connecticut Children's	Services
Medical Center	Waterbury Hospital
Griffin Hospital	Western Connecticut
Hartford Health Care	Health Network
New Milford Hospital	

HISTORICAL FINANCIALS

Company Type: Private

Income Statement   FYE: September 30

	REVENUE ($ mil.)	NET INCOME ($ mil.)	NET PROFIT MARGIN	EMPLOYEES
09/15	2,388	107	4.5%	22,000
09/14	2,360	120	5.1%	—
09/13	2,360	120	5.1%	—
09/09	1,237	52	4.3%	—
Annual Growth	11.6%	12.5%	—	—

2015 Year-End Financials

Return on assets: 6.4%   Cash ($ mil.): 101
Return on equity: 4.5%
Current ratio: 0.90

YAVAPAI COMMUNITY HOSP ASSN

EXECUTIVES

Ceo, John Amos

Prin, Timothy Barnett

Dev Co-Ordinator, Susie Haulle

Coordinator, Cindy Moore

Human Resources Director, Mark Timm

Director, Mary Sterling

Coordinator, Jason Bigelow

Director, Jeanne Briggs

Chief of Obstetrics/Gynecology, Connie Buckner

Human Resources Manager, Dee D Newton

Training and Direc, Ellen Benson

LOCATIONS

HQ: YAVAPAI COMMUNITY HOSP ASSN
1003 WILLOW CREEK RD, PRESCOTT, AZ 863011641
Phone: 928 445-2700
Web: WWW.YRMC.ORG

HISTORICAL FINANCIALS

Company Type: Private

Income Statement				FYE: December 31
	REVENUE ($ mil.)	NET INCOME ($ mil.)	NET PROFIT MARGIN	EMPLOYEES
12/17	347	48	13.9%	1,780
12/16	219	3	1.5%	—
12/15	146	(31)	—	—
12/14	150	(14)	—	—
Annual Growth	32.4%	—	—	—

2017 Year-End Financials
Return on assets: 6.5%
Return on equity: 13.9%
Current ratio: 3.20
Cash ($ mil.): 116

YORK HOSPITAL

York Hospital operating as WellSpan York Hospital takes its name from the community whose health it seeks to preserve. Part of WellSpan Health the medical center has about 570 beds and serves residents of York and surrounding area of south-central Pennsylvania. It is a regional leader in cardiovascular and orthopedic care and has programs in other specialty areas including oncology behavioral health and geriatrics. Additionally WellSpan York Hospital operates a Level 1 trauma center offers outpatient surgery emergency home health and diagnostic imaging services. It is also has teaching and research programs. The hospital was founded in 1880.

Operations
WellSpan York Hospital has been recognized as a top 100 US hospital by US News for more than five years in a row. It is also recognized for its cardiovascular and orthopedic programs. The center employs about 700 doctors.

The hospital's education programs include five allied health schools and seven residency programs. Affiliated organizations include the medical schools of Drexel University Pennsylvania State University and University of Maryland.

Strategy
WellSpan York Hospital is working to improve its specialist programs to meet the growing medical needs of area residents. In 2011 for instance it collaborated with technology firm Cerner and pharmaceuticals firm Hospira to form an infusion management program for its intensive care unit; the program aims to reduce infusion-related errors. In addition it launched a urinary catheter removal protocol to reduce infection rates and it implemented an aortic valve replacement program (making it one of three facilities in Pennsylvania to offer the open-heart surgery alternative).

EXECUTIVES

Vice President, Peter Hartmann
Medical Director, Cathy Penton Carpenter
Pharmacy Manager, Courtney Rodgers
Medical Director, Creston Tate
Pharmacist Manager, Tony Bixler
Managing Director Trauma Surgeon, Jesse Goddard
Clinic Director, Ralph Whitaker

LOCATIONS

HQ: YORK HOSPITAL
1001 S GEORGE ST, YORK, PA 174033645
Phone: 717 851-2345
Web: WWW.YORKHOSPITAL.EDU

COMPETITORS

Ascension Health	Hanover Healthcare
Catholic Health Initiatives	Hershey Medical Center
Geisinger Health System	Holy Spirit
Guthrie Healthcare	Lancaster General Memorial Hospital (PA)
	PinnacleHealth System

HISTORICAL FINANCIALS

Company Type: Private

Income Statement				FYE: June 30
	REVENUE ($ mil.)	NET INCOME ($ mil.)	NET PROFIT MARGIN	EMPLOYEES
06/18	1,063	181	17.0%	6,200
06/16	990	17	1.8%	—
06/15	925	82	9.0%	—
06/14	853	136	16.0%	—
Annual Growth	5.7%	7.3%		

2018 Year-End Financials
Return on assets: 1.6%
Return on equity: 17.0%
Current ratio: 2.40
Cash ($ mil.): 16

YOSEMITE FARM CREDIT, ACA

EXECUTIVES

Pres, Leonard Van Eldern
Cfo, Tracy Sparks
Vice President, Brian Lemons
Vice President Marketing, Melba Miyamoto
Manager, Ray Koopman
Vice President, Robert Fuller

LOCATIONS

HQ: YOSEMITE FARM CREDIT, ACA
806 W MONTE VISTA AVE, TURLOCK, CA 953827242
Phone: 209 667-2366
Web: WWW.YOSEMITEFARMCREDIT.COM

HISTORICAL FINANCIALS

Company Type: Private

Income Statement				FYE: December 31
	ASSETS ($ mil.)	NET INCOME ($ mil.)	INCOME AS % OF ASSETS	EMPLOYEES
12/17	2,889	53	1.8%	100
12/16	2,661	43	1.6%	—
12/15	2,368	41	1.7%	—
12/14	2,154	38	1.8%	—
Annual Growth	10.3%	11.2%		

2017 Year-End Financials
Return on assets: —
Return on equity: 48.9%
Sales ($ mil): 108

YOUNG LIFE

EXECUTIVES

Svp, Ted Johnson
Vice President, Ken Knipp
Senior Vice President Western Division, John Franklin
Auditors: CAPIN CROUSE LLP COLORADO SPR

LOCATIONS

HQ: YOUNG LIFE
420 N CASCADE AVE, COLORADO SPRINGS, CO 809033352
Phone: 719 381-1800
Web: WWW.YOUNGLIFE.ORG

HISTORICAL FINANCIALS

Company Type: Private

Income Statement				FYE: September 30
	REVENUE ($ mil.)	NET INCOME ($ mil.)	NET PROFIT MARGIN	EMPLOYEES
09/16	343	18	5.5%	3,100
09/15	331	29	9.0%	—
09/14	311	31	10.3%	—
09/13	276	17	6.5%	—
Annual Growth	7.6%	1.4%		

2016 Year-End Financials
Return on assets: 4.9%
Return on equity: 5.5%
Current ratio: —
Cash ($ mil.): 55

YSLETA INDEPENDENT SCHOOL DISTRICT

EXECUTIVES

Supt, Xavier Delatorre
Dir, Mary Haynie
Staff, Shannon Carroll
Designer, Liliana Sepulveda
Assistant Superintendent, Patricia Ayala
Instructional Media D, Virginia Rey
Auditors: WHITLEY PENN LLP HOUSTON TEX

LOCATIONS

HQ: YSLETA INDEPENDENT SCHOOL DISTRICT
9600 SIMS DR, EL PASO, TX 799257225
Phone: 915 434-0240
Web: WWW.YISD.NET

HISTORICAL FINANCIALS

Company Type: Private

Income Statement				FYE: June 30
	REVENUE ($ mil.)	NET INCOME ($ mil.)	NET PROFIT MARGIN	EMPLOYEES
06/17	471	150	32.0%	7,155
06/16	462	257	55.6%	—
06/15	449	(3)	—	—
06/14	442	5	1.2%	—
Annual Growth	2.1%	203.6%		

2017 Year-End Financials
Return on assets: —
Return on equity: 32.0%
Current ratio: —
Cash ($ mil.): 392

YUMA REGIONAL MEDICAL CENTER INC

Yuma Regional Medical Center (YRMC) is an acute care hospital that provides medical services for Yuma Arizona and its surrounding communities. The not-for-profit hospital which has more than 400 beds and 400 doctors provides general medical surgical and emergency services. YRMC also operates about 30 additional facilities around Yuma including a rehabilitation hospital laboratories a wound care clinic primary care clinics and diagnostic imaging centers.

Operations

YRMC offers a free program called Silver Care in which patients who are 55 and older are encouraged to live active and healthy lives by being offered a number of benefits such as discounts at local stores specially reduced rates on selected lab tests including cholesterol and blood glucose screenings. Additionally Silver Care members are eligible for free membership in the Fit for Life cardiac wellness program.

The hospital's medical personnel have completed advanced procedures such as a transcatheter aortic valve replacement and a one-level cervical disc replacement using Mobi-C technology.

Strategy

Being a regional hospital YRMC works hard to recruit physicians who might otherwise be drawn to larger teaching hospitals with more advanced technological equipment and complex patient cases. In order to lure in such specialists the hospital offers extended medical education career weekends and a number of specialized centers in which physicians can perform procedures solely in their specialty such as a neonatal ICU and a pediatric sub-specialty unit.

The system has grown by adding new specialty clinics to its network. For example its newest clinic is the YRMC Plastic and Reconstructive Surgery center. It expanded and renovated its emergency department (adding two heliports) in 2017.

EXECUTIVES

Vp Information Technology And Cio, Gene Shaw
Interim President And Ceo, Camie Overton
Vp Patient Care Services And Chief Nursing Officer, Deb Carver
Cfo, David Willie
Interim Vp Medical Affairs And Chief Medical Officer, Robert Cannell
Physical Therapy Director, Jennifer Breen
Vice President Treasurer And Assistant Secretary, Michelle Martinez
Infection Control Director, Valerie Payne

LOCATIONS

HQ: YUMA REGIONAL MEDICAL CENTER INC
2400 S AVENUE A, YUMA, AZ 853647170
Phone: 928 344-2000
Web: WWW.YUMAREGIONAL.ORG

PRODUCTS/OPERATIONS

Selected Services
Children
Cancer Care
Children's Rehabilitative Services
Critical Care
Diabetes Education
Diagnostic Imaging
Emergency Department
First Health Medical Supply
Gastroenterology
Heart

Hospitalist Program
Lab
Medical Staff Services
Nursing Units
Outpatient Surgical Center
Pharmacy
Spiritual Care and Patient Advocacy
Surgical Services
Weight Loss
Women's Services
Wound Care Center

COMPETITORS

Banner Health
Community Health Systems
Dignity Health
HCA
John C. Lincoln Health Network

Northern Arizona Healthcare
Phoenix Children's Hospital
Providence St. Joseph Health
Scottsdale Healthcare

HISTORICAL FINANCIALS

Company Type: Private

Income Statement | | | | FYE: September 30

	REVENUE ($ mil.)	NET INCOME ($ mil.)	NET PROFIT MARGIN	EMPLOYEES
09/17	442	50	11.5%	2,400
09/16	410	37	9.2%	—
09/15	371	(8)	—	—
09/14	328	30	9.2%	—
Annual Growth	10.5%	19.0%	—	—

2017 Year-End Financials

Return on assets: 4.5%   Cash ($ mil.): 37
Return on equity: 11.5%
Current ratio: 0.70

ZEN-NOH GRAIN CORPORATION

EXECUTIVES

Ceo, John D Williams
Dir, Yoshihiro Sugiyama
Dir, Yoshinori Ohara
Dir, Hiroyuki Kawasaki
Sr. Vice President, Charles E Colbert
Cfo, Shin Inoue
Contlr, Robin Gerarve
Controller, Cindi Ernst
Senior Vice-President, Chris Schuster
Manager, Barbara Campbell
Manager, Sean Burke

LOCATIONS

HQ: ZEN-NOH GRAIN CORPORATION
1127 HWY 190 E SERVICE RD, COVINGTON, LA 704334929
Phone: 985 867-3500
Web: WWW.CGB.COM

HISTORICAL FINANCIALS

Company Type: Private

Income Statement | | | | FYE: May 31

	REVENUE ($ mil.)	NET INCOME ($ mil.)	NET PROFIT MARGIN	EMPLOYEES
05/18	6,971	101	1.5%	188
05/17	7,047	67	1.0%	—
05/16	5,722	37	0.7%	—
05/15	6,000	86	1.4%	—
Annual Growth	5.1%	5.7%	—	—

2018 Year-End Financials

Return on assets: 1.0%   Cash ($ mil.): 43
Return on equity: 1.5%
Current ratio: 0.10

Hoover's Handbook of

Private Companies

Index of Executives

Index of Executives

A

Aardsma, Wayne 503
Aaron, Kimberly 141
Aaron, Todd 542
Aarons, Miriam 69
Aarons, Brian 525
Aaronson, Diane 298
Aasland, Brent 249
Abbamondi, Desa 690
Abbasi, Masoud 402
Abbeele, Annick D. Van den 153
Abbott, Karen 64
Abbott, Mary J 261
Abbott, Jody 387
Abbott, Greg 540
Abbott, Charles 541
Abdallah, Chaouki T. 648
Abdelhafiz, Gada M 227
Abdullah, Sakinah 505
Abel, Anju 248
Abelsen, James N 505
Abercrombie, Les 206
Aberle, Jim 697
Abernathy, Cammy 642
Abhold, Kathleen 446
Abhyankar, Vivek 324
Abish, Jeffrey D. (Jeff) 6
Able, Pamela 348
Ables, Dorothy M. 519
Aboody, Linda 325
Abraham, Edward 673
Abrahamson, Tom 278
Abramowitz, Bernard H 376
Abrams, Ryan 693
Abregu, Martin 581
Abrell, Lane 430
Abreu, Lorena 508
Abshire, Kathy 116
Abshire, Kathryn 116
Abutaleb, Sam 616
Acereda, Alberto 175
Acerra, Peter 205
Acevedo, Debby 466
Achat, Catherine 144
Ackaret, Gary 268
Acker, H William 660
Ackerman, John 152
Ackerman, Melissa Melshenker 441
Ackerman, Lyle 499
Ackerman, Jeffrey (Jeff) 581
Ackley, John 255
Ackroyd, Jim 4
Acord, Suzette 661
Acosta, Philip A 508
Acosta-Trant, Ivette 59
Acres, Harold R 146
Adadevoh, Dela 92
Adair, Donald D 551
Adam, Mary 47
Adam, Sharon 198
Adame, Theresa 22
Adame, Bonita 28
Adame, Pedro 690
Adamovich, David 429

Adams, Stan 7
Adams, John V 22
Adams, Michelle 28
Adams, James R. 73
Adams, Cathy 128
Adams, Kevin D 139
Adams, Louis 181
Adams, Hank 228
Adams, Gregory 239
Adams, William 260
Adams, Joe M 271
Adams, Lana 279
Adams, Martin L. 297
Adams, Joseph (Joe) 360
Adams, Nicole 464
Adams, Dan 483
Adams, Jennifer 483
Adams, Bradley 515
Adams, Michele 521
Adams, Lawrence 525
Adams, Jason 537
Adams, Justin 596
Adams, Holly 608
Adams, Cecelia 620
Adams, Samantha 622
Adams, Mary Jane 638
Adams, Nancy D 685
Adamson, Nancy 187
Adamson, John 559
Aday, Daniel 218
Addis, Jason 276
Addiscott, Lynn 637
Addison, Paul 404
Addison, Janine 630
Adelman, Fredie 506
Adepeder, Suzanne 155
Ades, Susan 506
Adian, Jim 678
Adix, Kenneth 425
Adkins, Britni 408
Adkins, Dana 493
Adkins, Jim 571
Adkins, Greg 634
Adler, Michael M. 355
Adler, Vitaly 688
Adome, Amy 498
Adonnino, Joseph 409
Adrah, Robert 568
Advani, Pratibha K 556
Afwerke, Issac 474
Agee, Nancy Howell 95
Agee, Krista 528
Aggarwal, Nidhi 69
Agner, Rebecca 385
Agnew, John 690
Agostaro, Russell 378
Agrawal, Gail B. 611
Agree, Jonathan 619
Aguilar, Ashley 91
Aguilar, Gayla 386
Aguilar, Jorge 470
Aguilar, Mike 622
Aguilar, Patrick R 637
Ahearn, Brian 198
Ahern, Anthony J 88
Aherne, Chris 357

Ahlgrimm, Marijo 34
Ahmed, Riffat K 234
Ahn, Henry 488
Aho, Todd R 234
Ahola, Orrin 129
Ahrabi-Nejad, Nadine 321
Ahrens, Chris 125
Ahrens, Jere M 185
Ahuja, Seema S 637
Ai, Lin 642
Aiken, Jefferson K. (Jeff) 287
Aing, Melissa 324
Aini, Maria 618
Ainslie, Carolyn N. 606
Airhart, Jim 486
Aishman, Lisa 250
Aja, Cathy 545
Ajalla, Pius 382
Ajmani, Deep 398
Akers, Jeffery 404
Akers, Harlan 478
Akers-Pecht, Anna 610
Akin, Bilal 226
Akin, Terry 594
Akin, David 640
Akins, Nick 10
Akins, Nicholas K 32
Akpoguma, Andrea 68
Al-Ghanoudi, Ashirf 215
Alabsi, Samir Y 252
Alami, Maher 417
Alarhayem, Abdulqader 637
Alba, Alex 549
Albano, Charles 3
Alberici, John S 18
Alberici, John S 19
Alberici, John S 19
Alberry, Andrew 680
Albers, Nancy 254
Alberti, Harry 487
Alberts, Jim 271
Albertson, Paul 373
Albrecht, Raymond P 341
Albright, Tenley 313
Albright, Jody 413
Albright, Glen 421
Albright, Randolph 422
Albright, Steven 540
Albury, Beverly 92
Alcantar, Alberto 664
Alcock, Charles R. 506
Alcorn, Karen 322
Aldersley, Stephen 464
Aldrich, Peter D 488
Aldrich, Sister Barbara 536
Aldridge, Bryan 52
Aldridge, Susan C. 165
Aldy, Sonya 680
Alekh, Kshitiz 685
Alesandro, Michael J 244
Alesch, Anne 106
Alessandrini, Robert G. 588
Alexaitis, Irene 497
Alexander, Jackie 27
Alexander, Jim 167
Alexander, Tempie 170

Alexander, Barbara J 211
Alexander, Barbara 211
Alexander, Gaylord 234
Alexander, Wendy 279
Alexander, Sherrie 335
Alexander, James 349
Alexander, Rosemary 395
Alexander, Gene 397
Alexander, Craig H 422
Alexander, Kelly 518
Alexander, Pamala 633
Alexander, Jeffery 635
Alexander, Gordon 662
Alexiou, Joy 482
Alfieri, Laurie 551
Alfieri, Robert 676
Alford, William C. 76
Alford, Katherine 489
Alford, Barbara 554
Alger, Robert 282
Alger, Robert E 589
Algoe, Eric 563
Alhadeff, Kathie 428
Alhand, Liz 226
Ali, Michael 126
Alicea, Maria 83
Alicea, Marisa 155
Alicea, Jaime 551
Aligheri, Tim 258
Alimard, Kristina 658
Alkins, Brett 183
Allavie, Kathy 462
Allcock, Nicole 511
Allen, Michael D. 14
Allen, Les 73
Allen, Jennifer 145
Allen, Christy 160
Allen, Michael 223
Allen, Melissa 235
Allen, Robert 251
Allen, Rob 251
Allen, Clay M 279
Allen, Linda 303
Allen, Kim 363
Allen, Steve 365
Allen, David J. 379
Allen, Chris 416
Allen, Adrienne 419
Allen, Mark 431
Allen, Robert 456
Allen, Zaruba 466
Allen, Becky 480
Allen, Janine 486
Allen, Kim 499
Allen, Shelly 538
Allen, Gloria 543
Allen, Dennis 559
Allen, Jodi J 584
Allen, Elizabeth Heller 593
Allen, Elizabeth 593
Allen, Richard D 602
Allen, Beth 630
Allen, Gary K. 647
Allen, Andrew T. 653
Allen, Andrew 680
Alley, C. Thomas (Tom) 179

Barry, Ellen 338
Barry, Don 493
Barry, Thomas E 514
Barry, John 653
Barry, Kyle 692
Barsanti, Amy 612
Barstad, Joanne 650
Bart, Kelly 315
Bartel, Charles R. (Chuck) 169
Bartel, Trish 238
Barter, Jim 115
Barter, Brian 429
Barth, Catherine 281
Bartlett, Bryan 64
Bartlett, Danielle 377
Barto, Nick 100
Bartol, Ian 406
Bartoli, Andrea 494
Bartolomei, Tom 361
Bartolucci, Tony 10
Barton, Liza 10
Barton, Robert F. 31
Barton, Michelle 43
Barton, Jacqueline K. 91
Barton, Randolph 364
Barton, Alan 404
Bartosh, Robert J. 62
Bartsch, Matthew 550
Bartschat, Michael 268
Baruch, Wayne 608
Barwani, Gulamali 126
Barwani, Muradali 126
Barwell, Owen 25
Barwell, Michael 154
Barwood, Marlene A 261
Barycki, Elvera 295
Barzilay, Jonathan 445
Bas, Leo 208
Basch, Kenneth 99
Basch, Ken 99
Baschky, Linda 640
Bascom, Steven 357
Bascope, Nicole 298
Basden, Daniel 111
Baselga, José 325
Baselice, Marsha 482
Basford, Matt 455
Bashaw, Michael 690
Basilio, Esther 532
Baskerville, Bob 488
Basnet, Gandhi 572
Basnett, Stan 451
Basoglu, Mehmet 226
Bass, Scott A. 37
Bass, William L. 105
Bass, Justin 149
Bass, Theodore 496
Bass, Theodore 642
Bassett, Donal J 361
Bassett, Mary Beth 670
Bassham, Terry D 271
Basterrechea, Jose 33
Basulto, Jose 508
Batal, Courtney 67
Batalla, Rachael 139
Batchelor, Cheryl 194
Bateman, Kevin 441
Bateman, Mark T. 471
Bateman, Christopher M 543
Bateman, Gray 594
Bates, Jonathan R. (Jon) 45
Bates, Crandall 55
Bates, Angela 201
Bates, Martin W 218
Bates, Peter W. 303
Bates, Melissa 314
Bates, Ruth 331
Bates, Douglas 332
Bates, Jim 478
Bates, Ondrea 671
BATHLOW, JACKIE 536
Batholomay, William C 113
Batres, Francisco 136
Batt, Douglas A. 417
Batteiger, Tamara 525

Battenfield, Keith 104
Batts, Arnisha 475
Batulis, Scott 409
Baucum, Carlton E 243
Bauer, Tyler 390
Bauer, Daniel (Dan) 616
Bauerle, Gary 368
Baugh, Mike 630
Baum, Kristin 425
Baum, Shannon 512
Bauman, Rachael 254
Baumann, Caroline 506
Baumann, Joseph 694
Baumgardner, Jeffrey 80
Baumgarten, Alan S 346
Baumgartner, Michael A. 58
Bauters, Fred J 149
Bautista, Javier Velez 222
Bauwel, Chantal Van 80
Bavasi, Chris 195
Bavazls, Marcelo 46
Bawden, Lori 685
Baxley, Anthony 608
Baxter, Jack 178
Baxter, Warner L. 179
Baxter, Marlene 551
Baxter, Jeffrey 616
Bay, Lea 224
Baybars, Ilker 96
Bayer, Ronald K 406
Bayless, Victoria W 39
Bayless, George 208
Baylor, Denise 208
Bayt, Phil 672
Bazeley, Joe 339
Bea, Javon R 329
Beacher, Bob 190
Beachman, Michael 141
Beadie, William M 40
Beadie, William M 686
Beaghler, Mark A 135
Beal, Steven 323
Beal, Graham W J 577
Beam, Jesse 616
Beaman, John 434
Beaman, Jamie 697
Bean, Ron 72
Bean, Darlene 174
Bean, James C. 392
Bean, Richard E 421
Bean, Brian 537
Bear, John R. 342
Beard, Amy 86
Beard, Dave 164
Beard, Michelle 425
Beard, Cheryl 431
Beard, Kirk 460
Bearden, Jay 157
Beasley, Hunter 279
Beasley, Scott 563
Beasley, Christian 567
Beassie, Rhonda 563
Beatty, Robert W 11
Beatty, Ellen M. 564
Beauchamp, Philip K 627
Beauchant, Phil 352
Beaudoin, Edward 24
Beaulieu, Aaron 170
Beavers, Nancy 616
Beberness, Benjamin 447
Becerra, Jose 291
Becerra, Xavier 540
Bechler, Kent 143
Bechtle, Mavis 593
Bechtol, Nancy 506
Beck, Chuck 67
Beck, Gretchen 96
Beck, Gregory 139
Beck, Hilda 262
Beck, Teresa 596
Beck, Mary 649
Becker, Russell 40
Becker, Randall 53
Becker, Rik 69
Becker, Ralph 241

Becker, Anne 292
Becker, Bernard 543
Becker, Douglas A 624
Becker, Jeff 656
Becker, Kendall 681
Beckett, Evelyn 135
Beckett, Kim 699
Beckford, Paulette 350
Beckford, Avril 680
Beckius, Larry 45
Beckman, Lawrence 21
Beckman, Seth 169
Beckman, Joni 686
Beckmeyer, Laura 155
Beckum, Renee 529
Beckwith, Robert 113
Becoats, Eric 170
Bedard, Terri 484
Bedford, Charles E. 595
Bedi, Singh 629
Bednar, Tony 333
Bedner, Marie 52
Beebe, Lynda 92
Beecher, Barbara 92
Beecher, Bradley P. 578
Beechner, Christine 220
Beeler, Don 119
Beeler, Jason 324
Beem, Janel 610
Beeman, Thomas E. (Tom) 589
Beeman, Tom 619
Beene, Delwin 134
Beer, Robert 200
Beerman, Martin W. 117
Beeson, John N 692
Behal, Raj 538
Behan, Katherine 43
Behm, Michael J. 456
Behm, Marcia 465
Behrens, Matt 252
Beilby, Dione 431
Beilock, Sian 610
Beine, Beverly 390
Beissel, Andy 25
Beiter, Stephanie 463
Bejarano, Joelle 273
Belanger, Patti 481
Belcher, Barry J 47
Belda, Annmarie 654
Belden, Doug 131
Belfort, Michael A. 560
Belhumeur, Geaorge 480
Belikoff, Michael 544
Belknap, Gary 435
Bell, Douglas 74
Bell, Alastair 80
Bell, Sergeant 123
Bell, Eldrin 143
Bell, Kathy 284
Bell, Troy 291
Bell, Deborah 344
Bell, Greg 430
Bell, Joanne 482
Bell, Jeffery A 493
Bell, Brent 523
Bell, Jack 537
Bell, Bonnie 561
Bell, Kathy 612
Bellack, Janis P. 419
Bellanti, Tim 49
Bellenfant, William 353
Beller, Mark 40
Bellinger, Terry 404
Bello, Kathy 609
Bellone, Steven 145
Belmore, Jane 301
Belsito, Charlene E 632
Belt, Katrina 584
Belton, Paul 498
Beltran, Andrea 170
Beltran, Chris 661
Belzley, Cody 3
Bembry, Gary 59
Bembry, Gary L 281
Bemiller, Todd 693

Ben, Mark 625
Benak, Timothy 94
Benavides, Jeffrey 226
Benavides, Dr Alda T 278
Benbow, Camilla 615
Bencivenga, Carol 325
Bender, Judy 464
Bender, Andria 540
Bendickson, Marcus J 170
Bendler, Matt 11
Benedetto, Florence Di 548
Benedicto, Dawn 22
Beneke, Andrea 646
Benenati, Susan V 665
Benham, Stephanie 15
Benjamin, Mike 552
Benn, David P. 548
Bennack, Frank A. 597
Bennet, Deborah 276
Bennett, Thomas 30
Bennett, Susan 94
Bennett, Karen 148
Bennett, Chris 232
Bennett, Melanie 289
Bennett, W. Bradley (Brad) 315
Bennett, Greg 410
Bennett, John 668
Bennett, James 694
Bennie, James 295
Bennorth, Kara 683
Benoit, Garrett 347
Benrubi, Guy 642
Benscoter, Sam 553
Bensema, David J. 58
Benson, Cedric 60
Benson, Ed 191
Benson, Helen 282
Benson, Bruce 601
Benson, Lora J 606
Benson, Paul H. 611
Benson, Richard 669
Benson, Ellen 699
Bent, Dennis 89
Benthuysen, Maureen Van 303
Bentine, John 36
Benton, Joe 86
Benton, Cory 188
Benton, Brent 200
Benton, Jeff 239
Benton, David 282
Benton, Andrew K. 423
Benvenuto, Joe 61
Benz, Gary 350
Benzin, Sandy 174
Berdahl, Robert M. (Bob) 5
Berdan, Barclay E. 562
Bereche, Alfred C 363
Berenis, Joseph 105
Berenzweig, Harold 562
Beresford, Michael 339
Berg, Jessica 98
Berg, David 402
Berg, James 562
Berg, Alicia 610
Berg, Joel H. 658
Berg, James 697
Berger, Vince 6
Berger, Chadd 141
Berger, Anne 146
Berger, Lisa 179
Berger, Alan 642
Bergeson, Steven 26
Berghuis, Peter 441
Bergman, Carol A 286
Bergman, Chris 572
Bergman, Jessica 613
Bergquist, Lauren 452
Bergren, Carnan 448
Beringer, Ken 15
Berkau, Barbara 413
Berkay, H Sinan 529
Berke, Ethan M 154
Berkey, Dennis D 695
Berkley, William R. (Bill) 377
Berkowitz, Martin A 602

Carter, Paul 179	Casto, David 307	Champlin, Ryan 141	Chen, Kevin 610
Carter, Ella 243	Caston, Kim 460	Chan, Eugene 376	Cheney, Bradley 621
Carter, Donald E 273	Castrejana, Josie 294	Chan, Hayley 449	Cheng, Adelia 38
Carter, Don 273	Castro, Ricardo 251	Chan, Neville 496	Cheng, Dr Rita 393
Carter, Ellen 298	Castro, Mercedes 583	Chan, Kenyon S. 658	Chengat, Vipindas 687
Carter, David 331	Caswell, Jim 273	Chance, Kenneth B. 98	Chenoweth, Inge 307
Carter, Paige 356	Catalano, David A 328	Chance, Mary 144	Chermak, Jerome 398
Carter, Debra 368	Catalano, Robert 525	Chance, Linda 208	Chernault, Daniel L 468
Carter, Jim 433	Catalano, Mark J. 696	Chancellor, James 260	Chernets, Natalie 618
Carter, Jeri 435	Catha, Connie 403	Chandler, Ryan R 193	Cherry, Richard 434
Carter, Gregory 483	Catherman, Betty 441	Chandler, Jason 224	Cherry, Melody 517
Carter, Lonnie N. 509	Catlender, Katie 369	Chandler, Willis 632	Chertoff, Michael 383
Carter, Michael 516	Catmull, Lori 368	Chandler, Catherine 692	Cheshire, Bryan 632
Carter, Richard 573	Catt, Michael S 466	Chandra, Gautam 687	Chesley, Philip 458
Carter, Belinda 584	Cattarusa, Sandy 480	Chane, E-J 56	Chesnutt, Jim 410
Carter, Lugeion Y 597	Cauce, Ana Mari 658	Chanen, Daniel 344	Chessare, John B 208
Carter, Donna 617	Caudill, Anthony 663	Chang, Owen 132	Chessare, John 219
Carter, Julien 628	Caughey, Andrew 671	Chang, Brian S 158	Chester, Nicholas 421
Carter, Jimmy 636	Caughman, S Wright 182	Chang, Rosemarie 270	Cheung, Keith 231
Carter-Robertson, Kira 518	Cauley, Shannon 54	Chang, Brian 332	Cheung, Christine 375
Carthew, Geoffrey 361	Cauthron, Nazaneen 118	Chang, Florence 357	Cheung, Ramsey 538
Cartwright, Kay 457	Cavalier, Rodney 627	Chang, Derek 488	Chevrette, John 75
Carugno, Paola A 292	Cavallo-Miller, Linda 529	Chang, Daphne 538	Chhean, Forster 631
Caruselle, Nicholas 541	Cavanagh, Brandy 449	Chang, James 553	Chiappone, Michael 528
Caruso, Michael 506	Cavanaugh, Alison 379	Chang, Andrew 553	Chicas, Carlos 93
Caruso, Dave 543	Cavanaugh, Steven M. 613	Chang, Lay Nam 669	Chick, Phillip 611
Carvalho, Damon 212	Caveney, John E. (Jack) 416	Channamsetty, Vijay 298	Chilante, Diane 568
Carvallo, Jorge 96	Cavey, Brian 128	Chao, Jon 191	Child, Jeffrey S. (Jeff) 450
Carvelli, Joe 561	Cawley, Patrick J. 592	Chapa, Phillip 157	Child, Curtis 450
Carver, Bridget 265	Caylor, Gordon 370	Chapin, Susan 521	Child, William H. (Bill) 450
Carver, Deb 701	Cazares, Sara L 543	Chapman, Christopher P 3	Childers, Robert 246
Carwein, Vicky L. 449	Cazurra, Alvaro C 655	Chapman, Martha 53	Childers, Bob 246
Carwein, Vicky L. 627	Cbet, John 403	Chapman, Janet 60	Childers, Dexter 551
Carwell, Mark 137	Ccrn, Joscelyn 226	Chapman, Dr John E 97	Childress, Brian 421
Cary, John 461	Cctc, Jennifer 300	Chapman, Robert 179	Childs, Kleta 184
Cary, James 644	Cebrun, Hearold L 459	Chapman, Diana 307	Childs, Michelle 321
Caryer, Steve 135	Cecchi, Joseph L. 648	Chapman, Larry 474	Childs, Craig 339
Casalegno, Gina 96	Celepcikay, Oner Ulvi 226	Chapman, Carl L 514	Childs, Bobby 591
Casarez, Timothy W 40	Cella, Peter L 112	Chapman, Catherine A 612	Chiles, Kisha 60
Casas, Jaime R. 367	Cellucci, Annemarie 302	Chapman, Timothy M. 668	Chiles, Thomas 625
Casazza, Peter 69	Ceman, Jamie 109	Chapman, Adrian P. 687	Chimene, Kim 397
Casazza, Elizabeth 148	Centeno, Betsy 227	Chappell, George 444	Chin, Helen 548
Case, Edward B 457	Centiva, Andres F Costas- 639	Chapple, Scott 410	Chindemi, Craig 310
Case, Thomas S 546	Ceragioli, Teresa 624	Chappuis, Cameron 279	Ching, Patrick D 493
Case, Thomas S 605	Cerilli, Brian 104	Charbonneau, Laura 66	Chinn, Terri 536
Case-Wirth, Jill 680	Cerise, Frederick P. (Fred) 152	Chard, David 514	Chinniah, Nim 397
Casello, Mario 450	Cerniglia, Linda 298	Charette, Scott 29	Chiodi, Kim 684
Casente, Salvador 179	Cerone, Phyllis 396	Charette, Gary C 40	Chiovatero, Georgia 503
Casey, Lois 91	Cerritelli, John 378	Charlat, Martin 488	Chipollini, Jose 101
Casey, Helen 226	Cesareo, Kerry 696	Charles, John 313	Chisholm, Bill 167
Casey, Margaret 692	Cesco, Craig 480	Charles, Timothy L 331	Chisholm, Moody L. 251
Cash, Jordan 250	Cesheshyan, Emelina 251	Charles, Kerwin 610	Chisler, Matt 635
Casinelli, Lisa 425	Cevillano, Brenda 88	Charos, Rae 532	Chisolm, Moody 538
Cason, Randy 537	Cha, Sam Ho 437	Charsha, Dianne 576	Chiszar, Vicky A 282
Cassandra, Williams 377	Chabino, Doug 301	Charvat, Peter 602	Chithran, Payyanadan V 184
Cassano, Richard 15	Chack, Karen H 282	Chasalow, Eric 82	Chiu, Lisa 98
Casseb, George 136	Chacko, Jacob 51	Chase, Dan 295	Chiu, Melissa 506
Cassel, Kerry 186	Chac--n, Chanda Cashen 560	Chase, Pam 449	Chiu, Edward 688
Cassel, Kari 497	Chad, Purdy 188	Chase, Arlo 540	Cho, Pat 172
Cassel, Brian 644	Chadbourne, Elizabeth 311	Chatman, Mary 484	Cho, Pat 173
Cassell, Jack C. 37	Chaddha, Shashi 189	Chauvin, Kathy 204	Cho, Jessica 495
Cassels, Bill 108	Chaden, Caryn 155	Chauvin, Robert F. (Bob) 267	Choi, Augustine M.K. 143
Cassels, W. T. (Tobin) 512	Chadwich, Jerry 223	Chavez, Lori 3	Choi, Kyung Hee 239
Cassels, W. T. 512	Chadwick, Edward G. (Ed) 234	Chavez, Jennifer 161	Chojnowski, Daniel 311
Cassels, Bill 577	Chae, Min 482	Chavez, Isabel 407	Chonko, Marcie 574
Cassilly, Joseph 660	Chaffee, Dudley 401	Chavez, Earl 454	Chopey, Stephen 540
Cassimy, Barbara 294	Chaffee, Taylor 402	Chawla, Ashish 693	Chopp, Robin 526
Cast, Stacey 382	Chaffin, Patrick 468	Chaya, Mary 617	Chopra, Raj 428
Cast, William R. 627	Chahin, Jaime 563	Cheatham, Ollie 372	Chopra, Ekta 586
Castaneda, Hugo 119	Chain, Leon 42	Cheatham, Gabriele 601	Chor, Ting Sik 517
Castaneda, Luis 237	Chaisson, Mary 145	Cheatman, Lora C 271	Chotiner, Alan 159
Castano, Robert 516	Chalifoux, Martha 294	Checketts, Robert S 274	Chou, Shang 313
Casteel, Camille 109	Challenger, Brett 128	Checketts, Lannie 472	Choudhury, Shafi 292
Castellano, Jerry 410	Chaltraw, William 662	Checketts, Lannie 624	Choudry, Tauseef 361
Castellucci, Paul 398	Chamberlain, John W. 31	Cheek, Kayla 201	Chouraqui, Fabrice 399
Casten, Peter G 577	Chamberlain, April B. 336	Chelin, Julie 131	Choutka, Michael J. 235
Castille, Philip 643	Chamberlain, Karen A. 684	Chellappan, Sriram 364	Chow, Marjorie 642
Castillo, Consuelo Del 102	Chambers, H D 22	Chelminiak, Lee 419	Chrest, Travis 511
Castillo, Mona 113	Chambers, Bradley S. 321	Chelton, Scott A. 167	Chris, Fjellstad 586
Castillo, Hugo Del 211	CHAMBERS, MARGARET 418	Chen, Ashley W. 6	Chrislan, Cathy 577
Castillo, Alberto 245	Chambers, Yohna 560	Chen, Eric 7	Chrisman, George 514
Castillo, Raul 294	Champion, Larry 216	Chen, Jennifer 237	Chrisostomidis, Vasilios 632
Castillo, Kimberly 497	Champion, Bret A 276	Chen, Shiming 268	Christekos, Vincent 233
Castillo-Cullather, Melanie 627	Champion, Bret 276	Chen, Chunguang 378	Christensen, William 25
Castleberry, Deana 416	Champion, Bret A 284	Chen, Hanmei 466	Christensen, Gwendolyn 51

Christensen, John 78
Christensen, Mylia 94
Christensen, Dianne 268
Christensen, Marc P. 514
Christensen, Patty 22
Christenson, Greg S. 689
Christian, Dan 1
Christian, Timothy 216
Christian, Ronald E 514
Christian, Carol 538
Christian, John 682
Christiansen, Karen 206
Christiansen, Dave 341
Christiansen, Amira 550
Christiansen, Douglas L. 615
Christianson, David 537
Christianson, Mathias J 602
Christino, Grace 315
Christman, Laura 568
Christmas, Bernard 669
Christoforo, John 71
Christoph, Janna 166
Christophe, Pierrot 210
Christophe, Scott 402
Christopher, Norman C. 118
Christopher, Rugg 121
Christopher, Gail C 672
Christopoulos, James 415
Christoun, Kevin 272
Chronister, Ronnie 170
Chu, Edward 462
Chua, Nicolas 610
Chubb, Jack 637
Chucri, Theresa 334
Chulick, Michele 116
Chumbley, Bud 48
Chun, Gregory H. (Greg) 320
Chung, Alexander N 68
Chung, Chui 218
Chung, David 227
Chung, William 359
Chung, Melody 517
Church, Tracy 227
Church, Craig 529
Churchill, Arthur L 231
Churchill, Gary 424
Churchill, Brian 530
Churchwell, Kevin 570
Chute, Tammie 546
Chvez, Dr Jess H 466
Ciaccia, Julius 392
Ciaccio, Teresa 462
Cianchette, Charlie 121
Ciccarone, Rachel 212
Cicero, Richard 280
Cichocki, Andrew R. (Andy) 15
Cichowski, Lorraine 566
Ciello, Ronald Del 329
Cigarroa, Francisco G. 656
Cirillo, Janice 692
Cirino, Eileen 279
Ciriza, Gloria 120
Clabaugh, Samuel F. 577
Clair, Bernadette St 359
Clair, Anne St 692
Clamp, Luke 289
Clancy, Kevin 191
Clancy, Makkie 340
Clanton, Lori 354
Clardy, David 242
Clarfeld, Richard 413
Clark, Frank 78
Clark, Jeffrey 139
Clark, Talisa R 144
Clark, Christopher 172
Clark, Randy 174
Clark, Dedra 200
Clark, R. Mel 250
Clark, Ed 251
Clark, Linda 268
Clark, Jeffrey 269
Clark, Jeff 269
Clark, Karri 276
Clark, Colby 305
Clark, Ron 319

Clark, Mark T 337
Clark, Susan 339
Clark, Carrie 340
Clark, Greg 361
Clark, Steven 380
Clark, Kathy 385
Clark, Terri 406
Clark, Jennifer 407
Clark, Lonnie 418
Clark, Mark T 422
Clark, Edward Stuart 439
Clark, Debra V 445
Clark, Tim 467
Clark, Joseph T. (Joe) 485
Clark, Virginia B. (Ginny) 506
Clark, Kathy 528
Clark, Patricia 551
Clark, Joan S. 562
Clark, Tara 568
Clark, Mark T 574
Clark, Gary 593
Clark, Laverne 598
Clark, Erin 611
Clark, Carol 646
Clark, Mark 662
Clark, Nigel 682
Clark, James 684
Clark, Don 690
Clarke, Stephen L 39
Clarke, Stephen L 39
Clarke, Sharon M 461
Clarke, Cyril 669
Clarkson, Frances E 646
Class, Becky 347
Clausen, Linda 81
Clautics, Douglas 302
Clavelle, Joanne 487
Claxon, Christi 239
Clay, Reed 50
Clay, Sharon Ten 127
Clay, Judy 428
Clay, Robert 485
Clay, Amy 487
Clay, Reed 540
Clay, Lori 562
Claypool, Pamela J. (Pam) 15
Claypool, Forrest 113
Claypool, Blain 538
Clayton, Chris 128
Clayton, James B. (Jim) 489
Cleary, Gerard 2
Cleary, James J 177
Cleary, James J 466
Cleaver, Chuck 310
Clebsch, Bill 288
Cleland, Richard C 186
Clem-Haniff, Jennifer 381
Clemens, Peter 485
Clemens, Laurie 663
Clemensen, Hal 13
Clement, Mark 463
Clement, Richard W. 648
Clemente, Paul 68
Clements, Doug 452
Clemons, Laticia 530
Clennan, Sharri Mc 359
Cleveland, Karrie 74
Cleveland, Laura 692
Clickner, Kathryn 454
Cliff, Suzy 548
Clifford, Lynn 652
Clift, Armando 271
Clift, Ruth 411
Clifton, Karmar 99
Clifton, Mark A. 522
Cline, Natalie H 207
Cline, Candy 624
Clinton, Brenden 339
Clinton, Shaun 562
Clinton, Malissia 564
Clontz, Tim 595
Cloonan, Annmarie 189
Clore, Sharon 480
Close, Brett 537
Closter, Harold A. 506

Cloud, Mike 256
Cloud, Carol 299
Cloud, Andrew 692
Clough, G Wayne 211
Clough, Jeanette G 353
Clouse, Anne 250
Clowers, Jennifer 412
Clure, Gail D Mc 672
Clutter, Cathy 642
Clymer, Karen 449
Clymo, Eileen 539
Cmes, Brody 390
Coaker, Emily 584
Coakley, John 134
Coate, Alexander 172
Coate, Alexander 172
Coates, Spencer 200
Coates, Eddye 332
Coats, Sam 152
Cobau, Ed 246
Cobb, Sue 303
Cobb, Jay 544
Cobb, Steven D. 611
Cobb, Clif 664
Cobbs, Bob 623
Cobine, Stew 627
Coborn, Chris 130
Cobos, Vicki 225
Coburn, George F 309
Coccagno, James A. 90
Coccagno, Jim 90
Cochran, Greg 148
Cochran, Karen 472
Cochran, Barry S. 577
Cochran, Cory 627
Cochrane, John Gregory 363
Cochrane, Andy 387
Cochrell, Patty 227
Cockrell, Kevin 26
Cockrell, Phillip 613
Coco, Denae 121
Coco, Jeffrey 621
Coco, Eric 624
Cocorullo, L Mark 310
Cocorullo, L Mark 310
Codkind, Gregory 109
Codner, Nancy 78
Cody, Kenneth 68
Cody, Thomas G. 115
Coe, Susan 645
Coel, David 510
Coen, Bill 339
Coffell, Shannon 42
Coffman, Kyle 343
Coffman, Joan 475
Coffman, Doug 635
Cogdill, Matthew 289
Cogdill, Richard A. (Rick) 604
Coggin, Bill 470
Cohen, Stephanie 22
Cohen, Carol 34
Cohen, Dennis 145
Cohen, Paula Marantz 165
Cohen, Caitlin 224
Cohen, David I. 302
Cohen, Elisa 377
Cohen, Bruce 378
Cohen, Jay 501
Cohen, David L. 607
Cohen, Gary 636
Cohen, Pinchas 656
Cohill, Mike 548
Cohn, Leslie 55
Colaizzi, Meredith 301
Colalillo, Anna 19
Colandrea, Joe 200
Colangelo, Carmon 616
Colbert, Tom 482
Colbert, Charles E 701
Colby, Ruth 503
Coldiron, Jenny 208
Coldiron, Den Ellen 638
Cole, Amanda 13
Cole, Beth V. 83
Cole, Charles T. 94

Cole, Rischa 172
Cole, Chris 256
Cole, George 275
Cole, Bennie L 396
Cole, Randy 410
Cole, Mr Cliff 421
Cole, Johnnetta B. 506
Cole, David 591
Cole, Jeffrey 598
Cole, Randy 677
Cole, Jay 682
Colella, Carmine 352
Coleman, John 172
Coleman, Lewis W 216
Coleman, Chris 225
Coleman, Sabrina 236
Coleman, Mark 290
Coleman, Willi 658
Colenda, Christopher 681
Coles, Allen 461
Coletti, Larry 617
Colgan, Kevin 611
Colhoun, Dan 147
Collard, Steve 66
Collazo, Cynthia 123
College, Eugene 191
Collett, Tiffany 318
Collett, Raquel 605
Colli, Michael 109
Collias, Art 104
Collier, Bradley W 260
Collier, John 314
Collier, Joe 441
Collier, Mary Sue 638
Collignon, David 6
Collings, Stacey 22
Collingsworth, J M 341
Collins, Joshua L. (Josh) 76
Collins, Courtney 88
Collins, Lance R. 143
Collins, Gregory F 183
Collins, Linn 245
Collins, Tommy H. 469
Collins, James 528
Collins, Bill 603
Collins, Liam 606
Collins, Rose 622
Collins, Michael F. 645
Collopy, Fred 99
Collura, Corren 545
Colmers, John 266
Colombo, Costantino (Chris) 313
Colones, Robert L 319
Colonna, Jerome 67
Colsman, Peggy 112
Colton, Sabine 456
Coltrane, Scott 651
Colucci, Eugene 220
Colucciello, Michael 440
Colvin, Jeff 10
Colvin, Kent 51
Colwell, Gale R 692
Combs, Robert 356
Combs, Joseph D. 615
Comeaux, Preston 429
Comegys, Glenn 125
Comey, Kimberly 628
Comizzoli, Pierre 506
Compton, Kris 30
Compton, Carol 110
Compton, James M 141
Compton, Rocky 537
Comstock, Karolyn 546
Conahan, Danielle 244
Conceicao, Cassio 502
Concordia, Elizabeth B. 652
Condia, Anthony 631
Condon, Robert 430
Condon, Michael A. 514
Condron, Robert 300
Condron, Gary D 575
Cone, Steve 1
Cone, Jason 321
Confare, Amy 51
Conforti, James E. 548

Culbert, John 155
Culbreath, John 427
Cullen, Michael R 69
Cullen, Michael 511
Culling, Robert (Doug) 492
Cullison, Dan 591
Culloch, Cathy Mc 484
Culnan, Mary Beth 537
Culp, Susan 406
Culpepper, Karen 198
Culwell, Curtis 208
Cumberledge, George 622
Cummings, Anita M 113
Cummings, Heather 276
Cummings, Bruce D. 283
Cummings, Gary 482
Cummings, Lori 521
Cummins, Chris 17
Cuneo, Jack 82
Cuningham, David 543
Cunningham, Mike 26
Cunningham, Larry 120
Cunningham, Jennifer 286
Cunningham, Christopher 392
Cunningham, John 645
Cunningham, Jodi 663
Cunningham, Phil 679
Cunnion, Bill 692
Cupp, Ronnie 575
Cupps, Nancy 301
Cupps, Donald L. 647
Curl, Kim 421
Curnow, Randy 328
Curphy, Rona 56
Curran, Michael J. 321
Curran, Jennifer 342
Curran, Michael J. 342
Curran, Greg 630
Current, Pam 183
Currie, Dean W. 90
Currie, Phyllis 342
Currie, Scott 343
Curry, Janet 118
Curry, Robert 122
Curry, Denise 135
Curry, Wanda C 184
Curry, Maridee 320
Curry, Susan J. 611
Curry, Jeffrey T 686
Curry-Briggs, Doreen 39
Curtis, Marilyn 202
Curtis, Lynda D. 373
Cusher, Andrew 631
Cushing, Robert 18
Cushman, Audrey 314
Cusick, Betty 356
Custer, Scott 292
Cutietta, Robert A. 656
Cutler, Juanita 99
Cutler, Alexander 174
Cutliff, Scott 454
Cuyler, Justin M 445
Cwalina, Marianne 82
Cwikla, Kelly 412
Cygan, James 48
Cyndi, Framme 188
Cyphers, Sue 225
Cyr, Alaina 562
Cyr, Carole 603
Czajkowski, Andrew 238
Czerniejewski, Stacy 651
Czumak, Michael 325
Czyz, Annemarie 532

D

D, Pedro Cazabon M 403
D, Gregory A Franklin Ed 630
D, Eric Dickson M 632
Dabbs, Lorrie 243
Dadalt, Peter J 652
Dadey, Bryan 613
Dadic, Paul 461
Daeihagh, Pirouz 385

Daffron, Eric 242
Daghe, Noelle 128
Dahl, Robert 440
Dahlheimer, Tim 40
Dahling, James D 116
Dahlstrom, Richard (Rick) 320
Dahnert, Wolfgang F 51
Daici, Silvia 184
Dailey, John 489
Dailey, John R. (Jack) 506
Dale, Nancy 298
Dale, Ken 566
Daleo, Robert D. (Bob) 200
Daley, Elizabeth M. 656
Dallala, Daniel 96
DalSanto, Robert J. 684
Dalton, Jessica 26
Dalton, William 225
Dalton, Lisa 361
Dalton, James T. 456
Dalton, Ellie 597
Dalton, Mark F. 615
Daly, Ronald E. 2
Daly, Christine 147
Daly, Ashley 327
Daly, Marilyn 369
Daly, Audrey 676
Damanaki, Maria 596
Dameron, Jeffrey C 110
Dammon, Robert M. 96
Damore, Joseph 346
Damschroder, Patricia 613
Dan, James R. 9
Dan, Foster 255
Dan, Joe 444
Danch, Stephen M 660
Dandy, April 624
Danes, Mike 49
Dang, Thanh 391
Dang, Minh 602
Dangerfield, Clyde R 212
Daniel, Chuck 39
Daniel, Karen L 75
Daniel, Bobby 88
Daniel, Karen L 88
Daniel, Patricia 168
Daniel, Biediger 194
Daniel, Becky 242
Daniel, Jacob 274
Daniel, Tammy 421
Daniel, Becky 562
Daniel, Charles 668
Daniels, Jodie 101
Daniels, Stephen 114
Daniels, Clive 141
Daniels, Ronald J. (Ron) 266
Daniels, Mitchell E. (Mitch) 449
Daniels, Mark 521
Daniels, Ikeisha 610
Daniels, Bobbi 646
Danielson, Jean 21
Dankner, Wayne 417
Danner, Dean 48
Danza, Franck 290
Danziger, Kay 281
Dao, Mark 356
Daprile, Joseph R 179
Daprile, Jospeh R 378
DAquila, Richard 698
Darcy, Mike 137
Dardano, Raymond 309
Dark, Dana 594
Darkow, Grant 79
Darnall, Alexander 526
Darnell, Lindsay 13
Darrington, Jim 251
Darrow, Bruce 355
Darsey, Larry 694
Dart, Richard C. 160
Das, Tuhin 325
DaSilva, Jack 616
Dasta, Vince 167
Datema, Craig 29
Daubner, Thomas 620
Dauer, Daniel M 406

Daughters, Shelly 559
Daum, John 627
Daurio, Jennifer 128
Daurio, Nancy 302
Dauterive, F Ralph 403
Dave, Naimesh 125
Davenport, DeWitt 92
Davenport, Mel 435
Davenport, Christopher 548
Davenport, Ronald 621
Davenport, Mary 666
Davenport, Mely 697
Davert, Marshall 361
David, Prabu 341
Davidoff, Ravin 80
Davidson, Curt 18
Davidson, Richard 106
Davidson, Robert G 331
Davidson, Lisa 356
Davidson, Sherwin 434
Davidson, Brian 536
Davidson, Catherine 571
Davidson, Gary 588
Davidtz, Judy 53
Davies, Neal 333
Davila, Diana 242
Davis, Ashley 3
Davis, Heather 6
Davis, Steve 8
Davis, Yolanda 11
Davis, James C. (Jim) 24
Davis, Elizabeth 64
Davis, Tommye Lou 64
Davis, Ray 66
Davis, Mary 68
Davis, Jonathan G. 82
Davis, Jason 89
Davis, Brandon 96
Davis, Pamela Bowles 98
Davis, Richard 106
Davis, Carolyn 118
Davis, Scott 120
Davis, Richard K 126
Davis, Dr Kent 157
Davis, Adora 170
Davis, Pamela 176
Davis, Brian 176
Davis, Ricky 178
Davis, Pamela 181
Davis, Joanne 196
Davis, Matt 199
Davis, Chris 234
Davis, Mary Jane 240
Davis, Steven 246
Davis, Shirley 247
Davis, Dawn 260
Davis, Beth 292
Davis, Cory 300
Davis, Auston 300
Davis, Leslie C 301
Davis, Jonathan S. 336
Davis, Tim 345
Davis, Don 345
Davis, Craig 352
Davis, Kenneth L 355
Davis, Eric 359
Davis, Will 359
Davis, Jed 368
Davis, Kay 368
Davis, Owen 376
Davis, Mathew 386
Davis, Richard E. 399
Davis, Alphonse G 410
Davis, Elaine P 420
Davis, Quincy 465
Davis, David 470
DAVIS, CHERYL 473
Davis, Jonathan S. 492
Davis, Anne 498
Davis, Steve 503
Davis, Kenneth 509
Davis, Dr Eddie J 559
Davis, Myra 560
Davis, Shawn 560
Davis, Dawn 565

Davis, Joan S. 576
Davis, Greg 579
Davis, Jeff 590
Davis, Ladeva 603
Davis, Debra A. 613
Davis, John 618
Davis, Michael 625
Davis, Bo 636
Davis, Jennifer 641
Davis, Leslie C. 652
Davis, Tyler 658
Davis, Deborah 665
Davis, A. Jack 669
Davis, Traci 677
Davis, Mike 684
Davis, Glenn 694
Davison, J Scott 407
Davoren, Peter J 608
Davy, Alan 455
Dawes, Christopher 288
Dawes, Christopher 300
Dawley, Mary 50
Dawson, Michelle 136
Day, Sarah 171
Day, Tracy 233
Day, Samantha 252
Day, Kim 330
Day, Debbie 357
Day, John 437
Day, Lynn Carmen 462
Day, Janet 574
Day, James H 625
Day, Howard 671
Day, Bill 677
Dayal, Gaurov 523
Days, Karen 365
DC, Sister Bernice Coreil 47
DC, Sister Maureen McGuire 47
DDS, Will Daniels 68
DDS, L Kenneth Heuler 115
DDS, Daniel D Louie 226
DDS, Duane Voshell 525
DDS, Maurice Gregory 545
De, Arlette 14
Deacon, Steven D 155
Deal, Gale 97
Deal, Philip 141
Deal, Bradley 467
Dean, Edward 53
Dean, James D 75
Dean, Kathy 163
Dean, Doug 179
Dean, Campbell 214
Dean, Ronald E 242
Dean, Patti 291
Dean, Linda 357
Dean, Pam 385
Dean, Morre 417
Dearth, Randall S. (Randy) 90
Deaver, Lori 233
Deaver, Jim 233
Deavers, Michael 243
Debenedetti, Pablo G. 606
Debenedictis, Nicholas 42
Debergalis, Joseph 365
Deblasi, Michael 179
Deboer, Dave 191
Debolt, Mary Kay 253
Deborah, Pine 68
Debruin, Christopher 545
Decastro, Victoria 115
Dechiro, Carlo V 519
Dechow, Joe 359
Decker, Andrea 329
Decknatel, Patty 602
Decleene, Judy 220
Decoeur, Dan 694
DeCoeur, Daniel 694
Decorte, Raymond 173
Dedeke, Brian 188
Dee, Timothy 416
Dee, Tim 416
Deering, Michael 296
Defenbaugh, Raymond E 73
Deford, Meghan 196

Eckels, Dan 675
Eckels, Dan 676
Ecker, Jeffrey Lawrence (Jeff) 590
Ecker, Kraig 696
Eckert, Matthew 52
Eckert, Barbara 390
Eckert, Robert 497
Eckhart, Brad 579
Eckhart, Gloria 620
Eckhoff, Heidi 601
Edd, Edward A Sussman 164
Edd, Gary Orsinger 164
Edd, Ed Potter 164
Eddinger, Ronnie 80
Eddins, Brad 561
Eddowes, Geoffrey W. 589
Eddy, Geno 219
Edelman, Ann 3
Edelstein, Jeffrey P 565
Edema, Douglas 518
Edens, Stacey 196
Edgar, Ted 183
Edgar, Robert V 374
Edgar, Robert 374
Edge, Jillian 299
Edge, Tom 512
Edgell, Eleonore 456
Edgett, Paul W. 100
Edinger, Tammy 126
Edminster, Susan 12
Edmonson, W 188
Edmunds, Karen 686
Edney, Jerry 49
Edward, Cheryl 45
Edwards, Cheryl 45
Edwards, Glendia 51
Edwards, Steven L 75
Edwards, Steve L 88
Edwards, Michael 99
Edwards, Lisa 109
Edwards, Mary Ann 135
Edwards, Cecil 248
Edwards, Bill 256
Edwards, Crystal 284
Edwards, Gordon 285
Edwards, Lyndon 294
Edwards, Marcie L. 297
Edwards, Brady 298
Edwards, Janet 417
Edwards, Pearse 433
Edwards, Susan 442
Edwards, Gerry 458
Edwards, Rebecca 464
Edwards, C H 490
Edwards, Clarence 490
Edwards, Teresa L. (Terrie) 492
Edwards, Terrie 492
Edwards, Chris 651
Edwards, Sherman 682
Efraimov, Angelina 565
Egan, Karen 174
Ege, Fred 371
Eger, Paul 446
Eghert, David 402
Egidi, Kenneth 422
Egloff, Doug 368
Egsieker, Erik 434
Ehara, George S 551
Ehlert, Carey 591
Ehlinger, Jon D 166
Ehlinger, Forrest G 227
Ehrler, Richard 414
Ehrlich, Robert 312
Ehrman, Larry 300
Ehrmann, Jean 449
Eichelberger, Mitch 112
Eichhorn, Barbara 549
Eichorn, Marvin 356
Eick, Aaron 451
Eidam, Jo Ellen 6
Eiland, Mattie 514
Eiler, Justin 458
Eipper, D 6
Eisenbrandt, Peter 301
Eisenkraft, James 355

Eisgruber, Christopher L. 606
Ejaz, Hassan 606
Ekola, Timothy 518
Ektarian, Victoria 15
El-Bayoumi, Jehan 321
Elachi, Charles 90
Elam, Travis 521
Elamine, A K 511
Elbaghdady, Heba 431
Elbaum, Richard 103
Elberfeld, Adrienne 576
Eldayrie, Elias G. 642
Elder, Mike 281
Elderkin, Greg 519
Eldern, Leonard Van 700
Eldredge, Derrek 300
Eldridge, Thomas 284
Eldridge, Kristin 446
Elfering, Steve 435
Elgohary, Nivin 128
Elia, Lois 9
Elia, Maryellen 237
Elias, Richard 429
Elices, Simone 561
Elizondo, Geraldine 435
Eljaiek, Lester 492
Elkin, Jim 624
Elkins, Beth 348
Elkins, Carla 480
Elko, Kristin 658
Ellard, Beth 2
Ellehuus, Christoffer 102
Ellen, Jonathan M. 264
Eller, Jeff 7
Eller, Carl 484
Eller, Mike 516
Ellerbrook, Niel C 514
Ellington, Chris 649
Elliot, Charles 549
Elliott, Brett 350
Elliott, Julie 415
Elliott, Bob 501
Elliott, Bruce 591
Ellis, Andrea Shaffer 115
Ellis, Jeremiah 192
Ellis, John W 208
Ellis, Keith 271
Ellis, Suzanne 318
Ellis, Karen 329
Ellis, Karen 460
Ellis, Nancy 486
Ellis, John 601
Ellis, Mary 633
Ellis, James G. 656
Ellison, Lois 3
Ellison, Greg 148
Ellsworth, Kathryn 210
Elnashai, Amr S. 600
Elrich, Marc 144
Elrod, James K 692
Elsabrout, Kerri 688
ElSawy, Amr A. 383
Elsbrock, Natalie 115
Elson, Clifford 360
Elster, Nanette 299
Elstrott, John B. 690
Eltz, Amanda 168
Elvekrog, John 577
Ely, Lisa 478
Emami, Azita 658
Embry, Kevin 144
Emerick, Joyce 685
Emerson, Bertrand M 265
Emerson, Rob 518
Emmans, John 92
Emmert, Mark A 363
Emmons, Christopher W. 303
Empey, Dennis 40
Empey, Dennis 624
Emrich, Richard 398
Encarnacion, Beverly 627
Encelewcki, Greg 511
Endacott, Dorothy 648
Eney, Alexander 278
Eng, Bland 207

Eng, Nelson 528
Engel, Robert B. 128
Engel, Mary 247
Engel, Heather 464
Engel, Sandra 480
Engelby, Katy 363
Engels, Kerry 51
Engler, Grace 235
Englert, Brad 656
Engles, Gregg L. 689
English, Alison 80
English, Kathy 117
English, Hopeton 291
Englund, Melissa 601
Ennis, Daniel G. 266
Ennis, Patti 497
Ennis, Mitch 627
Ennis, Karen 674
Enos, Deborah C. 419
Enriquez, Javier 118
Enriquez, Alexandra 352
Entwisle, Beverly J 626
Entwistle, David 538
Epelman, Marina 456
Epmeier, Bruce E 156
Epsilanty, Alexandra 552
Epstein, Irving R. 82
Epstein, Norman P 546
Erdmann, Bryan 223
Erdmann, CherylL 456
Erekson, O. Homer 560
Eremia, Alex 79
Erickson, Sue 333
Erickson, Andrew 552
Erickson, Tina 593
Erickson-King, Chris 357
Ericson, Brent 221
Erika, Hofmann 419
Ermis, Tommy 511
Ernie, Barry 514
Ernst, Cindi 701
Erpenbeck, Donald A 361
Errichetti, Ann 9
Errotabere, Leeann 670
Erskine, Arthur 350
Erskine, Alistair 582
Ervin, Bryan 128
Ervin, Teri 174
Ervin, Susan 451
Erwin, Duane 48
Erwin, Duane L. 48
Erwin, Steven 87
Erwin, Terry 307
Escarrer, Gabriel 160
Esch, Steve 139
Eschete, Marlise 475
Escobar, Daniel 508
Escobedo, Dr Francisco 120
Escoffery, Shawn 548
Escover, Norman 361
Escuyer, Vincent 231
Esham, Pat 457
Eshee, Denver 501
Eshelbrenner, Adam 616
Eshghi, Fleur 200
Eshleman, Denise 621
Esparza, Ryan 258
Esparza, Alma 430
Espeseth, Katherine 178
Espey-English, Patricia 682
Espey-English, Patti 683
Espich, Samuel 301
Espich, Dan 425
Espinoza, Aurora 420
Espinoza, Jose 508
ESPLIN, DEBRA 251
Esposito, Michael 540
Esposito, Sonia 603
Esquith, Stephen L. (Steve) 341
Esquivel, Orcar 120
Esrock, Brett 444
Essenberg, Janice 67
Esser, Richard W 277
Essex, James 684
Essig, Marshall 128

Essman, Christian 99
Estabrook, Crystal 106
Estavillo, Roxanne 233
Esteban, A. Gabriel 155
Estes, Rob W. 187
Estes, Melinda L. 473
Esther, Chet 221
Estrada, Betty 480
Estrada, Cindy 557
Etchemendy, John W. 288
Etcheverry, Marcia 244
Etesse, Gerald 238
Etheridge, Don 363
Etim, Linda 247
Etorrez, Alex 425
Etre, Kathy Armijo 537
Etten, Peter Van 168
Etter, Carl J. 488
Ettl, Robert 228
Eubanks, Clifford 184
Eubanks, Clay 554
Evans, Robert 69
Evans, Brian K. 83
Evans, Doug 111
Evans, Sandra 129
Evans, Wallace 161
Evans, Crystal 182
Evans, Darliene 194
Evans, Cindy 246
Evans, Jeremy S 277
Evans, Kari 300
Evans, Gail 303
Evans, Stephen R. T. 321
Evans, Susan 326
Evans, Jane 419
Evans, Donnie W 420
Evans, Peggy 493
Evans, Scott 498
Evans, James 509
Evans, Craig 597
Evans, Richard 602
Evans, Karen 616
Evans, Robert 624
Evans, Arthur T 640
Evans, Mariah 677
Evanson, Paul J 350
Eveland, Callie 176
Eveland, Dan 176
Everett, Judy 220
Everett, Greg 334
Everson, Monty 256
Everson, Dawn 305
Everson, Mike 337
Evitts, Beth 680
Ewald, Sandra 51
Ewert, Brian H 309
Ewert, Phil 478
Ewing, Marilyn E 249
Eyeington, Thomas 508
Eysenbach, Ted 542
Eze-Nliam, Chete 97
Ezer, Dorit Ben 115

F

Fabrey, Robert 480
Facciabene, Grace 528
Fache, Jameson Smith 101
Fache, Joseph Winick 225
Fache, Gregory 496
Factor, Saul 255
Fadem, Steve 566
Faehnle, Stephen T 233
Fagan, Mary 452
Fagan, Tiffani 472
Fagan, Shiraz M. 488
Fagen, Richard E. (Rich) 90
Fagen, Elizabeth C 628
Fague, Philip 109
Fahey, Walter J. 302
Fahim, Shafei 51
Fahle, Susan 120
Failor, Courtney M 637
Fails, Don 557

Giguere, Jillian 450
Gilbane, William J. (Bill) 212
Gilbane, Thomas F. (Tom) 212
Gilbert, Dana 9
Gilbert, Janet 157
Gilbert, Ozzie 217
Gilbert, Denis P 228
Gilbert, David 232
Gilbert, Vicky 257
Gilbert, Deanne 275
Gilbert, Lisa 300
Gilbert, Bob 321
Gilbert, Linda 441
Gilbert, Joanne T 459
Gilbert, Christopher B 474
Gilbert, Jorge 481
Gilbert, Samantha 581
Gilbert, Peter N. 631
Gilbert, Susan 651
Gilcher, Richard 516
Gilchrist, Richard I 521
Gilcrease, Buck 30
Gilcrease, Beck 30
Giles, Scott 346
Giles, Bobbi 537
Giles, Scott 666
Gilkey, Steven 188
Gill, Nicole 12
Gill, James F 63
Gill, Laura D. 172
Gill, Bhupinder 216
Gill, Margaret 324
Gill, Magaret 484
Gill, Alan H 565
Gillean, John A. 119
Gillespie, Jeffrey 531
Gillespie, Michael 570
Gillespie, Ed 594
Gillett, Aracely 163
Gillett, Bob 519
Gillette, Melissa 500
Gilley, Bryan 200
Gilliam, Derek 134
Gilliam, Chris 277
Gilliam, Lisa 663
Gilligan, Tommy 112
Gilliland, Lake 308
Gilliland, Terry 492
Gilliland, Brian 511
Gillis, Robert 38
Gillman, John 61
Gillming, Mark R 334
Gillrie, Dave P. 76
Gillund, Chris 125
Gilman, Fred 96
Gilmartin, Rich 281
Gilmore, Grover C. (Cleve) 98
Gilstrap, Mike 591
Gilstrap, Jamie K 666
Gilyard, Scott 599
Gingras, Mercy 613
Gini, Becky 347
Ginn, William (Bill) 596
Ginsberg, Harold 564
Ginter, John 6
Ginter, Tom 51
Gintzig, Donald R. 674
Giordano, Joseph 321
Giordano, Karen 374
Giovani, John Di' 531
Giovanni, Lisa 525
Giovanni, Lisa 533
Giovinazzo, Kathy 461
Girard, Jon D 340
Girardot, Jennifer 425
Girguis, Mark 479
Girlich, Anna 610
Girten, Damian 634
Gisler, Jacob 415
Giudice, William (Bill) 554
Given, Christopher 189
Given, Barbara 518
Givens, Carla 13
Givens, Gregg W. 167
Givens, Donna 563

Glade, Doug 150
Gladys, Taylor 99
Glandt, Eduardo D. 607
Glant, Tibor 467
Glanvill, Derek W. 318
Glanzer, Joshua D 196
Glaros, Dean 266
Glaser, Tom 1
Glasgow, Mary Ellen Smith 169
Glasner, Greg 249
Glaspie, John 410
Glass, Ms Sheronda 272
Glass, Thomas 386
Glass, Gene 561
Glass, Steven C. 574
Glassberg, Helene L 607
Glasscock, Dave 100
Glasscock, Melbern G 559
Glaun, Braeme 290
Glaunert, Curtis 677
Glavey, Patrick 360
Glay, Garry 157
Glazier, Paula 20
Glazier, Alysha 122
GLEASON, SUSAN 234
Gleason, Thomas R 312
Gledhill, Matt 368
Glenn, Linda 115
Glenn, Richard 620
Glenney, Chris 120
Glesby, James W O 96
Glick, Alvin 27
Glick, Randy 27
Glick, Barry 27
Glied, Sherry A. 377
Glimcher, Laurie H. 153
Glitch, Keri 342
Glodowski, Jonah 48
Gloor, Michelle 511
Gloria, Ana 635
Glover, Ron 6
Glover, Connie 52
Glover, Andy 128
Glover, Jason 285
Glover, Walter 636
Glover, Joseph (Joe) 642
Glovier, Cliff 663
Glubka, Terry 175
Glyar, David 135
Glynn, Ted 518
Glynn, Hilton 666
Gmelch, Walter H. 654
Goar, Michael 345
Goday, Swapna 685
Goddard, Jesse 700
Godenzi, Alberto 625
Godina, Susie 508
Godsey, Tracy 60
Godsil, Patrick 664
Godsted, Matt 684
Godusky, Brenda 634
Godwin, Janet E. 5
Godwin, Robin 42
Godwin, John T. 104
Godwin, David 417
Godwin, Donald 653
Godwin, Dwayne 673
Goeb-Burkett, Michelle 323
Goedecke, Nancy Collat 315
Goedecke, Glenn 315
Goedken, Thomas J. 5
Goel, Ashutosh 324
Goel, Anita 640
Goeppinger, Kathleen H 343
Goetz, William 386
Goetz-Krummel, Melissa 268
Goffnett, Carol 48
Goffney, Dr Latonya 20
Gogue, Jay 51
Goh, Eng Lim 502
Goh, Francis 510
Golanowski, Marie 51
Golato, Andrea 563
Golbey, Anita R 376
Gold, Jeffrey P. 78

Gold, Barbara 646
Goldbeck, John 331
Goldberg, Jonathan 27
Goldberg, Dror 32
Goldberg, Alexander 107
Goldberg, Neal B 241
Goldberg, Richard 321
Goldberg, Mark A. 417
Goldberg, Dori 632
Golden, Beth 321
Golden, Jed 381
Golden, John 541
Golden, Andrew K. 606
Golden, Andrew 640
Golden, Robert 659
Goldenberg, Neil 264
Goldenberg, Rodney 670
Goldfarb, Michael 321
Goldfarb, Timothy M. 497
Goldfeld, Robert 377
Goldhaber, Jeanne 658
Goldhahn, Laura 68
Golding, Stephen D. 607
Goldman, Phil 184
Goldman, Howard 597
Goldsbury, Richard 125
Goldschmidt, Lawrence E 223
Goldschmidt, Nancy 410
Goldsmith, David L. 263
Goldstein, Brian 128
Goldstein, Stacy A 204
Goldstein, Lisa A 376
Goldstein, Eliot 565
Goldstein, Allan Moises 590
Goldstein, Brian P 649
Goldstien, Gerald 685
Goldstine, Abner 32
Goldszer, Robert C. 355
Goldwin, Richard 638
Goler, Michael R. 280
Golia, Kanak R 424
Golia, Prebha 424
Golitko, Dave 8
Golkiewicz, Tamara 613
Goll, Harold 219
Golson, Kelly Jo 9
Golub, Todd 567
Golz, Judy Briscoe 136
Goman, Elizabeth J 598
Gombar, Greg A 569
Gomes, Maria 296
Gomez, Teresa 123
Gomez, Edwin 127
Gomez, Jaime 131
Gomez, Olegario 142
Gomez, Rick 163
Gomez, Jennifer 250
Gomez, Julie 456
Gomez, Clarisa 550
Gomez, Jacqueline 564
Gomez-urquiza, Jose 610
Gonick, Lev S. 44
Gonick, Lev 98
Gonick, Denise V. 360
Gonsman, Shana 53
Gonyea, Paula 614
Gonyea, Dave 672
Gonzales, Doc 136
Gonzales, Anita 141
Gonzales, Frank 305
Gonzales, Elizabeth 517
Gonzales, Erika 550
Gonzales, Gil 648
Gonzalez, Sandra 30
Gonzalez, Arthur A. 160
Gonzalez, Michael 225
Gonzalez, Manny 239
Gonzalez, Dolores 245
Gonzalez, Roberto 249
Gonzalez, Kathy 292
Gonzalez, Elizabeth 397
Gonzalez, Carmen 478
Gonzalez, Tina 569
Gonzalez, Elizabeth 586
Gonzalez, Fernando 631

Gonzalez, Jacqueline L 665
Gonzalez, Dena 670
Gonzalez, Linda 688
Goocher, Robert 514
Good, Michael 642
Good, Glenn E. 642
Goode, Wilson S 668
Goodfellow, Kathy 218
Goodhew, Ian 658
Goodman, Stacy 32

Goodman, Phyllis Goodman 115
Goodman, Jay S 329
Goodman, Larry J 467
Goodman, Wayne H. 564
Goodnow, John 68
Goodreau, Nicole 146
Goodrich, Loren 664
Goodrion, Sean 139
Goodrum, Ryan 563
Goodspeed, Dennis 281
Goodwim, Terry W 450
Goodwin, Linda 292
Goodwin, Kiani 305
Goodwin, Barry 344
Goold, Alex 27
Goorevich, Charlie 495
Gord, Dave 482
Gordeon, Tom 102
Gorder, Christopher D. Van 488
Gordon, Scott R. 45
Gordon, Tom 102
Gordon, Abram 115
Gordon, Pam 121
Gordon, Eric 126
Gordon, Bernard 279
Gordon, Andrew 406
Gordon, Victor 410
Gordon, Jean 461
Gordon, Jeffrey 685
Gordon, Howard 693
Gordon-Scott, J 420
Gore, Steve 432
Goree, Dr T Lamar 89
Gorham, Doug 586
Gorin, Joanna 175
Gorlewski, Todd 528
Gorman, Eric 104
Gorman, Galen 108
Gorman, Maureen J 270
Gorman, Timothy 425
Gormley, Ken 169
Gormley, Alice 309
Gormley, Kathleen K. 674
Gornall, Susan 391
Gorney, David J. 564
Gorno, Mary Louise 610
Gorrie, Thomas M. 168
Gorski, Bill 550
Gosevitz, Bernie 61
Goshay, Allison 332
Gosmak, Peter D 640
Gosser, James 109
Gosser, Alex 542
Gossett, Cindy 272
GOSTOUT, BOBBIE S 316
Gotanda, John Y. 667
Gothard, Joe 247
Gotlib, Ian 288
Gott, Sharon 124
Gottardy, Brian G 386
Gottlieb, Katherine 511
Gottlieb, Kevin 511
Gough, Fredric 391
Gough, Michael W 398
Gould, R Marcia 32
Gould, Rod 123
Gould, Karen 608
Gould, Andrea 666
Gouldie, Nichole 342
Goulding, Philip L 350
Gouveia, Jeffrey 545
Gove, Matt 428
Govier, George A 330
Govil, Sanjay 248

Gurne, Tanya 531
Guse, Brad 694
Gusler, Tim 334
Gustafson, Jennifer 577
Gutch, Barbara 355
Gutenberger, Thomas 653
Guterman, Neil B. 610
Guth, Amy 170
Gutholc, Robert 508
Guthrie, Linda 398
Guthrie, Kevin 398
Guthrie, Chris 615
Gutierrez, Richard 154
Gutierrez, Wanda 262
Gutierrez, Angela 444
Gutierrez, Brian G. 560
Gutmann, Amy 607
Gutnick, Michael P. 325
Gutowski, Paul 292
Gutter, Ellen 107
Gutteridge, Thomas G. (Tom) 613
Guva, Lorie 670
Guynn, Kevin 599
Guzick, David S. 497
Guzick, David S. 642
Guzik, Bill 4
Guzman, Ramon De 6
Guzman, Andrew T. 656
Guzman-Petter, Teresa 482
Guzzardo, Marc 211
Gwinn, Nancy E. 506
Gwithen, Kaye 378
Gyland, Kevin 207
Gyles, Jackie 207
Gyurci, John 333
Gyurisin, Margie 546

H

Haagenson, Deb 100
Haake, Anne 464
Haakenstad, Stein 301
Haan, Luci De 2
Haas, Mark P. 341
Haas, Jeffrey 439
Haas, Gerard 510
Haas-Kogan, Daphne 153
Haber, Rebecca 109
Haber, Daniel A. 590
Haberern, Andrew 128
Haberman, Shelley 12
Habermehl, William 408
Habgood, Debbie 157
Habib, Hadi 206
Habingreither, Robert 563
Hachten, Richard 147
Hacker, Ted 528
Hackerman, Nancy 505
Hackett, Steven G. (Steve) 438
Hackett, Sylvia 459
Hackney, Carol 458
Haddad, Gabriel G. 452
Haddad, Nick 481
Haddad, Ghassan 510
Haddad, Fadi 548
Hadel, Lorie 134
Haden, James E 310
Hader, Jillian 584
Hadjiliadis, Dennis 241
Hadley, David 250
Hadlock, Harmony 241
Haefner, Jeremy A. 464
Haenni, Chris 307
Hafeez, Tariq 696
Hafer, Greg 469
Hagan, Kevin 216
Hagan, Anna 396
Hagan, Julie 466
Hagans, Robert R. 1
Hagberg, Robert 227
Hagel, Shawn R. 438
Hagen, Kelly 29
Hagen, Mary E 252
Hagen, Bruce 405

Hagen, Thomas B 422
Hagens, William 514
Haggard, Keith 265
Haggerty, Shannon 501
Haghighat, Dennis 535
Hagler, Mendel 373
Hagner, Nancy 692
Hahey, Joanne 645
Hahn, William C. 153
Hahn, Cheri 526
Haile, Elizabeth 606
Haile, Kempton C. 616
Haines, Diana 78
Haines, Kathy 408
Hair, Liz 96
Hair, Ken 243
Haken, Jean 137
Hakim, Veronique 371
Hakim, Hossein 695
Hakimzada, Ahmad 381
Halamka, John D. 71
Halberg, Stuart 196
Hale, Donna 146
Hale, Dana 157
Hale, Philip 299
Hale, Glen 307
Hale, Vicki 361
Hale, Sharon 446
Hale, David F. 452
Hale, Mark S. 488
Hale, Jordan 540
Halford, Philip E 444
Hall, Steve 21
Hall, Jim 73
Hall, Peggy 109
Hall, Tony 144
Hall, Christopher 182
Hall, Veronica M. 234
Hall, Claudia 242
Hall, Tammy 246
Hall, Mark J 351
Hall, Robert 401
Hall, Jodi 422
Hall, Claude 504
Hall, Spencer 538
Hall, Cynthia 600
Hall, Susan 602
Hall, Kathryn A. 606
Hall, Donna 622
Hall, Ruth 630
Hallada, Tony 127
Halladay, Chris 286
Hallahan, Molly 627
Hallberg, Jacqueline 216
Hallberlin, Cindy 216
Halley, Lisa 239
Hallford, Brad 427
Halligan, Donald A 312
Halligan, Denise 323
Hallmark, Jeff 140
Hallock, Kevin F. 143
Halloran, Janice 163
Halperin, Kenneth J 617
Halpin, Jean 405
Halseth, Donald 305
Halsey, Drew 182
Halsey, Casey S. 256
Halsey, Casey S. 257
Halstead, Candace 200
Halt, Lynn 416
Halverson, John 51
Halverson, Thomas 128
Halvorson, Bob 344
Hamburg, Erin 577
Hamburgh, Rita 85
Hamby, Leigh S. 428
Hamel, Cathy 208
Hamill, Geoffrey S 346
Hamilton, Gregg 75
Hamilton, Dennie 284
Hamilton, Andrew 377
Hamilton, Shaya 391
Hamilton, Nikki 460
Hamilton, Theresa 461
Hamilton, Leann 515

Hamilton, Pat 528
Hamilton, Katie 560
Hamilton, Jennifer 620
Hamilton, Mark 664
Hamlin, Scott J. 115
Hamline, Steve 256
Hamline, Steve 257
Hamm, Bradley 398
Hammer, Doug 251
Hammer, David 286
Hammer, Holly 692
Hammerstone, Jim 99
Hammes, Chris 249
Hammes, Chris 250
Hammond, Scott 105
Hammond, Patti 180
Hammond, Harlan 251
Hammond, Ulysses B. 283
Hammond, James Q 407
Hammond, Michael 412
Hammond, Sally 595
Hammons, John 1
Hamner, Grace 511
Hamory, Bruce H. 208
Hampson, Chad 261
Hampton, Barbara 211
Hampton, Claudia 249
Hampton, Jason 307
Han, Jenny 3
Han, Joseph 116
Han, John 306
Han, Yunsung 495
Han, Kevin 544
Hanbury, George L. 398
Hance, James H. (Jim) 267
Hanchett, Edward 213
Hancock, William 28
Hancock, Todd 119
Hancock, Michele 272
Hancock, Lynne 570
Hancock, K. Kelly 574
Hand, Jack 436
Handlesman, Ralph 695
Handley, Jack 275
Hanes, Tom 281
Hanes, Lesley 471
Haney, Annette 134
Haney, Kevin 157
Haney, Susan 435
Haney, Mark 680
Hankey, Brandon 535
Hankins, Tad 133
Hankins, Deb 627
Hanks, Joe 1
Hanks, Lynn 129
Hanks, Jonathan 661
Hanley, Richard J 146
Hanlon, Robin 496
Hanlon, Philip J 626
Hanly, Donna 405
Hann, Michael 334
Hanna, Nader B 319
Hannah, Joe 297
Hannasch, Luann 531
Hannay, Robert 172
Hanneman, Kathryn 469
Hannigan, Anne 288
Hannon, Rita 314
Hanrahan, Johnathan 402
Hans, Bill 383
Hansberry, Kristin 329
Hanselman, Lisa 682
Hansen, Mike 10
Hansen, John 22
Hansen, James 27
Hansen, Mark 40
Hansen, Jan 92
Hansen, Sherry 94
Hansen, Lynn L 148
Hansen, Darel 233
Hansen, Amanda 268
Hansen, Don 409
Hansen, William 436
Hansen, Dr David 462
Hansen, Jenifer 508

Hansford, Lisa 479
Hanson, Stephen C. 58
Hanson, Victoria 316
Hanson, Gary A. 423
Hanson, Vicki 464
Hantman, Perla Tabares 602
Haq, Aftab 637
Haque, Nawal 575
Harbarger, Claude W 529
Hardeman, Kasonya 23
Harden, Tim 51
Harden, Billy 141
Harden, Diane 158
Harden, James 325
Harden, Kelly 391
Harden, M C 512
Harden, Robert 562
Harder, Veronica 109
Harder, Andrew J 627
Hardie, Jennifer 306
Hardin, Scott 51
Hardin, Kathrine 482
Hardin, Marie 600
Harding, Douglas J 53
Harding, Scott 95
Harding, Joe 171
Harding, P Russell 288
Harding, John 339
Hardister, Wanda 194
Hardman, Scott 396
Hardman, Susan J. 458
Hardwick, M Susan 514
Hardy, Marie 71
Hardy, Cody 111
Hardy, Chavonne 181
Hardy, Dana 516
Harford, Simon N. R. 417
Hargadon, Donald 693
Hargenes, Donna 260
Hargens, Donna 260
Hargraves, Gordon 244
Hargrove, Sirena 181
Hargrove, Karen 375
Haring, Don 550
Harker, Patrick T 641
Harkins, Bonnie 135
Harkness, Charles L. 242
Harless, Donna 97
Harlovic, Michael 23
Harlow, Susan 214
Harlow, Angela 231
Harmeson, Dan 549
Harmon, Georgann 108
Harmon, Gordon 174
Harmon, Alexandra 428
Harmon, Brad 478
Harmon, Lori 500
Harmon, Scott 661
Harms, Albert 528
Harned, Chrystine 464
Harness, Carl 144
Harney, Earl Reginald 592
Haroutunian, Karen 624
Harper, Gregory 183
Harper, David 361
Harper, Ryan 377
Harper, Erin 422
Harper, Raymond 469
Harpole, Eileen 60
Harra, Robert 692
Harralson, Beverly 528
Harreld, J. Bruce 611
Harrell, Colleen 329
Harrelson, Katie 84
Harrelson, Gary 108
Harriman, Bob 59
Harriman, Morril 640
Harrington, John 57
Harrington, Jeff 114
Harrington, Jeffrey 114
Harrington, John 200
Harrington, Darrell 226
Harris, Chelene 3
Harris, Bill 26
Harris, Brianne 28

Ishiguro, Tadashi 86
Ishmael, Omar 568
Ishtiaq, Ahmer 381
Isidro, Judith 124
Isley, Megan 115
Isom, Gary E 449
Ison, Tamara 680
Israel, Leslie 297
Israel, Michael D 683
Isreal, Toni 286
Isserman, Jacob 355
Italiano, Deborah 538
Itzkowitz, Fredric H 193
IV, W R Sronce 166
IV, Calvin Thomas 217
Ivanoff, Henry 69
Ivanoff, Kevin 69
Ivashkiv, Lionel B 376
Ivers, Lewis 489
Iversen, Lorraine 83
Iverson, Kirk 7
Iverson, Erik 693
Ivey, Jerry 692
Ivie, Warren 255
Ivie, Brandon 255
Ivie, Brian 446
Ivy, Laura 435
Iwanik, Diana 440
Iyer, Kris 238
Iyer, Vijayalakshmi 270
Iyoya, Martin 263
Izadi, Azade 69
Izaguirre, Gladys 475

J

J-amie, White 205
Jaber, Adeeb 39
Jablin, Burton F. 488
Jabro, Mark 498
Jacangelo, Joseph 361
Jackiewicz, Thomas E. 656
Jackson, Fred L 47
Jackson, Paul 88
Jackson, Bobby 144
Jackson, D T 164
Jackson, Rosa P 177
Jackson, Anthony 191
Jackson, Dimetria 194
Jackson, Richard L. 258
Jackson, R. Shane 258
Jackson, Andrea 262
Jackson, Fred 276
Jackson, Ron 291
Jackson, Jolinda 315
Jackson, Drew 318
Jackson, Laurisa 327
Jackson, Larry 328
Jackson, Melissa 331
Jackson, Maureen 427
Jackson, Kimberley 453
Jackson, Steven 462
Jackson, Lisa 464
Jackson, Grace 501
Jackson, Rosa P 515
Jackson, Michael 558
Jackson, David 562
Jackson, Claire 563
Jackson, Jamere 584
Jackson, Susan 680
Jackson-Elmoore, Cynthia 341
Jacob, Ken 89
Jacob, Jeffrey 372
Jacob, Richard 699
Jacobino, Lucy 325
Jacobs, Richard F. 45
Jacobs, Michael 99
Jacobs, Richard B. 102
Jacobs, Christy 108
Jacobs, Jill 122
Jacobs, Hannah 205
Jacobs, John 256
Jacobs, John 257
Jacobs, Joyce 292

Jacobsen, Leland 406
Jacobson, Pam 192
Jaconette, Paul 482
Jacques, Lori 392
Jadlowski, Mary 149
Jaeke, Erik 393
Jafarnia, Korsh 335
Jaffrey, Jonathan D 671
Jagger, Hal 501
Jaggers, Richard 54
Jaggers, Richard 54
Jahanian, Farnam 96
Jahn, Timothy 58
Jahn, Barb 531
Jahns, Tracy 613
Jain, Sahil 96
Jain, Nitin 282
Jain, Anshu 346
Jaiswal, Jyoti 113
Jakino, Mike 480
Jakosky, Donn 415
Jakub, Paula 32
Jalace-vasold, Melissa 692
Jalona, Sanjay 282
Jamar, John 36
Jamarik, Marissa 298
James, Marianne F. 115
James, David 128
James, Dick 133
James, Fred 174
James, Scott 345
James, Jan 436
James, Rank 463
James, Hal 463
James, Michael 498
James, Andino 528
James, Laura 535
James, Curtis 537
James, Jerry 562
James, Gena 620
James-Francis, Ma 384
James-Nielsen, Lori 476
Jameson, J. Larry 607
Jamieson, Dick 98
Jamieson, T J 259
Jamieson, Lee 259
Jamison, David 252
Janas, Jane 296
Janda, Kenneth 134
Janell, Joseph E 83
Janeway, Dean 275
Jani, Gita 164
Janis, Robert (Bob) 155
Janis, Bob 155
Janise, Carlton 89
Janish, Thomas 40
Janiszewski, Chuck 11
Jankelowitz, Larry 440
Janki, Daniel 210
Jankos, Dianna 349
Jankowski, Joseph 99
Jankowski, Gary 309
Jankowski, Cecelia 586

Jannasch, Charlyn 420
Janney, John 448
Janney, Jeremy 516
Janney, Karen 550
Jansen, Robert 680
Janser, Kevin 508
Janski, Mary 602
Jantz, Tricia 556
Jantzen, Daniel 154
Janus, Tammy 329
Janzekovich, Cathleen 107
Jaramillo, Richard 312
Jaramillo, David 433
Jarman, Samuel Y 27
Jarocki, Larry 670
Jarrett, Adam 239
Jarrett, Mark 390
Jarrett, Dr Ehren 464
Jasinski, Joseph 491
Jasko, Brian 392
Jasko, Donna 660

Jaskunas, Jeremy W 333
Jaurequi, Pat 480
Javallana, Maria 560
Javersack, Dawn 79
Javidroozi, Mazyar 184
Jaworski, Brandy 697
Jayachandran, Priya 671
Jazwinska, Klaudia 286
JD, J Richard Ludgin MD 51
JD, Howard R Grant 279
JD, Howard R Grant 279
Jean, Grace 33
Jean, Christopher Des 290
Jean-Felix, Eddy 564
Jedlicki, Anne 646
Jeffers, Linda 135
Jeffers, Lewis 436
Jefferson, Timothy 217
Jefferson, Larry 560
Jeffrey, Hanks 143
Jeffrey, William 522
Jeffrey, David E 602
Jeffs, Mike 136
Jelks, Dionne 603
Jelle, Lorraine 74
Jellinek, Michael 380
Jenkins, Jo Ann C. 1
Jenkins, Janet 110
Jenkins, Decosta 178
Jenkins, Sheterra 226
Jenkins, Amanda 252
Jenkins, Julia 252
Jenkins, Ladenea 268
Jenkins, Jeff 548
Jenkins, Justin 556
Jenkins, Marjorie 595
Jenkins, Barbara 599
Jenkins, Jeff 616
Jenks, Maria 271
Jenne, Joan 533
Jenness, Calvin E. 76
Jennifr, K 387
Jennings, Gary 49
Jennings, William M 83
Jennings, Reynold J 129
Jennings, Lorie 282
Jennings, Lynn A 286
Jennings, Stephen 452
Jennings, Reynold J. 680
Jennings, William M. (Bill) 698
Jenrette, John 102
Jensen, Jaclyn 102
Jensen, Richard 125
Jensen, Linda A 188
Jensen, Thomas J 188
Jensen, Tom 188
Jensen, Carolann 252
Jensen, Eric 342
Jensen, Craig 487
Jensik, Emily 131
Jentz, Alan 634
Jepson, Brian D. 405
Jernigan, Donald 7
Jernigan, Emily 81
Jerome, Brian S 277
Jerpe, David 421
Jeske, Julie 527
Jesko, Danielle 128
Jesse, Robert J 421
Jester, Clyde A 133
Jesus, Carmencita De 295
Ji, Seo Na 592
Jiambalvo, James 658
Jiampetti, Brenda 603
Jiang, Tina 288
Jiang, Shibo 372
Jiang, Joseph 511
Jianwen, Shen 664
Jicinsky, Terry 282
Jick, Daniel 71
Jiga, Anthony 377
Jilg, Robyn 640
Jimenez, Ed 497
Jimerson, Linda 480
Jinks, Mark 122

Jipping, Jon E 252
Jishi, Mohannad 526
Jith, Gayathri S 663
Jockett, Joan 620
Johannes, Carol 646
Johansen, Jakob V 182
Johansen, Breanna 464
Johnk, Kellee 481
Johnnie, Mark 55
Johns, Bobbie 170
Johnsen, Tim 250
Johnsen, David C. 611
Johnsgaard, Dag 185
Johnson, Robert 26
Johnson, Matt 27
Johnson, Kimberly 32
Johnson, Donna 42
Johnson, Charlotte 45
Johnson, Merida 47
Johnson, Michele 52
Johnson, George 52
Johnson, George 53
Johnson, Dennis 58
Johnson, Darron 60
Johnson, Kendal 63
Johnson, Gerald D. (Jerry) 76
Johnson, Paula 86
Johnson, Peter S 87
Johnson, Bret 94
Johnson, Brooke 106
Johnson, Bertica 108
Johnson, Linda 110
Johnson, Kelly M. 114
Johnson, Boyce 120
Johnson, Clinton L 123
Johnson, Heather 131
Johnson, Kathryn 134
Johnson, J D 145
Johnson, Cindy 147
Johnson, Steve 151
Johnson, Vivian 152
Johnson, Bruce E. 153
Johnson, H Keith 161
Johnson, Greg 166
Johnson, David L 170
Johnson, Deborah C 174
Johnson, David 178
Johnson, Mike 183
Johnson, Barbara 184
Johnson, Harry 185
Johnson, Jt 187
Johnson, Earl 200
Johnson, Lynn 225
Johnson, Steven P. 230
Johnson, Patsy 240
Johnson, Ruthenia 240
Johnson, Christina 242
Johnson, Janice 243
Johnson, Michelle R 247
Johnson, Mark 252
Johnson, Patrice 268
Johnson, Neil 275
Johnson, Janice 279
Johnson, Patricia 286
Johnson, Erik S 288
Johnson, Carrie 300
Johnson, Colleen 312
Johnson, Anthony 313
Johnson, Kathleen 320
Johnson, Oliver M. 321
Johnson, Noila 325
Johnson, Rodney D. 333
Johnson, Brad 337
Johnson, Barbara 340
Johnson, Karen D 343
Johnson, Bernadeia 345
Johnson, Steven 345
Johnson, Cleveland 352
Johnson, Mellisa 356
Johnson, Karen 360
Johnson, David D 363
Johnson, Tracy 391
Johnson, Diane 395
Johnson, Darrell 409
Johnson, Lorette 417

Khan, Tanveer A 263
Khan, Maryam 286
Khan, Adeel 459
Khan, S S 508
Khan, M Aness 531
Khan, Samir 610
Khan, Alia 681
Khanchandani, Ashok 410
Khator, Renu 643
Khazanchi, Shal 464
Khouri, Lara 571
Khoury, Aldo 531
Khurana, Sanjay 2
Khym, Danny 495
Kian, David 196
Kickbusch, Laura 104
Kiel, Lori 269
Kiely, Ann 621
Kikumoto, C. David 14
Kilborn, Jim 32
Kilbride, Marc 183
Kile, Pam K 125
Kile, Pam 125
Kiley, Tom 313
Kilguss, Matt 357
Kilian, Mitchell 337
Kilian, Craig 677
Kilic, Serkan 226
Kilkenny, Rosemary 582
Killebrew, Lester H 548
Killeen, Thomas 333
Killeen, Nora 409
Killion, Kathleen 474
Killmer, Jonathon 238
Kilpatrick, David 395
Kilsgaard, Jill 599
Kim, Yup 17
Kim, Ginny 103
Kim, Miah 107
Kim, Earl 124
Kim, Joanne Y 324
Kim, Dong Eun 368
Kim, Taeeuk 437
Kim, Changyoung 437
Kim, Jinho 437
Kim, James K 495
Kim, Mike 495
Kim, Betty 495
Kim, Robert 496
Kim, Mikyoung 562
Kim, Jung-In 601
Kimball, Kathy 321
Kimball, Scott 659
Kimbell, Jimmy 39
Kimmel, Bradford 133
Kimmerle, David 164
Kimmerle, Sandra Sue 164
Kimmins, Mary 425
Kimmons, Herb 452
Kimura, Yoshimasa 35
Kinane, Denis F. 607
Kinard, John 501
Kincannon, Elizabeth 417
Kincheloe, Duncan 347
Kinder, Richard D 366
Kinder, Richard D 495
Kindred, Bryan N. 577
King, Susan 8
King, Tommy 30
King, Randy 60
King, Chris 81
King, Gena 120
King, Adrian 122
King, Winney 141
King, Yolanda 143
King, David 170
King, Corey 196
King, Jerry 210
King, Michele 301
King, Karen 305
King, John 342
King, Tami 365
King, Jack 396
King, Meg 423
King, Daniel 426

King, Jared 474
King, Jeffrey 493
King, Rick 498
King, Vernon J 536
King, Kirk 562
King, Kara 569
King, Charles 575
King, David 591
King, Michelle 595
King, Michael (Mike) 671
King-Shaw, Ruben J. 645
Kingbury, Mike 206
Kingsley, Mary 79
Kingsley, Scott 514
Kingsmore, Stephen 452
Kingston, Robert E. 590
Kini, Narendra M 665
Kinman, Thomas 115
Kinneer, Mike 133
Kinney, Doug 298
Kinsey, Jon 178
Kinslow, Anthony D 99
Kintigh, Denise 474
Kintz, Ronald 404
Kinyon, Craig C 457
Kinyon, Craig 457
Kipp, Cathy 435
Kippenhan, Matthew 398
Kipps, David 163
Kirby, Phil 61
Kirby, Ed 276
Kirby, Tim B. 336
Kirby, Tracy 387
Kirby, Bob 515
Kirby, James 541
Kirby, Rex B. 545
Kirby, Michelle 562
Kirby, Adrienne 576
Kirchner, Jeffrey 589
Kirchner, James 592
Kirejczyk, Wanda M 241
Kirk, Roger L 72
Kirk, Ron 145
Kirk, Joyce 145
Kirk, Rich Van 161
Kirk, Warren J 163
Kirk, Joseph 206
Kirk, Bruce M 290
Kirk, Norma 353
Kirk, Evelyn 430
Kirk, Peggy 457
Kirk, Paul 695
Kirkemo, Erik 185
Kirkendall, Bill 579
Kirkevold, Dee 553
Kirkpatrick, R. James 341
Kirsch, Peter 183
Kirsch, Becky 249
Kirschenbaum, Norman 225
Kirschner, Sid 428
Kirstetter, Axel 333
Kirton, Nancy 281
Kisch, Horst 128
Kiser, Janice 110
Kiser, Terry 346
Kiser, Christopher 368
Kish, Janine 486
Kishan, Neel 96
Kishore, Ashok 623
Kissel, Mark A 131
Kistner, Tim 185
Kittoe, Michael 158
Kittoe, Michael E. 280
Kiwall, Walter J 674
Klabe, Jim 692
Klaich, Daniel 370
Klasek, Bob 396
Klasek, Robert 396
Klasko, Stephen K. 618
Klaus, Rusty 166
Klawiter, Jeffrey 337
Klehr, Joan 48
Kleiber, Dan 437
Klein, David G 64
Klein, David 172

Klein, David 172
Klein, Martin H 173
Klein, Larry 187
Klein, Ben 196
Klein, Tammy 213
Klein, Irving 244
Klein, Barry 297
Klein, Vickie Barrow 304
Klein, Jason 325
Klein, Cathy 344
Klein, Howard 402
Klein, Kathy 434
Klein, Steve 447
Klein, Roger D 574
Klein, David 632
Kleinhanzl, Thomas A. 205
Kleinman, Kent 143
Kleinman, Ronald Ellis 590
Klemm, Sara 591
Klemt, Les 422
Kligman, Michelle 446
Klim, Maria 51
Kline, Douglas B. 258
Kline, Mark W. 560
Klingner, Mary 583
Klinitchek, Darryl 511
Klipp, Todd 80
Kloberdanz, Mark 424
Kloehn, Steve 96
Klonowski, Lisa 158
Klontz, Richard 634
Klopfenstein, Joshua 610
Klosson, Michael 485
Klostermeier, Janice 663
Klueg, Steven P 305
Klug, Janet 281
Klug, Candice 591
Klugherz, Greg 602
Kluth, Doreen 537
Kluyver, Cornelis A. (Kees) de 651
Knackstedt, Beth 361
Knapp, Michelle 217
Knapp, Kyra 321
Knauer, Dallas 568
Knaus, Ron 519
Knauth, Tanner 501
Knelly, Shirley J 39
Knepp, Lynn E 207
Knepper, Chris 136
Knesek, Michael J 341
Knight, Thomas 21
Knight, Charles 131
Knight, Richard 154
Knight, Tim 247
Knight, Keith 256
Knight, Calvin (Cal) 263
Knight, Cal 263
Knight, George 330
Knight, Gordon D Jr 592
Knight, Phil 616
Knight, Alton 631
Knipp, Ken 700
Knoll-finn, Mj 377
Knott, Irene 526
Knott, Irene 616
Knott, Jack H. 656
Knowles, Jane 336
Knowlton, Timothy 619
Knox, Tanya 134
Knox, Mark 688
Knudson, Dennis 276
Knuth, Barbara A. 143
Knutson, Brad 435
Koch, Alan 7
Koch, Robert 87
Koch, Cheryl 265
Kochard, Lawrence E 658
Kochem, Gary J. 17
Kochem, Gary J 18
Kocher, Angela 422
Kodama, Hugh 357
Koder, Tim 329
Kodish, Jan 574
Koelmel, John R. 375
Koeneke-hernandez, Ludwig 619

Koenig, Tracy 151
Koenig, Carol 397
Koenig, Harris F 479
Koenig, Joseph G. (Joe) 696
Koeper, John 518
Koepke, Diane 67
Koeppel, Holly 32
Koeppel, Carol 693
Koerner, Spencer 103
Koerner, Erich 396
Koerner, Gert 544
Koerschner, Carl 335
Koestler, Robert J. 506
Kohler, Missey 583
Kohn, Emily 60
Kohn, Rachel 269
Kohnen, Rhonda 298
Koil, Thomas 174
Kojima, Elaine 339
Kolb, Dianne C. 92
Kolb, Matthew 95
Kolb, Greg 106
Kolb, Kenneth 119
Kolb, Edward (Rocky) 610
Kolbash, Ronald 610
Koleci, Carolann 695
Koli, Roshni 270
Kolker, Dov 355
Kollar, Kevin 51
Kolluri, Pavan 47
Kolniak, Tiffany A 353
Kolpasky, Paul 234
Koltz, MarisaE 218
Komar, June 488
Komiske, Bruce 225
Komuniecki, Patricia R. 613
Kondapalli, Swathi 568
Konop, Amanda 465
Konzelman, Sharon 275
Koo, Yun 103
Koocher, Gerald P. 155
Koogler, David 453
Kookesh, Albert M. 489
Koonce, Scott 15
Koontz, Bill 455
Koopman, Trish 692
Koopman, Ray 700
Kooy, Donald 319
Kopec, Mike 307
Koper, Alex 482
Kopf, Chris 213
Kopfensteiner, Thomas R. 100
Kopicki, John 105
Koppenhoefer, Kathleen 622
Koppolu, Prasad 297
Kopra, Amanda 285
Kopstain, Eric 615
Korenaga, Kendall 19
Koretzky, Gary 143
Korey, Lowder 304
Korner, Barbara O. 600
Korsmeyer, Mark 150
Koscielniak, Lucy 205
Koshurba, Sherry 354
Kosiyangkakul, Tai 471
Koss, Kristen K 543
Kost, Beth 272
Kosteba, Linda 359
Kosturko, Maryellen 83
Kothari, Manish 522
Kotkin, Jeffrey 188
Kotlikoff, Michael I. 143
Kottman, Bill 176
Koustareva, Kate 94
Kovack, Kristen 430
Kovacs, Greg 322
Koval, Erin 386
Kovoch, Dan 61
Kowal, Nadine 588
Kowalczyk, Dave 315
Kowals, Kathy 111
Kowalski, Kevin P. 321
Kozar, Joseph 611
Kozel, Kenneth 645
Kozicz, Gregory J 18

Kozicz, Gregory J 19
Kozicz, Gregory J 19
Kozoman, Robert L. (Bob) 155
Kozusnik, Maryann 688
Krabbenhoft, Kelby K 481
Kraetsch, Jeff 41
Kraev, Igor 180
Krafft, Robert 539
Kraft, Stephanie 417
Kraft, John 642
Kraich, Rick 669
Krajewski, David 290
Krakauer, Lawrence 313
Krakaur, Ken 492
Kramar, John 90
Kramer, Lorne 122
Kramer, Adam 441
Kramer, Don 462
Kramer, Robin C 584
Kramer, Jennifer 630
Krane, Jeffrey 567
Krapek, Karl J 139
Krapels, Marco 559
Kraszewski, Andrew 376
Kratz, Karen 115
Krause, Brian 72
Krause, Melissa 119
Krause, Alan J. 360
Krause, Roger 415
Krause, Catherine 648
Krause, David 663
Krauss, Marty W. 82
Krauss, Dora 361
Krauss, Jim 492
Kraut, Jeffrey A. 390
Krawczyk, Tammy 693
Krawiec, Ronald 186
Krebsbach, Karen 624
Kremer, Donald 112
Krenk, Chris 94
Krenke, Brian 278
Krenz, William C. (Willie) 564
Krepps, John 503
Kretzinger, Cut 231
Kreutcer, Alva 622
Krevans, Sarah 548
Krhovsky, David M 519
Kricka, Larry 241
Krider, Holly 478
Krieger, Kenneth F. (Ken) 588
Kriehn, Judy 208
Krier, Greg 640
Kriesand, Dave 56
Kriesberg, Barry 227
Krishna, R. Murali 250
Krishnamoorthy, Gnana 325
Krishnan, Ramayya 96
Kriskie, Michele 184
Kristensen, Douglas A. (Doug) 78
Kristofka, Michael 610
Krmpotic, Deb 56
Krmpotic, Deb 187
Kromm, Elizabeth 266
Kronfeld, David 182
Kronlage, Dan 162
Kroot, Irwin 597
Kropilak, Mark J 42
Kropiunik, Frank C 18
Krouse, Michael 405
Krow, Reggie 363
Kruczlnicki, David G 213
Krueger, Eric 500
Krueger, Dennis 520
Kruger, Cynthia V 231
Kruis, Tresa 84
Krull, Henry 106
Krupicki, Shawnda 528
Krupka, Jacqueline 35
Kruse, Mark 102
Kruse, Shelly 221
Kruse, Lowell 231
Kruse, Brent 426
Krych, Ron 614
Kryda, Michael 473
Krysti, Galvin 379

Krystopolski, Ruth 481
Krzmarzick, Brent 646
Kubish, Kristine 671
Kubista, Jennifer 553
Kucera, Margaret 610
Kucera, Kevin 613
Kuczmanski, John D. 320
Kudravetz, Douglas 37
Kuehne, Will 286
Kuhlmann, Lucas 5
Kuhn, Rebecca (Becky) 56
Kuida, Elliot 310
Kukelhan, Allison 6
Kukura, Joe 293
Kula, Tom 391
Kulikowski, Eileen 603
Kulkarni, Sanjeev R. 606
Kumar, Arvind 210
Kumar, Sunil 266
Kumar, Ranjan V 404
Kumar, Arvind K 479
Kumar, Vinod 556
Kundra, Raj 696
Kuntschik, David 368
Kuntz, Kyle 173
Kuntz, Kevin 318
Kunz, Michael 115
Kunze, Shane 448
Kuper, Jacob 255
Kuperus, Cindy 98
Kuppuswamy, Murali 584
Kurdle, Florence B 39
Kures, Peter 413
Kurin, Richard 506
Kurkowski, John 149
Kurtz, Norma 230
Kurtz, Michelle 557
Kurzatkowski, Amy 189
Kusinski, Denise 430
Kutateladze, Andrei 132
Kutch, John M 624
Kutcher, Gregory R 316
Kutryk, Terrance 25
Kvistad, Gregg 132
Kwetkowski, Brian G 695
Kwong, Melsen 102
Kyger, Carolyn 424
Kyle, April 511
Kyler, Chrisopsher 661
Kyler, Christopher 661

L

Labass, Bob 247
Labay, Charles 166
LaBelle, James 488
Laborde, Sarah 569
Labosky, Laura 123
Labrecque, Andre G 24
Lacasse, Paul E 81
Lacey, Erin 253
Lacey, Diane E. 373
Lacey, Bonita Washington 457
Lacey, David 670
Lackey, Beth 214
Lacue, Amanda 619
Ladd, Edward H. (Ted) 71
Ladd, Ruta 83
Ladd, Kevin 200
Ladd, Steven 221
Lafianza, Nancy 380
Laflamme, Catie 292
Lafond, Debbie 113
Lafrankcis, Janine 231
Lage, Jose L. 514
Lagenfeld, Michelle 220
Lager, Jeffrey T 32
Lagerlef, Brenda 431
Lago, Jim 174
LaHatte, Bernard 616
Lahey, John L 450
Laing, Tom 385
Laing, Ann 451
Lake, Linda 684

Lakin, Kenneth S 79
Lakin, Peter D 80
Lakin, Edwin A 80
Lalas, Jose W 143
Lally-Green, Maureen 169
Lamar, Jim 216
Lamattere, Shelly De 193
Lamb, Jim 105
Lamb, John 309
Lamb, Carolyn 353
Lamb, Todd 540
Lamb, Angy 554
Lamb, Amy 674
Lambdin, James 660
Lambert, Karen A. 9
Lambert, Leo M 181
Lambert, Courtney 310
Lambert, Robert 404
Lambert, Phil 496
Lambertson, Stephen 616
Lamonte, Steve 51
LaMorte, Debra 377
Lampert, Steven 50
Lamstein, Joel H 269
Lancaster, Rick 219
Lancaster, Tim 233
Lancaster, Bonita 584
Lance, Phil 250
Lance, Donald W 602
Lance, Garrett 627
Landau, Alan 391
Lande, Ruth 325
Lander, Eric 567
Landers, Peter 629
Landes, Barbara L. 445
Landess, C Barton 202
Landewee, Cassy 339
Landin, Linda 300
Landry, Dustin 347
Landry, Stephen G. 494
Landry, Ronnie 621
Lane, Danny 49
Lane, Michael 143
Lane, Conan 232
Lane, Mark 254
Lane, Kevin 395
Lane, Linda 430
Lane, Melissa 480
Lane, Kevin 503
Lane, Charles E. 642
Lanell, Randle 20
Laney, Mark 231
Laney, Mark 232
Laney, D. Randy 579
Lang, Karen 446
Lang, Marcina 654
Langberg, Michael L. 102
Langberg, Joanna 191
Langdon, Matt 356
Lange, Wade 31
Lange, Kristin 408
Langer, Dennis 133
Langford, Barbara 27
Langford, Stephen 67
Langham, Charles 64
Langham, Catherine 580
Langhauser, Diana 321
Langley, W. John 315
Langlois, Melissa 47
Lango, Cynthia 282
Langton, Clara 69
Lanham, Cindy 503
Lanham, Roger M. 684
Lanier, Gina 52
Lanier, Andrea 471
Lankford, Wendy 276
Lanning, John E 372
Lanning, Shelley 566
Lannon, David 690
Lansford, Gordon E. 256
Lansford, Gordon E. 257
Lansing, Alexis 202
Lansing, Linda 485
Lant, Stephen 106
Lantos, Phyllis R. 597

Lantz, Paul 147
Lapeer, James 519
Lapiana, John K. 506
Lapidas, Gary 632
Lapkin, Robert A 241
Lapkin, Robert 241
LaPorte, Todd 487
Laprade, Patricia 54
Lara, Miguel 127
Laratonda, Susan 693
Laraway, Dennis L. 56
Laraway, Dennis 324
Lardi, Marco G 620
Larimore, Jim 5
Lark, Vercie 167
Lark, J Peter 282
Lark, David C 457
Larobina, Mark 221
Larocque, Lynda 647
Larose, Doug 41
Laroux, Leonard 51
Larsen, Rachel 53
Larsen, Christian 179
Larsen, Shild 185
Larsen, Brenda 406
Larsen, Matthew 506
Larsen, David 666
Larsen, Dan 684
Larsen, David 685
Larsh, Herbert 480
Larson, Angela 157
Larson, Elwin 229
Larson, April 246
Larson, Jamie E 346
Larson, Kenneth S 439
Larson, Thomas R 589
Larson, Lynette 677
Larson, Erik 694
Larsson, Randi 498
Larsson, Christian 636
Lasaga, Manuel 59
Lasala, Joseph A 88
Lashier, Mark E. 112
Lashier, Mark E 112
Lasiter, Paul B. 423
Laskey, Sara 593
Lassiter, Wright L. 234
Latacki, Nancy 463
Laten, Steve 27
Lathan, Grenita 242
Lathrop, Ann 149
Latifzai, Khoshal 292
Latorre, Sarah 632
Lattanzio, Nicole 535
Latushie, Dick 453
Latz, Greg 138
Lau, Paul 470
Lau, Luther 522
Laubach, Harold E. 399
Laube, Marcus 431
Lauf, Michael K. (Mike) 92
Lauffer, Marlee 235
Laughlin, Michael 536
Laughridge, Mason 620
Laughton, Kim 486
Launius, Steve 170
Lautenbach, Denise K 598
Lauter, Keith 524
Lavelle, Tom 440
Lavelli, Lucinda 642
Lavely, Patty 224
Lavender, Sunee 639
Laver, Michael 377
Lavery, Michelle 480
Lavoie, Blair 361
Lavrusky, Nancy 160
Law, David 40
Law, Tom 271
Law, Michelle 691
Lawler, James 167
Lawler, Michael A 232
Lawler, Maria 352
Lawler, Will 605
Lawler, Paul J 672
Lawless, Stephen T 22

Lindo, Michelle 603
Lindsay, Mike 26
Lindsay, Julie 101
Lindsay, Jane 218
Lindsay, Aaron 462
Lindsay, Gail 479
Lindsey, H. Eugene (Gene) 50
Lindsey, Leslie 439
Lindsey, Steven L 520
Lindsey, John 537
Lindsey, Don 554
Lindstrom, Donnie 256
Linesch, William E 439
Link, Denise W 126
Link, Dave 481
Linn, Joe 252
Linn, Michael 416
Linnehan, Frank 165
Linton, William A. (Bill) 443
Linzer, Daniel I. 397
Lipani, Laura 333
Lippeveld, Theo 269
Lippman, Frederick 398
Lippoldt, Diana 681
Lipscombe, Ailsa 610
Lipsky, Matt 566
Lipton, Lisa 505
Lisenby, Michael 172
Lisieski, Sharman 484
Liss, Samuel 167
Listengardt, Joe 431
Listengart, Joseph 366
Lister, Noel 458
Liszt, Mark 284
Liszt, Max 284
Litaker, Tom 446
Litavec, Viliam 201
Litchfield, Debra 448
Litos, Dennis 249
Little, Bobby 36
Little, George A 228
Little, George A 228
Little, George 228
Little, George A. 229
Little, Gregory D 289
Little, Darlene 292
Little, Denise 330
Little, Michael D 408
Little, Daniel 456
Little, James H 583
Little, Thomas A 666
Little, Lou 680
Little, Niki 694
Littlejohn, Bill 498
Litwin, Jim 247
Litz, William 43
Liu, Ke-Cheng 7
Liu, Deborah 90
Liu, Marsha 396
Liu, Edison T. 587
Lively, David 398
Livermore, Craig 158
Livingston, Randall S. (Randy) 288
Livingston, Keith 618
Lizhong, Yu 377
Lizo, Ralph 597
Lll, Hunt M 310
Lloyd, Lisa Kay 563
Lloyd, James 642
Lo, Francis 690
Lobach, Carmen 480
Lochhead, Jim 159
Lochow, Gary 686
Locke, Cherie 500
Locken, Dale 13
Lockhart, Laura 120
Lockhart, Melanie 242
Lockwood, Charles J. 197
Lodge, Terry L. 15
Lodhi, Mujib 676
Loeffler, Arthur A 539
Loeffler, Jay S. 590
Loera, Patricia 658
Loessin, Bruce 98
Loethen, Michael 347

Loewentheil, Sanford 278
Lofaro, John 179
Loffler, Alicia 398
Loffredo, Joe 464
Lofgren, Diane Gage 498
Lofgren, Richard P. 631
Loftin, Karen 242
Lofton, James 25
Lofton, Kevin E. 100
Lofton, Kevin E 101
Loftus, Phillip 523
Logan, Jonathan B. 128
Logatto, Vincent 541
Logeman, David 105
Logemann, Cari 48
Lohr, Dan 227
Lohrer, Bernadette 486
Lohse, John 468
Lokman, Lawrence 600
Lollar, Donald 410
Lollock, Rita 564
Lomax, Stephanie 276
Lombardo, Thomas 425
Lomeli, Bernardo 608
Lomeo, Jody L 186
Loney, Andrew 17
Long, Toby 107
LONG, GARY 188
Long, Laura 233
Long, Thomas 237
Long, Gary 255
Long, Shayla 293
Long, Jerry 333
Long, David 343
Long, Thomas D 343
Long, Ronald R. (Ron) 562
Long, Nathan 572
Long, Greg 618
Long, Larry 692
Longfellow, Michael 323
Longhi, William G 408
Longlais, Brett J 687
Longley, S. Catherine (Katy) 587
Longo, Christie 692
Longstaff, William 479
Longstreet, Christopher 309
Longsworth, Nora 613
Longton, Kyle 32
Looker, Travis 626
Loomis, Anna 357
Loomis, Nancy 479
Looney, John 380
Loose, Jeffrey 475
Loosmore, Casey 141
Looten, Kathy 522
Lopatto, Bill 339
Lopez, Amy 119
Lopez, David S. 152
Lopez, Ann 315
Lopez, Jorge 325
Lopez, Jody 433
Lopez, Nestor A Ramirez 530
Lopez, Noemi 597
Lopez, Mary 635
Lopman, Abe 699
Loran, Jarrod 159
Lord, W. Leighton 509
Lord, Janet E 552
Lord, Kathy 687
Lorei, Greg 256
Lorei, Greg 257
Lorenz, Dan 73
Lorenz, Paul E 482
Lorenzen, Angela 690
Lorenzo, Heather 333
Lorenzo, Lisa 577
Loreto, Sheila 589
Loring, Eileen 510
Lorino, Lisa 571
Lorio, Renee 637
Lorne, Eric 293
Lorton, Donald E 95
Loshin, David S. 399
Losntos, Juan De 386
Lott, Wayne J. 83

Lott, Tanya 94
Lott, Ken 172
Lott, Douglas 277
Lott, Lori 293
Lottig, Jim 211
Lotze, Timothy 560
Loudermilk, Kerry 427
Loudermilk, Beth 680
Louge, Michael W. (Mike) 405
Loughin-Vance, Kristy 622
Loughman, Tim 696
Loui, Shelley 270
Louie, Lindsay A 236
Louis, David N. 590
Loup, Stephen 476
Louttit, Gordon 564
Louvis, Soterios 223
Lovato, Marty 207
Love, Phillip E 13
Love, Debra 27
Love, Ron 119
Love, Karen 134
Love, Tolli 142
Love, Katie 238
Love, Alexandra 431
Lovelady, James 32
Loveless, Steve 537
Lovett, Robert 623
Low, Lewis 285
Low, Robert E. 371
Lowder, Dr Steve 543
Lowe, Sheila 92
Lowe, Karen 128
Lowe, Terril 135
Lowe, Kenneth W. (Ken) 488
Lowe, Vicky 493
Lowe, William J. 627
Lowe, Ada 692
Lowenberg, John 310
Lowenfels, Fred 623
Lower, Dennis 75
Lower, William 277
Lowry, Donna 129
Lowther, Aaron 111
Lowther, Mike 382
Loyd, Peggy 537
Lozada, Leonardo J. 473
Lozano, Sandra 348
Lu, Billy 284
Lubert, Rachel 565
Lubert, Ira M. 600
Lucado, Pat 194
Lucas, Philip 243
Lucas, Julie 313
Lucas, John 324
Lucas, Ken 337
Lucas, Bruce 354
Lucas, Darren 437
Lucas, Connie 540
Lucas, Bryan 560
Lucas, Mary 570
Lucca, Marc 42
Lucero, Barbara 281
Lucey, Morag 52
Luchini, Joseph 188
Luciano, Melba 603
Lucier, Suzy 6
Lucier, Jake 15
Lucier, Christopher 658
Luckas, Nancy 134
Luckey, Jeane 670
Lucks, Cheryl W. 365
Lucore, Charles 530
Ludden, Paul W. 514
Ludington, Bob 604
Ludwig, Todd 677
Ludwig-Beymer, Patti 176
Luffler, Ann Marie 549
Luginbuhl, William E 570
Lugo, Luz 525
Lukaszewski, Michael 421
Luken, Ellen 168
Luker, Bob 443
Lumbard, Lisa 105
Lumsdaine, Dianne 164

Lumsden, Chris A. 492
Luna, Bower 14
Luna, James 420
Luna, Rachel 516
Luna, Nallibe 587
Lund, Ed 25
Lund, Mary 151
Lund, Dennis 300
Lundequam, Michael 442
LUNDGREN, DAVID 203
Lundin, Douglas 66
Lundy, Rich 595
Lunn, Eric 29
Lurie, Robert F. 375
Lusignan, Sara 48
Lusk, Liska 559
Lustgarten, Joyce 162
Lutlow, Shannon 159
Luttinger, Raymond 264
Lutz, Tom 575
Lutz, John M. 615
Luu, Bao Q 488
Lyash, Jeffrey J. (Jeff) 179
Lyden, Shawn 118
Lydstone, Elizabeth 298
Lyford, Robert M 45
Lyle, John 620
Lyles, Donna 289
Lyman, Gregory A 672
Lymer, Scott 212
Lynch, Brian P 155
Lynch, Timothy W 203
Lynch, Diane 235
Lynch, Donald M 261
Lynch, Jack 302
Lynch, Katie 371
Lynch, Timothy G. 456
Lynch, Mel 694
Lyndaker, Matthew 693
Lyngdoh, Sheppard 248
Lynn, Mary 218
Lynn, Scott J. 468
Lyon, Robert C. 367
Lyon, Glenn S. 579
Lyons, Amy 285
Lyons, Mitch 341
Lyons, Althea 391
Lyons, William 648
Lysen, Jan 238
Lyssy, Samuel L. (Sam) 367
Lyttle, Lance 433
Lytton, Marcia 6
Lytton, Alexander 544
L'Heureux, Scott 258
L'Homme, Bert 170

M

Ma, Mahau 356
Ma, Qingyun 656
Maakestad, Paul 394
Maas, John 212
Maass, Paul T. 604
Mabe, Johnny 183
Mabe, David 475
Macaluso, Diane 24
Macaulay, Caitlin E 279
Maccarone, Diane 440
Maccarone, Connie 684
Macdonald, Eileen B 39
Macdonald, Linda 100
MacDonald, Walt 175
Macdonald, Ellen A 226
Macdonald, John 479
Macdonald, Carrie 641
Macdougall, Betty 34
MacDougall, Harriett 398
Mace, Alexander 514
Macechko, Nicholas 693
Macha, Mark 441
Machamer, Virginia 692
Machen, Robert 34
Machuk, Paul 79
Macina, Robert P. 589

Macinnes, Dennis M 352
Macisaac, Don 406
Mack, Kristina A 159
Mack, Jill 179
Mack, Winifred 516
Mack, Judith 652
Mack-Brooks, Pamela 241
MacKeen, Ray 616
Mackell, Lisa 306
MacKenzie, Wayne 99
Mackenzie, Jake 338
Mackey, Bob 239
Mackey, John P. 690
Mackinnon, Matt 360
Mackler, Mitchell 693
Macko, David 209
Macko, David 582
Macko, Terence 696
Mackowiak, Edward 616
Maclaren, Catherine 174
Maclasco, Robert 491
Maclennon, John 442
Macmaster, Gregory 404
Macner, Anne 595
Macnutt, James 535
Macomber, Marina 392
Macon, James 380
Macphail, Winborne 485
Macpherson, Ross 301
MacVane, Jessica 218
Macveigh, Matt 254
Madalena, Ralph J 376
Maddalone, Dom 509
Madden, Nancy 399
Madden, Thomas 611
Madden, Donald 623
Maddox, Mark 130
Madel, Denise 12
Madeley, Paul E 64
Maden, Nicholas 185
Madigan, Angie 133
Madison, Dennis 515
Madrid, Bonita 433
Madrigal, Calvin 612
Madson, Deborah 238
Maeda, Tsuyoshi 426
Maeder, Jeff 616
Maehara, Jenny 482
Maestas, Juan 685
Mafi, Gabriela 208
Magdziarz, Wayne F 299
Magee, Deb 416
Mageli, John 26
Magenheimer, Richard C 21
Maggelakis, Sophia 464
Maggitti, Patrick G. 667
Magid, Bruce R. 82
Magill, M. Elizabeth 288
Magner, Johnette 75
Magruder, Joan 346
Magruder, Joan 525
Maguin, Stephen 145
Maguire, Kate 247
Mahaffey, Jenny 225
Mahalingam, S. 555
Mahan, Michelle 205
Mahan, Chip 292
Mahan, James S 292
Mahaney, Sheryl 276
Mahar, Derek 91
Mahase, Kishan 227
Mahendran, Bagavathy 228
Maher, John 362
Maheshwari, Umesh 382
Mahil, Amandip 163
Mahjoub, Ali 381
Mahler, Carl 554
Mahler, Anthony 683
Mahone, Barbara 692
Mahoney, Robert J. 159
Mahoney, Edward J. 325
Mahoney, Joanne M. 375
Mahoney, Kelly 540
Mai, Shayne 368

Maibach, Doug 61
Maibach, Ben C. 61
Maibach, Ryan 61
Maibach, Benjamin C 61
Maibach, Douglas L 61
Maibach, Sheryl B 61
Maidlow, Spencer T 146
Maier, Mike 383
Mail, Ingrid M 306
Mailand, William 290
Maines, Josh 484
Mains, Kenneth G 344
Maisel, Bruce 684
Maislin, Stephen 220
Mak, Janet 325
Maki, Mark A 342
Maklan, David 682
Makori-Nelson, Benadette 129
Makulec, Jude 464
Malakof, Stacey L 376
Maland, David 216
Malave, Rockwell 293
Malavé, Andrés 399
Malcolm, Georgette 593
Maldonado, Ricardo 163
Maldonado, Raul 415
Maldonado, Debbie 540
Maldonado, Lisa 546
Malek, Ryan 354
Maley, Michael 15
Maley, Christopher 589
Malhotra, Meena 296
Malhotra, Roopali 656
Mallakis, Kosta 433
Mallen, Ben 245
Mallett, Chris 392
Mallette, Michael 136
Mallison, Nathan 363
Mallot, Kyle M 167
Mallott, Anthony 489
Malloy, Tom 2
Malloy, William 337
Malloy, Thomas E. 654
Malone, Mike 13
Malone, Steve 200
Malone, Jacqueline 300
Malone, Dean 343
Malone, Dean P 343
Malone, Anthony J 396
Malone, Blake 400
Malone, Jan 413
Malone, K K 469
Malone, Marguerite G. 483
Malone, Laura 565
Malone, John T 660
Malone, Nancy 675
Maloney, William 186
Maloney, Patrick 203
Maloney, Katie 220
Maloney, Rosario 415
Maloney, James F 631
Maloney, G P 688
Maloney, G 688
Maloy, June 387
Malte, Bob 275
Mamet, Michele 331
Mamon, Harvey 567
Manacchio, Margot 699
Manasia, Anthony 355
Manbeck, Keith 690
Mancheste, George 617
Mancoridis, Spiros 165
Mancuso, Anthony 197
Mancuso, Anthony 302
Mandel, Don 21
Mandel, Lawrence 275
Mandel, Carol A. 377
Mandel, Adrienne A. 676
Mandell, James 570
Mander, Gurpreet 530
Mandeville, Kathy 315
Mandichak, Mark 310
Mandola, Kim 313
Mandrella, Karen 654
Maneker, Amy 118

Maner, Bobbie 465
Maneri, Phil 184
Mangel, Allen W. 458
Mangel, Barry 680
Manget, Christine 508
Mangin, Wendy 213
Mangoni, John 244
Mangura, Paul 384
Manheimer, Mark L 520
Manias, William G 185
Manica, Virgil 629
Manigan, Elizabeth 200
Manigault, Pierre 94
Manis, Jonathan (Jon) 548
Mankiller, Kristen T 569
Manley, Kathy 621
Mann, James 10
Mann, Jeff 15
Mann, Christopher 141
Mann, Robert 160
Mann, Maria A. 167
Mann, Lindsay K 271
Manna, Frank 20
Manna, Rebecca 269
Manning, Martin F. (Marty) 9
Manning, Robin E. (Rob) 179
Manning, Peggy 247
Manning, Michael 590
Manning, Mike 685
Mannix, Margaret 2
Mannix, Mary N 51
Mannon, David 430
Mannon, George 621
Manoogian, Lisa 35
Manos, Steven S. 82
Manrique, Olga 59
Mansfield, Stephen L. (Steve) 336
Mansky, Patrick 205
Manson, Dave 482
Mantella, Philomena V. 392
Manthe, Junior 281
Manuel, Ethan 326
Manuel, Terri 439
Manuel, Bill 501
Manuel, Shasta 523
Manzano, Wilhelmina 597
Manzari, Margie 516
Manzo, Paul E 470
Manzon, Wendy 235
Mapes, Michelle 191
Maples, John T. 507
Marano, Robert P 630
Marcaccio, Mario J 102
Marcellino, David L 81
March, Keith 350
Marchael, Tom 633
Marchbein, Deane 320
Marchese, Sara 452
Marchetti, Paul K 422
Marchik, Katie 252
Marchin, George 270
Marchozzi, Tom 227
Marciniak, Richard 628
Marco, Bob 238
Marco, Mario J. San 684
Marcus, Judith 285
Marcus, Philip 472
Marcus, Ruth 508
Marcus, W. Andrew 651
Marek, Liz 22
Marella, Punnaiah 187
Marestaing, Alex 430
Margetts, Marty 119
Margol, Kanoe 601
Maria, Peter J De 688
Mariani, Harry 244
Marinello, Kathryn V 584
Marinello, Tony 639
Marinez, Lauren 341
Maring, Trent 424
Marinich, Season 84
Marino, Linda 532
Marion, Melissa 692
Maritz, W. Stephen (Steve) 307
Mark, William 522

Markell, Peter K. 419
Markell, Peter K. 626
Markewicz, Jeremy 315
Markinson, Bryan 355
Markle, Jami 243
Markley, Steve 162
Marks, George 48
Marks, Julia 227
Marks, Cindy 348
Marks, Stanley W. 508
Markson, Larry 71
Markus, Tim 13
Markus, Donna 218
Marlow, Gary P 391
Marlow, Patty 668
Maron, Michael 239
Marottolo, Lucille 450
Marovich, Milan 282
Marquardt, Patti 68
Marquardt, R. Scott 304
Marquardt, Robert 304
Marquardt, Jeanne 625
Marquez, Merly 192
Marquez, Rose 245
Marquis, Jeffrey A. 223
Marra, Michele 387
Marra, Michel 387
Marrano, Steve 42
Marrero, Cecilia 161
Marrs, Rick 423
Mars, Galen 192
Marsch, Jean 220
Marsden, Noel 83
Marsh, Andrew 185
Marsh, Celeste 251
Marsh, Randy 368
Marsh, Edward 371
Marsh, Allen J 483
Marsh, Beth 522
Marsh, Amy K 651
Marsh, Peter 673
Marshal, Jim 368
Marshall, Devona 392
Marshall, Era L. 506
Marshall, David 517
Marshall, Cynthia 623
Marshall, Ken 638
Marshall, Lynne 693
Marsicano, Michael 202
Marsteller, Brent A 88
Martel, Ron 267
Martel, Amina 482
Marter, Kenneth W 321
Marthens, Thomas 293
Martin, Julia 6
Martin, Cynthia 22
Martin, Michael 46
Martin, Dan 96
Martin, Michelle 96
Martin, Glen 110
Martin, David 123
Martin, Michael 132
Martin, Sandy 141
Martin, Dan 163
Martin, David 191
Martin, Michael M. 200
Martin, David 226
Martin, Colleen 281
Martin, Barbara 303
Martin, Alexa 313
Martin, Kathryn 325
Martin, Beth 361
Martin, Antonio 373
Martin, Alison 383
Martin, Josh 422
Martin, Andrew D. 456
Martin, Daniel B 466
Martin, Thomas 466
Martin, Gina 475
Martin, Julie 482
Martin, Diane 530
Martin, Kip 569
Martin, John 603
Martin, Michelle 603
Martin, Mark 620

Miceli, Matilda 587
Miceli, Charles 614
Michael, Amanya 251
Michael, Kelly 331
Michaelis, Dennis 444
Michaels, Judy 252
Michaelson, DK 170
Michaelson, Dr Steve 598
Michalerya, William 286
Michalski, Gene 692
Michalsky, Bryan 271
Michaud, Christopher 501
Michaud, Peter L. 507
Michel, Euclid 89
Michel, Howard E. 586
Micheletti, Andrew 53
Michels, David P 131
Michels, Becky 248
Michelucci, Aaron J 65
Micinski, Gary 254
Mickey, Aileen 275
Mickus, Steven 329
Middendorf, Tom 580
Middleton, Alan 382
Middleton, Debra 613
Middleton, Mike 647
Midgett, Alex 183
Midgley, Clare 567
Midkiff, Scott F. 669
Midlo, Luke 535
Midyett, Ron 41
Mielak, Gary 176
Mielak, Gary 176
Mignagna, Gary 660
Migoya, Carlos A. 446
Mihran, Robin 517
Mijares, Al 408
Mika, Teresa 353
Miklaszewski, Elana 60
Milam, Sabrina 664
Milam, Hof 673
Milby, Ron 221
Miles, Steven 24
Miles, Larry 149
Miles, John 192
Miles, Amy E. 455
Miles, Samantha 601
Miles, Thomas J. 610
Miles, Keith 648
Milhiser, Jim 479
Miliband, David 251
Mill, Jack De 450
Mill, Georgia 466
Millard, Robert B. 313
Millard, Jayne 629
Millard, Suzanne Turtle 629
Miller, Paul 9
Miller, Bill 42
Miller, Dale 53
Miller, Toni 79
Miller, Keith 87
Miller, Leo 89
Miller, Alex 115
Miller, Margaret 131
Miller, Jonathan 135
Miller, Michael 140
Miller, David 155
Miller, Bob 155
Miller, Timothy (Tim) 162
Miller, Mark 170
Miller, Nathan 184
Miller, Adam 190
Miller, Jennifer 201
Miller, Clark 207
Miller, Lynn 208
Miller, Lynn 209
Miller, Deborah 209
Miller, Lorie 212
Miller, Don 216
Miller, Dan 231
Miller, Cathy 231
Miller, Edwin (Glen) 235
Miller, Deloris 239
Miller, Derek 242
Miller, Vickie 247

Miller, Wentz J 249
Miller, Robert 255
Miller, Diane 256
Miller, Gragg 259
Miller, Mary Kay 274
Miller, Kyle 294
Miller, Bob 301
Miller, Andrew 302
Miller, Henry 323
Miller, Matthew 326
Miller, Melissa 327
Miller, Peter C 339
Miller, Brian 357
Miller, Rick 365
Miller, Frank R 372
Miller, H. Gilbert 383
Miller, Darlene 399
Miller, Susi 405
Miller, Linda 412
Miller, Thomas 431
Miller, James 464
Miller, John 483
Miller, Alex 483
Miller, Janice 487
Miller, Jan 487
Miller, Tim 487
Miller, Scott 506
Miller, Rob 507
Miller, Barbara 511
Miller, Glenn 514
Miller, Marge 516
Miller, Karen 516
Miller, Josh 519
Miller, Jon 534
Miller, Betsy 538
Miller, David R 552
Miller, Kurt 553
Miller, Jim 557
Miller, Randy 563
Miller, Logan 566
Miller, Wes 567
Miller, Franklin C. (Frank) 568
Miller, Pamela 589
Miller, Ceil 602
Miller, Ezra 603
Miller, Patrice 619
Miller, Amy 635
Miller, Trevor 636
Miller, Phillip 648
Miller, Jeffrey 656
Miller, Fletcher 666
Miller, J. J. 684
Miller, Al 692
Miller, Erin 693
Millett, David 439
Millican, Anthony 120
Milligan, Paul T 102
Milligan, Gretchen 482
Millikan, J. Scott 74
Millinor, Payton 164
Millman, Robert L 344
Millman, Richard G 344
Mills, Brandon 19
Mills, Dawn 52
Mills, Stephanie 54
Mills, Curt 155
Mills, Kathy 201
Mills, Don 339
Mills, Stephen S 381
Mills, Jane 415
Mills, Angel 496
Milner, Sheila 158
Milner, Eve 172
Milnes, Susan 239
Milone-Nuzzo, Paula 600
Milovich, David 90
Milton, Jerrod 114
Minami, Brad 38
Minardi, Christina 690
Minarovic, Michael J 42
Minarovic, Rosanne 486
Minasian, Brenda 356
Mincin, Wes 624
Minehan, Cathy E. 590
Miner, Jim 344

Miner, James D. 588
Mines, Michael A. (Mick) 406
Minhas, Hamza 568
Minnehan, Mike 677
Minnick, Mike 444
Minor, Lloyd 288
Minotti, Anthony J 193
Minter, Cindy 348
Mintz, Karly 60
Mintz, Alan 297
Minutoli, Robert 616
Minyard, Nelson 174
Mion, Anna 359
Mirabal, Emanuel 552
Mireles, Kelli 40
Mirkopoulos, Nicholas S 72
Misencik, Mark 104
Misita, Bill 426
Mislan, Tim 346
Misra, Sanghamitra 560
Mistry, Nilesh 696
Misuraca, Tami H 624
Misuraca, Tami H 624
Mitchell, Andrea 78
Mitchell, Laura 121
Mitchell, Susan 176
Mitchell, Susan 176
Mitchell, J. Stuart 230
Mitchell, Jim 248
Mitchell, Christopher 259
Mitchell, Sheena 279
Mitchell, Michael R 290
Mitchell, Harmon 464
Mitchell, Jenny 529
Mitchell, Robert (Rob) 616
Mitchell, Stephanie 630
Mitchell, Larry 681
Mitchell, Amy 694
Mitra, Subhro 386
Mitrick, Joseph M. (Joe) 58
Mitrovich, Mark 361
Mitry, Norman F 663
Mitschke, Gina 284
Mittal, Lalita 617
Mittelman, Monty 441
Mittermaier, Pascal 596
Mittl, Cheryl 20
Mitzner, Jennifer 238
Mix, Heidi 463
Miyamoto, Patti 242
Miyamoto, Mike 538
Miyamoto, Melba 700
Miyazaki, Shigeki 35
Miyazaki, Higeki 35
Mladenovic, Jeanette 410
Mleczko, Dan 575
Mnning, Carol 695
MO, Weiwei 659
Moag, Tony 616
Moats, Dan 36
Moberg, Kirk 95
Mock, Kathy 238
Mock, Fred 244
Mock, Robert C. 267
Mock, Angie 440
Modde, Margaret Mary 146
Modjeska, Alicia 134
Mody-Baily, Priti 73
Moe, Jeanan 693
Moehling, John 576
Moelis, Ron 278
Moeller, Mark 223
Moeller, Clair J. 342
Moen, Kayla 481
Moersch, Brian 174
Moffet, Brian L 505
Moffett, Randy 637
Moffitt, John 339
Moffitt, Jamie 651
Moffitt, Michael 651
Mofor, Lapah 96
Mogan, Tom 625
Mogan, Thomas 626
Mogg, Denise 474
Moghadam, Shams 603

Mohlman, Kurt 609
Mohn, Ross 613
Mohr, Todd M. 10
Mohr, Steven 294
Mohr, David 492
Mohrman, Michael 467
Moilien, Phillip 151
Moje, Elizabeth Birr 456
Molek, Noreen 516
Molen, Matt 552
Molina, Dolores 90
Molina, Luis 160
Molina, Claudia 243
Molina, Jennifer 293
Molina, Natalie 372
Molina, Rita 390
Molinaro, James 461
Moline, Kathy 329
Molinie, Bernard 379
Moliterno, David 273
Molko, Cindy 474
Molle, Josephine 234
Mollet, Chris 176
Mollet, Chris 176
Molloy, Melinda 113
Molmen, David 29
Molnar, Cindy 104
Molnar, Richard 313
Molnar, Carol 694
Moloney, Ellen 380
Moloney, Jacquie 645
Moltrup, Doreen 532
Monaco, Mark 194
Monaco, Donna 302
Monahan, Thomas L 102
Monahan, Mike Null 398
Monan, J. Donald 625
Moncher, Daniel 193
Moncrief, Kit Tennison 561
Mondragon, Brian 123
Monette, Todd 112
Monette, Perry 685
Money, Celista 668
Monge, Cathie 675
Monighetti, Daniel 441
Moniuskzo, Richard 461
Monk, David H. 600
Monlezun, Mike 170
Monroe, Sheila 525
Monroe, Alex 572
Monson, Thomas S. 83
Monson, Dale D. 130
Monson, Jeffrey 681
Montanaro, Tom 230
Montano, Cathy 537
Montebello, Philippe De 594
Monteiro, Ken 581
Montemurro, Michael 282
Montenegro, Sara 560
Montero, Alejandro 456
Montgomery, Richard 198
Montgomery, Toni-Marie 398
Montgomery, James 461
Montgomery, Robert 471
Montgomery, Gregory 493
Montgomery, Lisa P. 591
Montgomery, James 621

Montgomery-Talley, La June 672
Monti, Philip 501
Montminy, Sandy 434
Montonye, Brian 141
Montoya, Victoria 189
Montoya, Jessica 410
Montoya, Lillian 537
Montrond, Deborah 148
Montry, Mindy 460
Mood, Shawn 101
Moody, Allison 6
Moody, Felice 39
Moody, Michael 170
Moody, Russell 391
Moody, Lori 497
Moody, Sharmin 537
Mookherjee, Disha 535

Rhoten, Marilyn 147
Rhyne, Jerry 291
Riano, Jewell 344
Ribe, Ken 70
Riccioni, Mich 482
Rice, Patricia M 22
Rice, William 112
Rice, Steve 182
Rice, Larry 267
Rice, John L 277
Rice, Will 439
Rice, Bret 509
Rice, Jennifer 537
Rice, Ling 598
Rich, Robert E. (Bob) 574
Richard, Michelle 69
Richard, John 82
Richard, Sylvia 279
Richard, Andy 483
Richard, Harrington 521
Richards, David 68
Richards, James J 134
Richards, Nicole 176
Richards, Patricia R. 251
Richards, Jeanne 311
Richards, James J 359
Richards, Michael 480
Richards, Larry 627
Richards, Thomas 647
Richardson, Todd 48
Richardson, Trena 106
Richardson, Fred 123
Richardson, Lisa 126
Richardson, Thomas C. 138
Richardson, Danielle G 168
Richardson, Dee 197
Richardson, Kathy 238
Richardson, David 286
Richardson, Christy 331
Richardson, Mark 410
Richardson, Hunter 412
Richardson, Cliff 539
Richardson, David E. 642
Richer, Alvin 46
Richey, Linda 115
Richey, Mike 542
Richey, Bernadina 562
Richland, Scott 91
Richmond, Estelle 134
Richmond, Craig 336
Richmond, Craig 593
Richter, Karen 118
Richter, Alfred 292
Richter, Michael F 550
Richtsmeier, William 590
Richvalsky, James 107
Ricke, David 556
Rickel, Todd A. 613
Ricken, Chris 660
Rickenbach, Josef H. von 417
Ricker, Bob 459
Rickett, Tyler 19
Rickley, Brian 21
Ricks, Michael 238
Rico, Jean 663
Ridenour, Nancy 648
Ridinger, James H 308
Ridinger, Loren 308
Ridinger, Loren 308
Ridlen, Debbie 257
Ridley, Kevin 113
Ridolfi, Kaye 99
Riebel, William 574
Riecken, Regina 368
Riedel, Judy 473
Riegelhaupt, Kathleen 598
Rieger, Michael 332
Rieker, Karen 525
Rieman, Brooke 617
Riemer, Hans 144
Riendeau, Nicole 451
Riese, Werner De 299
Rigales, Luis 537
Riggs, Mel G. 367
Riggs, Daniel 429

Riggs, Kirsten 459
Riggs, Jean 603
Rigler, Mark L 163
Riley, Donna 40
Riley, Judith 88
Riley, Shane 200
Riley, Brian 254
Riley, Cheryl 275
Riley, Trent 439
Riley, Denise 449
Riley, Charles 567
Riley, Anne 613
Riley, James 692
Riley-Brown, Michelle 560
Rilloraza, Francisco 412
Rimar, Stephen 381
Rimon, Karen 228
Rincon, Francisco Del 103
Rincon, Luis 375
Rine, Mary 109
Rinehart, Lucy 155
Rinehart, Doug 589
Rinere, Monique 597
Riney, Robert G. (Bob) 234
Rinker, Franklin M 224
Rinshed, Rick 432
Rion, Deborah 522
Riordan, Keith 343
Riordan, Mark 562
Riphagen, Derek 25
Ripoly, Josie 352
Ripper, Karen 310
Ripperda, Amanda 246
Risan, Michael 62
Risio, Gary De 53
Rislow, Deb 223
Rispone, Rodi F 347
Risse, Thomas 444
Rissi, Daniel 283
Ritch, Jill A Alexander 649
Rittenmeyer, Ronald 52
Ritter, Gretchen 143
Ritter, David 159
Ritter, Michael 345
Ritter, Thad 536
Ritter, Tim 557
Ritter, Teresa 573
Ritter, Jane 636
Rivas, Saul 105
Rivas, Ray 127
Rivas, Isadore 233
Rivas, Manual 391
Rive, Lyndon R. 559
Rive, Peter J. 559
Rivera, Rosa 152
Rivera, Andrea 362
Rivera, Maria 381
Rivera, Anna 430
Rivera, Mario 648
Rivero, Diana 630
Rivers, Bill 441
Rivest, Jeffrey A. 644
Rivkin, Natalya 128
Rivkin, Michael 570
Rizk, Norman W. 538
Rizzo, Gregory 519
Rizzo, Richard J 630
Rn, Joan 315
Rn, Laura Espinosa PHD 335
Rn, Ann Cella 529
Roach, Jill 620
Robaina, Ashley 637
Robb, Gary 333
Robb, Chuck 473
Robb, Walter E. 690
Robbins, Tracy 168
Robbins, Sheldon 283
Robel, Susan M. 208
Robel, Lauren 627
Robelia, Lance 295
Robert, Carrie 108
Robert, Lucas 145
Robert, Debbie 398
Roberts, Samuel 67
Roberts, Carrie 108

Roberts, Peter W. 116
Roberts, Angie 143
Roberts, Phyllis 204
Roberts, Kevin V 209
Roberts, Dale 218
Roberts, M. Parker 303
Roberts, William R. 321
Roberts, R Don 359
Roberts, Kristine 361
Roberts, Fred 420
Roberts, Janet 477
Roberts, John G. 506
Roberts, James 578
Roberts, Rebecca 587
Robertson, Cliff 21
Robertson, Laura 56
Robertson, Cliff A. 100
Robertson, Cliff 148
Robertson, Jessica 209
Robertson, Pamela 269
Robertson, William G. (Bill) 357
Robertson, Euan 372
Robertson, A E 408
Robertson, Joseph (Joe) 410
Robertson, Bruce 492
Robertson, Debbie 501
Robertson, Carla 517
Robertson, Pat 572
Robertson, Gordon 572
Robertson, Thomas S. 607
Robertson, Anne Walters 610
Robertson-Keck, Karen 204
Robeson, Ziggy 630
Robillard, Barbara 521
Robillard, Jean 643
Robinett, Pam 363
Robinette, Gary E. 432
Robins, Doug 183
Robinson, Breanna 33
Robinson, Ron 58
Robinson, Jeffrey 79
Robinson, Daniel 96
Robinson, Chase 140
Robinson, Debra 173
Robinson, Patricia 187
Robinson, Donna 193
Robinson, Vicki 198
Robinson, John R 215
Robinson, Aaron 230
Robinson, Nina B 238
Robinson, Becky 239
Robinson, Rebecca 239
Robinson, Warren 314
Robinson, Jason 332
Robinson, Lisa 359
Robinson, Edward 359
Robinson, Timothy C. 365
Robinson, Myron 378
Robinson, John 422
Robinson, Thomas L 462
Robinson, Risa 464
Robinson, Phil 471
Robinson, Larry A. 494
Robinson, William J. (Bill) 497
Robinson, Raymond E 510
Robinson, Dave 512
Robinson, Jack 531
Robinson, Susan 536
Robinson, Dick 550
Robinson, Albert 557
Robinson, David 562
Robinson, Wt 566
Robinson, Shirley 630
Robinson, Linda 641
Robinson, Boyd 642
Robinson, Samara 649
Robinson, Douglas 649
Robinson, Lester 678
Robinson, Carl 692
Robinson, Randy 695
Robison, Mark 81
Robison, Kenneth L 148
Robitaille, Robert 124
Robitaille, Mark E 310
Robitaille, Mark 310

Robledo, Raymond 587
Robles, Monica 125
Robles, Norberto (Bert) 373
Robles, Wilma 399
Robles, Janet C 426
Robyn, Betts 68
ROC, Pierre 381
Roccasalvo, Andrea 589
Rocha, Julie 284
Roche, Joe 91
Roche, Kimberly De 190
Roche, Brian 260
Roche-Carter, Noreen 470
Rochedieu, Patricia 283
Rochin, Gerardo 521
Rock, Jessica 169
Rock, Bernard 623
Rockett, Kathryn 296
Rockwood, John D. 321
Rodarte, Robert 433
Rodell, Angela 17
Roderick, Ryan 458
Rodewald, Renee 40
Rodgers, Susan L 149
Rodgers, Karri 488
Rodgers, Ron 659
Rodgers, Courtney 700
Rodi, Lynn 175
Rodis, John 472
Rodman, Cheryl 339
Rodriguez, Rudy 159
Rodriguez, Vicki 191
Rodriguez, Jackie 199
Rodriguez, Camille 201
Rodriguez, Rick 208
Rodriguez, Mandy 239
Rodriguez, Manuel 242
Rodriguez, Richard 271
Rodriguez, Zina 273
Rodriguez, Deb 294
Rodriguez, Angela 387
Rodriguez, Daniel B. 398
Rodriguez, Leticia 415
Rodriguez, Michelle 415
Rodriguez, Barbara 478
Rodriguez, Domingo C 510
Rodriguez, Carlos 623
Rodriguez, Ricardo 635
Rodriguez-Mackintosh, Pat 22
Roe, Deanna 97
Roe, Amy 692
Roebuck, Mark 516
Roeder, Craig 443
Roemer, Dennis R. 589
Roeser, William 518
Roesler, Jodi 151
Roessle, Randy 629
Rogalski, Robert J 686
Rogan, Randall G. (Randy) 673
Rogers, Sandy 59
Rogers, Deb 97
Rogers, Don 103
Rogers, Harlan 141
Rogers, David 231
Rogers, Greg 343
Rogers, Joseph 384
Rogers, Ralph 399
Rogers, Bobby 450
Rogers, Mark 557
Rogers, James E. (Jim) 596
Rogers, Amy 681
Rogers, Rebecca 692
Rogge, Matt 19
Rogos, Aaron 154
Roheim, John 368
Rohit, Mehra 456
Rohlfing, Ron 631
Rohman, Cindy 289
Rohr, James E. (Jim) 96
Rojas, Manuel F 70
Rojas, Lili 144
Rojas, Eddy 611
Rojek, Kenneth J 384
Rokicki, Mike 602
Rolak, Loren A 309

INDEX OF EXECUTIVES

Shelley, Alexa 478
Shelton, Jean 106
Shelton, John A 158
Shelton, Mary 480
Shelton, M. Dwight 669
Shelton, Suzanne 669
Shelton, Todd 696
Shen, Sam 288
Shen, Kyle 610
Shendell-Falik, Nancy 65
Shepard, Ann 100
Shepard, Janet 109
Shepard, Ken 293
Shepardson, Andrew 68
Sheperd, David 694
Shepheard, Hillary 561
Shepherd, Julie 233
Shepherd, Richard 275
Shepherd, Mary 395
Shepherd, Rick 430
Shepherd, Jane 682
Sheppard, Brooke 359
Sheppard, Dennis 522
Sheppard, William D 522
Sheppard, Ben 537
Sher, Susan S. 611
Sherer, Matt 554
Sheridan, Tom 15
Sheridan, Chris 98
Sheridan, Richard 488
Sheridan, John P. 576
Sheridan, Patrick 671
Sherin, Jonathan 671
Sherlock, Lori 682
Sherman, Debbie 81
Sherman, Karen 284
Sherman, Mark 488
Sherman, Diane 538
Sherman, Gail 603
Sherman, Malcolm L 628
Sherron, Tammy 96
Sherry, Bernie 619
Sherwin, R Lawrence 520
Shi, Patricia 372
Shibrowski, Michael 40
Shields, Christine 121
Shields, Kevin 616
Shikiar, Mindy 79
Shiltz, LauraA 456
Shimada, Michael 505
Shimamoto, Kevin 662
Shimizu, Shaun 19
Shindler, John 415
Shingles, Stan 106
Shipley, Kathy 663
Shippey, Mike 171
Shippy, Jared 293
Shirley, Douglas E. 576
Shirvani, Hamid Augustine 386
Shively, Kari 361
Shivery, Toni 645
Shmerling, James E. 114
Shmerling, James E. 138
Shoaf, Kirby 134
Shoaf, Donnie 183
Shockey, Elizabeth G 612
Shockley, Carolyn R. 179
Shoemake, James 318
Sholar, Shondra 86
Shook, Douglas 656
Shope, Darwin G 676
Shopper, Glenn 20
Shor, David 398
Shore, Melissa 153
Shore, Lynn 192
Short, Steve 197
Short, Andrew K 318
Short, Jeffrey B 581
Shortridge, John 81
Shoulders, Patrick A. 627
Shoup, Scot 311
Shows, W T 141
Shows, Susan 288
Shrewsbury, Amber 225
Shriner, Kimberly 244

Shuck, Theresa 537
Shufflebarger, Thomas G 571
Shugrue, Dianne 213
Shukis, Mariela 699
Shuler, Kathryn 15
Shuler, Tomma 239
Shulman, Brian B. 494
Shultz, Cindy 435
Shum, Jennifer 589
Shumann, C R 231
Shumar, Brenda 686
Shupe, Rachel 560
Shuster, Sandra L 361
Shuster, Keith 564
Shutt, Cheryl 639
Shutty, Jessica 392
Si, Stephanie L 144
Sibergleid, Steven 25
Sibert, Leslie R 211
Sibley, James M 288
Sicca, Darlene 290
Sickles, Jenny 584
Sicola, Tom 319
Sicotte, Luc 684
Sidar, Avinash 531
Siddall, Brenda 282
Sideras, John F. 98
Sidrys, Paul 113
Siebenborn, Bill 150
Siebers, Dan 190
Siegel, Deana 553
Siegel, Allen 660
Siegert, Thomas 586
Siegfried, Scott 474
Siegismund, Lee 517
Siegle, Candy 664
Siegrist, Joie 538
Siemer, Kristine A 359
Siepman, Milton 63
Sietman, Milton 63
Sievers, Glen 424
Siewertsen, Jim 3
Sigler, Lisa 45
Sigmon, William 53
Siko, Carol 686
Silberberg, Allison 122
Silbiger, Martin 129
Silfen, David M. 607
Silins, Andris J 312
Sill, Tammy 148
Sillman, Michael 307
Siltzer, Jody 324
Silva, Judith 419
Silva, Pamela 515
Silvagni, Anthony J. 399
Silveira, Fernando 549
Silver, Richard 487
Silver, Richard 487
Silver, Christopher 642
Silveria, Richard 80
Silveria, Cheri 159
Silverman, Barry J. 399
Silverman, Caleb 400
Silverman, Daniel C 505
Silvers, J. B. 593
Silversten, Scott 196
Silvey, Brent J 675
Silvia, Clarence J 241
Sim, Edward 58
Sim, Sugin 131
Simeck, Shirley 412
Simerly, Rick 255
Simers, Kim 107
Simio, Frank 200
Simione, Mark A. 383
Simko, Bill 491
Simmons, Randall 42
Simmons, Shelly M 47
Simmons, Sharon 86
Simmons, Adele 112
Simmons, Jodi 251
Simmons, Jay 295
Simmons, Tj 301
Simmons, Eileen 332
Simmons, Elizabeth H. 341

Simmons, Rob 428
Simmons, Corrine 465
Simmons, Brad 474
Simmons-Oliver, Cheryl 292
Simms, Susan 421
Simon, Dennis 6
Simon, Mary 197
Simon, Carrie 251
Simon, Debbie 252
Simon, John D 286
Simon, Lou Anna K. 341
Simon, Don 390
Simon, Darryl 521
Simon, Linda 531
Simon, Marianne 574
Simon, Alex 602
Simone, Alan Del 681
Simonian, T Michael 660
Simons, Pat 166
Simonsen, Carolyn 333
Simpson, Ryan 231
Simpson, Glenn 320
Simpson, Karen 497
SIMS, SUZANNE 152
Sims, Demarlo 297
Sims, Dominique 514
Sims, Damon 600
Sims, Stefanie 621
Sinagra, Jack 629
Sine, Jeffrey A. 37
Sinek, Jim 79
Singer, Steven R 153
Singer, Neil 293
Singer, Peter 395
Singer, Bruce H 470
Singer, Samantha 567
Singer, Ethan 627
Singh, Nonihal 57
Singh, Bhupi 162
Singh, Pooja 292
Singh, Anup V. 382
Singh, Vijayeta 392
Singh, Jasvinder 535
Singh, Premjith L 609
Singh, Sabi 643
Singhal, Aparna 189
Singhal, Raj 456
Singleton, J Knox 21
Singleton, Joanna 197
Singleton, Kali 277
Singleton, J Knox 298
Singleton, Palmer C 359
Singleton, H. Wells 399
Singleton, Arnold R. 509
Sipilovic, Bridget 276
Sipple, Lanette 685
Sipser, Michael 313
Siragusa, Paul 426
Sirianni, Frank 200
Sirstins, Max 164
Sisam, Allison 477
Sisisky, Richard L 512
Sisitsky, Todd B. 485
Sisler, Andrew 125
Sisney, Brett 161
Sisson, William G. 58
Sitherwood, Suzanne 520
Sitterding, Mary 115
Siu, Albert 355
Siva, Chokkalingam 646
Sivakumar, Balasubramaniam 532
Six, Beth 266
Sizemore, Vicki 55
Sizemore, Thomas 307
Sizemore, Mark 444
Sjulin, Renee 87
Skabelund, Hoyt 56
Skadin, John 473
Skaggs, Robert 207
Skaine, Theresa M 484
Skaloot, Ed 548
Skarka, Kathy 362
Skarulis, Patricia C. 325
Skaruppa, Cindy 435
Skeans, John 528

Skehan, Michael 310
Skelsey, Maral 322
Skelton, Bryce 544
Skiendzielewski, John 209
Skill, Thomas D. (Tom) 611
Skinner, Anne 346
Skinner, Mary L 431
Skinner, Stephen 445
Skinner, Stephen 545
Skinner, Douglas J. 610
Sklar, Michelle 654
Skluth, Nancy 333
Skoda, Sophia 172
Skolrood, Kent 59
Skonieczny, Michael 390
Skorkowsky, Patrick 125
Skorton, David J. 506
Skory, John E 574
Skrivanos, Stephen F 75
Skrocki, Denise 632
Slack, Charlene 220
Slade, Charlyn 9
Slader, Salene 187
Slatas, Brian 102
Slater, Jana Kay 214
Slater, Dave 446
Slater, Mark 487
Slatky, Larry I 362
Slaton, Shawn 111
Slattery, William (Willie) 167
Slattery, Kerrie 421
Slaughter, James G. 469
Slaughter, Veronica 635
Slavick, Amy 535
Slavin, Peter L. 419
Slavin, Peter L. 590
Slaybaugh, Chris 692
Slinkard, John 546
Sloan, Jacob 64
Sloan, Gayle 476
Sloat, Jean 96
Slominski, Donald D. (Don) 320
Slomsky, David 545
Slon, Dennis 299
Slonim, Sheryl 239
Sluka, Joseph 456
Slusher, Martin 262
Slusky, Lorie A 374
Slyter, Mark F 63
Small, Alliant 6
Small, Jeff 171
Small, Andrew 431
Small, David R. 446
Small, J. Radford 559
Small, Deborah A 606
Smalley, James 227
Smalls, Kenyell 372
Smart, James 306
Smart, Denise T. 563
Smedes, Tina 105
Smeenk, Sharon 198
Smeltzer, David P 42
Smet, John H 32
Smilde, Renee 488
Smit, Charl 61
Smith, Wade 10
Smith, Scott 10
Smith, Lisa 26
Smith, Robert 27
Smith, Stephan 33
Smith, Jenni 38
Smith, Rosi 45
Smith, David 49
Smith, Lamont 50
Smith, James 51
Smith, Arthur 52
Smith, Debra 52
Smith, Ryan 56
Smith, Tyler 61
Smith, Gerald 67
Smith, Lloyd V 68
Smith, Hal E 75
Smith, Taylor 78
Smith, Connie D 81
Smith, Catherine 83

Terra, Patricia 193
Terranova, Carleen 692
Terrasi, Francesco M 102
Terrazas, Miguel 443
Terrell, Ransom 125
Terrell, Michael 207
Terrell, Helen 449
Terrell, Carla 694
Terri, Klopfenstine 255
Terrill, Mark 681
Terry, Monte 101
Tersigni, Anthony R 47
Terwilliger, Jerry 405
Tessier, Pamela 227
Testa, Steve 365
Testy, Kellye 658
Teufel, Sharon 132
Thacker, Lynda 584
Thadani, Sharmila 182
Thakur, Anita 133
Thakur, Netra 204
Thames, Thomas B. 492
Thames, Bruce A 552
Thandri, Ananthan 326
Thanopoulos, George 335
Thao, MAI 91
Tharp, William W 197
Tharp, Jeffrey 680
Thatavakorn, Amy 637
Thatcher, Linda 666
Thaw, James 87
Theodoredis, Roger E. 689
Thibodaux, Vincent 624
Thibodeaux, Wayne 561
Thiele, Ron 255
Thieme, Dennis 370
Thiessen, Allen 661
Thilmany, Andrea 410
Thimmesch, Timothy 218
Thimmesch, Tim 218
Thoeny, Lysa 693
Thom, Patrick 5
Thom, Jonathan 188
Thoman, Thomas S. 15
Thomas, Marshall 3
Thomas, Savageau 68
Thomas, Mary 89
Thomas, Jake 92
Thomas, Jacob 125
Thomas, Robin 125
Thomas, Michael J 142
Thomas, Larry 144
Thomas, Stephanie 160
Thomas, Jess 160
Thomas, Tony 171
Thomas, Elaine 172
Thomas, Ryan 173
Thomas, Kenneth 179
Thomas, Pamela 193
Thomas, Dana 248
Thomas, Michelle 252
Thomas, Michael S. 263
Thomas, Rony 291
Thomas, Michael 292
Thomas, Ramona 310
Thomas, Debbie 323
Thomas, Beverly 339
Thomas, Donna 359
Thomas, Olivia 365
Thomas, Jill 422
Thomas, Dan 433
Thomas, Becky 435
Thomas, Tim 436
Thomas, Bill 446
Thomas, Jeff 530
Thomas, Sarah 613
Thomas, Rebecca S. 673
Thomas, Roger 694
Thomason, Jaime 271
Thomason, Alesia 422
Thomason, Keith 594
Thompsen, Kelvin 515
Thompson, Denton 15
Thompson, Dwight 29
Thompson, Jolene 36

Thompson, Arthur 75
Thompson, Arthur 136
Thompson, Linda Valdez 152
Thompson, Jerry E 185
Thompson, Jeffrey E 223
Thompson, Katherine 231
Thompson, Bryan 232
Thompson, Matt 243
Thompson, Gloria 247
Thompson, Dale 249
Thompson, Gigi 249
Thompson, Owen 249
Thompson, Mark 252
Thompson, Susan K. 252
Thompson, Steve 271
Thompson, Julie 281
Thompson, Patrick 291
Thompson, Craig B. 325
Thompson, Dale 345
Thompson, Brittany 346
Thompson, Ray 353
Thompson, Doug 369
Thompson, Timothy 374
Thompson, Barbara 416
Thompson, Steve 427
Thompson, Vicki 435
Thompson, Todd 460
Thompson, Charles 461
Thompson, Lisa 465
Thompson, Richard 476
Thompson, Glynn 480
Thompson, Donna 498
Thompson, William P. 523
Thompson, Aida 537
Thompson, David 554
Thompson, Doyle 559
Thompson, Ryker 561
Thompson, James L 598
Thompson, Staci 602
Thompson, Greg A 620
Thompson, Lewis E 620
Thompson, Kim 636
Thompson, Ken 647
Thompson, Thomas J 660
Thompson, Audrey 669
Thompson, M Keith 672
Thompson, Nell 681
Thompson, Beverly Brooks 695
Thomson, Laura 356
Thomson, Greg 634
Thomson, Joanne 645
Thorne, James 137
Thornhill, Hugh 405
Thornton, Rhonda 45
Thornton, Brian 96
Thornton, Connie 308
Thornton, Lether 389
Thornton, Glenda 554
Thornton, Ann 573
Thornton, Leslie 687
Thorp, Gorman M 233
Thorp, H. Holden 616
Thorpe, Linda 56
Thorpe, Ruth 399
Thorpe, Edith D 548
Thorson, Dave 13
Thorson, Michael 219
Thorup, Schuyler 101
Thoven, Glenn 308
Thrasher, Kelsey 299
Thrasher, Terrell 299
Thullbery, Joan 537
Thunell, Adam 135
Thurman, Ramona 143
Thurman, Lindsay 601
Thway, Myint 496
Thyberg, Gordon 563
Tibbitts, Mark 46
Tibbitts, Betsy 210
Tibbs, E. W. 105
Tice, Casandra 99
Tichenor, Stuart 148
Ticker, Jay 376
Tickles, Chuck 271
Tiddettes, Shawn 668

Tiedemann, Peter 28
Tiencken, John 105
Tierney, Thomas J. 596
Tiesi, Jeffrey 688
Tietjen, Deb 208
Tighe, Thomas 162
Tilds, Eric 293
Tilford, Tim 310
Till, Frank 149
Tilley, Martha 109
Tilley, Luke 692
Tillman, Linda 418
Tillman, Michael C 635
Tilton, David 379
Tilton, Jesse C 385
Tim, Snyder 673
Timanus, Timothy 490
Timberlake, Rebecca 538
Timm, Mark 699
Timmerman, Greg 254
Timmerman, Timothy T. 298
Timmers, Martha 442
Timmons, Darla 486
Tin, Judy A 184
Ting, Henry 597
Tinns, Holly 164
Tipton, Richard 450
Tirman, Kerry R 86
Tirrell, Matthew 610
Tischner, Kl 368
Tison, Jack 416
Titinger, Jorge L. 502
Titov, Debbee 430
Tkach, Dennis 457
Tkaczyk, Greg 393
Toadvine, Stephen 584
Tobin, Jim 283
Tobin, Philip T 565
Tobin, Thomas J 565
Todd, Aaron D. 14
Todd, Amy 288
Todd, Irene 300
Todd, Timothy J 343
Todd, Brenda 406
Todd, Andrew N 418
Todd, Andrew 697
Todd, Andrew N 697
Toellner, Ann 646
Toeniskoetter, Charles 480
Toffey, Bryan 10
Tohrnan, Kathy 532
Tokunaga, Christine 245
Tol, Daryl 323
Tolley, Howard 661
Tolman, Ruth 168
Tom, Melissa 511
Tom, Crystal 570
Tomasik, Andy 341
Tomasky, Susan 32
Tombesi, Paolo 399
Tomlin, Bob 284
Tomlinson, Eric 385
Tomlinson, Monica 566
Tomo, Ronald 362
Toms, Shannon 628
Toncray, Debby 183
Toner, Renee 160
Toni, Christine 189
Tonkinson, Robert 568
Tonn, Barbara 247
Tonner, Paul 318
Tooke, David 431
Toombs, Ross 182
Toomey, April 179
Topper, Joan 208
Topper, John E 331
Topper, Joseph V. (Joe) 667
Toppin, Bruce 388
Toppin, Bruce 389
Torbert, Ronald J 61
Torchiana, David F. 419
Torchiana, David 419
Toresdahl, Brett 376
Torgerson, James P 609
Torino, Christopher 484

Torkelson, Thomas E 245
Tornek, Scott 439
Torossian, Lynn M. 234
Torrance, Kelly 235
Torre, Bonnie 480
Torres, Chris 302
Torres, Marilyn 338
Torres, Ceci 393
Torres, Estella 572
Torres, Eddie 632
Torres, Daniel 642
Torres, Donna 693
Torres-Springer, Maria 372
Torrey, William 68
Tossava, Kendra 243
Totherow, Bill 521
Totten, Elizabeth 606
Touchet, Jennifer 220
Toulme, Patrick 395
Tourangeau, Roger 682
Tournillon, Toby 475
Tousignant, Michael 128
Towarak, Tim 69
Towers, Kelly 584
Townes, Wlliam 188
Townes, Emilie M. 615
Townsel, Beadie H 490
Townsel, Beadie H 490
Townsend, Ted 252
Trabold, Tina 330
Trabulsi, Ann 69
Trach, Natalie 384
Tracy, Diane 456
Tracy, James A. (Jim) 470
Tracy, Jan 549
Tragni, Lauren M 573
Trahey-Romanuk, Gina 218
Trainer, Michael 118
Trakimas, Ann 128
Trammell, Shelly 685
Tramontana, Anthony 261
Tramontana, Nick 562
Tramontozzi, Domenick 123
Tran, Peter 96
Tran, Chris T 109
Tran, Thomas 145
Tran, Phat 208
Tran, Dana 275
Tran, Lan 458
Tran, Vicki 631
Transue, Darren 198
Trapani, Stephen 215
Traquina, Perry M. 82
Trask, Amanda 100
Trask, David 435
Trauth, Denise M. 563
Traviolia, Brad 566
Travis, Troy 339
Travisano, Jacqueline A. 399
Treadway, Carol 563
Treadwell, Melinda 659
Treasure, Jeffrey 213
Treasure, Jeff 276
Trebesch, Butch 38
Trefethen, Angela 407
Trembulak, Frank 208
Trembulak, Frank J 209
Trembulak, Frank J 209
Trembulak, Frank J 209
Trembulak, Frank J 582
Tremone, Carl 627
Tremper, Glendora 120
Trendel, Jennifer 301
Trepa, Kevin M. 76
Tresch, Richard 625
Trevino, Alyssa 162
Trevorah, Danielle 486
Treworgy, Samantha 78
Treynor, Elizabeth 676
Trezza, Steve 363
Tribble, J Lee 288
Trice, Barry G. 223
Triesenberg, Ryan 575
Triggs, Susan 524
Trimble, Fred 479

Watkins, W Juan 75
Watkins, Jesse 177
Watkins, Glissandia 460
Watkins, Brad 561
Watkins, Anthony 675
Watriss, Whitney 506
Watson, Scott 300
Watson, Alan 314
Watson, George E 359
Watson, Christopher 398
Watson, Mike 422
Watson, Brad 452
Watson, Leslyn 482
Watson, Bud 486
Watson, Amy E. 520
Watson, Aaron 529
Watson, Dean 554
Watson, James M. 611
Watt, Kelley A 298
Watt, Abby 370
Watt, Andrew 515
Watt, Robert M 694
Watters, James H. 464
Watts, Karen 152
Watts, Dr Calvin J 273
Watts, Richard 421
Watts, Charles 550
Waugh, Alex 30
Waugh, Scott 419
Waugh, Wendi 516
Way, Chrisanne 40
Waye, Janice 27
Wayling, Brian 251
Wayne, John C. 432
Wayne, Rodney 541
Wayson, Amy 410
Weathers, Hugh E 13
Weaver, Michael 108
Weaver, George 175
Weaver, Carl 417
Weaver, Jeremy 453
Weaver, Jennifer 567
Weaver, Donald 658
Weaver, Gail 697
Webb, David 15
Webb, Sandra 30
Webb, David 64
Webb, Sandra 81
Webb, Donna 95
Webb, Patricia G. (Pat) 100
Webb, Marie 178
Webb, Christopher 201
Webb, Kim 277
Webb, Steven 378
Webb, Maryjo 498
Webb, Kathleen M. 611
Webb, Steven T 664
Webber, Henry S. 615
Webber, Rhonda 637
Webber, Michael J. 654
Weber, Roger 15
Weber, Amy 261
Weber, Lance 301
Weber, Emily 321
Weber, Jeff 338
Weber, Scott 441
Weber, Rhonada 525
Weber, Keith 539
Weber, Emily 641
Weber, Stephen 691
Webster, Keith 96
Webster, Rick 619
Webster, Marshall W. 652
Weekly, Julia Willett 174
Weeks, Albert 60
Weeks, Susan 560
Wegehaupt, Olga 9
Wegel, Michael 8
Wegener, Mildred 613
Weglarz, Liliam 603
Wegman, Jill 141
Wehe, Brad 29
Weibel, Kurt 56
Weibelt, Daniel 605
Weigley, David E. 8

Weih, Lori 252
Weil, Robert J. 100
Weil, Robert J. 208
Weiland, Ed 481
Weiler, Nathan 48
Weimer, Loren Karp 106
Weinberg, Meryl 373
Weinberg, Ido 590
Weiner, Jeffrey M 306
Weiner, Toby 414
Weiner, Jack 531
Weiner, Edward G. 623
Weingart, Saul N 628
Weinraub, Michelle 683
Weinstein, Michael Arthur 14
Weinstein, James 154
Weinstein, Susan 223
Weinstein, James 371
Weinstein, Debra 590
Weinstock, Richard 278
Weintraub, Jonathan 144
Weir, Walter 78
Weir, George 257
Weir, David 376
Weirick, Cecilia 204
Weis-Smith, Linda 473
Weisberg, James 182
Weise, Lori 103
Weisensel, Bill 281
Weiser, Anna 571
Weisickle, John 33
Weismann, Marty 308
Weiss, George 59
Weiss, Tamara 264
Weiss, Howard 290
Weiss, Aaron 303
Weiss, Allen S 361
Weissman, Martin 308
Weissman, Neil J. 321
Weissman, Seth R. 559
Weissman, Paul 688
Weitzel, David 105
Welage, Lynda S. 648
Welborn, Tom 347
Welborn, Thomas O 347
Welborn, Gregory S. (Greg) 367
Welborn, Ruth B. 563
Welch, Debi 145
Welch, Kevin 208
Welch, Carrie 251
Welch, Joseph L 252
Welch, Kevin 255
Welch, Patrick J 268
Welch, Joseph L 340
Welch, Michael F 418
Welch, Susan 600
Welch, Michael F 697
Welch, Michael F 697
Welcome, Dorothy 249
Weldon, Terry 188
Weldon, Aaron 197
Weldy, John 670
Welkie, Katherine A. (Katy) 251
Welle, Patricia 486
Wellendorf, Don 301
Weller, Matthew 269
Weller, Simcha 628
Wellman, Laura Meyer 202
Wells, Brooks 10
Wells, Kelly 108
Wells, Beverly 243
Wells, Alex 268
Wells, David A 346
Wells, John 359
Wells, Karla 407
Wells, Samuel 616
Welsh, James 211
Welsh, Cary 281
Welsh, Jon 343
Welsh, Richard 391
Welsh, Peter 545
Welsh, Jeff 567
Welty, Bonnie 500
Welu, Todd 149
Welz, Edward A. (Ed) 375

Wenaas, Jeffrey K. (Jeff) 235
Wendland, Andy 548
Wendt, Stephen C 164
Wendy, Warring 570
Weng, Kirsti 288
Wenger, Philip R. 589
Wenta, Ted 188
Wente, James W 511
Wente, Susan 615
Wentworth, Carlos 252
Wentz, Deanna 22
Wentz, Robert J 410
Wenzel, Patricia 340
Wenzell, Jeffrey A 188
Werft, Ronald C 482
Wermers, Michael 621
Werner, Todd S. 56
Werner, Patrick 352
Wernick, Mark 22
Wernick, Joel 427
Werrbach, John 22
Wersal, Ann 301
Werth, Dennis L. 379
Werthman, Ronald J 265
Werthman, Ronald 266
Wertman, Linda 588
Wescoe, Nicole 690
Wesley, Mary Lou 680
Wesolowski, Karen 136
Wesp, Clyde 663
Wessel, Tyler 257
Wessells, Chris 653
Wessler, Alan 339
West, Judy 29
West, Patrick H 123
West, Robert F. (Rob) 128
West, George 208
West, David 341
West, Tom 399
West, Mark D. 456
West, Karen 460
West, Sarah 510
West, Lashonda 599
Westad, Erik 185
Westapher, Bernard 416
Westbrook, Bennett D. 468
Westby, Ross 151
Wester, K Scott 412
Westering, Karen Van 598
Westermann, Marit 565
Westervelt, Karen S 597
Westle, Marc B 345
Westman, Carl E 361
Weston, Ivy 123
Weston, Andrew 499
Westphal, Kenneth 164
Westphal, Dan 384
Westrick, Karl J 305
Westrick, Karl 305
Wetherly, Mark 129
Wetmore, Griffin P. 503
Wetterer, Diana 398
Wetzel, Todd 449
Wetzel, Laura 474
Wetzel, Leslie 654
Wexner, Abigail S. 365
Weymouth, Tara 149
Whalen, Chad 90
Whalen, Anna 273
Whalen, Thomas V. 287
Whalen, Anna 296
Whaley, Justin 101
Whaley, Ron 101
Whaley, Alan 248
Wharton, Junaye 571
Wheaton, Pam 528
Wheaton, Craig 670
Wheeler, Dane 6
Wheeler, Penny Ann 26
Wheeler, Zach 42
Wheeler, Debi 251
Wheeler, Brett 319
Wheeler, Steven M. (Steve) 487
Wheeler, Melanie 567

Wheeler, James R 591
Wheeler, Peter 595
Wheeler, Kelsey 626
Wheeler, Bradley C. (Brad) 627
Wheeler, Brad 627
Wheeler, Paul 660
Wheeler-Fair, Martha 344
Whelan, John 627
Whelpley, Rodd 246
Whichard, Betty M 649
Whiddon, Georgia 563
Whigham, Teresa 110
Whiitely, B Glen 145
Whipple, John 444
Whitaker, Sandy 281
Whitaker, Erin 332
Whitaker, Hal 444
Whitaker, John 473
Whitaker, Candace 501
Whitaker, Grant 661
Whitaker, Ralph 700
Whitbread, Mary 234
Whitcomb, Lisa 329
White, Matthew 12
White, Allen 42
White, Doug 46
White, Rev. William W. 57
White, William W 59
White, Cooper 118
White, Joseph 121
White, Terry 123
White, Keith A. 125
White, Paul 125
White, Cris A 131
White, Jennifer 134
White, Jeffery 149
White, Erika 149
White, James M 158
White, Bob 158
White, Andrew 161
White, Paul 175
White, Andrea 181
White, Steven T 191
White, Greg 220
White, Joseph E 232
White, James 250
White, Christine 266
White, Marietta R 270
White, Joseph 298
White, Kevin 303
White, David 327
White, Eric 339
White, Don 345
White, Judy D 352
White, Rita 369
White, Robert 377
White, Jacob 400
White, Thomas D 400
White, Sam 415
White, Christine 433
White, Stephen F 462
White, Curt 500
White, Lori 514
White, Douglas 562
White, Michael 618
White, Winona 627
White, Raymond E 639
White, Owen C 641
White, Craig G. 648
White, Amy 661
White, Brendan M. 684
White, Charles 684
White, Wendy 692
White-Coleman, Debra 243
Whitehair, Kevin 342
Whitehall, Ellen 52
Whitehead, Angela 63
Whitehead, Benjamin 75
Whitehead, David 617
Whitehead, Dave 617
Whitelaw, Kelly 162
Whitely, B Glen 145
Whiteman, Keith 377
Whiteman, Charles H. 600
Whitener, Pam 297

Womack, Robert R 476
Womack, Daniel 540
Womack, Mark 605
Womble, Aaron 363
Wondafrash, Worku 319
Wong, Marissa 99
Wong, Stephen 288
Wong, Christina 292
Wong, Michael 299
Wong, Colleen 627
Woo, Tracy 601
Woo, Melissa 651
Wood, Jo 60
Wood, Kevin 105
Wood, William 161
Wood, Bill 161
Wood, Kurt 166
Wood, Laura 266
Wood, Carolyn 377
Wood, Carl 449
Wood, Rhonda 518
Wood, Nancy 550
Wood, Steve 640
Wood, Patrick 693
Woodall, Doyle 174
Woodall, Niki 639
Woodard, Beth 436
Woodard, Elizabeth 436
Woodard, Eric 506
Woodcock, John 54
Woodcock, John 54
Woodruff, David 313
Woods, Don 49
Woods, Joseph 144
Woods, Clyde 218
Woods, Mike 221
Woods, Brian T 396
Woods, Randall 416
Woods, Andrea 527
Woods, Christopher 545
Woods, Eugene A 569
Woods, Chris 616
Woods, Tiffany 621
Woods, Dan 680
Woods-Moss, Julie 556
Woodson, Nathaniel D 609
Woodson, Jonathan 697
Woodward, James L 333
Woody, Craig W. 132
Woody, Bill 239
Wool, Julius 373
Wool, Norman 467
Wooldridge, Sherry 443
Wooley, Mylowe 398
Woolfolk, James W 89
Woolridge, Anthony 255
Woolridge, Diane 345
Woolridge, Victor 645
Woolston, Kristina 111
Wooten, Scott 58
Wooten, Michelle 462
Worcester, Hilary 342
Wordell, Doug 521
Work, Victor 632
Workman, Sue B. 98
Worl, Rosita F. 489
Worsham, Richard 491
Worth, Denny 221
Worth, Greg 676
Wortham, E Dale 226
Worthen, Kevin J. 83
Worthey, Tracy 612
Worthington, Bill 482
Worthington, Randall T 660
Wortman, Mandy 107
Wortman, Mandi 107
Wotring, Debora 154
Wotton-Gantner, Kelley 66
Wozniak, Debbie 81
Wozniak, Greg 535
Wray, Christine R. 321
Wright, Rodney L 14
Wright, Craig 46
Wright, Tom 158
Wright, Mike 184

Wright, Robert 184
Wright, Michaella 228
Wright, W Cameron 240
Wright, Alexander 241
Wright, Lori A 271
Wright, Jamal 275
Wright, David H. (Dave) 297
Wright, Rachel 354
Wright, Kenneth 354
Wright, Dale 376
Wright, Adam 394
Wright, Lori 415
Wright, John 461
Wright, Anika 464
Wright, Robert S 482
Wright, Victor 528
Wright, Mark 566
Wright, Daniel 634
Wright, Steve 659
Wright, Daniel 667
Wright, Clarice 692
Wrighton, Mark S. 615
Wroblewski, Jo 57
Wrubel, Harvey 182
Wu, Chwan Hwa 51
Wu, Ye 196
Wu, Jiang 215
Wu, Wendy 482
Wu, Ming 559
Wuellner, James 535
Wunderlich, Daniel 343
Wussow, Luanne 316
Wutke, Steve 371
Wyatt, David 356
Wyatt, Bill 433
Wyatt, Mark 519
Wye, John Van 346
Wyffels, Chad 521
Wylie, Kevin 141
Wyllie, Robert 574
WyllieAndrews, Victoria 395
Wymore, Kelle 533
Wynia, Marvin 191
Wynn, Barry 509
Wynne, Susan 588
Wynne, Kaye 604
Wynter, Rudolph L 371
Wyrsch, Martha B 561

X

Xiang, Ester 557
Xiao, Dana 613
Xie, Andrew 116
Xu, Lily 390

Y

Yacob, Desalegn 365
Yaeger, Jackie 224
Yale, Craig 14
Yale, Neha 66
Yamada, Donna 270
Yamadi, Asghar 168
Yamakawa, Mark 601
Yamamoto, Lisa 276
Yamauchi, Tim 441
Yammout, Saleh 464
Yancey, Bryan 224
Yang, Mary 339
Yang, Honggang 399
Yang, Daniel 405
Yang, Jenny 495
Yanisch, Stephen 36
Yao, Benjamin 557
Yarbrough, Todd 359
Yarbrough, Shelly 662
Yardley, William T 22
Yardley, Bill 22
Yardley, William T. (Bill) 519
Yarobough, Martin 201
Yates, Stacy 170

Yates, Faellen 170
Yates, Vinson M. 405
Yates, Deirdre 494
Ybarra, Leticia 560
Yeakley, Rourke 534
Yedla, Anupama 584
Yee, Aynna 482
Yeh, David 510
Yehiely, Fruma 398
Yeigh, Bjong Wolf 658
Yellin, Jason 566
Yeomans, Tim 450
Yepes, Maria 296
Yeroshek, David 630
Yeshoalul, Melon 617
Yeskie, Andrew 312
Yin, Deryu 7
Yip, Byron 22
Yip, Angela 480
Yochum, Alice 96
Yocum, Deb 543
Yocum, Patricia R 550
Yoder, Lamont 56
Yoho, Quentin 556
Yoho, Ryan 567
Yoldas, Erol 87
Yoo, Peter 479
Yoo, Scott 480
Yoon, Michael S 2
Yortsos, Yannis C. 656
Yost, Kevin C. 689
Youatt, June 341
Youcis, Stacey 589
Young, Kevin 8
Young, Robert H. 15
Young, Russell 19
Young, James N 27
Young, Kerry 72
Young, K. Richard 83
Young, Lynn 96
Young, Jason 103
Young, Stephen 103
Young, Christopher 125
Young, Brittney 136
Young, Wayne 187
Young, Mark 189
Young, Christine 192
Young, Tammy 231
Young, Blaine 247
Young, Tom 249
Young, Carol 271
Young, Eric 307
Young, Bonny 316
Young, Carmen 340
Young, Joanna 341
Young, Sandra 346
Young, Theresa 370
Young, Cassie 441
Young, Alan 493
Young, Gary S. 576
Young, Randy 581
Young, Fred 603
Young, Ann 613
Young, Theresay 672
Youngblood, Mike 319
Youngdahl, Lyle 207
Younger, Jon 550
Youngquist, Gene 73
Youngs, Michael 152
Younkle, Kim 220
Youso, Steven R. 208
Yu, Nancy 333
Yu, Angel 377
Yu, Sue 557
Yultyev, Aleksandr 215
Yunck, Kara 67
Yunker, Jean 52
Yurovitsky, Alyssa 290
Yvonne, Luttschwager 543

Z

Zaas, David 167
Zaas, David 168

Zabaneh, Samir 232
Zabetakis, Paul 290
Zablo, Allison 361
Zacharias, Rhonda 281
Zacharius, Sherrie 564
Zachary, Beth D. 7
Zachary, Jayton 299
Zafft, Wayne 269
Zafirau, William 574
Zafonte, Ross D. 590
Zale, Hisashima 270
Zammer, William 92
Zammit, Wade 489
Zamora, Abel 278
Zanavich, W Marie 609
Zanetich, Thomas N. 689
Zang, David 664
Zapotocky, John 422
Zaren, Howard 92
Zarubi, Kathy 487
Zauk, Adel M 531
Zauner, Alois 482
Zavala, Donna 145
Zebot, Cy 183
Zeevi, Gary 493
Zehnder, William A 539
Zehnder, Drew 539
Zeidel, Mark L. 71
Zeitler, Denise 662
Zeller, Pat 478
Zemore, Pamela 456
Zepeda, Carl 119
Zeppos, Nicholas S. 615
Zernicke, Paul 392
Zetter, Bruce 570
Zhang, Cherry 78
Zhang, Harry 249
Zhang, Jin 392
Zhang, MEI 466
Zhang, Marianna 610
Zhang, Daisy 619
Zhao, Susan X 482
Zhou, Jason 610
Zhu, Haizhen 147
Zibrov, Andre 149
Zick, Kenneth 673
Zickefoose, John Z 143
Ziecheck, Hal 352
Ziegler, Richard A 37
Ziegler, Michael 441
Zielinski, Trudy 133
Zielinski, Marybeth 361
Ziemianski, Karen 186
Zierden, Ann 602
Ziffer, Jack A. 57
Zilbermann, Mark 567
Zilieris, Nick 59
Zillmer, Eric 165
Ziman, Richard S. 459
Zimmer, Mark 399
Zimmer, Kris A. 523
Zimmer, Robert J. (Bob) 609
Zimmerli, Bert 246
Zimmerli, Bert R. 251
Zimmerman, Jennifer 72
Zimmerman, Trinity 207
Zimmerman, Linda K 418
Zimmerman, Gail 451
Zimmerman, Doris 451
Zimmerman, Mark 493
Zimmerman, James 564
Zimmerman, Michael 591
Zingaretti, Michael 218
Zinkan, Lynn 571
Zinkan, Rob 627
Zinkin, Peter 55
Zinner, Michael J. 57
Zionts, Paul 155
Zipparro, Vincent 361
Zirbser, Glenn 298
Zmich, Kenneth W. 104
Zmrhal, Gary 230
Zohn, Patrick 126
Zoilo, John 118
Zolenas, Joseph 266

This Page left intentionally blank